GRANDMA'S SECRET

GRANDMA'S SECRET SPOT REMOVER®

Grandma's wipes out a wide range of stains from food to grease to blood! Fast working and easy-to-use. Convenient, take-along size is perfect at home or on the go. Non-toxic & Eco-friendly.

$3.99 ea.

$4.99 ea.

GRANDMA'S SECRET WRINKLE REMOVER®

If you have Wrinkles but don't have time to iron, Grandma can help. Just spray and you're on the way! Clean springtime scent. Non-toxic & Eco-friendly.

GRANDMA'S SECRET® MIRACLE MOISTURIZER

Grandma's original recipe for soft skin brings a trusted solution to a new generation. Simply apply a small amount to re-hydrate skin. Greaseless, Stainless and Fragrance Free. Non-toxic & Eco-friendly.

$4.99 ea.

PHONE ORDERS 1-800-605-SOAP (7627) • www.GrandmasSoap.com

tri-state
printing co.
800-642-1166

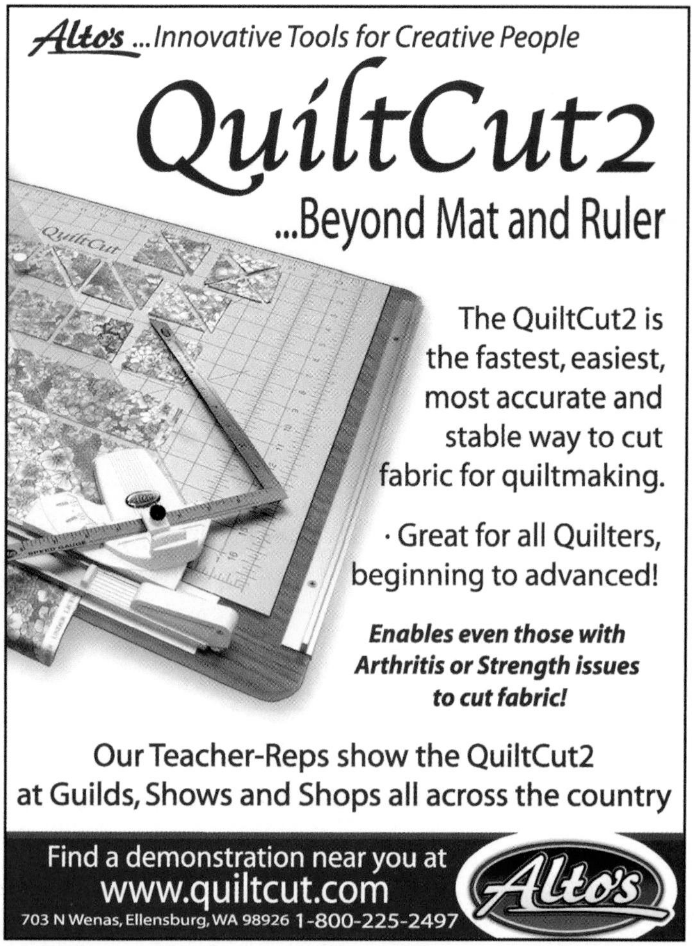
Alto's ...Innovative Tools for Creative People
QuiltCut2
...Beyond Mat and Ruler
The QuiltCut2 is the fastest, easiest, most accurate and stable way to cut fabric for quiltmaking.
· Great for all Quilters, beginning to advanced!
Enables even those with Arthritis or Strength issues to cut fabric!
Our Teacher-Reps show the QuiltCut2 at Guilds, Shows and Shops all across the country
Find a demonstration near you at
www.quiltcut.com
703 N Wenas, Ellensburg, WA 98926 1-800-225-2497
Alto's

Meetinghouse Hill Designs, LLC
Wool Appliqué Art Designed For Distinction
Kathy J. Gaul
Artist
Ask for these and other wool appliqué patterns at your local retailer.
Or Contact Me @
(719) 282-3518
www.meetinghousehilldesigns.com

StudioKat Designs
Switch Bags in a SNAP!
with a
PortaPockets Purse Insert
#1400
see the complete line at
www.StudioKatDesigns.com
or call: 866-409-8634 (tollfree)

Fort Worth fabric studio
Check us out at:
www.FortWorthFabricStudio.com
Same day shipping!
Online quilt shop ~ fabrics ~ kits
patterns ~ bundles ~ fat quarters
~ weekly Bundle Batch™ ~
monthly Fab Fats ~ simply inspiring!

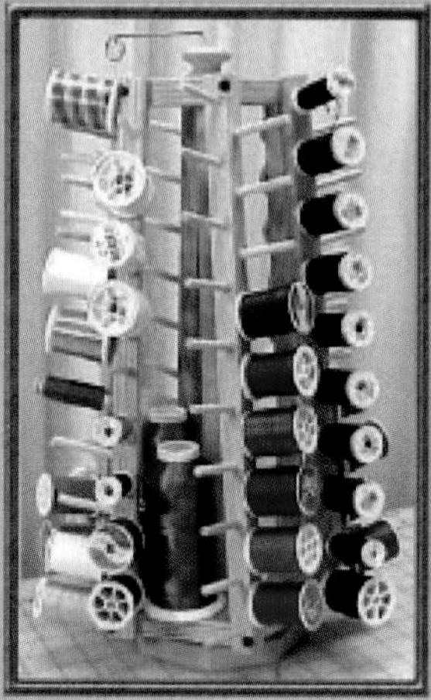

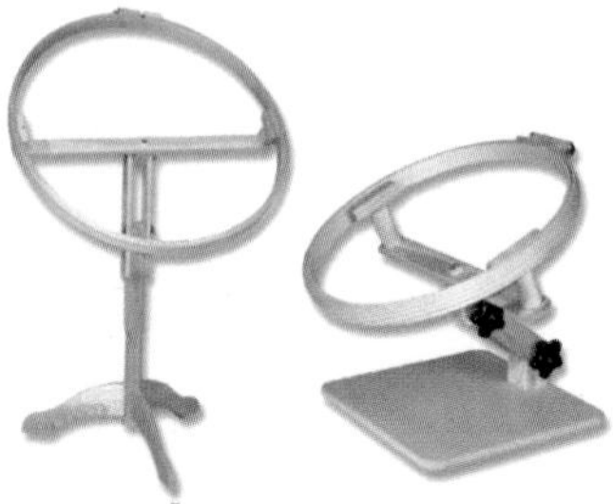

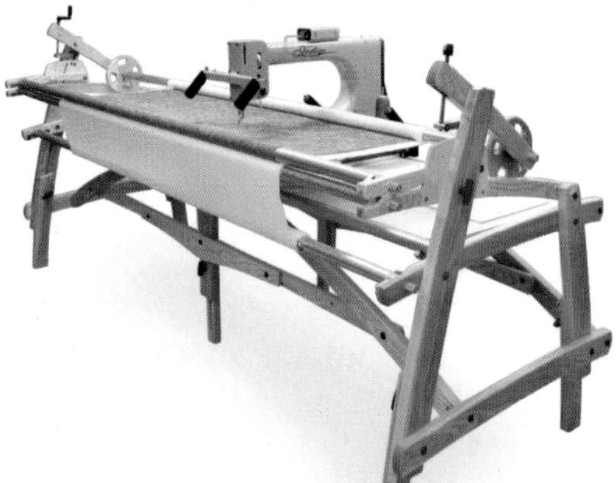

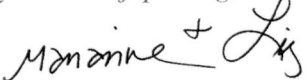

Quilters' Gift Shop

No Fabric
No Notions
No Patterns

Nothing But Gifts for Quilters!

A website dedicated to gifts with the quilter in mind. So next time you need a unique gift for a quilting buddy (or yourself) visit our online shop. Over 1,200 items to choose from. Many items found nowhere else.

2506 Robinson St.
Colorado Springs
Colorado 80904
719-685-5041
orders@quiltersgiftshop.com

www.quiltersgiftshop.com

Quilters' Travel Companion

11th Edition 2010 - 2012

Published by:
Chalet Publishing
2506 Robinson St.
Colorado Springs, CO 80904

Edited by:
Audrey Swales Anderson,
Thomas Culp
& Jack Murphy

Special thanks for your help to:
Sandra Clark, Teresa Gallegos,
Linda Graham, Kyle Heath,
Wesley Lehman, Pam McInturff,
& Cynthia Taylor.

800-959-4587
info@quilterstravelcompanion.com
www.quilterstravelcompanion.com
Fax: (719) 685-2347

Illustrations by:
Leere Aldrich
"At the Cabin"
from Provo Crafts
and Desk Gallery-Mega Bundle

How to Use this Guide

How to Use the Quilter's Travel Companion (QTC)

FEATURED SHOPS: This QTC contains over 2050 ***featured quilt shops***, located all over North America. Each listing allows you to learn more about the shop, and the ***maps*** will enable you to get right to their doorstep. The listings are organized by state, and listed geographically, so that close-by shops are close together in the book. You can use the shop number and the ***state map*** to find shops close to where you are, and where you might want to be. You should use commercial maps in addition to our state maps (which provide a good general guide to locations).

ADDITIONAL INFORMATION in the QTC: The QTC also provides you with more information about the quilting world:

1. At the end of each state listing we also include a listing of ***all quilt shops***. Information for the shops in this list that are bolded was correct at time of publication..
   We would suggest calling first before visiting the non-bold shops.
2. In addition, we provide as a service to the quilting community a listing of ***quilt shows***, organized by state and time of year. Shows change quite a bit, and so make sure to check the given contacts on our website before you travel to attend one.

INFORMATION ON OUR WEBSITE: You can find lots of valuable information on our website: www.quilterstravelcompanion.com.

1. Unfortunately, shops do move, change or go out of business. We are constantly ***updating*** this information on our website. In addition, we provide an *Up-to-Date Newsletter* to help you keep track of these changes; this is ***free*** when you provide us with your e-mail address! If you know about new shops or changes needed, please ***contact us***; we strive to have the most up-to-date and accurate information possible.
2. The website also includes updates and new information on ***quilt shows***. Let us know about additions or corrections!
3. The website includes an extensive list of ***quilt guilds,*** organized by state. If your guild is not listed or needs changes, please contact us: the listing is ***free***.
4. We also include a listing of ***shop hops*** – check to see if there is a shop hop in an area you might be visiting!
5. We also include a nice group of ***quilt retreat facilities*** – so you and your friends can plan a great getaway!

Chalet Publishing's mascots: Cauchy & Blaise

HAVE FUN WITH THE QTC! Bring your QTC along when you ***travel***, so that you can find quilt shops you might have missed otherwise. Or ***plan a trip*** with family and friends, just to visit the quilt shops you find in the QTC! Many of our customers have the shops ***sign their books*** as they visit them. There is no replacement for actually ***visiting*** the many beautiful ***brick & mortar quilt shops*** all across North America. Please send us stories of your travels.

Your one stop for shops, shows, guilds, hops and retreats.

www.quilterstravelcompanion.com

Quilters' Travel Companion

Table of Contents

U.S.A. Shops

Canadian Shops

Have a Great Trip

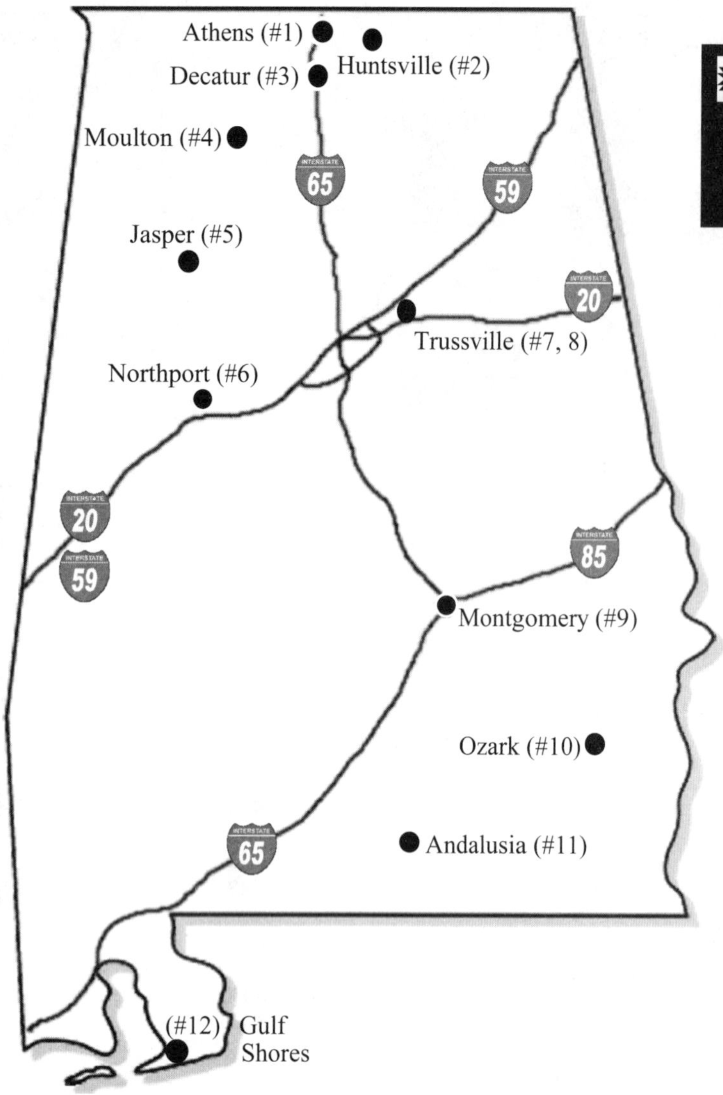

12 Featured Shops ALABAMA

Athens, AL #1

Mon - Sat 10 - 5

Heart of Dixie

630B S. Jefferson St. 35611
(888) 239-0941
Owner: Brenda Armstrong
Est: 1998
web@heartofdixiequiltshop.com
www.heartofdixiequiltshop.com

Small town Southern friendly quilt shop just a few miles from the Interstate.

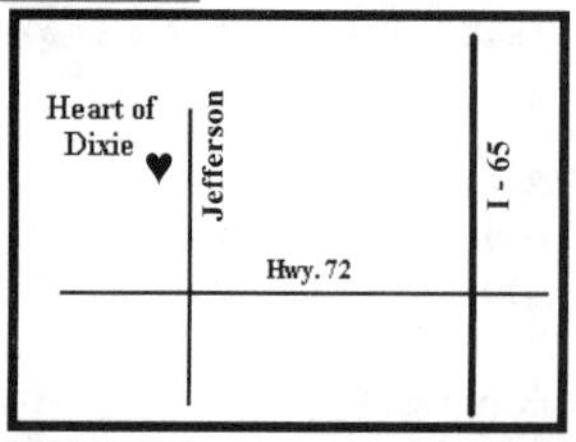

Huntsville, AL #2

Mon - Sat 10 - 5

Patches & Stitches

603 Humes Avenue 35801
(256) 533-3886
1-877-SHE-SEWS
www.patchesandstitches.biz
Est: 1978 2500 sq.ft.

"Quilting, Cross Stitch & Needlepoint"

We are located in one of Huntsville's Historic Mill Villages. Call for directions if you can't find us. We are off of Andrew Jackson Way behind O'Reilly Auto Parts

Decatur, AL #3

Mon - Fri 10 - 6 Sat 10 - 3

Quilter's Refuge ...where creativity soars!

1000 Beltline Rd. SW #V2 35601
(256) 552-9410

Est: 2005 3000 sq.ft. 2500 Bolts
Online Newsletter
www.quiltersrefuge.com
Your one stop quilt shop! We carry everything you need to get started on a quilt project including notions, fabrics, thread, patterns, backings, flannel, batting & advice.

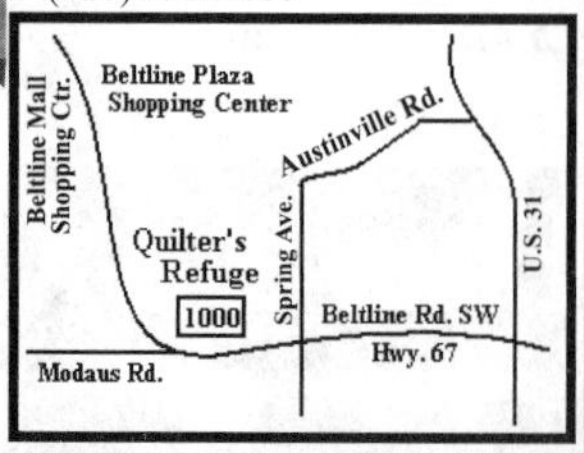

Moulton, AL #4

M, T, Th, F 9 - 6 Wed & Sat 9 - 5:30

Granny's Quilt Shop

15314 Court St. 35650
(256) 974-6244
Est: 2008 3600 Sq.ft.
1600+ Bolts

Owners: Judy & Jerry Whitworth
judetogo@charterinternet.com
www.grannysquiltshop.net
"Southern Hospitality, Hometown Touch, and Family Values."
Fabric from many respected manufacturers.

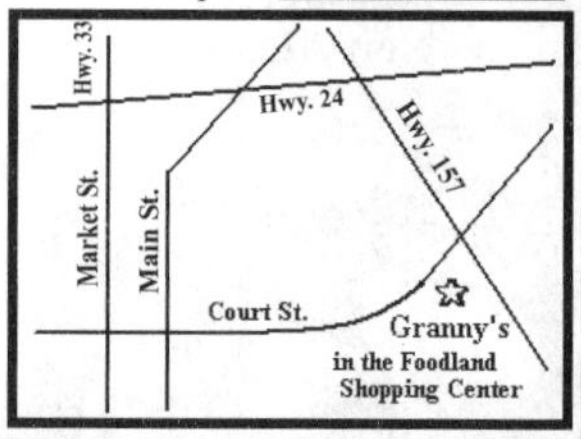

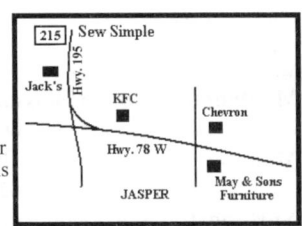

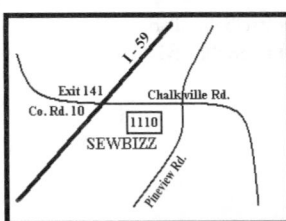

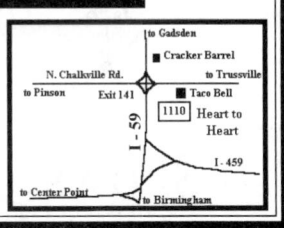

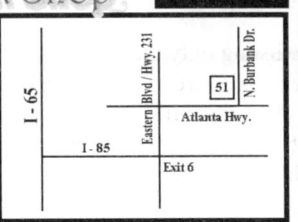

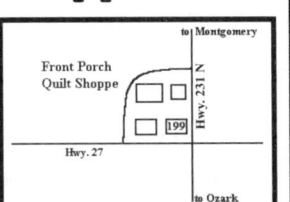

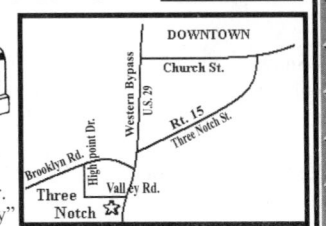

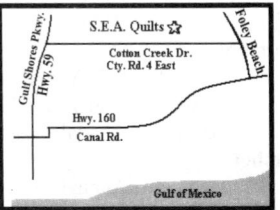

Alabama Quilt Shops

Andalusia Three Notch Cottage Quilt Shop, 161 W Valley Rd.
334-427-8458 **See ad #11, page 13**

Athens Heart of Dixie Quilt Shop, 630-B S. Jefferson St.
256-232-0508 **See ad #1, page 12**

Athens Quilts to Remember, 27344 Elkins Rd 256-233-2585
Boaz Wilson Fabric Outlet, 1524 US HWY 431 N 256-593-6501
Centreville Cahawba Quilt Shop, 1204 Walnut St. 205-225-0060
Collinsville A Time 2 Sew, 76 Main St. 256-524-3296

Decatur Quilter's Refuge, 100 Beltline Rd. SW #V2
256-552-9410 **See ad #3, page 12**

Dothan Dothan Sewing Center, 2797 Ross Clark Circle 334-794-3177
Florence Calico Rose Quilt Shop, 1707 Darby Drive 256-760-8227

Gulf Shores S.E.A. Quilt Shoppe, 22131 Cotton Creek Dr
251-968-7327 **See ad #12, page 13**

Hanceville Kats Korner Fabrics, 111 Bangor Ave. NE 256-352-2999
Huntsville Creative Sewing, 8415-R Whitesburg Dr. 256-883-4414

Huntsville Patches & Stitches, 603 Humes Ave. NE
256-533-3886 **See ad #2, page 12**

Jasper Sew Simple, 215 Hwy. 195
205-295-2229 **See ad #5, page 13**

Killen Quilters Haven & More, 7054 Co. Rd. 31 256-272-0583
Magnolia Springs Magnolia Quilt Company, 300 River Rt 251-965-3625
Montgomery Jo's Sew & So Quilting, 5734 Carriage Hills Ct. 334-271-1715

Montgomery Kudzu Blossom Quilt Shop, 51 N Burbank Dr.
334-396-6600 **See ad #9, page 13**

Moulton Grannys Quilt Shop, 15314 Court St.
256-974-6244 **See ad #4, page 12**

Northport Sew Delightful Northport, 80 McFarland Blvd.
205-752-1700 **See ad #6, page 13**

Oneonta Hearts Desire Quilts, 312-314 1st Ave. E 205-274-4374
Opelika Opelika Sewing Center, 3305 Pepperell Parkway 334-749-9522
Oxford Sew What!, 1720 Hwy. 78 E #7 256-831-9599

Ozark Front Porch Quilt Shoppe 199 N. Hwy 231
334-445-3521 **See ad #10, page 13**

Russellville Parker's Discount, Hwy. 24 E 205-332-4539

Trussville SEWBIZZ, 1110 N. Chalkville Rd. #160
205-655-7060 **See ad #7, page 13**

Trussville Heart to Heart Quilt Shop, 1110 N. Chalkville Rd.
205-661-0537 **See ad #8, page 13**

Alabama Quilt Shows

About Shows: We are listing only the very basic information about shows that happen on a regular schedule here. Please check out our website for more details on each show. Also this information tends to change quite often so please verify the event with our website or a local source before you venture far. Or if you're in the right area at the right time, give it a shot.

If you are a show organizer, please keep us updated on your event.
shows@quilterstravelcompanion.com www.quilterstravelcompanion.com

On our website you will also find:
- Exact dates (when we have them)
- Contact Information
- Events happening on a one-time basis
- Sponsor Information
- Description of Event

Month	City	Schedule	Show	Location with address
February				
	Robertsdale	Odd Years, 1st weekend in February	United Methodist Women Quilt Show	Robertsdale United Methodist, 22220 Hwy. 59
March				
	Troy	Odd Years: Mid February thru Late March	Pioneer Museum Show	Pioneer Museum of Alabama, 248 U.S. Hwy. 231 N
	Florence	Annual, 2nd Fri & Sat in March	Quilts by the River	Edgemont UMC, 1330 Eau Claire Ave.
June				
	Mobile	Odd Years, 1st weekend in June	Azalea City Quilters' Guild	Cranford Burns Middle School, 6175 Girby Rd.
	Cullman	Annual, 2nd week of June	Quilt Symposium of Alabama	St. Bernard Retreat Center, Hwy. 278 E
	Birmingham	Odd Years, 3rd weekend in June	QuiltFest	Oak Mtn. Middle School, 5650 Cahaba Valley
September				
	Huntsville	Odd Years, 3rd weekend in September	Heritage Quilters Show	Von Braun Center, 700 Monroe St. SW
	Gadsden	Odd Years, Fall	Gadsden Quilt Guild Show	Kiwanis Pavilion, 1500 Noccalula Rd. (Hwy. 211)
	Collinsville	Annual, Last weekend of September	Sew 'N Sews Show	Walking Tour of Historic Collinsville
October				
	Oneonta	Annual, 4th weekend in October	Blount County Quilters Guild Show	Palisades Park, 1225 Palisades Pkwy.

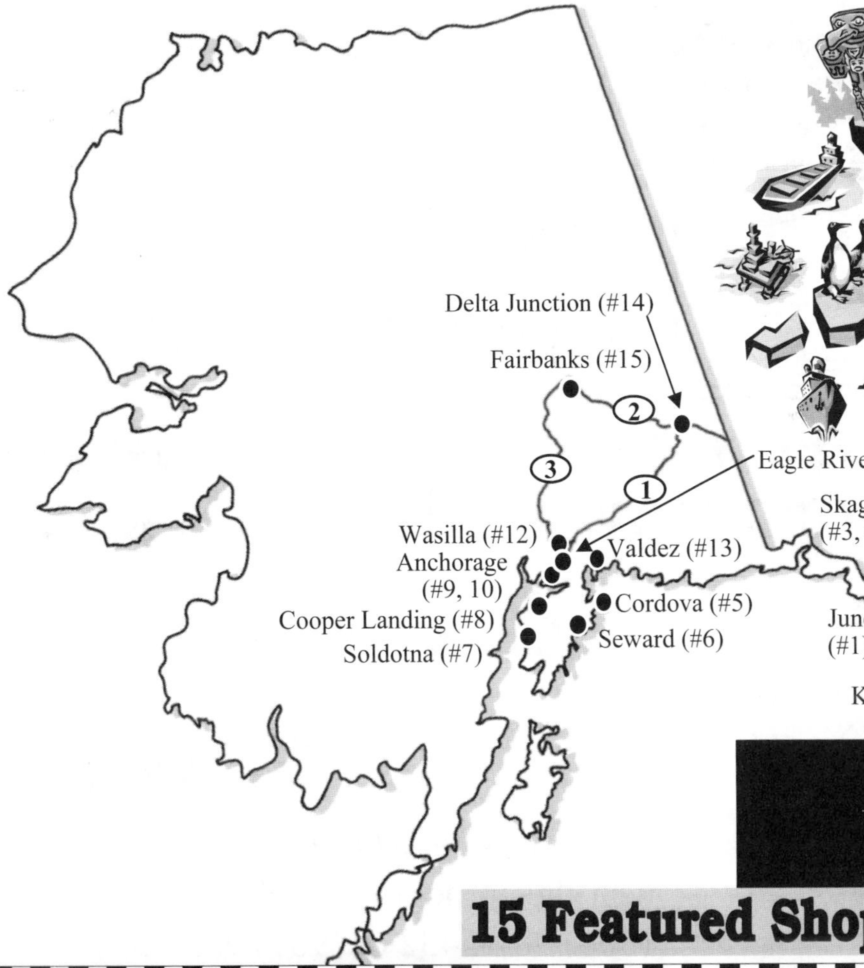

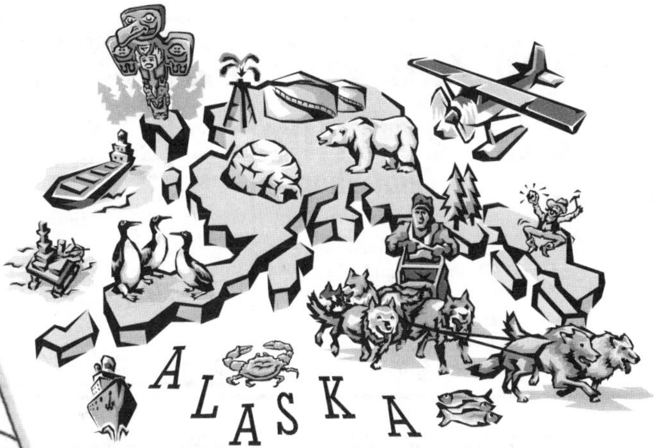

Alaska

15 Featured Shops

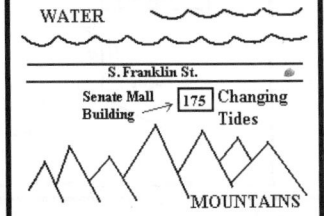

Ketchikan, AK #2

Winter
Mon - Sat 10 - 5
Summer Sun 8 - 4
& Mon-Sat 8 - 6

The Silver Thimble

Quilt Shoppe

5 Salmon Landing #204 99901
(907) 225-5422
Owner: Beatriz T. Gale Est: 1984
silverthimble@kpunet.net
www.silverthimblealaska.com
Available: Alaska quilt kits, fabrics, patterns & gifts.

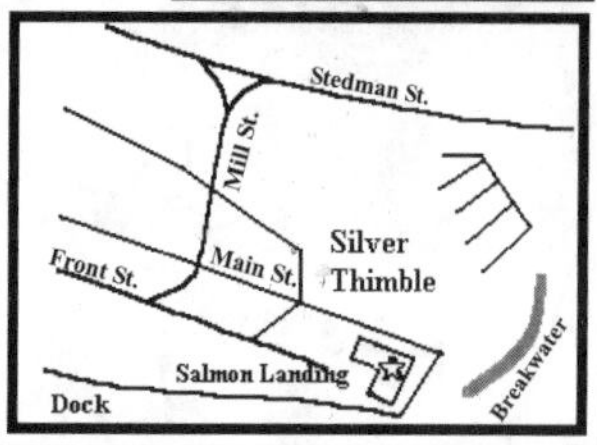

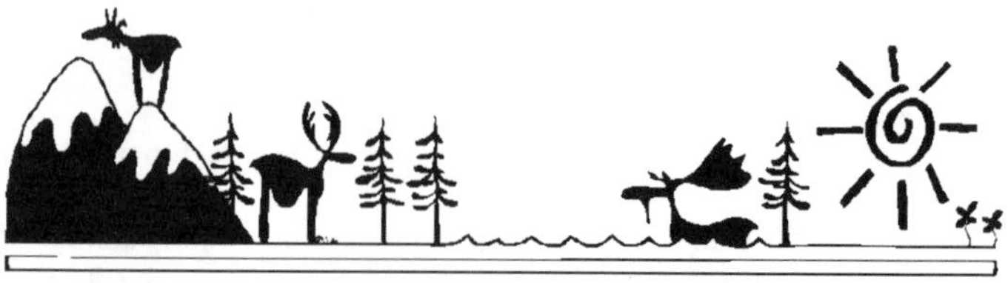

Two Great Shops, now under ONE Roof!

Rushin' Tailor's Quilt Alaska

Changing Threads

370 Third Ave, P.O. Box 135 99840
near the corner of Broadway & 3rd
(800) 981-5432 or (907) 983-2397

Skagway, AK #3 & 4

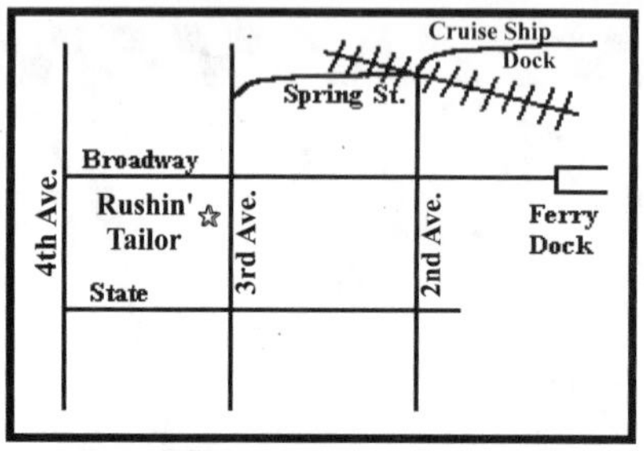

Summer Hours:
Daily 8:30 - 5:30+
Open Year-Round

Quilt Kits, Alaskan Patterns & Animal Fabrics.
Fat Packs & Bundles! Batiks!
Cross Stitch & Needlepoint by Regional Artists. Qiviut and Luxury Yarns, many dyed in Alaska.

Visit Us FIRST at: www.quiltalaska.com or www.changingthreads.com

Alaskan Quilt Shop & Needlework Haven!

Cordova, AK #5

Mon, Wed
Fri & Sat
12 - 6
or by Appt.

Forget-Me-Not Fabrics

1 Old Sawmill/Whitshed Rd.
P.O. Box 1109 99574
(907) 424-3656
Owner: Diana Rubio
Est: 1993 3600+ Bolts
forget@gci.net
Full line fabric store. All your family's needs. We carry a little bit of everything--leather, vinyl, fur corduroy, satins, laces, wool, etc. We have a variety of quilting & handicraft classes in the evenings.

Seward, AK #6

Tues - Sat
11 - 5
Summer Time
Open 7 Days

Sew 'n Bee Cozy

211 4th Ave. 99664
P.O. Box 2962

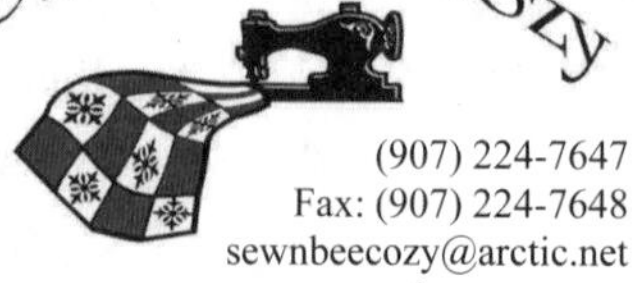

(907) 224-7647
Fax: (907) 224-7648
sewnbeecozy@arctic.net
www.sewnbeecozy.com
Alaska themed fabrics, books & patterns.
Premium quilter's cotton, flannel and batiks.
1000+ Bolts and notions galore!

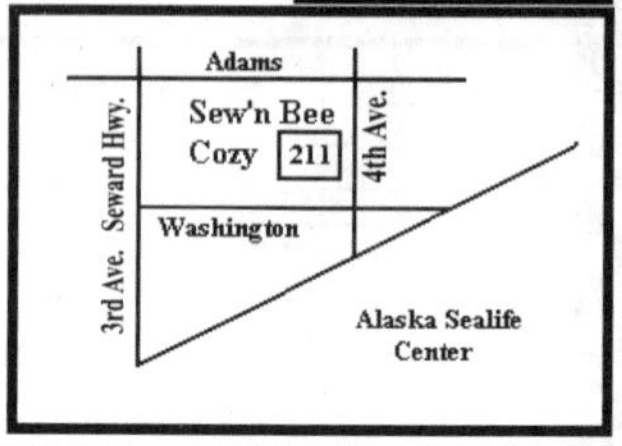

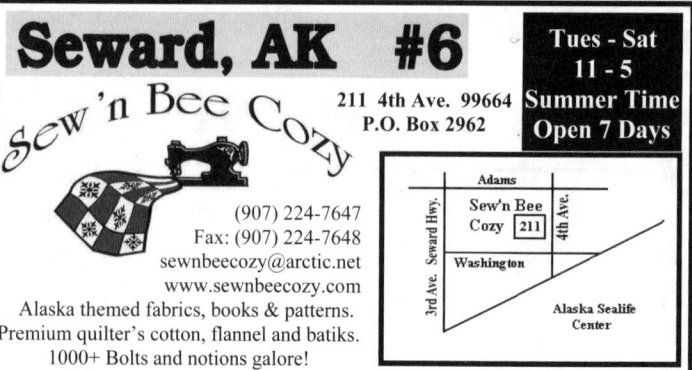

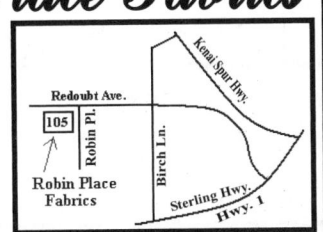

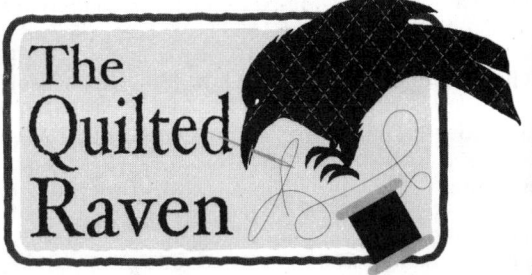

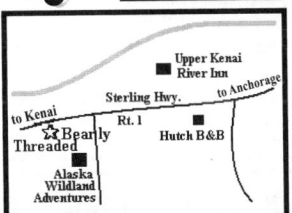

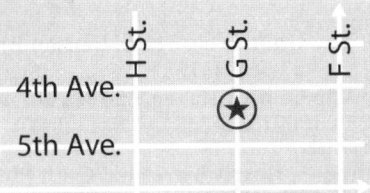

Dina's Cozy Cabin Quilts

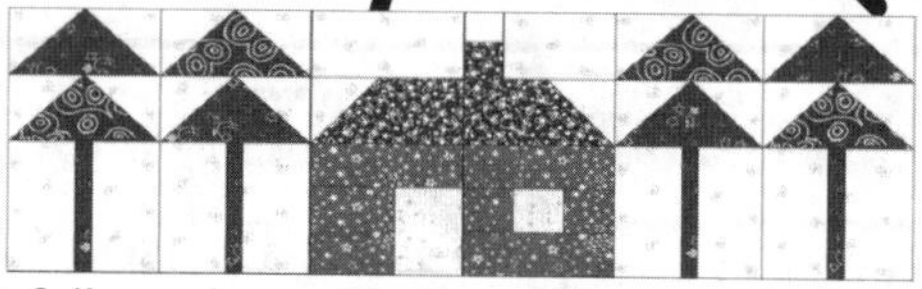

We have a full-service quilt shop with a wonderful classroom all in a very spacious shop with high ceilings and all on one level! We carry over 2000 bolts of fine-quality fabrics. We specialize in batiks, florals, flannels, woodland and cabin prints, and full spectrum collections. We stock a full variety of notions, books and patterns. Hinterberg Frames and Nolting Longarm Machines. Our store is a quilt show every day!

Mon - Fri 10 - 7
Sat 10 - 6
Sun Noon - 5

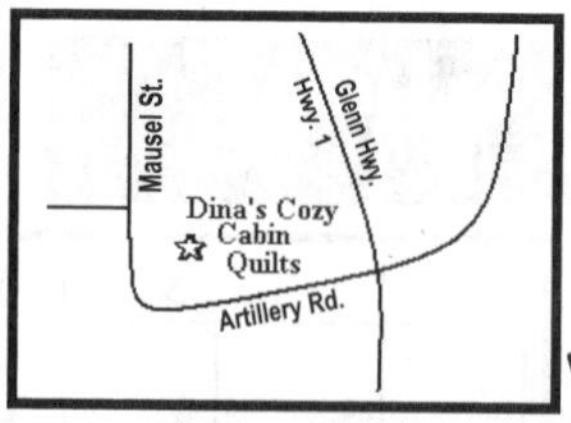

10901 Mausel St. 99577
(907) 696-3462
Owner, Author & Teacher:
Dina Pappas
dccq@mtaonline.net
www.dinascozycabin.com

Eagle River, AK #11

Wasilla, AK #12

Mon - Fri 10 - 6
Sat 10 - 5

Sylvia's Quilt Depot

1261 S. Seward Meridian Pkwy. #E 99654
Corner of Parks Hwy. & Seward Meridian
(907) 376-6468 Fax: (907) 376-6403
sylvia@sylviasquiltdepot.com
www.sylviasquiltdepot.com
Books & Patterns by Alaskan Artists.
Offering quality fabrics, kits and the latest patterns, books & notions. All who enter are friends and we would love to say "Hello".

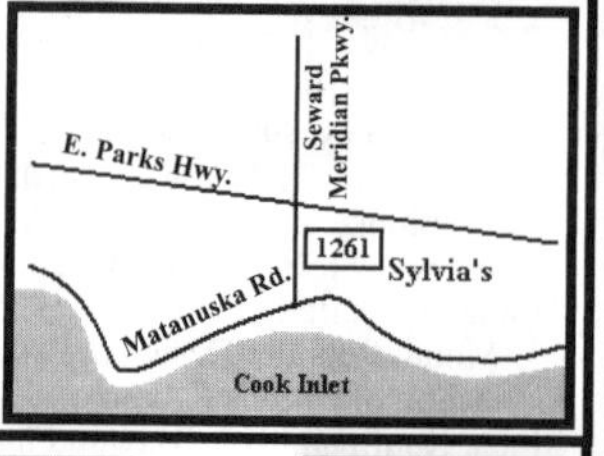

Valdez, AK #13

Mon - Fri 10 - 5:30
Sat 10 - 5

The Calico Whale

354 Fairbanks Dr. 99686
(907) 835-4263 Fax: (907) 835-3265
Owner: Shelly Stubblefield
Est: 1995 1500 sq.ft.
calicowhale@valdezak.net

Good selection of fabrics, books, patterns, quilting supplies, needlework, yarn and knitting supplies.

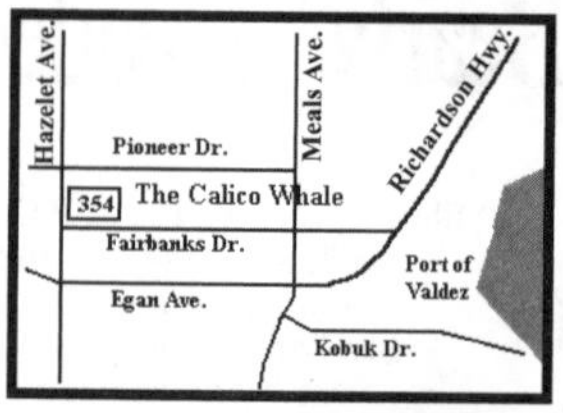

Delta Junction, AK #14

Mon - Sat 10 - 5
Fri til 9

The CALICO COW

1380 Richardson Hwy. 99737
(907) 895-9895

Est: 2003
1600 sq.ft.
1800 bolts

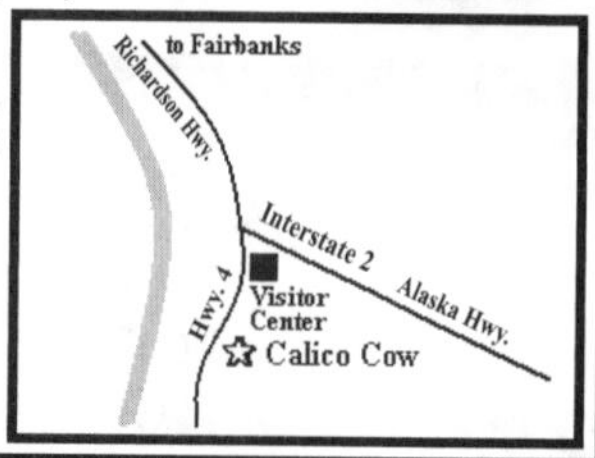

Owners: Maribeth Miller & Jackie Becker
info@thecalicocow.com
www.thecalicocow.com
Specializing in quilting cottons, especially Alaskan prints, flannels, wide backings & notions. We're your area HandiQuilter Rep.

Fairbanks, AK #15

Mon - Sat 10 - 6
Sun 12 - 5

1875 University Ave. #2 99709
(907) 455-0299
Owner: Marie Noah

NORTHERN THREADS

customerservice@northernthreads.net
www.northernthreads.net
PFAFF & Singer Sewing Machines. Fabrics, Notions, Classes, Yarn, Knitting Supplies, Professional Quilting Service.

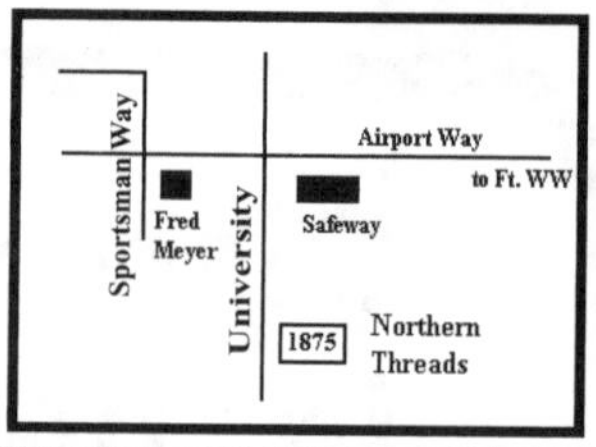

Alaska Quilt Shops

Anchorage **The Quilt Tree, 341 E. Benson Blvd. #5**
907-561-4115 **See ad #9, page 17**

Anchorage **The Quilted Raven, 650 W. 4th Ave.**
(907) 278-3521 **See ad #10, page 17 & 200**

Anchorage Seams Like Home, LLC, 3901 Old Seward Hwy. 907-677-8790

Cooper Landing **Bearly Threaded Quilt Store**
Mile 47 1/2 Sterling Hwy. 907-401-0544
See ad #8, page 17

Cordova **Forget-Me-Not Fabrics, 1 Old Sawmill Rd.**
907-424-3656 **See ad #5, page 16**

Craig Wild Rose Quilt Shop 311 Easy Street 907-826-2234

Delta Junction **The Calico Cow, 1380 Richardson Hwy.**
907-895-9895 **See ad #14, this page**

Eagle River **Dina's Cozy Cabin Quilts, 10901 Mausel St**
907-696-3462 **See ad #11, this page**

Fairbanks **Northern Threads, 1875 University Ave. Suite #2**
907-455-0299 **See ad #15, this page**

Fairbanks Quilts Unlimited, 1918 Jack St. 907-452-1918
Fairbanks The Material Girls, 3065 College Rd. 907-474-8118
Haines Material Girls LTD, 322 Main St /Po Box 1063 907-766-3391
Homer Seams To Bee, 1103-A Ocean Dr 907-235-6555

Juneau **Changing Tides, 175 S. Franklin St.**
585-993-0840 **See ad #1, page 15**

Juneau Rain Tree Quilting, 9131 Glacier Hwy. #7 907-789-7900
Kenai Kenai Fabric Center, 115 N. Willow St. 907-283-4595
Ketchikan Rainforest Crafts, 2417 Tongass Ave. #115 907-247-2738

Ketchikan **Silver Thimble, 5 Salmon Landing #204**
907-225-5422 **See ad #2, page 16**

Kodiak Flying Geese Fabric & Quilts, 202 Center St. #320 907-486-8700
Palmer Just Sew, 579 S. Alaska St. 907-745-3649
Petersburg Fabric Basket, P.O. Box 248 907-772-4077
Petersburg Island Bound Quilting, 101 Louis Ln., P.O. Box 358 907-772-3249

Seward **Sew'n Bee Cozy, 211 4th Ave.**
907-224-7647 **See ad #6, page 16**

Sitka Abby's Reflection, 231 Lincoln St. 907-747-3510

Skagway **Rushin' Tailor's QuiltAlaska, 370 3rd Ave.**
907-983-2397 **See ad #3, page 16**

Skagway **Changing Threads, 370 3rd Ave.**
907-983-3700 **See ad #4, page 16**

Soldotna **Robin Place Fabrics, 105 Robin Pl.**
907-262-5438 **See ad #7, page 17**

Valdez **The Calico Whale, 354 Fairbanks Dr.**
907-835-4263 **See ad #13, this page**

Wasilla **Sylvia's Quilt Depot, 1261 S. Seward Meridian**
907-376-6468 **See ad #12, this page**

Alaska Quilt Shows

8 Shows

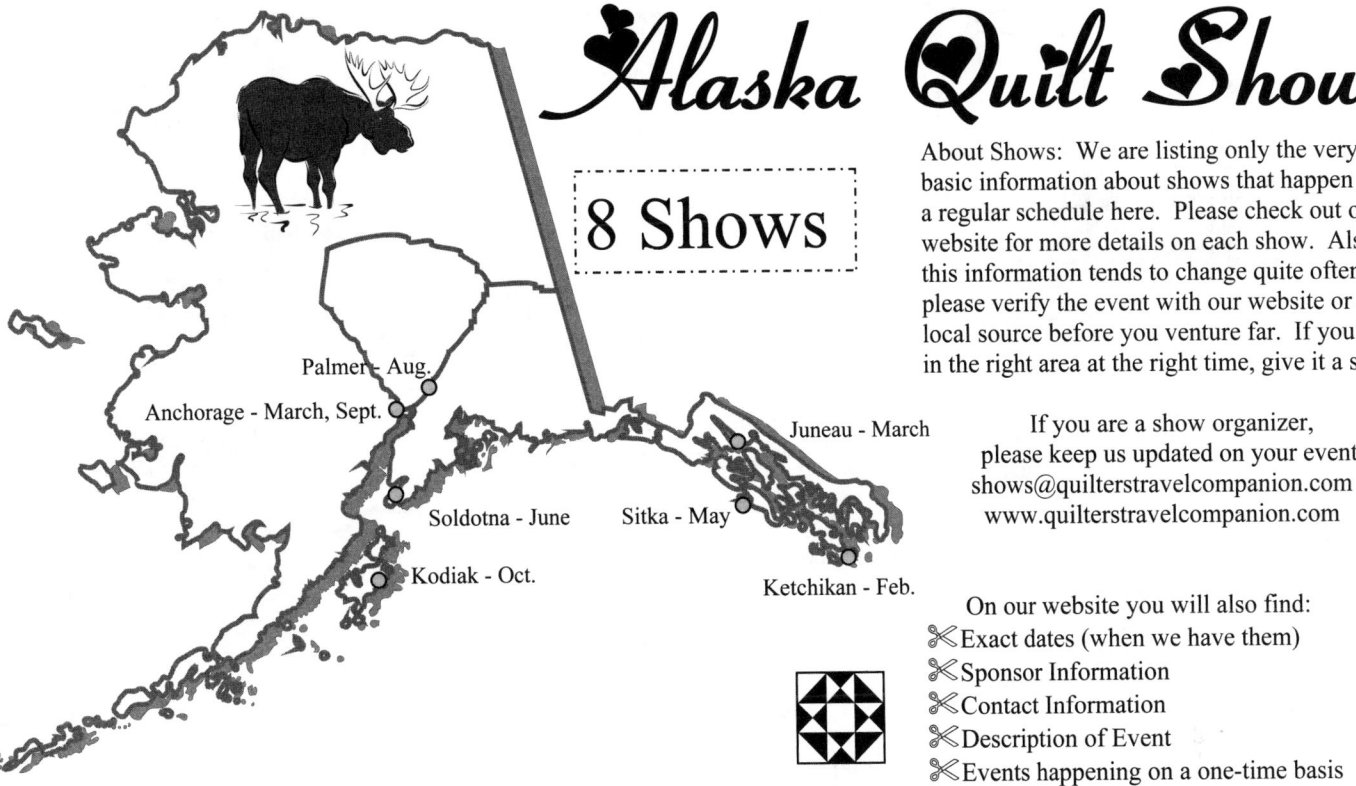

About Shows: We are listing only the very basic information about shows that happen on a regular schedule here. Please check out our website for more details on each show. Also this information tends to change quite often so please verify the event with our website or a local source before you venture far. If you're in the right area at the right time, give it a shot.

If you are a show organizer, please keep us updated on your event.
shows@quilterstravelcompanion.com
www.quilterstravelcompanion.com

On our website you will also find:

- Exact dates (when we have them)
- Sponsor Information
- Contact Information
- Description of Event
- Events happening on a one-time basis

Month	City	Schedule	Show	Location with address
February				
	Ketchikan	Annual, 2nd weekend in February	Quilting in the Rain	Plaza Mall, 2417 Tongass Ave.
March				
	Anchorage	Even Years, 2nd week in March	Alaska Fiber Festival	Conoco Phillips Atrium, 700 G St.
	Juneau	Annual, 2nd weekend in March	Capital City Quilters Show	Centennial Hall, Willoughby and Egan Dr.
May				
	Sitka	Annual, 1st weekend in May	Ocean Wave Quilters Show	Harrigan Centennial Hall, 330 Harbor Dr.
June				
	Soldotna	Annual, 4th weekend in June	Robin Place Fabrics Show	Robin Place Fabrics, 105 Robin Place
August				
	Palmer	Annual, late August to Labor Day	Alaska State Fair Quilt Exhibition	Alaska State Fair, 2075 Glenn Hwy.
September				
	Anchorage	Annual, 2nd weekend in September	Great Alaska Quilt Show	Conoco Phillips Atrium, 700 "G" St.
October				
	Kodiak	Annual, 1st weekend in October	Kodiak Bear Paw Quilters Show	Gerald Wilson Auditorium, Rezan St.

Notes

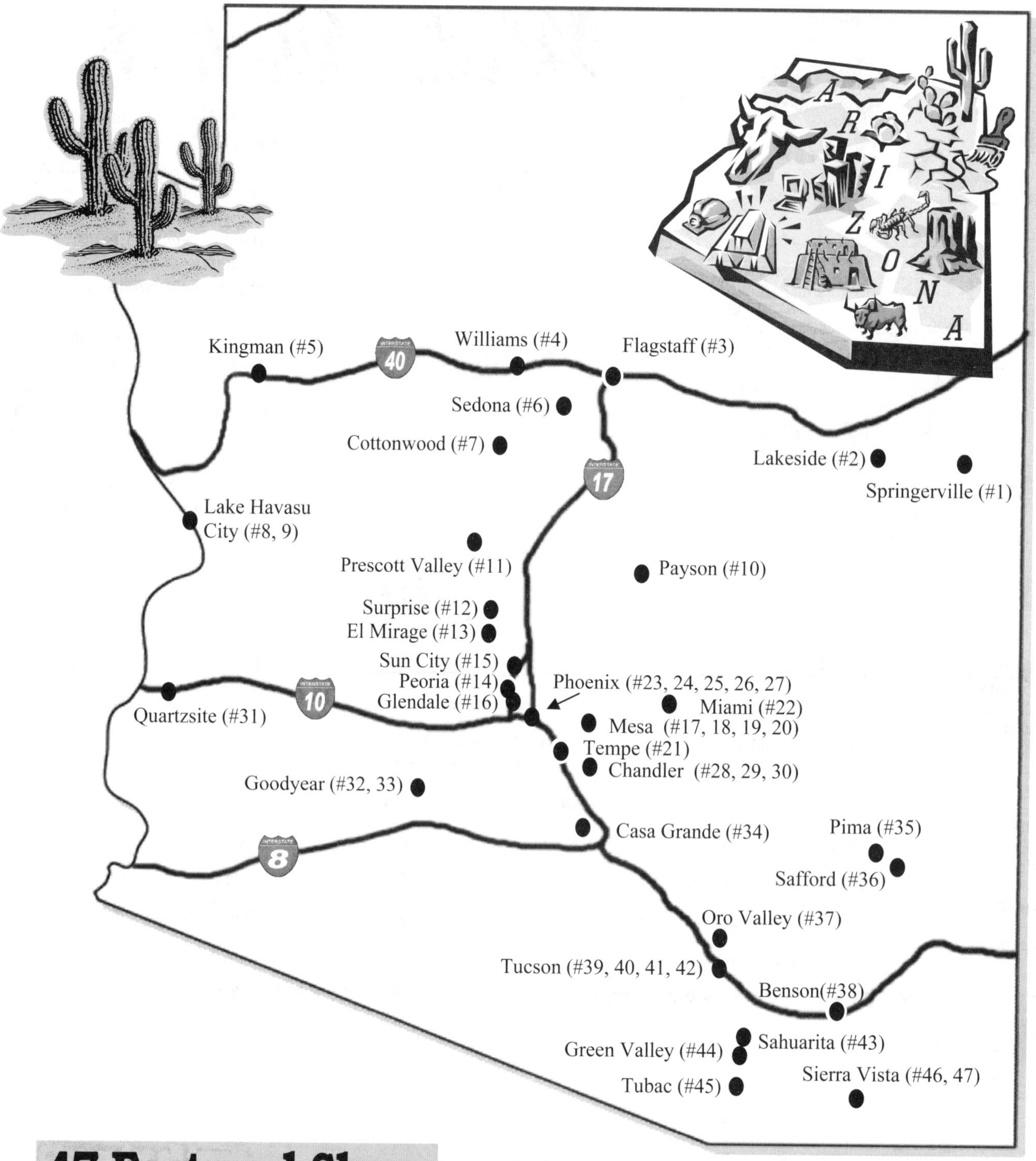
ARIZONA
Kingman (#5)
40
Williams (#4)
Flagstaff (#3)
Sedona (#6)
Cottonwood (#7)
17
Lakeside (#2)
Springerville (#1)
Lake Havasu City (#8, 9)
Prescott Valley (#11)
Payson (#10)
Surprise (#12)
El Mirage (#13)
Sun City (#15)
Peoria (#14)
Glendale (#16)
Phoenix (#23, 24, 25, 26, 27)
Miami (#22)
Mesa (#17, 18, 19, 20)
Tempe (#21)
Chandler (#28, 29, 30)
Quartzsite (#31)
10
Goodyear (#32, 33)
Casa Grande (#34)
Pima (#35)
Safford (#36)
8
Oro Valley (#37)
Tucson (#39, 40, 41, 42)
Benson(#38)
Green Valley (#44)
Sahuarita (#43)
Tubac (#45)
Sierra Vista (#46, 47)

47 Featured Shops

ARIZONA

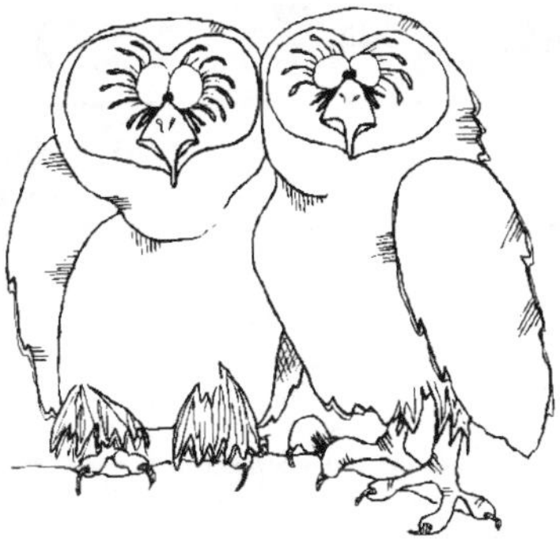

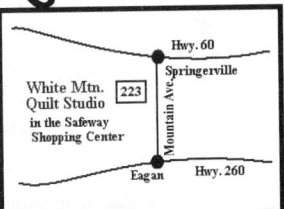

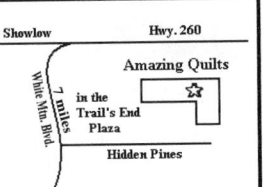

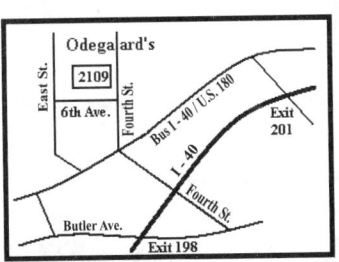

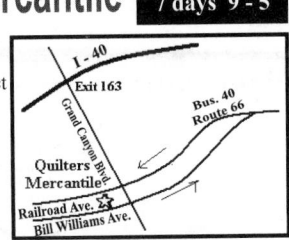

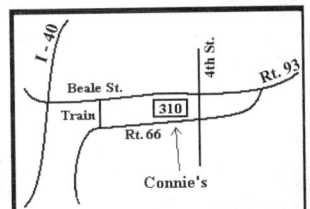

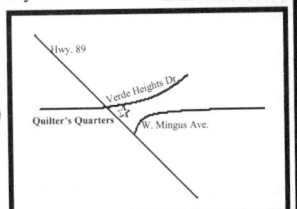

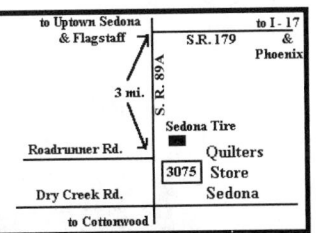

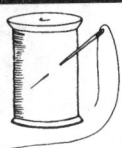

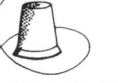

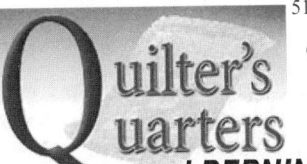

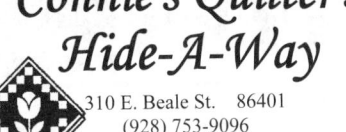

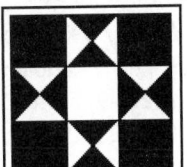

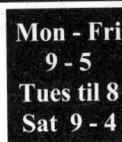

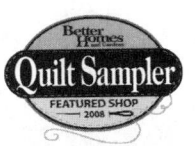

Lake Havasu City, AZ #8

Summer 6/1 - 11/1
Mon - Fri 9 - 4
Sat 9 - 2
Winter
Mon - Fri 9 - 5
Sat & Sun 9 - 4

JonAli Quilt n'

289 Lake Havasu Ave. S. 86403
(928) 854-2002
jonali@citilink.net www.jonali.net
Fabric • Quilting Notions • Classes
Patterns • Books

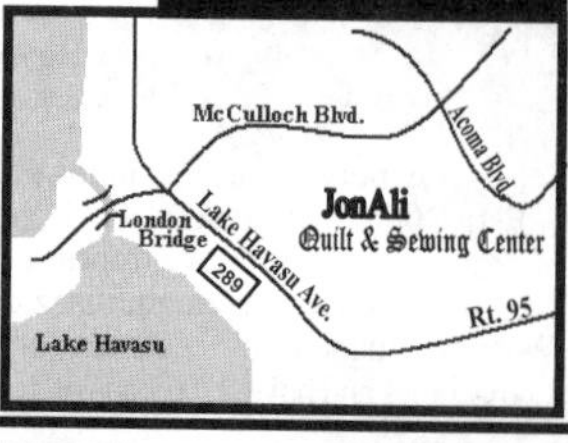

Lake Havasu City, AZ #9

Mon - Sat
9 - 4

Sew What ?

2876 Sweetwater Ave., #2 **(Right off Hwy. 95)** 86406
Phone: (928) 453-4040 **Owner:** Jeanette Kennedy
Email: jeanette@sewwhat-quilting.com
Web Site: www.sewwhat-quilting.com

Est: 1995
4000 Bolts

Largest selection of fabrics, books, patterns & quilting supplies on the lower Colorado River and the American Home of the London Bridge.

Payson, AZ #10

Mon - Sat
10 - 5
Sun 11 - 4

Quilting Sisters

904 N. Beeline, Suite E 85541
(928) 468-6360 Fax: (928) 474-9550
Owners: Cheryl & Richard Dolby
Est: 2001 4500 sq.ft.
cheryl@quiltingsistersaz.com
www.quiltingsistersaz.com
Inspiring a new generation of quilters while assisting the more experienced to rediscover their enthusiasm and passion. Bernina Dealership.

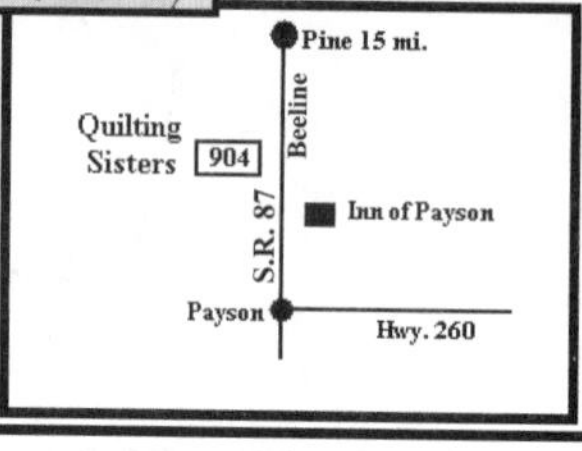

Prescott Valley, AZ #11

Mon - Fri
9 - 5
Sat 9 - 4

A Quilter's Dream

8732 E. Hwy. 69 86314
(928) 772-0864
Owner: Sherrill Chapman
aquiltersdream@cableone.net

Beautiful 100% Cotton Fabrics. Great Selections of Books, Patterns & Notions. Unique Gifts. Classes for all Levels of Quilting.

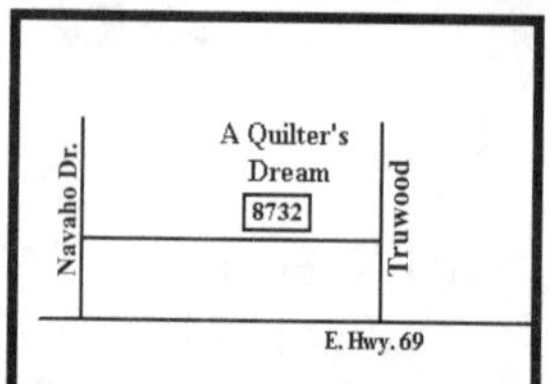

El Mirage, AZ #13

Mon - Sat
9 - 5

35TH AVE. SEW & VAC

12213 NW Grand Ave. 85335
(623) 583-0070 Fax: (623) 583-2946
Free Online Newsletter
info@35thavesewandvac.com
www.35thavesewandvac.com

Fabric - Quilting Supplies
Sewing Machines - Classes

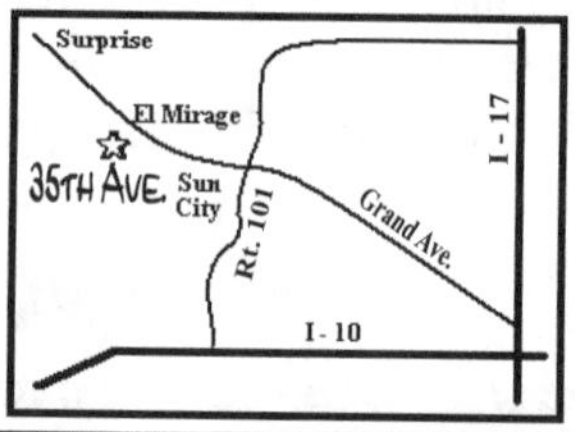

Your center for education and creativity...

Surprise, AZ #12

The Quilted Cactus

15459 W. Bell Rd. #109
Surprise, AZ 85374
(623) 975-9356
Owner: Kathy Rodolph
Fax: (623) 975-9427
Est: 2008 3800 sq.ft.
info@TheQuiltedCactus.com

www.TheQuiltedCactus.com

Mon - Fri 9 - 5 Sat 9 - 4

- 4,000+ Bolts of Fabric
- Books, Patterns & Notions
- Classes & Groups
- Online Newsletter
- Janome Sewing Machines
- Sales & Service
- Friendly, helpful staff

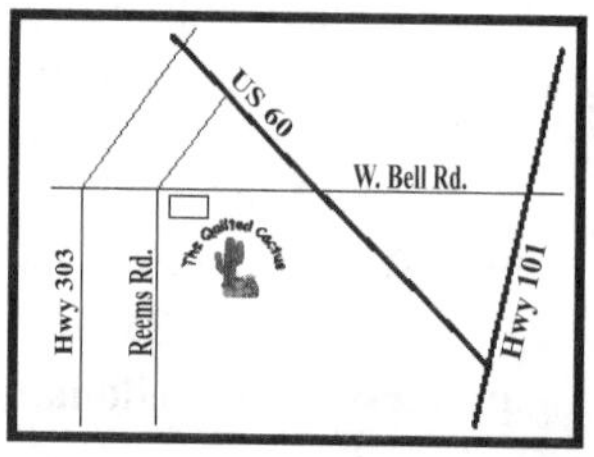

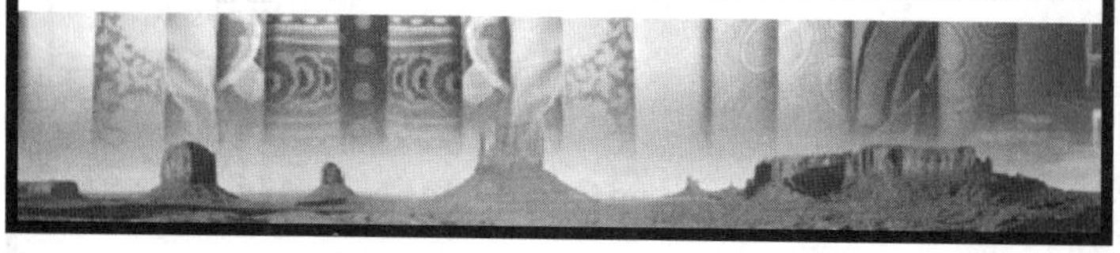

Peoria, AZ #14

Mon - Fri
9:30 - 6
Tues til 9
Sat 9:30 - 5

THE QUILTER'S BEE

7549 W. Cactus Rd. #111 85381
(623) 334-9359 Fax: (623) 334-9481
Owner: Margaret Baker
Est: 2002 1800 sq.ft. Online Newsletter
info@quiltersbeeaz.com
www.quiltersbeeaz.com

Books, patterns, notions, classes, and fabric: Southwest, batiks, flannels, Civil War and 30's reproductions and much more with friendly, helpful service too.

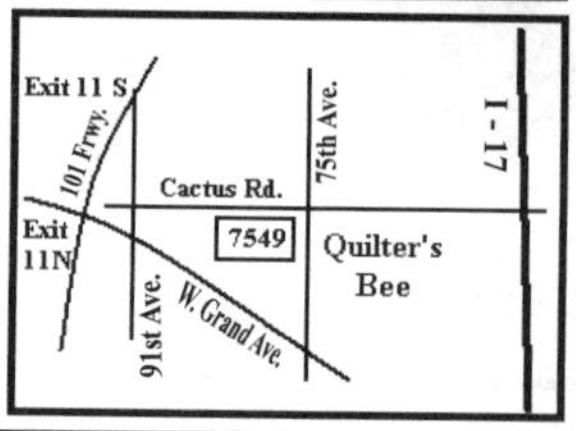

Sun Valley Quilts

Mon - Fri 9:30 - 5
Wed til 6
Sat 9:30 - 4
Sun 12 - 4

BERNINA

Sun City, AZ #15

* **Visit our Online Store at: www.sunvalleyquilts.com**
* Largest fabric selection in West Valley!
* Large Selection of Southwest Fabrics.
* Books, notions, gifts & more.
* Books 20% off everyday
* 65+ classes and clubs every month
* Full Service Bernina Dealer.

Nothing Sews Like A Bernina. Nothing.
BERNINA®

9857 W. Bell Rd.
85351
(623) 972-2091
Fax:
(623) 972-6085
Est: 2001 5700 sq.ft.
8000+ Bolts

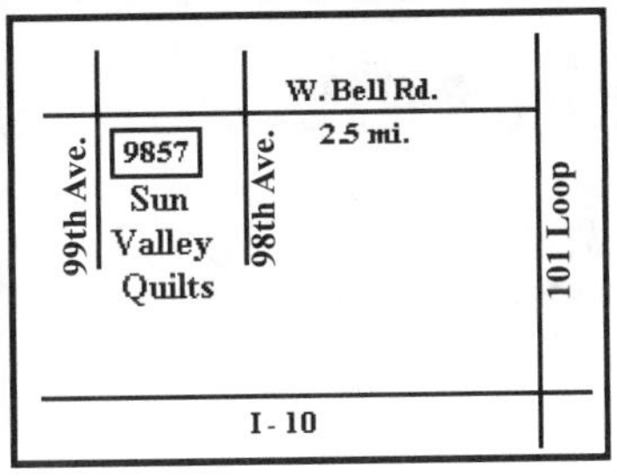

Dawn S. Maher, Owner

www.sunvalleyquilts.com

2 GREAT LOCATIONS

Owner: Pat Mulqueen
Family Owned and Operated since 1977
singersewing @yahoo.com

Mulqueen sewing & vacuum centers

Mesa, AZ #17

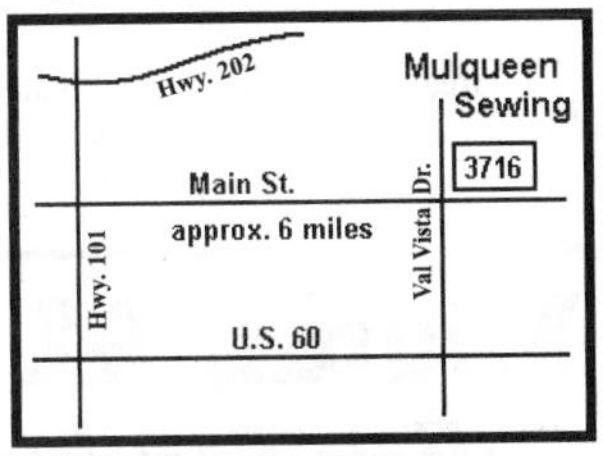

3716 E. Main St.
Mesa, AZ 85205
480-545-0778

Over 10,000 bolts of fabric. Books, Quilting Supplies, Embroidery Supplies & Software, Kits, Threads, and more. June Tailor Products. Brother, Janome & Singer Machines--Sales & Service.
GAMMILL QUILTING MACHINES

Both Shops: Mon - Sat 9:30 - 5:30

Glendale, AZ #16

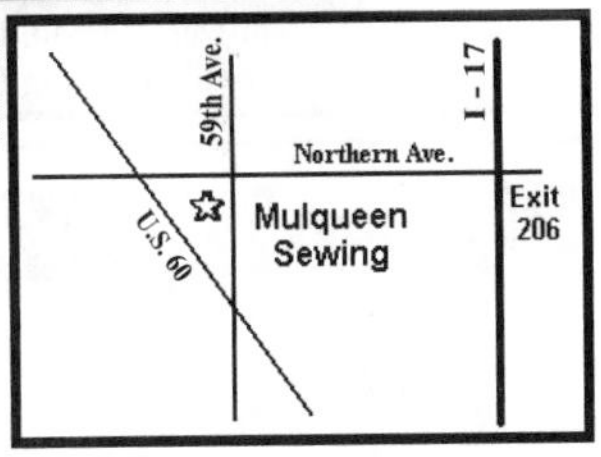

7838 N. 59th Ave.
Glendale, AZ 85301
623-934-0084

Also visit us at: www.sewshop.com

Mesa, AZ #18

SCRAPBOOKS, ETC.

Mon 10 - 7 Tues - Sat 10 - 9

Specializing in current and bright designer fabrics, notions, patterns, idea books, classes and so much more.

2820 E. University Dr. #111
Mesa, AZ 85213
(480) 854-2303
Est: 1999
10,000 sq.ft. 500 bolts

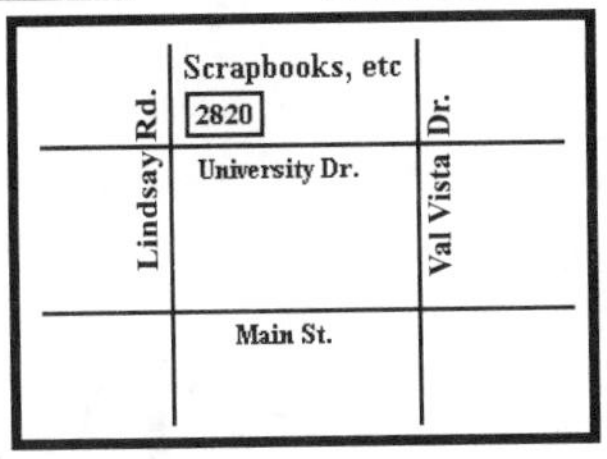

Take the US 60 to Gilbert Rd. or the North 202 to Gilbert Rd. Go east (1 mile to Lindsay and University)

www.scrapbooks-etc.com

A Quilters Oasis

9963 E. Baseline Rd., Suite #105 85209
(480) 354-4077 www.aquiltersoasis.com
Fax: (480) 354-8415 Est: 2005 1600 sq.ft.
Owner: Kathy Reynolds 2500+ Bolts
Online Newsletter & Blog kathy@aquiltersoasis.com

Mon - Fri 9:30 - 5
Tues til 7 Sat til 4

Mesa, AZ #19

* **A fun, friendly place to inspire and supply the quilter and sewing enthusiast.**
* **Friendly, knowledgeable staff.**
* **Great selection of 100% cotton fabric.**
* **Books, Patterns & Notions.**
* **Classes: Beginner to Advanced.**

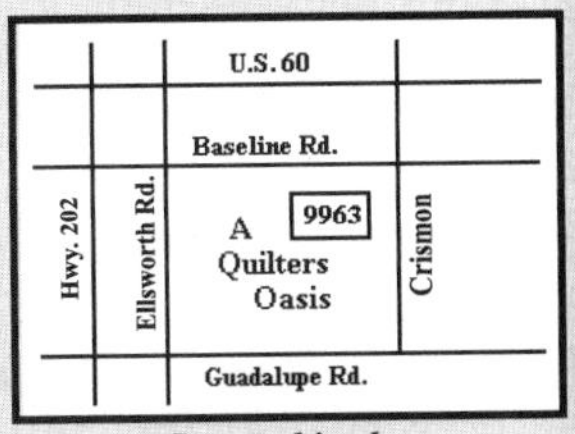

Located in the Augusta Ranch Marketplace.

Mesa, AZ #20

Mon - Sat 9 - 5 Summer Hrs. Vary

Fashion Fabrics

9849 E. Main St. 85207
(480) 986-3243 Fax: (480) 380-2778
Owner: Louise Hales
Est: 2001 1500 sq.ft. 5000 Bolts

Great fabrics, notions and patterns. We have a longarm quilting machine in-house and offer classes.

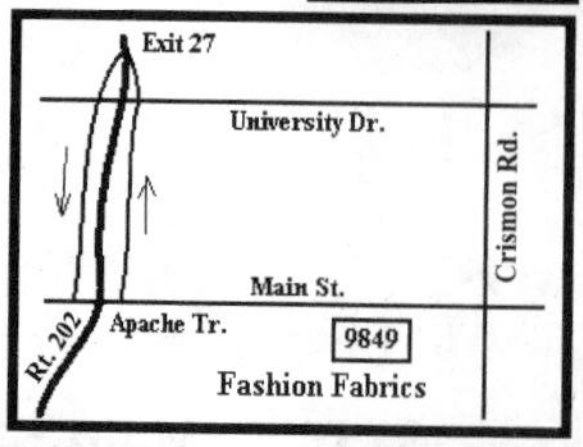

Miami, AZ #22

Mon - Sat 10 - 6

Julie's Sewing Corner

600 Sullivan St. 85539
(928) 473-7633
Owners: Don & Julie Reiman
Est: 2006 1500+ Bolts
juliessewingcorner@yahoo.com
Western & Southwestern, batik, brightly colored fabric & blenders. books, patterns, notions, batting, stabilizers, thread, felting, and fabric inks. Husqvarna Viking Dealer.

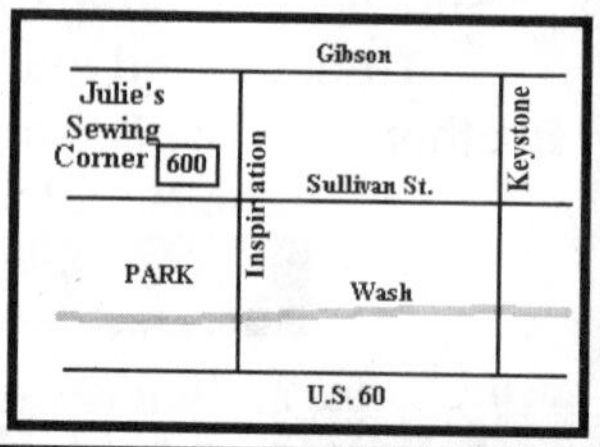

Tempe, AZ #21

Est: 1982

THE QUILTER'S RANCH

1721 E. Warner Rd. #C9
85284
(In Cobblestone Village Shopping Center)
(480) 838-8350
quiltersranch@juno.com

Visit our website
www.quiltersranch.com

Authorized Bernina dealer.

BERNINA

Mon - Sat 9:30 - 5
Thurs til 8 Sun 12 - 4

Owner: Susan Visotsky

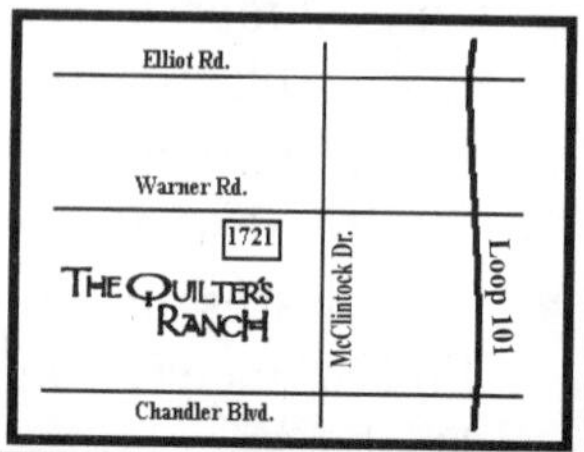

Phoenix, AZ #23

Mon - Sat 9:30 - 5 May - Aug 9:30 - 4

The Quilted Apple

3043 N. 24th St. 85016
(602) 956-0904
Fax: (602) 956-3082

Est: 1978 4200 sq.ft. 3000 bolts
thequiltedapple@gmail.com Online newsletter
www.quiltedapple.com
Arizona's Oldest Quilting Store.
For all your quilt-making & rug hooking needs.

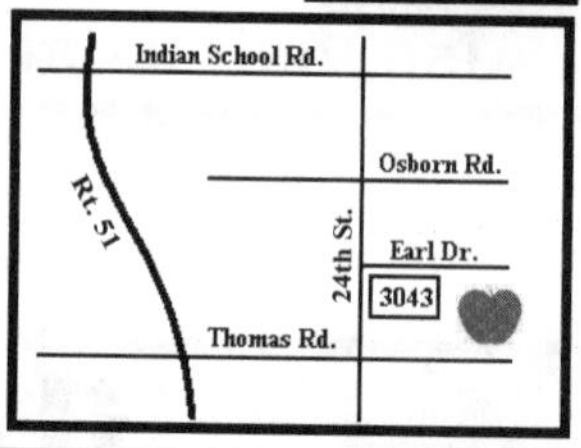

Phoenix, AZ #24

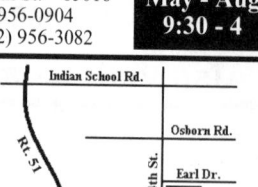

Mon - Sat 10 - 5 Closed Mondays June thru Aug

The Olde World Quilt Shoppe

30855 N. Cave Creek Rd. #134 85331
(480) 473-2171 Fax: (480) 473-2066
Est: 2008 2800 sq.ft. 3500 Bolts
Online Newsletter
mail@theoldeworldquiltshoppe.com
www.theoldeworldquiltshoppe.com
Come visit our 'home' away from home to see how to use/display your quilts and projects. Over 100 kits available. Top Ten shop Fall 2009.

Quilt Sampler

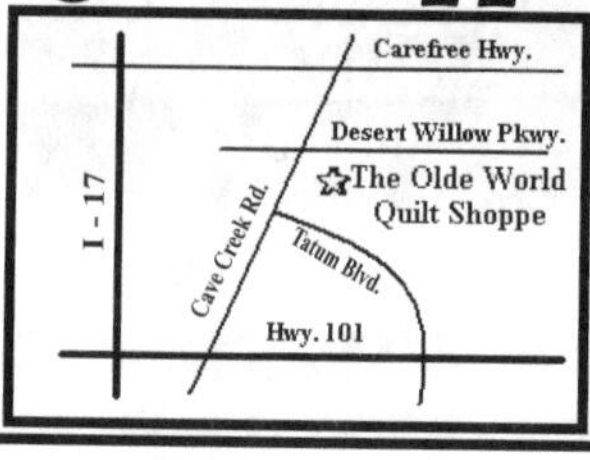

Phoenix, AZ #25

Mon - Fri 9:30 - 6 Wed til 9 Sat 9:30 - 5

3 Dudes Quilting

5053 E. Elliot Rd. 85044
(480) 598-8601
Fax: (480) 705-9531
Est: 2009
1600 sq.ft.
2400 bolts

Owners: Ray Steeves, Jeff Carr, Frank Costa
3dudesquilting@live.com Online Newsletter
www.3dudesquilting.com
Fabric, Notions, Patterns, Books, Classes
We believe that by helping our customers become better quilters we are creating a more valuable pastime for them.

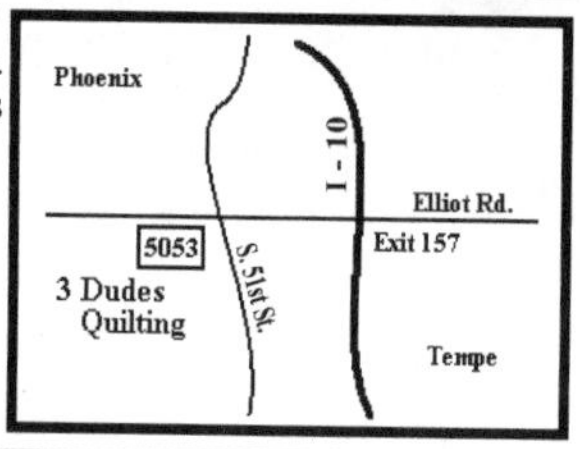

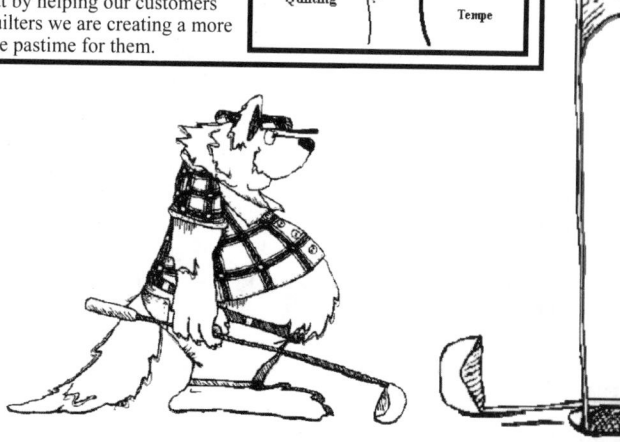

LARGEST FABRIC STORE IN ARIZONA

Phoenix, AZ #26

3500 W. Northern
Phoenix, AZ 85051
(602) 841-5427
Fax: (602) 841-3131
info@35thavesewandvac.com
Est: 1990 1500 sq.ft.

www.35thavesewandvac.com

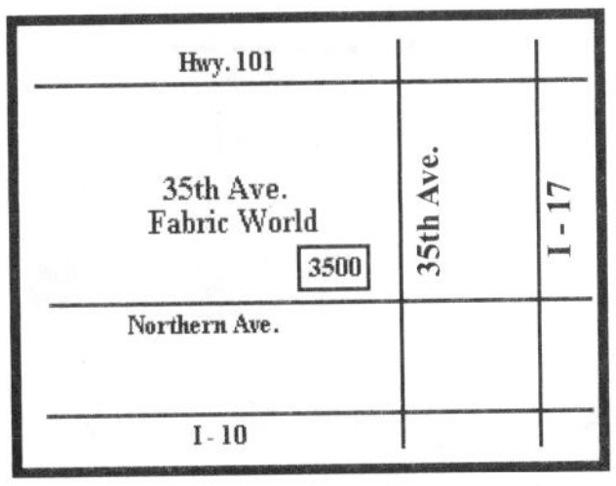

* Fabric (over 17,000 bolts)
* Books, Classes, Kits
* Complete Collection of Threads
* Notions and Quilting Supplies
* Magazines
* Pfaff / BabyLock / Elna / Singer
* Quilting Frames
* Quilters / Embroidery Sewing Machines
* Free Shipping over $50
* Free Online Newsletter

Quiltz

...Your Quilting Destination

8,000 sq, ft. of Inspiration
Over 7,000 Bolts
Owner: Cindy Coleman
Store Manager: Jennifer Rossetti

20% OFF
ALL BOOKS! ALL THE TIME!

Check for our COLOR OF THE MONTH
20% off
Every month a Different color.

Come visit our specialty departments:

* Fantastic Florals
* Batik Beauties
* Simply Southwest
* Vintage 30's
* Basically Bright
* Flannel Fun
* Christmas Corner (year round)

and a fantastic staff to help you

Each of these departments is full of FABRIC, PATTERNS, GIFTS & IDEAS

Come see for yourself!

Quiltz Hours:
Mon—Sat 10 to 5
Sunday 12 to 4
Tuesday to 8

Quiltz
13825 N. 32nd St. #8
Phoenix, Az 85032
(602)482-4141
www.QuiltzAz.com
email: contact@quiltzaz.com

Easy Freeway Access!

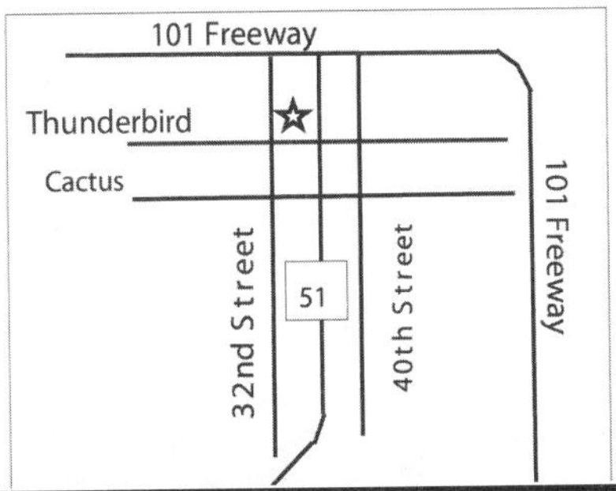

Phoenix, AZ #27

Zoe's Trunk

Chandler, AZ #28

Owner: Mary Lucille

2990 North Alma School Rd., Suite 3
Chandler, AZ 85224
480-857-4833
quilts@zoestrunk.com
Est: 2000 3500+ Bolts

www.zoestrunk.com

Monday thru Saturday 9:30 - 5:30
Tues til 7:30

A place to set your creativity free!
Fabric, books and classes for all your quiltmaking adventures.
Hand-dyed wool, patterns, classes and kits for rug hooking and penny rugs.
The Valley's largest selection of batiks, brights, 19th Century & 1930's reproduction fabrics.

Kits available - we would be happy to customize one for you, just ask!

Mail order available

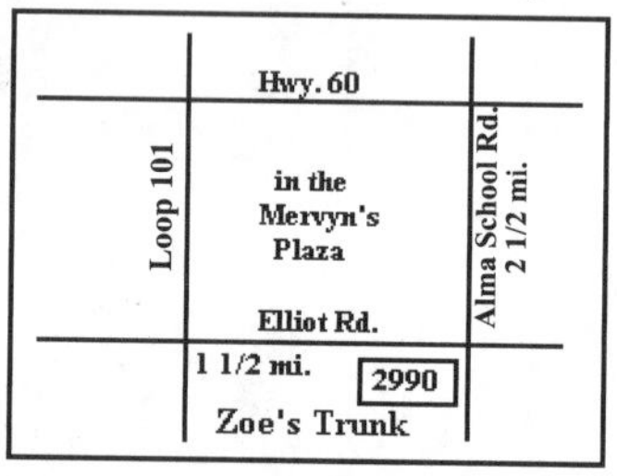

Visit these Restaurants in the area to get more energy for shopping at Zoe's Crackers & Co., Burrito Express, & TC Eggington's

Cutting Edge Quiltworks

1949 W. Ray Rd. #33 85224
(480) 857-3443
Fax: (480) 857-6945
Est: 2001

Mon - Fri 10 - 6
Thur til 8
Sat 10 - 5
Labor Day to Mothers Day
Sun 12 - 4

Chandler, AZ #29

- Premium Quality Fabric for Quilters.
- Check Out Our Build Your Stash Corner.
- Huge Moda Selection and Blender Wall.
- Lots of Samples and Kits.

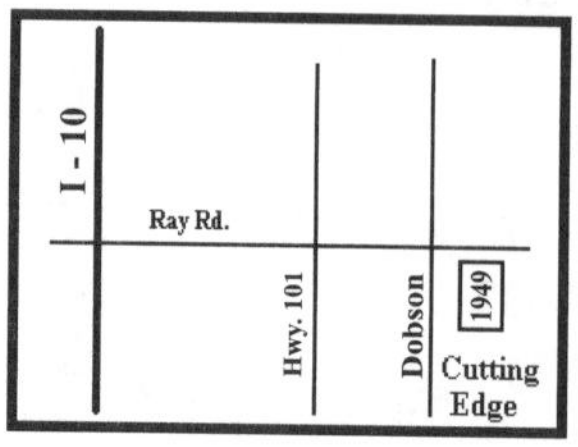

Take Ray Rd. Exit from I - 10 or 101. East on Ray to Dobson (SE corner)

www.cuttingedgequiltworks.com

Chandler, AZ #30

35th Ave. Sew & Vac

Mon - Fri 9 - 6
Sat 9 - 5
Sun 10 - 4

4939 W. Ray Rd. #27 85226
(480) 961-7363 Fax: (480) 705-0065
Free Online Newsletter
info@35thavesewandvac.com
www.35thavesewandvac.com

Fabric - Quilting Supplies
Sewing Machines - Classes

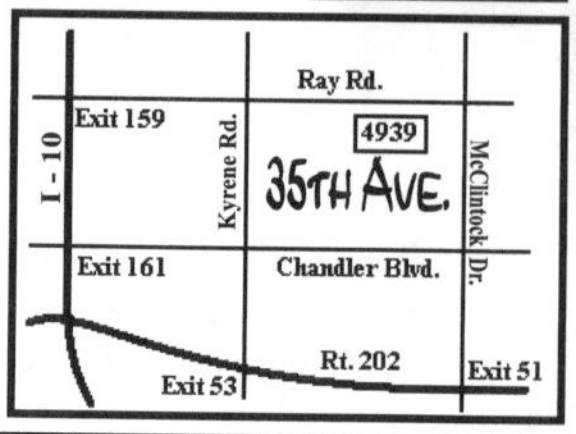

Quartzsite, AZ #31

Desert Fabric

Mon - Sat 9 - 5
May - Aug 9 - 1

185 Washington Ave 85346
(928) 927-7447 Fax: Same
1400 sq. ft. 1100+ Bolts
jbarc@tds.net

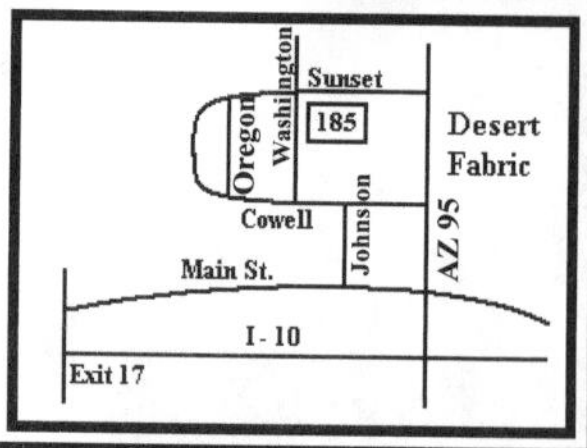

Quality fabric selection to satisfy any quilter's taste. Excellent selection of southwest prints to remember your Arizona visit.

Goodyear, AZ #32

Tue - Sat 10 - 6
Closed Sun - Mon

Bearly Stitchin Sewing Center

14270 W. Indian School Rd. C-5 85395
(623) 243-5552
Fax: (623) 243-5570
bstitchin@earthlink.net
www.bearlystitchin.com
2000 Bolts Newsletter Online

We have all the fabric, thread, books, patterns and inspiration for your next quilting adventure. We also offer Husqvarna Viking.

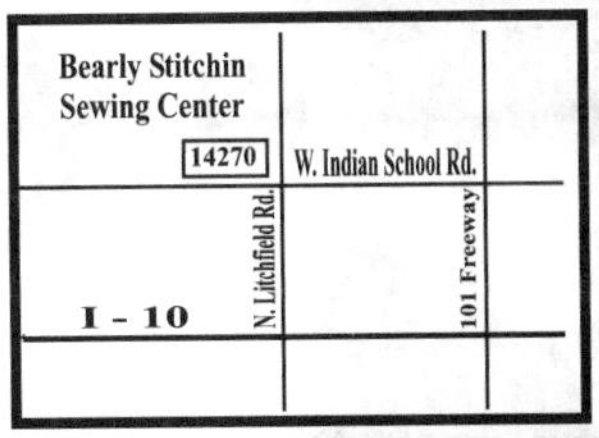

Casa Grande, AZ #34

Mon - Fri 9 - 5
Sat by Appt.

Eagles Wings Quilting

118 E,. 1st St. 85122
(520) 431-1905
Owner: Dena Dority Est: 2010
eagleswingsquilting@yahoo.com

Custom & long arm quilting.
Coming soon:
Fabrics, notions and sewing machines.

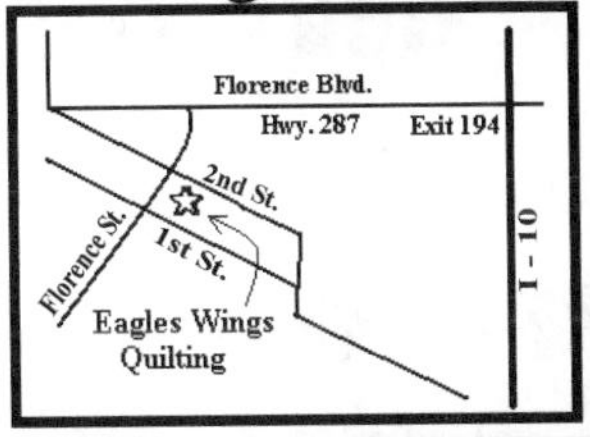

Pima, AZ #35

Mon - Fri 10 -6
Sat 10 - 4

Stitches

211 W. Center St. 85543
(928) 485-2511
Owner: Nelda Potter
stitches@aznex.net

Lots of Fabrics - Batting - Patterns - Notions
Machine Embroidery Threads
Hemstitching - Long Arm Quilting.

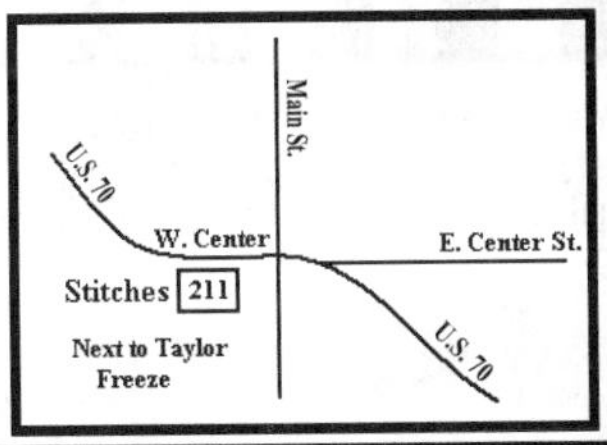

creative pursuitsetc

HQ 18
AUTHORIZED REP

Safford, AZ #36

Quilting Fabric and Notions.
Plus unique Home Décor, Gifts, and Scrapbooking Supplies. Drop in classes.
Pfaff & Brother Machines
Long-Arm Quilting Services

Mon - Fri 10 - 5:30
Sat 10 - 4

701 S. 5th Ave. 85546
(928) 348-7597
Owner: Rita Standage
ritastandage@yahoo.com
www.creativepursuitsetc.com

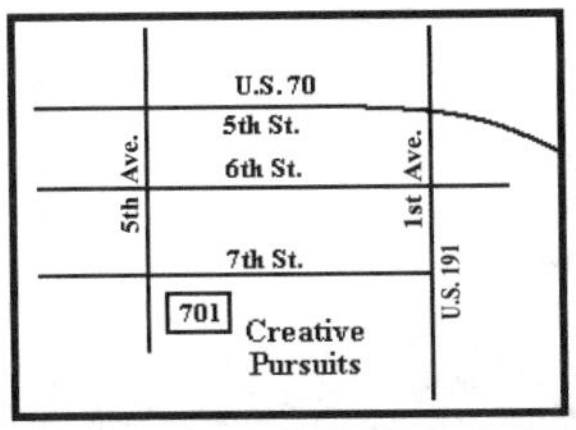

Fine Fabrics • Notions • Threads • Patterns • Gifts

In Stitches! Fabric

Mon - Sat 10-6

623-935-6596

Start a New Project Today!

www.institchesfabric.com

Full collections of quilt shop quality fabrics!

- Robert Kaufman
- Timeless Treasures
- Michael Miller
- Andover
- Benartex
- Makower

and so much more!

We also carry a wide selection of Fairy Frost.
Sign Up Now for Classes

Get Your AccuQuilt GO Here!

accuquilt

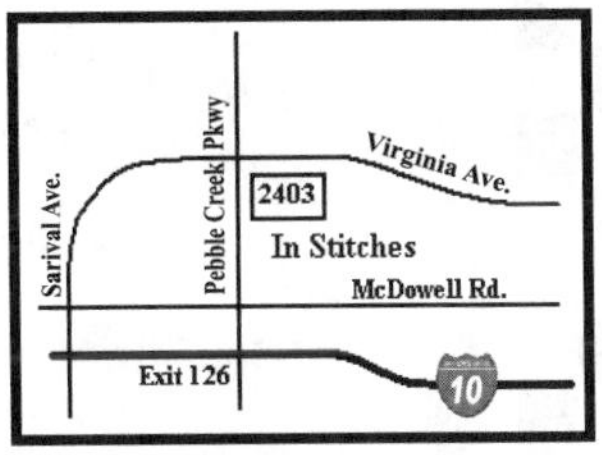

2403 N. Pebble Creek Pkwy #109 85395
Next to Papa John's
1/2 miles N of McDowell

Goodyear, AZ #33

Oro Valley, AZ #37

Mon - Fri 9 - 5
Sat 9 - 4

Catalina Quilting

11941 N. 1st Ave. 85737
(520) 825-8800
Owner: Betty Riddle
Est: 2006 Online Newsletter
briddle@catalinaquilting.com
Shop online for all your quilting needs.
www.catalinaquilting.com
Fabrics, Patterns, Classes, Books, Threads.

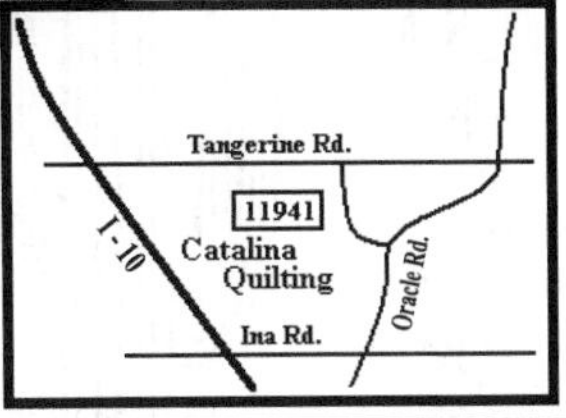

Benson, AZ #38

Mon - Sat 9 - 5

Cowgirl-Up Quilts

370 E. 4th St. 85602
(520) 586-1616
Owner Laura Mucci
Est: 2008 1600 sq.ft.
cowgirl-upquilts@hotmail.com
www.cowgirl-upquilts.com

We carry a large selection of western & southwestern fabric. We also carry Moda, Kaufman, Rowan, Hoffman and others

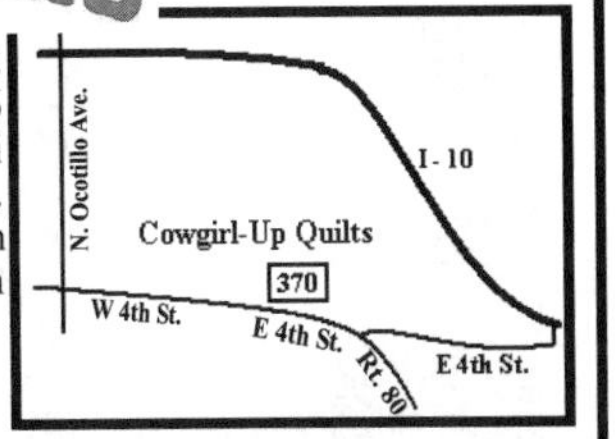

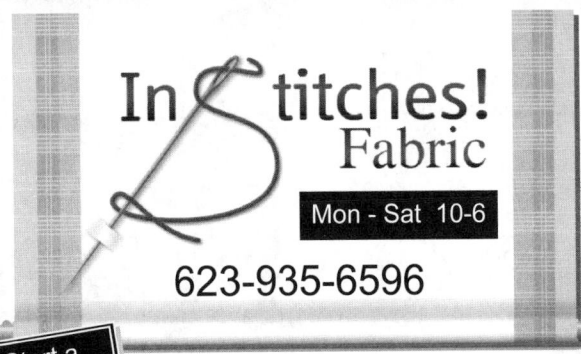

Quilter's Market

Better Homes and Gardens
Quilt Sampler
FEATURED SHOP

Tucson, AZ #39

- Colorful, exciting fabrics
- Experienced, enthusiastic teachers
- Helpful, knowledgeable staff
- Inspiring classes for all skill levels
- Fun and friendly atmosphere

7601 E. Speedway
Tucson, AZ
520-747-8458
www.thequiltersmarket.com

Monday–Friday 9:30-5:30
Saturday 9–5
Sunday 11–4

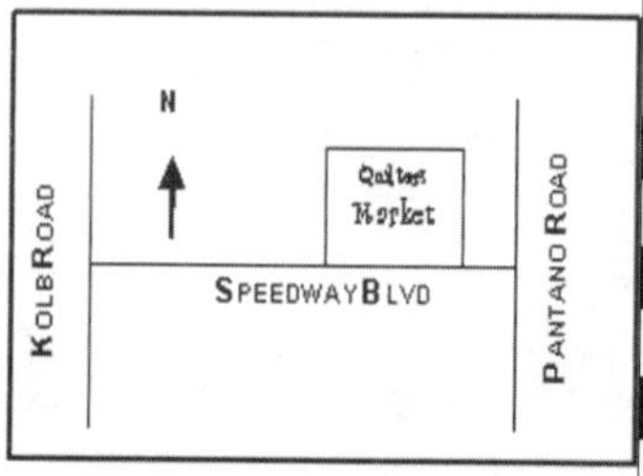

Tucson, AZ #40

Cactus Quilt Shop

Mon - Fri 9:30 - 5
Sat 9:30 - 4:30
Summer Hours:
Memorial to Labor Day
We close at 4 pm

6482 N. Oracle Rd.
Plaza Del Oro Shopping Center
In The NE Corner - Under the Clock
(520) 498-4698
Fax: (520) 498-4708
www.cactusquiltshop.com
Owner: Nancy Landon Est: 1997
1890 sq.ft. 3000+ Bolts

Everything for the Quilter
Plus Treasures.
We specialize in reproduction fabrics--largest collection in the South West!
And don't miss our Kitty Corner.

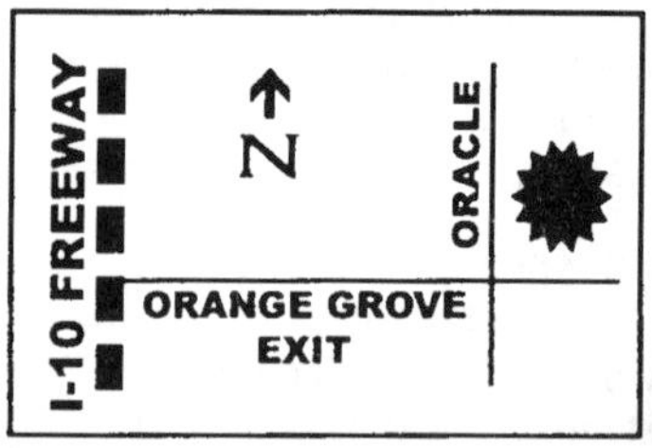

Tucson, AZ #41

The Quilt Basket

A Friendly Place for all your Quilting Needs

Mon - Sat 9:30 - 5

www.quiltbaskettucson.com

Hope to see you soon!

6538 E. Tanque Verde #130
Tucson, AZ 85715
(520) 722-8810
Owner: Lena Tsuruda

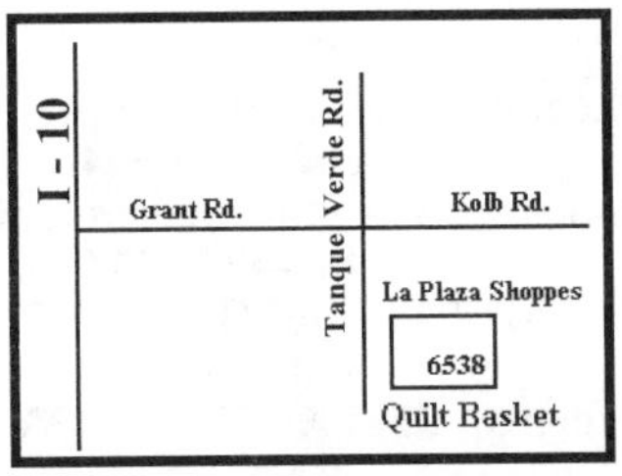

Sahuarita, AZ #43

QUILTERS DESERT PATCH

Mon - Sat 9 - 5
Summer Hours (June, July, August) Fri & Mon 9 - 5 or by Appt.

16121 S. Country Club Rd. 85629
(520) 399-2877 or (520) 648-1533
Owner: Phyllis Sirrine
Est: 1985 5000+ Bolts

1800 sq.ft. stuffed with Bolts & Flat Folds. We're happy to open by appointment for travelers in the summer call (520) 648-1533

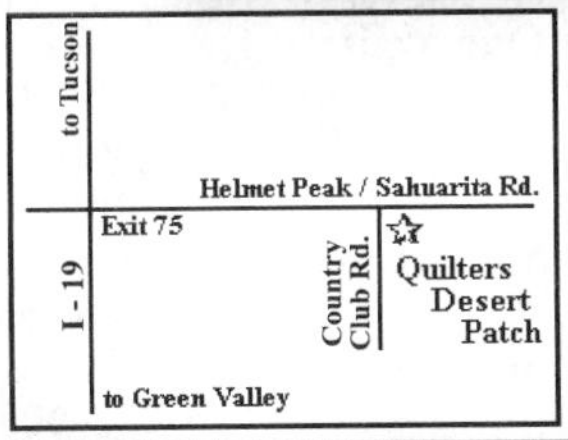

Green Valley, AZ #44

Hearts and Hands

Mon - Sat 9 - 5

110 E. Duval Rd. 85614
(520) 399-2050 Fax: (520) 399-3064
Est: 2002 3025 sq.ft. 2500+ Bolts
www.heartsandhandsquilts.com

Authorized Bernina Dealer - Sewing Machine Repair. Machine Embroidery Designs and threads. Specializing in bright, contemporary fabrics. Visit our new 'southwest corner' filled with southwest fabrics, patterns and designs.

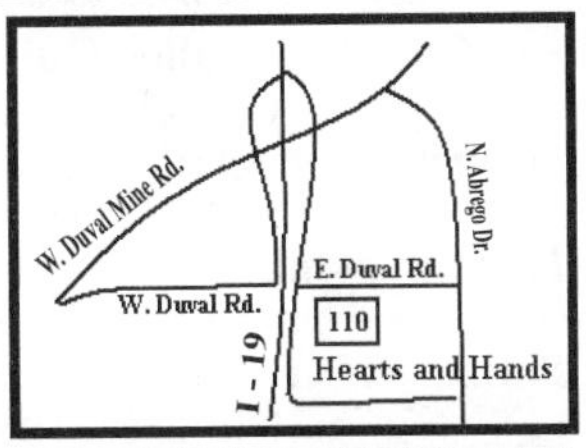

Tubac, AZ #45

Quilts LTD Gallery

Open Daily Nov - May Summer Weekends Only

7 Camino Otero, P.O. Box 2211 85646
(800) 255-2306
Est: 2004 1000 sq.ft.
quiltsltd@gmail.com www.quiltsltd.net

We specialize in Southwestern, Vintage and One-of-a-Kind quilts. Wearable art, quilters gifts, books, fat quarters & fun!

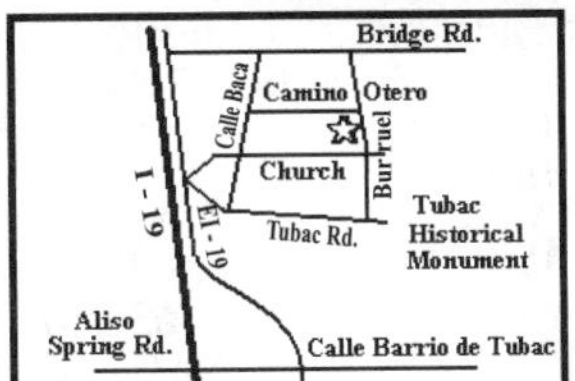

Tucson, AZ #42

Bella Quiltworks

Largest selection of 1800 - 1930 Reproduction and Batik fabrics in the area

KITS ~ KITS ~ KITS

- Block of the month programs. Yes, we mail!
- Hand-dyed wool.
- Original patterns by staff and local designers.
- Classes with award winning teachers.
- Supplies & Gifts.
- Knowledgeable and helpful staff.

www.bellaquiltworks.com
(520) 514.7000

5648 E. BROADWAY BLVD. TUCSON

MONDAY-FRIDAY • 10–5:30 • SATURDAY • 10–5

Owner, Joelee Furrier ~ Est. 2003

Sierra Vista, AZ #46

Mon - Fri 10 - 5
Sat 10 - 4

The Squirrel's Nest
Quilting & Beyond

4049 E. Camino Principal 85650
(520) 417-1070 Fax: (520) 417-1071
info@fibernuts.com
www.fibernuts.com
Est: 1990 6000 sq. ft. 6000 bolts
HandiQuilter HQ16 - Avanté
Brother Sewing & Embroidery Machines
Spinning - Weaving - Lacemaking - Knitting

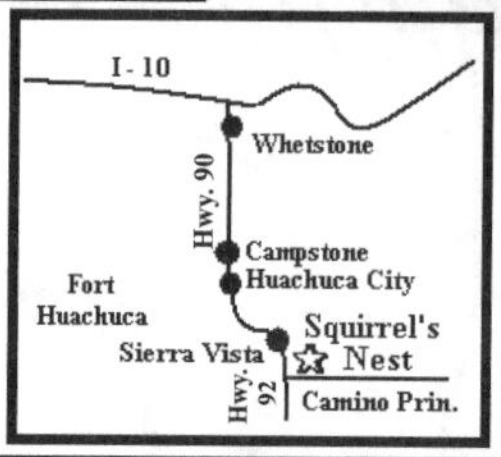

Sierra Vista, AZ #47

Mon - Sat 10 - 5

Thimbleweed Quilts

124 El Camino Real 85635
(520) 458-3221
Owner: Pat Boeck Est: 2001
www.thimbleweedquilts.com

Over 2,000 bolts of fabric.
Lots of Kits, Block of the Month's, Patterns and Classes. Professional machine quilting available on a Gammill machine.

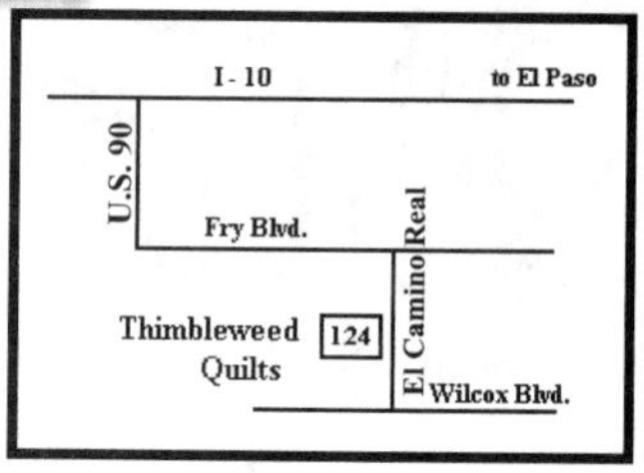

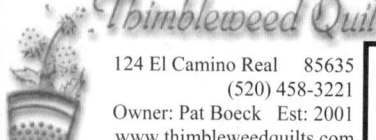

Arizona Quilt Shops

Benson — **Cowgirl-Up Quilts, 370 E. 4th St.** 520-586-1616 — See ad #38, page 27
Casa Grande — **Eagles Wings Quilting, 118 E. 1st St.** 520-4311905 — See ad #34, page 27
Casa Grande — Quilters Corner, 424 N. Florence St. 520-421-9484
Chandler — **Zoe'sTrunk 2990 N. Alma School Rd., Suite 3** 480-857-4833 — See ad #28, page 26
Chandler — **Cutting Edge Quiltworks, 1949 W. Ray Rd.** 480-857-3443 — See ad #29, page 26
Chandler — **35th Ave Fabric World II, 4939 W Ray Rd # 27** 480-961-7363 — See ad #30, page 26
Cottonwood — **Quilter's Quarters, 51 Verde Heights Dr.** 928-634-8161 — See ad #7, page 21
El Mirage — **35th Ave Fabric World III 12213 NE Grand Ave** 602-583-0070 — See ad #13, page 22
Flagstaff — **Odegaard's Sewing Center, 2109 N. Fourth St.** 928-774-2331 — See ad #3, page 21
Fountain Hills — Desert Flower, 16858 Ave of the Fountains 480-836-2441
Gilbert — Patchwork Pieces Quilt, 1250 N. Sailors Way 480-545-7096
Glendale — **Mulqueen Sewing Center, 7838 N. 59th Ave.** 623-934-0084 — See ad #16, page 23
Goodyear — **Bearly Stitchin Sewing Ctr, 14270 W Indian School** 623-243-5552 — See ad #32, page 27
Goodyear — **In Stitches Fabric, 2403 N. Pebble Creek Pkwy.** 623-935-6596 — See ad #33, page 27
Green Valley — **Hearts and Hands, 110 E. Duval Rd.** 520-399-2050 — See ad #44, page 29
Kingman — **Connie's Quilter's Hide-A-Way, 310 E. Beale St** 928-753-9096 — See ad #5, page 21
Lake Havasu City — **JonAli Quilt & Sewing Center 2097 N. McCulloch Blvd.** 928-854-2002 — See ad #8, page 22
Lake Havasu City — **Sew What ?, 2876 Sweetwater Ave. #2** 928-453-4040 — See ad #9, page 22
Lakeside — **Amazing Quilts, 2964 W. White Mountain Blvd.** 928-368-5567 — See ad #2, page 21
Mesa — **Mulqueen Sewing Center, 3716 E. Main St.** 480-545-0778 — See ad #17, page 23
Mesa — **Scrapbooks, Etc., 2820 E University Dr. # 111** 480-854-2303 — See ad #18, page 23
Mesa — **Fashion Fabrics, 9849 E. Main St.** 480-986-3243 — See ad #20, page 24
Mesa — **A Quilters Oasis, 9963 E. Baseline Rd. #105** 480-354-4077 — See ad #19, page 23
Mesa — Sally's Fabrics, 1235 E. Main St. 480-833-7201
Miami — **Julie's Sewing Corner, 600 Sullivan St.** 928-473-7633 — See ad #22, page 24
Oro Valley — **Catalina Quilting, 11941 N. 1st Ave. #141** 520-825-8800 — See ad #37, page 27
Payson — **Quilting Sisters, 904 N. Beeline, Suite E** 928-468-6360 — See ad #10, page 22
Peoria — **The Quilter's Bee, 7549 W Cactus Rd., Ste. 111** 623-334-9359 — See ad #14, page 22
Phoenix — **The Quilted Apple, 3043 N. 24th St.** 602-956-0904 — See ad #23, page 24
Phoenix — **The Olde World Quilt Shoppe, 30855 N. Cave Creek** 480-473-2171 — See ad #24, page 24
Phoenix — **3 Dudes Quilting, 5053 E. Elliot Rd.** 480-598-8601 — See ad #25, page 24
Phoenix — **35th Ave Fabric World, 3500 W. Northern Ave.** 602-841-5427 — See ad #26, page 25
Phoenix — **Quiltz, 13825 N 32nd St., Ste. 8** 602-482-4141 — See ad #27, page 25
Phoenix — The Bernina Connection, 4219 E Indian School Rd. 602-553-8350
Pima — **Stitches, 211 W. Center St.** 928-485-2511 — See ad #35, page 27
Prescott Valley — **A Quilter's Dream 8732 E. Hwy. 69** 928-772-0864 — See ad #11, page 22
Prescott Valley — Quilt n' Sew Connection, 6546 E. 2nd St., Ste A 928-775-9580
Quartzsite — **Desert Fabric, 185 N. Washington St.** 928-927-7447 — See ad #31, page 26
Safford — **Creative Pursuits 701 S 5th Ave # A** 928-348-7597 — See ad #36, page 27
Sahuarita — **Quilters Desert Patch, 16121 S. Country Club Rd.** 520-648-1533 — See ad #43, page 29
Sedona — **Quilter's Store Sedona, 3075 W. Hwy. 89A** 928-282-2057 — See ad #6, page 21
Sierra Vista — **The Squirrel's Nest 4049 E. Camino Principal** 520-417-1070 — See ad #46, this page
Sierra Vista — **Thimbleweed Quilts, 124 El Camino Real** 520-458-3221 — See ad #47, this page
Springerville — **White Mountain Quilt Studio, 223 S. Mountain** 928-333-1333 — See ad #1, page 21
Sun City — **Sun Valley Quilts, 9857 W. Bell Rd.** 623-972-2091 — See ad #15, page 23
Surprise — **The Quilted Cactus, 15459 W. Bell Rd. #109** 623-975-9356 — See ad #12, page 22
Tempe — **Quilters' Ranch 1721 E Warner Rd #C-9** 480-838-8350 — See ad #21, page 24
Tubac — **Quilts Ltd. Gallery, 7 Camino Otero** 800-255-2306 — See ad #45, page 29
Tucson — **Cactus Quilt Shop, 6482 N. Oracle Rd., Plaza del Oro** 520-498-4698 — See ad #40, page 28
Tucson — **Bella Quiltworks, 5648 E. Broadway Blvd.** 520-514-7000 — See ad #42, page 29
Tucson — **Quilt Basket, Inc., 6538 E. Tanque Verde Rd. #130** 520-722-8810 — See ad #41, page 29
Tucson — **The Quilter's Market, 7601 E. Speedway Blvd.** 520-747-8458 — See ad #39, page 28
Tucson — Madison's Quilts, 10940 E. Desert Senna Rd. 520-731-1474
Tucson — Quilters Bee, 3860 N. El Moraga Dr. 520-743-0391
Wickenburg — M's Quilting Inspirations, 37825 S. Camino Blanco 928-684-6353
Williams — **Quilters Mercantile, 226 W. Rt. 66** 928-635-5221 — See ad #3, page 21
Yuma — Log Cabin Quilts, 136 W. 32nd 928-344-3800
Yuma — Quilting Bee, 2360 W. 32nd St. 928-726-3000

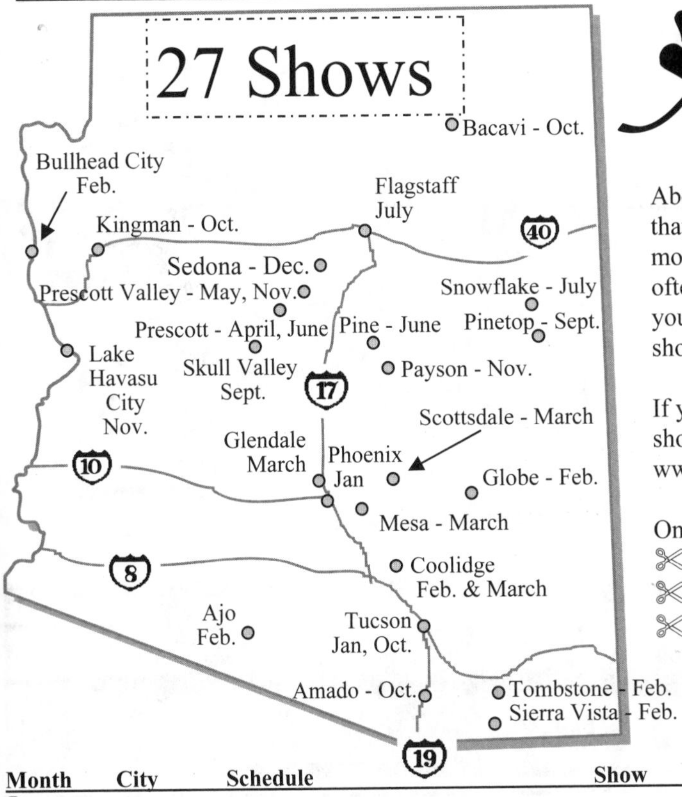

Arizona Quilt Shows

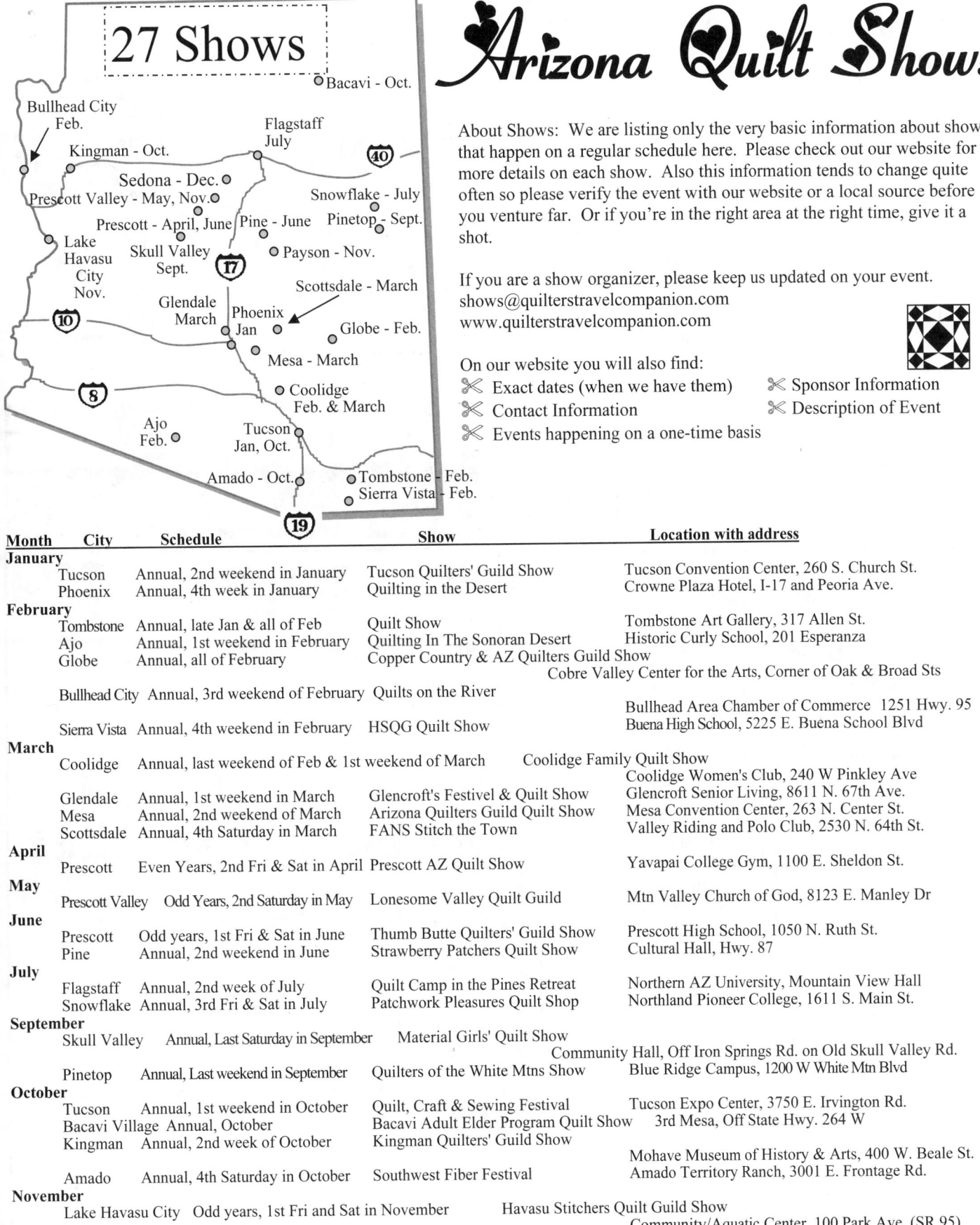

About Shows: We are listing only the very basic information about shows that happen on a regular schedule here. Please check out our website for more details on each show. Also this information tends to change quite often so please verify the event with our website or a local source before you venture far. Or if you're in the right area at the right time, give it a shot.

If you are a show organizer, please keep us updated on your event.
shows@quilterstravelcompanion.com
www.quilterstravelcompanion.com

On our website you will also find:
- Exact dates (when we have them)
- Contact Information
- Events happening on a one-time basis
- Sponsor Information
- Description of Event

Month	City	Schedule	Show	Location with address
January				
	Tucson	Annual, 2nd weekend in January	Tucson Quilters' Guild Show	Tucson Convention Center, 260 S. Church St.
	Phoenix	Annual, 4th week in January	Quilting in the Desert	Crowne Plaza Hotel, I-17 and Peoria Ave.
February				
	Tombstone	Annual, late Jan & all of Feb	Quilt Show	Tombstone Art Gallery, 317 Allen St.
	Ajo	Annual, 1st weekend in February	Quilting In The Sonoran Desert	Historic Curly School, 201 Esperanza
	Globe	Annual, all of February	Copper Country & AZ Quilters Guild Show	Cobre Valley Center for the Arts, Corner of Oak & Broad Sts
	Bullhead City	Annual, 3rd weekend of February	Quilts on the River	Bullhead Area Chamber of Commerce 1251 Hwy. 95
	Sierra Vista	Annual, 4th weekend in February	HSQG Quilt Show	Buena High School, 5225 E. Buena School Blvd
March				
	Coolidge	Annual, last weekend of Feb & 1st weekend of March	Coolidge Family Quilt Show	Coolidge Women's Club, 240 W Pinkley Ave
	Glendale	Annual, 1st weekend in March	Glencroft's Festivel & Quilt Show	Glencroft Senior Living, 8611 N. 67th Ave.
	Mesa	Annual, 2nd weekend of March	Arizona Quilters Guild Quilt Show	Mesa Convention Center, 263 N. Center St.
	Scottsdale	Annual, 4th Saturday in March	FANS Stitch the Town	Valley Riding and Polo Club, 2530 N. 64th St.
April				
	Prescott	Even Years, 2nd Fri & Sat in April	Prescott AZ Quilt Show	Yavapai College Gym, 1100 E. Sheldon St.
May				
	Prescott Valley	Odd Years, 2nd Saturday in May	Lonesome Valley Quilt Guild	Mtn Valley Church of God, 8123 E. Manley Dr
June				
	Prescott	Odd years, 1st Fri & Sat in June	Thumb Butte Quilters' Guild Show	Prescott High School, 1050 N. Ruth St.
	Pine	Annual, 2nd weekend in June	Strawberry Patchers Quilt Show	Cultural Hall, Hwy. 87
July				
	Flagstaff	Annual, 2nd week of July	Quilt Camp in the Pines Retreat	Northern AZ University, Mountain View Hall
	Snowflake	Annual, 3rd Fri & Sat in July	Patchwork Pleasures Quilt Shop	Northland Pioneer College, 1611 S. Main St.
September				
	Skull Valley	Annual, Last Saturday in September	Material Girls' Quilt Show	Community Hall, Off Iron Springs Rd. on Old Skull Valley Rd.
	Pinetop	Annual, Last weekend in September	Quilters of the White Mtns Show	Blue Ridge Campus, 1200 W White Mtn Blvd
October				
	Tucson	Annual, 1st weekend in October	Quilt, Craft & Sewing Festival	Tucson Expo Center, 3750 E. Irvington Rd.
	Bacavi Village	Annual, October	Bacavi Adult Elder Program Quilt Show	3rd Mesa, Off State Hwy. 264 W
	Kingman	Annual, 2nd week of October	Kingman Quilters' Guild Show	Mohave Museum of History & Arts, 400 W. Beale St.
	Amado	Annual, 4th Saturday in October	Southwest Fiber Festival	Amado Territory Ranch, 3001 E. Frontage Rd.
November				
	Lake Havasu City	Odd years, 1st Fri and Sat in November	Havasu Stitchers Quilt Guild Show	Community/Aquatic Center, 100 Park Ave. (SR 95)
	Payson	Annual, 2nd weekend of November	Rim Country Quilt Roundup	Rim Country Quilt Roundup, 100 W. Main St.
	Prescott Valley	Annual, usually the weekend before Thanksgiving	Lonesome Valley Quilt Guild Show	Mountain Valley Church of God, 8123 E. Manely Dr.
December				
	Sedona	Annual, late December to mid-February	Sedona Public Library Quilt Show	Sedona Public Library, 3250 White Bear Rd.

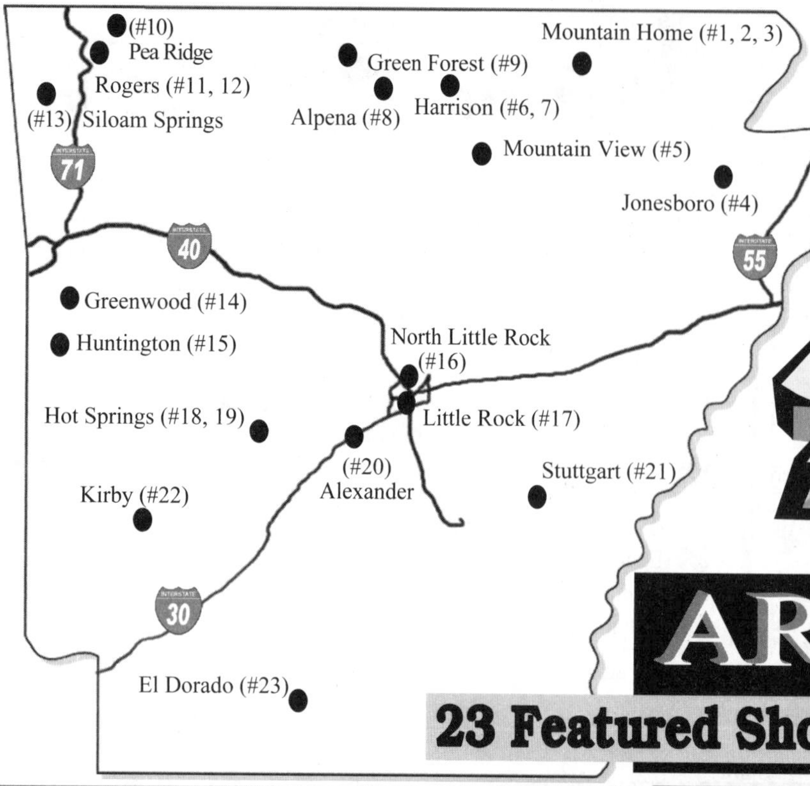

ARKANSAS

23 Featured Shops

Mountain Home, AR #1 & 2

ALL YOUR SEWING NEEDS UNDER ONE ROOF

307 S. Main St.

870-425-7670 870-425-8202

REMEMBER ME QUILT SHOP

- 4000 sq.ft.
- Fabrics & Notions
- Books & Patterns
- Gift Shop
- Samples
- Sewing Classes

Tues - Fri
9:30 - 5
Sat 9:30 - 3
Owner: Linda Siebert

MTN HOME SEWING CENTER

- Sewing Machines
- Embroidery Machines
- Sergers, Cabinets
- Embroidery Headquarters
- Service All Make & Models

Mon - Fri
9:30 - 5
Sat 9:30 - 2
Owner: Jerry Walcott

R.V. & Bus Parking * Handicap Access

One Block North of Downtown

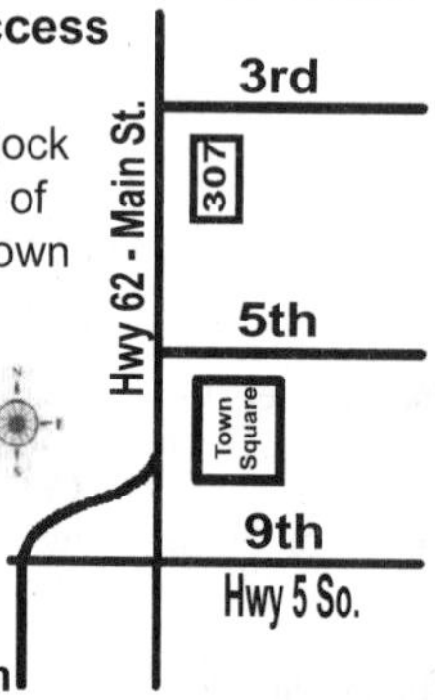

www.remembermequiltshop.com
http://mountainhomesewingcenter.com

Mountain Home, AR #3

Tues - Fri 9:30 - 5 Sat 9:30 - 3

Sew Unique

960 E. 9th St. 72653
(870) 424-4739 Est: 2006 2500 sq.ft.
Owner: Debbie Horton 500+ bolts
sewmickey50@gmail.com Online newsletter
www.sewuniquemh.com
We offer fabrics, notions and patterns, sewing clubs, seminars, machine sales and service. Our goal is to share our knowledge and make our store a fun place for you to come and enjoy your hobby.

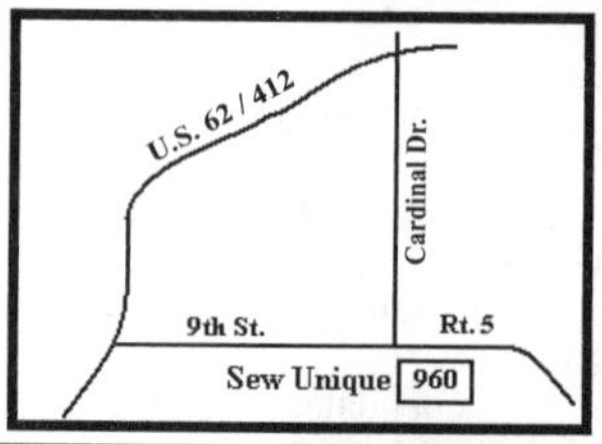

Jonesboro, AR #4

Tues - Fri 10 - 5:30 Sat 10 - 3 Mon by Appt.

THE CORNER QUILTER
YOUR COMPLETE SATISFACTION IS OUR FIRST PRIORITY

2010 Wilkins 72401
(870) 931-1138
Est: 1996

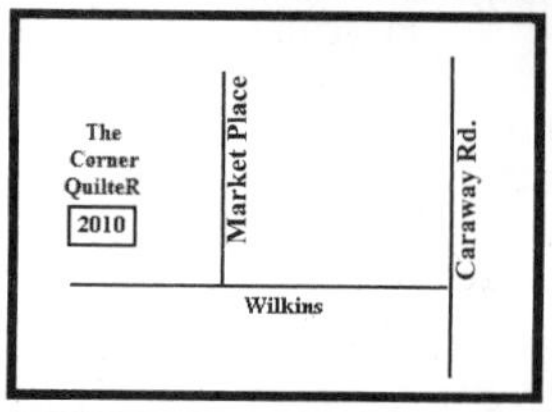

Owners: Leonard & Ann Davis
www.thecornerquilter.com
Handi Quilter & Elna Machines
All kinds of quilting classes & products.
Friendly Service and a great place to visit.

Mountain View, AR #5

Mon - Sat 10 - 5

The Quilting Bee

www.quiltingbeear.com
212 W. Main St., P.O. Box 2360 72560
(870) 269-9302
Owners: Daphne Higginbotham Est: 2002
ddhigg@mvtel.net 600+ Bolts
Located in the "Ozark Folk Music Capital of the World". 2000 sq.ft. of Fabrics, Notions, Books, Gifts & Good Times!

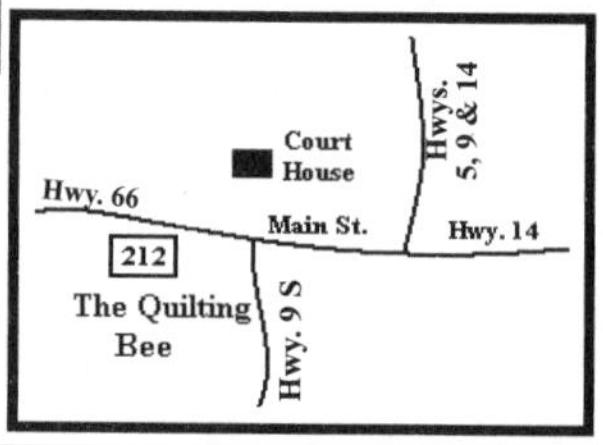

Country Corner Quilt Shop

10872 Hwy 392
Harrison, AR 72601
870-437-2299

Arkansas' Largest Independently Owned Fabric & Quilt Shop Since 1986

MON - SAT 8 - 5

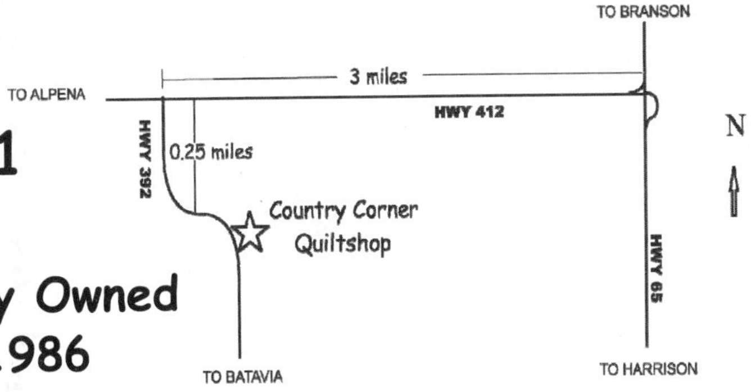

- The most friendly and knowledgeable staff
- More than 4000 bolts of the best cotton fabrics
- Books & Patterns galore, many patterns are our originals
- Nolting Longarm Machine Quilting Studio with multiple machines quilting in our studio six days a week
- Nolting Machine Sales and Service for 20+ years.

We are the fun place to shop! Located on a convenient travel route between Branson, MO and Eureka Springs, AR

Harrison, AR #6

Harrison, AR #7

Mon - Sun
9 - 5

Heart Quilt Shop

8874 Hwy. 62 W
72601
(870) 437-5400

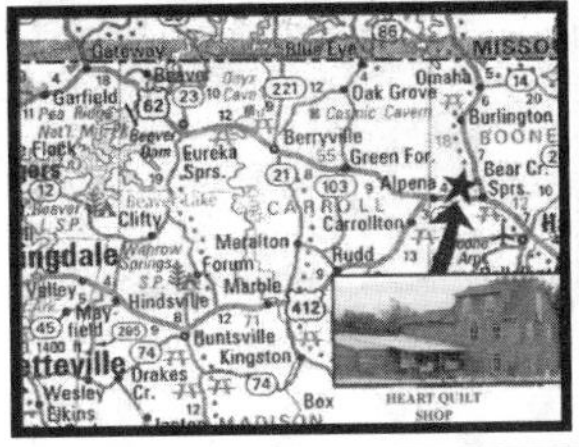

www.heartquiltshop.com
We have a variety of quilts.
We have fat quarters and charm packs.
Come by and See Us!

Alpena, AR #8

Mon - Sat
9 - 4

BJ's RAG BARN

307 E. Elm St. 72611
(870) 437-2325
Owners: Tom & Betty Wymore
Est: 1973
2400 sq.ft.

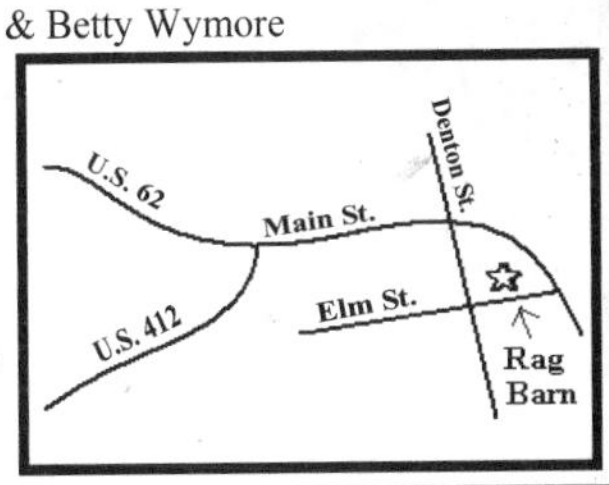

"We're the Big Red Barn"

Tons of quilt fabrics on bolts. 1000's of yards of flat folds. 90" quilting material. Lace, buttons & gifts. Quilts for sale.

McKee Sewing Center

64 Sparrow Road
870-437-2862 or 800-533-4531
Monday-Friday 9:00 - 5:00
Saturday 9:00 - 4:00

Quilting Fabric & Supplies
Embroidery Machines & Supplies
Authorized Brother, Janome, & Husqvarna Dealers
Handi Quilter 16 Mid-Arm Quilter

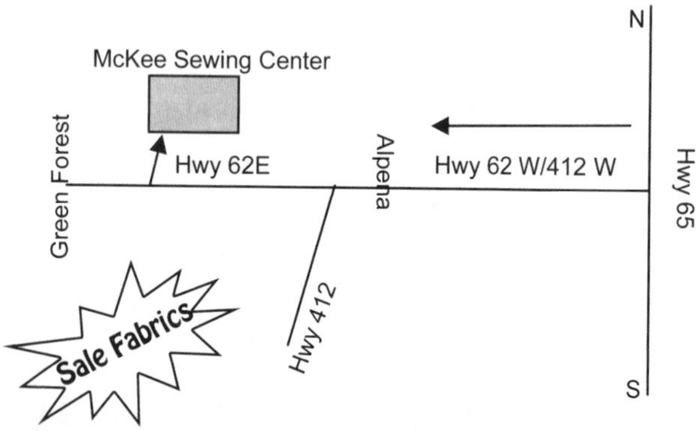

We specialize in quality quilting fabrics-2000+ bolts, Notions & classes. Friendly service always available. New customers are just friends we haven't met yet!

Green Forest, AR #9

Pea Ridge, AR #10

Tues - Fri 8 - 5
Sat 8 - 12

SEW N SEW QUILT SHOP

346 Lee Town Rd. 72751
(479) 457-1685 Fax: Same
sewnsewquiltshop@yahoo.com
Est: 2005
2000 sq.ft.
2500+ bolts
Free Newsletter

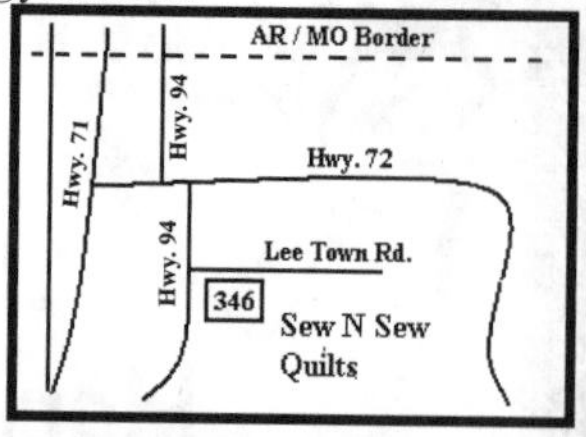

Fabrics, notions, books & patterns. Great classes, too! We'll finish your quilts with a Gammill Long-Arm Statler Stitcher.

Rogers, AR #11

The Rabbit's Lair

Home of fabrics fresh from market, lots of wool and hand dyed fibers that titillate and samples that inspire. This store has a dynamic energy that can sweep you up until the creative juices are flowing and you simply have no choice but to create something beautiful.

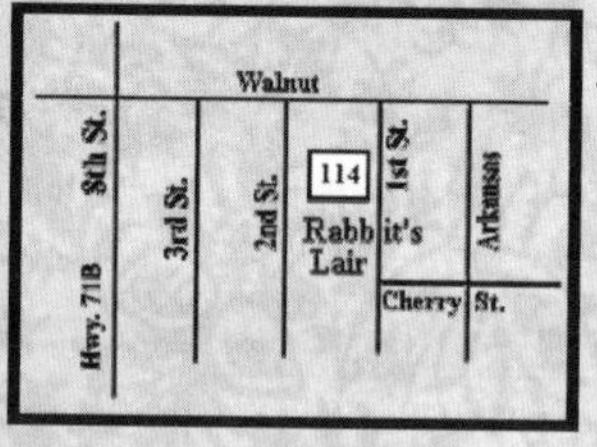

114 S. First St.
Rogers, AR 72756
(479) 636-3385
info@therabbitslair.com

Located in Historic Downtown Rogers

Mon - Sat 9:30 - 5
Open until 7 on Tues & Thurs
Mary Schopp Est: 2004
www.therabbitslair.com

Rogers Sewing Center

Since 1973

1802 Hwy. 71B South (8th street)
P.O. Box 280, Rogers, AR 72756

- Bernina "Dealer of the Year" 2000 and 2004.
- Repair, Parts and Accessories for all makes of machines and sergers.
- Lots of Fat Quarters
- Sewing Classes
- Machine embroidery & Software Supplies
- Drop By - We would love to meet you!

Mon - Fri 9 - 5
Sat 9 - 4

Rogers, AR #12

(479) 636-8240

Fax: (479) 636-1703
mail@rogerssewingcenter.com

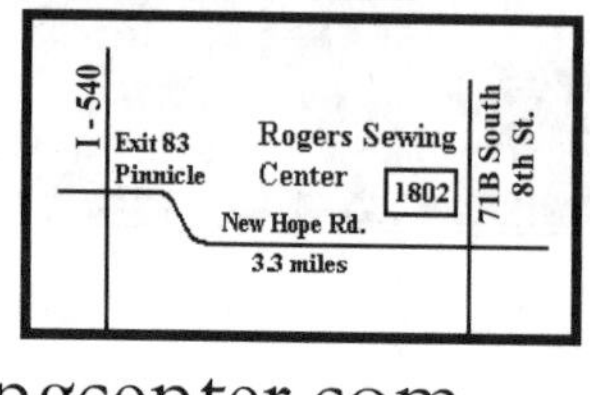

www.rogerssewingcenter.com

Siloam Springs, AR #13

Tues - Fri 9:30 - 5:30
Sat 9:30 - 4

SAGER CREEK QUILTS & YARNWORKS

304 E. Central Historic District 72761
(479) 524-5244 Est: 2000
www.sagercreekquilts.com

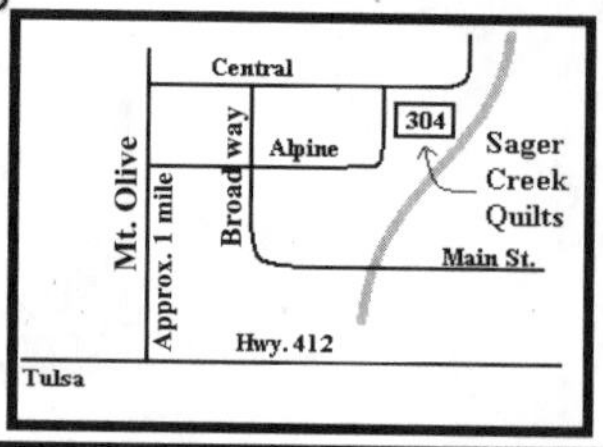

1800 bolts of 100% cottons, books, patterns, notions and batting. Wool for rug hooking & penny rugs. Knitting & Crocheting supplies plus a full line of needles & hooks.
Your One Stop Quilt Shop

Crooked Creek Quilt Shop
Greenwood, Arkansas

1736 West Center 72936
(479) 996-5808
Est: 1995 2000 sq.ft.
ccquilts@centurytel.net
Owners: Margie Love & Marcella Pickett

Fabric & Notions. Experienced long-arm quilters specializing in edge to edge, Heirloom and Trapunto. We have more than 45 years of quilting experience and would love to talk to you about your quilting needs. We do classes in piecing & appliqué.

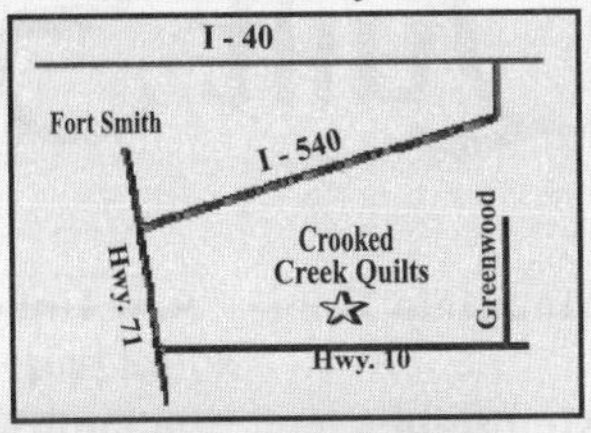

Tues - Fri 10 - 5 Sat 10 - 4

9 miles south of Fort Smith and one mile on Hwy. 10 spur East.

#14 **www.crookedcreekquiltshop.com**

Huntington, AR #15

Wed & Sat 9:30 - 5

MAMA'S LOG HOUSE

3715 E. Clarks Chapel Rd.
72940
(479) 928-1600 or
(479) 883-0254 Est: 1982
mamaslog@valuelinx.net
www.mamasloghousequiltshop.com

Quilting Supplies - Crafts
Split Oak Baskets - 100% Cotton Fabric

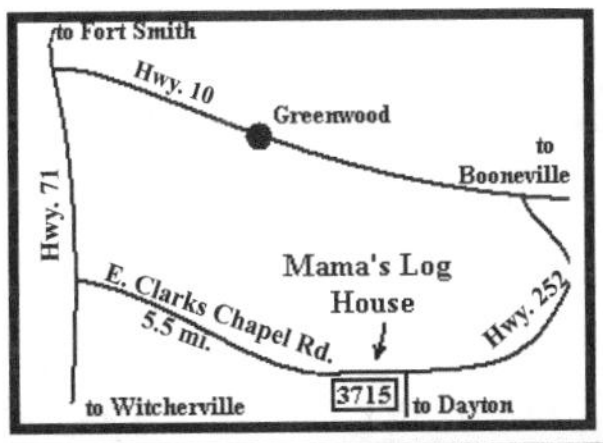

North Little Rock, AR #16

Tues - Fri 10 - 5 Sat 10 - 2

Sew Much More

100 E. 13th St. 72114
(501) 753-6050
Est: 1996 6000 sq.ft.
2000 Bolts Online Newsletter
www.sewmuchmoreinc.com

- Over 2000 Bolts of Fabric
- Wide Variety of Sewing and Quilting Notions
- Pfaff, Janome and Juki Authorized Dealers

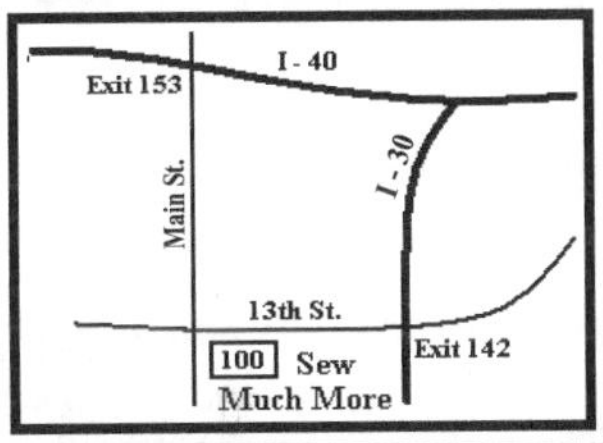

Little Rock, AR #17

Mon - Fri 10 - 5 Sat 10 - 4

The Stitchin' Post

1520 Macon Dr. #A2 72211
(501) 227-0288
Owners: Jane Bell & Linda Bowlby
info@stitchinpostinc.com
www.stitchinpostinc.com

100% cotton quilting Fabrics
Patterns ✂ Notions ✂ Classes

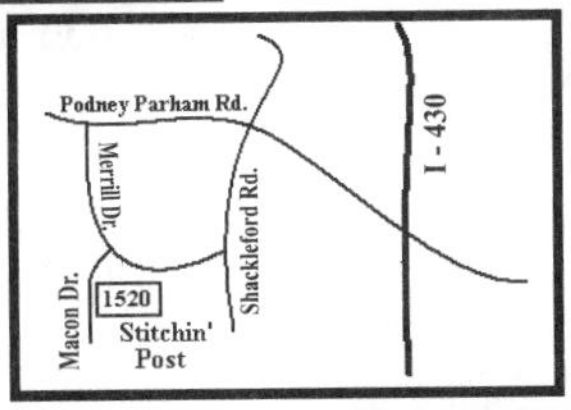

Hot Springs, AR #18

327 N. Hwy. 7 71901
(501) 318-2739
Owner:
Norma McKinnon
Est: 2008
1500 sq.ft.
750 Bolts
info@hhqsewingcenter.com

Hickory Hill Quilts

Mon - Sat 10 - 5

www.hhqsewingcenter.com

Full service quilt shop with fabric & notions. Full range of classes available. Authorized Dealer for **BERNINA**

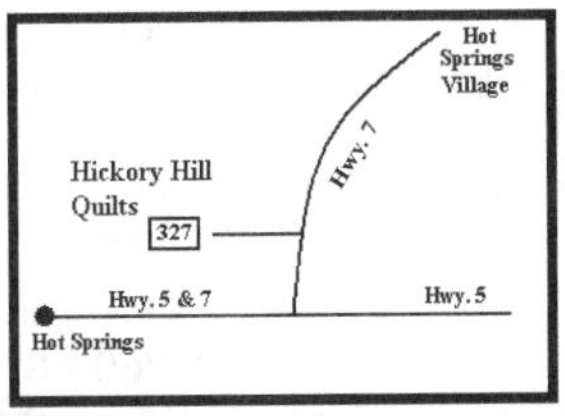

Hot Springs, AR #19

Mon - Fri 8 - 5:30 Sat 8 - 2

Cathy's Quiltin' Square
& Monogrammin' Designs

3256 Albert Pike 71913
(501) 760-6099
Owner: Cathy Anderson
Est: 1999 3600 sq.ft.
caquiltingsq@att.net

Quilt Fabric, Patterns, Books, Notions, Custom Machine Quilting, Embroidery and Screen Printing.

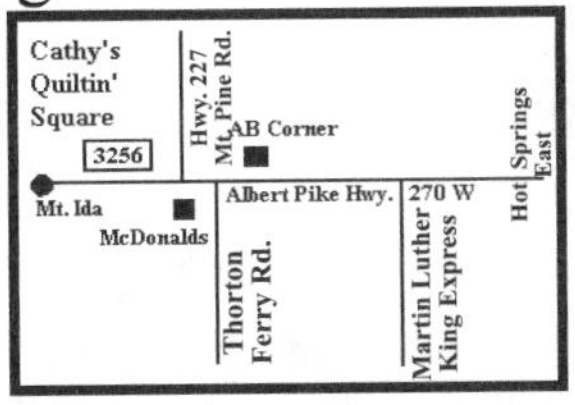

Alexander, AR #20

Tues - Fri 10 - 5:30 Sat 10 - 3

Pinwheel Fabrics

7915 Hwy. 5 North 72002
(501) 847-4177
pinwheelfabric@sbcglobal.net
www.pinwheelfabrics.com
Owner: Charlotte Williams
Est: 2004 1800 sq. ft.
2000 Bolts Free Newsletter

Quilting Fabric, Books, Notions & Patterns. Classes Available. Gammill Longarm rental avail.

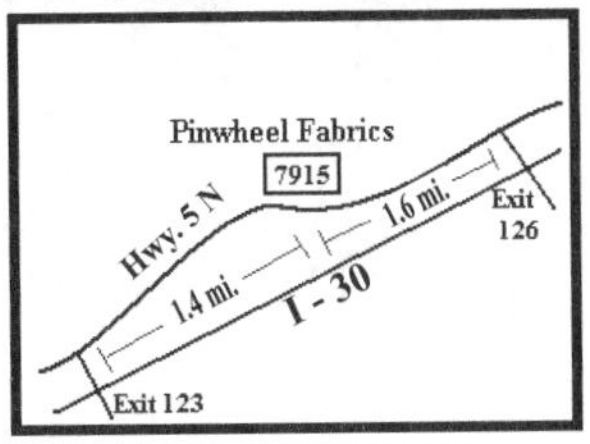

Stuttgart, AR #21

Mon - Fri 9:30 - 5 Sat 10 - 2

The French Seam

2015 S. Buerkle St. 72160
(870) 673-8156 Fax: (870) 673-6280
www.frenchseam.com

Authorized Bernina Sales & Service.
Quilting Fabric & Notions
Machine Embroidery Supplies
Fashion Fabric & Sewing Notions

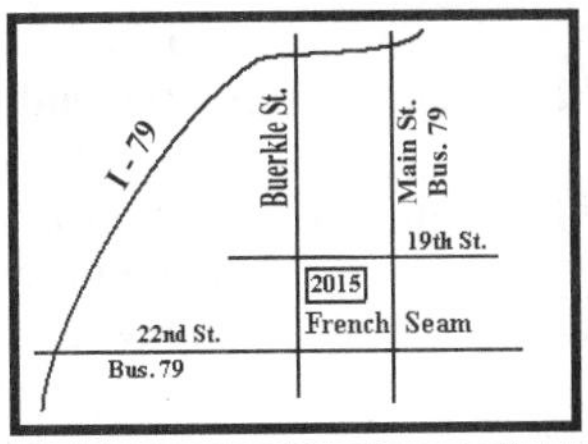

Kirby, AR #22

Tues - Fri 9 - 5
Sat 9 - 4

Vickie's Quilting Shack

3049 Hwy. 70 W 71950
(870) 398-4109
Owner: Vickie Handley
Est: 2001 1650 sq.ft. 1500 bolts

Fabrics, Notions, Machine Quilting, Quilts for Sale, Custom Quilting Pre-cut Quilt Kits.

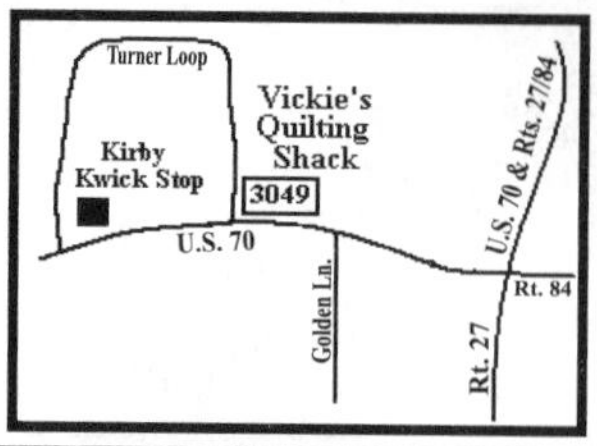

El Dorado, AR #23

Open By Appointment Mon, Tues & Fri

MNM Quilt Shop

154 Pete Mason Rd. 71730
(870) 862-0580 Fax: Same
Owner: Nannette Moss
Est: 2001 1200 sq.ft.
mnm@seark.net Over 1,000 Bolts
Custom Machine Quilting, Large Selection of Books, Rulers, Notions & Fabrics. Quilting Classes. Individually owned & operated.

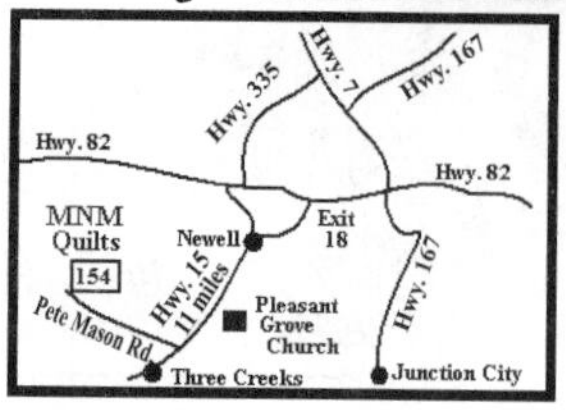

Arkansas Quilt Shops

Alexander **Pinwheel Fabrics, 7915 Hwy. 5 North**
501-847-4177 **See ad #20, page 35**

Alpena **B J's Rag Barn, 307 E. Elm St.**
870-437-2325 **See ad #8, page 33**

Batesville Marshall Dry Goods Company, 310 W. Main St. 870-793-2405
Bentonville Sew a Stitch, 106 NW 2nd St. 479-273-6064
Blytheville Village Shoppe, 5221 Southside Dr 870-532-4144
Cave City Quilt Rack, 1094 Hwy 230 870-283-2429
Clarksville Ginny Fabrics, 2205 W. Main St. 479-754-0196

El Dorado **MNM Quilt Shop, 154 Pete Mason Rd.**
870-862-0580 **See ad #23, this page**

Eureka Springs The Quilt Shop, 2 Center St. 479-253-2093
Eureka Springs Treasures from the Pacific, 435 W. Van Buren 479-253-8681
Eureka Springs Digital Quiltz, 36 Hwy. 23 South 479-253-9049
Flippin Curiosity Shop, 9084 Hwy. 62 E 870-453-5300
Fort Smith Just for Fun Fabrics, 2801 Old Greenwood Rd. 479-424-1219
Gassville R-Gems Inc, 5435 Hwy 62 W 870-430-5225
Glencoe Quilt Palace, Hwy. 62 E, P.O. Box 75 870-895-2999

Green Forest **McKee Sewing Center, 64 Sparrow Rd.**
870-437-2862 **See ad #9, page 34**

Greenwood **Crooked Creek Quilts, 1736 West Center St.**
479-996-5808 **See ad #14, page 35**

Harrison **Country Corner Quilt Shop, 10872 Hwy. 392**
870-437-2299 **See ad #6, page 33**

Harrison **Heart Quilt Shop, 8874 Hwy. 62 West**
870-437-5400 **See ad #7, page 33**

Heber Springs HQuilters Corner Fabric, 122 E Main St. 501-362-8612
Holiday Island Sew in Heaven, 3 Parkcliff Dr. 479-253-0770

Hot Springs **Hickory Hill Quilts & Sewing Ctr, 327 N. Hwy 7**
501-318-2739 **See ad #18, page 35**

Hot Springs **Cathy's Quiltin' Square, 3256 Albert Pike**
501-760-6099 **See ad #19, page 35**

Huntington **Mama's Log House, 3715 E. Clarks Chapel Rd.**
479-928-1600 **See ad #15, page 35**

Jonesboro **The Corner Quilter, 2010 Wilkins**
870-931-1138 **See ad #4, page 32**

Kirby **Vickie's Quilting Shack, 3049 Hwy. 70 W**
870-398-4109 **See ad #22, this page**

Little Rock **The Stitchin' Post, 1520 Macon Dr. #A2**
501-227-0288 **See ad #17, page 35**

Mountain Home **Remember Me Quilt Shop, 307 S. Main St.**
870-425-7670 **See ad #1, page 32**

Mountain Home **Mountain Home Sewing Ctr, 307 S. Main St.**
870-425-8202 **See ad #2, page 32**

Mountain Home Thus & Sew, 2612 Hwy. 5 S 870-424-3243

Mountain Home **Sew Unique, 960 E. 9th St.**
870-424-4739 **See ad #3, page 32**

Mountain View **The Quilting Bee, 212 W. Main St.**
870-269-9302 **See ad #5, page 32**

North Little Rock **Sew Much More, 100 E. 13th St.**
501-753-6050 **See ad #16, page 35**

Pea Ridge **Sew N Sew Quilts, 346 Lee Town Rd.**
479-451-1685 **See ad #10, page 34**

Rogers **The Rabbit's Lair, 114 S. 1st St.**
479-636-3385 **See ad #11, page 34**

Rogers **Rogers Sewing Center, 1802 Hwy. 71B S (8th St.)**
479-636-8240 **See ad #12, page 34**

Siloam Springs **Sager Creek Quilts, 304 E. Central**
479-524-5244 **See ad #13, page 34**

Stuttgart **The French Seam, 2015 S. Buerkle**
870-673-8156 **See ad #21, page 35**

Sulphur Springs The Quilt Corner, 110 S. Hibler Ave. 479-298-3006

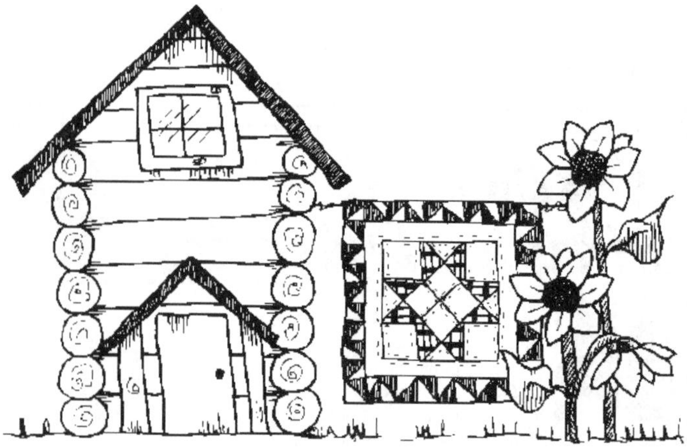

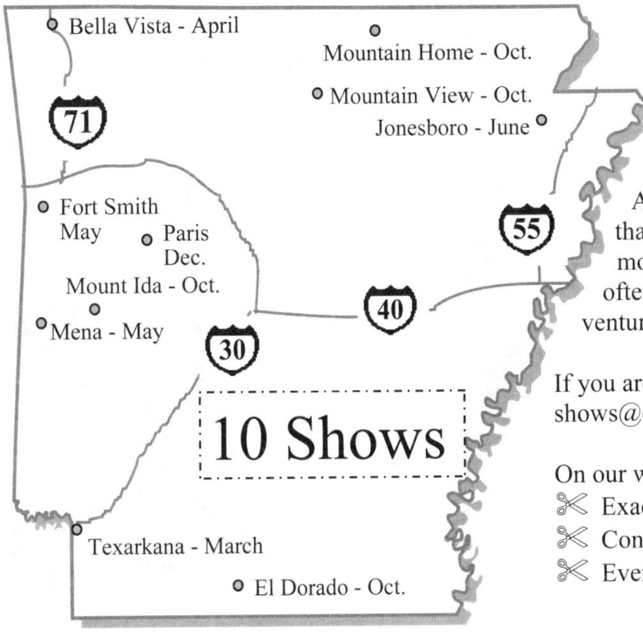

Arkansas Quilt Shows

About Shows: We are listing only the very basic information about shows that happen on a regular schedule here. Please check out our website for more details on each show. Also this information tends to change quite often so please verify the event with our website or a local source before you venture far. Or if you're in the right area at the right time, give it a shot.

If you are a show organizer, please keep us updated on your event.
shows@quilterstravelcompanion.com www.quilterstravelcompanion.com

On our website you will also find:
- Exact dates (when we have them)
- Contact Information
- Events happening on a one-time basis
- Sponsor Information
- Description of Event

Month	City	Schedule	Show	Location with address
March				
	Texarkana	Annual, 1st Fri & Sat in March	Miller-Bowie Quilt Show & Sale	Four States Fairground, 3700 E. 50th St.
April				
	Bella Vista	Even Years, 1st weekend in April (Unless Easter)	Calico Cut-Ups Quilt Show	St. Bernard Catholic Church, 1 St. Bernard Ln.
May				
	Fort Smith	Annual, 3rd Fri & Sat in May	The Belle Point Quilters Guild Show	Knights of Columbus Hall, 10203 Columbus Acres
	Mena	Annual, last weekend in May	Ouachita Quilt Show	Historical Armory, 211 DeQueen St.
June				
	Jonesboro	Annual, 1st weekend in June	Threads of Life Quilt Show St.	Bernards Auditorium, 505 E. Washington
October				
	El Dorado	Odd Years, 2nd Sat. in October	Union County Quilt Guild Show	Best Western King's Inn--Conference Center, 1920 Junction City Hwy.
	Mt. Ida	Annual, 2nd weekend in October	Quartz, Quiltz & Craftz Festival	Montgomery County Fairgrounds, Fairgrounds Rd.
	Mountain Home	Odd Years, last weekend in October	Hill 'n Hollow Quilter's Show	Baxter County Fairgrounds, 1507 Fairgrounds Dr.
	Mountain View	Odd Years, 4th weekend in October	Stone County Extension Homemakers Quilt Show	Ozark Folk Center, Hwy. 382
December				
	Paris	Annual, 1st Fri-Sat of December	Arkansas Fiberarts Extravaganza	The Lodge at Mt. Magazine, 6878 Hwy 309 S

Notes

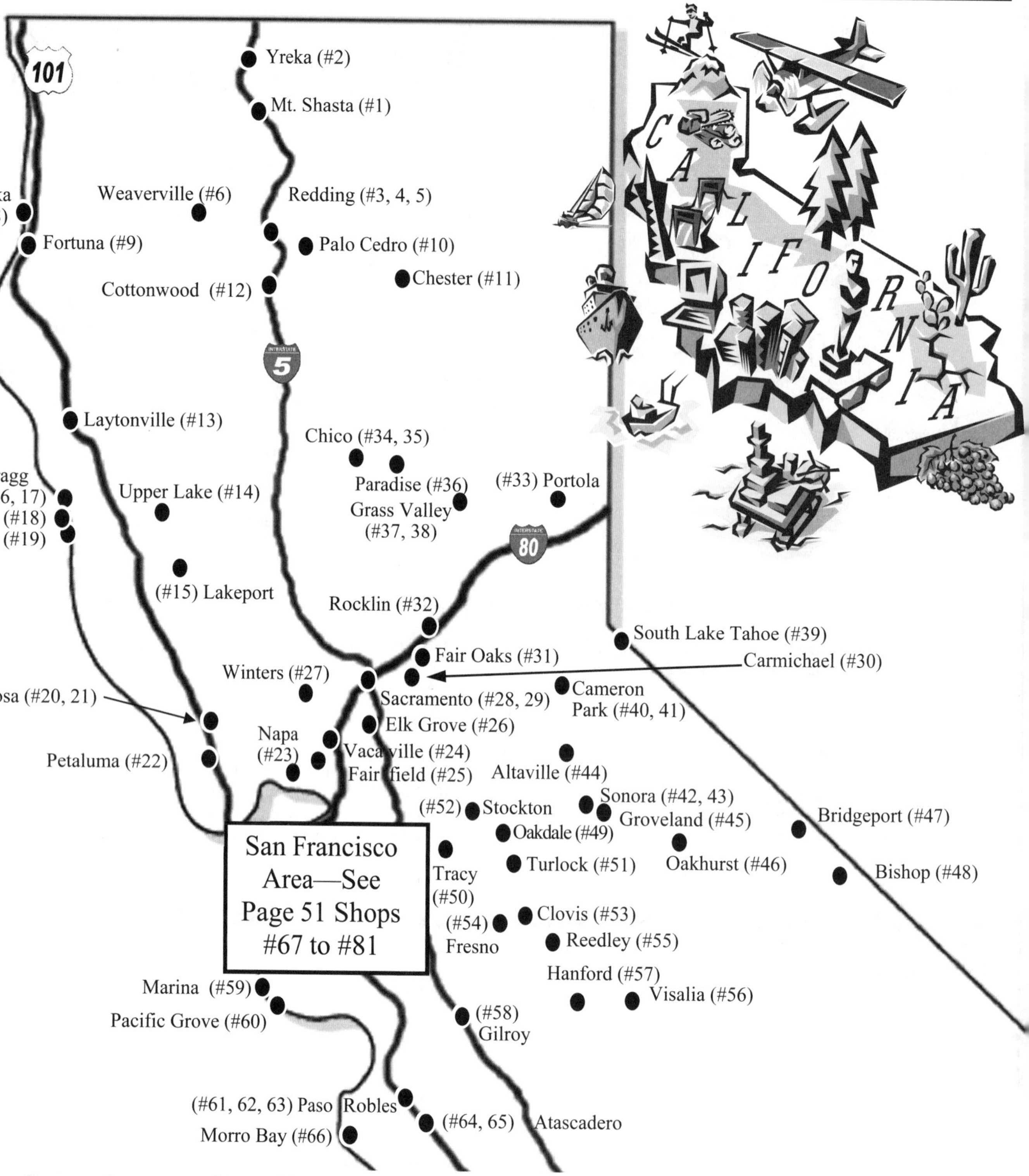

For Southern California See Page 55 Shops #82 thru #129

CALIFORNIA

129 Featured Shops

Mt. Shasta, CA #1

Tues - Sat
10 - 5
Some Mondays

Weston's
Quilting and Crafts

414 Chestnut St. 96067
(530) 926-4021
Owner: Michaela Weston
Est: 1968 1900 sq.ft.

Fabric - Yarns - Needle Arts
Serving you for over 40 years.

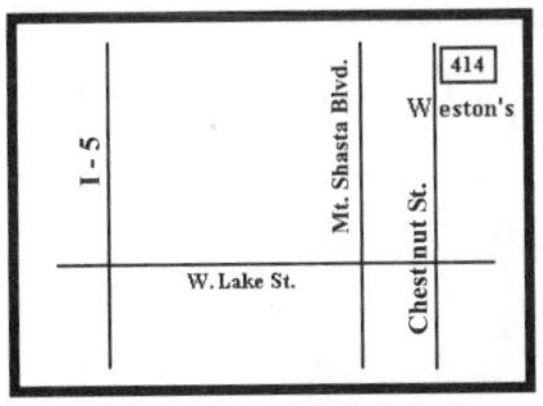

Redding, CA #3

Mon - Fri
10 - 5:30
Sat 10 - 5

SEW WHAT!
QUILTING WITH AN ATTITUDE

2609 Bechelli Ln. 96002
(530) 242-0177
Owner: Lori Orlando Est: 2002 3500 sq.ft.
www.sewwhatquilts.com
Over 3500 bolts, specializing in Kaffe Fassett and Brights & Batiks. Notions, Books, & Patterns, & we also carry yarn. Friendly, helpful Staff.

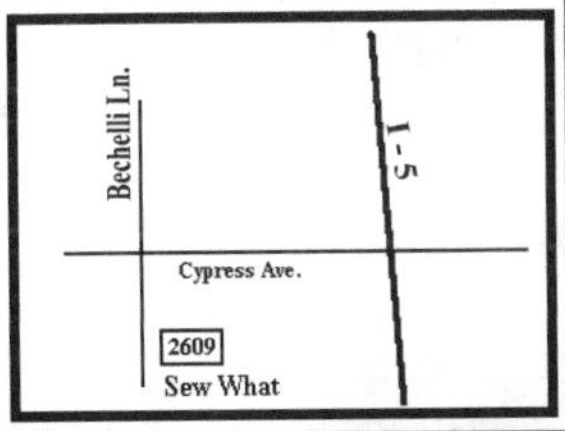

Redding, CA #4

Mon - Sat
10 - 6
Sun 12 - 5

The Sewing Room Quilt Shop

2665 Park Marina Dr. 96001
(530) 246-2056 Fax: (530) 246-0109
Owners: Karon Trybom & Cyndi Piearcy
Est: 2001 5000 sq.ft. 4000 bolts

Come see our selection of 4000 bolts of fabric. 30's and Batiks. We specialize in embellishments. Notions, patterns, books and classes.

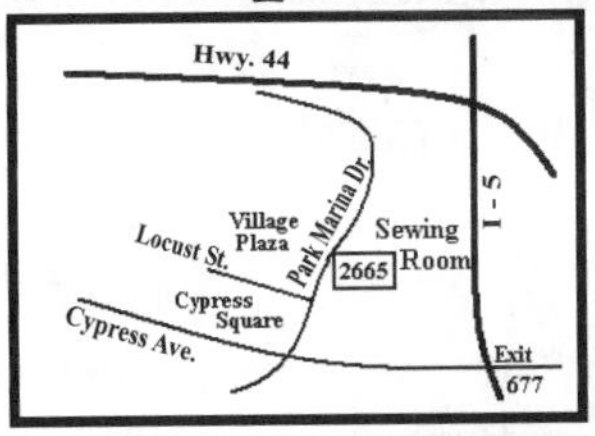

Redding, CA #5

Mon - Sat
9 - 5

Sew Simple

2223 Larkspur Lane 96002
(530) 222-1845 Fax: (530) 265-0300
Est: 1990 Newsletter
simplesew@aol.com

4000 bolts of fabric, notions, books, classes.
HandiQuilter and Bernina Dealer
Knowledgeable, friendly staff.

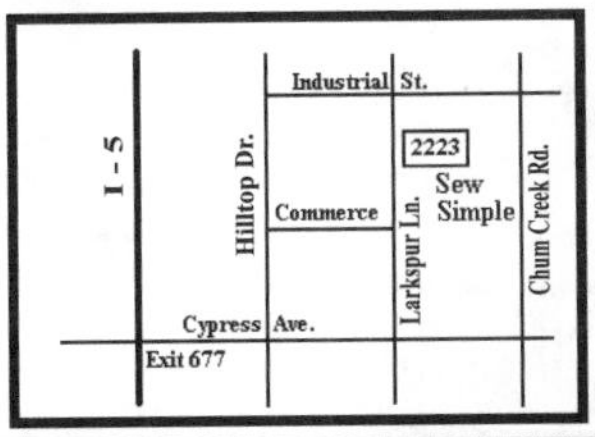

Weaverville, CA #6

Tues - Fri
10 - 6
Sat 10 - 4

Textile Traditions Quilt Shop

555 A Main St.
P.O. Box 3277 96093
(530) 623-6454
Owners: Sue Rhodes & Brenda Houston
www.textiletraditions.com

Quilt shop & dry goods emporium in historic Weaverville. We feature reproduction & art fabrics, notions, classes & FUN!

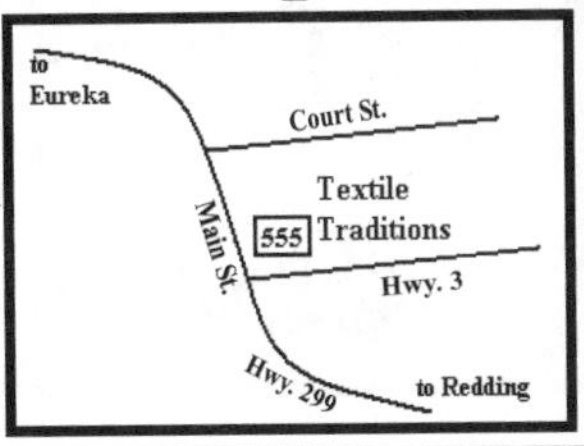

Yreka, CA #2

WOODEN SPOOLS

304 N. Main St.
Yreka, CA 96097
(530) 842-4562

Hours: Tuesday - Saturday
10 am - 4 pm
Closed Sundays & Mondays

★ Fabric ★ Notions ★
★ Quilt Supplies ★
★ Custom Machine Quilting Service ★
Vintage Singer Featherweight Sales, Service & Restoration
Authorized HQ 16 Tech / Representative

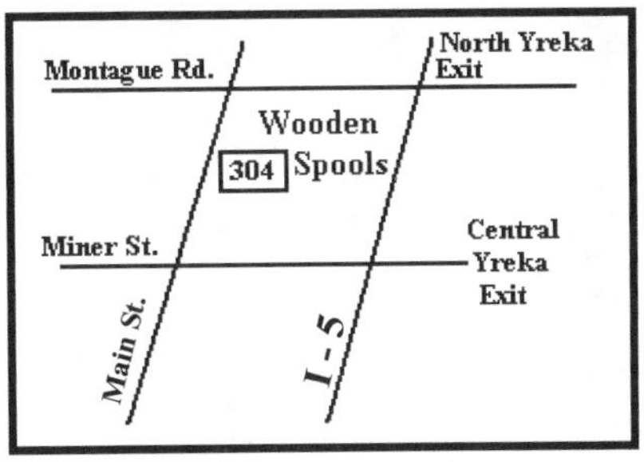

Scottie Dog Quilts

301 W. Harris St. Eureka, CA 95503
(707) 444-9662
www.scottiedogquilts.com
ScottieDogQuilts@aol.com
Owners: BrendaLou Scott & Liz Scott Adams

Mon 10 - 9
Tues - Fri
10 - 5:30
Sat 10 - 4

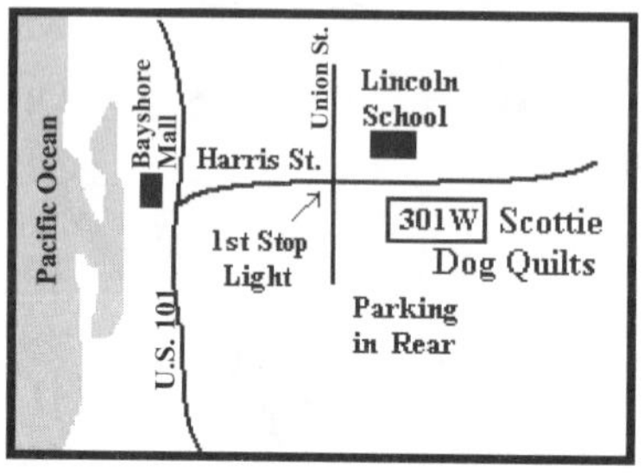

Wonderful selection of 100% Cotton Fabrics. Full line of Patterns, Books, Notions & Gifts. Classes, Retreats and Quilting Cruises for beginning through advanced quilters.

Eureka, CA #7

Eureka, CA #8

Ocean Wave Quilts

305 V Street 95501
(707) 444-0252
Owner: Suzie Pawlus
www.oceanwavequilts.com
Est: 1994 2000 Bolts

Open 6 days
9:30 - 5:30
Closed Tues

1800 sq ft of fabulous fabrics and hundreds of quilting books. Lots of patterns, some by our wonderful local artists. Find us in historic "Old Town" in the two story house built in 1904, in the Victorian Seaport of Eureka. Formerly of Trinidad, now one block off Hwy 101 South.

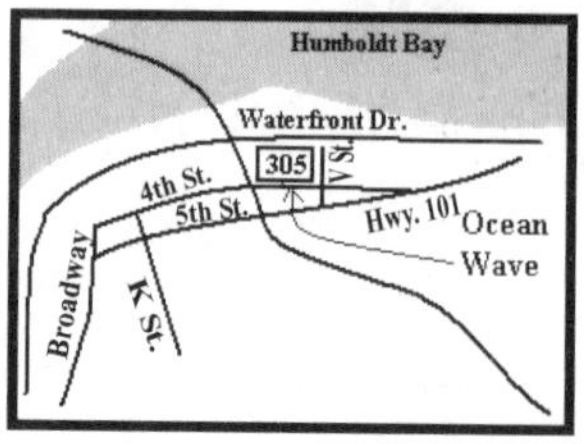

Fortuna, CA #9

Fortuna Fabrics & Crafts

Mon - Fri
10 - 5:30
Sat 10 - 4

2045 Main St. (in Rays Shopping Ctr.)
(707) 725-2501 Fax: Same
Est: 1994 1900 sq.ft.
Pretty much everything you need for all your handmade works of art. Fabrics, Notions, Books, Patterns, Wool Felt, DMC Floss & Pearls, Glass Beads, Fabric Dyes, Stamped Goods for embroidery etc, etc, etc...

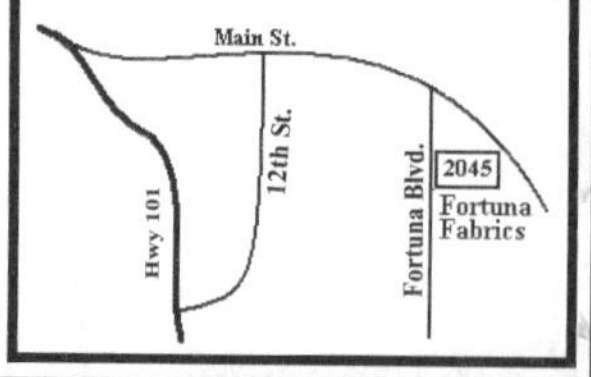

Chester, CA #11

Mtn. Maid Quilters

Oct 1 - May 30
Mon - Sat 10 - 5
June 1 - Sept 30
Mon - Sat 10 - 5
Sun 12 - 4

135 Main St. #6E
P.O. Box 546
96020

Est: 1992
1500 sq.ft.
3000 Bolts Owner: Sharon Paine
(530) 258-3901

Fabric, Notions, Specialty Threads, X-stitch, Dyes, and Silk Ribbon. We're next to beautiful Mt. Lassen and Lake Almanor. Classes Offered.

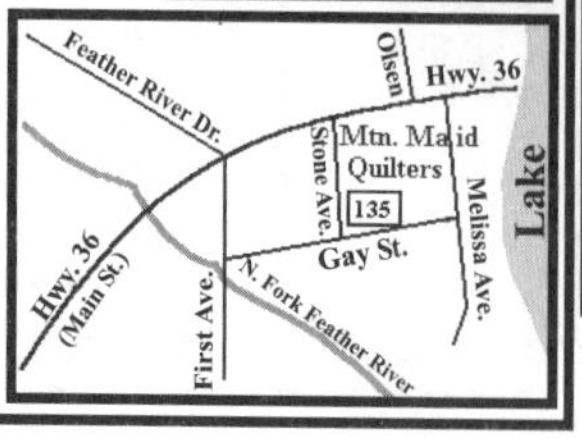

JJ's Log Cabin Quilt Shop

- Fabrics
- Notions
- Books
- Patterns
- Classes

9348 Deschutes Rd.
Palo Cedro, CA 96073
530-547-2228
Open 7 Days a Week
www.jjslogcabin.com

#10

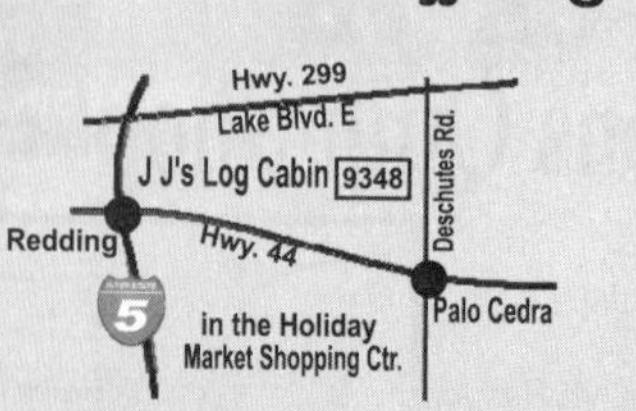

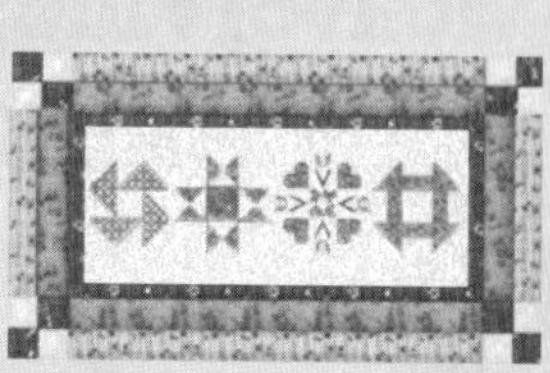

Just plain fun !

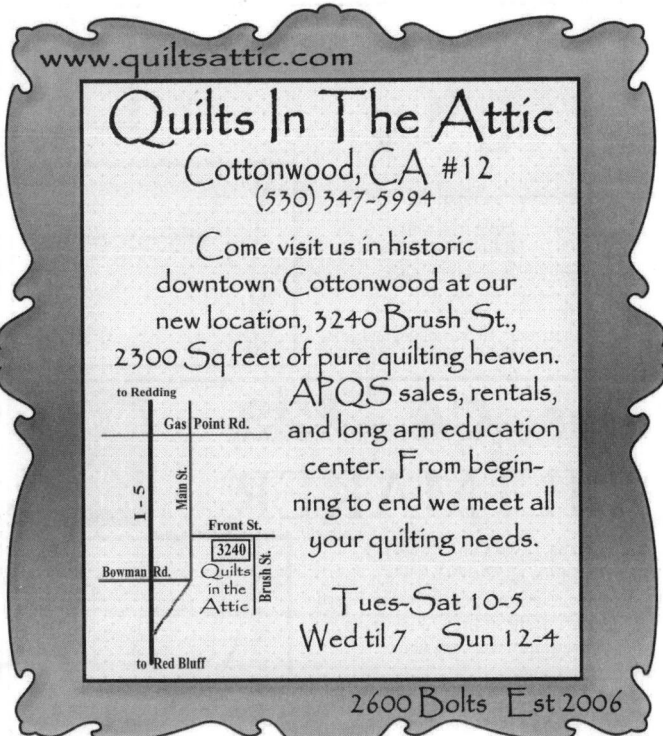

www.quiltsattic.com

Quilts In The Attic

Cottonwood, CA #12

(530) 347-5994

Come visit us in historic downtown Cottonwood at our new location, 3240 Brush St., 2300 Sq feet of pure quilting heaven. APQS sales, rentals, and long arm education center. From beginning to end we meet all your quilting needs.

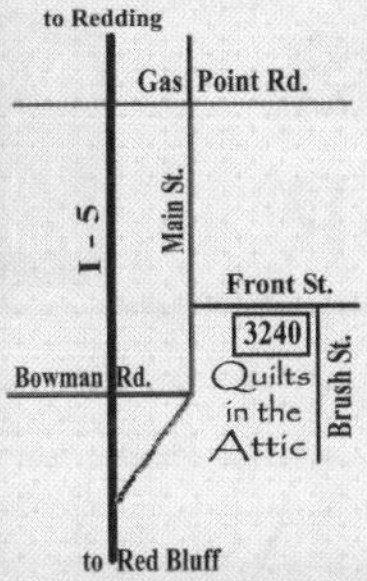

Tues-Sat 10-5
Wed til 7 Sun 12-4

2600 Bolts Est 2006

Laytonville, CA #13

Tues - Sat 10 - 5

The Fat Quail Quilt Shop

44550 N. Hwy. 101, P.O. Box 641 95454
(707) 984-6966
thefatquail@earthlink.net
Owner: Debbie Bowles

A fabric shop with warm country charm, friendly atmosphere and personalized attention. Right on the highway. Batiks, prints, books, patterns.
www.laytonville.org/fat_quail/fat_quail.html

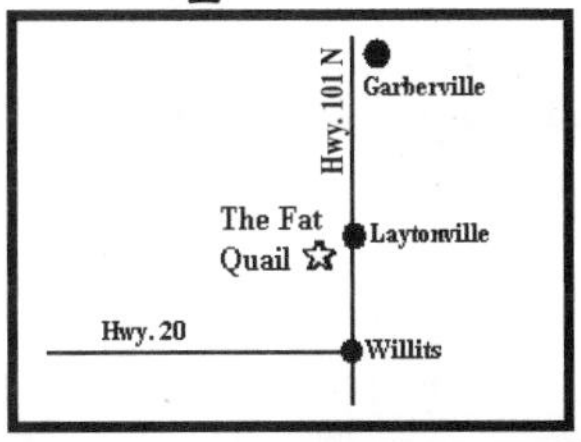

Upper Lake, CA #14

Open 6 days 10 - 5 Closed Wed.

Gracious Ladies

9460 Main St.
P.O. Box 975 95485
(707) 275-2307
Owners: Danna & J P Sarlande

Since 1998 in Historic Upper Lake
An emporium of gift items crafted by local artisans. Enjoy our eclectic collection of fabric & sewing notions as well as vintage books & patterns. Quilts, wall-hangings & pillow-quilts for sale.

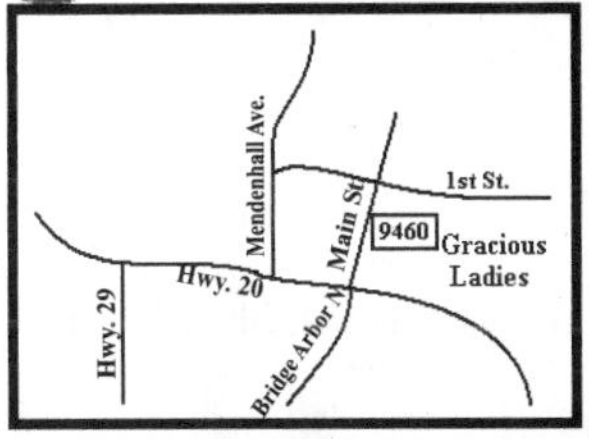

Lakeport, CA #15

Tues - Sat 10 - 4 Except Wed 1 - 8

Kerrie's Quilting

1853 N. High St. 95453
(707) 263-8555
KQ@pacific.net
www.kerriesquilting.com

100% Cottons	Notions	Classes
Books	Elna	Retreats

Quilter's vacation rental available.

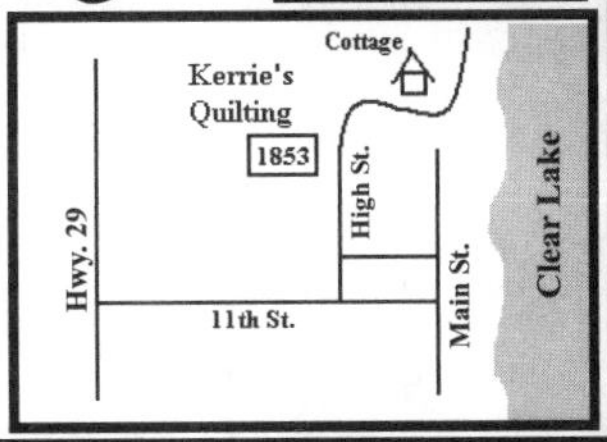

Fabric Indulgence & Art Supply

WWW.FABRICANDART.COM

- huge selection of fabric paints and dyes
- pfd Fabrics
- traditional japanese fabrics
- aboriginal prints
- batiks
- authentic african fabrics
- sustainable and organic fabrics
- fair trade silks from Asia
- ribbons and trims
- beads and findings

181 BOATYARD DRIVE
CORNER OF HWY 1 AND HWY 20
FORT BRAGG 707-964-6365

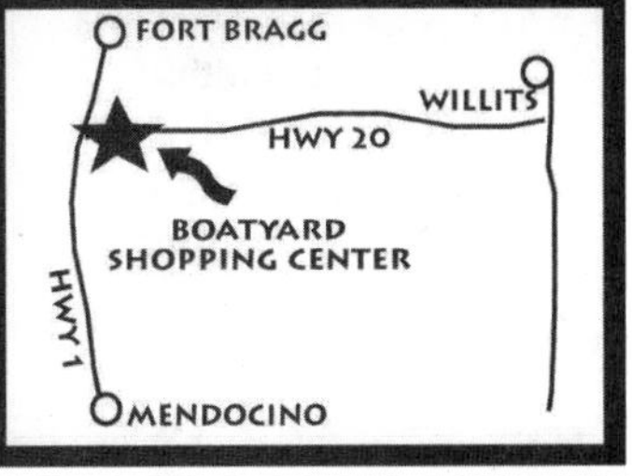

Fort Bragg, CA #17

Tues - Fri 10 - 5 Sat 10 - 3

Sew'n Sew

890-A N. Franklin St. 95437
(707) 964-4152
Fax: (707) 964-7046
Owner: Nancy Lamphear

Lots of classes. A large colorful collection of Quilting Fabrics and a great selection of books & patterns. Husband Friendly.

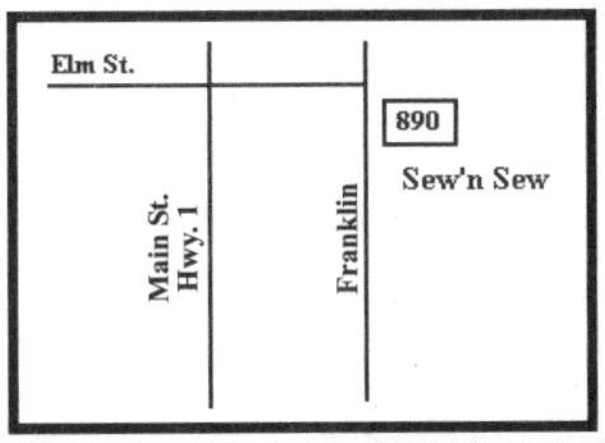

Mendocino, CA #18

Daily 10 - 5:30

OCEAN QUILTS OF MENDOCINO

45270 Main St., P.O. Box 1692 95460
(707) 937-4201 oceanq@mcn.org
www.oceanquiltsmendocino.com Est: 1999
Great selection of finished Quilts.
Gifts for quilters and folk art.

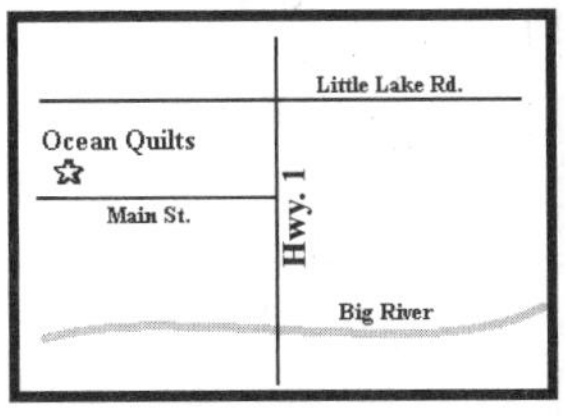

Albion, CA #19

Phone for Appointment

Rainbow Resource Co.

P.O. Box 222 95410
(707) 937-0431
rainbow@mcn.org
Est: 1969
Owner: Charlene Younker

My own line of hand silk-screened fabric for quilters, along with related fabrics from various companies. Also hand-dyed rick rack & other items. Unusual Buttons, & Fun Stuff.

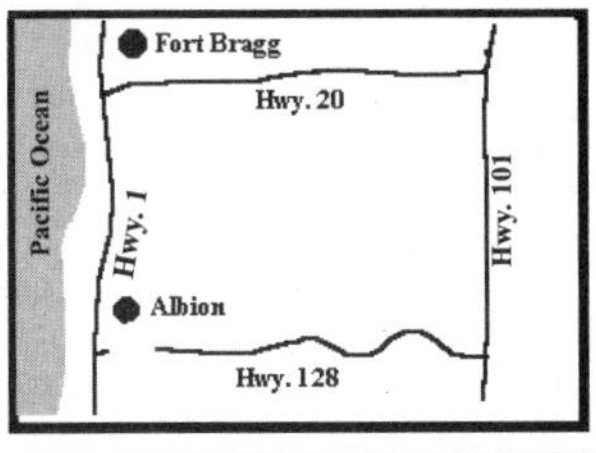

Santa Rosa, CA #20

Mon - Sat 10 - 6
Sun 12 - 5

The Material Girl
FABRICS AND QUILTING SUPPLIES

6119 Old Redwood Hwy. #B1
Windsor Village Ctr. 95403
(707) 836-0114
Fax: (707) 836-9575 Est: 2006
Nicole Cowlin, proprietor 1900 sq.ft.
www.materialgirlfabric.com
2500+ Bolts, Retro & Vintage Reproductions, Vintage Quilt Repair, Gifts, Classes and other fun Goodies.

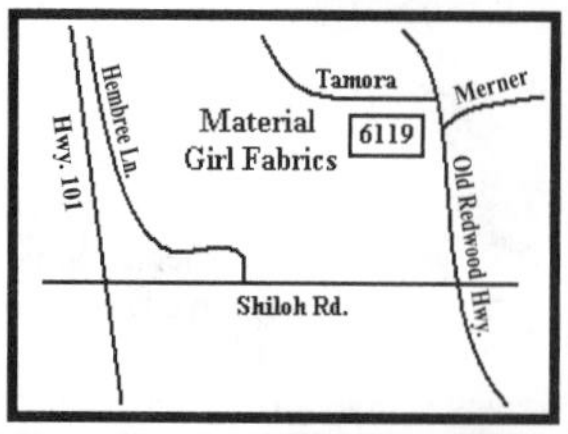

Santa Rosa, CA #21

Mon - Sat 10 - 5
Sun 12 - 4

Quilted Vine

1591 Farmers Ln. 94505
(707) 546-0750
Owner: Lynda McLean
Est: 2007 Online Newsletter
quiltedvine@sbcglobal.net
www.quiltedvine.com
Located in the heart of beautiful Sonoma County. One-stop quilt shop with fabric, notions and gifts. We strive to provide amazing customer service.

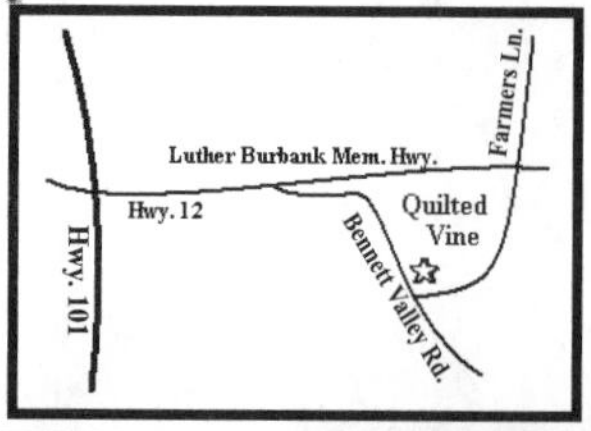

Petaluma, CA #22

Mon - Sat 10 - 5:30
Sun 12 - 4

Quilted Angel

200 G St. 94952
(707) 763-0945
Owner: Barbara & Jim Meikle
Est: 1991 3600 sq.ft. 4500+ Bolts
angels@QuiltedAngel.com
www.QuiltedAngel.com
A "destination" Quilt Store. Fabrics from all major suppliers, books (800 titles), notions, patterns, and classes.

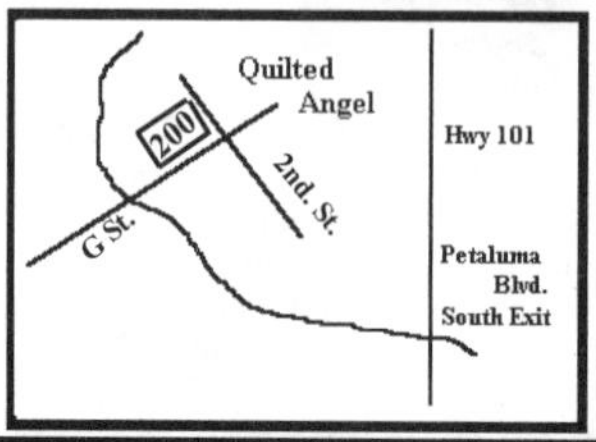

Napa, CA #23

Mon - Fri 10 - 5
Tues til 7
Sat 10 - 3

QUILTMAKER

1275 Napa Town Center 94559
(707) 252-6793
Owners: Diane Massey-Todd & Nancy Eberlin
Est: 1996 1500 sq.ft. 3000+ bolts
www.quiltmakernapa.com

We are all things quilting! The best in quilt classes, tools, books and fabrics.

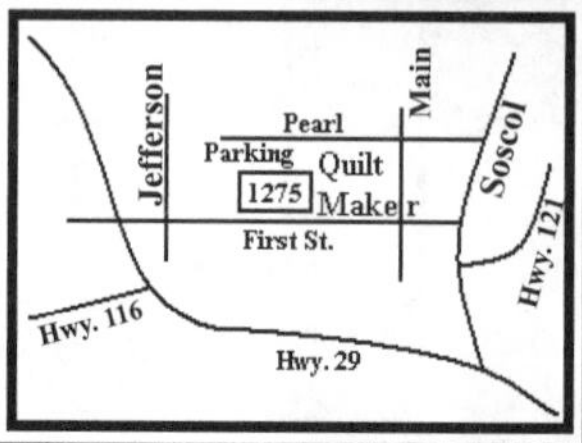

Vacaville, CA #24

A Quilted Heart

878 Alamo Drive, Vacaville, CA 95688
(707) 447-9000
www.aquiltedheart.net
Owners: Connie Ward & Michelle Craft

Hours: Mon - Fri 10 - 6, Sat 10 - 5, Sun 11 - 4

BOOKS • PATTERNS • NOTIONS • KITS

Quality Quilting Fabric
Check out our website for class schedules and more information about our store.

Located with:
ABS SEW N VAC
sewing machines
Pfaff & Brother

Easy access on and off the freeway

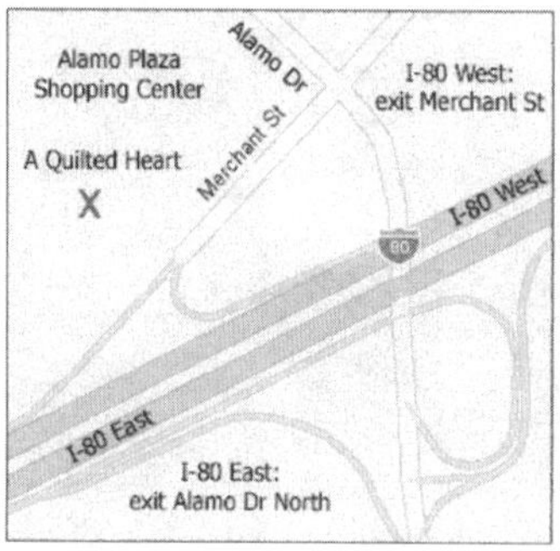

Fairfield, CA #25

Mon - Fri 10 - 6
Sat 10 - 5
Sun 11 - 4

Cornerstone Quilt Shoppe

1001 Texas St. #A 94533
(707) 438-2969 Fax: (707) 438-0304
cornerstonequilt@sbcglobal.net
www.cornerstonequiltshoppe.com
Owner: Beverly Cavazos
3300 sq. ft. Free Newsletter
2500+ bolts, notions, books & classes with a friendly staff. All your quilting needs in one shop. Longarm quilting is our specialty.

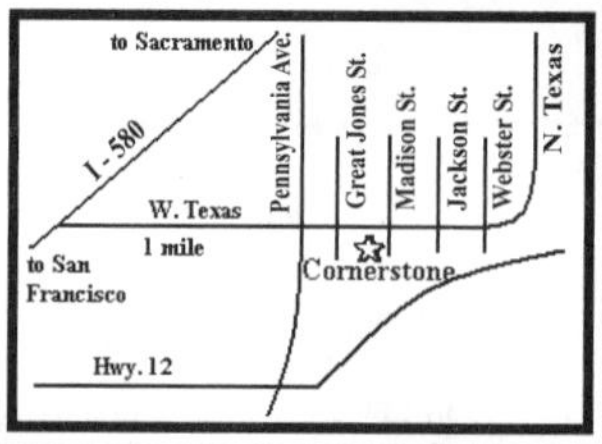

Elk Grove, CA #26

Mon - Fri 10 - 6
Sat 10 - 5

Country Sewing Center

9414 Elk Grove Florin Rd. 95624
(916) 685-8500 Est: 1993
Owners: Susan & Bill Zimlich
4000 sq.ft. 3000+ Bolts
www.countrysewing.net

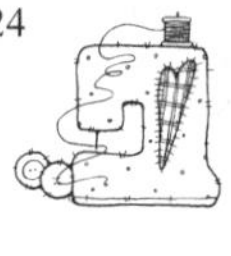

Great selection of 100% cotton fabrics, books & notions. Friendly, small-town service. Bond Rd. Exit from Hwy. 99 or I - 5 then East.

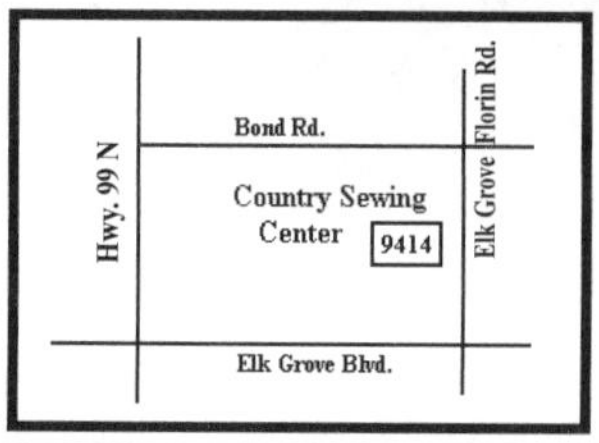

Winters, CA #27

Tues - Fri 10 - 6
Sat 10 - 5
Sun 10 - 4

Cloth Carousel

9 Main St. 95694
(530) 795-2580 Owner: Jan Bawart
www.clothcarousel.com
Featuring Friendly, Knowledgeable Staff. Offering Fabric, Notions, Books, Patterns, Classes and more for both Traditional and Contemporary Quilters. Eleven miles North of Vacaville off I - 505. Visit Winters on the 2nd Saturday in June for the Textile Art Festival.

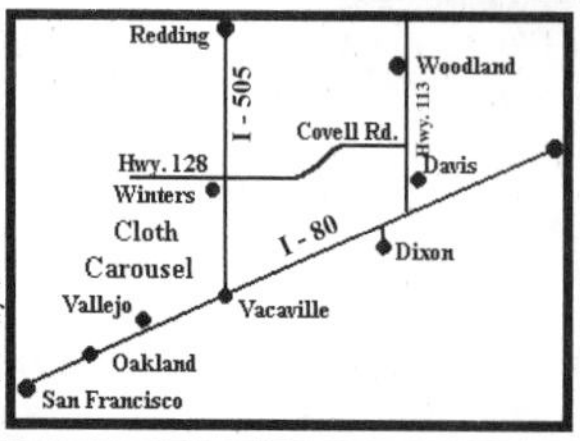

Sacramento, CA #28

Mon - Fri 10 - 6
Sat 10 - 4
Sun 12 - 4

Lindy Munday
Bearpaws & Hollyhocks
A Quilt Shop

4128 El Camino Ave. #5 95821
(916) 971-9392
bpandhh@sbcglobal.net
Est: 2005
2800 sq. ft.
2000 Bolts
Free Newsletter
Lindy Munday
100% Cotton Fabrics - Wool - Books - Patterns
Notions - Needlepunch - Classes
Bernina Location
Arrow Sewing Cabinets - Eclectic Gifts
www.bearpawsandhollyhock.com

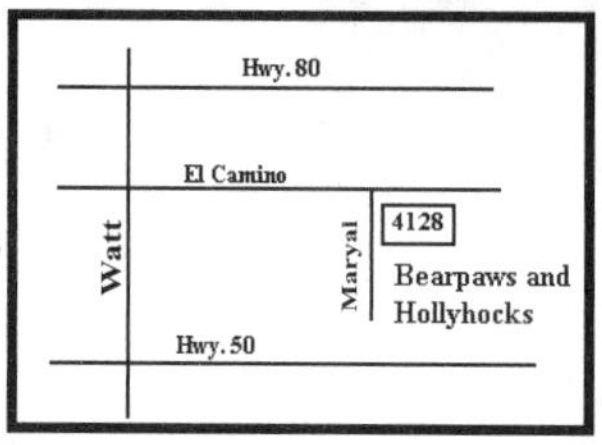

Sacramento, CA #29

Quilters' Corner

9792 B. Business Park Dr.
Sacramento, CA 95827
(916) 366-6136
Fax: (916) 366-6105
www.quilterscornersac.com

Mon - Fri 10 - 6
Sat 10 - 4
Sun 12 - 4

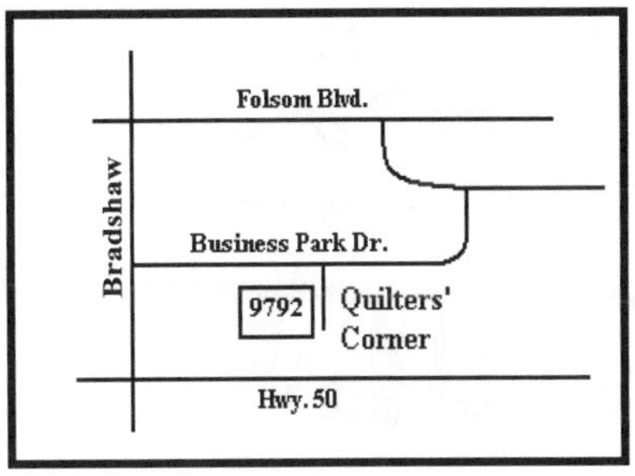

Full Service Quilt Store.

Over 3,000 sq.ft. of fabrics, books, patterns, notions, and gifts.
We have numerous clubs and yearly retreats.

Take Hwy. 50 to Bradshaw Rd., We are north of the Freeway. Turn on Business Park Dr. About 1/2 mi. turn into Driveway 9792 (Across from Marsh's Carpets)

Carmichael, CA #30

Mon - Fri 9 - 9
Sat 9 - 7
Sun 10 - 5

Beverly's

6456 Fair Oaks Blvd. (at Marconi Ave.)
(916) 486-8374 95608
www.beverlys.com

We cater to Quilters! High Quality Fabrics from Top Companies! Lots of Notions, Books, Classes. Very Friendly, Helpful Customer Service.

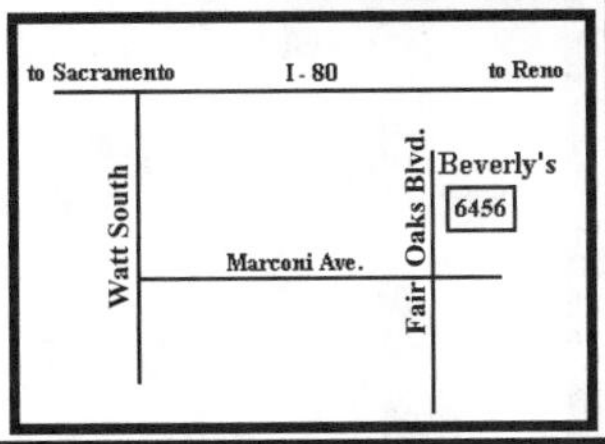

Fair Oaks, CA #31

Mon - Fri 10 - 5:30
Sat 10 - 5
Sun 12 - 4

Tayo's Fabrics & Quilts

10127 Fair Oaks Blvd. 95628
(916) 967-5479
Owner: Phyllis Williams Est: 1983
info@tayosfabrics.com
www.tayosfabrics.com

Fabrics, books, patterns & notions for traditional & contemporary quilting, wearable art & fashion sewing. Felted wool, crazy quilting supplies. Classes. Personal & friendly service.

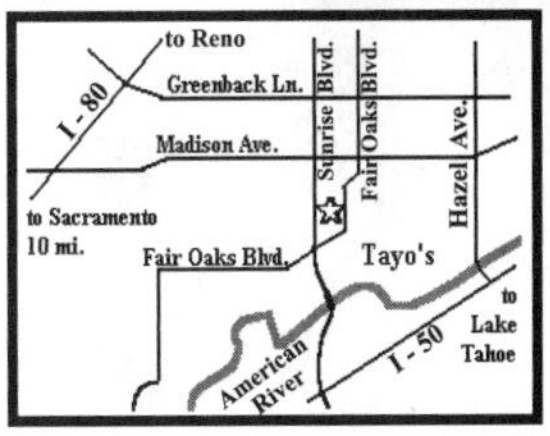

Rocklin, CA #32

Mon - Fri 10 - 5
Sat 10 - 4

The Quilter's Stash

1150 Sunset Blvd
Suite 158 95765
(916) 435-2103

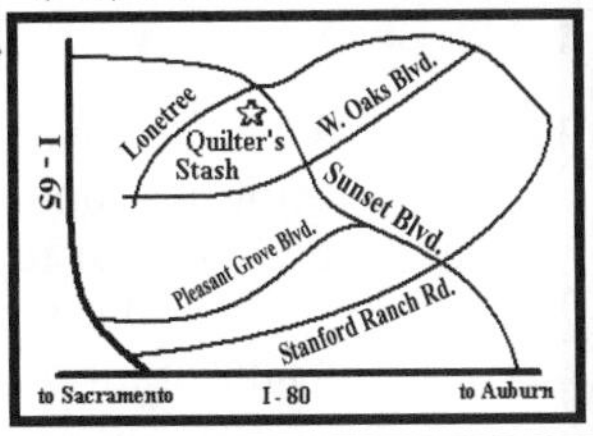

Owners: Betty & Karol
Est: 2007 Free Email Newsletter
thequilterssstash@att.net
www.thequiltersstash.net
Fabrics, Notions, Patterns & Classes for Quilters. We are on the corner of Lonetree and Sunset Blvd. in Rocklin.

Portola, CA #33

Mon - Sat 10 - 4

Homestead Fabrics

141 Nevada St. 96122
(530) 832-0446
Owner: Lorraine Wakefield
Est: 1993 1000 sq.ft. 1000 Bolts
loriwake@sbcglobal.net

100% cotton fabrics, patterns, kits, books and gifts. Friendly staff. Located in old town Portola. 49 miles to Reno.

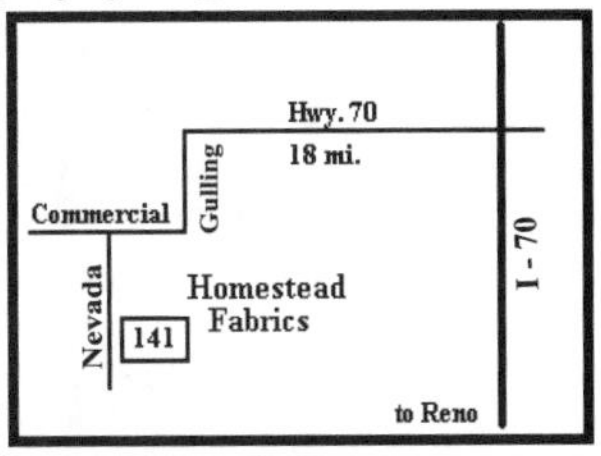

Chico, CA #34

Mon - Sat 10 - 5:30
Sun 11 - 4

Honey Run Quilters

1230 Esplanade 95926
(530) 342-5464
Owner: Carmen Rolfe
www.honeyrunquilters.com

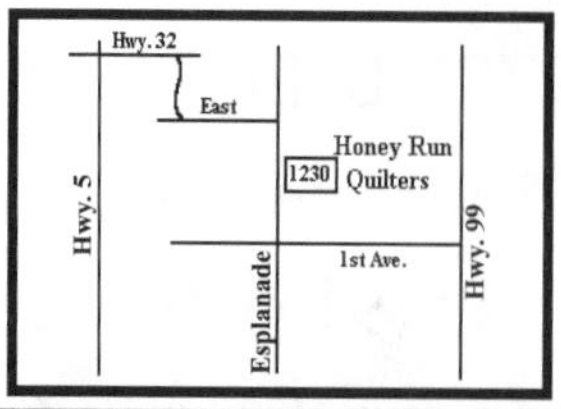

Better Homes Quilt Sampler Featured Shop

We carry a unique mix of fabrics and our own kits as well as the latest books, patterns and notions. We offer friendly and knowledgeable service.

Chico, CA #35

Mon - Fri 10 - 6
Sat 10 - 4

The Rabbit Hole Quilt Shop

2607 Esplanade 95973
(530) 345-5015
Owner: Cassandra Scott Est: 2004
1800 sq.ft.

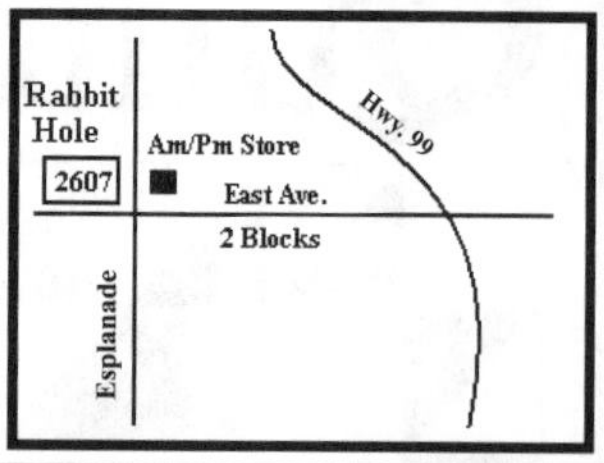

Large 3500 bolt inventory includes Batik, Flannel, Asian, Novelty, Black & Whites and Panels. Patterns, Books, Notions, and Longarm Machine.
therabbithole@digitalpath.net
www.rabbitholequiltshop.com

Paradise, CA #36

Morning Star QUILTS

Over 3,000 bolts of top quality quilting fabrics, including over 1000 bolts of batiks. Large selection of quilting notions, patterns and classes.

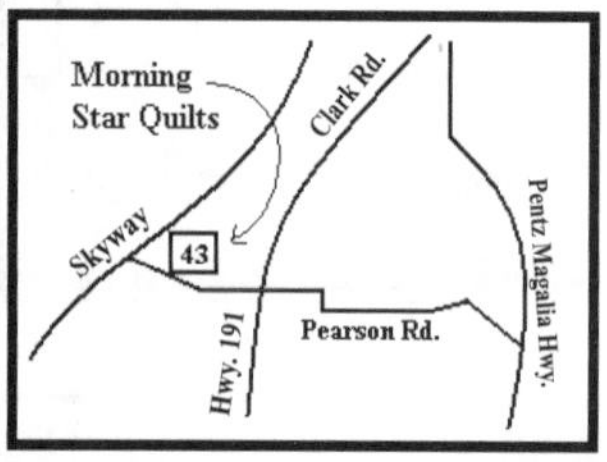

43 Pearson Rd. 95969
(530) 876-3243
morningstarquilts@sbcglobal.net

Mon - Fri 9 - 5 Sat 10 - 4

www.morningstarquilters.com

Better Homes Quilt Sampler Featured Shop

Grass Valley, CA #37

Mon - Fri 9 - 8
Sat 9 - 6
Sun 10 - 6

Ben Franklin Crafts and Frames

Ideas & Inspiration

598 Sutton Way 95945
(530) 273-1348 Est: 1973
www.benfranklin-crafts.com

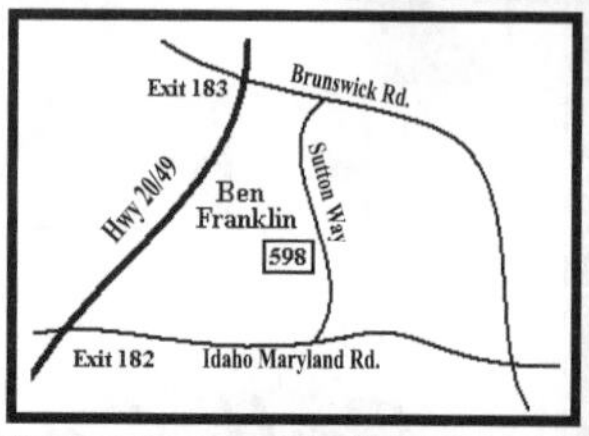

100% Cotton Fabrics, Patterns, Books, Notions, Art Quilt Supplies, Yarn, Needlework Supplies, Beads, Paper Crafts, Art Supplies, Home Décor, and Gifts.

South Lake Tahoe, CA #39

Nov - March
Fri, Sat, Mon 10-4
April - Oct.
Tues - Sat 10 - 6
All Year Sun 11 - 4

Quilting Tahoe

2264 Lake Tahoe Blvd. #7 96150
(800) 476-9065 or
(530) 544-9797
Owner: Penny Burroughs
Est: 2003 900 sq.ft. 2000 Bolts
quiltingtahoe@gmail.com
www.quiltingtahoe.net

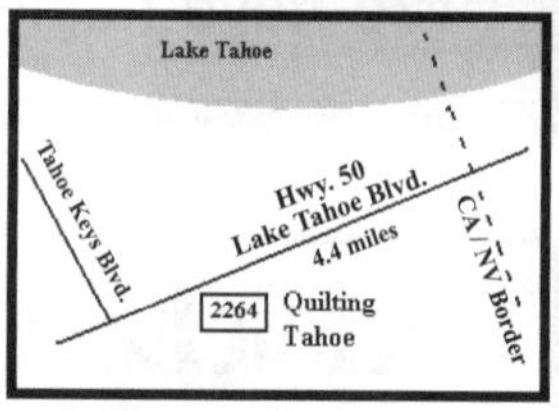

Quality fabrics from top manufacturers. Backgrounds and blenders are a specialty, textures too. Classes on demand.

SUGAR PINE Quilt Shop

452 South Auburn St., Grass Valley, CA 95945
(530) 272-5308 Est: 2002 1200 sq. ft.
Don't miss our fabulous selection of quilting fabrics, books, patterns & gifts.

Grass Valley, CA #38

www.sugarpinequiltshop.com

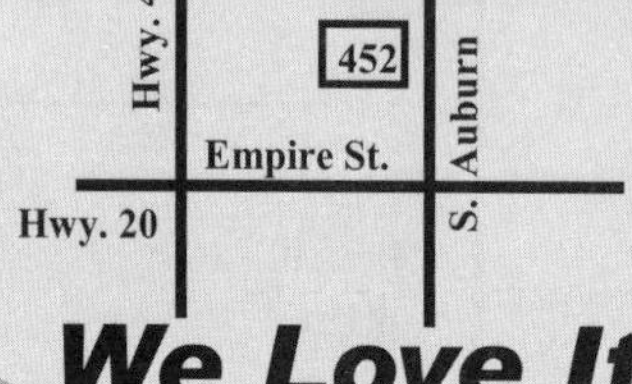

Tues - Sun 10-5
Closed Mon

We Love It All!

Cameron Park, CA #40

SHARED STITCHES

2650 Cameron Park Dr.
Suite 300 95682
(530) 676-4739
www.sharedstitches.com
Fax: (530) 676-4484
2500 sq.ft. 2500 bolts
sharedstitches@att.net
Email newsletter

Mon - Fri 9:30 - 5:30
Sat 9:30 - 5 Sun 12 - 4

Est: 2008

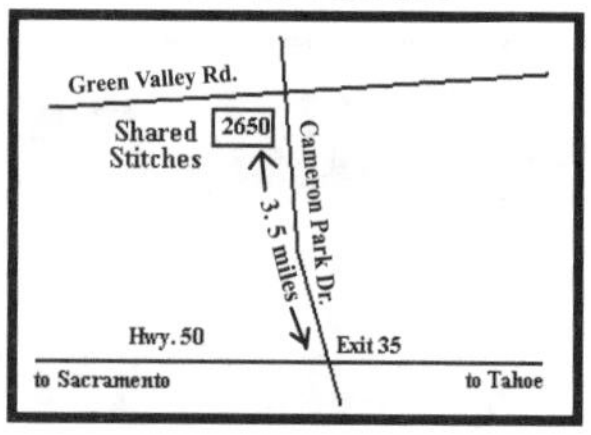

We have a wide array of quilting fabrics, notions, books, patterns, and classes.
Featuring Civil War reproductions, 30's, Batiks & Kids.
Our staff is here to help.
10% discount on regular priced merchandise to 1st-time customers.

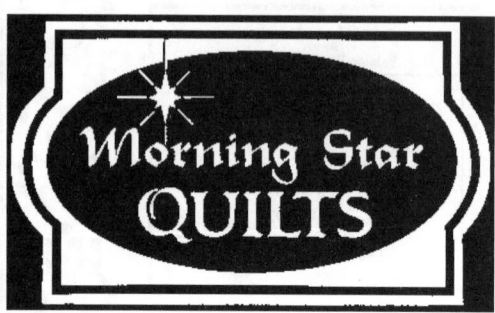

Cameron Park, CA #41

HIGH SIERRA QUILTERS

In the Bel Aire Shopping Center, Hwy. 50 at Cameron Park Dr.
30 miles east of Sacramento

ON THE ROAD TO SOUTH LAKE TAHOE

3490 Palmer Drive, #3G
Cameron Park, CA 95682
Phone 530-677-9990
Fax 530-677-9992
Owners: Linda Van Dyke & Doug Hodder
1,400 sq. ft. shop 4,000+ bolts of 100% cottons

Mon - Fri 10 - 5:30
Sat 10 - 5 Sun 12 - 4

Friendliest shop in El Dorado County featuring a great selection of flannel, batiks, Asian, and novelties from all the major manufacturers, quilting supplies, full line of quilting notions, quilting books, patterns from local artists, classes from beginner to advanced skill levels, gift items, and more ….

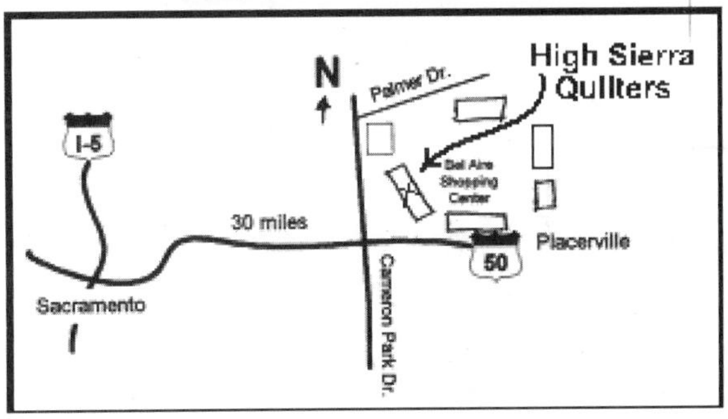

www.highsierraquilters.com

Bearly Quilting
...fabric, friends, fun

Est: 2006

Sonora, CA #42

Junction Shopping Center
13769 Mono Way #E, Sonora, CA 95370
(209) 694-0226 fax: (209) 694-0227
bearlyquilting@att.net
Owners: Larry & Nancy Bertuccelli

Bearly Quilting is the newest and largest full service quilt store & sewing center located in the Sierra foothills. We stock over 4,000 bolts of fabric, offer a large selection of notions, books, kits, finished quilts, unique giftware, and provide a variety of classes for all levels of quilters. We also carry a full line of Baby Lock sewing, quilting, and embroidery machines, and Koala studio sewing cabinets. Stop by and say hi to our mascot, "Sewphia" who greets all of our customers. We are a "must see" destination for the traveling quilter.

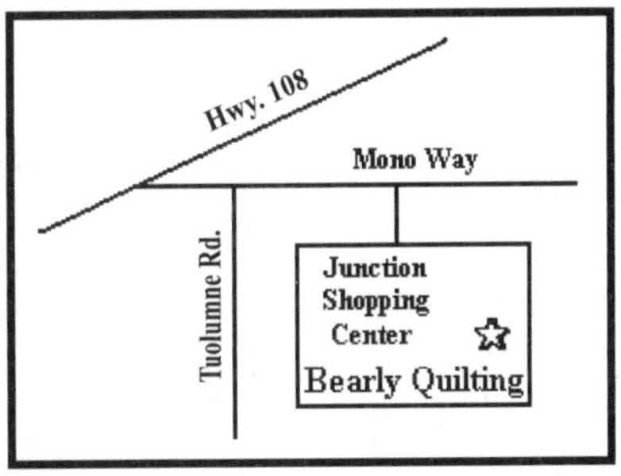

Mon - Sat 10 - 5 Sun 11 - 4

www.bearlyquilting.net

Sonora, CA #43

Tues - Sat 10 - 5

Timeless Calico Designs

11916 Hwy. 49 95370
(209) 533-0200
Owner: Lindy Miller
timelesscalico@goldrush.com
www.timelesscalicodesigns.com
We have the largest selection of 19th century historic reproduction fabrics in Northern CA. From traditional to modern art, your quilt projects will stand out when you use these gorgeous designs from the past. Books, Patterns & Kits.

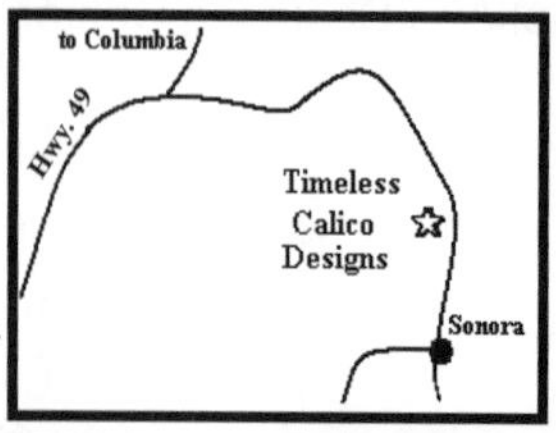

Altaville, CA #44

Mon - Sat 10 - 5 Summer Sundays

The Country Cloth Shop

457 S. Main St. P.O. Box 868
"Angels Camp" 95221
(209) 736-4998 Est: 1980
Owners: Ginger & Chuck Duffy
ccshop@goldrush.com 1600 sq.ft.
www.countryclothshop.com
Authorized Bernina Dealer
Located in historic Angels Camp in the Mother Lode foothills. Good selection of fabrics, books, patterns & threads.

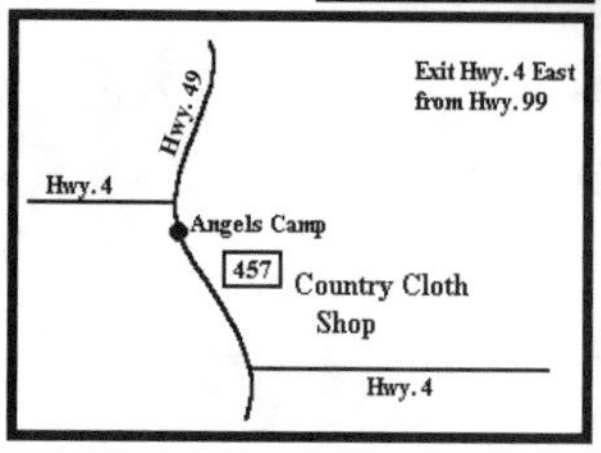

Groveland, CA #45

Mon - Fri 9 - 4

WinDee's Quilting Bees

21081 Lytle Loomis Rd., P.O. Box 237 95321
(209) 962-0421
Owner: Dee Small
Deedesmall@inreach.com

Longarm Quilter, Piecing Classes & Quilts for Sale.
I would love to help you finish your quilts.
Stop by on your way to Yosemite.

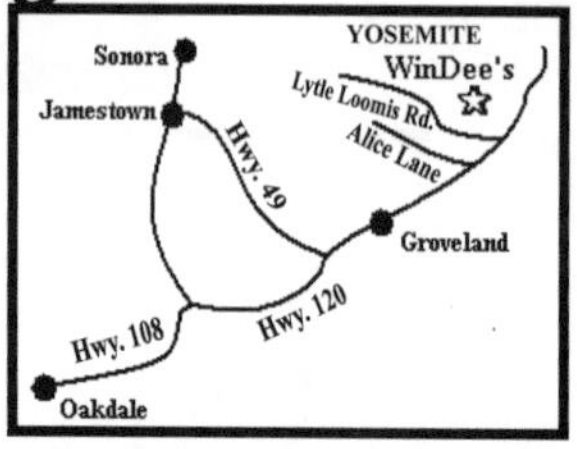

Oakhurst, CA #46

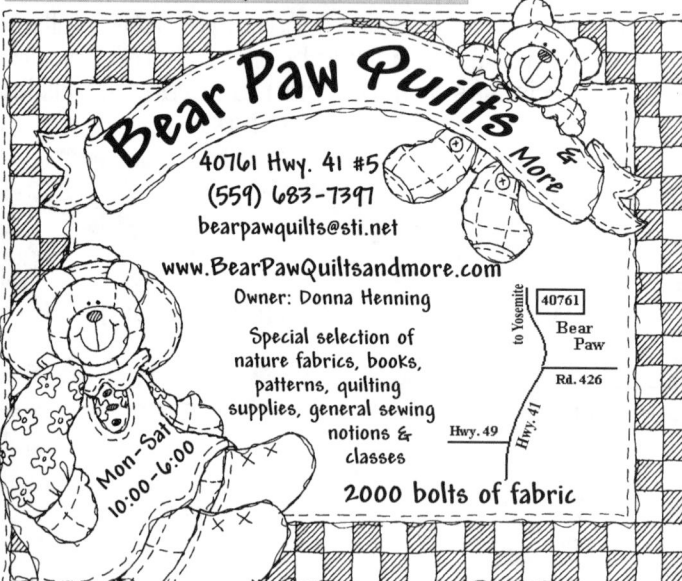

Bear Paw Quilts & More

40761 Hwy. 41 #5
(559) 683-7397
bearpawquilts@sti.net
www.BearPawQuiltsandmore.com
Owner: Donna Henning
Special selection of nature fabrics, books, patterns, quilting supplies, general sewing notions & classes
Mon-Sat 10:00-6:00
2000 bolts of fabric

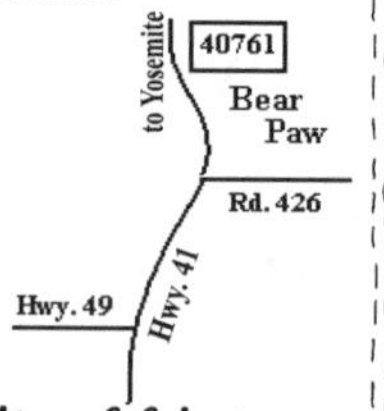

Hampton House

261 Main St., P.O. Box 264 93517
(760) 932-1145
Owners: Cole and Melanie Hampton
hamptonquilts@aol.com

March - October Mon - Sat 10 - 4

Moda, Robert Kaufman, Heirloom fabrics, Laces, Books, Patterns, Notecards, Gifts, Handmade Gifts, and Notions.

A comfortable and fun shop to visit!

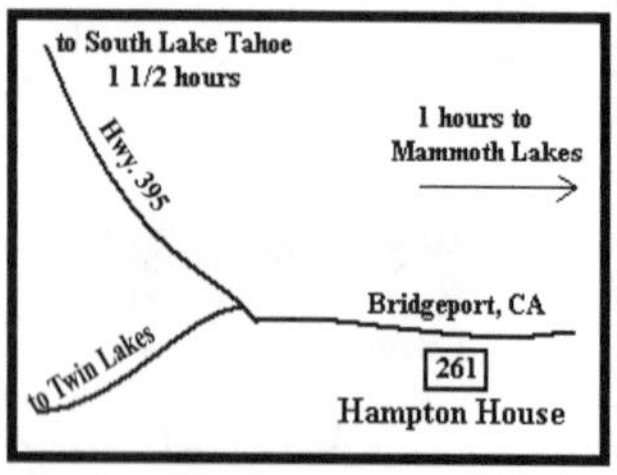

Bridgeport, CA #47

Bishop, CA #48

**Mon 11 - 3
Tues - Fri 10 - 6
Sat 10 - 5
1st & 3rd Sun 1 - 4**

Quilting in the Sierras

169 East Line (760) 872-4769
"Your quilts will be divine." 93514
Est: 2006 700 sq. ft.
www.quiltinginthesierras.com
We specialize in quality quilting fabrics. Clubs & Classes. Check out our BOM's. Come share our joy of quilting in our 100 yr. old house in the Sierras.

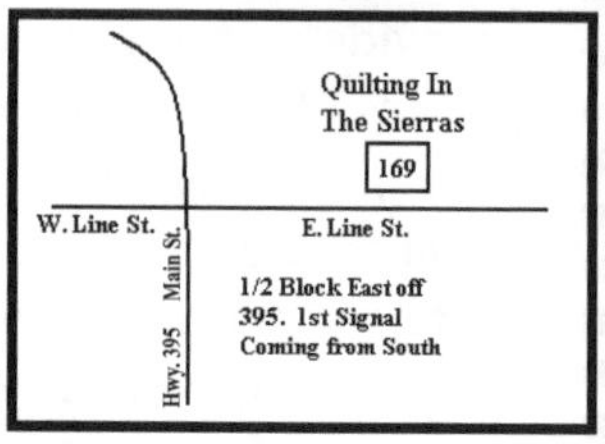

Oakdale, CA #49

**Mon - Fri 10 - 5
Sat 10 - 4**

Quilters Cabin

630 N. Yosemite Ave. 95361
(209) 847-4487
Owner: Marie Lewerenz

Est: 2005 1450 sq.ft. 3500+ bolts
marie2thecabin@comcast.net
The shop features a large variety of fabrics.
A very large section of batiks.
Patterns & Books.
Long arm services available.

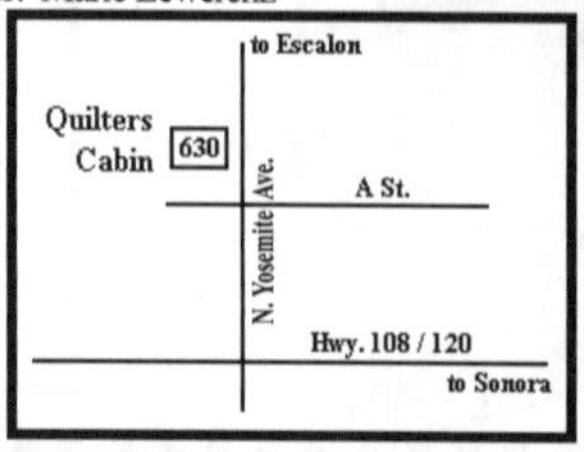

"A Fabric Store and Sew Much More . . . . "

Sew Many Quilts

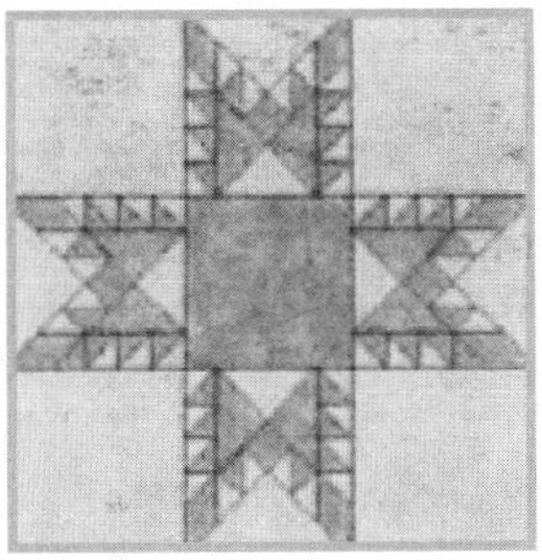

71 E 10th Street, Tracy, CA 95376
(209) 836-5426 sewmanyquilts@sbcglobal.net
Fax: (209) 836-5584 Owner: Colette Lenoir
www.sewmanyquiltsca.com

Tracy, CA #50

Est: 2001 2000 sq. ft.

Sun 11 - 4 Mon 11 - 3
Tues - Sat 10 - 5

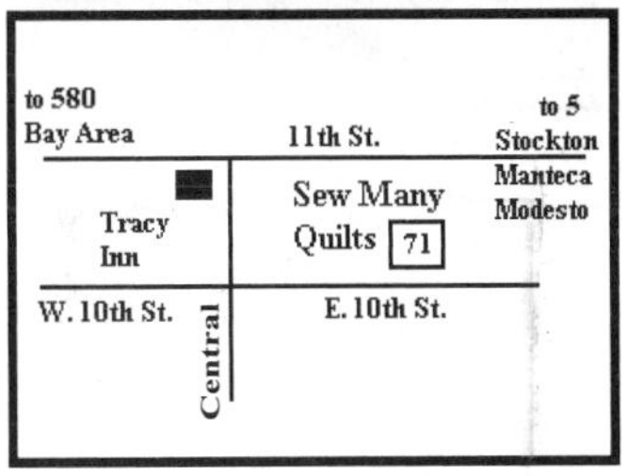

Located in the historic downtown section of Tracy, California; Sew Many Quilts carries over 7000 bolts of 100% cotton fabrics for quilting and other sewing and craft projects. This is a full service quilting store featuring a complete line of notions, decorative buttons, gifts, 'minkee', charm packs, jelly rolls, embellishments, books and patterns. Come and see the "International Room" showcasing Australian, Hawaiian, African, Native American and Asian fabrics as well as African mudcloth and African and Indonesian Batiks. Stop in and pick up a class schedule. Beginning to advanced quilting classes are offered with guest lectures and quilt trunk shows to keep you up to date on the newest trends.

"Your Quilting Link Between the East Bay and the Central Valley"

Turlock, CA #51

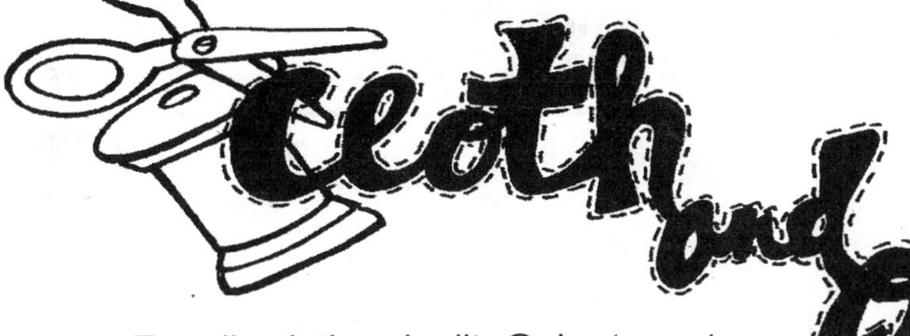

625 E. Main St.
Turlock, CA 95380
(209) 632-3225

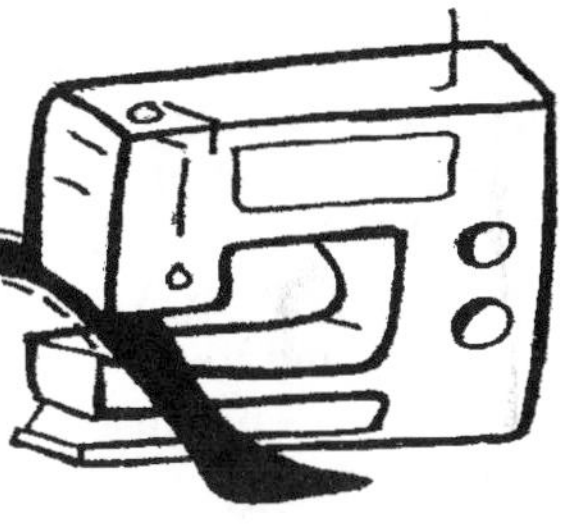

E-mail: clothandquilts@charter.net
Fax: (209) 632-3354
Est: 2001 3900 sq.ft.
Owners: Cindy Kooistra,
Debbie Sanders, & Margaret Labno

Mon - Sat 9:30 - 5:30

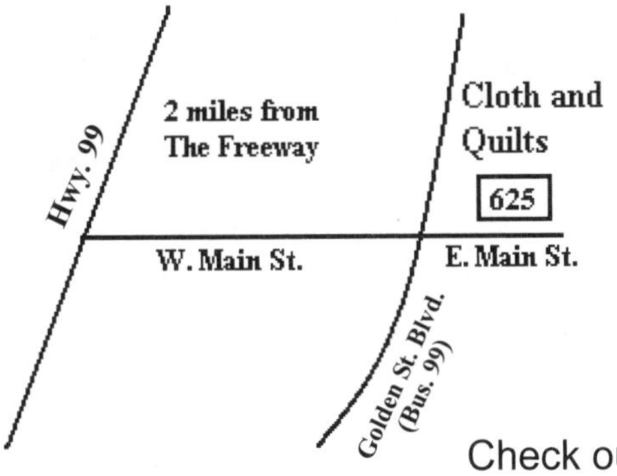

Your One Stop Quilt Shop!

Over 5000 Bolts of Fabrics, Books,
Patterns and Notions. Long Arm Quilting Avail.
BERNINA® Sales and Service.
Classes Available

www.clothandquilts.com

Check out what we're up to--download our newsletter from the website.

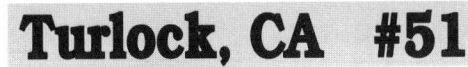

Stockton, CA #52

Quilters Quarters

4343 Pacific Ave.
Stockton, CA 95207
(209) 462-0161

Fabric, Classes & Supplies

Stockton's <u>only</u> Quilt Shop

We're located in University Square

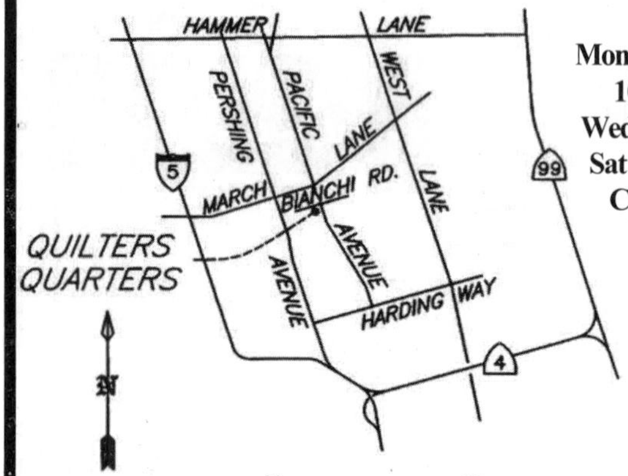

Hours:
Mon, Tue, Thurs, Fri 10 AM - 6 PM
Wed 10 AM - 7 PM
Sat 10 AM - 4 PM
Closed Sunday

quiltersquarters@comcast.net
www.quiltersquarters-stkn.com

Clovis, CA #53

Quilters' Paradise, Inc.
Inspiring Quilters for over 30 Years

Located in Historic Old Town Clovis
Gateway to Yosemite National Park

Owners: Kathy Beechinor, Colette Belt, Barbara Pontius

We specialize in "QP" original patterns and custom kits. Our selection of textured fabrics includes Minkee, Chenille, wool on the bolt and a wide array of hand dyed wool.

Wide Selection of Blocks of the Month
Full Service Website - We ship international, too.

339 Pollasky,
Clovis, CA 93612
(559) 297-7817
FAX (559) 297-0838

Store Hours
Mon.-Fri. 10-6
Sat. 10-5
Sun. 12-4

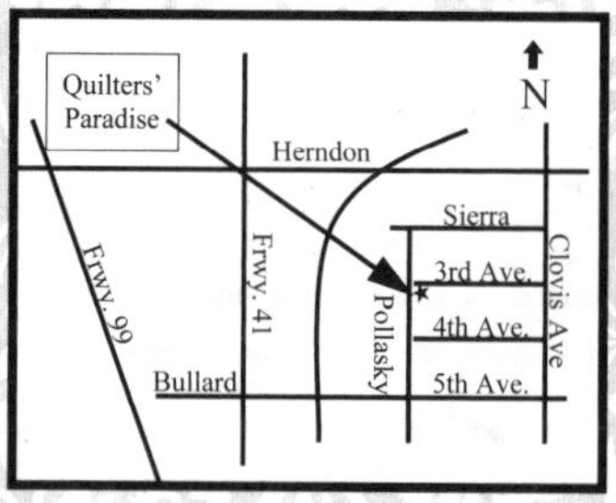

www.quilters-paradise.com

Cottage Quilts

Located in northwest Fresno, Cottage Quilts is one of the valley's newest quilt stores. We're known for our friendly staff, fabric selection, kits, and block of the months. With the addition of our Sew Creative Studio, we now carry Pfaff, Viking, and Singer sewing machines; Horn and Regal cabinets; and sewing notions. It's not just about quilts anymore!

Owners: Carolyn & David McCray
Est: 2004 3800 sq.ft.
Free online newsletter
cottagequilts@comcast.net

Mon - Fri 10 - 5
Sat 10 - 4

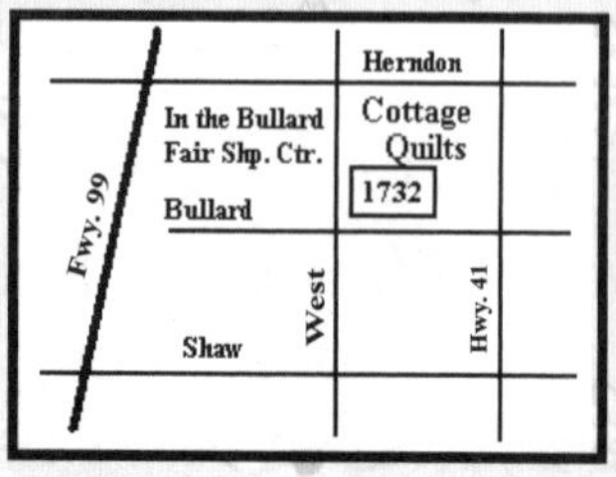

1732 W. Bullard Ave. 93711
(559) 447-0599 www.cottage-quilts.com

Fresno, CA #54

Reedley, CA #55

Mon - Fri 10 - 5
Sat 10 - 4

Mennonite Quilt Center

1012 "G" St. 93654
(559) 638-3560 2500 sq.ft.
Mgrs: Mary Elizondo
mennoquilts@yahoo.com
www.mennonitequiltcenter.com

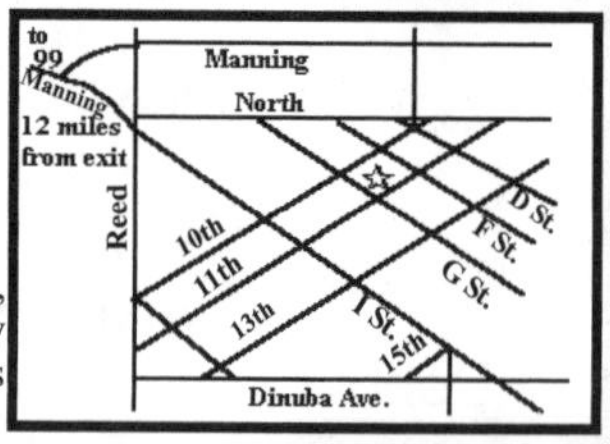

100% Cotton Fabrics, Notions, Books, Patterns, & Battings. Quilters on site Monday mornings. Quilt show year around. Tours Available. 12 mi. E of Hwy. 99 on Manning.

Visalia, CA #56

Mon - Fri 9:30 - 5:30
Thur til 7
Sat 9:30 - 4:30

Thimble Towne

400 W. Caldwell Ave. #F 93277
(559) 627-5778
Est: 2000
Owner: Kathy Veltkamp
thimbletown@sbcglobal.net
www.thimbletowne.com

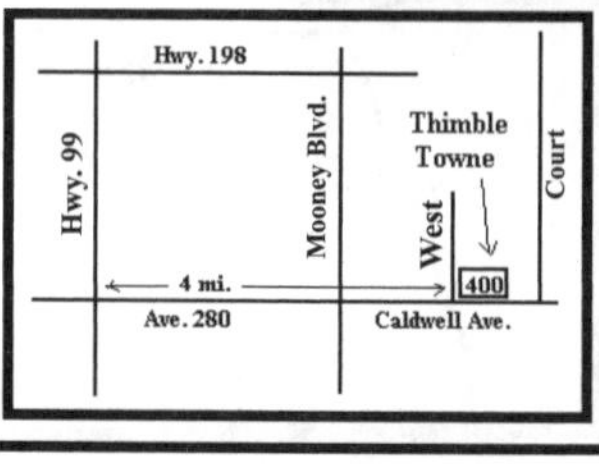

100% cotton fabrics; books and patterns galore; mail order welcome; newsletter; classes; Bernina Sewing Machines

Quilters Quarters

880 N. Irwin St. 93230
559.584.6899
Fax: 559.584.6899
Owner: Linda Carter
Est: 2004 4000 sq. ft.
2500+Bolts

www.quiltersquarters.net

Hanford, CA #57

Mon - Fri 9:30 - 5:30
Sat 9:30 - 4:30

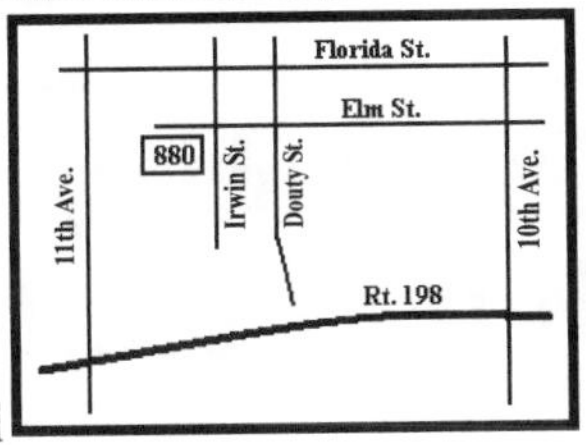

We specialize in quality quilting fabrics, by well known designers: quality threads, and the latest and greatest notions. We have classroom availability for 20 students. We also offer special arrangements for day "group" events or classes. Long Arm Quilting Available. Premier Husqvarna Viking Dealer Sales and Service.

Husqvarna VIKING

Gilroy, CA #58

Mon - Fri 10 - 5
Sat 10 - 4

THE NIMBLE THIMBLE

7550 Monterey St.
95020
(408) 842-6501 Fax: Same

Est: 1977 2000+ sq.ft.
thimble@garlic.com
www.nimblethimble.com
A charming little shop offering the beginning or accomplished quilter a unique resource for fabric, books, patterns, classes and gifts.
In house long-arm quilting is also offered.

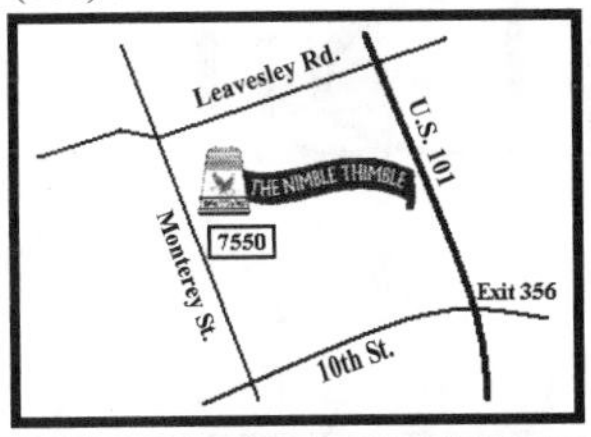

Marina, CA #59

Mon - Sat
9:30 - 5:30

Your Home Town Sewing Center, Inc.

215-L Reservation Rd. 93933
(831) 582-2595
Fax: (831) 582-2597
Owner: Roberta Brunet
Est: 2004 5000 sq. ft.
3000 Bolts
www.hometownsewing.com
Great Selection of fabric for quilting & sewing.
Books - Patterns - Classes - Fabric Paints - Dyes
Authorized Bernina & Pfaff Dealer
Long Arm Quilting

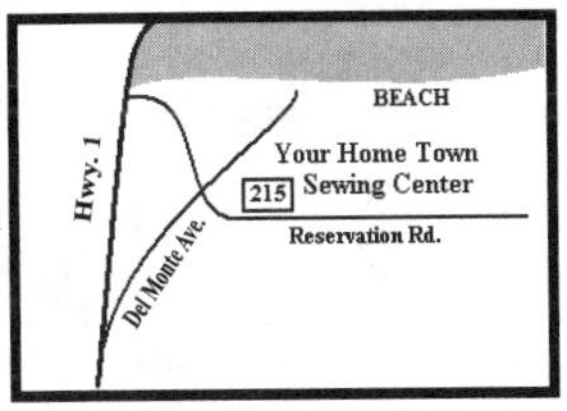

Back Porch Fabrics

Mon - Sat
10 - 5
Sun 12 - 4

157 Grand Ave. at Central 93950
(831) 375-4453 Fax: (831) 375-3755
info@backporchfabrics.com
Owner: Gail Abeloe Est: 1996

Pacific Grove, CA #60

- **Top Shop 2003 "Quilt Sampler"**
- **Unique fabrics, books and patterns for quilting and wearable art.**
- **Home of the "Back Porch Press" pattern company.**
- **Continuous shows in our Quilt Gallery featuring prominent, local quilters.**

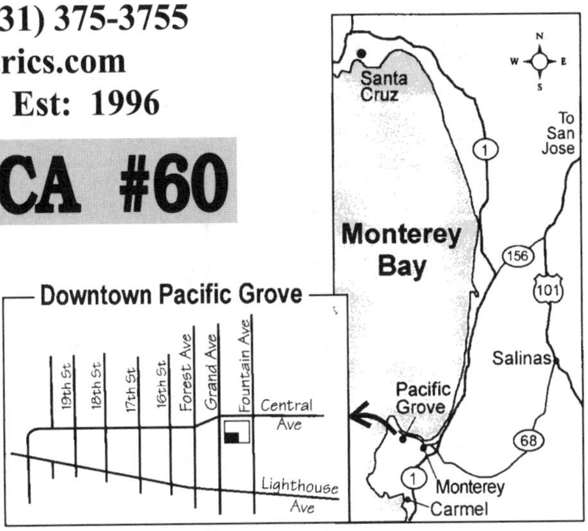

Located 90 miles south of San Francisco on the Monterey Peninsula.

Visit Us on the Web At: www.backporchfabrics.com

www.fabricworm.com

Birch Fabrics

Mon - Sat 9 - 5

1244 Pine St. #D, Paso Robles, CA 93446
805.239.8888 fax 805.239.8807

We specialize in Modern Quilting Cottons and Japanese Import Fabrics. We also carry fabrics for children, organic fabrics and a great selection of patterns. Come check out our selection of handmade gifts. Be sure to visit our website also: www.fabricworm.com

Paso Robles, CA #61

Paso Robles, CA #62

Mon - Fri 10 - 5 Sat 11 - 4:30

The Quiltery

1413 Riverside Ave. 93446
(805) 227-4561
Owner: Sherline Lockhart
Est: 1999 1500 Bolts
www.thequiltery.net

A great selection of quality fabric (still at $5 Yd.) books, patterns, notions and in-house longarm quilting. Quilting is our specialty and passion!

Paso Robles, CA #63

Mon - Fri 10 - 5 Sun 12 - 4

Wine Country Quilts

705 Pine St., Suite D 93446
(805) 239-8976
Owners: Wilda & Gentry Sprayberry
Est: 2007 3000 sq.ft.
wcquilting@aol.com

Beautiful fabrics in every color of the rainbow. Natural cotton fabrics and batting. A warm cozy atmosphere, that makes you feel you are among old friends. Quilts of a bygone era to contemporary abstract quilts. Great fun classes.

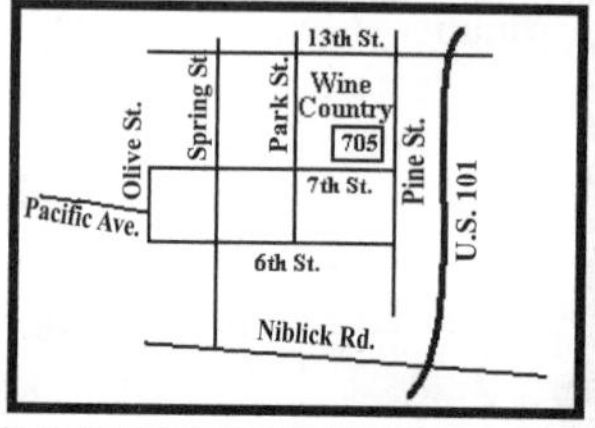

Atascadero, CA #65

Mon - Thurs 10 - 6 Fri & Sat 10 - 5 Sun 12 - 5

Sew Fun

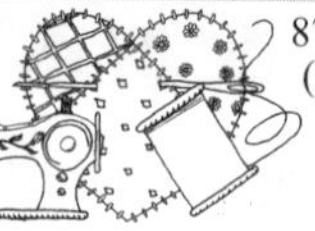

8775 El Camino Real 93422
(805) 462-9739 Est: 1996
Owner: Lynn Barksdale

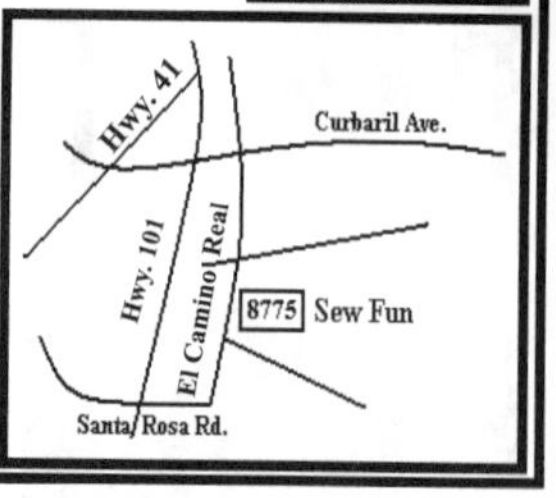

Est: 1996 3200 sq.ft. Lynn@atsewfun.com
www.atsewfun.com Complete Quilt Shop.
5000+ bolts of cotton fabrics - Outrageous selection of Batiks and Asian Fabrics! Large Quilt Display daily. You'll find it all here - Books, kits, notions, classes, plus great friendly service.
Home of Janome Sewing Machines.

Quilter's Cupboard

Atascadero, CA #64

5275 El Camino Real 93422
(805) 466-6996
Fax: (805) 466-6555
Owner: Lori Getz
Est: 1997 2000 sq.ft.

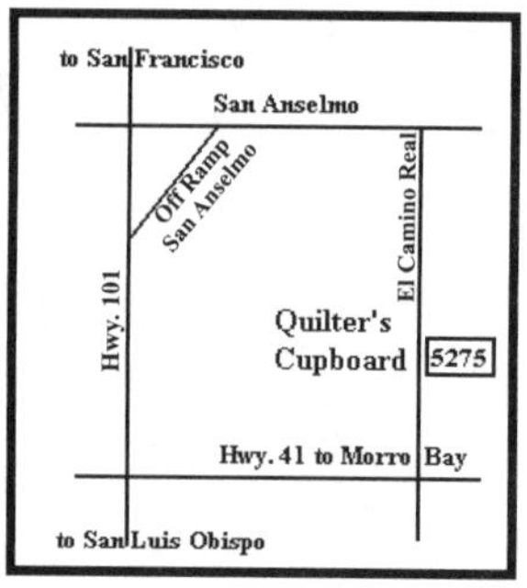

Monday - Saturday 10 - 5 Closed Sundays

Complete Quilt Shop

with over 2500 bolts of 100% cotton fabric, stencils, notions, books, patterns, classes & gifts.

www.quilterscupboard.com

Morro Bay, CA #66

Mon - Sat 10 - 5 Sun 12 - 4

The Cotton Ball

1199 Main St. 93442
(800) 895-7402 or 805.772.2646 Fax: 805.772.6357
Owner: Judi Appell Est: 1969
www.thecottonball.com
Great selection of quilting fabric, decorating fabric, books, patterns and notions.
Pfaff Sewing Machine Dealer. *Great, friendly service!*

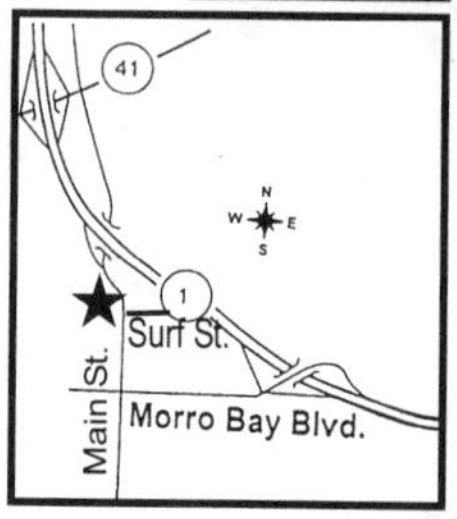

San Francisco Area

15 Featured Shops

Shops #67 to #81

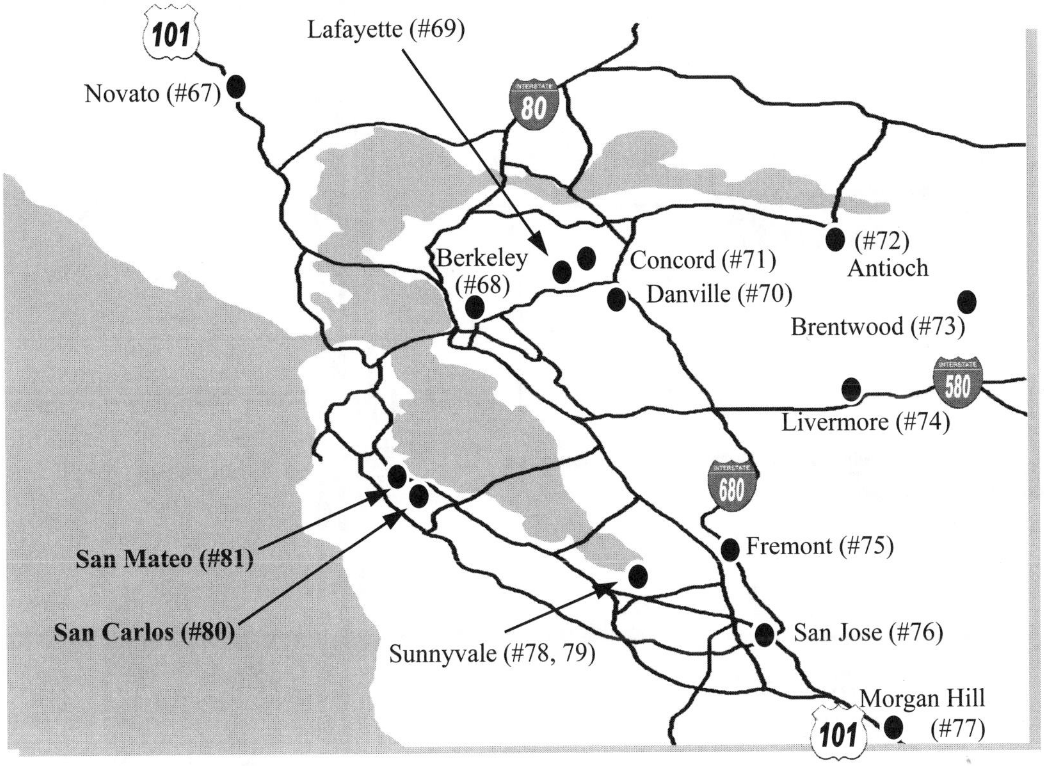

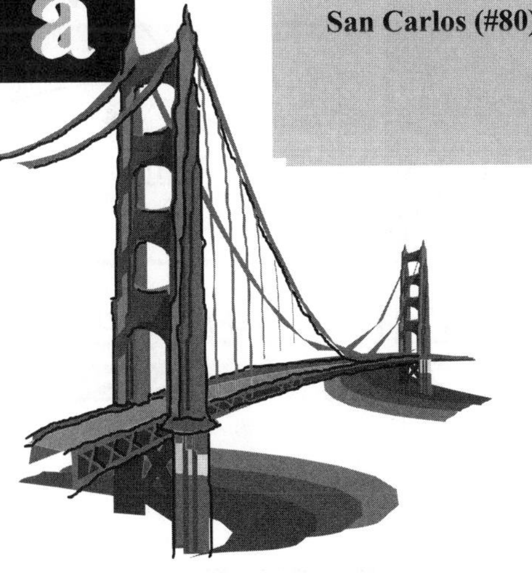

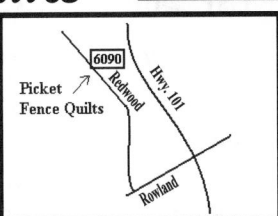

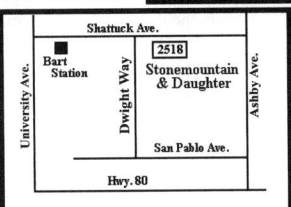

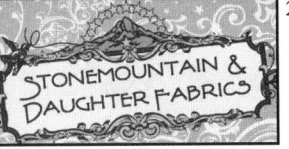

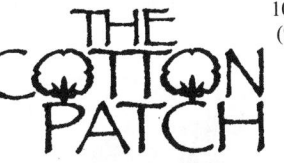

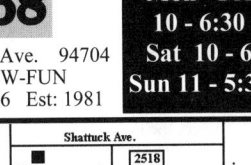

Danville, CA #70

The Quilter's Inn

125 F Railroad Ave.
Danville, CA 94526
(925) 837-8458
Fax: (925) 837-8463
thequiltersinn@aol.com
Owner: Jane Lewis Est: 2004
2000 sq. ft. 4000 Bolts

www.thequilters-inn.com

Selected as a Top Ten Shop by Quilt Sampler Magazine.

Mon - Sat 9:30 - 5

Our knowledgeable staff welcomes you to our cozy atmosphere where quilters come together to create a happy community and sisterhood. Free Newsletter.

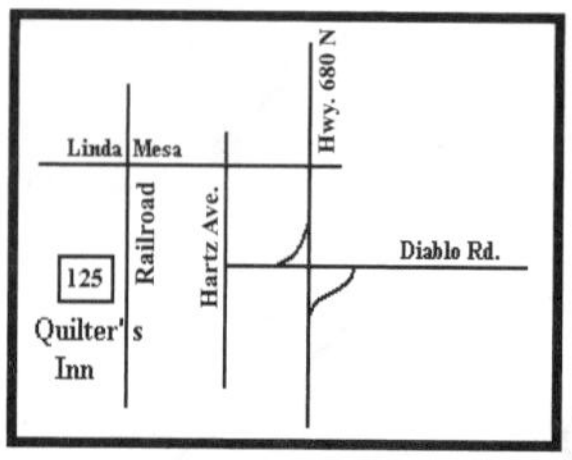

Concord, CA #71

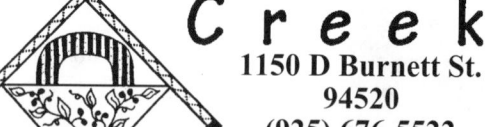

Thimble Creek

1150 D Burnett St.
94520
(925) 676-5522
Owners:
Roxie & Joe Wood
Est: 1994 6000 sq.ft.
6000 Bolts
roxie@thimblecreek.com

Wonderful quilts on display in a spacious, friendly atmosphere. Great selection of books, patterns, notions, fabric & classes! Check our website for fabulous new kits, Block of the month programs and retreats.

Mon - Fri 10 - 5
Tues & Thur til 8
Sat 10 - 5
Sun 12 - 4

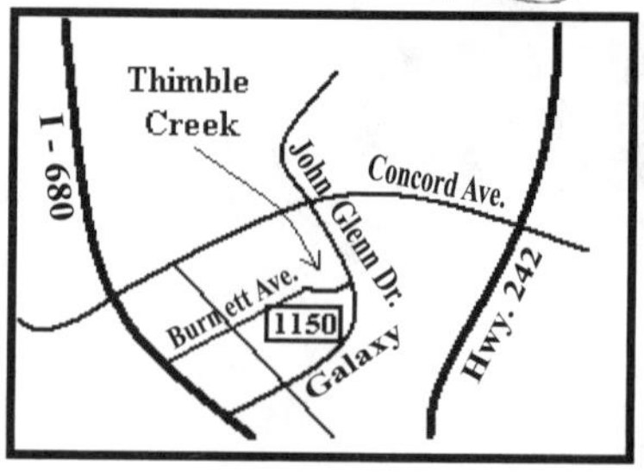

www.thimblecreek.com

Queen B's Quilt Shop

Address: **720 West 2nd Street 94509**
Phone: **(925) 978-4587**
FAX: **(925) 756-2445**
E-Mail: **info@queenbsquiltshop.com**
Website: **www.queenbsquiltshop.com**
Owner: **Bernie**
Est: 2001 1550 sq.ft. 4000 bolts

We Are Your Full Service Quilting Store.

- **Friendly, knowledgeable & helpful staff.**
- **Fabric galore and more arriving daily.**
- **Patterns, books and notions.**
- **Classes for all levels.**
- **Professional custom machine quilting.**
- **Visa and Master Card.**
- **Easy freeway access & 1 block to Amtrak.**

Antioch, CA #72

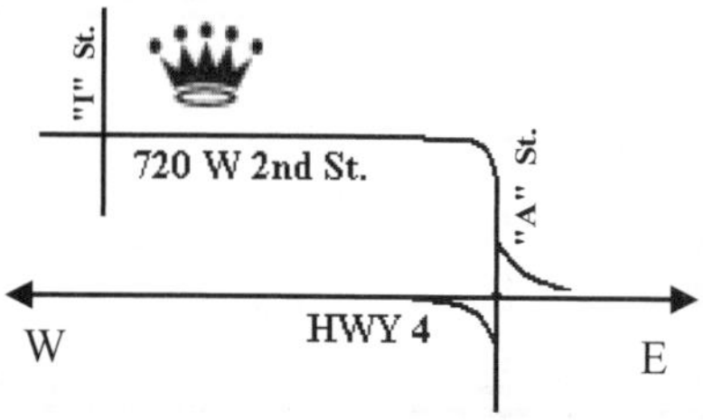

Monday - Saturday
10 AM - 5:30 PM
Sunday
11 AM - 4 PM
Closed Wednesday

Brentwood, CA #73

Mon - Fri 10 - 5:30
Tues til 8
Sat 10 - 5

Sew Ewe Quilt

470 Harvest Park Dr.
Suite E 94513
(925) 634-7153 Fax: (925) 634-5692
Owner: Nancy Haney
sewewequilt@sbcglobal.com
www.sewewequilt.com
"Where the Flock Gathers to Quilt & Sew"
Fabrics - Specialize in Moda, Kaufman, Retro & Batiks. Notions, Books, Patterns, Classes Beginning to Advanced.

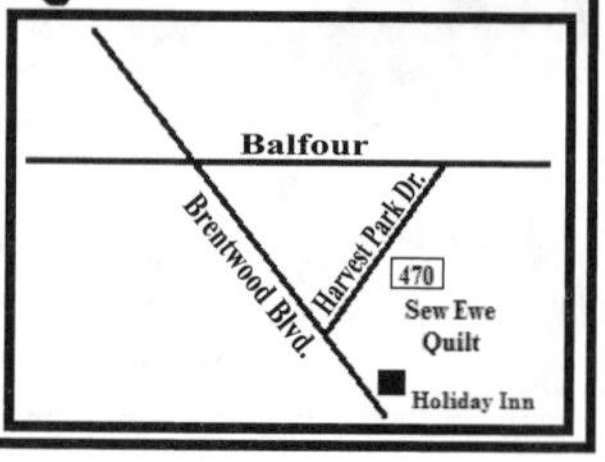

IN BETWEEN STITCHES

a place where friendships grow

inbetweenstitches.com

#74

Established in 2002, this delightful quilt and gift store offers the latest books, patterns, and fabric. Check out the website and join the email list to receive more information about the store and classes. You'll not want to miss the beautiful ***Quilting in the Garden Show*** in late September at the Alden Lane Nursery, hosted by both the nursery and In Between Stitches.

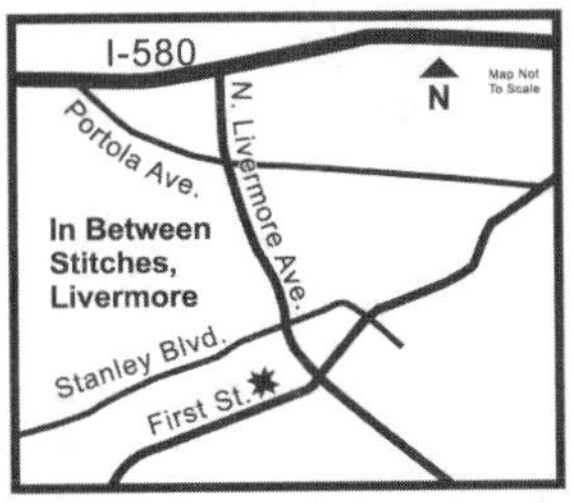

925-371-7064

M-F 10-5:30
Sat 10-5
Sun 10-3

Better Homes and Gardens Quilt Sampler Featured Shop 2010

2190 First St., **Livermore, CA** 94551

Fremont, CA #75

Wed - Sat 10 - 6
Sun 10 - 4

Sisters N Stitches

Quilt Shop & Quilting School

3270 Seldon Court #4 94539
(510) 490-7586 Fax: Same Est: 2005
Owner: Denise Mullenix Online newsletter
sistersnstitches@yahoo.com
www.sistersnstitches.com
A complete quilt shop with an extensive class offering. Many standing programs each week. Also single session classes.

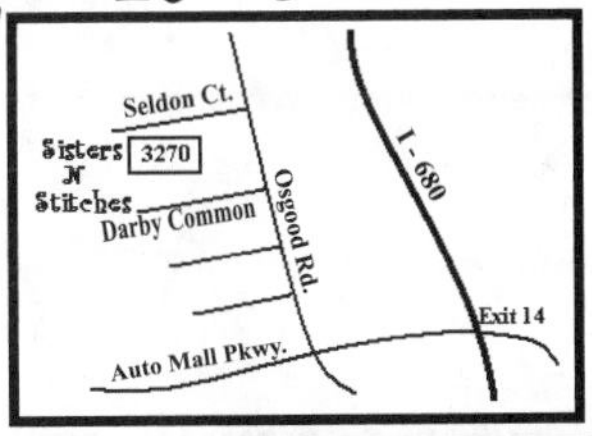

San Jose, CA #76

Tues - Sun 10 - 5
1st Fri 8 - 11 pm

San Jose Museum of Quilts & Textiles

520 S. 1st St. 95113
(408) 971-0323 Fax: (408) 971-7226
Est: 1977 Admission Charged
Non-profit Public Benefit Museum
www.sjquiltmuseum.org

Regularly changing exhibits of Quilts and Textiles. Museum Store has extensive assortment of books on quilting.

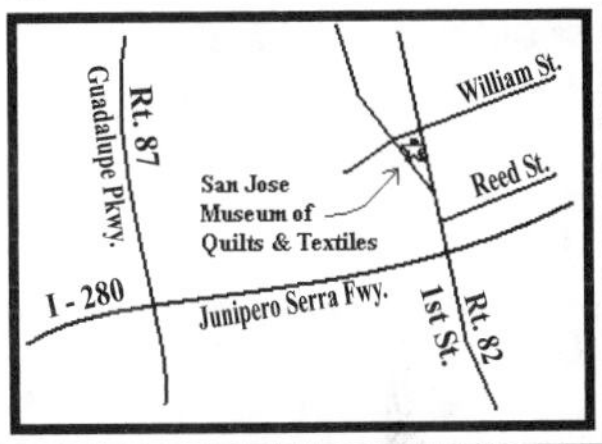

Morgan Hill, CA #77

Mon - Fri 10 - 5ish
Sat 10 - 4ish

Quilts and Things

16985 Monterey St. #316 95037
(408) 776-8438 Fax: Same
quiltclass@aol.com
www.quiltshopmorganhill.com
Located between the San Francisco and Monterey Bay Areas, Quilts and Things is a cozy shop filled with must-have fabrics. Large selection of Kits.

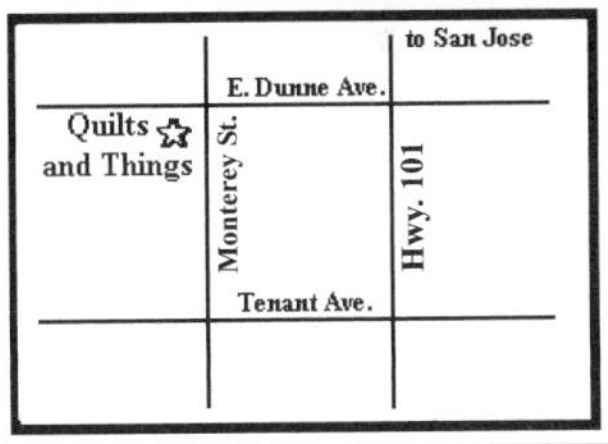

1326 S. Mary Ave., Sunnyvale, CA 94087
♥(408) 735-9830♥www.thegranaryquilts.com

Sunnyvale, CA #78

Your Friendly Neighborhood Quilt Shop!

- ♥ 100% Cotton Fabrics
- ♥ Quilting Supplies
- ♥ Books & Patterns
- ♥ Gifts for Quilters
- ♥ Notions
- ♥ Classes

Owner: Paula Ivers

Shop Hours:
Mon - Sat 10am - 6pm
Thurs til 8pm
Last Sunday of the month
10am - 4pm

Easy Freeway Access!

The place to go when you want to sew! Largest Selection! We have it all!

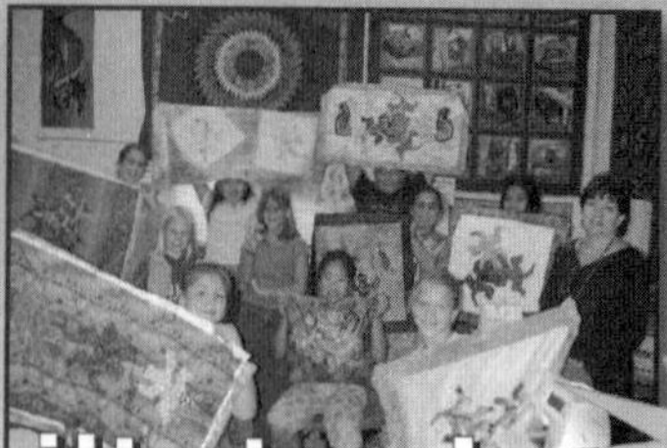

California's cutting edge quilt store!

We give out-of-state fabric discounts

The most quilting and sewing supplies under one roof!

- classes
- books
- furniture
- fabric
- buttons
- zippers
- knits
- batiks
- minkee
- rayon
- wool
- flannel
- notions galore
- thread haven
- sashiko supplies
- angelina fibers
- 12+ batting varieties
- embroidery machines
- 49+ sewing machines
- world's best sergers
- friendly fabric finders
- over 4500 bolts of fabric
- award-winning quilts
- free abundant parking

www.eddiesquiltingbee.com

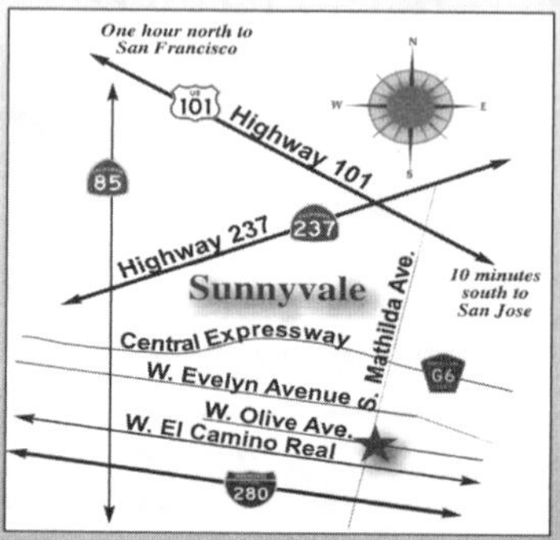

Open 7 Days a Week
Mon-Fri 9am-8:30pm
Sat 9am-5:30pm
Sun 11am-5:00pm

Eddie's Quilting Bee

Toll free: 1-888-QUILTER
Local: (408) 830-9595 (1-888-784-5837)
480 S. Mathilda Ave., Sunnyvale
1 block north of El Camino, next to BofA

Factory Authorized Dealer!

Husqvarna VIKING · baby lock · BERNINA Nothing Sews Like A Bernina. Nothing. · JANOME · KOALA CABINETS · Tin Lizzie 18 Your Affordable Longarm quilter · HORN of America COLLECTION

San Carlos, CA #80

Mon - Sat
10 - 5

The Laurel Leaf

648 Laurel Street 94070
(650) 591-6790
Owner: Julie Murphy
Est: 1983 2200 sq.ft.
www.laurelleafquilts.com
Longarm Quilting Service.
100% Cotton Fabric, Books, Patterns, Quilting Supplies and Classes.
Authorized Bernina Dealer.

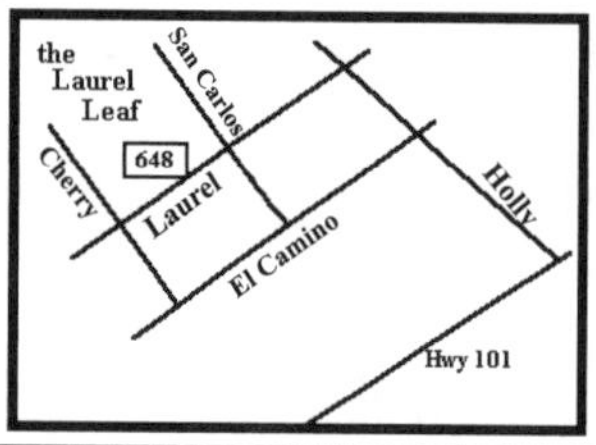

San Mateo, CA #81

Mon - Sat
10 - 4
Sun 1 - 4

Always Quilting

4230 Olympic Ave. 94403
(650) 458-8580 Fax: (650) 349-3248
Owners: Kit Morse & Julie McAuliffe
Est: 2003 6000 sq.ft. 4500+ bolts
info@alwaysquiltingonline.com
www.alwaysquiltingonline.com
Visit our friendly shop where creativity and community come together.
Authorized Handi-Quilter Dealer.

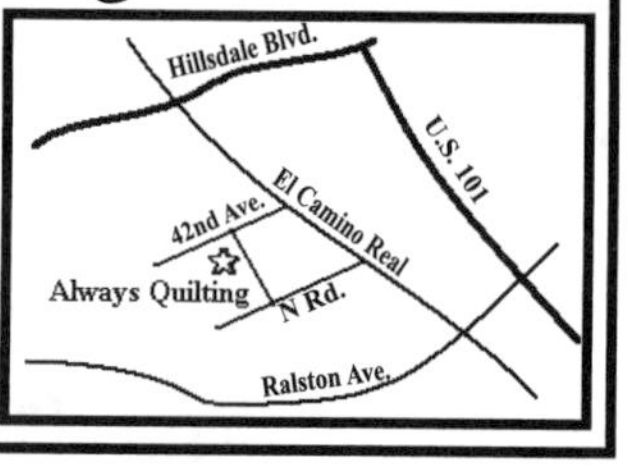

SOUTHERN CALIFORNIA

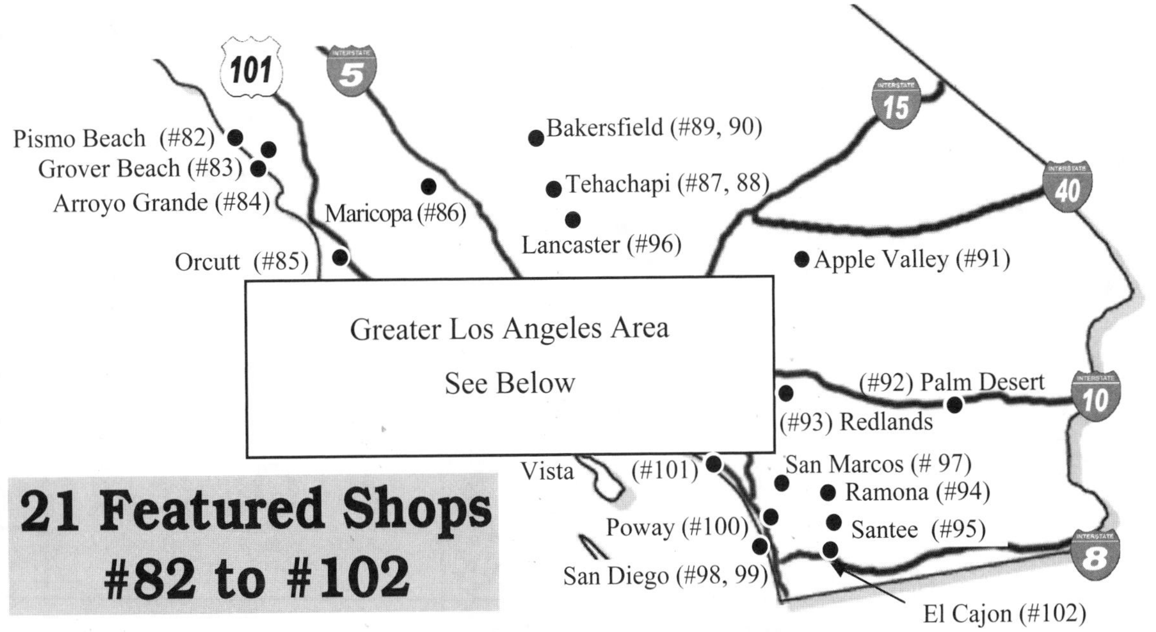

21 Featured Shops #82 to #102

Greater Los Angeles Area

27 Featured Shops #103 to #129

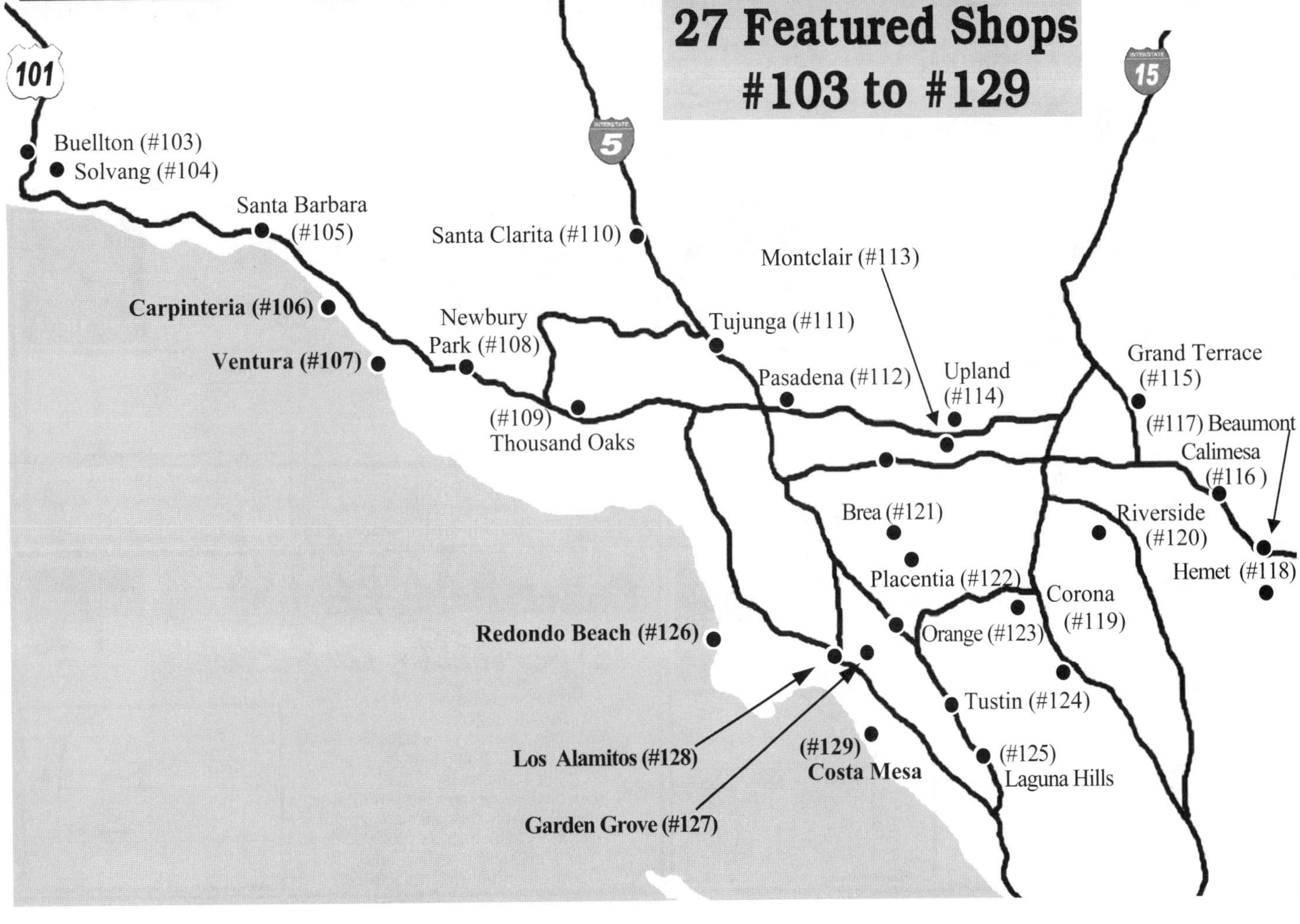

Quiltin' Cousins

330 Pomeroy 93449
(805) 773-4988
Owner: Shawn Lombardo

Check out our new website
www.quiltincousins.net

Fabric • Books • Notions
Patterns & Gifts

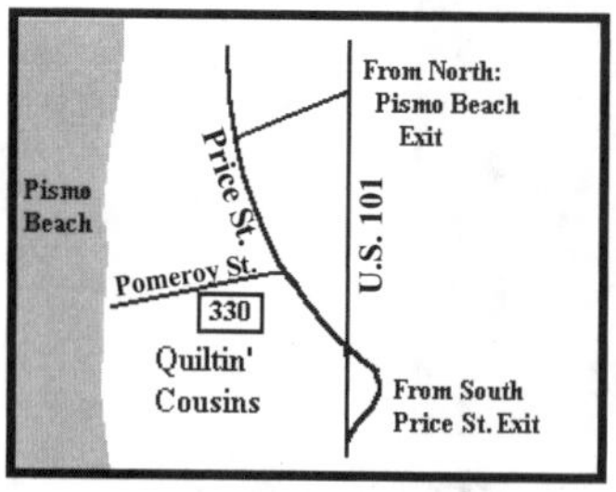

Tues - Fri
10 - 5
Sat 10 - 4

Pismo Beach, CA #82

Grover Beach, CA #83

Tues - Sat
10 - 5

Sew Stitchin' Quilt Shop

197 S. 8th St. 93433
(805) 904-6145
Fax (805) 904-6146

Est: 2009 750 sq.ft. 1200 Bolts
Email Newsletter Avail.
sewstitchinquiltshop@charter.net
We're a quilt shop with a friendly atmosphere. We offer only the finest 100% cotton fabric, notions, books, patterns, threads, kits, BOM's, stitcheries and classes.

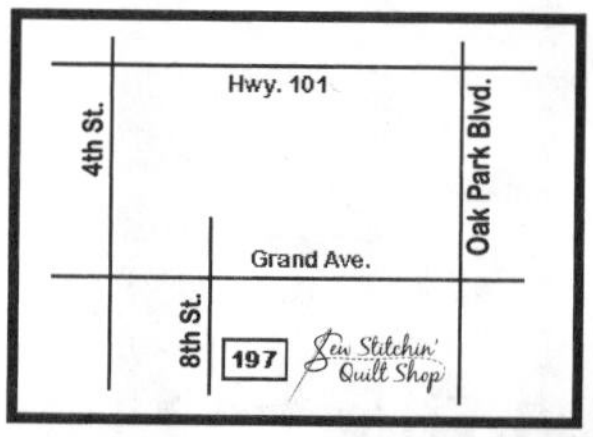

Arroyo Grande, CA #84

Mon - Sat
10 - 5
Sun 12 - 4

The Quilt Attic

106 Bridge St. 93420
(805) 474-0717 Est: 1998
TheQuiltAttic@aol.com 2000 sq.ft.
www.quiltspot.com

Cotton fabrics, books, patterns, notions, gifts and classes for quilters. We have Computer Software to design your quilts.
Authorized elna dealer.

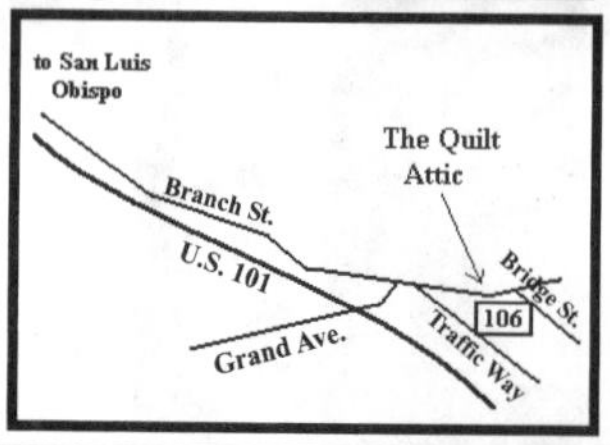

Orcutt, CA #85

Mon - Fri
10 - 5:30
Sat 10 - 4

Old Town Quilt Shop

165A W. Clark Ave. 93455
(805) 938-5870 Fax: (805) 938-5875
Owner: Maxine Campbell Online Newsletter
Est: 2005 1500 sq. ft. 2000 Bolts
www.OldTownQuiltShopOrcutt.com
100% cotton fabrics, flannels, patterns, books, notions and classes.
On the Central Coast Quilt Shop Tour.

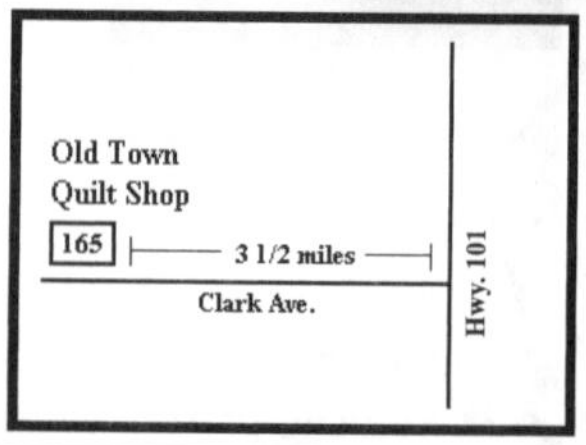

Maricopa, CA #86

Tues - Fri
10 - 5:30
Sat 10 - 2

Maricopa Quilt Company

370 California St. 93252
(661) 769-8580 Fax: (661) 769-8676
Owner: Vicki Destrampe
Est: 2006
vickigd@bak.rr.com
Long arm quilting services, 100% cotton fabrics. Western, Civil War, Minkee, Batiks and over 3000 bolts of fabric.

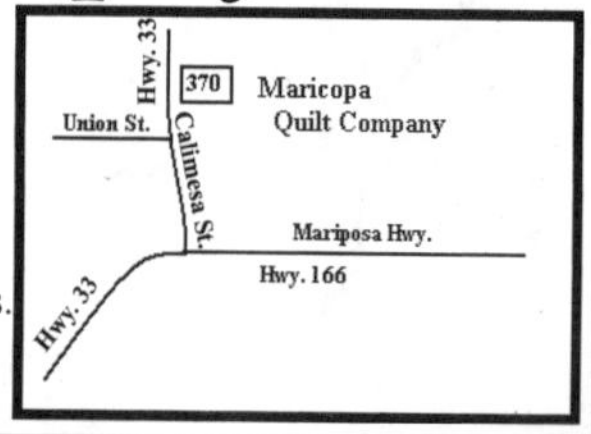

Tehachapi, CA #87

Mon 12 - 5
Tues - Fri
9 - 5
Sat 10 - 4

Debbie's Fabrics

New Location:
112 E. Tehachapi Blvd. 93561
(661) 823-7114
Owner: Debbie Szydlowski

Great prices on quilt shop quality fabrics from RJR, Moda, SSI, P&B, Benartex, etc.
Longarm quilting service
Old fashioned, friendly staff.

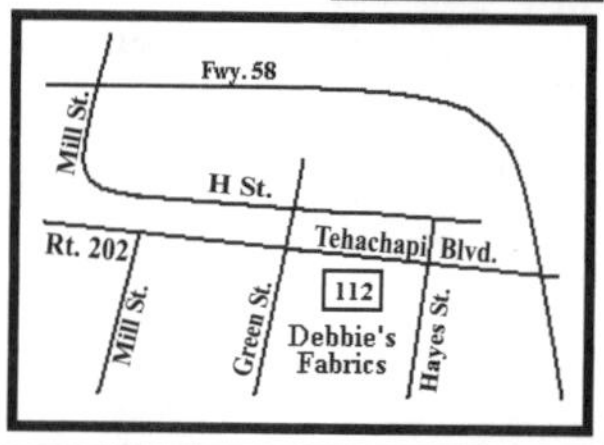

Tehachapi, CA #88

Tues - Fri
9:30 - 3:30
Sat 10 - 3

* 5 Heart Quilts & Fabric *

Est: 1993
1900 sq.ft.
1600 Bolts

104 W. Tehachapi Blvd. 93561
(661) 822-8709 Owner: Claudia Blodget
www.5heartquilts.webs.com
A Quilters Heaven with all of the Colors - 100% Cotton, Hoffman, Alex. Henry, Northcott, Benartex, Books, Notions and Classes - For Your Needs. Also Fine Jewelry. Husqvarna Viking Dealer.

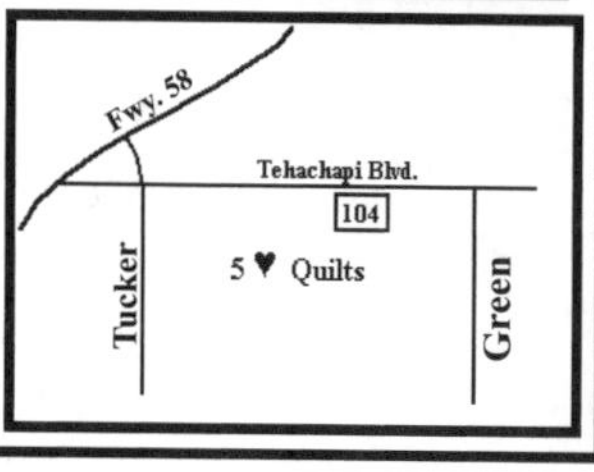

Bakersfield, CA #89

Mon - Sat
9:30 - 5:30

To Quilt 'n Sew

3510 Allen Road #102 93314
(661) 589-8863 Fax: (661) 587-3974
toquiltnsew@sbcglobal.net www.toquiltnsew.com
Owner: Robin Laiblin
Est: 2000 3400 sq.ft. 2000+ Bolts
"The happiest quilting store in Kern County"
Complete quilt store specializing in customer service. 200+ book titles and 200+ distinct Quilting stencils and patterns.
Classes for beginners to advanced.

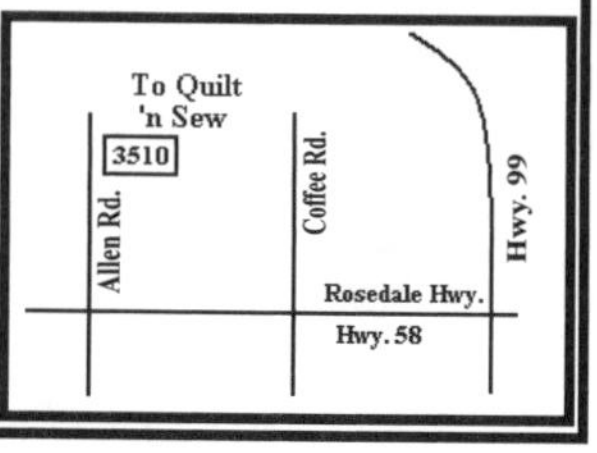

Bakersfield, CA #90

STRAWBERRY PATCHES

6439 Ming Ave. #C,
Bakersfield, CA 93309
(661) 835-1738
Owner: Suzanne Zingg Est:1985 2500 sq.ft.

www.strawberry-patches.com

Voted one of America's Top Ten quilt shops by American Patchwork & Quilting Magazine. Selection, Service, Smiles.

Authorized BERNINA Dealer

Mon - Fri 10 - 5:30
Sat 10 - 5

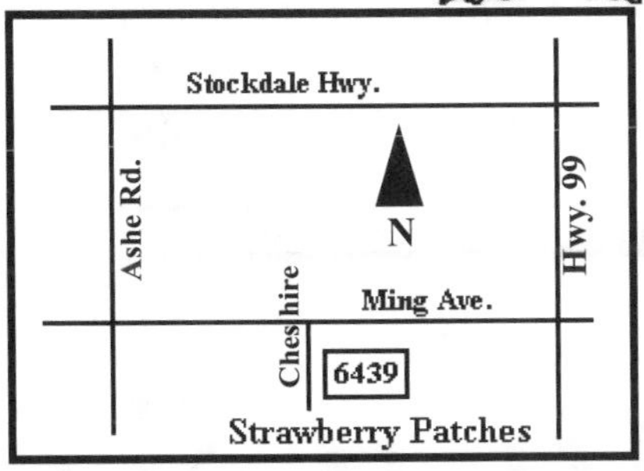

Apple Valley, CA #91

Mon - Sat 10 - 5

Cozy Quilt'n

21810 Hwy. 18 #9 92307
(760) 240-7778 Fax: (760) 240-7738
Owner: Sue Tumbleson
Est: 2002 2000 sq.ft. 5000+ bolts

Anniversary "Quilts on Parade" - an Outdoor Display of Quilts made in our Classes - is held in Late May, call for dates.

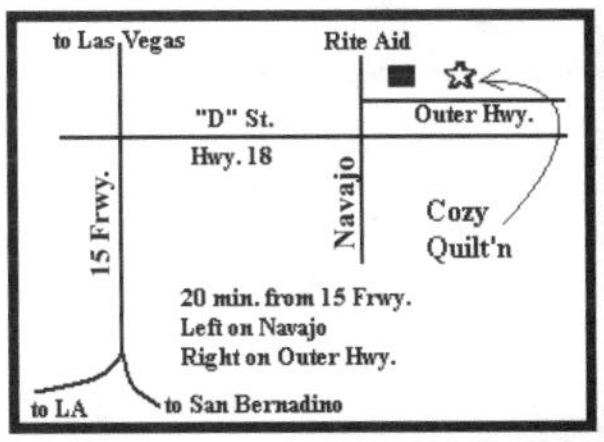

Palm Desert, CA #92

Mon - Sat 9:30 - 5:30
Sun 11 - 4

Monica's Quilt & Bead Creations

77-780 Country Club Dr. #C & D 92211
(760) 772-2400 Fax: (760) 772-2324
Owner: Monica Gonzales 4500 bolts
monicasqbc@aol.com
www.monicasquiltandbead.com

We are a full service quilt shop carrying 100% cotton fabrics and a complete bead store for your jewelry making needs.

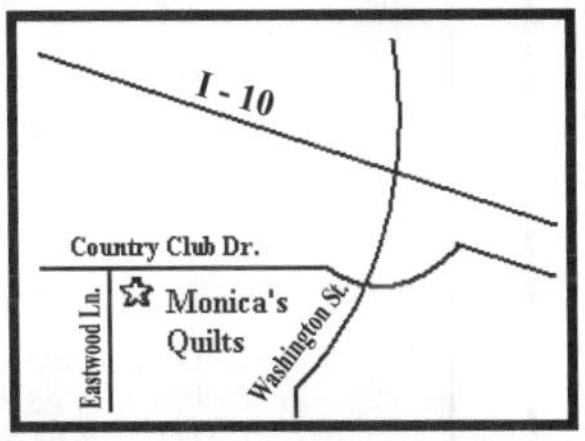

Redlands, CA #93

Est: 1986

The Calico Horse

461 Tennessee St.
Suite J 92373
(909) 793-1868 or
(909) 824-6198
Donna@thecalicohorse.com
Owner: Donna Sheridan

Mon - Fri 10 - 6
Sat 10 - 4

Large selection of 100% cotton fabrics and supplies including flannels & reproduction fabrics.

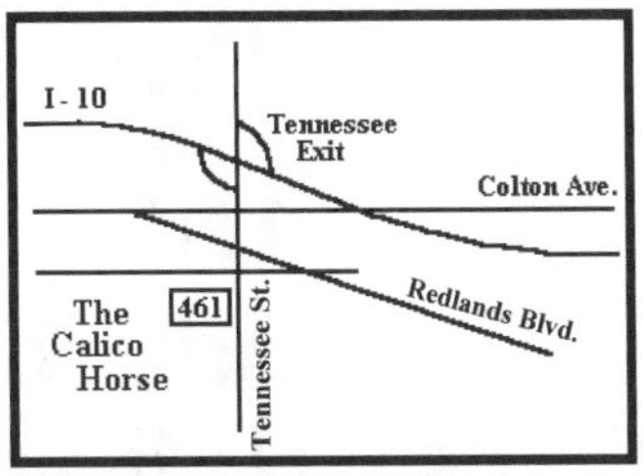

Patterns & Books.

Friendly, expert advice. Mail Order Available.

www.thecalicohorse.com

Ramona, CA #94

Mon - Fri 9:30 - 5
Tues til 7
Sat 10 - 5

The Crazy 9 Patch

1174 Main St. 92065
(760) 789-4050
www.crazy9patch.com

Take Scripps Poway Pkwy East Turn Left onto CA-67. This becomes Main St. in Ramona.

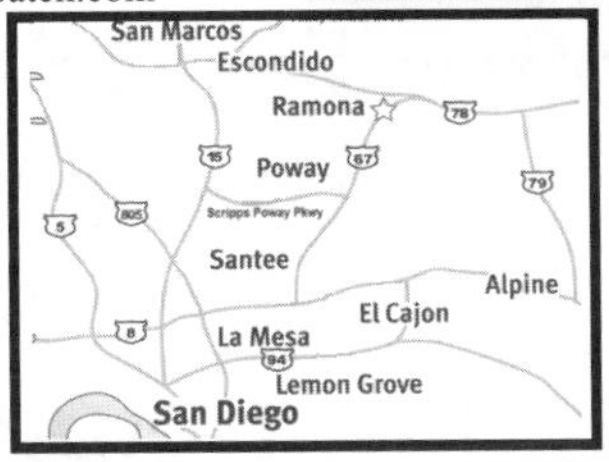

A Groovy Little Shop With A Focus on Brights & Batiks.

Santee, CA #95

Mon - Fri 9:30 - 6
Sat 9:30 - 5
Sun 11 - 5

Memory Lane Quilt Shop

225 Town Center Parkway 92071
(619) 562-2288 Fax: (619) 562-2299
Owner: Chris Stiasny
www.memorylanequiltshop.com

Our goal is to create a warm, friendly and fun environment for our quilting family. We strive to provide great products, fabulous classes and of course excellent personal service! All the latest in fabrics, books, patterns and notions.

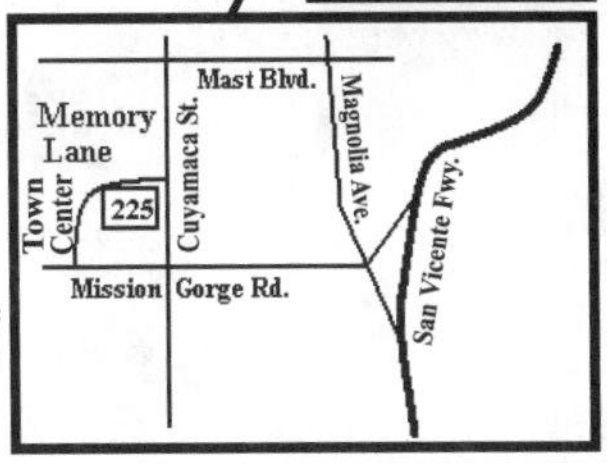

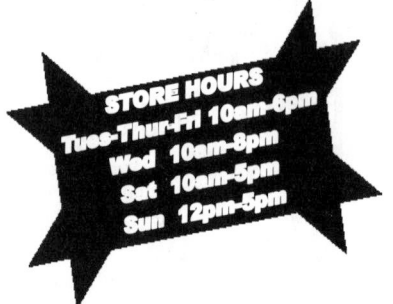

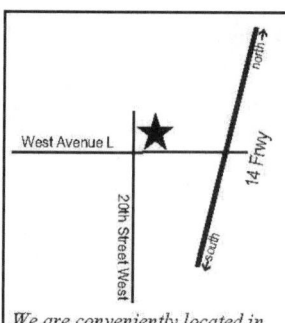

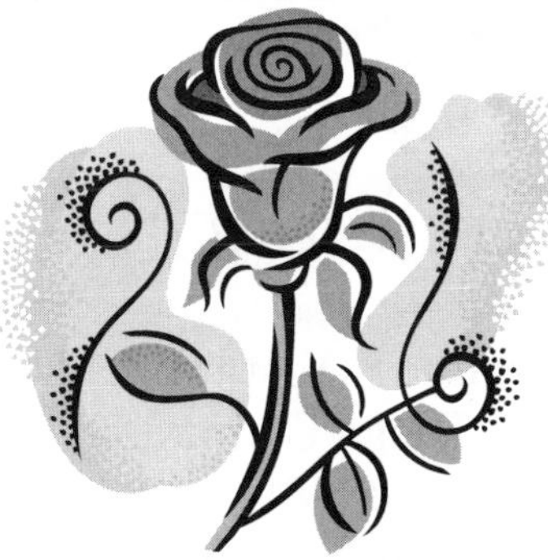

Rosie's Calico Cupboard

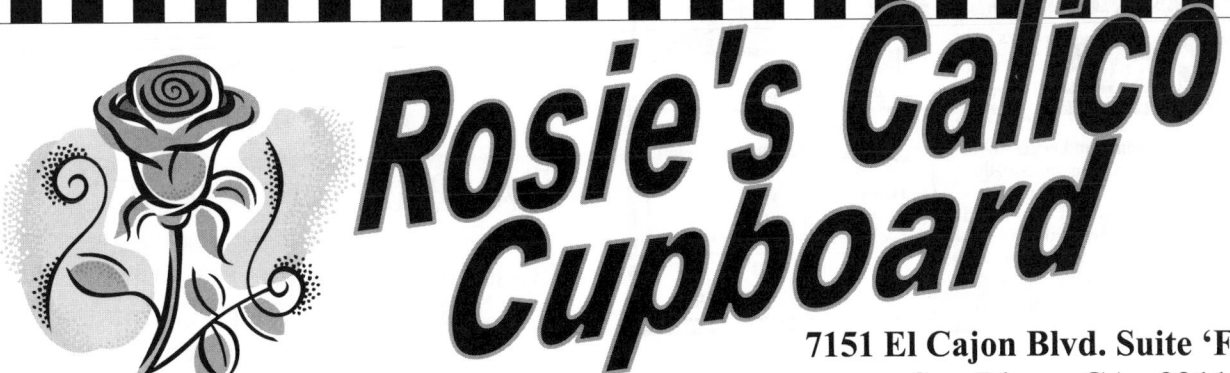

7151 El Cajon Blvd. Suite 'F'
San Diego, CA 92115
(619) 697-5758
Fax: (619) 465-8298
rozgonzalez@cox.net
www.rosiescalicocupboard.com

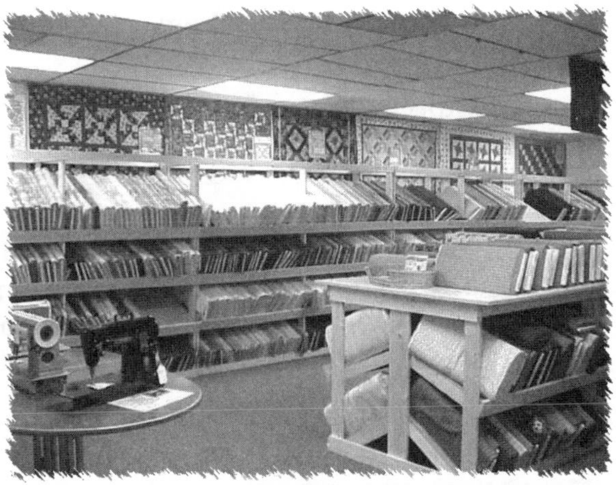

Offering over 8000 sq. ft. (stocked to the brim) with over 20,000 bolts of First Quality 100% Cotton Prints at everyday DISCOUNT prices. Books, Batting, Notions, Patterns, Quilting Thread and Machine Embroidery Thread, Machine Embroidery Designs, ACCU GO Cutters, and Quilting and Crafting related Gift items. Jim Shore also! Authorized JANOME Sewing Machine Dealer -- Sales, Service, Repair, Janome Sewing Club, Janome Embroidery Club and Janome Sewing Machine classes, plus much much more.

accuquilt
better cuts make better quilts

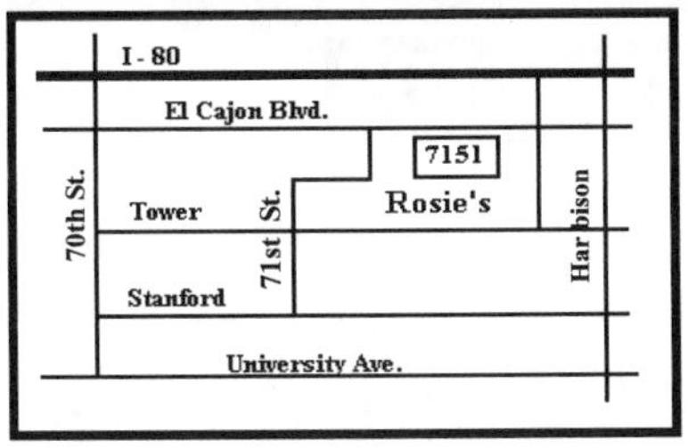

Visit our new online shop at:
www.rosiescalicocupboard.com/InternetSalesPage.html

Monday - Friday 9 - 5 Wednesday til 8
Saturday 8 - 5 Sunday 11 - 5

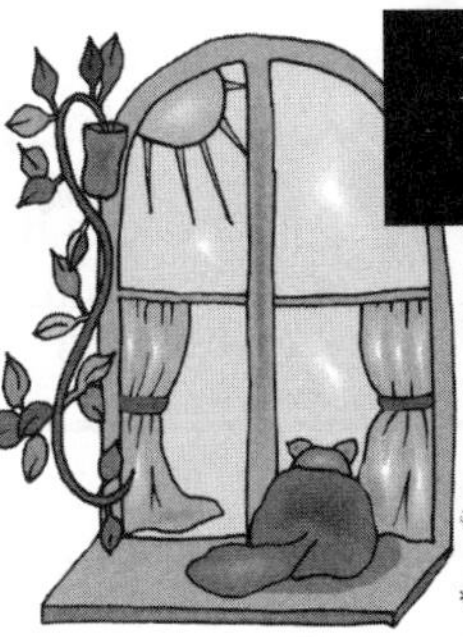

Hwy. 8 (East or West) — take 70th St. exit, travel south on 70th St. for 1/2 mile to El Cajon Blvd., turn left (east) onto El Cajon Blvd., travel for 1 1/2 blocks.
Hwy. 94 (East or West) — take the Mass. exit, travel north to University Ave., turn left, follow to 70th St., turn right, follow to El Cajon Blvd., turn right.
We are freeway close from all points of San Diego and the trolley stops ONE mile from our shop.

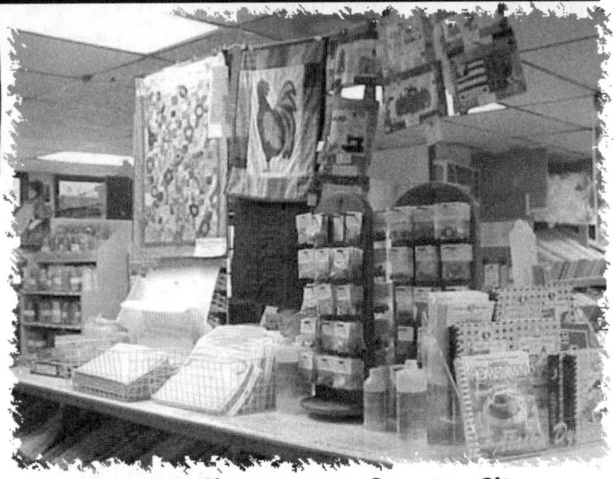

- Well stocked sale rack with values from 25 to 75% off suggested Retail Prices.
- New stock arriving daily.
- 1100 sq.ft. Classroom with a full calendar of Quilting & Crafting Classes year round.
- http://www.rosiescalicocupboard.com/NEWSLETTER.html. Find monthly Coupons in our Newsletter
- Mail Orders and Special Orders Welcome
- Visa, MC, Discover, ATM Cards

A Full Service Quilt Shop Catering to Quilters and Crafters Since 1983

San Diego, CA #98

San Diego, CA #99

Tues - Sun 10 - 4

Quilt Visions
THE ART OF THE QUILT

2825 Dewey Rd., #100 92106
(619) 546-4872
visions@quiltvisions.org www.quiltvisions.org

Located in Liberty Station, San Diego's new center for arts and culture. Our state-of-the art gallery presents a new exhibition every two months featuring the work of established and emerging fiber and fabric artists from around the world. In addition we sponsor the biennial Quilt Visions juried international exhibition at the Oceanside Museum of Art.

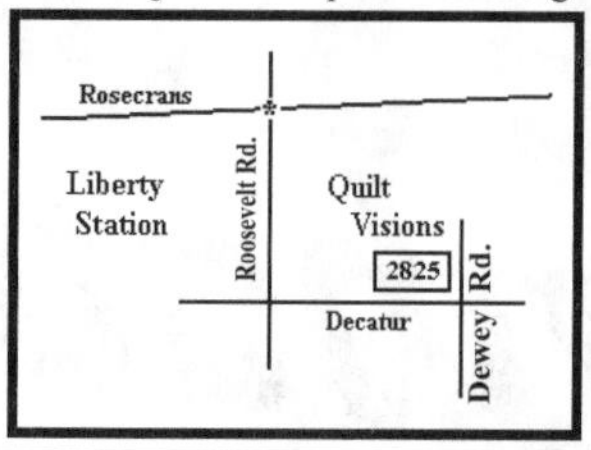

Poway, CA #100

Mon, Wed, Fri Sat 10 - 5 Tues & Thur 10 - 7

Amidon Quiltworks

12625 Danielson Ct. #111
92064
(858) 486-0696 Est: 1994
Fax: (858) 486-1618
Owner: Nancy Amidon
3800 sq.ft. 5000 Bolts aqw@cox.net
www.amidonquiltworks.com
A full service quilt shop carrying fabrics, books, patterns, notions and gifts.
Mail Order Available.

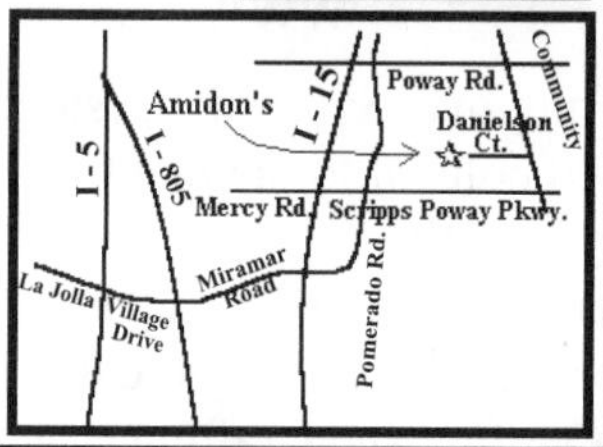

#101

Fat Quarters Quilt Shop

728 Escondido Avenue ~ Vista, CA 92084
North San Diego County
760-758-8308
www.fatquartersquiltshop.com

Monday thru Saturday 10 am – 5:30 pm
Closed on Sunday

Stop by and be inspired -
Meet your friends at Fat Quarters Quilt Shop!

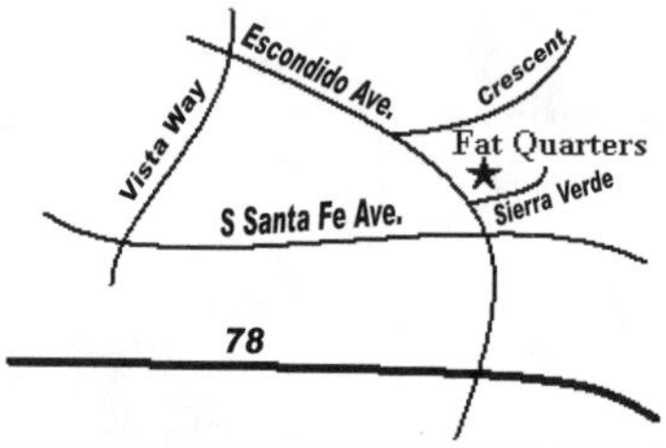

Established 1999
2,800 Square Feet with Over 4000 bolts of the NEWEST fabrics.

El Cajon, CA #102

15 minutes from downtown San Diego

Cozy Quilt Shop and **SewCozy Sewing Center**

Hours:
Mon-Sat 9:30-5:30
Thur til 6:30
Sun: noon – 4

2940 Jamacha Rd, Ste H, El Cajon, CA 92019
619-670-0652 cozyquilt.com

Home of the Strip Club and *Strip Clubbing* and publishers of Cozy Quilt Designs original patterns, books and tools!

With 4,500 square feet of brightly lit space, we offer over 3,000 bolts of 100% cotton fabric and a Bernina creative sewing center.
We are a **Must See** in San Diego.

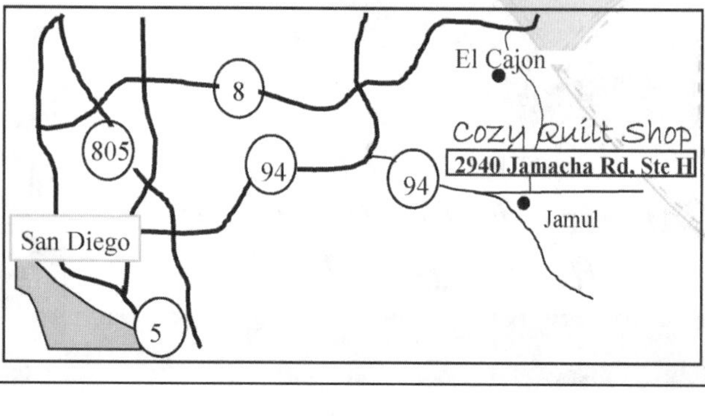

Directions

From San Diego: 94 East. Stay on 94 until it turns from freeway to city street (Do not be tempted to take 125 or turn right at Jamacha Blvd). Left at the stop light of Cuyamaca College Drive West. (Target, TGI Fridays and Staples will be on your right.) Left into parking lot. Next to Eroma Day Spa.

From East County: I-8 to Second Street exit. Go South. Second Street Turns into Jamacha Rd. We are about 6 miles from the freeway on your right.

Buellton, CA #103

www.thecreationstation.com

The Creation Station! FABRIC & Quilt Shop

252 E. Hwy. 246, Unit A
Buellton, CA 93427
(805) 693-0174

Fax: (805) 693-0164
Est: 2001 2800 sq.ft.
info@thecreationstation.com
Owners: Dawn & Patrick Farrier

Shop our Online Store!

Wed - Sat 10 - 5
Sun 10 - 4

All fabric $6.00 per yard!
(price subject to change)
Unique selection of 100% cotton & flannel fabrics amidst our fun & funky nostalgic setting

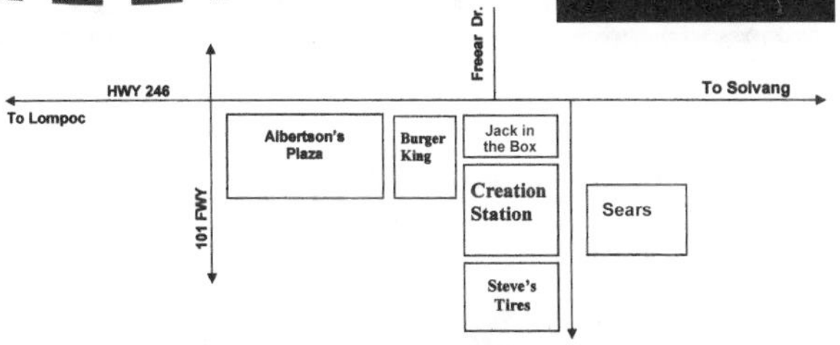

Solvang, CA #104

Rasmussen's Solvang

Mon - Sat 9 - 5:30
Sun 9 - 5

1697 Copenhagen Dr. 93463
(805) 688-6636 Fax: (805) 688-2847
info@rasmussenssolvang.com
www.rasmussenssolvang.com

We offer a large selection of quilting fabric, patterns, and books; as well as needlework and knitting supplies. We welcome phone and mail orders.

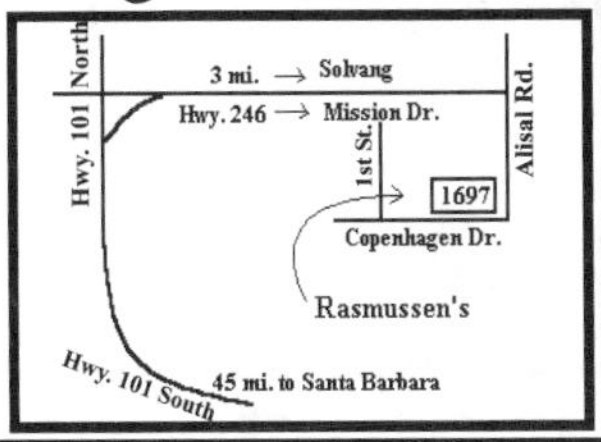

Santa Barbara, CA #105

The Fabric Quarter Quilt Shop

Tues - Fri 10 - 5:30
Sat 10 - 5

5708-C Hollister Ave. Goleta, CA 93117
(805) 683-3300
Owner: Wendy Ladd
Est: 2010 1200 sq.ft.
www.thefabricquarter.com
Contemporary, eclectic fabrics, notions and books for the experienced to new quilter.
Located in Old Town Goleta.
Five minutes from Santa Barbara.

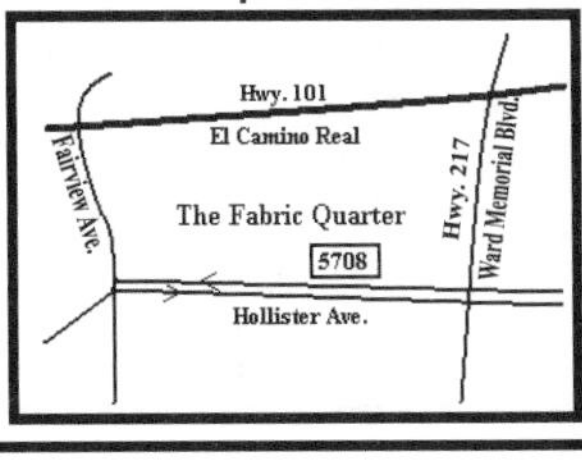

Ventura, CA #107

Quilt Ventura

Tues - Thur 10 - 6
Fri & Sat 10 - 5
Sun 11 - 4

4572 Telephone Rd.
Suite 908 93003
(805) 658-9800
www.quiltventura.com
Owner: Joey Strait
Delighting quilters with contemporary fabrics, books, notions and awesome classes!

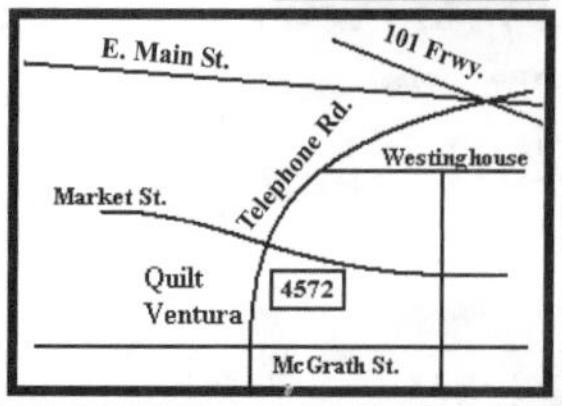

Newbury Park, CA #108

THE QUILTERS' STUDIO™

1090 Lawrence
Dr. #101
91320

Mon - Sat 10 - 5
Thur til 6
Sun 12 - 4

(805) 480-3550 Owner: Eileen Alber
Est: 1999 2500+ Bolts Newsletter
Eileen@quiltersstudio.com
www.QuiltersStudio.com
Our shop focuses on providing customers with an enriching environment where they can explore their own passion. Check out our online class schedule--we have the largest classroom around.
Bring in this ad for 10% off your purchases.

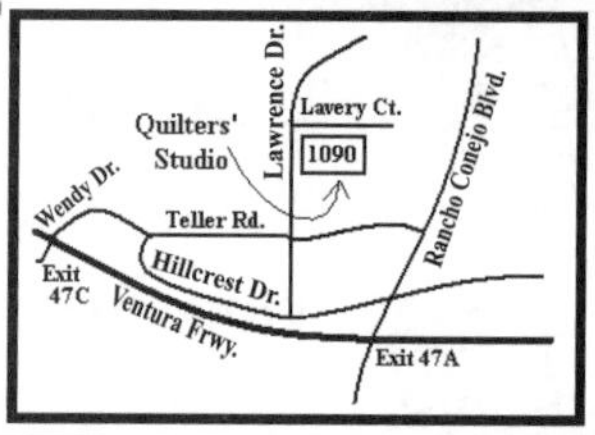

Your Quilting Destination!

Cotton & Chocolate Quilt Company

Thousand Oaks, CA #109

We feature fabulous fabric, exciting kits, as well as a full line of notions, books & patterns. AND, of course, no shopping is complete without some irresistible chocolate!!

Mon - Thur 10 - 6
Fri & Sat 10 - 5 Sun 12 - 4

1724 Avenida De Los Arboles, Unit E,
Thousand Oaks, CA 91362
805-241-0061
2800 sq. ft. 4000+ Bolts Free Newsletter

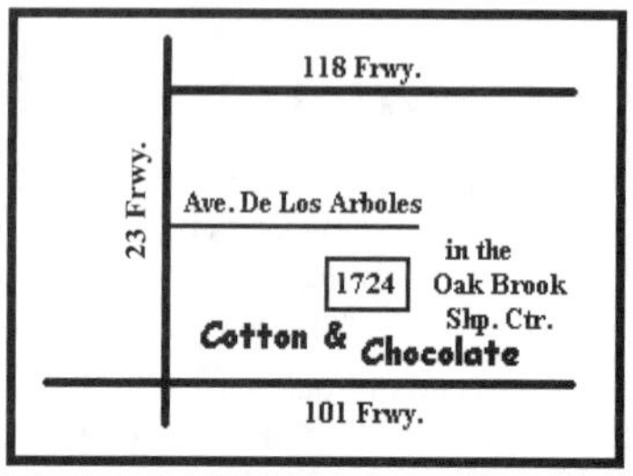

www.cottonandchocolate.com

Santa Clarita, CA #110

Mon - Sat 10 - 5

Loving Stitches QUILT SHOPPE

(661) 254-1296

21515 Soledad Canyon Rd. #121 91350
www.lovingstitchesquiltshoppe.com
Over 3000 bolts of fabric.
A large selection of Orientals and Batiks plus Books & Patterns.

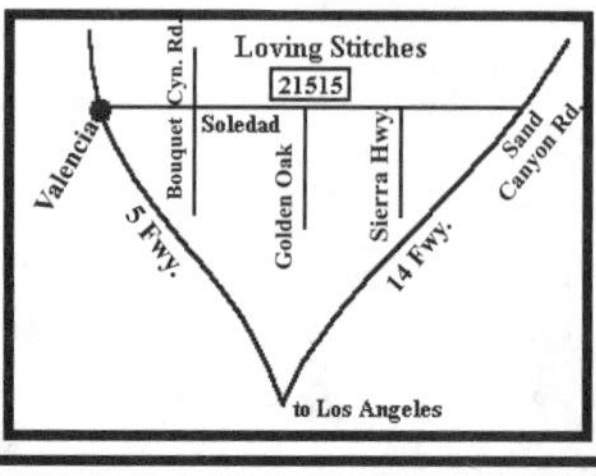

Tujunga, CA #111

Mon, Tue, Wed & Fri 10 - 6
Thur 10 - 7
Sat 10 - 5 Sun 12 - 4
Open some holidays

Patchwork Penguin

6245 Foothill Blvd., 91042
(818) 248-7390
Owner: Crissa DuCharme
patchworkpenguin@yahoo.com
www.patchworkpenguin.com
Quilt & Yarn Shop
Quality fabrics, gifts, classes AND
Fabulous Customer Service.

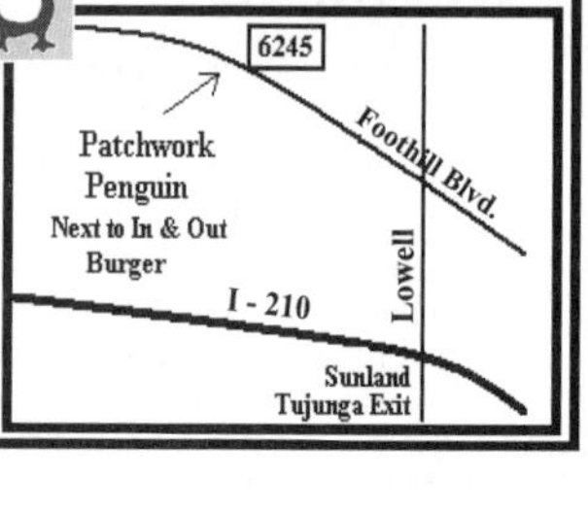

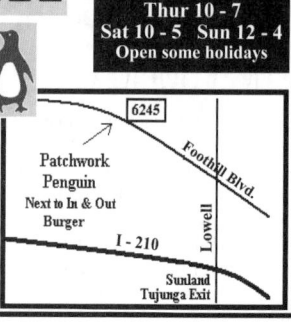

#112

NEW MOON TEXTILES

www.newmoontextiles.com

1393 E. Washington Blvd.
Pasadena, CA 91104 626-296-6663

With over 4000 bolts of fabric, we are one of the brightest and most colorful stores in Southern California. We have loads of books, patterns, notions, and classes. In addition, we carry many fabrics and supplies for surface designers and wearable artists

Directions: Exit the 210 freeway at Hill Ave., go north 1.1 miles and turn left on Washington and right into our parking lot.

Hours: M-W 10 am-6pm, Th- F 10am-7pm
Sat 10am-5pm, Sun 12pm-4pm

Upland, CA #114

Ginger's Quilt Shoppe

Tue - Fri 10 - 7
Sat 10 - 5
Sun 11 - 4

1120 Dewey Way, Suite B 91786
(909) 920-3099
Owners: Ginger Hennessee & Linda Polley
gingerandlinda@yahoo.com
www.gingersquiltshoppe.com
The newest quilting corner in Southern California! Our 3000 sq.ft. shop is full of thousands of high quality fabrics that just shout for a quilting project. Ready made kits, enjoy our books in a comfy chair with a cup of coffee and share your ideas.

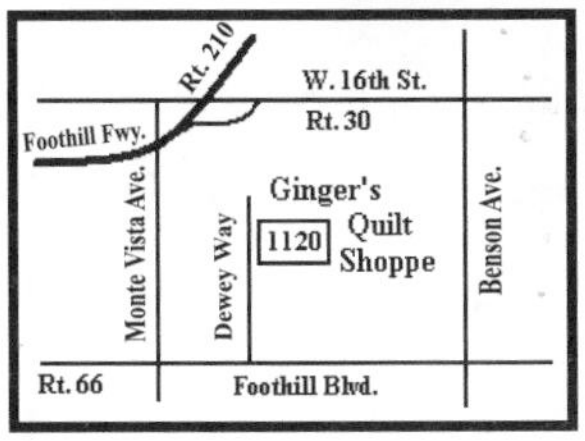

Grand Terrace, CA #115

Bluebird Quilts & GALLERY

Sun 12 - 5
Mon - Thurs 10 - 6
Fri 10 - 3
Closed Sat

22320 Barton Rd.
Ste. A 92313
(909) 514-0333

Tweet - Tweet - Tweet
Owners: Janet & Stephen Bottroff
Fax: (909) 514-0330
Est: 2008 900+ sq.ft. 1000+ bolts
bluebirdquilts@att.net
Watercolor Quilt Specialist with 30 years of quilt experience. Kaffe Fassett, Batiks, Asian and more! Free e-mail newsletter.
Come see what all the talk is about!

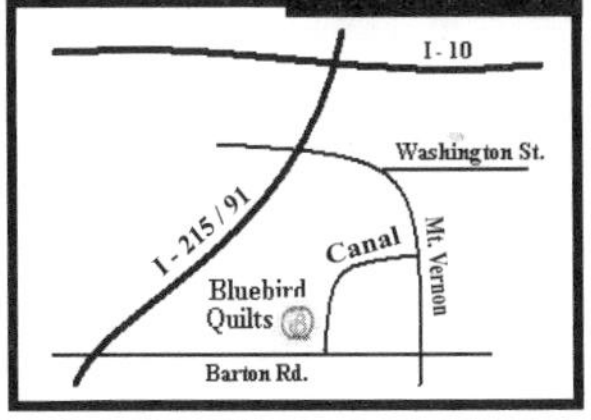

Montclair, CA #113

"Your Idea Place"

500 Books
Gifts for Quilters
Notions and Supplies
Classes for all Skill Levels
5,000 Bolts of Cotton Fabric
7500 square feet
Featured in Quilt Sampler Magazine
Authorized Janome & Horn Dealer

(909) 985-9000
Mon - Sat 10 - 5
Sun 12 - 3

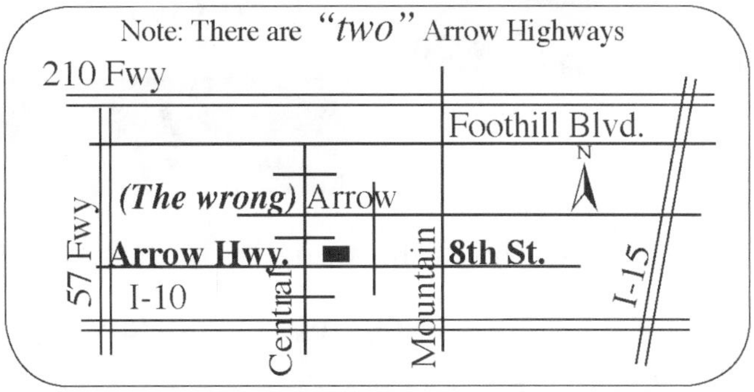

5436D Arrow Hwy., ✷ Montclair CA 91763
www.thefabricpatch.com

Calimesa, CA #116

Mon - Fri 10 - 5
Sat 10 - 3

Busy Bee Quilt Shop

1007 Calimesa Blvd., Suite J 92320
(909) 795-2778
Owner: Heidi Stagno

We specialize in Hoffman Batiks, 1930's reproductions. Juki sewing machine dealer. We offer a unique one-of-a-kind pattern line designed by the owner and sold only at our shop.

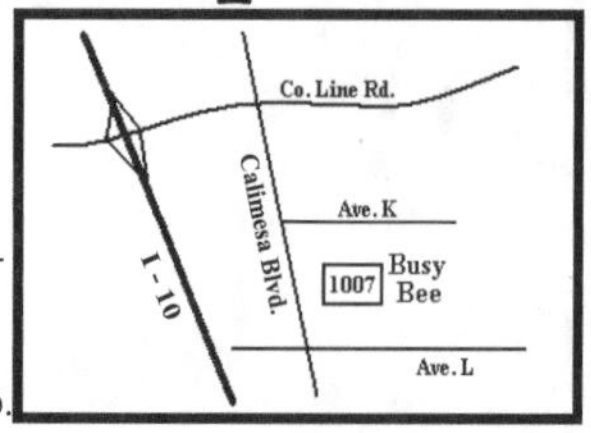

Beaumont, CA #117

Mon - Fri 10 - 6
Sat 10 - 5

Georgia's Quilting Obsession

232 W. 6th St. 92223
(951) 845-8009 Fax: Same
antqgal@aol.com Est: 2003
www.georgiasquiltingobsession.com

All the newest fabrics at prices you will love.
We also carry Dakota Embroidery Designs.
Check out our great classes.
"Quilting is Obsessively Addicting."

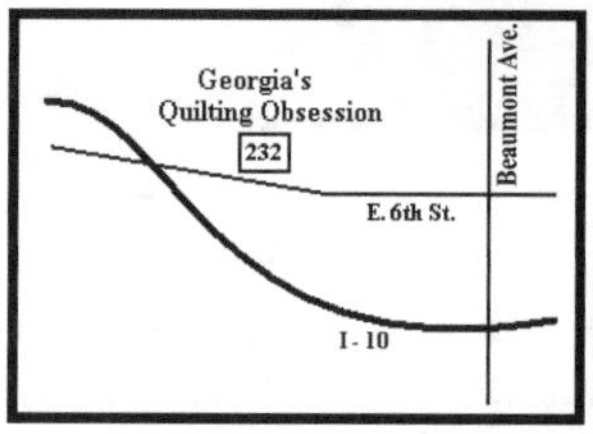

Hemet, CA #118

Mon - Fri 10 - 5
Sat 10 - 4

BUTTERFIELD QUILT CO.

130 N. Juanita St. 92543
(951) 658-4115
Online Newsletter
Fine Quilting Fabric including Moda, Benartex, Northcott, Timeless Treasures, P&B, Specialty Notions. Patterns & Books. Prices well worth the trip. Great line-up of classes.
info@butterfieldquiltco.com
www.butterfieldquiltco.com

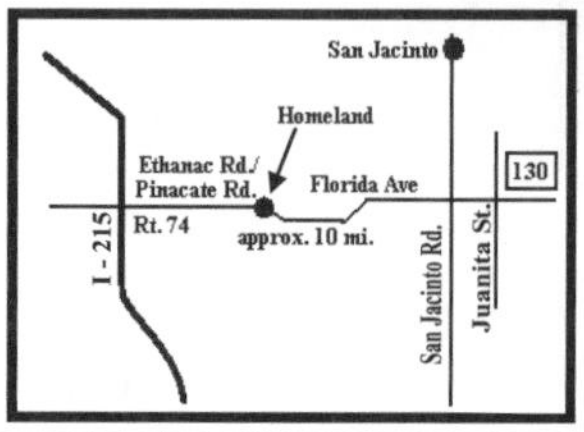

Corona, CA #119

Mon - Sat 10 - 5
Sun - Closed

Stars & Scraps Quilt Shop

2175 Sampson Ave. #121 92879
(951) 737-3959
starsandscrapsquiltshop@msn.com
www.starsandscrapsquiltshop.com
Owner: Raquel James Est: 2002
2400 sq.ft. with 2000+ bolts. Notions, books & patterns. Classes too. See website for current information and schedules.

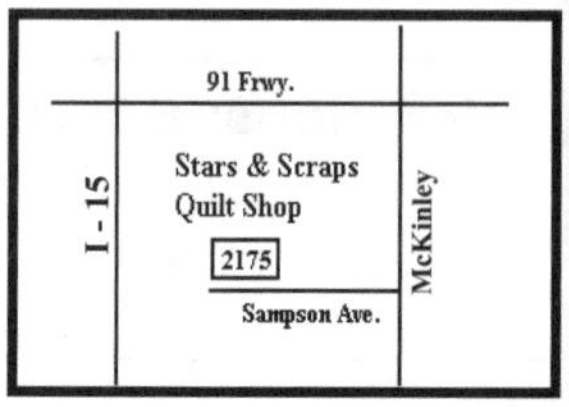

Riverside, CA #120

The Quilter's Cocoon

"Your Full Service Quilt Shop"
10248 Indiana Ave., Riverside, CA 92503
951-351-0346
thequilter@quilterscocoon.com
www.quilterscocoon.com

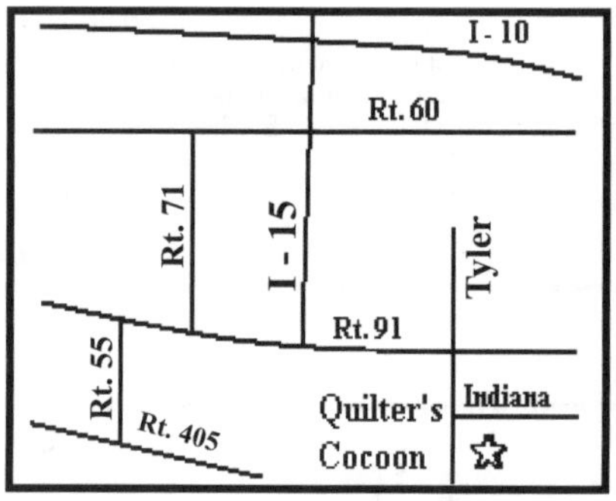

Tues - Sat 10:00 - 5:00
Wed 10:00 - 8:00 Closed Sun & Mon

Home of the highest quality fabrics at the lowest overall prices guaranteed.
Offering: Fabric, Notions, Books, Patterns, Batting, Fabulous Service and more.
Machine quilting on the premises using a Gammill Optimum with Statler Stitcher
Handi Quilter and Pro-Stitcher Represenative – Sales and Service
Quilt Classes for all skill levels.

Brea, CA #121

Mon - Thur 10 - 8
Fri & Sat 10 - 5
Sun 12 - 4

Cozy Cottage Fabrics

740 N. Brea Blvd. 92821
(714) 529-2999
Owner: Kris Giannetti
Est: 2003
2000 sq.ft.

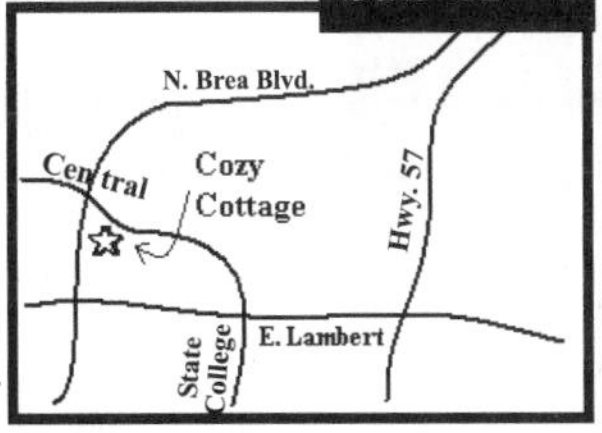

www.cozycottagefabrics.com
Info@cozycottagefabrics.com
We offer a large selection of quilting fabrics, software, books, notions, patterns and classes. You'll love our wide selection of 1930's reproductions, batiks, flannels and novelty fabrics. We also carry yarn, knitting & crochet supplies.

Placentia, CA #122

Mon - Fri 10 - 5:30
Sat 10 - 5
Sun 10 - 4

The Calico House

1279 E. Imperial Hwy. 92870
(714) 993-3091 Fax: (714) 993-2316
Owner: Cindy Zechter
calicohousequilting@yahoo.com
www.calicohousequilting.com
Est: 1981 2500+ Bolts

Complete Quilt Shop.
Books, Fabrics, Notions, Classes.
Helpful, Friendly Staff

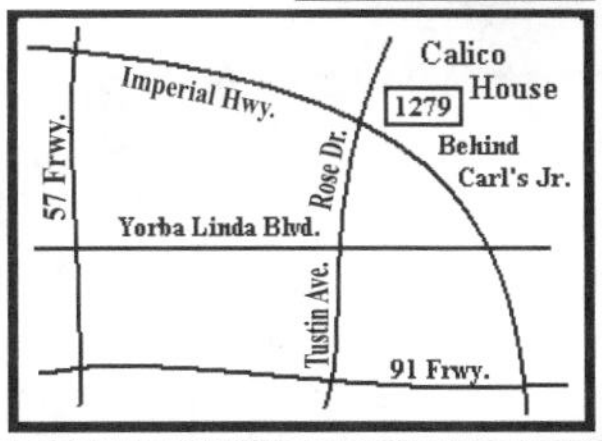

Orange, CA #123

www.orangequiltbee.com

Orange Quilt Bee

Mon-Fri 10-8
Sat 10-5 Sun 12-4

We are a full service quilt shop providing an excellent selection of fabrics, books, patterns, notions and in-store machine quilting. OQB offers a full array of classes including quilting for all levels, garment sewing, handbags and hand embroidery. We have a large spacious classroom that includes pinning/cutting tables and natural lighting. We pride ourselves in offering outstanding customer service.

628 E. Katella Ave.
92867
(714) 639-3245
Owners:
Pebble Gilb & Lisa Wiltse
Est: 2009 3750 sq.ft.
2500 Bolts
Fax: (714) 639-3391
oqbshop@orangequiltbee.com

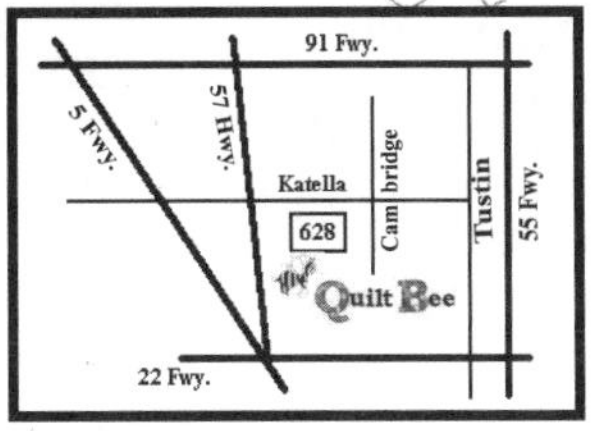

Near Disneyland

Tustin, CA #124

Flying Geese Fabric
A Quilter's Shop & More

307 El Camino Real
Tustin, CA 92780
(714) 544-9349
www.flyinggeesefabric.com
...in the heart of Old Town Tustin

GREAT CLASSES AVAILABLE
Beginner and Intermediate Quilting
Machine and Hand Quilting
Machine and Hand Applique
Beginner and Children's Sewing
Wool Samplers

- Moda • RJR
- Michael Miller
- Kaffe Fassett
- Alexander Henry
- Marcus Brothers
- Lake House
- Kaufman
- Thimbleberries
- Asian Fabrics

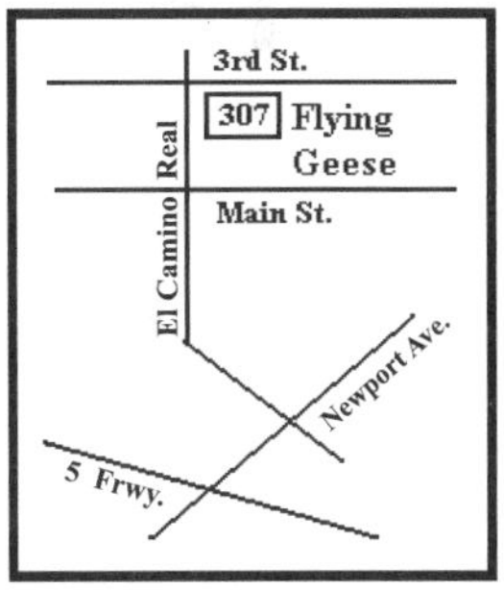

Mon, Tues, Thurs 10 - 6 Wed 10 - 7
Fri & Sat 10 - 5

Laguna Hills, CA #125

Mon - Fri 10 - 6
Sat 10 - 5
Sun 12 - 5

A TIME TO SEW

27071 Cabot Rd. #101 92653
(949) 282-0084 Fax: (949) 282-2764
Owner: Martha Hurlburt
Est: 2008 3700 sq.ft. Online Newsletter
atimetosew1@sbcglobal.net
www.a-time-to-sew.com
Wide selection of fabric, books, patterns and notions for quilts. Classes also.

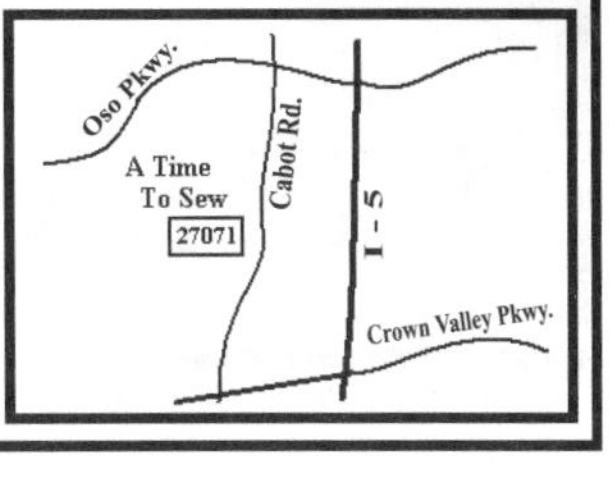

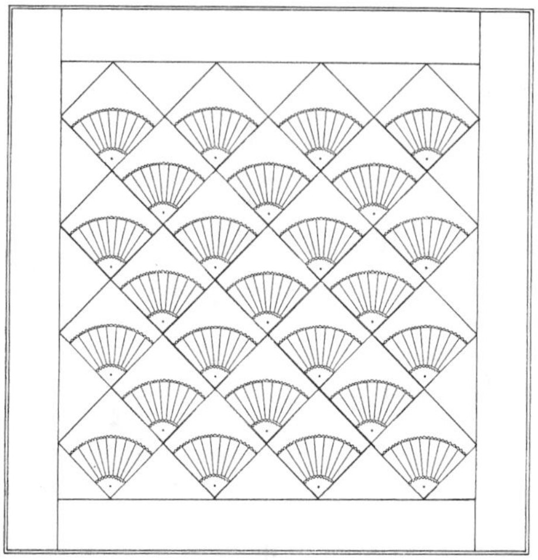

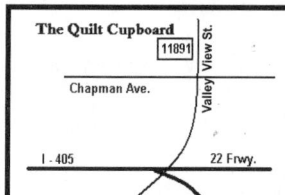

California Quilt Shops

Albion The Quilt Complex, 30701 Middle Ridge Rd. 707-937-0739
Albion Rainbow Resource, 33875 East Lane 707-937-0431 See ad #19, page 41
Altaville The Country Cloth Shop, 457 S. Main St. 209-736-4998 See ad #44, page 46
Anaheim Soft Expressions, 1230 N. Jefferson St. #M 714-630-7414
Anaheim Timeless Quilts, 1135 E. Lincoln Ave. 714-520-5304
Anaheim Tall Mouse, 5437 E. La Palma 714-693-4900
Anaheim Embroider That Quilt, 3315 E. Miraloma Ave. 714-985-9839
Anderson Carol's Quilt Shop, 17456 Flowers Ln. 530-357-2575
Anderson Quilter's Paradise, 16325 Tacoma Ln. 530-357-4864
Antioch Queen B's Quilt Shop, 720 W. 2nd St. 925-978-4587 See ad #72, page 52
Apple Valley Cozy Quilt'n, 21810 US Hwy 18 #9 760-240-7778 See ad #91, page 57
Apple Valley The Fabric Garden, 20601 Highway 18 760-961-0662
Arcata Daisy Drygoods, 959 H St. 707-822-1893
Arcata Fabric Temptations, 942 `G' St. 707-822-7782
Arroyo Grande The Quilt Attic, 106 Bridge St. 805-474-0717 See ad #84, page 56
Atascadero Sew Fun, 8775 El Camino Real 805-462-9739 See ad #65, page 50
Atascadero Quilter's Cupboard, 5275 El Camino Real 805-466-6996 See ad #64, page 50
Auburn Cabin Fever Quilt Shoppe, 826 Lincoln Way 530-885-5500
Avalon Catalina Crafters, 115 Sumner Ave. 310-510-3590
Bakersfield Strawberry Patches, 6439 Ming Ave. #C 661-835-1738 See ad #90, page 57
Bakersfield To Quilt 'n Sew, 3510 Allen Rd. #102 661-589-8863 See ad #89, page 56
Bakersfield Tod's Sew & Vac, 905 19th St. 661-323-7504
Bakersfield Quilter's Haven, 3040 Brundage Ln. 661-336-0100
Barstow Route 66 Quilt Shop, 24525 W. Main St. 760-253-5307
Beaumont Georgia's Quilting Obsession, 232 W 6th St 951-845-8009 See ad #117, page 64
Berkeley Stonemountain & Daughter Fabrics, 2518 Shattuck Ave. 510-845-6106 See ad # 68, page 51
Berkeley New Pieces, 766 Gilman 510-527-6779
Bishop Quilting In The Sierras, 169 East Line St. 760-872-4769 See ad #48, page 46
Brea Cozy Cottage Fabrics, 740 N. Brea Blvd 714-529-2999 See ad #121, page 65
Brentwood Sew Ewe Quilt, 470 Harvest Park Dr. Suite E 925-634-7153 See ad #73, page 52
Bridgeport Hampton House, 261 Main St. 760-932-1145 See ad #47, page 46
Buellton The Creation Station !, 252 E Hwy. 246 Unit A 805-693-0174 See ad #103, page 61
Calimesa Quiet Mouse Quilt Shop, 1096 Calimesa Blvd. #B 909-446-1000
Calimesa Busy Bee Quilt Shop, 1007 Calimesa Blvd. Suite J 909-795-2778 See ad #116, page 64
Camarillo Baron's Fabric, 379 Carmen Dr. 805-482-9848
Cambria Pine Tree Patchworks, 815 Main St 805-927-3869
Cameron Park High Sierra Quilters, 3450 Palmer Dr.Suite #8 530-677-9990 See ad #41, page 45
Cameron Park Shared Stitches, 2650 Cameron Park Dr. #300 530-676-4739 See ad #40, page 44
Campbell Golden State Sewing Center, 2435 S. Winchester 408-866-1181
Capitola Judy's Sewing Center, 1501 41st Ave. #J 831-464-8181
Carmichael Creative Sew & Vac, 4141 Manzanita Ave #150 916-483-1414
Carmichael Beverly's Fabrics, 6456 Fair Oaks Blvd 916-486-8374 See ad #30, page 43
Carpinteria The Treasure Hunt, 919 Maple Ave. 805-684-3360 See ad #106, page 61 & 410
Castro Valley Bolt's End Fabrics, 2743 Castro Valley Blvd. 510-537-1684
Cerritos Tall Mouse Arts & Crafts, 13233 E. South St. 310-865-0800
Chester Paper Stuff, 425 Main St. 530-258-3966
Chester Mountain Maid Quilters, 135 Main #6E 530-258-3901 See ad #11, page 40

Chico — **Honey Run Quilters, 1230 Esplanade** — **530-342-5464** — **See ad #34, page 44**

Chico — **Rabbit Hole, 2607 Esplanade** — **530-345-5015** — **See ad #35, page 44**

Chula Vista — Amethyst Quilts, 786 3rd Ave. Suite A — 619-585-0020

Chula Vista — Quilter's Choice, 417 3rd. Ave. — 619-425-2545

Clovis — **Quilters' Paradise, 339 Pollasky Ave.** — **559-297-7817** — **See ad #53, page 48**

Colfax — Whistlestop Quilt Shop, 54 S. Main St — 530-346-8482

Concord — **Thimble Creek, 1150-D Burnett St.** — **925-676-5522** — **See ad #71, page 52**

Corona — **Stars & Scraps Quilt Shop, 2175 Sampson Ave. #121** — **951-737-3959** — **See ad #119, page 64**

Costa Mesa — **Piecemakers Country Store, 1720 Adams Ave.** — **714-641-3112** — **See ad #129, page 67**

Cottonwood — **Quilts in the Attic, 3240 Brush St.** — **530-347-5994** — **See ad #12, page 41**

Danville — **The Quilter's Inn, 125-F Railroad Ave.** — **925-837-8458** — **See ad #70, page 52**

Drytown — The Old General Store, 15907 State Highway 49 — 209-245-6914

Dublin — Dublin Sewing Center, 7367 Village Parkway — 925-829-6511

El Cajon — Quilters' Connection, 260 W. Douglas Ave. — 619-444-8800

El Cajon — **Cozy Quilt Shop, 2940 Jamacha Rd. Suite H** — **619-670-0652** — **See ad #102, page 60 & 196**

Elk Grove — **Country Sewing Center, 9414 Elk Grove Florin** — **916-685-8500** — **See ad #26, page 42**

Encinitas — Starry Night Hollow, 895 Saxony Rd — 760-944-3700

Escalon — Purple Patch Quilting, 2212 Arroya St. — 209-838-7249

Escondido — Bits & Pieces Bernina Studio, 426 West 2nd Ave. — 760-745-5878

Escondido — Quilter's Paradise, 1451 Montiel Rd. #140 — 760-738-9677

Eureka — **Scottie Dog Quilts, 301 W. Harris St.** — **707-444-9662** — **See ad #7, page 40**

Eureka — **Ocean Wave Quilts, 305 V St.** — **707-444-0252** — **See ad #8, page 40**

Fair Oaks — Jeanette's Fabrics, 11045 Fair Oaks Blvd — 916-482-1899

Fair Oaks — **Tayo's Fabrics & Quilts, 10127 Fair Oaks Blvd.** — **916-967-5479** — **See ad #31, page 43**

Fairfax — Rainbow Fabrics, 50 Bolinas Rd. — 415-459-5100

Fairfield — **Cornerstone Quilt Shoppe, 1001 Texas St. #A** — **707-438-2969** — **See ad #25, page 42**

Fallbrook — Quilter's Cottage, 131 East Fig St. Suite 6 — 760-723-3060

Ferndale — Itsy Bitsy Quilt Shop, 580 Main St. #3 — 707-786-9002

Folsom — Meissner Sewing Maching Co., 1013 Riley St. — 916-984-7071

Fort Bragg — **Sew'n Sew Fabrics, 890-A N. Franklin St.** — **707-964-4152** — **See ad #17, page 41**

Fort Bragg — **Fabric Indulgence & Art Supply, 181 Boat Yard Dr** — **707-964-6365** — **See ad #16, page 41**

Fortuna — **Fortuna Fabrics & Crafts, 2045 Main St.** — **707-725-2501** — **See ad #9, page 40**

Fortuna — All Washed Up, 685 Spring St — 707-725-9773

Fountain Valley — Fun 2 Sew, 17195 Newhope St. #108 — 714-444-1895

Fremont — Color Me Quilts and More, 37495 Niles Blvd. — 510-792-6567

Fremont — **Sisters 'N Stitches, 3270 Seldon Court #4** — **510-490-7586** — **See ad #75, page 53**

Fresno — **Cottage Quilts, 1732 W. Bullard Ave** — **559-447-0599** — **See ad #54, page 48**

Galt — Creative Quilts, 10393 Twin Cities Rd — 209-745-0633

Garden Grove — Bear's Quilt Shop, 10722 Trask Ave. #A — 714-590-9209

Garden Grove — **The Quilt Cupboard, 11891 Valley View St.** — **714-891-8639** — **See ad #127, page 66**

Gilroy — **The Nimble Thimble, 7550 Monterey St.** — **408-842-6501** — **See ad #58, page 49**

Goleta — **The Fabric Quarter, 5708 C Holister Ave** — **805-683-3300** — **See ad #105, page 61**

Granada Hills — Patchwork N' Things, 12355 Jolette Ave. — 818-360-2828

Grand Terrace — **Bluebird Quilts & Gallery, 22320 Barton Rd. #A** — **909-514-0333** — **See ad #115, page 63**

Grass Valley — Creative Machine Arts, 231 E. Main St. — 530-477-6629

Grass Valley — **Ben Franklin Crafts, 598 Sutton Way** — **530-273-1348** — **See ad #38, page 44**

Grass Valley — **Sugar Pine Quilt Shop, 452 S. Auburn St.** — **530-272-5308** — **See ad #37, page 44**

Grass Valley — Fabrics on Mill Street, 140 Mill St. — 530-273-9386

Groveland — Bunny Rose & Co., 18743 Main St. — 209-962-4438

Groveland — **WinDee's Quilting Bees, 21081 Lytle Loomis Rd.** — **209-962-0421** — **See ad #45, page 46**

Grover Beach — **Sew Stitchin' Quilt Shop, 197 S 8th St** — **805-904-6145** — **See ad #83, page 56**

Gualala — The Loft, 39225 S. Hwy. 1 — 707-884-4424

Hanford — **Quilter's Quarters, 880 N. Irwin St.** — **559-584-6899** — **See ad #57, page 49**

Healdsburg — Fabrications 116 Matheson St. — 707-433-6243

Hemet — **Butterfield Quilt Company, 130 N Juanita St** — **951-658-4115** — **See ad #118, page 64**

Hollister — Homespun Harbor, LTD., 341 Tes Pinos Rd. #101 — 831-630-9438

Inyokern — Quilted Patches, 300 Mark Ct., PO Box 1176 — 760-377-5378

Jackson — Sewing Cottage, 11974 W. State Hwy. 88 — 209-223-0393

June Lake — Sierra Cottons & Wools, 2784 State Highway 158 — 760-648-7875

La Jolla — Jane's Fabrique, 7547 Girard Ave. — 858-459-5828

La Mesa — The Country Loft, 4685 Date Ave. — 619-466-5411

Lafayette — **The Cotton Patch, 1025 Brown Ave.** — **925-284-1177** — **See ad #69, page 51**

Laguna Hills — **A Time to Sew, 27071 Cabot Road, Ste 101** — **949-282-0084** — **See ad #125, page 65**

Laguna Niguel — Tall Mouse Crafts, 23932 Aliso Creek Rd. — 949-360-5777

LaHabra — Calico Corner Quilt Shop, 2094 W. LaHabra Blvd. — 562-694-3384

Lakeport — **Kerrie's Quilting, 1853 N High St** — **707-263-8555** — **See ad #15, page 41**

Lancaster — **Bolts in the Bathtub, 1965 West Ave L** — **661-945-5541** — **See ad #96, page 58**

Lancaster — Cozy Quilts, 42555 32nd St. W — 805-945-1207

Laverne — Custom Creations, 4009 Kimberly Ave — 909-223-2023

Laytonville — **The Fat Quail Quilt Shop, 44550 N. Hwy. 101** — **707-984-6966** — **See ad #13, page 41**

Lemon Grove — Ethnic Quilts & Fabrics, 2607 Lemon Grove — 619-461-0783

Livermore — **In Between Stitches, 2190 First St.** — **925-371-7064** — **See ad #74, page 53**

Lodi — Quilter's Friend, 521 W Lodi Ave — 209-333-2075

Los Alamitos — **Bunney Hutch Quilt 'N Sew, 4478 Cerritos Ave.** — **714-226-9647** — **See ad #128, page 66**

Los Gatos — Natural Expressions of Los Gatos, 18 N. Santa Cruz — 408-354-5330

Magalia — Seams To B, 14543 Grinnell Ct. — 530-873-2670

Manteca — Ladybug's Quilts, 1236 N. Main St. #A — 209-824-0485

Maricopa — **Maricopa Quilt Company, 370 California St** — **6617698580** — **See ad #86, page 56**

Marina — **Your Home Town Sewing Center, 215-L Reservations Rd.** — **831-582-2595** — **See ad #59, page 49**

Martinez — Main Street Quilts, 533 Main St. — 925-372-3700

Marysville — Sew So Shop, 425 D St. — 530-742-7626

Mendocino — **Ocean Quilts of Mendocino, 45270 Main St.** — **707-937-4201** — **See ad #18, page 41**

Mission Viejo — Moore's Sewing and Fabric, 25390 Marquerite — 949-580-2520

Montclair — **The Fabric Patch, 5436 D Arrow Hwy.** — **909-985-9000** — **See ad #113, page 63**

Montrose — Quilt 'n' Things, Inc., 2411 Honolulu Ave. — 818-957-2287

Morgan Hill — **Quilts & Things, 16985 Monterey St. #316** — **408-776-8438** — **See ad #77, page 53**

Morro Bay — **The Cotton Ball, 1199 Main St.** — **805-772-2646** — **See ad #66, page 50**

Morro Bay — LINA G'-All the Trimmings, 468 Morro Bay Blvd. — 805-772-7759

Mt. Shasta — **Weston's Quilting and Crafts, 414 Chestnut St.** — **530-926-4021** — **See ad #1, page 39**

Napa — Nor Mar Fabrics, 1327 Main St. — 707-253-8577

Napa — **Quiltmaker, 1275 Napa Town Center** — **707-252-6793** — **See ad #23, page 42**

Newbury Park — **The Quilters' Studio, 1090 Lawrence Dr. #101** — **805-480-3550** — **See ad #108, page 62**

Nipomo — Creative Patches House, 136 A&B North Thompson — 805-929-3704

Norco — Fabric Flea Market, 343 6th St. #I — 951-371-4349

Norco — Tattered Rabbit Quilt Shop, 1660 Hamner Ave. #16 — 951-278-9108

Northridge — Candy's Quiltworks, 8549 Reseda Blvd. — 818-349-7397

Novato — **Picket Fence Quilts, 6090 B Redwood Blvd.** — **4158928380** — **See ad #67, page 51**

Oakdale — **Quilters Cabin, 630 N. Yosemite Ave.** — **209-847-4487** — **See ad #49, page 46**

Oakhurst — **Bear Paw Quilts & More, 40761 Hwy. 41 #5** — **559-683-7397** — **See ad #46, page 46**

Oceanside — Aretoy Quilts, 1656 Ord Way — 760-630-9234

Orange — **Orange Quilt Bee, 628 E Katella Ave** — **714-639-3245** — **See ad #123, page 65**

Orcutt — **Old Town Quilt Shop, 165-A West Clark Ave.** — **805-938-5870** — **See ad #85, page 56**

Pacific Grove — **Back Porch Fabrics, 157 Grand Ave.** — **831-375-4453** — **See ad #60, page 49**

Palm Desert — Ralph's Sewing & Vacuum, 73741 Hwy. 111 — 760-568-2226

Palm Desert — **Monica's Quilt & Bead, 77-780 Country Club Dr.** — **760-772-2400** — **See ad #92, page 57**

Palo Cedro — **JJ's Log Cabin, 9348 Deschutes Rd** — **530-547-2228** — **See ad #10, page 40**

Paradise — Debbie's Quilt Shop, 6455 Skyway — 530-877-8458

Paradise — **Morning Star Quilts, 43 Pearson Rd.** — **530-876-3243** — **See ad #36, page 44**

Pasadena **New Moon Textiles, 1393 E Washington Blvd 626-296-6663** See ad #112, page 63

Paso Robles **Wine Country Quilts, 705 Pine St, Ste. "D" 805-239-8976** See ad #63, page 50

Paso Robles **Birch Fabrics, 1244 Pine St Ste D 805-239-8888** See ad #61, page 50

Paso Robles **The Quiltery, 1413 Riverside Ave. # B 805-227-4561** See ad #62, page 50

Petaluma **Quilted Angel, 200 G St. 707-763-0945** See ad #22, page 42

Pico Rivera S & J Quilts, 7860 Paramount Blvd. 310-942-7784

Pismo Beach **Quiltin Cousins, 330 Pomeroy 805-773-4988** See ad #82, page 56

Placentia **The Calico House, 1279 E. Imperial Hwy. 714-993-3091** See ad #122, page 65

Pleasant Hill Beverly Fabrics & Crafts, 8 Capri Ln. 925-462-9340

Portola **Homestead Fabric, 141 Nevada St. 530-832-0446** See ad #33, page 43

Poway **Amidon Quiltworks, 12625 Danielson Ct. #111 858-486-0696** See ad #100, page 60

Poway Baker's Sewing Center, 12935 Pomerad Rd 760-745-4140

Ramona **The CraZy 9 Patch, 1174 Main St. 760-789-4050** See ad #94, page 57

Ramona Keepsake Quilte Shoppe, P.O. Box 282 760-788-5652

Redding **The Sewing Room, 2665 Park Marina Dr. 530-246-2056** See ad #4, page 39

Redding **Sew What!, 2609 Bechelli Lane 530-242-0177** See ad #3, page 39

Redding **Sew Simple, 2223 Larkspur Ln. 530-222-1845** See ad #5, page 39

Redlands **The Calico Horse, 461 Tennessee St. Suite J 909-793-1868** See ad #93, page 57

Redondo Beach The Cotton Shop, 1922 Artesia Blvd 310-376-3518

Redondo Beach **Luella's Quilt Basket, 1512 Aviation Blvd. 310-798-1282** See ad #126, page 66

Reedley **Mennonite Quilt Center, 1012 "G" St. 559-638-3560** See ad #55, page 48

Reseda Boothill Patches, 7620 Tampa Ave. 818-344-2678

Ridgecrest The Quilted Quail, 901 N. Heritage Drive #104 760-446-7420

Ridgecrest Casa Java Roasting Co., 972 N. Norma St. 760-446-5282

Ridgecrest Quilt 'N Home, 425 E. Ridgecrest Blvd. 760-371-9060

Ripon Horsefeathers Quilt Shop, P.O. Box 1288 209-823-1633

Riverside Moore's Sewing Center, 10357 Magnolia Ave. #L 951-688-6254

Riverside **The Quilter's Cocoon, 10248 Indiana Ave. 951-351-0346** See ad #120, page 64

Riverside Sewing Shack, 7000 Indiana Ave Suite 103 951-680-1739

Rocklin **The Quilter's Stash, 1150 Sunset Blvd., Ste. 158 916-435-2103** See ad #32, page 43

Sacramento **Bearpaws & Hollyhocks, 4128 El Camino Ave. # 5 916-971-9392** See ad #28, page 42

Sacramento **Quilter's Corner, 9792 B Business Park Dr. 916-366-6136** See ad #29, page 43

Sacramento Meissner Sewing Machine Co, 2417 Cormorant Way 916-920-2121

San Carlos **The Laurel Leaf, 648 Laurel St. 650-591-6790** See ad #80, page 54

San Diego **Rosie's Calico Cupboard, 7151 El Cajon Blvd. 619-697-5758** See ad #98, page 59

San Diego **Quilt Visions Art Quilt Gallery, 2825 Dewey Rd. 619-546-4872** See ad #99, page 60

San Diego Once Upon A Quilt, 4594 30th St 619-563-4164

San Diego Sew Hut, 4226 Balboa Ave. 858-273-1377

San Francisco Mendels' Far Out Fabrics, 1556 Haight St. 415-621-1287

San Francisco Fabric Creation, 1846 26th Ave. 415-731-7539

San Jose **San Jose Museum of Quilts & Textiles, 520 South 1st St. 408-971-0323** See ad #76, page 53

San Jose Quilter's Nest, 1375 Blossom Hill Rd. #57 408-723-4133

San Jose Prairie Queens Quilt Shop, 14922 Camden 408-559-6735

San Luis Obispo Betty's Fabrics, 1229 Carmel St. 805-543-1990

San Marcos **Quilt in a Day, 1955 Diamond St. 800-777-4852** See ad #97, page 58

San Mateo **Always Quilting, 4230 Olympic Ave. 650-458-8580** See ad #81, page 54

San Rafael California Sewing & Vacuum, 1435 4th St. 415-457-3326

Santa Ana Quilting Possibilities, 2207 S. Grand Ave. 714-546-9949

Santa Ana Unique Quilting, 1969 Ritchey St 714-258-0311

Santa Barbara Grant House Sewing, 128 E. Cannon Perdido 805-967-3680

Santa Clarita **Loving Stitches Quilt Shoppe, 21515 Soledad Canyon 661-254-1296** See ad #110, page 62

Santa Cruz Hart's Fabric Center, 1620 Seabright Ave. 831-423-5434

Santa Maria Betty's Fabrics, 1627 S. Broadway 805-922-2181

Santa Maria Santa Maria Sewing, 127 E. Main St. 805-922-1784

Santa Rosa **The Material Girl Fabrics and Quilting Supplies 6119 Old Redwood Hwy., Ste. B1 707-836-0114** See ad #20, page 42

Santa Rosa **Quilted Vine, 1591 Farmers Ln 707-546-0750** See ad #21, page 42

Santee **Memory Lane Quilt Shop, 225C Town Center Parkway 619-562-2288** See ad #95, page 57

Scotts Valley Judy's Sewing Center , 222 G Mt. Hermon Rd. 831-440-1050

Sebastopol Sewannes Fabrics, 4770 Daywalt Rd. 707-823-9968

Silverado Cottonwood Quilting, 28189 Thisa Way 714-649-2203

Simi Valley Quilters Country Cottage, 4449-B Cochran St 805-520-1243

Sky Forest Mountain Quilters Cottage, 935 S. Kuffel Canyon 909-337-1521

Sky Forest Yarn & Sew Shop, 28589 Hwy. 18 909-336-0080

Solvang **Rasmussen's, 1697 Copenhagen Dr. 805-688-6636** See ad #104, page 61

Sonora **Bearly Quilting, 13769 Mono Way #E 209-694-0226** See ad #42, page 45

Sonora Sew Country Quilts and Fabrics, 19060 Standard 209-533-5015

Sonora **Timeless Calico Designs, 11916 Hwy 49 209-533-0200** See ad #43, page 46

South Lake Tahoe **Quilting Tahoe, 2264 Lake Tahoe Blvd #7 800-476-9065** See ad #39, page 44

South Pasadena Mosaic Quilt Studio, 917 Fremont Ave. 626-799-5998

Stockton **Quilters Quarters, 4343 Pacific Ave. #B2 209-462-0161** See ad #52, page 48

Sunnyvale **The Granary, 1326 S. Mary Ave. 408-735-9830** See ad #78, page 53

Sunnyvale **Eddie's Quilting Bee, 480 S. Mathilda Ave. 408-830-9505** See ad #79, page 54 & 412

Tehachapi **5 Heart Quilts & Fabric, 104 W. Tehachapi Blvd. 661-822-8709** See ad #88, page 56

Tehachapi **Debbie's Fabrics Etc., 112 E Tehachapi Blvd 661-823-7114** See ad #87, page 56

Temecula Temecula Quilt Co., 33353 Temecula Parkway 951-302-1469

Temecula Quilter's Coop, 28677 Old Town Front St. 951-694-3600

Temecula Temecula Valley Sewing, 28780 Old Town Front St. 951-694-9576

Thousand Oaks From Here to Quilternity, 296 Via Brava 805-427-6474

Thousand Oaks **Cotton & Chocolate Quilt Company 1724 Avenida de los Arboles, Ste. E 805-241-0061** See ad #109, page 62

Torrance AAA Sewing, Fabrics, 3770 Sepulveda Blvd. 310-791-1190

Trabuco Canyon Cotton Boutique, 21851 Via De La Luz 949-709-1696

Tracy **Sew Many Quilts, 71 E. 10th St. 209-836-5426** See ad #50, page 47

Tujunga **Patchwork Penguin, 6245 Foothill Blvd. 818-248-7390** See ad #111, page 62

Turlock **Cloth & Quilts, 625 E Main St 209-632-3225** See ad #51, page 47

Tustin **Flying Geese Fabrics, 307 El Camino Real 714-544-9349** See ad #124, page 65

Upland **Ginger's Quilt Shoppe, 1120 Dewey Way, Ste. B 909-920-3099** See ad #114, page 63

Upper Lake **Gracious Ladies 9460 Main St., P.O. Box 975 707-275-2307** See ad #14, page 41

Vacaville **A Quilted Heart, 878 Alamo Dr. 707-447-9000** See ad #24, page 42

Valley Center Inspirations Quilt Shop, 27350 Valley Center 760-751-9400

Ventura **Quilt Ventura, 4572 Telephone Rd, Suite 908 805-658-9800** See ad #107, page 62

Victorville Andrea's Quiltin' Quarters, 12370 Hesperia Rd 760-955-9777

Visalia **Thimble Towne, 400 W. Caldwell Ave. #F 559-627-5778** See ad #56, page 48

Vista **Fat Quarters Quilt Shop, 728 Escondido Ave. 760-758-8308** See ad #101, page 60

Weaverville The Golden Needles, 493 Main St 530-623-5850

Weaverville **Textile Traditions Quilt Shop, 555 A Main St. 530-623-6454** See ad #6, page 39

Westminster Moore's Fabric Shop, 16472 Beach Blvd. 714-596-3999

Willows Quilt Corral, 245 W Wood St 530-934-8116

Winters **Cloth Carousel, 9 Main St. 530-795-2580** See ad #27, page 42

Woodland Red Hen Quilt Shop, 14080 County Road 99A 530-661-6677

Woodland Hills The Quilt Emporium, 4918 Topanga Canyon 818-704-8238

Yorba Linda Cranberry Quiltworks, 3810 Prospect Ave. #A 714-223-1701

Yorba Linda Tall Mouse, 17506 Yorba Linda Blvd. 714-996-0101

Yreka **Wooden Spools, 304 N. Main St. 530-842-4562** See ad #2, page 39

Yucca Valley Quilting Between Friends, 7379 Hopi Tr. 760-365-4519

Yucca Valley Stitchin & Quilting, 57353-A 29 Palms Hwy. 760-365-1744

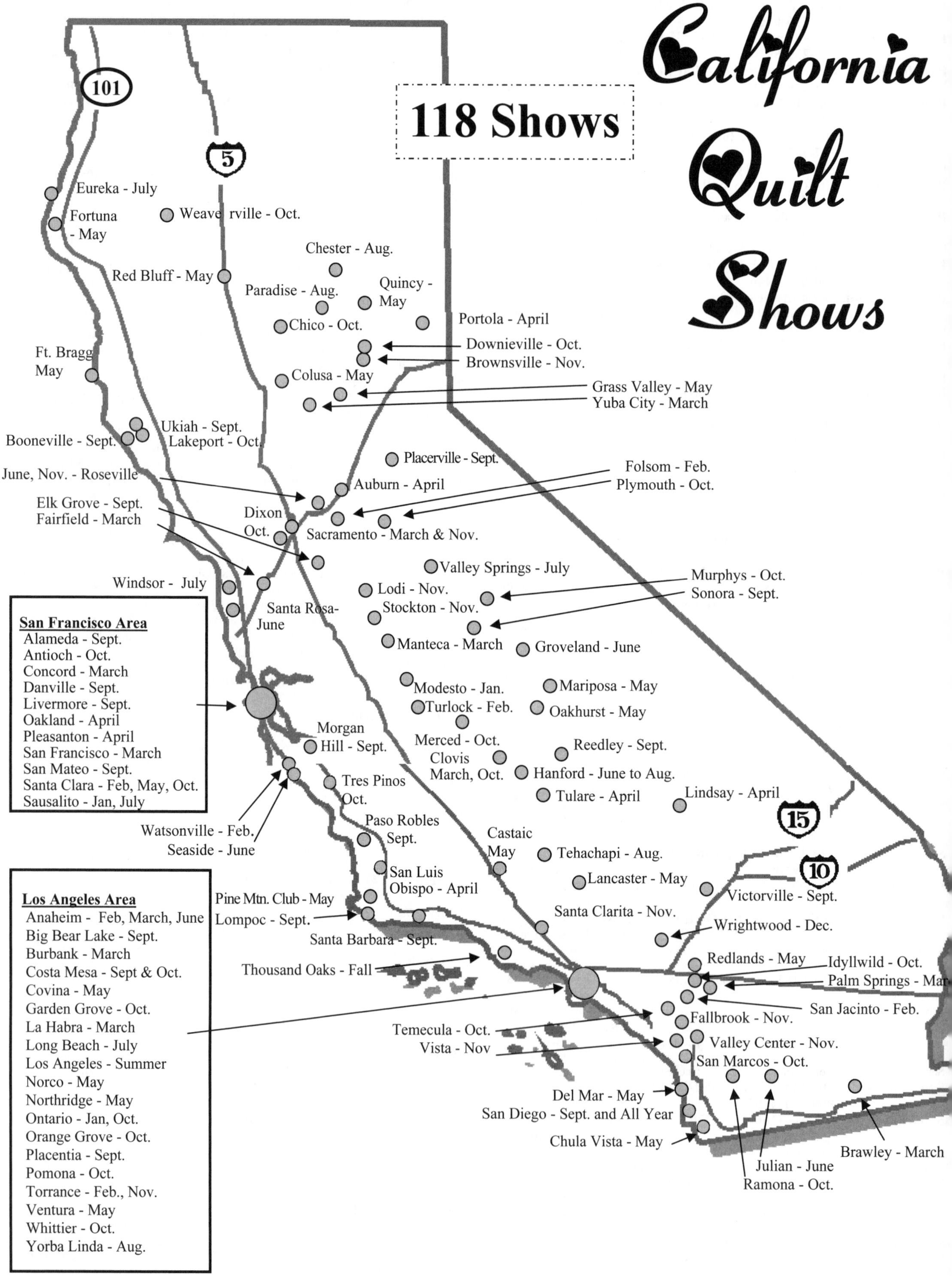
California Quilt Shows
118 Shows
101
5
15
10
Eureka - July
Fortuna - May
Weave rville - Oct.
Red Bluff - May
Chester - Aug.
Paradise - Aug.
Quincy - May
Chico - Oct.
Portola - April
Downieville - Oct.
Brownsville - Nov.
Ft. Bragg May
Colusa - May
Grass Valley - May
Yuba City - March
Ukiah - Sept.
Lakeport - Oct.
Booneville - Sept.
Placerville - Sept.
June, Nov. - Roseville
Auburn - April
Folsom - Feb.
Plymouth - Oct.
Elk Grove - Sept.
Fairfield - March
Dixon Oct.
Sacramento - March & Nov.
Valley Springs - July
Windsor - July
Lodi - Nov.
Murphys - Oct.
Sonora - Sept.
Santa Rosa - June
Stockton - Nov.
Manteca - March
Groveland - June
San Francisco Area
Alameda - Sept.
Antioch - Oct.
Concord - March
Danville - Sept.
Livermore - Sept.
Oakland - April
Pleasanton - April
San Francisco - March
San Mateo - Sept.
Santa Clara - Feb, May, Oct.
Sausalito - Jan, July
Modesto - Jan.
Mariposa - May
Turlock - Feb.
Oakhurst - May
Morgan Hill - Sept.
Merced - Oct.
Reedley - Sept.
Clovis March, Oct.
Hanford - June to Aug.
Tres Pinos Oct.
Tulare - April
Lindsay - April
Watsonville - Feb.
Seaside - June
Paso Robles Sept.
Castaic May
Tehachapi - Aug.
San Luis Obispo - April
Lancaster - May
Victorville - Sept.
Los Angeles Area
Anaheim - Feb, March, June
Big Bear Lake - Sept.
Burbank - March
Costa Mesa - Sept & Oct.
Covina - May
Garden Grove - Oct.
La Habra - March
Long Beach - July
Los Angeles - Summer
Norco - May
Northridge - May
Ontario - Jan, Oct.
Orange Grove - Oct.
Placentia - Sept.
Pomona - Oct.
Torrance - Feb., Nov.
Ventura - May
Whittier - Oct.
Yorba Linda - Aug.
Pine Mtn. Club - May
Lompoc - Sept.
Santa Clarita - Nov.
Wrightwood - Dec.
Santa Barbara - Sept.
Thousand Oaks - Fall
Redlands - May
Idyllwild - Oct.
Palm Springs - Ma
San Jacinto - Feb.
Temecula - Oct.
Fallbrook - Nov.
Vista - Nov
Valley Center - Nov.
San Marcos - Oct.
Del Mar - May
San Diego - Sept. and All Year
Chula Vista - May
Brawley - March
Julian - June
Ramona - Oct.

California Quilt Shows

About Shows: We are listing only the very basic information about shows that happen on a regular schedule here. Please check out our website for more details on each show. Also this information tends to change quite often so please verify the event with our website or a local source before you venture far. Or if you're in the right area at the right time, give it a shot.

If you are a show organizer, please keep us updated on your event.
shows@quilterstravelcompanion.com www.quilterstravelcompanion.com

On our website you will also find:
- Exact dates (when we have them)
- Contact Information
- Events happening on a one-time basis
- Sponsor Information
- Description of Event

Month	City	Schedule	Show	Location with address
All Year				
	San Diego	Annual, all year	Quilt Visions Quilt Gallery	Visions Art Quilt Gallery, 2825 Dewey Rd. #100 (Liberty Station)
January				
	Sausalito	Annual, 1st full week, Jan	Golden Gate Fiber Institute Winter Intensive	Point Bonita YMCA Camp, 981 Fort Barry
	Ontario	Annual, 3rd weekend of January	Road to California	Ontario Convention Ctr, 2000 Convention Ctr Way, Vineyard Exit off I-10
	Modesto	Odd Years, last weekend of January	Heart of the Valley Quilts & Textile Arts Show	Modesto Centre Plaza, Corner of 10th and K
February				
	Folsom	Annual, 1st weekend in February	Folsom Quilt & Fiber Guild Show	The Folsom Community Center, 52 Natoma St
	Anaheim	Annual, 2nd Sun - Wed of February	CHA Winter Convention	Anaheim Convention Center, 800 W. Katella Ave.
	San Jacinto	Annual, 2nd Fri & Sat of February	Valley Quilters Show	Valley Wide Recreation Center, 901 W. Esplanade
	Torrance	Annual, 3rd Weekend in February	South Bay Quilters Guild Show	Torrance Cultural Arts Center, 3330 Civic Center Dr. N
	Turlock	Annual, 3rd weekend in February	Turlock Quilt Guild Quilt Fair	Stanislaus Co. Fairgrounds, 900 N. Broadway
	Watsonville	Annual, 4th Weekend in February	Pajaro Valley Quilt Association Show	Santa Cruz County Fair Grounds, Hwy. 152, 2601 E. Lake
	Santa Clara	Annual, Last Thur. - Sun. February	Stitches West	Santa Clara Convention Center, 5001 Great America Pkwy.
March				
	Clovis	Even, 1st weekend in March	San Joaquin Valley Quilt Guild Show	Clovis Memorial Building, 453 Hughes Ave.
	La Habra	Even Years, 1st weekend of March	Friendship Square Quilt Guild Show	La Habra Community Center, 101 W. La Habra Blvd.
	Manteca	Annual, 1st weekend of March	Manteca Quilters Quilt & Cloth Doll Show	MRPS Hall, 133 N. Grant
	Palm Springs	Annual, 1st Fri & Sat of March	Desert Guilds Quilt Show	Palm Springs Pavilion, 401 S. Pavilion Way
	San Francisco	Odd Years, 1st weekend in March	San Francisco Quilt Guild Show	San Francisco Exhibition Center, 635 8th St. at Brannan
	Burbank	Annual, a weekend in March	Glendale Quilt Guild Show	Burbank Airport Marriott, 2500 Hollywood Way
	Brawley	Odd Years, 3rd weekend in March	Imperial Valley Desert Quilters	Lions Center, 225 A St
	Concord	Annual, 3rd weekend on March	Guild of Quilters of Contra Costa County	Clayton Faire Shopping Ctr., 5298 Clayton Rd
	Fairfield	Odd Years, 3rd week of March	North Wind Quilters Guild Show	Fairfield Senior Center, 1200 Civic Center Drive
	Yuba City	Annual, 3rd weekend in March	Yuba Sutter Valley Quilt Guild Show	Yuba Sutter Fair Grounds, 442 Franklin Ave
	Anaheim	Annual, Last Fri-Sun March	Newton's Yarn Country Spring Fling Seminar	Shrine El Bekal, 1320 S. Sanderson Ave.
	Sacramento	Annual, last weekend of March	Quilt, Craft and Sew Festival	Cal Expo/State Fairgrounds, 1600 Exposition Blvd.
April				
	Auburn	Annual, 2nd weekend in April	Foothill Quilters Guild Show	Gold Counrty Fairgrounds, 1273 High St
	Oakland	Even Years, 2nd weekend in April	East Bay Heritage Quilters Show	Oakland Convention Center, 550 Tenth St. at Broadway
	Lindsay	Annual, 3rd weekend in April	Best of the Valley	McDermont Fireld House, 365 N. Sweet Brier
	Portola	Annual, 3rd weekend in April	Cabin Fever Quilt Guild Show	Memorial Hall, Hwy 70
	Tulare	Annual, 3rd Fri - Sun in April	California Antique Farm Equipment Show	International Agri-Center's Heritage Complex 4500 S. Laspina St.
	San Luis Obispo	Annual, last weekend of April	Seven Sisters Quilt Show	Alex Madonna Expo Center, 100 Madonna Rd.
	Pleasanton	Odd Years, Last weekend in April	Amador Valley Quilters Show	Alameda County Fairgrounds, 4501 Pleasanton Ave
May				
	Covina	Even Years, 1st weekend in May	TLC Quilters Showcase	Covina Woman's Club, 128 S. San Jose Ave.
	Fortuna	Annual, early May	Quilters' Escape Retreat	River Lodge Conference Center, 1800 Riverwalk Dr.
	Grass Valley	Annual, 1st weekend in May	Pine Tree Quilt Guild of Nevada County	Nevada County Fairgrounds, 11228 McCourtney Rd
	Mariposa	Even Years, 1st Saturday in May	Mariposa Ourdoor Quilt Show	Mariposa Museum & History Center, Jessie St at Hwy. 140
	Norco	Odd Years, 1st weekend of May	Inland Empire Quilters Guild Show	Norco Community Center, 3900-A Acacia
	Ventura	Annual, 1st weekend in May	Camarillo Quilters Association Show	Ventura County Fairgrounds, 10 W. Harbor Blvd.
	Colusa	Odd Years, 2nd Saturday in May	Pacific Flyway Quilters Quilt Show	Scout Cabin/Will S. Green Park, 901 Parkhill St
	Del Mar	Annual, 2nd weekend in May	Quilt, Craft & Sewing Festival	Del Mar Fairgrounds, 2260 Jimmy Durante Blvd.

May Continued

Red Bluff	Odd Years, 2nd weekend in May	Sun Country Quilters Show	Tehama district Fairgrounds, 650 Antelope Blvd
Santa Clara	Annual, 2nd weekend in May	Santa Clara Valley Quilt Association Show	Santa Clara Convention Ctr, 5001 Great America Parkway
Chula Vista	Annual, 3rd Fri & Sat in May	Chula Vista Quilters Guild Show	Community Congregational Church, 276 F St
Lancaster	Annual, 3rd weekend in May	Antelope Valley Quilt Association Show	Antelope Valley Fairgrounds (Eliopulos Pavilion), 2551 West Ave H (at the 14 Frwy.)
Northridge	Annual, 3rd weekend in May	Quilting in the Valley Quilt Show	Student Union--California St. Northridge, 18111 Nordhoff St.
Oakhurst	Odd Years, 3rd weekend in May	Sierra Mountain Quilters Association Show	Yosemite High School, 50200 School Road
Pine Mountain Club	Odd Years, 3rd Sat. in May	Pine Mountain Scrappers Quilt Show	The Village Center
Quincy	Annual, 3rd weekend in May	Quincy Crazy Quilters Show	Plumas-Sierra County Fairgrounds, 204 Fairgrounds Rd
Redlands	Annual, Saturday after Mother's Day	Citrus Belt Quilt Show	Smiley Park by the Lincoln Memorial Shrine, 125 W. Vine St. (Between Eureka and 4th)
Fort Bragg	Annual, Memorial Day Weekend	Fort Bragg Quilt Show	Town Hall & Laurel & Main St., 363 N Main & 213 E. Laurel
Castaic	Annual, Last Fri-Sun, May	Griffin Dyeworks Fiber Retreat	Camp Verdugo Oaks, 38001 Golden State Hwy

June

Santa Rosa	Annual, 1st weekend in June	Moonlight Quilters of Sonoma County Show	Santa Rosa Veterans Mem Bldg, 1351 Maple Ave.
Groveland	Odd Years, 2nd Sat. in June	Pineneedlers Quilt Stroll	Downtown Hwy. 120
Los Angeles	Odd Years, Summer	Santa Monica Quilt Guild Show	Loyola Marymount University, 1 LMU Dr. (4 mi. N. of LAX)
Seaside	Even years, 2nd weekend in June	Monterey Peninsula Quilters Guild Show	Seaside High School Gym, 2200 Noche Buena St. (Exit Hwy. 1 at Fremont)
Anaheim	Odd Years, 3rd weekend of June	Orange County Quilters Guild Show	Anaheim First Christian Church, 520 W South St
Hanford	Annual, 6 weeks of mid Summer	Kings Art Center's Quilt Show	Kings Art Center, 605 N. Douty St.
Roseville	Annual, 4th weekend in June	Roseville Quilters Guild Quilt Show	Placer County Fairgrounds, Washington Blvd.
Julian	Last week in June	Heritage Quilt Show	Town Hall, 2129 Main St

July

Windsor	Annual, 1st Sunday in July	Windsor Farmer's Market Annual Quilt	Old Downtown Windsor Green, Old Redwood Hwy.
Eureka	Odd years, 3rd weekend in July	Heart of the Redwoods Quilt Show	Redwood Acres Fairgrounds, 3750 Harris
Valley Springs	Even Years, 3rd weekend in July	Loose Threads Quilt Guild	Valley Springs Elementary School, 240 Pine St.
Sausalito	Annual, 4th Mon-Sun, July	Golden Gate Fiber Institute Winter Intensive	Point Bonita YMCA Camp and Conference Center, 981 Fort Barry
Long Beach	Annual, last weekend in July	International Quilt Festival	Long Beach Convention Center, 300 E. Ocean Blvd.

August

Chester	Even Years, 1st weekend in August	Chester Piecemakers Quilt Guild Show	Chester High School, 612 First St.
Yorba Linda	Even Years, 1st weekend in August	Quilt Daze Yorba Linda	Community Center, 4501 Casa Loma
Paradise	Even Year, August	Ridge Quilter's Show	Paradise Intermediate School, 5657 Recreation Dr.
Tehachapi	Odd Years, 3rd weekend of August	Tehachapi Mountain Quilt Guild Show	West Park Activity Center, 410 W "D" St.

September

Big Bear Lake	Annual, Sat & Sun of Labor Day Weekend	Busy Bears Quilt Guild Show	Big Bear Middle School, 41275 Big Bear Blvd.
Elk Grove	Odd Years, 1st weekend after Labor Day	Elk Grove Quilt Guild Show SES	Portuguese Hall, 10427 E. Stockton Blvd. (Hwy. 99 at Grantline Rd.)
Santa Barbara	Even Years, last weekend in September	Coastal Quilter Guild Show	Earl Warren Showgrounds, 3400 Calle Real
Paso Robles	Even Years, 2nd weekend of September	Almond Country Quilters Guild Show	Mid State Fairgrounds, Riverside Ave.
Placentia	Odd Years, September	North Cities Quilt Guild Show	George Key Ranch, 625 W. Bastanchury Rd.
Victorville	Annual, 2nd weekend in September	Quilters Piece Corps Quilt Show	San Bernardino County Fairgrounds, 14800 7th St.
Booneville	Annual, 3rd Fri-Sun, Sept	California Wool & Fiber Festival	Mendocino Cty Fairgrounds, 16640 CA Hwy. 128
Danville	Odd Years, 4th weekend of September	Diablo Valley Quilters Quilt Show	Charlotte Wood Middle School, 600 El Capitan
San Diego	Annual, 3rd weekend in September	San Diego Quilt Show	San Diego Convention Center, Hall A, 111 W. Harbor
San Mateo	Annual, 3rd weekend in September	Quilt, Craft & Sew Festival	San Mateo Event Center, 2495 S. Delaware St.
Sonora	Annual, 3rd weekend of September	Sierra Quilt Guild Show	Mother Lode Fairgrounds, 220 Southgate Dr.
Ukiah	Annual, 3rd weekend in September	Grapevine Quilt Show	Ukiah Valley Conference Ctr, 200 S. School St.
Costa Mesa	Even Years, last Fri & Sat of September	Orange Grove Quilters Guild Show	Orange County Fairground, Bldg. #12, 88 Fair Dr.
Livermore	Annual, 4th weekend of September	Quilting in the Garden	Alden Lane Nursery, 981 Alden Lane
Lompoc	Odd Years, Late September	Quilters Etc. of Lompoc	Anderson Recreation Center, 125 W. Walnut Ave.
Reedley	Odd Years, 4th weekend in September	Kings River Quilt Festival	Immanuel High School, 1128 Reed Ave.
Alameda	Annual, last weekend of September	The Alameda Quilt Show	Alameda High School Gym, 2201 Encinal Ave.
Morgan Hill	Annual, last weekend in September	South Valley Quilt Association Show	Morgan Hill Community & Cultural Center, 17000 Monterey Rd.
Placerville	Even Years, last weekend in September	Eastern Expression In Cloth	El Dorado County Fairgrounds, 100 Placerville Dr.

October

Dixon	Annual, 1st Sat in October	Lambtown USA Fiber Fair	Dixon May Fair Grounds, 655 S 1st St.
Downieville	Odd Years, 1st weekend in October	Mountain Star Quilters Show	Downieville Comm. Center, Main St. (Hwy. 49)
Lakeport	Annual, 1st weekend in October	Ladies of the Lake Quilt Guild	Lake County Fairgrounds, 401 Martin St.
Merced	Odd Years, 1st weekend in October	Gateway Quilters' Guild Quilt Show	Merced County Fairgrounds, 900 Martin Luther King Jr. Way
Plymouth	Odd Years, 1st weekend of October	Sierra Gold Harvest Quilt Show	Plymouth Fair Grounds, 18621 Sherwood St.
Pomona	Annual, 1st weekend in October	Quilt Craft & Sewing Festival	Fairplex, 1101 W. McKinley Ave.
Temecula	Annual, 1st Saturday in October	Old Town Temecula Outdoor Quilt Show	Old Town Temecula Comm. Theater, 42051 Main St.
Tres Pinos	Annual, 1st weekend in October	Quilt Show at the County Fair	San Denito Cty Fairgrounds, 9000 Airline Hwy.

October Continued

Weaverville	Annual, 1st Saturday in October	Thursday Night Strippers Quilt Guild Show	Historic District, Hwy. 299 between Mill and Court St.
Whittier	Even Years, 1st weekend in October	Los Angeles County Quilt Guild Show	The Ritz Gardens, 11201 1st Ave.
Orange Grove	Annual, Mid October	Orange Grove Quilters Auction & Tea	Garden Grove United Methodist Church, 12741 Main St.
Ramona	Annual, 2nd weekend in October	Ramona Back Country Quilters Show	Mountain View Community Church, 1191 Meadowlark Way
Santa Clara	Annual, 2nd weekend in October	Pacific International Quilt Festival	Santa Clara Convention Center, 5001 Great America Pkwy.
Thousand Oaks	Odd Year, Fall	Conejo Valley Quilters Show	Cal Lutheran College-Gilbert Sports Arena, 60 W. Olsen Rd.
Costa Mesa	Odd Years, 3rd weekend in Oct.	Flying Geese Quilt Show	Orange County Fair Grounds, Blvd. 14, 88 Fair Dr.
Idyllwild	Annual, 3rd weekend in October	Mt. Quilters of Idyllwild	Idyllwild Elementary School, 26700 Hwy. 243
Ontario	Odd Years, 3rd weekend of October	Nite Owl Quilters Guild Show	Ontario Senior Center, 225 E. "B" St.
San Marcos	Odd Years, October	Fall Festival of Quilts	Cal State University San Marcos Clarke Field House, E. Barham Dr.
Chico	Annual, 4th weekend in October	Annie's Star Guild Show	Silver Dollar Fairgrounds, 2337 Fair St.
Garden Grove	Odd Years, 4th Sat. in October	Orange Grove Quilters Guild Show	Garden Grove United Methodist Church, 12741 Main St
Murphys	Annual, last weekend in October	Mountain Heirloom Quilt Faire	Ironstone Vineyards, 1894 Six Mile Rd.
Antioch	Annual, last weekend of October	Delta Quilters Quilt Shop	Contra Costa Fairgrounds, 18th St. & L St.

November

Brownsville	Annual, 1st weekend in November	Mountain Quilt Guild Show	Ponderosa Community Center, 17103 Ponderosa Way
Fallbrook	Odd Years, 1st Fri & Sat in November	Fallbrook Quilt Guild Show	Presbyterian Church CAC, 463 S. Stage Coach Ln.
Lodi	Even Years, 1st weekend of November	Tokay Stitch 'N' Quilt Guild Show	Lodi Grape Festival Grounds, 413 E. Lockeford St.
Roseville	Annual, 1st or 2nd Fri & Sat in November	Pioneer Quilters' Guild Quilt Show	Maidu Community Center, 1550 Maidu Dr.(take Douglas Blvd. E exit off I-80)
Torrance	Annual, 1st Sun, Nov	Weaving & Fiber Festival	Torrance Cultural Arts Center, 3350 Civic Center Dr
Valley Center	Annual, 1st Sat. in November	Quilt Auction	Bates Nut Farm, 15954 Woods Valley Rd.
Vista	Annual, November & December	Pacific Quilt Artists	Rancho Buena Vista Adobe Gallery, 651 E. Vista Way
Santa Clarita	Odd Years, 2nd Sat. in November	Santa Clarita Valley Quilt Guild Show	Golden Valley School, 27051 Robert Lee Pkwy.
Sacramento	Annual, 3rd weekend in November	River City Quilters Guild Show	Scottish Rite Temple, 6151 H St.
Stockton	Odd Years, 3rd weekend in November	Tuleburg Quilt Guild Show	Scottish Rite Masonic Center, 33 W. Alpine Ave.

December

Wrightwood	Annual, 2nd Sat. in December	Pine Needles Guild Wrightwood Holiday Home Tour	Wrightwood, San Gabriel Mtns--15 Freeway

Shop information is constantly changing!!
We offer a newsletter to help you keep up with these changes.
This newsletter is free to email addresses or $8 for mail paper copies.
We publish the newsletter every 6 months for a total of
3 editions to go with this book,
(Dec. 2010, June 2011 and Dec. 2011)

Just send us an email with your address and email address requesting the
newsletter to info@quilterstravelcompanion.com
Or send the information to 2506 Robinson St.
Colorado Springs, CO 80904
Or call 800-959-4587.

The History of the Quilters' Travel Companion

The 1st edition was published in 1992 for just the states West of the Mississippi. I didn't want to bite off more that I could chew. It included 125 shops, was 9" by 5" and was 96 pages. We followed that up with the East of the Mississippi edition in 1993. That book included 227 shops in 160 pages.

Travelers were asking for just one book so by the 3rd edition in 1994 we put the entire country together in one book. This edition had 750+ shops and was 320 pages. In 1995 we tried a supplement to keep travelers better up to date. It added 150 more shops and was 64 pages. Later we switched to a newsletter to update shop information.

We still offer this newsletter, free to email addresses every 6 months.

In 1996 we were pleased to add Canadian stores to the QTC in the North American Edition, which had 1000+ shops in 416 pages.

In 1998 we adopted our larger 8 1/2" by 11" format to accommodate over 1350 shops in 384 pages. We went to this size because the book would have been too thick for the binding to hold up at the previous size. We just had so many shops at this point that it was dictated!!

QTC History continued on page 417.

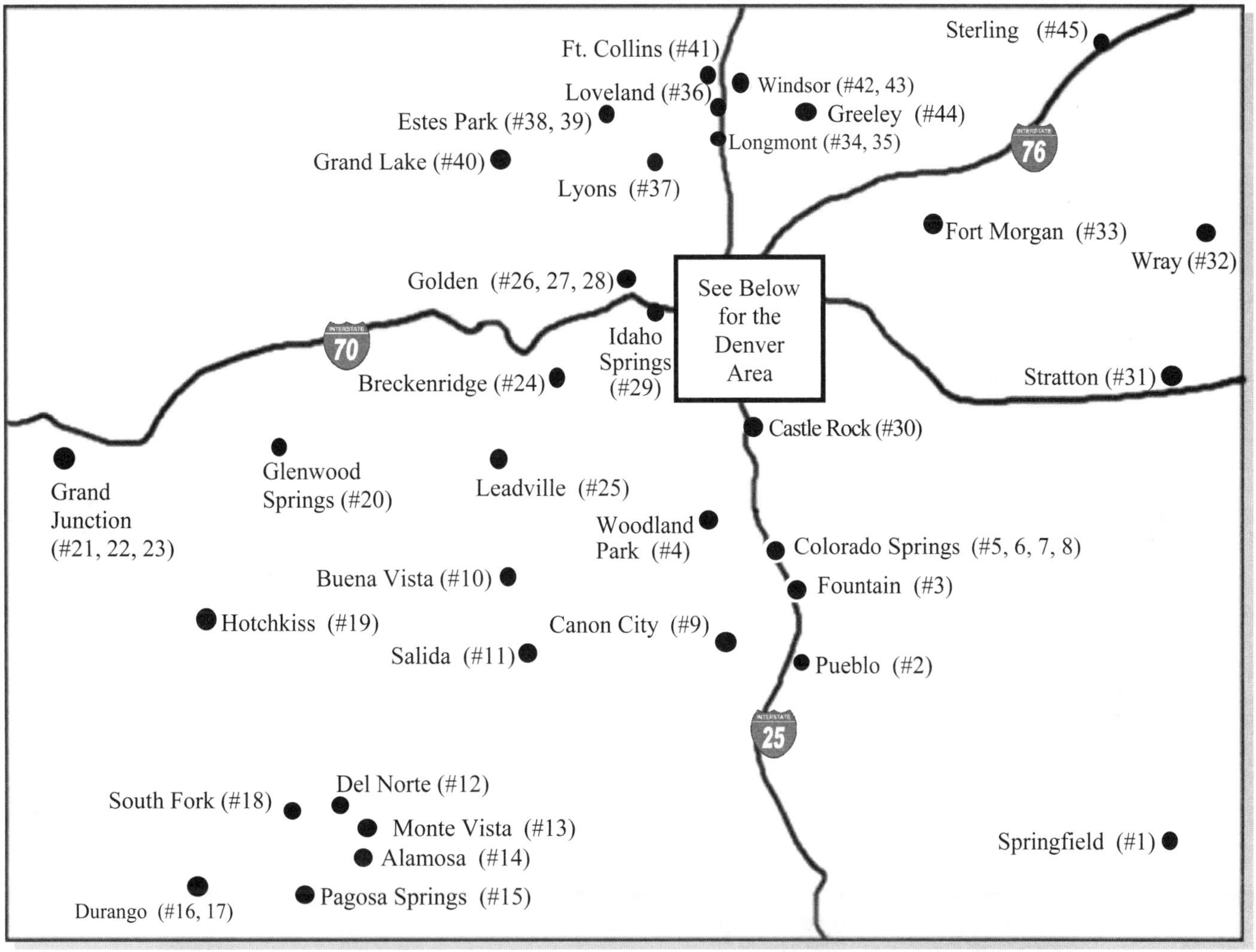
Ft. Collins (#41)
Loveland (#36)
Windsor (#42, 43)
Estes Park (#38, 39)
Greeley (#44)
Longmont (#34, 35)
Grand Lake (#40)
Lyons (#37)
Sterling (#45)
76
Fort Morgan (#33)
Wray (#32)
Golden (#26, 27, 28)
See Below for the Denver Area
70
Idaho Springs (#29)
Breckenridge (#24)
Stratton (#31)
Castle Rock (#30)
Grand Junction (#21, 22, 23)
Glenwood Springs (#20)
Leadville (#25)
Woodland Park (#4)
Colorado Springs (#5, 6, 7, 8)
Buena Vista (#10)
Fountain (#3)
Hotchkiss (#19)
Canon City (#9)
Salida (#11)
Pueblo (#2)
25
Del Norte (#12)
South Fork (#18)
Monte Vista (#13)
Alamosa (#14)
Springfield (#1)
Durango (#16, 17)
Pagosa Springs (#15)

COLORADO

55 Featured Shops

C O L O R A D O

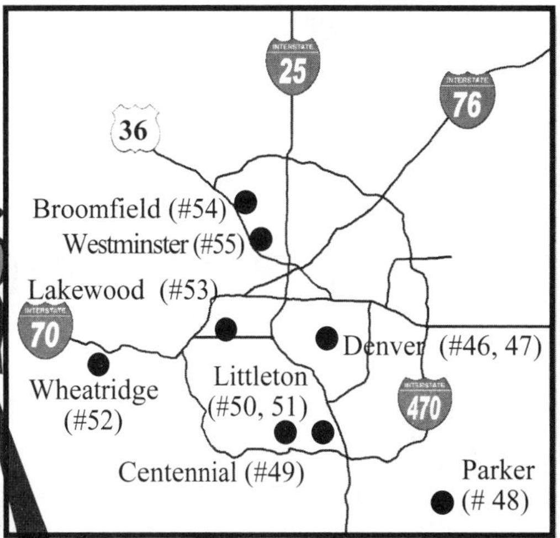
25
76
36
Broomfield (#54)
Westminster (#55)
Lakewood (#53)
70
Denver (#46, 47)
Wheatridge (#52)
Littleton (#50, 51)
470
Centennial (#49)
Parker (# 48)

Springfield, CO #1

Mon - Fri 9 - 5

Justa Stitchin'

965 Main 81073
(719) 523-4985 Fax: Same
Owner: Mari Lee Freiberger
Est: 2001 2175 sq.ft. 1000 Bolts
justa_34@hotmail.com

Quilting Classes. Block of the Month, Thimbleberries Club, Notions, Books, Patterns, Alterations, Batting, Quality Fabrics.

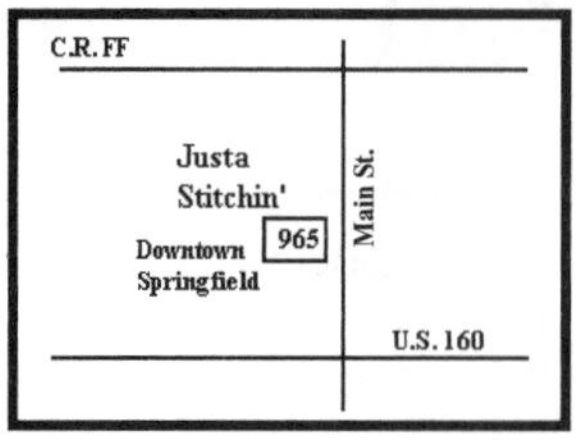

Pueblo, CO #2

Tues - Fri 10 - 5 Sat 10 - 4

Stitcher's Garden

"Where beautiful quilts grow."
308 S. Union Ave. 81003
(719) 545-3320 Fax: (719) 545-3307
Owners: Susie Cunningham & Nancy Piazza
stitchers_garden@yahoo.com

Located in the historic district, we feature fine cotton fabrics, patterns, books, classes and supplies for quilting.

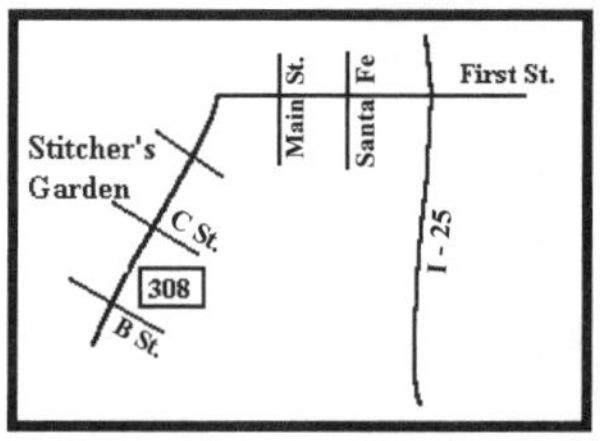

Fountain, CO #3

Tues - Sat 10 - 6

117 S. Main St. 80817
(719) 382-6252
Est: 2008
Owners: Nani Kaai & Laura Farnham
1700 sq.ft. 1000 bolts Newsletter
nalasquiltique@gmail.com

Fabrics, Classes & Notions.
Authorized APQS Representative.
Sales * Service * Education

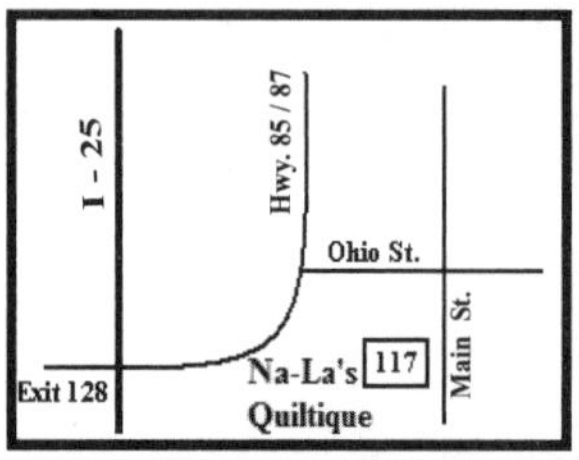

Woodland Park, CO #4

Mon - Sat 10 - 6 Sun 12 - 6

Nuts N Bolts
Needleworks

200 S. Chestnut St. 80863
(719) 687-2272 Fax: (719) 687-9439
Est: 2008 3500 sq.ft. Online Newsletter
www.nutsnboltsneedleworks.com

Fabric, needleart supplies, classes
Sewing & quilting notions.

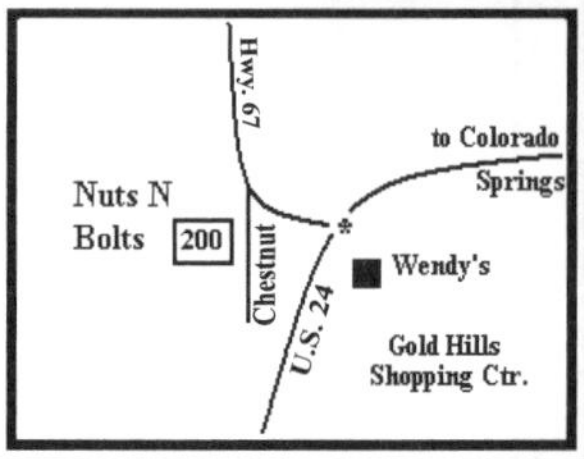

High Country Quilts

Offering only the best in
Fabric • Books • Classes
Notions • Patterns
Friendly customer service
Serving you since 1983

4771 N. Academy Blvd.
Colorado Springs, CO 80918
(719) 598 1312
www.hcquilts.com

Bernina Sales and Service
APQS Sales and Service

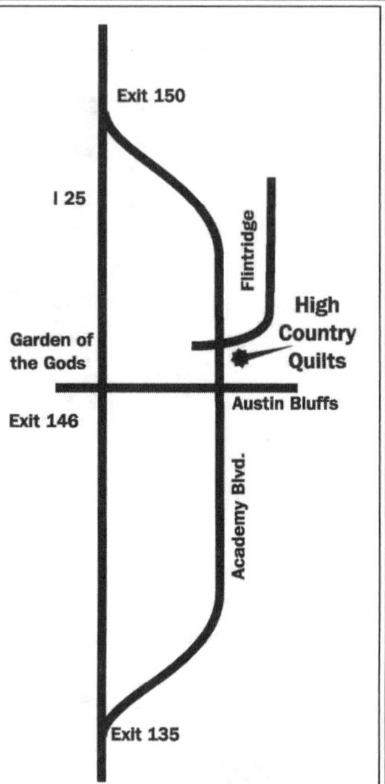

Colorado Springs, CO #5

APQS AMERICAN PROFESSIONAL QUILTING SYSTEMS

BERNINA

BBB

Husqvarna VIKING

Ruth's Stitchery

www.ruthsstitchery.com

Colorado Springs, CO #6

Handi Quilter®
Designed by a Quilter, for Quilters.

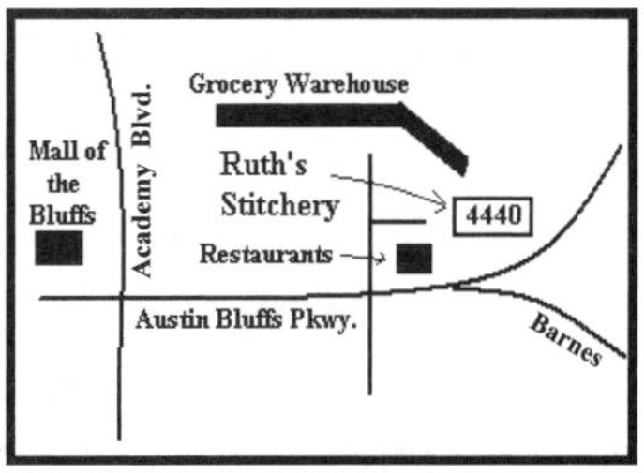

4440 Austin Bluffs Pkwy. 80918
Toll Free (888) 591-8803
(719) 591-1717 Fax: (719) 591-5356
Owner: Ruth V. Warren
Est: 1984 7500 sq.ft. RStitchery@pcisys.net
6500 Bolts 1200 Quilt Book Titles
M/C-Visa-Discover-American Express

Featured in Quilt Sampler Fall, 2006

Mon - Sat 9 - 6 Thur til 9 Sun 12 - 5

- Hand & Machine Quilting
- Beginning to Advanced Sewing
- Counted X-Stitch / Hardanger

Authorized Husqvarna Viking Sewing Machine / Serger Dealer and Service center for Colorado Springs area.

Lady Bug Hill quilts

Fun, fabric and inspiration!
A friendly place to let your quilting imagination grow!

From I-25 take Exit #145 east to Arcadia. Just past Arcadia turn right into the Fillmore Business Park. We are on the southeast corner. Safe Travels!

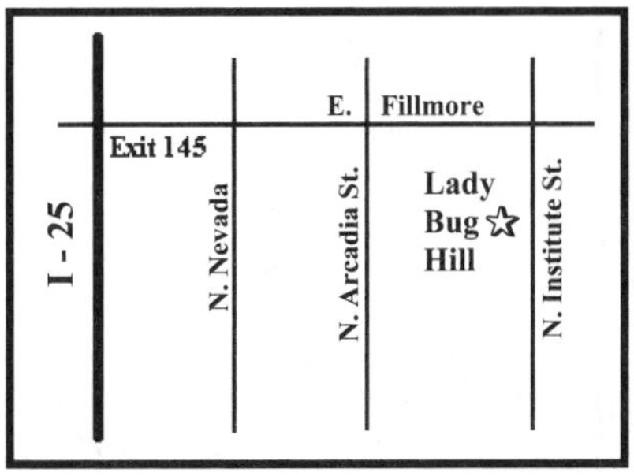

Ladybug is a home away from home; a fun, friendly place to let your quilting imagination grow. We hope we have an opportunity to meet you if your travels bring you our way...

Colorado Springs, CO #7

For information about all our classes and projects visit our website at www.ladybughillquilts.com

• 955 E. Fillmore St • Colorado Springs, CO 80907 •
• Phone: 719-593-5949 • Toll Free 1-866-593-5949 •

Store Hours:
Mon-Fri 10 to 5:00
Sat 9:30 to 5
Sun 1 to 4

Colorado Springs, CO #8

Needleworks
by Holly Berry

2409 W. Colorado Ave.
Colorado Springs, CO 80904
(719) 636-1002

Visit the home of the all new
Art Quilting Patterns and Kits
by Kathryn Read of
Holly Berry House Originals!
Also Needlepoint...Knitting...Rug Hooking

Est: 1998

**Mon - Sat
10 - 5
Sun 1 - 4**

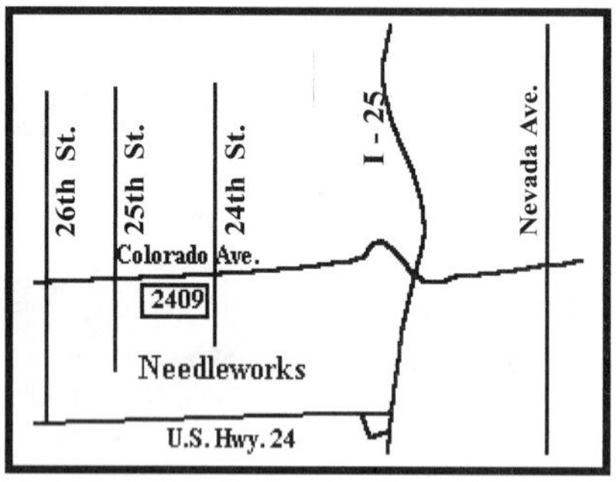

www.hollyberryhouse.com

Fax: (719) 636-2765 hbho@earthlink.net

The Creative Cloth Closet

Quality Quilting Fabrics, Books,
Patterns, Threads, Notions & Gifts.

Mon - Sat 10 - 6

www.quiltingfabriccolorado.com

508 Main St. 81212
(719) 269- SEWS (7397)
creativecloth@qwestoffice.net
Owner: Denise Hovey

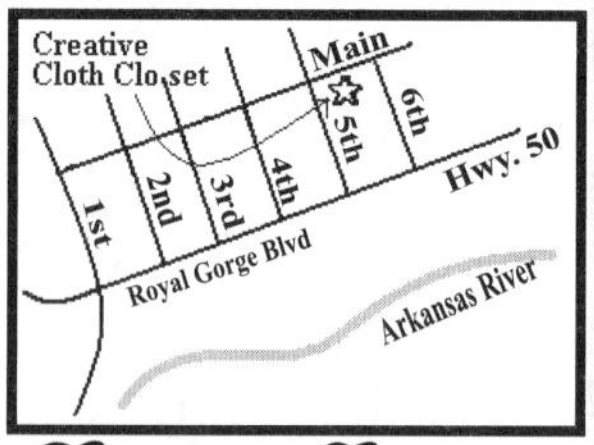

A Place to explore your Creative Energy!

Canon City, CO #9

Buena Vista, CO #10

**Mon - Fri
9:30 - 5
Sat 9:30 - 3**

Bev's Stitchery

202 Tabor St. P.O. Box 1773 81211
1/2 block North of the Stop Light
(719) 395-8780
Owner: Bev Zabloudil Est: 1977

Quilting, Fabrics, Notions & Tools. Fine Needlework Supplies. Large Selection of Books. Quilting, Counted Cross-Stitch, Crochet & Knitting. Classes too!

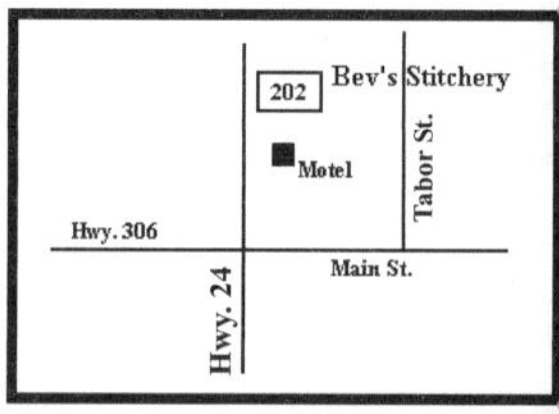

fringe

mon-sat 10-6
sun 12-5

quilting / knitting / sewing / felting / locker rug hook
fabric, patterns, & threads - yarn & needles
gifts - music, candy, moda home, and much more.

Salida, CO #11

139 f street 81201
(719) 539-4006
est: 2009 1700 sq.ft.
800+ bolts

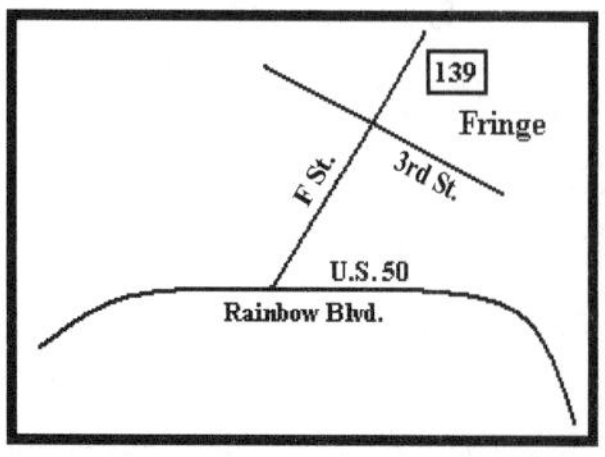

www.fringefab.com

Del Norte, CO #12

**Mon - Sat
10 - 5**

Kathy's Fabric Trunk

16179 W. Hwy. 160 81132
(877) 873-0211
Owner: Kathy Black
Est: 2001
kathysfabrictrunk@q.com

Fabrics, Patterns, Notions, Classes, Books, Floss
One day classes for busy travelers.
BabyLock Sewing Machines.

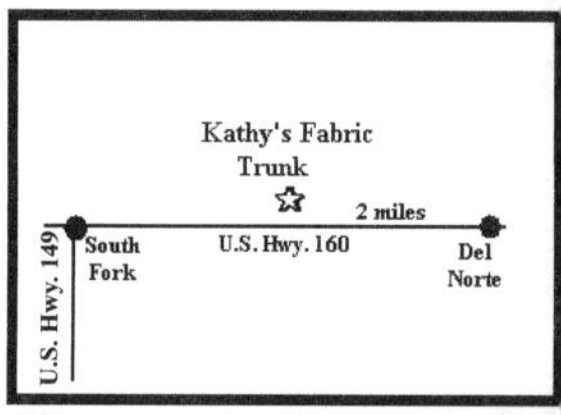

Monte Vista, CO #13

**Mon - Fri
10 - 5
Sat 10 - 3**

Shades, Quilts & Etc.

129 Adams St. 81144
(877) 852-2179
(719) 852-2179 Fax: Same
marilyn.davey@gmail.com

Window Covering & Quilt Shop.
Quilting Supplies including a wide selection of fabrics, notions, books & patterns. DMC Floss, Janome Sewing Machines.

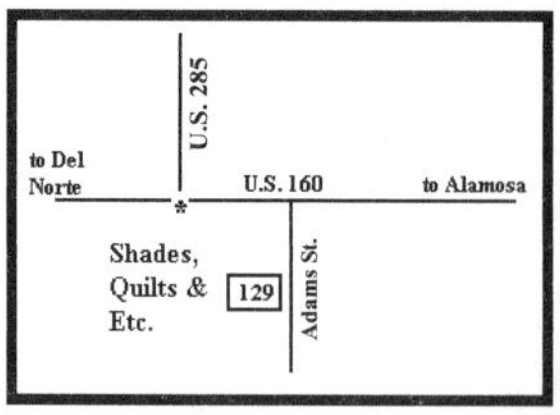

Alamosa, CO #14

Mon - Fri 9:30 - 5:30
Sat 9:30 - 4

Gray Goose Fabrics

616 Main St. 81101
(719) 589-6982
Owners: Gail Mattive & Kerry Worley
2000+ Bolts 800 Books / Patterns
ggoose@gojade.org
100% Cottons & quilting notions & supplies, books, patterns, DMC floss & Oklahoma Embroidery Take Out.
Daytime, evening and Saturday Classes.

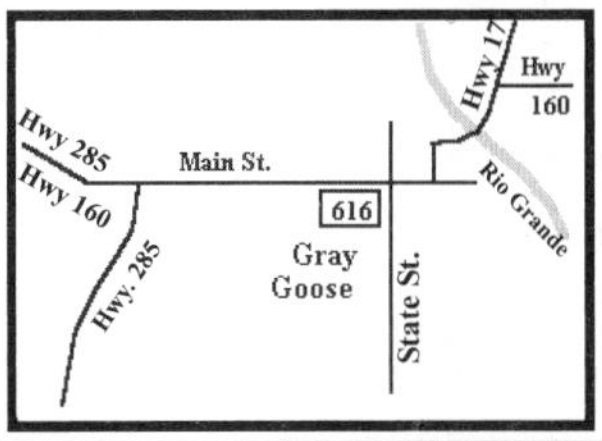

Pagosa Springs, CO #15

Summer Mon- Sat 9 - 6
Winter (Jan-May) 9 - 5:30

EAGLE MOUNTAIN MERCANTILE

56 Talisman Dr., #8C P.O. Box 1800 81147
(970) 731-9900 Fax: (970) 731-9901
laura@eaglemountainmerc.com
www.eaglemountainmerc.com
Colorado's most unique shopping experience.
We are a combination Quilt Shop and Sporting Goods store.
"The perfect his-n-her destination."

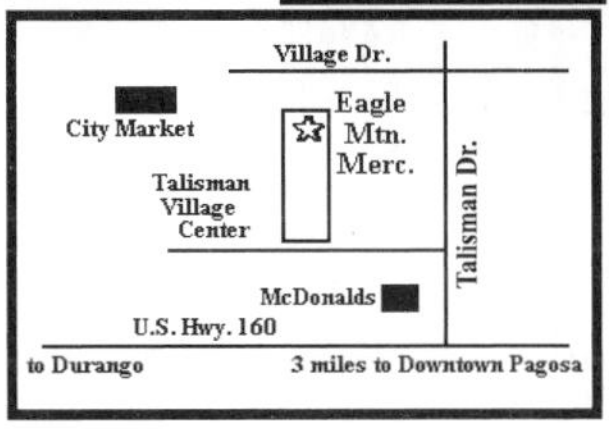

Durango, CO #16

Mon - Sat 10 - 6

Durango Sewing Center

Wide variety of fabrics
Authorized Janome Dealer--Sales & Service
Notions, Books & Patterns
We offer Classes for beginners to experts
Batiks with a large selection of Kaffe Fassett

1111 Camino Del Rio, Suite #104A
Durango, CO 81301
970-382-8809
Est: 2005 2000 bolts
gamato88@durango.net

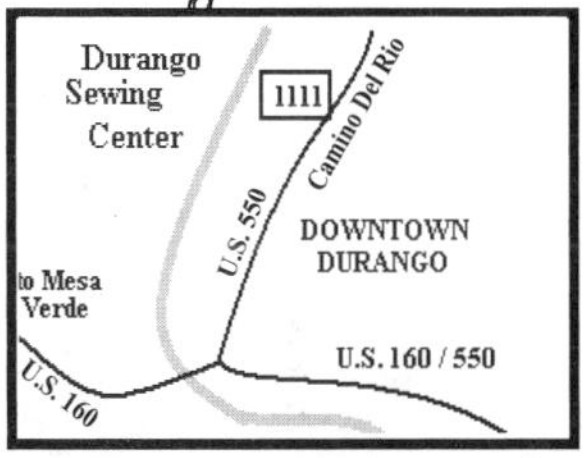

Durango is a tourist's paradise, come enjoy our natural beauty. Durango/Silverton Narrow Gauge Railroad
Mesa Verde National Park is close by!

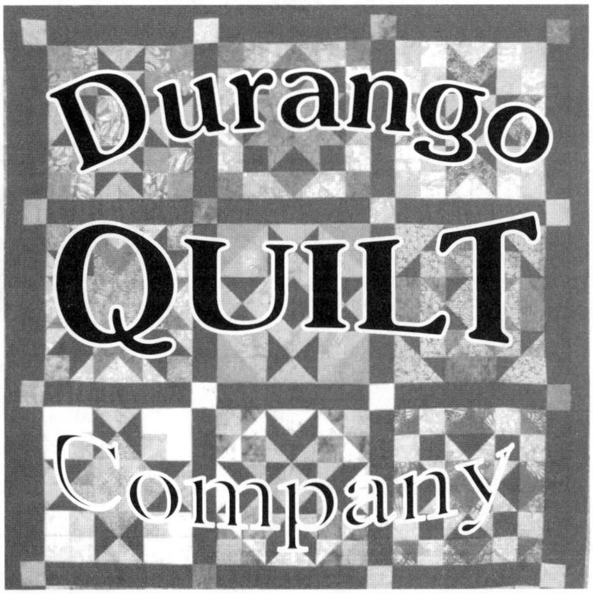

Durango #17

21516 Hwy. 160 W
Durango, CO
81303
(970) 247-2582
Fax: (970) 375-0259

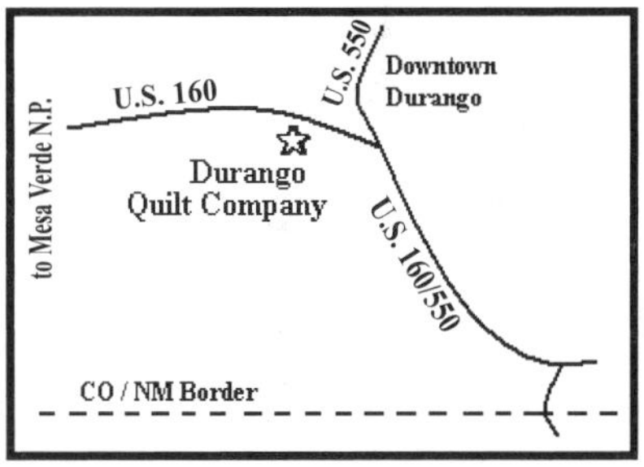

Mon - Sat 9:30 - 5:30
Sundays 12 - 5

- Authorized dealer for Baby Lock sewing machines.
- Over 4000 bolts of quality cotton. Complete collections by Moda, RJR, Benartex and many more
- Four Corners 'Eleanor Burns' Learn to Quilt store
- Flannel Fantasy Section has 100's of bolts of the newest collections.
- Batik Bonanza
- Over 4000 feet of ***amazing*** displays and samples to spark your creativity
- Original quilt kits. Over 300 Quilt book titles in stock.
- Free use of our Baby Lock sewing machines and quality tools when attending our classes.

South Fork, CO #18

Wed - Sat 10 - 4

Beaver Mountain Quilts, Etc.

31070 W. Hwy. 160, P.O. Box 346 81154
(719) 873-1222 Fax: (719) 873-1223
Owner: Barbara Franke
Est: 2004 1300 sq. ft.

We are a consignment quilt gallery and gift shoppe featuring a large selection of handmade quilts by quilters of the San Luis Valley.
Our gift line features the beautiful Heartwood Creek Collection by master sculptor, Jim Shore, and water colorist, Diane Phalen.

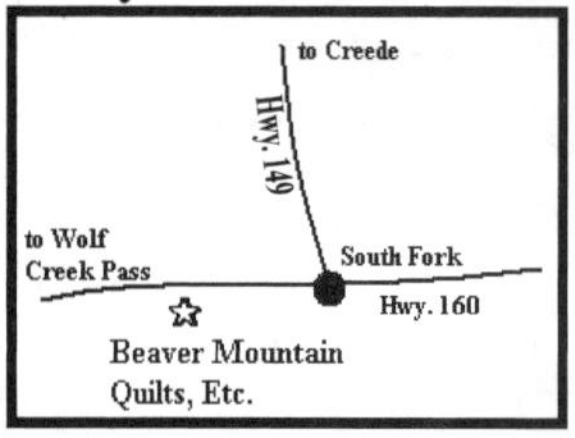

Hotchkiss, CO #19

Tues - Sat 9 - 5

The Quilt Patch

148 Bridge St. 81419
(970) 872-2688
Owner: Virginia Harkleroad
Twenty miles east of Delta

Small town country store atmosphere. Pull up a chair and visit. Over 1400 bolts.

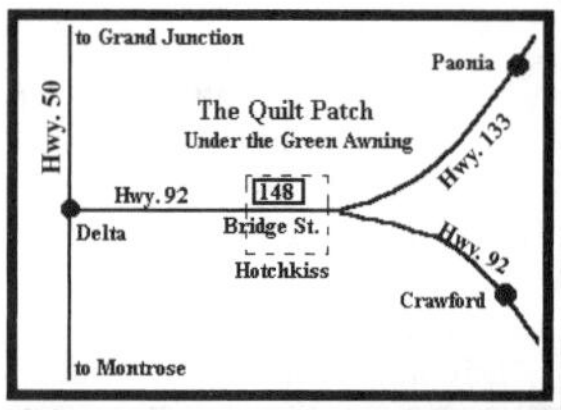

Glenwood Sew

822 Grand Avenue, Glenwood Springs, CO 81601
(970) 945-5900 - (800) 371-5967 - www.glenwoodsew.com

sandy@glenwoodsew.com
Owners: Bob & Sandy Boyd
Est: 1977 5000 sq.ft. 2500 Bolts

**Mon - Sat 10 - 6
Sun 11 - 4**

Glenwood Springs, CO #20

- ❖ Over 2,500 bolts
- ❖ Great Batiks!
- ❖ Original Ideas and Unusual Fabrics - Inspiration
- ❖ Full line of books & notions
- ❖ Quilting classes & workshops
- ❖ Husqvarna Viking Sewing Machine Sales & Service.

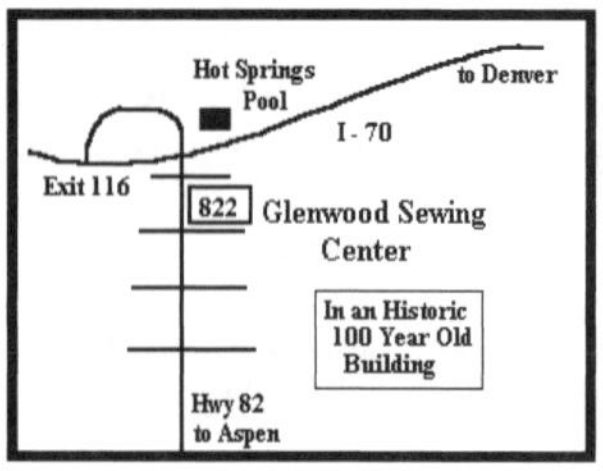

Take 1 - 70 to exit 116. First block after the bridge in downtown.

Grand Junction, CO #21

Mon - Sat 9:30 - 5:30

Hi Fashion FABRICS Inc. The FABRIC STORE

2586 Patterson Rd. 81505
(970) 242-1890
Fax: (970) 243-0360

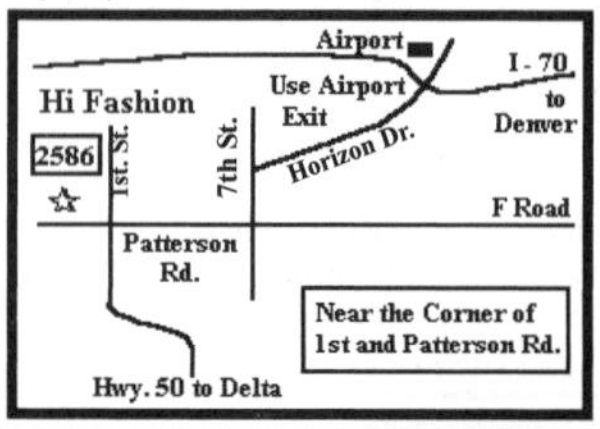

Bernina and Handi Quilter Dealer. Est: 1965
Owner: Jeff Vogel jpvlefty@aol.com
Over 10,000 Bolts of quilting cottons. One of the few full line independent fabric stores remaining. We have 18,000 square feet of fabric including fashion goods, outer wear, home decorating and upholstery.

Grand Junction, CO #22

Open 7 Days a Week

Quilters' Corner, Inc.

421 Colorado Ave. 81501
Downtown Historic Grand Junction
(970) 255-8838 or (888) 255-4863
www.quilterscornergj.com
Over 3000 bolts, hundreds of books and patterns.

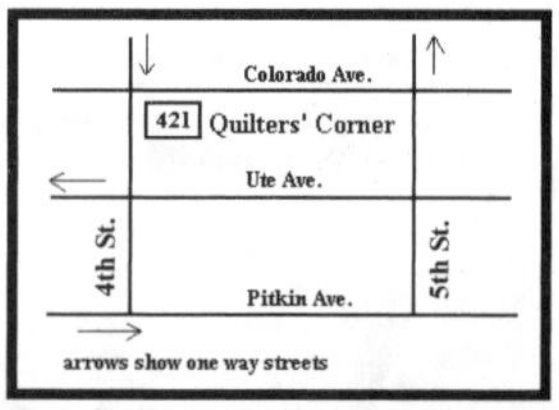

Quilting & Knitting Supplies

#24 BRECKENRIDGE, CO.

Visit Us Upstairs
For a Cup
of tea!

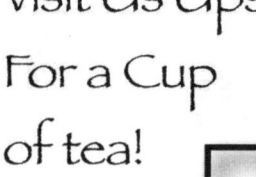

DIRECTIONS TO BRECKENRIDGE

From
Denver International Airport (DEN):
Breckenridge is 104 miles (166km) from Denver International Airport. Take Interstate 70 west to exit 203. Continue south on HWY 9 to Main St., Breckenridge. Hope to see you soon!

"Come in as strangers and leave as friends"

Tea Time Quilting & Stitchery

122 S. Main St. "Upstairs" Breckenridge, CO.
970-547-8300
Hours:
Monday - Saturday 10 - 5 Sunday Noon - 4
www.teatimequiltingandstitchery.com

Better Homes and Gardens Quilt Sampler FEATURED SHOP 2008

Grand Junction, CO #23

**T, W, TH 10 - 5
M, F, S by Appt.**

Fabric Arts Studio LLC — A place to be creative.

2297 Tall Grass #9 81505
(970) 263-7907
Fax: (970) 263-8078
Owner:
Jane Aldoretta

fabricartsstudio@me.com
www.fabricartsstudio.com

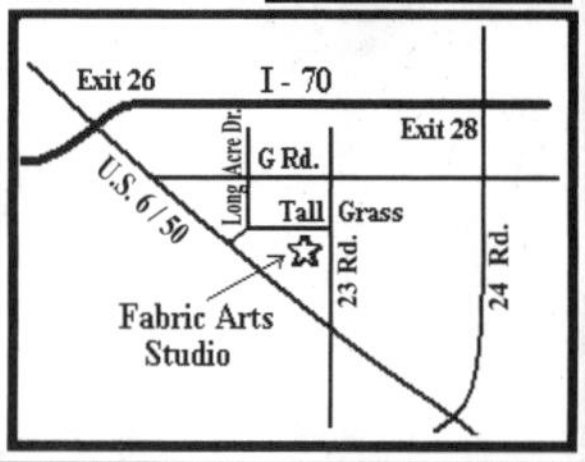

A new state-of-the-art, specialized studio/classroom that caters to the exploration of fabric surface design. Studio time, longarm time, good times!! "Coolest Collage" Club & "Dyeing to Come" Club.

Leadville, CO #25

Hrs. Vary Please Call First

Mtn. Top Quilts

129 E. 7th St. 80461
(719) 486-3454
Owner: Gwendolyn Shepherd
Est: 1983 ccsmtq@chaffee.net

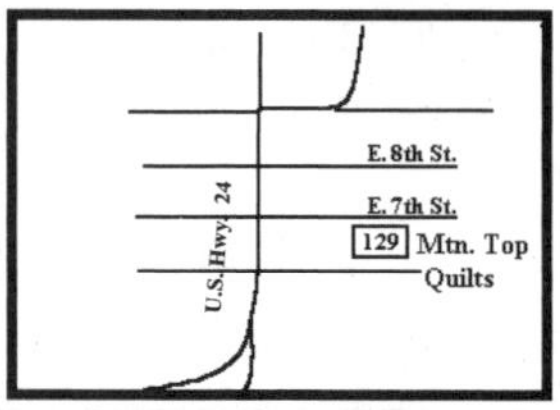

Antique quilts, old quilt blocks & tops, vintage fabrics and laces, feed sacks, buttons & embellishments, out of print quilt books, sewing collectables.

Golden, CO #26

Mon - Sat 10 - 4 Mem to Labor Day Sun 12-4

Rocky Mountain Quilt Museum

1213 Washington Ave. 80401
(303) 277-0377
www.RMQM.org
Est: 1990
Quilt Market - Gift Shop

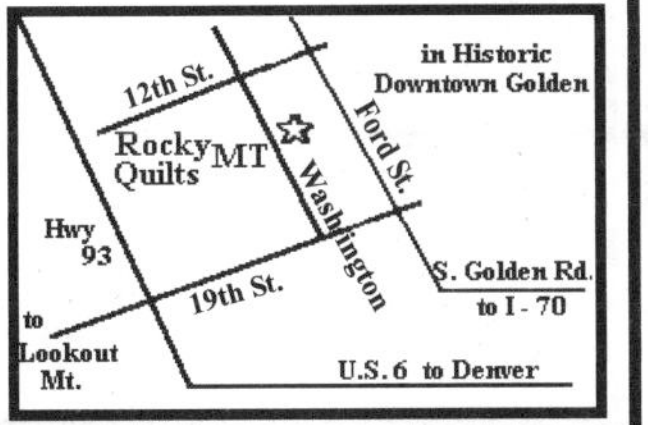

"Revealing the Diversity of Quilts"
The Rocky Mountain Quilt Museum offers exhibits that change quarterly.
Admission Charged.

Golden, CO #27

Mon - Sat 10 - 5:30 1st Fri til 8 Sun 12 - 4

"Purveyors of Fine Fabrics"
1108 Washington Ave. 80401
(303) 277-0717

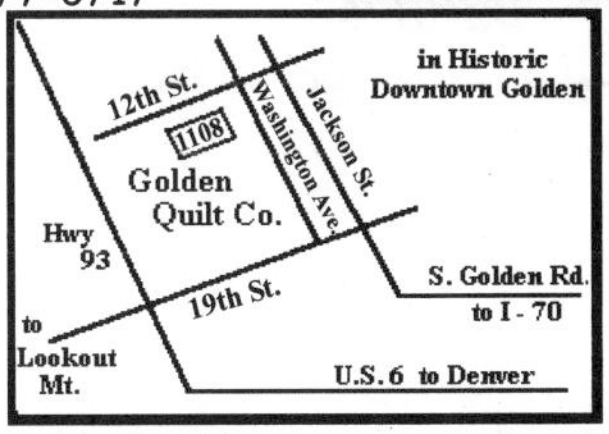

www.goldenquiltcompany.com
One block north of the Rocky Mountain Quilt Museum

Golden, CO #28

Mon - Fri 10 - 5 Closed Weekends

CREATIVE CRAFTS GROUP QUILT GALLERY

741 Corporate Cir., Suite A 80401
(303) 215-5600
www.quiltersvillage.com

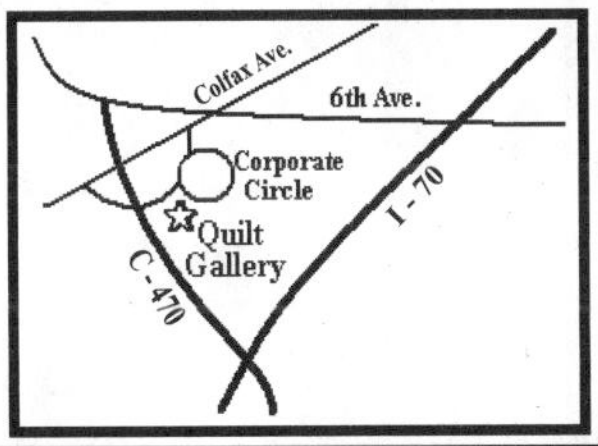

Visit today for a free, self-guided tour showcasing fine quilt collections in our office gallery.

CALL FOR MORE INFORMATION

Idaho Springs, CO #29

Hen House Quilts & Gifts

"Best little Quilt Shop in these here hills."

Exceptional shopping experience with over 3,500 bolts of fabric. Good selection of flannels. Notions, Patterns, Books, Classes. Special Gifts for Quilters.

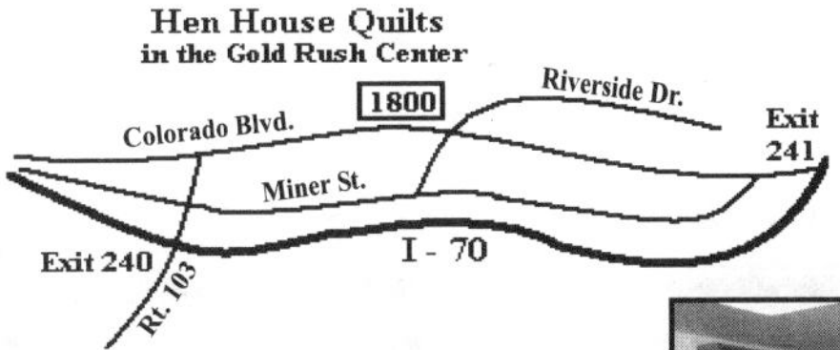

Mon - Sat 10 - 5:30

1800 Colorado Blvd. #1
Idaho Springs, CO 80452
303-567-4092
Fax: 303-567-4093
2000 sq.ft.
henhousequilts@wispertel.net

www.henhousequiltsgifts.com

Castle Rock, CO #30

Mon - Fri 10 - 6 Thur til 7 Sat 10 - 5

SEW-CIETY, Inc.
Bringing you the Whole Nine Yards

4714 Milestone Ln., Unit J 80104
(720) 733-8102 Fax: (720) 773-8103
carol@sew-ciety.com
www.sew-ciety.com

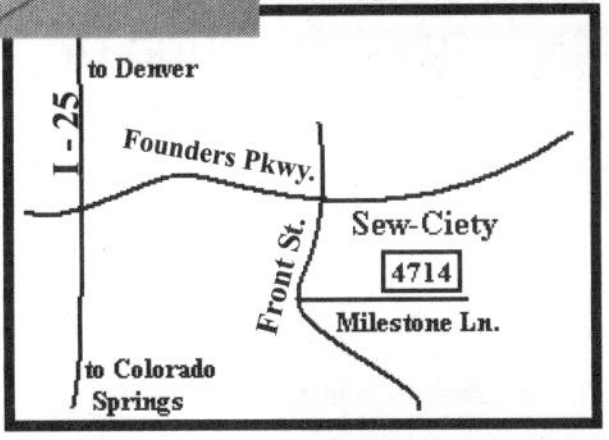

We carry the whole nine yards . . . .
Viking and PFAFF machines, Quilt Fabrics, Notions, Thread and much more.
Friendly & Fun Service!

Stratton, CO #31

Tues - Sat 10 - 6 PLEASE CALL FIRST

Benay's Country Quiltin'

32131 County Rd. HH 80836
(970) 362-4650 or (719) 348-5650
Owner: Benay Brachtenbach
Est: 1999 1250 bolts

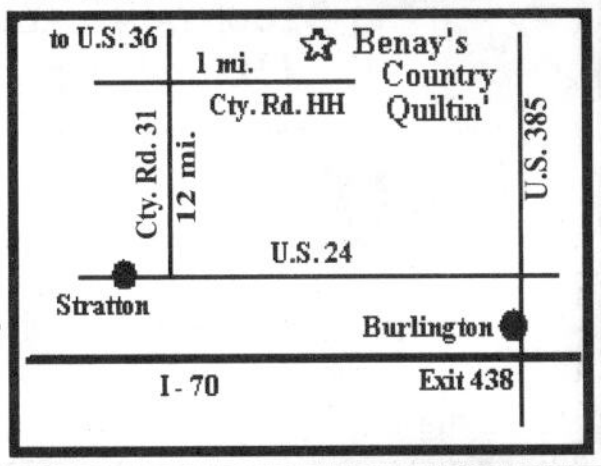

10 years in business. Machine Quilting, Classes, Notions, Fabric plus Patterns & Books.
N39.48230 W102.57193

Wray, CO #32

Mon - Fri 9:30 - 5:30 Sat 9:30 - 2

Rainbow Fabrics & Crafts

409 Main St. 80758
(970) 332-4343
Owner: Wanda Harford
Est: 1994 2500 sq.ft. 3000+ bolts
rainbow@plains.net

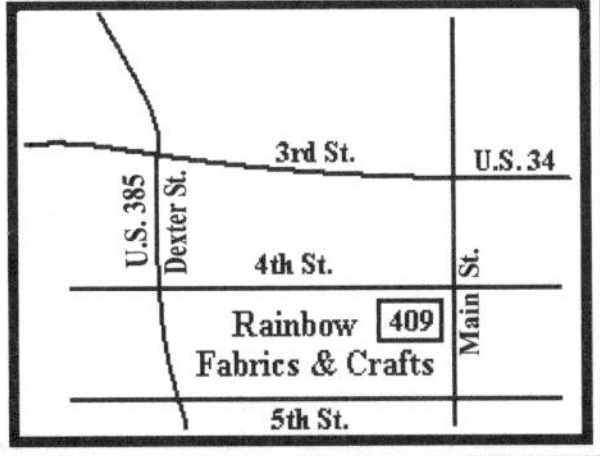

Quilting Fabrics & Notions.
Books & Patterns AccuQuilt Go Cutter
Janome Sewing Machines.

Ft. Morgan, CO #33

Mon - Sat 10 - 5

Inspirations Quilt Shop

423 Main St. #300 80701
(970) 542-0810 Owner: Nancy Hocheder
shop@inspirationsquiltshop.com
www.inspirationsquiltshop.com

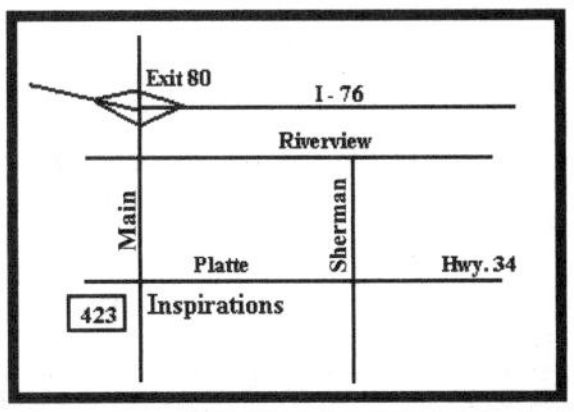

Top quality fabrics, books, patterns and lots of kits to choose from. You'll enjoy seeing our large selection of models.

Longmont, CO #34

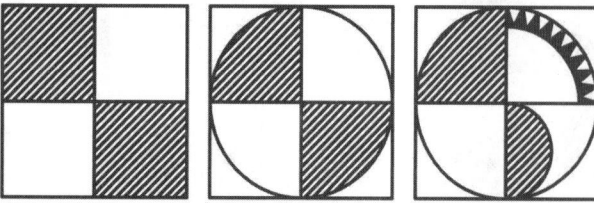

The Quilter's Studio LLC
a place to create
364 Main St. 80501
303-776-6444
www.thequiltersstudio.com

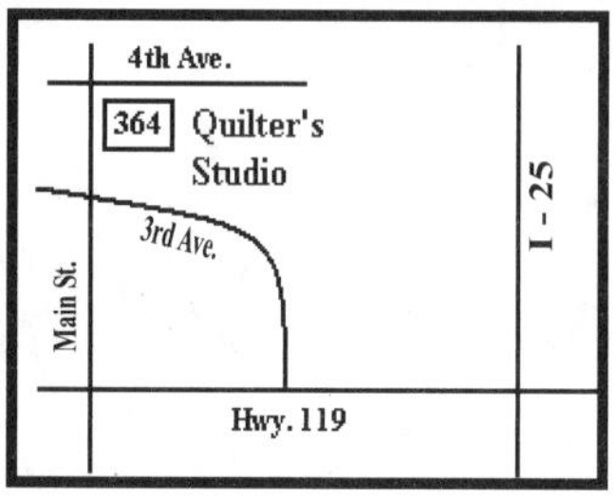

Owners: Sheri Diesburg, Dawn Koltz & Ann Marceca
Est: 2005 2800 sq.ft.
1600 Bolts

Mon - Sat 10 - 6

Batiks, Cotton Prints, Hand-Dyed Cottons, Kits, Books, Patterns and Notions for the Traditional to Contemporary Quilter.
Classes for Beginners to Advanced in Piecing, Quilting and Art Quilting
Shop Online at www.thequiltersstudio.com

Longmont, CO #35

Mon - Sat 9:30 - 6
Sun 11 - 3

THREAD BEAR QUILTS
1755½ Main St. 80501
(720) 652-9001
Owner: Penny D. Mullen
www.threadbearquilts.com

We carry FULL LINES of fabric.
Largest selection North of Denver.
Online Newsletter.

baby lock FOR THE LOVE OF SEWING
Dealer

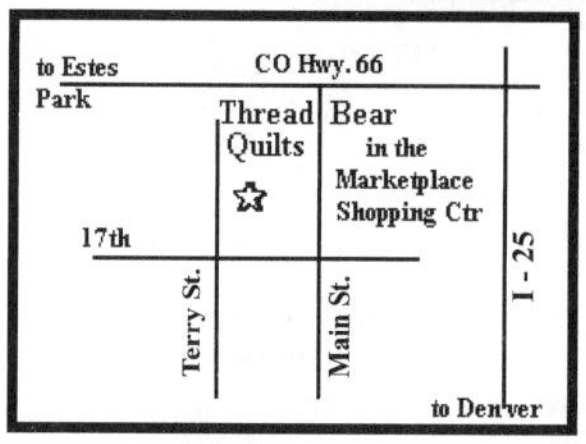

Loveland, CO #36

Sweetheart QUILT SHOPPE
970-461-3452
517 N. Denver Ave. 80537
www.sweetheartquilt.com
Est: 2005

Mon - Sat 10 - 6

Over 4,000 bolts of 100% cotton quilting fabric. Thimbleberries, Kansas Troubles, batiks, flannels, brights, pastels, lots of great blenders and everything in between.... And comfortable chairs for the husbands.
Large selection of books, patterns, notions & threads.
Friendly, knowledgeable staff. Free parking.
Free Newsletter Online.

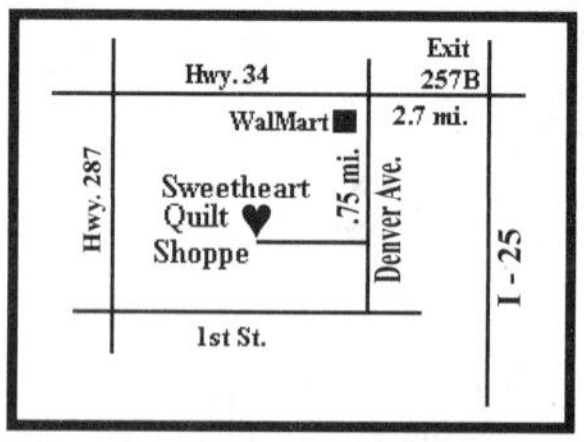

We carry 100% cotton fabrics available for making quilts, along with books, patterns, notions, threads, batting and stencils. With over 5,000 bolts of fabric, we carry a wide variety of styles such as Batiks, Asian, Australian, 30's, children's and flannels. Fat quarters available for all our fabrics.

Lyons, CO #37

424 Main St.
P.O. Box 1342 80540
(303) 823-6067
Owner: Jan Rold
Est: 2000 1600 sq. ft.

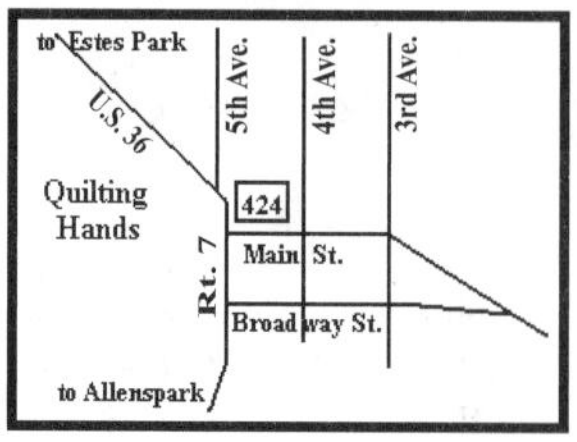

www.quiltinghandsshop.com

Estes Park, CO #38

Mon - Sat 10 - 5
Sun 12:30 - 4:30

930 Big Thompson Ave.
P.O. Box 436 80517
(970) 586-5330

MOUNTAIN LADY QUILT SHOP INC.
www.mtnladyquilt.com
mtnladyqlt@estesvalley.net

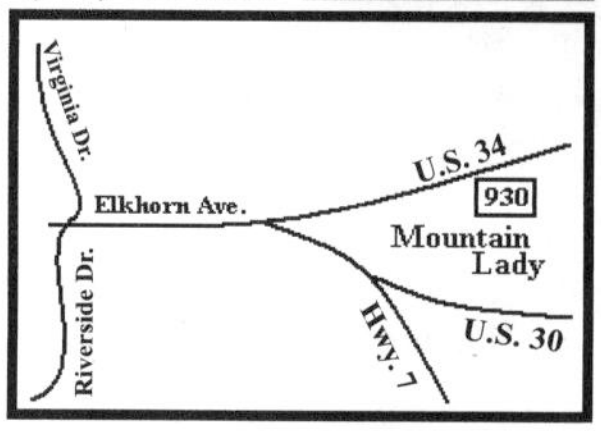

Quality supplies for Quilters.
We specialize in Mountain Theme Fabrics and Kits. Classes, mail order.

Estes Park, CO #39

Year 'round 10 - 5
Closed Wed.

Maggie Mae's Quilts 'N
242 Moraine Ave. P.O. Box 3580
(970) 586-4257 80517
Owner: Margaret McCormick
Est: 1990 1200 sq.ft.

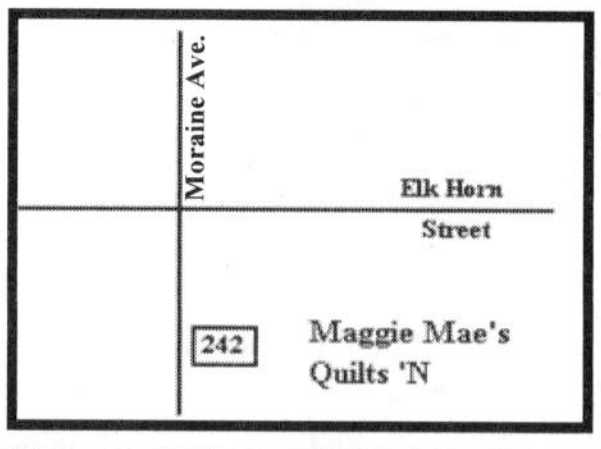

Featuring Patterns by Colorado Designers
Kits - Fabrics - Christmas Projects.
Largest specialty selection of Aunt Gracie's Scrap & 1930's.

Cabin Quilts & Stitches

"A Unique Place to Shop"

For the serious quilter
Fabric, Books, Patterns, Notions & Yarn
Unique Gifts all in one "Cozy" Store

908 Grand Avenue
(970) 627-3810
Grand Lake, CO 80447
Owner: Judy K. Jensen
cabinquilts@rkymtnhi.com

Grand Lake, CO #40

Located on the Boardwalk in beautiful Grand Lake, Colorado

Open Year Round

Directions:
From Denver take I-70 west to U.S.40
Go North to Granby. From Granby take
U.S.34 North to Grand Lake (15 miles)
at the entrance to Rocky Mountain National Park

Ft. Collins, CO #41

The Fig Leaf

2700 S. College, Unit 1 80525
(970) 495-1766
Owners: Rob & Laura Shotwell
Est: 1982 16,000 sq.ft.
thefigleaf@qwestoffice.net

Over 3500 Bolts of Fabric
(includes 500 Bolts of Flannel)
Books, Patterns, Notions.

Mon - Sat 10 - 6 Sun 12 - 5

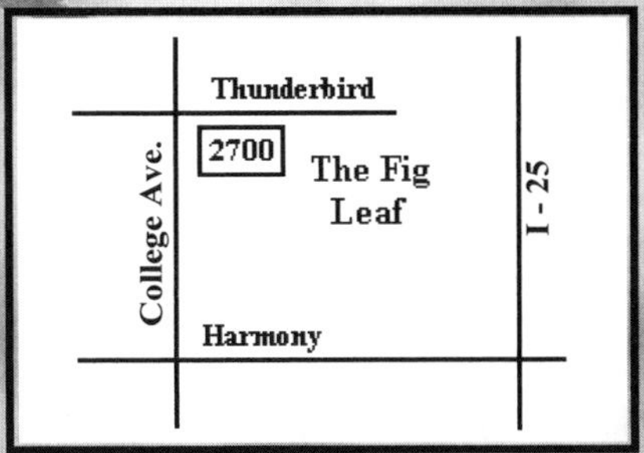

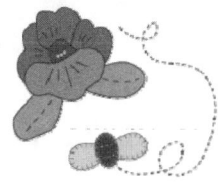

Greeley, CO #44

Mon - Fri 10 - 5
Sat 10 - 4
Call for Holiday Hrs.

wild'n woolly

2030 35th Ave., Unit A 80634-3944
(970) 356-0335
Owner: Ruth Dixon
Est: 1978 2500 Bolts

Yarn and Quilt Shop. Over 2500 Bolts Patterns, classes, supplies for knitting, crochet, Needlepoint & hardanger.

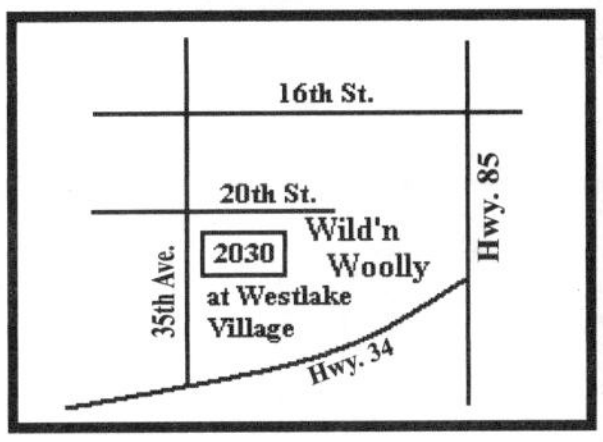

Sterling, CO #45

Mon - Fri 9 - 5:30
Sat 9 - 5

Quilts-N-Creations

201 Ash P.O. Box 991 80751
(970) 522-0146 Est: 1987
www.sew2000.com/qnc
1000 Bolts of Printed & Solid Cottons
Bridal Headquarters for N.E. Colorado including Bridal Fabric & Trims. Tuxedo Rentals from Jim's Formal Wear and Randall's Formal Wear.
Authorized Bernina Dealer. Custom sewing including crafts, quilts, garments or Bridal.
Custom, Traditional & Heirloom Quilting.

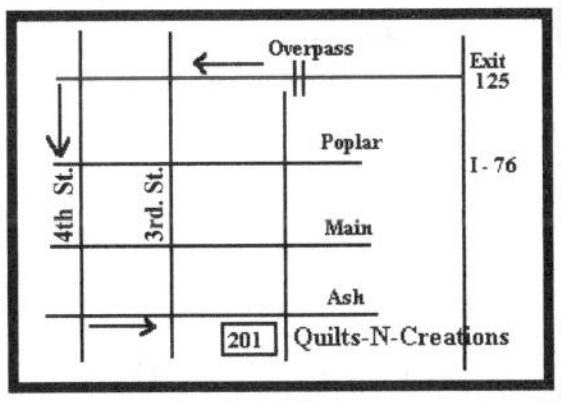

Brazilian Embroidery

...and so much more!

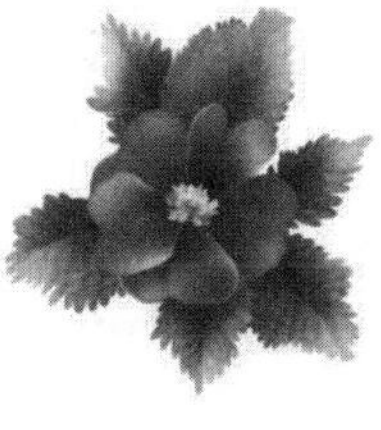

4444 Morrison Road
Denver, Colorado 80219-2446
(303) 522-6866 (phone)
(303) 934-0568 (fax)
info@brazilianembroidery.biz

We are the only shop to stock all the Brazilian Embroidery EdMar threads, gold-plated charms, Mill Hill beads, Kreinik, Rajmahal and much more! A full line of all the designers. Specialty threads and ribbons for embellishing. Call for an appointment. We also do mail order with Visa/MC.

See www.ChristineHause.com for class schedules with the only certified instructor in the state and information on the Colorado Brazilian Embroidery Guild.

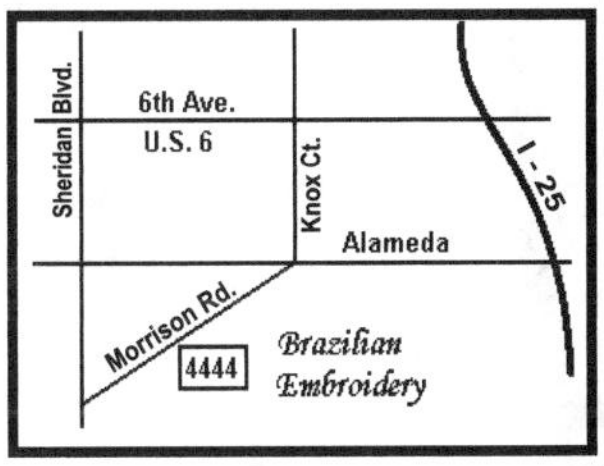

Your one-stop shop for ***everything*** Brazilian Embroidery!
www.brazilianembroidery.biz

Denver, Colorado #46

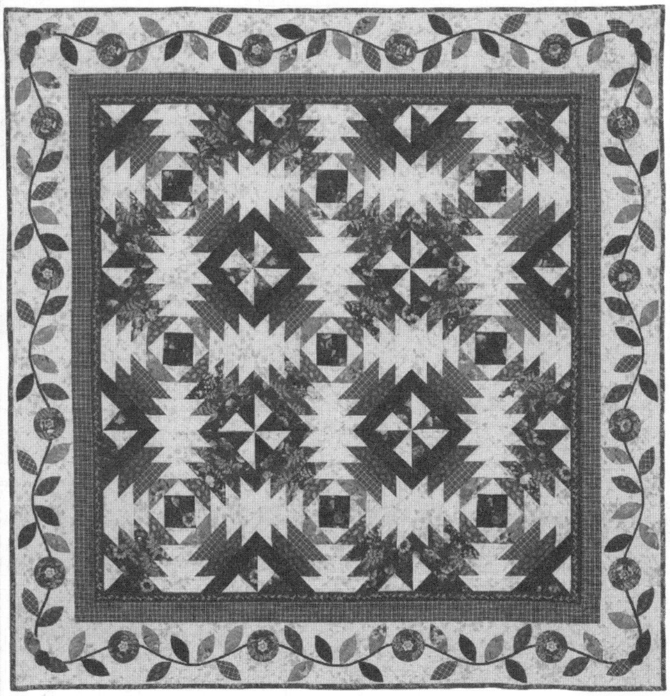

Great American Quilt Factory

Owners Lynda Milligan & Nancy Smith

#47

- Home of POSSIBILITIES® books
- Over 5,000 bolts of cotton fabric plus books, notions, patterns, kits, and gifts
- Fabrics include batiks, reproductions, Kaffe Fasset/Westminster, flannels, and other great designers and styles
- Huge selection of quilting embellishments & books including Angelina Fibers, Jacquard paints, air-dry clay, shrink plastic, and so much more!

Shop Hours
Mon, Tues, Thurs & Fri • 10:00 to 6:00
Wed • 10:00 to 8:00 Sat • 10:00 to 5:00
Sun • 12:00 to 5:00

Great American Quilt Factory
303-740-6206 greatamericanquilt.com
8970 E. Hampden Ave • Denver, CO 80231

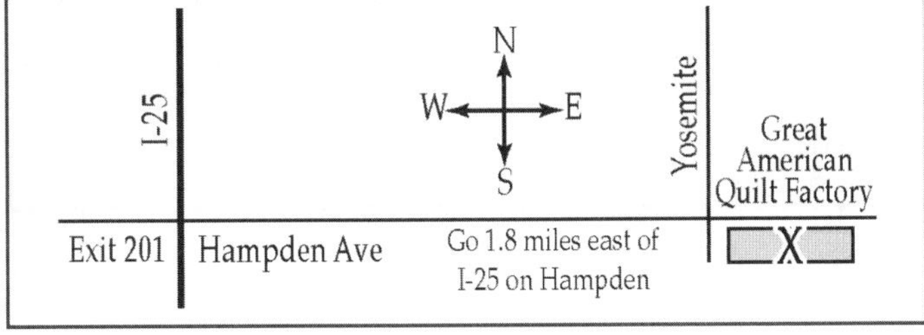

High Prairie Quilts

Store hours:
Mon – Fri 9:30-6:00 ✦ Sat 9:30-5:00
Sun 12:00-5:00
www.highprairiequilts.com

Over 2000+ bolts of fabric and lots of models in styles for everyone!
We have a great selection of classes for all levels of quilters.
A variety of Blocks of the Month available, check out our website for more details!

18870 E. Plaza Dr.
Parker ✦ CO ✦80134
303-627-0878

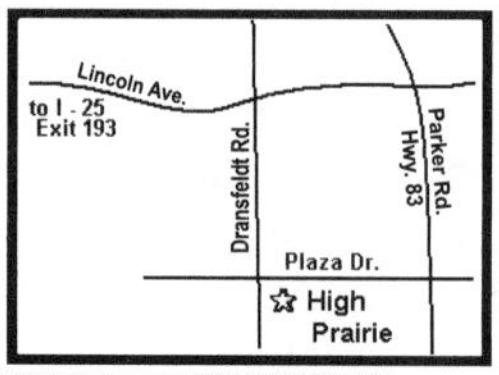

Parker, CO #48

Centennial, CO #49

Holly's Quilt Cabin

Mon - Sat 9:30 - 6
Tues til 7
Sun 12 - 4

Quilting and Gifts

Come enjoy our great selection of the newest fabrics, gifts and the latest Mountainpeek Creation patterns.

Home of: Mountainpeek Creations™

8210 S. Holly St. 80122
888-768-5922
www.hollysquiltcabin.com

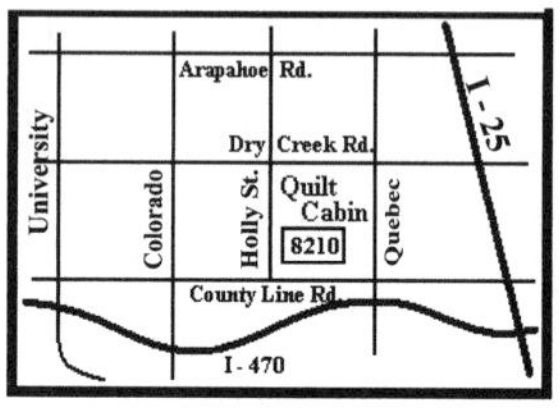

Harriet's Treadle Arts-

Your home for everything quilting!

Established in 1981 and specializing in the art and education of quilt making for 29 years. Family owned and operated by Harriet Hargrave and her daughter Carrie.

Harriet's Treadle Arts
A Premier Quilt Shop

We offer classes in hand and machine quilting and appliqué as well as machine piecing. We carry over 5000 bolts of cotton fabric, 200+ titles of books, 100's of patterns and stencils and oodles of notions to meet all your quilting needs. We also carry one of Colorado's largest selection of vintage reproduction fabrics from 1790-1930.

Come visit our warm homey store for inspirations or let our helpful, friendly sales staff guide you to a new project. We are here to help and support you in all your quilting endeavors.

Mon - Fri 10 - 5
Sat 10 - 4

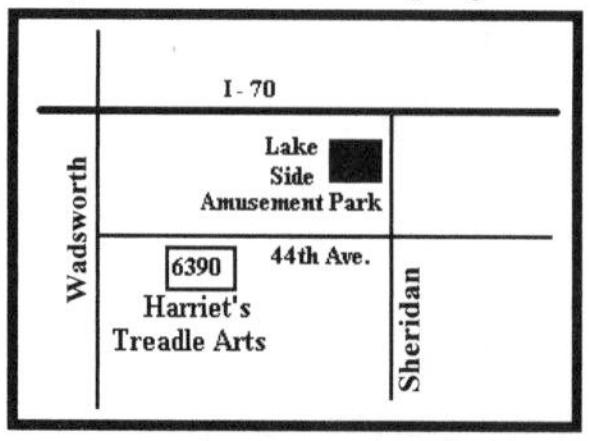

• 6390 W. 44th Ave. • Wheat Ridge, CO 80033 •
• 303-424-2742 • www.harriethargrave.com •

Wheat Ridge, CO #52

Littleton, CO #50

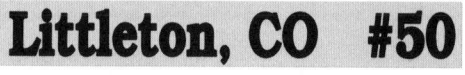

Mon & Tues 10-7
Wed - Sat 10 - 5
Sun 12 - 4

The Creative Needle

6905 South Broadway #113 80122
(303) 794-7312
Owner: Marge Serck
Est: 1978 3500 sq.ft. 4500 Bolts
www.thecreativeneedle.com

One stop for quilting, cross-stitch, heirloom and smocking. Elna and Baby Lock machine sales and service.

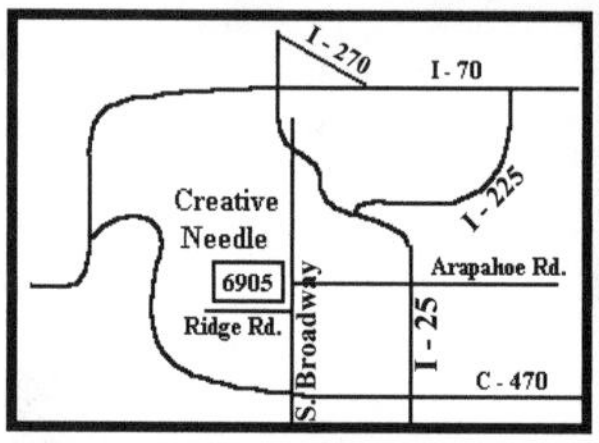

Littleton, CO #51

Mon - Fri 9:30 - 6
Tues til 8
Sat 10 - 5
Sun 12 - 5

Fabric Expressions

3625 W. Bowles Ave. #13 80123
(303) 798-2556
Owner: Alison Dale
Est: 1994 4200 sq.ft. 3500+ bolts
fabricexpressions@msn.com
www.fabricexpressions.com
100% Cottons, Batiks, Flannels, Plaids, Books, Notions, Classes.
A Unique Quilt Shop

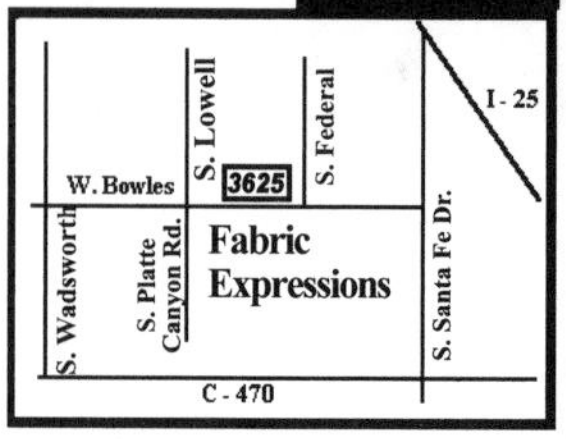

www.emilyssewing.com
Mon-Fri 10-5:30
Sat 10-4

Emily's Sewing Basket

Fabric - Notions - Patterns
Books - Heirloom Quilting
Hand & Machine Embroidery
Help for Beginners and
Advanced Learners
Classes
Friendly, Customer Oriented

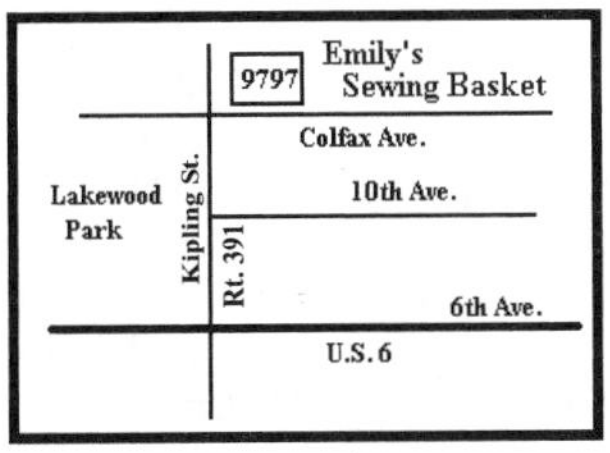

9797 W. Colfax Ave., Lakewood, CO 80215
303-238-3100 Est: 2008 2600 sq.ft.
info@emilyssewing.com 1500 bolts
"WE ARE JUST A YARD AWAY"

Lakewood, CO #53

the Quilt Store

A Quilt Store by Quilters for Quilters

Large selection of quality fabric
Books, patterns, notions
Gifts & Kits
Classes

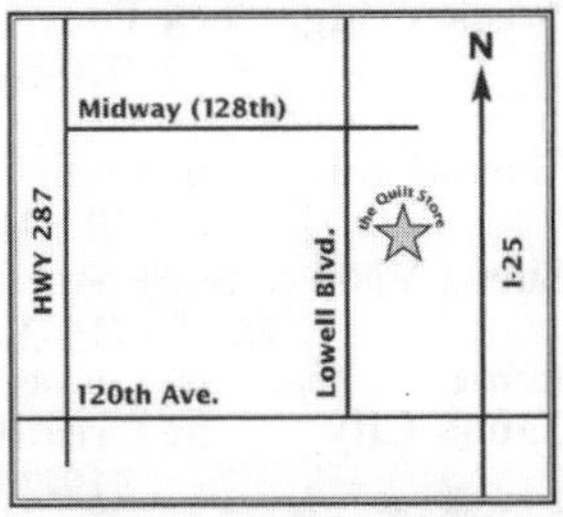

Broomfield, CO #54

12710 Lowell Blvd.
(303) 465-0750
quilters@thequiltstore.net
www.thequiltstore.net

Store Hours
Weekdays 10-6
Saturday 10-5
Sunday 10-3

Stop By For Inspiration!

Just 30 minutes north of Denver

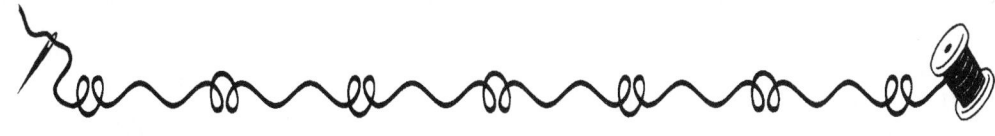

Tomorrow's Heirlooms

One Stop Shopping

#55

BERNINA
Sewing and Embroidery Machines

Gammill
QUILTING SYSTEMS

Statler Stitcher
COMPUTERIZED QUILTING SYSTEMS

Quilting Sewing
Embroidery

Store Hours
Monday- Friday 10:00 to 6:00
Saturday 10:00 to 5:00
Sunday Closed

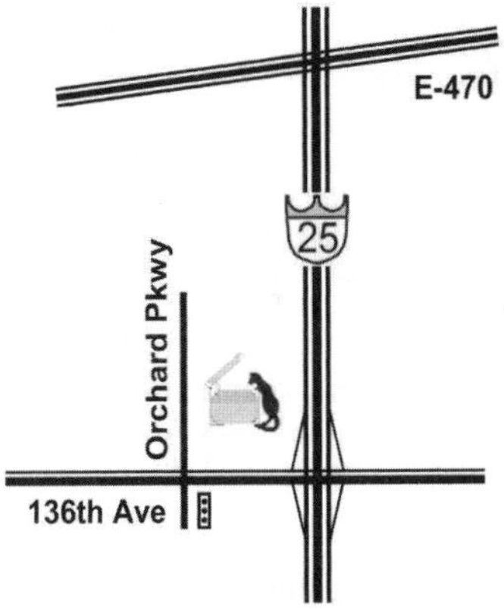

NW Corner of
136th and I 25

50,000 Yards of Fresh Fabric * Threads Galore
Patterns * Kits * Notions * Books * Classes

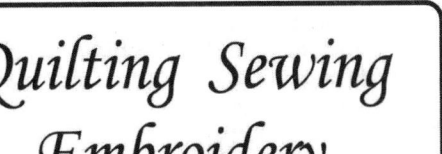

13644 Orchard Pkwy #600, Westminster Colorado 80023 303-457-3888 www.quiltshop.us

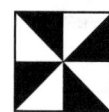

Colorado Quilt Shops

Alamosa Gray Goose Fabrics, 616 Main St. 719-589-6982 See ad #14, page 79
Arvada Quilted Moose Quilt Shop, 5762 Olde Wadsworth 303-423-6232
Arvada Shared Threads Quilt Shop, 10050 Ralston Rd. 303-420-5720
Bailey A Quilt Top Shop @ Wolf Mountain, 279 Wisp Creek 303-838-5557
Boulder Elfriede's Fine Fabrics, 2425 Canyon Blvd. 303-447-0132
Breckenridge Tea Time Quilting & Stitchery, 122 S. Main St. 970-547-8300 See ad #24, page 80
Broomfield Quiltequipt, 6811 120th Ave. #1E 303-466-8129
Broomfield The Quilt Store, 12710 Lowell Blvd 303-465-0750 See ad #54, page 87
Buena Vista Bev's Stitchery, 202 Tabor St. 719-395-8780 See ad #10, page 78
Cahone Ann Neely's Quilting Shop, 14064 Hwy. 491 970-562-4655
Canon City The Creative Cloth Closet, 508 Main St. 719-269-7397 See ad #9, page 78
Castle Rock Sew-Ciety, 4714 Milestone Ln. #J 720-733-8102 See ad #30, page 81
Centennial Holly's Quilt Cabin, 8210 S. Holly St. 720-529-9659 See ad #49, page 86
Cheyenne Wells Rambling Rose Quilt Shop, 44408 Cty. Rd. Q 719-767-2813
Colorado Springs Ruth's Stitchery, 4440 Austin Bluffs Pkwy. 719-591-1717 See ad #6, page 77
Colorado Springs LadyBug Hill Quilts, 955 E. Filmore 719-593-5949 See ad #7, page 77
Colorado Springs High Country Quilts, 4771 N. Academy 719-598-1312 See ad #5, page 76
Colorado Springs Needleworks by Holly Berry House 2409 W. Colorado Ave. 719-636-1002 See ad #8, page 78
Colorado Springs Mill Outlet Fabric Shop, 2906 N. Prospect St. 719-632-6296
Cortez Quiltin' Chicks Quilt Shop, 15 E. Main St. 970-565-7541
Del Norte Kathy's Fabric Trunk, 16179 W. Hwy. 160 877-873-0211 See ad #12, page 78
Denver Great American Quilt Factory, 8970 E. Hampden 303-740-6206 See ad #47, page 85
Denver Brazilian Embroidery, Inc., 4444 Morrison Rd. 303-522-6866 See ad #46, page 85
Durango All for the Love of Quilts, 1474 Main Ave. #205 970-259-1454
Durango Durango Quilt Company, 21516 Hwy. 160 W 970-247-2582 See ad #17, page 79
Durango Durango Sewing Center, 1111 104A Camino Del Rio 970-382-8809 See ad #16, page 79
Estes Park Maggie Mae's Quilts 'N, 242 Moraine Ave. 970-586-4257 See ad #39, page 82
Estes Park Mountain Lady Quilt Shop, 930 Big Thompson 970-586-5330 See ad #38, page 82
Estes Park Cottage Bliss, 870-A Moraine Ave.Hwy 36 970-577-1557
Evergreen Crafty Lady Quilts, 28566 Clover Ln 303-674-3126
Fort Collins The Fig Leaf, 2700 S. College Ave., Unit 1 970-495-1766 See ad #41, page 83
Fort Morgan Inspirations Quilt Shop, 423 Main St. #300 970-542-0810 See ad #33, page 81
Fort Morgan Sew & Sew Quilts, 731 State St 970-542-0144
Fountain Na-La's Quiltique 117 S. Main St. 719-382-6252 See ad #3, page 76
Glenwood Springs Glenwood Sewing Center, 822 Grand Ave. 970-945-5900 See ad #20, page 80
Golden The Rocky Mountain Quilt Museum 1213 Washington Ave. #200 303-215-9001 See ad #26, page 81
Golden Golden Quilt Company, 1108 Washington Ave. 303-277-0717 See ad #27, page 81
Golden Creative Crafts Group, 741 Corporate Cir. Suite A 303-215-5600 See ad #28, page 81
Grand Junction HI Fashion Fabrics, 2586 Patterson Rd. 970-242-1890 See ad #21, page 80
Grand Junction Fabric Art Studios, 2297 Tall Grass #9 970-263-7907 See ad #23, page 80
Grand Junction Quilters' Corner, Inc., 421 Colorado Ave. 970-255-8838 See ad #22, page 80
Grand Lake Cabin Quilts & Stitches, 908 Grand Ave. 970-627-3810 See ad #40, page 83
Greeley Wild 'N Woolly, 2030 35th Ave. Unit A 970-356-0335 See ad #44, page 85
Hotchkiss The Quilt Patch, 148 Bridge St. 970-872-2688 See ad #19, page 80
Idaho Springs Hen House Quilts & Gifts, 1800 Colorado 303-567-4092 See ad #29, page 81
Lakewood Emily's Sewing Basket, 9797 W. Colfax Ave. 303-238-3100 See ad #53, page 87
Leadville Mountain Top Quilts, 129 E. Seventh St. 719-486-3454 See ad #25, page 80
Littleton The Creative Needle, 6905 S. Broadway #113 303-794-7312 See ad #50, page 86
Littleton Fabric Expressions, 3625 W. Bowles Ave. #13 303-798-2556 See ad #51, page 86
Littleton Denver Fabrics, 2777 W. Belleview Ave. 303-730-2777
Longmont Bernina Sewing Center, 1744 Collyer St 303-776-6704
Longmont The Quilter's Studio, 364 Main St. 303-776-6444 See ad #34, page 82
Longmont Thread Bear Quilting Fabrics, 1755 1/2 Main St. 720-652-9001 See ad #35, page 82
Loveland Sweetheart Quilt Shoppe, Inc. 517 N. Denver Ave. 970-461-3452 See ad #36, page 82
Loveland The Wool Basket, 526 N. Cleveland 970-203-0999
Lyons Quilting Hands Quilt Shop, 424 Main St. 303-823-6067 See ad #37, page 82
Merino D & J Country Antiques, PO Box 29 970-842-5813
Monte Vista Shades, Quilts, & Etc, 129 Adams St. 719-852-2179 See ad #13, page 78
Pagosa Springs Eagle Mountain Mercantile, 56 Talisman 970-731-9900 See ad #15, page 79
Parker High Prairie Quilts, 18870 E. Plaza Dr. 303-627-0878 See ad #48, page 86
Pine A Quilt Top Shop, 316 Mt. Evans Blvd. #B 303-838-5557
Pueblo Stitcher's Garden, 308 S. Union Ave. 719-545-3320 See ad #2, page 76
Salida Fringe, 139 F Street 719-539-4006 See ad #11, page 78
South Fork Beaver Mtn Quilts, Etc., 31070 W. Hwy. 160 719-873-1222 See ad #18, page 80
Springfield Justa Stitchin', 965 Main St. 719-523-4985 See ad #1, page 76
Sterling Quilts-N-Creations, 201 Ash St. 970-522-0146 See ad #45, page 85
Stratton Benay's Country Quiltin', 32131 County Rd HH 970-362-4650 See ad #31, page 81
Westcliffe The Silver Needle Quilt Shop, 307 Main St. #A 719-783-9699
Westminster Tomorrow's Heirlooms, 13644 Orchard Pkwy. 303-457-3888 See ad #55, page 87
Wheatridge Harriet's Treadle Arts, 6390 West 44th Ave. 303-424-2742 See ad #52, page 86
Windsor The Little Wool Shoppe, 429 Main St. 970-686-5642 See ad #42, page 84
Windsor Quilter's Stash 1180 West Ash St., Ste. 100 970-686-5657 See ad #43, page 84
Woodland Park Nuts 'n Bolts Needleworks, 200 S. Chestnut 719-687-2272 See ad #4, page 76
Wray Granma's Charms, 301 S. Main St. 970-332-5556
Wray Rainbow Fabrics and Crafts 409 Main St. 970-332-4343 See ad #32, page 81

Colorado Quilt Shows

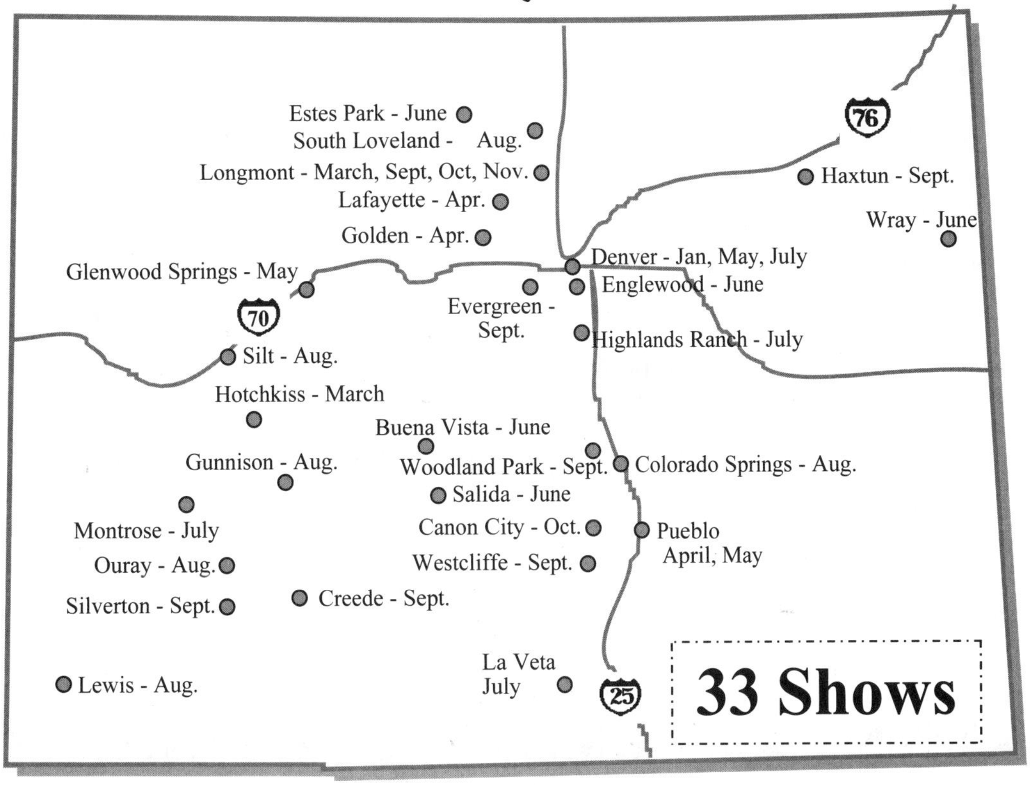

About Shows: We are listing only the very basic information about shows that happen on a regular schedule here. Please check out our website for more details on each show. Also this information tends to change quite often so please verify the event with our website or a local source before you venture far. Or if you're in the right area at the right time, give it a shot.

If you are a show organizer, please keep us updated on your event.
shows@quilterstravelcompanion.com www.quilterstravelcompanion.com

On our website you will also find:

- Exact dates (when we have them)
- Contact Information
- Events happening on a one-time basis
- Sponsor Information
- Description of Event

Month	City	Schedule	Show	Location with address
March				
	Longmont	Annual, 1st Sat of March	Interfaith Quilters Show & Sale	First Lutheran Church, 803 3rd Ave
	Hotchkiss	Odd Years, 2nd weekend of March	S&B Quilters Quilt Show	Delta County Fairgrounds, Heritage Hall, 196 W Hotchkiss Ave
April				
	Pueblo	Annual, 2nd Fri & Sat in April	Quilt and Stitch Expo of Pueblo	Pueblo Convention Center, 320 Central Main St
	Golden	Annual, 3rd Saturday in April	Rocky Mountain Quilt Museum Auction	Calvary Church, 1320 Arapahoe St
	Lafayette	Annual, April	Quaking Aspen Quilt Guild Show	Lafayette Public Library, 755 W. Baseline Rd.
May				
	Pueblo	Annual, Last week of April into May	Pride City Quilt Guild	Southeastern Colorado Heritage Center, 201 W B St
	Denver	Annual, first weekend in May	Denver National Quilt Festival	Denver Merchandise Mart, I - 25 and 58th St.
	Glenwood Springs	Annual, Mother's Day weekend	Quilters of the Rockies Show	West Glenwood Mall, Hwy. 6 & 24
June				
	Englewood	Even Years, 2nd weekend in June	Arapahoe County Quilters Show	First Plymouth Congregational Church, 3501 S. Colorado
	Estes Park	Even Years, 3rd Wed - Sun of June	Quilt Colorado	Rocky Mountain Park Inn-Holiday Inn Conference Ctr, 101 S. St. Vrain
	Salida	Annual, 3rd weekend in June	Monarch Quilters Show	Salida Middle School, 520 Milford St
	Wray	Annual, 3rd Fri & Sat of June	Quilts of the Plains	Main Street

Colorado Shows Continued

Month	City	Schedule	Show	Location with address
July				
	Buena Vista	Annual, late June or early July	Chaffee County Quilt & Textile Show	Buena Vista Community Center, 715 E Main St
	La Veta	Annual, 1st weekend in July	Scrappy Ladies Quilt Show & Sale	La Veta Community Center, Downtown
	Denver	Annual, 2nd weekend in July	Quilt, Craft & Sewing Festival	Denver Merchandise Mart, 451 E. 58th Ave.
	Montrose	Annual, 2nd weekend in July	Black Canyon Quilt Show	Montrose Pavilion, 1800 Pavilion Dr
	Highlands Ranch	Annual, 3rd weekend in July	Firehouse Quilts Show & Sale	Cherry Hills Community Church, 3900 Grace Blvd.
August				
	Ouray	Annual, Late July thru most of August	Ouray County Historical Society Museum Show	Historical Society Museum, 420 6th
	Silt	Annual, 1st Saturday in August	Anvil Points Quilt Guild Show	Outdoors at the Historical Park, 8th and Orchard, Exit 97 off I-70
	Gunnison	Annual, Parts of August & September	Land of the Rainbow Quilt Festival	Gunnison Arts Center, 102 S. Main St.
	Lewis	Annual, 3rd weekend in August	Armchair Quilters	Lewis Arriola Comm Center, 1 mile east of Arriola on CR South
	Loveland	Annual, 3rd weekend in August	Rocky Mountain Quilt Festival	The Ranch (Larimer Cty. Fairgrounds), 5280 Arena Cir.
	Colorado Springs	Annual, September & October	Exhibition of Quilts & Fine Woodworking	Colorado Springs Pioneers Museum, 215 S. Tejon St.
September				
	Westcliffe	Annual, Labor Day Weekend--Thurs to Mon	Olde Schoolhouse Quilt Show	Silver Needle Quilt Shop, 304 S. 4th St.
	Silverton	Odd years, 1st weekend after Labor Day	Silverton Threads Show	Silverton School Gymnasium, 12th & Reese Sts
	Woodland Park	Annual, 2nd Saturday in September	Quilters Above the Clouds	Ute Pass Cultural Center, Midland Ave.
	Creede	Even Years, 3rd weekend of September	Silver Threads Quilt Guild Show	Creede Community Center, 503 Froest Service Rd. #9
	Longmont	Annual, 4th Fri & Sat of September	Quilt-A-Fair	Boulder County Fairgrounds, Nelson Rd.
	Evergreen	Annual, last Sat. of September	Evergreen's Outdoor Quilt Festival	Hiwan Homestead Museum, 4208 S. Timbervale
	Haxtun	Annual, Last Saturday in September	Corn Festival Quilt Show	Haxtun Community Center, 125 N. Wilson
October				
	Canon City	Odd years Last half of October	Royal Gorge Quilt Council Show	Pueblo Community College, 51320 W Highway 50
	Longmont	Annual, 3rd Saturday in October	Longmont Quilt Guild Quilt Show	Boulder County Fairgrounds, Nelson Rd.
November				
	Longmont	Annual, 1st weekend in November	Handweavers Guild of Boulder Show	Boulder County Fairgrounds, Nelson & Hover

Notes

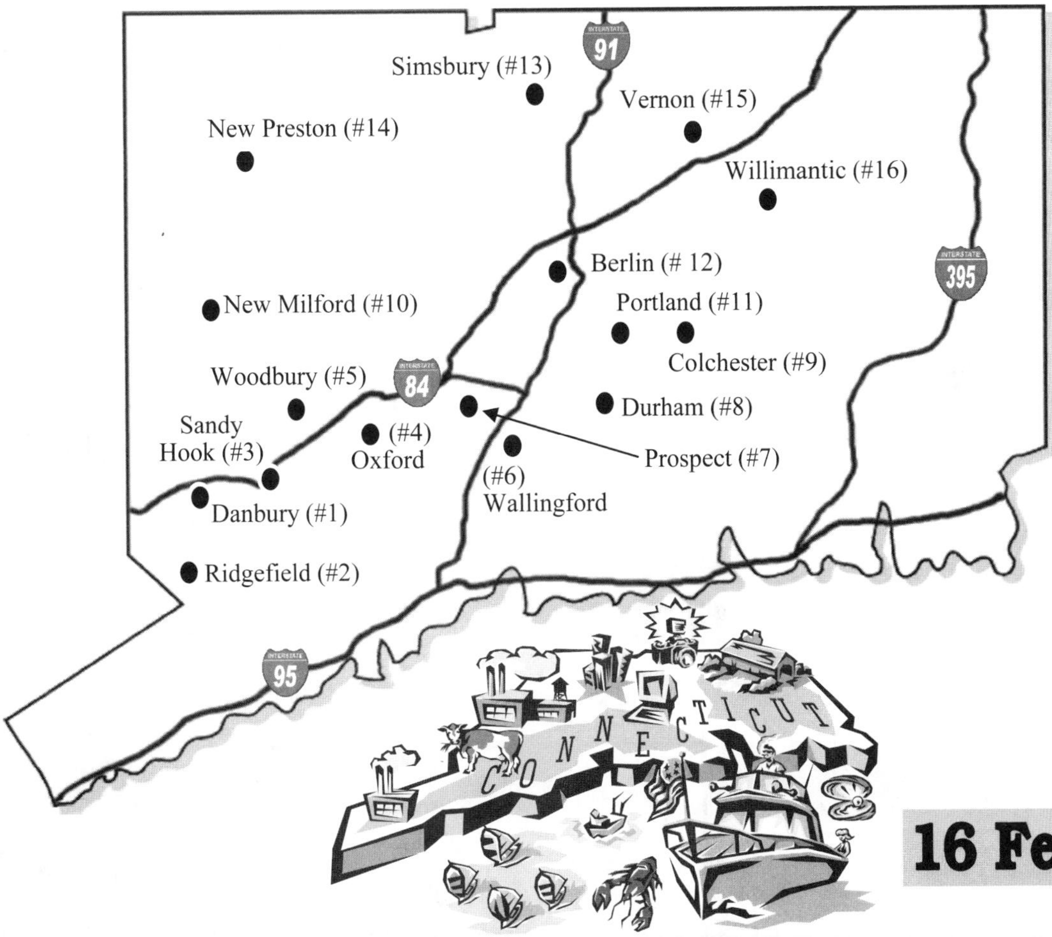

CONNECTICUT

16 Featured Shops

THE QUILT SHOP

Danbury, CT #1

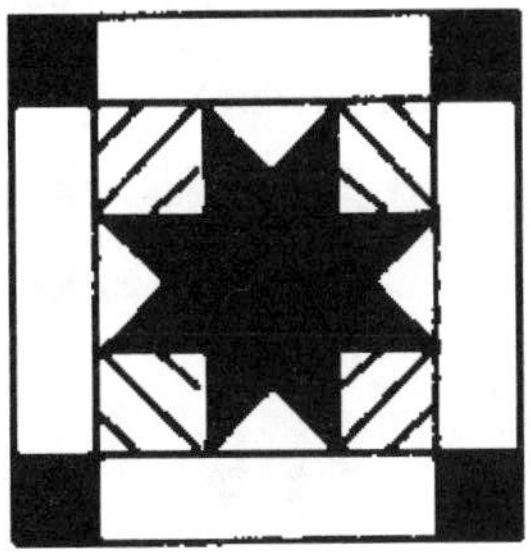

5 Padanaram Rd.
Rt. 37 06811
(203) 743-0543
wamquilt@aol.com
Owner: Ginny Murphy
www.thequiltshoponline.com

Over 3000 Bolts of Contemporary Cotton Fabrics.
Including Westminster, Moda, Art Gallery & Riley Blake
Area's Authorized BERNINA Dealer
Featuring Complete Line of Machines & Accessories.

FOR ALL YOUR QUILTING SUPPLIES

Mon - Sat 9 - 5
Thurs til 8
(Sept - May) Sun 12 - 4

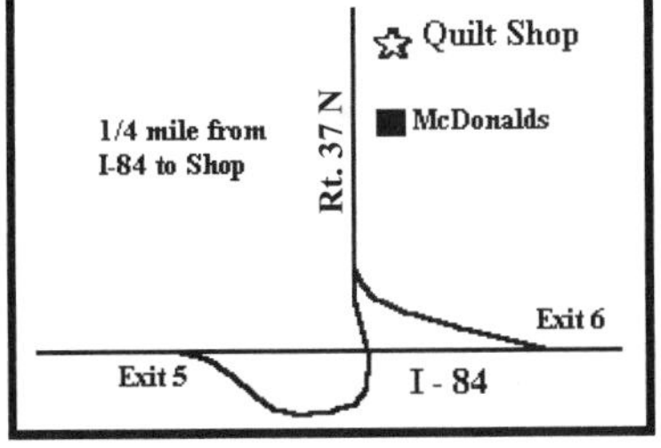

"Worth The Trip"

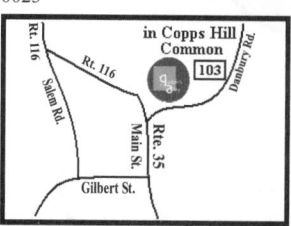

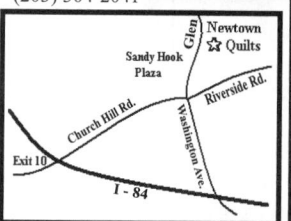

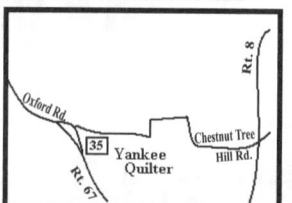

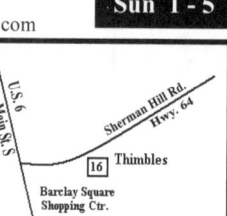

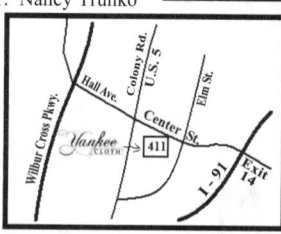

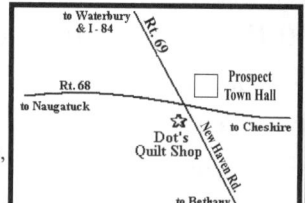

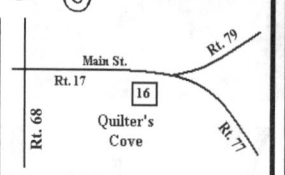

Quilter's Corner

In the Red Barn

Meet Q.C. our shop dog

312 Danbury Rd. (Rt. 7)
New Milford, CT 06776
(860) 355-4516

Est: 1999

Owner: Becky Frazer
Fax: (860) 355-9510
2300 sq.ft. 3000+ Bolts

Mon - Sat 10 - 5
Wed til 8 on class nights

Your source for fabrics, supplies, classes and unique gifts.

New Milford, CT #10

Spacious, well lit shop filled with 100% cotton fabrics, books, patterns, notions, gift items and a friendly, helpful staff.

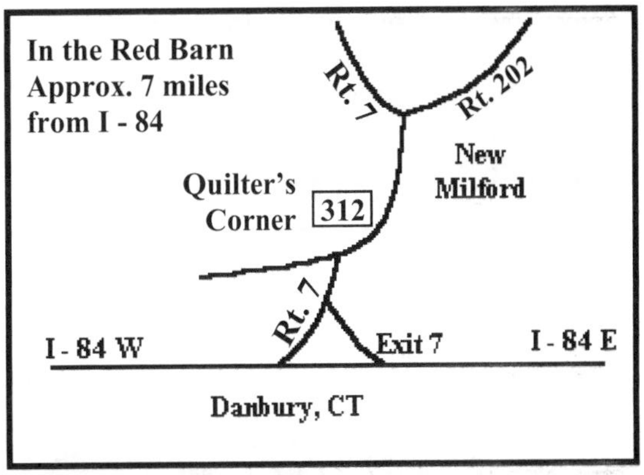

www.quilterscorneronline.com

Portland, CT #11

Tues - Fri 10 - 5
Sat 10 - 3

Patches & Patchwork

216 Main St. 06480
(860) 342-4567 Fax: (860) 342-1615
patches_patchwork@sbcglobal.net Est:1980
Owner: Jane Wilk Sterry 1200 sq.ft.

We carry the unusual in fabrics.
Latest books, patterns and notions. Classes.
Antique quilt repair! Commission quilts.
Hand and machine quilting available.

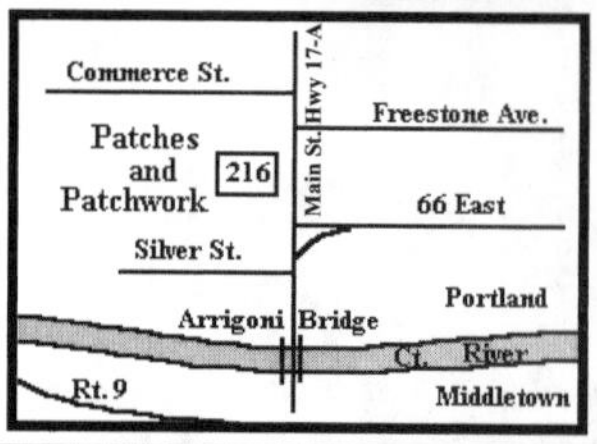

Berlin, CT #12

Tues - Sat 10 - 5
Thur til 8
Sun 12 - 5

Lisa's Clover Hill Quilts

116 A Mill St. 06037
(860) 828-9325

lisa@cloverhillquilts.com
Owner: Lisa Salonia

Quality Fabric, Notions & Classes

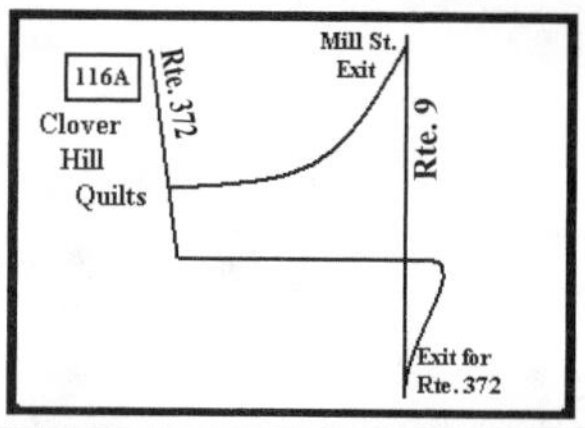

Sew Inspired Quilt Shop & Studio

Design. Create. Complete.

A fun and friendly shop with over 4,000 bolts of fabric

Hundreds of book titles plus the latest patterns and quilting notions; Quilting "art" supplies; Classes, clubs and events for all levels.

Simsbury, CT #13

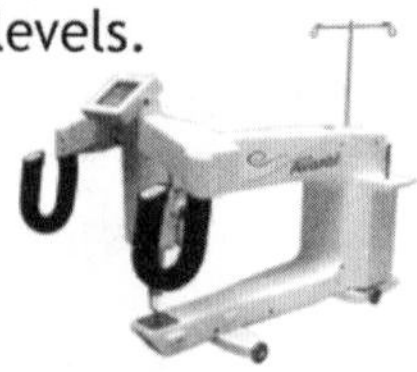

- **Authorized Handi Quilter® Representative**
- Mid- and Long-arm quilting classes
- Custom Quilting Services
- Gammill/Statler Rental
- Accuquilt GO! Fabric Cutter Dealer

Inside Fiddler's Green
Simsbury Center
8 Wilcox Street, Simsbury, CT 06070
860-651-8885
www.sewinspiredquilts.com
Bus trips welcome - please call ahead

Mon, Fri, Sat 10-6
Tues, Wed, Thurs 10-8
Sun 12-4

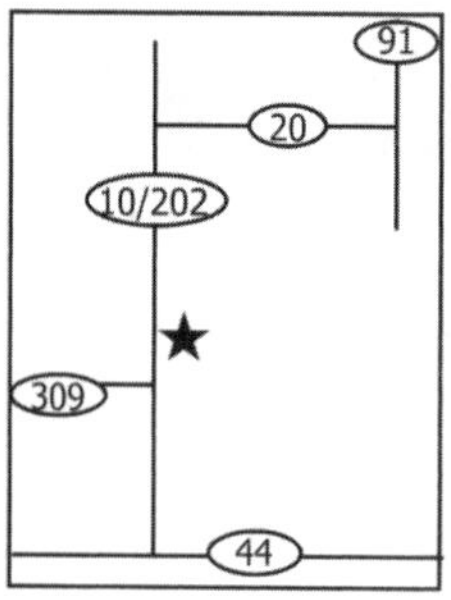

New Preston, CT #14

Tues - Thur 10 - 4
Fri 10 - 5:30
Sat 9 - 3
Sun 10 - 2

Common Threads Quilt Shop

168 New Milford Tpke. 06777
Stonemill Commons
(860) 868-2658

Owner: Corinne Thompson Est: 2001
commonthreads1@aol.com
www.commonthreadsquiltshop.com
"Quilt Gallery with an every changing display to inspire your creativity." Authorized Janome Dealer.
Civil War Repro's, Homespuns, Batiks, Tone-on-Tone

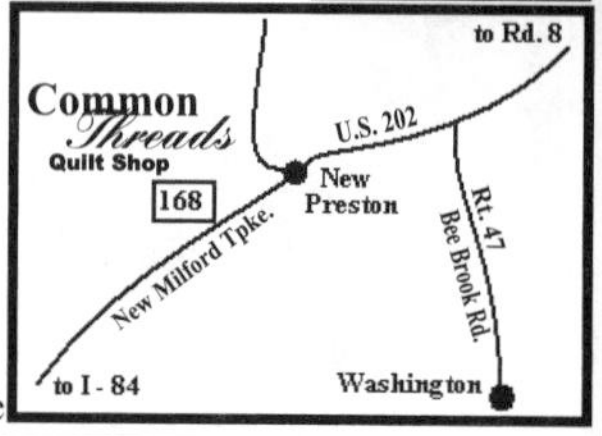

QUILTING By The Yard

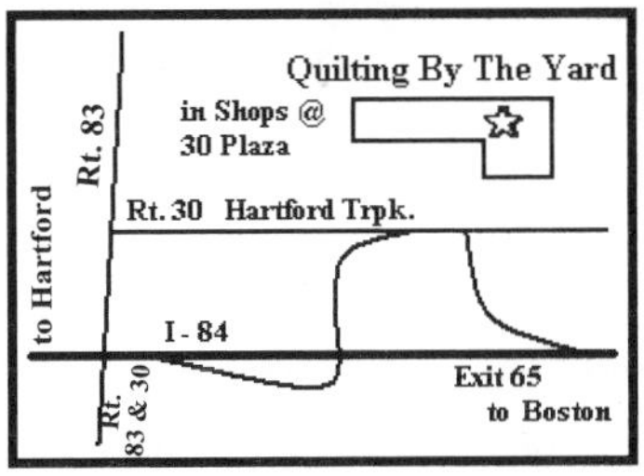

Easy on and off I-84.

Vernon, CT #15

435-O Hartford Turnpike 06066
(860) 896-1056
Est: 2000 2600 sq.ft. 4600 Bolts

WOW! Complete supply of quilting fabrics, kits, books, patterns and the latest notions.
Classes offered days, evenings and weekends.
Spacious, well lit shop.
Extensive collections of batiks, Thimbleberries fabrics, novelty prints and much, much more.

www.quiltingbytheyard.com

Mon - Fri 10 - 5 Thur til 8 Sat 10 - 4 Sun 11 - 4

"Everything You Need To Make Your Quilting Experience A Dream"

Nearly 5000 Bolts of Fabric

Including Hoffman, Benartex, P & B, Moda, Maywood, South Seas, Kona Bay, and many more.

We Carry Tons of Books, Supplies, Patterns, Kits, Batiks, Fat Quarter Bundles, Gadgets and Quilters Tools.

We offer quilt retreats featuring our extremely talented teachers and their original designs.

Willimantic, CT #16

Quilter's Dream

Located in a lovely Victorian building situated in the downtown of an historic mill town, blocks from the Windham Textile and History Museum

Visit our Web Site at
www.quiltersdream.com
Monday - Saturday, 10 AM - 6 PM
Thursday, 10 AM - 8 PM,
Sunday, 12 Noon - 5 PM

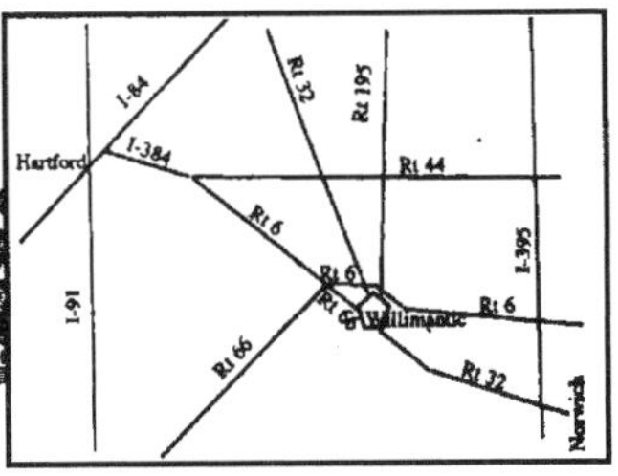

Bus Tours Welcome* • Free Gift to All
(*Please call ahead if you wish to plan a group visit.)

1158 Main Street
Willimantic, CT 06226
(860) 456-7629

Larisa and James Key

Connecticut Quilt Shops

Berlin **Lisa's Clover Hill Quilts, 116A Mill St.**
860-828-9325 **See ad #12, page 94**

Bethel Homestead Viking, 5 Front St. 203-744-3118

Bridgeport The Barn, 50 Hurd Ave. 203-367-1010

Bristol Lin's Quilt Source, 162 Wanderbilt Rd 860-583-2099

Colchester **Colchester Mill Fabrics, 120 Lebanon Ave.**
860-537-2004 **See ad #9, page 92**

Danbury **The Quilt Shop, 5 Padanaram Rd. Rte. 37**
203-743-0543 **See ad #1, page 91**

Danbury Stitch in Time Sewing Center , 66 Sugar Hollow Rd. 203-748-7283

Danbury Fabric Tree, 19 Sugar Hollow Rd 203-792-5252

Durham **Quilter's Cove, 16 Main St. Unit #301**
860-349-0007 **See ad #8, page 92**

Glastonbury Close to Home, 2717 Main St. 860-633-0721

Milford Close to Home, 952 Boston Post Rd. 203-878-1654

New Milford **Quilter's Corner, 312 Danbury Rd.**
860-355-4516 **See ad #10, page 93 & 407**

New Preston **Common Threads Quilt Shop, 168 New Milford**
860-868-2658 **See ad #14, page 94**

North Haven Quadrille Quilting, 118 Quinnipiac Ave. 203-497-8348

Old Saybrook Coastal Sewing & Fabrics, 27 N. Main St. 860-388-1832

Oxford **Yankee Quilter, 35 Old State Rd. 67, Bldg 2, Unit J**
203-888-9196 **See ad #4, page 92**

Portland **Patches & Patchwork, 216 Main St.**
860-342-4567 **See ad #11, page 94**

Prospect **Dot's Quilt Shop, 6 New Haven Rd.**
203-528-0161 **See ad #7, page 92**

Ridgefield **The Quilter's Alley, 103 Danbury Rd**
203-431-0023 **See ad #2, page 92**

Rocky Hill Affordable Fabrics, 2119 Silar Deane Hwy. 860-563-7647

Sandy Hook **Newtown Quilts, 10 Glen Rd.**
203-304-2041 **See ad #3, page 92**

Simsbury **Sew Inspired Quilt Shop, 8 Wilcox St.**
860-651-8885 **See ad #13, page 94**

Simsbury Caroline's Quilts, 542 Hopmeadow St #119 860-658-4677

Unionville Close To Home, 45 S. Main St. 860-675-4481

Vernon **Quilting By The Yard, 435-O Hartford Tpke**
860-896-1056 **See ad #15, page 95**

Wallingford **Yankee Cloth, 411 Center St.**
203-265-1932 **See ad #6, page 92**

Willimantic **Quilter's Dream, 1158 Main St.**
860-456-7629 **See ad #16, page 95**

Woodbury **Thimbles 16 Sherman Hill Rd.**
203-266-0337 **See ad #5, page 92**

Connecticut Quilt Shows

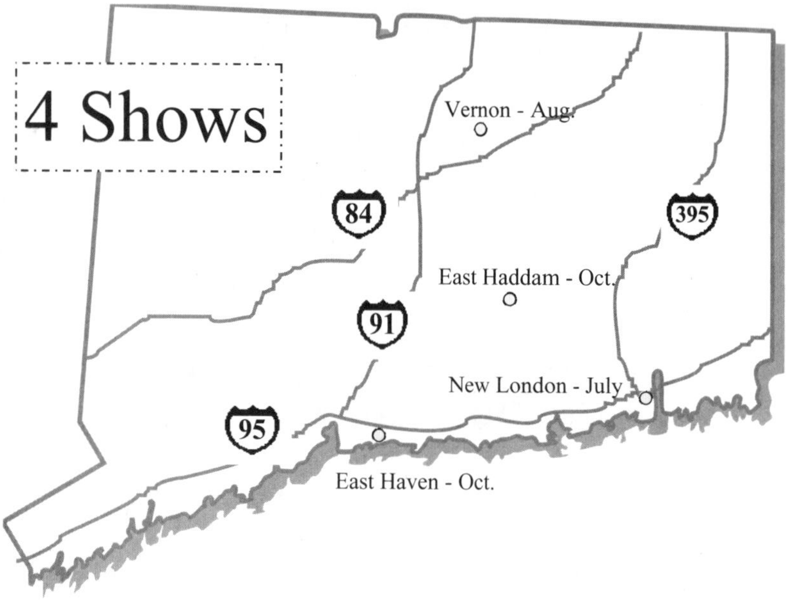

About Shows: We are listing only the very basic information about shows that happen on a regular schedule here. Please check out our website for more details on each show. Also this information tends to change quite often so please verify the event with our website or a local source before you venture far. Or if you're in the right area at the right time, give it a shot.

If you are a show organizer, please keep us updated on your event. shows@quilterstravelcompanion.com www.quilterstravelcompanion.com

On our website you will also find:

- Exact dates (when we have them)
- Sponsor Information
- Contact Information
- Description of Event
- Events happening on a one-time basis

Month	City	Schedule	Show	Location with address
July				
	New London	Even Years, July	Clamshell Quilt Guild Show	College Center at Crozier-Williams Connecticut College
August				
	Vernon	Odd Years, 3rd week of August	Greater Harford Quilt Guild Show	To be Determined
October				
	East Haddam	Annual, Columbus Day weekend in October	Quilt & Needle Arts Show	First Church of Christ, 499 Town St.
	East Haven	Odd Years, 3rd weekend in October	Shoreline Quilters Guild Show	East Haven High School, 35 Wheelbarrow Ln.

Quilter's Hive

fabric classes supplies

1800 Capitol Trail
Newark, DE 19711
(302) 737-5699
www.quiltershive.com

5000 sq. ft. of all the fabric, gadgets and goodies that quilters love

- over 4000 bolts of the latest 100% cotton fabrics
- Books, patterns and notions
- classes from beginning hand and machine quilting to advanced Baltimore Album style applique

HOURS
Mon, Tues & Fri 10-5
Wed 10-8
Thurs 10-4
Sat 10-4

Newark, DE #1

LOCATED AT THE CORNER OF KIRKWOOD HIGHWAY AND HARMONY ROAD

TAX FREE SHOPPING CLOSE TO I-95

From I-95 take Exit 3 on to Rt. 273 West (towards Newark) Turn right on Harmony Road at the first traffic light. Follow Harmony Road for 2.1 miles to Rout 2 (the 5th traffic light). Turn left on Rt.2 (stay in left lane) and make a U turn to get back to the Quilter's Hive parking lot.

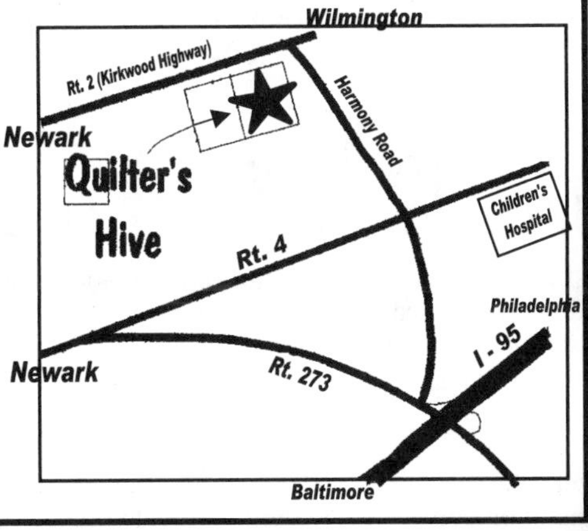

DELAWARE

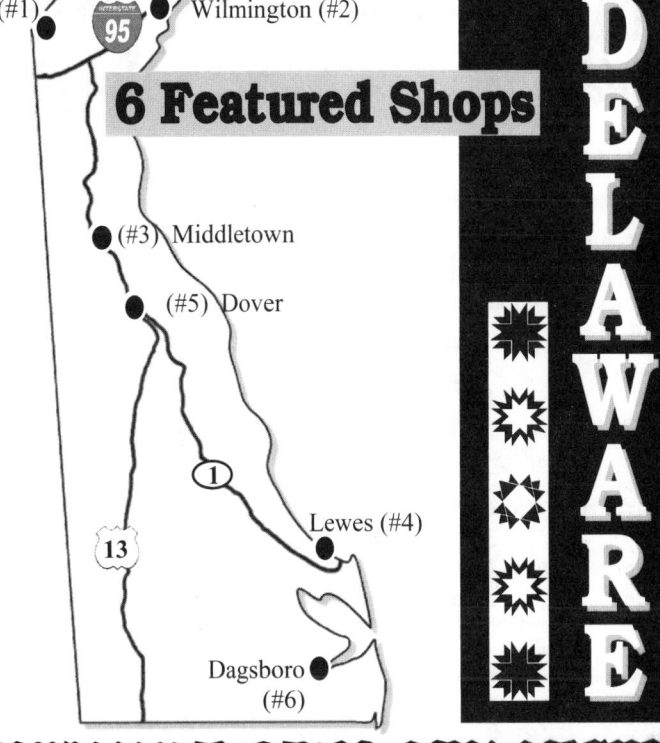

6 Featured Shops

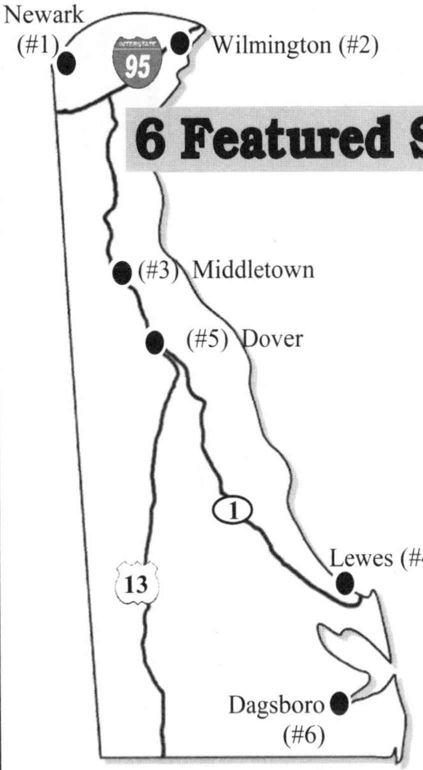

Wilmington, DE #2

HAYES SEWING MACHINE Co.

4425 Concord Pike 19803
(302) 764-9033
Owner: Trev Hayes

Mon & Fri 10 - 9
Tues, Wed Thur 10 - 6
Sat 10 - 5

Est: 1969 Fax: (302) 478-0908
trevhayes@aol.com www.trevhayes.com
Wilmington's oldest sewing machine center.
Over 3000 bolts of fabrics.
5000 sq.ft. showroom. We carry Bernina, BabyLock & Singer sewing machines sales and service. Free estimates. Family Business.

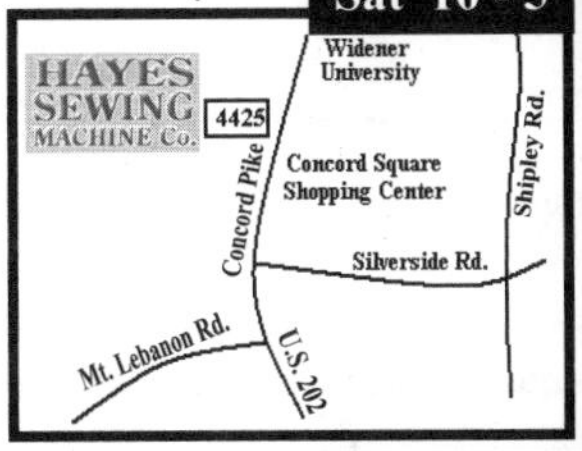

Middletown, DE #3

Lil Country Shoppe

Mon - Fri 10 - 5
Sat 10 - 4

551 Boyds Corner Rd. 19709
(302) 378-5568
Est: 2002 3500 sq.ft. 3000+ Bolts
Lilcountryshoppe@juno.com
www.lilcountryshoppe.com

Quality 100% Cottons, Books, Patterns, Notions & Rug Hooking notions, Foundation, Hand-dyed Wool. Bolts of Wool. Handi-Quilt Dealer
Groups/Buses Welcome. Please call in advance.

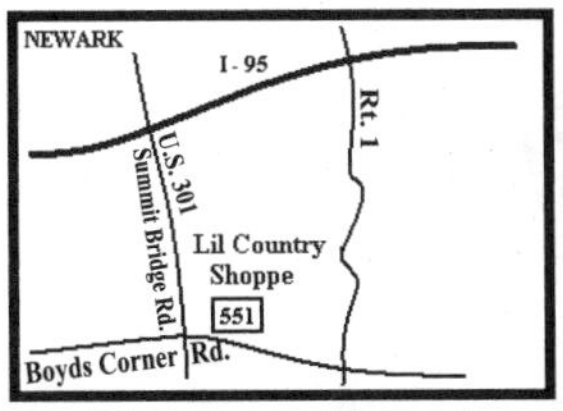

Mare's Bears

QUILT SHOP

At the "Beacon Motel"
528 E. Savannah Rd. 19958
(302) 644-0556
www.maresbearsquiltshop.com
Owner: Maryann McFee
Est: 1995 2000 sq.ft.

Mon - Sat 10 - 5
Sun 12 - 4
Closed Sun Thanksgiving to Mem. Day

- 3500 Bolts of Fabric
- Notions
- Books & Patterns
- Classes

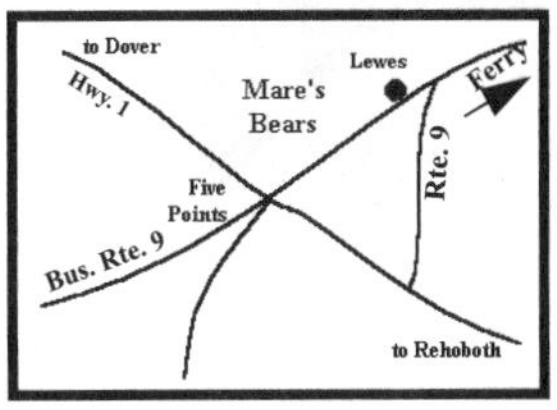

Home of Appliqué by the Bay with Elly Sienkiewicz
First week of December

Lewes, DE #4

Dover, DE #5

Shady Lane Selections

Mon, Tues, Wed 8 - 5
Fri 8 - 6
Sat 8 - 4

1121 Victory Chapel Rd. 19904
Owner: Salina Yoder
Est: 1982 2900 sq.ft. 500+ Bolts

Quilts in all sizes — We do special orders. Custom Hand Quilting. Lots of small crafts, rag rugs, etc. Fabric from Hoffman, RJR, P&B, etc.

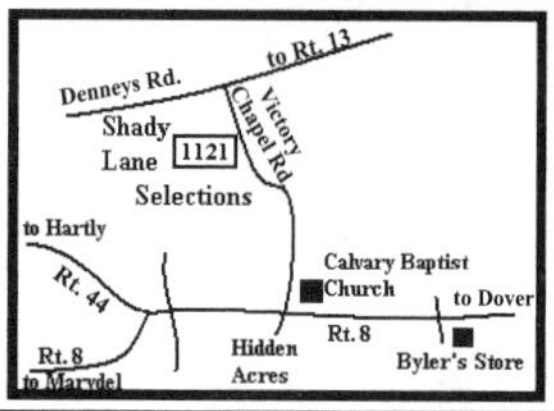

Dagsboro, DE #6

Mon 10 - 7
Tues - Fri 10 - 5
Sat 10 - 4

33119 Main St.
P.O. Box 41 19939
(302) 732-6304

Owner: Kathy Lewis Est: 2008
1800 sq.ft. 2000+ bolts Email Newsletter
www.serendipityquiltshop.com

100% cotton, flannel, washed wool, notions, latest books & patterns, many classes, plus block-of-the-month programs.

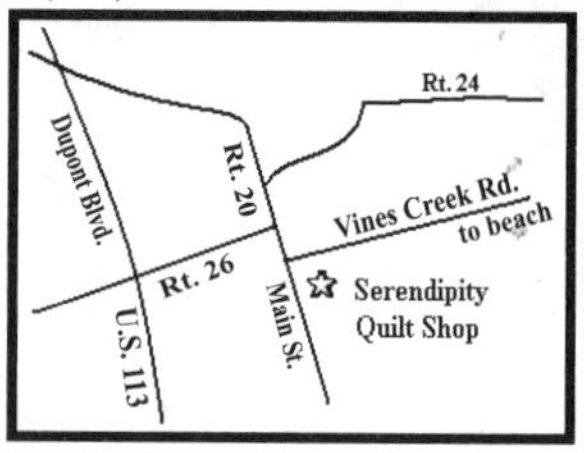

Delaware Quilt Shops

Dagsboro **Serendipity Quilt Shop, 33119 Main St.**
302-732-6304 **See ad #6, this page**

Dover **Shady Lane Selections, 1121 Victory Chapel Rd.**
no phone **See ad #5, this page**

Dover Rose Valley Quilt Shop, 280 Rose Valley School Rd.
Dover Chicks -n- Stitches, 1151 E. Lebanon Rd. #F 302-535-8438
Dover Delaware Sewing Center, 1716 S. Governors Ave. 302-697-2445

Lewes **Mare's Bears Quilt Shop, 528 E. Savannah Rd.**
302-644-0556 **See ad #4, page 97**

Middletown **Lil' Country Shoppe, 551 Boyds Corner Rd.**
302-378-5568 **See ad #3, page 97**

Newark **Quilter's Hive, 1800 Capitol Tr., Ste. 2**
302-737-5699 **See ad #1, page 97**

Wilmington **Hayes Sewing Machine Co., 4425 Concord Pike**
302-764-9033 **See ad #2, page 97**

Delaware Quilt Shows

About Shows: We are listing only the very basic information about shows that happen on a regular schedule here. Please check out our website for more details on each show. Also this information tends to change quite often so please verify the event with our website or a local source before you venture far. Or if you're in the right area at the right time, give it a shot.

If you are a show organizer, please keep us updated on your event.
shows@quilterstravelcompanion.com www.quilterstravelcompanion.com

On our website you will also find:
- Exact dates (when we have them)
- Contact Information
- Events happening on a one-time basis
- Sponsor Information
- Description of Event

Month	City	Schedule	Show	Location with address
September				
	Middletown	Annual, last Saturday in September	Backyard Quilt Show	Lil' Country Shoppe, 551 Boyds Corner Rd.
October				
	Milford	Odd Years, 3rd weekend in October	Kent Sussex Quilt Show	Milford Senior Center, 111 Park Ave.

District of Columbia Quilt Shops

Washington Appalachian Spring, 1415 Wisconsin Ave. NW 202-337-5780
Washington Appalachian Spring, 50 Massachusetts Ave. NE 202-682-0505

District of Columbia Quilt Shows

We don't know of any shows in the District of Columbia.
Please submit any shows you may know of, thanks.

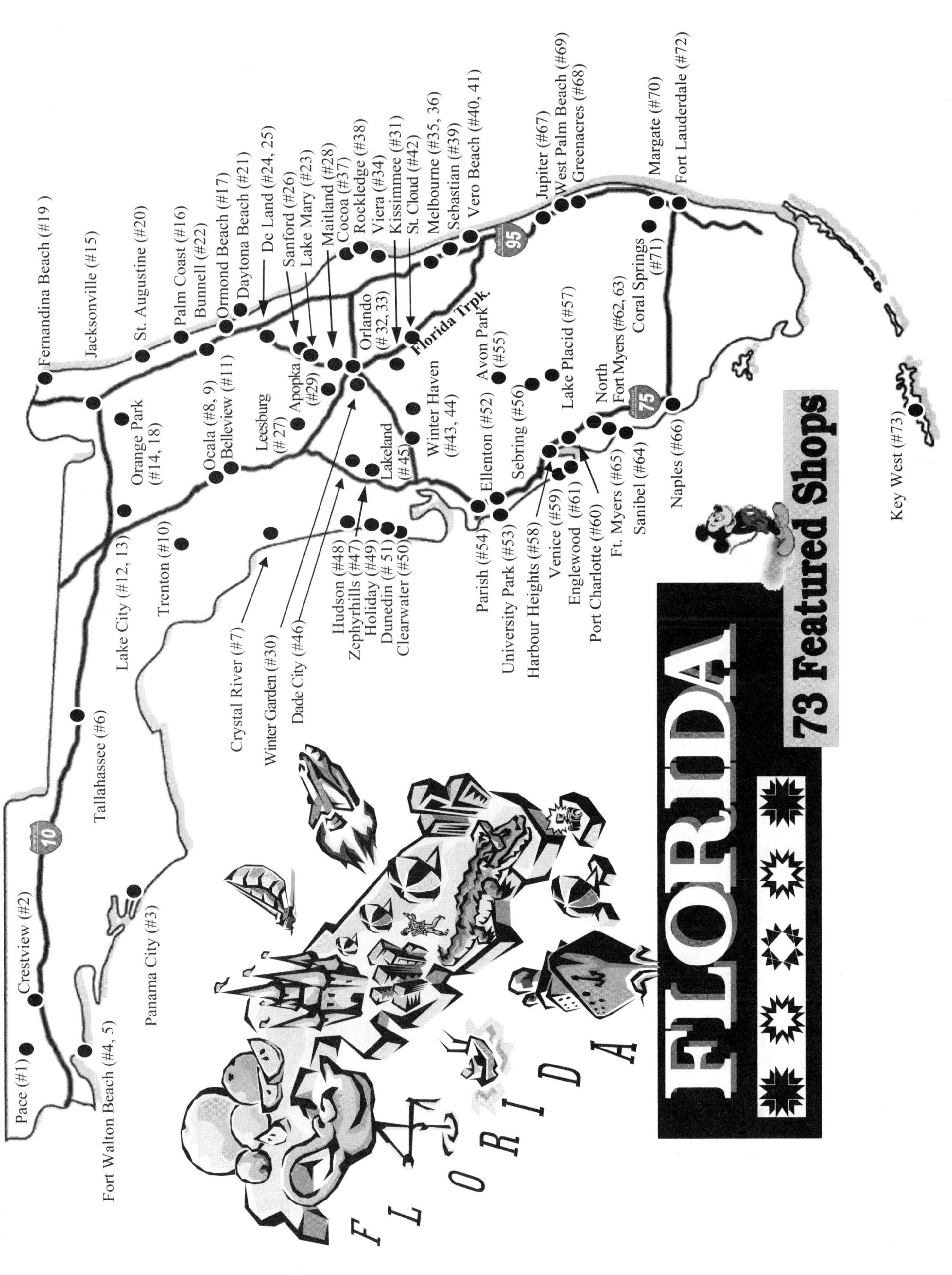
Pace (#1)
Crestview (#2)
Fort Walton Beach (#4, 5)
Panama City (#3)
10
Tallahassee (#6)
Lake City (#12, 13)
Trenton (#10)
Fernandina Beach (#19)
Jacksonville (#15)
Orange Park (#14, 18)
St. Augustine (#20)
Palm Coast (#16)
Bunnell (#22)
Ormond Beach (#17)
Daytona Beach (#21)
Ocala (#8, 9)
Belleview (#11)
Leesburg (#27)
Crystal River (#7)
Winter Garden (#30)
Dade City (#46)
De Land (#24, 25)
Sanford (#26)
Lake Mary (#23)
Maitland (#28)
Apopka (#29)
Cocoa (#37)
Rockledge (#38)
Viera (#34)
Kissimmee (#31)
St. Cloud (#42)
Orlando (#32, 33)
Florida Trpk.
Melbourne (#35, 36)
Sebastian (#39)
Vero Beach (#40, 41)
95
Winter Haven (#43, 44)
Lakeland (#45)
Hudson (#48)
Zephyrhills (#47)
Holiday (#49)
Dunedin (# 51)
Clearwater (#50)
Ellenton (#52)
Parish (#54)
University Park (#53)
Harbour Heights (#58)
Avon Park (#55)
Sebring (#56)
Lake Placid (#57)
Venice (#59)
Englewood (#61)
Port Charlotte (#60)
North Fort Myers (#62, 63)
Ft. Myers (#65)
Sanibel (#64)
75
Naples (#66)
Jupiter (#67)
West Palm Beach (#69)
Greenacres (#68)
Coral Springs (#71)
Margate (#70)
Fort Lauderdale (#72)
Key West (#73)
FLORIDA
FLORIDA
73 Featured Shops

Pace, FL #1

The Quilting Station

Mon - Fri 9:30 - 5
Thurs til 6
Sat 9 - 5

4507 Chumuckla Hwy. 32571
(850) 994-1610 Phone/Fax
quiltingstation@bellsouth.net
Est: 2003 2500 sq.ft. 3000 Bolts
www.quiltingstation.com

Specialized in batiks and brights. Quilting supplies, thread, books, patterns, kits, classes (kids too!). ***Come on in and have fun.***

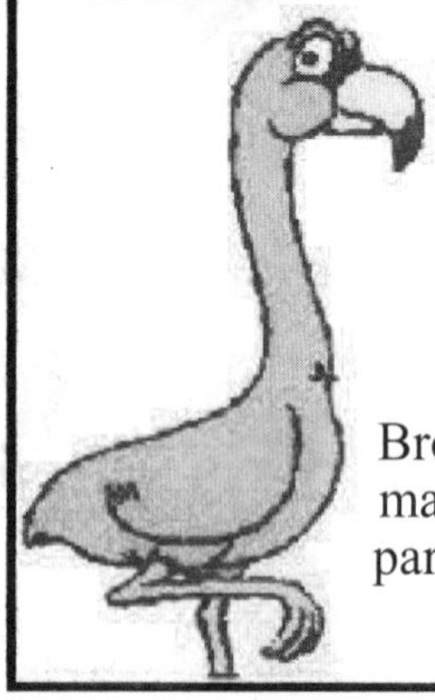

Brother sewing machine dealer parts & service.

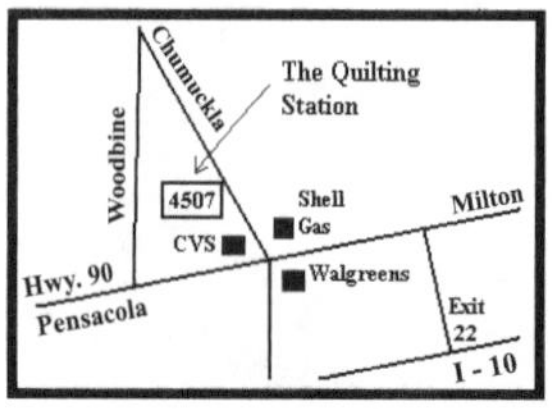

Margie's

Sew Much Fun

Since 1971

Bernina

Janome

2014 Lacey Ln. 32536
866-739-6274 (Toll Free)
(850) 682-6920
(850) 689-3655
www.margiessewmuchfun.com

Largest Independent Fabric Shop in Florida's Panhandle. Classes for all interests (garments to quilting) Fabrics include Bridal, Party, Children, Knits, Quilt etc. Over 3400 bolts of fabric, over 700 books, & quilting supplies.

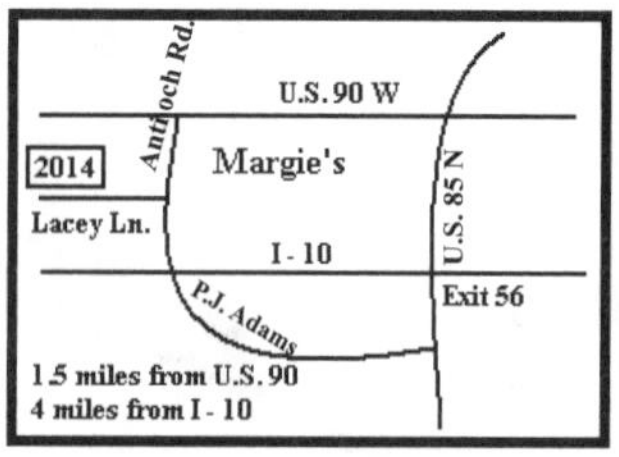

Mon - Sat 9am - 6pm

Crestview, FL #2

Panama City, FL #3

Quilting by the Bay

Quilt · Sew · Create

www.quiltingbythebay.com

Friendly knowledgeable staff
Block of the Month programs
Quilting supplies and kits
Over 4000 bolts of fabric
10,000+ Fat Quarters

2303 Winona Drive, Panama City, FL 32405
866-632-QBTB(7282)

Monday through Friday
10:00 am to 5:00 pm
Saturday 10:00 am to 4:00 pm

Better Homes Quilt Sampler Featured Shop

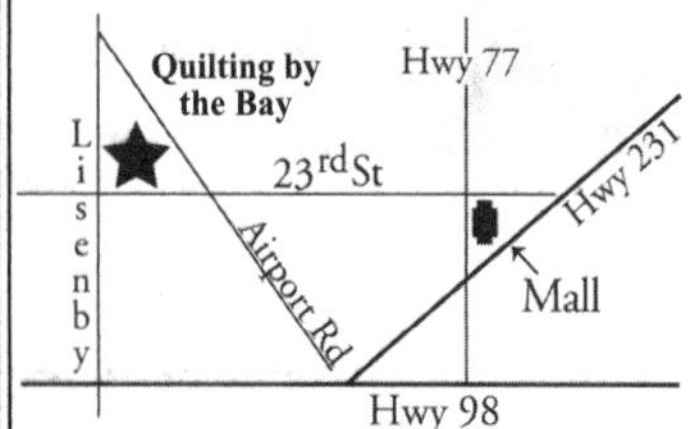

- Just north of 23rd Street between Airport and Lisenby
- 3 miles E of Hathaway Bridge
- 3 miles W of Panama City Mall

Fort Walton Beach, FL #4

Mon - Fri 10 - 5:30
Sat 10 - 4

745 N. Beal Pkwy. #4 32547
(850) 864-4555
Owners: Lynn & Travis Griffith

Lynn's SEWING CENTER

lynnsewing@earthlink.net
www.lynnsewing.com
We are not just a sewing store, we are a sewing boutique. We sell BERNINA Sewing Machines, TinLizzie18, Happy Embroidery Machines and quilting and smocking supplies.

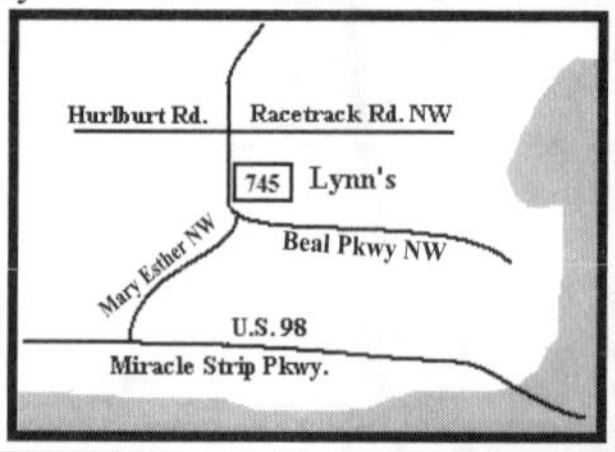

Fort Walton Beach, FL #5

Tues - Fri 9:30 - 6
Sat 9 - 3

The Sewing Center Around the Block

913 N. Beal Pkwy. #F 32547
(850) 243-8261 Fax: Same
Est: 1998 2600 sq.ft. 2400 bolts
Online newsletter
1000's of bolts of fabric.
Clubs and Classes.
We offer a wide variety of services from selling and servicing sewing machines and vacuums to custom long arm quilting to complete your quilt tops.
info@sewitbetter.com
www.aroundtheblockquilting.com

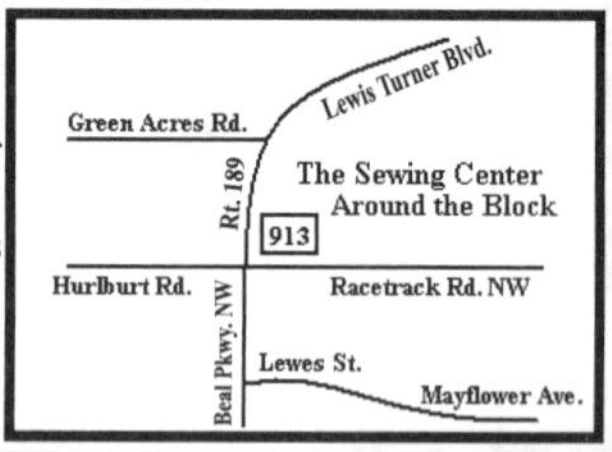

Tallahassee, FL #6

Mon - Fri 10 - 5:30
Sat 10 - 4

1400 Village Sq. Blvd. #4 32309
(850) 386-7697
Owners: Lynn & Travis Griffith

Lynn's SEWING CENTER

lynnsewing@earthlink.net
www.lynnsewing.com
We are not just a sewing store, we are a sewing boutique. We sell BERNINA Sewing Machines, TinLizzie18, Happy Embroidery Machines and quilting and smocking supplies.

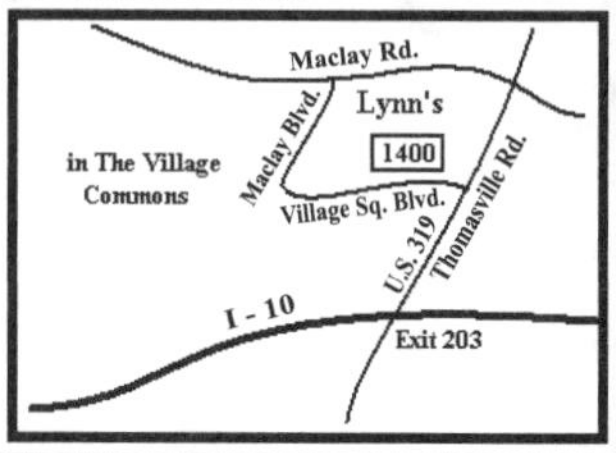

Tomorrow's Treasures Quilt Shop

Two locations to serve you!

www.crquilts.com

Authorized BERNINA Sales and Service

802 N. Suncoast Blvd.
Crystal River, FL 34429
(352) 795-2600
ttcrs@embarqmail.com

Mon - Sat 9 - 4
Tues 9 - 6

Crystal River, FL #7

Huge Classroom. We Love Helping You Choose Fabric! Distinctive Designs, Original Patterns, Kits, Notions & books. Large Selection of Stencils. Mail Order. 4000 Bolts of the Finest 100% Cotton Quilting Fabrics. Horn Cabinets.

HandiQuilter with Pro Stitcher

6126 SW Hwy. 200
Ocala, FL 34476
(352) 690-1915
ttocala@embarqmail.com

Mon 9 - 6
Tues - Sat 9 - 4

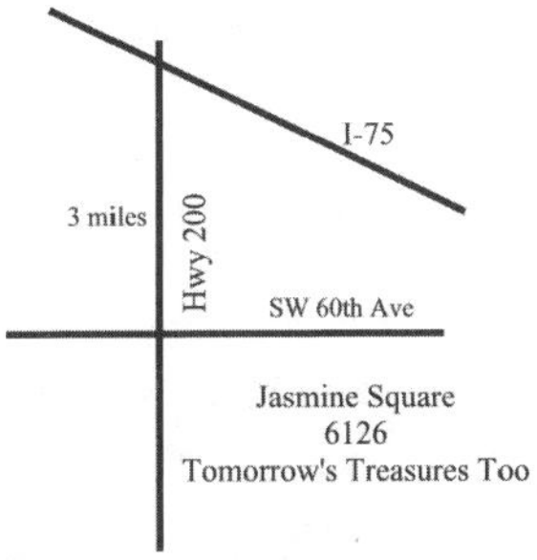

Ocala, FL #8

Innovative Classes and Clubs. Warm Personal Service. Inspirational Samples and Kits. Unusual Notions and Gadgets. Mail Order. Over 2000 Bolts of Quality Designer Fabrics.

Happy Voyager Commercial Embroidery Machine

Ocala, FL #9

Peggy's Heirlooms of Tomorrow, Inc.

Created Today. Cherished Forever

4414 SW SR 200 #1510
Visit us in our new 3200 sq.ft location at "Market Street", beside Panara Bread

www.heirloomsoftomorrow.com
(352) 351-8282 Owner, Peggy Vogt
peggy@heirloomsoftomorrow.com

Mon - Sat
10 - 6

Peggy and The Girls invite you to come in as a customer and leave as a friend! Fabric, Notions, Books, Patterns, Heirloom Supplies, Shiva Paints, Hot Ribbon Appliqué, and Copic Painting Supplies. "Premier Handi Quilter Shop" Featuring a complete line of Handi Quilter Machines and accessories.

Handi Quilter

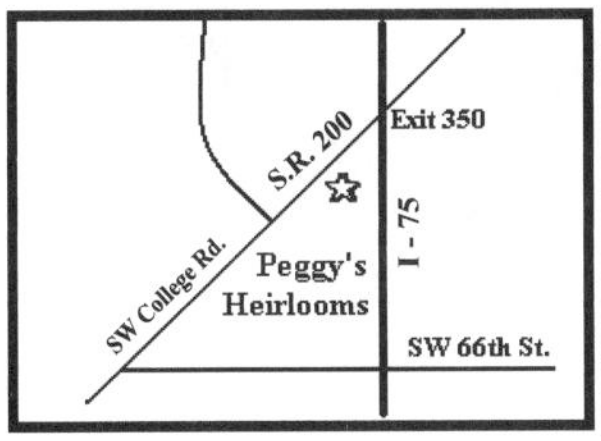

1/2 mile west of I-75, exit 350

Suwannee Valley Quilt Shoppe

517 N Main Street, Trenton, FL (352) 463-3842

Florida's Most Unique Quilt Shop & Antique Village

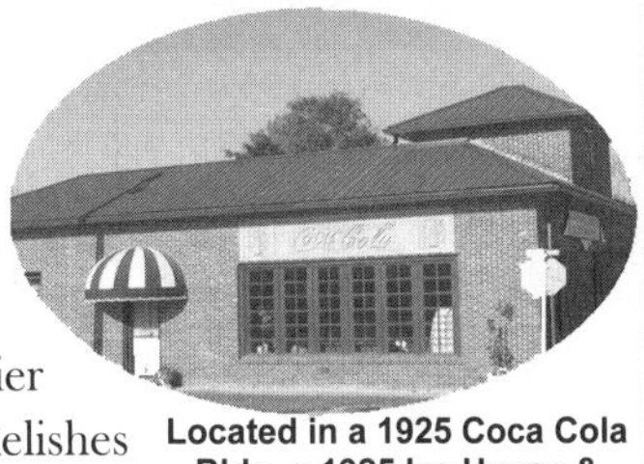

- Fabric & Classes
- Books & Supplies
- Machine Quilting
- Stained Glass
- Cross Stitch
- Antiques
- Framing
- Chocolatier
- Jams & Relishes
- Hair Salon

Located in a 1925 Coca Cola Bldg, a 1925 Ice House & a 1910 Dry Goods Store

Visit our Suwannee Rose Café
For lunch & pastries homemade daily

Open Mon - Sat
10 to 5

Home to over 6000 bolts of fabric plus an extensive selection of quilt supplies & books.

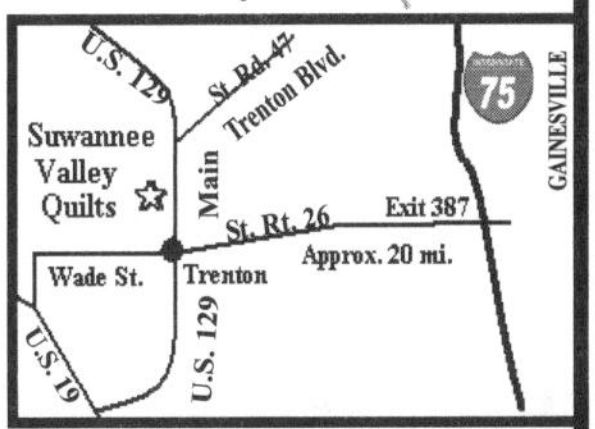

#10

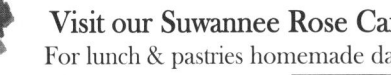

www.suwanneeshops.com

Belleview, FL #11

Mon - Sat 10 - 5

Whippoorwill Station

7655 SE 126th Place #3 34420
(352) 347-9400 Fax: (352) 307-0615
3000 sq.ft. Newsletter
whippoorwillsta@aol.com
www.whippoorwillstation.biz
Visit us on Facebook.
We are a full service quilt shop with a friendly and helpful staff.

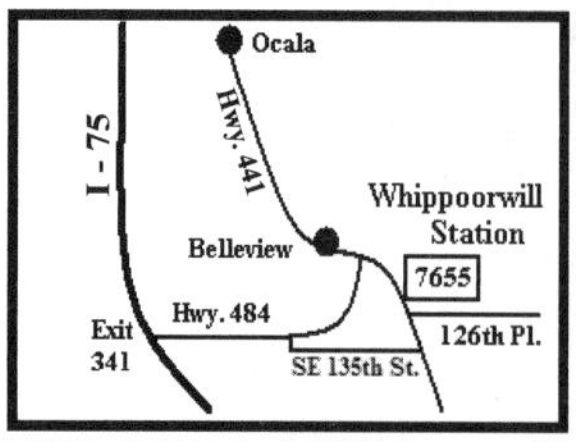

Lake City, FL #12

Mon - Fri 10 - 5:30
Sat 10 - 4

AmyGene's Quilt Store

218 N. Marion Ave. 32055
(386) 754-3741 Fax: (386) 754-3743
Est: 2007 2000 sq.ft. Newsletter
amygenes@bellsouth.net
www.amygenes.com
Your source for quilting fabric from well know sources. We also carry supplies, patterns, Gutterman threads and books as well as notions. Husqvarna Viking dealer. Voted 2009 best fabric store!

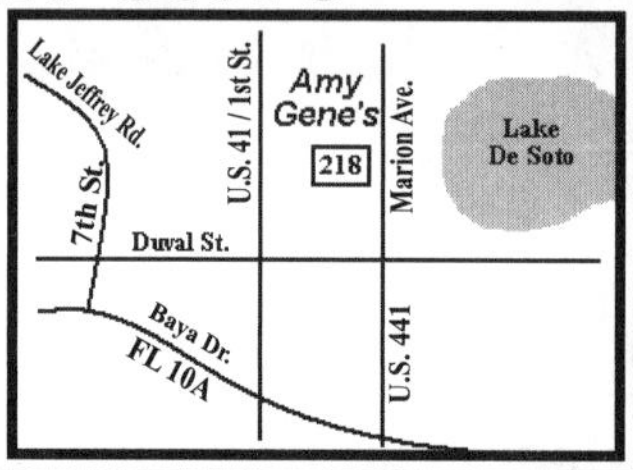

FABRIC ART SHOP

Open 7 days:
Mon-Sat 10-6
Sun 1-5

A specialty fiber art store to provide you with items to make your most wonderful creations!

Over 3500 bolts of quality fabrics, Specialty books, tools, threads; Large variety of embellishments; Unique gifts, art supplies, education in the shop and on the road.

Lake City, FL #13

Distributor of EASY GLIDE CREATOR, PENNYWINKLE PROFESSIONAL & SUNSHINE 16 quilting machines. Also distributing EASY GLIDE Tools, Roll'n Glide, Quacker Glides, MicroStitch and JANOME products.

QUACKER GLIDES

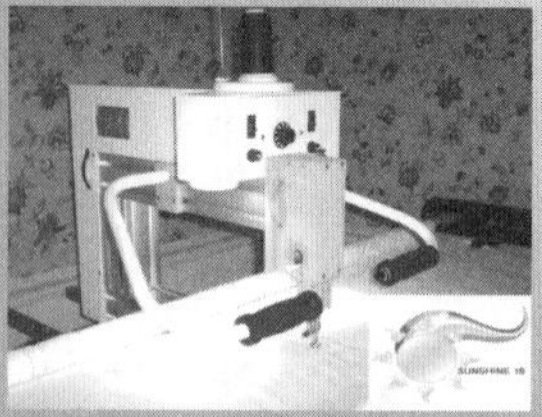

Barbie@fabricartshop.com
Phone: 386-755-0179
Tollfree: 877-755-0179
Fax: 386-755-8530
www.fabricartshop.com

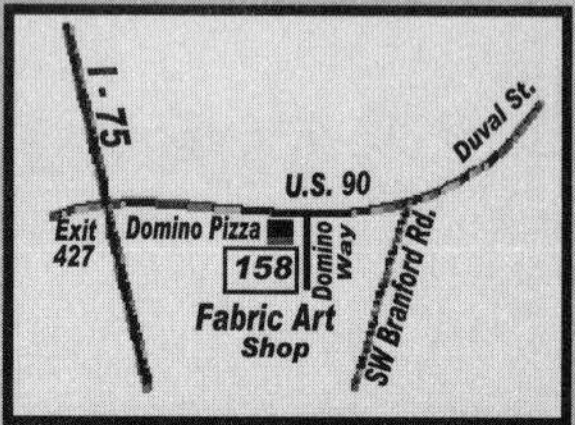

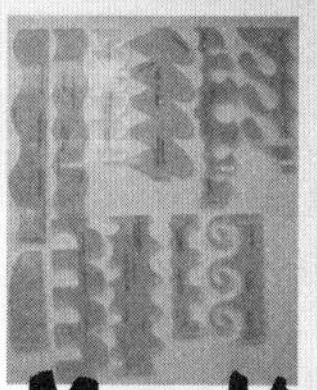

FABRIC ART SHOP
158 SW Domino Way
Lake City, FL 32025

THE FIRST QUILT SHOP IN NORTH FLORIDA OFF I-75, EXIT 427, east 7/10 mile on US 90, turn right at Domino's Pizza, purple building on right.

May You Be Moved to Create!

Orange Park, Fl #14

Authorized Bernina Dealer

Over 2500 bolts of premium
100% cotton fabric
Patterns, books, kits, thread
Long Arm quilting machine

calicostationinc@bellsouth.net

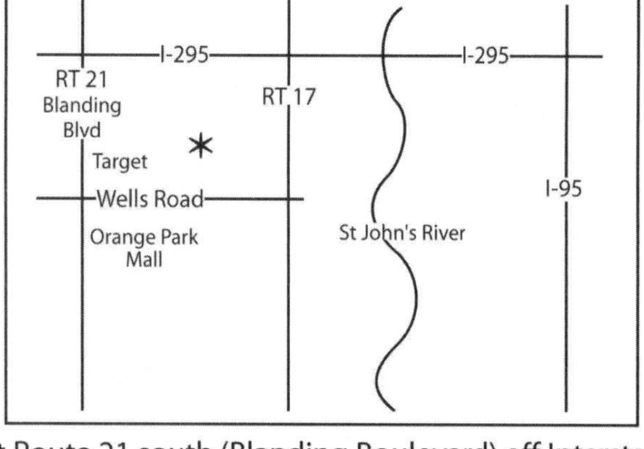

Exit Route 21 south (Blanding Boulevard) off Interstate 295 turn left on Wells Road, turn left at second light

1857 Wells Road Orange Park, Florida 32073

Sharing a passion for
Calico Station
Quilt shop est. 1980
fabric, friends & FUN!

www.calicostation.com 1-904-269-6911

Monday-Thursday	9:00-6:00
Friday	9:00-5:00
Saturday	10:00-4:00

The Olde Green Cupboard

10950-26 San Jose Blvd., Jacksonville, FL 32223 (904) 880-6656 Mon - Sat 10 - 6

Picked as one of the TOP 10 Quilt Shops to visit by

American Patchwork Quilting in September 2004 Issue & Top 20 in 2007

★Full Service Quilt Shop	★Quilting Classes	★ 4000 + Bolts of Fabric
★Longarm Quilting	★Furniture	★Moda
★Home Decor	★ Cross-Stitch	★Primitives
★Antiques	★10,000 Sq. Ft	★ Batiks
★One-of-a-Kind Items	★Samples Galore!	★Books, Patterns, Notions
★Homespuns	★Reproduction Fabric	★Florals

I-295 to San Jose Blvd South. First shopping center on your right across the street from Wal-Mart.

Jacksonville, FL #15

If you're coming to visit from out-of-town.... call ahead and we'll put on a fresh pot of coffee!

A QUILTSHOP YOU'LL NEVER FORGET!

www.oldegreencupboard.com

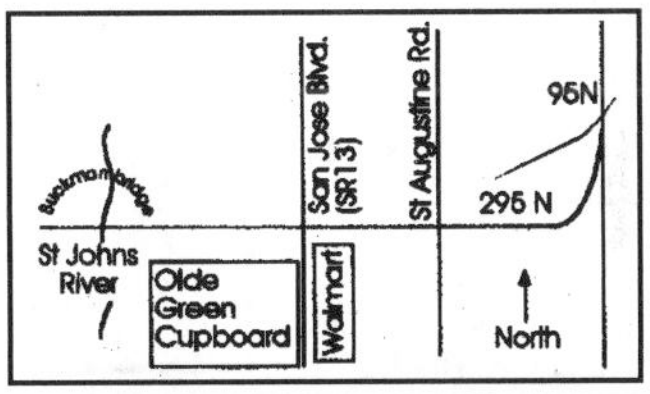

Byrd's Nest Quilt Shop & PFAFF Sewing Center

Ormond Beach, FL #17 & Palm Coast, FL #16

2 Locations to Serve You

- Over 5000 bolts of fabric
- Batiks—Over 500 bolts
- Books, Patterns & Kits
- Quilting Classes & Clubs
- PFAFF/Babylock Sewing/Embroidery Machines
- PFAFF/Babylock Sergers
- Long-arm Gammill Rental
- We appreciate your business & will treat you as so!

Owner: Kathy Byrd
Both Locations: Mon thru Sat 10 - 5

156 E. Granada Blvd
Ormond Beach, FL 32176
(386) 615-8789
Large classroom, busses welcome.
Located just 5 miles east of I-95
Or 2 blocks west of AIA on Highway 40.
Across from Outback Steakhouse.

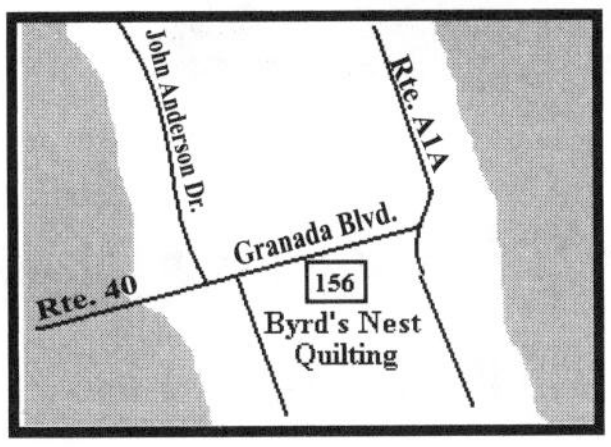

160 Cypress Point Pkwy.
Unit A 108
Palm Coast, FL 32164
(386) 447-1103

2 minutes from I-95
Next to Steak 'n Shake
off the Palm Coast Pkwy NW

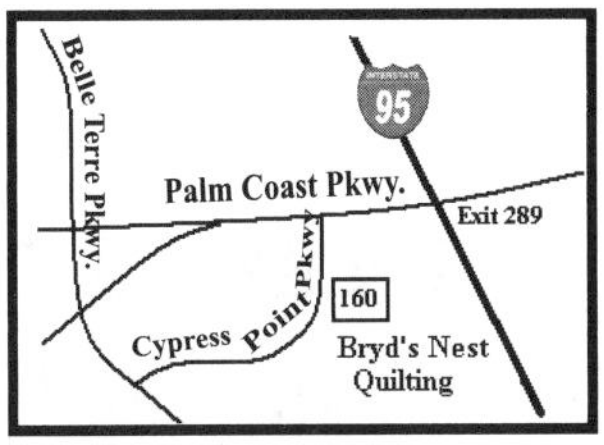

byrdsnestquilt@bellsouth.net **www.byrdsnestquiltshop.com**

Orange Park, FL #18

Mon - Fri 10 - 5
Sat 10 - 4

Country Crossroads

799-3 Blanding Blvd. 32065
(904) 276-1011
TheMice@CountryCrossroad.com
www.CountryCrossroad.com
Owners: Bob & Lynn Provencher
Est: 1988 2400 sq.ft. 1000+ Bolts
"Customer Friendly" offering custom long-arm quilting, books, patterns, notions, classes. 100% cotton fabrics with emphasis on brights and novelty.

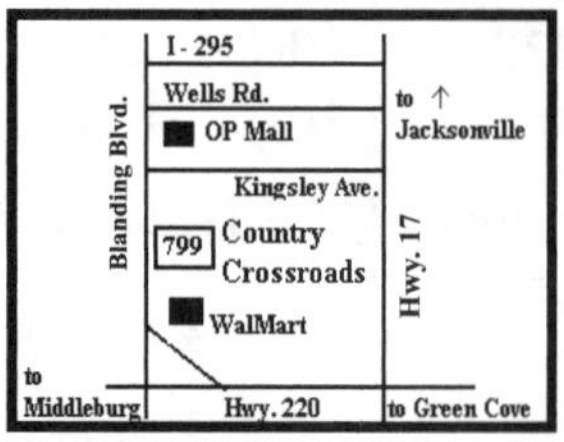

Fernandina Beach, FL #19

Mon - Fri 10 - 5
Sat 10 - 4

Jan's Quilt -n- Stitch

474388 East SR 200 (A1A) 32034
(904) 310-6735
billjan599@cs.com

Large selection of fabric, books and notions.

baby lock FOR THE LOVE OF SEWING
Sales & Service.

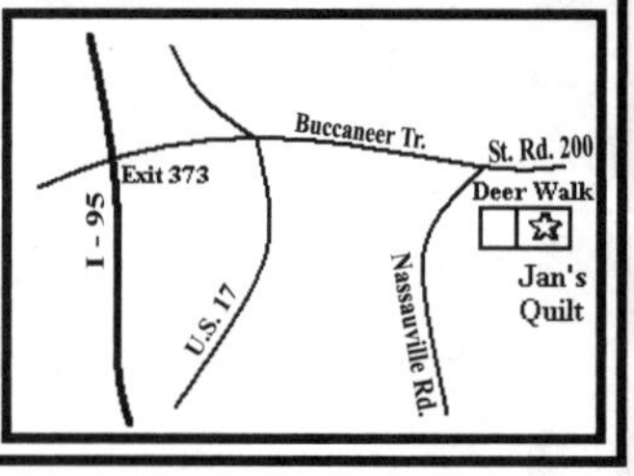

St. Augustine, FL #20

Mon - Sat 10 - 5:30

MAGRIETA'S QUILT SHOP

142 C King St. 32084
(904) 829-3137 Fax (904) 819-9250
Owner: Magrieta Hanekom
Est: 2007 2400 sq.ft. Online Newsletter
magrieta@customquilting.net
www.magrietasquiltshop.com
"The Big Little Shop!"
Quilting Classes, Lots of Batiks, Notions, Kits, Samples, Patterns, & Books.

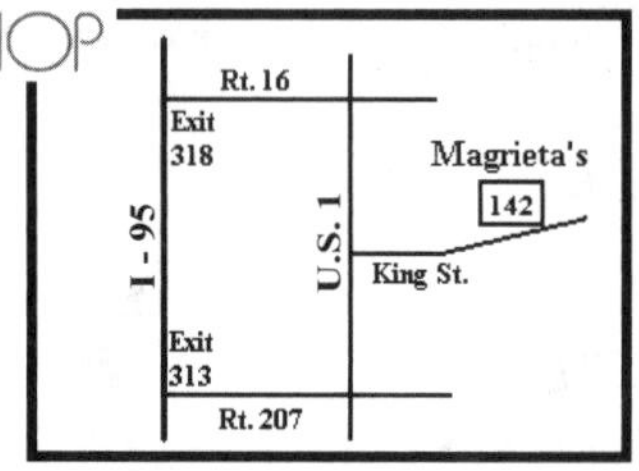

Daytona Beach, FL #21

Mon - Fri 9 - 5:30
Sat 9 - 4

The Sewing Garret

Sewing Machine Sales and fabric shop.
949 Beville Rd., Bldg. #2 32119
(386) 767-3545
Est: 2001 4000 sq.ft. Newsletter Online
thesewinggarret@bellsouth.net
www.sewinggarret.com
Cottons, silks, laces, patterns, kits and loads of samples.
Babylock, Elna, Janome & Brother dealer.
"We're all about knowing when it comes to sewing!"

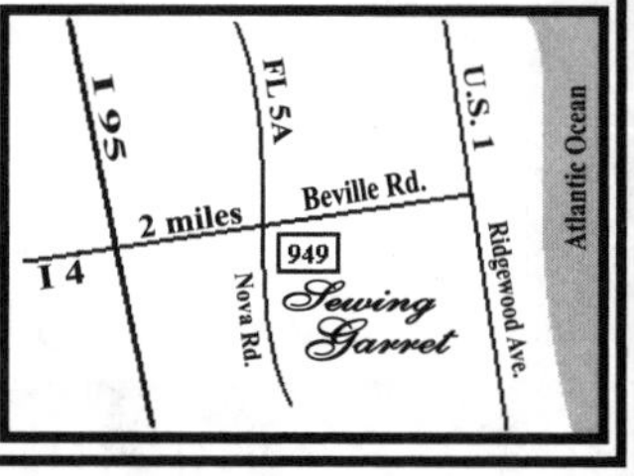

Sew & Quilt Shop

Proud to offer Quality Products, Classes & Services
Quilting, Sewing, & Knitting Supplies

BERNINA Happy brother at your side Gammill QUILTING SYSTEMS

Bernina ... The most technologically advanced sewing machines.
Brother ... Exclusive Licensee of "Project Runway" Season Seven.
Gammill ... Your Quilting Partner meeting all of your longarm needs.
Happy HSC Voyager ... The ultimate high yield embroidery machine.

Bunnell, FL #22

Stop by & join the fun; your creativity is limited only by your imagination!

Exit 284 off I-95—Just 2 miles west on left—Marvin's Garden Business Center

4601 E. Hwy 100, Bunnell, FL 32110 (877) 586-5409 M-Sat 10-5 (Wed eve till 8)

www.sewandquiltshop.com

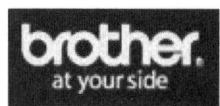

The "must see" shop in Central Florida

Bernina
SEWING CENTRE

sewithappens.com Est: 1997

Over 5000 square feet of inspiration!
Beautiful fabric selection!
Books, patterns and notions!

Lake Mary, FL #23

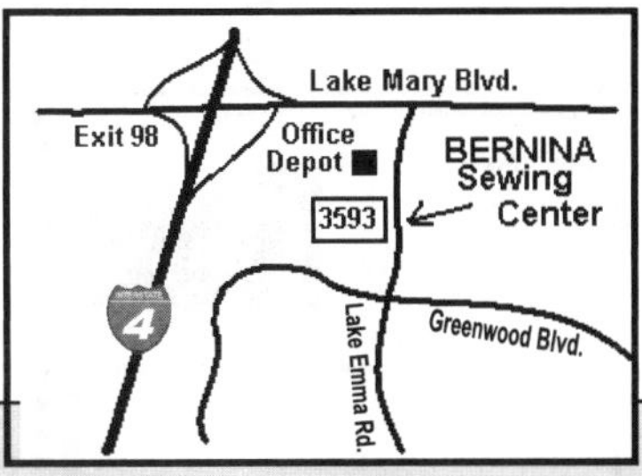

Embroidery online.com | Handi Quilter | TinLizzie18 | Loralie Designs — Touching the heart with fun art! | accuquilt GO! fabric cutters

Mon, Wed, Fri 9:30 -6
Tues & Thurs 9:30 - 8
Sat 9:30 - 4
Sun 12 - 4

3593 Lake Emma Rd. 32746
407-805-9300
Owners: Melody & Steve Hicks
2500+ Bolts Online Newsletter
melsews@aol.com

Quilt Shop of DeLand, Inc.

115 W. Rich Ave.
DeLand, FL 32720
866-734-8782 or
386-734-8782
Owner: Judy Hansen
Est: 2001
quiltshopofdeland
@hotmail.com

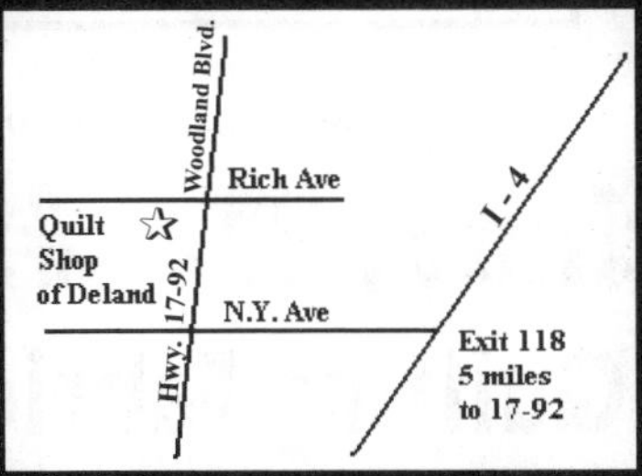

- **Featuring over 4000 bolts--huge variety-BATIKS, ORIENTALS, FLORALS, CIVIL WAR, AND 30'S, BEAUTIFUL HOLIDAY PRINTS YEAR AROUND.**
- **50% Sale Section too!**
- **Newest PATTERNS & BOOKS on the market.**
- **4 Shop Hops a year.**
- **Pick up your autographed copy of Judy's Books and Patterns.**

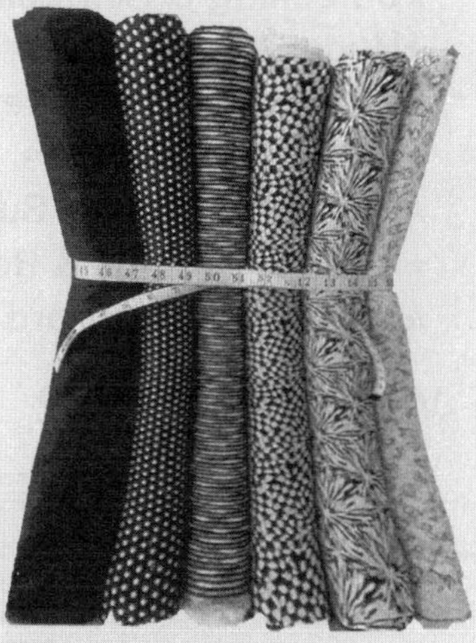

Books by Judy Hansen

Mon - Sat 10 - 5

NOW SHOP ONLINE!
www.quiltshopofdeland.com

DeLand, FL #24

Beautiful, Historic Downtown DeLand - Just 45 minutes north of Disney World and 30 minutes southwest of Daytona Beach! Visit us soon!

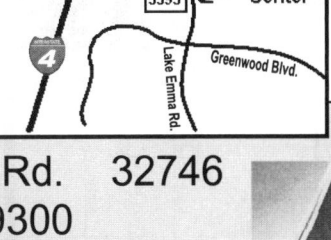

DeLand, FL #25

By Appt. Only
Phone or e-mail

Lake Nanu's Quilted Rooster

Gammill Statler Stitcher
Long Arm Quilting Service
Est: 1999 Pet & Smoke free
lakenanu@cfl.rr.com
www.lakenanusquiltedrooster.com
(386) 717-8645 Fax: (386) 736-4822
Crib to King. We have batting.
Edge to Edge pano's 1¢ per inch
Visa Discover Master Card Accepted
Send via: UPS - US Mail - FedEx Fast Turn Around

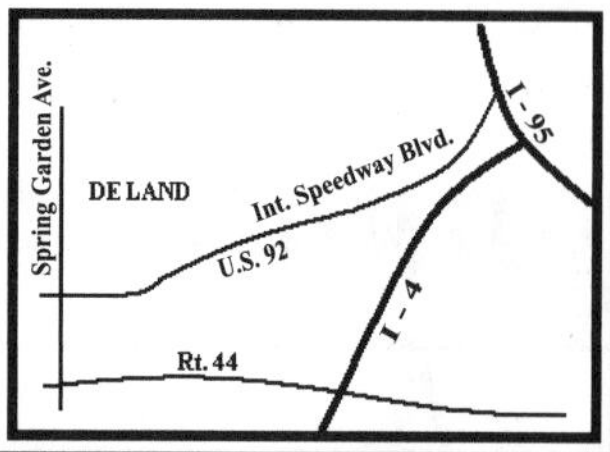

Sanford, FL #26

Mon - Sat
10 - 6

Fireside Quilts

1301 S. Park Ave.
32771
(407) 322-0065

& Gifts & Quilting Retreats
& Harts Sisters Tea Room

Owners: Kenda & Scott Race
kenda@firesidequilts.com
www.firesidequilts.com
1500 to 2000 bolts
Classes: Day and Evening, and Saturdays
We carry books, notions, patterns, and kits.

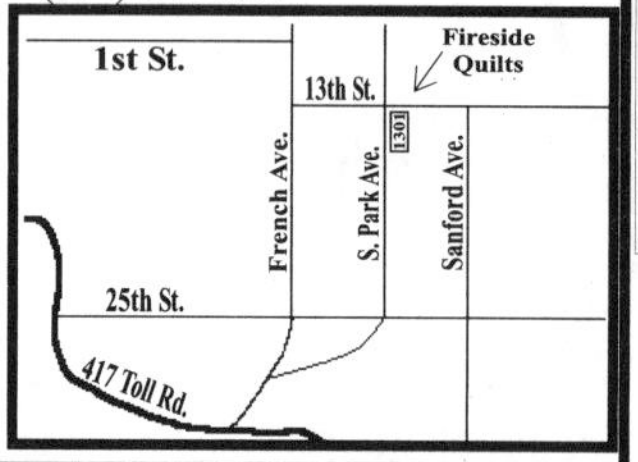

A QUILTER'S DREAM

Leesburg, FL #27

Mon - Fri
9 - 5
Sat 9 - 2

Great Fabrics from Hoffman, Timeless Treasures, P&B, Benartex and more.
We participate in 3 shop hops each year!
"Always a friendly Smile"

719 W. Main St. 34748
(352) 728-1482
Owner: Connie Czernuch
Est: 2002
aqd@embarqmail.com

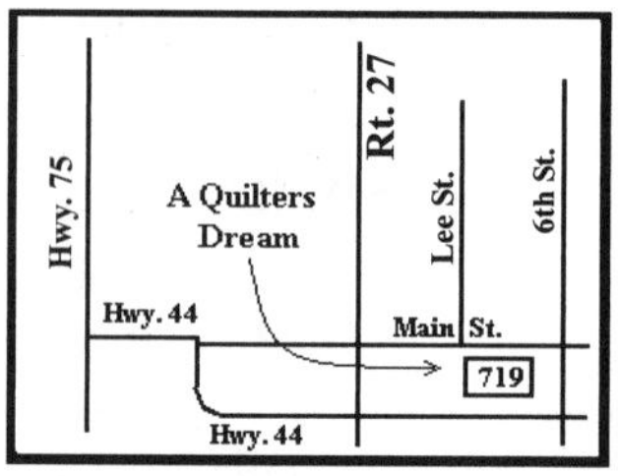

www.aquiltersdream.biz

★Full Quilting Dept.: Fabrics, Patterns, and Books
★Full Line of Quilting and Sewing Notions
★Smocking & Heirloom: Fabrics, Patterns and Plates
★Huge Selection of Bridal & Evening Wear Fabrics
★Lycra, Spandex, Stretch Velvets, Crushed Velvets
★Silks, Linens, Trims, Notions
★Buttons, Buttons, Buttons
★Drapery Fabrics & Home Décor Trims
★We have many 'Hard to Find' Items!

Mon - Fri 9:00 - 8:30
Sat 9:00 - 5:30 Sun 12 - 5

Koala studios

baby lock
FOR THE LOVE OF SEWING

BabyLock Sewing Machines Sales and Service

Visiting Orlando ? Don't miss - - -

Sewing Studio
Fabric Superstore

1/4 mile North of Maitland Blvd.
Overpass on Hwy. 17-92

9605 S. Hwy. 17-92, Maitland, FL 32751
800-831-1492 407-831-6488
www.sewing.net

Maitland, FL #28

Central Florida's Largest Selection of Quilting Fabrics

Apopka, FL #29

Mon - Fri 10 - 6 Sat 9 - 4

Apopka Quilt Company

74A Semoran Commerce Pl. #102 32703
(407) 889-0077 Est: 2006
Owner: Barbara McCauley 2000+ Bolts
info@apopkaquilts.com Newsletter
www.apopkaquilts.com
"Full Service Quilt Shop"
PATTERNS - FABRIC - NOTIONS
CLASSES - LONG ARM

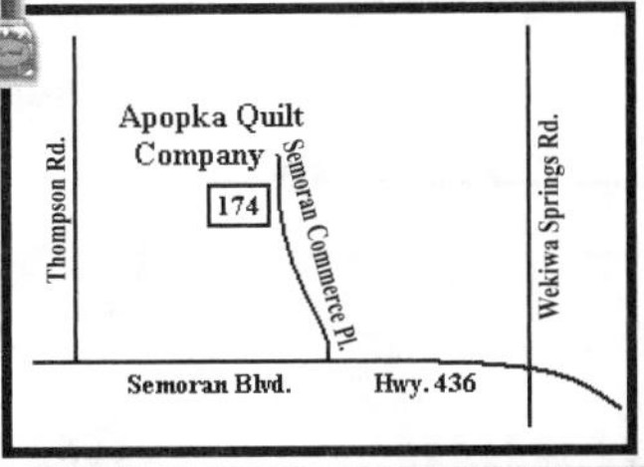

Kissimmee, FL #31

Mon - Sat 10 - 6

Queen Ann's Lace

305 Broadway Ave. 34741
(407) 846-7998
Owner: Pat Gilreath
Authorized Bernina Dealer
Est: 1991 3000 sq.ft.
Newsletter/Sales: www.queenannslace.com
Fine 100% cotton fabrics, quilting books, patterns, notions & classes for all your needs. Located closest to Disney World in Historic Downtown Kissimmee

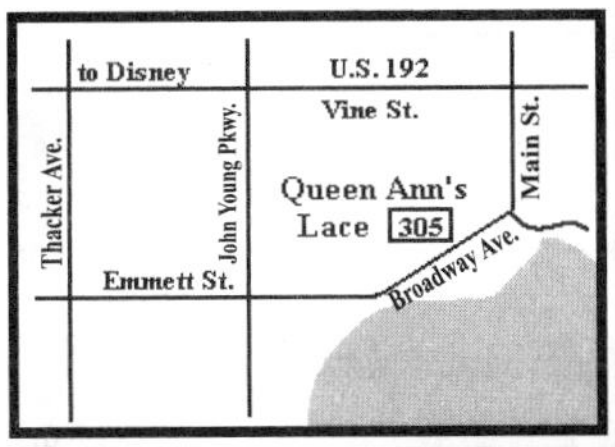

Orlando, FL #32

Mon - Fri 10 - 6 Tues & Thur til 9 Sat 10 - 4 Sun 12 - 4

Quilter's Cove of Central FL

2500 Curry Ford Rd. 32806
(407) 894-8333
Owner: Denise DiVittorio
www.QuiltersCoveofCFL.com

Orlando's Friendliest Quilt Shop.
Lots of Novelty Fabrics and a large selection of patterns & books.
Easy to get to from the attractions.

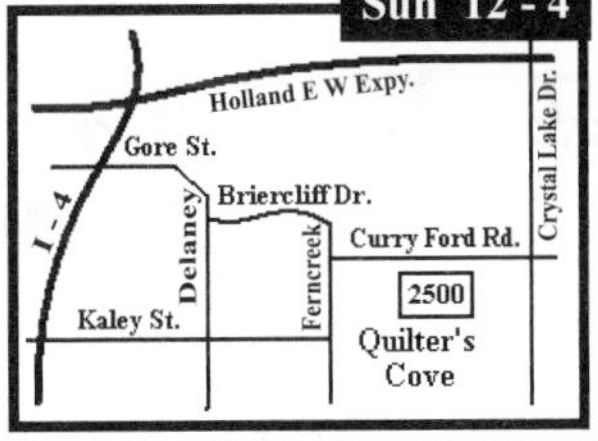

My Quilt Shack

5575 Schenck Ave, Ste 7
Viera FL 32955
Phone: 321-433-1948
Fax: 321-433-1971

JANOME Authorized Dealer

Books ~ Patterns
Notions ~ Classes
Thread ~ Fabric

Email: email@myquiltshack.com
Web: www.myquiltshack.com

Viera, FL #34

Winter Garden, FL #30

Nancy's Quilt Shop

Mon - Fri 10 - 4 Sat 10 - 2

Inside
Carter Family Bowl
(use single door entrance)

Authorized Janome Dealer
We carry all supplies for the Janome Machines. Machine, computer digitizer and quilting classes.

Free-hand or computer quilting on any size quilt. Quilting done on a millennium long-arm machine: quick turn around.

We carry all the brand name quilting fabrics and have over 2500 bolts in stock. Books, patterns and basic sewing supplies too!

715 S. Dillard St. 34787
407-905-8879
Fax: 407-656-1422
Owner: Nancy Carter
nanccarter@aol.com

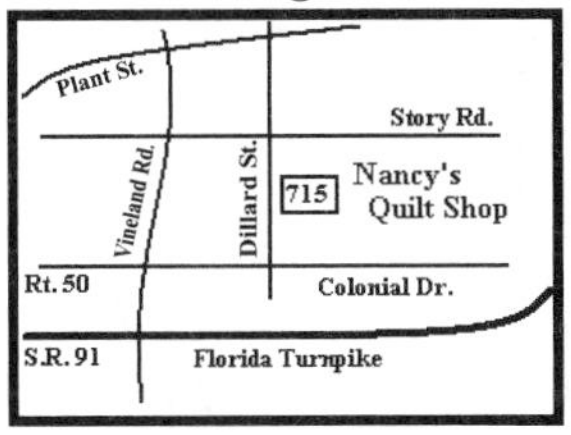

www.quiltingbynancy.com

Orlando, FL #33

Mon - Fri 10 - 6 Sat 10 - 3

Cornerstone Quilt Shop, Inc.

5953 E. Colonial Dr., Suite 2 32807
(407) 207-6500 Fax: (407) 207-6444
Est: 2005 2200 sq. ft.
cornerstonequilt@cfl.rr.com
www.Cornerstonequiltshop.net

Featuring the Gammill Statler Stitcher for Quilting Services, Notions, Books, Quality Fabrics and More.

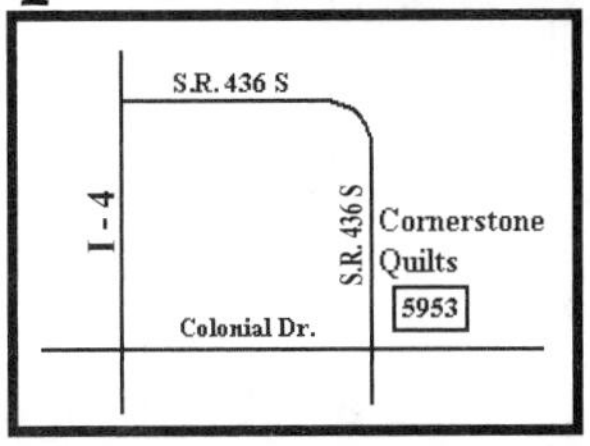

Melbourne, FL #35

Mon - Fri 9:30 - 5 Wed til 7 Sat 9:30 - 4

Boutique 4 Quilters

2945 W. New Haven Ave. 32904
(321) 768-2060 Fax: (321) 768-0065
Owner: Anita Kelly
Est: 2005 2500 sq.ft.
4quilters@bellsouth.net

A shop with a Scandinavian ambiance. Large selection of Kaffe Fasset, Loralie, Batiks, Asians, Silks and Hand-Dyed fabrics.

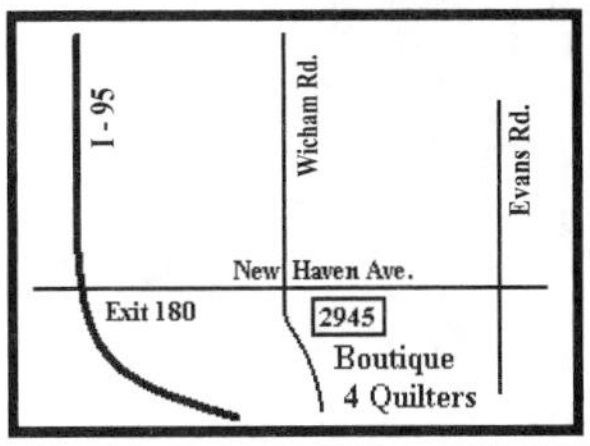

Quilting Folks & Sewing Gallery

Complete source for all of your quilting and sewing needs.

Cocoa, FL #37

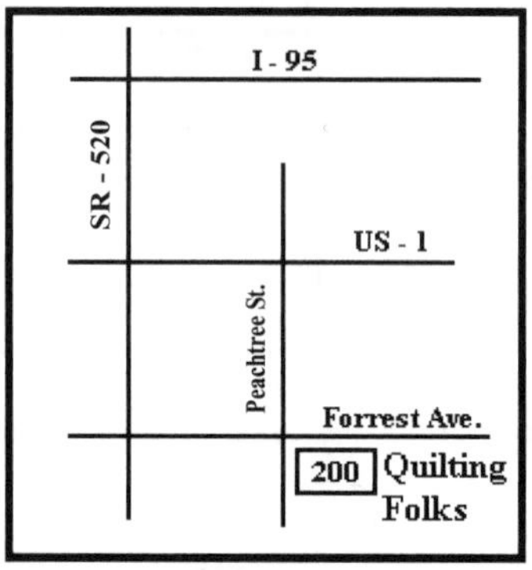

(321) 631-8601
200 Forrest Ave
Cocoa, FL 32922

Melbourne, FL #36

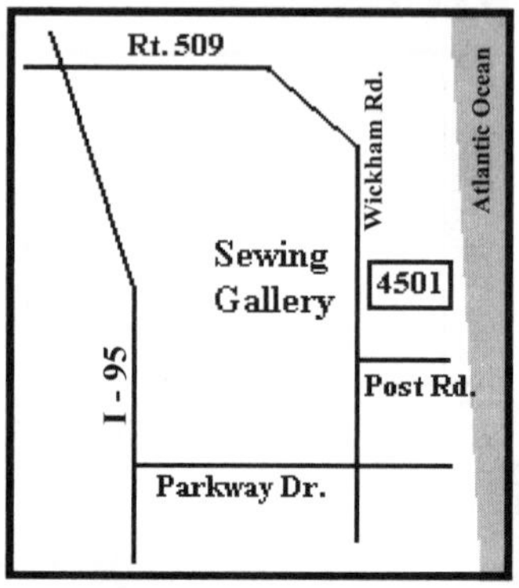

(321) 253-3882
4501 N. Wickham Rd.
Melbourne, FL
32935

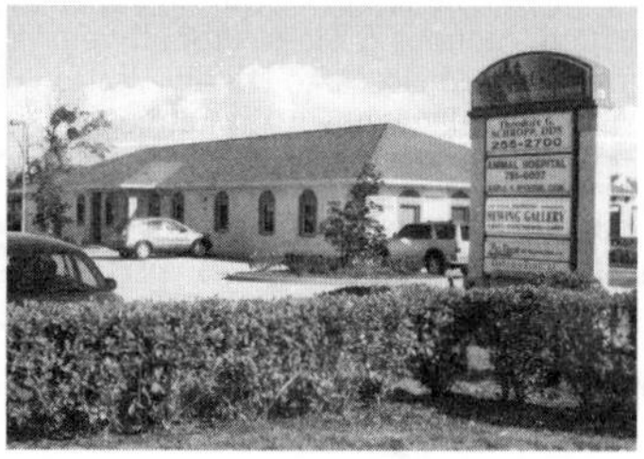

Both Shops:
Mon - Fri 10 - 5
Sat 10 - 3

Owners: Linda Joseph & Bernadette Schecher

www.QuiltingFolks.com

- Largest selection of first quality fabrics
- Year round Christmas room and Halloween Hollow
- Largest selection of wool, wool felt, fiber arts, threads and embellishments
- Books, patterns and notions.
- Knowledgeable staff
- Classes for all types of sewing
- Custom Longarm quilting service
- On-site repairs/service for all brands of machines.

Get inspired!! Quilting Folks Sewing Gallery is the ultimate sewing source. We are the longest established quilt shop in Brevard and stock only the best quality fabrics and supplies. We offer products for all types of sewing and have something for everyone's sewing style. With the best classes in town, visit our website and take a class when you visit.

Nothing Sews Like A Bernina. Nothing.
BERNINA®

JANOME

HORN of America

Handi Quilter®

The Quilt Place #38

Florida's Favorite Quilt Shop

575 Barton Blvd. Rockledge, FL 32955

Friendly & Experienced Staff...Customers are our priority.

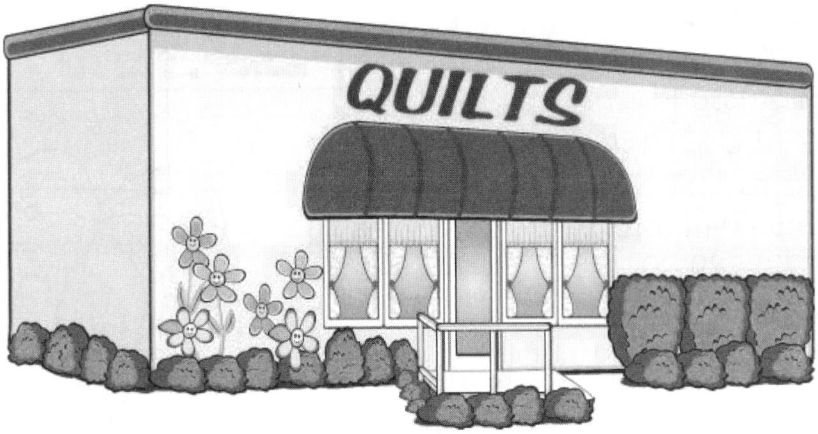

Open Monday through Saturday 10:00-5:00

Over 8,000 square feet of fabric, notions & quilting supplies

Email to request a catalog

Home of the Exclusive Square Deals!!

A Square Deal kit is 42, 10" squares (2 each of 21 different fabrics), and a pattern.

These kits are theme coordinated so choosing your favorite fabric is already done.

Whether you like patriotic, tropical, large or small florals, Robyn Pandolph, Kaffe Fasset, black and white, Civil War, safari, Christmas, Fall, Batik, 30s, or musical you'll find something to suit your taste.

Once you choose your "theme" then you choose from one of the 13 patterns and you're ready to sew. Check out our web site for all the details.

- **Over 9,000 Bolts of Fabric**
- **Quilting Classes**
- **Long Arm Classes**
- **Long Arm Rental**
- **Patterns, Books, Kits**

shop@thequiltplace.com

www.thequiltplace.com

321-632-3344

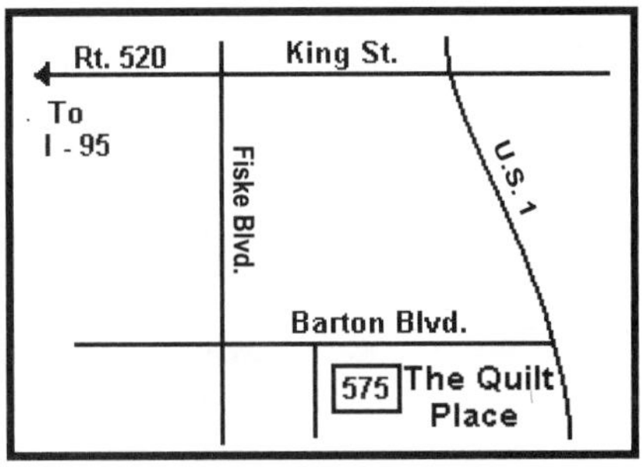

Marilou's Quilting & Sewing Center

"A Better Place to Buy"

Custom Machine Quilting, Quilting Supplies, Fabric, Books, Husqvarna Viking Sewing Machines, Sales and Service. Quilts for sale.
Classes in Quilting, Sewing, Embroidery & Computer.

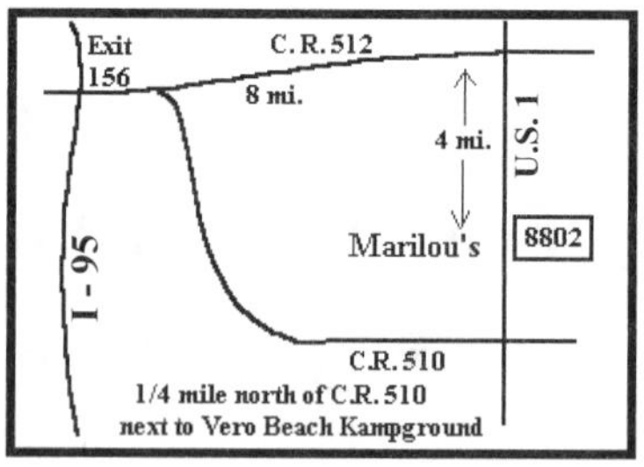

Sebastian, FL #39

Wabasso Plaza
8802 N U.S. Hwy 1,
Sebastian, FL 32958
for GPS enter Wabasso for city
(772) 589-0011
Fax: (772) 589-5682

Mon - Fri 10 - 5
Sat 10 - 4

Est: 1996

Owner: Marilou Keen
e-mail: Quilting 2125@aol.com
www.marilousquiltingandsewingcenter.com

The Quilted Lily

1110 Old Dixie Hwy. Suite 1A
Vero Beach, FL 32960
(772) 567-4220
www.thequiltedlily.com
1000 sq.ft.
600+ bolts free newsletter
SEWING & QUILTING CLASSES

Mon - Fri 10 - 5
Thur til 7
Sat 10 - 4

The unique quilt shop with bold to beautiful fabrics, notions, patterns and many classes. Visit our friendly and experienced ladies.

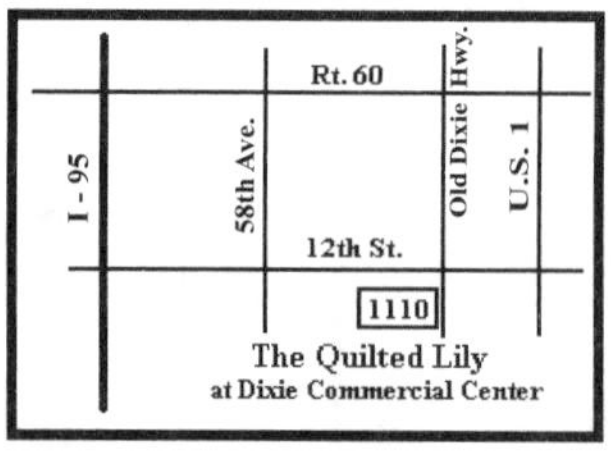

Vero Beach, FL #40

Vero Beach, FL #41

The Dragonfly Quilt Shop

1910 Old Dixie Hwy. off Rt. 60
Vero Beach, FL 32960
(772) 567-9600
Mon - Sat 10 - 5 Sunday by Chance

Most Adorable Quilt Shop Around.
Unique hand-made gifts, notions, books, patterns, beautiful 100% cotton fabrics, classes and much more.
Owner: Christina Fratcher

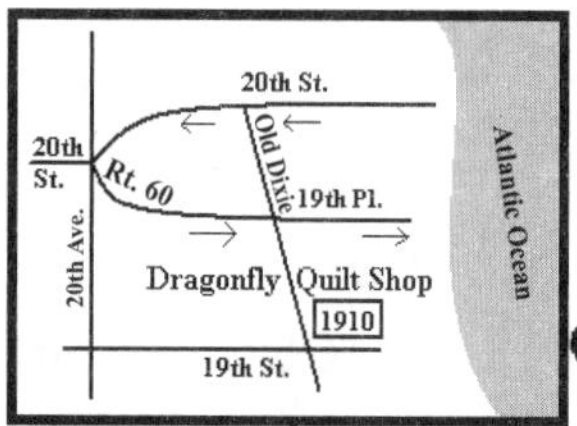

Lillie's Quilting Loft

Fabrics, Books, Patterns and More!

315 Commerce Center Dr.
St. Cloud, FL 34769
407.891.1078
pamela@lilliesquiltingloft.com

Tue - Sat 10 - 4, Wed til 9
Closed Sun & Mon

www.lilliesquiltingloft.com

We carry the highest quality 100% cotton fabric.

Drop by our shop in St. Cloud or shop on our website 24/7.

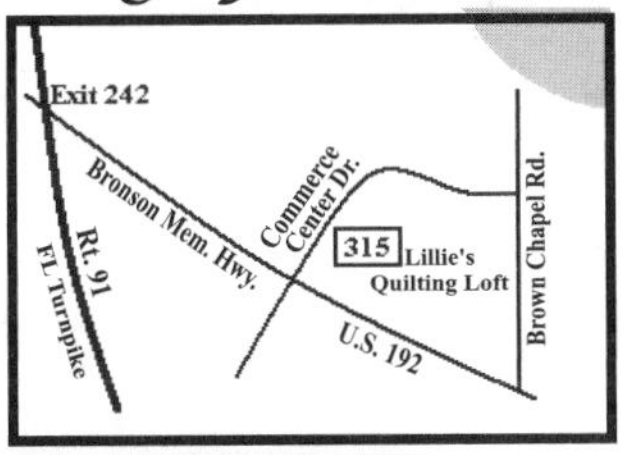

St. Cloud, FL #42

Winter Haven, FL #43

Mon, Wed, Fri 9 - 5
Tues & Thurs 9 - 9
Sat 9 - 4

Heartfelt Quilting & Sewing

365 5th St. SW 33880
(863) 299-3080
Owner: Patricia Roberts
4000 sq. ft.
4000+ Bolts

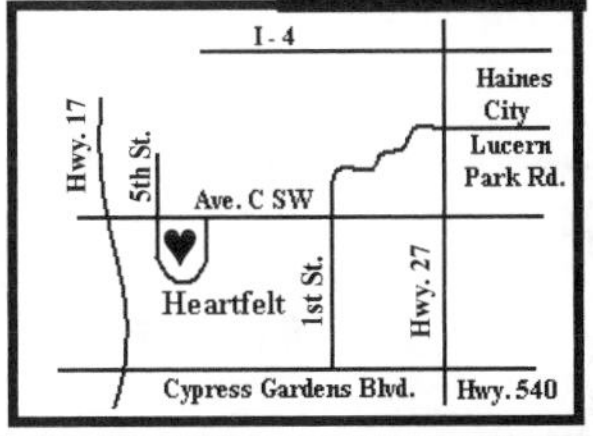

A Fun One of a Kind Quilt Shop with Quality Cottons & Batiks, Janome Sewing & HQ Quilting Machines.
Visit our website: www.heartfeltquilting.net

Winter Haven, FL #44

Mon - Sat 9 - 5
Tues til 8

Heart to Heart
QUILTING AND SCRAPBOOK SHOPS

102 Post Ave. SW 33880
(863) 298-8185
Fax: (863) 294-3685

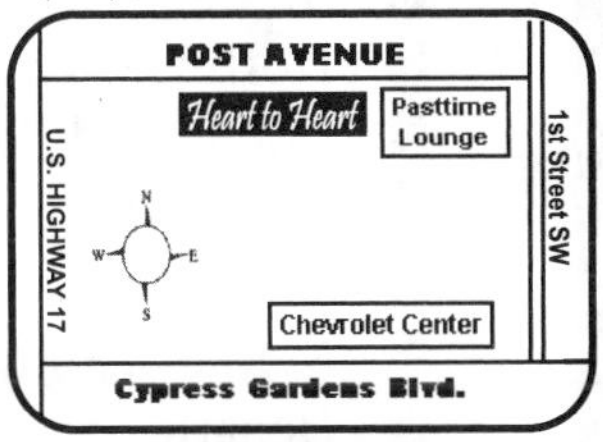

Owner: Pat Brenchley Est: 2000 3000+ bolts
Quilting & Scrapbooking Shop Specializing in 100% Cotton Fabrics, Sewing Machine Sales & Service. Acid & Lignin Free Archival Safe Papers, Stickers & Albums
Baby lock Sewing Machines

Lakeland, FL #45

Mon - Fri 10 - 5
Sat 10 - 4

Patchwork Pig

228 E. Pine St. 33801
(863) 682-4774 Fax: (863) 680-9943
patchworkpig@verizon.net
www.patchworkpigoflakeland.com
Est: 2003 3000 sq.ft. 5000+ bolts
Everything for the quilter - except more time!
Expert color coordinators.
Jo Morton Club

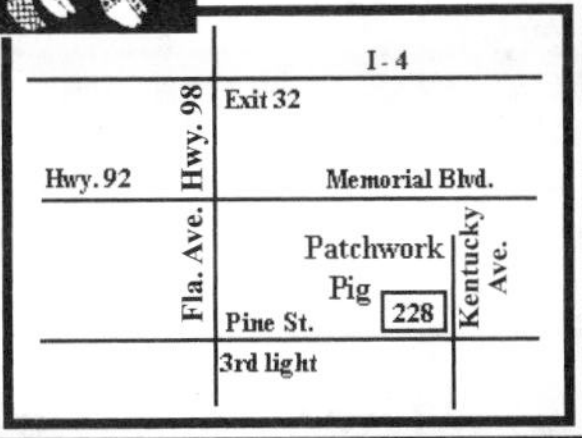

Dade City, FL #46

Quilts on Plum Lane

Located in Dade City's Downtown Antique District. Large selection of Books & Patterns, notions, classes. New Brand-Name 100% Cottons, Flannels, Batiks & Kits.

Mon - Sat 10 - 5
Thurs til 9
1st Sat til 7

14215 7th St. 33523
(352) 518-0003

Fax: (352) 518-0022
plumlanedl@cs.com
Owner: Donna Lillibridge
Mgr. Carol Bradshaw
Est: 2003

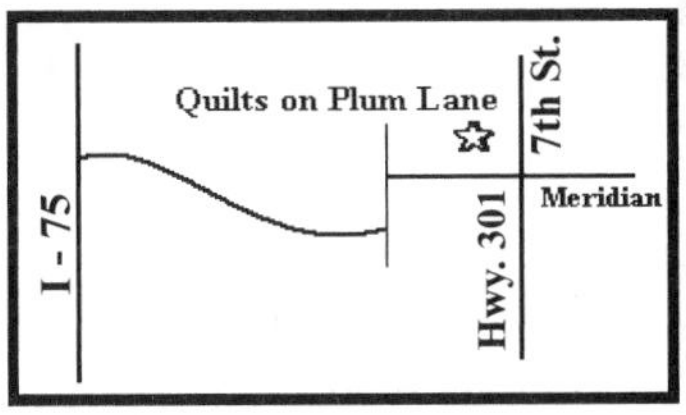

www.quiltsonplumlane.com

Zephyrhills, FL #47

Mon - Fri 10 - 5
Sat 10 - 3

QUILTER'S QUARTERS

4833 Allen Rd. 33541
(813) 779-2615 Fax: Same
quiltersqrtrs@verizon.net
www.quiltersqrtrs.com
Owner: Yvonne Pederson
Est: 2003 1000+ bolts
"The comforts of home are quilted!"
100% cotton fabric, books & patterns, sewing notions, classes & friendly, helpful service.

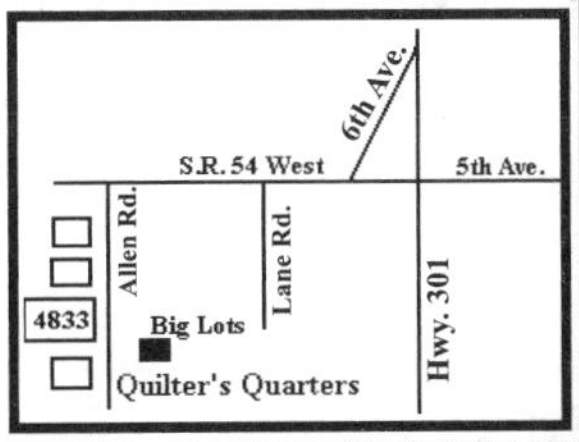

Hudson, FL #48

Tues - Fri 10 - 5
Sat 10 - 3

Quilt Til You Wilt
& Embroidery Studio

9609 Fulton Ave. 34667
(727) 862-6141 Fax: (727) 868-4765
Owner: Pat Wilkinson
Est: 1998 2000 sq.ft.
pipsqeak@gte.net www.QuiltTilYouWilt.net
Professional machine quilting. Quilt & Bear making classes, Supplies for both. Over 2500 bolts of fabric!! One room of embroidery, for all your professional embroidery needs.

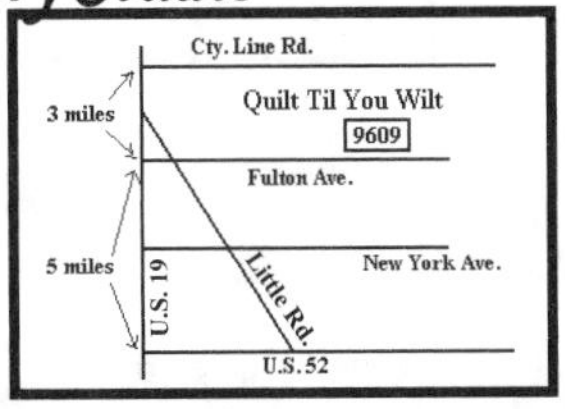

Holiday, FL #49

Tue - Fri 10 - 5
Sat 10 - 3

A & A White Sew Fabric

2621 U.S. 19 34691
(727) 937-6510 Fax: (727) 937-6590
Est: 1979 2400 sq.ft. 3500+ bolts
www.aawhitesewfabric.com
Dealer for Bernina, Pfaff, Babylock, Elna, Brother, Craftmaster, Singer, Riccar-- Repairs on all Makes, Classes. Everything You Would Need For Quilting.

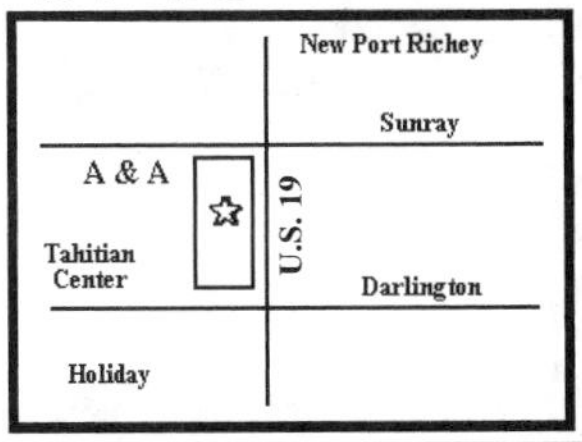

Country Quilts & Bears

Country Store with a Christian Heart

- Moda
- Hoffman
- Michael Miller
- RJR Fabrics
- Timeless Treasures
- Marcus Brothers
- Benartex
- P&B Fabrics
- In the Beginning
- Clothworks
- South Seas Imports
- Davids Textiles
- Maywood Studios
- Red Rooster

Mon - Sat
9 - 5

1983 Drew Street 33765
(727) 461-4171
Owners: Marilyn & John Humphries
www.countryquiltsandbears.com

A fully stocked quilt shop —
4000 bolts of cotton fabrics.
Large selection of flannels.
Friendly Service, notions, books & patterns.
We also carry quilt kits for making some of
the currently popular quilt patterns.

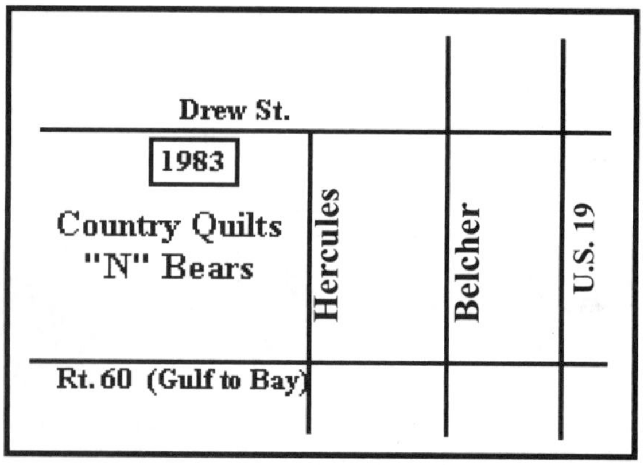

Beginner, advanced and limited
edition Teddy Bear classes
taught by Francy Gordon.
Mohair, luxury plush acrylic
fur, glass eyes, joints and bear
accessories available.

Est: 1986

Clearwater, FL #50

3300 sq.ft.

Dunedin, FL #51

RAINBOWS END QUILT SHOPPE

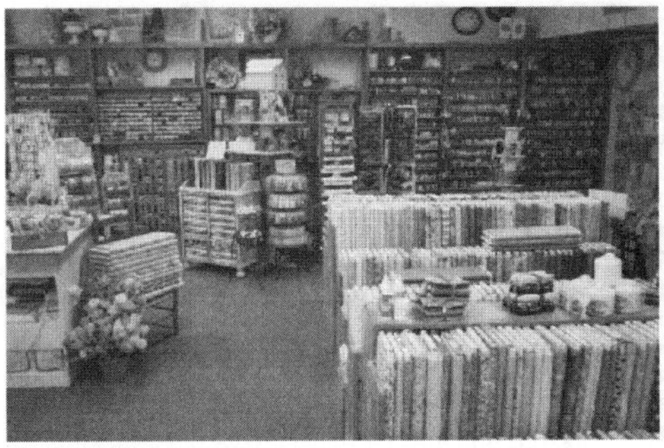

941 BROADWAY STREET (ALT 19)
DUNEDIN, FLORIDA 34698
(727)733-8572 (800) 353-1928 FAX (727)736-0235

LARGEST COMPLETE QUILT SHOPPE IN FLORIDA

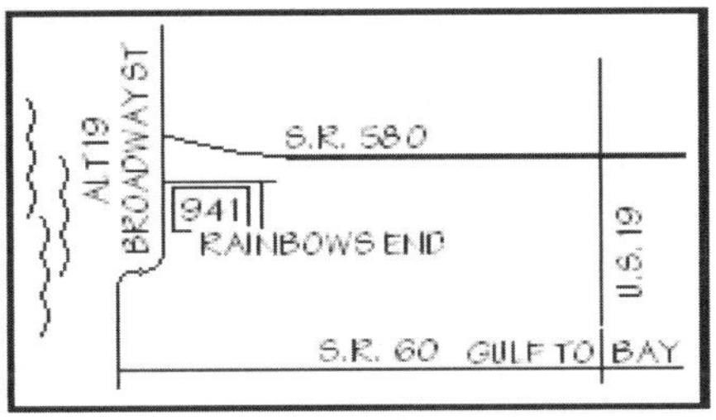

EST. 1982 7200 SQ. FT.

HOURS -
MON- SAT 10 AM TO 5 PM
WED 10 AM - 8 PM

WWW.RAINBOWS-END.COM
WWW.RAINBOWSENDQUILTSHOPPE.COM
WWW.RAINBOWSENDQUILTSHOPPE.BLOGSPOT.COM

OVER 18,000 BOLTS OF 100% COTTON FABRIC
QUILT, WALLHANGING & BLOCK OF THE MONTH KITS
HUNDREDS OF BOOKS, PATTERNS, NOTIONS, STENCILS, GIFT ITEMS, QUILTING SOFTWARE
LARGE COLLECTION OF SAMPLES OF CLASSES, PATTERNS, BOOKS & KITS
AUTHORIZED ELNA & PFAFF SALES & SERVICE
SEWING MACHINE CENTER

Quilters Haven & More

Ellenton, FL #52

Est: 1996

2418 U.S. Hwy. 301 N 34222
(800) 775-4445 or (941) 729-0511
www.quiltershavenandmore.com

Nov - April
Mon - Sat 9:30 - 4
May - Oct
Tues - Sat 9:30 - 4
Or by Appt.

"Favorite Location of Quilters for over 25 Years!!"

Exceptional Fabric Selection. Knowledgeable & Friendly staff specializing in color coordination. Classes for all Skill Levels. **Over 3,000 Bolts**, Books, Notions & Patterns. Authorized Sales & Service of Husqvarna Viking Sewing Machines & Sergers. Free Lessons with any Machine Purchased.

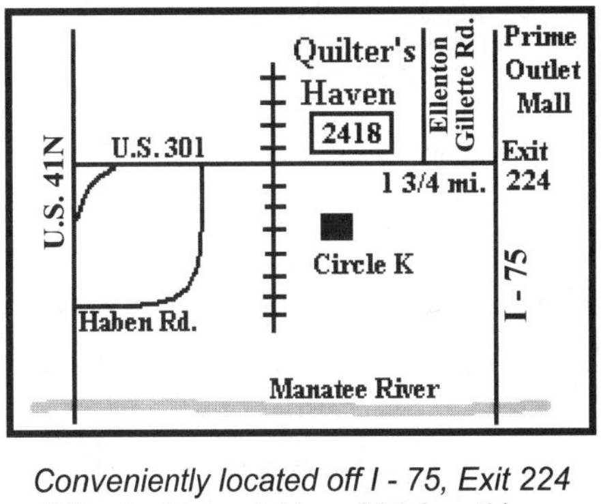

Conveniently located off I - 75, Exit 224 (Ellenton) turn right on 301 (south), go approx. 1 3/4 miles. We are on right side (north) directly across from Circle K

Husqvarna VIKING

University Park, FL #53

Cotton Patch Quilt Shop

located off University Pkwy West of I-75, exit 213, Sarasota/Bradenton
8480 Cooper Creek Blvd. #101 34201
(941) 359-3300

♥ ♥ ♥ ♥ ♥ ♥ ♥ ♥ ♥ ♥ ♥ ♥ ♥

Visit us in our new location!

Fabulous Fabrics ♥ 1,000's of fat quarters
$5 Markdowns ♥ Something for everyone
Friendly, helpful staff and great parking.

Mon - Sat 10 - 5
Sundays Nov. - March
Noon - 4

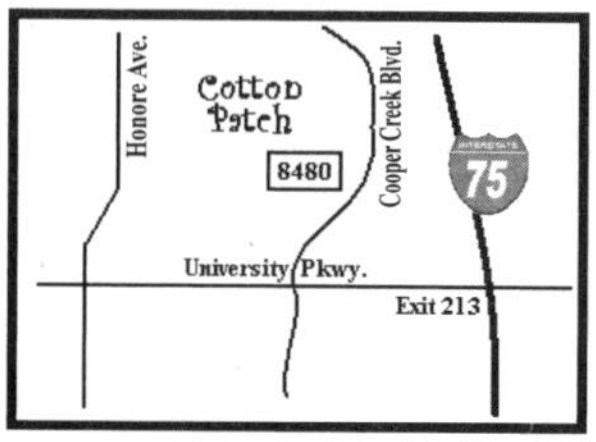

Owners:
Tim and
Laura Flynn

www.cottonpatchquiltshop.com

Parrish, FL #54

Mon - Fri 9 - 5
Sat 9 - 4

Patches Galore Inc.

8915 U.S. Hwy 301 North 34219
(800) 470-7002 or (941) 776-5669
Online newsletter
www.patchesgaloreinc.com

Great selection of fabrics and notions.
Authorized BERNINA Dealer

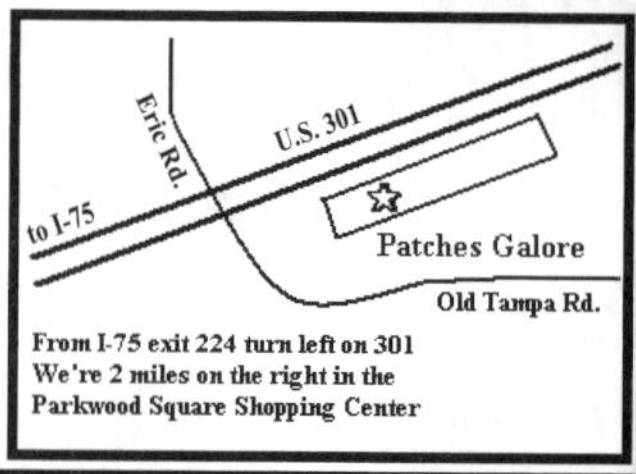

Avon Park, FL #55

Mon - Sat 10 - 4
Thur til 8

Heart to Heart

QUILTING AND SCRAPBOOK SHOPS

1103 W. Circle St. 33825
(863) 453-3100

Owner: Pat Brenchley Est: 2000 3000+ bolts
Quilting & Scrapbooking Shop Specializing in 100% Cotton Fabrics, Sewing Machine Sales & Service. Acid & Lignin Free Archival Safe Papers, Stickers & Albums
Baby lock Sewing Machines

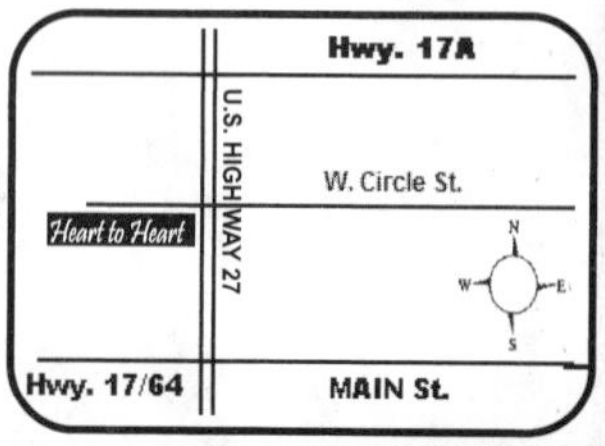

Sebring, FL #56

Mon - Fri 9 - 5
Sat 9 - 3
Closed Mon during Summer

Crafty Quilters

13221 Hwy. 98 33876
(863) 655-4600 Est: 1990
Owner: Dee Dee Bedard
www.craftyquiltersfl.com

For all your Quilting Needs.
Quilting Frames. Classes Available.
Factory Authorized Dealer of New Home & JANOME. Repairs on all Machines.

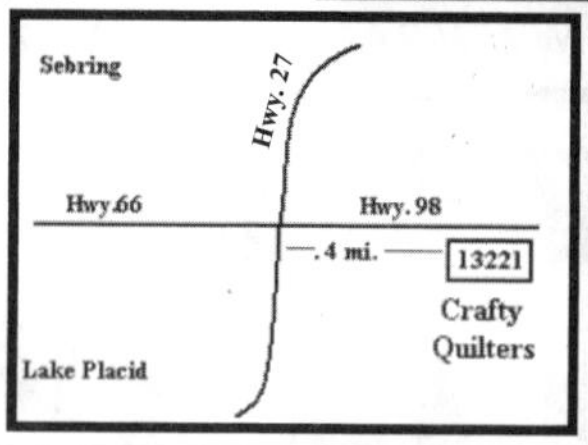

Lake Placid, FL #57

Tues - Fri 10 - 5
Sat 9 - 1

Sew-Biz

299 E Interlake Blvd. 33852
(863) 699-2228 Fax: (863) 699-2272
nancy@sewbiz.biz www.sewbiz.biz
Owners: Paul & Nancy Vasilchik
Est: 1992 2400 sq. ft. 1100 Bolts.

Home of playful pets and Little Town to Go and other Quilt Patterns and Books.
Enjoy fellowship with fellow fabricholics.

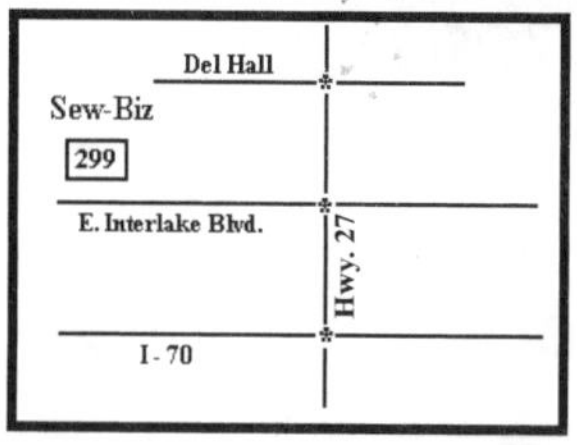

Harbour Heights, FL #58

Mon - Fri 9 - 5
Sat 9 - 4

Sandy's Quilt Shop LLC

3083 Sulstone Dr. 33983
(941) 255-1117 Est: 2007
Owners: Kathy Web & Nora Baker
sandysquiltshop@yahoo.com
www.sandysquiltshopllc.com

Let our courteous and knowledgeable staff help you with your next quilting project.
We have hundreds of colors and patterns in stock at all times.

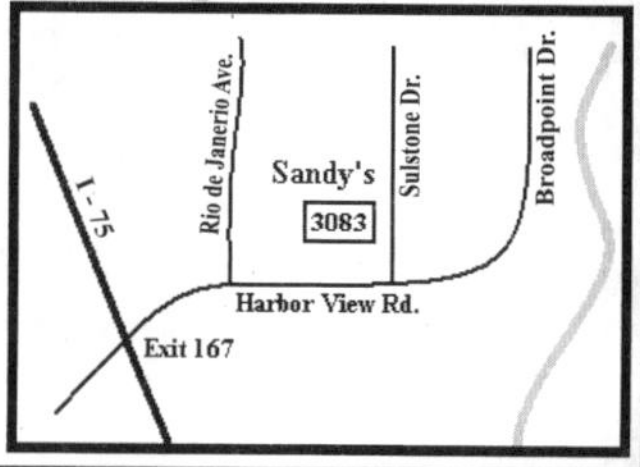

Venice, FL #59

Mon - Fri 10 - 5
Sat 10 - 2
Closed Sat. May - Sept.

Deborah's Quilt Basket

337 W. Venice Ave. 34285
(941) 488-6866 Fax: Same
Est: 1984 2000 Bolts
debsquiltbasket@aol.com

Visit historic downtown Venice.
See a large variety of fabrics in addition to lots of books, patterns, notions and gifts.

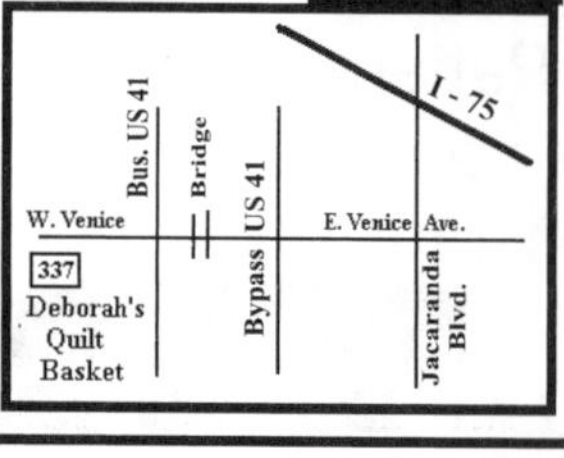

Port Charlotte, FL #60

Mon - Fri 10 - 5
Sat 10 - 3

Quilts n' More!

822 Tamiami Tr. 33953
(941) 255-9330
Owner: Linda MacDougall
Est: 2000

quiltsnmore@ewol.com www.quiltsnmore.net
2500+ bolts of 100% cotton fabrics, books, notions, patterns. Janome authorized dealer. Horn cabinets. Friendly, helpful service. Authorized Tin Lizzie Dealer. Long Arm Quilting Services Available.

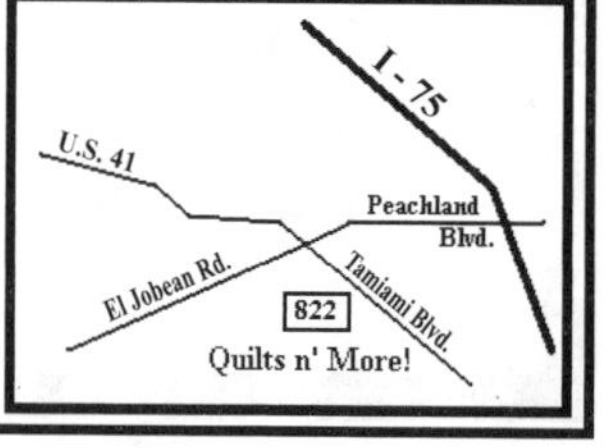

Englewood, FL #61

A Quilter's Cottage

Mon - Fri 9 - 5
Sat 9 - 4

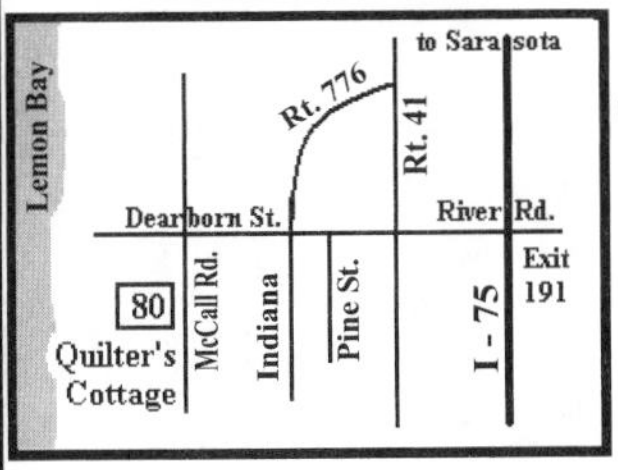

80 S. McCall Rd.
Englewood, FL 34223
941-475-5906
www.aquilterscottage.com
aqc04@daystar.net
Owner: Chris Raver
Online Newsletter
Est: 2005
3300 sq.ft. 4000+ Bolts

Your one-stop shop for all of your quilting needs! Long Arm and handquilting services, classes, fabrics, notions, books, patterns. Over 900 bolts of Batiks!

North Fort Myers, FL #62

"The Place Where Friends Meet Friends & Stitching and Laughter Are One!"

Quilt Lovers' Hangout

Largest Quilt Shop in SW Florida

4,500 sq. ft. OF FUN AND FABRIC

13494 N. Cleveland Ave.
Hancock Bridge Square
N. Ft. Myers, FL 33903
239-995-0045
Est: 2005 Online Newsletter
Owners: Debbie Olive & Gayle Cowdin

Our shop Showcases 6000 bolts of Quilting Fabrics along with a Large Selection of Books & Patterns. Professional Long-arm Machine Quilting. Quality classes & Teachers.

Show and Tells are Always Welcomed!

Open 7 Days a Week
Mon, Thurs, Fri 9-6
Tues, Wed 9-8
Sat 9-4 Sun 12-4

Bus Tours & Quilt Guild Welcome. Lots of Parking Many Eateries in Walking Distance

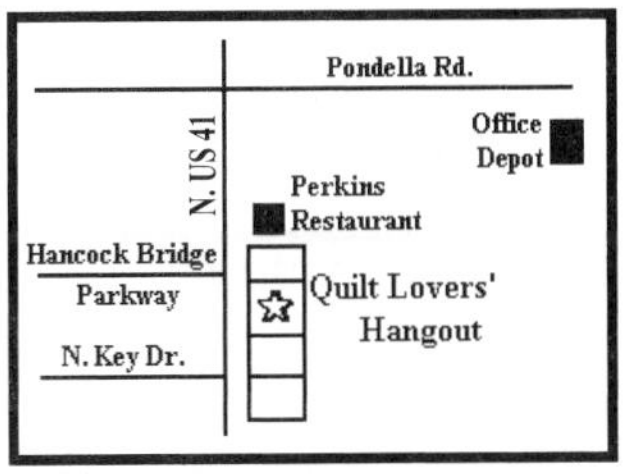

www.quiltlovershangout.com

North Fort Myers, FL #63

Susie Q's Quilts

239-656-2722
1890 N. Tamiami Trail
N Ft. Myers, FL 33903
www.susieqquilts.com

Friendly - Full Service Quilt Shop
Long Arm Quilting Services with Statler Stitcher.
Over 4500 bolts of fabrics.
Large selection of Books, Patterns & Notions.
Classes from Beginner to Advanced.
Christmas year round.

susieqquilts@embarqmail.com
Owner: Renee' Kennedy
Fax: 239-997-2722
Est: 2000 3500 sq. ft.
Online Newsletter

Authorized...Janome and Handi Quilter Dealer

Believe in Your Creativity
JANOME

Statler Stitcher

Mon - Fri 9 - 6
Sat 9 - 4
Call for Summer Hours

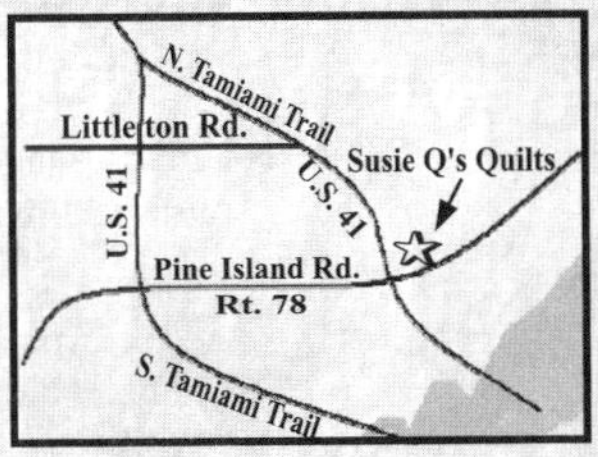

Sanibel, FL #64

Quilting
Books
Beads
Fabric

Mixed Media
Scrapbooking
Art Supplies
Shell Crafts

Three Crafty Ladies®

Mon - Sat 10 - 5

1628 Periwinkle Way
Heart of the Island Plaza
Sanibel, FL 33957
(239) 472-2893
threecraftyladies@gmail.com

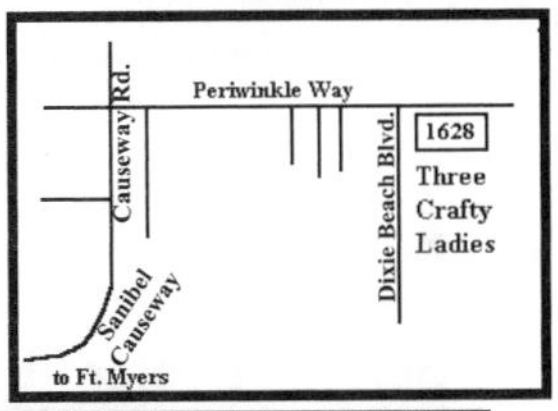

www.threecraftyladies.com

Ft. Myers, FL #65

Mon - Fri 10 - 5
Sat 10 - 4

SEW Studio

9671 Gladiolus Dr. 33908
The Plaza at Gladiolus Preserve
(239) 432-2898

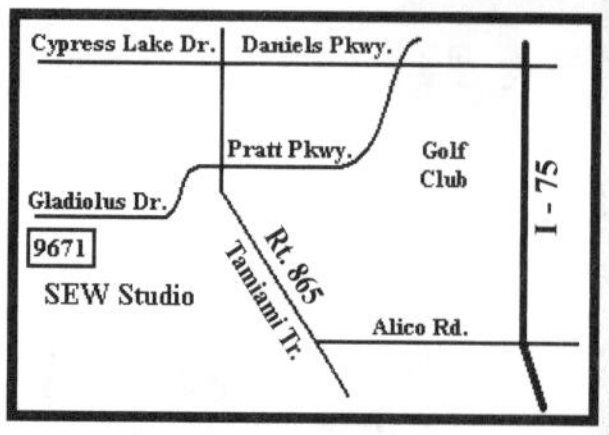

Owner: Rita Decker
www.sewstudio.com

100% Quality Quilting Cottons Patterns
Books Notions Classes
Authorized Bernina Dealer.

Naples, FL #66

Mon - Fri 9:30 - 5
Wed til 8
Sat 9:30 - 4

SEW Studio

2360 Immokalee Rd. 34110
Greentree Center
(239) 598-3752 Est: 1992
3200 sq.ft.

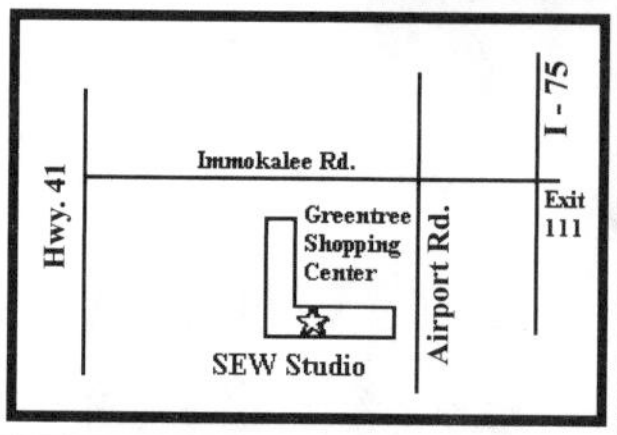

Owner: Rita Decker Fax: (239) 598-9113
www.sewstudio.com
Unique collection top quality cottons for quilting. Notions, Kits, and Classes.
Authorized Bernina Dealer.
Rental Machines. 18 years in Naples.

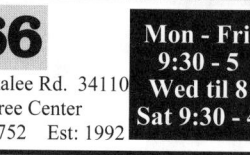

Quilters Choice

BERNINA

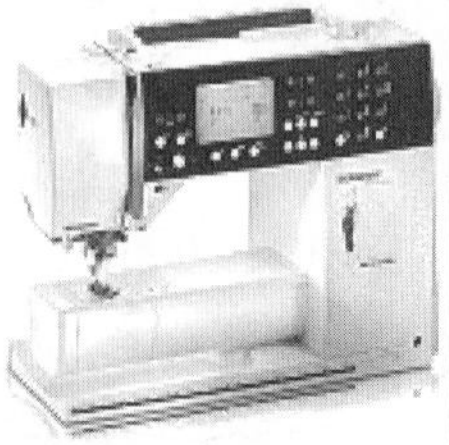

661 Maplewood Dr. #14
Jupiter, FL 33458
(561) 747-0525
quilterschoice@bellsouth.net
Owner: Vivian Irwin
Est: 1992 Newsletter

Mon - Fri 10 - 5
Sat 10 - 4

Authorized Bernina dealer
Sale & Service
Loads of great quilting fabrics, notions, books and patterns.
We'd love to meet you!

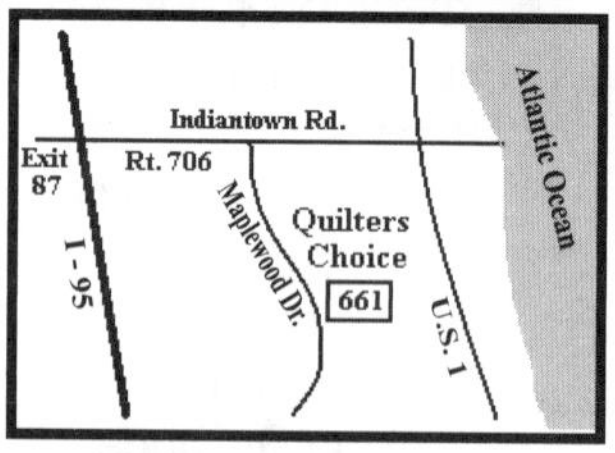

Jupiter, FL #67

Greenacres, FL #68

Mon - Fri 9:30 - 5:30
Sat 9:30 - 4:30

Buttonwood Quilts

3046 Jog Rd. 33467
(561) 304-7211 Fax: (561) 304-7212
Owners: Robin Puma & Ann Taylor
pumaemail@aol.com
www.buttonwoodquilts.com
Est: 2006
Full service quilt shop with long arm quilting service.
Authorized Janome dealer.

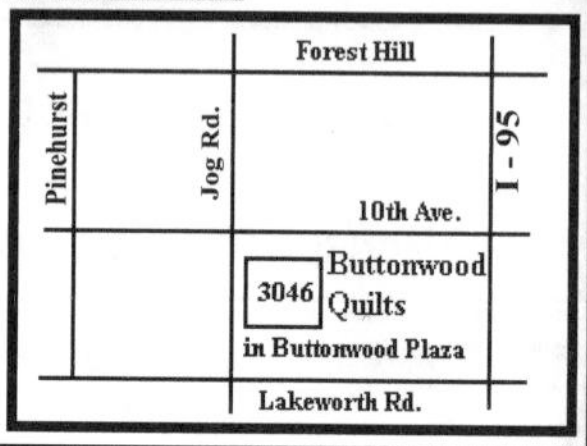

My Quilt Shoppe

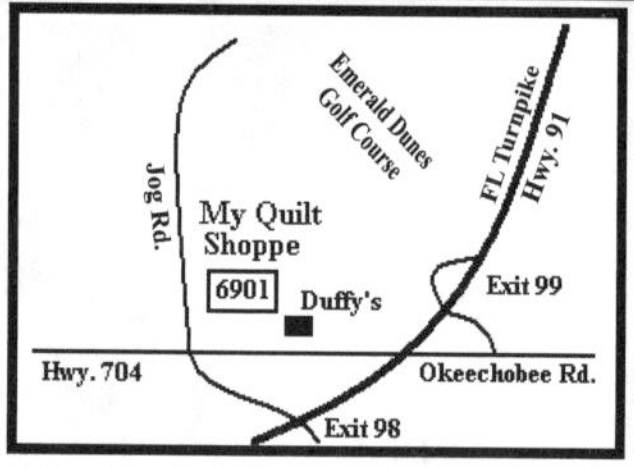

6901 W. Okeechobee Blvd. #D-11 33411
(561) 684-0020
myquiltshoppefl@bellsouth.net
www.myquiltshoppefl.com

Let Us Make "My Quilt Shoppe" Your Quilt Shop!

Mon - Fri 10 - 5
Sat 10 - 4

- 6000 Bolts of Fabric
- Patterns & Books
- Kits
- Classes
- Bernina Dealer

Est: 1999

Nothing Sews Like a Bernina. Nothing.
BERNINA

West Palm Beach, FL #69

SUNSHINE SEWING COMPANY

Authorized Janome Dealer
Authorized Tin Lizzie Dealer

Largest QUILT SHOP in South Florida

FABRICS, BOOKS, NOTIONS, CLASSES
MAGAZINES, SOFTWARE, PATTERNS

Home of
Fay Nicoll Judaica Designs
Year-Round Judaica
www.faynicolljudaicadesigns.com

-- Store Hours --
Mon, Tues, Wed, Fri: 10 am - 5 pm
Thur: 10 am - 9 pm Sat: 10 am - 4 pm
Call for Summer Hours

1821 Banks Road
Banks Business Park
(Greater Fort Lauderdale Area)
Margate, FL 33063
(954) 971-4810

www.sunshinesewing.com

#70

Coral Springs, FL #71

Tues - Fri 10 - 4:30 Sat 10 - 4

Jamie's Country Stitches

11471 W. Sample Rd.
33065
(954) 755-2411
Est: 1982
Your one stop Quilting Shoppe.
You'll be glad you came !

www.jamiescountrystitches.com

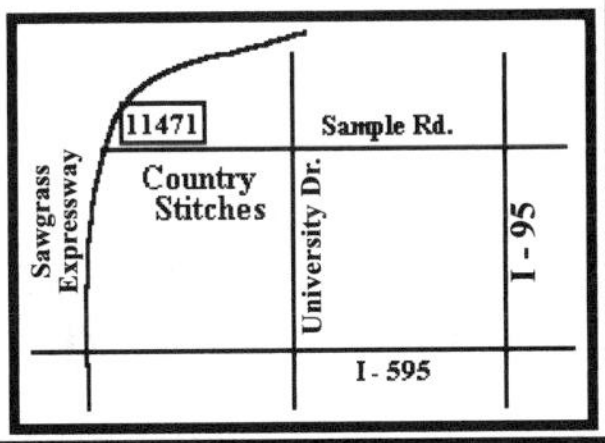

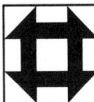

3404 Griffin Road * Ft. Lauderdale, FL 33312
954/987-8827 * OUAQ@bellsouth.net *
www.onceuponaquilt.com
Shop Hours: Tuesday-Friday 9:30-4:30 Saturday 930-4:00

We are a full service **Quilt** and **Knit Shop** & a proud **Bernina Authorized Dealer** with a bit more -- Hand dyed wool, rug hooking, punch needle, yarn, ribbon, lace and embellishments too. We are proud to say that we were selected as one of 10 featured shops in the 2004—Sampler issue of American Patchwork and Quilting Magazine. Visit us and you will experience a warm welcome and friendly atmosphere.

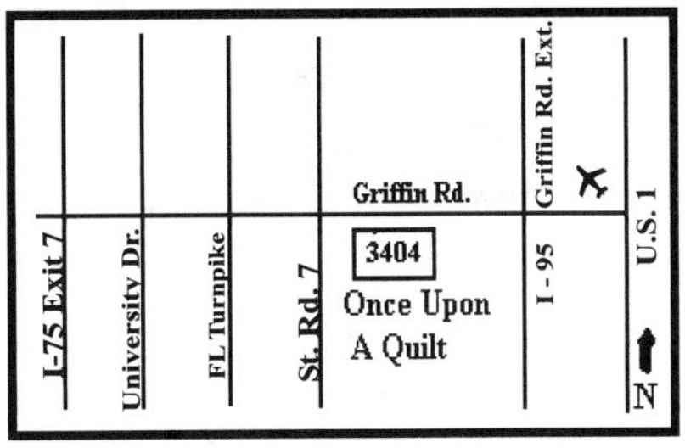

Ft. Lauderdale, FL #72

Nothing Sews Like a Bernina. Nothing.

BERNINA®

Long Arm machine quilting on premises
Sewing Machines Repair all makes and models

On Griffin Road between I-95 and SR 441 - 4 Miles From the Hollywood/Ft. Lauderdale Airport

Key West, FL #73

Mon - Thur 9 - 5 Fri 9 - 4 Sat 10 - 2

Seam Shoppe

1114 Truman Ave. 33040
(305) 296-9830 Fax: (305) 296-9630
Owners: Cindy & Doug Meyer Est: 1986
seamshoppe@aol.com
www.tropicalfabricsonline.com

Quilters and Fabric Collectors ! We stock mostly tropical fabrics for fashion, quilting and upholstery including palms, batiks, florals and vintage look.

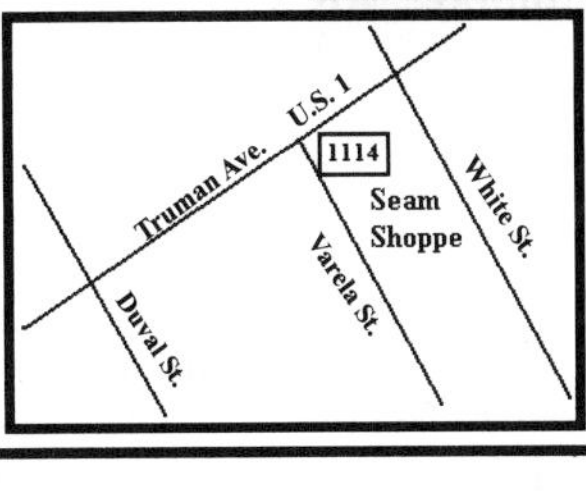

Florida Quilt Shops

Alachua Button & Bows-A Qulting Boutique, 14823 Main St. 3864180194

Apopka Apopka Quilt Company, 174A Semoran Commerce Pl. 407-889-0077 See ad #29, page 107

Apopka Material Girl Quilt Shop, 993 W. Orange Blossom Trail 407-884-0660

Avon Park Heart to Heart Fabrics & More, 1103 W. Circle 863-453-3100 See ad #55, page 114

Belleview Whippoorwill Station, 7655 S.E. 126 Place, Unit 3 352-347-9400 See ad #11, page 102

Beverly Hills Fabrics-To-Go, 3593 N. Lecanto Hwy. 352-527-8740

Brooksville Nana's Quilt Shop, 18851 Cortez Blvd. 352-796-0011

Bunnell The Sew & Quilt Shop, 4601 E. Hwy. 100 Unit B6 386-586-5409 See ad #22, page 104

Clearwater Country Quilts "N" Bears, 1983 Drew St. 727-461-4171 See ad #50, page 112

Clermont Clearmont Sewing & Quilting, 741 W. Montrose St. 352-243-4568

Cocoa Quilting Folks & Sewing Gallery, 200 Forrest Ave. 321-631-8601 See ad #37, page 108

Coral Springs Jamie's Country Stitches, 11471 W. Sample 954-755-2411 See ad #71, page 117

Crestview Margie's Sew Much Fun, 2014 Lacey Ln. 850-682-6920 See ad #2, page 100

Crestview Granny's Attic, 337 N. Main St. 904-682-3041

Crystal River Tomorrow's Treasures, 802 N. Suncoast Blvd. 352-795-2600 See ad #7, page 101

Dade City Quilts on Plum Lane, 14215 7th St. 352-518-0003 See ad #46, page 111

Daytona Beach The Sewing Garret, 949 Beville Rd., Bldg #2 386-767-3545 See ad #21, page 104

Deland Quilt Shop of Deland, 115 W. Rich Ave. 386-734-8782 See ad #24, page 105

Deland Lake Nanu's Quilted Rooster, 1220 Glen Royal Ter. 386-717-8645 See ad #25, page 106

Dunedin Rainbow's End Quilt Shoppe, 941 Broadway 727-733-8572 See ad #51, page 113 & 414

Ellenton Quilters Haven & More, 2418 US Hwy. 301 N 941-729-0511 See ad #52, page 113

Englewood A Quilter's Cottage 80 S. McCall Rd. 941-475-5906 See ad #61, page 115

Fernandina Beach Jan's Quilt-n-Stitch, 474388 E SR 200/A1A 904-310-6735 See ad #19, page 104

Fort Lauderdale Once Upon a Quilt, 3404 Griffin Rd. 954-987-8827 See ad #72, page 117

Fort Walton Beach Lynn's Sewing Center, 745 N. Beal Pkwy. 850-864-4555 See ad #4, page 100

Fort Walton Beach Sewing Center, Around the Block Quilting 913 N. Beal Pkwy #F 850-243-8261 See ad #5, page 100

Fruitland Park Sew Cherished, 2468 Hwy. 441, Ste. 104 352-787-5001

Ft. Myers SEW Studio, 9671 Gladiolus Dr. 239-432-2898 See ad #65, page 116

Greenacres Buttonwood Quilts, 3046 Jog Rd. 561-304-7211 See ad #68, page 116

Haines City P's and Q's Patchwork 621 Ingraham Ave. 8634216222

Harbour Heights Sandy's Quilt Shop, 3083 Sulstone Dr. 941-255-1117 See ad #58, page 114

Holiday A&A White Sew Vac & Fabric, 2621 US 19 727-937-6510 See ad #49, page 111

Homosassa Winder's Fabric Outlet, 6971 Gordon Point 352-628-5752

Hudson Quilt 'Til You Wilt & Embroidery Studio 9609 Fulton Ave. 727-862-6141 See ad #48, page 111

Jacksonville The Olde Green Cupboard, 10950-26 San Jose Blvd. 904-880-6656 See ad #15, page 103

Jacksonville Paula's Fine Fabrics, 8358 Point Meadows Dr. #4 904-519-7705

Jupiter Quilter's Choice, 661 Maplewood Dr. #14 561-747-0525 See ad #67, page 116

Key West The Seam Shoppe, 1114 Truman Ave 305-296-9830 See ad #73, page 117

Kissimmee Queen Ann's Lace, 305 Broadway 407-846-7998 See ad #31, page 107

Lake City AmyGene's Lake City Quilt Store, 218 N. Marion 386-754-3741 See ad #12, page 102

Lake City Fabric Art Shop, 158 SW Domino Way 386-755-0179 See ad #13, page 102

Lake Mary Bernina Sewing Center, 3593 Lake Emma Rd 407-805-9300 See ad #23, page 105

Lake Placid Sew-Biz, 299 E. Interlake Blvd. 863-699-2228 See ad #57, page 114

Lakeland Patchwork Pig, 228 E. Pine St. 863-682-4774 See ad #45, page 111

Lakeland Fabric Warehouse, 3030 N. Florida Ave. 863-680-1325

Leesburg A Quilter's Dream, 719 W. Main St. 352-728-1482 See ad #27, page 106

Lutz Scrap and Sew, 17681 N. Dale Mabry Hwy. N 813-963-5200

Maitland The Sewing Studio Fabric Superstore 9605 S. Hwy. 17-92 407-831-6488 See ad #28, page 106

Margate Sunshine Sewing Co., Inc., 1821 Banks Rd. 954-971-4810 See ad #70, page 116

Melbourne Quilting Folk & Sewing Gallery 4501 N Wickham Rd 321-253-3882 See ad #36, page 108

Melbourne Boutique 4 Quilters, 2945 W. New Haven Ave. 321-768-2060 See ad #35, page 107

Miami The Quilt Scene, 8801 SW 132nd St. 305-969-9886

Naples SEW Studio, 2360 Immokalee Rd. 239-598-3752 See ad #66, page 116

North Fort Myers Susie Q's Quilts, 1890 N Tamiami Trail 239-656-2722 See ad #63, page 115

North Fort Myers Quilt Lovers' Hangout, 13494 N. Cleveland 239-995-0045 See ad #62, page 115

Ocala Tomorrow's Treasures Quilt Shop, 6126 SW Hwy. 200 352-690-1915 See ad #8, page 101

Ocala Peggy's Heirlooms of Tomorrow, 7651 SW SR200 352-351-8282 See ad #9, page 101

Orange Park Country Crossroads, 799-3 Blanding Blvd. 904-276-1011 See ad #18, page 104

Orange Park Calico Station, Inc., 1855-6 Wells Rd. 904-269-6911 See ad #14, page 102

Orlando Quilters Cove, 2500 Curry Rd 407-894-8333 See ad #32, page 107

Orlando Cornerstone Quilt Shop, 5953 E. Colonial Dr. 407-207-6500 See ad #33, page 107

Ormond Beach Byrd's Nest Quilting, 156 E. Granada Blvd. 386-615-8789 See ad #17, page 103

Pace The Quilting Station, 4507 Chumuckla Hwy. 850-994-1610 See ad #1, page 100

Palm Coast Byrd's Nest Quilt Shop & PFAFF Sewing Center 160 Cypress Pt Parkway Unit A 108 386-447-1103 See ad #16, page 103

Panama City Quilting by the Bay, 2303 Winona Dr. 850-215-7282 See ad #3, page 100

Parrish Patches Galore, Inc., 8915 US Hwy 301 N 941-776-5669 See ad #54, page 114

Port Charlotte Quilt's N More, 822 Tamiami Trail #2 941-255-9330 See ad #60, page 114

Port Charlotte Charlottes Sewing Studio, 2421 S. Tamiami Tr. 941-235-3555

Port Richey A&A White's Sewing & Fabric, 11720 US 19 727-697-1892

Punta Gorda The Golden Thimble, 25201 Marion Ave 561-702-4307

Punta Gorda Aunties Quilt Shop, 1080 Taylor St. #112 941-613-1959

Rockledge **The Quilt Place, 575 Barton Blvd**
321-632-3344 **See ad #38, page 109**

Sanford **Fireside Quilt Shop and Gifts & Quilting Retreats**
1301 S. Park Ave.
407-322-0065 **See ad #26, page 106**

Sanibel **Three Crafty Ladies, Inc., 1628 Periwinkle Way**
239-472-2893 **See ad #64, page 115**

Sarasota Alma Sue's Quilt Shop, 3667 Bahia Vista St 941-330-0993
Sarasota Sew Worth It!, 5507 Palmer Crossing Circle 9419245600

Sebastian **Marilou's Quilting & Sewing Center**
8802 N. U.S. Hwy. 1
772-589-0011 **See ad #39, page 110**

Sebring **Crafty Quilters, 13221 Hwy. 98 South**
863-655-4600 **See ad #56, page 114**

St. Augustine **Magrieta's Quilt Shop, 142-C King St.**
904-829-3137 **See ad #20, page 104**

St. Cloud **Lillie's Quilting Loft, 315 Commerce Center Dr.**
407-891-1078 **See ad #42, page 111**

Stuart JaM Patch, 932 SE Central Pkwy 772-283-9889

Tallahassee **Lynn's Sewing Center, 1400 Village Square Blvd.**
850-386-7397 **See ad #6, page 100**

Tallahassee Florida's History Shop, 500 S Bronough St 850-245-6375
Tampa Keep Me In Stitches, 14833 N. Dale Mabry Hwy. 813-908-3889
Temple Terrace Heritage Quilt & Needlework, 10939 N. 56th St. 813-989-3993

Trenton **Suwannee Valley Quilt Shoppe, 517 N. Main St**
352-463-3842 **See ad #10, page 101**

University Park **Cotton Patch Quilt Shop**
8480 Cooper Creek Blvd. #101
941-359-3300 **See ad #53, page 114**

Venice **Deborah's Quilt Basket, 337 W. Venice Ave.**
941-488-6866 **See ad #59, page 114**

Vero Beach **DragonFly Quilt Shop, 1910 Old Dixie Hwy**
772-567-9600 **See ad #41, page 110**

Vero Beach **The Quilted Lily, 1110 Old Dixie Hwy, Ste 1A**
772-567-4220 **See ad #40, page 110**

Viera **My Quilt Shack, 5575 Schenck Ave. #7**
321-433-1948 **See ad #34, page 107**

West Palm Beach **My Quilt Shoppe, 6901 W. Okeechobee**
561-684-0020 **See ad #69, page 116**

Winter Garden **Nancy's Quilt Shop, 715 S. Dillard St.**
407-905-8879 **See ad #30, page 107**

Winter Haven **Heart to Heart Fabrics, 102 Post Ave. SW**
863-298-8185 **See ad #44, page 111**

Winter Haven **Heartfelt Quilting & Sewing, 365 5th St. SW**
863-299-3080 **See ad #43, page 111**

Zephyrhills **Quilter's Quarters, 4833 Allen Rd.**
813-779-2615 **See ad #47, page 111**

34 Shows

Florida Quilt Shows

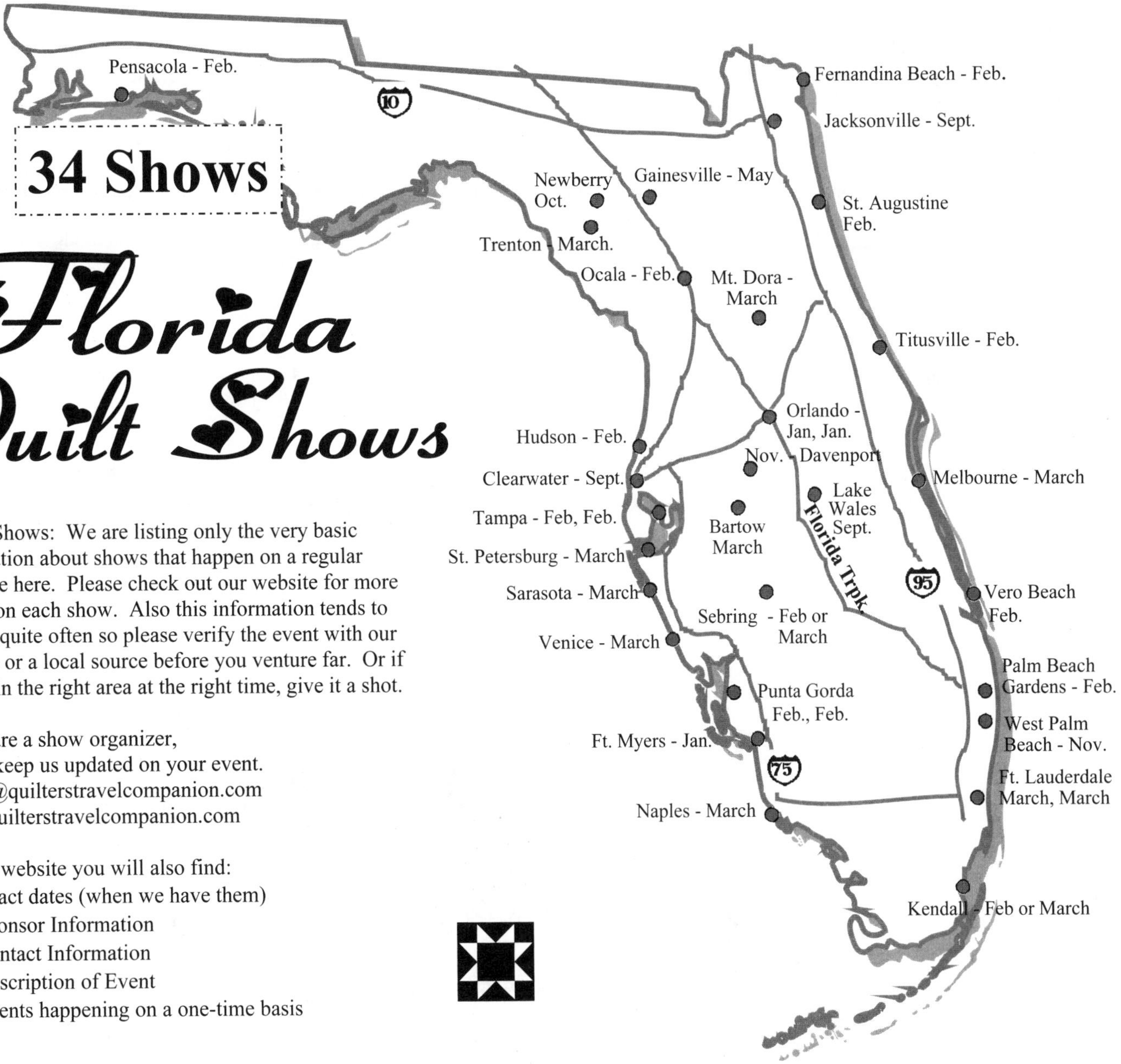

About Shows: We are listing only the very basic information about shows that happen on a regular schedule here. Please check out our website for more details on each show. Also this information tends to change quite often so please verify the event with our website or a local source before you venture far. Or if you're in the right area at the right time, give it a shot.

If you are a show organizer,
please keep us updated on your event.
shows@quilterstravelcompanion.com
www.quilterstravelcompanion.com

On our website you will also find:

- Exact dates (when we have them)
- Sponsor Information
- Contact Information
- Description of Event
- Events happening on a one-time basis

Month	City	Schedule	Show	Location with address
January				
	Fort Myers	Even Years, 2nd weekend in January	Southwest Florida Quilt Show	Lee Civic Center, 11831 Bayshore Rd.
	Orlando	Even Years, 3rd weekend in January	Quilt Magic	Central Florida Fairgrounds, 4603 W. Colonial Dr.
	Orlando	Odd Years, 3rd or 4th Weekend in January	Florida Quilt Show	Central Florida Fairgrounds, 4603 W. Colonial Dr.
February				
	Hudson	Even Years, 2nd weekend in Feb.	West Pasco Quilters' Guild Show	Veterans Memorial Park, 14333 Hicks Rd.
	St. Augustine	Annual, 2nd weekend of February	Retreat: Quiltstock	Ramada Inn, San Jose Blvd.
	Ocala	Even years, 3rd weekend in February	Belleview Busy Bees Quilt Show	Silver Springs Shores Presbyterian Church, 674 Silver
	Tampa	Odd Years, 3rd weekend of February	World of Whimsy Quilt Show	The Salvation Army Worship Center, 1100 W. Sligh Ave.
	Tampa	Annual, 3rd Thur - Sat in February	Original Sewing & Quilt Expo	Tampa Convention Center, 333 S. Franklin St.
	Titusville	Odd Years, 3rd Sat & Sun of February	Quilting from the Heart Brevard	Community College, 1311 N. Washington Ave.
	Vero Beach	Odd Years, usually 3rd Fri & Sat of February	SunBonnetSue Quilters Guild Show	Indian River County Comm. College--Richardson Ctr., 7955 58th Ave. -- South of Rt. 60 at 58th Ave.
	Clearwater	Odd Years, 4th Fri & Sat in February	Quilters' Crossing of Palm Harbor Quilt Show	Countryside Recreation Center, 2640 Sabal Springs Dr.
	Ferandina Beach	Every 3rd Year, Late February	Fernandina Beach Quilters Guild	The Peck Center, S. 10th & Elm
	Pensacola	Even Years, 4th weekend of February	Pensacola Quilters' Guild Show	Pensacola Fairgrounds, 6655 Mobile Hwy.
	Punta Gorda	Even Years, February	Disconnected Piecers Quilt Guild Show	Charlotte Harbor Event Center, 75 Taylor St.
	Sebring	Odd Years, Feb or March	Quilting in the Highlands	Agri CenterGeorges, Blvd. & U.S. 27 S
	Kendall	Annual, End of Feb or beginning of March	Ocean Waves Quilt Fest	Elk's Lodge, 10301 Sunset Dr.
	Palm Beach Gardens	Even Years, late February	Palm Beach County Quilters Guild Show	North Palm Beach Community Center, 1200 Prosperity Farms
	Punta Gorda	Odd Years, last weekend in February	Southwest Florida Quilt Festival	Charlotte Harbor Event & Conference Ctr, 75 Taylor St.
March				
	Mt Dora	Annual, 1st Thurs & Fri of March	FANtastic Quilt Show	Lake Receptions, 4425 Hwy. 19A
	Naples	Annual, 1st weekend in March	Stitches in Time	The Community School of Naples, 13275 Livingston Road
	St. Petersburg	Even Year, first weekend of March	Suncoast Quilting Circle Show	Gibbs Campus Gym--St. Peterburg College, 6605 5th Ave. N
	Bartow	Annual, 2nd weekend in March	Bloomin' Art Festival Quilt Show	
	Fort Lauderdale	Even Years, March Quilt	Show by the Sea	War Memorial Auditorium, 800 NE 8TH St.
	Melbourne	Even Years, 2nd Fri & Sat in March	Seaside Piecemakers Quilt Show	Melbourne Auditorium, 625 E. Hibiscus Blvd.
	Sarasota	Odd Years, 2nd Fri & Sat in March	Friendship Knot Quilters' Guild Show	Sarasota Municipal Auditorium, 801 N. Tamiami Tr.
	Trenton	Annual, March	Springhouse Quilters' Guild Show	
	Fort Lauderdale	Odd Years, 3rd weekend in March	Broward Quilt Expo	War Memorial Auditorium, 800 Sandy Ninninger Dr.
	Venice	Even Years, 3rd weekend in March	Venice Quilters' Guild Show	Venice Area Community Center, 326 Nokomis Ave.
May				
	Gainesville	Odd Years, 1st weekend in May	Tree City Quilters' Guild Show	Best Western Gateway Grand Hotel, 4200 NW 97th Blvd. (I-75 Exit 390)
September				
	Lake Wales	Annual, September thru November	Depot Museum's Quilt Exhibit	The Depot Museum, 325 S. Scenic Hwy.
	Jacksonville	Annual, 4th weekend in September	QuiltFest Inc. of Jacksonville	Prime Osborn Convention Center, 1000 Water St.
October				
	Newberry	Annual, last Sat. of October	Quilters of Alachua County Day Guild Show	Dudley Farm Historic State Park, 18730 W. Newberry Rd.
November				
	Davenport	Annual, 2nd Fri & Sat in November	Quilts and Tea Festival	Davenport Historic District, 1 S. Allapaha Ave.
	West Palm Beach	Annual, 2nd weekend in November	World Quilt Show	Palm Beach Cty. Convention Center, 650 Okeechobee

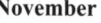

GEORGIA

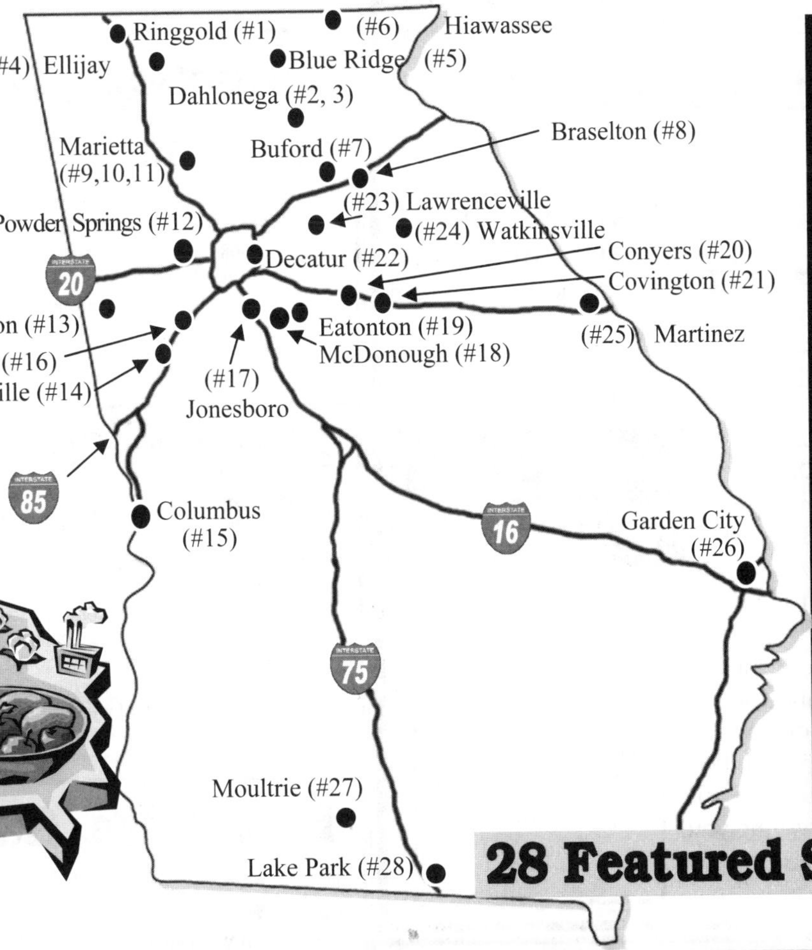
Ringgold (#1)
(#6)
Hiawassee
(#4) Ellijay
Blue Ridge (#5)
Dahlonega (#2, 3)
Braselton (#8)
Marietta (#9,10,11)
Buford (#7)
(#23) Lawrenceville
(#24) Watkinsville
Powder Springs (#12)
Decatur (#22)
Conyers (#20)
Covington (#21)
20
Carrollton (#13)
Eatonton (#19)
McDonough (#18)
(#25) Martinez
Newnan (#16)
Hogansville (#14)
(#17)
Jonesboro
85
Columbus (#15)
16
Garden City (#26)
75
Moultrie (#27)
Lake Park (#28)

GEORGIA

28 Featured Shops

"The one stop shop for your quilting and knitting supplies."

Dahlonega, GA #2

Magical Threads

315 Church St.
Dahlonega, GA 30533
(706) 867-8918
info@magicalthreads.com
Owner: Laurelanne Hackinson
Est: 2001 5000+ sq.ft.
www.magicalthreads.com

Authorized Handi Quilter Dealer

Monday - Saturday
10 am - 5 pm
Sunday by Appt. Only

Located in historic Dahlonega in a house built in 1846, our store showcases over 7500 bolts of 100% cotton fabric along with a full line of yarns and knitting supplies. Our great blend of the contemporary and the traditional, in addition to all of the books, patterns, and notions truly make us "the one stop shop" for everything you need to make your next project simply "magical".

Dahlonega, GA #3

Mon - Fri 10 - 5
Sat 10 - 4

The Common Thread

598 Grove St. N 30533
(706) 864-0740 Fax: Same
Est: 2008 1700 sq.ft. 3000 Bolts
thecommonthread@windstream.net
www.thecommonthread.bravehost.com

For all your quilting and sewing needs.
Long-Arm Quilting Service.

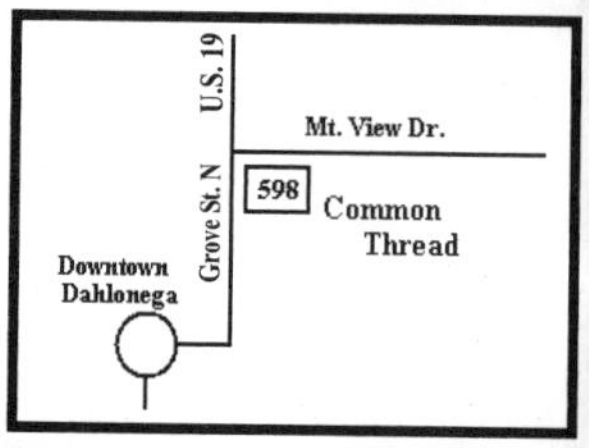

Ellijay, GA #4

Mon - Sat 10 - 5

Quilt Shop on the Square

44 North Main St. 30540
706-635-1135
Owner: Pamela K. Clark
quiltshoponthesquare@etcmail.com
www.quiltshoponthesquare.com
We have many new and exciting things planned for the store and we hope we will have a chance to meet everyone in the area interested in sewing and quilting.

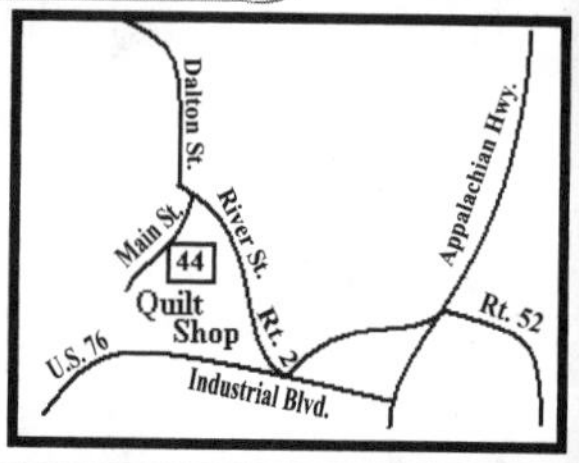

Blue Ridge, GA #5

Mon - Sat 10 - 5

COUNTRY STITCHES Inc.

30 W. Main St. 30513
(706) 632-3070
Owner: Priscilla Ryan
countrystitches@tds.net
www.countrystitchesinc.net
We are a full service quilt shop which offers a wide variety of fabrics, patterns, notions and friendly assistance so that you can obtain what you need for your projects in one location.
Babylock and Janome Dealer.

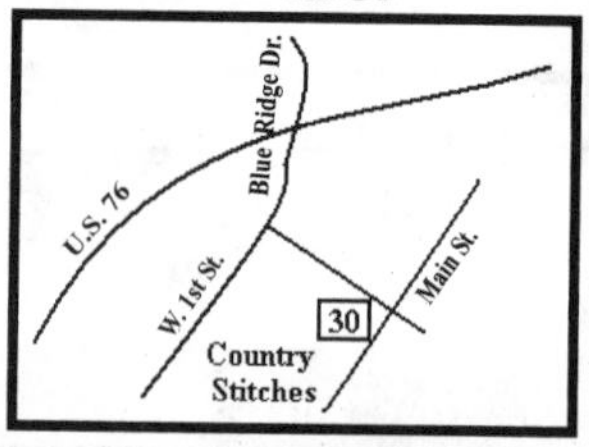

Hiawassee, GA #6

Mon - Sat 10 - 4

Log Cabin Patchworks

312 Big Sky Dr. 30546
(706) 896-7275
www.LogCabinPatchworks.com
Est: 1980 2000 sq.ft. 1500 Bolts

We specialize in Thimbleberries, Homespuns, Moda, Flannels and Reproduction fabrics.
Better Homes & Garden Quilt Sampler Shop 2002

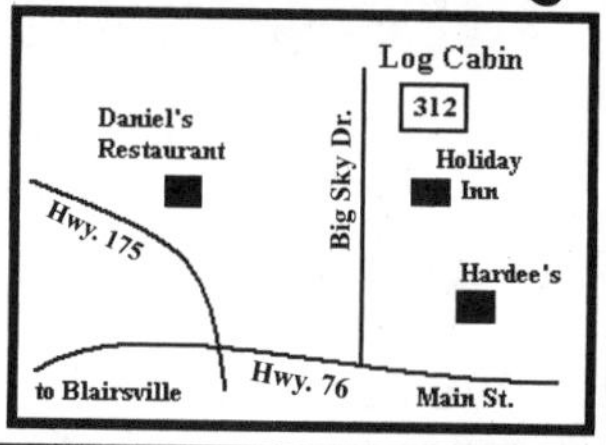

Buford, GA #7

Georgia Sewing & Quilting, Inc.

Mon-Sat
10:00-6:00
Tue/Thur til 8:00

1651 Horizon Pkwy.
Suite 800
Buford, GA 30518
770 831-7990

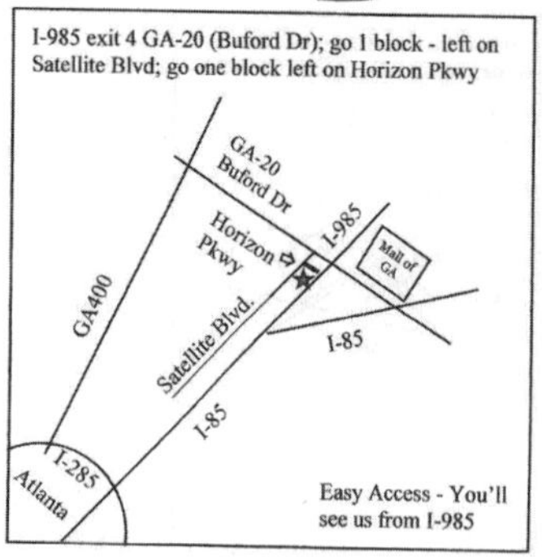

Convenient to I-985-exit 4
I-85-exit 115 & GA400 -exit 14

www.GeorgiaSewingAndQuilting.net

- Georgia Hospitality!
- Huge selection of 100% cotton quilting fabrics
- Batiks, Flannels & more
- Patterns, tools, sewing notions
- Classes, Lectures, Workshops, Trunk Shows
- Free on-line newsletter
- Software—quilting & embroidery—with classes!

Braselton, GA #8

Mon 12 - 5
Tues - Sat 10 - 5

Betty Sue's quilt shop
Designer Fabric and more

7419 Spout Springs Rd.
30542
(770) 965-3380

Owner: Susan Cowan Est: 2007
1500 sq.ft. Online Newsletter
bettysue@prodigy.net www.bettysues.com
We are a family owned business here to serve your quilting needs. Fabrics from major manufacturers. Notions, Batting & Classes.

Marietta, GA #9

Tiny STITCHES

2520 E. Piedmont Rd.
Suite H 30062
(770) 565-1113

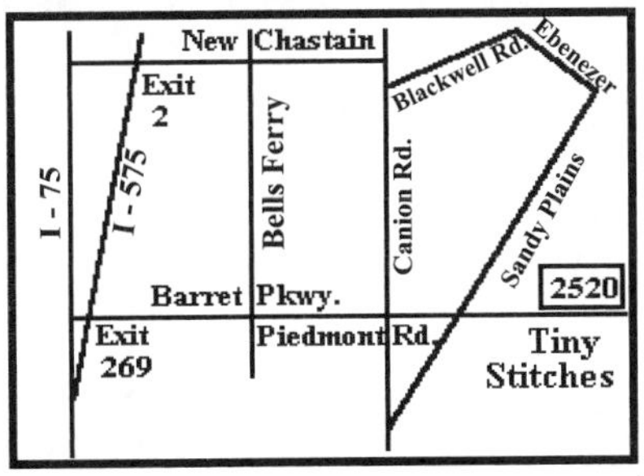

Visit Georgia's Largest Quilt Shop

We are a fully stocked quilt shop
— Over 6000 bolts of cotton fabrics — over 500 book titles —
Large selection of the newest notions
Friendly, knowledgeable service
Classes offered in quilting, clothing and accessories

Be sure to check our website frequently for upcoming retreats and events.

Just off I-75, Tiny Stitches is a convenient stop for the traveling Quilter. Exit 269, east onto Barrett Pkwy. This becomes E. Piedmont. We are located at 2520 E. Piedmont.

We gladly ship both online and phone orders.
Visit our website: www.tinystitches.com

Est: 1992

Mon - Sat 9:30 - 5:30 Fri til 7 Sun 1 - 5

Red Hen Fabrics

Fabric and Quilting Emporium

305 Cherokee St. Marietta, GA 30060
770-794-8549 www.RedHenFabrics.com
Owner: Mary Anne Henderson
Est: 2004 Fax: 770-794-8292
Online Newsletter motherhen@redhenfabrics.com

Mon - Sat 10 - 6 Sun 1 - 5

Over 6000 square feet and 6000 bolts of the very best fabric at discount prices!
FREE GIFT with your fabric or notion purchase on your FIRST visit.
COME SHOP WITH THE BEST!!

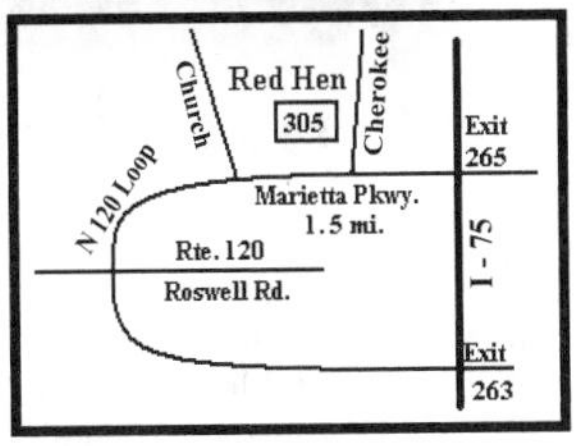

Marietta, GA #10

Marietta, GA #11

Little Quilts®

est. 1986

1450-C Roswell Rd.
"Near Historic Marietta"
Phone: 770-578-6727
Fax: 770-509-9748

"Step Into Our World"

Fabrics, books and patterns by Little Quilts

Our cozy shop has reproduction fabrics, wool, Kaffee Fassett, Moda & more!
Wool for rug hooking, rug punching yarn, needle punch, stitchery, gifts . . . and lots of inspiration!

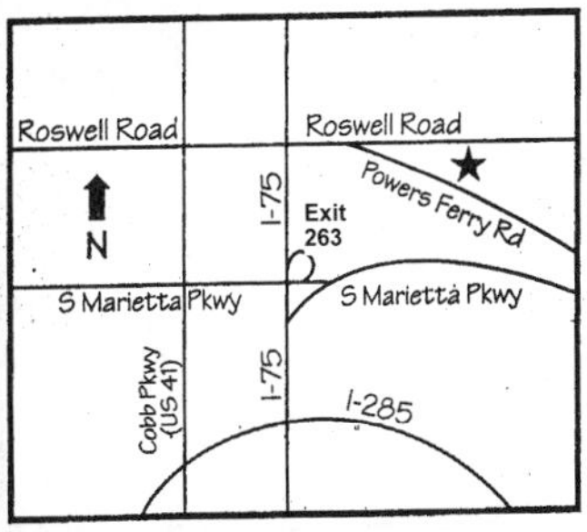

Mon - Sat 10 - 5

Top Ten Shop
American Patchwork & Quilting 2004

www.littlequilts.com

Powder Springs, GA #12

Tues - Sat 10 - 6

Kiwiquilts

3200 Hopeland Industrial Dr. #500 30127
(770) 243-3749
Owner: Tracy Morgan
Est: 2009 1400 sq.ft.
www.kiwiquilts.com

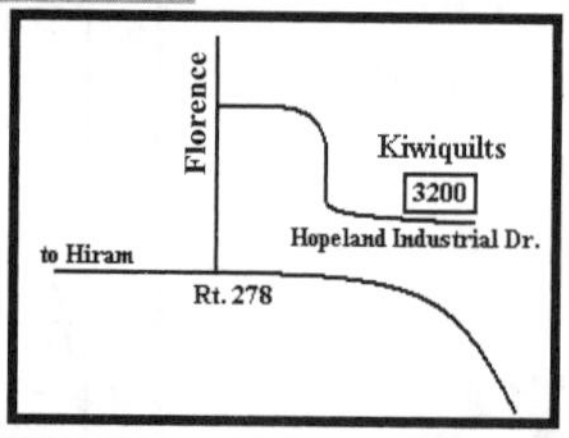

Wide variety of fabrics from traditional to trendy. Classes, patterns, notions and books.

Carrollton, GA #13

Mon - Sat 10 - 6

Qwiltz Quilt Shop

206 Adamson Square 30117
(678) 601-3623
qwiltz@bellsouth.net Est: 2005
www.qwiltz.com
Owner: Robbi Leeper Free Newsletter
Welcome to Qwiltz. We offer a full range of Fabric, Patterns, Books & Notions.
Beg-Adv Classes. Machine Quilting.
Come on in - The coffee's on!

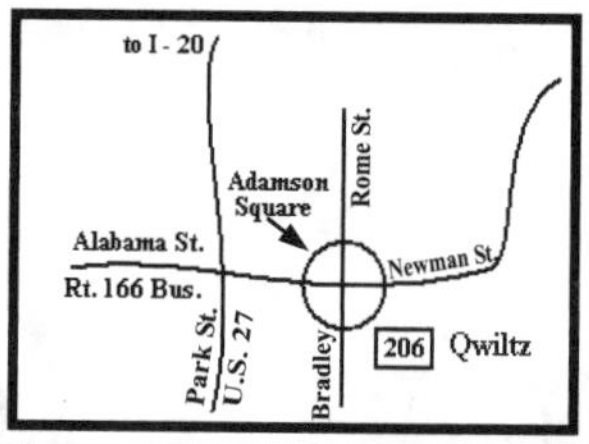

Hogansville, GA #14

1910 House Quilt Shop

104 High St., Hogansville, GA 30230
(706) 637-6556
1910house@bellsouth.net

* 2000 bolts of 100% Cotton Fabric
* Books, Patterns, and Notions
* Classes Offered

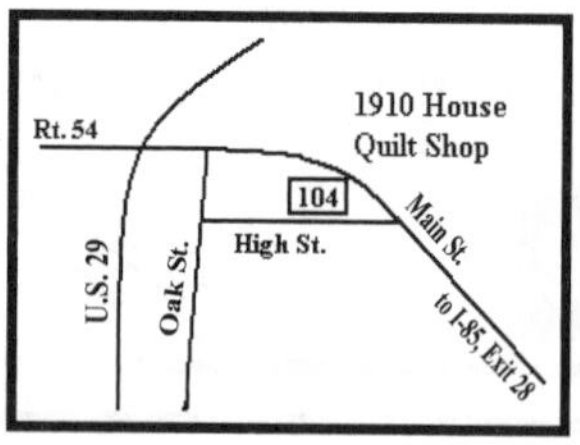

Tuesday—Saturday
10:00 a.m. to 5:00 p.m.
1st Sunday of each month
1:00 p.m. to 5:00 p.m.

Located in Historic Downtown Hogansville
2.5 miles off Interstate 85, Exit 28

Columbus, GA #15

**Mon - Fri 9:30 - 6
Sat 9:30 - 4**

Sew Much Fun

7801 Veteran's Pkwy. 31909
(706) 317-0024 Fax: (706) 317-0032
Owner: Lain Stowe
Est: 2004 Online Newsletter
sewmuchfun@knology.net
www.sewmuchfunincolumbus.com
Over 7000 Bolts of Fabric - Complete Line of Notions, Books and Patterns - LongArm Quilting Services and Lots of Fun!

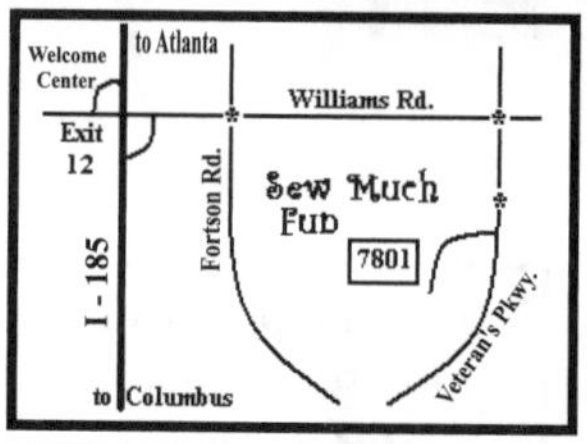

Newnan, GA #16

Mon - Sat 10 - 5

On the square in historic downtown Newnan

Heritage Quilts & Fabrics

22B W. Court Square 30263
770-683-9058

*2000 bolts of 100% Cotton Fabric
*Great selection of books & patterns
*Longarm Quilting
*Classes available

info@heritagequiltsandfabrics.com
www.heritagequiltsandfabrics.com

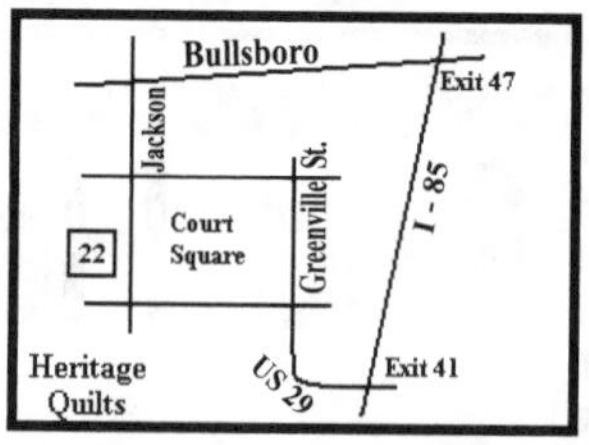

Jonesboro, GA #17

Mon - Sat 10 - 5

Quilts and Fixins

7986 N. Main St. 30236
(770) 472-0015 Fax: (770) 471-8822
www.quiltsandfixins.org
Est: 1998 6000 Bolts
100's of samples, books, patterns, & notions.
Many classes and gifts.
Exit 235 off I - 75 S. (Hwy 19&41-Tara Blvd.) Go S 4 mi, turn L onto Hwy 138. At next light (N. Main) turn R. We're on the left.

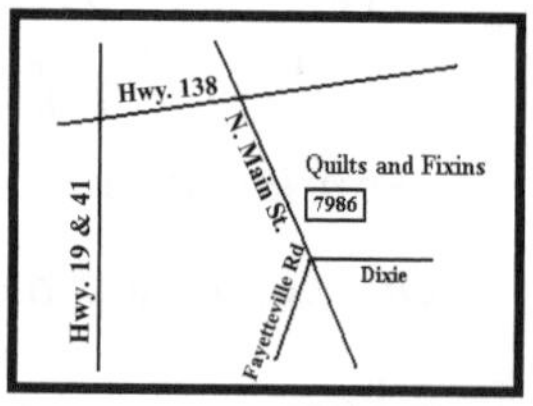

McDonough, GA #18

**Mon - Fri 10 - 6
Sat 10 - 4**

Handi Quilter
baby lock

A Scarlet Thread

Store is slated to move, please call first
3159 Jodeco Rd. 30253 (678) 583-2296
7500 + bolts of quilting fabrics
info@ascarletthread.com
www.ascarletthread.com
Sewing, Quilting & Embroidery Supplies & Machines. Baby lock authorized dealer.

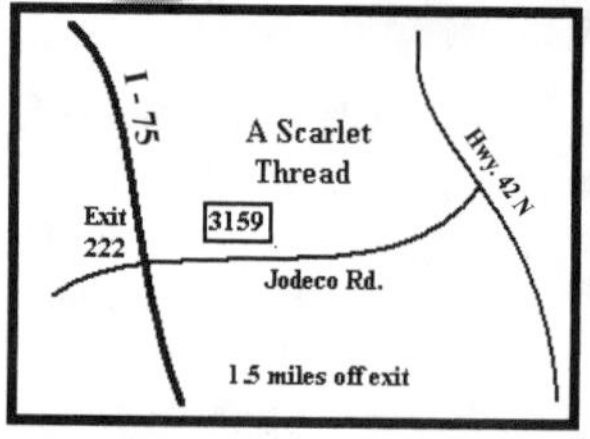

Eatonton, GA #19

**Tues - Fri 10 - 5
Sat 10 - 4**

The Stitching Barn

105 Clack Circle #400
31024
The Shoppes at Fore Magnolias

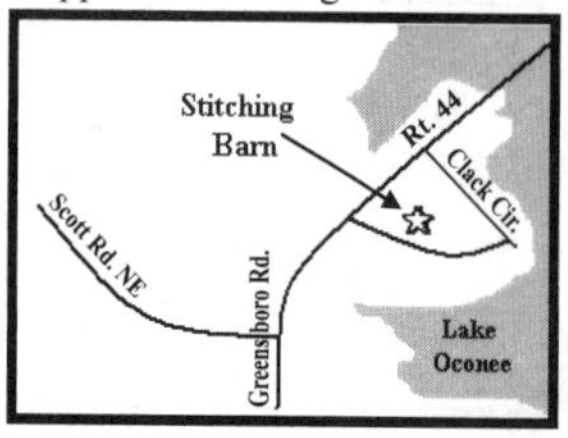

(706) 485-0028
Owner: Becky Pitman Newsletter
stitchingbarn@yahoo.com
Join the crafty folks in the Lake Oconee area for quilting, sewing, knitting, crocheting.
Quality products and service.

Conyers, GA #20

**Tues - Fri 9:30 - 6
Sat 9:30 - 4**

Sweet Home Quilt Co.

1004 Green St. SW 30012
(678) 413-1611
Owners: Melisa & Mike Morrison
info@sweethomequiltco.com
www.sweethomequiltco.com
100% cotton fabrics from all leading manufacturers - MODA fabrics are our specialty. Great selection of books, patterns, notions & gifts.

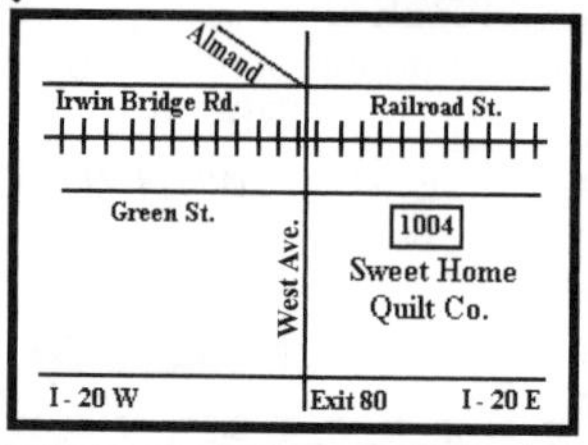

AN OLD FASHIONED GENERAL STORE

PATRICK'S

Est. 1950

10285 Covington Bypass Rd.
Covington, GA 30014
(770) 786-3220

3500+ bolts

Monday - Friday 9 - 5:30
Sat 9 - 3:30

100% Cotton Fabrics
Including
Flannels, Reproductions,
Florals & Prints.
100's of Quilt Patterns

Covington, GA #21

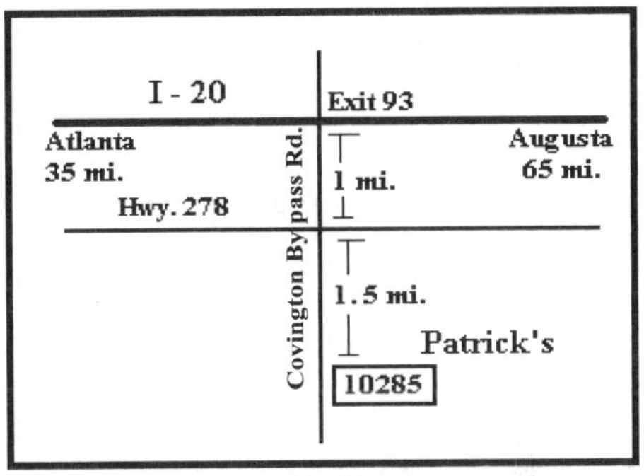

MasterCard VISA AMERICAN EXPRESS DISCOVER

Decatur, GA #22

Intown Quilters, Inc.

Open 7 days a week in our permanent home in Decatur since 2006.

Hours Sunday 1p-6p
Monday-Saturday 10a-6p

Established 2002 and moved to a permanent bright, sunny home in 2006 with over 4000 bolts.

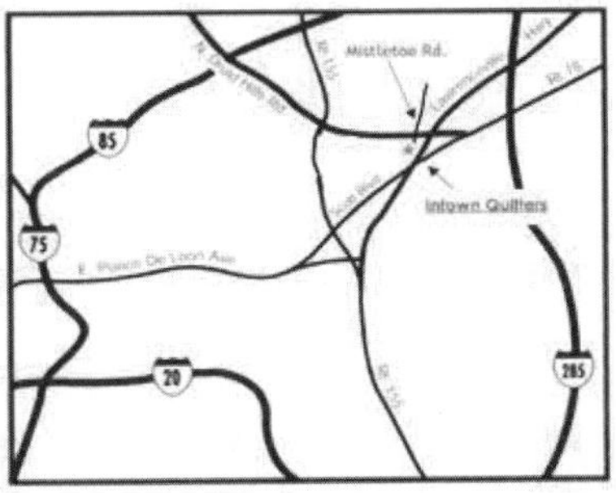

Specializing in all things bright and beautiful! You will find many of your favorite designers such as Kaffe Fassett, Brandon Mably, Philip Jacobs, Amy Butler, Heather Bailey, Patty Young, Sandy Henderson, Anna Maria Horner, a large collection of Asian fabrics, tons of batiks, many kits, books, patterns and notions.

1058 Mistletoe Road
Decatur, Ga. 30033
404-634-6924
www.intownquilters.com
www.intownquilters.blogspot.com

Lawrenceville, GA #23

Tues - Fri 10 - 5
Sat 10 - 4

Patchwork Cottage

2070 Sugarloaf Pkwy
Suite 1100 30045

(770) 237-5455
Owner: Mita Chatterjee 1500+ bolts
info@patchworkcottagequilting.com
www.patchworkcottagequilting.com
We carry a huge selection of reproduction fabric, the latest Moda, RJR, Kauffman and P&B Textiles. Creative patterns, books and a huge selection of notions. We offer classes for tweens and grandmas and all those in between!

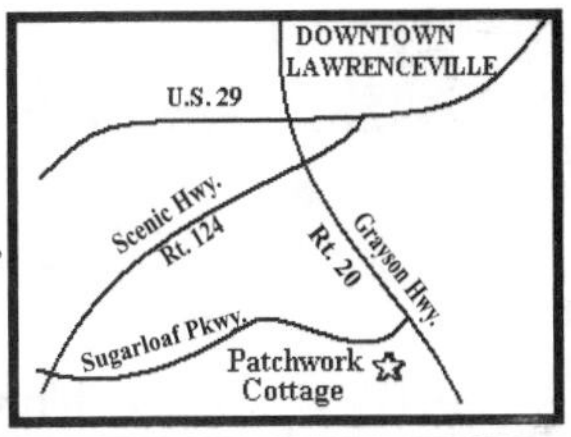

Watkinsville, GA #24

Tues - Sat 10 - 5
Thur til 7

Dragonfly QUILT SHOP

1260 Mars Hill Rd. #103
30677
(706) 769-0070

Fax: (706) 769-0071 Est: 2007 1750 sq.ft.
1700 bolts Online newsletter
info@dragonflyquiltshop.com
www.dragonflyquiltshop.com

A Small Town Shop With Contemporary Flair
"Where Your Creative Dreams Take Flight"

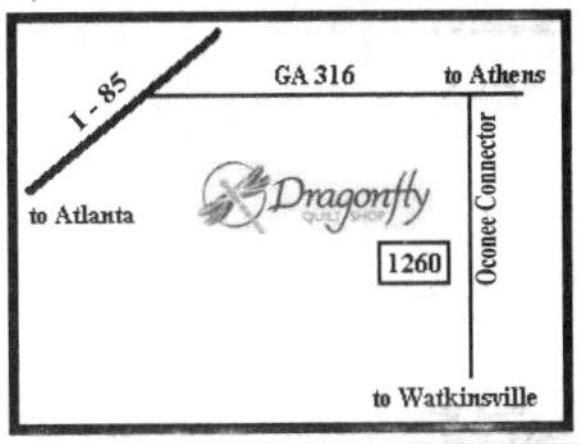

Martinez, GA #25

Mon - Fri 9 - 6
Sat 9 - 5

BRANUM'S
SEWING & VACUUM SUPERSTORE

3230 Washington
30907
Online Newsletter

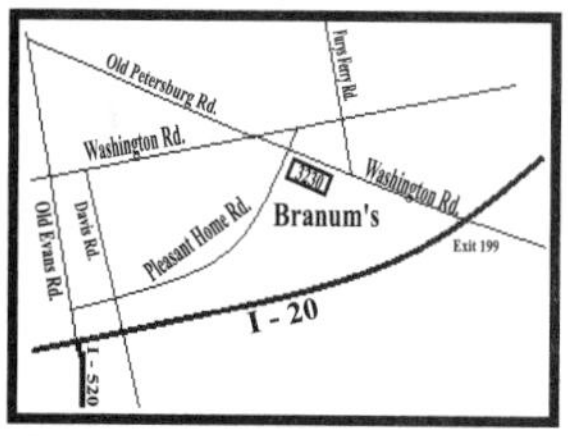

(706) 860-5434 Fax: (706) 855-1314
(800) 462-1457
branums@hotmail.com
www.branums.com
We carry 100% cotton quilting fabric, heirloom fabric and laces, smocking supplies, patterns, and notions. A full service Bernina center with in-house sewing machine repair.

Garden City, GA #26

Mon - Fri 10 - 5
Sat 10 - 4

Sew Much More

4831 Augusta Rd. (Hwy. 21) 31408
(912) 966-5626 Fax: (912) 964-7067
bonnie@sewmuchmore.com
www.sewmuchmore.com
High Quality Quilting Fabrics and Notions from all the best manufacturers (1500+ bolts).
Batiks, Flannels and Heirloom.
Authorized Pfaff Dealer.

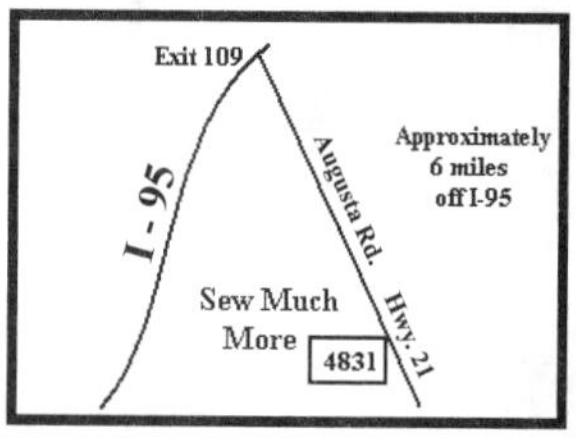

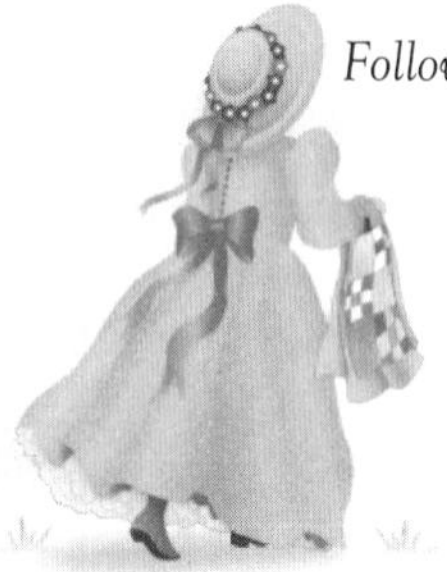

Follow me to...

Suzanne's Quilt Shop Inc.

www.suzannesquilts.com
"Cherishing Quilts of the Past and Inspiring Quilters of the Future."

Suzanne Leimer
Original Owner
Since 1988

Come shop our extensive online catalog or our 5000 square foot store
1800's & 1930's Reproductions, Florals, Batiks, Novelty, Asian, Children's, Holiday, Modern Retro, Flannels, Plaids, Tropicals, LakeHouse, Moda, Thimbleberries and More!!!

- Notions, Books, Patterns & Quilt Kits Galore
- Suzanne's Original Designs!
- Classes, Clubs & Private Lessons
- Handi Quilter Training
- Suzanne's Quilt Escape Retreats

Find us on Facebook
Follow us on Twitter!
Suzy sayz blog

Handi Quilter
Authorized Dealer

9 First Street SE Moultrie, Georgia 31768
888-798-0934 toll free - 229-616-1013
Monday-Saturday 10-5:30 p.m.

#27

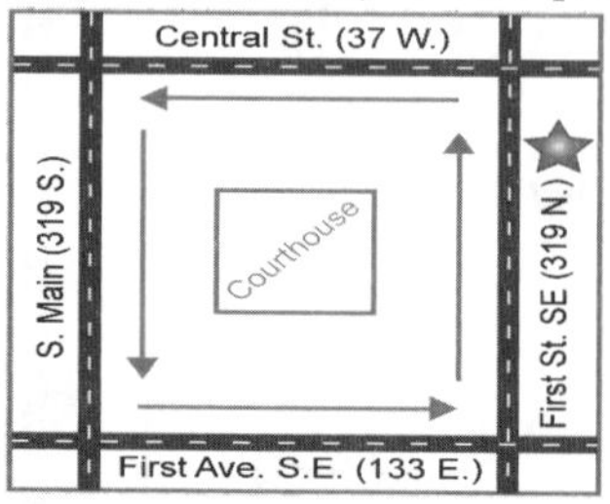

From Valdosta, GA & I-75 Exit 25, Rt. 122 West
From Tifton, GA & I-75 Exit 41, Rt. 37 South
From Tallahassee, FL & I-10 Exit 203, Rt. 319 North
On the Courthouse Square

Don't pass through Georgia without visiting Suzanne's!

Lake Park, GA #28

Mon - Sat 10 - 5

Gone Quiltin'

1244 Lakes Blvd. 31636
(229) 559-1888
Fax: (229) 559-1222
Est: 2009
2500 sq.ft.

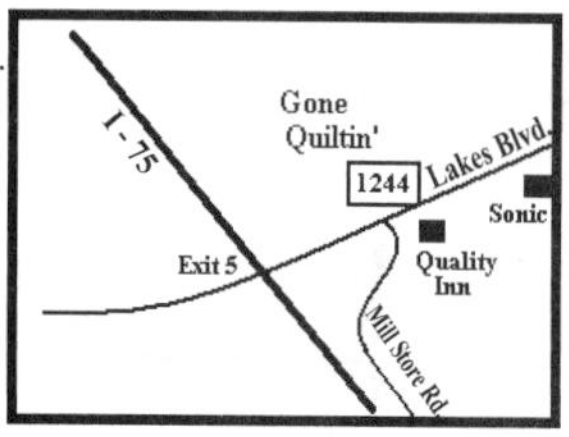

Owner: Rachael Kreyling
gonequiltin1226@att.net
www.gonequiltin.net
Janome Dealer Longarm services available.
Great fabrics, AccuQuilt, Feather Weights.
Visit us for all your quilting needs.

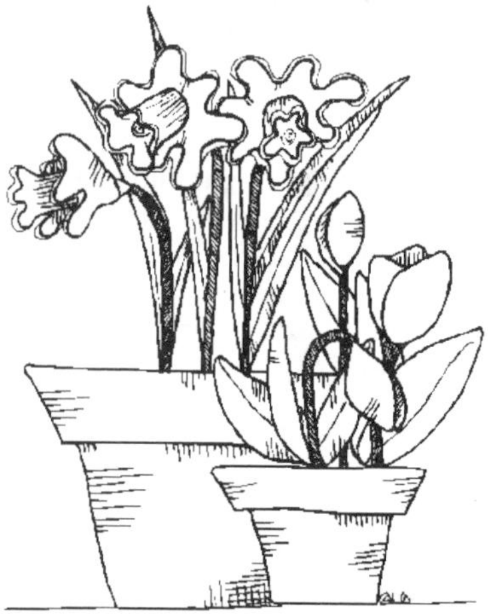

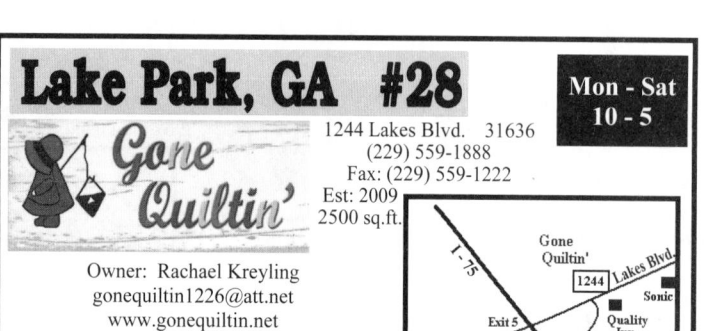

Georgia Quilt Shops

Alpharetta — Share the Spirit Quilting, 3680 Aubusson Trace — 770-642-7350
Bainbridge — Janet's Fashion Fabrics, 124 E. Broughton St. — 912-246-5674
Blairsville — Fabric Center & Quilt Shop, 307 Cleveland St — 706-745-6918

Blue Ridge — **Country Stitches, Inc., 30 W. Main St.**
706-632-3070 **See ad #5, page 122**

Braselton — **Betty Sue's Quilt Shop, 7419 Spout Springs Rd.**
770-965-3380 **See ad #8, page 122**

Buford — **Georgia Sewing & Quilting, Inc.**
1651 Horizon Pkwy., Ste 800
770-831-7990 **See ad #7, page 122**

Carrollton — **Qwiltz Quilt Shop, 206 Adamson Sq.**
770-258-3201 **See ad #13, page 124**

Chickamauga — Memories & More, 121 Gordon St. — 706-375-5300

Columbus — **Sew Much Fun, 7801 Veteran's Pkwy.**
706-317-0024 **See ad #15, page 124**

Columbus — Southern Sewing Center, 2911 Airport Thruway — 706-327-1231

Conyers — **Sweet Home Quilt Co., 1004 Green St. SW**
678-413-1611 **See ad #20, page 124**

Covington — **Patrick's, 10285 Covington Bypass Rd**
770-786-3220 **See ad #21, page 125**

Dahlonega — **Magical Threads, 315 Church St.**
706-867-8918 **See ad #2, page 122**

Dahlonega — **The Common Thread, 598 Grove St. N**
706-864-0740 **See ad #3, page 122**

Dawsonville — Sew Memorable Inc., 4055 Hwy. 53 E #110 — 706-265-2121

Decatur — **Intown Quilters, Inc., 1058 Mistletoe Rd.**
404-634-6924 **See ad #22, page 125**

Duluth — Atlanta Sewing Center, 2255 Pleasant Hill Rd. 770-622-1880

Eatonton — **Stitching Barn, 105 Clack Cir. ste 400**
706-485-0028 **See ad #19, page 124**

Ellijay — **Quilt Shop On The Square, 44 N Main St**
706-635-1135 **See ad #4, page 122**

Garden City — **Sew Much More, 4831-A Augusta Rd.**
912-966-5626 **See ad #26, page 126**

Hiawassee — **Log Cabin Patchworks, 312 Big Sky Dr.**
706-896-7275 **See ad #6, page 122**

Hogansville — **1910 House Quilt Shop, 104 High St.**
706-637-6556 **See ad #14, page 124**

Jackson — The Gardeners Quilt, 658 W 3rd St — 770-504-8222

Jonesboro — **Quilts & Fixins, 7986 N. Main St.**
770-472-0015 **See ad #17, page 124**

Lake Park — **Gone Quiltin', 1244 Lakes Blvd.**
229-559-1888 **See ad #28, page 126**

Lavonia — Ola's Quilt Shop, 1178 E Main — 706-356-1562

Lawrenceville — **Patchwork Cottage, 2070 Sugarloaf Pkwy**
770-237-5455 **See ad #23, page 125**

Marietta — **Little Quilts, 1450 C Roswell Rd.**
770-578-6727 **See ad #11, page 123**

Marietta — **Red Hen Fabrics, 305 Cherokee St.**
770-794-8549 **See ad #10, page 123**

Marietta — **Tiny Stitches, 2520 E. Piedmont Rd.**
770-565-1113 **See ad #9, page 123**

Martinez — **Branum's Sewing Center, 3230 Washington Rd.**
706-860-5434 **See ad #25, page 126**

Martinez — Jeff's Sewing Center, 3833 Washington Rd — 706-863-0090

McDonough — **A Scarlet Thread, 3159 Jodeco Rd.**
678-583-2296 **See ad #18, page 124**

Morrow — Olde Towne Quilts, 1065 Olde Morrow Towne Rd — 770-961-4242

Moultrie — **Suzanne's Quilt Shop, 9 First St. S.E.**
229-616-1013 **See ad #27, page 126**

Nashville — Nana's Quilt Shop 807 Adel Rd.2296863378

Newnan — **Heritage Quilts & Fabrics, 22B W. Court Square**
770-683-9058 **See ad #16, page 124**

Pooler — The Guild, 1109 E. Hwy. 80, #B — 912-748-4188

Powder Springs — **Kiwiquilts, 3200 Hopeland Industrial Dr.**
770-243-3749 **See ad #12, page 124**

Ringgold — **Sew Bee It, 6103 Alabama Hwy.**
706-937-9142 **See ad #1, page 121**

Savannah — Colonial Quilts & Crafts, 11710 A Largo Dr — 912-925-0055
St. Simons Island — Stepping Stones Quilts, 301 Skylane Rd. — 912-638-7128
Statesboro — Deb-Bees Creations, 17943 Hwy. 80 W — 912-764-5423
Tucker — Home Spice Décor 2615 Mountain Ind. Blvd. 770-934-4224

Watkinsville — **Dragonfly Quilt Shop, 1260 Mars Hill Rd., #103**
706-769-0070 **See ad #24, page 125**

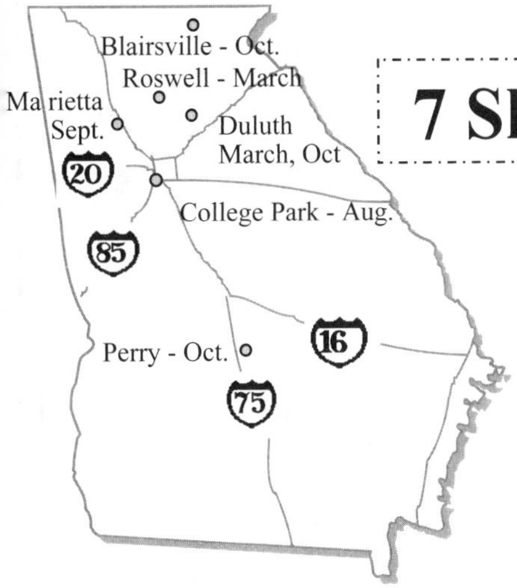

7 Shows

Georgia Quilt Shows

About Shows: We are listing only the very basic information about shows that happen on a regular schedule here. Please check out our website for more details on each show. Also this information tends to change quite often so please verify the event with our website or a local source before you venture far. Or if you're in the right area at the right time, give it a shot.

If you are a show organizer, please keep us updated on your event.
shows@quilterstravelcompanion.com www.quilterstravelcompanion.com
On our website you will also find:

- Exact dates (when we have them)
- Contact Information
- Events happening on a one-time basis
- Sponsor Information
- Description of Event

Month	City	Schedule	Show	Location with address
March				
	Duluth	Annual, 2nd Thur - Sat in March	Original Sewing & Quilt Expo	Gwinnett Center, 6400 Sugarloaf Pkwy.
	Roswell	Annual, 2nd week of March	Bulloch Hall Quilt Guild Show	Bulloch Hall, Bulloch Ave.
August				
	College Park	Odd Years, 1st week in August	Brown Sugar Stitchers Show	South Fulton Arts Center, 4645 Butner Rd.
September				
	Marietta	Odd Years, 3rd weekend in September	Georgia Celebrates Quilts	Cobb County Civic Center, 548 S. Marietta Pkwy. (2 mi. W of I-75)
October				
	Perry	Annual, 1st Thur thru 2nd Sat. in October	Georgia National Fair Quilt Competition	Georgia National Fairgrounds, 401 Larry Walker Pkwy.
	Blairsville	Odd Years, 2nd weekend in October	Misty Mountain Quilters Guild Show	North Georgia Technical College, 434 Meeks Ave.
	Duluth	Annual, 3rd weekend of October	Georgia Quilt Show	Gwinnett Center, 6400 Sugarloaf Pkwy.

8 Featured Shops

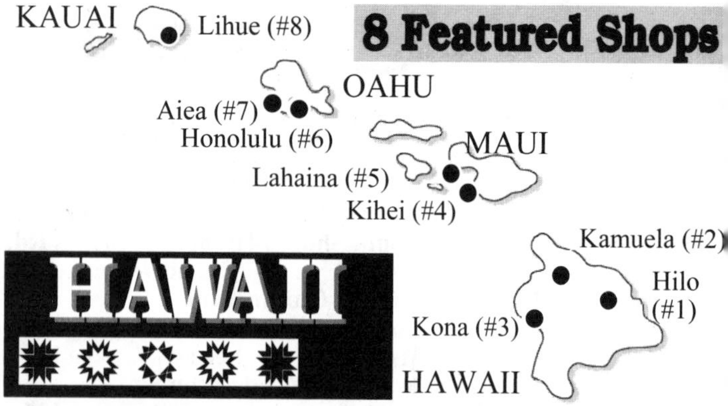

Hilo, Hawaii, HI #1

Mon - Fri 9:30 - 5
Sat 9 - 5

Fabric Impressions

206 Kamehameha Ave. 96720
(808) 961-4468
Owners: Tamarra Bennett & Mary Pierson
fabricimps@aol.com Est: 1988
www.fabricimpressions.com

Hawaiian, Oriental and Batik fabrics, fat quarters, kits, books and patterns for quilters. Handmade in Hawaii quilts and gift items.

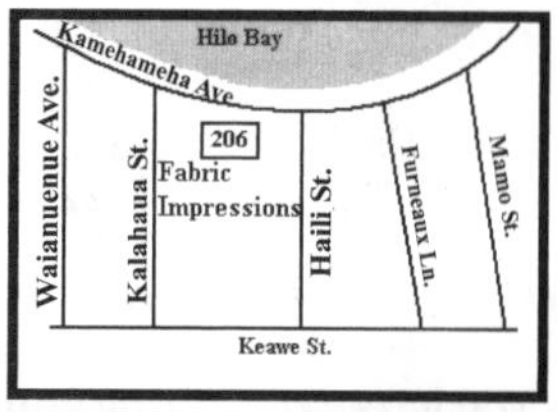

Kamuela, Hawaii, HI #2

Mon - Fri 9:30 - 4
Sat 9 - 1

64-1067 Mamalahoa Hwy.
Holomua Center 96743

TOPSTITCH

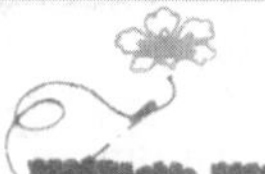

(808) 885-4482
Owner: Liz Moiha Est: 1978
topstitchhawaii@gmail.com
A fine collection of cotton fabrics including tropical prints, quilting solids, and batiks. Needlecraft supplies and Hawaiian Quilts.

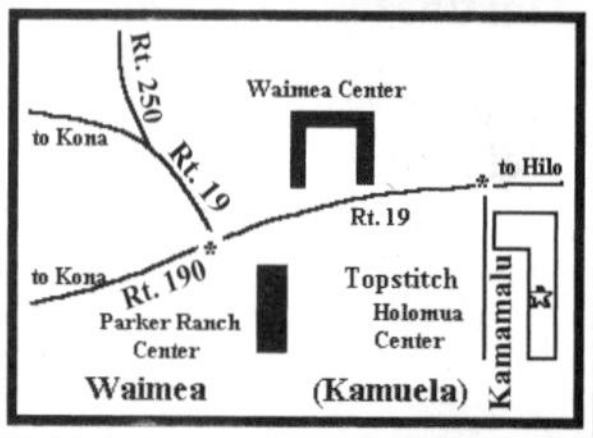

Kona, Hawaii, HI #3

Mon - Fri 10 - 5
Sat 10 - 4

Quilt Passions

75-5626 Kuakini Hwy., # 4 96740
(808) 329-7475
www.quiltpassions.net

Owner:
Karen Barry

Tropical & Batik Fabrics • Yarn & Counted Cross Stitch • Supplies for all your Quilting and Needlework Inspirations!

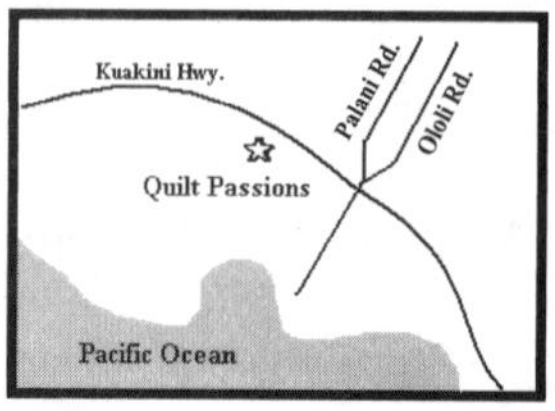

Kihei, Maui, HI #4

Mon - Sat 10 - 6

The Maui Quilt Shop

Azeka Shopping Ctr., Makai, 1280 S. Kihei Rd.
P.O. Box 2322 96753
(808) 874-8050
Fax: (808) 874-8380
Est: 2004
www.mauiquiltshop.com

Unique Collection of Island Quilt Kits and Patterns. Tropical Florals, exotic Batiks & Asian Designs can be found in our shop.

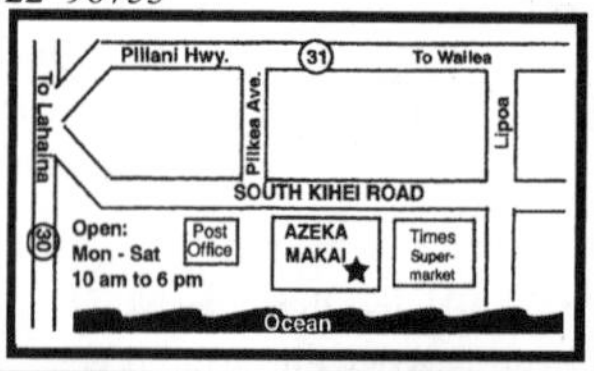

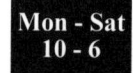

Lahaina, Maui, HI #5

Mon - Sat 10 - 5

The Needlework Shop

136 Dickenson St. #3 96761
(808) 662-8554 Fax: Same
needlept505@aol.com
www.theneedleworkshop.com
Est: 2000
Specializing in Hawaiian quilting. Patterns and tropical batiks. Hawaii quilt lessons available. Other quilt related merchandise. A comfortable shop with aloha.

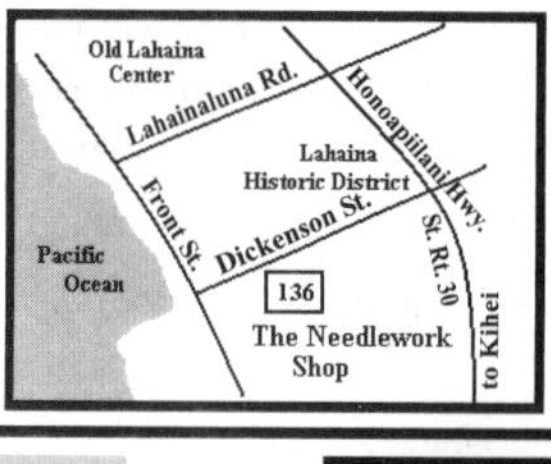

Honolulu, HI #6

Tues - Sat 10 - 5

Anne's Hawaiian Quilt

Watumull Building, 8th Floor
307 Lewers St. #804 - 805 96815
(808) 922-3451 Fax: (808) 922-3451
info@anne-hawaiianquilt.com
www.anne-hawaiianquilt.com

We offer Hawaiian Quilt Lessons! Fabrics, tools, threads for Quilts are all available only at this shop in Waikiki!

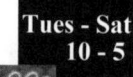

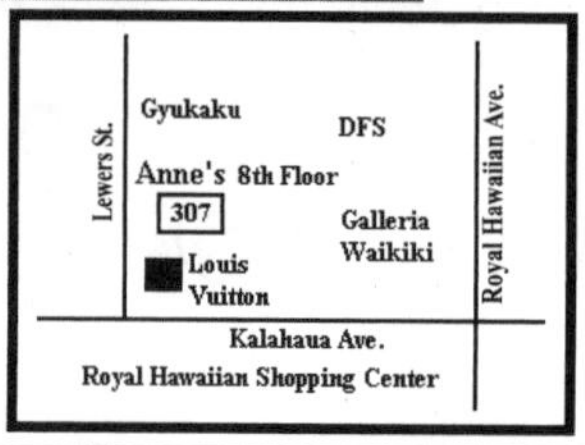

Aiea, Oahu, HI #7

Tues - Sat 9 - 5

The Quilt Hut

"A Quilter's Paradise"

98-029 Hekaha St., Suite 24 96701
(808) 486-6690 Est: 2003 1600 sq.ft.
newz@thequilthut2.com 1800+ Bolts

A complete resource center for the truly obsessed Quilter. Whether you live on the islands or are planning a visit you must experience our Quilter's Paradise.

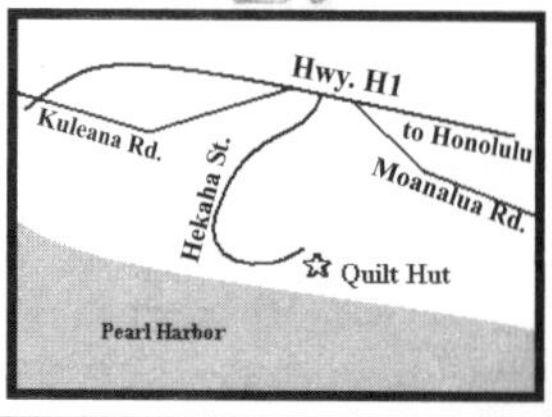

Lihue, Kauai, HI #8

Mon - Sat 9 - 5

Kapaia Stitchery

P.O. Box 1327 96766
3-3551 Kuhio Hwy.
(808) 245-2281 Fax: (808) 245-1772
Est: 1973 Visa, MC, Discover, Amex

We Love Quilting !
The best selection of Tropicals, Batiks, & Quality 100% Cottons for Quilting.

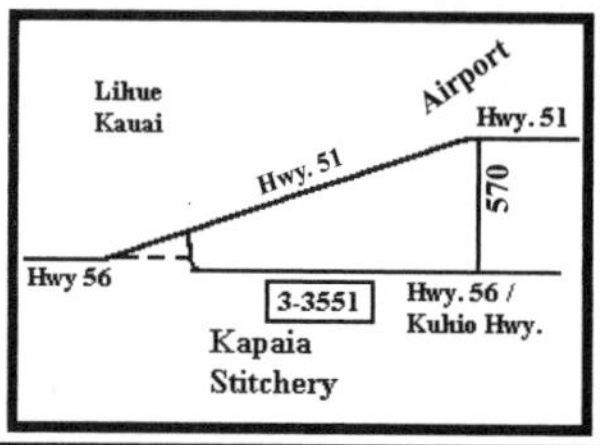

Hawaii Quilt Shops

Aiea **The Quilt Hut, 98-029 Hekaha St Suite 24**
808-486-6690 **See ad #7, page 128**

Hilo **Fabric Impressions, 206 Kamehameha Ave**
808-961-4468 **See ad #1, page 128**

Hilo Kilauea Kreations II, 680 Manonost 808-961-1100
Honolulu My Little Secret, 1050 Ala Moana Blvd. #B2 808-596-2990
Honolulu Hawaiian Style Quilts, 1071 Luapele Dr. 808-487-3700

Honolulu **Anne's Hawaiian Quilt, 307 Lewers St. # 804 - 805**
808-922-3451 **See ad #6, page 128**

Honolulu Kaimuki Dry Goods, 1144 10th Ave. 808-734-2141
Honolulu Viking & Singer Sewing & Vacuum, 670 Auahi St. 808-521-7966
Honolulu Island Crafts & Fabrics, 1284 Kalani St #D102 808-847-0603
Honolulu The Calico Cat, 1223 Koko Head Ave. 808-732-3998
Honolulu Berina of Hawaii, 320 Ward Ave. #114 808-536-6931
Kahului Sew Special, 275 W. Kaahumanu Ave. 808-877-6128
Kamuela Upcountry Quilters, P.O. Box 2631 808-885-7666

Kamuela **Topstitch 64-1067 Mamalahoa Hwy**
808-885-4482 **See ad #2, page 128**

Kapaa Vicky's Fabric Shop, 1326 Kuhio Hwy #4 808-822-1746
Kealakekua Kimura's Fabrics, P.O. Box 435 808-322-3771

Kihei, Maui **The Maui Quilt Shop, 1280 S. Kihei Rd.**
808-874-8050 **See ad #4, page 128**

Kona **Quilt Passions, 75-5626 Kuakini Hwy.**
808-329-7475 **See ad #3, page 128**

Lahaina **The Needlework Shop, 136 Dickenson St. #3**
808-662-8554 **See ad #5, page 128**

Lahaina Quilts 'n Fabric Land, 658 Front St #134B 808-662-0951
Lahaina Ka Honu Gift Gallery, 277 Wili Ko Pl. #40 808-661-0173

Lihue, Kauai **The Kapaia Stitchery, 3-3551 Kuhio Hwy.**
808-245-2281 **See ad #8, page 128**

Volcano Kilauea Kreations, 27 1/2 M M Old Volcano Hwy. 808-967-8090
Wahiawa The Pineapple Patch, 64-1550 Kamehameha Hwy. 808-622-3494

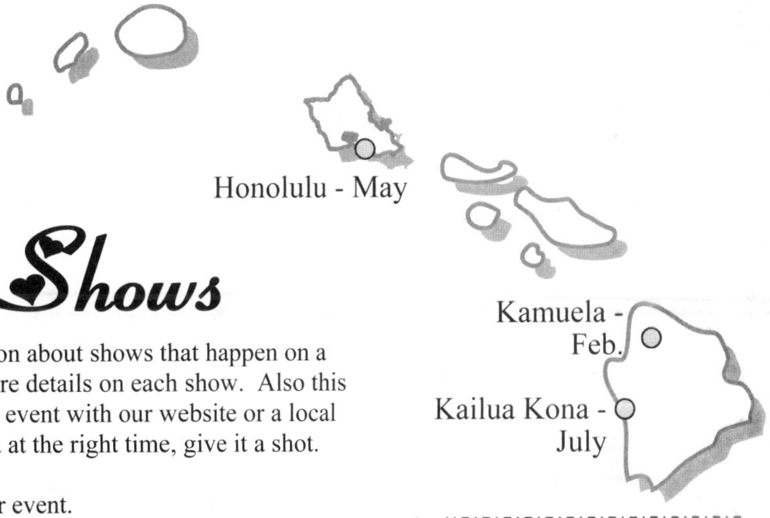

Hawaii Quilt Shows

About Shows: We are listing only the very basic information about shows that happen on a regular schedule here. Please check out our website for more details on each show. Also this information tends to change quite often so please verify the event with our website or a local source before you venture far. Or if you're in the right area at the right time, give it a shot.

If you are a show organizer, please keep us updated on your event.
shows@quilterstravelcompanion.com www.quilterstravelcompanion.com

3 Shows

On our website you will also find:
- Exact dates (when we have them)
- Contact Information
- Events happening on a one-time basis
- Sponsor Information
- Description of Event

Month	City	Schedule	Show	Location with address
February				
	Kamuela	Odd Years, Presidents' Day Weekend in February		Ka Hui Kapa Apana O'Waimea Kuhio Hale
May				
	Honolulu	Annual, 4th week of April thru 1st week of May	Hawaii Quilt Guild Show	Honolulu Academy of Arts--Linekona School, 1111 Victoria St
July				
	Kona	Annual, week of July 4th	Quilt Ventures	Sheraton Keauhou Bay, 78 - 128 Ehukai St

IDAHO

16 Featured Shops

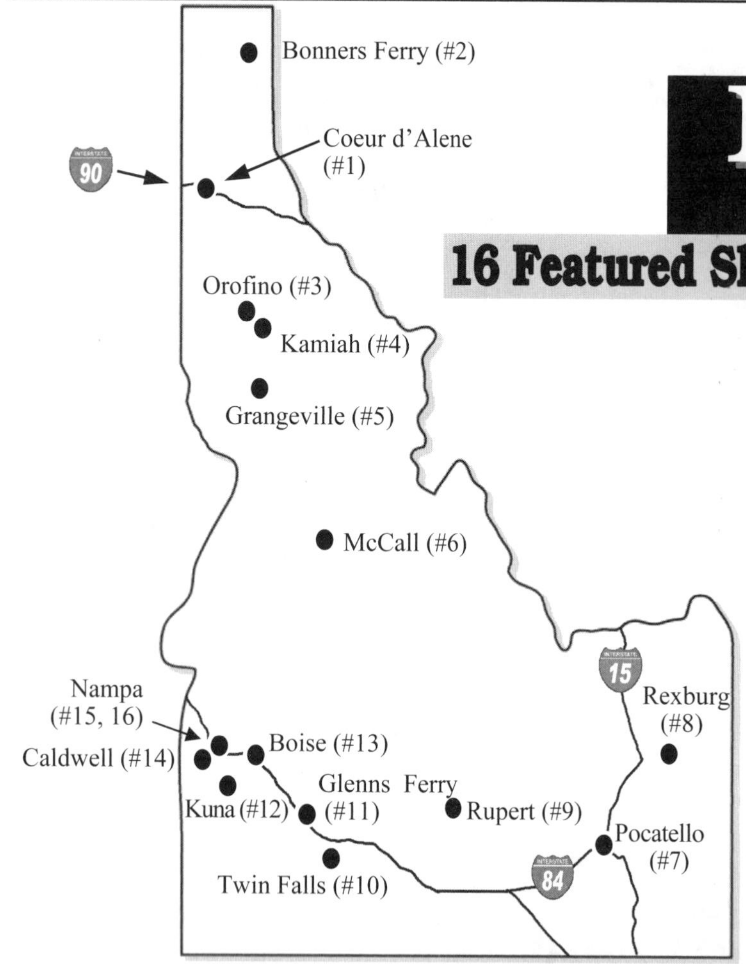

Est: 2002

Coeur d'Alene, ID #1

BEAR PAW QUILTING AND BERNINA

- 6300 sq. ft. of Inspiration!!
- BERNINA Sales & Service
- 5000+ bolts of quality cotton fabrics
- Quilting books, patterns & notions
- Embroidery Supplies
- Wool appliqué & Stitchery supplies
- Gund Bear Distributor
- Many gift ideas for quilters and friends

600 W. Kathleen Ave. #10, Coeur d'Alene, ID 83815
(208) 664-1554 Fax: (208) 664-7739
bearpawquilting@roadrunner.com
www.bearpawquilting.net
Owners: Sandy Goedde & Kathryn Boss

Mon, Tues, Fri 9:30 - 6:00 Sat 10:00 - 5:00
Wed & Thurs 9:30 0 8:00 Sun 11:00 - 5:00

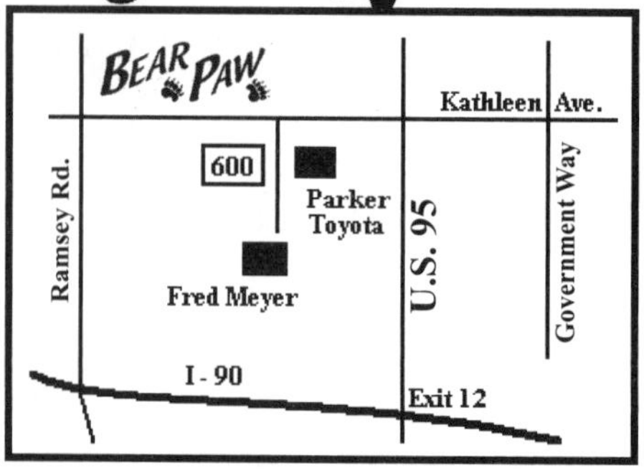

Bonners Ferry, ID #2

Tue - Thur 9:30 - 5:30
Fri 9:30 - 5
Sat 10 - 2

Callie's Niche

6429 Bonner St.
83805
(208) 267-1583
Owner: Callie Gahr

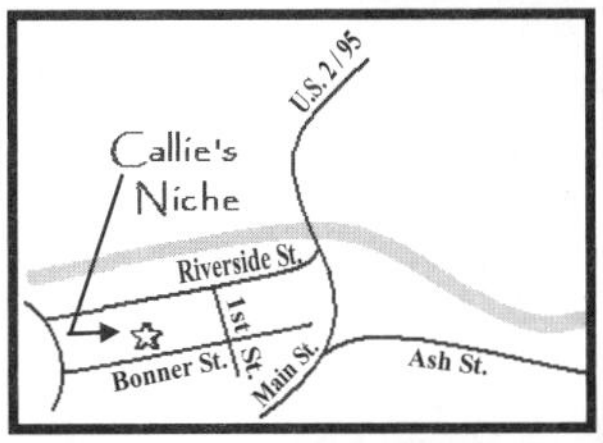

calliesniche@gmail.com
Fun Fabrics Patterns & Notions
Mending & Alterations

Orofino, ID #3

Mon - Fri 9:30 - 5
Sat 9:30 - 2

Wild Hare

222 Johnson Ave., P.O. Box 1061 83544
(208) 476-3358 Fax: (208) 476-3358
Owner: Tina Harper
wildhare@cebridge.net

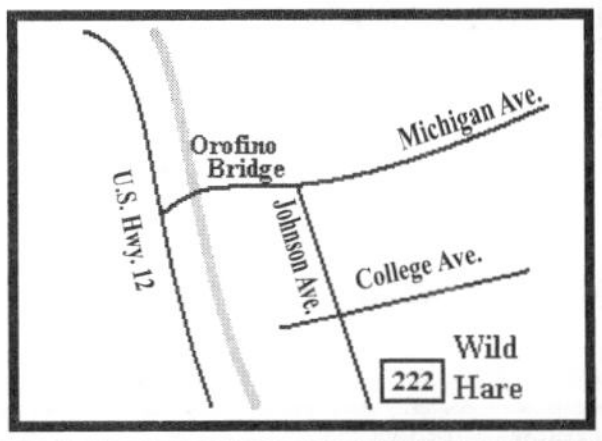

Quality quilting fabric, notions, books, patterns & kits. Friendly, small-town atmosphere, classes, locally made gifts. Also beads, yarns & crochet threads.

Kamiah, ID #4

Tues - Sat 10 - 5
Call first for B & B

Quilt House
BED & BREAKFAST and QUILT SHOP

247 Flying Elk Dr. 83536
Toll free 877 QUILT BB (784-5822)
(208) 935-7668 Elaine Hutchison
www.quilthousebedandbreakfast.com

Directions: After going through Kamiah, cross bridge, take immediate left. This is the Woodland Rd., follow for 12 miles past the Woodland Friends Church. (12 miles, stay left) Take all 1st lefts after the church. (2 more miles to the Quilt House) Pass the Quilt House to the driveway.

Country mountain setting, 14 miles from Kamiah. Enjoy a week-end or week long quilt retreat in a beautiful 3 story log B&B with fabulous views. Sleeps up to 14.

Grangeville, ID #5

Mon - Fri 10 - 5
Sat 10 - 3

Melinda's Fabrics

207 W. Main 83530
(208) 983-0254
Est: 1988 1625 sq.ft. Free Newsletter
melindasfabrics@mtida.net
"A Unique Quilt Stop"
Quality quilting fabrics, notions, accessories & classes. Friendly, relaxed atmosphere.
Come & Enjoy

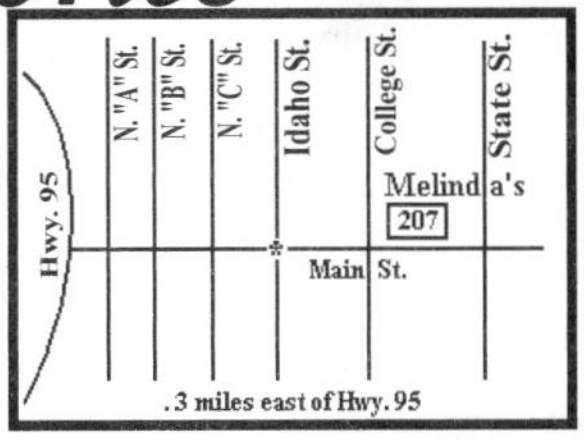

McCall, ID #6

Mon - Sat 11 - 5

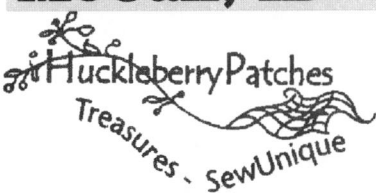

HuckleberryPatches
Treasures - SewUnique

136 E. Lake St. 83638
(208) 634-4933
Owners: Katie Granger & Lisa Murrant
www.huckleberrypatches.com

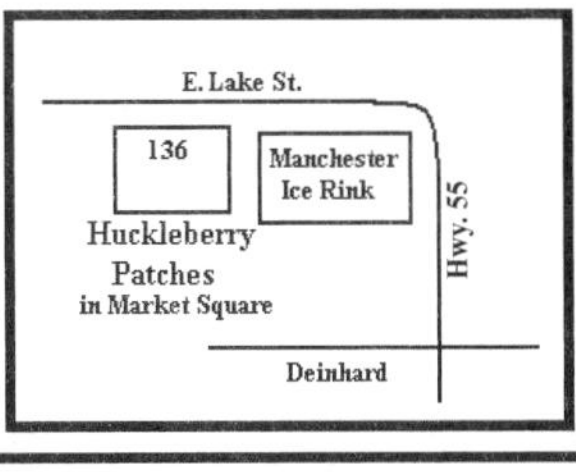

BENARTEX • HOFFMAN • MODA • MAYWOOD • KAUFMAN • WESTMINSTER • MICHAEL MILLER • NORTHCOTT MONARCH • SHANNON • BLANK • TIMELESS TREASURES •

THE AREA'S FINEST QUILT SHOP

We proudly feature quilt fabrics, patterns and programs by the best designers in the industry.

- Quilt programs -- Pre-cut Kits
- Largest selection of flannels in stock everyday!
- Huge selection of batiks!
- Selection of beautiful fabric packets for your convenience.
- Specialty yarns.
- Huge beading department.
- Complementary home décor collection.

Stop in soon, we look forward to seeing you!

We do special orders, and we ship anywhere!

4150 YELLOWSTONE
1-877-I Quilt 2 • (208) 237-1014

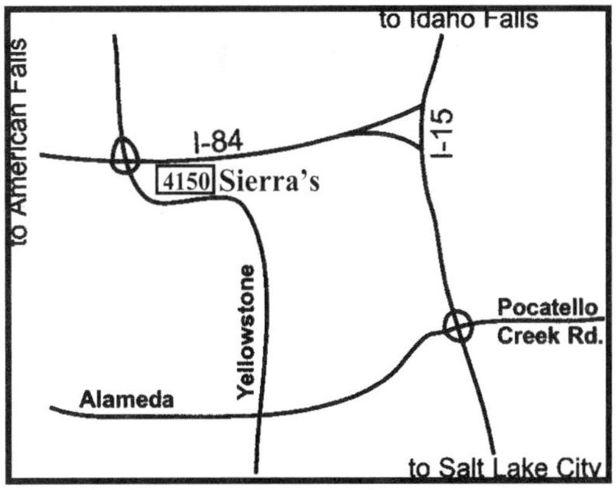

OPEN 7 DAYS A WEEK
M-F 9am-8pm SAT 9am-7pm SUN 11am-5pm
sierrascrafts.blogspot.com ▪ www.sierrasstores.com
Owner: Emma Gebo Est. 1993

Pocatello, ID #7

Rexburg, ID #8

Tues - Fri 10 - 5:30
Sat 10 - 4

Rosemary's Stash

44 N. 2nd East 83440
(208) 356-4181
Owner: Rosemary Ravsten Est: 2008

Quilting fabrics, books, patterns, Batiks, modern and retro prints. Large selection of solid fabrics and tone-on-tone fabrics.

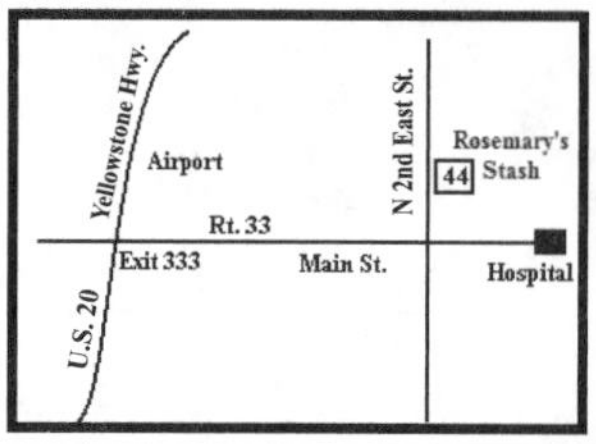

Rupert, ID #9

THE GATHERING PLACE

524 6th St. (On the Square)
Rupert, ID 83350
(208) 436-0455
Fax: (208) 436-9875
info@gatheringplacequilts.com
Owners: Ron & Joyce Jensen
10,000 sq.ft. 10,000+ Bolts

Featured Shop in Quilt Sampler 2006

Idaho's largest quilt shop
www.gatheringplacequilts.com

Mon - Fri 10 - 5:30 Sat 10 - 5

10,000+ bolts of your favorite fabrics.
Machine quilting.
Fun Classes.
Friendly Service.

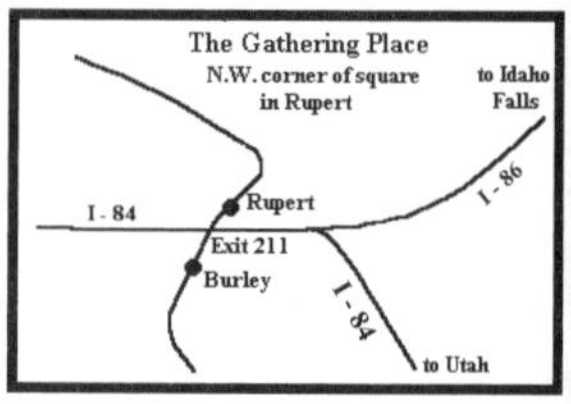

Located just 4 miles North of I - 84

Stitchin' Time

143 Main Ave. E
Twin Falls, ID 83301
208/735-4094
Fax 208/735-1469

PFAFF
Supreme Dealer
stitchintime@qwestoffice.net
www.stitchintime.ws
In downtown, where all the unique shops are.

Mon - Thur 10 - 5:30
Fri & Sat 10 - 5

Shop in a friendly, well-lit atmosphere. 5,000 sq. ft. store with over 3,500 bolts of quality 100% cotton. Loads of quilts on display to spur your imagination.
Huge selection of Books, Patterns & Notions. Professional Machine quilting available.

Metered Parking in front, Free Parking in back. Yes, there is a back door! GPS Coordinates are: N42° 33.330' W114° 28.136'

Twin Falls, ID #10

Glenns Ferry, ID #11

Mon - Sat 9 - 6

Three Island Quilts

97 N. Commercial St. 83623
(208) 366-3031 or (888) 606-0268
www.threeislandquilts.com 600+ bolts
Unique Quilt Shop in Downtown Glenns Ferry specializing in Quality Quilting Fabrics, Notions, Books & Patterns.
Friendly, Fun Service. Longarm service avail.

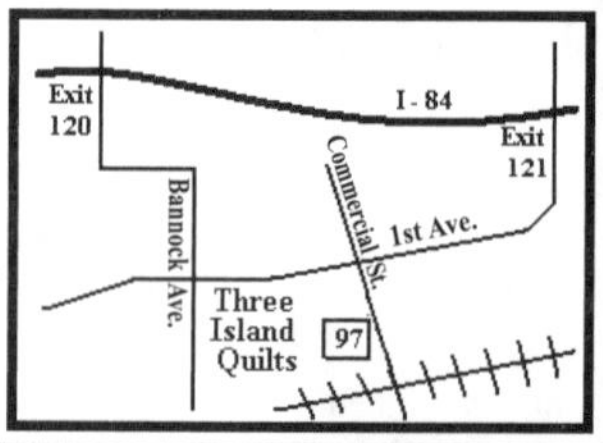

Kuna, ID #12

Mon - Fri 10 - 6
Thur til 8
Sat 10 - 5

Knit One Quilt Too

Yarns • Fabrics • Notions • Classes

762 E. Wythe Creek Ct. #101 83634
(208) 922-1906
Jennifer "JP" & Diane • Owners
www.roomtolearn.biz
Come see us for all of your quilting needs; Quality fabrics, notions, patterns and classes. For a class schedule visit our website.

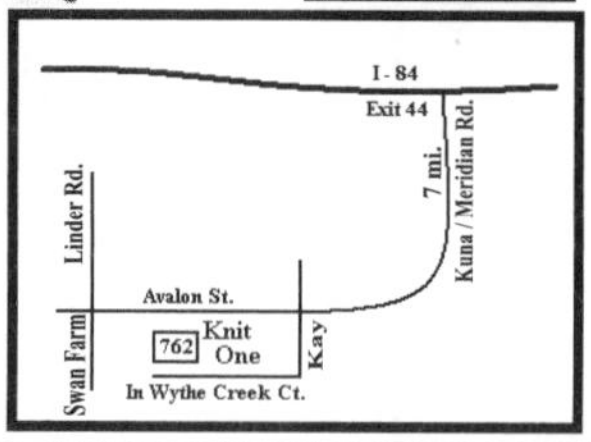

Boise, ID #13

Mon - Sat 10 - 6
Sun 12 - 5

The Quilt Crossing

5725 Fairview Avenue 83706
(208) 376-0087 Owner: Patty Hinkel
Est: 1987 10,000 sq.ft. 4000 Bolts
info@quiltcorssing.com
http://blog.quiltcrossing.com
www.quiltcrossing.com
Specializing in distinctive 100% cotton fabrics, classes, books, gifts & quilt patterns.
Bernina Sewing Machines.

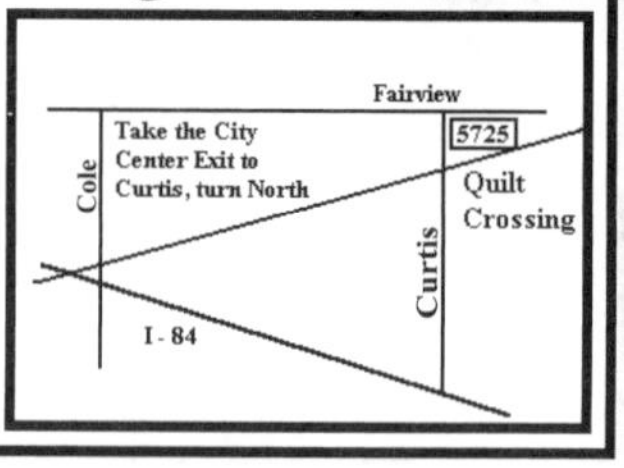

Caldwell, ID #14

Mon - Fri 10 - 5
Sat 10 - 3

Cindy's Quilt Shop

720 S. Kit Ave. 83605
(208) 453-8228 Fax: (208) 453-5152
cindy@cindysquiltshop.com
www.cindysquiltshop.com
Owner: Cindy Martin
Est: 2002 2000 sq.ft. 2500 Bolts
The friendliest quilt shop in the valley of Idaho. Stop by for a visit.

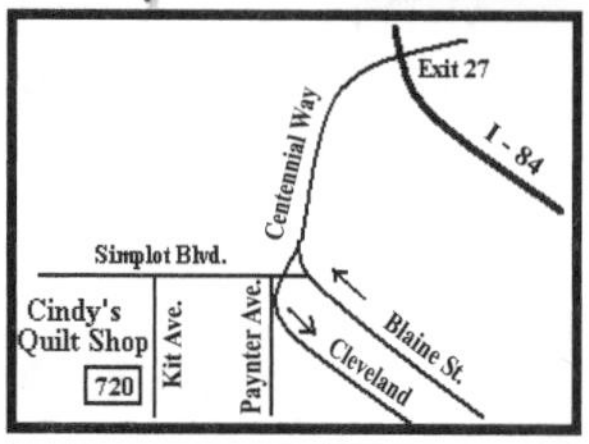

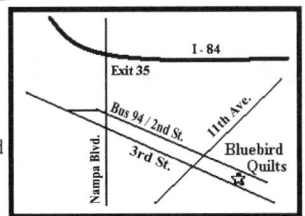

Idaho Quilt Shops

Athol Auntie Linda's Quilt Shop, 8949 E. Scout Tr. 208-683-8948
Blackfoot Bernina's Best by Jolene, 701 W. Hwy. 39 208-684-9100
Boise The Quilt Crossing, 5725 Fairview Ave.
208-376-0087 See ad #13, page 132
Boise The Country Quilter, 966 S. Vista Ave. 208-424-3188
Boise Idaho Sewing Center, 4500-A Overland Rd 208-338-0144
Boise Hollands Sew Shoppe, 6555 W. Overland Rd. #110 208-322-4211
Boise Idaho Yankee Pastime, 300 Greensboro 208-866-6404
Bonners Ferry Callie's Niche, 6429 Bonner St.
208-267-1583 See ad #2, page 131
Burley Hem-Stitching Etc., 1238 Overland Ave. 208-878-0236
Burley Walter Times Two, 1020 E 17th St 208-678-1317
Burley Mill End Fabrics, 1358 Overland Ave. 208-878-5713
Caldwell Cindy's Quilt Shop, 720 S. Kit Ave.
208-453-8228 See ad #14, page 132
Clark Fork Quilt Patch, 54080 Hwy. 200 208-266-1422
Coeur d'Alene Bear Paw Quilting, 600 W Kathleen Ave # 10
208-664-1554 See ad #1, page 130
Coeur d'Alene Lyle's, 600 E. Best Ave. 208-765-9627
Council Pins & Needles, 110 Illinois Ave 208-253-4672
Craigmont Canyon Creek Fabrics, 2059 Younger Rd. 208-937-2631
Deary The Crazy Quilter, 508 2nd Ave. 208-877-1214
Eagle Seams Etc., 124 E. State St. 208-939-8227
Emmett Missing Pieces, 103 N Commercial Ave 208-365-4848
Garden City Quilt Expressions, 9165 Chinden Blvd. #107 208-338-8933
Garden Valley Stitch n' Snip, 342 S. Middle Fork Rd. 208-462-4602
Glenns Ferry Three Island Quilts, 94 N. Commercial St.
208-366-3031 See ad #11, page 132
Grangeville Melinda's Fabrics, 207 W. Main
208-983-0254 See ad #5, page 131
Hailey Sun Valley Fabric Granary, 122 S. Main St. Suite B 208-788-1331
Idaho Falls Granny's Quilts, 390 N. Karey Ln. 208-522-0930
Idaho Falls Porter's Craft and Frame, 2455 E. 25th St. 208-522-5882
Idaho Falls Madsens Crafts & Framing, 2125 W. Broadway 208-523-6074
Idaho Falls Blackbird Haven, 140 S. Freeman Ave. 208-528-7879
Kamiah Quilt House Bed & Breakfast, 247 Flying Elk Dr.
208-935-7668 See ad #4, page 131
Kootenai Admit One Fabrics, 4300 McGhee Rd., Bld. 4, Ste E 208-265-0931
Kuna Knit One, Quilt Too, 762 East Wythe Creek
208-922-1906 See ad #12, page 132
Lewiston Becky's Fabrics & Bernina, 1702 21st St. 208-743-4448
Lewiston Emerald Garden, 2125 14th Ave. 208-743-1849
Mackay Lost River General Store, 4372 W. Houston Rd. 208-588-2270
McCall Huckleberry Patches, 136 E. Lake St.
208-634-4933 See ad #6, page 131
Meridian The Calico Garden, 6235 Joplin Rd. 208-286-9509
Meridian 2 Sisters Quilting Shoppe, 35 E. Fairview 208-887-4707
Montpelier Thimblewood Creations, 843 Washington St. 208-847-1931
Moscow Stitches & Pedals, 872 Troy Rd. #120 208-882-5672
Nampa The Unique Spool, 1303 West Elmore Ave.
208-465-4412 See ad #16, this page
Nampa Bluebird Quilt Studio, 1309 2nd St. So., Ste A
208-467-4148 See ad #15, this page
Nampa FabriQue, 1124 1st St. South 208-442-9276
Orofino Wild Hare, 222 Johnson Ave.
208-476-3358 See ad #3, page 131
Orofino Lura's Fabrics, 10494 Hwy. 12, P.O. Box 1052 208-476-7781
Pocatello Sierra's, 4150 Yellowstone
208-237-1014 See ad #7, page 131
Pocatello Sages Creek Quilt Company, 1625 N 2nd Ave 208-232-0709
Pocatello The Quilt Shop, 119 S. Main 208-233-6611
Preston Fabric Farm & Quilts, 1173 S 1600 E 208-852-1419
Rexburg Rosemary's Stash, 44 N 2nd East
208-356-4181 See ad #8, page 132
Rexburg Porter's Craft & Frame, 19 College Ave 208-359-0786
Rigby The Quilt Shoppe, 243 W Main St 208-745-5151
Rigby Abbots Variety, 120 E Main St 208-745-7738
Rigby Sew-N-Sew Quilts, 5 N 4000 E 208-745-7101
Rupert The Gathering Place, 524 6th St.
208-436-0455 See ad #9, page 132
Salmon Sophie's Quilts and Fabric, 527 Main St. 208-756-1547
St. Maries Mrs. Sew-n-Sew's Quilt Shop, 816 Main Ave. 208-245-6656
Twin Falls Stitchin' Time, 143 Main Ave. E.
208-735-4094 See ad #10, page 132
Twin Falls Tiffany Square, 132 Main Ave. N 2087367286
Twin Falls Idaho Quiltworks, 1563 Fillmore St. #2A 208-736-7500
Viola Grammy G's Treasures and Notions, 1051 Chaney . 208-883-9500
Wendell The Fat Quarter Quilt Shop, 1955 Frontage Rd. S 208-536-6240

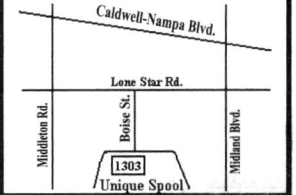

20 Shows

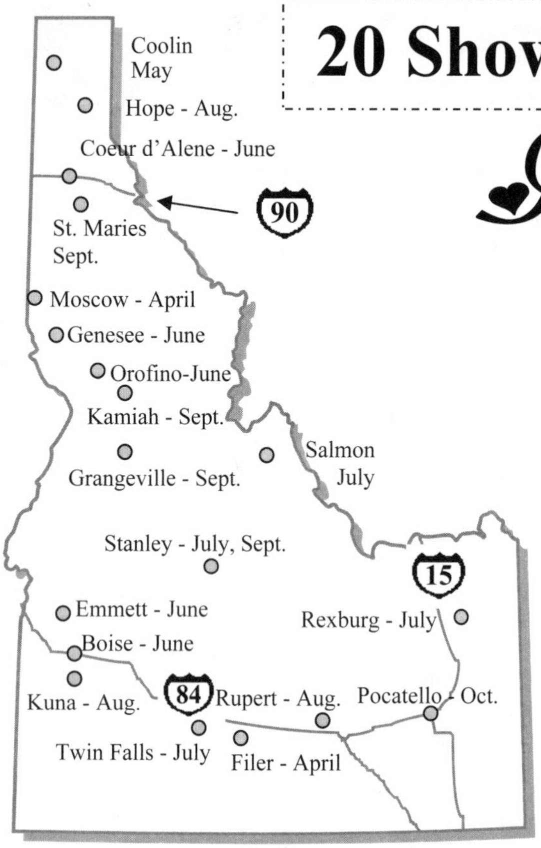

Idaho Quilt Shows

About Shows: We are listing only the very basic information about shows that happen on a regular schedule here. Please check out our website for more details on each show. Also this information tends to change quite often so please verify the event with our website or a local source before you venture far. Or if you're in the right area at the right time, give it a shot.

If you are a show organizer, please keep us updated on your event.
shows@quilterstravelcompanion.com www.quilterstravelcompanion.com

On our website you will also find:

- Exact dates (when we have them)
- Contact Information
- Events happening on a one-time basis
- Sponsor Information
- Description of Event

Month	City	Schedule	Show	Location with address
April				
	Filer	Odd years, 1st weekend in April	Desert Sage Quilt Guild Quilt Show	Twin Falls County Fairgrounds
	Moscow	Annual, 2nd weekend in April	Palouse Patchers Quilt Show	Latah County Fairgrounds - Exhibit Building, 1021 Harold
May				
	Coolin	Annual, Memorial Day Weekend	Coolin Days Quilt Show	Priest Lake, Hwy. 57, Corner of Dickensheet & Cavanaugh
June				
	Emmett	Annual, 2nd weekend in June	Valley of Plenty Quilters Show	Emmett Jr. High School, 301 E. Fourth St.
	Genesee	Annual, 2nd Saturday in June	Genesee Quilt Guild Show	Genesee Senior Center, 140 E Walnut St.
	Orofino	Odd Years, 2nd weekend in June	Clearwater Quilt Guild Show	Orofino Jr. High School Gym, 429 Michigan Ave.
	Boise	Annual, last weekend of June	Boise Basin Quilters Show Boise	Centre on the Grove, 850 Front St.
	Coeur d'Alene	Odd Years, last weekend of June	North Idaho Quilters Show	Kootenai County Fairgrounds, 8056 N. Government Way
July				
	Salmon	Annual, weekend before July 4th	Lemhi Piecemakers Quilt Show	Salmon City Center, Main St.
	Twin Falls	Annual, 1st Fri & Sat in July	Historic Downtown Quilt Walk	Downtown, Twin Falls
	Stanley	Annual, 3rd weekend in July	Sawtooth Mountain Mamas Quilt Show	Downtown Stanley, Main St.
	Rexburg	Annual, last Sat & Mon of July	Mountain Valley Quilt Guild Show	The Bed Place, 59 E. Main St.
August				
	Hope	Annual, 1st Sat of August	Clark Fork Valley Guild Show	Memorial Community Center, Hwy. 200
	Kuna	Annual, 1st weekend in August	Idaho Piece Makers Quilt Show	Kuna High School, 637 E. Deer Flat Rd.
	Rupert	Annual, 1st Mon - Sat in August	Minidoka Quilt Show	Minidoka County Fairgrounds, 85 E. Baseline
September				
	Kamiah	Annual, Labor Day weekend September	Central Idaho Quilters' Guild	St. Catherine Catholic Church, 407 7th St.
	St. Maries	Annual, Labor Day weekend	Valley Piecemakers Quilt Show	Heyburn Elementary Gym, 1405 Main Ave.
	Stanley	Annual, 3rd weekend in September	Sawtooth Mountain Mamas Quilt Festival	Stanley Community Center, Hwy. 21
	Grangeville	Even Years, 4th weekend in September	Camas Prairie Flowers Grangeville	Elementary School, 400 S. Idaho
October				
	Pocatello	Annual, 3rd weekend in October	Happy Hands Quilt Club Show	Booth Barn, Off Pocatello Creek Rd. Exit

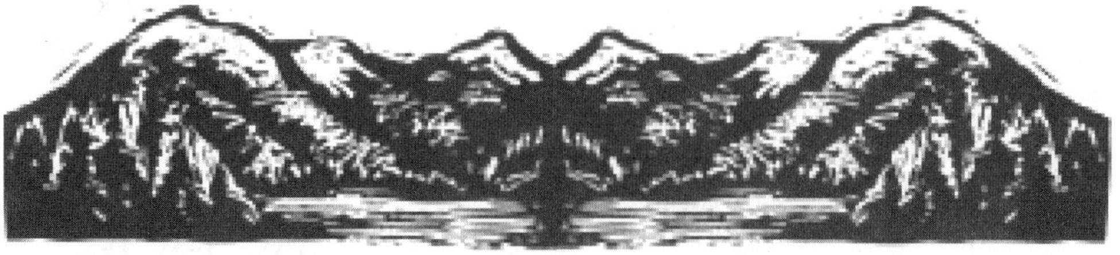

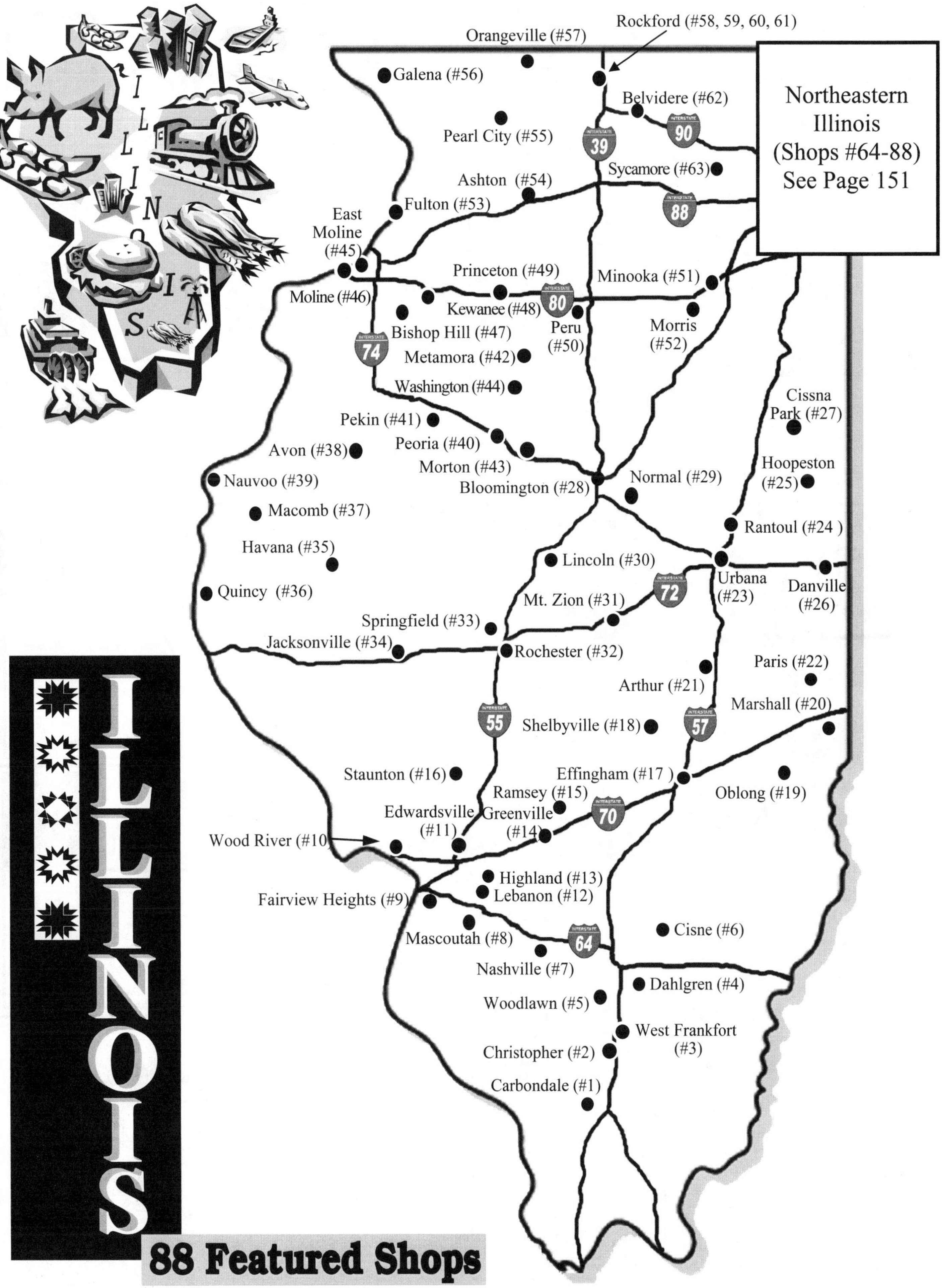
ILLINOIS
88 Featured Shops
Northeastern Illinois (Shops #64-88) See Page 151
Rockford (#58, 59, 60, 61)
Orangeville (#57)
Galena (#56)
Belvidere (#62)
Pearl City (#55)
Sycamore (#63)
Ashton (#54)
Fulton (#53)
East Moline (#45)
Princeton (#49)
Minooka (#51)
Moline (#46)
Kewanee (#48)
Peru (#50)
Morris (#52)
Bishop Hill (#47)
Metamora (#42)
Washington (#44)
Cissna Park (#27)
Pekin (#41)
Peoria (#40)
Avon (#38)
Morton (#43)
Hoopeston (#25)
Normal (#29)
Nauvoo (#39)
Bloomington (#28)
Macomb (#37)
Rantoul (#24)
Havana (#35)
Lincoln (#30)
Quincy (#36)
Urbana (#23)
Danville (#26)
Mt. Zion (#31)
Springfield (#33)
Jacksonville (#34)
Rochester (#32)
Paris (#22)
Arthur (#21)
Marshall (#20)
Shelbyville (#18)
Staunton (#16)
Effingham (#17)
Ramsey (#15)
Oblong (#19)
Edwardsville (#11)
Greenville (#14)
Wood River (#10)
Highland (#13)
Lebanon (#12)
Fairview Heights (#9)
Mascoutah (#8)
Cisne (#6)
Nashville (#7)
Dahlgren (#4)
Woodlawn (#5)
West Frankfort (#3)
Christopher (#2)
Carbondale (#1)
39
90
88
80
74
72
55
57
70
64

Carbondale, IL #1

Mon - Fri 10 - 6
Thur til 8
Sat 10 - 5

Calico Country Sew & Vac

2525 Fairview Dr. 62902
(618) 529-5665
Online Newsletter
Est: 1995
5000 sq.ft.

www.calicocountry.com
Large selection of fabric, notions, books, patterns & embroidery supplies. Babylock, Bernina, Janome & elna sewing machines, embroidery machines & sergers.

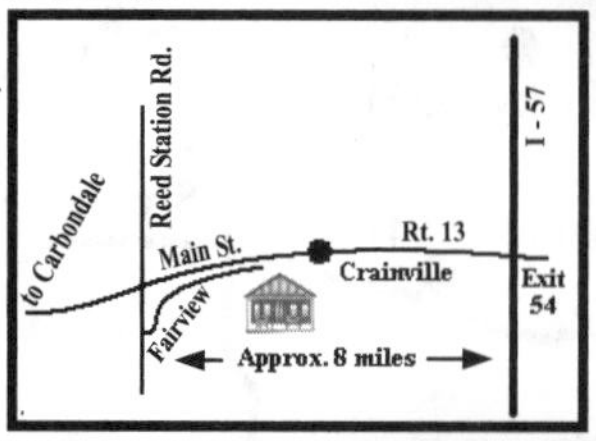

Christopher, IL #2

Mon - Sat 10 - 4
Wed & Sun Closed

Quilters Corner

211 W. Sylvia Ave. 62822
(618) 724-2817
quilterscorner1@verizon.net

Small shop on the corner. We carry main brand fabrics at an affordable price. Ceramic giftware and also embroidery blocks.

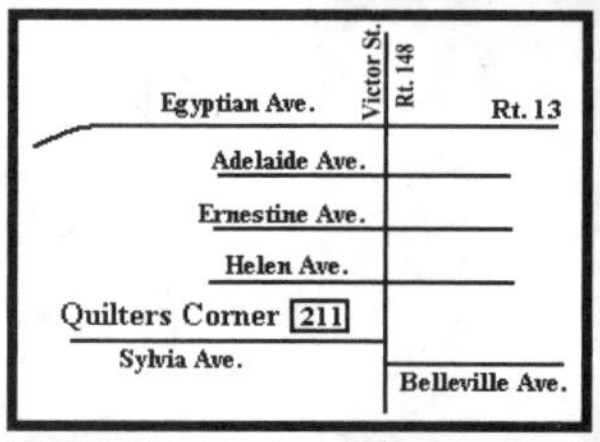

West Frankfort, IL #3

Mon - Sat 9 - 5
Thur tl 8

Calico Country Sew & Vac

310 S. Logan/RT 37 S 62896
(618) 932-2992
Online Newsletter
Est: 1988
5000 sq.ft.

www.calicocountry.com
Large selection of fabric, notions, books, patterns & embroidery supplies. Babylock, Bernina, Janome & elna sewing machines, embroidery machines & sergers.

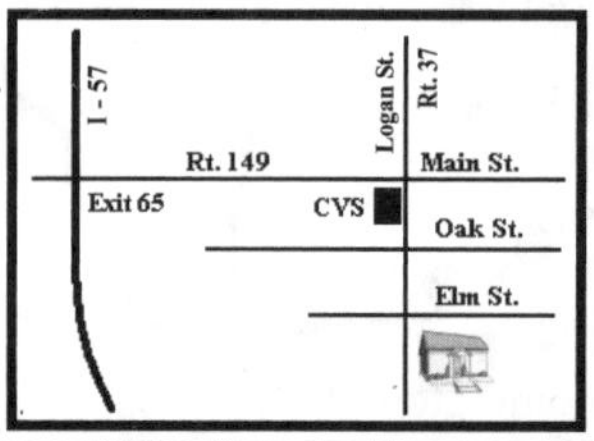

Dahlgren, IL #4

M, T, Th, F 9 - 5
Sat 9 - 3

Joyce's Country Quilts

R.R. #1, Box 54-B 62828
(618) 736-2385
1000+ bolts

100% Cotton Fabric, Notions, Books, Hand-Quilting, Custom Quilts, Kits. A friendly country shop where everyone's welcomed!

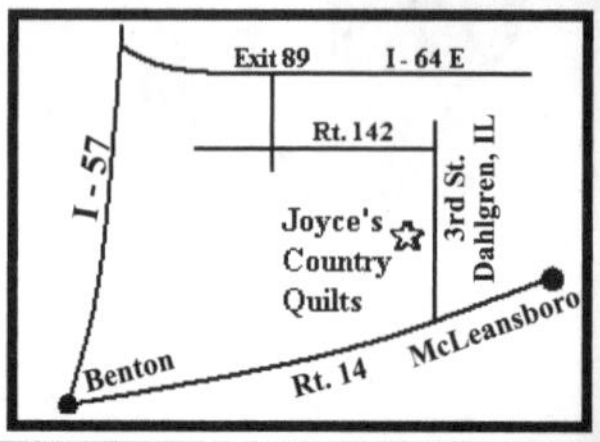

COTTON PATCH

Tues - Fri 10 - 6
Sat 9 - 4
After hours Appt. Welcomed

6194 E. Hobbes Rd. 62898
(618) 735-2483
Owner: Lynne Mears
cottonpatch@frontiernet.net
www.mycottonpatchquiltshop.com

Woodlawn, IL #5

Quality Fabric
Books, Notions
Classes

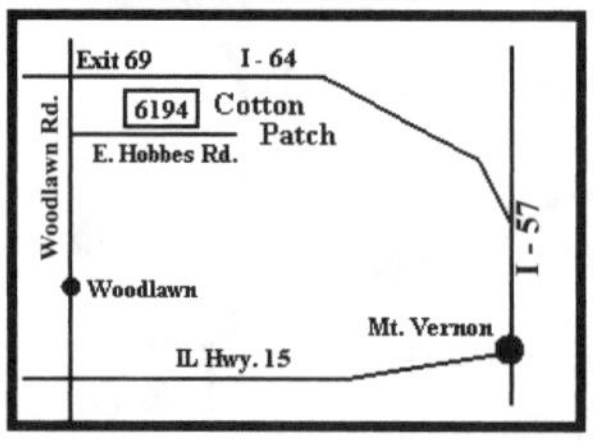

Cisne, IL #6

Mon, Tues, Thur 5 - 8
Sat 8 - 2

Your Quilting Stash

Route 1, Box 90 62823
(618) 835-2681
Owners: Cheryl & Rick Matthews
Est: 2009 1000 sq.ft. 950 bolts
Newsletter
Large selection of Modas and Aunt Graces. Kits available. Long arm quilting available. We are also available by appointment.

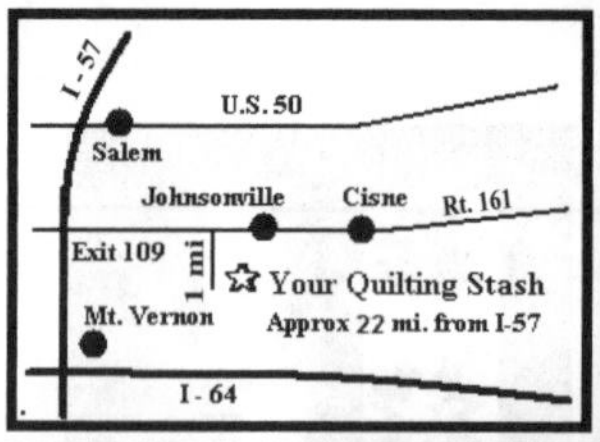

Nashville, IL #7

Mon - Thur 8 - 5:30
Fri 8 - 6
Sat 8 - 5

Lee's Quilting & Craft Center

212 E. St. Louis St. 62263
(618) 327-8898

Supplies for all your quilting needs. Over 1500 bolts of fabric. Over 600 quilting stencils. 114 quilt block designs to embroider.

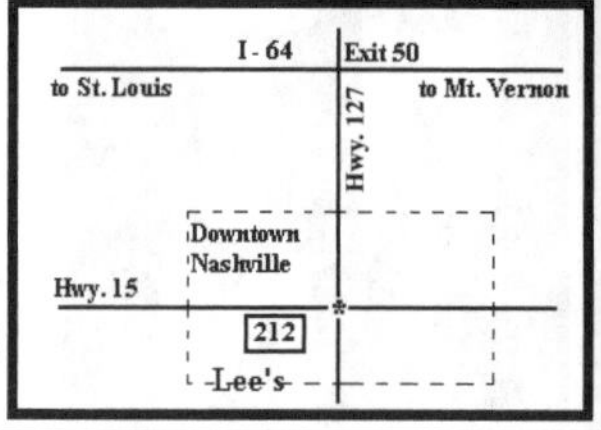

Mascoutah, IL #8

Tues 2- 5
Wed - Fri 10 - 4
Sat 10 - 2

Patchwork Corner Crafts

200 N. Jefferson St.
62258
(618) 566-2652

We have a large supply of quilting fabrics and supplies. We have pieced quilt tops, finished quilts and handmade crafts.

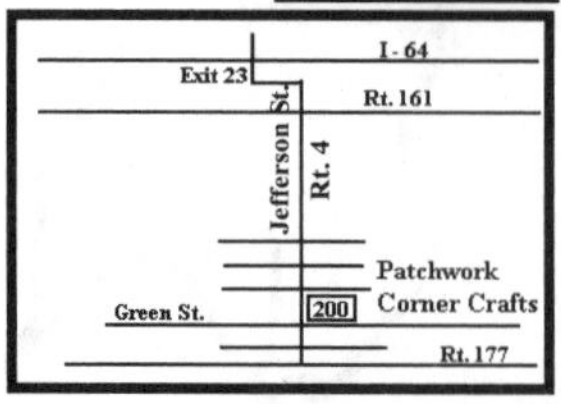

Jackman's Fabrics

Since 1903

www.jackmansfabrics.com

Quilt Superstore - Fairview Heights, Illinois

Babylock Sergers, Embroidery & Sewing Machines

Only 15 minutes from downtown St. Louis

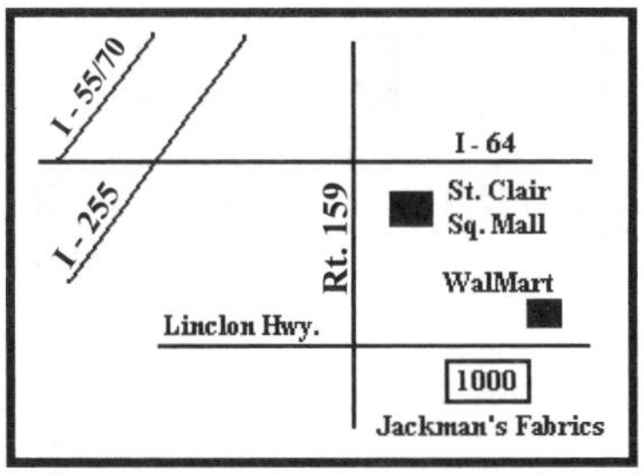

618-632-2700 · 1000 Lincoln Hwy., 62208

Mon. & Thurs. 10:00 - 9:00 · Tues., Wed., Fri. 10:00 - 6:00
Sat. 10:00 - 5:30 Sun. noon - 5:00

Fairview Heights, IL #9

Over 100,000 yards of quilting cottons!
Hoffman, Moda, Benartex, Art Gallery, Lakehouse, Timeless Treasures, P&B, Wilmington, Blank and more ...

Fabrics designed by French General, Amy Butler, Urban Grey, Nancy Halvorson, etc.

Huge collection of batiks, marbles, novelties, patterns, books, etc.

Tremendous displays! Great new ideas!

Bus Groups Welcome! Please Call.
Show us this ad and you will receive a 1 time 15% discount on your entire non-sale purchase.

Patchwork Plus

Est: 1999

Wood River, IL #10

62 E. Ferguson Ave. 62095
(877) 529-9562 or (618) 251-9788
shop@patchworkplus.net
Owner: Jan Copeland
2000+ Bolts of 100% Cotton

Mon - Thur 9 - 5
Fri & Sat 9 - 4 Sun 12 - 4

Home of "Naked Without My Quilts" original designs.

Indulge your fabric craving in a relaxed atmosphere. Our knowledgeable and friendly staff can help you with color selection or any quilting problem you may have. Stop in and say "hello".

We specialize in reproduction fabrics from 1800-1920.

Bring in your Quilters' Travel Companion book and receive a free fat quarter with purchase.

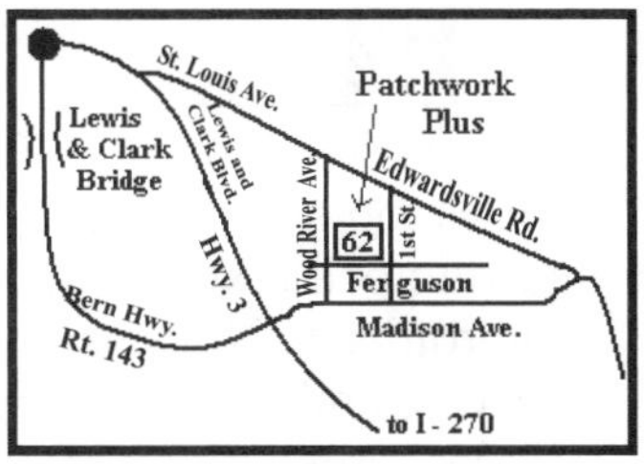

www.patchworkplus.net

Edwardsville, IL #11

The Quilted Garden

Visit our lovely shop in an historical brick home built in the 1830's where we are known for our friendliness, beautiful cotton fabrics, supplies, classes, original designs, Hinterberg/Voyager dealer, and yes, our restroom. ***"We love being your inspiration…."***

Mon - Fri 9:30 - 5 Sat 9:30 - 4 Sun 12 - 4

1310 N. Main St. 62025
618-656-6538
thequiltedgarden@charter.net
Owner: Jenice Belling
Est: 2000 1500 Bolts

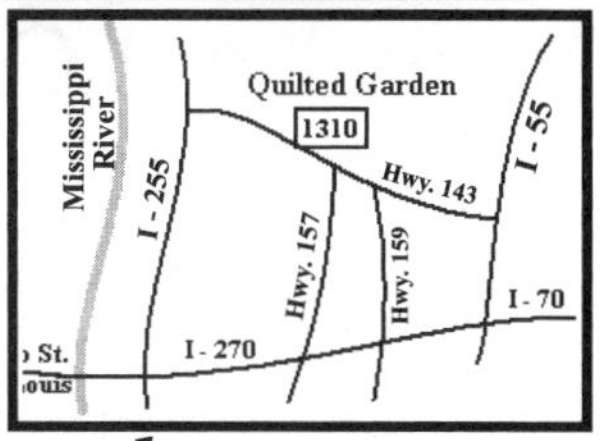

www.quiltedgarden.com

Calico Moon in Historic Lebanon, Illinois

Primitives ★ Folk-Art ★ Home Décor
Woolens ★ Homespuns
Rug Hooking Supplies & Classes

Calico Moon
Est. 1993

Calico Moon offers Moda Fabrics specializing in the warm, primitive color palettes. We offer the largest selection of 100% mill-dyed and hand-dyed wools.

Rug Hooking classes and supplies available.

Hours
Tues - Sat 10am - 5pm

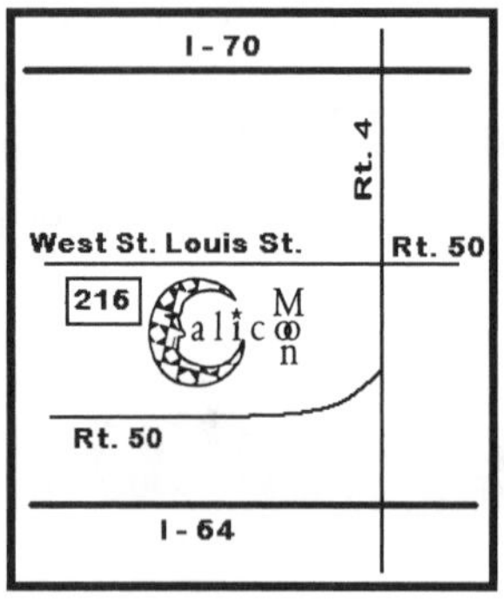

216 W. St. Louis St.
Lebanon, IL 62254
618-537-6240

Visit us at: www.ShopCalicoMoon.com

Lebanon, IL #12

Highland, IL #13

Tues - Fri 9 - 4
Sat 9 - 3

Rosemary's Fabric & Quilts

812 Ninth St. 62249
(618) 654-5045
Owner: Rosemary Seifried
Est: 1988
Rosemarys_Quilts@charter.net

Largest Thimbleberries Selection in St. Louis Area.
Over 3000 Bolts of Fabric.
Everything a Quilter Needs!

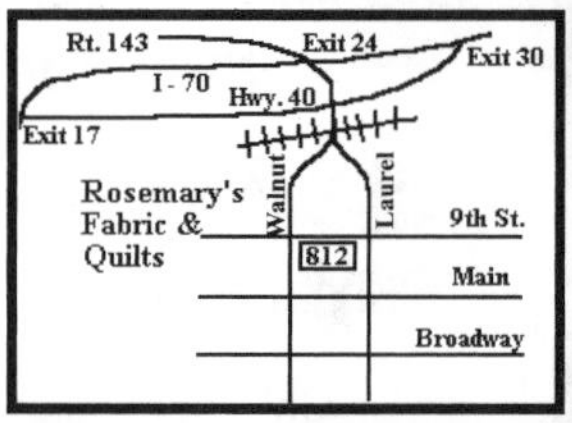

Greenville, IL #14

Tues - Thur 9 - 5
Fri 9 - 7
Sat 9 - 3

Farmland Quilting & Embroidery

201 S. 4th St. 62246
(888) 483-4794 or (618) 664-2139
Owners: Lora Kennedy & Virginia Schewe
farmlandqande@celerityinc.com
www.farmlandquilting.com

Cotton, fleece, flannel, batting, notions, yarn, patterns, books, stamped goods, classes, crystal & porcelain gifts, handmade jewelry, custom machine quilting & embroidery.

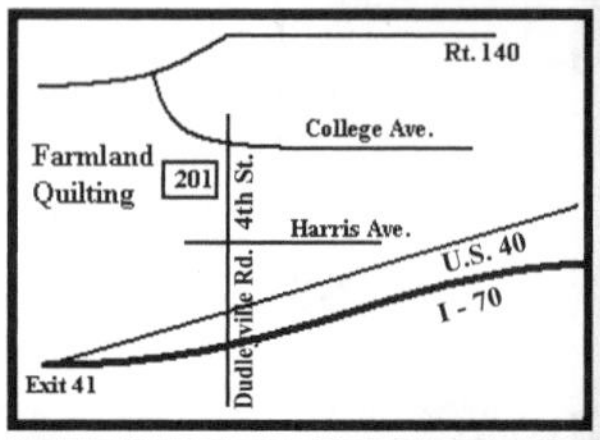

Ramsey, IL #15

Tues - Fri 9 - 5
Sat 9 - 2

The Quilt Top Shop

332 S. Superior St. 62080
(618) 423-1239
Owner: Patti Van Uytven
Est: 2007 Newsletter
quilttopshop@yahho.com
www.quilttopshop.com

We have over 1500 bolts of fabric, quilt kits, books, patterns, and quilting supplies. We also carry embroidery blocks, tops, and floss. Longarm machine quilting services available.

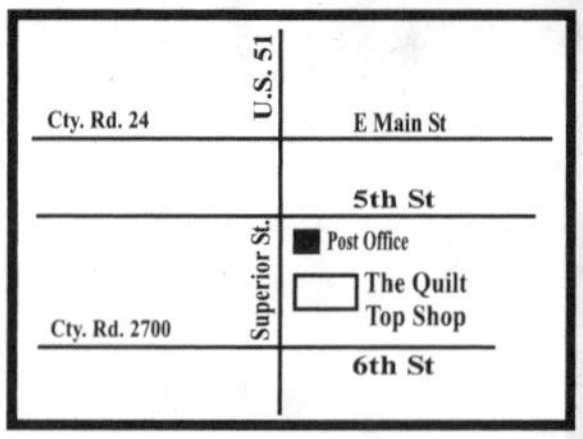

Staunton, IL #16

Tues - Sat 10 - 4

Main Street Mini Mall

Quilt Shop and More

124 E. Main St. 62088
(618) 635-5509
Owner: Helen (Jody) Zarr Est: 2002
100% Cotton Fabrics - Notions - Quilting Books - Fat Quarters - Classes - Pre-stamped Embroidery Blocks - Guetermann Cotton Threads - Batting - Machine Quilting Available. 5000 bolts of fabric.

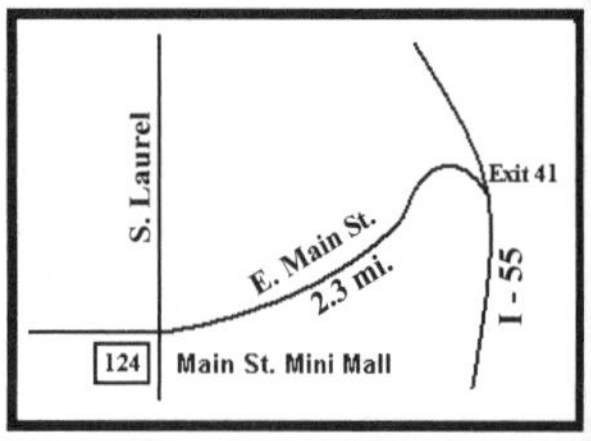

Shelbyville, IL #18

Mon - Sat 9 - 5

Main Street Quilt Company

200 E. Main St. 62565
(217) 774-3484
Est: 2008 Online Newsletter
www.mainstreetquiltcompany.com

A full service quilt shop just minutes from Lake Shelbyville. Fabrics, notions, patterns, classes, longarm machine quilting & much more!

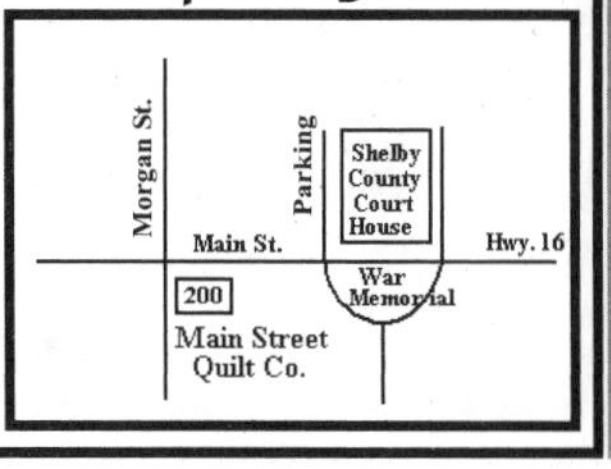

Angie's Nine Patch

Mon - Fri 9 - 6
Sat 8 - Noon
Closed Sun

Effingham, IL #17

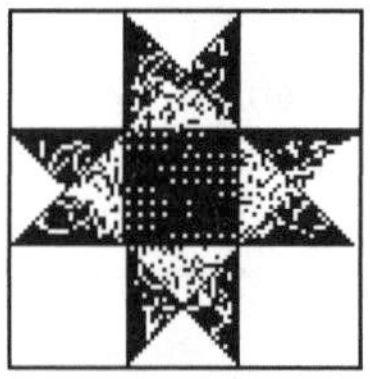

804 S. Henrietta 62401
Exit 159, turn right on Henrietta
(217) 347-9669 3000 Bolts

Large selection of fabrics, books, patterns and stamped textiles for embroidery. Notions, laces, embroidery flosses, crochet thread
Low Prices.

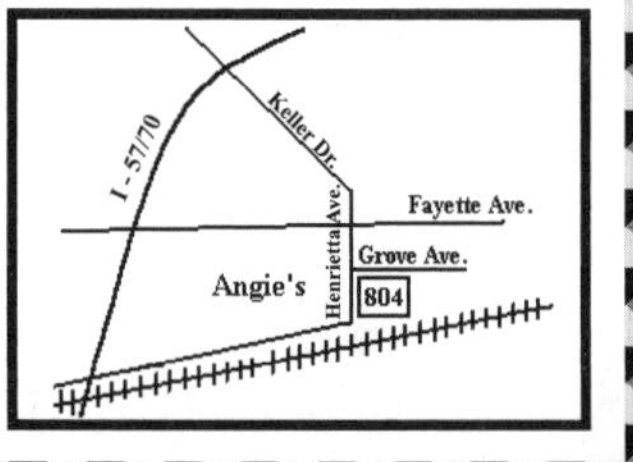

Oblong, IL #19

Mon - Sat 9 - 5 Evenings by Appt.

The Village Stitchery

108 E. Main 62449
(618) 592-4134 2400 sq.ft.
Owner: Lisa Pinkston Est: 1982
www.villagestitchery.com
Visit our unique shop which carries a complete line of fabrics and supplies for the beginning to expert quilter.

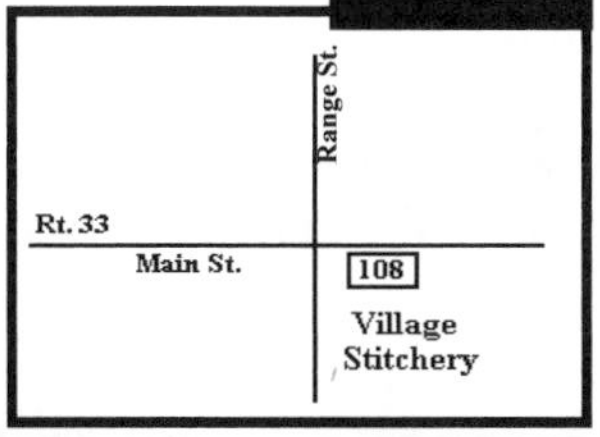

Marshall, IL #20

Mon & Wed 3-6 Tues & Thur 10-2 Fri 10-6 Sat 10-5

White Stallion Creations

620 Archer Ave. 62441
(217) 826-3787
Owner: Edie Wittenmyer
witt_biz@yahoo.com
www.whitestallioncreations.com
Visit the studio in historic downtown Marshall, IL and receive a 10% discount with purchase of quality quilting fabric!

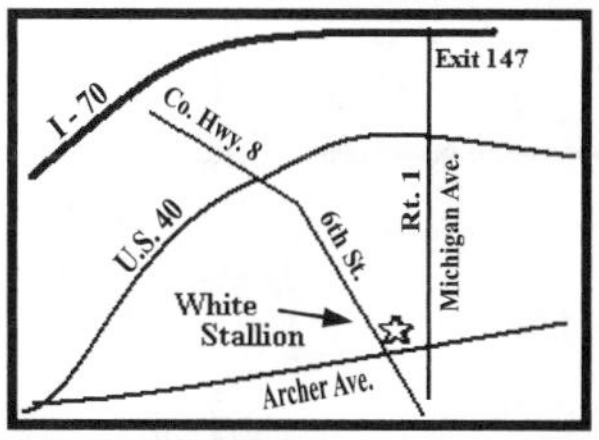

Arthur, IL #21

Mon - Sat 8:30 - 5

Stitch & Sew Fabrics

220 S. Vine St. 61911
(217) 543-2287
Est: 1994
stitchandsew@consolidated.net
Owners: Sam & Dorothy Herschberger

Over 2000 Bolts of high quality name brand Quilting Cottons, Pre Stamped Embroidery Blocks, Embroidery Floss, Long Arm Quilting, Quilting Supplies, Books and Notions. Authorized Babylock Dealer.

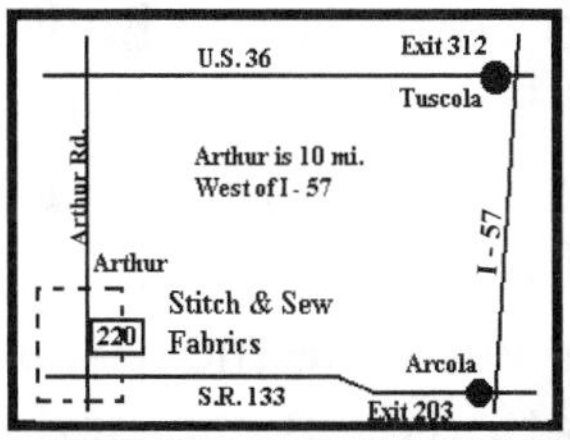

Paris, IL #22

Lori's Pins 'n Needles

(217) 465-5541
loris@comwares.net
www.lorisviking.com

Husqvarna VIKING

"Quilting Headquarters"

- Over 3000 bolts of name brand 100% cotton fabrics
- Books, patterns and quilting tools
- Large classroom area—classes and demonstrations
- Authorized Husqvarna Viking Sewing Machine Sales and Service.

Monday - Thursday 9-6
Friday 9-8
Saturday 9-5

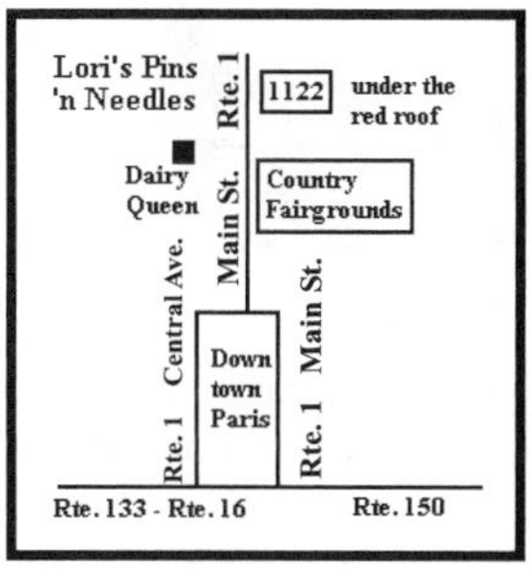

1122 N. Main St.
P.O. Box 815 61944

156A Lincoln Square Mall
Urbana, IL 61801
217-328-1591
www.sewsassyinc.com
sewsassy@sbcglobal.net

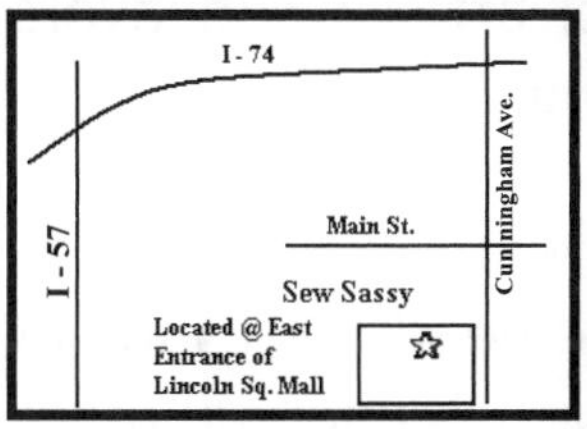

Sew Sassy

Owners: Joyce Day & Nancy Muncaster

Mon - Fri 10 - 6:30 Sat 10 - 6 Sun 10 - 5

Urbana, IL #23

Sew Sassy is not your traditional quilt shop. Bright colors and unique designs as well as traditional patterns can be found displayed on its walls. You will also find a large collection of batiks, fabric collections by Laurel Burch, many colorful fabrics as well as traditional fabrics. We also offer Pfaff, Bernina and Janome.

Rantoul, IL #24

Tues - Fri 10 - 5 Sat 10 - 4

The Needle & I

801 Arends Blvd. #102 61866
(217) 892-2638
needleI@egix.net

Visit our shop located in the former headquarters building on the converted Chanute Air Force Base. Filled with all your quilting needs! Elna sales and service.

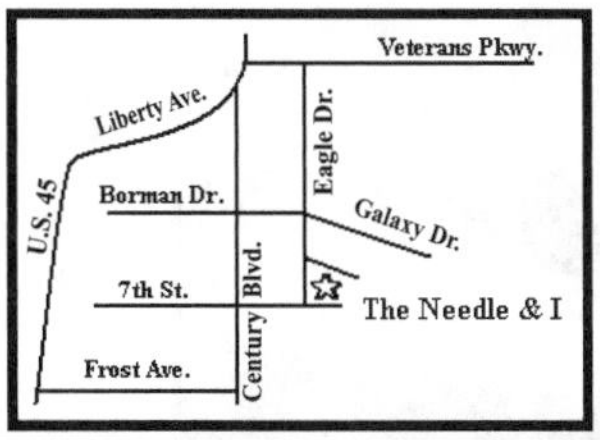

Hoopeston, IL #25

Mon - Fri 9 - 5:30 Sat 9 - 3

The Sewing Boutique

222 E. Main St. 60942
(217) 283-7125 Fax: (217) 283-5580
vkeller5@verizon.net or
jbauer6@hotmail.com
Est: 1980 2200 sq.ft.

A fabric shop stocking basics and quality cottons for quilting.
Authorized Husqvarna Viking dealer.
Classes Galore!

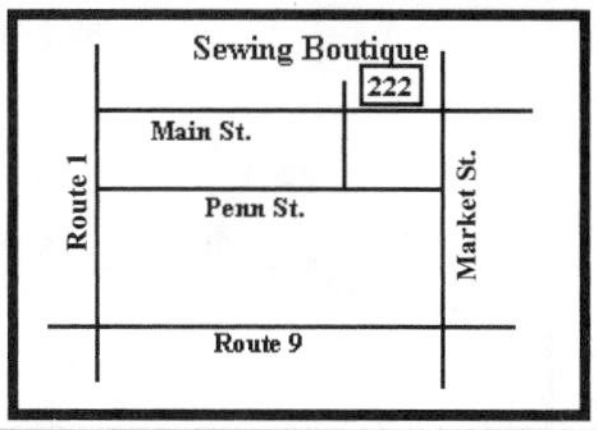

Threads and Beds
Retreat Center

www.threadsandbedsretreat.com

207 S. Buchanan St.
Danville, IL 61832
1-866-431-9202
threadsoftimefab@aol.com

Welcome to Threads and Beds Retreat Center! Our unique facility allows you to relax, explore your creativity, and have a fantastic time sewing with friends and fellow craftswomen. Our goal is to provide you with the most spacious and gracious accommodations you can find -- a facility specifically designed for artistic endeavors of sewing, quilting, and scrapbooking.

We look forward to hosting you and providing for your artistic needs, both in our retreat center and in the fabulous attached quilt shop, Threads of Time, with more than 4000 bolts of fabric, hundreds of the newest notions, and a complete book and pattern studio.

- 9,500 sq. ft. of retreat area
- Two large sewing areas with custom-made sewing tables and plush leather chairs
- Sewing space for 60 sewers at a time
- Minimum of 2/ Maximum of 36 overnight sewers
- Horn cutting tables, irons and ironing-boards
- 5 Large Design Walls (8' x 6')
- Totally handicapped accessible, one-level facility with no stairs
- 6 individual restrooms, 3 shower rooms - (separate from restrooms)
- 2 Large kitchens / dining rooms with seating for 24 each
- Refrigerators, microwaves, toaster ovens, large counter space for serving
- Wireless Internet and Cable TV in dining areas
- Connected to Threads of Time, the region's premier quilt shop (see opposite page)

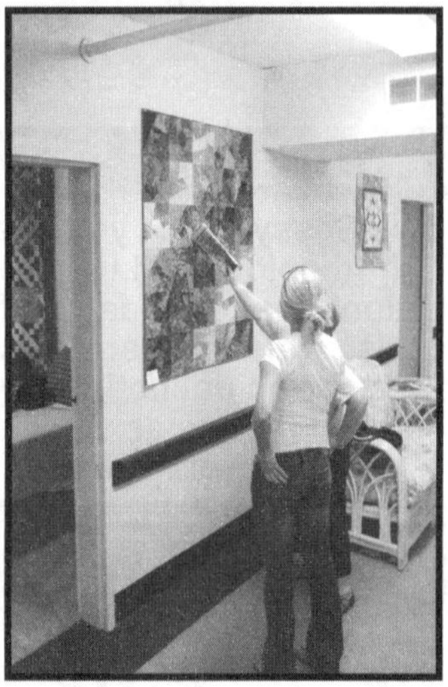

"For the times of your life and the fabric of the times..."

Threads of Time

Creative Sewing & Retreat Center

Owners: Bill & Melissa Gouty
Est: 2006

www.threadsoftimefab.com

Danville, IL #26

207 S. Buchanan St.
Danville, IL 61832

M-F 9:00am-6:00pm
Sat 9:00am-3:00pm

217-431-9202
1-866-431-9202
email: threadsoftimefab@aol.com

6,000 sq. ft. of fabric, notions, and displays!

Full line of world's finest Janome sewing machines

Horn Cabinets & Accessories

Sewing machine repairs

Over 4,000 Bolts of Fabric

Extensive collection of books and patterns

I-74 to Exit #216 South to Perrysville Rd
Go Right on Perrysville Rd 6 blocks
Look for the big English Street Clock

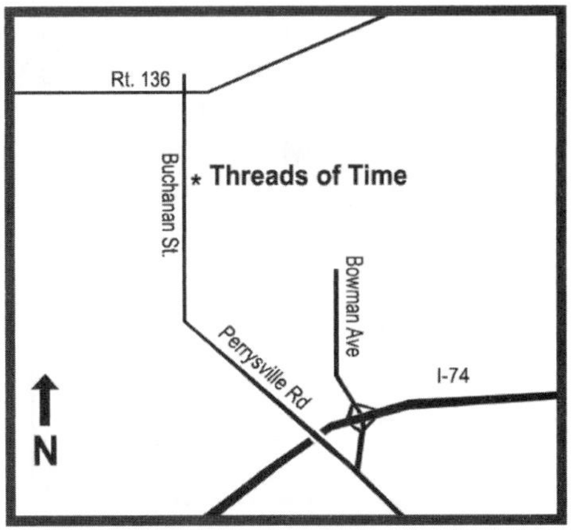

"For the times of your life and the fabric of the times..."

Prairieland Quilts

Over 2000 square feet of shopping with thousands of Bolts of Fabric, large selection of books, patterns, and supplies. Janome sewing machine sales and service; machine and hand quilting service available; home of QuiltersWarehouse.com serving the world with an online catalog of over 3,500 quilt books and patterns.

Mon - Fri 9 - 4
Sat 9 - 3

JANOME

101 N. 2nd. St. (Rt.49) 60924
(815) 457-2867
www.prairielandquilts.com
Owner: Suzanne Bruns Est: 1993

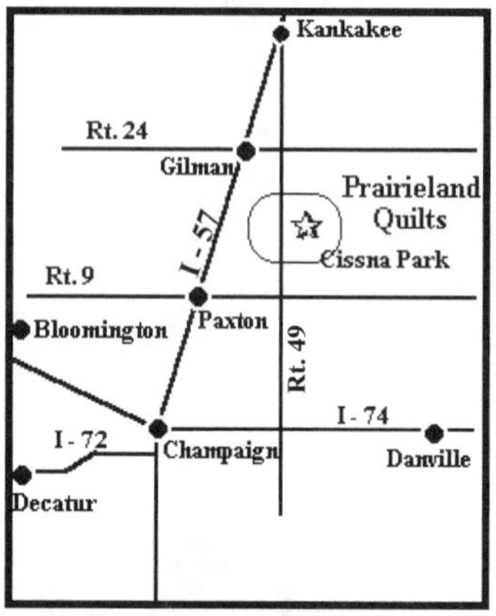

Cissna Park, IL #27

Bring your 'Travel Companion' with you and receive a one time 10% discount on your purchase.

Bloomington, IL #28

The Treadle

Est: 1976

Wed 10 - 5
Thur 10 - 6
Fri 10 - 5
Sat 10 - 4
Sun 12 - 4

2101 Eastland 61704
(309) 662-1733
10,000 Bolts, largest selection of quilt books in central Illinois.

20% discount, on anything regular price, whenever you pay cash (green)!

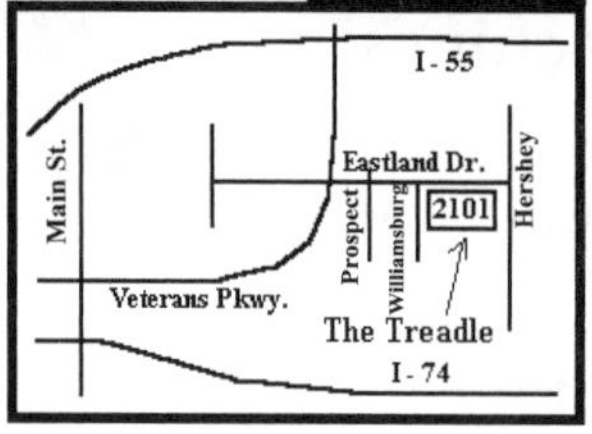

Normal, IL #29

Sewing Studio

Mon - Fri 9:30 - 6
Sat 9:30 - 5
Sun 12 - 4

1503 E. College, Suite C 61761
(309) 452-7313
Owners: Margaret Couch
Est: 1983 2600 sq.ft.
nsewstu@mindspring.com

Quality quilting and fashion fabrics. Quilting & sewing classes, books. Quilting & heirloom supplies & notions. Bernina / Viking / Dealer

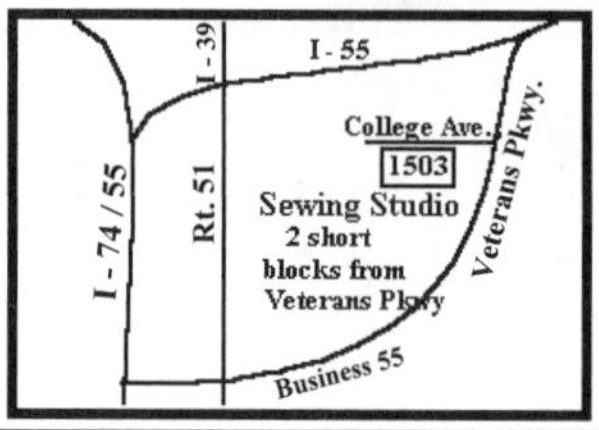

Lincoln, IL #30

LOG CABIN QUILT SHOP

M, W, F 10-3
Sat 9-3

118 N. McLean St. (Downtown Lincoln)
(217) 871-1864 62656
Owner: Donna Becke
donna@logcabinquiltshoplincoln.com
www.logcabinquiltshoplincoln.com
Small town friendly shop offering longarm machine quilting, fabrics, books, patterns, batting, thread, backing fabrics, notions, collectibles & gifts.

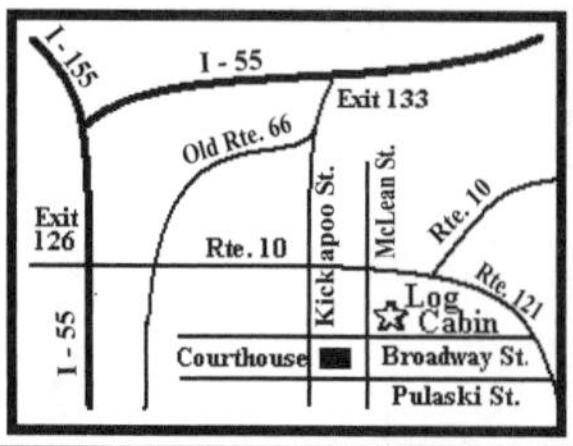

Mt. Zion, IL #31

Stewart's sewing machines

Tues - Fri 9 - 5
Sat 10 - 2

415 N. State Hwy. 121,
P.O. Box 227 62549
(217) 864-6142

Fax: (217) 864-6812
Est: 1964 1500 Bolts
www.stewartssews.com
Quilting fabrics, notions, patterns, classes and seminars. Authorized dealer: *Babylock, Janome, Elna and Brother*

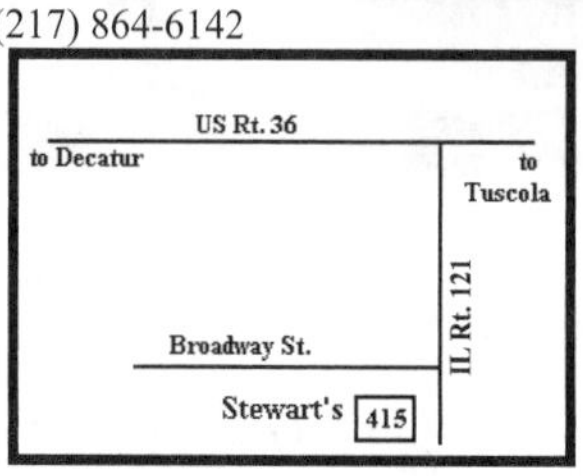

Mon - Fri
10 - 5
Thur til 8
Sat 10 - 4

peace & Appliqué Quilt Shop

145 E. Main St.
Rochester, IL 62563
Phone/Fax: (217) 498-6771
Owners: Gretchen Quistgaard
& Lois Weissberg
quilter@peacenapplique.com

www.peacenapplique.com

In a charming historic brick building, we offer over 6,000 bolts of Moda, Hoffman, Benartex, P & B, and others, including reproductions, 30's, flannels, primitives, and brights.

Central Illinois largest BERNINA dealership, focused on machine sales and repair, great classroom training, embroidery designs and supplies lots of inspiration!!! Nothing Sews Like A Bernina. Nothing. BERNINA®

Our 4,000 square foot building showcases our love for wool, needlepunch, wearables, purses and primitives. Filled with great quilts and kits, you are sure to find something you will love.

Come join us at the shop just 4 miles southeast of Springfield on Route 29 and one block north of the silo in Rochester.

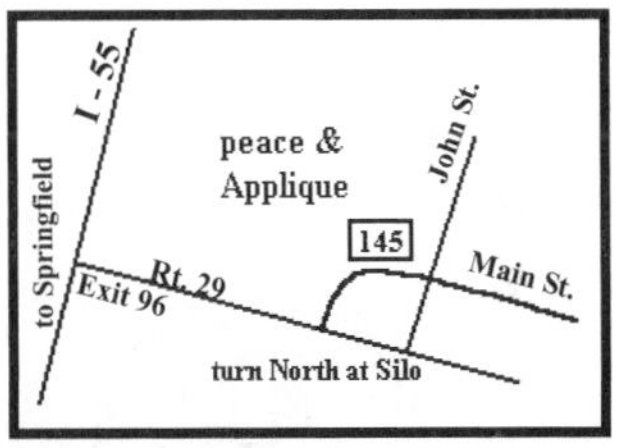

"Every Day is a Great Day to peace & Applique"

Rochester, IL #32

Springfield, IL #33

Tues - Thurs 10 - 5
Fri 10 - 4
Sat 10 - 2

Sew Unique

1050 N. Grand Ave. West
(217) 523-4293
Owner: Bonnie Jameson
www.sewunique.org
Email: sewunique@sewunique.org
Top Quality Bright & Contemporary Quilting Fabrics, Supplies, Patterns, Books, Notions & Classes.
Authorized Sales & Service:
Brother & Tin Lizzie18

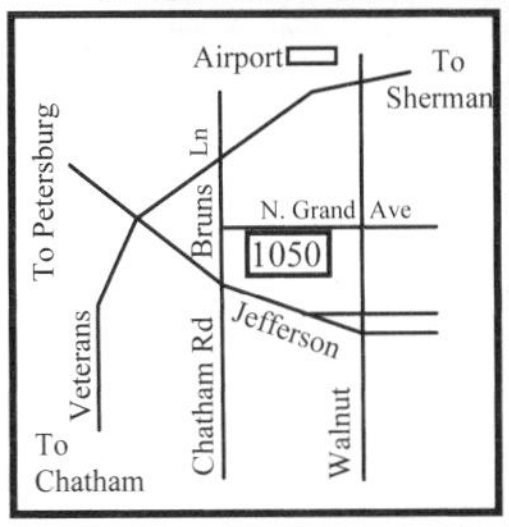

Jacksonville, IL #34

Mon 10 - 7
Tues - Fri
10 - 5
Sat 10 - 3

Times Square Sewing Complex

806 Hardin Ave. 62650
(217) 245-5445
Owner: Sue Fox Online Newsletter
Est: 1996 timessquare@mchsi.com
www.timessquaresewing.com
Visit our wonderful sewing machine store!
Authorized Janome Sewing Machine Dealer.
Free class & 1 year service with purchase of a sewing machine

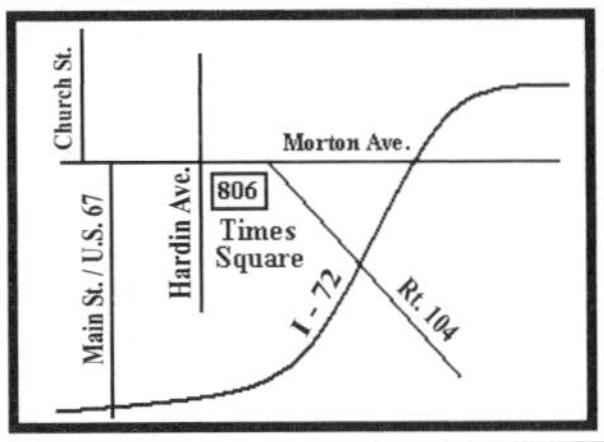

Havana, IL #35

Long Arm Quilting

It's A Must Have

Ma's Got'a Notion

MON. ~ FRI.
9:00AM ~ 5:00PM
SAT. 10:00AM ~ 4:00PM
305 W. Main St.
HAVANNA, IL 62644
309-543-6613

We carry 100% Cotton Fabrics, Patterns, Books, Sewing Notions, Classes.

Owner:
Sue Schaeffer
Est: 2003
2000 sq.ft.
masgotanotion
@grics.net

Long Arm Quilting done by appt. We offer Computerized and/or Hand-guided work on Gammill Machines.
We are the largest retailer in the Midwest for 108" wide backing, over 250 colors & prints.

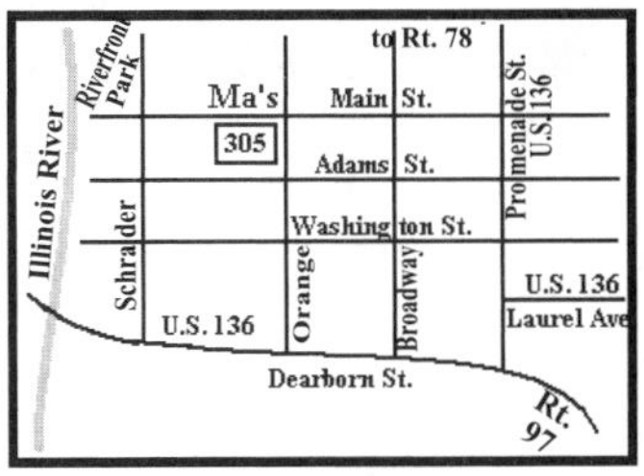

We've Got Your Back

Quincy, IL #36

Times Square Sewing Complex #2

Mon 10 - 7
Tues - Fri 10 - 5
Sat 10 - 3

420 N. 24th St. 62301
(217) 222-7458
Owner: Sue Fox Online Newsletter
timessquare@mchsi.com
www.timessquaresewing.com
Authorized Janome Sewing Machine Dealer.
New Classroom! Sewing Machine Instruction, Cabinets, Software & Accessories. Quilting, Machine Embroidery & Appliqué Block of the Months.

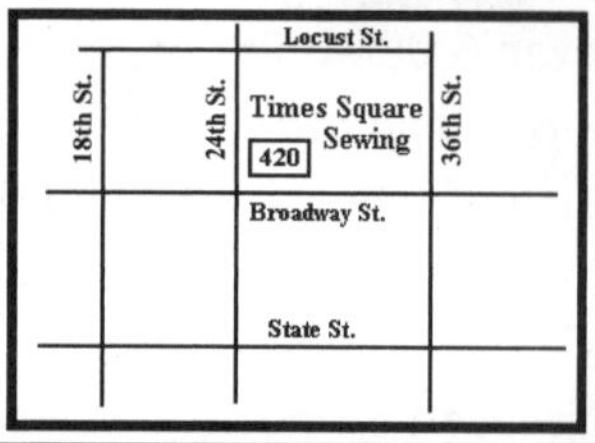

Macomb, IL #37

Piece to Peace Treasures Quilt Shop

Mon - Fri 9 - 5
Sat 9 - 4

341 N. Lafayette St. 61455
(309) 836-5999
quilts@macomb.com

Owner:
Kathleen Percy
Est: 2004
1500 sq.ft.

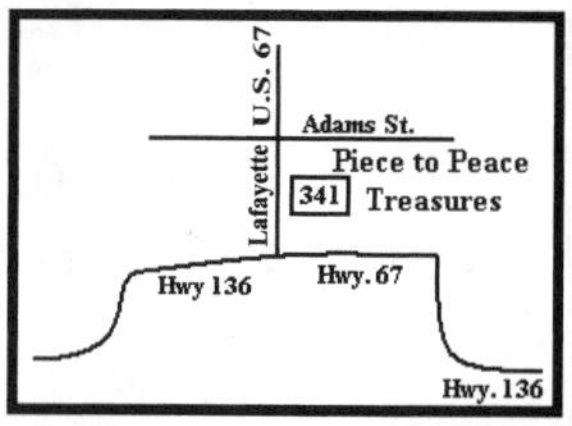

Everything for the quilter!
Cottons, books, patterns, notions and gifts.

Avon, IL #38

The Clothesline Quilt Shop

Tues - Sat 10 - 5

102 N. Main
P.O. Box 122, Avon, IL 61415
(309) 465-3850 quiltshop@grics.net

Large selection of patterns, books, notions and 100% cotton quilt fabrics.

We also custom machine quilts with a good selection of battings.

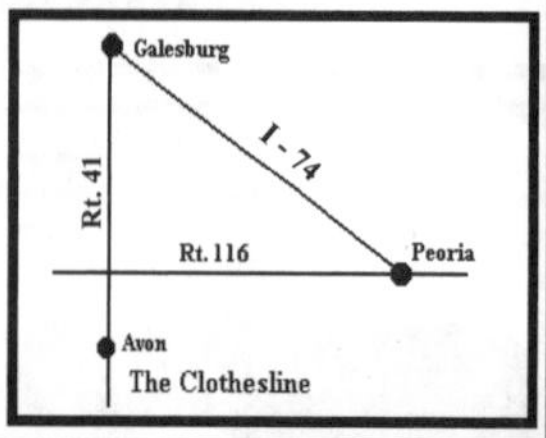

Nauvoo, IL #39

Sew Inspired Quilts

Mon - Sat 10 - 6

1360 Mulholland St., P.O. Box 76 62354
(217) 453-9909 Fax: (217) 847-6449
Owner: Barbara Wilson
sewinspiredquilts@mchsi.com
www.quiltsofnauvoo.com

Fabrics to inspire you, patterns and kits to delight you, and project support for any question

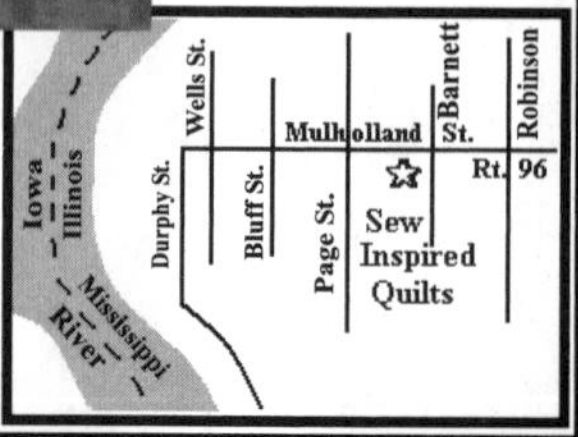

Peoria, IL #40

Prairie Points

Mon - Fri 9:30 - 6
Sat 10 - 4

8839 N. Knoxville Ave. 61615
at North Point Shopping Center
(309) 692-4340
cozy@mtco.com
www.mybeststitch.com

Buses Welcome
Premier Husqvarna Viking Dealer

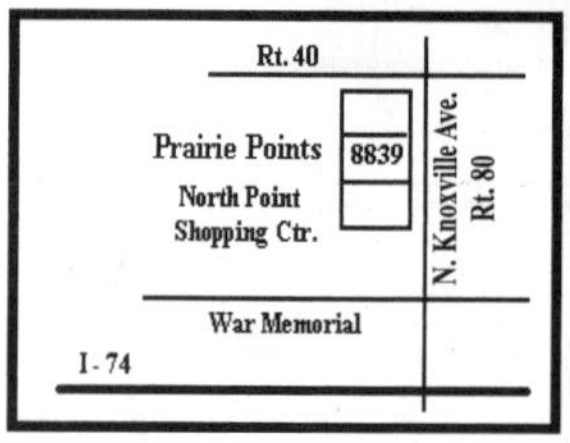

Pekin, IL #41

Cotton Stitches

Mon & Fri 9:30 - 7
Tues - Thur 9:30 - 5
Sat 10 - 4

2938 Court St. (Sunset Shp. Plaza) 61554
(309) 347-7399
cozy@mtco.com
www.mybeststitch.com

Buses welcome.
Premier Husqvarna Viking Dealer
Dedicated to your success!

Metamora, IL #42

Cozy Corner

Mon & Fri 9:30 - 6
Tues - Thur 9:30 - 5
Sat 10 - 4

101 W. Partridge St.
P.O. Box 409 61548
(309) 367-9303
cozy@mtco.com
www.mybeststitch.com

Buses Welcome
fun ~ friendly ~ historic
Premier Husqvarna Viking Dealer

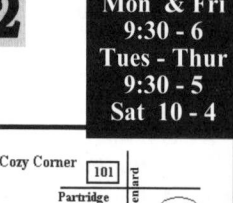

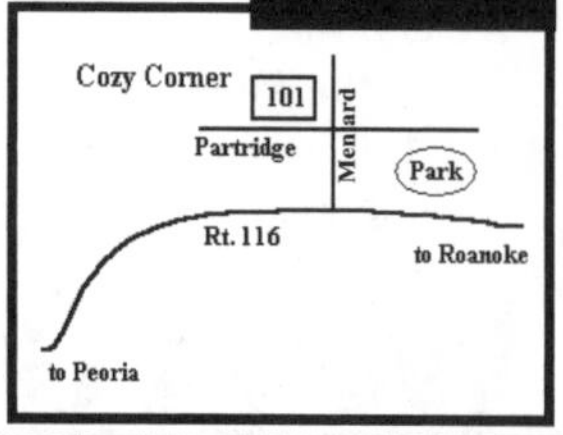

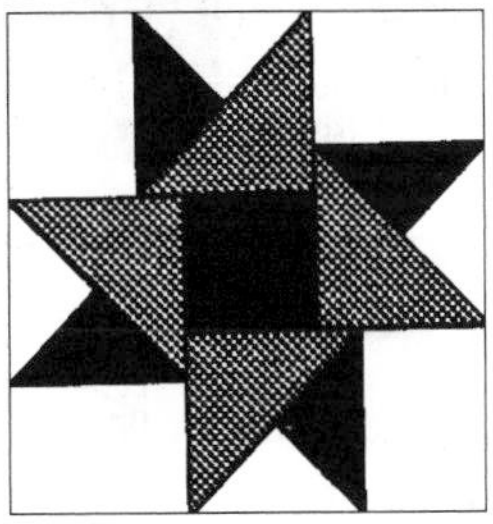

The Quilt Corner

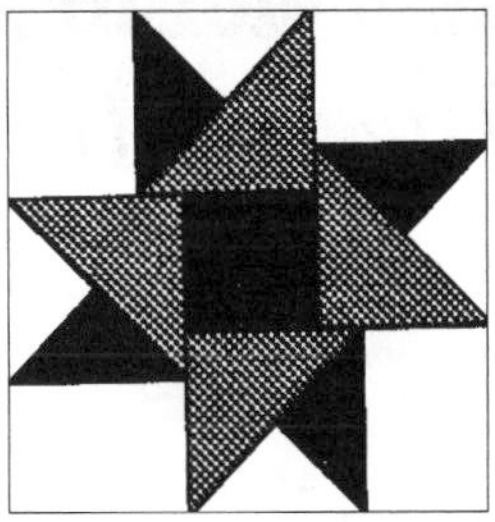

- Complete line of Quilting Fabrics
- Large selection of Batik and Flannel Fabrics
- Books, Patterns & Notions
- Kits are our Specialty
- Large selection of Wool, Wool Embroidery and Patterns
- Punch Needle & Embroidery Supplies and Patterns

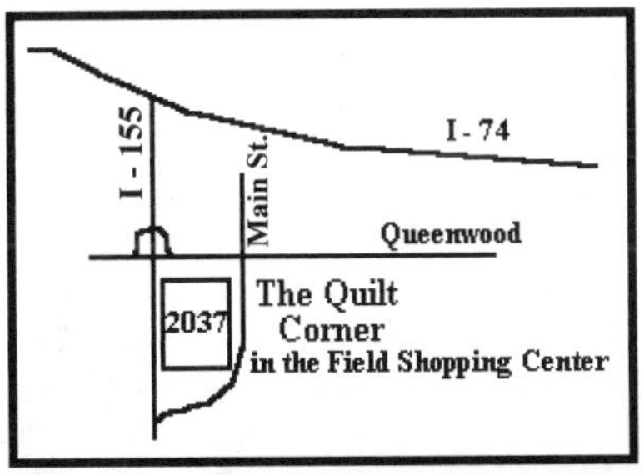

Morton, IL #43

2037 S. Main St. 61550
(309) 263-7114
Owner: Karen Bailey
Est: 1988 5000 sq.ft. 5500 Bolts
quiltcnr@mtco.com

Mon - Thur 9:30 - 8 Fri - Sat 9:30-4:30

www.thequiltcorner.biz

Peddler's Way Quilt Co.

Washington, IL #44

Visit our shop adjacent to Historic Washington Square. We are newly expanded to double the size of our shop including the addition of specialty yarns. We feature only top quality quilting fabrics and exhibit a large variety of samples to ignite your imagination. We welcome groups and will make special arrangements for your visit to include demonstrations if you contact us ahead of time. We look forward to your visit.

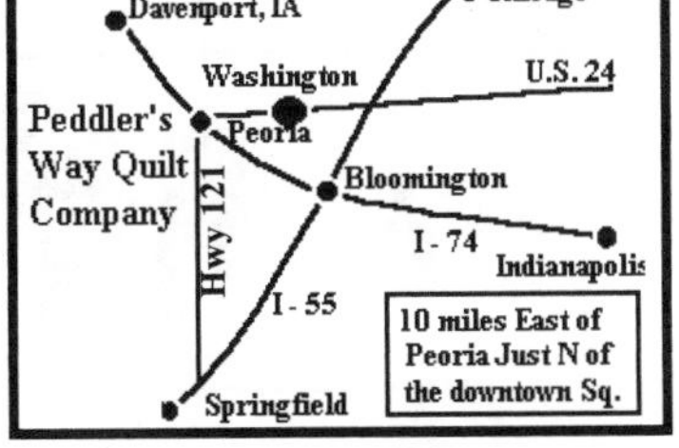

Open 7 Days a Week

- ★ Large selection and variety of top quality quilting fabrics
- ★ The latest books, patterns and notions
- ★ A variety of kits and samples
- ★ Lots of Classes
- ★ A friendly and knowledgeable staff available to assist you
- ★ Specialty yarns for those who also knit and crochet

127 Peddlers Way 61571
(309) 444-7667
6000 sq.ft. Est: 1985
Owners: Linda Calvert, Debbie Myers & Gail Warning

www.peddlersway.com pwqc@mtco.com

Authorized Pfaff Sewing Machine Dealer

East Moline, IL #45

Tues, Thur, Fri 9:30 - 5
Mon & Wed 9:30 til 9
Sat 9:30 - 4

The Quilt Basket

627 Avenue of the Cities 61244
(309) 755-9750
Owner: Ann Filiatreau
Est: 2002

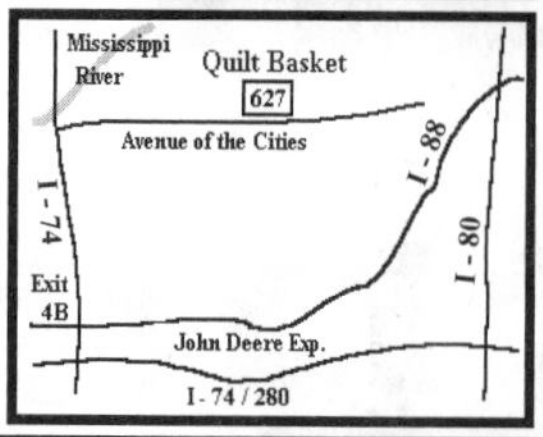

Machine quilting, 100% Cotton Fabric, large selection of Flannels, Notions, Books, Patterns, Quilt Classes. Hand made wood items by local craftsmen.

Moline, IL #46

Mon - Fri 10 - 5
Sat 10 - 2
Call Ahead for Special Appt.

Quilts by the Oz

...has you covered...

5341 Avenue of the Cities
(Enter from 22nd Ave.) 61265
(309) 762-9673 or
(800) 735-9673
Owner:
Harlene Rivelli
Est: 1987
2400 sq.ft.

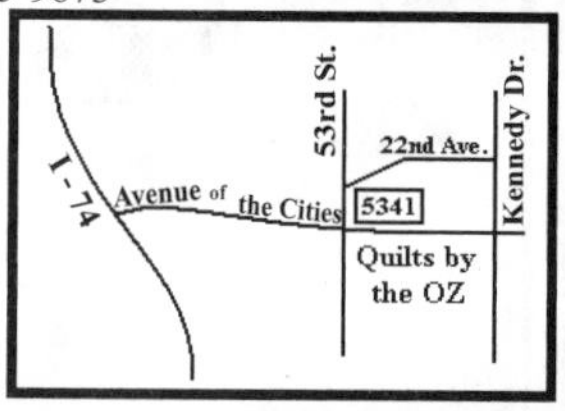

www.quiltsbytheoz.com
5000+ bolts of 100% cottons & novelties.
Thimbleberries, 30's / Civil War, Hoffman, Kaufman, Northcott, Timeless Treasures, etc.
Books -- Patterns -- Notions

Bishop Hill, IL #47

Mon - Sat 10 - 5
Sun 12 - 5

Village Smithy

309 N. Bishop Hill St. 61419
(309) 927-3851 Fax: (309) 937-5438
marilyn@VillageSmithyQuilts.com Est: 1984
www.VillageSmithyQuilts.com 1000 Bolts
Owner: Marilyn Nelson 2900 sq.ft.

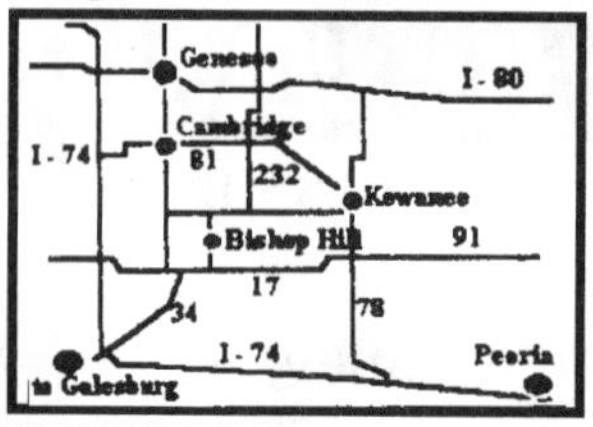

We feature vintage quilts, quilting supplies, fabrics, patterns, Antiques and Collectibles. Located in a charming historical village. Custom longarm quilting.

Kewanee, IL #48

Tues 10 - 6
Wed - Fri 10 - 5
Sat 10 - 4

The Quilt Box

109 E. Third St. 61443
(309) 854-9000 Est: 2003
QuiltBox@kewanee.com

We cater to Quilters!
Full line of 100% cotton fabrics.
Notions - Books - Patterns
Floss - Gifts - Classes - Visa & MC

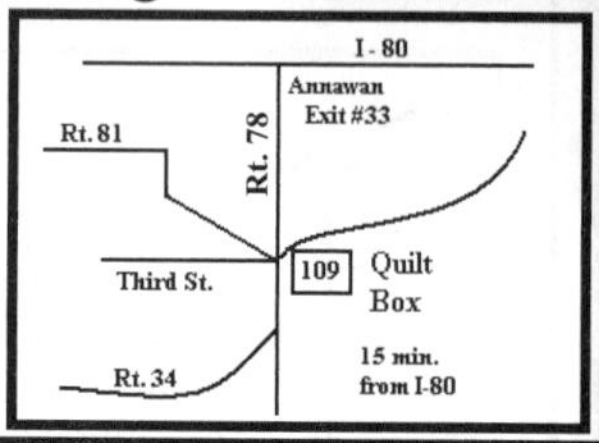

Princeton, IL #49

Quilter's Garden

Stroll our garden of quality fabrics, patterns and books. We offer a wide variety of yarns and supplies. Over 2000 bolts of cotton fabrics including Moda, Batiks, Civil War and much more. We are a certified AccuQuilt Go dealer.

527 S. Main St. 61356
Phone/Fax: (815) 879-3739
www.quiltersgardenonline.com
quiltersgarden@yahoo.com
Owners: Beth Rosene & Carol Keller
Est: 2000 1700 sq.ft. 300 sq. ft. Yarn Loft

"Stairway to Stitchin"
a sewing retreat center
is available.
Home of the zany
quilt guild program,
"A Visit from Aunt
Sewzy."
Call or e-mail for
details.

Mon - Fri 10 - 5 Sat 10 - 4

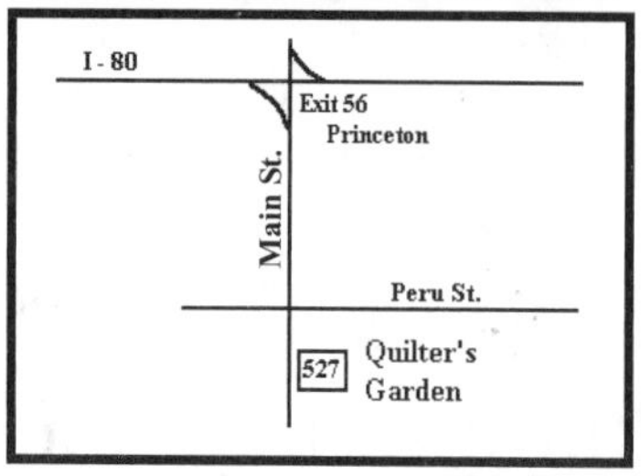

D's Sewing Center & Quilt Shop

Est: 2005

2700 sq. ft.

www.dssewingcenters.com

We are a full service quilt shop where we have over 3000 bolts of quality quilting fabric and a large supply of quilting books, patterns, and notions. We are also certified dealers for Janome sewing machines & sergers, and the HQ Avante quilting machine by Handi Quilter.

Monday thru Friday 10 - 6, Saturday 9 - 3

4377 Venture Dr. 61354
(815) 223-7231
Fax: (815) 220-3501
dssewing@comcast.net
Free online Newsletter

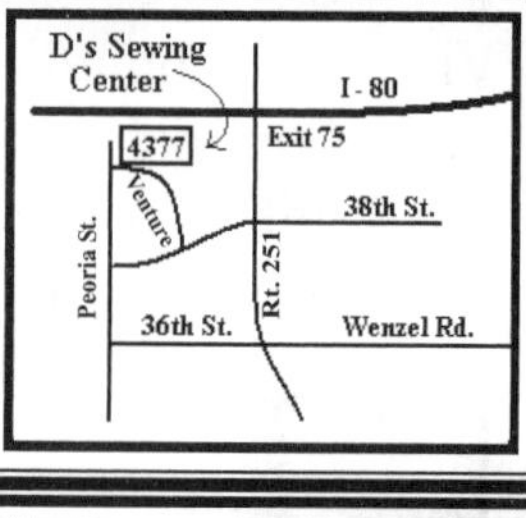

Peru, IL #50

Minooka, IL #51

Mon - Fri 10 - 5
Sat 9 - 4
Sun 11 - 4

Quilted Turtle

849 Ridge Rd. 60447
(815) 521-1505 Fax: (815) 521-1575
Owners: Robbie Presbitero & Amie Rush
Est: 2008 qtinfo@quiltedturtle.com
www.quiltedturtle.com

Fabrics, notions, patterns.
Everything a quilter needs. Newsletter
Friendly Staff. 1 1/2 miles south of I-80

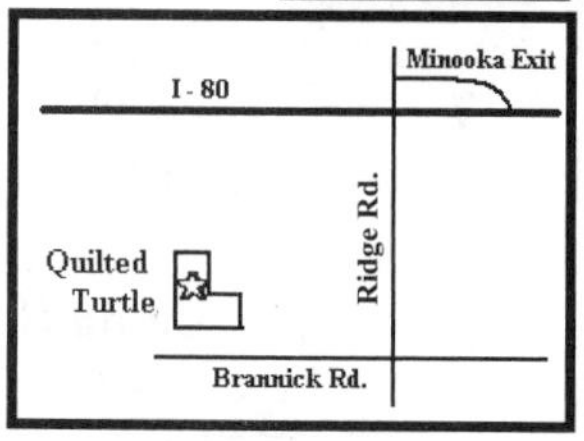

- Over 7,000 bolts of cotton fabric (discounted 20% everyday)
- Largest selection of Hoffman fabrics in IL
- Also featuring Moda, RJR, Timeless Treasures, Michael Miller, Kona, Benartex, Hi-Fashion, Springs, Kaufman, P&B, Northcott, Maywood & MORE.
- Quilting notions, stencils, patterns, books and quilting frames.
- Brother & Janome Dealer.

THE FABRIC CENTER

"A SEWING MACHINE SUPERSTORE"

Morris, IL #52

OPEN

Mon - Fri
9:00 - 5:30
Thurs 9:00 - 7:00
Sat 9:00 - 5:00

A Quilters Dream

301 Liberty Street
Morris, IL 60450
815-942-5715

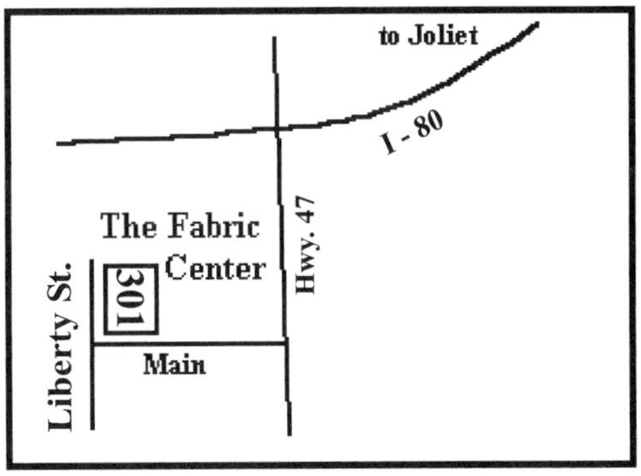

"In Historic Downtown Morris"

Stop in to see the Tin Lizzie TL18LS Quilting System

Fulton, IL #53

SUSAN'S CALICO CREATIONS

1108 4th St.
Fulton, IL 61252
(815) 589-2221
Owner:
Susan May

susancalicocreations@hotmail.com
www.susancalicocreations.com
Over 4000 Bolts of Fabric, Notions, Books, Patterns, Stencils, Machine Quilting, Classes.

Tues - Sat 10 - 5
Thurs 10 - 8
Sunday 12 - 4

Also Visit: "Attic Woods" solid wood unfinished furniture for every room in the house.

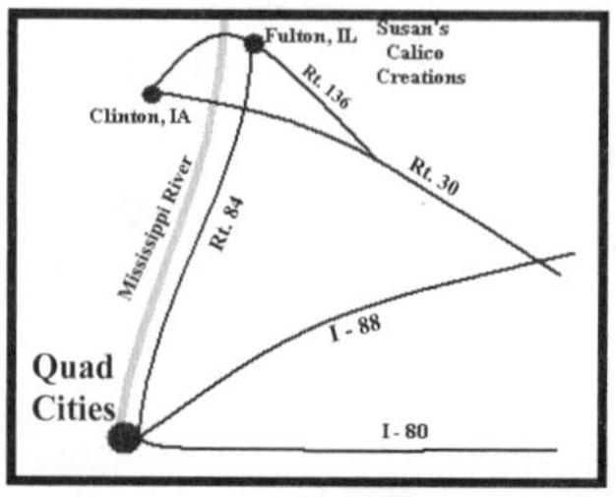

Ashton, IL #54

Tues - Fri 10 - 5
Sat 10 - 2

Cottage Garden Quilts

705 N. First St. (IL Rt 38)
P.O. Box 571 61006
(815) 453-7534
www.cottagegardenquilts.com

Our quality fabrics, patterns and kits will inspire your creativity. A full service quilt shop offering long-arm machine quilting.

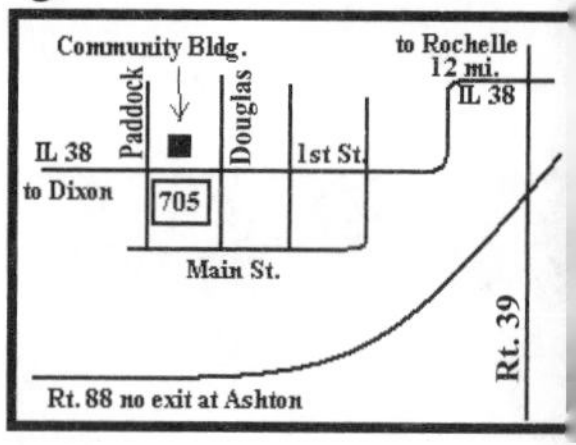

Pearl City, IL #55

Mon - Thur 11 - 7
Fri 11 - 5
Sat 10 - 5
Sun 12 - 4

Sew Many Antiques

140 - 160 S. Main St., P.O. Box 55
(815) 443-2211 61062
Owners: Jill & Dave Shaulis and Vicki & Dave Olsen
Est: 1992 4300 sq.ft.
sewmanyantiques@gmail.com
www.sewmanyantiques.com
Filled with over 2000 bolts of fabric, patterns, books, gifts, and antiques. We offer classes, retreats & always a friendly welcome.

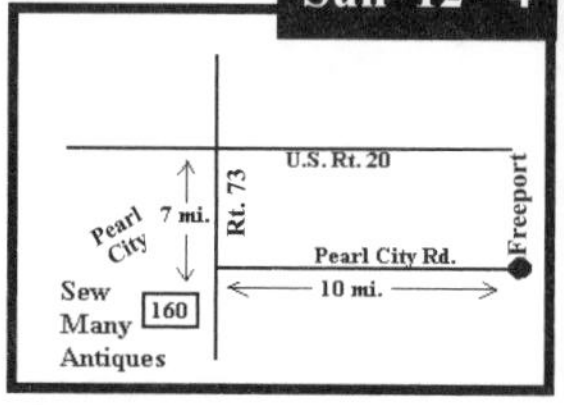

Galena, IL #56

Mon - Sat 10 - 5
Sun 11 - 3

PHAT 1/4's

303 S. Commerce 61036
815-776-0034
Est: 2004
2000 sq.ft.
pqquilting@aol.com

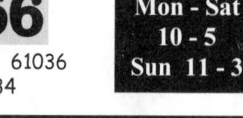

www.phatquartersquilting.com
Phat 1/4's offers over 2000 bolts of fabric, thread, books, patterns, notions and of course Pretty Hot And Tempting Quarters.
Authorized Bernina Dealer Sales & Service.

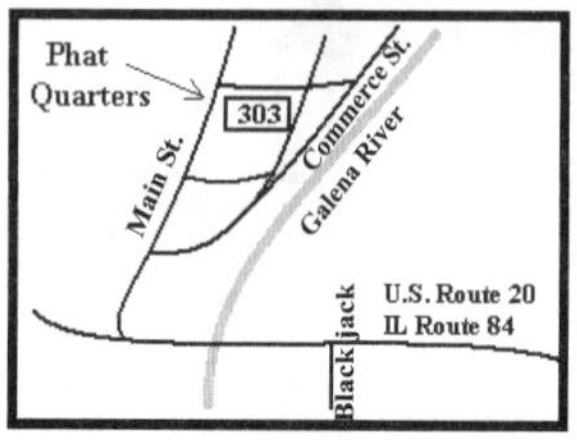

Orangeville, IL #57

Mon - Sat 9 - 5

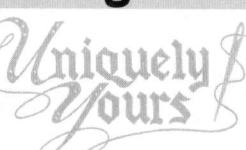

Uniquely Yours

12530 Hwy. IL 26 N
P.O. Box 55 61060
(815) 789-434 Cell: (608) 558-5158
Owners:
Sandy & Gene Haffele
Est: 1990
2100 sq.ft.
uniquelyyours20@netzero.com
www.uniquelyyoursquilting.com
Full Service Quilt Shop. 6500 Bolts
Over 20 years in business serving the needs and wants of quilters world-wide.

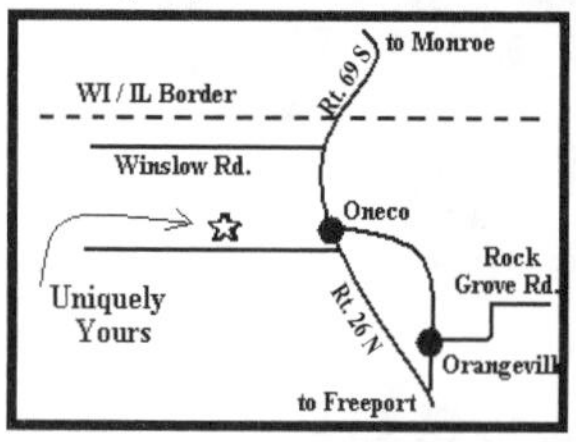

Rockford, IL #59

Tues - Fri 10 - 5
Sat 10 - 4:30

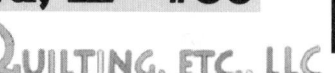

IT'S FOR QUILTING, ETC., LLC

2252 New Milford School Rd. 61109
(815) 874-0152 or (877) 454-3032
Owner: Diane Nordlof Est: 2006
2000 sq.ft. 2000+ bolts Newsletter via email
info@itsforquilting.com
www.itsforquilting.com
Where color lives; from the soft and subtle to the wild and bold. Moda, Westminster Fibers, Contemporary Fabric, Art Quilt Supplies and classes.

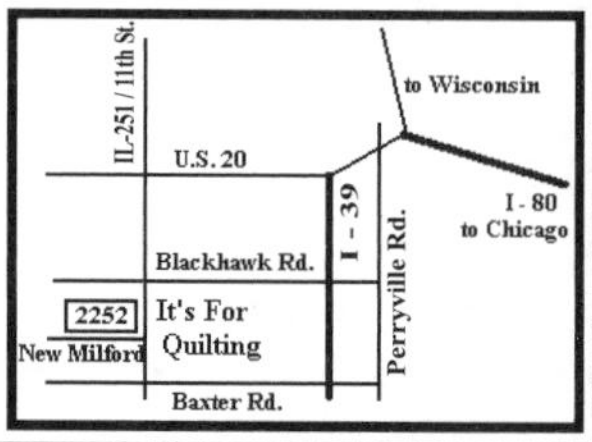

Rockford, IL #58

Acorn Quilts

Mon - Fri 10 - 6 Sat 10 - 4

Urban chic meets vintage charm
An eclectic combination of contemporary and reproduction prints in an inspiring atmosphere.

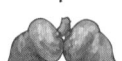

6409 E. Riverside Blvd. 61114
815-977-5275

acornquilts2@gmail.com
Fax: 815-977-5275
Est: 2009
1800 sq.ft.
1500 Bolts
Free Newsletter

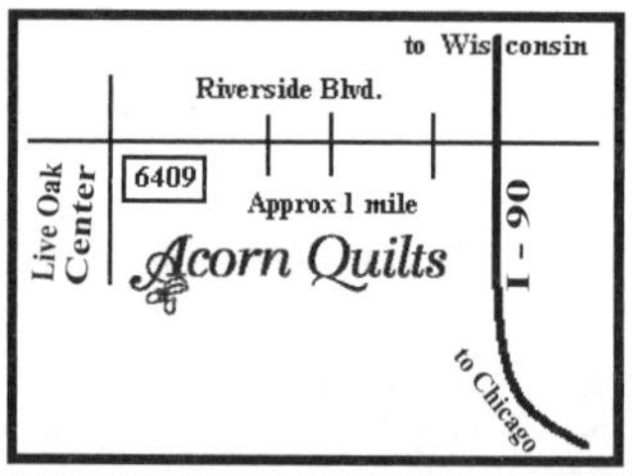

Rockford, IL #60

Quilters HAVEN

4616 E. State St. 61108
(815) 227-1659
Owners: Stephanie Gauerke & Cathy Johnson
Est: 1995 1200 sq.ft.

www.quilterhaven.com

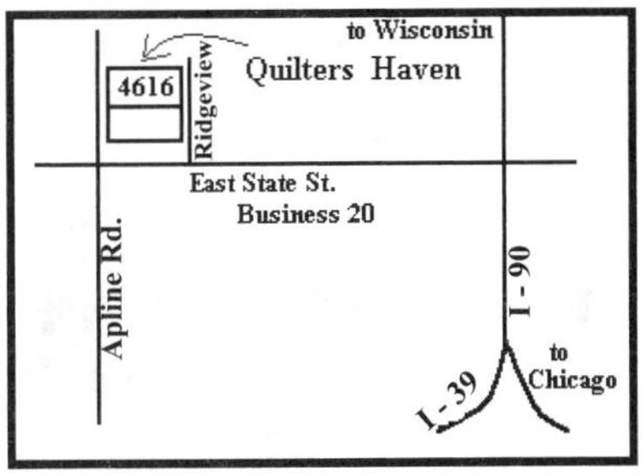

Located on the north side of the building lower level entrance.

Quilters Haven carries a wide variety of 100% cotton fabrics (numbering 3000+), books, patterns and notions. We offer a unique combination of classes and have several samples to inspire you! Friendly, individual attention is what we are known for. We do special order and shipping on request.

TOP 20

HandiQuilter Rep

Trained and authorized Rep for:
- *HQ[18] Avante[tm]*
- *HQ Sixteen® Machines*
- *HQ Pro-Stitcher®*
- *HQ Fusion®*

Mon - Sat 10 - 4 Wed til 7

Rockford, IL #61

QUILTER'S GENERAL STORE INC.

6903 Harrison Ave. 61108
815-397-5160
Fax: 815-399-5025
E-Mail: quiltnut0302@aol.com
Web Site: www.quiltersgeneralstore.com
Owner: Deb Peterson

Mon - Fri 10 - 5 Sat 10 - 4

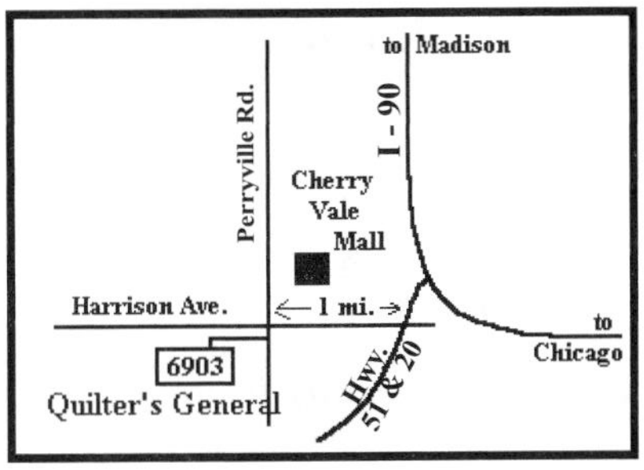

"Featured in American Patchwork and Quilting "Sampler 2001"

This "country in the city" shop boasts 3500+ bolts of cotton fabric, books, patterns, notions, fabric kits, and a friendly, helpful staff of quilters. Located in a beautiful 1875 farm house. Classes for all levels. Newsletter and special orders upon request.

Belvidere, IL #62

All My Stitches
Quilt Shop

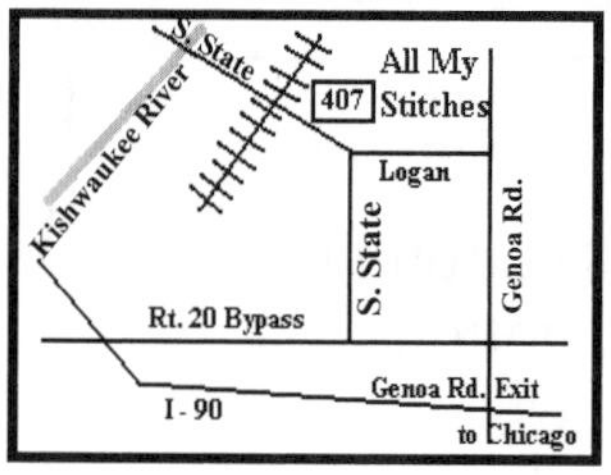

815-547-1099
407 S. State Street
Belvidere, IL 61008
Belvidere exit off I-90
QuiltShop13@yahoo.com

Tues - Fri 10 - 4 Sat 10 - 3

Thimbleberries, 30's Reproductions & Collections of 100% Cotton Fabrics from all the best manufacturers

Sycamore, IL #63

The place to go for brights!

Tammy Tadd Designs
RETAIL STORE AND DESIGN STUDIO

Better Homes and Gardens Quilt Sampler FEATURED SHOP 2009

Tammy Tadd Designs is proud to be selected as a Top 10 Quilt Shop in the Fall 2009 Issue of Quilt Sampler Magazine!

- **2000 bolts** *of fabric with new lines arriving weekly.*
- *Full-service quilt shop with the* **latest** *fabrics, notions, books & patterns.*
- *We* **specialize** *in bright, contemporary, non-traditional fabrics & a nice selection of batiks & 1930's reproductions.*
- *A bright, happy shop with fun,* **personalized** *service.*
- *Machine* **quilting** *services available.*
- *Bus* **groups** *welcome.*

Conveniently located on Prairie Drive, just west of the Farm Bureau building off Peace Rd in the Prairie Commons Business Center in Sycamore, IL

VISIT US:
920 W. Prairie Drive, Suite J
Sycamore, IL 60178
Toll Free 877-999-8233
www.tammytadddesigns.com

REGULAR STORE HOURS:

Mon., Tues., Wed. & Fri.	10-5
Thurs.	10-8
Saturday	10-4
Sunday	Closed

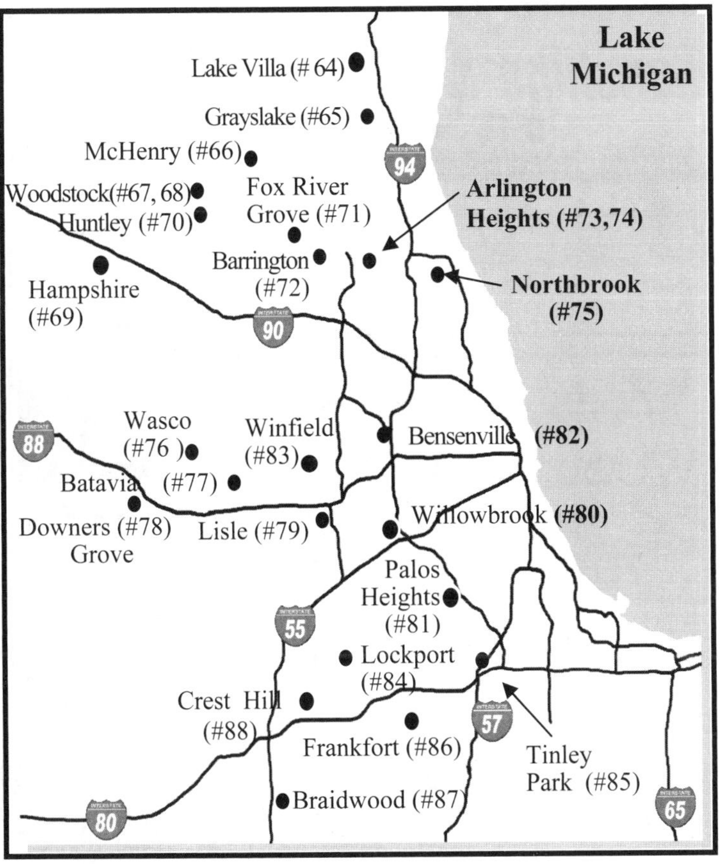

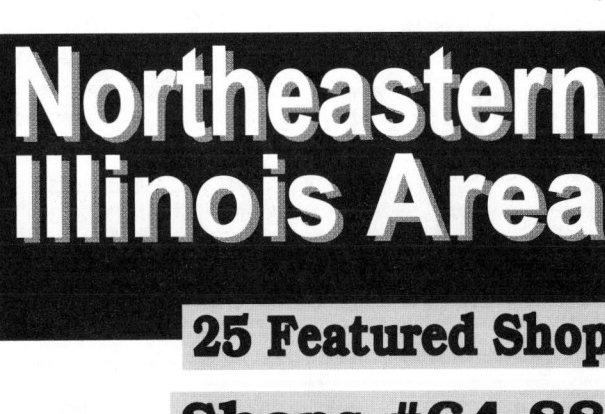

Northeastern Illinois Area

25 Featured Shops

Shops #64-88

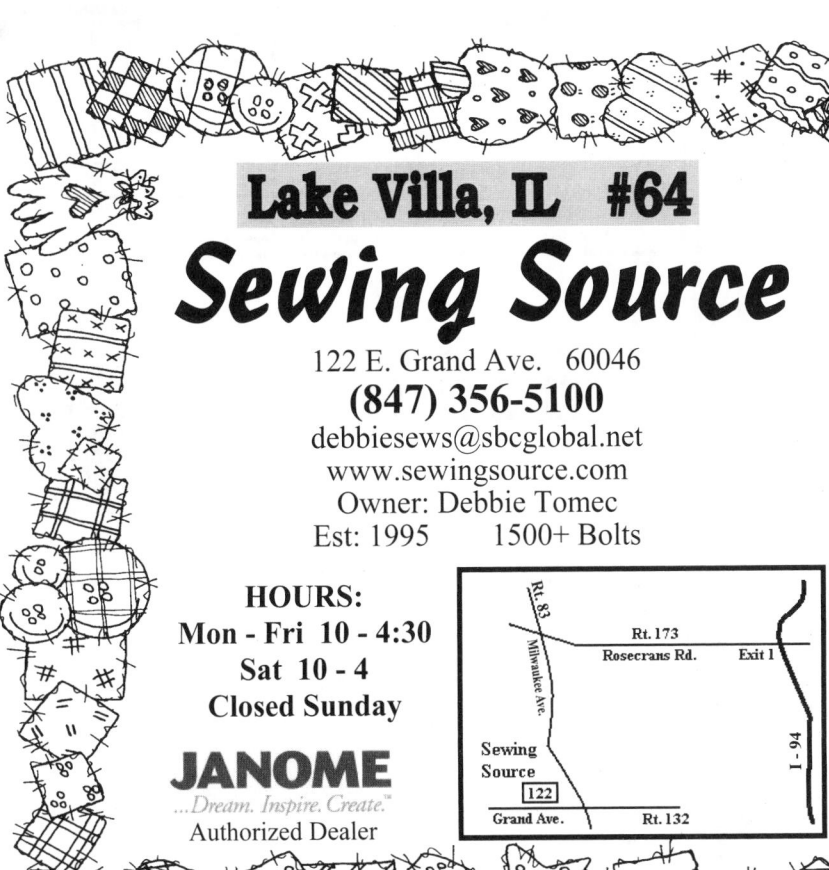

Lake Villa, IL #64

Sewing Source

122 E. Grand Ave. 60046
(847) 356-5100
debbiesews@sbcglobal.net
www.sewingsource.com
Owner: Debbie Tomec
Est: 1995 1500+ Bolts

HOURS:
Mon - Fri 10 - 4:30
Sat 10 - 4
Closed Sunday

JANOME
...Dream. Inspire. Create.™
Authorized Dealer

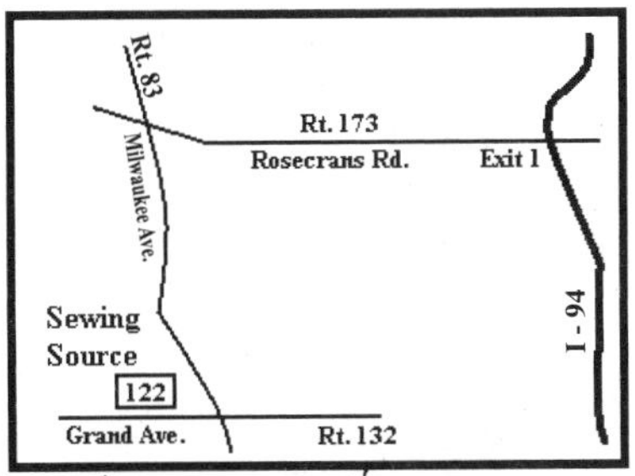

We sell Quilting and Embroidery Machines.
Horn Cabinets
A full line of Quilting Fabrics
Over 400 Books and Patterns
Specialty Threads
Classes Available

Repairs on all makes of Sewing Machines & Scissor Sharpening by Joe.

Professional Long Arm Quilting and Custom Work
We teach for the college of Lake County

We are a drop-off point for project Linus & Conker Cancer

Grayslake, IL #65

Mon - Sat 10 - 4
Wed til 7
Sun 12 - 4

quiltplay

62 Center St. 60030
(847) 548-4967
Owner: Shelley MacGregor
info@quiltplayshop.com
www.quiltplayshop.com
Full service quilt shop with long arm quilting.
Patterns, Fabrics, Notions and more.
After 10/01/2010, call for location.

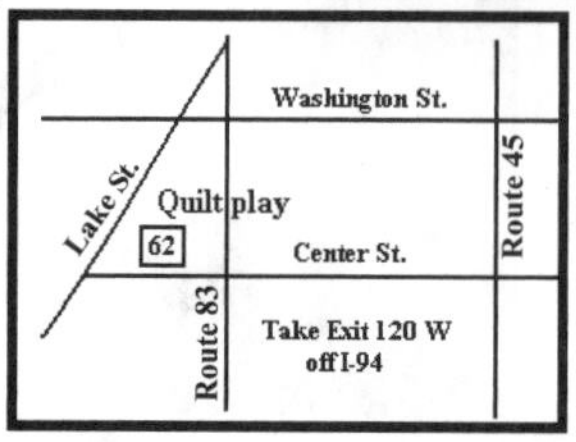

McHenry, IL #66

Tues - Thur 11 - 4
Fri 11-7
Sat 11-6
Call ahead for Sun

Sunshine & Shadow
Quilt Shoppe
Quilting, Needle Arts & Gifts

1241 N. Green St. 60050
815-385-5003
www.sunshineshadowquiltshop.com

Quality Fabrics, Books, Patterns & Classes,
Machine Repairs. All sales cash or check only.

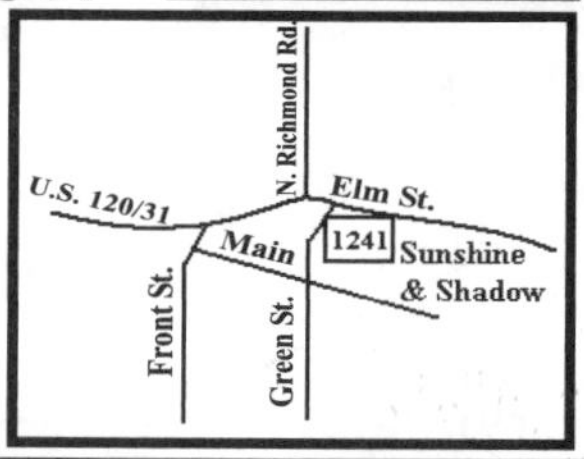

Woodstock, IL #67

Mon - Fri 12 - 8
Sat 10 - 4

That Quilt Shop INC.

1818 S. Rose Farm Rd.
60098
(815) 338-9353
Owner: Therese Dominas
thatquiltshopinc@yahoo.com
www.thatquiltshopinc.com

Classes • Fabric • FUN
Long-Arm Quilting Available.

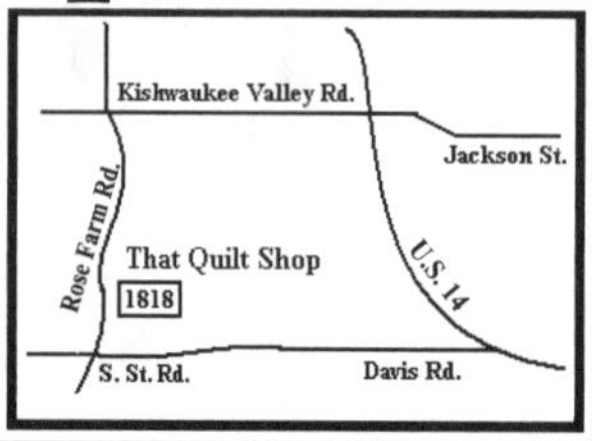

Woodstock, IL #68

Mon - Fri 10 - 4:30
Sat 10 - 4

Woodstock Quilts, Inc.

216 S. Seminary 60098
(815) 338-1212
Owner: Debbie Best Est: 2002

Fabric, Quilting Supplies.
2 Blocks East of the
Historical Woodstock Square

You Stitch Love Into Every Quilt,
Choose Your Fabric With Love

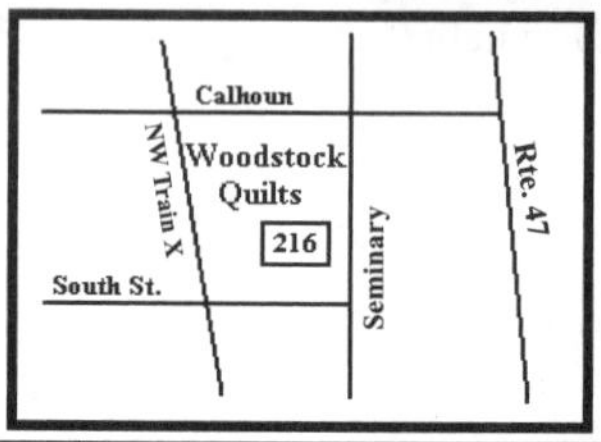

Hampshire, IL #69

Judy's Quilt 'n' Sew

Where Good Things Begin....

290 South State St
Hampshire, IL 60140
(847) 683-4739

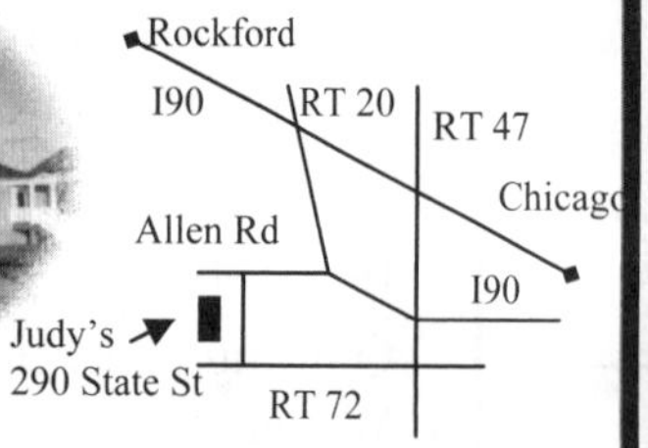

3000 Bolts of Fabric, Kits, classes, books, patterns and notions.
Pfaff & Bernina Sales and Service.

www.judysquiltnsew.com
10-5 Mon-Fri Thur til 8 10-3:30 Sat & 12-3 Sun

Huntley, IL #70

Mon, Wed, Fri 10 - 5
Tues & Thur 10 - 8
Sat 10 - 5

10709 Huntley / Dundee Rd. 60142
(847) 669-1722 Fax: (847) 669-1727
Owner: Kathi Dayon
Est: 2007
1400 sq.ft.
1800+ Bolts
Free Newsletter
quiltinjoy@quiltinjoy.com
www.quiltinjoy.com

Our welcoming team is
inspirational and knowledgeable.
We feature brights, batiks, and novelty prints.
Always over 200 bolts at $6 per yard.

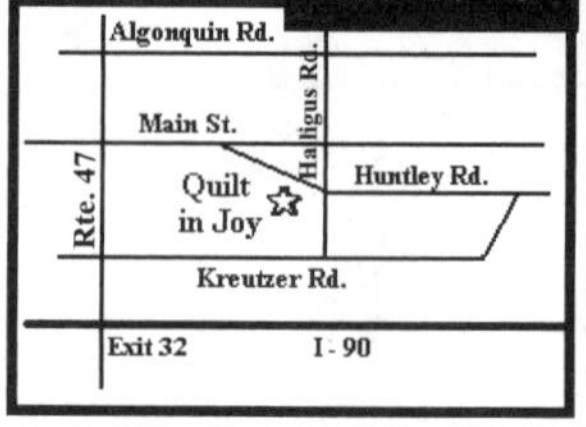

Fox River Grove, IL #71

Tues & Wed 10 - 9
Thurs - Sat 10 - 5

Pieceful Gathering Quilt Shop

106 Northwest Hwy. (Rt. 14) 60021
(847)516-7911 or (866) 455-7911
Owners: Carrie Quinn & Katie Reed
Est: 2006
Quality Fabrics, Kits,
Notions, Books, Patterns.
Classes for all levels.
Friendly and helpful Staff
Longarm Quilting Service.
carrie@piecefulgathering.com
www.piecefulgathering.com
Come Visit Our Pieceful Shop.

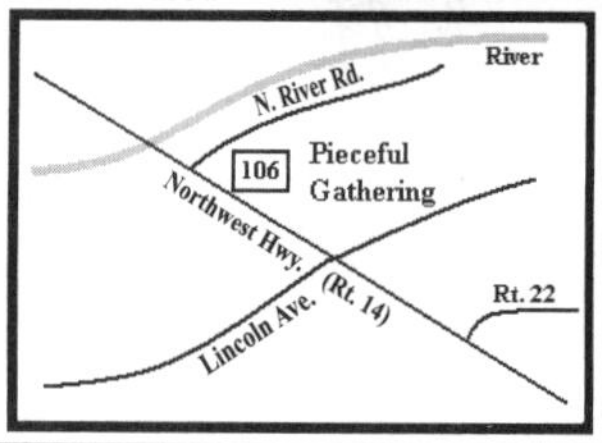

Barrington, IL #72

A Touch of Amish

130 Applebee St. 60010
(847) 381-0900
(888) 5-QUILTS (578-4587)
Owner: Lynn Rice
Est: 1986 2500 sq.ft.

Tues - Sat 10 - 4

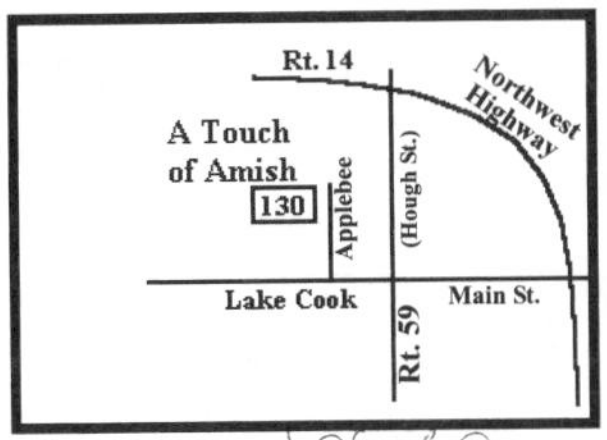

Wonderful fabrics, books, patterns, custom quilting, classes, and always great service.

Visit us at:
www.atouchofamish.com

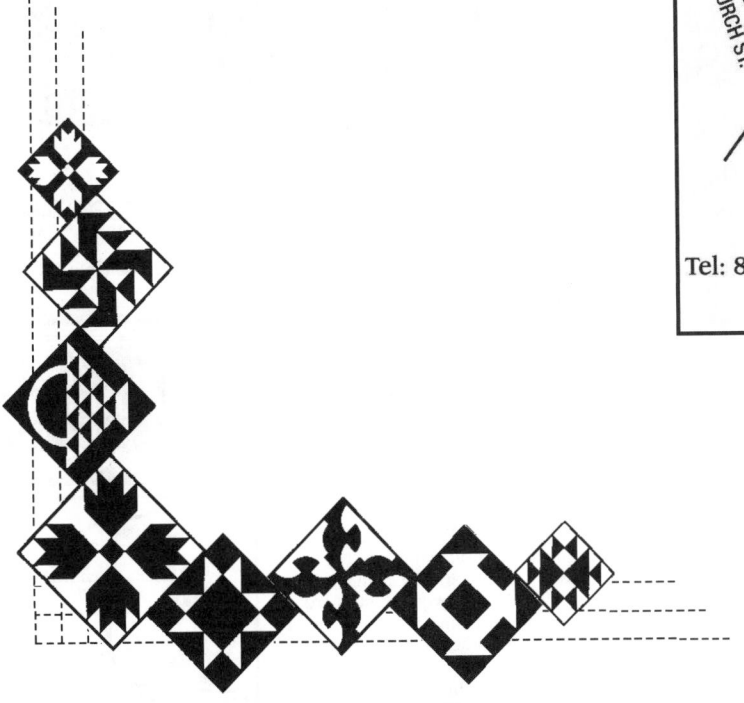

Arlington Heights, IL #73

Open 7 days a Week

BERNINA baby lock PFAFF Husqvarna VIKING

LINDA Z's SEWING CENTER

1030 E. Central Rd.
60005
(847) 394-4590
www.lindazs.com

Specialty threads
On-site service all brands
40+ years in business.
Classes offered from beginner to expert.

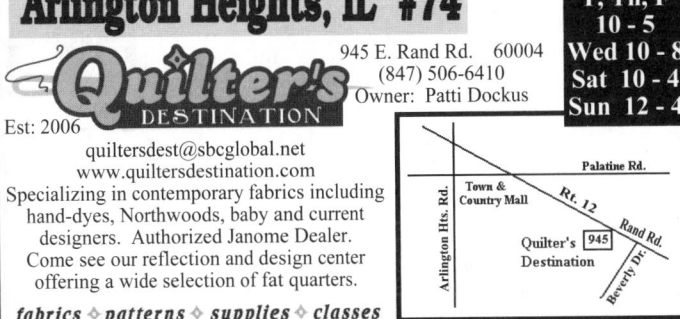

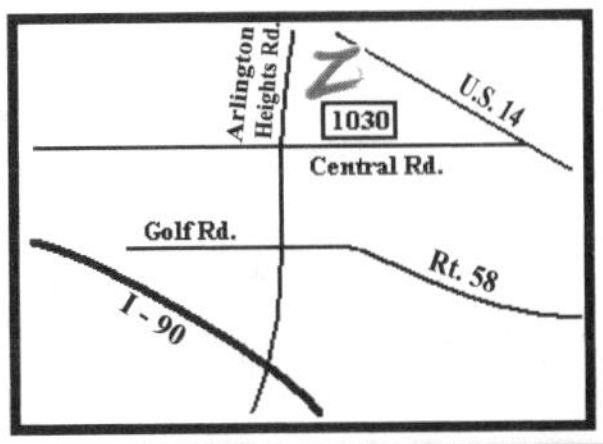

Arlington Heights, IL #74

T, Th, F 10 - 5
Wed 10 - 8
Sat 10 - 4
Sun 12 - 4

Quilter's DESTINATION

945 E. Rand Rd. 60004
(847) 506-6410
Owner: Patti Dockus

Est: 2006

quiltersdest@sbcglobal.net
www.quiltersdestination.com
Specializing in contemporary fabrics including hand-dyes, Northwoods, baby and current designers. Authorized Janome Dealer. Come see our reflection and design center offering a wide selection of fat quarters.

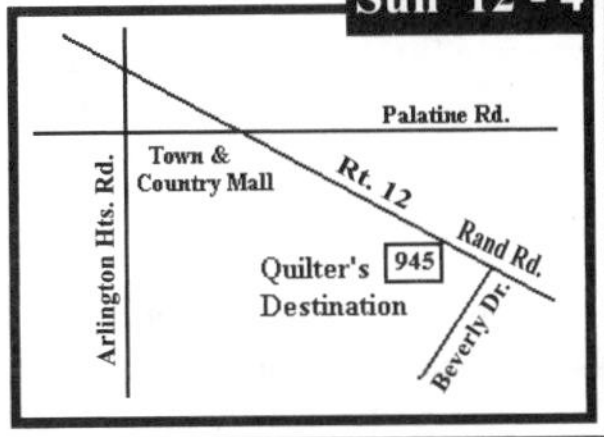

fabrics ◊ patterns ◊ supplies ◊ classes

QUILTER'S HEAVEN

The fabric store you've been praying for!

Specializing in brights, batiks, and designer fabrics — Kaffe Fasset, Amy Butler, Moda — 3000+ bolts. Books, patterns, notions galore.

Hours: Mon 10-7, Tue-Fri 10-5, Sat 9-5, Sun Closed

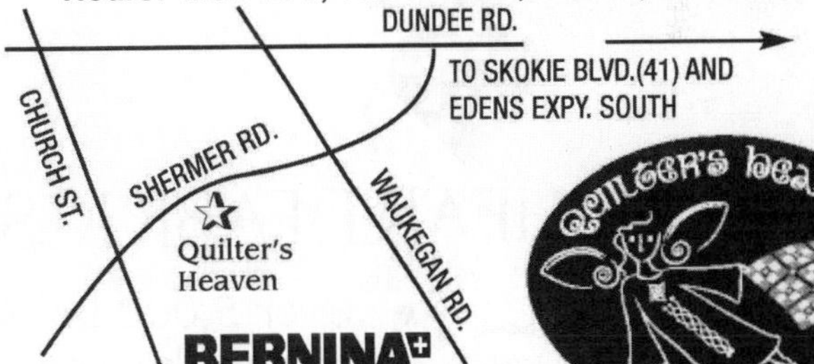

#75

BERNINA Dealer

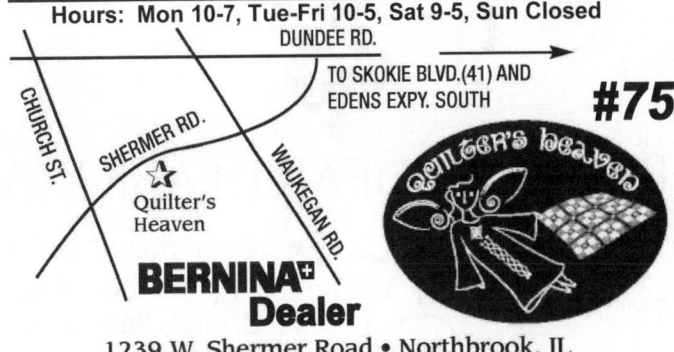

1239 W. Shermer Road • Northbrook, IL
Tel: 847-272-7245 • e-mail: quiltersheaven@sbcglobal.net
www.quiltersheaveninc.com

Wasco, IL #76

Open by Chance or Appointment

Karen's Quilt & Bead Shop

40 W 514 IL Rte 64 60183
(630) 377-5965
karen@karensquiltshop.com
www.karensquiltshop.com

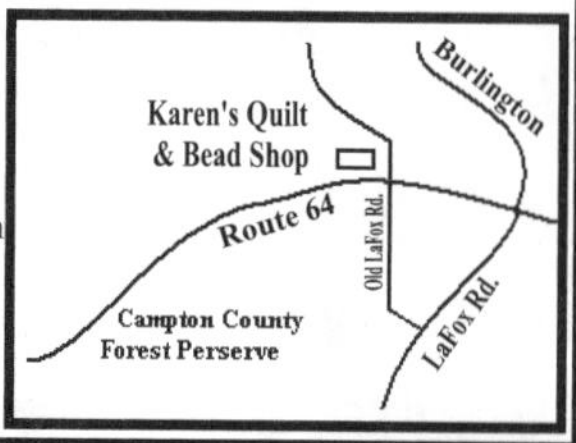

Come visit our WAREHOUSE for our online shop when in the St. Charles area. We carry an eclectic assortment of fabrics from novelties to reproductions to Asian & batiks from quality manufacturers at GREAT prices. *We offer **professional** LONGARM quilting services too!*

Batavia, IL #77

PRAIRIE SHOP QUILTS

QUILTING WITH A MISSION

1911 West Wilson Street Batavia, IL 60510
phone: 630-406-0237
www.prairieshopquilts.com

With over 3500 bolts of fabric, hundreds of notions, books, patterns and terrific class offerings, PSQ is your one stop shop for all your quilting needs! ***You can also rent time on our Gammil Long Arm quilting machine or we'll quilt it for you!***

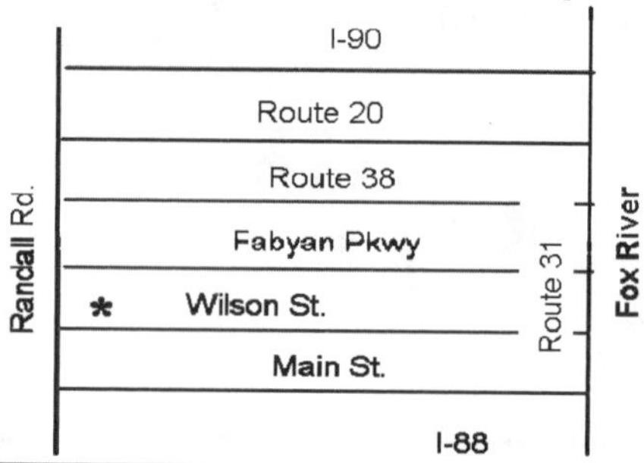

Monday - Friday 10 to 6
Thursday 10 to 8
Saturday 10 to 5
Sunday Noon to 4

We are located at the NE corner of Randall Rd. & Wilson St. next to Ace Hardware!

Downers Grove, IL #78

Mon - Sat 10 - 5 Thur til 8

THE QUILT BASKET

1012 Curtiss St.
60515
(630) 515-8820

1200 sq.ft. 1700 bolts
qltbasket3@yahoo.com
www.thequiltbasket.com

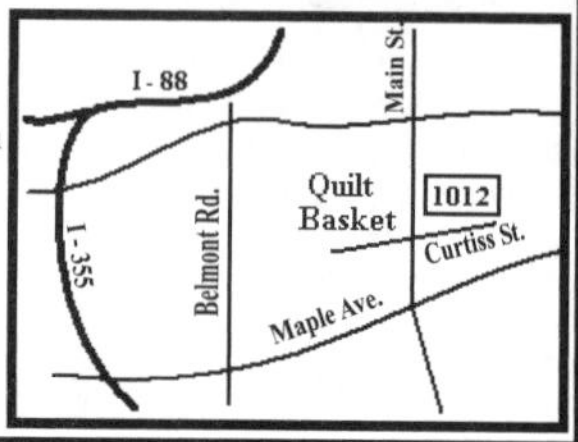

We've got plenty of fabrics to tempt and inspire you! We've got some fun new classes to tempt you and some old favorites. Check out our club offerings.

Follow Your Heart....

You can find us with a map but something inside will also know the way. Our shop is filled with fabric that calls to you, inspires and rewards you for making the trip. So come and touch...see...discover us!

PIECEFUL HEART FABRICS

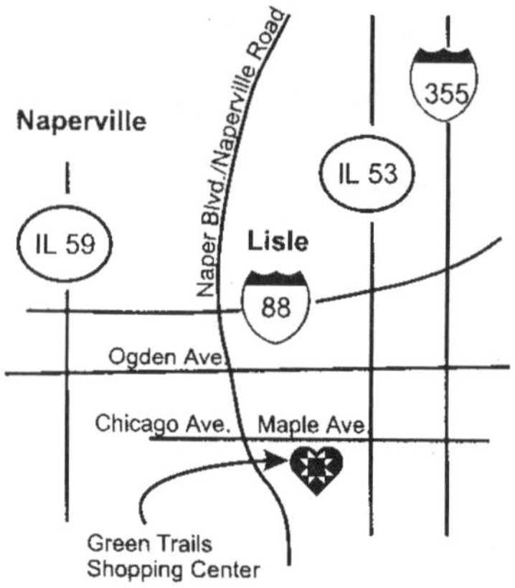

- Over 5,000 bolts of pure heaven
- Books, Patterns, Classes and lots of fresh ideas.
- Hours:

Mon & Thurs 10-8
Tues, Wed, Fri 10-5
Sat 10-4 Sun 12-4

2723 W. Maple Ave. Lisle, IL 60532
(630) 718-0112 www.phfab.com
(1/2 Block East of Naper Blvd.)

Lisle, IL #79

Willowbrook, IL #80

Tues, Wed Thur 10 - 5 Fri & Sat 10 - 4 Sun 12:30 - 4

quiltfabric.com

888 75th St. Corner of Rt. 83 & 75th, 60527
630.321.9051

Large Store
Large Selection

Come in for some inspiration! Bright, friendly atmosphere. Kits, models, top quality fabrics, patterns, books and notions. PFAFF & JANOME authorized dealer.

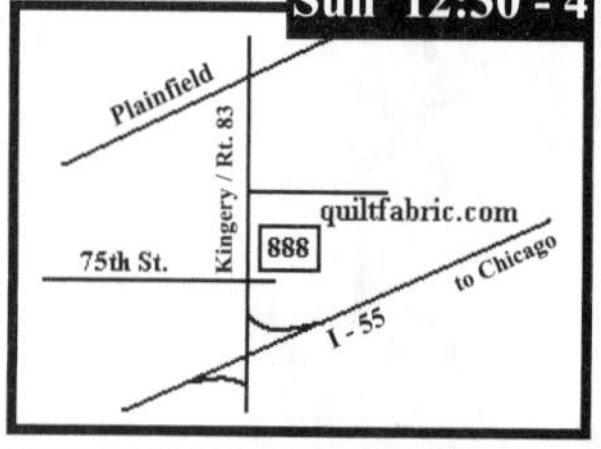

Palos Heights, IL #81

Mon, Tue, Wed Fri 10 - 5 Thur 10 - 7 Sat 9 - 4

Susan Marie's

6515 W. 127th St. 60463
708.371.9314
3000 sq.ft. 1000+ bolts
susanmarie@susanmariesinc.com
www.susanmariesinc.com
Newsletter Available Two Large Classrooms

We carry the complete line of Bernina sewing and Embroidery machines, sergers and accessories. Large selection of Batiks, books, patterns, threads, stabilizers and notions.

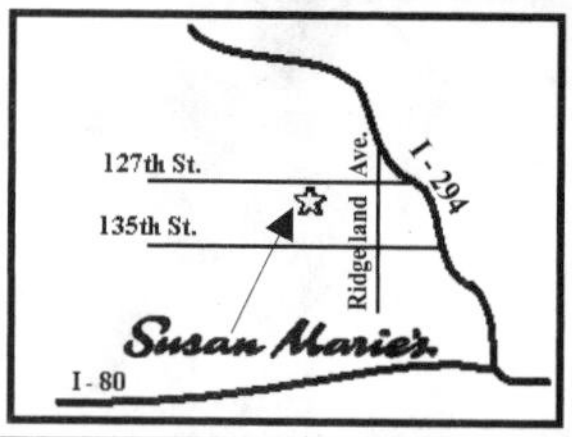

Chicagoland's Premier Quilting & Sewing Center

Fabrics etc.2

Where it's always time to sew!

1105 S. York Rd.
Bensenville, Il 60106
630-238-8000

AUTHORIZED DEALER

baby lock

BERNINA

elna

#82

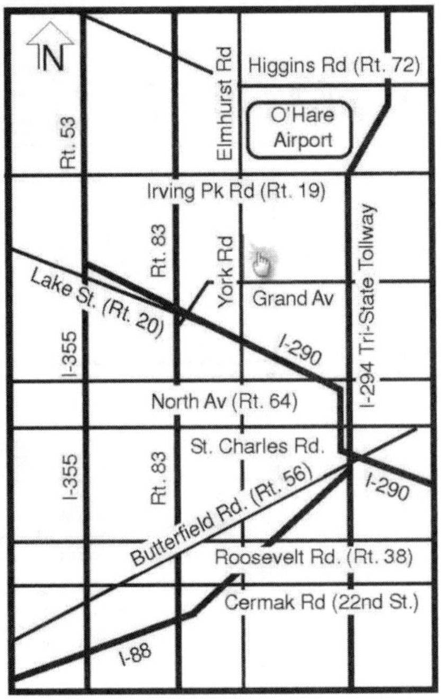

Easy to get to: I-290 Exit 12 (York Rd.)
15 minutes from:
- O'Hare Airport • Schaumburg • Itasca
- Bloomingdale • Lombard • Oakbrook
- Riverside • Oak Park • Park Ridge

- Always Friendly, Courteous and Willing to Help
- Over 4,500 Bolts of Fine Quality Quilting Fabrics
- Area's largest selection of Batiks, Asians & Flannels
- Fat Quarters • Patterns • Kits • Books
- Sewing Machines • Notions • Classes
- In-Store Rental Machines Available
- On-site Machine Service & Repairs

Chicagoland's largest quilt shop.

Bus Tours Welcome!

Mon, Wed, Fri 10-5
Tues, Thur 10-8
Sat 10 - 5 Sun 12-5

www.fabricsetc2.com

Winfield, IL #83

The Quilt Merchant

27 W 209 Geneva Rd. (Prairie Trails Shopping Ctr) Winfield, IL 60190
(630) 480-3000 www.thequiltmerchant.com

Dedicated to bringing quilters everywhere the best in both Reproduction and Modern fabrics, patterns, books and notions.
Devoted Jo Morton store, as well as Kaffe Fassett, batiks and the best from Michael Miller, Marcus Brothers, Windham, Blue Hill Fabrics and more.
We also carry supplies for wool appliqué and redwork embroidery.
We invite you to come visit anytime you are in the Chicagoland area.
Several restaurants close by - make a day of it!

Mon - Sat 10 - 5
Thur til 8 Sun - Closed

Better Homes and Gardens Quilt Sampler FEATURED SHOP

A top ten shop featured in Better Homes and Garden fall 2007 Quilt Sampler Magazine.

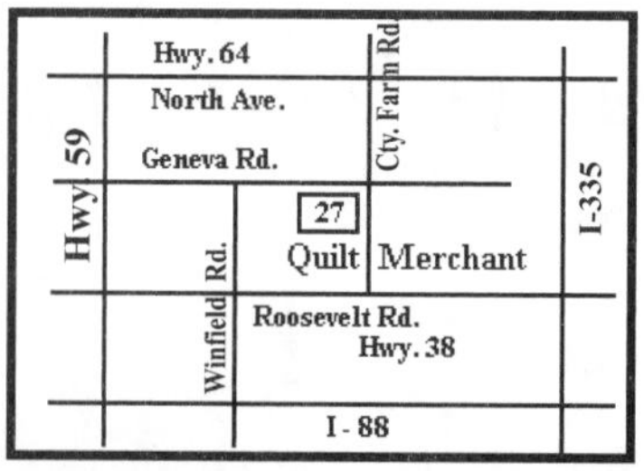

Lockport, IL #84

Thimbles

Mon, Wed, Fri, Sat 9:30 - 4
Thur 9:30 - 7
Sun 12 - 4
Closed Tuesdays

940 S. State St. 60441
(815) 836-8735 Fax: (815) 836-8174
thimblesquilts@sbcglobal.net

Located on Lockport's Historic State St.
3000 Bolts Fabric, Books, Patterns, Notions & Classes.
Authorized Bernina Dealer

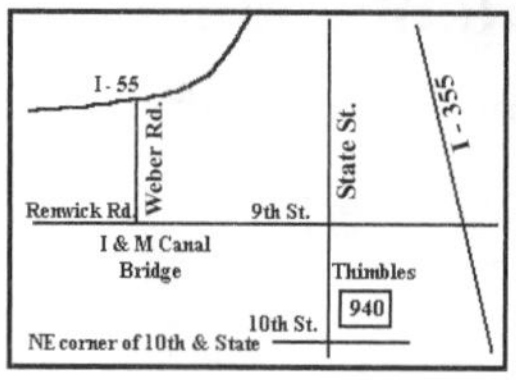

Tinley Park, IL #85

Sew Creative

Mon - Fri 10 - 5:30
Thur til 7
Sat 10 - 4

7020 Centennial Dr. 60477
(708) 429-6056 Est: 1993
sewcreativeinc@me.com
www.sewcreativequilting.com
We have a lot to offer in the way of quality quilting fabrics. You will find one room devoted to Batiks and Asians as well as heirloom sewing. Janome Sewing Machines and Gammil long arm quilting services.

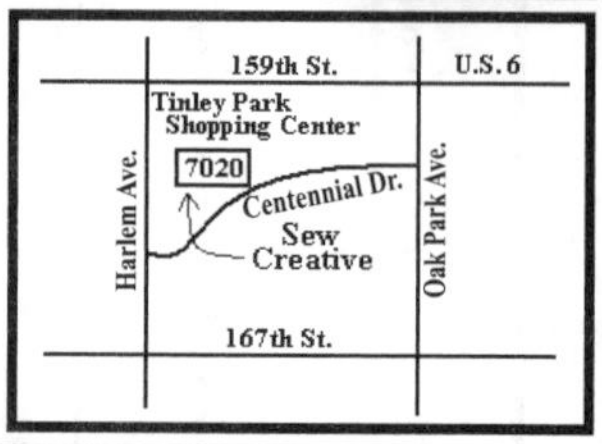

Frankfort, IL #86

Top Shelf Quilts

M, T, W, F 10 - 5
Th 10 - 8
Sat 10 - 4
Sun 12 - 4

10 Elwood St. 60423
(815) 806-1694
Est: 2003 2000 sq. ft. Free Newsletter
topshelfquilts@yahoo.com
www.topshelfquilts.com
Over 3000 bolts of fabric including Thimbleberries, batiks, brights, novelty, Moda, flannel, blenders. Notions, books, etc.
Longarm quilting services.

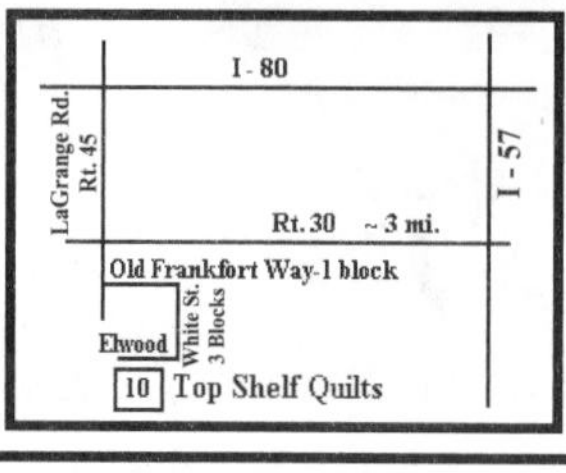

Braidwood, IL #87

Countryside Village

Mon - Sat 9 - 5
Sun 10 - 5

1540 N. Division St. 60408
Easy access on I-55 and Rt 113 Exit 236E
(815) 458-2191
countrysidevillage@yahoo.com

9,000 Sq. Ft. of Gifts, Fabric, Home Décor and more.

www.countrysidevillagegifts.com

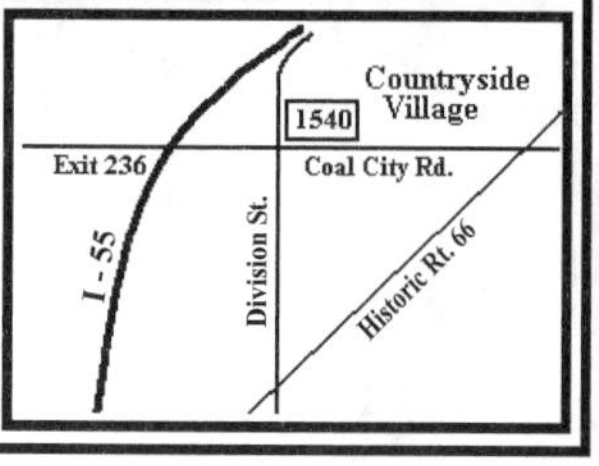

Roberts Sewing Center

A Quilter's Paradise

12,000 sq. ft. !

Est. 1930

Owner: Ken Roberts

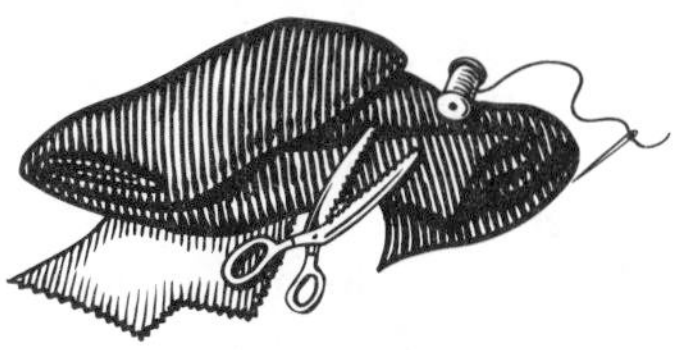

2011 Weber Rd. Crest Hill, IL 60403

(800) 273-9111 or (815) 729-1600

Bus Tours Welcome—Please Call Ahead

e-mail: rsckk1@aol.com

Crest Hill, IL #88

OVER 7,000 bolts of fabric

Large Inventory of:

- Books
- Patterns
- Notions
- Thread
- Embroidery Designs

Map not to scale

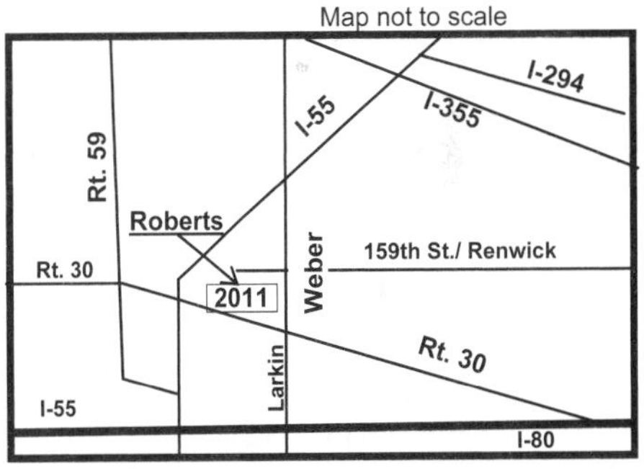

Kits

Kits

Kits!!

www.robertssewingcenter.com

shop on-line for kits and more at

www.aquiltersparadise.com

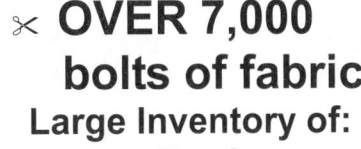

PFAFF Husqvarna VIKING

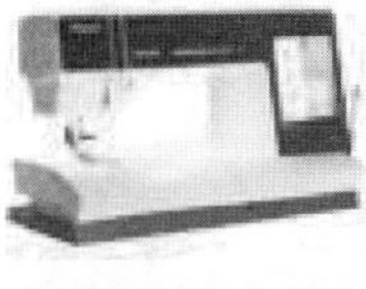

authorized dealer

Home and Industrial Machines

Mon, Wed, Fri & Sat 9:30am—5:30pm Tues & Thurs 9:30am—7:00pm

(Closed Sunday)

Illinois Quilt Shops

Aledo Stone House Quilting, 2028 Ridge Rd. 309-582-8611
Altamont Quilts & More, 9 S. Main St 618-483-5629
Arlington Heights Linda Z's Sewing Center, 1030 E. Central
847-394-4590 See ad #73, page 153
Arlington Heights Quilter's Destination, 945 E Rand Rd
847-506-6410 See ad #74, page 153
Arthur Stitch & Sew Fabrics, 220 S. Vine St.
217-543-2287 See ad #21, page 139
Ashton Cottage Garden Quilts, 705 N. 1st St. #C
815-453-7534 See ad #54, page 148
Avon The Clothesline Quilt Shop, 102 N. Main
309-465-3850 See ad #38, page 144
Barrington A Touch of Amish 130 Applebee St.
847-381-0900 See ad #72, page 153
Batavia Prairie Shop Quilts 1911 W. Wilson St.
630-406-0237 See ad #77, page 154
Belvidere All My Stitches, 407 S. State St.
815-547-1099 See ad #62, page 150
Bensenville Fabrics Etc. 2, 1105 S. York Rd.
630-238-8000 See ad #82, page 155
Big Rock Esther's Place, 201 W. Galena St. 630-556-9665
Bishop Hill The Village Smithy, 309 N. Bishop Hill St.
309-927-3851 See ad #47, page 146
Bloomington The Treadle, 2101 Eastland Dr.
309-662-1733 See ad #28, page 142
Braidwood Countryside Village 1540 N. Divison St.
815-458-2191 See ad #87, page 156
Carbondale Calico Country Sew & Vac, 2355 Sweets Rd.
618-529-5665 See ad #1, page 136
Carpentersville Grist Mill Ends & Things, 39 E. Main St. 847-426-6455
Chicago QUILTOLOGY-The Urban Quilt Space, 2625 N Halsted St 773-880-5994
Christopher Quilters Corner, 211 W. Sylvia Ave.
618-724-2817 See ad #2, page 136
Cisne Your Quilting Stash, Rt. 1 P.O. Box 90
618-835-2681 See ad #6, page 136
Cissna Park Prairieland Quilts, 101 North 2nd. St. (Rt 49)
815-457-2867 See ad #27, page 142
Clare Basketcases Unlimited, 26271 Malta Rd 815-393-3414
Clinton Quilters Delight, 301 W. Washington St. 217-937-0159
Collinsville Cross Patches, 110 W. Main St. 618-345-3661
Crest Hill Roberts Sewing Center, 2011 Weber St.
815-729-1600 See ad #88, page 157
Crete Just Between Friends, 219 Milburn Ave. 708-672-5641
Crystal Lake Fabric Shop at Geiseke Dept. Store, 21 N. Williams 815-459-2084
Crystal Lake Needlinaround Inc, 3910 Steeple Run 847-309-1995
Dahlgren Joyce's Country Quilts, R.R. #1, Box 54-B
618-736-2385 See ad #4, page 136
Danville Threads of Time, 207 S. Buchanan
217-431-9202 See ad #26, page 141
Downers Grove The Quilt Basket, 1012 Curtiss St.
630-515-8820 See ad #78, page 154
East Moline The Quilt Basket, 627 Ave. of the Cities
309-755-9750 See ad #45, page 146
Edgewood Rutledge Quilting, 507 Rt. 37 618-238-4544
Edwardsville The Quilted Garden, 1310 N. Main St.
618-656-6538 See ad #11, page 137
Effingham Angie's Nine Patch, 804 S. Henrietta
217-347-9669 See ad #17, page 138
Effingham Calico Shoppe, 1108 N. Merchant St. 217-342-6628

Elburn Silver Oaks Quilt Shop, 40W686 Campton Wood Dr 630--9458631
Fairview Heights Jackman's Fabrics, 1000 Lincoln Hwy.
618-632-2700 See ad #9, page 137
Fox River Grove Pieceful Gathering Quilt Shop, 106 NW Hwy.
847-516-7911 See ad #71, page 152
Fox River Grove Window Box Gardens, 38 Manchester Ct. 847-516-2496
Frankfort Top Shelf Quilts, 10 Elwood St
815-806-1694 See ad #86, page 156
Fulton Susan's Calico Creations, 1108 4th St.
815-589-2221 See ad #53, page 148
Galena Phat Quarter's, Inc., 303 S. Commerce St.
815-776-0034 See ad #56, page 148
Geneseo Quilts-N-Blooms Quilt Shop, 101 S, State 309-944-8739
Grayslake Quiltplay, 62 Center St
847-548-4967 See ad #65, page 152
Greenville Farmland Quilting & Embroidery, 201 South 4th
618-664-2139 See ad #14, page 138
Hampshire Judy's Quilt 'n' Sew290 S. State St.
847-683-4739 See ad #69, page 152
Havana Ma's Got'a Notion, 106 N. Schrader St.
309-543-6613 See ad #35, page 143
Highland Rosemary's Fabric and Quilts, 812 9th St.
618-654-5045 See ad #13, page 138
Hoopeston The Sewing Boutique, 222 E. Main St.
217-283-7125 See ad #25, page 139
Huntley Quilt in Joy, 10709 Huntley/Dundee Rd.
847-669-1722 See ad #70, page 152
Jacksonville Times Square Sewing Complex, 806 Hardin Ave.
217-245-5445 See ad #34, page 143
Kewanee The Quilt Box, 109 E. Third St.
309-854-9000 See ad #48, page 146
Lake Villa Sewing Source, 122 E. Grand Ave.
847-356-5100 See ad #64, page 151
Lebanon Calico Moon, 216 W St. Louis St
618-537-6240 See ad #12, page 138
Lemont That Thread Shop, P.O. Box 325 708-301-3172
Lincoln Log Cabin Quilt Shop, 118 N. McLean
217-871-1864 See ad #30, page 142
Lisle Pieceful Hearts Fabrics 2723 W. Maple Ave.
630-718-0112 See ad #79, page 154
Lockport Thimbles, 940 S. State St.
815-836-8735 See ad #84, page 156
Loves Park J Rose Sewing Studio, 6130 E Riverside Blvd. 815-229-3112
Macomb Piece to Peace Treasures, 341 N. Lafayette St.
309-836-5999 See ad #37, page 144
Mahomet A Quilting Bee, 415 E. Main St. 217-714-1809
Marshall White Stallion Creations, 620 Archer Ave.
217-826-3787 See ad #20, page 139
Mascoutah Patchwork Corner Crafts, 200 N. Jefferson St.
618-566-2652 See ad #8, page 136
McHenry Sunshine & Shadow Quilt Shoppe, 241 N. Green
815-385-5003 See ad #66, page 152
McLeansboro Burris Fabrics, RR 2 Box 486 618-643-2275
Metamora Cozy Corner Quilts, 101 W. Partridge St.
309-367-9303 See ad #42, page 144
Milford Dixie Cloth Shop, 130 E. Jones 815-889-5349
Minooka Quilted Turtle, 849 Ridge Rd.
815-521-1505 See ad #51, page 146

Moline **Quilts by the Oz, 5341 Ave. of the Cities**
309-762-9673 **See ad #46, page 146**
Moline Always In Stitches, 1413 16th Ave. 309-757-0017
Morris **The Fabric Center, 301 Liberty St.**
815-942-5715 **See ad #52, page 147**
Morris Quilting Memories, 906 Edgewood Dr. 815-730-9537
Morton **The Quilt Corner, 2037 S. Main St.**
309-263-7114 **See ad #43, page 145**
Mt. Zion **Stewart's Sewing Machines, 415 N. St. Hwy. 121**
217-864-6142 **See ad #31, page 142**
Nashville **Lee's Quilting & Craft Center, 212 E. St. Louis St.**
618-327-8898 **See ad #7, page 136**
Nauvoo **Sew Inspired Quilts, 1360 Mulholland St**
217-453-9909 **See ad #39, page 144**
Normal **Sewing Studio, 1503 E. College Ave. #C**
309-452-7313 **See ad #29, page 142**
Northbrook **Quilter's Heaven, 1239 Shermer Rd.**
847-272-7245 **See ad #75, page 153**
Oblong **The Village Stitchery, 108 E. Main St.**
618-592-4134 **See ad #19, page 139**
Odin Mary's Vogue Shop, 105 Green US Hwy 50 618-775-8371
Olney Quilts & Clutter, 713 W. Main St. 618-395-0114
Orangeville **Uniquely Yours Quilt Shop, 12530 N. Oneco Rd.**
815-789-4344 **See ad #57, page 148**
Oregon Stitches In Time, 300 W. Washington 815-732-4599
Oswego Prairie Stitches Quilt Shoppe, 72 S. Main St. 630-554-9701
Palos Heights **Susan Marie's Quilt Shop 6515 W 127th St**
708-371-9314 **See ad #81, page 154**
Paris **Lori's Pins 'N Needles, 1122 N. Main St.**
217-465-5541 **See ad #22, page 139**
Pawnee Flying Needles Quilting, 607 7th St. 217-625-7187
Pearl City **Sew Many Antiques, 160 S. Main St.**
815-443-2211 **See ad #55, page 148**
Pekin **Cotton Stitches, 2938 Court St.**
309-347-7399 **See ad #41, page 144**
Peoria **Prairie Points, 8839 N. Knoxville Ave.**
309-692-4340 **See ad #40, page 144**
Peru **D's Sewing Center & Quilt Shop, 4377 Venture**
815-223-7231 **See ad #50, page 146**
Princeton **Quilter's Garden, 527 S. Main St.**
815-879-3739 **See ad #49, page 146**
Princeton Old Times--Quilter Heaven, 954 N. Main St. 815-872-9841
Quincy **Times Square Sewing Complex, 420 N. 24th St.**
217-222-7458 **See ad #36, page 144**
Ramsey **The Quilt Top Shop, 332 S Superior St**
618-423-1239 **See ad #15, page 138**
Rantoul **The Needle & I, 801 Arends Blvd. #102**
217-892-2638 **See ad #24, page 139**
Rochester **Peace & Applique Quilt Shop, 145 E. Main St.**
217-498-6771 **See ad #32, page 143**
Rockford **Quilter's Haven 4616 E. State St.**
815-227-1659 **See ad #60, page 149**
Rockford **Quilter's General Store, 6903 Harrison Ave.**
815-397-5160 **See ad #61, page 149**
Rockford **Acorn Quilts, Inc., 6409 E. Riverside Blvd.**
815-289-9771 **See ad #58, page 148**
Rockford **It's For Quilting, etc., 2252 New Milford School**
815-874-0152 **See ad #59, page 148**
Rockford Golden Needles, 5530 Weatherford Dr. 815-873-0300
Salem Itch'n to be Stitch'n, 220 E Rogers St 618-740-1238
Salem Barbaras Fabrics & Finds, 105 N. Maple 618-548-0028
Sandwich Quilter's Heart, 603 E Railroad St 815-786-6066

Shelbyville **Main Street Quilt Company, 200 E. Main St**
217-774-3484 **See ad #18, page 138**
Springfield **Sew Unique, 1050 N. Grand Ave. W**
217-523-4293 **See ad #33, page 143**
Staunton **Main Street Mini Mall, Quilt Shop, 124 E. Main**
618-635-5509 **See ad #16, page 138**
Sycamore **Tammy Tadd Store, 920 W. Prairie Drive**
877-999-8233 **See ad #63, page 150**
Tinley Park **Sew Creative, 7020 Centennial Dr**
708-429-6056 **See ad #85, page 156**
Towanda Bolines at Indian Creek, 6 Pepperwood Ct. 888-214-3819
Troy Sweet Annies Quilt Shoppe, 112 E. Market St. 618-667-8002
Urbana **Sew Sassy, 156 A Lincoln Sq. Mall**
217-328-1591 **See ad #23, page 139**
Wasco **Karen's Quilt & Bead Shop, 40W514 IL Rte 64**
630-377-5965 **See ad #76, page 154**
Washington **Peddler's Way Quilt Co, 127 Peddler's Way**
309-444-7667 **See ad #44, page 145**
West Frankfort **Calico Country Sewing, 310 S. Logan St.**
618-932-2992 **See ad #3, page 136**
Wheaton Craftique/Never Enough Knitting, 119 N. Main St. 630-221-1007
Willowbrook **Quiltfabric.com, 888 75th St.**
630-321-9051 **See ad #80, page 154**
Winfield **The Quilt Merchant, 27 W 209 Geneva Rd.**
630-480-3000 **See ad #83, page 156**
Wood River **Patchwork Plus, 62 E. Ferguson Ave.**
618-251-9788 **See ad #10, page 137**
Woodlawn **Cotton Patch, 6194 E. Hobbes Rd.**
618-735-2483 **See ad #5, page 136**
Woodstock **That Quilt Shop, Inc., 1818 S Rose Farm Rd**
815-338-9353 **See ad #67, page 152**
Woodstock **Woodstock Quilts, 216 S. Seminary**
815-338-1212 **See ad #68, page 152**

33 Shows

Illinois Quilt Show

Chicago Area Shows
Batavia - July
Glencoe- Nov.
Glen Ellyn - March
Grayslake - Feb, Sept. or Oct.
Hinsdale - Feb. or March
Hoffman Estates - Sept.
Rosemont - April
Schaumburg - March
South Holland - Oct.

About Shows: We are listing only the very basic information about shows that happen on a regular schedule here. Please check out our website for more details on each show. Also this information tends to change quite often so please verify the event with our website or a local source before you venture far. Or if you're in the right area at the right time, give it a shot.

If you are a show organizer, please keep us updated on your event.
shows@quilterstravelcompanion.com www.quilterstravelcompanion.com

On our website you will also find:
- Exact dates (when we have them)
- Sponsor Information
- Contact Information
- Description of Event
- Events happening on a one-time basis

Month	City	Schedule	Show	Location with address
February				
	Grayslake	Annual, 2nd Sat in February	Winter Festival and Quilt Walk	Downtown Grayslake
March				
	Bensenville	Annual, 1st weekend in March	Fischer Farm Quilt Show	Fischer Farm, 16W860 Old Grand Ave.
	Bloomington	Annual, March or April	Quilt Spectrum	Interstate Center, 2301 W. Market St., (I-55/74 at Rt. 9 Exit)
	Hinsdale	Even Years, Feb or March	Salt Creek Quilt Guild Show	The Community House, 8th and Madison
	Crest Hill	Even Years, 2nd weekend in March	Pride of the Prairie Quilt Show	Richland Grade School, 1919 Canton Farm Rd.
	Glen Ellyn	Odd Years, 2nd Sat in March	Quilt Gathering	Abbington Banquet Center, Rt. 53 & Butterfield Rd.
	Highland	Annual, 2nd Fri & Sat in March	Highland Historical Society Quilt Show	Faith Countryside Atrium Apts., 1331 26th St.
	Ottawa	Odd Years, 3rd weekend in March	Little Cabin in the Woods Quilt Show	St. Columba School, 1110 LaSalle St.
	Ottawa	Even Years, March	Illinois Valley Quilt Guild	Knights of Columbus Hall, 401 W. Main St.
	Princeton	Odd Years, 3rd weekend in March	Covered Bridge Quilt Guild Show	Bureau County Fairgrounds, W. Peru St.
	Springfield	Even Years, 3rd Fri & Sat in March	Q.U.I.L.T.S. Quilt Show	Illinois State Fairgrounds--Orr Building
	Decatur	Annual, last Fri & Sat of March	Decatur Quilt Guild Show	Decatur Civic Center, Corner of Rt. 51 N & Rt. 36 E
	Schaumburg	Annual - Late March	Original Sewing & Quilt Expo	Schaumburg Convention Center, 1551 N. Thoreau Dr.
April				
	Greenville	Annual, 2nd Sat in April	Heritage Day Quilt Show	St. Lawrence Catholic Church Hall, 512 S. Prairie St.
	Quincy	Odd Years, 3rd weekend of April	Stitches In Time Quilt & Needlework Show	Quincy Senior High School, 33rd & Main St.
	Rosemont	Annual, 3rd weekend in April	International Quilt Festival	Donald Stephens Center, 5555 N. River Rd.
	Arthur	Annual, last weekend in April	Arthur Quilt Show	Arthur Community Bldg., 120 E. Progress
May				
	Rockford	Odd Years, 1st weekend in May	Sinnissippi Quilters Quilt Show	Indoor Sport Center, 8800 E. Riverside Blvd. (just off I-90)
	Bishop Hill	Annual, 3rd weekend in May	Bishop Hill Quilt Show	The Colony School Bldg., Main St.
June				
	O'Fallon	Odd Years, 2nd weekend in June	Hearts 'n' Hands Quilt Guild	Marie Schaefer School, Corner of U.S. 50 & Cherry St.
July				
	Danville	Annual, all of July	Vermilion County Museum Society	Vermilion County Museum, 116 N. Gilbert
	Rochester	Annual, 2nd Fri & Sat of July	Peace & Applique Charity Quilt Show	Masonic Hall, E. Main St.
	Batavia	Annual, 3rd weekend in July	Batavia Quilt & Textile Show	Shannon Hall and the Eastside Comm Center, 14 N. Van Buren
	Jacksonville	Annual, last Fri & Sat of July	River Country Quilt Show	Jackonville High School, 1211 N. Diamond St.
August				
	Galesburg	Even Years, 2nd weekend in August	Piecemakers Quilt Guild Show	Carl Sandburg College, 2232 S.Lake Storey Rd.
September				
	East Peoria	Odd Years, 3rd weekend in September	Gems of the Prairie Quilt Guild Show	East Peoria Event Center, 4200 E. Washington (Rt. 8)
	Effingham	Annual, 3rd Fri & Sat in September	Crossroads Quilters Guild Show	Hendelmyer Recreation Center, 1906 S. 4th St.
	Hoffman Estates	Odd Year, 2nd Fri & Sat after Labor Day	NW Suburban Quilt Guild Show	Prairie Stone Sport & Wellness Center, 5050 Sedge
October				
	Grayslake	Odd Years, September or October	Village Quilters Show	Lake Country Fairgrounds, 1060 E. Petersen Rd.
	Mt. Vernon	Annual, 1st Fri & Sat in October	Itchin' To Be Stitchin' Quilt Show	Pleasant Hill Baptist Church, 19479 N. Illinois Hwy. 37
	Salem	Annual, 3rd weekend in October	Happy Hearts Quilt Guild Show	Salem Community Center, 416 E. Oglesby St.
	South Holland	Odd years, 3rd weekend in October.	Midwest Fall QuiltFest	Thornwood High School, 170th & South Park Ave.
November				
	Glencoe	Annual, 1st full Thurs to Sat in November	Illinois Quilters Show	Chicago Botanic Garden, 1000 Lake Cook Rd.

59 Featured Shops

INDIANA

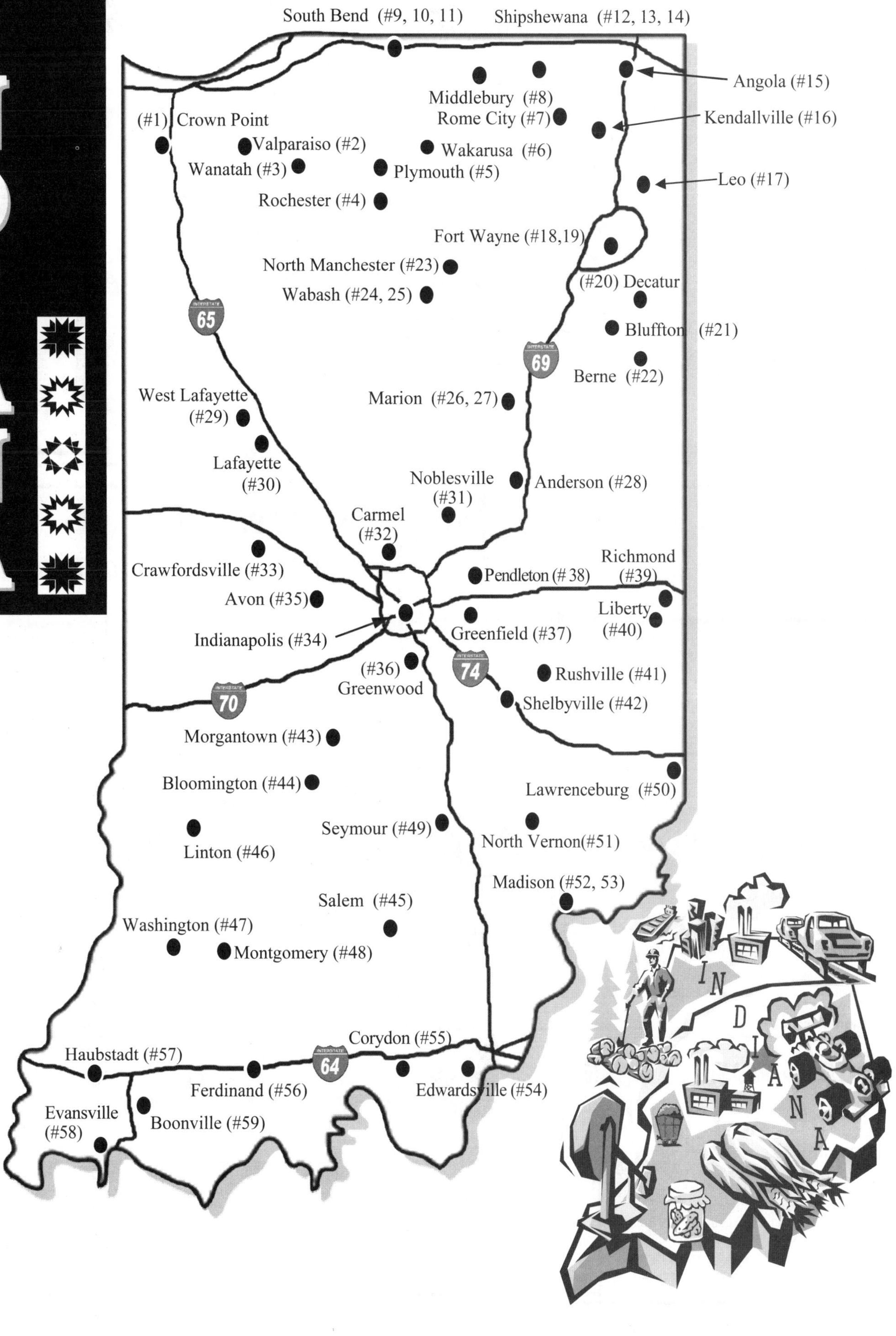
South Bend (#9, 10, 11)
Shipshewana (#12, 13, 14)
Angola (#15)
Middlebury (#8)
Rome City (#7)
Kendallville (#16)
(#1) Crown Point
Valparaiso (#2)
Wakarusa (#6)
Wanatah (#3)
Plymouth (#5)
Leo (#17)
Rochester (#4)
Fort Wayne (#18,19)
North Manchester (#23)
(#20) Decatur
Wabash (#24, 25)
65
Bluffton (#21)
69
Berne (#22)
West Lafayette (#29)
Marion (#26, 27)
Lafayette (#30)
Noblesville (#31)
Anderson (#28)
Carmel (#32)
Richmond (#39)
Crawfordsville (#33)
Pendleton (# 38)
Avon (#35)
Liberty (#40)
Indianapolis (#34)
Greenfield (#37)
(#36) Greenwood
74
Rushville (#41)
70
Shelbyville (#42)
Morgantown (#43)
Bloomington (#44)
Lawrenceburg (#50)
Seymour (#49)
North Vernon(#51)
Linton (#46)
Madison (#52, 53)
Salem (#45)
Washington (#47)
Montgomery (#48)
Corydon (#55)
Haubstadt (#57)
64
Ferdinand (#56)
Edwardsville (#54)
Evansville (#58)
Boonville (#59)

Crown Point, IN #1

Mon - Fri 10 - 6
Tues & Fri til 8
Sat 10 - 5

bits 'n pieces

732 N. Main St. 46307
(219) 662-9030
Est: 1997 4000 sq.ft.
second floor NOW OPEN!

Quality quilting fabrics, notions, books & patterns featured in a friendly sewing room atmosphere. New classes each month. Join Us!

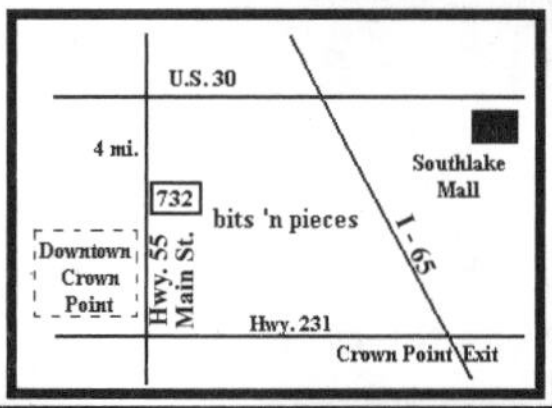

Valparaiso, IN #2

Mon - Fri 10 - 5:30
Thur til 7
Sat 10 - 3

Needle & Thread

60 W. Jefferson 46383
(219) 462-4300 Est: 1990
Owner: Marlene Rock 1500 sq.ft.
2900 Bolts Free Newsletter

Visit our old Victorian house with everything you need for quilting. We carry Civil War repros, 30's, homespuns, batiks, flannels, Asians, brights, ... fabric to die for!

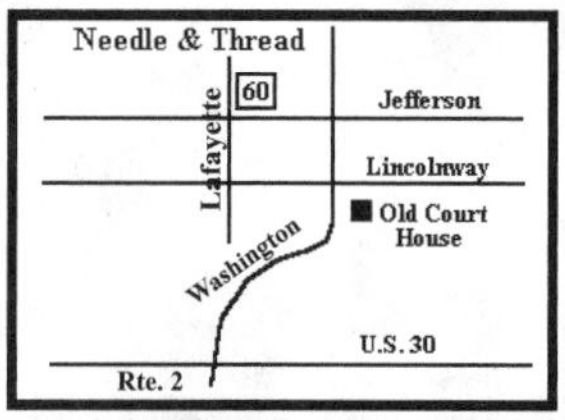

Wanatah, IN #3

Wed, Thur, Fri 5:30 - 8:30
Sat 10 - 5
Sun 11 - 4

SCRAPYARD QUILTING

10505 W 1000 S 46390
(219) 733-9980
Owner: Judy Parker

Est: 2009
800 sq.ft.
Newsletter
herveyparker@earthlink.net
www. scrapyardquilting.com
A collection of fine fabrics and crafts.
A complete line of quality products at prices you can afford. We also offer classes.
"Your One Stop Creative Shop"

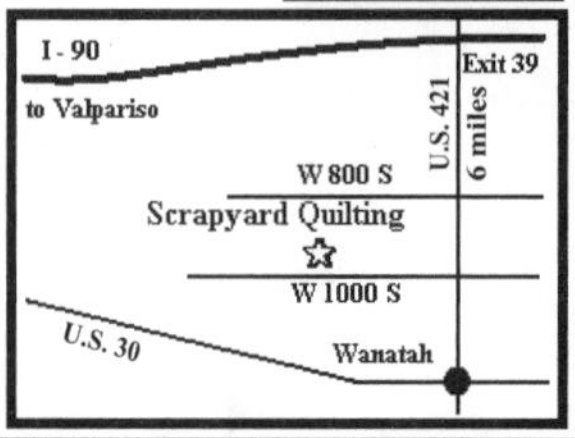

Rochester, IN #4

Mon - Fri 12 - 6
Tues & Wed til 8
Sat or Sun by Appt.

The Thread Shed

610 Main St., P.O. Box 501 46975
(574) 223-4959
Est: 1979 1500 bolts
sewwhat@rtcol.com

100% cotton fabrics for quilting & crafts, including over 20 bolts of double quilted fabric. The latest quilting notions, & DMC floss & supplies for embroidery work. Free Tues. & Weds. night classes. Lap quilts are made here for the Indiana Veteran's Home.

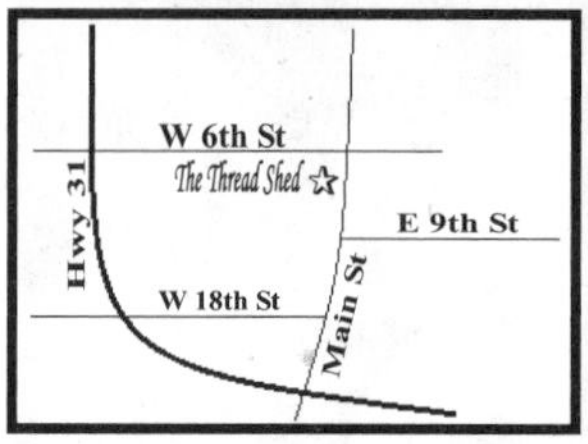

Plymouth, IN #5

Call to Schedule Your Event

Lucky Breezes Crafter's Cottage

We're a small retreat center located northwest of Plymouth

Located in a picturesque country setting, and just 10 minutes from downtown Plymouth. Lucky Breezes Crafter's Cottage is a fully equipped 3 bedroom (no bunk beds), 2 1/2 bath house with an oversized heated/air conditioned sewing/crafting room attached, for all day, or night comfort. The house can easily accommodate 4-11 people. Felt board, cutting mats, ironing boards, irons, and laundry room with slop sink are all supplied for your use. Bring your food, your friends, your projects, and stay as long as you like. Please visit our website, or contact Deborah direct @ 574-223-4959 or sewwhat@rtcol.com.

Wakarusa, IN #6

Mon - Fri 9 - 5
Sat 9 - 2

Jeanette's Fabric Boutique

105 S Elkhart St., P.O. Box 511 46573
(574) 862-4207 Fax: (574) 862-1637
Owner: Jeanette Prenkert
Est: 1981 2500 sq. ft. 2000+ Bolts
jeanettes1@verizon.net
www.jeanettesfabric.com

Large selection quilting fabrics; many classes; personal help anytime; authorized Janome and Baby Lock dealer; unique store in a small town.

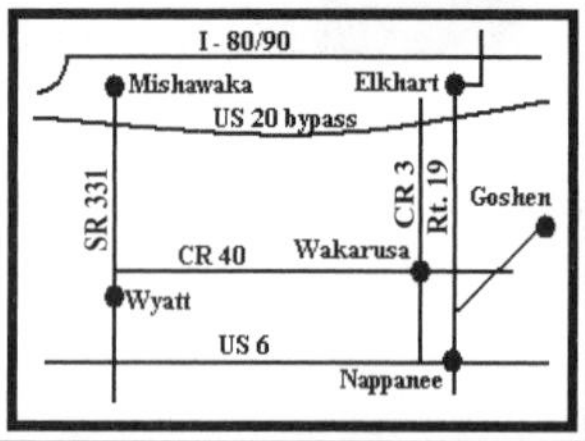

Rome City, IN #7

Mon - Fri 9 - 5
Wed til 8
Sat 9 - 3

Caroline's Cottage Cottons

195 Weston St. 46784
(260) 854-3900
Owners: Caroline & David North
Est: 2007 1500+ Bolts
www.carolinescottagecottons.com
We are located in the historic lake community. The shop is a little brick home that was built in 1870. Each room has a different theme. We specialize in Civil War, 1920's & 1930's fabrics & wool for penny rugs. Supplies, books, patterns and classes.

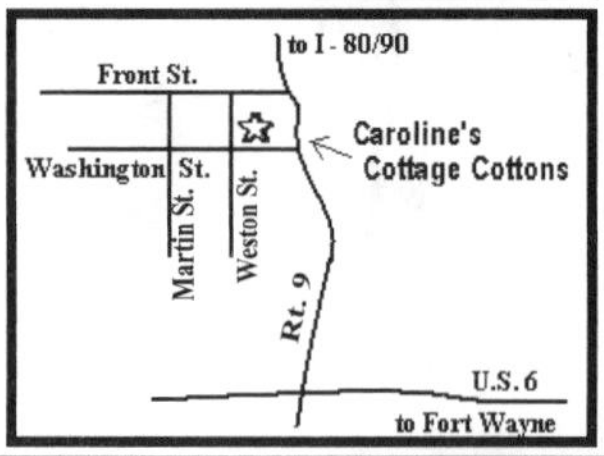

Middlebury, IN #8

Mon - Thur 9 - 7
Fri & Sat 9 - 8
Winter Hrs. Vary

The Quilt Shop at the Essenhaus

240 U.S. 20, P.O. Box 1217 46540
(574) 825-9471 x300 or (800) 455-9471 x300
thequiltshop-roz@live.com
www.essenhausuilts.com
Fabrics • STENCILS • Patterns • Notions
Locker hooking • Quilt Magic
Locally/Amish made Quilts, Dolls & Gifts
Custom Orders Welcome!
"It's a Joy to serve you" Rosilynn Stoffel

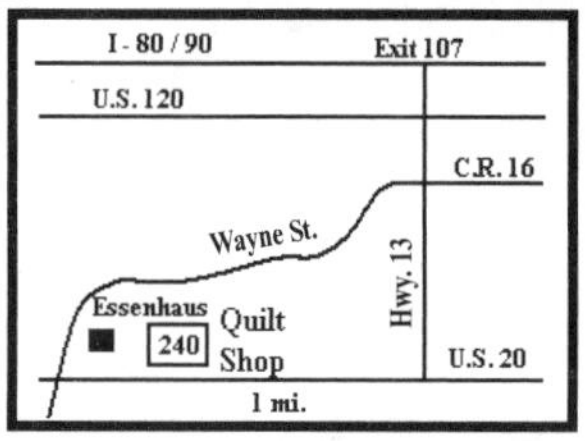

South Bend, IN #9

Mon - Sat 10 - 6
Thur til 8

Stitch 'N Time Fabrics

2305 Miami St. 46614
(574) 234-4314 Est: 1993
Fax: (574) 968-4314
stitchntimefabrics@sbcglobal.net
www.stitchntimefabrics.com 4000+ Bolts
Owner: Valerie Strycker 3800 sq.ft.
Large Selection of Notions, Books & Patterns.
Singer, Pfaff & Janome sewing machines.
Service of all makes. Classes.

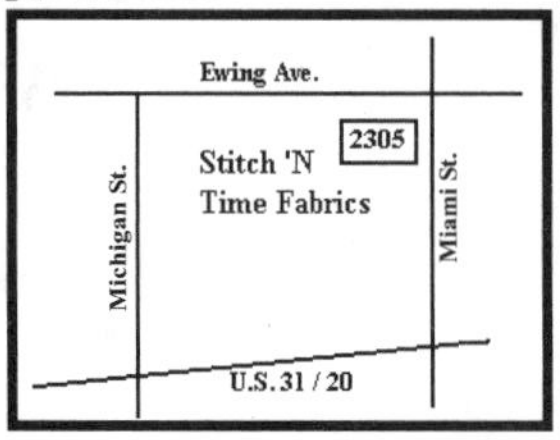

South Bend, IN #10

Tues - Fri 10 - 5
Sat 10 - 3

Heckaman's Quilts + Yarns

We Finish What Grandma Started

63028 U.S. 31 South 46614
(574) 291-3918
www.naturalquiltsandyarns.com

Quilts for Sale. Custom Orders Welcome
Let us Quilt your Heirlooms by Hand or Machine. Beautiful Yarns. Ashford Spinning Wheels. Rug Hooking Supplies

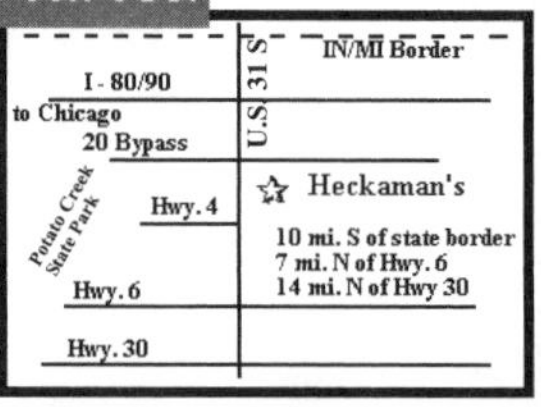

South Bend, IN #11

Erica's

©Erica

HOURS
Monday 9:30-5:30
Tuesday 9:30-5:30
Wednesday 9:30-5:30
Thursday 9:30-8:30
Friday 9:30-5:30
Saturday 9:00-4:00
Sunday 12:00-4:00

1320 N. Ironwood Dr., South Bend, IN 46615
(574) 233-3112
www.ericas.com http://blog.ericas.com

Almost 5000 bolts of fabric including Moda, Benartex, South Sea Imports, RJR, Windham and designers Nancy Halvorsen, Deb Strain, Thimbleberries and many others!
Books, patterns, notions and more!
Shop in store or online.

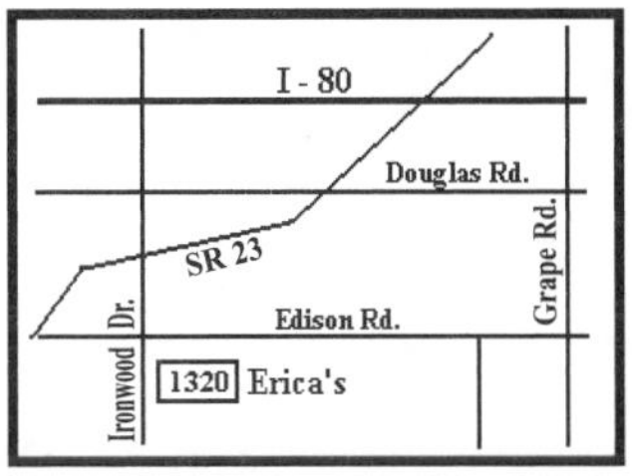

There's only one . . .

YODER DEPARTMENT STORE

♦Quilting
♦Fashion
♦Bridal

Every Major Manufacturer and More Represented.

#12

12,000+ Bolts of Fabric In Stock

Silk • Velvet • Wool • Linen • Denim

Quilting Supplies & Kits
Notions Patterns Books

Shipshewana, IN

260-768-4887

Yoder's Shopping Center
300 S. Van Buren St. (SR 5)
Shipshewana, IN

M-Sat 8a-5:30p

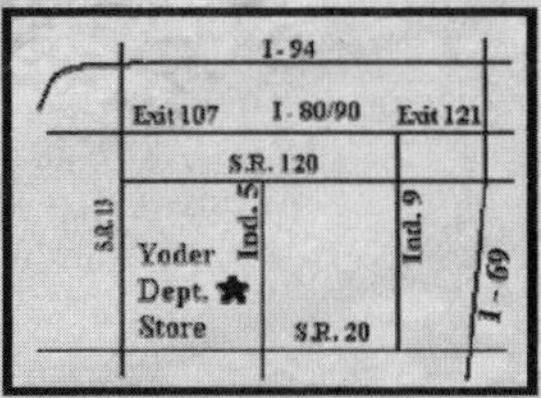

www.YoderDepartmentStore.com

Shipshewana, IN #13

Mon - Sat 10 - 5
Winter Hrs. Vary
Please Call Ahead

Rebecca Haarer Folk Arts & Antiques

165 Morton St. 46565
Mailing: P.O. Box 52
(260) 768-4787 Est: 1971
Owner: Rebecca Haarer Free Brochure
Antique Quilts, Quilt Tops, Quilt Blocks and Fabric. Amish Quilts, Dolls, Rockers and Stencils. Amish Quilt Lectures.
Area's largest selection of vintage Quilts

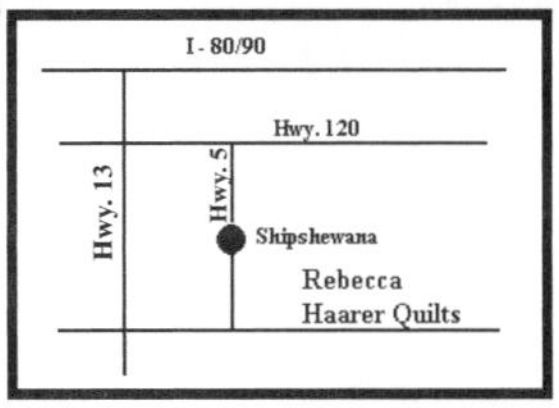

Shipshewana, IN #14

Mon - Sat
Jan - March
10 - 5
April - Dec
9 - 5

Lolly's Fabrics & Quilts

255 E. Main St., P.O. Box 1095
(260) 768-4703
lollys@lollys.com
Est: 1981
5000+ sq.ft.
14,000 bolts

www.lollys.com Online Newsletter
Every Quilter's Dream!
We provide the Inspiration.
Fabrics, Patterns and everything you need to complete your project.
Exceptional Customer Service.

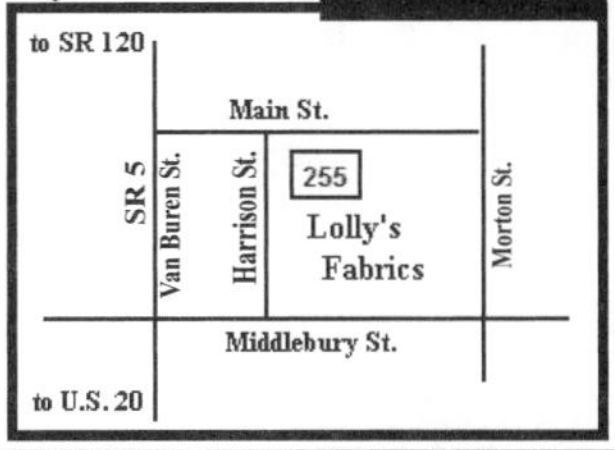

Angola, IN #15

Mon - Fri
10 - 6
Sat 9 - 4

Sewing Treasures

1605 S. Wayne St. 46703
(260) 665-6948 Fax: (260) 665-6948
Est: 1999 2600 sq.ft. 1200 Bolts
sewlutions@locl.net
www.sewingtreasures.net
Your full service quilt store in the Indiana Lake Country. Stop by and say "hi".

Husqvarna VIKING

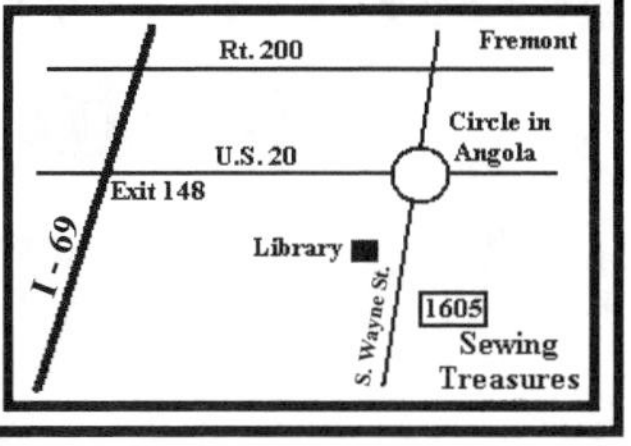

Kendallville, IN #16

Mon - Fri
10 - 6
Sat 10 - 3

Nancy's Stitches

704 S. Main St. 46755
(260) 343-2627
Est: 2003 1200 sq.ft. 900 Bolts
Free Newsletter

We do cater to Quilters through Fabric, Notions, Patterns and Longarm Quilting.
We also do alterations and give classes.

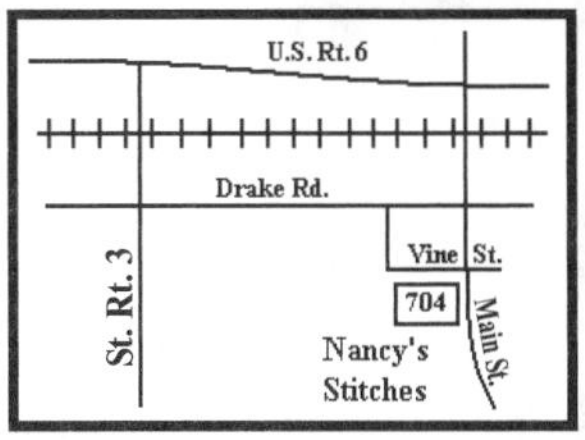

Leo, IN #17

Mon - Fri
10 - 5
Thur til 8
Sat 10 - 3

A Quilt of Many Colors

15026 St. Rd. 1 46765
(260) 627-2907
aqomc4751@verizon.net

www.quiltofmanycolors.com
Small town shop with world view of fabric.
"Where Customers are Friends"

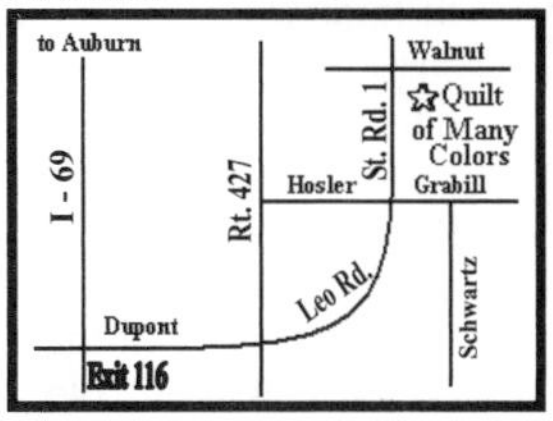

Husqvarna VIKING

vikingsewingcenter@hotmail.com
www.vikingsewingcenters.com

Viking Sewing Centers

Tues-Thur 9-5 Fri 9-4 Sat 10 -3

Husqvarna-Viking Sewing Center. We carry books, patterns, thread, stabilizers and software, embroidery designs, sewing machine cabinets and much much more. Our staff is happy to greet you with a smile and help you find what you need. Stop in for a cup of coffee.

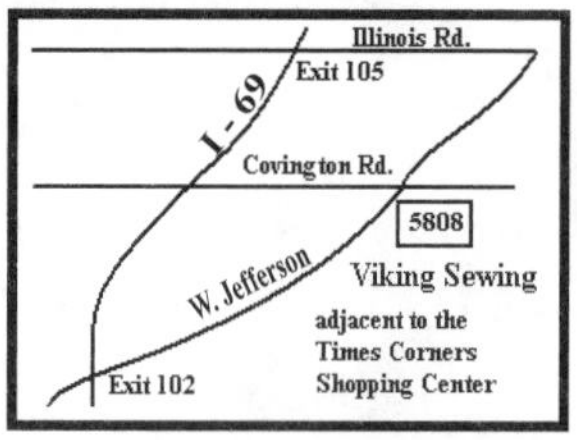

5808 W. Jefferson St. 46804
800-657-9233 or
260-432-9000
Est: 2005 1600 sq.ft.

Fort Wayne, IN #18

Pieced Together QUILT SHOP

6037 E. State Blvd.
Fort Wayne, In 46815
260-486-4217
Est: 2007 Online E-News

Tuesday - Friday 10 - 5
Saturday 10 - 4
By Appointment

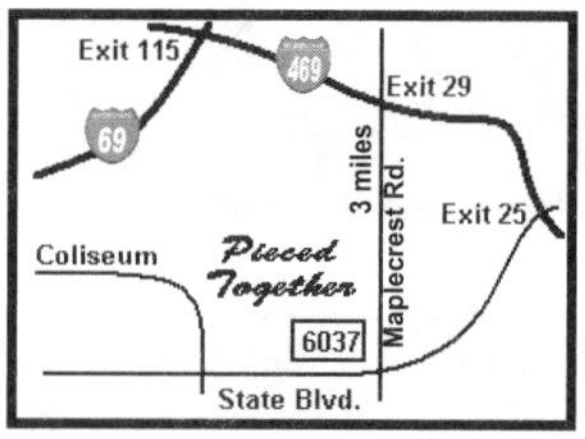

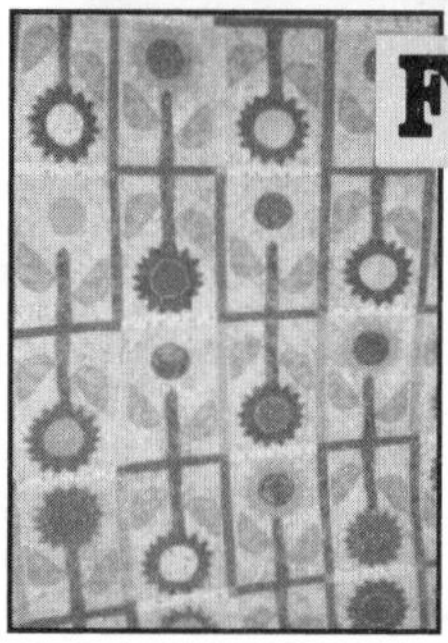

Fort Wayne, IN #19

Over 3500 Bolts of Quality Cottons.
Classes, Clubs, Books, Patterns, Kits
Notions, Jelly Rolls, & Charm Packs
Custom Quilts & Long Arm Quilting
FUN & FRIENDS
piecedtogether@verizon.net
www.ptquilts.com

Decatur, IN #20

Country Creations

Mon - Fri 10 - 5
Sat 9 - 2

5342 N 400 W 46733
(260) 547-4535
Owners: Bev and Gene Weber
Est: 1998 3000 sq.ft.
fabrics2@onlyinternet.net

Cotton for quilting, supplies, books, patterns, classes. Custom long-arm quilting

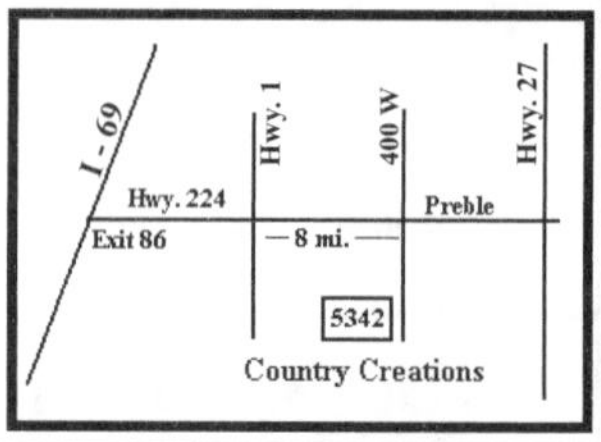

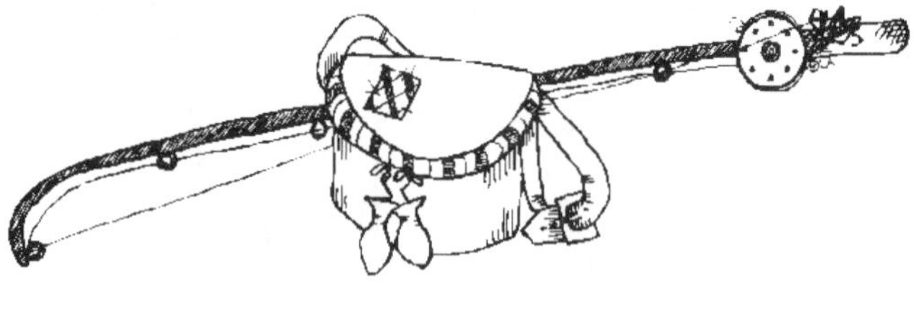

Bluffton, IN #21

Quilts n Gifts LLC

2035 Commerce Dr.
Behind Lowe's 46714
(260) 565-4438
quiltsngifts@adamswells.com

"Your one-stop Quilt Shop."

Tues, Wed, Fri 9:30 - 5
Mon & Thur 9:30 - 6
Sat 9:30 - 3

- over 2500 Bolts of Fabrics
- over 300 patterns
- threads from Gutterman, Robison Anton, Superior, King Tut
- classes from beginners to advanced
- long arm service Gammill Statler
- customer service our #1 priority
- various blocks-of-the-months www.quiltsngifts.blogspot.com
- facebook quilts & gifts

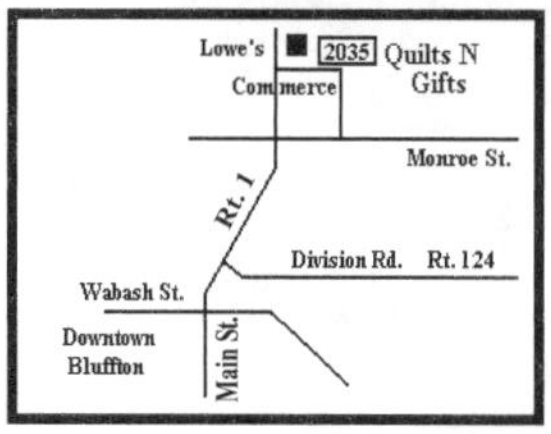

www.quiltsngifts.net

Berne, IN #22

Engine House Quilt Shop

Mon - Fri 9 - 5
Sat 9 - 3

160 W. Main St. 46711
(260) 589-3060 Est: 2006
Owner: Deb Tumbleson Online Newsletter
deb@enginehousequiltshop.com
www.enginehousequiltshop.com
You will find favorite fabrics such as: Red Rooster, Maywood Studios, & Blank.
We also have Flannel, Minkee, Homespun and Chenille.
Also Patterns, Kits and Books.

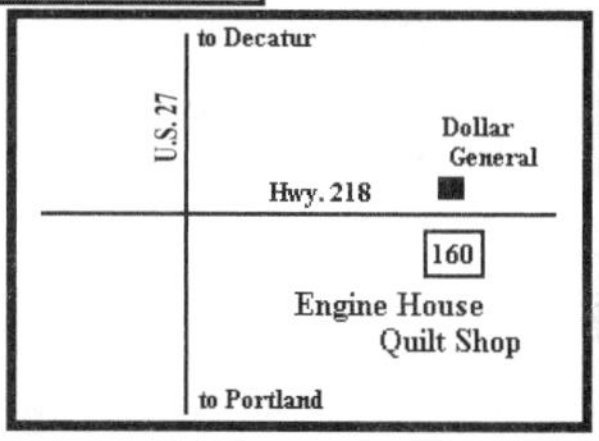

N. Manchester, IN #23

The Creative Stitch Quilt Shop

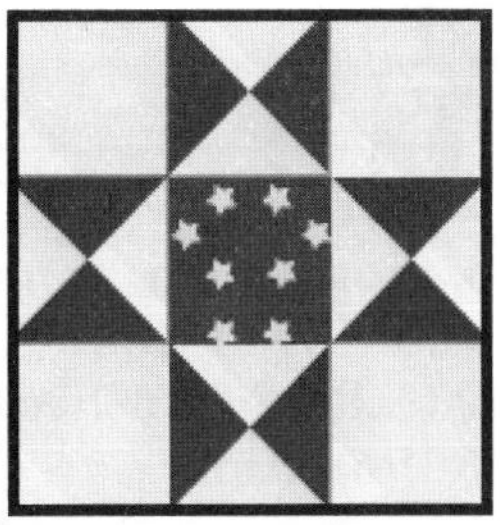

- Large selection of quilting fabrics, books, patterns, notions and kits
- Large classroom - Several BOM offerings
- Lots of Creative Ideas displayed with Great Samples
- Quality Long Arm Quilting provided - Statler Stitcher
- Friendly, helpful staff - personal service.

Tues - Fri 10 - 5 Sat 10 - 3

208 E. Main St. 46962
(260) 982-1080
creativestitch@verizon.net
Owner: Linda Cearbaugh

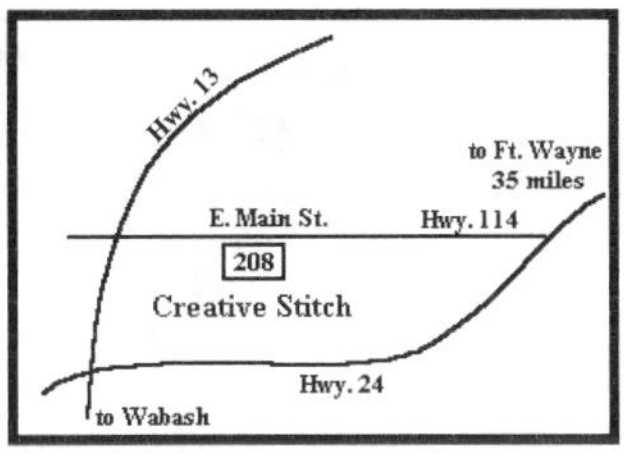

Wabash, IN #24

Mon - Fri 10 - 5:30 Sat 10 - 5

Nancy J's Quality Fabrics

1604 S. Wabash St. 46992
Toll Free (866) 563-3505 Est: 1980
Owners: Nancy Jacoby & Miriam Peebles
www.colorsgonewild.com
The latest & greatest Fabrics.
Books and Patterns for quiltmaking.
Plan to spend a day in Historic Wabash!

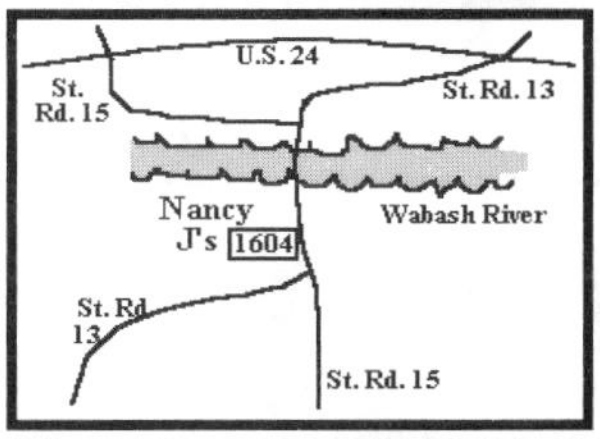

Wabash, IN #25

Mon - Fri 9 - 5 Sat 9 - 3

Heaven on Earth

4767 N. St. Rd. 15 46992
(765) 833-5461
Owner: Cheryl Ross
Est: 1996 Free Newsletter
aandchoe@dishmail.net
www.heavenonearthofwabash.com
Lots of inspiration, friendly service all in a cozy log cabin. Tons of books, patterns, and notions. Over 2000 bolts of fabric from Moda, Red Rooster, & Wyndham. Long arm quilting service.

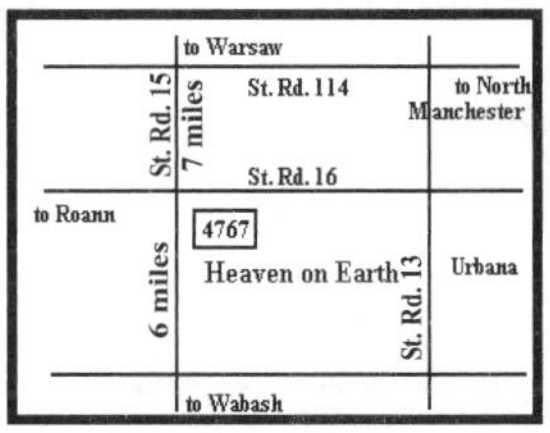

Marion, IN #26

Wed - Sat 10 - 3

The Quilters Hall of Fame

926 S. Washington, P.O. Box 681 46952
(765) 664-9333 Fax: Same
quiltershalloffame@sbcglobal.net
www.quiltershalloffame.net

Renovation of the historic Marie Webster Home is complete. Annual Celebration featuring quilt shows, lectures, workshops, and more - third weekend in July. Call for schedule.

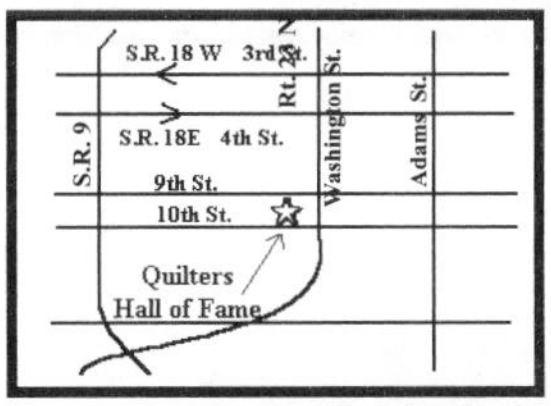

Marion, IN #27

Mon - Fri 10 - 6 Closed Wed & Sun Sat 10 - 3

SEW BIZ

"Where Sewing Is Exciting"

3722 South Western Ave. 46953
(800) 500-3830 or (765) 674-6001
Fax: (765) 674-5992 5000 sq.ft.
1983-2010 Celebrating 27 years!
sewbiz@indy.rr.com
www.sewbizmarion.com
Owner: Donelle McAdams

Viking Sewing Machine Dealer-Mid and Long arm Quilting Machines. 100% cottons, books, patterns, classes. A place to share ideas and get inspired.

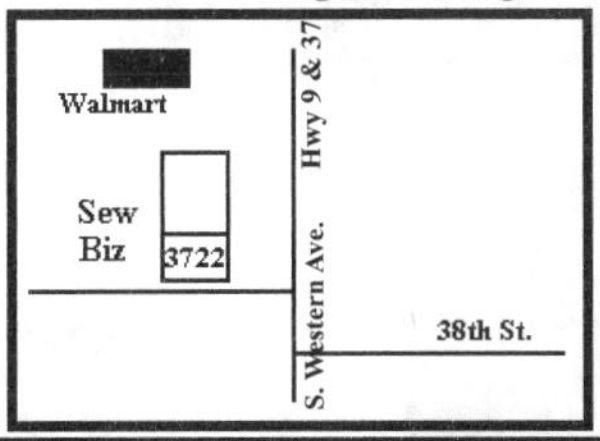

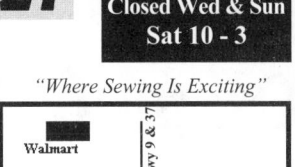

Anderson, IN #28

Tues - Fri 10 - 5 Sat 9 - 3

The Quilt Shoppe

112 W. Grand Ave. 46012
(765) 649-9102
Fax: (765) 649-2311
Owner:
Dawn R. Cornell
Est: 2004
3000 sq.ft. 2500 bolts
www.thequiltshoppeonline.com

The most up-to-date high quality fabrics from Moda, RJR, P&B. Uniquely packaged kits & collections, Gifts, antiques and a fun, feeling good environment to visit again and again.

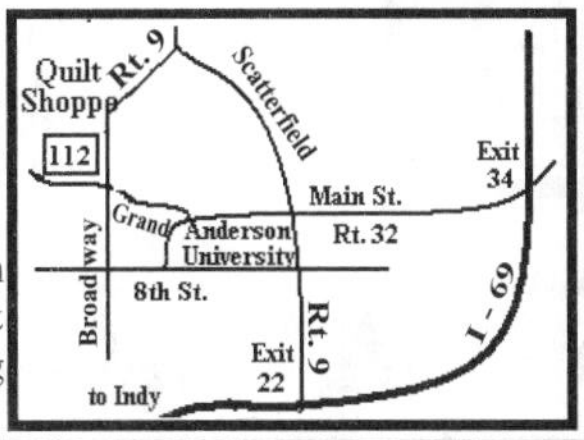

Cheryl's Quilt Shop

& More !

1227A Sagamore Pkwy N
(Eastway Plaza)
47904
(765) 447-5400
cherylsquiltshop@verizon.net
www.cherylsquiltshop.com

West Lafayette, IN #29

Please inquire about our great 5 bed retreat area!!

**Mon 12 - 7
Tues - Fri
10 - 5:30
Sat 9 - 3**
Please check website to confirm hours before traveling.

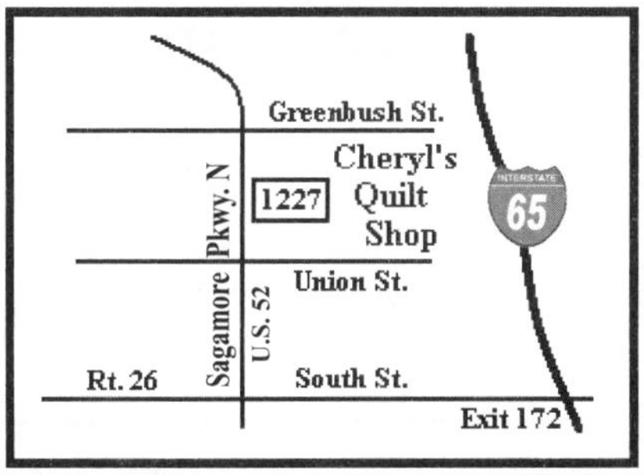

**Full line of quilting fabrics and notions
Authorized Janome dealer.
Always helpful, friendly advice!**

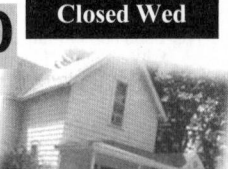

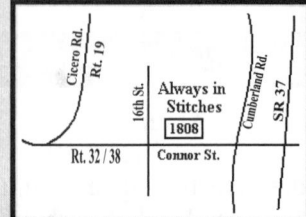

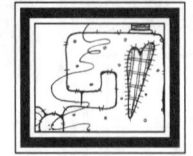

Est. 1977

CaldwellSewVac.com

Fabric, Sewing Machines, Vacuums & More!

116 S. Green St. Crawfordsville, IN 47933

765-362-7360

info@caldwellsewvac.com

www.caldwellsewvac.com

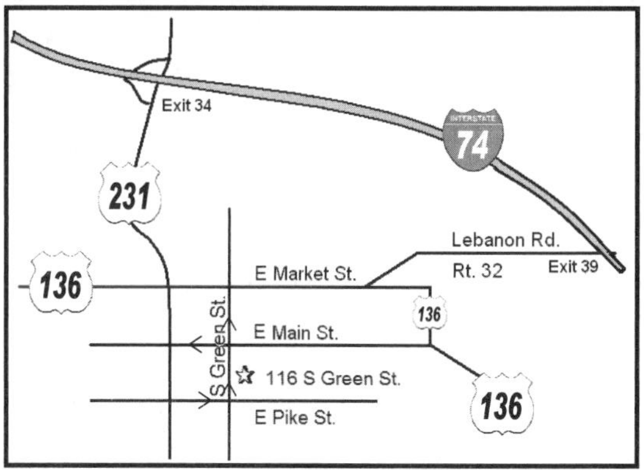

We do alterations too!

#33

QUILTS PLUS

Est: 1977

1748 E. 86th Street
Northview Mall
Indianapolis, IN 46240
(800) 840-2241
or (317) 844-2446
shop@quiltsplus.com
Owner: Jeanne Moosey

www.quiltsplus.com

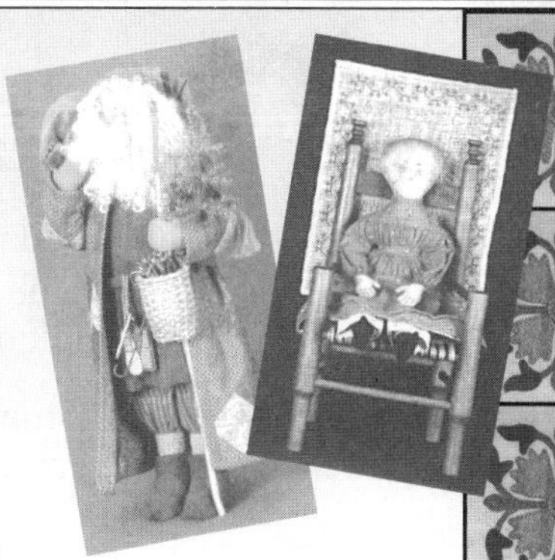

Selected by Better Homes and Gardens American Patchwork & Quilting as one of the Top Ten Quilt Shops in 2005!

- **Visit us and enjoy our great atmosphere and personalized service.**
- **We specialize in Reproductions, Wool, and Chenille Projects**
- **Block of the Month Programs available.**

Mon - Sat 10 - 5
Sun 12 - 4

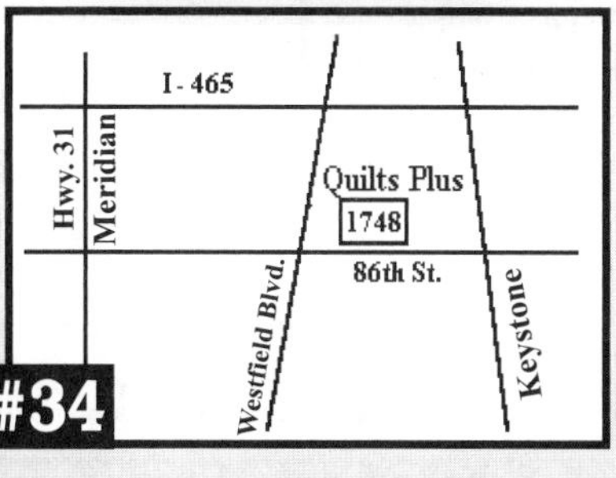

Indianapolis, IN #34

Avon Quiltery
and Bernina Sewing Center

5201 E. US 36, #105 46123
(317) 745-2626
Fax: (317) 745-2774
Owners: Dian & Russ Himes
Est: 2005 2500 sq. ft.
info@avonquiltery.com
www.avonquiltery.com

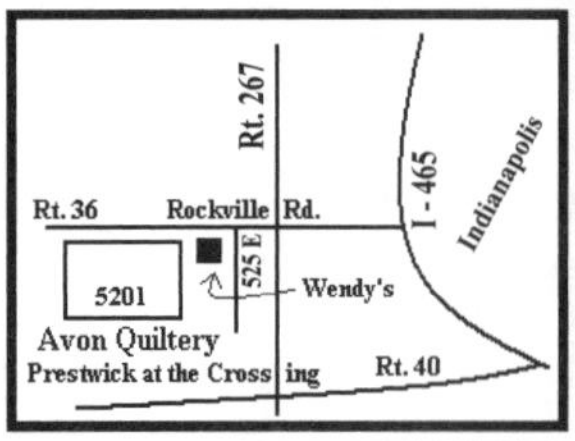

Nothing Sews Like a Bernina. Nothing. BERNINA®

Authorized Janome & Bernina Dealer

We're all about bright colors. Large selection includes retro, batiks, Japanese, hand-dyed rayons, quilting supplies, books, patterns, notions, Tsukineko Inks, Paint sticks, Angelina etc. Everything for the fabric artist/sewer. Sewing machines & sergers too! Classes and friendly staff await your every need.

Avon, IN #35

Mon - Fri 10 - 6
Sat 10 - 5

Est: 1973 **Greenwood, IN #36** 5600 sq.ft.

The Back Door, Inc.

2503 Fairview Place #W 46142
(317) 882-2120 teribackdoor@indy.rr.com
www.backdoorquilts.com
Owners: Linda Hale & Teri Dougherty

Mon - Thur 9:30 - 9
Fri & Sat 9:30-5
1st & 3rd
Sundays 1 - 4

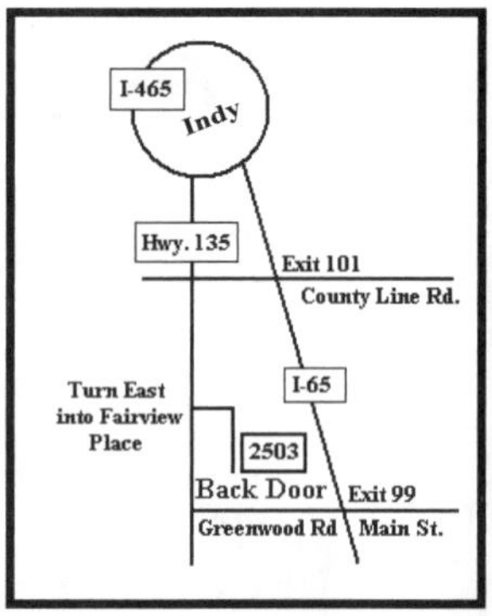

Quilting Supplies,
Wool, Punchneedle
Embroidery & Stitchery
Better Homes and Gardens
Top Ten Shop

Liberty, IN #40

Pohlar Fabrics

Mon - Sat
9 - 5

Over 4000 bolts of Fabrics.
- Moda - RJR - Hoffman - Benartex -
- Northcott - Thimbleberries -

Sewing & quilting notions, books, patterns and ready made gifts.
Machine Quilting.
Mail Order Welcome.
Exciting quilt classes!

Authorized Bernina Dealer Sales & Service. BERNINA

6439 S. State Rd. 101 47353
(800) 357-3152

or (765) 458-5466
pohlarfabrics@yahoo.com
Owners:
Kenny & Rose Pohlar
Est: 1984
1150 sq.ft.

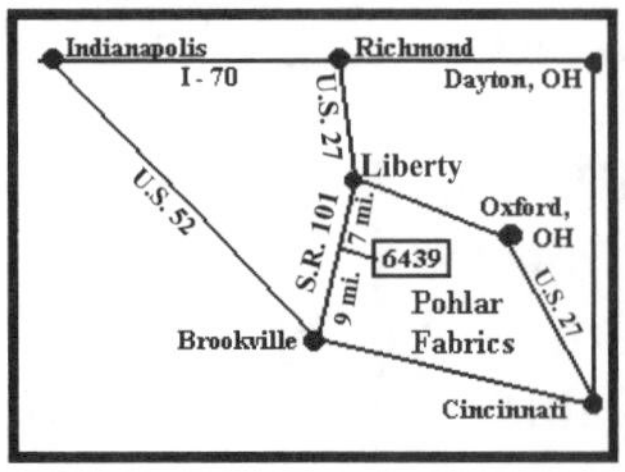

www.pohlarfabrics.com

Greenfield, IN #37

By Appointment

Zig-Zag Corner
Quilts & Baskets

7872 N. Troy Rd. 46140
(317) 326-3115
www.zigzagcorner.com
Est: 2002 1500+ bolts
Supplies and classes for:
Quilting -- Tatting -- Basket Weaving
Smocking -- Embroidery -- Heirloom Sewing
Rent our Training / Special Events Center.

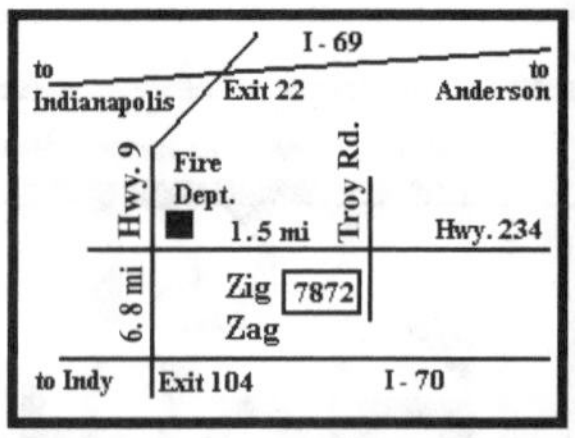

Pendleton, IN #38

Mon - Sat
10 - 5

Ruth's Legacy Quilting

104 W. High St. 46064
(765) 778-2488
Est: 1996 2700 sq.ft.
www.RuthsLegacyQuilting.com

Fabric, classes, patterns, notions and friendly service.
Long-arm machine quilting service available.

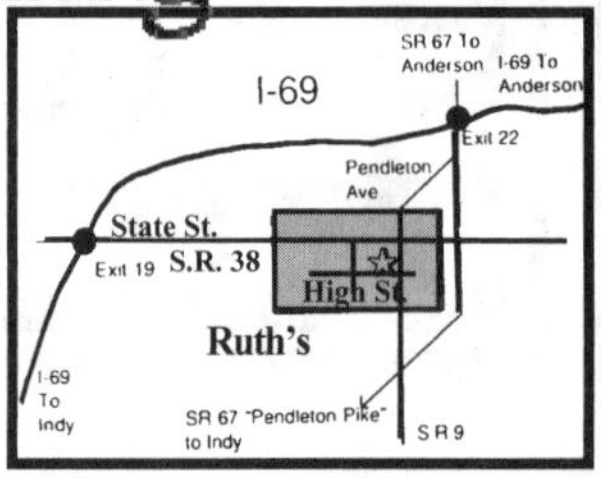

Richmond, IN #39

M, T, W, TH
10 - 6
Fri 10 - 7
Sat 10 - 5

The Stitching Nook

4629 National Rd. E 47374
(765) 962-7678 Est: 1982
stitchingnook@verizon.net
www.stitchingnook.com

100% Cotton Fabrics, Quilting Notions, Classes, Viking/Husqvarna Machine Sales, and Friendly Personal Attention.

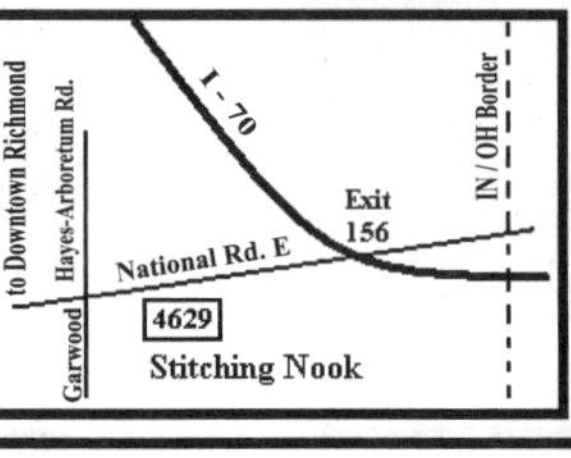

Rushville, IN #41

**Mon - Fri 10 - 5
Sat 10 - 2**

In Stitches

837 W. Third St. 46173
(765) 938-1818 Fax: (765) 938-1819
Owner: Cathy Burkett Est: 2003
institches@mach1pc.com
www.institchesquiltshop.com
Over 1000 bolts of 100% cotton fabrics including Benartex & Moda. Lots of samples to inspire.
Classes, patterns & books.
"A fun place to shop!"

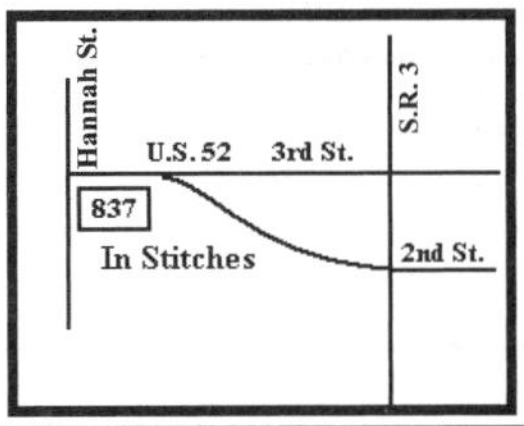

Shelbyville, IN #42

**Mon - Fri 10 - 5
Sat 10 - 3**

The River's Edge Fabric Company

425 E. Washington St. 46176
(317) 392-1550 Fax: (317) 392-8845
riversedge1550@sbcglobal.net
Owners: Nancy & Paul Mason
Est: 2007
5000 sq.ft.
5000+ Bolts
Online Newsletter
www.riversedgefabric.com
Quality Cottons, Books, Notions, Patterns.
Gammill Longarm Quilting, Kits and Classes.
Authorized Janome Dealer

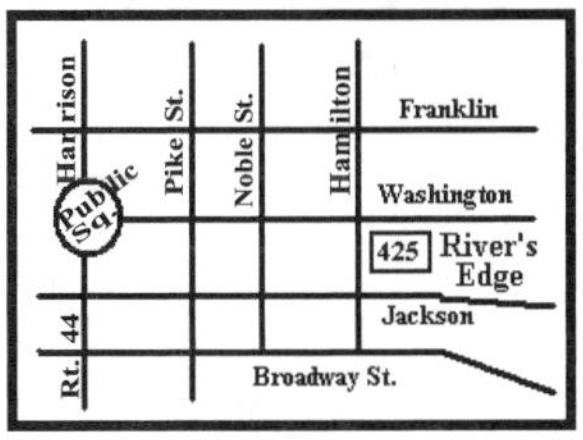

Morgantown, IN #43

**Mon - Sat 10 - 5
Wed til 8**

Ady's Fabric & Notions

79 W. Washington St, P.O. Box 492 46160
(812) 597-0578
Est: 2001 2000 Bolts
adysfabric@sbcglobal.net
www.adysfabrics.com

Large selection of 100% cotton fabrics. Complete line of notions, patterns & classes. Gifts for the Quilter.

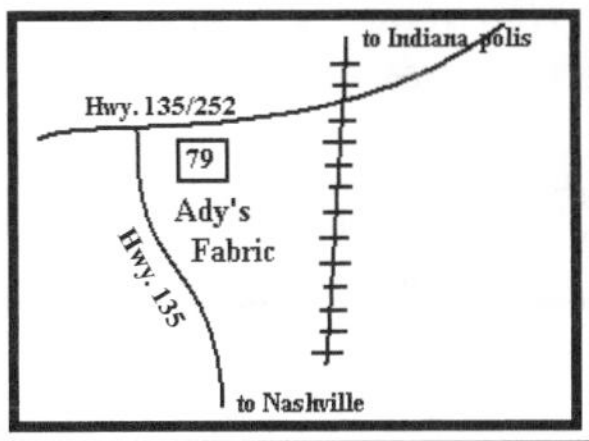

Bloomington, IN #44

**Tues, Fri, Sat 10 - 5
Wed & Thur 10 - 6**

Shiisa Quilts

2536 W. Industrial Park Dr., Suite 5 47404

(812) 333-8311
Owner: Janet Mease
Est: 2008 Free online newsletter
janet@shiisaquilts.com www.shiisaquilts.com
Bernina Sales and Service • Embroidery software and supplies • We specialize in moderns/Asians/brights • Classes available
Block of the Month programs available.

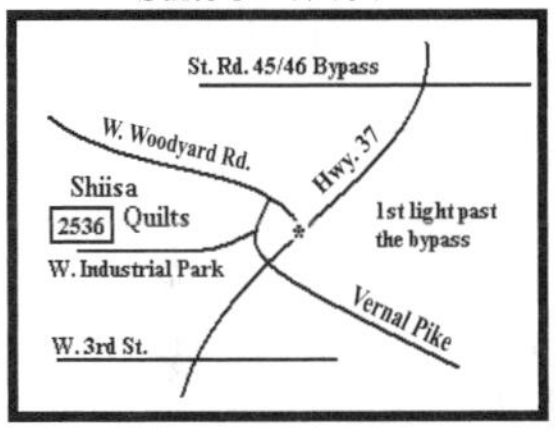

Salem, IN #45

Craft Town Fabrics

Over 7,000 bolts of 100% Cotton fabrics. Large selection of books, patterns and quilting notions. Check out our website.

www.crafttownfabrics.net

We usually ship within 24 hours.

21 Public Square, Salem, IN 47167
Phone/Fax 812-883-6860
robin@crafttownfabrics.net

Monday - Friday 9:00 - 5:00 Saturday 9:00 - 4:00

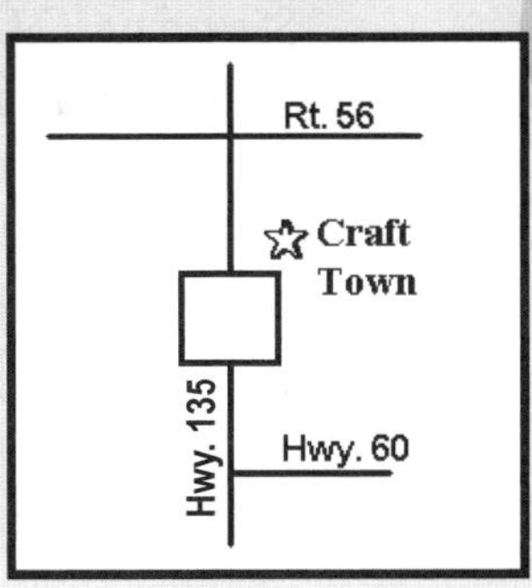

Est: 1973
7000 sq. ft.

Linton, IN #46

Tues & Wed 8 - 4
Thur 8 - 7
1st & 2nd Sats 8 - 2

Busy Bees

R.R. #4, Box 1050 47441
(812) 847-2417
2000+ Bolts

A gold mine for quilters!
A charming country setting with friendly atmosphere and great pricing!
Green County's best kept secret!

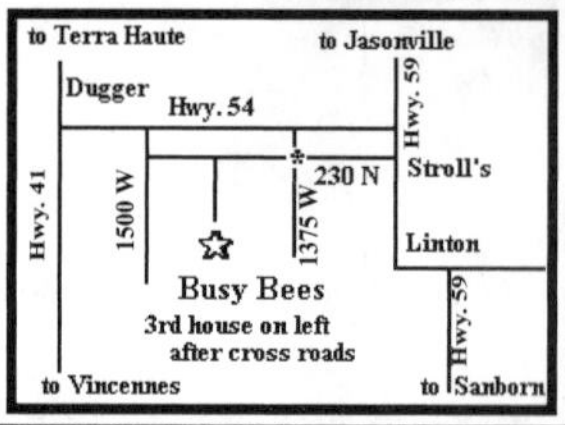

Washington, IN #47

Mon - Sat 10 - 5
Eastern Time

The Stitching Post

"Your Country Quilt Store"

401 E. Main St. 47501
(812) 254-6063 Est: 1986
Owner: Mary Dell Memering 4000 sq.ft.
www.stitchingpostquilts.com
Southwest Indiana's largest selection of quality quilting fabrics--10,000 bolts 100% cottons including 1930's & Civil War fabrics, Thimbleberries, Moda, Benartex & More

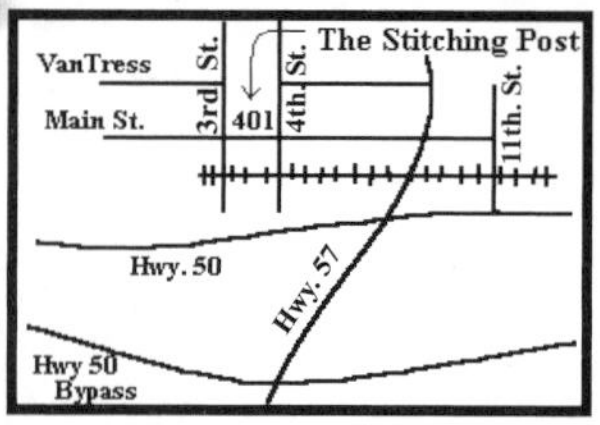

Montgomery, IN #48

Mon - Sat Daylight Hours

David V. Wagler's Quilts

4413 E 200 N 47558
(812) 486-3836
Owners: David & Anna Wagler
Est: 1980 1900 sq.ft. 1500+ Bolts

Hand Made Quilts on display. Quilts made to order, applique, pieced, & wholecloth tops. 100% Cotton Fabrics, Stencils, Books, Patterns, Kits

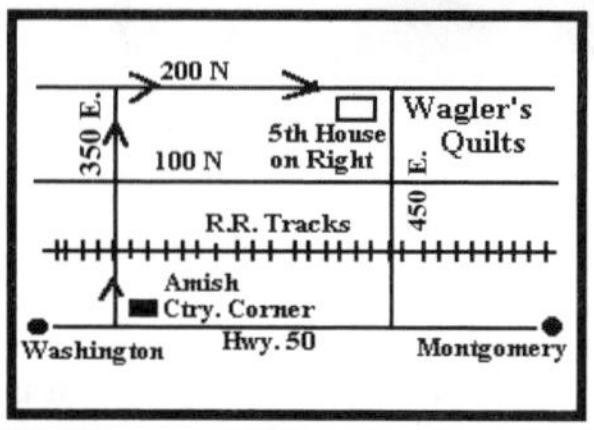

Seymour, IN #49

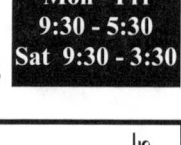

Mon - Fri 9:30 - 5:30
Sat 9:30 - 3:30

Loose Threads

The unique Quilt Shoppe

205 S. Maple St. 47274
(812) 524-2013 Fax: 523-0096
alicewest@verizon.net
Est: 2002
Owner:
Alice West
3500 sq.ft.
www.loosethreadsonline.com

Loose Threads is truly the unique quilt shoppe.
Offering 4000+ bolts of fabric, and Hundreds of Books and Patterns.

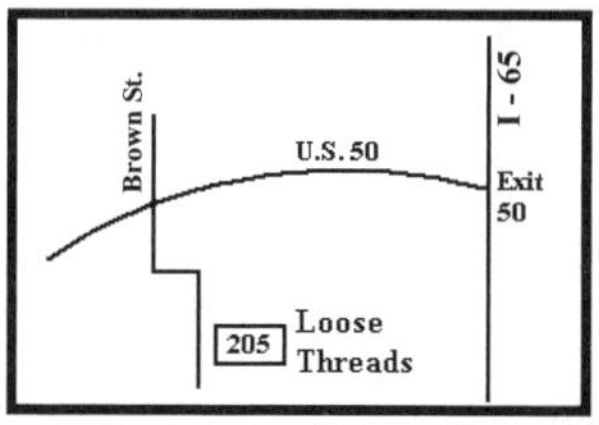

Quilt Bug

84 E. High Street
Lawrenceburg, Indiana 47025
812-539-4939
Owners: Bev DeSalvo & Susie Terrell
Est: 2002
Hours: Monday thru Friday 10:00 to 5:00
Saturday 10:00 to 3:00
Closed Sundays to be with our friends and family

2000 plus bolts of quality 100% cotton fabric at fantastic prices. Complete line of notions, books and patterns. Gift certificates available. Call about our class & club schedule, or give us your email address to be added to our mailing list.

Get Bit
By
The Bug

Check out our website for the latest in classes, clubs, retreats and all your quilting needs.

Lawrenceburg, IN #50

www.quiltbug.net

NORTH VERNON, IN. #51

Sharynn's Quilt Box

EST. 1994

1551 North State Street
North Vernon, IN 47265
812-346-4731

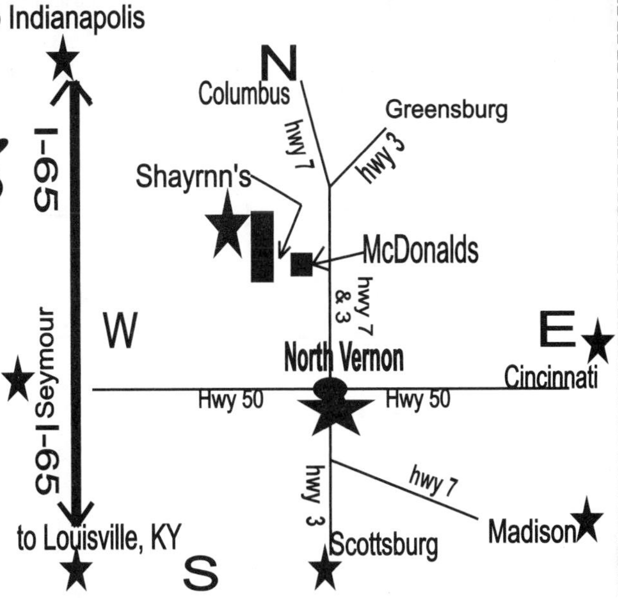

Authorized Janome Dealer
Handi Quilter Sales Rep

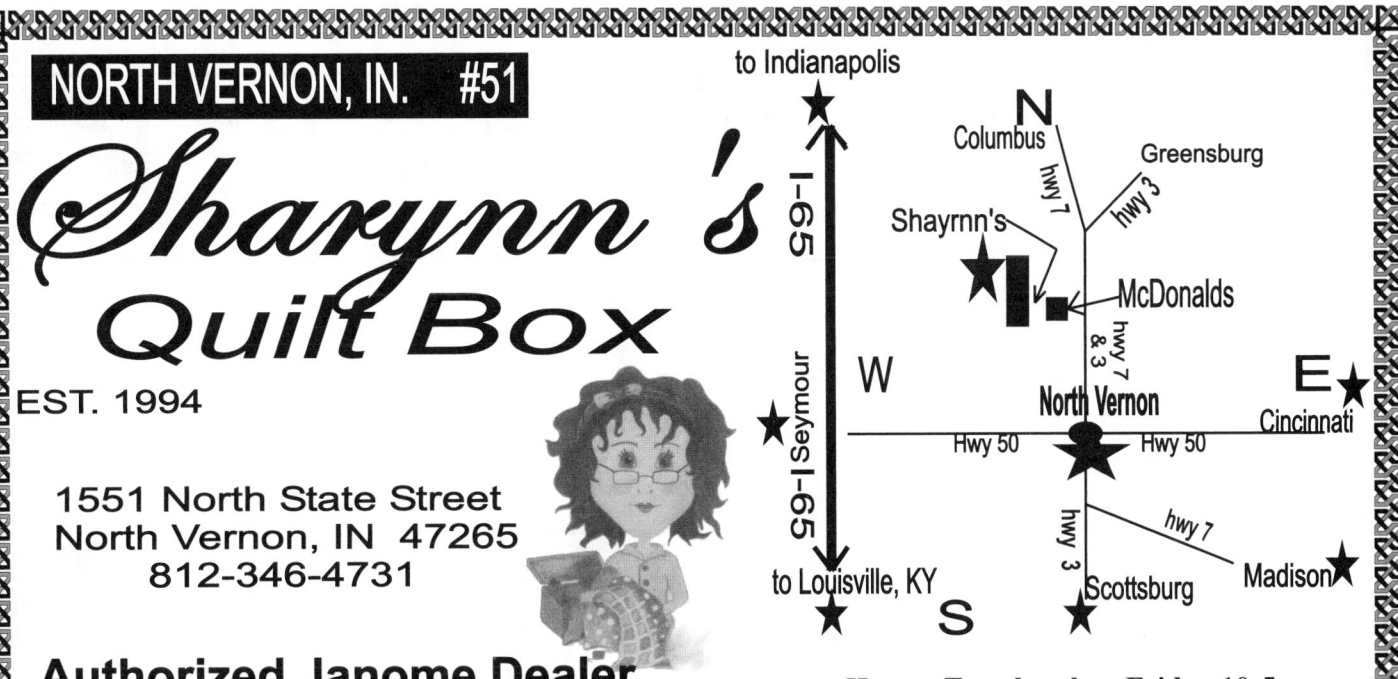

Hours: Tuesday thru Friday 10-5 pm
Saturday 10-3 pm

2000+ bolts of 1st quality 100% cotton fabric. Kits, books, patterns, notions, and gift certificates. Knowledgeable and friendly staff, Block of the Month, Thimbleberries Club, Janome Club. Shop on line at **www.sharynns.com**

Madison, IN #52

Mon - Sat 9 - 5

L & L Yard Goods

1814 Taylor St. 47250
(812) 273-1041
Owner: Lenora C. Green Est: 1986
www.landlyardgoods.com
Selection of Fabrics from Marcus Civil War & etc., Moda, Nancy Halverson by Benartex, Thimbleberries, Batiks from Hoffman, Andover's Renée Nanneman and other quality fabric lines to meet the quilters desires. Lots of wonderful Samples! Classes. Longarm Quilting.

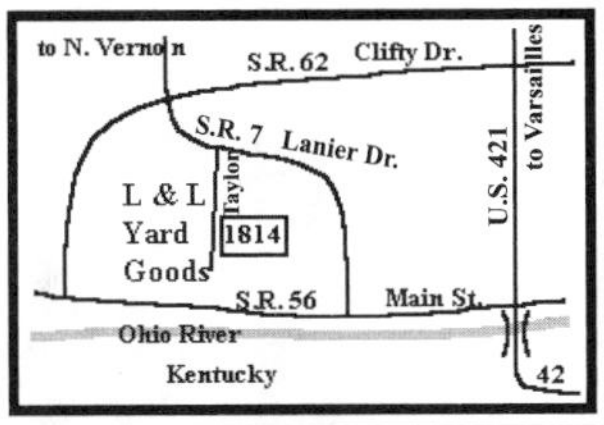

Madison, IN #53

Margie's Country Store

www.margiescountrystore.com

Mon - Sat 10 - 5
Sun 1 - 5

721 W. Main St. 47250
1-877-395-6263
Owner: Marjorie Webb
Est. 1970

Books, Patterns, many Hand Embroidered Patterns. Fabrics include MODA, Kaffe Fassett, Batiks, Marcus, Wingham, RJR, and Andover.

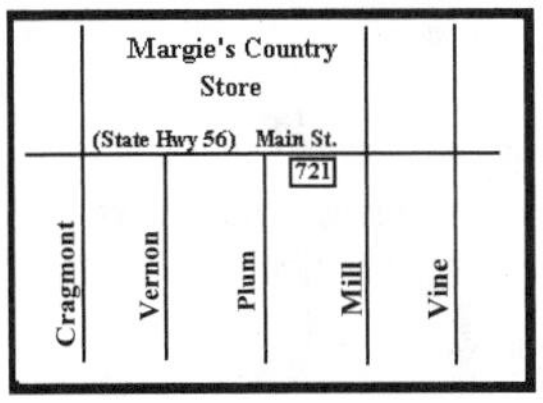

Specializing in 1800s Reproduction Civil War Fabrics. 100 or more rotating samples. Kind, professional, and gracious assistance. Four cellar rooms featuring Rowe Pottery, Bennington Pottery, Swan Creek candles, Village Paints, and much more.

Edwardsville, IN #54

Tues - Fri 10 - 6
Sat 10 - 3

the Quilting Bee

For all your quilting needs!

4904 Old Georgetown Rd. 47122

(877) 784-5823 or (812) 542-1236
Fax: (812) 542-1332 Est: 2006 3000+ Bolts
www.quiltingbeeshop,.com

We offer a large selection of the finest "Quilt Quality" 100% cotton fabrics from the major quilt fabric manufacturers and designers. The latest patterns, books and notions. Kits also.

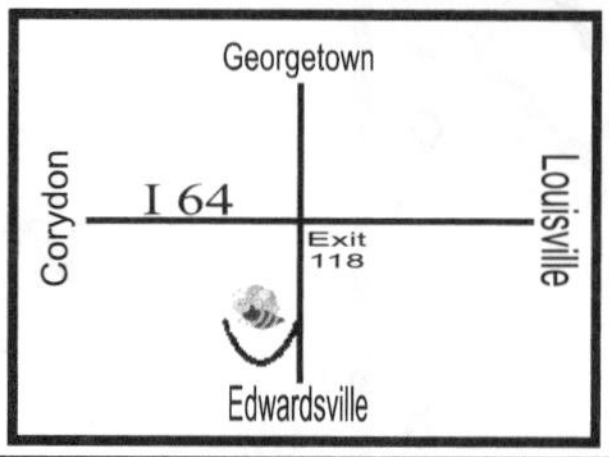

Corydon, IN #55

Mon - Fri 9:30 - 5:30
Tues til 8
Sat 9:30 - 3

HollyHock Quilt Shop

1148 Hwy. 62 NW 47112
(812) 738-1312
www.HollyHockQuiltShop.com

Fabric ~ Patterns ~ Notions
Books ~ Classes ~ Gifts
Long Arm Rental
Handmade Quilts
Singer Sewing Machines

Directions from I~64
Corydon Exit

At end of the Exit Ramp
Turn Right
Go SOUTH on IN~135
Turn Right on IN~62
HollyHock Quilt Shop on Right!

Ferdinand, IN #56

Mon, Tues, Thur 9 - 6
Wed & Fri 9 - 8
Sat 9 - 4

VAAL'S Furniture & Appliance

515 Main St.
P.O. Box 176 47532
(812) 367-1750 Fax: Same
Est: 1945

Huge selection of quilting fabrics.
Linings - Books - Notions - Stencils - Crafts
Quilt Blocks - Floss - Yarn

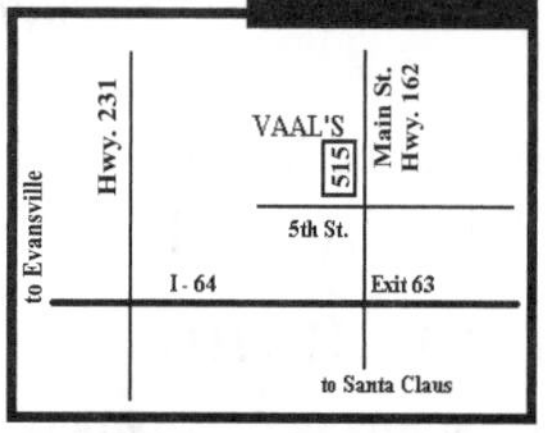

Haubstadt, IN #57

Tues 2 - 8
Fri & Sat 10 - 4

Quilts n' Bloom

879 W 1000 S 47639
(812) 768-6009
Owners: Kathy & Rick Will

Quilting supplies, Books, Patterns, quality cotton Fabrics, Classes, Featherweight Parts & Service, Country Setting & Flower Garden.

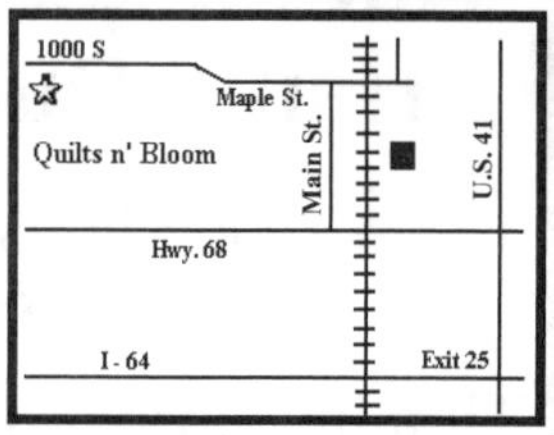

Let us help you create a unique quilt.

Quilter's Nest

2814 Mt. Vernon Ave.
Evansville, IN 47712
812-423-6378
www.quiltersnest.net

Mon, Tues, Thurs 10 - 6 Fri 10 - 5 Sat 10 - 4

Come visit our warm & friendly shop where you always receive personalized attention.
Over 2000 bolts of 100% cotton.
Large selection of patterns, books, notions and kits.
Extensive class schedule.

Owners: Holly Yingling
& Mary Brass
quiltersnestinc@aol.com
Est: 2008 1200 sq.ft.
Free Online Newsletter

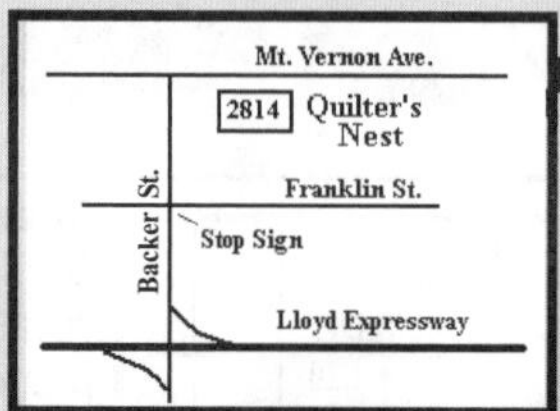

Evansville, IN #58

Indiana Quilt Shops

Anderson **The Quilt Shoppe, 112 W Grand Ave**
765-649-9102 **See ad #28, page 165**

Angola **Sewing Treasures, 1605 S. Wayne St.**
260--66-5-6948 **See ad #15, page 163**

Avon **Avon Quilting, 5201 E. US 36, Suite 105**
317-745-2626 **See ad #35, page 168**

Beech Grove The Fussy Cut Quilt Shop, 201 Bethel Ave. #A-1 317-786-9289

Berne **Engine House Quilt Shop, 160 W. Main St.**
260-589-3060 **See ad #22, page 164**

Berne Gathering House, 105 W. Main St. 260-589-8466

Bloomington **Shiisa Quilts, 2536 W Industrial Dr., Suite 5**
812-333-8311 **See ad #44, page 169**

Bluffton **Quilts n Gifts, LLC, 2035 Commerce Dr.**
260-565-4438 **See ad #21, page 164**

Boonville **The Village Mercantile, 123 S. 2nd. St.**
812-897-5687 **See ad #59, this page**

Carmel **Quilt Quarters, 12405 N. Meridian St.**
317-844-3636 **See ad #32, page 166**

Corydon **HollyHock Quilt Shop, 1148 Hwy. 62 NW**
812-738-1312 **See ad #55, page 172**

Crawfordsville **Caldwell Sew & Vac, 116 S Green St**
765-362-7360 **See ad #33, page 167**

Crown Point **bits 'n pieces, 732 N. Main St.**
219-662-9030 **See ad #1, page 162**

Decatur **Country Creations, 5342 N 400 W**
219-547-4535 **See ad #20, page 164**

Edinburgh Martha's Quilts & Gift Shop, 6463 E. Orchard Dr. 812-526-2931

Edwardsville **The Quilting Bee, 4904 Old Georgetown Rd.**
812-542-1236 **See ad #54, page 172**

Evansville **Quilter's Nest Inc, 2814 Mt. Vernon Ave**
812-423-6378 **See ad #58, page 172**

Evansville Sew Tech, 4651 Bayard Park Rd. 812-477-8477

Ferdinand **Vaal's Furniture & Appliance, Inc., 515 Main St.**
812-367-1750 **See ad #56, page 172**

Fort Wayne **Pieced Together Quilt Shop, 6037 E. State Blvd.**
260-486-4217 **See ad #19, page 164**

Fort Wayne **Viking Sewing Center, 5808 W. Jefferson St.**
260-432-9000 **See ad #18, page 164**

Ft. Wayne Edwards Sewing Center, 4114 N. Clinton 260-486-3003
Geneva Geneva Hometown Variety, 340 E. Line St. 260-368-7444
Goshen Calico Point, 24920 County Rd. 40 574-862-4065

Greenfield **Zig-Zag Corner Quilts & Baskets, 7872 N. Troy**
317-326-3115 **See ad #37, page 168**

Greenwood **The Back Door, 2503 Fairview Place Suite W**
317-882-2120 **See ad #36, page 168**

Haubstadt **Quilts 'n Bloom, 879 W 1000 S**
812-768-6009 **See ad #57, page 172**

Indianapolis **Quilts Plus, 1748 E. 86th St.**
317-844-2446 **See ad #34, page 167**

Kendallville **Nancy's Stitches LLC, 704 S. Main St.**
260-343-2627 **See ad #16, page 163**

Lafayette **Quilter's Harvest, Inc., 2307 State Rd 25 W**
765-474-2057 **See ad #30, page 166**

LaGrange Homespun Treasures, 205 E. Wayne St. 260-463-8499

Lawrenceburg **Quilt Bug, 84 E. High St**
812-539-4939 **See ad #50, page 170**

Leo **A Quilt of Many Colors, 15026 State Rd. 1**
260-627-2907 **See ad #17, page 163**

Liberty **Pohlar Fabrics, 6439 S. State Rd. 101**
800-357-3152 **See ad #40, page 168**

Linton **Busy BeesRR 4 Box 1050**
812-847-2417 **See ad #46, page 170**

Madison **Margie's Country Store, 721 W. Main St.**
812-265-4429 **See ad #53, page 171**

Madison **L & L Yard Goods, 1814 Taylor St.**
812-273-1041 **See ad #52, page 171**
Madison Fabric Shop, 220 E. Main St. 812-265-5828
Marion **Sew Biz, 3722 S. Western Ave.**
765-674-6001 **See ad #27, page 165**
Marion **Quilter's Hall of Fame, 926 S. Washington St.**
765-664-9333 **See ad #26, page 165**
Middlebury **The Quilt Shop 240 US 20**
800-455-9471 x300 **See ad #8, page 162**
Monroe Wilmen's Country Store, 421 E 100 S No Phone
Montgomery **David V. Wagler's Quilts, 4413 E. 200 N.**
812-486-3836 **See ad #48, page 170**
Morgantown **Ady's Fabrics & Notions, 79 W. Washington St.**
812-597-0578 **See ad #43, page 169**
Muncie Quilters' Toy Box, 804 W. McGalliard Rd 765-288-7316
Nappanee Martin's Quilt Shop, 25387 Cty. Rd. 46 574-831-2256
New Albany Jan's Sewing Things, 201 Hausfeldt Ln. 812-945-8113
New Paris Three Sisters Fabric, 69295 CR-23 574-903-4847
Noblesville **Always In Stitches, 1808 E. Conner St.**
317-776-4227 **See ad #31, page 166**
Noblesville Arbuckle's Railroad Place, 1151 Vine St. 317-773-3985
North Manchester **The Creative Stitch Quilt Shop**
208 E. Main St.
260-982-1080 **See ad #23, page 165**
North Vernon **Sharynn's Quilt Box, 1551 N. State St.**
812-346-4731 **See ad #51, page 171**
Pendleton **Ruth's Legacy, 104 W. High St.**
765-778-2488 **See ad #38, page 168**
Plymouth **Lucky Breezes Retreats, 5856 Redwood Rd**
574-223-4959 **See ad #5, page 162**
Rensselaer From The Needles Point, 125 N. Front St. 219-866-5353
Richmond **The Stitching Nook, 4629 National Rd. East**
765-962-7678 **See ad #39, page 168**
Richmond Nancy's Fancys Sewing Corner, 340 NW 5th St. 765-939-0465
Rochester **The Thread Shed, 610 Main St.**
574-223-4959 **See ad #4, page 162**
Rockville Fiber Closet, 109 W. High St. 765-569-2953
Rome City **Caroline's Cottage Cottons, 195 Weston St.**
260-854-3900 **See ad #7, page 162**
Rossville Rossville Quilts, 356 W. Main St. 765-379-2900

Rushville **In Stitches, 837 W. Third St.**
765-938-1818 **See ad #41, page 169**
Rushville Country Quilt Barn, 5026 W. US 52 765-663-5882
Salem **Craft Town Fabrics, 21 Public Square**
812-883-6860 **See ad #45, page 169**
Seymour **Loose Threads, 205 S. Maple St.**
812-524-2013 **See ad #49, page 170**
Shelbyville **The Rivers Edge Fabric Co., 425 E Washington**
317-392-1550 **See ad #42, page 169**
Shipshewana **Rebecca Haarer Folk Arts & Antiques, 165 Morton**
260-768-4787 **See ad #13, page 163**
Shipshewana **Yoder's Department Store, 300 S. Van Buren**
260-768-4887 **See ad #12, page 163 & 402**
Shipshewana **Lolly's Fabrics & Quilts, 255 E. Main St.**
260-768-4703 **See ad #14, page 163**
Shipshewana Little Helpers Quilt Shop, 1030 N 1000 W 260-768-4278
Shipshewana Bernina Sewing Center, 350 S. Van Buren St. 260-768-7393
South Bend **Stitch 'n Time Fabrics, 2305 Miami St.**
574-234-4314 **See ad #9, page 162**
South Bend **Heckaman's Quilting & Yarns, 63028 U.S. 31 S**
574-291-3918 **See ad #10, page 162**
South Bend **Erica's Craft & Sewing Ctr, 1320 N. Ironwood**
574-233-3112 **See ad #11, page 163**
Valparaiso **Needle & Thread, 60 W. Jefferson St.**
219-462-4300 **See ad #2, page 162**
Wabash **Nancy J.'s Fabrics, 1604 S. Wabash St.**
260-563-3505 **See ad #24, page 165**
Wabash **Heaven on Earth, 4767 N St. Rd. 15**
765-833-5461 **See ad #25, page 165**
Wakarusa **Jeanette's Fabric Boutique, 105 S. Elkhart**
574-862-4207 **See ad #6, page 162**
Wanatah **Scrapyard Quilting, 10505 W 1000 S.**
219-733-9980 **See ad #3, page 162**
Warsaw Lowery Sewing Center, 707 E. Winona Ave. 574-267-8631
Washington **The Stitching Post, 401 E. Main St.**
812-254-6063 **See ad #47, page 170**
West Lafayette **Cheryl's Quilt Shop, 1227 Sagamore Pkwy. N**
765-447-5400 **See ad #29, page 165**
Winamac Just Plain Annie's, 606 E 13th St 574-946-0496

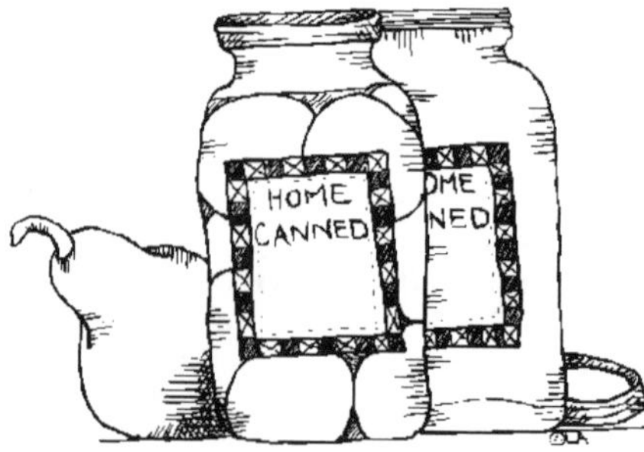

Indiana Quilt Shows

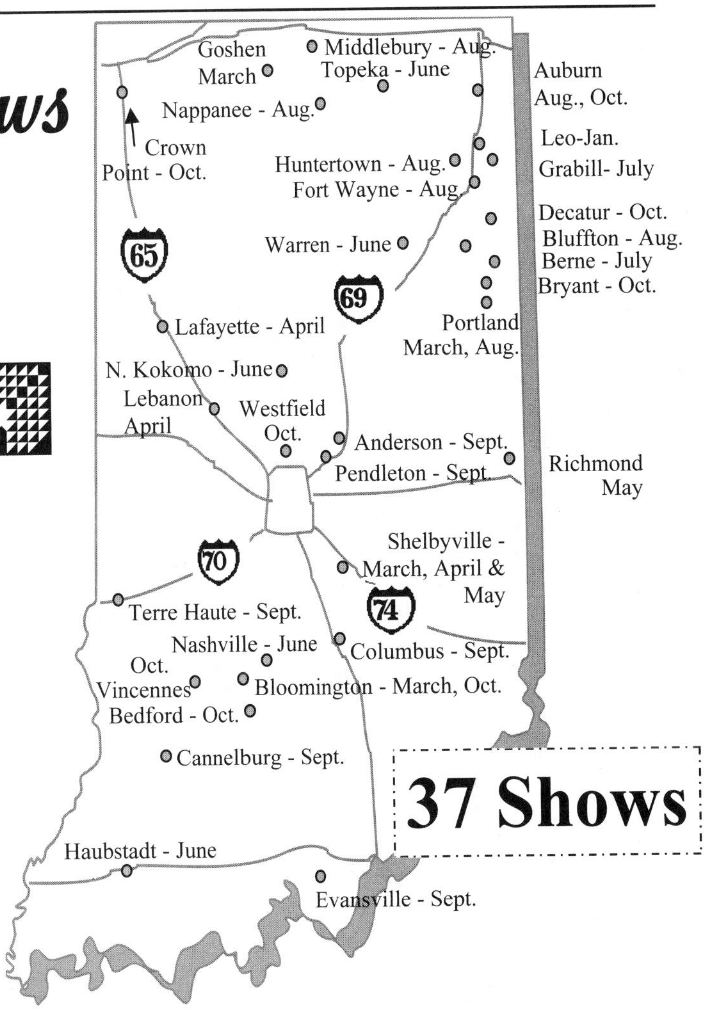

About Shows: We are listing only the very basic information about shows that happen on a regular schedule here. Please check out our website for more details on each show. Also this information tends to change quite often so please verify the event with our website or a local source before you venture far. Or if you're in the right area at the right time, give it a shot.

If you are a show organizer, please keep us updated on your event.
shows@quilterstravelcompanion.com
www.quilterstravelcompanion.com

On our website you will also find:

- Exact dates (when we have them)
- Contact Information
- Events happening on a one-time basis
- Sponsor Information
- Description of Event

Month	City	Schedule	Show	Location with address
January				
	Leo	Annual, last full week of January	Olde Church Shoppes Show	Olde Church Shoppes, 10629 Main St. (10 min. east of I-69)
March				
	Bloomington	Annual, Late Feb or Early March	Indiana Heritage Show	Bloomington Convention Center, 302 S. College Ave.
	Portland	Annual, 2nd Thur-Sat in March	Fiber Fest & Spin-In	Jay County Fairgrounds, 806 E. Votaw St. (4-H Bldg.)
	Shelbyville	Annual, 2nd Sat of March	Quilting for All Seasons Quilt Show	Family Art Building, Shelby Cty. Fairgrounds, Fair Ave. & Frank
	Goshen	Annual, 3rd Saturday of March	A Gathering of Quilters	Elkhart Country Fairgrounds, 17746 CR 34
April				
	Shelbyville	Annual, April & May	Shelbyville Quilt Show	Grover Museum, 52 W. Broadway St.
	Lafayette	Even Years, Early in April	Old Tippecanoe Quilt Guild Show	Christ United Methodist Church, 3610 S. 18th St.
	Lebanon	Annual, 4th Saturday in April	Boone County Homemakers	Boone County Fairgrounds-Health Services Pavilion, I - 65 Exit 138
May				
	Richmond	Odd Years, 3rd weekend of May	Wayne Cty. Extension Homemakers Quilt Show	Wayne County Fairgrounds, 861 Salisbury
June				
	Nashville	Annual, 1st weekend of June	Brown County Historical Quilt Show	Brown County Historical Society Bldg., 1934 St. Rd. 135 N
	North Kokomo	Odd Years, 1st Fri & Sat in June	Kokomo Piecemakers Quilt Guild	Johanning Civic Center, U.S. 31
	Haubstadt	Annual, 3rd Sat in June	Quilt 'N Bloom Outdoor Quilt Show	Quilts 'n Bloom, 879 W 1000 S (1/2 mi. W on Maple St.)
	Topeka	Annual, last Wed - Sat in June	Topeka's Quilt Show & Sale	Topeka United Methodist Church, Pine & Babcock St.
July				
	Warren	Annual, 1st Fri & Sat of July	Festival of Quilts	Warren Church of Christ, 3rd and Wayne St.
	Grabill	Odd Years, 3rd weekend of July	Little Marvels	Grabill Missionary Church, 13637 State St.
	Berne	Annual-last full weekend of July	Swiss Days Quilt Show	South Adams High School, 1000 Parkway St.
August				
	Huntertown	Annual, 1st weekend in Aug.	Huntertown Heritage Days	Huntertown Elementary School, Old Lima Rd.
	Nappanee	Annual, 1st weekend of August	Amish Acres Arts & Crafts Festival	Amish Acres Historic Farm, 1600 W. Market St.
	Bluffton	Annual, 2nd weekend in August	Creative Quilters Too Quilt Show	Wells County, 4-H Park, St. Rd. 1
	Fort Wayne	Even Years, 2nd weekend in August	Appleseed Quilt Show	Memorial Coliseum, 4000 Parnell Ave.
	Middlebury	Annual, 2nd full Thurs - Sat in August	Essenhaus Quilt Show & Sale	Essenhaus Inn & Conference Center, 240 U.S. 20
	Portland	Annual, 4th weekend in August	Stitch 'n Chatter Quilt Show	Arts Place, Inc., 113 E. Walnut St.
	Auburn	Annual, Sat & Sun before Labor Day	Home of the Classics Quilt Show	National Automobile Museum, 1000 Gordon M Buehrig
	Cannelburg	Annual, Sat before Labor Day	Amish Quilt Auction	Simon J. Graber Comm. Bldg. Cy. Rd. 900 E. (North of US 50)
	Northern Indiana	Annual, Late Summer to October	Quilt Gardens Tour Various Cities	Elkhart, Goshen, Middlebury, Nappanee, Shipshewana
September				
	Pendleton	Annual, 2nd Thur - Sun in September	Spring Valley Quilt Show	Pendleton Historical Museum Falls Park
	Anderson	Odd Years, 3rd weekend in September	Redbud Quilt Guild Show	North Anderson Church of God Scatterfield Rd.
	Evansville	Odd Years, 3rd weekend of September	Harvest of Quilts	Vanderburgh 4-H Center 201 E. Boonville-New Harmony Rd.
	Terre Haute	Even Years, 3rd weekend of September	Quilts Along the Wabash	Terre Haute Family Y, 951 Dresser Dr.
	Columbus	Even Years, end of Sept. or beginning of Oct.	A Gathering of Quilts	Donner Center 22nd & Sycamore Sts.
October				
	Auburn	Annual, 1st weekend in October	Quilt Show First	United Methodist Church, 1203 E 7th St.
	Bedford	Even Years, 1st weekend of October	Quarry Quilters Quilt Show	Comfort Inn, Constitution Ave.
	Crown Point	Odd Years, usually 1st weekend in October	Heritage Quilters of Crown Point	Timothy Ball School, 720 W. Summit St.
	Vincennes	Annual, 2nd Fri & Sat in October	Grouseland Quilt & Fiber Arts Festival	Green Activities Center, 3 W. Scott St.
	Bryant	Annual, 3rd weekend in October	Bearcreek Farms Quilt Lover's Get-A-Way	Bearcreek Farms, 8339 N 400 E
	Decatur	Annual, Last full weekend in October	Callithumpian Quilt Show	Riverside Center, 231 E. Monroe St. (U.S. 224)
	Westfield	Odd years, late Oct.	Quilters' Guild of Indianapolis Show	Westfield Middle School, 345 W. Hoover St. (US 31 at 181st.)
	Bloomington	Every third year from 2008, fall	Quilts from the Heartland	Bloomington Convention Center, 302 S. College Ave.

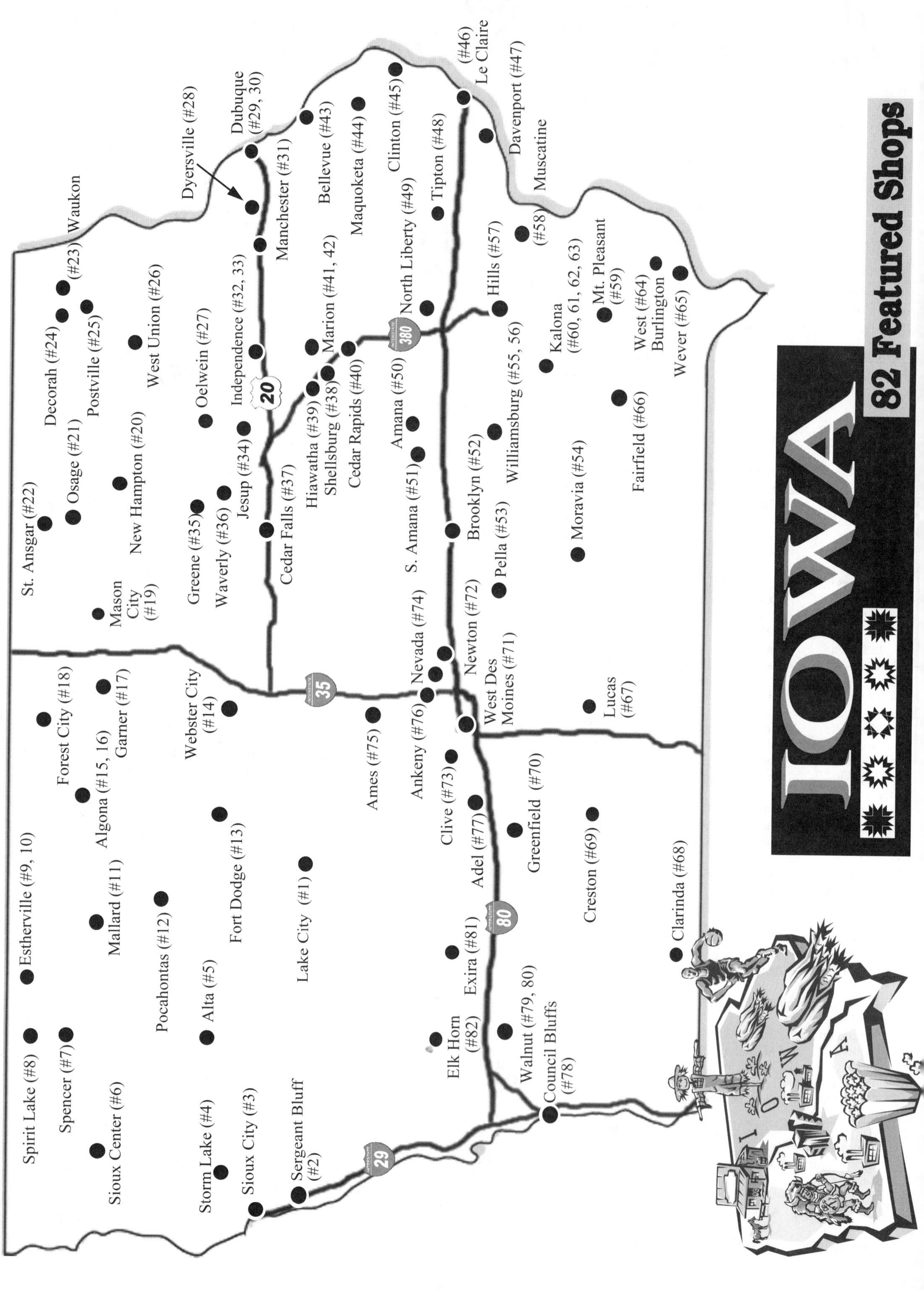
IOWA
82 Featured Shops
Spirit Lake (#8)
Spencer (#7)
Sioux Center (#6)
Estherville (#9, 10)
Mallard (#11)
Pocahontas (#12)
Alta (#5)
Storm Lake (#4)
Sioux City (#3)
Sergeant Bluff (#2)
Lake City (#1)
Fort Dodge (#13)
Algona (#15, 16)
Forest City (#18)
Garner (#17)
Webster City (#14)
Ames (#75)
Ankeny (#76)
Nevada (#74)
Newton (#72)
West Des Moines (#71)
Clive (#73)
Adel (#77)
Exira (#81)
Elk Horn (#82)
Walnut (#79, 80)
Council Bluffs (#78)
Greenfield (#70)
Creston (#69)
Clarinda (#68)
Lucas (#67)
St. Ansgar (#22)
Osage (#21)
Mason City (#19)
New Hampton (#20)
Greene (#35)
Waverly (#36)
Jesup (#34)
Cedar Falls (#37)
Decorah (#24)
(#23) Waukon
Postville (#25)
West Union (#26)
Oelwein (#27)
Independence (#32, 33)
Hiawatha (#39)
Shellsburg (#38)
Cedar Rapids (#40)
Marion (#41, 42)
Amana (#50)
S. Amana (#51)
Brooklyn (#52)
Pella (#53)
Williamsburg (#55, 56)
Moravia (#54)
Fairfield (#66)
Kalona (#60, 61, 62, 63)
Mt. Pleasant (#59)
West Burlington (#64)
Wever (#65)
Hills (#57)
(#58) Muscatine
North Liberty (#49)
Tipton (#48)
Clinton (#45)
Maquoketa (#44)
Bellevue (#43)
Manchester (#31)
Dyersville (#28)
Dubuque (#29, 30)
Davenport (#47)
(#46) Le Claire
20
35
380
80
29

Towne Square Quilt Shoppe

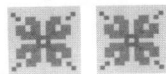

Mon - Fri 10 - 6 Sat 9 - 4

103 E. Main St.
Lake City, IA 51449
712-464-7477
tsqs@iowatelecom.net
www.tsquilts.com
Owner: Christi Savage
Est: 2001 1500 sq.ft.

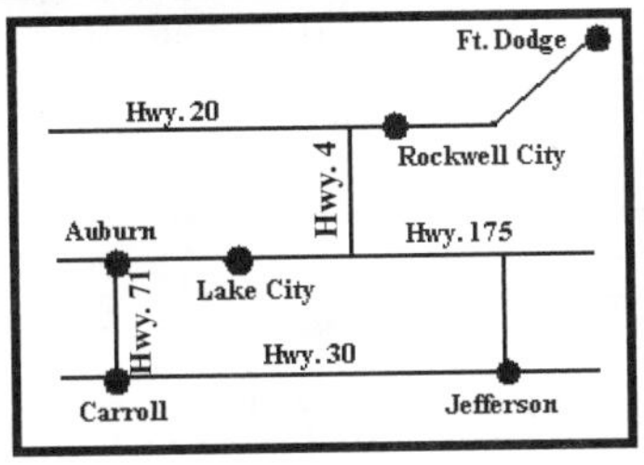

Located 25 miles NE of Carroll in charming Lake City. Features fabric, patterns and quilting supplies. Come see the quilt block on the classroom floor.

Lake City, IA #1

Sergeant Bluff, IA #2

Mon - Fri 10 - 6
Sat 9:30 - 4
Closed Sun and major holidays

My Quilt Shop is Your Quilt Shop

206 1st St.
P.O. Box 314 51054
(712) 943-9486

"DON'T FORGET THE FABRIC"

Nestled inside the Pioneer Mall, we cater to the novice and experienced quilters as well. Our staff is patient and helpful, our fabrics are bright and beautiful. See us for Horn Cabinets, Janome and Tin Lizzie sales and service.

Owner: Kim Gray Est: 2001
diamond3@longlines.com www.kimsquilts.com

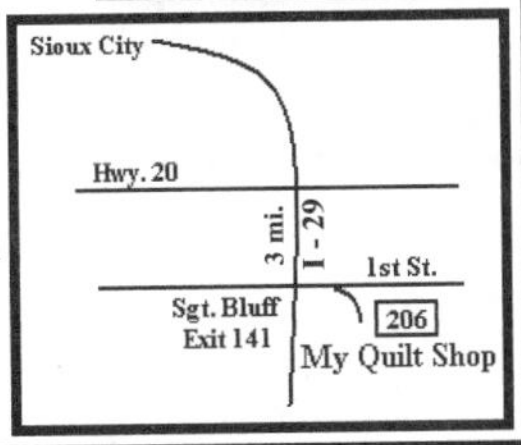

We feature an antique-filled atmosphere that compliments the quilting fabrics, patterns & books, sewing notions, gift items and greeting cards. A helpful staff and lots of samples on display.

Heart & Hand Dry • Goods • Company

Mon - Fri 10 - 5:30
Thurs til 6
Sat 10 - 5

3011 Hamilton Blvd.
Sioux City, IA 51104
(712) 258-3161
hrthand@yahoo.com
www.heartandhand.com
Owner: Ann Brouillette
4000 sq.ft. 5000 Bolts

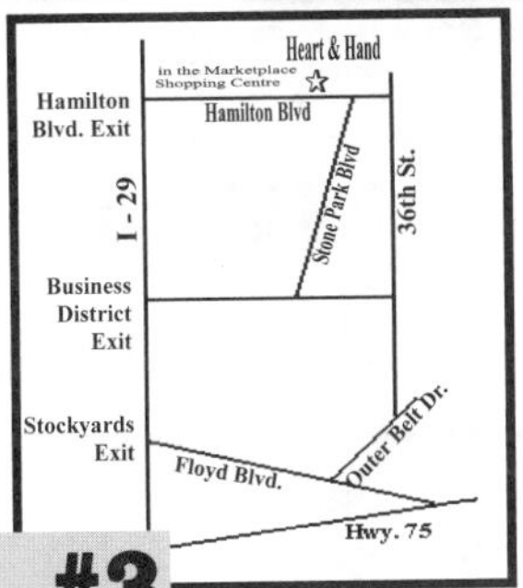

Sioux City, IA #3

Est: 1996

Featured in 1999 Quilt Sampler Magazine

Storm Lake, IA #4

Inspired By Time Quilts

Mon - Fri 9 - 5
Sat 9 - 4

516 Lake Ave. 50588
(712) 213-1100
Owner: Tracy Irwin Est: 2006
irwitra@iowatelecom.net Newsletter

100% cotton fabrics. Great selection of notions & gifts plus books & patterns. Large selections of Brights & Batiks. We also offer classes (March - Sept).

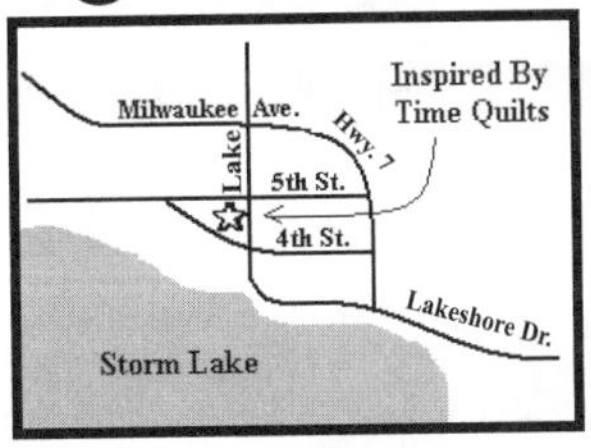

Alta, IA #5

The Quilt Shoppe

By Chance or Appointment, Please call ahead

206 S. Main 51002
(712) 284-2724
Owner: Pat Patten
Est: 1987 1200 sq.ft.
pptqs@yahoo.com

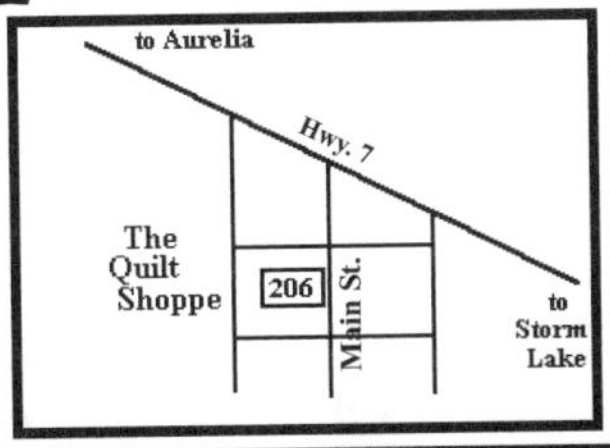

Big discounts on quilt supplies, books, patterns, quilts, quilted items. Kits for sale. Custom work available, UFO's completed for you.

Sioux Center, IA #6

Roelofs Store

Mon - Fri 9 - 5:30
Wed til 8
Sat 9 - 5

24 3rd St. NW 51250
(712) 722-2611
Owner: Dixie Roelofs Est: 1976
roelofs@mtcnet.net 2000 sq.ft.

Quilting Fabrics & supplies; Fabric craft patterns and supplies; kits; hemstitched flannel receiving blankets ready for crochet edge; Bernina Sewing Machines.

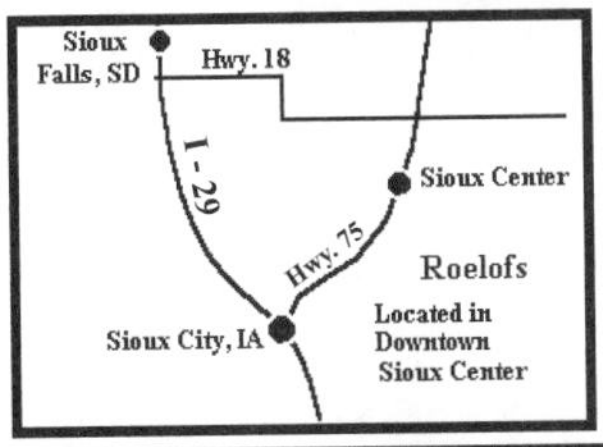

Spencer, IA #7

Mon - Fri 9:30 - 5:30
Thur til 7
Sat 9:30 - 4

Quilts on Grand

211 Grand Ave. 51301
(712) 262-2738
quiltsog@ncn.net

Owners: Neila Rohan & Sue Stevenson
Est: 2002 3000 sq.ft.
2500+ Bolts

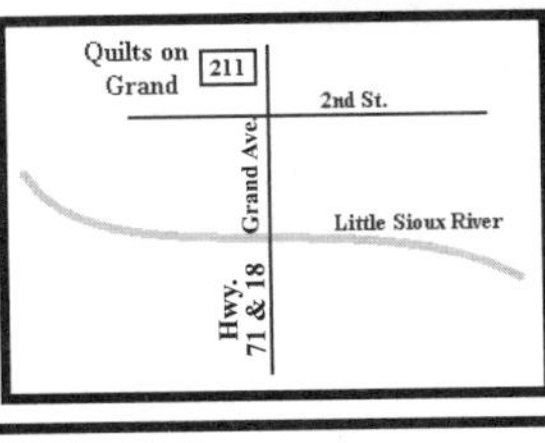

Customer friendly. Quality 100% cotton fabrics, flannels, books, notions, gifts, pottery, classes, finished quilts. Something for everyone. Buses welcome.

Spirit Lake, IA #8

Quilt "n" Stitches

Mon - Fri 10 - 5
Sat 10 - 4

816 Lake St. 51360
(712) 336-2708
quiltnstitches09@yahoo.com
Free Newsletter

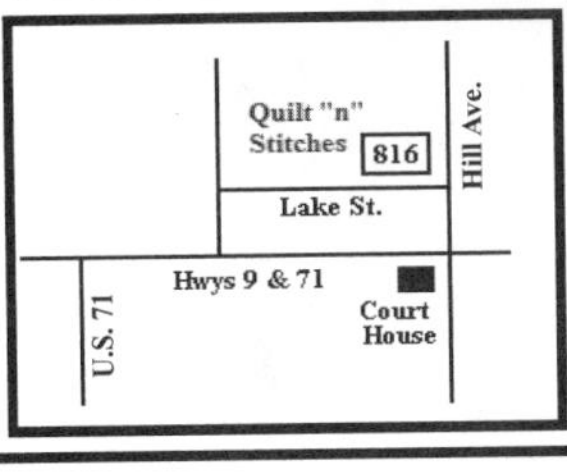

Full service quilt shop with classes, custom quilt making, and long arm quilting services. Check out our retreats!

Estherville, IA #9

Mon - Fri 9 - 5
Sat 9 - 4

Homespun Quilt Shop

202 Central Ave. 51334
(712) 362-5100 Fax: Same
Owner: Candy Fredericksen
homespun202@yahoo.com
www.homespunquiltshop.com

Fabulous selection of Civil War fabrics ~ Unique Kits ~ McCalls Country Candles ~ Block of the Month ~ Custom made quilt racks, shelves & wooden frames!
"Your Destination for a Quilting Adventure!"

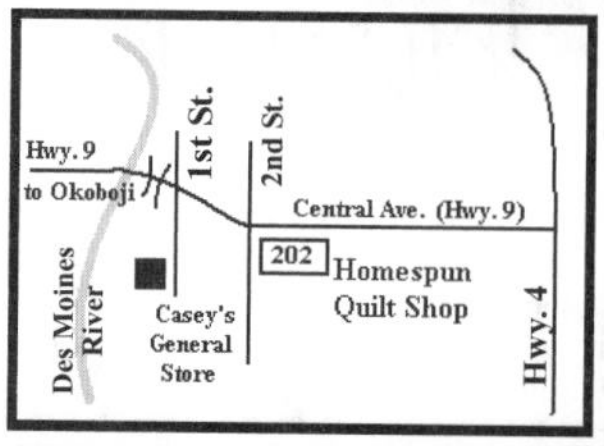

Estherville, IA #10

Mon - Fri 9 - 5:30
Sat 9 - 4

The Wooden Thimble

4 N. 16th St. 51334
(712) 362-2561
mary@woodenthimble.com
www.woodenthimble.com
Owner: Mary Hart Est: 1983

Large selection of fabric, quilting, cross-stitch and craft supplies, books and patterns. Many hand made gifts and lots of friendly service.

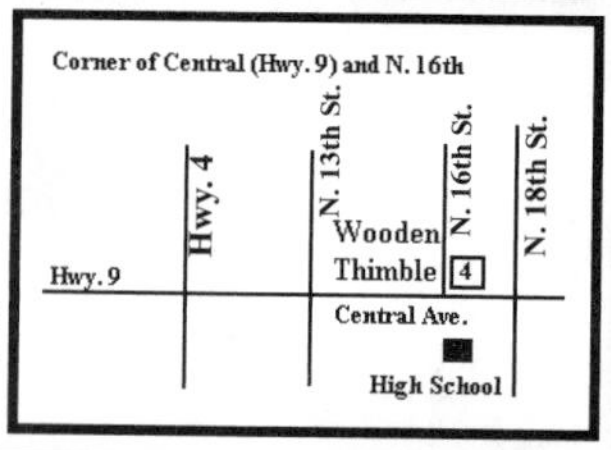

Mallard, IA #11

Most Days
Mon - Fri 10 - 4
Or by Chance or Appt.

The Quilter's Portable

607 Inman, P.O. Box 313 50562
(712) 425-3478 Est: 2001
qportable@ncn.net
www.quiltersportable.com
Owner: Deborah Travis
40-50 Machines Available

Unique Sewing machine shop specializing in Brother & Singer 221 (accessories & machines available).
Dealer for Hinterberg Voyager Quilting System.
Notions & Accessories for Quilters.

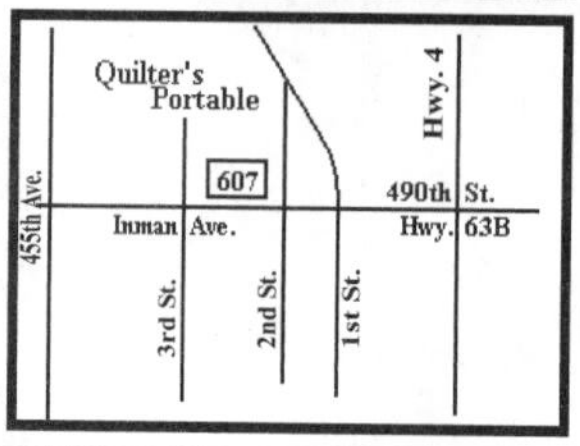

Pocahontas, IA #12

Mon - Fri 8:30 - 5
Wed til 6
Sat 8:30 - 1

Quilting on Main

229 N. Main 50574
(712) 335-3969
Owner: Bonnie Wood Est: 2000
patches@evertek.net

We have an ever expanding line of 2000+ bolts of quilting fabrics that include Moda, Maywood & RJR. Stop in and see our wide array of colors in the brights, pastels, and flannel. Many samples and kits fill our shop. Let us help you with all your quilting needs.

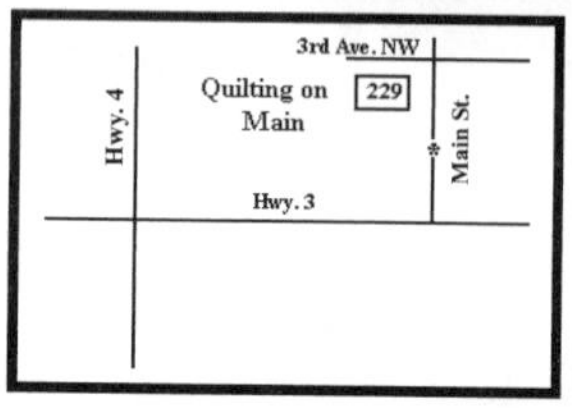

Fort Dodge, IA #13

Mon - Fri 9 - 5
Sat 9 - 1

The Family Quilt Shop

1200 A St. W 50501
(515) 576-0295
Owner: Cindy Kaufman
cysperch@frontiernet.net
www.thefamilyquiltshop.com

Quilters bring your spouse, we have a '3 hole' golf course and cart available while you shop.

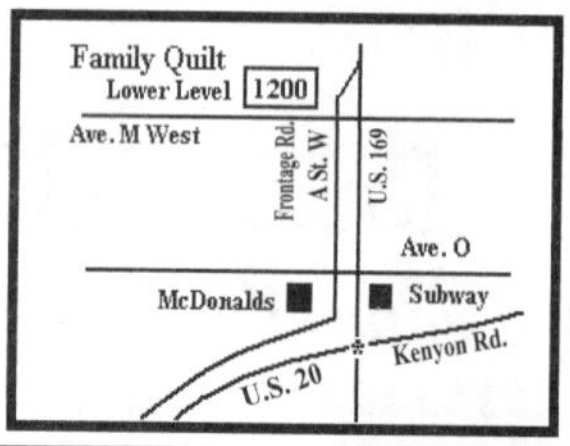

Webster City, IA #14

Mon - Fri 9:30 - 5:30
Sat 9:30 - 2

Gingerbread House

309 Bank St. 50595
(515) 832-1492
Fax: Same
Est: 1974 2000+ Bolts

"as unique as you are"
CHECK US OUT
We are one of the most diversified stores around.

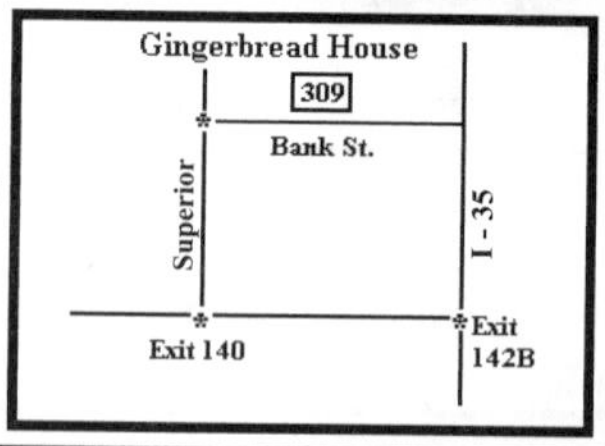

Algona, IA #15

Mon - Fri 10:30 - 5
Sat 10 - 2

Heartland Quilt Shop

107 S. Harlan 50511
(866) 469-1428 or (515) 295-3036
Owner: Pat Lucas
Est: 2001 2200 sq.ft. 1400 bolts
myquilts@netamumail.com
Website coming soon

Warm country style featuring large selections of Moda, Thimbleberries, Aunt Gracie's and much more!
Classes, samples & friendly service.

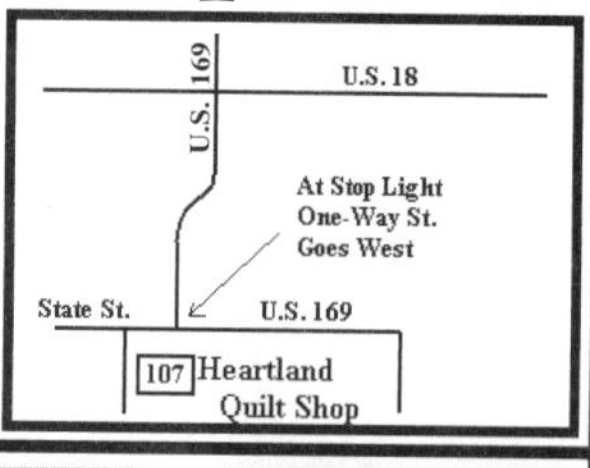

Algona, IA #16

Mon - Fri 10 - 5
Sat 10 - 3

Seams To Me

17 E. State St. 50511
515-295-5841
Owner: Karen Boyken Est: 1987
kboyken@netamumail.com
www.seamstome.com

Quality 100% cotton fabrics.
Full line of notions & crafts.
Walls filled with models & displays. Mail Order.

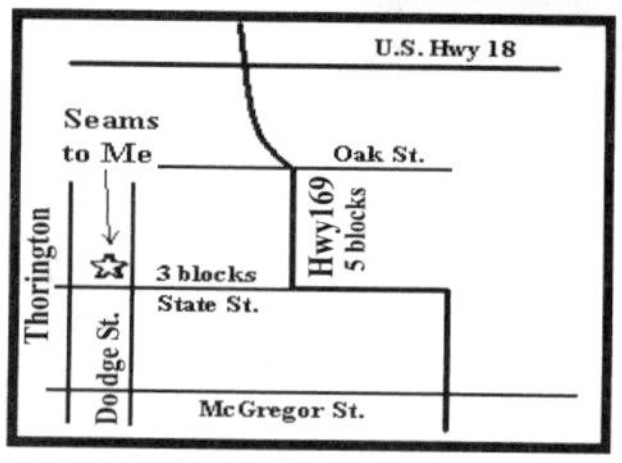

Garner, IA #17

April - Oct.
Mon - Sat 9 - 5
Nov. - March
Tues - Sat 9 - 5

2345 Palm Ave. 50438
(641) 923-3893

Owners: Mary Etherington & Connie Tesene
Est: 1983 5000 Bolts
Goat Gazette newsletter $12.00/year
info@countrythreads.com
www.countrythreads.com
Your full service quilt shop in a chicken coop!

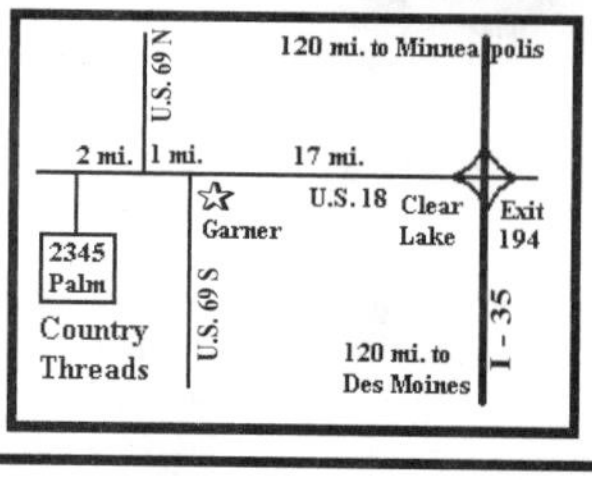

the Quilted Forest

205 North Clark, Forest City, IA 50436
Phone: 641-585-2438 or 877-985-2438
Hours: Monday-Friday: 10 a.m. to 5 p.m.
Saturday: 10 a.m. to 4 p.m.
www.thequiltedforest.com

Owner:
Shelley Robson
Established:
1998

Our friendly, spacious shop is a delight to quilters and knitters. We have a diverse selection of fine quality fabrics, notions, books and yarns. Pieced Tree Patterns is our original pattern line featuring a variety of projects. www.piecedtreepatterns.com

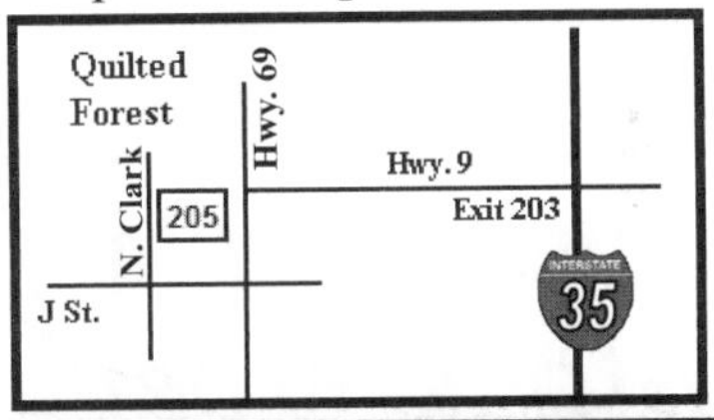

Forest City, IA #18

Mason City, IA #19

Mon - Fri 10 - 6
Sat 10 - 4

Saintly Stitches

1631 - 4th St. SW 50401
#115 Willowbrook Mall
(641) 423-5176

www.saintlystitches.com
holly@saintlystitches.com

Great selection of fabrics, kits, patterns and notions. Samples galore to inspire and friendly, knowledgeable staff to assist you with all your quilting needs...

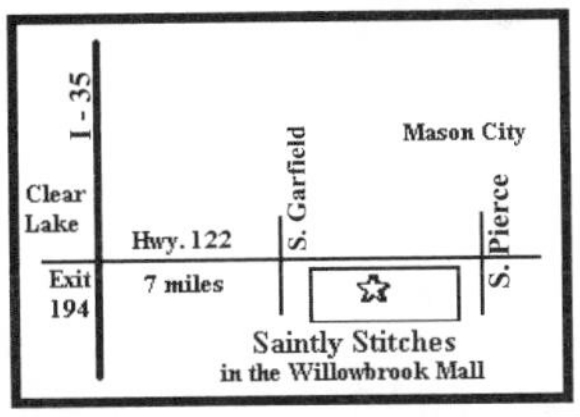

New Hampton, IA #20

Mon - Fri 9 - 5
Thur til 7
Sat 9 - 4

Quilter's Window

Opening your window to creativity

101 E. Main St. 50659
(641) 394-6900
Est: 2005

denise@quilterswindow.com
www.quilterswindow.com

Better Homes Quilt Sampler Featured Shop 2008

PFAFF Sewing Machine Sales
Service on All Brands * Fabrics * Notions *
Classes * Publications * Machine Quilting

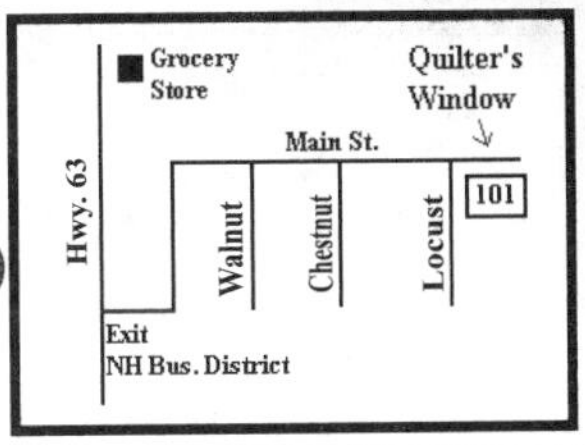

Osage, IA #21

Mon - Sat 9 - 5

Debbie's Quilt Shop & Gifts

605 Main St. 50461
(641) 732-1474
2500+ bolts Free Newsletter
debbies@osage.net

A 1919 Theater building filled with fabric, samples, kits, patterns, notions and gifts. "We would love to help you choose that 'perfect' piece."

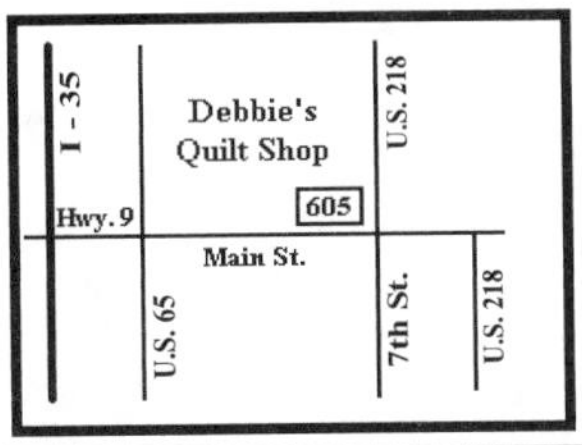

St. Ansgar, IA #22

Mon - Sat 9 - 5

Saintly Stitches

308 W. 4th St. 50472
(641) 736-2300
holly@saintlystitches.com

www.saintlystitches.com
Online Newsletter

Knowledgeable, friendly service always! ...3000 bolts, notions, books, patterns, classes and Heirloom sewing supplies. Shop St. Ansgar - a tourist destination; buses & groups welcome. Call ahead so we can plan a special day for you.

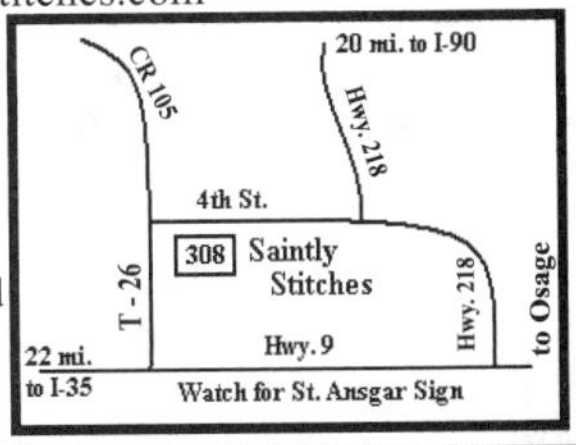

Waukon, IA #23

Country Stitchin'

915 Hwy. 76 South, Waukon, IA 52172
(563) 535-7376
jsnitker@acegroup.cc
Owners: Jane Snitker & Peg Mathis Est: 1997

"A Charming Country Atmosphere"

Unique Quilt shop, located on a 4½ acre farm. Specializing in Custom HAND Quilting.
Many samples on display.
All samples are for sale.
Quilt Tops--several to choose from
Quilt Classes Year Round
Large selection of fabrics, books, patterns & notions.

Mon - Sat 9 - 5

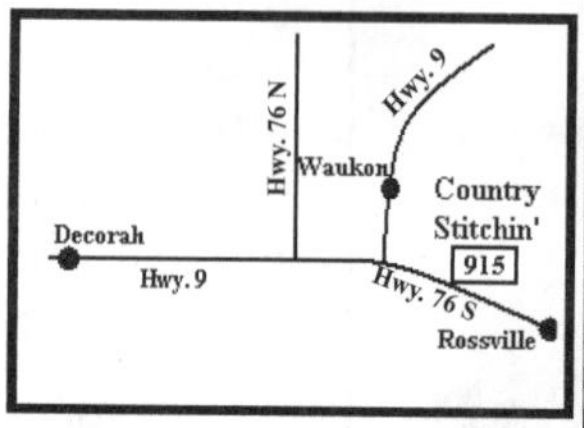

Decorah, IA #24

Mon - Fri 10 - 5
Sat 10 - 4

415 W. Water St. 52101
(563) 382-4646
Fax: (563) 382-6020

Pine Needles
sew good for your life

Owners: Marcia Nagel & Suzie Diemer
Est: 1999 3700 sq.ft. 4000 bolts
info@pnqs.net www.pnqs.net
Bernina, APQ, Accuquilt, loads of fabric & publications and the best customer service around! 2 locations! The area's largest quilt shop!

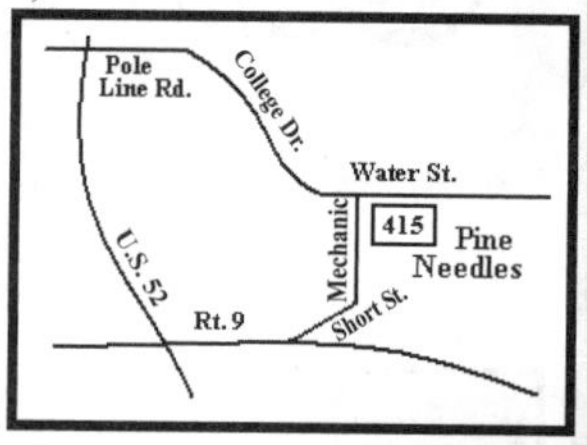

Postville, IA #25

Mon - Sat 10 - 6

Forest Mills Quilt Shop

650 Forest Mills Rd. 52162
(563) 568-3807
Est: 2003 3000+ bolts
forestmillsquilts@gmail.com

Specializing in Civil War reproductions, Batiks and wildlife.
Gift items for the country enthusiast.
Seasonal shop hops. Scenic rural setting.

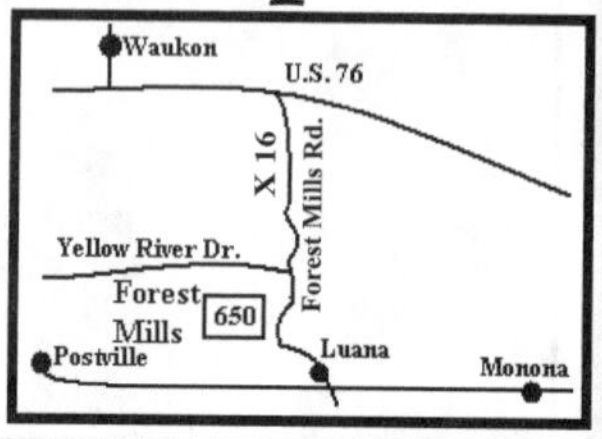

West Union, IA #26

Mon - Fri 10 - 5
3rd Thur til 9
Sat 9 - 3

One Block Over

322 E. Main St. 52175
(563) 422-3822 Fax: (563) 422-3822
Est: 2004 Free online newsletter
322@oneblockoverquiltshop.com
www.oneblockoverquiltshop.com
A Quilters' Shop--classes for all levels of quilters, quality fabrics, complete Jinny Beyer Palette, love Batiks, helpful staff.

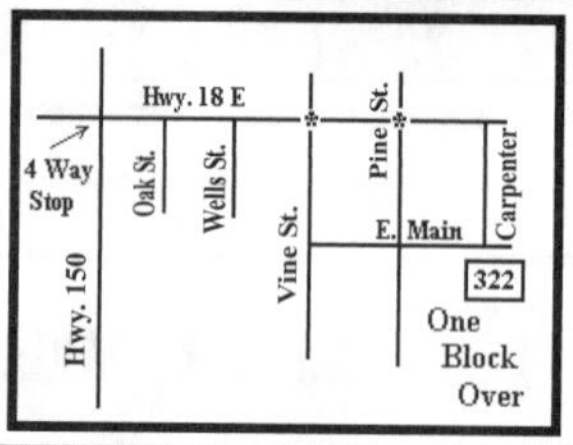

Oelwein, IA #27

Mon - Fri 10 - 5
Sat 10 - 4

LouAnn's Quilt Garden & Retreat

21 E. Charles 50662
(319) 283-5165
Owner: LouAnn Milks Est: 1991
louannsfabrics@hotmail.com
Full service quilt shop. We carry Baby Lock Sewing Machines, Books, Kits, Patterns, Notions, Koala Kabinets.
Quilt retreat designed especially for group events to quilt, sew, or craft with friends.
24 person capacity for overnight guests.

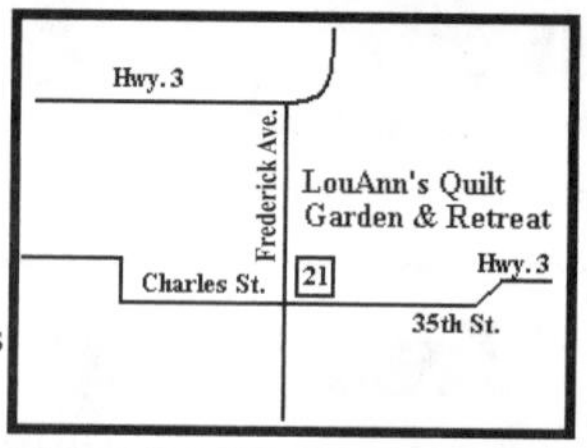

Dyersville, IA #28

Vintage Threads

Quilt Shoppe

234 1st Ave. E 52040
(563) 875-7330
vintagethreads@iowatelecom.net
website: www.vintagethreads.net

Creating quilted memories piece by piece.

Owners: Sue Maloney & Deb Jaeger

A warm & friendly shop filled with fabric, wool, notions, books, patterns, kits, classes & Horn Cabinets.

Mon - Fri 9 - 5 Sat 9 - 2

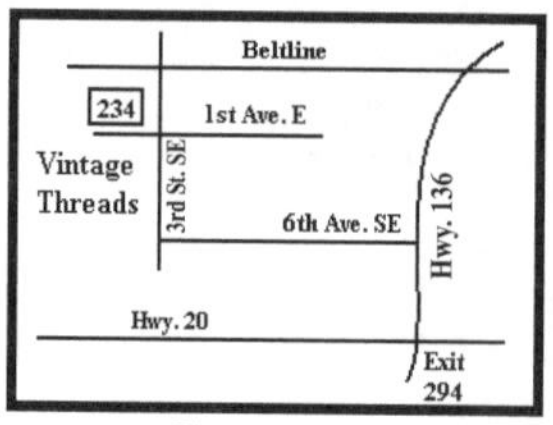

Vintage Loft Retreat Center

- Located above Vintage Threads
- Accommodations for 8 guests
- Call Vintage Threads for reservations

Dubuque, IA #29

Mon - Fri 10 - 5
Sat 10 - 4

3220 Dodge St. #106
52003
(563) 556-3163

Quilt Shack

- fabrics
- threads
- notions
- classes
- one day retreats

quiltshack@mchsi.com
www.quiltshackdbq.com

Husqvarna VIKING

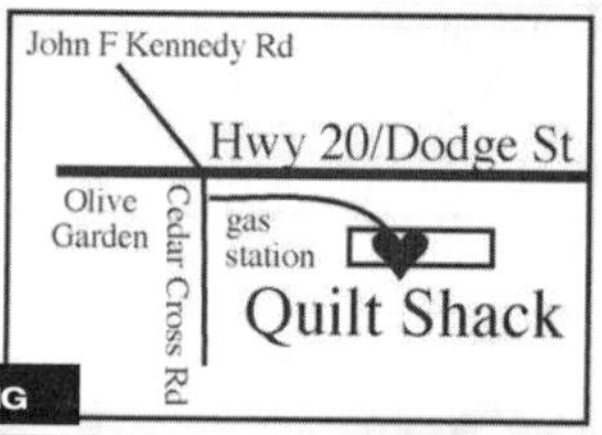

Dubuque, IA #30

Mon - Fri 10 - 5
Sat 10 - 4

The Cotton Cabin Quilt Shop

1075 Main St. 52001
563-582-0800 Owner: Kathy Regan
info@cottoncabinquilts.com Est: 2000
www.cottoncabinquilts.com
A newly expanded quaint shop. Large assortment of civil war prints, flannel, 100% cotton collections, kits, fat quarters and 100% wool. We've recently added YARN. Knowledgeable, Friendly Staff!

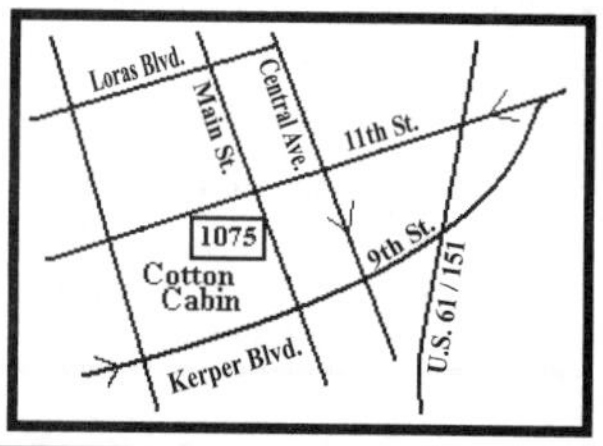

The Quiltmaker's Shoppe

110 East Main St. Manchester, IA 52057
(563) 927-8017
Owner: Kathy Wilgenbusch
www.thequiltmakershoppe.com

Mon - Fri 9 - 5
Thur til 7
Sat 9 - 4

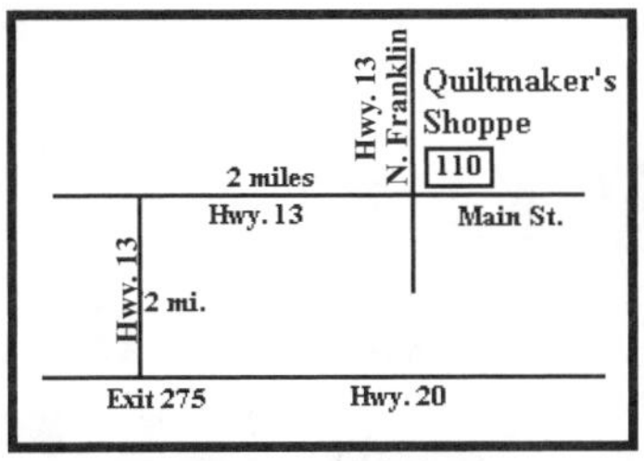

Manchester, IA #31

We offer 100% cotton fabric from the top lines, the latest in books & patterns and a full line of notions. We also have kits, hand-crafted quilt racks & quilt hangers.

Come in and see what we have in store for you!

Independence, IA #32

Mon - Fri 10 - 5
Sat 9 - 5

Quilter's Quarters

213 First St E 50644
(319) 334-4443 5000+ bolts
info@quiltersquartersonline.com
www.quiltersquartersonline.com
Owners: Mark & Melinda Engelbrecht

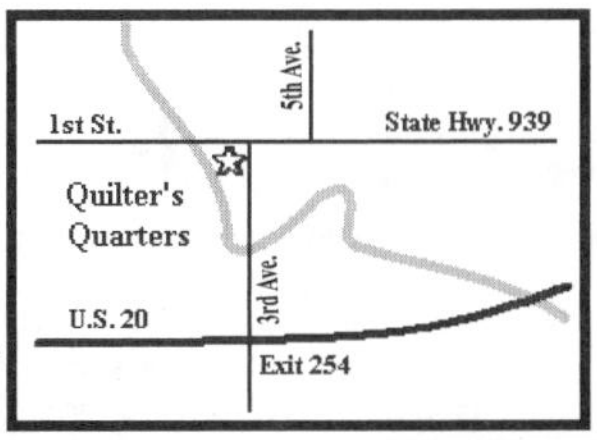

Quality Quilting Fabrics and Flannels, Books, Patterns, Supplies, Notions. Authorized Dealer for PFAFF sewing machines.

Independence, IA #33

Mon - Sat
10 - 5

Vineyard Gift & Quilt Shoppe

915 First St. W 50644
(319) 334-2211

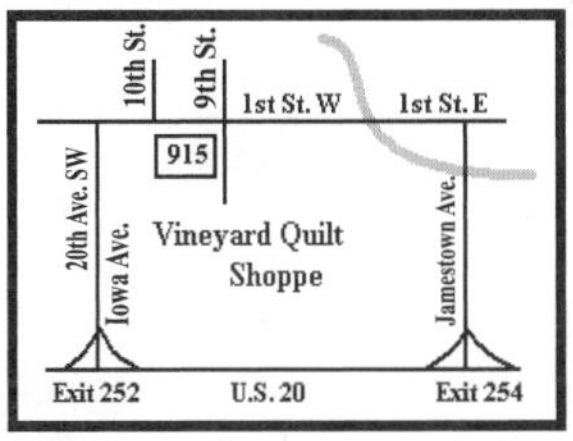

www.barbsvineyard.com
Historic Setting: Quaint, Cozy & Cute!
Fabric & Wool, Notions & Books,
Patterns & Classes
"Friendships Grow Here"

The Moose Patch Quilt Shop

Waverly • Iowa

"A quilter's dream come true!"

- 2,000 sq. ft. of Pure Quilting Delight
- All the Latest Fabrics & Designers
- Free Fat Quarter Therapy Club!
- Lots of Samples & Displays to Inspire You
- Knowledgeable, Friendly Staff

Mon - Fri 10 - 5
Thur 10 - 7
Sat 10 - 4

www.sewdear.com

205 E. Bremer
Waverly, IA 50677
(319) 352-5040
2000 sq. ft.

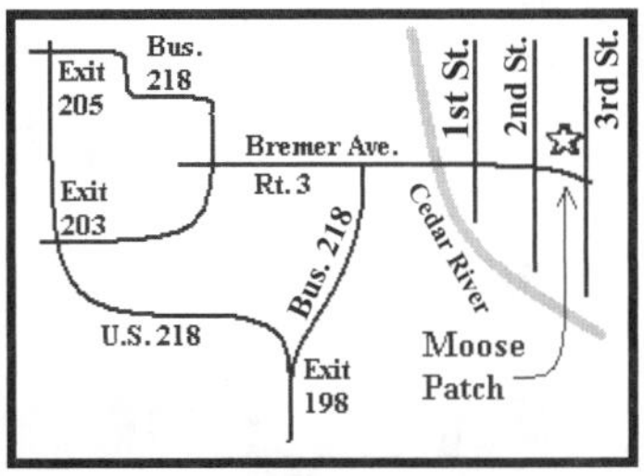

Waverly, IA #36

Jesup, IA #34

Tues - Fri 10 - 5
Thurs 10 - 7
Sat 10 - 4

Merry's Stitchins

Always something new stitched up to inspire you!

1923 Baker Rd. 50648
(319) 827-6703
Owner: Merry Backes merrys@jtt.net
www.merrysstitchins.com
Must see quilt shop! Many samples & kits.
4000+ bolts of fabrics -- many full lines.
Home of: Patch Abilities, Inc.

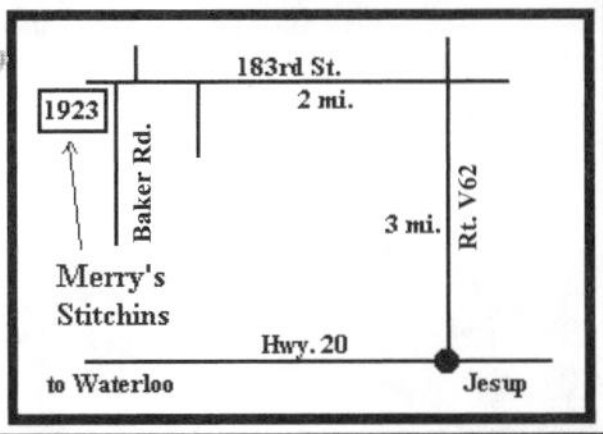

Greene, IA #35

Mon - Fri
7:30 - 5:30
Sat 8 - 2

Dralle's

122 E. Traer St.
P.O. Box A 50636
(641) 816-4158 Est: 1896

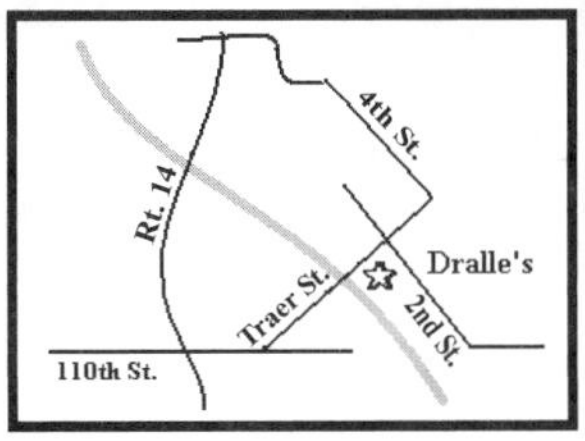

jpd@omnitelcom.com
www.drallesdeptstore.net
North Iowa's Only TRUE Dept. Store!
Quilting Fabric & Patterns
Embroidery Supplies - Classes - Gifts
Janome Sewing Machines
When in town visit the bakery. Open Wed-Sat.

Cedar Falls, IA #37

Mon - Fri 10 - 5:30
Thur til 8
Sat 10 - 4

Crazy To Quilt Shop

707 W. First St., 50613
(319) 277-1360
Owners: Jeni Moravec & Liz Wehrmacher

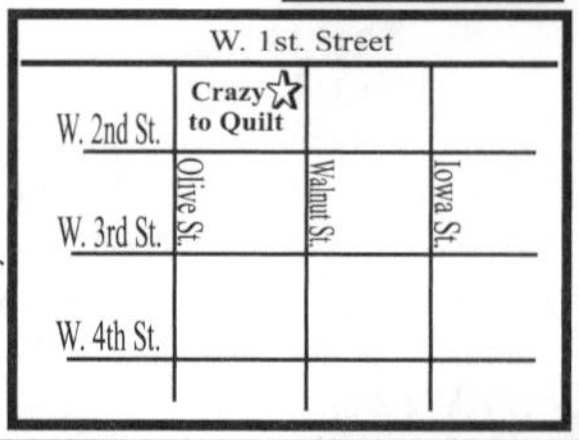

www.crazytoquilt.com
Quality quilting supplies and fabrics; large selection of batiks and flannels; friendly, helpful staff; a variety of classes; special orders welcome.
Authorized **PFAFF** Dealer Sales & Service.

Shellsburg, IA #38

April 1 - Dec 31
Wed - Fri 12 - 6
Sat 10 - 4

MyTyme Creations

"A Craft Show Everyday"

115 Main St., P.O. Box 243 52332
(319) 540-6243
www.mytymecreations.com
An extraordinary gift shop with more than 25 consignors who keep the store stocked with their one-of-a-kind items. Quilts, Baby Room Items, Cross Stitch Pictures, Afghans, Baskets and more all at very reasonable prices. All hand made!!

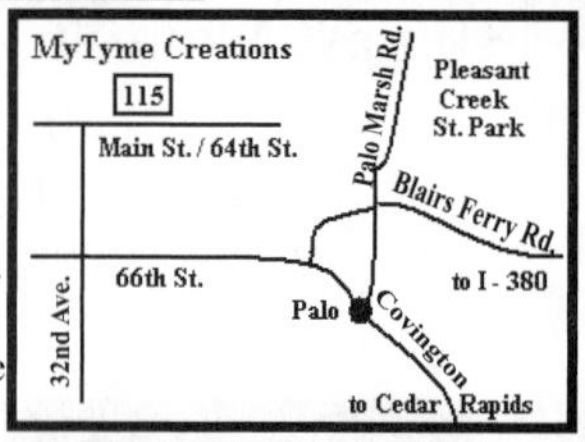

Hiawatha, IA #39

Mon - Fri 8 - 4

Nolting Mfg., Inc.

1265 Hawkeye Dr. 52233
(319) 378-0999 Fax: (319) 378-1026
nolting@nolting.com
www.nolting.com
Est: 1987 12,000 sq.ft. Free Catalog

The original Longarm Quilting Machine Manufacturer. See machines being made. Try new and refurbished Longarms. Machine Quilting Shop, Patterns, Accessories.

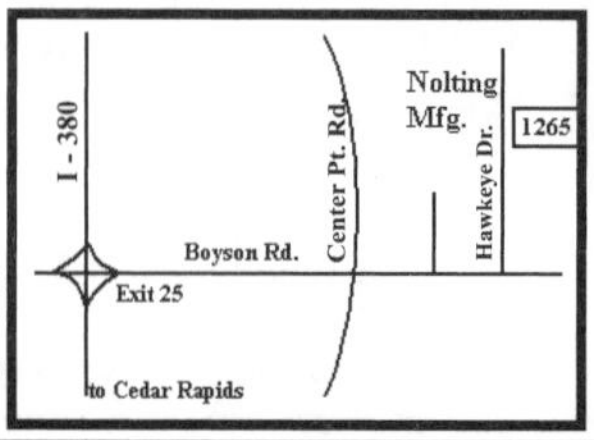

Marion, IA #41

Connie's Quilt Shop

785 8th Ave. 52302
(319) 373-9455
CONNIESQUILTSHOP@wmconnect.com
Est: 1992 Owner: Connie Moyer

Over 4000 bolts of reproduction prints, batiks, brights, novelties, and flannels. We carry a large selection of books, patterns & notions; including English Paper Piecing Patterns.
Stop in and See Us!!

Mon - Sat 10 - 5

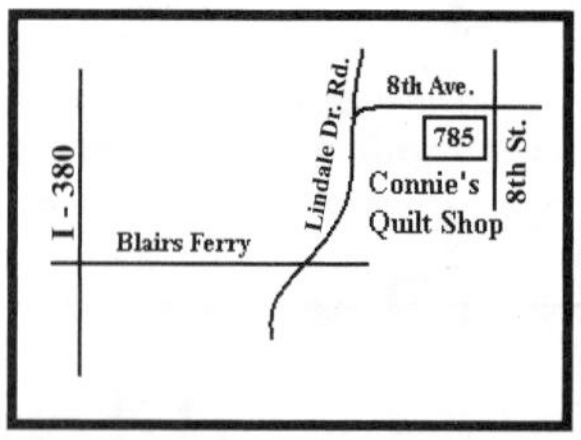

pine needles Sewing Center

1000 Old Marion Rd. 52402
319-373-0334 * sew@pineneedles.net
Est: 2003 * 7000 square feet

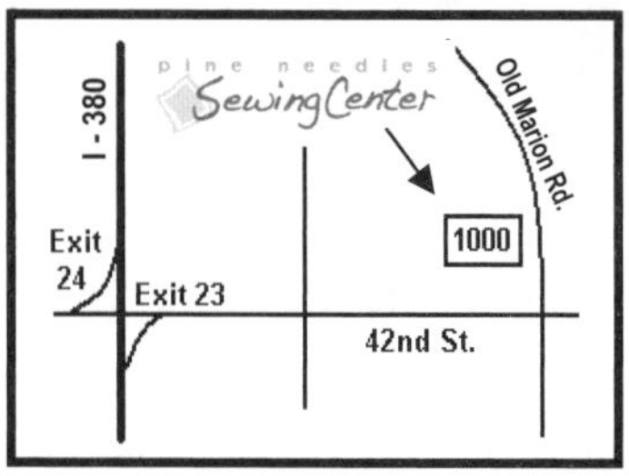

Store Hours:
Mon - Fri 10 - 5
Sat 10 - 4 Sun 12 - 4

Nothing Sews Like A Bernina. Nothing.
BERNINA®

This spacious store is home to fabric in abundance, creative energies everywhere and a full service BERNINA sewing machine dealer.

www.pineneedles.net

Cedar Rapids, IA #40

319-377-1482 **Open 7 Days**

"the cottage rose" a quilt shop™

1048 7th Ave.
Marion, Iowa 52302

www.cottagerosequiltshop.com

Mon - Fri 10 - 6
Thu 10 - 7
Sat 10 - 5 Sun 12 - 4

Located in Historic Uptown Marion, Iowa
100% Cotton Fabrics from "quilt shop only" Mills and Designers. Patterns, Books & Wool.

Featured is
"Rosies Bungalow" Quilt Retreat Center, for the Prefect Quilting Get Away.

A Truly Great Quilt Shop, plus Unique Specialty Shops, Antiques, and Great Food, in the area. This is worth the trip.

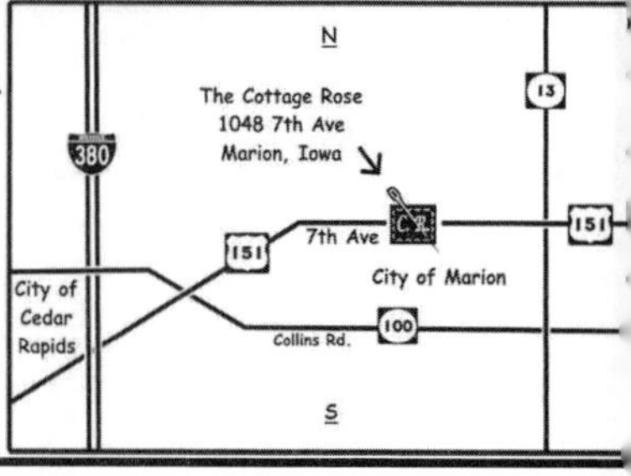

#42

Bellevue, IA #43

Thur - Mon 11 - 5

JoQuilter Fabrics

128 S. Riverview Dr.
52031
(563) 872-3473
joquilter@iowatelecom.net
Owner: Jo Fifield
Est: 2002

A cozy quilt shop on Bellevue's main street with a spectacular Mississippi River view. Now carrying all 100 colors of Fossil Fern from Benartex!

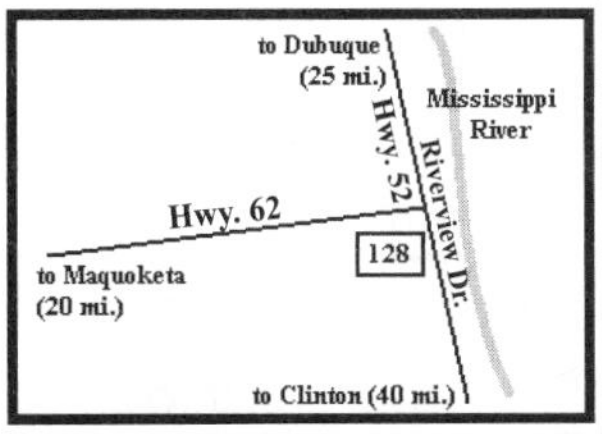

Maquoketa, IA #44

Mon - Fri 9 - 5 Weekends Call First

Hermes Auto & Upholstery, Inc.

1325 E. Platte St. 52060
(563) 652-2279
Owner: Brenda Hermes Est: 1984
blhermes@hotmail.com
www.hermesauto.com

- Quilting Fabric, Upholstery for Home, Antiques, Auto and Farm.

Also Custom Blinds and Window Treatments.

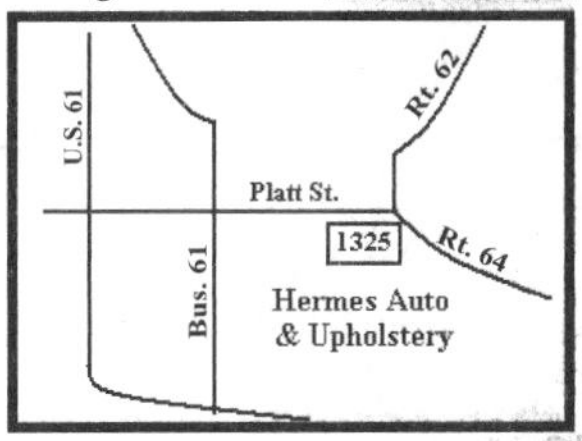

Sew Many Things!

Clinton, IA #45

1015 13th Ave. N, Suite E
Clinton, IA 52732
(563) 242-6135
www.iasews.com

We are a hands on sewing center featuring 100% cotton fabrics. We carry a large selection of books and patterns for all of your creative sewing needs. We offer classes in quilting, sewing (home decorating and garment construction), and machine embroidery.
We also carry a large selection of Robison Anton, Sulky and Mettler sewing and machine embroidery threads.
We are the Premier Dealer of Husqvarna Viking Sewing, Serger, and Embroidery Machines.
We offer on-site service and repair of all makes and models of sewing machines.

We have a dedicated staff to help you with all your quilting, sewing, and embroidery needs.

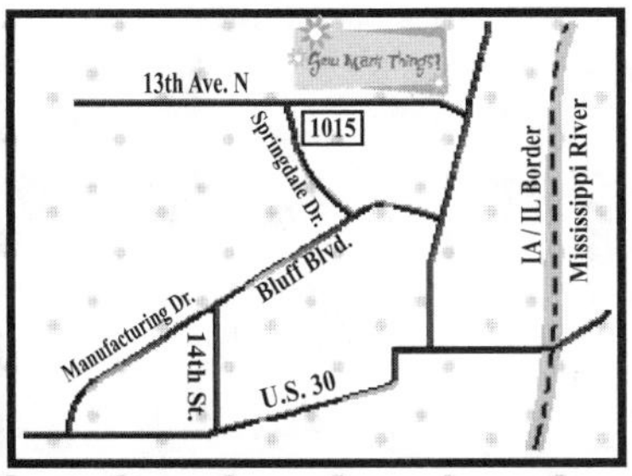

**Mon 10 - 8
Tues - Thur 10 - 5
Sat 10 - 3**

Owner: Stephanie Nickles
Est: 2008 3000 sq.ft.
2500+ Bolts
Newsletter Online

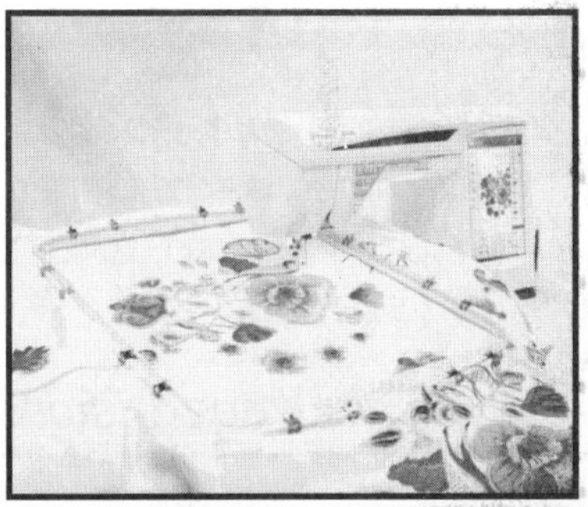

Husqvarna VIKING

Le Claire, IA #46

Mon - Fri 10 - 5 Sat 10 - 4

Expressions in Threads

208 S. Cody Rd. 52753
(563) 289-1447
2800 sq. ft.

expressinthread@aol.com
www.expressionsinthreads.com

2 miles from the Iowa Welcome center.
Fine Fabrics for Quilting

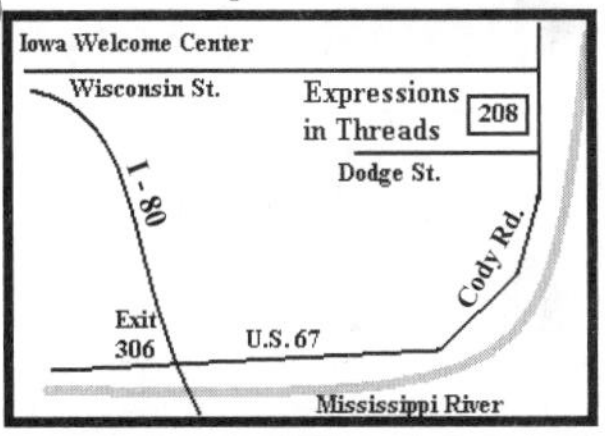

Davenport, IA #47

Mon - Sat 9 - 5

Denise Quilts

1536 W. Locust St. 52804
(563) 323-1890
Owner: Denise Hale Est: 2009
denisequilts@mchsi.com 2400 sq.ft.
denisequilt.tripod.com

Denise Quilts offers longarm quilting. Fabric, notions, quilting classes. Learn to use the longarm and finish you own tops.

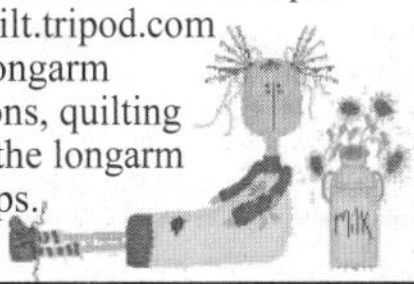

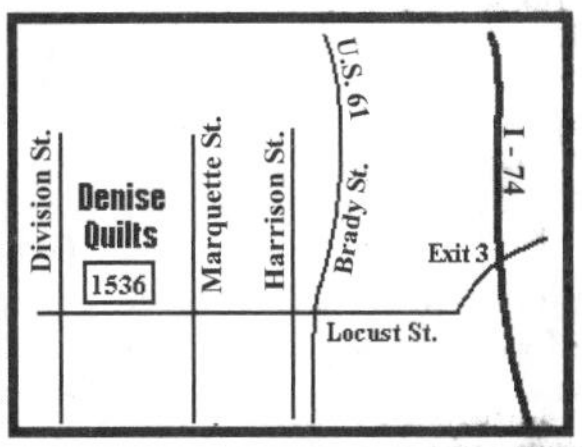

Tipton, IA #48

The Fabric Stasher
Quilt Store and More!

Mon, Tue, Fri 9 - 6
Wed 9 - 4
Thur 9 - 7
Sat 10 - 4

505 E. Cedar St. 52772
(563) 886-1600
Owners: Sheila Powelka & Kerri Smith
fabricstasher@iowatelecom.net
www.thefabricstasher.com

Large selection of fabric, books, patterns & notions. Yarn and much more. Classes offered.

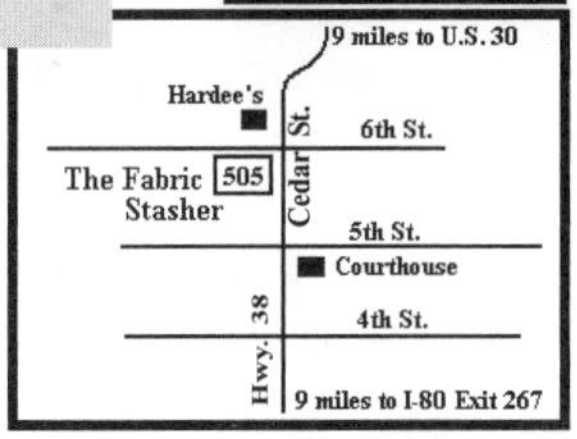

North Liberty, IA #49

Mon - Fri 10 - 6
Thur til 8
Sat 10 - 5

480 W. Zeller St.
P.O. Box 546 52317
(319) 626-3160

Common Threads
Quilt Shoppe

Owner: Peg Griffin-Wood
www.ctquiltshoppe.com

Quality Fabrics Notions
Classes Longarm Services
Longarm Supplies & Instruction
Quilt Commissions

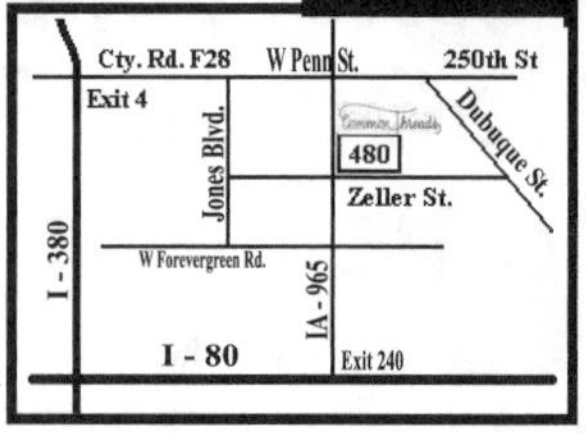

Heritage Designs

Quilting & Needlework

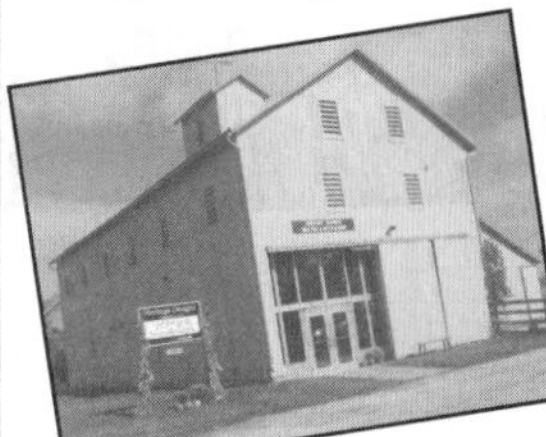

Quilt Sampler Featured Shop 2009

2009 Top 10 Quilt Shop
Buses Welcome
Please Call Ahead

Est: 1976

Open Daily
Mon - Sat 9-5
Sun 11-4

Our shop is located in a renovated granary, built in 1895.

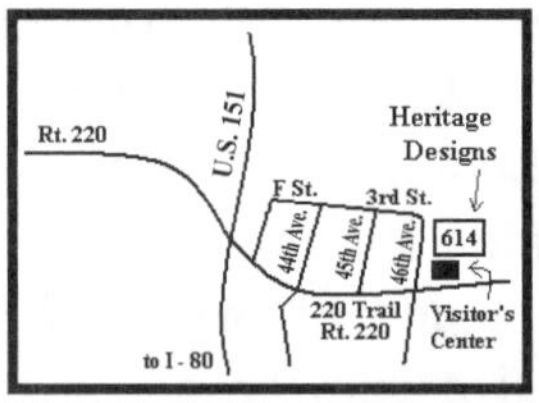

www.AmanaColonies.com

- 4000 Fabrics Contemporary to Traditional
- Kits
- Books & Patterns
- Notions & Unique Accessories
- Cross-Stitch
- Tatting
- Dovo Scissors
- Featured Local Designs
- Punchneedle
- Embroidery & appliqué patterns

Amana, IA #50

614 46th Ave. 52203
Next to the Visitors Center in
Historic Amana, Iowa
(319) 622-3887

www.heritagedesignsquiltshop.com

Experience a store where fabric is designed!

Est: 1987

Fern Hill

103 - 220th Trail 52334
(319) 622-3627
Fax: (319) 622-6120
fernhill@southslope.net

Fern Hill's own designer, Stephanie Brandenburg, creates beautiful Fern Hill lines sold internationally. Tour her design studio, our fabric loft with over 4,000 bolts of fabric, a library of patterns and books, and shop our original patterns and kits.

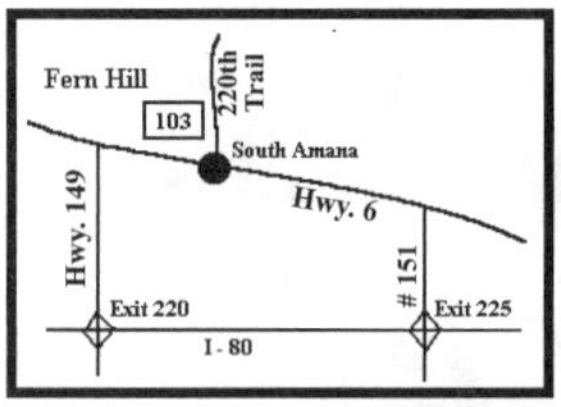

Mon - Sat 9:30 - 5
Sun 11 - 4

www.fernhill.net

South Amana, IA #51

Brooklyn, IA #52

Mon - Fri 8 - 6
Sat 8 - 5

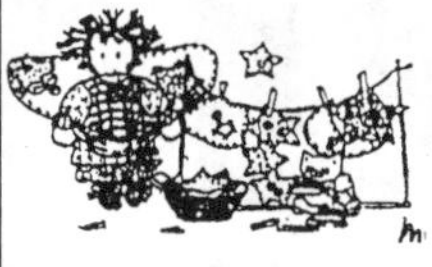

True Value

118 W. Front St.
52211
(888) 522-7712
brooktruevalue@netins.net

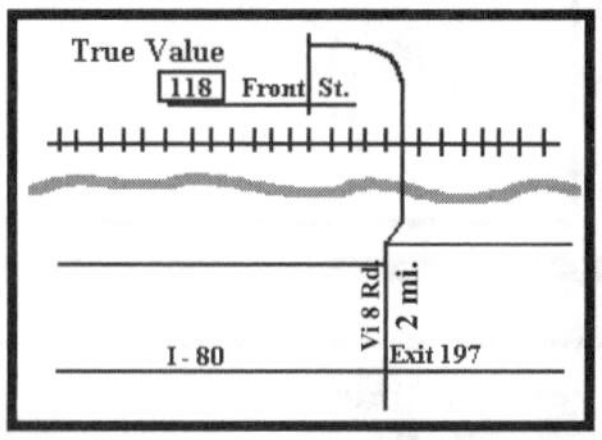

600 bolts of Quality Cotton Quilting Fabric, (Blank, Flannels, Moda), DMC Floss, Craft Patterns, Rubber Stamps, Silk Ribbon. Quilting & Craft Supplies. Lots of Models. Scrapbooking & ideas.

Pella, IA #53

Vande Lune Fabrics
and Quilt Shop

Mon - Fri 9 - 5:30
June to Aug. Thur til 7
Sat 9 - 4:30

701 Franklin St. 50219 Est: 1972
(641) 628-3350 Fax: (641) 628-8968
Located on the SE corner of Town Square

Large selection of the latest Books, Notions & Fabrics (over 3,000 bolts). Come visit our Vibrant Store. We are known for our unusual samples with available kits.

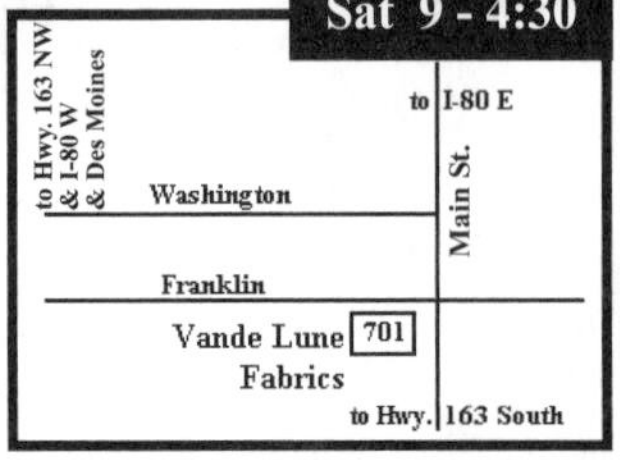

Moravia, IA #54

Wed - Fri 10 - 6
Sat 10 - 4

Shops at Granny's House

2797 600th Ave. 52571
(641) 724-3131 Est: 2006
400 sq.ft. 500 bolts

shopsatgrannyshouse@yahoo.com

Quilt fabric & beads for jewelry making in a charming 1905 farm house. Located 4 miles w of Moravia. Watch for our blue highway sign.

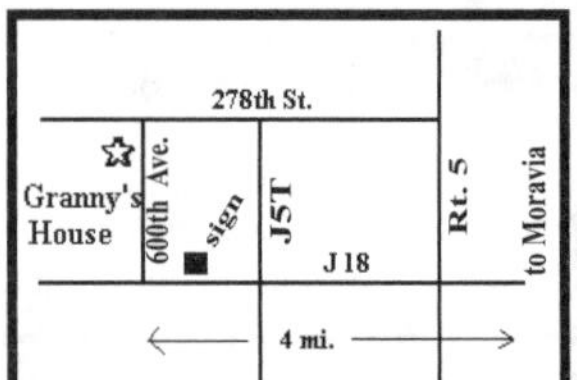

Williamsburg, IA #55

Rainbows & Calico Things

A unique shop located on a three generation farm just outside of historic Williamsburg, Iowa.

2811 240th St. 52361
(319) 668-1977
Owner: Barbara Wardenburg
Est: 1994 1600 sq.ft.

We carry a wonderful selection of Black and White, Hoffman Christmas, Batiks, Juvenile Flannels and Bright 100% Cotton Fabrics by Hoffman, Timeless Treasures, Moda, Kaufman, Benartex, Michael Miller, Lakehouse Direct and more. (2000 bolts) Also a great supply of Books, Patterns, Rulers and Notions. Electric Quilt Software Programs with on demand demo.

Wed - Sat 9 - 4
Other Times by Chance or Appt.

If coming from the **East** use I-80 Exit 225 follow map & signs.
If coming from the **West** use I-80 Exit 220 go into Williamsburg.
Turn east on **State St., (F-46)**, **240th St.** go 3½ miles.

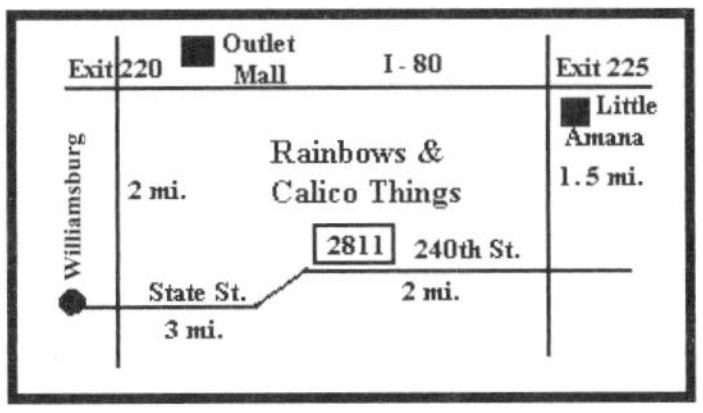

E-mail: barbaraw@rainbowsandcalicothings.com
Web Site: www.rainbowsandcalicothings.com

The Woolen Needle

~Iowa's Largest Wool Selection~

Reproduction Cottons~Penny Rugs
Rug Hooking ~Punch Needle

225 West Welsh ~ PO Box 10
Williamsburg, Iowa 52361
319-668-2642

#56

www.thewoolenneedle.com
email ~ woolenneedle@iowatelecom.net

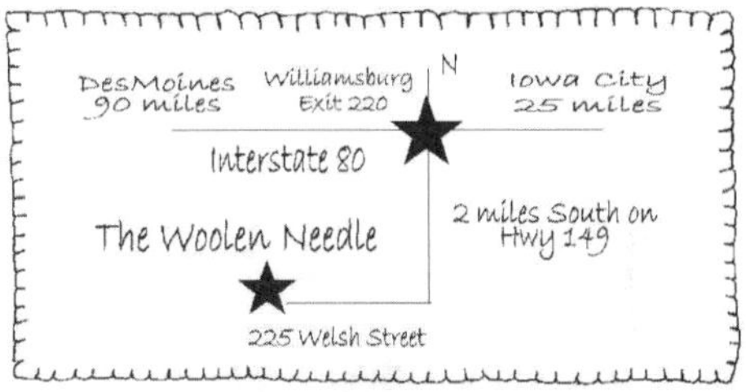

~Open~
Tuesday thru Friday 9 to 5
Saturday 9 to 1

Muscatine, IA #58

Mon - Sat 9 - 4

The Cotton Shop

331 E 2nd St. 52761
(563) 262-5709

cottonshop@machlink.com
www.cottonshoponline.com

A hands-on store offering classes & support for quilters & crafters.
Over 3000 bolts of 100% cotton fabric.
Wool felt and wools for rughooking. Now carrying cross-stitch patterns to compliment our great selection of books and patterns.

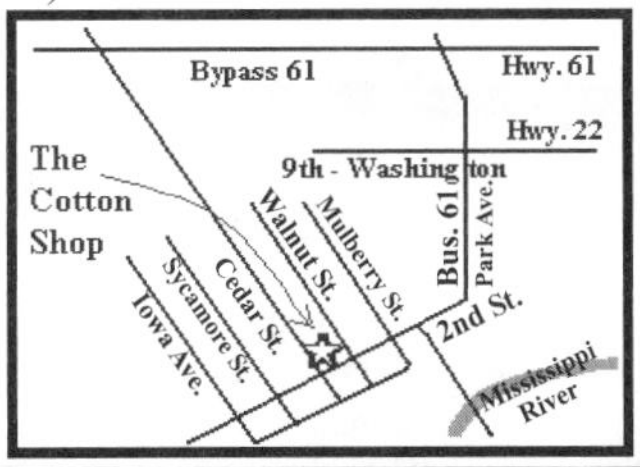

Hills, IA #57

Inspirations

Quilt fabric ✻ notions ✻ gifts ✻ whatnot

120 Main St., Hills, IA 52235
319-679-2207
Owner: Nancy Lackender
inspirations-quilts@msn.com

- Reproduction fabrics are our specialty
- Great selection of patterns for children, aprons and handbags
- Treat yourself to lunch at our sister shop located in the same building.

Morning Glory Bakery & Tearoom
reservations recommended 319-679-2208

Tues - Sat 9:30 - 5

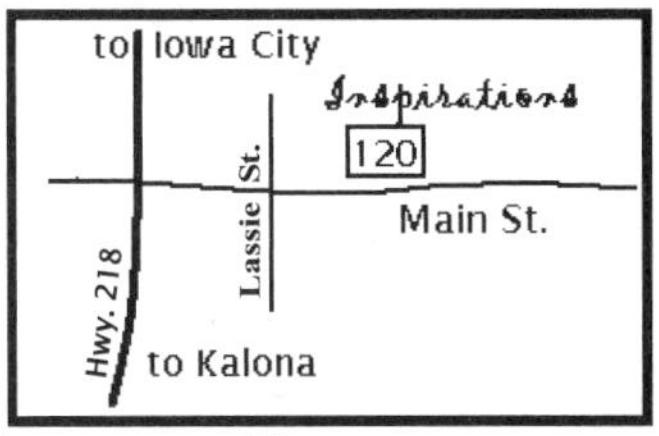

www.inspirations-quilts.com

Quilters Paradise

Est: 2001

120 N. Main St. 52641
(319) 385-1749
Owner: Cathy Hopkins
quiltersparadise@lisco.com

Mon - Fri 10 - 5
Sat 10 - 3

"Where Heaven is only a stitch away."
Love, laughter & friends are always welcome.

Offering quality cotton fabrics, books, patterns and notions. Longarm quilting available.

Retreat Center

Brand New Hideaway above the shop. 3 bedroom, large work area, full kitchen and bathroom facilities. A great getaway for you & your friends.

Mt. Pleasant, IA #59

Kalona, IA #60

Mon - Sat 9 - 5

Stitch N Sew Cottage

207 4th St. P.O. Box 351 52247
(319) 656-2923 Est: 1981
stitchnsewc@yahoo.com

Custom made Quilts, Fabrics, Notions, Quilting supplies, 3000+ Bolts, Books and Patterns.

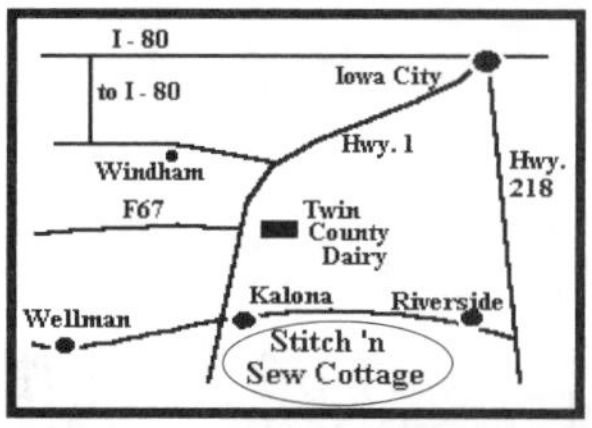

Kalona, IA #61

Summer 9:30 - 4 Winter 11 - 3

Kalona Quilt & Textile Museum

In the Kalona Historic Village on D Ave.
715 D Ave. 52247
(319) 656-3232
Two Quilt Galleries--Amish & Other American Quilts. Shows change every 3 - 4 months
Admission $4 or $7 for entire grounds. We can also arrange day-long excursion to Mennonite farms.

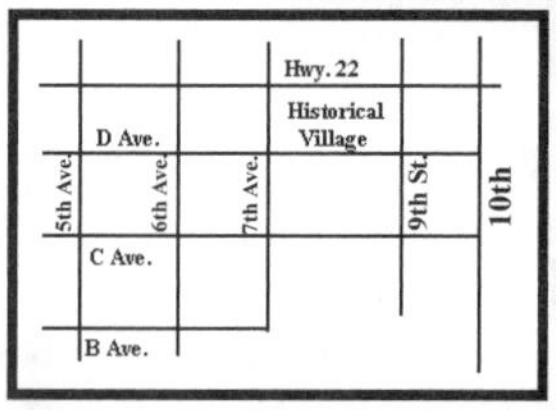

Kalona, IA #62

Mon - Sat 10 - 5

Willow Creek Quilting & Gifts

418 B Ave., P.O. Box 862 52247
(319) 656-3939
Owner: Juanita Troyer
www.willowcreekquilting.com
NEW FLANNEL ROOM. 100% cotton flannels--specializing in homespuns. 1000's of bolts of regular cotton fabrics. Huge selection of books & patterns for dolls, quilts, & stitchery with many models and quilts made up.
Many quilt kits available.

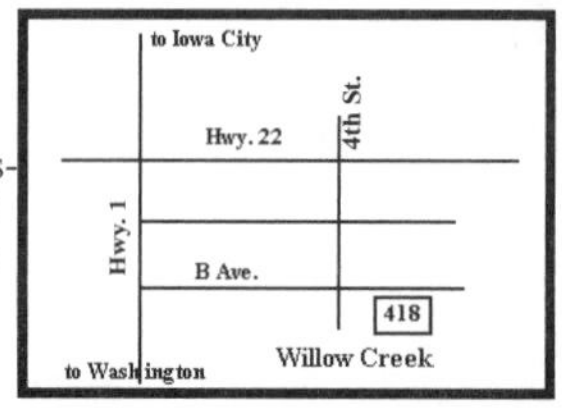

Kalona, IA #63

Mon - Sat 9 - 5

Woodin Wheel

515 "B" Ave., P.O. Box 627 52247
(319) 656-2240
www.woodinwheel.com

Over 300 New & Antique Quilts for Sale.
Sponsor of Annual Kalona Quilt Show & Sale.
Last Friday & Saturday of April.
Large selection of Heartwood Creek by Jim Shore.

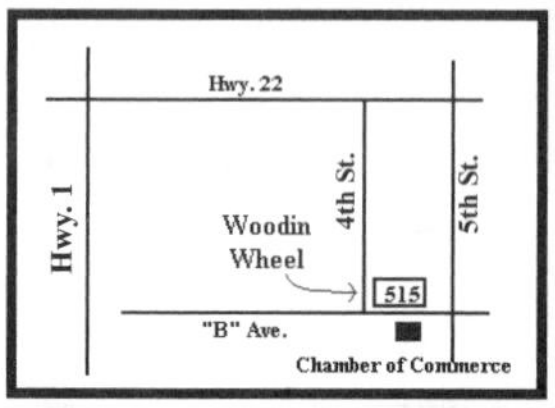

West Burlington, IA #64

Tues - Fri 10 - 5:30 Sat 10 - 3

The Quilting Corner

123 Broadway St. 52655
(319) 752-4288
Owners: Ellen & David Bloomberg

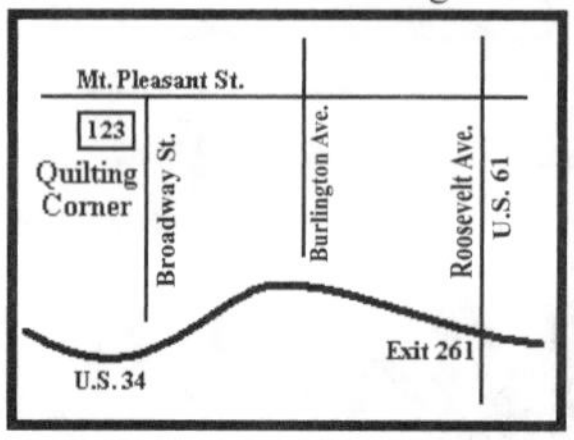

thequiltingcorner@live.com
Authorized PFAFF Dealer--Sales & Service.
Friendly staff, lots of Samples.
Fabrics, Patterns, Books Notions, Kits & more.

Wever, IA #65

Mon - Fri 10 - 5

On Hwy. 61, mile marker 29
(319) 470-8670

New fabrics and patterns arriving all the time. Wool, kits, & needful things.

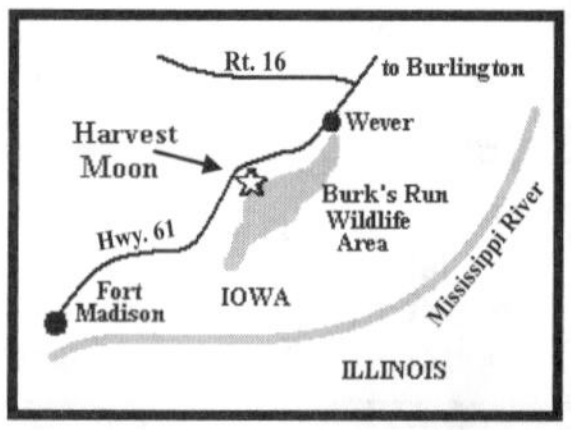

harwood@iowatelecom.net
www.harvestmoonquiltco.com

Fairfield, IA #66

Tues - Fri 10 - 5:30 Sat 9 - 3

C R Quilts

2255 Hwy. 1 S 52556
(641) 469-4534
Owner: Jeanie Belgarde
Free Newsletter
crq@iowatelecom.net
www.crquiltstore.com
We offer name brand fabrics including: Moda, Hoffman, RJR & More.
Classes, Patterns, Books, & Notions plus Long Arm quilting.

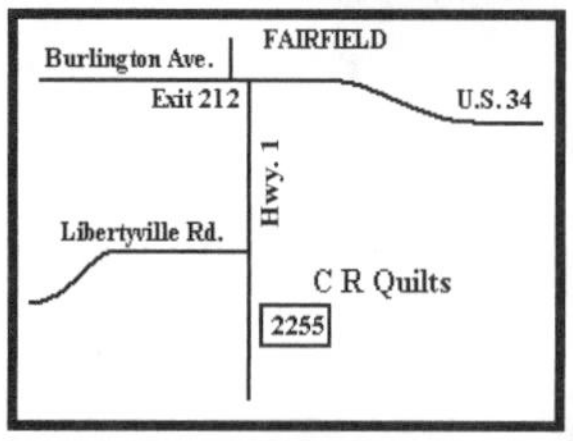

Lucas, IA #67

Mon - Sat 9 - 5 Wed til 8

Quilt With Us

100 E. Front St., P.O. Box 89 50151
(641) 766-6486
Owner: Mary Kinsey Est: 2002
quiltwithus@yahoo.com

Small town friendly quilt shop located in a 1915 hardware store featuring fabrics, notions, books, classes, large selection of 108" quilt backing, antiques & gifts.

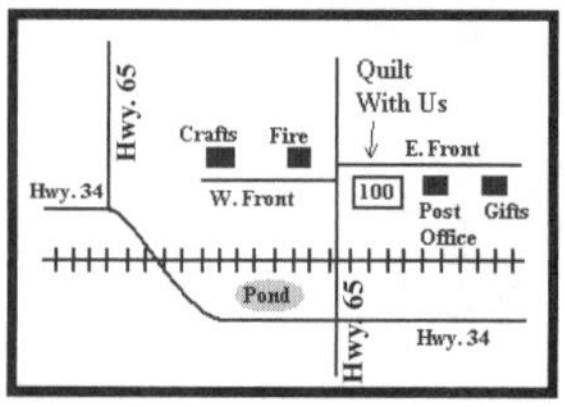

Clarinda, IA #68

Tues - Sat 10 - 5

The Quilt Coop

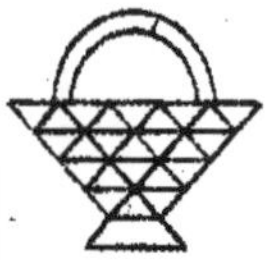

2377 - 270th St. 51632
(712) 582-3553
Owner: Robin Ripley
Est: 2004 3000+ Bolts
robin@quiltcoop.com
www.thequiltcoop.blogspot.com

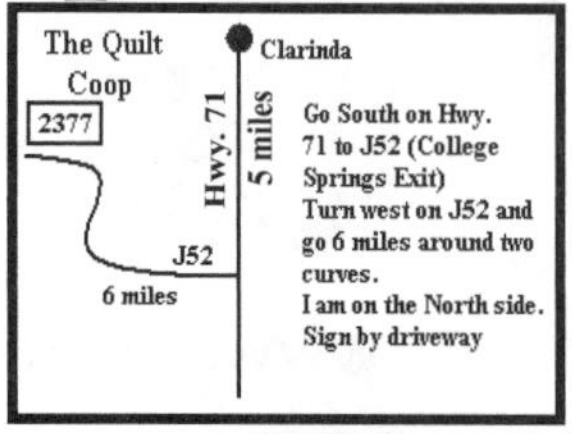

A Full Service Quilt Shop In The Country

Creston, IA #69

Mon - Sat 9 - 5:30 Mon & Thur til 8

Quilts and other Notions

209 W. Montgomery St. 50801
(641) 782-8874 Fax: (641) 782-6660
Owner: Joyce Franklin
Est: 1982 4000 sq. ft. Free Newsletter
quiltsandothernotions@gmail.com
www.quiltsandothernotions.com
7000 bolts of quilt fabrics. We sell and service Husqvarna Viking sewing machines and sergers.
28 years in business.

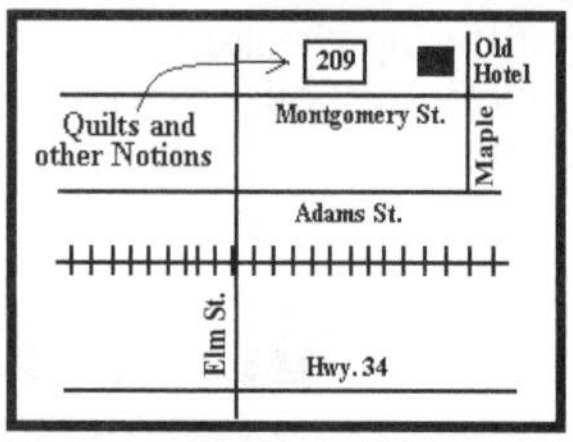

Greenfield, IA #70

FABRIC CREATIONS

Mon - Fri 8 - 5
Sat 8 - 12

111 SW Jackson 50849
(641) 343-7186
Owner: Kerin Ladd
ksladd@iowatelecom.net

Quilts, Quality Fabrics
Notions, Gifts, Alterations

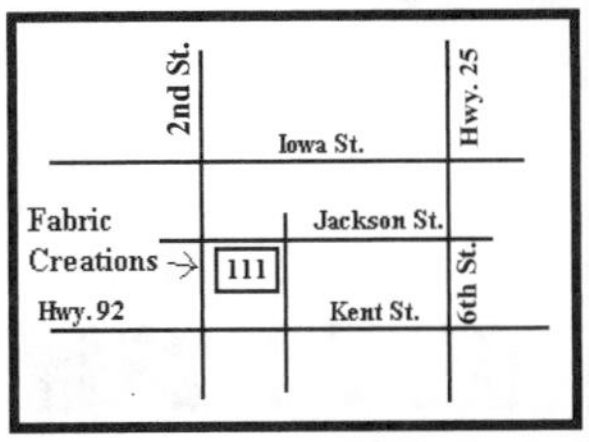

West Des Moines, IA #71

The Quilt Block

M -S 10 - 5
Thur 10 - 7
Sun 1 - 4

325 5th Street 50265
(515) 255-1010
Owner: Mary Miller
Est: 1987 3000 sq.ft. 2000 Bolts
www.iowaquiltblock.com

Full line quilt supply store--fabrics, notions, books, patterns. Authorized Bernina dealer.

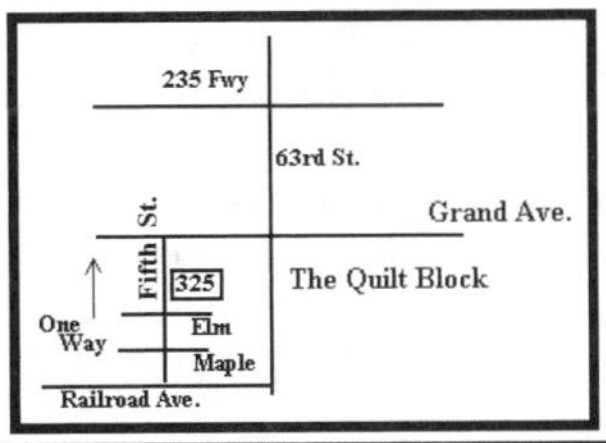

Newton, IA #72

CORNER STONE QUILTS

Quality Quilting Fabrics & Wool, Notions, Books, Patterns & More.
Come see our beautiful 1900 Craft house full of Civil War & 1930's reproduction fabrics.

426 1st Ave. E 50208
641-792-6274
Authorized Jenny Haskins Dealer
Online Newsletter
Lee@cornerstonequilts.net

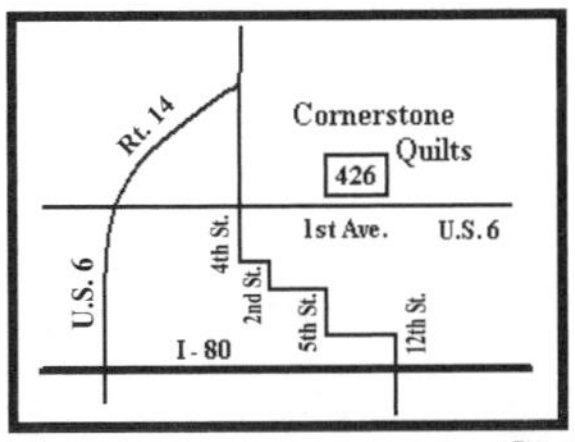

- Machine Embroidery
- Block of the Month Club
- Embroidery Club
- Civil War Club
- 30's Club
- Long Arm Quilters Support Group

Mon - Fri 10 - 5:30
Sat 10 - 4

Authorized PFAFF, brother and Tin Lizzie Sales and Service

www.cornerstonequilts.net

Creekside Quilting

9926 Swanson Blvd. 50325
(515) 276-1977
Owner: Connie Doern
Est: 2003 3600 sq. ft
www.creekside-quilting.com

- **5,000 bolts of fabric from Moda, P&B, Timeless Treasures, Kaufman, Hoffman, Bali, Maywood, Westminster & others.**
- **Extensive selection of batiks, reproduction fabrics, novelties, contemporary fabrics, Asian prints, and new collections.**
- **Over 200 book titles, patterns, and magazines. Many original patterns.**
- **Wide assortment of notions and threads**
- **Beautiful samples, many with kits**
- **On-line newsletter**
- **Friendly staff of experienced quilters**

Come and see us.
The coffee's always on !

Buses welcome; please call ahead

PFAFF authorized dealer

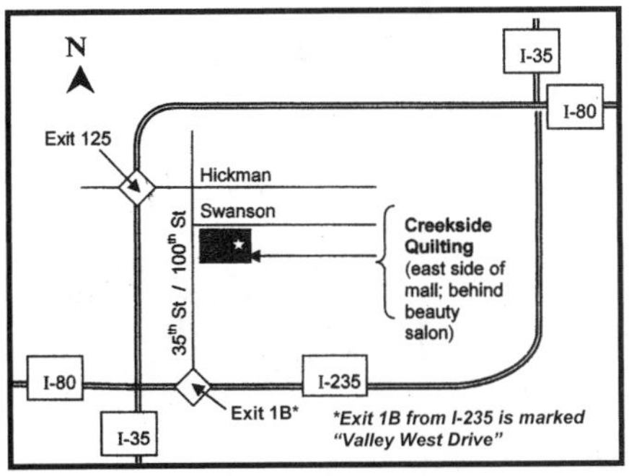

Hours:
Mon - Wed 10 - 5:30
Thur 10 - 7
Fri & Sat 10 - 5
Sun 1 - 4

Just 5 minutes from I - 35 & 80 exchange in western suburb of Des Moines

Clive, IA #73

Nevada, IA #74

BLOCK PARTY STUDIOS, INC.

Central Iowa's Quilt Shop In The Country!

Unique hand printed fabric & original quilt patterns
GLORIOUS fabrics · Warm welcomes
Come see what makes us beyond the ordinary!

The hand that guides the needle rules the world
Sew and your friends sew with you; Rip and you rip alone.
If quilting were a crime I'd be doing time!

Swatches from our hand printed "TQRT" series

Store Hours
Mon-Fri 8:30-5
Saturday 10-3
....
or 24/7 online!

Just 6 minutes east of I-35, in Nevada's West Industrial Park

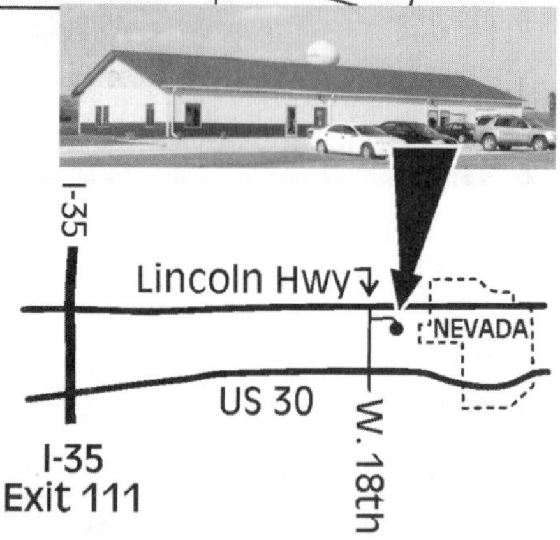

1503 West K Avenue · Nevada, IA · (800)419-2812
www.blockpartystudios.com

Ames, IA #75

Quilting Connection

Mon & Thur 10 - 8
Tues, Wed, Fri 10 - 5:30
Sat 10 - 5
Sun. by appt.

238 Main St. 50010
(515) 233-3048 Owner: Kelly Irwin
info@iaquilts.com www.iaquilts.com
5000 sq.ft 6000+ Bolts

Husqvarna VIKING

Great selection of 100% cotton fabrics.

Hundreds of books, patterns, notions and embroidery designs.

Complete Line of Husqvarna Viking Sewing Machines.

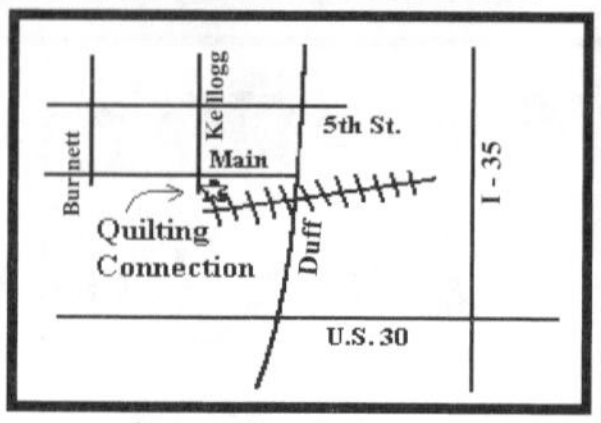

Conveniently located 2 miles West of I-35

Ankeny, IA #76

Mon - Fri 10 - 5:30
Thur til 7
Sat 10 - 5

Quilter's Cupboard

706 SW 3rd St. 50023
(515) 963-8758
2000 sq.ft. 2000 Bolts
quilterscupboard@yahoo.com
www.quilterscupboardiowa.com
Fabric, Notions, Books, Patterns
Classes and clubs available
Authorized Baby Lock Sewing Machine Dealer.
Friendly, knowledgeable staff available to serve.

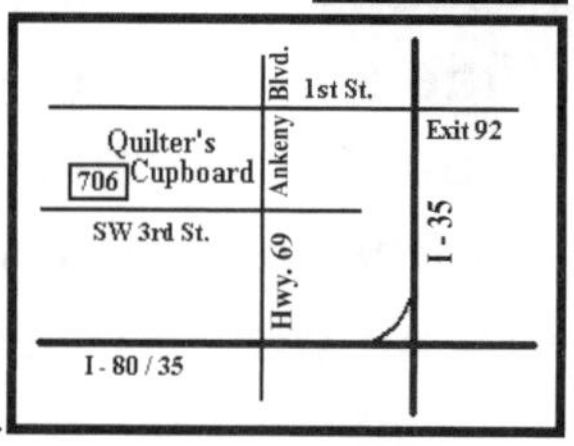

Adel, IA #77

Mon - Sat 9 - 5
Thur til 7

ADEL QUILTING & DRY GOODS Co.

909 Prairie St. 50003
(515) 993-1170
adelquilting@mchsi.com Est: 2002
www.adelquilting.com
Owners: Jacque & Frank Johnson
Come to the "Little Quilt Shop on the Prairie" for fabric, patterns, books, kits, notions, classes & friendly service.

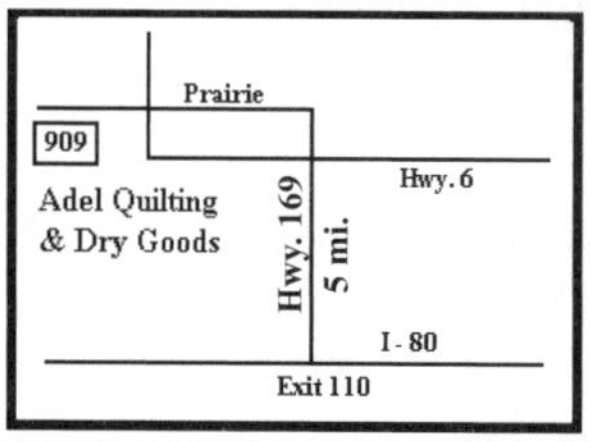

Council Bluffs, IA #78

Kanesville Quilting

19851 Virginia Hills Rd. 51503
(877) 294-1009 or (712) 366-6003
quilts@kq.omhcoxmail.com
www.kanesvillequilting.com
Owners: Mavis Hauser & Karen Krause
Est: 1990 3000 sq.ft.

Spacious, well lit shop, filled with 100% cotton fabrics, books, patterns, notions, and the latest magazines. We do machine quilting on your tops. Our friendly staff is always ready to assist you with your quilting needs.
PFAFF Authorized Dealer

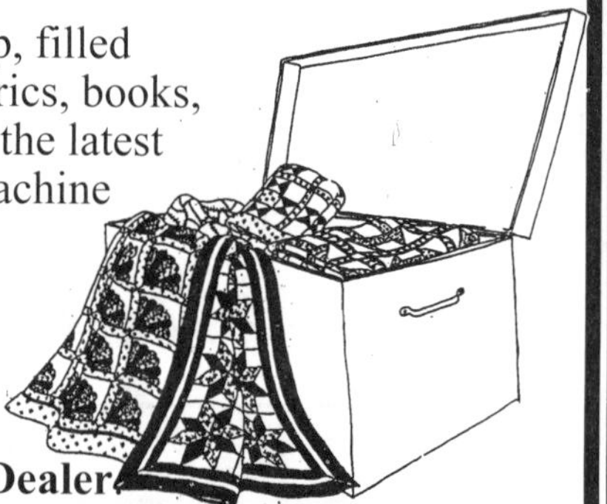

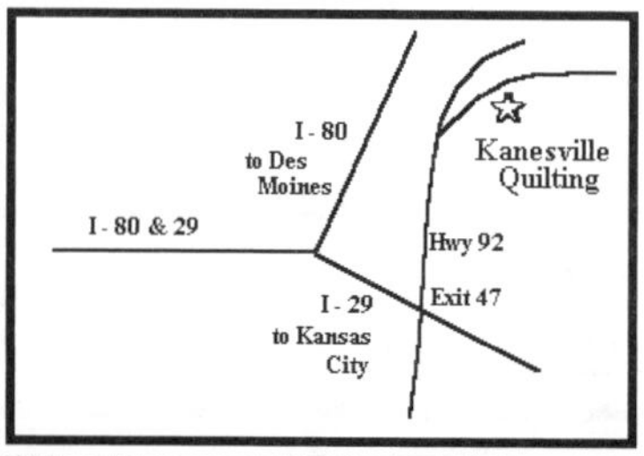

Mon - Fri 10 - 5:30
Sat 10 - 4

East on Hwy. 92

Walnut, IA #79

Mon - Sat 9 - 5 Sun 1 - 5

DR's Kalico Krafts

206 Antique City Dr., P.O. Box 332 51577
(712) 784-3865
Owner: Dorine K. Rasmussen
Est: 1995 1800 sq.ft.
kalicokrafts@walnutel.net

Fabric, Books and Supplies for Quiltmaking. Finished Wallhangings to Quilts. Custom orders. Needlework finishing. Machine appliqué and preprinted shirts, gifts and fleece.

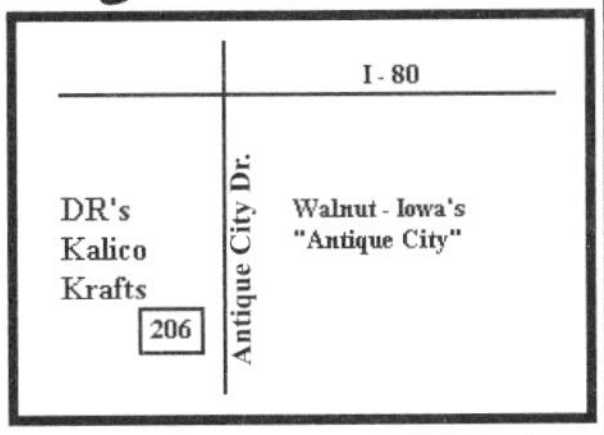

Walnut, IA #80

Mon - Sat 10 - 5

Olde Tyme Quilting

215 Antique City Dr.
P.O. Box 705 51577
(712) 784-3653 or (888) 784-3661

Fabrics including over 100 backings.
Quilting Notions.
Batting by the yard!

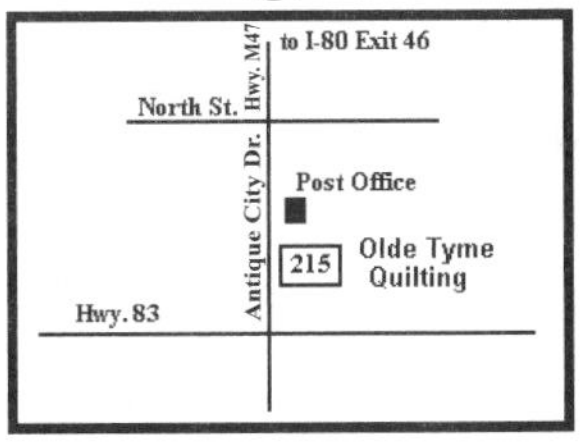

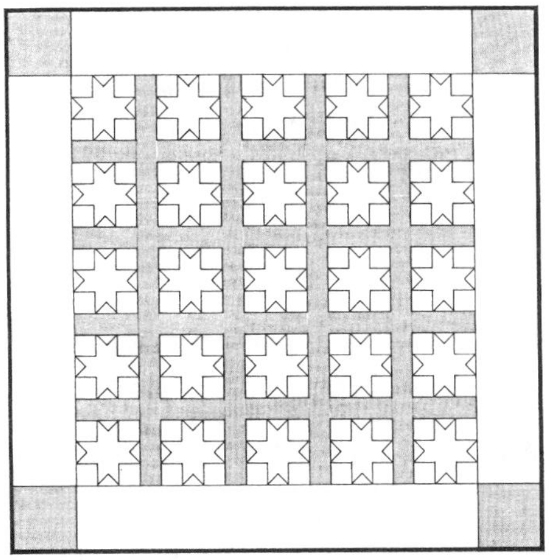

Exira, IA #81

Tues - Sat 10 - 5 Thur til 8

Log Cabin Quilting

111 W. Washington
P.O. Box 594 50076
(712) 268-2487
Owner: Margy Hansen
lcquilts@metc.net
www.logcabinquilts.blogspot.com
Machine guided quilting, fabric, notions, books, patterns, samplers / kits, classes& gifts.
Service with a smile behind the yellow door.

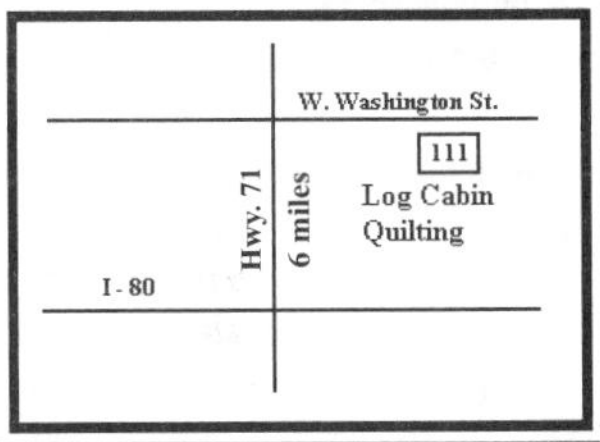

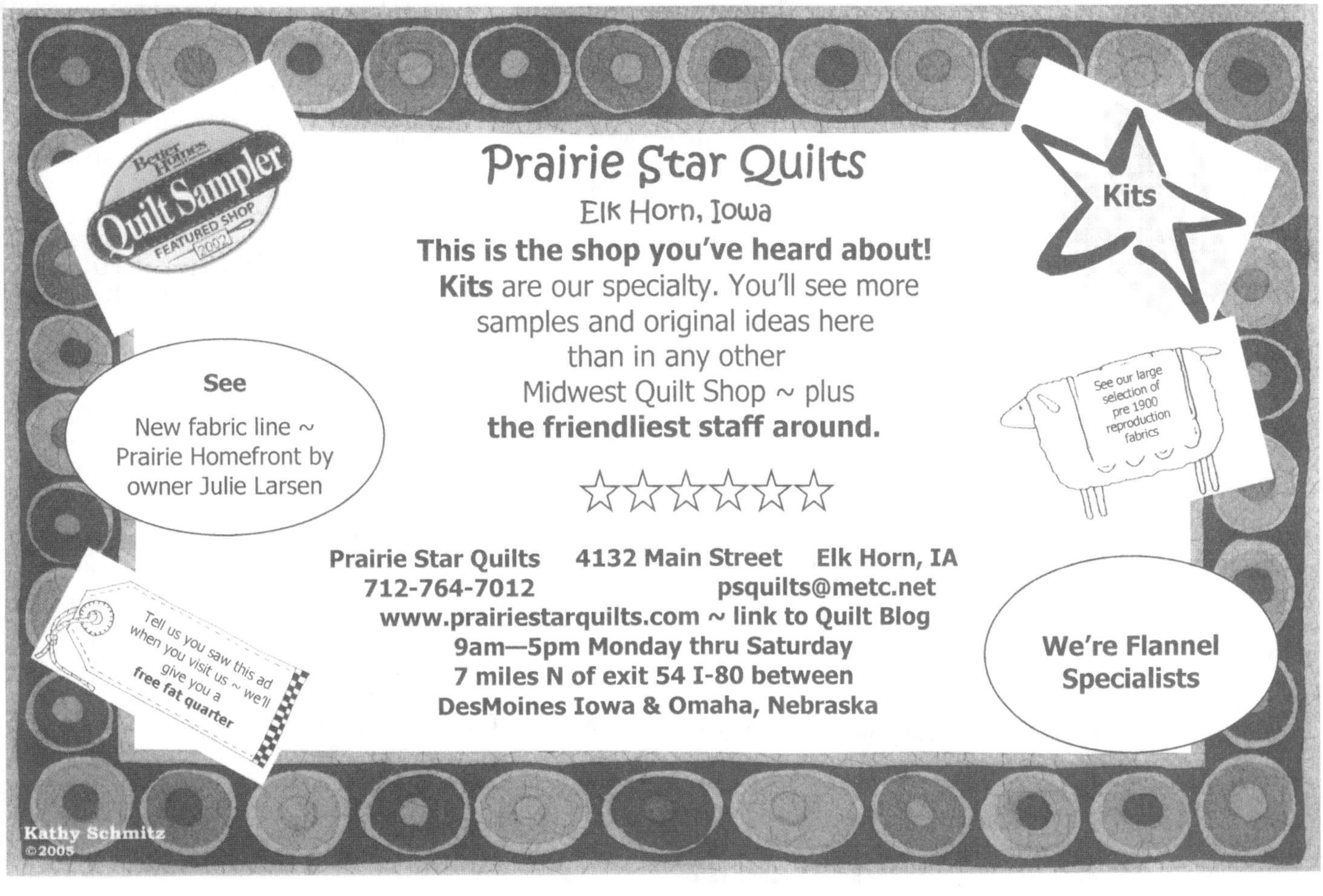

Iowa Quilt Shops

Adel **Adel Quilting & Drygoods, 909 Prairie St.** **515-993-1170** **See ad #77, page 188**

Algona **Heartland Quilt Shop, 107 S. Harlan St.** **515-295-3036** **See ad #15, page 178**

Algona **Seams To Me, 17 E. State St.** **515-295-5841** **See ad #16, page 178**

Alta **The Quilt Shoppe, 206 Main St.** **712-284-2724** **See ad #5, page 177**

Amana **Heritage Designs, 614 46th Ave.** **319-622-3887** **See ad #50, page 184**

Ames **Quilting Connection, 238 Main St.** **515-233-3048** **See ad #75, page 188**

Ankeny **Quilter's Cupboard, 706 SW 3rd ST** **515-963-8758** **See ad #76, page 188**

Aplington Jen's Needleworks, 900 Parriott 319-347-2793

Audubon Country Quilting, 1752 210th St 712-563-3257

Bellevue **JoQuilter Fabrics, 128 S. Riverview Dr.** **563-872-3473** **See ad #43, page 183**

Bonaparte La Donna's Quilting Shop, 411 Maple St. 319-592-3666

Brooklyn **True Value, 118 W. Front St.** **641-522-7712** **See ad #52, page 184**

Burlington The Sew 'N Sew Shop, 3206 Division St. 319-752-5733

Carroll Threads Etc., 907 Hwy. 30 E 712-792-4073

Carroll The Quilt Shop, 512 N. Adams St. 712-792-2890

Cascade Spools N Jewels, 24623 Hwy. 136 S 563-852-7765

Cedar Falls **Crazy to Quilt Shop, 707 W. 1st St.** **319-277-1360** **See ad #37, page 182**

Cedar Falls Quilting Bug, 7125 N Union Rd 319-266-1098

Cedar Rapids **Pine Needles Sewing Ctr, 1000 Old Marion** **319-373-0334** **See ad #40, page 182**

Cedar Rapids Treasures From The Attic, 2300 Grande Ave. SE 319-390-1929

Cedar Rapids Lulijune's Quilt Shop, 14303 University Ave. 319-961-0705

Cedar Rapids West Side Sewing Machine Shop, 2600 Edgewood Rd SW 319-365-3075

Chariton Betty's Gift & Quilt Shop, 907 Braden Ave. 641-774-2496

Chariton The Sampler, 102 S. Grand 641-774-2116

Charles CityStitches, 715 Kelly Mall 641-228-3383

Cherokee Quilt'n Kaboodle, 420 W. Main St 712-225-3600

Clarinda **The Quilt Coop, 2377 - 270th St.** **712-582-3553** **See ad #68, page 186**

Clinton **Sew Many Things, 1015 13th Ave N Ste. E** **563-242-6135** **See ad #45, page 183 & 208**

Clive **Creekside Quilting, 9926 Swanson Blvd.** **515-276-1977** **See ad #73, page 187**

Colfax Sugar Creek Sampler, 11627 N. 19th Ave. W

Conrad Conrad General Store, 101 N. Main St. 641-366-2043

Council Bluffs **Kanesville Quilting, 19851 Virginia Hills Rd.** **712-366-6003** **See ad #78, page 188**

Creston **Quilts & Other Notions, 209 W. Montgomery St.** **641-782-8874** **See ad #69, page 186**

Davenport **Denise Quilts, 1536 W. Locust St.** **563-323-1890** **See ad #47, page 183**

Decorah **Pine Needles Quilt Shop, 415 W Water St** **563-382-4646** **See ad #24, page 180**

Des Moines Miller's Perfect Place, 5255 NE 3rd St 515-282-8605

Dubuque **The Cotton Cabin and Yarn Shop, 1075 Main St** **563-582-0800** **See ad #30, page 180**

Dubuque **Quilt Shack, 3220 Dodge St. #106** **563-556-3163** **See ad #29, page 180**

Dyersville **Vintage Threads Quilt Shoppe, 234 1st Ave. E** **563-875-7330** **See ad #28, page 180**

Elk Horn **Prairie Star Quilts, 4132 Main St.** **712-764-7012** **See ad #82, page 189**

Estherville **The Wooden Thimble, 4 North Sixteenth St.** **712-362-2561** **See ad #10, page 178**

Estherville **Homespun Quilt Shop, 202 Central Ave.** **712-362-5100** **See ad #9, page 178**

Exira **Log Cabin Quilting, 111 W. Washington** **712-268-2487** **See ad #81, page 189**

Fairfield **CR Quilts, 2255 Hwy. 1 S.** **641-469-4534** **See ad #66, page 186**

Forest City **The Quilted Forest, 205 N. Clark St.** **641-585-2438** **See ad #18, page 179 & 206**

Fort Dodge **The Family Quilt Shop, 1200 A St. W** **515-576-0295** **See ad #13, page 178**

Garner **Country Threads, 2345 Palm Ave.** **641-923-3893** **See ad #17, page 178**

Greene **Dralle's Dept. Store, 122 E. Traer St. PO Box A** **641-816-4158** **See ad #35, page 181**

Greenfield **Fabric Creations, 111 SW Jackson St.** **641-343-7186** **See ad #70, page 187**

Harlan Stitchin' Tree Quilts, 616 Market St 712-755-3655

Hiawatha **Nolting's Manufacturing, Inc., 1265 Hawkeye** **319-378-0999** **See ad #39, page 182**

Hills **Inspirations, 120 Main St** **319-679-2207** **See ad #57, page 185**

Independence **Quilter's Quarters, 213 First St E** **319-334-4443** **See ad #32, page 181**

Independence **Vineyard Gift & Quilt Shoppe, 915 First St. W.** **319-334-2211** **See ad #33, page 181**

Indianola The Stitching Place, 127 N Buxtun 515-961-5162

Iowa City Home Etc Workshop, 207 N. Linn St. 319-337-4775

Iowa City Textiles Inc., 109 S. Dubuque St. 319-339-0410

Iowa Falls Iowa Falls Sewing Machine, 520 Washington 641-648-2379

Jesup **Merry's Stitchins, 1923 Baker Rd.** **319-827-6703** **See ad #34, page 181**

Jewell Prairie Rose Quilts & Bernina Too, 629 Main 515-827-6151

Kalona **Kalona Quilt & Textile Museum, 515 D Ave.** **319-656-3232** **See ad #61, page 186**

Kalona **Woodin Wheel Antiques & Gifts, 515 B Ave.** **319-656-2240** **See ad #63, page 186**

Kalona **Stitch 'n Sew Cottage, 207 4th St.** **319-656-2923** **See ad #60, page 186**

Kalona **Willow Creek Quilting & Gifts, 418 B Ave.** **319-656-3939** **See ad #62, page 186**

Kensett Heart & Sew Quilts, 908 Maple St. 641-845-2234

Keokuk Quilt 'N Etc., 300 Main St. #620 319-524-1327

Kirkville Patchwork Peddlers Post, 207 McCarroll St. 641-777-0279

Lake City **Towne Square Quilt Shoppe, 103 E. Main St.** **712-464-7477** **See ad #1, page 177**

Lamont Quilter's Quarters, 3290 150th St.

Le Claire **Expressions In Threads, 208 S Cody Rd.** **563-289-1447** **See ad #46, page 183**

Lemars Unique Fabric, 22 Plymouth St. SW 712-546-7464

Lucas **Quilt With Us, 100 E. Front St.** **641-766-6486** **See ad #67, page 186**

Mallard **The Quilter's Portable, 607 Inman** **712-425-3478** **See ad #11, page 178**

Manchester **The Quiltmaker's Shoppe, 110 E. Main St.**
563-927-8017 **See ad #31, page 181**

Maquoketa **Hermes Auto & Upholstery Inc, 1325 E. Platte**
563-652-2279 **See ad #44, page 183**

Marion **Connie's Quilt Shop, 785 Eighth Ave.**
319-373-9455 **See ad #41, page 182**

Marion **"The Cottage Rose" A Quilt Shop, 1048 7th Ave.**
319-377-1482 **See ad #42, page 182**

Mason City **Saintley Stitches 2, 1631 - 4th SW #115**
641-423-5176 **See ad #19, page 179**

Monona Suhdron Fabrics, 120 W. Center St. 563-539-2135

Montezuma 3 sisters Fabrics & Fashions, 305 E Main St 641-623-5640

Moravia **Shops at Granny's House, 2797 600th Ave.**
641-724-3131 **See ad #54, page 184**

Mt. Pleasant **Quilter's Paradise, 120 N. Main St.**
319-385-1749 **See ad #59, page 185**

Muscatine **The Cotton Shop, 331 East 2nd St.**
563-262-5709 **See ad #58, page 185**

Muscatine Neal's Vacuum & Sewing Center, 309 E. 2nd. St. 563-263-4543

Nevada **Block Party Studios Quilt Shop, 1503 West K**
513-382-3150 **See ad #74, page 188**

New Hampton **Quilter's Window, 101 E. Main St.**
641-394-6900 **See ad #20, page 179**

Shellsburg **My Tyme Creations, 115 Main St.**
319-540-6243 **See ad #38, page 182**

Sioux Center **Roelof's Store, 24 3rd St. NW**
712-722-2611 **See ad #6, page 177**

Sioux City **Heart in Hand Dry Goods, 3011 Hamilton Blvd.**
712-258-3161 **See ad #3, page 177**

South Amana **Fern Hill Gifts & Quilts, 103 220th Trail**
319-622-3627 **See ad #51, page 184**

Spencer **Quilts On Grand, 211 Grand Ave.**
712-262-2738 **See ad #7, page 177**

Spirit Lake **Quilt 'n' Stitches, 816 Lake St.**
712-336-2708 **See ad #8, page 177**

St. Ansgar **Saintly Stitches, LLC, 308 W. St. 4th St.**
641-736-2300 **See ad #22, page 179**

St. Olaf Country Calico Fabrics, 19035 Depot Rd. 563-783-2495

Storm Lake **Inspired by Time Quilts, 516 Lake Ave.**
712-213-1100 **See ad #4, page 177**

Strawberry Point Keppler Krafts, 35536 Hwy. 13 N 563-933-2310

Tipton **The Fabric Stasher, 505 E.Cedar St.**
563-432-6461 **See ad #48, page 184**

Volga Old Stone School Quilts & Tea l, 2077 Bell Rd. 563-767-4011

Walnut **Olde Tyme Quilting, 215 Antique City Drive**
712-784-3653 **See ad #80, page 189**

New Hampton Material Magic, 22 E. Main St. 641-394-2461

Newton **Cornerstone Quilts, 426 1st Ave. East**
641-792-6274 **See ad #72, page 187**

North Liberty **Common Threads, 480 W. Zeller St**
319-626-3160 **See ad #49, page 184**

Norwalk Harvest Table, 4837 R 57 Hwy. 515-981-4307

Oelwein **Lou Ann's Quilt Garden & Retreat**
21 E. Charles St.
319-283-5165 **See ad #27, page 180**

Onawa Susie's Quilts-N-More, 904 Iowa Ave. 712-423-9625

Osage **Debbie's Quilt Shop, 605 Main St.**
641-732-1474 **See ad #21, page 179**

Osceola Robinson's True Value, 127 S. Main 6413422154

Panora Quilting Market, 4926 Lynn Dr 641-755-4151

Pella **Vande Lune Fabrics, 701 Franklin St.**
641-628-3350 **See ad #53, page 184**

Pocahontas **Quilting on Main, 229 N. Main**
712-335-3969 **See ad #12, page 178**

Postville **Forest Mills Quilt Shop, 650 Forest Mills Rd.**
563-568-3807 **See ad #25, page 180**

Sac City Oak Door Fabrics, 107 N. 5th St. 712-662-4160

Sergeant Bluff **My Quilt Shop, 206 1st St.**
712-943-9486 **See ad #2, page 177**

Walnut **DR's Kalico Krafts, 206 Antique City Dr.**
712-784-3865 **See ad #79, page 189**

Waukon **Country Stitchin', 915 Hwy. 76 S**
563-535-7376 **See ad #23, page 180**

Waverly **The Moose Patch, 205 E. Bremer Ave.**
319-352-5040 **See ad #36, page 181**

Waverly Fiberworks, 108 E. Bremer Ave. 319-352-5464

Webster City **Gingerbread House, 309 Bank St.**
515-832-1492 **See ad #14, page 178**

West Burlington **The Quilting Corner, 123 Broadway St**
319-752-4288 **See ad #64, page 186**

West Burlington Sandi's Sewing Connection, 219 W. Mt. Pleasant 319-752-2226

West Des Moines **The Quilt Block, 325 5th St.**
515-255-1010 **See ad #71, page 187**

West Union **One Block Over, 322 E. Main St.**
563-422-3822 **See ad #26, page 180**

Wever **Harvest Moon Quilt Company, 1873 345th Ave.**
319-470-8670 **See ad #65, page 186**

Williamsburg **The Woolen Needle, 225 W. Welsh St.**
319-668-2642 **See ad #56, page 185**

Williamsburg **Rainbows and Calico Things, 2811 240th St.**
319-668-1977 **See ad #55, page 185**

Winterset Fons & Porter Quilt Supply, 54 Court 515-462-5416

Winterset Ben Franklin, 72 W. Court 515-462-2062

Iowa Quilt Shows

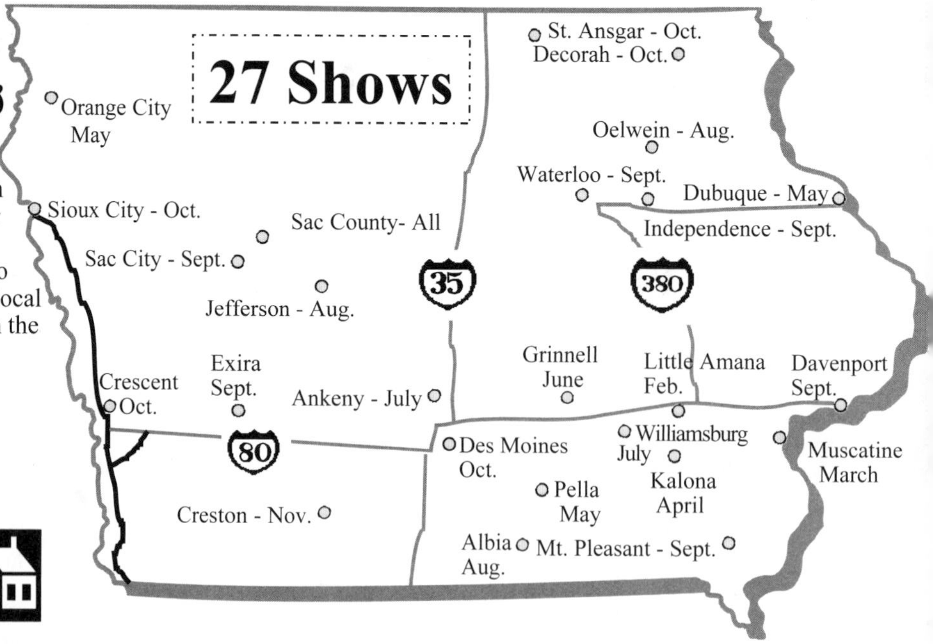

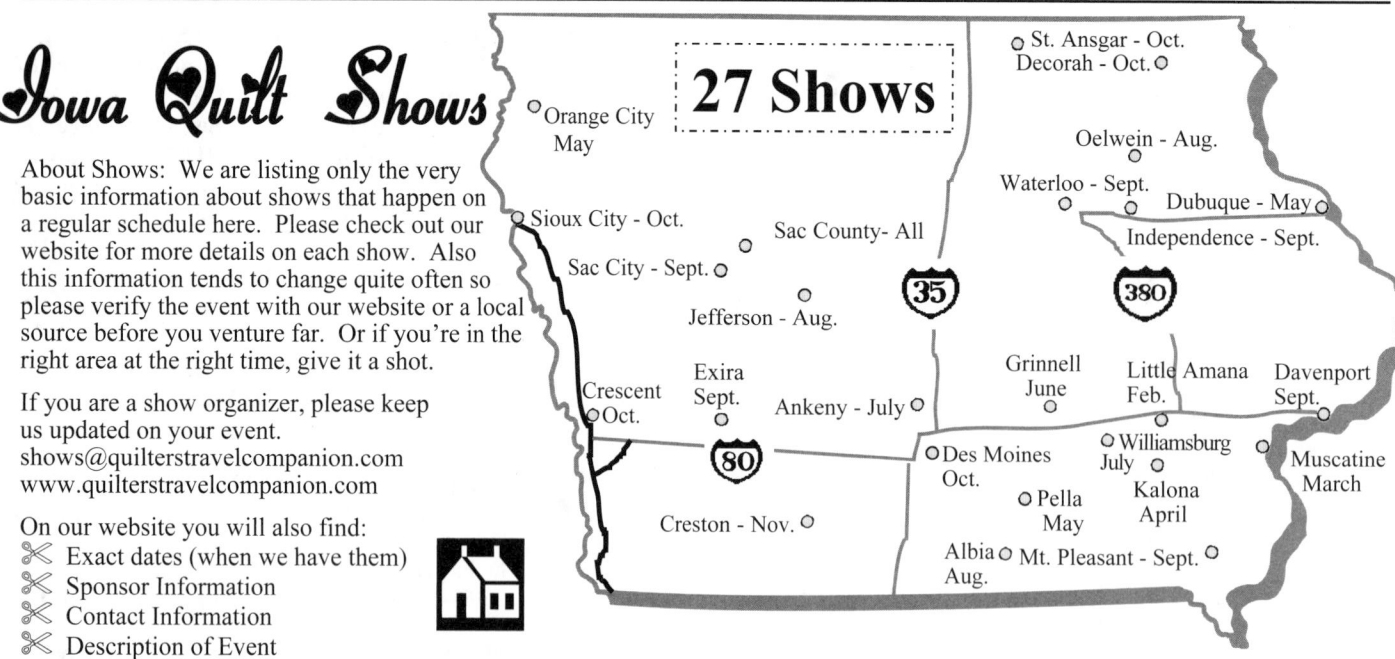

About Shows: We are listing only the very basic information about shows that happen on a regular schedule here. Please check out our website for more details on each show. Also this information tends to change quite often so please verify the event with our website or a local source before you venture far. Or if you're in the right area at the right time, give it a shot.

If you are a show organizer, please keep us updated on your event.
shows@quilterstravelcompanion.com
www.quilterstravelcompanion.com

On our website you will also find:

- Exact dates (when we have them)
- Sponsor Information
- Contact Information
- Description of Event
- Events happening on a one-time basis

Month	City	Schedule	Show	Location with address
All Year				
	Sac County	Annual, All Year Barn Quilts	Sac County	
February				
	Little Amana	Annual, Sun & Mon of Presidents Weekend	I-80 Quilt Shoppers Shopping Spree	Clarion Inn Exit 225 off I - 80
March				
	Muscatine	Odd Years, 2nd Fri & Sat in March	Muscatine Melon Patchers Quilt Show	First Baptist Church, 3003 Mulberry Ave.
April				
	Kalona	Annual, last Fri & Sat of April	Kalona Quilt Show & Sale	Kalona Community Center, Corner of 6th & D St.
May				
	Pella	Annual, 1st full Wed-Sat in May	Pella Area Quilters Guild Quilt Show	Pella Opera House, 611 Franklin St.
	Dubuque	Even Years, late May	Cable Car Quilters Guild Show	Dubuque County Fair Grounds, 14583 Old Hwy. Rd.
	Orange City	Annual, 2nd week of May	Stash Busters	Northwestern College - Bultman Center, 101 7th St. SW
June				
	Grinnell	Odd Years, usually 2nd Fri & Sat in June	Jewel Box Quilters Show	Grinnell Middle School, 132 East St.
July				
	Williamsburg	Odd Years, around the 4th of July	Iowa County Heartland Quilters Show	St. Mary's Catholic Comm Ctr, Exit 220 S off I-80
	Ankeny	Annual, 2nd Fri & Sat in July	Quiltfest	Faith Baptist Bible College, 1900 NW 4th St.
August				
	Albia	Annual, 3rd weekend in August	Albia Restoration Days Quilt Show	Trinity United Methodist Church, 1225 A Ave. E
	Oelwein	Annual, 3rd weekend in August	Creative Cut-Ups Open Quilt Show	Oelwein Community Plaza, 25 W. Charles St.
	Jefferson	Odd Years, last weekend in August	Cross County Quilters Show	Green County Community Center, 203 W. Harrison St.
September				
	Independence	Odd Years, 3rd weekend in September	It's All About Quilts	Falcon Center, 1305 5th Ave3. NE (Hwy. 150N)
	Sioux City	Odd Years, September or October	Siouxland Samplers Quilt Guild Show	Sioux City Convention Center, 801 4th
	Waterloo	Even Years, 3rd Fri & Sat in September	Keepsake Quilt Guild Show	Waterloo Center for the Arts, 225 Commercial St.
	Davenport	Even Years, last Fri & Sat of September	Mississippi Valley Quilters Guild Show	Mississippi Valley Fairgrounds, 2815 W. Locust St.
	Exira	Annual, last Sat. of September	Exira Community Fall Festival	Recreation Center, 106 N. Jefferson St.
	Mt. Pleasant	Odd Years, Late September	Mt. Pleasant Quilt Show	Iowa Wesleyan College, 601 W. Main St.
	Sac City	Odd Years, last weekend of September	Sac County Quilt-A-Fair	Sac County Fairgrounds, 416 Park Ave.
October				
	Crescent	Annual, Columbus Day Weekend	Crescent Fall Festival Quilt Show	Crescent Elementary School, 401 W. Welch
	Des Moines	Annual, 2nd weekend in October	Des Moines Area Quilters Guild Show	Des Moines Iowa Events Center
	Decorah	Even Years, 3rd weekend in October	Northeast Iowa Quilters Guild Show	Decorah Middle School, 405 Winnebago St.
	Des Moines	Annual, last weekend in October	Metropolitan Women's Expo	Iowa Events Center Hy-Vee Hall C, 730 3rd St.
	Des Moines	Annual, 2nd weekend in October	AQS Quilt Expo	Iowa Events Center, 730 3rd St.
	St. Ansgar	Annual, last Saturday of October	Quilt Extravaganza	All Over Town
November				
	Creston	Annual, first Thur - Sat after Thanksgiving	Deck the Halls Quilt Show	American Home Design Center (restored Power Plant), 101 N. Walnut St.

HINGELEY ROAD QUILT SHOP · FLOODWOOD, MN

HINGELEY ROAD Quilt Shop

Store Hours:
MON-FRI 10-5, SAT 9-4

Home of:
HINGELEY ROAD QUILT DESIGNS

.........PATTERNS

BOOKS..................

Only the Best: Top Quality, Quilt Shop Only Quilt Fabric

- Over 6,000 bolts, including all the Moda/Holly Taylor Groups and **Minnesota Charms Hoffman Exclusive Batiks**
- Huge selection of charms, bali pops, jelly rolls, layer cakes, turnovers and custom cuts/combinations.
- Northwoods Room dedicated to Northwoods Themed Fabrics
- Year-round selection of Holiday fabrics (Christmas, Halloween), 100's of baby prints and textures. 100's of northwoods prints in the Northwoods Room. Over 1,000 batiks and over 1,000 flannels.
- All products available with our **full-service online shopping cart!**

MinnesotaCharms.com Quilt Show 1st weekend of Oct. 2010
Visit our website for details. www.MinnesotaCharms.com

Store Map:
HOW TO FIND US...

Conveniently located right on Hwy 2 - 4 miles East of Floodwood, MN

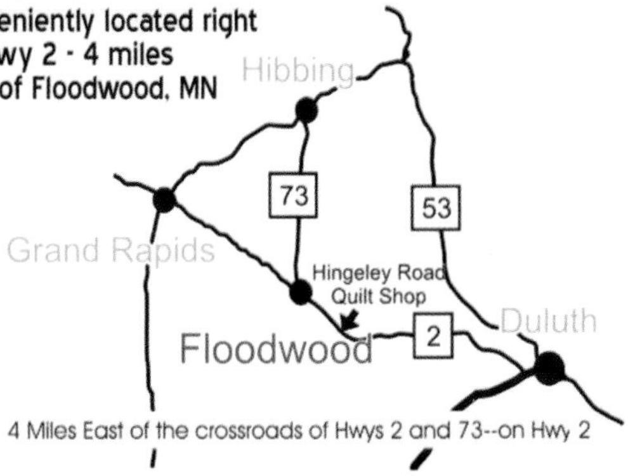

HOME OF 10,000 Charms & Hingeley Road Quilt Designs!
VISIT OUR WEBSITE: *MinnesotaCharms.com*
PARTICIPATING SHOP quiltminnesota.com

11284 HWY 2 · Floodwood, MN · 55736
4 Miles East of the HWY 2/73 Crossroads · 218-476-3139

www.HingeleyRoadQuiltShop.com
www.MinnesotaCharms.com

6 miles from Canadian Border

Dreamcrafters Quilt Shop

Akwesasne, NY

Located at the Wolf Pack Gift Shop on Rte. 37
1422 State Route 37, Hogansburg, NY 13655
(518) 358-4285 Owner: Dyan Swamp
E-Mail: dreamquilt@aol.com

Store Hours
Mon - Fri
9am - 7pm
Sat & Sun
10am - 6pm

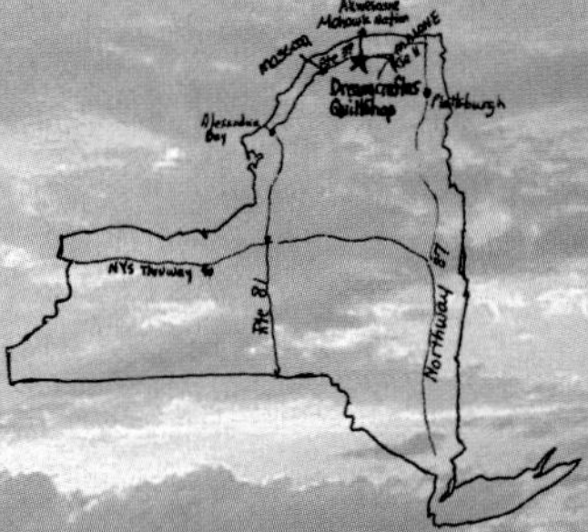

LARGEST QUILT SHOP IN NORTHERN NY SUPPLIES FOR ALL YOUR "DREAM" CREATIONS

- 6000+ Bolts of 100% Cottons, Hoffman, Kaufman, Batiks
- Notions: Batting, Thread & Stencils
- Huge Selection of Books & Patterns.
- Quilts For Sale
- Fat Quarters Galore!!!
- Yard Cuts & 1/2 Yard Cuts
- Kits
- Quilter's Gifts
- All purchases are tax-free

GINGER'S NEEDLEWORKS & QUILTING

www.quiltknit.com

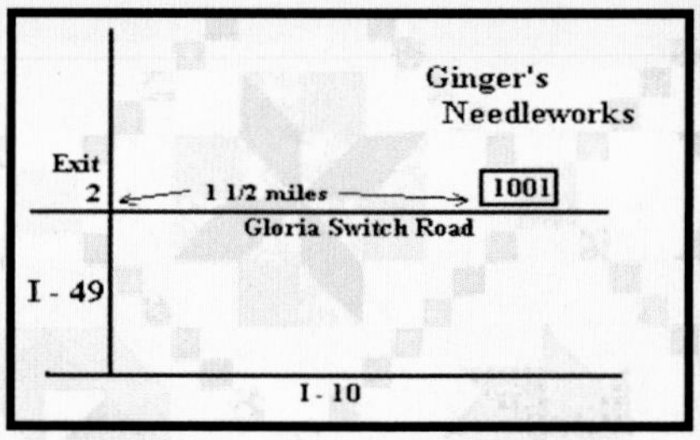

Store Hours: Monday - Friday 9 - 4

1001 East Gloria Switch Road 70507 (337) 232-7847

Owner: Ginger Moore Est:1985 2400 sq.ft.

9000 Bolts of Fabrics
Specializing in Civil War and 1930's Reproductions and Oriental Fabrics. We also have a large selection of Novelty Prints.
Lots of Notions, Patterns, and Books.

Fabric & Quilting Supplies!

Make <u>www.quiltknit.com</u> your one-stop online quilt store for all your quilting fabrics, notions, books and patterns. Secure online ordering and fast service.

Lafayette, LA

Stitch-N-Frame

Established 1983

A Quilter's Paradise

The largest quilting shop in Mississippi makes it worth your trip to come to Vicksburg!

Come visit us in our new 6000 sq. ft. location.

Owners Kay & Mark Elliot invite you to stop by and take a test drive on any or all of the Gammill longarm machines, you'll be glad you did!

We carry a full line of long arm supplies in addition to Jim Shore collectables and Laurel Burch fashion accessories. All the major fabric manufacturers are represented among our 10,000 bolts of 100% cotton fabrics. We have a large selection of 30's Reproductions and Civil War Collections, along with patterns, kits, Blocks of the Month, notions and ideas galore!

Custom machine quilting, machine sales and service; quilting classes are available as well as quilting machine time rental. Join the on-line newsletter to learn about our Thursday Specials.

Husbands, come play on our machines or enjoy our cozy husband waiting area.

Gammill® QUILTING SYSTEMS

Statler Stitcher

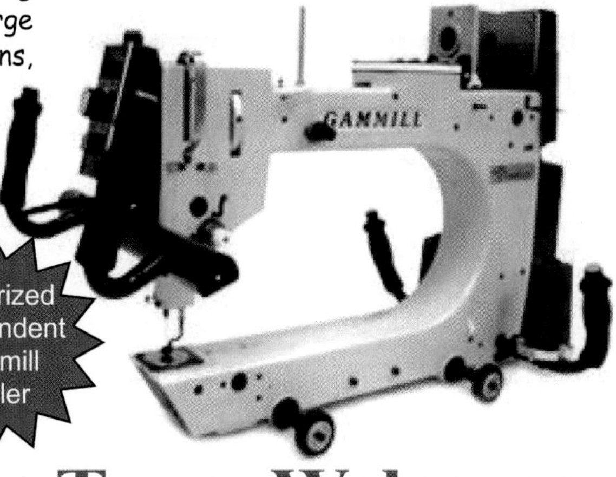

Authorized Independent Gammill Dealer

Bus Tours Welcome

Vicksburg, MS

Mon - Sat 9 - 5:30

31 Willow Creek Dr.
Vicksburg, MS 39183
Toll Free: (877) 634-1462
Phone: (601) 634-0243
Fax: (601) 634-0287
stitch-n-frame@att.net

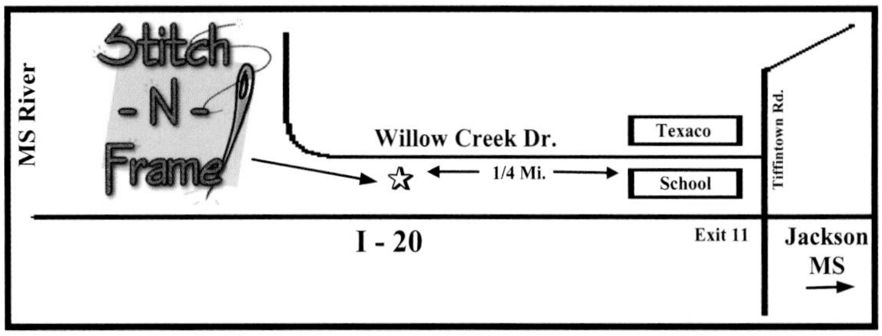

www.stitch-n-frame.net

Chester, VT

Country Treasures

Fabric • Quilts • Gifts • Books

One of the premier quilt shops in New England!

Stocked with over **8,000 BOLTS** of fabric, including flannels and brushed homespuns

Fat quarters bundles, color coordinated or complete lines

Great selection of books and patterns!

Quilt classes for every skill level

(802)875-4377
12 Common St.,
Chester, VT 05143

vermontquilting.com
sue@vermontquilting.com

Open: Monday ~ Saturday 10am - 5pm • Sunday 12pm - 4pm • Closed in April

El Cajon, CA

15 minutes from downtown San Diego

Cozy Quilt Shop and SewCozy Sewing Center

Hours:
Mon-Sat 9:30-5:30
Thur til 6:30
Sun: noon – 4

2940 Jamacha Rd, Ste H, El Cajon, CA 92019
619-670-0652 cozyquilt.com

Home of the Strip Club and *Strip Clubbing* and publishers of Cozy Quilt Designs original patterns, books and tools!

With 4,500 square feet of brightly lit space, we offer over 3,000 bolts of 100% cotton fabric and a Bernina creative sewing center. We are a Must See in San Diego.

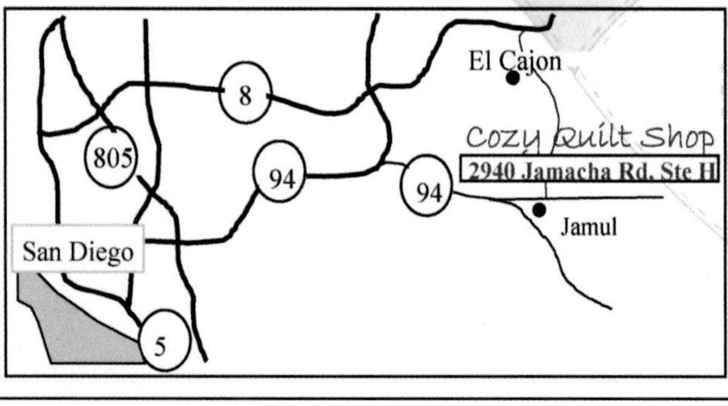

Directions

From San Diego: 94 East. Stay on 94 until it turns from freeway to city street (Do not be tempted to take 125 or turn right at Jamacha Blvd). Left at the stop light of Cuyamaca College Drive West. (Target, TGI Fridays and Staples will be on your right.) Left into parking lot. Next to Eroma Day Spa.

From East County: I-8 to Second Street exit. Go South. Second Street Turns into Jamacha Rd. We are about 6 miles from the freeway on your right.

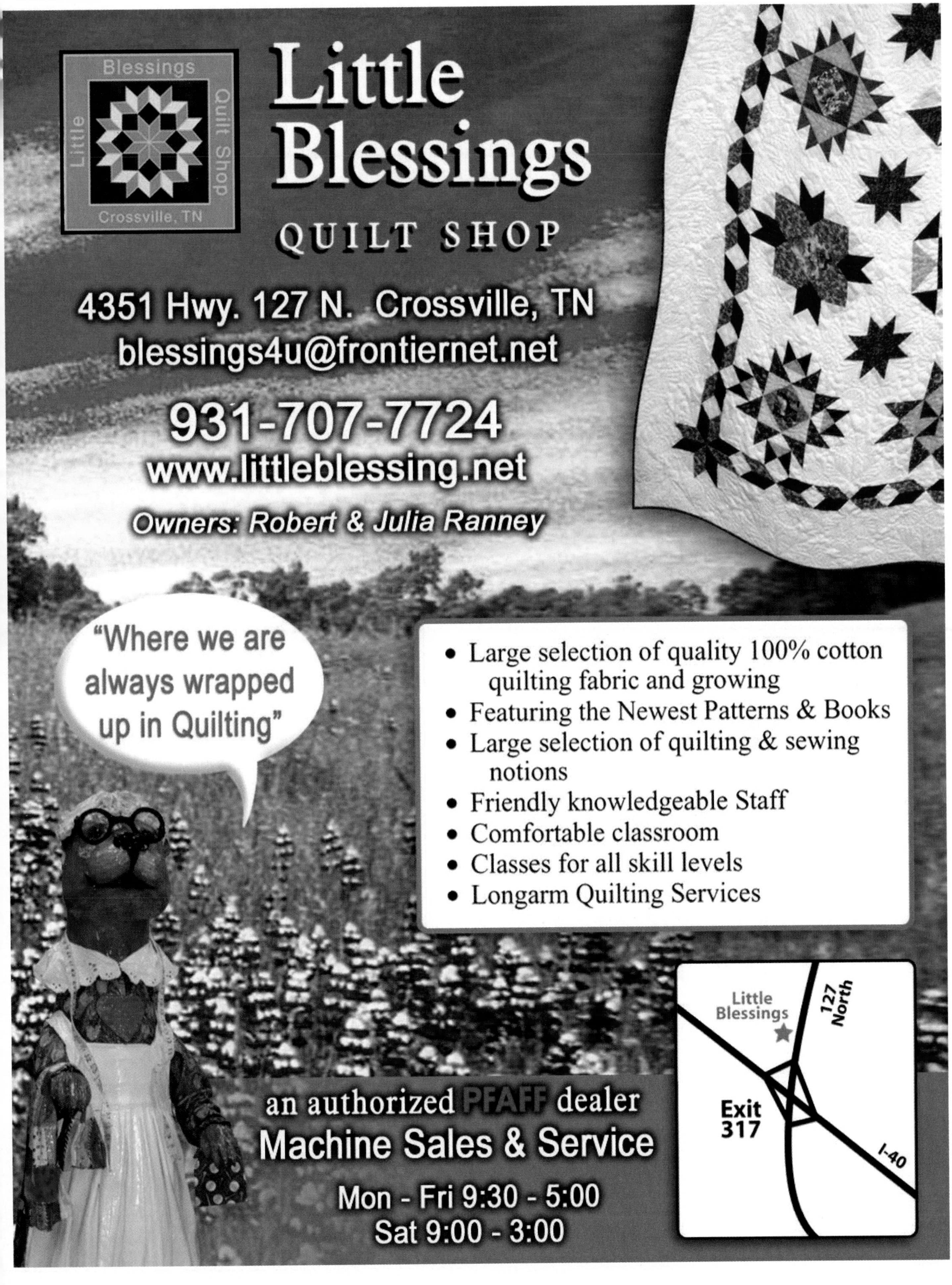

Blessings
Little
Quilt Shop
Crossville, TN
Little Blessings
QUILT SHOP
4351 Hwy. 127 N. Crossville, TN
blessings4u@frontiernet.net
931-707-7724
www.littleblessing.net
Owners: Robert & Julia Ranney
"Where we are always wrapped up in Quilting"
• Large selection of quality 100% cotton quilting fabric and growing
• Featuring the Newest Patterns & Books
• Large selection of quilting & sewing notions
• Friendly knowledgeable Staff
• Comfortable classroom
• Classes for all skill levels
• Longarm Quilting Services
Little Blessings
127 North
Exit 317
I-40
an authorized PFAFF dealer
Machine Sales & Service
Mon - Fri 9:30 - 5:00
Sat 9:00 - 3:00

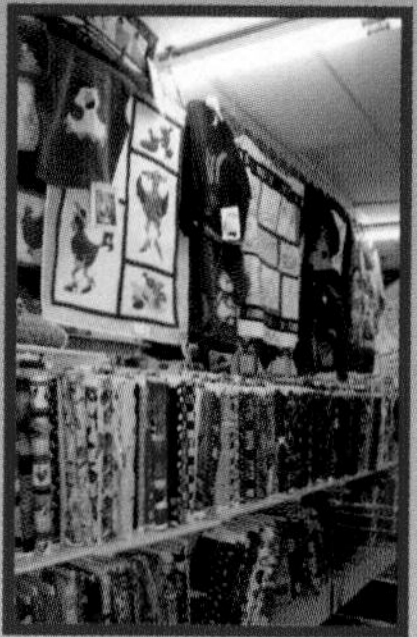

Quilts & Quilts

"It's like a Quilt Show everyday!"

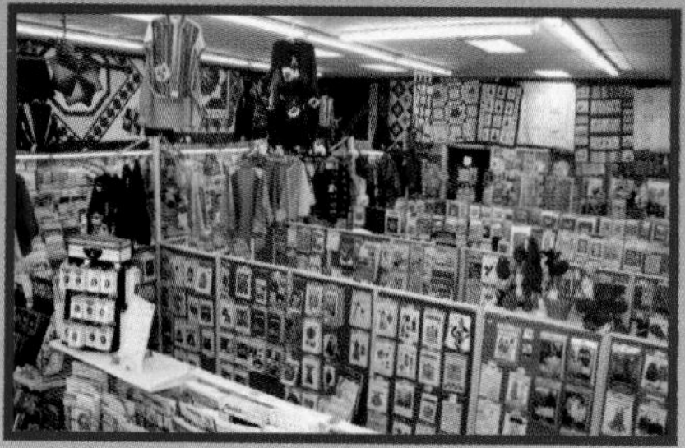

Branson, MO

1137 West Hwy. 76
65616
in Branson Heights Shopping Ctr.
(417) 334-3243
Owner: Marlys Michaelson
Est: 1981 8,000 sq.ft.

March - December
9 - 6 Mon - Sat 10 - 5 Sun
January & February
9 - 5 Mon - Sat Closed Sun
* hours may vary

- 10,000 Bolts of Fabric to choose from and our color pro's are always happy to help!
- Over 2,000 Book Titles
- Quilted Clothing, Runners, Purses, Quilts, Embroidery, Quilting Notions & more.

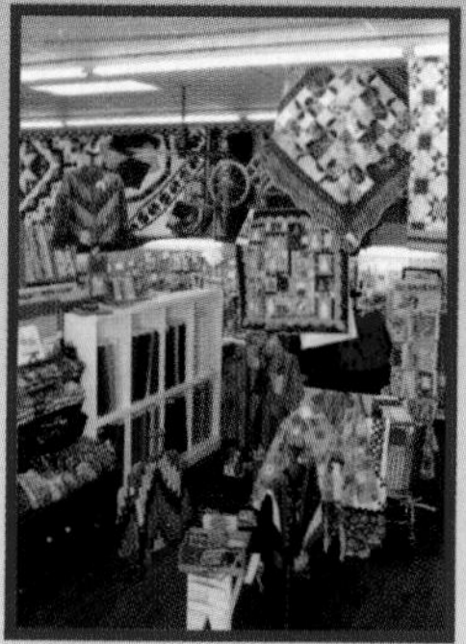

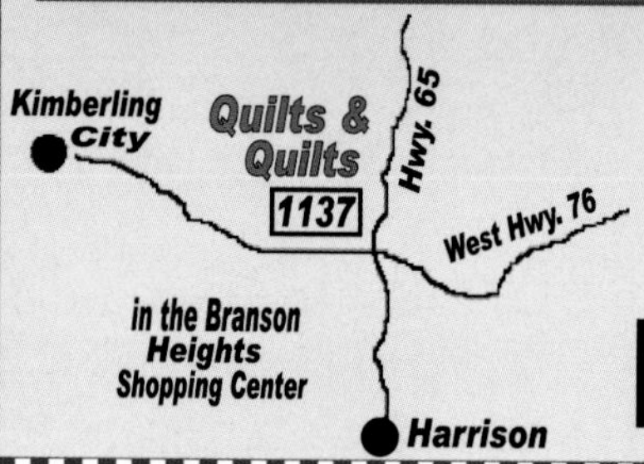

SAMPLES, SAMPLES, SAMPLES!
Inspiring Quilters everyday!

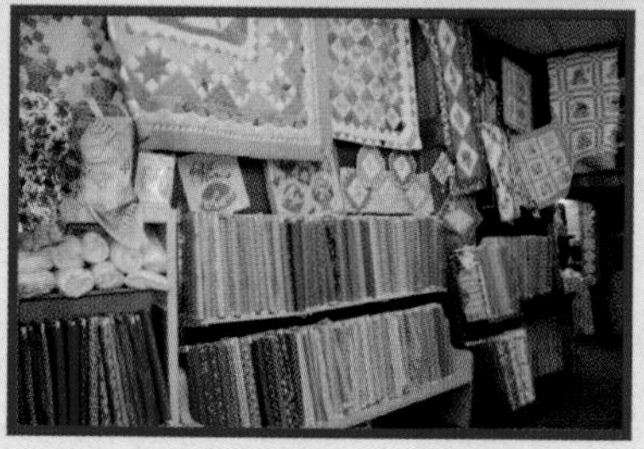

www.quiltsandquilts.com

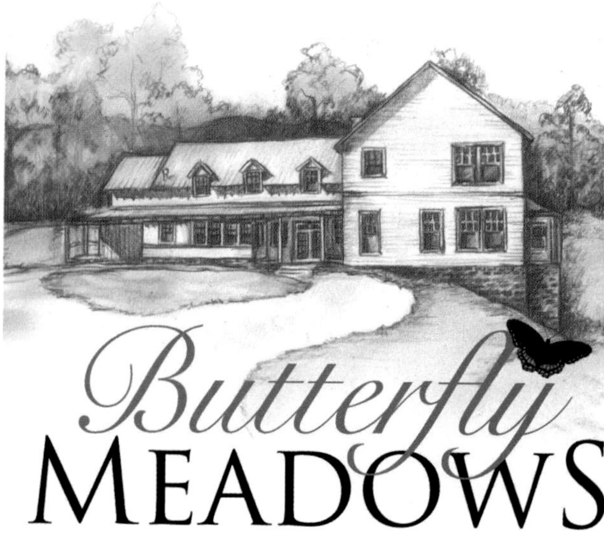

Butterfly MEADOWS
INN & FARM

We know quilters and have created a special place for you. Come relax at Butterfly Meadows Inn & Farm. We offer overnight accommodations in seven comfortable rooms and suites for you and your friends. Our spacious gathering rooms are ideal for quilting and enjoying the company of fellow quilters. Our Swallowtail room, with 1100 square feet, will be set up for your group with individual sewing tables and chairs, ironing and cutting stations. Enjoy scrumptious, home-cooked meals.

With the look and charm of a 100 year old farmhouse, surrounded by woods and meadows, you can step back in time to a simpler way of life and enjoy a special "piece-ful" retreat. Please call 877-671-4594 or email relax@butterflymeadowsinn.com to book your group stay *(up to 22 guests)*. Check our website, butterflymeadowsinn.com for our open retreats and specials.

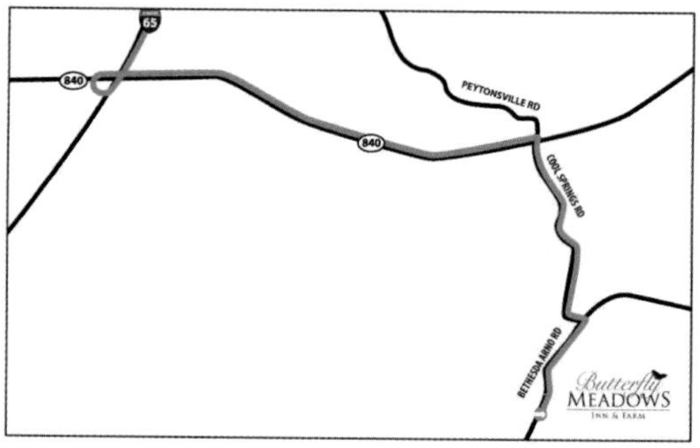

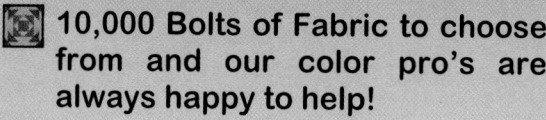

6775 Bethesda Arno Road, Franklin, Tennessee 37179
877-671-4594 ~ relax@butterflymeadowsinn.com
www.butterflymeadowsinn.com

Discover Quilting in the Last Frontier!

Downtown Anchorage on G Street between 4th & 5th Avenue

Open Daily 11 – 6
May – September

- Alaska-Themed Fabrics & Quilt Kits
- Fabrics by Local Artists, including Barbara Lavallee, Jon Van Zyle, & Cindy Shake
- A Wide Selection of Batiks
- Gifts for the Quilter, Handcrafted in Alaska
- Quilting & Cross-Stitch Patterns by Local Artisans
- Yarns, Locally Hand-Dyed

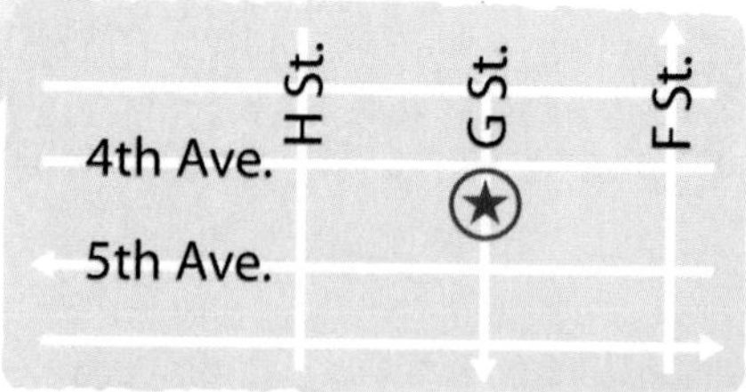

The Quilted Raven
650 West 4th Avenue
Anchorage, Alaska 99501
907.278.3521
www.quiltedravenalaska.com

The Quilted Raven

Anchorage, AK

Suzy's Quilt Shop

111 N. 6th Street, Garland, Texas 75040 972-272-8180
www.suzysquilts.com suzysquilts@aol.com

You are the Heart of our Business

Store Hours:
Mon-Fri 9:30am-5:00pm
Saturday 9:30am-4:00pm

Owner: Suzanne Cook
Est 1989 4200 sq ft.

Classes Are Fun!
See our Class Schedule on our website. www.suzysquilts.com Color Pictures of each class. Sign up by phone. Plan your trip to be here for one of our classes.

"The road to Suzy's is never long."

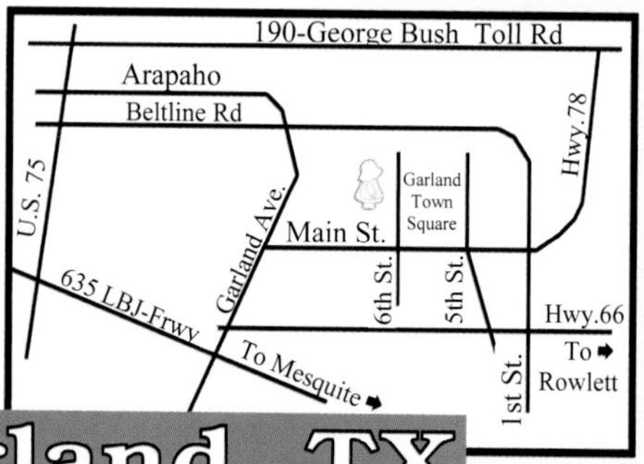

Patterns * Supplies * Books * Fabrics
Kits * Classes * Gifts * Original Patterns
Lots of Samples * 1st Sat Samplers

Clubs
Thimbleberries, 20-30's, Appliqué Lovers, Tea Party, Floss & Chocolate, Dear Jane, Scrap Swap, and Red-work/Embroidery, & Fat (hind) Quarter.

Mondays Are Fun
Every Monday Is Sit-n-Sew
Bring Your Project
Bring a Friend

Garland, TX

Deep in the *Square* of Texas!

The Revolutionary Quilting System Used by Thousands is Available in Historic Fredericksburg, Texas.

FREDERICKSBURG IS NESTLED IN THE HEART OF RICH TEXAS HISTORY *and* DISTINCTIVE CULTURE. Located in the Texas hill country–65 miles northwest of San Antonio and 70 miles west of Austin–it's the perfect setting for a quilter's paradise.

The Fredericksburg Pie Company is home to many Square in a Square™ quilting products and is located one block off Fredericksburg's renowned main street: 3.5 miles of unique shops, century-old homes, and days of enjoyment.

Jodi Barrows has developed a reputation in the quilting world of weaving her love of history into an extensive collection of custom fabric designs, as well as her historical novels. Fredericksburg is the perfect setting to experience this unique blend of quilting and history.

MEET JODI IN PERSON!

Don't miss out on your opportunity to meet Jodi Barrows in person at **The Fredericksburg Pie Company**!

Join us for book signings and lectures throughout the year. See Jodi's schedule at squareinasquare.com. We look forward to seeing you there!

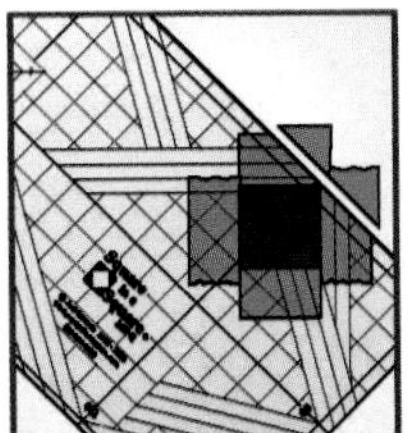

ONE SQUARE DOES IT ALL

The technique begins with a piece of fabric to which strips are attached, and then cut with a rotary cutter in a unique way. The results are entire blocks or parts of blocks quickly and accurately achieved. Learn more by watching videos on our website.

The Fredericksburg Pie Company
108 E. Austin Street
Fredericksburg, TX 78624
1 Block Off Main Street Between Adams & Llano
Parking in the rear
(830) 990-6992
Monday - Saturday: 10 am – 6 pm
Sunday: 11 am – 4 pm | *Closed Wednesday*

TOOLS, QUILTS, & PATTERNS

While in Fredericksburg, be sure to see the variety of products and quilts for sale at **The Fredericksburg Pie Company**, or visit squareinasquare.com.

SNS PUBLISHING (888) 624-6260 squareinasquare.com

Specialty Quilts

Jefferson City, MO

Monday - Friday
9:00 - 5:00
Saturday
10:00 - 2:00

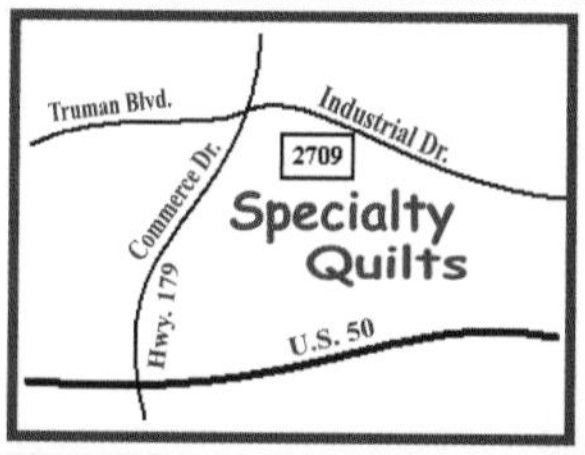

2709 D Industrial Dr.
(Rear Entrance from Metro Dr.)
Jefferson City 65109
573-761-7313
Owner:
Linda Foulk

www.specialtyquilts.com

Huge selection of Jelly Rolls, Honey Buns, Layer Cakes, Charms, Fat Quarter Bundles, Kits, Wide linings, embroidery blocks, etc.
Moda, Timeless Treasures, Benartex, Thimbleberries and much more. Books and patterns.
Custom Machine Quilting & Piecing Service.

Polka Dot pincushion inc.

4131 W. Streetsboro Rd. 44286
330-659-0233

A great place to find inspiration for your next sewing or quilting project. Choose from many kits, classes and workshops for all levels.
Sign up for our emails to receive news of special events and our newsletter.

Monday 12-5
Tuesday 10-5
Wednesday 10-5
Thursday 10-8
Friday 10-5
Saturday 10- 4
Sunday Closed

www.pdpincushion.com

Opened: 2005 3000 bolts
2450 square feet
Owner: Ronnie Rajkovich
ronnie@pdpincushion.com

Richfield, OH

Green River, WY

Keama's Quilts

Mon - Sat
9 - 6

Keama's Quilts proudly stocks 100% Cotton Fabrics, Books, Patterns, Batting, Notions, Threads, Classes, Quilting Services, and Much, Much More.
Come experience our Knowledgeable Assistance and Friendly Service. Gammill Rep.

Gammill Quilting Systems

(888) 875-5461
91 W. Flaming Gorge Way
Green River, WY 82935

Downtown Green River. Located on the main Business Route, we're very easy to find.

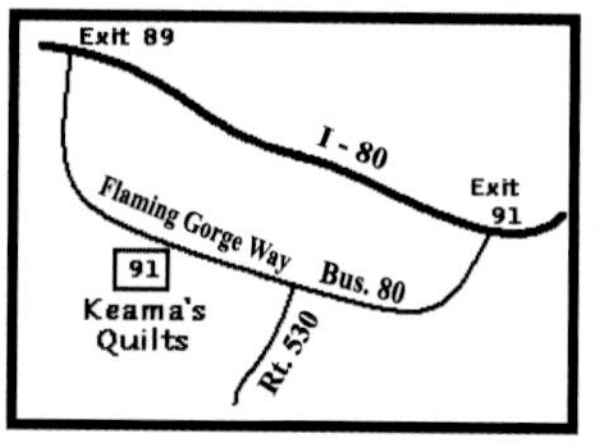

www.keamasquilts.com

Husqvarna VIKING

Appletree Quilting Center

www.AppletreeQuilting.com

- Super-Friendly, Professional Staff to help you! Over 350 years of combined sewing expertise!
- 5,000 square feet of Quilting Paradise - including 5000+ bolts. It's sew easy to pull a quilt at Appletree Quilting Center!
- Great selection of books, patterns, & notions.
- Heirloom sewing & smocking supplies.
- Classes, Classes, Classes! The largest selection of hands-on sewing classes in the Mid-Missouri area.
- Full line of quality built Husqvarna Viking sewing machines from Sweden. The same company that also builds Husqvarna chain saws!
- Open 7 days a week for your convenience.
- Lots of parking available. Buses and large groups are always welcome!

Directions to Our Shop:

Appletree Quilting Center is located in the heart of Missouri quilting country half way between St. Louis and Kansas City on **Interstate 70**. **Take exit #124** - Stadium Blvd. **Turn south on Stadium, then turn right on to Bernadette Dr.** (second stop light at Wendy's Restaurant). We are located in Bernadette Square, a shopping center on your right, just across from the Columbia Mall.

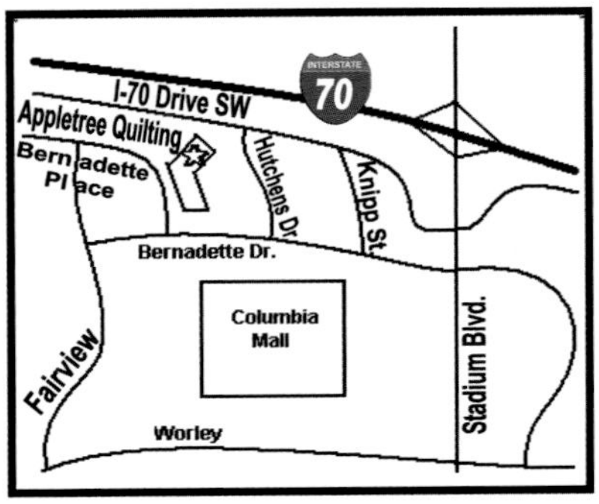

Appletree Quilting Center

2541 Bernadette Drive
Columbia, MO 65203
sewing@appletreequilting.com
(573) 446-2655 1-800-269-2655

HOURS: OPEN 7 Days a Week for Your Convenience!

10 – 5:30	Mon. – Thr.
10 – 5	Fri. & Sat.
1 – 4	Sunday

Established 1985
Millie & Floyd Kaiser, Owners

Quilted Treasures

A Fresh Look at Traditional Quilting

Est. 1998 • 4500 bolts
Owner: Mary Wilberg
Busses Welcome

Better Homes and Gardens Quilt Sampler FEATURED SHOP

QT Blogs
Pieces of Work
Sew Domestic
Classroom Chatter

Just 2.2 miles from Cabelas!

TO CABELAS FROM SHOP: Cross Hwy. 101 on 141st Ave. Right on Rogers Drive (near Walgreens). Left on South Diamond Lake Road. Right on George Weber Drive.

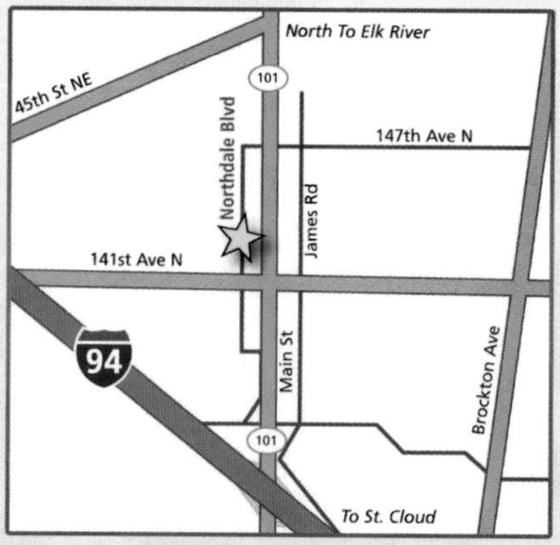

*We specialize in **quilt kits of all styles**, over 100 beautiful quilt samples, and inspirational displays throughout the shop*

Shop Hours:

M - F	10 - 5
Th	10 - 8
Sat	10 - 4
Sun	12 - 4

www.quiltedtreasures.net

Quilted Treasures of Rogers
14178 Northdale Blvd.,Rogers, MN 55374
763.428.1952
info@quiltedtreasures.net
www.quiltedtreasures.net

Rogers, MN

Sew Chic

I - 79
Exit 139

348 Meadowdale Rd. Fairmont, WV 26554
(877) 366-4135 or (304) 366-4135
Owner: Sue Henderson Est: 1996
Participant in Mountain Quilt Quest Shop Hop

- Over 2500 bolts of designer cottons
- Complete line of quilting supplies, books, patterns, and notions
- Huge thread assortment
- Machine Embroidery
- Year round classes
- Mail orders welcome
- Free newsletter online or by request
- Friendly, Knowledgeable Staff

BERNINA

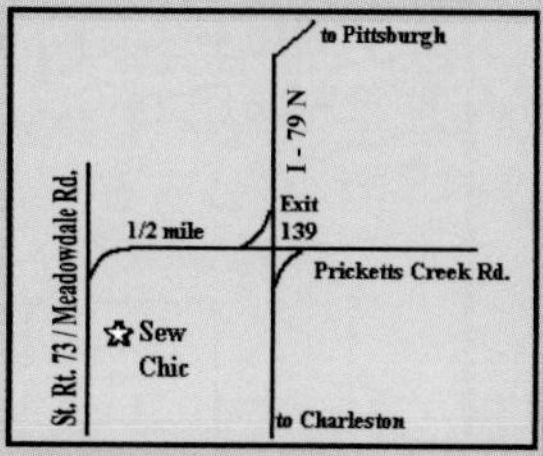

Fairmont, WV

Mon - Fri
10 - 6
Sat 10 - 2

www.sewchic.com

SewFlakes

fine quilt & fashion fabrics

www.sewflakesfabrics.com

- Quilt Fabric
- Fashion Fabric
- Pre-Cuts
- Block of the Months
- Patterns
- Kits
- Classes
- Events
- BERNINA

BERNINA

Christine Fornell
Est: 2004

106 S. Main
Broken Arrow, OK
918-251-7094
sewflakes@inbox.com

Mon- Fri 10 - 5
Thur til 8 Sat 10 - 4

We strive to meet your sewing needs no matter your project preference. We offer over 3,000 bolts of high quality, 100% cotton, quilting fabrics and also silks, wools, lycras, rayons, bamboo knits, faux furs, velvets and much more.

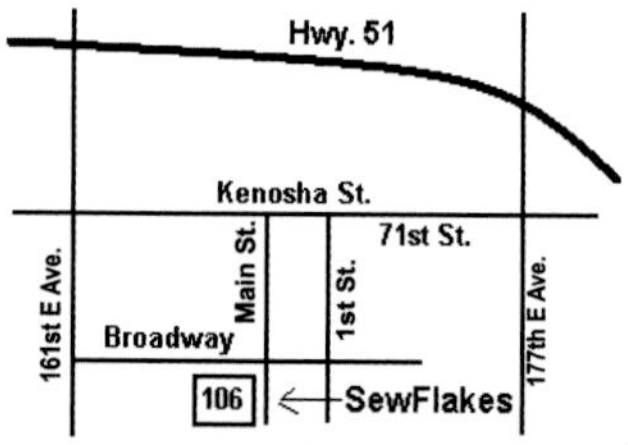

Broken Arrow, OK

olive juice Quilts LLC

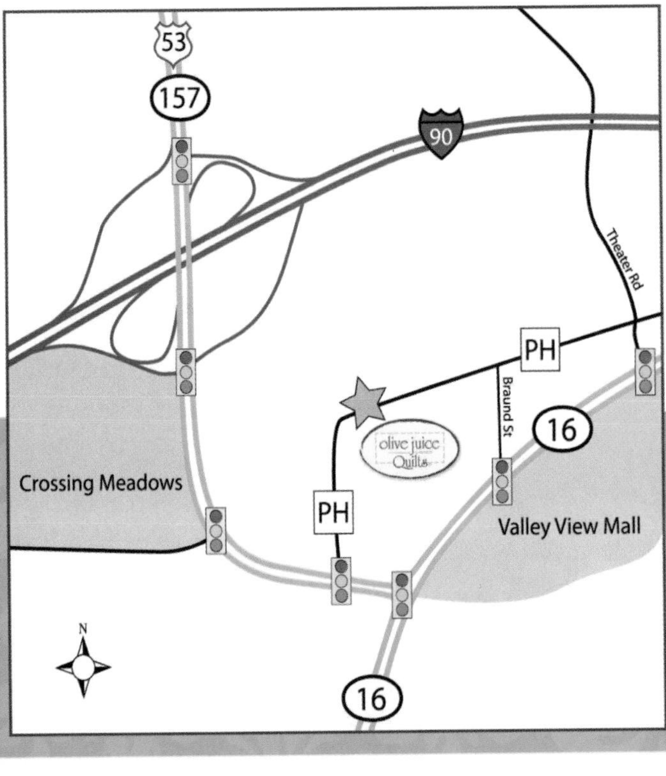

BERNINA

300 Book Titles • Notions
4,000 Bolts of Fabric
Arrow Cabinets • Horn Cabinets
Classes • Clubs • Newsletters

All Model Machine Repair
with 90 day guarantee

1258 County Road PH
Onalaska, WI 54650
(608) 782-3257
www.olivejuicequilts.com

mon - sat 10 - 5 | thurs 10 - 8 | sun 12 - 4

the Quilted Forest

205 North Clark, Forest City, IA 50436
Phone: 641-585-2438 or 877-985-2438
Hours: Monday-Friday: 10 a.m. to 5 p.m.
Saturday: 10 a.m. to 4 p.m.
www.thequiltedforest.com

Owner:
Shelley Robson
Established:
1998

Our friendly, spacious shop is a delight to quilters and knitters. We have a diverse selection of fine quality fabrics, notions, books and yarns. Pieced Tree Patterns is our original pattern line featuring a variety of projects. www.piecedtreepatterns.com

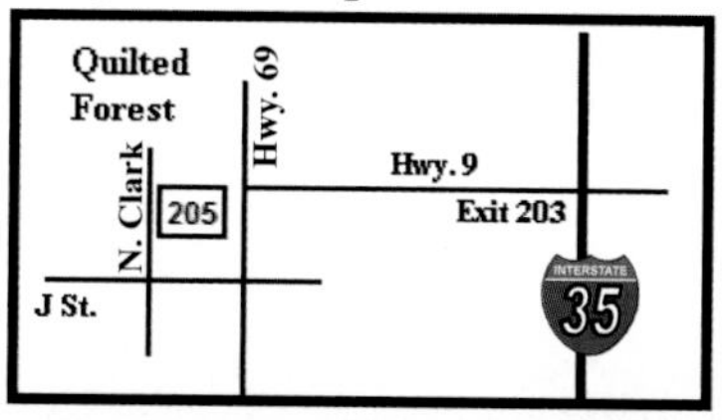

Forest City, IA

1st QUALITY FABRICS IN THE HEART OF INTERCOURSE, PA

Opening in March 2010!

- Fabrics, Notions, Patterns, Books & Supplies For Discriminating Quilters
- Experienced, Helpful Staff
- Specializing In Fabrics: Asians, Batiks, Reproductions & Brilliant Blenders
- BittyKinna's Own Inspired Line Of Patterns
- Individual Instruction & Group Classes

HOURS: M - SA 9AM - 6PM ◆ SU 12PM - 4 PM ◆ By Appointment

QUILT SHOP
BittyKinna's
Where Quilters Gather

BittyKinna

Etymology: Italian dialect.

1a: A term of endearment meaning "Little Mousie" referring to someone who is always scurrying around, getting into mischief;

1b: The owner's apt nickname when she was a little girl.

717.768.8885 ◆ 3466 Old Philadelphia Pike ◆ P.O. Box 330 ◆ Intercourse, Pennsylvania 17534 ◆ www.bittykinna.com

Las Vegas area's Ultimate **Quilt** & **Sewing Shop**

Just Minutes from the Las Vegas Strip

Family Owned Since 2003

Come enjoy our bright and contemporary atmosphere! Quiltique is a full service creative sewing center specializing in quilting, sewing and machine embroidery. You will find the best quilting fabrics on the market including great companies and designers such as Kaffe Fassett, Moda, Amy Butler, Hoffman Batiks, Free Spirit and Robert Kaufman, just to name a few! We also have the largest class selection in the area offering quilting, garment sewing, machine embroidery and even long-arm quilting. You will find everything you need to create the project you have been dreaming of including BERNINA Sewing Machines. *Don't miss this shop!*

2009 Better Homes and Gardens Quilt Sampler Top Shop.

- Best Selection in town! Over 6,400 sq. ft. and 6,000 bolts of designer fabrics.
- Find incredible deals on fabrics, patterns and notions in our well-stocked sale area.
- Friendly, Knowledgeable and Professional staff always ready to assist you.
- Antiques and Gifts too!

QUILTIQUE®

213 N. Stephanie Street, Suite E
Henderson, Nevada 89074

702-563-8600

info@quiltique.com
www.quiltique.com

Hours:
Monday – Saturday
10 am – 6pm

Better Homes and Gardens Quilt Sampler FEATURED SHOP 2009

BERNINA
Authorized Dealer

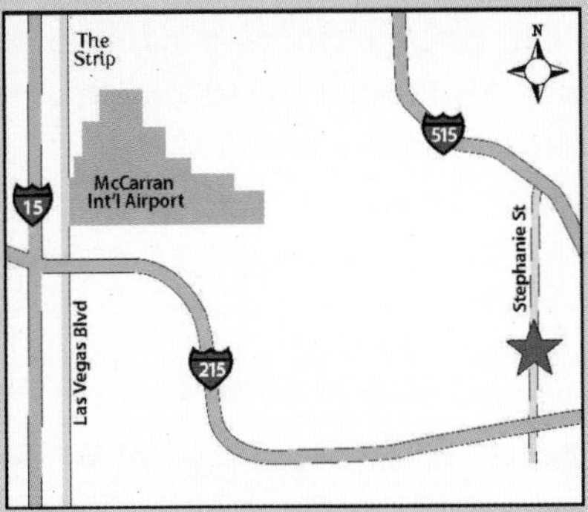

Directions:

- Take the I-215 freeway East toward Henderson
- Exit at Stephanie Street
- Travel North on Stephanie Street to American Pacific Dr.
- We are on the Northwest corner of Stephanie St. and American Pacific Dr. in the Stephanie Promenade Center

the FUN
"Experience with Us!"
Gardnerville, NV

The Quilt House, Inc.

Est 1999

Gardnerville, NV

Monday - Saturday 10am - 5pm
Closed Sundays

MasterCard VISA

* 3000+ Bolts and Growing
* "Block of the Month"
* "Thimbleberries Club"
* Large selection of Quality 100% cotton fabrics
* "Kits", gift items, books, patterns, and notions
* Knowledgeable and Friendly staff
* Welcoming and Fun atmosphere.
* Quality classes and teachers
* Gift Certificates
* Bus Tours and Quilt Guilds welcome (please call ahead)
* Mail Order Available

6400+ square feet of Shopping and Creative FUN !!

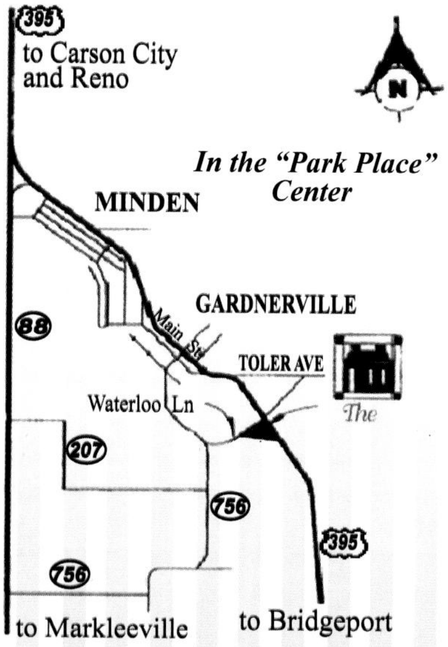

BBB Member Northern Nevada, Inc.

1328 US Hwy. 395 N. #105
Gardnerville, NV 89410
(775) 782-8845
theqlthouse@aol.com
Owners:
Gary and Janet Pierce

www.TheQuiltHouse.net

Better Homes and Gardens Quilt Sampler Featured Shop 2004

Better Homes and Gardens Creative Collection Best of Quilt Sampler 2007

Heavenly Seating Right Chair-Right Price

HORN of America

BERNINA

Sew Many Things!

Clinton, IA

1015 13th Ave. N, Suite E
Clinton, IA 52732
(563) 242-6135
www.iasews.com

We are a hands on sewing center featuring 100% cotton fabrics. We carry a large selection of books and patterns for all of your creative sewing needs. We offer classes in quilting, sewing (home decorating and garment construction), and machine embroidery.
We also carry a large selection of Robison Anton, Sulky and Mettler sewing and machine embroidery threads.
We are the Premier Dealer of Husqvarna Viking Sewing, Serger, and Embroidery Machines.
We offer on-site service and repair of all makes and models of sewing machines.

We have a dedicated staff to help you with all your quilting, sewing, and embroidery needs.

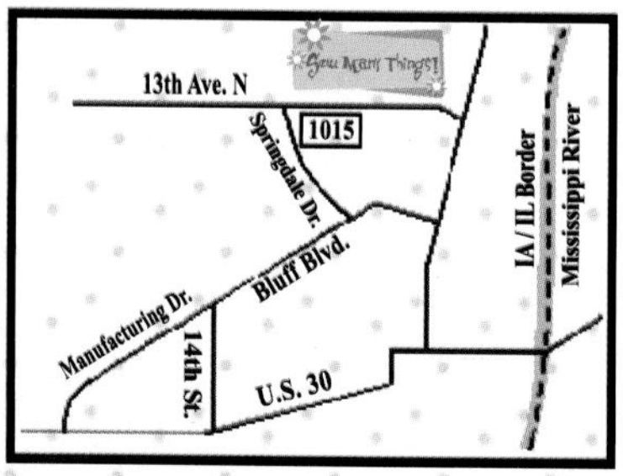

Mon 10 - 8
Tues - Thur 10 - 5
Sat 10 - 3

Owner: Stephanie Nickles
Est: 2008 3000 sq.ft.
2500+ Bolts
Newsletter Online

Husqvarna VIKING

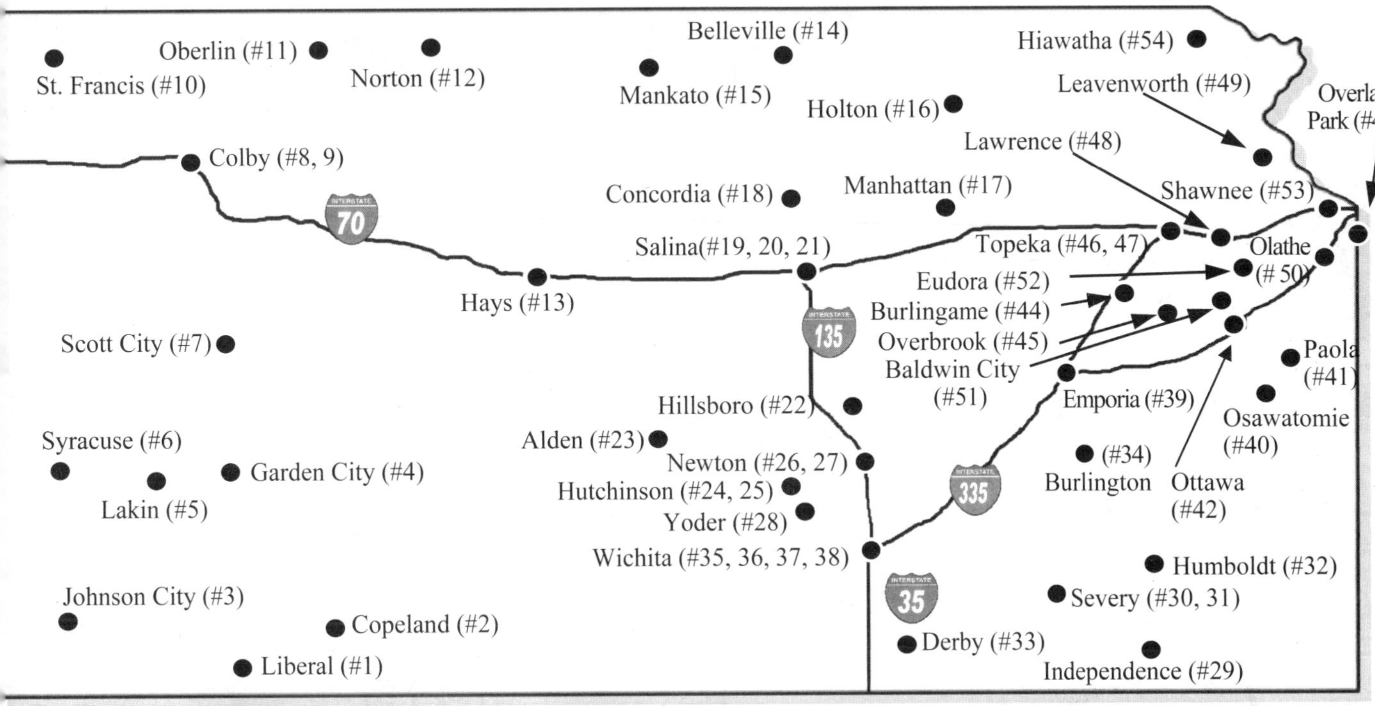

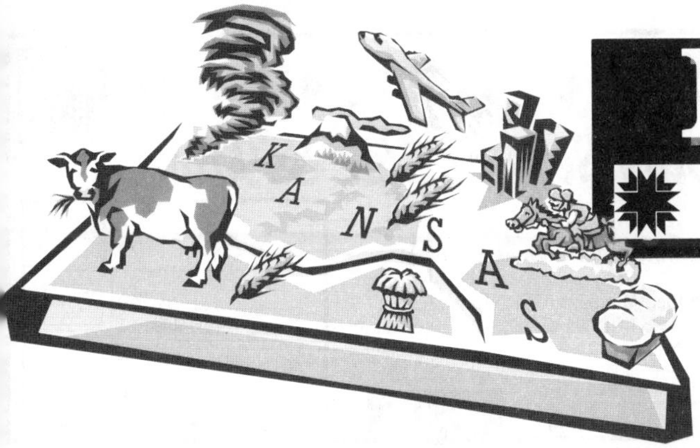

KANSAS

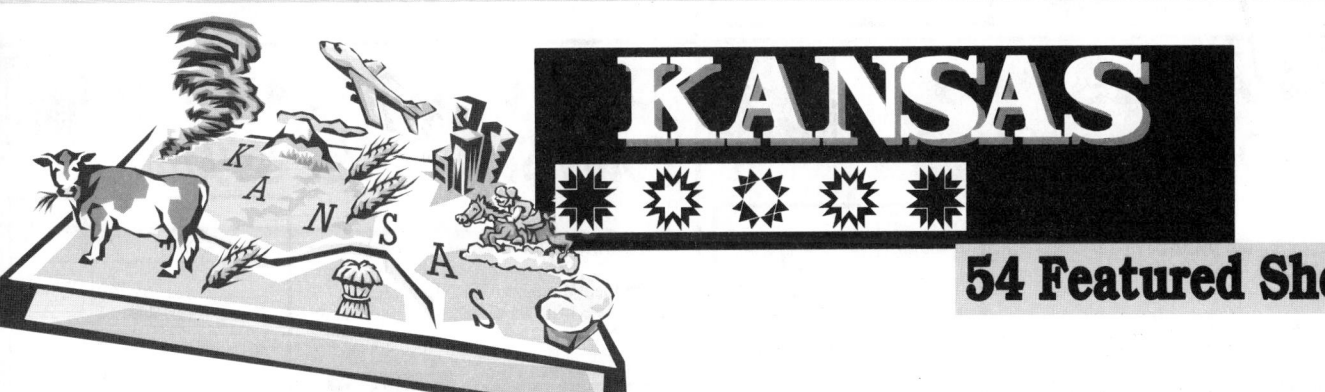

54 Featured Shops

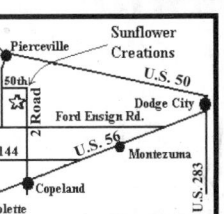

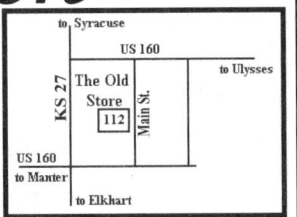

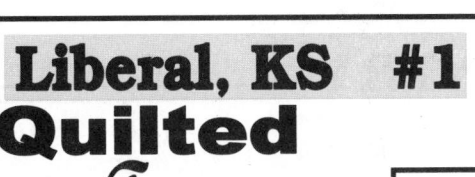

Lakin, KS #5

Tues - Fri 10 - 5
Sat 9 - 12

Red Rooster Quilt Shop

108 N. Main
Mailing: P.O. Box 57,
Kendall, KS 67857
(620) 355-7808
Owner: Crystal Owen

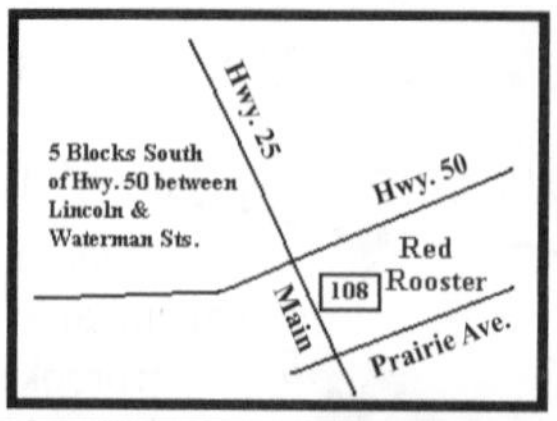

Lakin is located on Hwy. 50 - west of Garden City, KS. Turn south on Hwy. 25 (Main St.)
"Come see us!"

Syracuse, KS #6

Tues - Fri 11 - 5:30
Wed til 9
Sat 10 - 3

Quilter's Stash

123 N. Main 67878
(620) 384-5390 Fax: (620) 384-7639
quiltersstash@wbsnet.org
www.kansasquiltersstash.com
Owners: Carol Dikeman,
Melanie Eddy & Jenny Schwieterman
Est: 2004 2000 sq. ft. Free newsletter
Fabric, notions, patterns, books, serger thread, OESD embroidery thread and supplies, baby lock sewing machines & Dakota CD's.

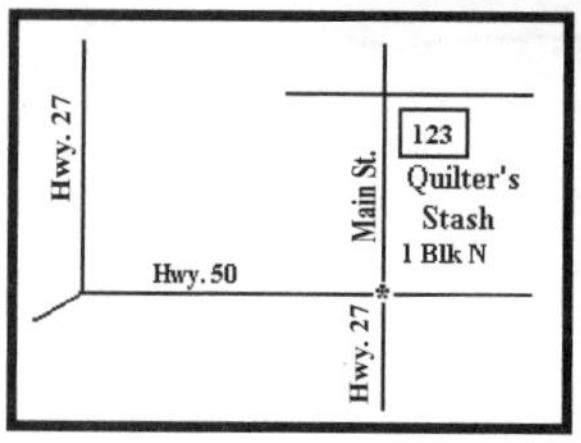

Scott City, KS #7

Mon - Fri 10 - 5:30

Buttons & More

415 Main 67871
(620) 872-7112
Owner: Linda Tilton

Quality Quilt Fabric
Books & Notions
Long-arm machine quilting services.

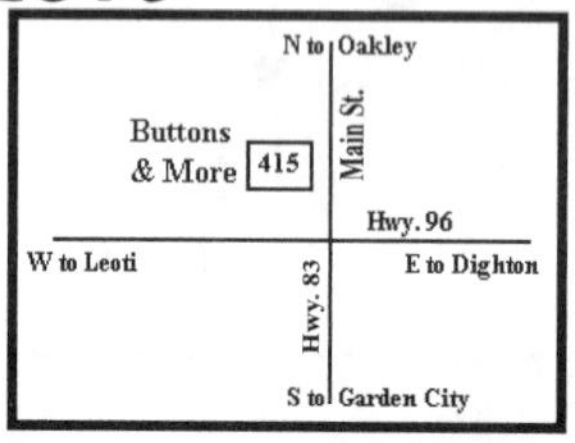

Colby, KS #8

Mon - Sat 9 - 5

Quilt Cabin

1525 S. Range Ave. 67701
(785) 462-3375
Est: 1988

5000 bolts of quality 100% cotton fabrics.
Books, patterns, notions and classes.
Decorator fabrics. Custom window treatments.
Janome Sewing Machine Sales & Service.

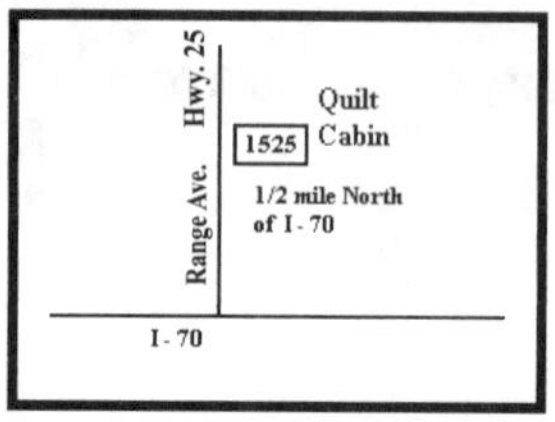

Colby, KS #9

Mon-Sat 9:30-5:30

Colby Sew & Vac & More

1015 Taylor Ave. 67701
(785) 460-1900
Owners: David &Ronda Mudloff
colbysew@st-tel.net
Brother, Viking & BERNINA Dealer.
Large selection of Fabrics, Patterns, Kits, Yarns & Knitting Notions & Threads. We cater to quilting & machine embroidery. We also carry Horn Cabinets.
Nothing Sews Like A Bernina. Nothing.
BERNINA VIKING

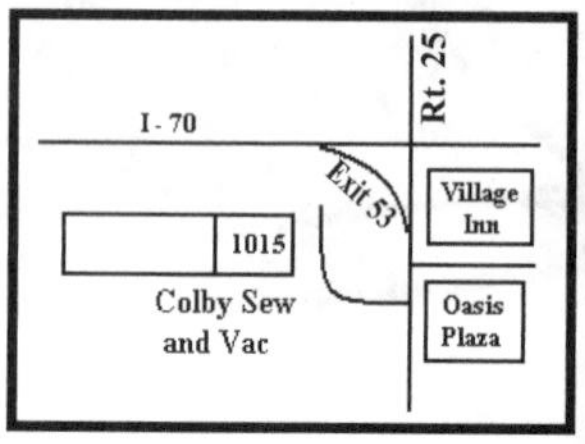

St. Francis, KS #10

Call First
Mon - Fri 10 - 5
Sat 10 - 12

Sainty Stitches

Fabric & Yarn Shoppe

113 W. Washington St. 67756
(785) 332-2339
Owner: Dorothy Smestad
Est: 2006 900 sq.ft.

Quilting Fabrics and Sewing Machine Repair

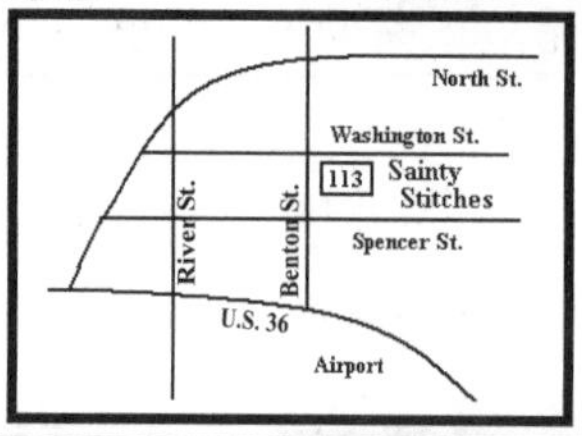

Norton, KS #12

Tues - Fri 9:30 - 5:30
Sat 9:30 - 3

Stitch Up A Storm

113 W. Main St. 67654
(785) 874-5152
Owners: Regina Stark & Jamie Wentz
Est: 2008 Newsletter
stitchupastorm@ruraltel.net

Great Selection of Quilting, Fabrics, Notions, and Books. We offer classes, custom quilting and embroidery. Huge selection of DMC Floss.

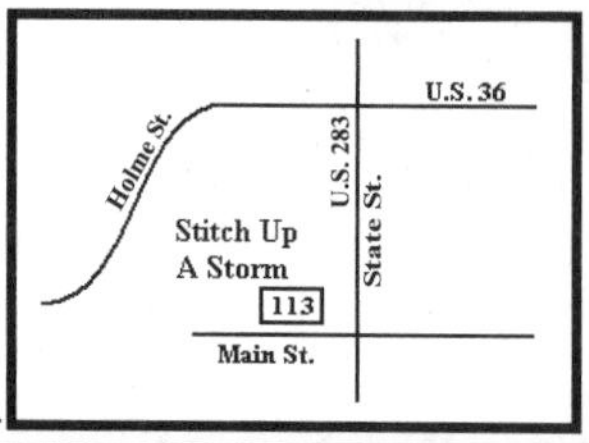

COUNTRY QUILTING & Keepsakes

Mon - Sat 10 am - 5 pm

#11

Fabrics
Books
Patterns
Notions
Batting
Classes

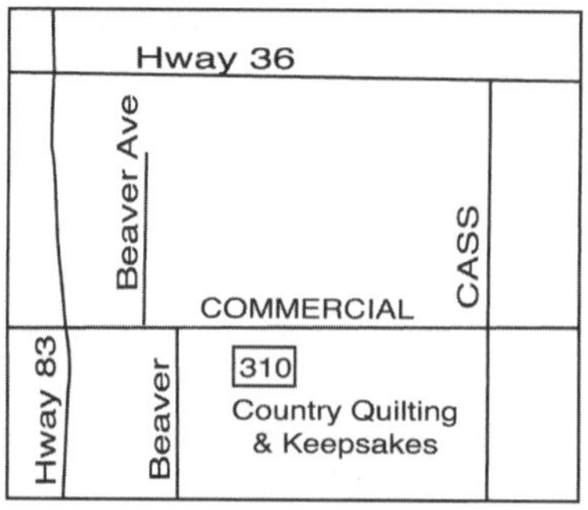

owner: Norma Carman

310 WEST COMMERCIAL; OBERLIN, KS. 67749
Ph: 785-475-2411

"Helping you create your quilt from start to finish."

Hays, KS #13

Quilt Cottage Co.

Mon - Fri 10 - 5:30
Sat 10 - 3

Yarn & Cross Stitch, Too!

2520 Vine (in the Centennial Mall) 67601

(785) 625-0080 www.quiltcottageco.com

Est: 1994 4800 sq.ft. 3500+ Bolts
Debbie Huebner & Kari Schultz

* Top quality quilting fabrics
* Excellent selection of books, patterns and notions
* Fine hand knitting yarns
* Knitting needles, notions and patterns
* Counted cross stitch fabrics, patterns and DMC floss

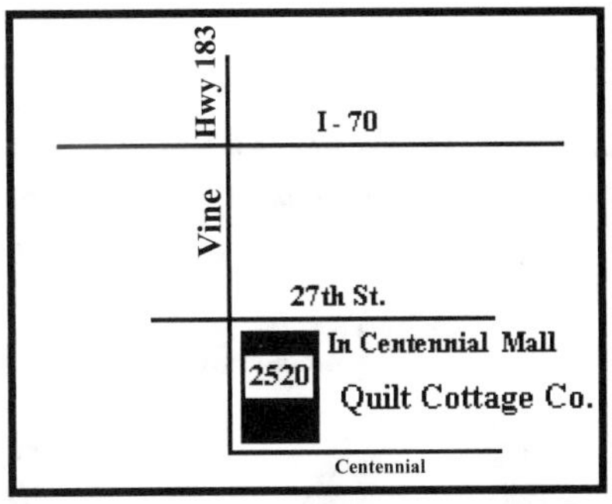

Mankato, KS #15

Hidden Treasures Quilt Shop

Mon - Fri 10 - 6
Sat 10 - 5

101 N. Commercial 66956
(785) 378-8020 Fax: (785) 378-8021
Owner: Luann Wilson
Est: 2008 1400 bolts Free Newsletter
hiddentreasuresquiltshop@nckcn.com

Fabric, Notions, Patterns, Gift Items, Custom Framing, and Quilts for Sale.
Look inside for the purple door!

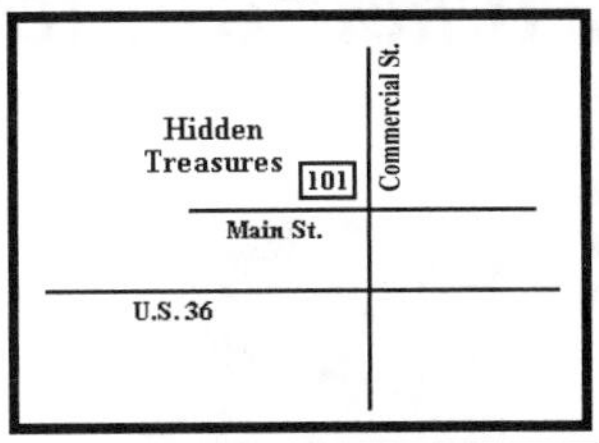

Belleville, KS #14

Sew Country

Fabric ♥ Notions ♥ Gifts

1834 M St. 66935
Phone & FAX 785-527-2332
Sheila Cornett, Owner
Established 1992
sewcountry@nckcn.com
www.sewcountryandgifts.com

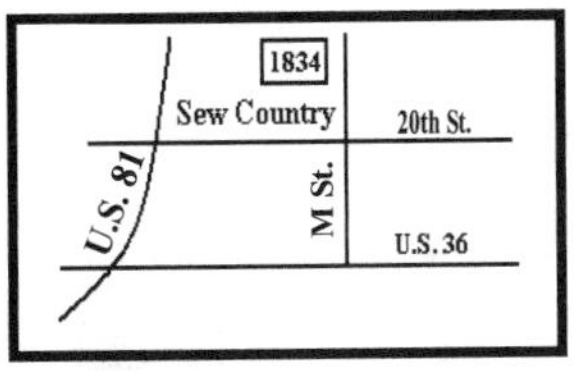

Monday - Friday 9 - 5:30 Saturday 9 - 5

Welcome to the Country!

3000+ Bolts of quality quilt fabric from Moda, Hoffman, Northcott, Andover and More! Largest Selection of Fat Quarters, Patterns and Books in North Central Kansas! Our own Hand-Dyed Wools and Full Line of Silk Ribbon Embroidery Supplies. Republic of Tea, Wind & Willow, Woodwick Candles and kitchen gadgets & more.

Holton, KS #16

Quilting on the Square

Mon - Fri 10 - 7
Sat 10 - 5

400 Pennsylvania 66436
(785) 364-4050
Est: 2005

Owners: Mark & Mary Pfeiler
qos@quiltingonthesquare.com
www.quiltingonthesquare.com

Your full service quilt shop in northeastern Kansas. All the latest fabrics, patterns and notions. Classes and online shopping too.

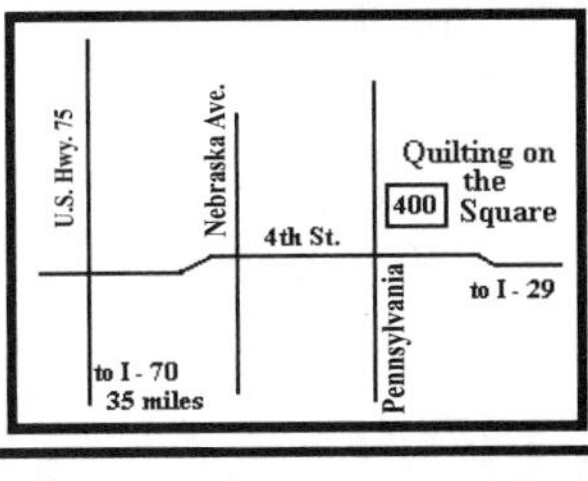

Manhattan, KS #17

All About Quilts — EST. 2005 — Manhattan, KS

Quilt Shop and Retreat House

We carry a large variety of fabrics (5000+ bolts), which include Moda, Benartex, Hoffman, RJR and Hoffman Batiks. Our store features such designers as Kansas Troubles. Large selection of Batiks & Brights. Books, Patterns, Quilting Notions.

www.about-quilts.com

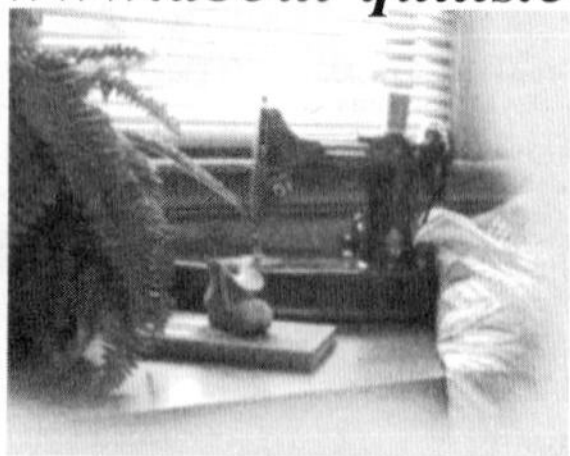

Mon 12 - 5:30
Tues - Sat 9 - 5:30

785-539-6759

BERNINA
Janome
Tin Lizzie
Koala & Horn Cabinets

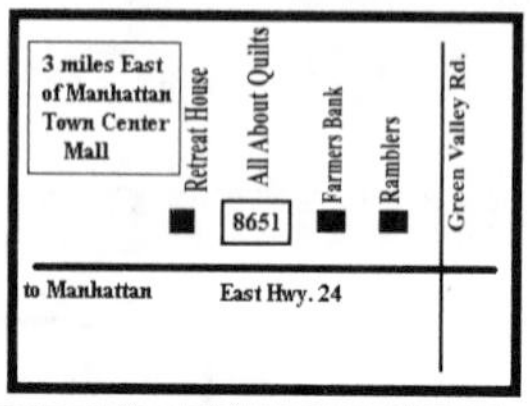

8651 E. US Hwy. 24 66502
allaboutquilts@yahoo.com
Owner: Karen Malone
Est: 2004 2400 sq.ft.

Concordia, KS #18

Tues - Fri 12 - 6
Thur 12 - 7
Sat 10 - 5

Fabric Essentials

116 West 6th St. 66901
(785) 243-4044

www.FabricEssentials.com

5000+ bolts of unusual quilting, fashion, toweling, home décor, and outdoor fabric. Concordia has many fine restaurants, museums, hotels, and attractions. Make Concordia your destination in North Central Kansas!

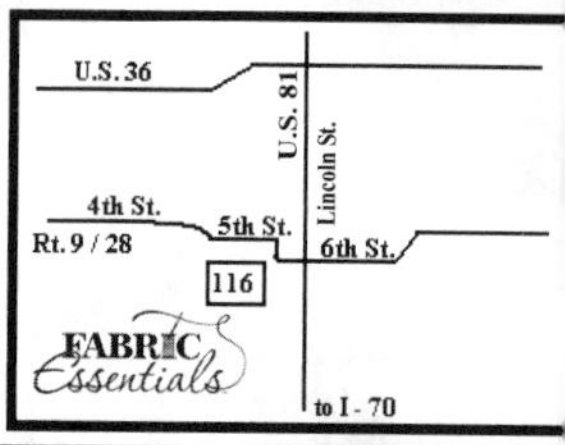

Salina, KS #19

Tues - Sat 12 - 5:30

Quilting Station

212 E. Iron 67401
(785) 493-5625
Owner: Kathryne Perney Est: 2002
kdperney@yahoo.com

Located in a cute antique gas station.
We specialize in giftware for the quilt lover.
Long arm quilting services.
Quilts by Kansas quilt makers.

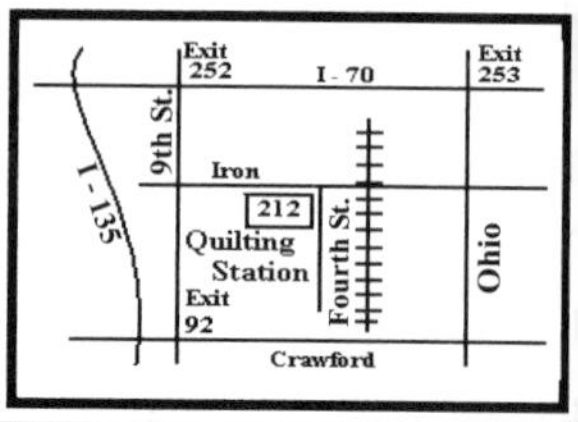

Salina, KS #20

Quilting Bee

Where Quilters want to "Bee"!

Mon - Fri 9:30 - 5:30
Sat 9:30 - 5

120 S. Santa Fe 67401
(785) 823-9376
Fax: (785) 823-7628
Owner: Sherril Bieberly
Est: 1979 4000 sq.ft.
info@quiltingbee.net

Come visit our full line quilt shop!

We feature Kansas Troubles quilters fabrics, books & patterns plus a large selection of other fabrics including Moda, Batiks, 30's, & flannels. Lots of kits.

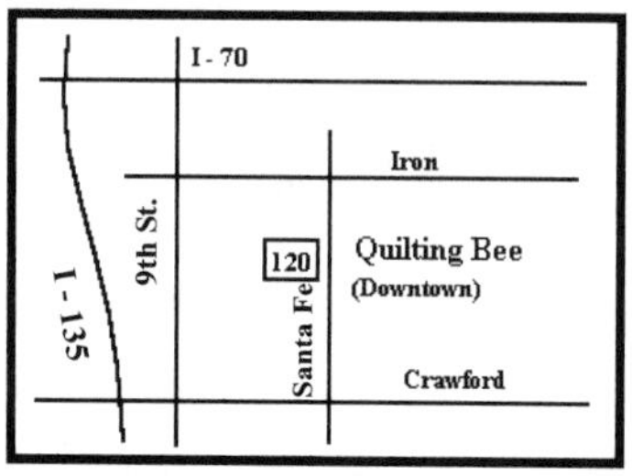

www.quiltingbee.net

Salina, KS #21

Mon - Fri 9 - 6
Sat 9 - 4

Emporium

1833 S. 9th St. 67401
(785) 823-1515 Fax: (785) 823-5818
Owner: Becky Rageth
Est: 1998 Newsletter
emporiuminc@yahoo.com
One-stop creative shop.
We sell and service sewing machines and vacuums. We also offer sewing cabinets, patterns, sewing accessories, cotton fabrics, notions & classes.

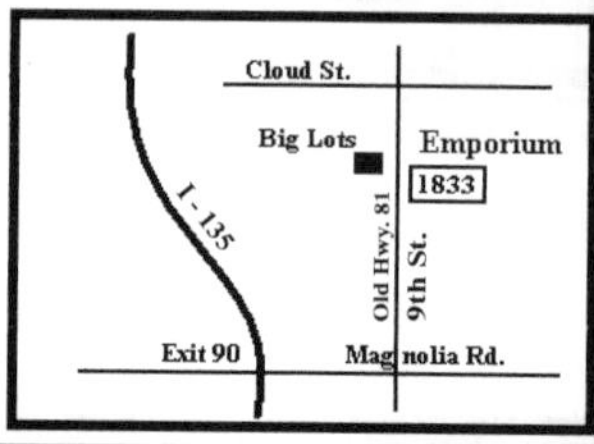

Hillsboro, KS #22

Mon - Fri 10 - 6
Sat 10 - 4

Quilts & QuiltRacks

130 N. Main St. 67063
(620) 947-2222
Est: 2002 1000+ bolts & growing
diane@quiltsandquiltracks.com
www.quiltsandquiltracks.com

More than 60 beautiful quilts and 20 quilt racks. All handcrafted, many locally.

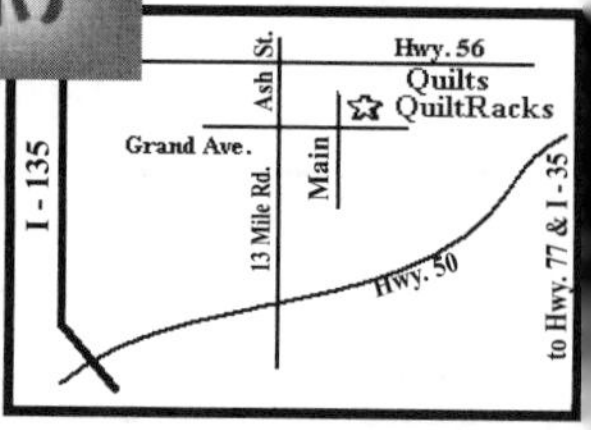

Alden, KS #23

Mon - Sat 10 - 4:30

Prairie Flower Crafts

205 Pioneer St. 67512-0158
(800) 527-3997 or (620) 534-3551
Owner: Sara Fair Sleeper Est: 1970
PrFlrCraft@aol.com 8600 sq.ft.
www.Aldenfabric.com

A Specialty Fabric Shop for Quilters

RJR, Hoffman, Michael Miller, Alexander Henry, Daiwabo Taupe Fabric, Moda, Kona Bay, SSI, Marcus Brothers, Robert Kaufmann, Benartex, Northcott, Timeless Treasures, In the Beginning, Andover, Free Spirit, UK, African & Asian Fabrics.

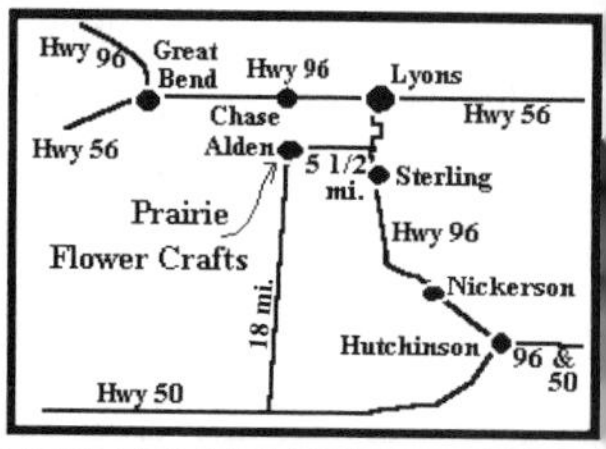

Cottonwood Quilts

fine fabrics, notions & gifts

Hutchinson, KS #24

126 N. Main 67501 (620) 662-2245

llove2quilt@kscottonwoodquilts.com

Est: 1998 3500 sq. ft. 3500 Bolts

www.kscottonwoodquilts.com

Mon - Sat 9:30 - 5 Thur til 8:30

We are located in a charming, historical building offering a wonderful selection from batiks and bold brights, to homespun & Thimbleberries. Let our friendly staff help you with all your quilting needs.

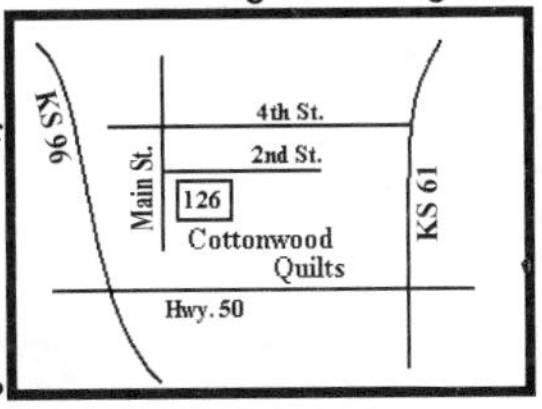

Kits - clubs - BOM's - Mail & web orders - notions - books - patterns

Hutchinson, KS #25

Mon - Sat 9:30 - 5

COUNTRY FABRICS

6411 W. Morgan Ave. 67501

(620) 662-3681 Est: 1977

Owners: Janet, Randy, & Leland Headings

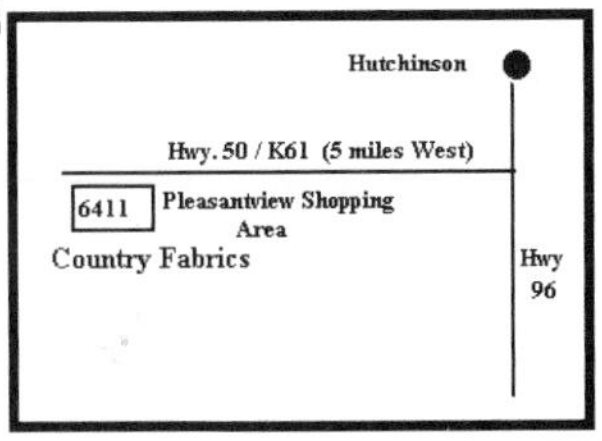

100% Cotton Solids and calicos.
Quilting Notions, Books, & Batting.
Fashion Fabrics, Sewing Notions & Patterns.

Newton, KS #26 & 27

Charlotte's Sew Natural

26th YEAR

UNIQUE FABRICS FOR QUILTING & FASHION

The BEST source for

Fabrics • Patterns • Buttons
Trims • Notions • Classes

710 N. Main 67114
(316) 284-2547
Over 4000 Bolts

Collect all of Charlotte's Original Patterns. Many for 5" square charm packs.

Owner: Charlotte Wolfe

Mon - Fri 9:30 - 5:30
Thur til 8 Sat 9:30 - 5

Now -- 2 unique STORES IN NEWTON!

Charlotte's Bargain Fabric & Stitchery

601 SE 36th St. #103

(316) 804-4660
in the Chisholm Trail Mall
4 miles south of downtown Newton

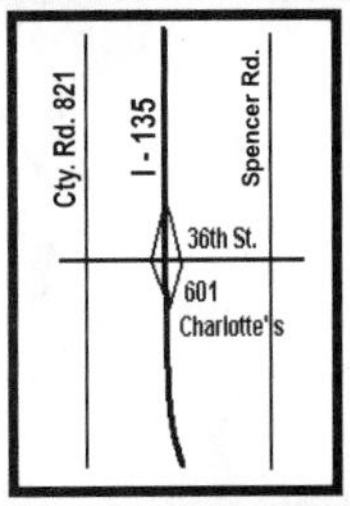

Sew Inexpensive Fabric,
DMC Floss & Stamped Needleart!

www.sewnatural.net

Yoder, KS #28

Mon - Sat 9:30 - 5

Demelia's Quilt Co.

3406 E. Red Rock Rd. 67585
620-465-2505
Owner: Cindy Mastro

demelias@sbcglobal.net
www.demeliasquiltco.com

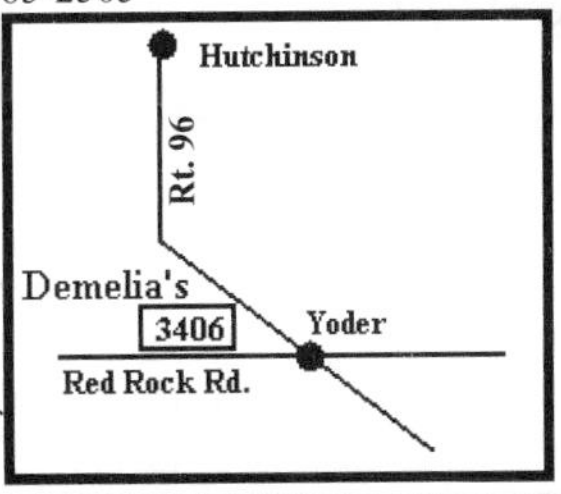

We are a destination shop located in the heart of Yoder. Our friendly staff invites you to stop in and visit us soon. We have over 1000 bolts of high quality cotton fabric and a great selection of notions, books and patterns. Classes offered.

Independence, KS #29

Lillie's Classic Quilts & Home Decor

113 W. Myrtle St. 67301
(620) 331-4690
Fax: (620) 331-3230

Tues - Sat 10 - 5

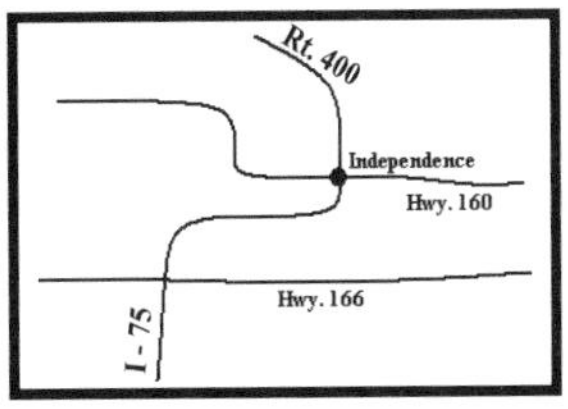

Est: 2001

We are a quilter's boutique, featuring complete lines of new & vintage fabrics. Moda Home and Home Décor.

Lillie's Classic Quilts & Home Décor has been chosen as one of the 10 featured shops across the U.S. and Canada for the spring issue of Quilt Sampler, 2008. Competition to be included in Quilt Sampler is keen. Over 3,000 quilt shops are eligible. Quilt shops submit a detailed application on their history, business promotions, charitable work, teaching schedules and design philosophies. A panel of quilt experts chooses the 10 shops and they are kept secret and unveiled at either the spring or fall International Quilt Market.

Better Homes and Gardens Quilt Sampler FEATURED SHOP

Please stop by for a visit.

www.lilliesclassicquilts.com

Severy, KS #30

Mon - Sat 9 - 5 Sun 1 - 5

Needle In A Haystack

207 Q Road 67137
(620) 736-2942 needle@sktc.net
www.needleinahaystack.com
Owner: Cynthia Washburne
Est: 1991 3000+ bolts

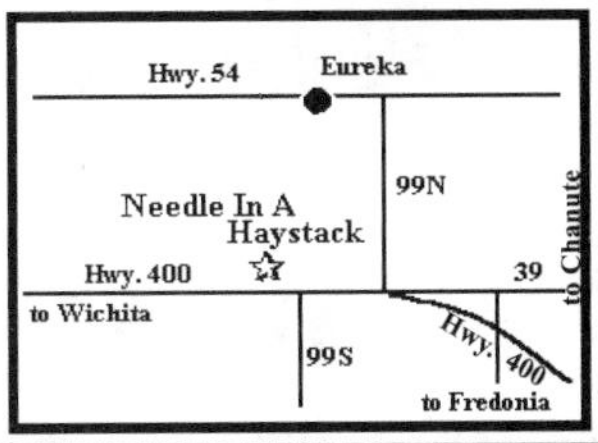

Fabrics -- Books -- Notions
BOM's -- Kits -- Classes

Severy, KS #31

Tues - Fri 9:30 - 5
Sat 9:30 - 4

Itchin to Stitch

1590 20th St. 67137
(620) 736-2040 Fax: (620) 736-2047
Owner: Wanda Nusz
Est: 2006 2500 sq.ft. 1500 Bolts
wanda@itchin-to-stitch.com

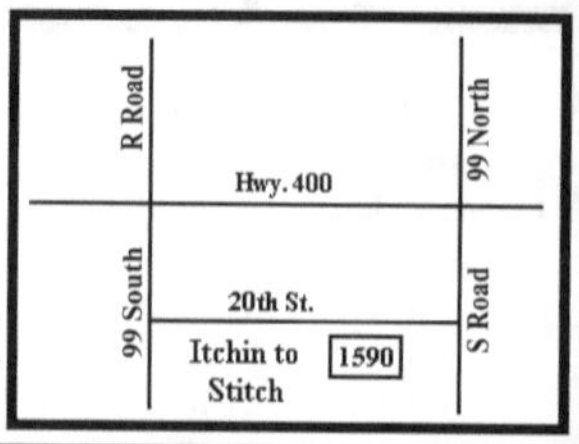

Full Service Quilt Shop offering Fabrics, Books, Patterns, Notions, Block of the Months, Classes, and Machine Quilting Available.

Best Little Quilt Shop in Southeast Kansas!

Heavenly Kneads & Threads Plus

724 Bridge St. 66748
620-473-2408

- Quilting Fabrics
- Quilting Supplies
- Books & Notions
- Machine Quilting
- Classes
- Knitting & Crochet
- Tatting Supplies

Mon - Fri 10 - 5
Sat 10 - 2

Est: 2006

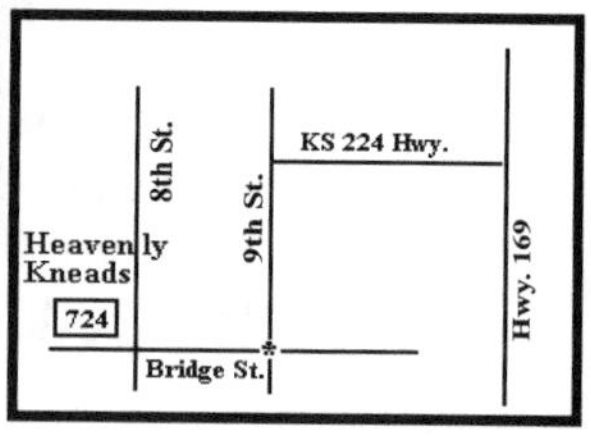

Featuring Moda, Thimbleberries, Timeless Treasure, Marcus Brothers, Civil War & 1930's Reproductions and many other name brand fabrics at reasonable prices.

Owners: Carolyn Zellner & Mary Bulk
heavenly_kneads@yahoo.com
Online Newsletter
1800 bolts & adding more

Humboldt, KS #32

Derby, KS #33

Sunflower Quilts

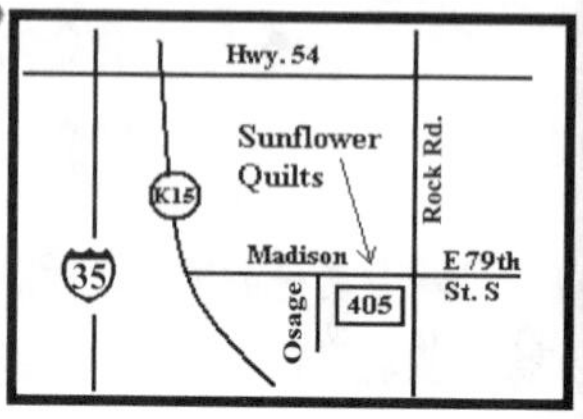

405 Osage Rd., Derby, KS 67037
Website: www.sunflowerquilts.com
Email: sunflowerquilts@sbcglobal.net

(316) 788-5120

Fabric - Notions - Patterns - Books
Classes - Wearables
Authorized Husqvarna Viking Sales & Service
Owner: Janeen Miller
Est: 2002 with 4000+ sq.ft., 3000+ bolts

Mon - Thur 9:30 - 6
Fri & Sat 9:30 - 5
Sun 1 - 5

Offering BOMs, Hinterberg Frames, Quilters Dream Batting, Fine fabrics from Benartex, Clothworks, Hoffman, Kona Bay, Moda, RJR, a large selection of batiks and more.

Burlington, KS #34

Mon - Fri 10 - 5:30
Sat 10 - 3
Sun by Appt.

Silver Threads & Golden Needles

321 Neosho, Hwy 75 66839
Owner: Jerry Anne Hoyt
(620) 364-8233
Est: 1985 2000 sq.ft.
stgn@mchsi.com

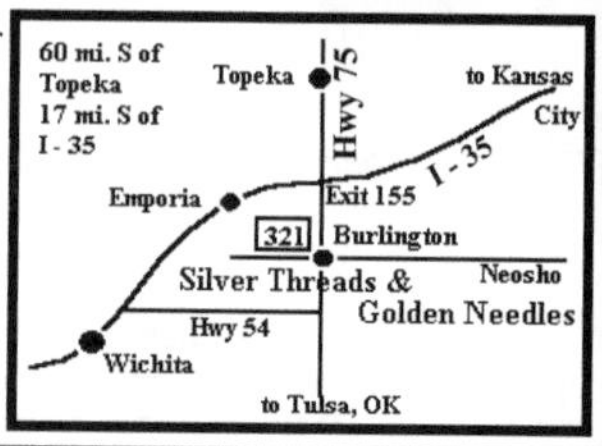

Fabrics, Patterns, Notions, Crafts, & Quilting Supplies
Serving the area for over 25 years!

Picket Fence Quilt Co.

7130 W. Maple #230
Wichita, KS 67209
(316) 558-8899
Fax: (316) 558-8877
pf-quilts@cox.net

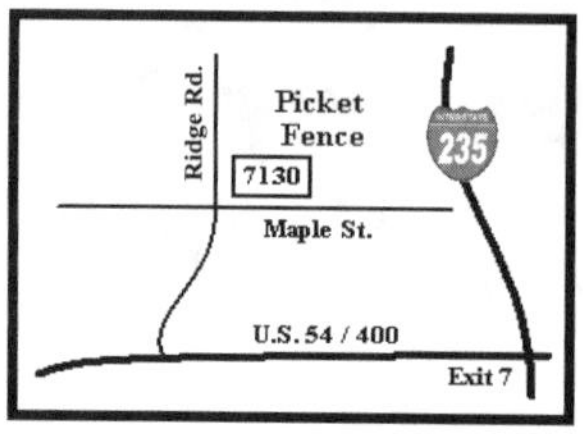

Mon - Thur 10 - 5:30
Fri & Sat 10 - 5

Over 2500 bolts of fine quality cotton fabrics for your shopping pleasure.
Notions - Books - Classes - Patterns - Batiks

Est: 2005

Wichita, KS #35

2500 Bolts

#36

Material Girls Quilt Shoppe

Mon - Sat 10 - 5:30

Complete selection of quilting supplies, fabrics, books, patterns & notions. - Various quilting classes

535 W. Douglas, Suite 140
Wichita, KS
In the Historic Delano District
316-684-5855
Owners: Jo Degner & Jan Munroe
3100 Sq. feet - Over 5000 Bolts

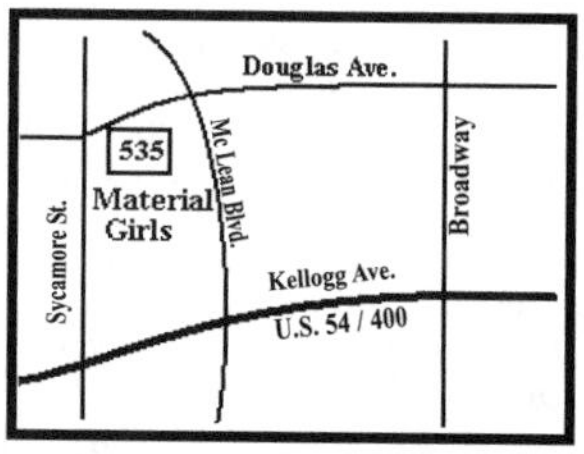

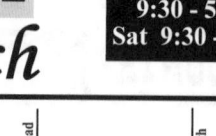

www.materialgirlsquiltshoppe.com

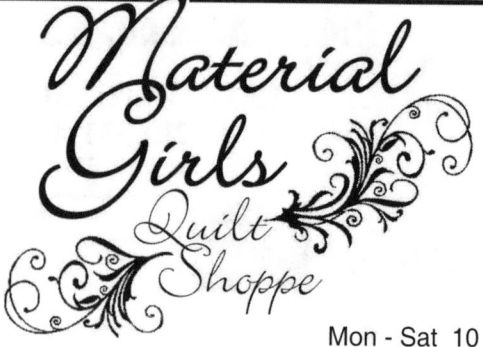

Gramma's Calico Cupboard

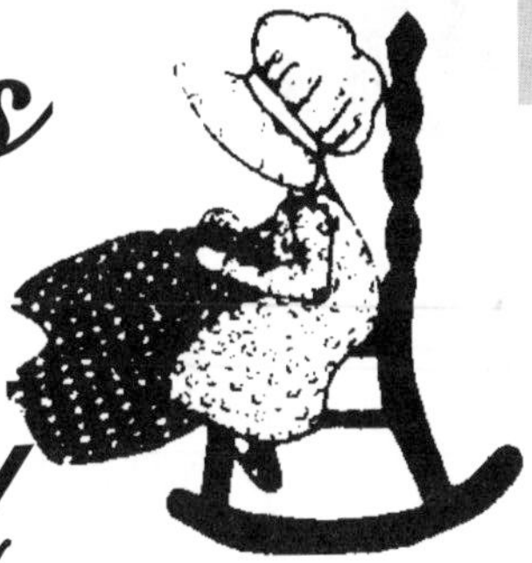

Wichita, KS #37

1945 S. Hydraulic 67211
(316) 264-0274
Owner: Betty Webb
Est: 1982 5500 sq.ft.
6000 Bolts

Quilting and Craft Patterns

Fantastic collections of fabric, includes 1930's reproductions, florals, flannels, juvenile prints, wool felt, & homespuns. Holiday fabrics always available. Christmas room open all year, full of fabrics, patterns and gifts.
Handmade rag dolls, quilts, quilted animals and antiques.

www.grammascalicocupboard.4t.com

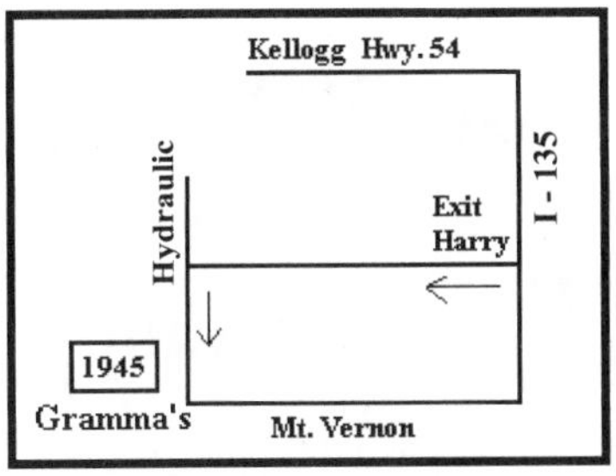

Mon - Sat 9:30 - 5

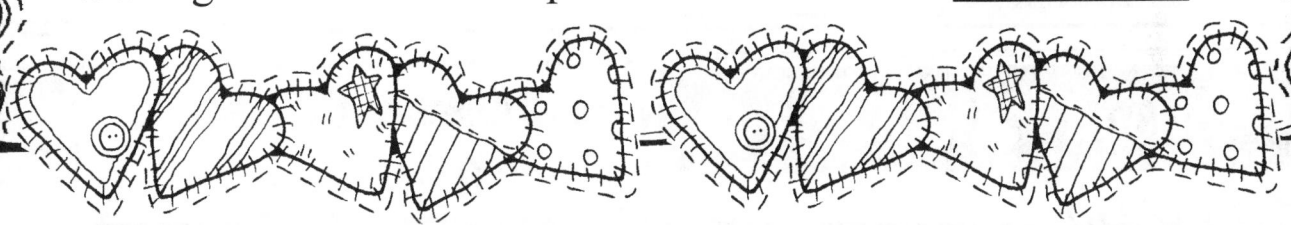

Hen Feathers Quilt Shop

Wichita, KS #38

At Hen Feathers you will find great fabric and a friendly atmosphere. Our selection includes florals, batiks, westerns & reproduction prints, plus fabrics for pet lovers.

We are easy to find and definitely worth stopping by. Don't forget to visit our sale corner.

Mon, Tues, Wed, Fri 10 - 5:30
Thur 10 - 7 Sat 10 - 5

110 N. Rock Rd. 67206
316-652-9599
henfeathers@cox.net

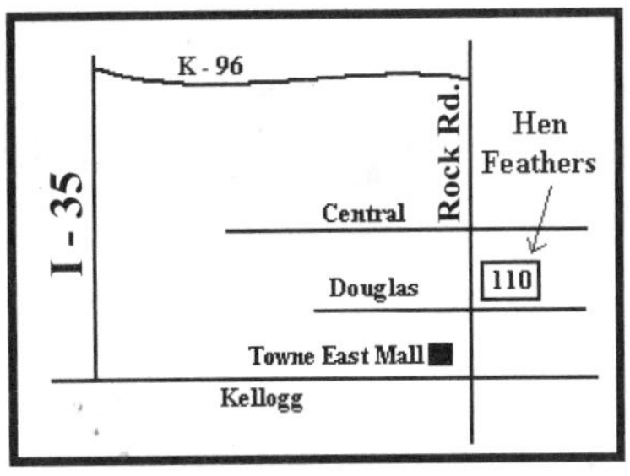

www.henfeathersquilts.com

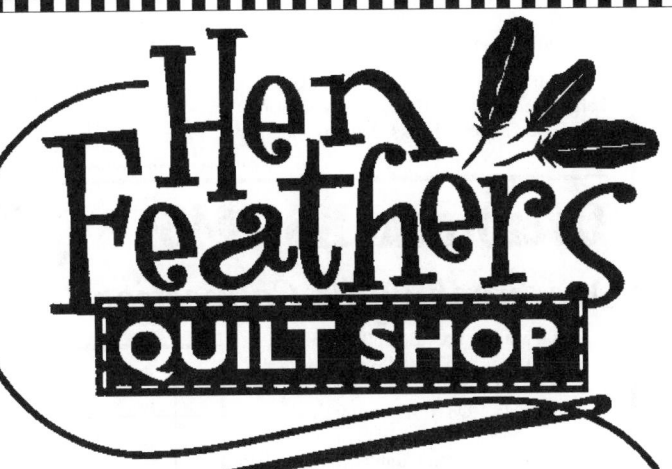

Emporia, KS #39

Tues - Fri 10 - 5
Sat 10 - 3

Prairie Pieces Quilt Shop

911 Commercial St. 66801
(620) 342-9110
Owner: Sue Blubaugh
Est: 1990 3000+ Bolts

www.prairiepiecesquiltshop.net

Full line quilt shop.
Hoffman, Moda and other fabric lines.
Small town service with a smile.

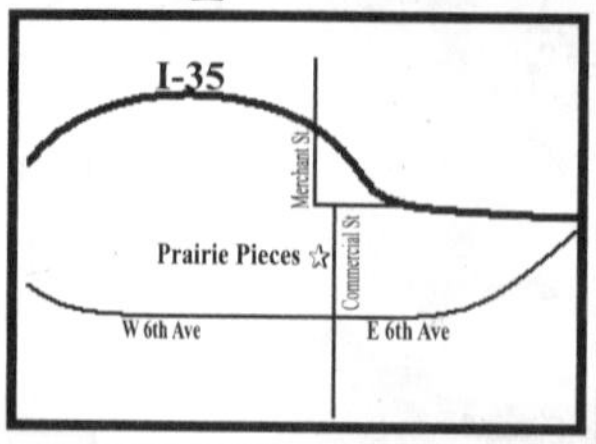

Osawatomie, KS #40

Tues - Fri 9 - 5
Sat 9 - 3

Happy Crafters

1935 Parker 66064
(913) 755-4360
Est: 1988 1800 sq.ft. 1500 Bolts
www.happycrafters.net

Full service quilt shop offering fabric, kits, patterns, books, classes, embroidery patterns, finished quilts, wall hangings and long-arm quilting services.

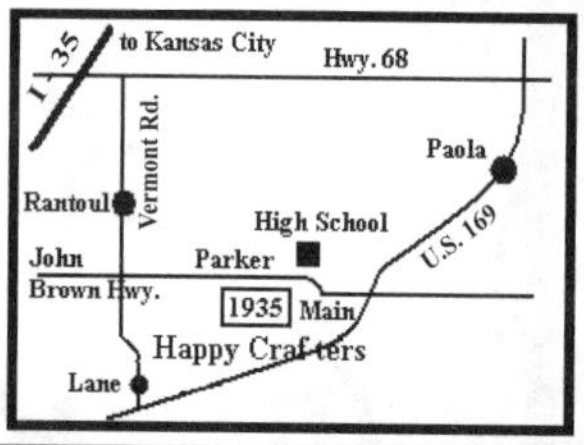

Paola, KS #41

Mon - Fri 10 - 5
Wed til 7
Sat 9 - 4

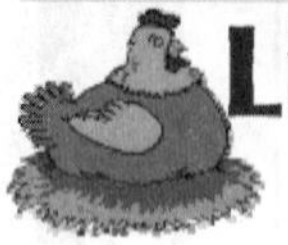

LiL' RED HEN Quilt Shop

913 N. Pearl, Suite 1 66071
(913) 294-5230 Fax: (913) 294-5231
Owner: Janna Renner Est: 2007
1500 sq.ft. 2000 Bolts Free Online Newsletter
LilRedHen2@att.net
www.Lilredhenquiltshop.com
Fabrics, Notions, Yarn & misc. gifts.

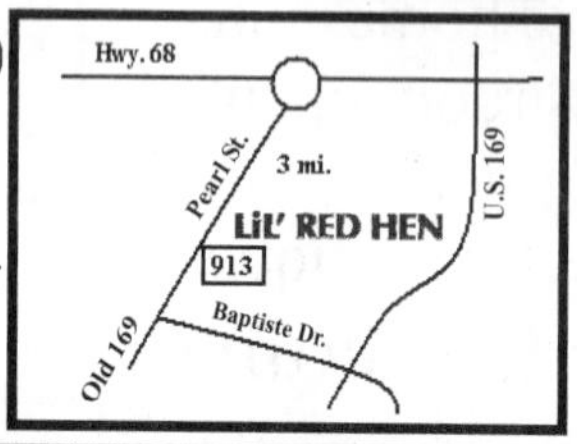

Ottawa, KS #42

Mon - Fri 9:30 - 5
Sat 9:30 - 3

Chris' Corner Quilt Shop

3593 N. Hwy. 59 66067
(785) 242-1922
Owner: Chris Campbell
Est: 1984 Newsletter
chriscorner@sbcglobal.net

Quality, Knowledge and Service is the norm not an exception. Fabrics, patterns, books, notions and classes.

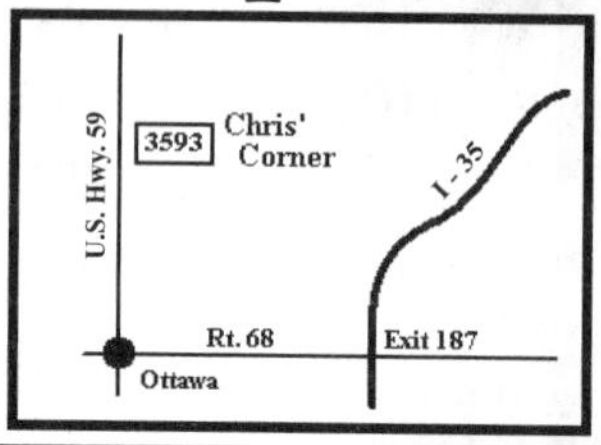

Overland Park, KS #43

Harper's Fabric & Quilt Co.

7918 Santa Fe Dr
Overland Park, KS 66204
913-648-2739
Toll-Free
877-780-2739
harpersfab@aol.com

Open 7 days a week
Mon-Thu 10 -7, Fri 10-6,
Sat 9-5, Sun 1-4

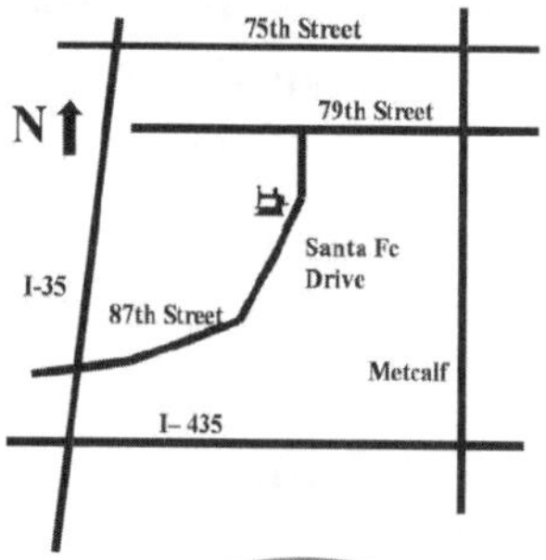

Kaffe Fassett, Amy Butler, Moda, Michael Miller, Windham, Hoffman, Benartex, Red Rooster, Marcus Brothers, Books, Quilting Supplies & Notions, Classes, Seminars & Workshops. Premier Huqvarna Viking Sewing Machines & Sergers

Better Homes and Gardens Quilt Sampler FEATURED SHOP 2008

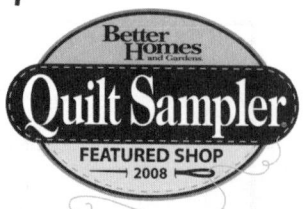

www.harpersfabricandquilt.com

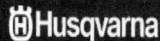

Husqvarna VIKING

Burlingame, KS #44

Tues - Fri 10 - 5
Sat 10 - 4

Great Plains Quilt Co.

119 W. Santa Fe Ave. 66413
(785) 654-3303
Est: 2004 2400 sq.ft. 1800 bolts
quiltplainsquilt@embarqmail.com

1930's reproduction fabrics, batiks. Large selection of fabrics, samples & ideas, classes, notions, books, patterns and long arm quilting.

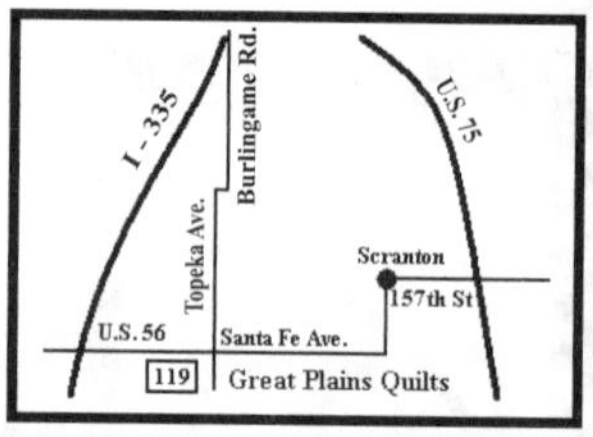

Overbrook, KS #45

Tue - Sat 10 - 5

Overbrook Quilt Connection

500 Maple P.O. Box 50 66524
(785) 665-7841 or (888) 665-7841
Owner: Roxane Fawl
Est: 1994 4300 sq.ft.
oqc@embarqmail.com
www.overbrookquilts.com

2000 bolt inventory, books, patterns, notions, classes. Mail order.

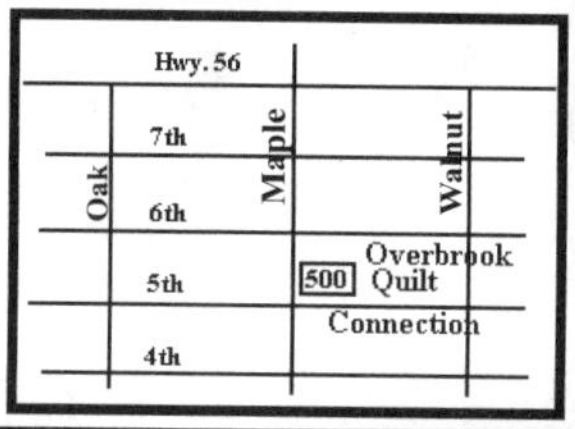

Topeka, KS #46

Mon - Fri 10 - 5:30
Thur til 7
Sat 10 - 3

Stitching Traditions Quilt Shop

3005 SW Topeka Blvd.
66611
(785) 266-4130
Est: 1997
2000 sq.ft.
750+ bolts

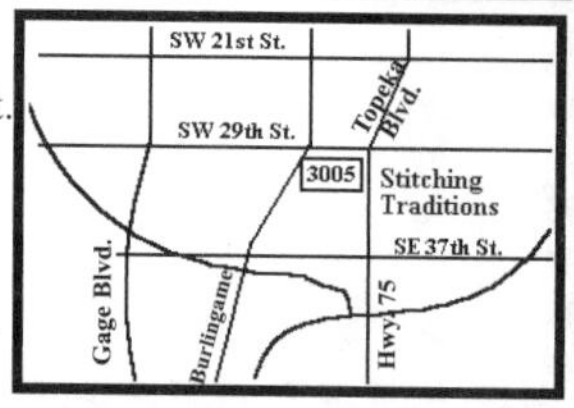

Full service quilt shop serving Topeka and the surrounding area. We offer a large selection of fabric, books, patterns, notions and classes.

Colleen Janssen
Proprietor

Est: 1992

Fabric Corner

(785) 271-7667
5331 SW 22nd Place 66614

Located in the Fairlawn Plaza Shopping Center at the Corner of 21st and Fairlawn

Topeka, KS #47

One can't imagine the awesome feeling of entering our more than 8,000 sq. ft. space with more than 3,000 bolts of quality quilting and fashion fabrics.

We carry over 400 titles of books for quilting, sewing and home décor.

Authorized BERNINA dealer and comprehensive sewing center.

Monday - Friday 10-5:30
Thursday 10-8
Saturday 10-5
Open Some Sundays
(Please Call First)

If you are traveling through our area, be sure to mention this ad and receive 10% off your purchase except our already discounted Berninas.

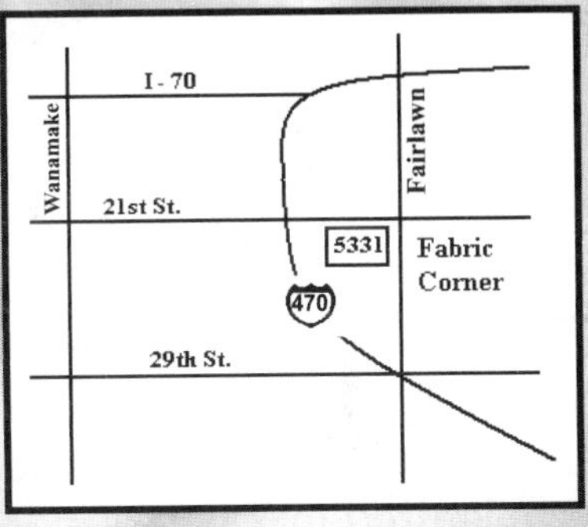

Nearly everything under one roof for the quilter or seamstress.

Stitch On Needlework Shop

Mon - Sat 10 - 5:30 Thur until 8 pm Sunday 1 - 4

926 Massachusetts St., Lawrence, KS 66044
785-842-1101 shop@stitchon.com
Est. 1976 3,000 sq.ft. 2500+ bolts of 100% Cotton
www.stitchon.com

Batiks, Flannels, 1930's. Large selection of books, patterns and Models. Counted Cross Stitch and fun buttons.
Large gift selection of Department 56, Vera Bradley, Lampe Berger, Aromatique, Polish Pottery & Much, Much more.

Lawrence, KS #48

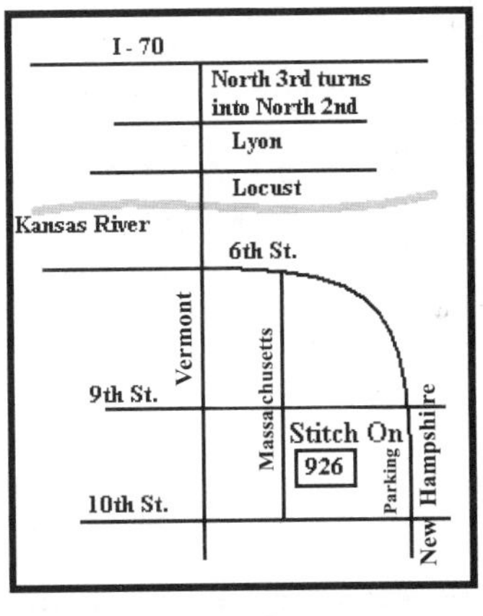

Quilter's Quarters

Kansas' Premier Quilt Shop

200 S. 5th St.
(Corner of Delaware and 5th)
Leavenworth, KS 66048
(913) 651-6510
www.quiltersqtrs.com
Owner: Jerry Ann Stube

Better Homes and Gardens Quilt Sampler FEATURED SHOP

Minutes from Kansas City, The Quilter's Quarters is dedicated to providing the best possible customer service in the friendliest atmosphere. Quilters will truly find a home in our civil war vintage building where the surroundings may be antique, but the fabric and ideas are cutting edge.

Mon - Fri 9:30 - 5
Sat 9:30 - 3:30

Leavenworth, KS #49

Just 15 minutes north of the new Kansas Speedway on Kansas Hwy. 7. Just outside the front gate of historic Fort Leavenworth.
Featured in 2 books-- "Kansas City Quilt Maker Portraits & Patterns" and "Kansas City Scrap Book" by Terri Atkinson.

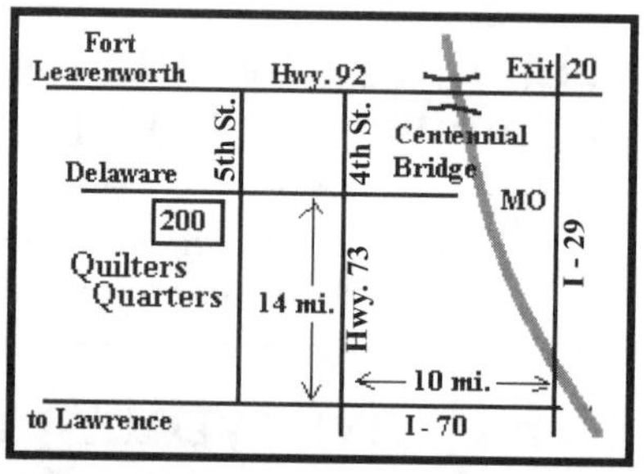

Quilters' Haven

Better Homes and Gardens Quilt Sampler FEATURED SHOP

Fabric ✱ Quilting Supplies ✱ Classes

Handi Quilter®

PFAFF
Sewing Machines
Original Built in Walking Foot

LARGE SELECTION OF QUILTERS' COTTONS
BATIKS
FLANNELS
BRIGHTS
ORIENTALS
AND
JAPANESE
TAUPES

All Books 20 % OFF Everyday

Over 100 Inspiring Samples

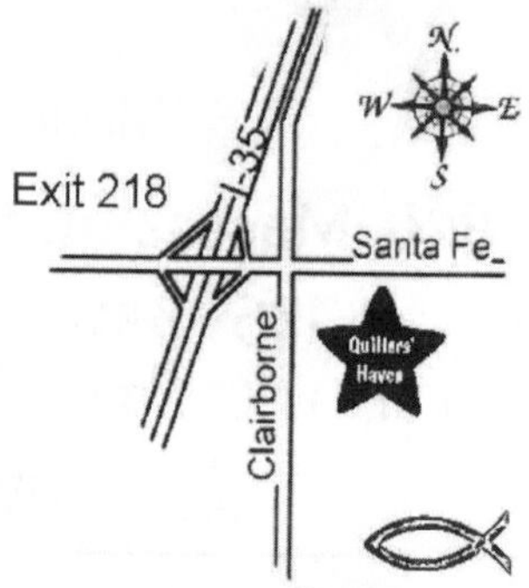

116 N. Clairborne Rd #B
Olathe KS 66062
913.764.8600

www.quiltershaven.com

Olathe, KS #50

Baldwin City, KS #51

Mon - Sat 10 - 5

Quilters' Paradise

713 8th St., P.O. Box 646 66006
(785) 594-3477 Est: 1986
Owner: Sharon A. Vesecky
quiltfabsupply@yahoo.com
www.quiltingfabricsupply.com

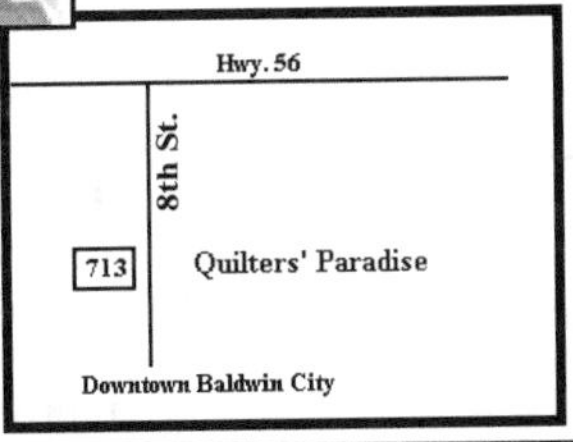

Quilting supplies, books, patterns, fabric—Hoffman, Jinny Beyer, Springs, Maywood Studio, Moda, Batiks & Flannels and many others. KenQuilt Quilting Machines.

Quilts on Display

Quilting Bits & Pieces

Over 5200 square feet of Quilter's Playland, with oodles of finished quilts to inspire you. Our special areas of interest include applique and embroidery. We carry only top quality fabrics with corresponding fat quarters, separated into special sections of 30's, batiks, contemporary and our famous color wall.

Eudora, KS #52

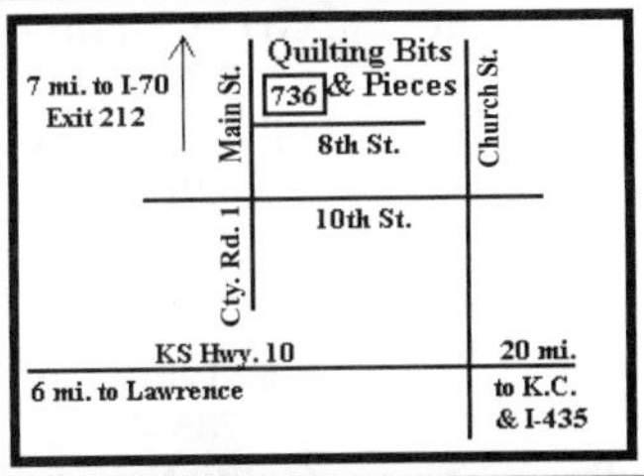

M, W, F 9:30 - 5 T & Th 9:30 - 7 Sat 9:30 - 4

Website: www.eudoraquiltshop.com
Est: 1997 (785) 542-2080
e-mail: bitsnpieces@sunflower.com

736 Main St. 66025 877-639-2080

Shawnee, KS #53

Prairie Point

Fabrics, Quilting Supplies & Classes

Better Homes and Gardens Quilt Sampler FEATURED SHOP 2006

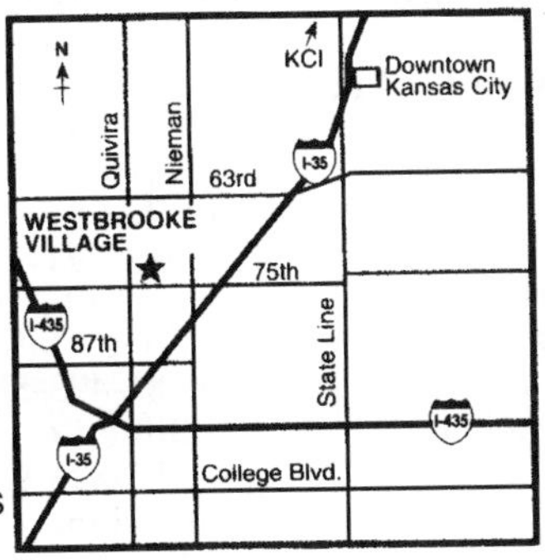

Prairie Point is a full service shop for all your quilting needs. 5000 bolts of the best fabrics, the newest notions, innovative books and patterns and a variety of kits will all make your quiltmaking a pleasure. We offer classes for all quilting levels and all quilting techniques. Our friendly and knowledgeable staff is ready to serve you.
Stop in for a visit!

Store Hours:
Mon & Wed 10:00-8:30
Tues & Thurs 10:00-5:30
Fri & Sat 10:00-5:00
Sunday 1:00-5:00

www.prairiepoint.com

Our website lists the current class offerings, special events and block-of-the-month programs that are so popular at Prairie Point.

Prairie Point is located in Suburban Kansas City

7341 Quivira Rd.
Shawnee, KS 66216
(913) 268-3333
Toll Free (888) 268-5606
email:prairieptquilts@aol.com

Hiawatha, KS #54

Tues - Fri 10 - 6
Sat 10 - 4

Sunflower Quilt Shop

718 Oregon St. 66434 (785) 742-4343
Owner: Linda Duesing Est: 2001
1550 sq.ft. 2000 Bolts
www.sunflowerquiltshop.net

Full service quilt shop offering fabrics, notions, books, patterns, classes, custom machine quilting. Friendly helpful service.

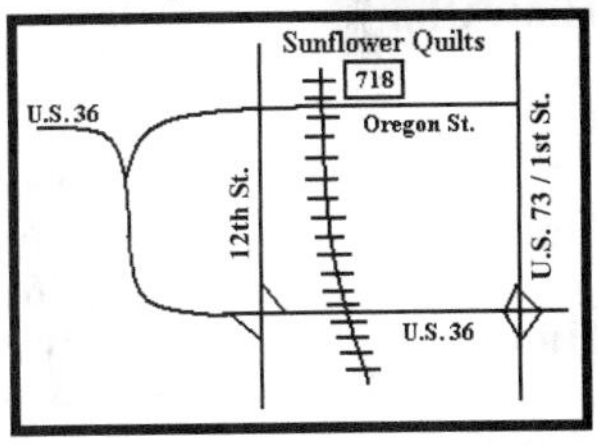

Kansas Quilt Shops

Abilene — Material Girls, 307 N. Cedar St. 785-263-7787

Alden — **Prairie Flower Crafts, 205 Pioneer St.** **620-534-3551** **See ad #23, page 212**

Argonia — Quilters Nook, 106 N Main St 620-435-6961

Baldwin City — **Quilters' Paradise, 713 8th St.** **785-594-3477** **See ad #51, page 219**

Belleville — **Sew Country, 1834 M St.** **785-527-2332** **See ad #14, page 211**

Burlingame — **Great Plains Quilt Co., 119 W. Santa Fe Ave.** **785-654-3303** **See ad #44, page 216**

Burlington — **Silver Threads & Golden Needles, 321 Neosho** **620-364-8233** **See ad #34, page 214**

Chanute — Simple Creations, 216 W Main St 620-212-3149

Chapman — Mother & Me Fabrics, 422 Glick 785-922-6190

Cimarron — Country Dumplings, 203 N. Main St. 620-855-4686

Colby — **The Quilt Cabin, 1525 S. Range Ave.** **785-462-3375** **See ad #8, page 210**

Colby — **Colby Sew and Vac,1015 Taylor Ave.** **785- 460-1900** **See ad #9, page 210**

Concordia — **Fabric Essentials, 116 W 6th St.** **785-243-4044** **See ad #18, page 212**

Copeland — **Sunflower Creations, 23403 2 Rd.** **620- 668-5584** **See ad #2, page 209**

Derby — **Sunflower Quilts, 405 Osage Rd.** **316-788-5120** **See ad #33, page 214**

Dexter — Creek Water Wool Works, 216 S. Maple 620-876-5666

Downs — Stuff N Such, 801 Morgan Ave. 785-454-3416

Emporia — **Prairie Pieces Quilt Shop, 911 Commercial St.** **620-342-9110** **See ad #39, page 216**

Eudora — **Quilting Bits & Pieces, 736 Main St.** **785-542-2080** **See ad #52, page 219**

Garden City — **Bar K Fabrics, 402 E. Fulton St.** **620-275-7689** **See ad #4, page 209**

Garnett — Country Fabrics, 108 E. 5th Ave. 785-448-0003

Hays — **Quilt Cottage Co., 2520 Vine St.** **785-625-0080** **See ad #13, page 211**

Hiawatha — **Sunflower Quilt Shop, 718 Oregon St.** **785-742-4343** **See ad #54, page 219**

Hillsboro — **Quilts & QuiltRacks, 130 N. Main St.** **620-947-2222** **See ad #22, page 212**

Holton — **Quilting on the Square, 400 Pennsylvania** **785-364-4050** **See ad #16, page 211**

Humboldt — **Heavenly Kneads & Threads Plus, 724 Bridge** **620-473-2408** **See ad #32, page 214**

Hutchinson — **Cottonwood Quilts, 126 N. Main** **620-662-2245** **See ad #24, page 213**

Hutchinson — **Country Fabrics, 6411-D W. Morgan Rd.** **620-662-3681** **See ad #25, page 213**

Independence — **Lillie's Classic Quilts, 113 W. Myrtle St.** **620-331-4690** **See ad #29, page 213**

Independence — Stella's Quilt-N-Frabrics, 4530 CR 6000 620-325-5378

Johnson City — **The Old Store, 112 S. Main** **620-492-1478** **See ad #3, page 209**

Kiowa — Clark's Fabric Shop, 605 Main St. 620-825-4985

Lakin — **Red Rooster Quilt Shop, 108 N. Main St.** **620-355-7808** **See ad #5, page 210**

Lawrence — **Stitch on Needlwork Shop, 926 Massachusetts** **785-842-1101** **See ad #48, page 217**

Lawrence — Sarah's Fabrics, 925 Massachusetts 785-842-6198

Leavenworth — **The Quilter's Quarters, Inc., 200 S. 5th St** **913-651-6510** **See ad #49, page 218**

Leavenworth — Sew Much More, 301 Delaware St. 913-651-6664

Leavenworth — Lac Quilt Shop, 426 Miami St. 913-682-7873

Leoti — Prairie Flower Quilt Co., 102 S. Indian Rd. 620-375-2044

Liberal — **Quilted Treasures, 215 N. Kansas** **620-624-8192** **See ad #1, page 209**

Manhattan — **All About Quilts, 8651 E. US Hwy. 24** **785-539-6759** **See ad #17, page 212**

Mankato — **Hidden Treasures Quilt Shop, 101 N. Commercial** **785-378-8020** **See ad #15, page 211**

Newton — **Charlotte's Sew Natural, 710 N. Main St.** **316-284-2547** **See ad #26, page 213**

Newton — **Charlotte's Bargain, 601 SE 36th St. #103** **316-804-4660** **See ad #27, page 213**

Norton — **Stitch Up A Storm, 113 West Main St.** **785-874-5152** **See ad #12, page 210**

Oberlin — **Country Quilting & Keepsakes** **310 W. Commercial** **785-475-2411** **See ad #11, page 210**

Olathe — **Quilters' Haven, 116 N. Clairborne Rd. #B** **913-764-8600** **See ad #50, page 218**

Osawatomie — **Happy Crafters Quilt Shop, 1935 Parker** **913-755-4360** **See ad #40, page 216**

Ottawa — **Chris' Corner Quilt Shop, 3593 N Hwy. 59** **785-242-1922** **See ad #42, page 216**

Overbrook — **Overbrook Quilt Connection, 500 Maple** **785-665-7841** **See ad #45, page 216**

Overland Park — **Harper's Fabrics, 7918 Santa Fe Dr.** **913-648-2739** **See ad #43, page 216**

Overland Park — Addadi's Fabrics, 9629 West 87th St. 913-381-9705

Paola — **Lil' Red Hen Quilt Shop, 913 N. Pearl #1** **913-294-5230** **See ad #41, page 216**

Phillipsburg — Quilting Fool, 204 E Union Rd 785-543-2635

Salina — **Quilting Station, 212 E Iron** **785-493-5625** **See ad #19, page 212**

Salina — **Quilting Bee, 120 S. Santa Fe Ave.** **785-823-9376** **See ad #20, page 212**

Salina — **Emporium, 1833 S. 9th St.** **785-823-1515** **See ad #21, page 212**

Scott City — **Buttons & More, 415 Main St.** **620-872-7112** **See ad #7, page 210**

Seneca — The Quilt Basket, 802 North St. 785-336-2133

Severy — **Itchin To Stitch, 1590 20th St.** **620-736-2040** **See ad #31, page 214**

Severy — **Needle in a Haystack, 207 Q Rd.** **620-736-2942** **See ad #30, page 213**

Shawnee — **Prairie Point Quilts, 7341 Quivira Rd.** **913-268-3333** **See ad #53, page 219**

St Francis — **Sainty Stitches Fabric, 113 W Washington St** **785-332-2339** **See ad #10, page 210**

Syracuse — **Quilter's Stash, 123 N. Main** **620-384-5390** **See ad #6, page 210**

Topeka — **Fabric Corner, 5331 SW 22nd Place** **785-271-7667** **See ad #47, page 217**

Topeka — **Stitching Traditions, 3005 SW Topeka Blvd.** **785-266-4130** **See ad #46, page 216**

Topeka — Bennett's Sewing Center , 2125 N. Kansas 785-232-9117

Wichita — **Material Girls Quilts, 535 W Douglas Ste 140** **316-684-5855** **See ad #36, page 214**

Wichita — **Gramma's Calico Cupboard, 1945 S. Hydraulic St.** **316-264-0274** **See ad #37, page 215**

Wichita — **Hen Feathers Quilt Shop, 110 N Rock Rd** **316-652-9599** **See ad #38, page 215**

Wichita — **Picket Fence Quilt Co., 7130 W. Maple #230** **316-558-8899** **See ad #35, page 214**

Wichita — Attic Heirlooms, 1705 W. Douglas 316-265-4646

Wichita — Needles and Notions, 2441 N. Maize Rd. 316-722-5959

Winchester — Aunt Sadie's Quilt Shop, 208 Winchester 913-774-7455

Yoder — **Demelia's Quilt Co., 3406 E. Red Rock Rd.** **620-465-2505** **See ad #28, page 213**

Kansas Quilt Shows

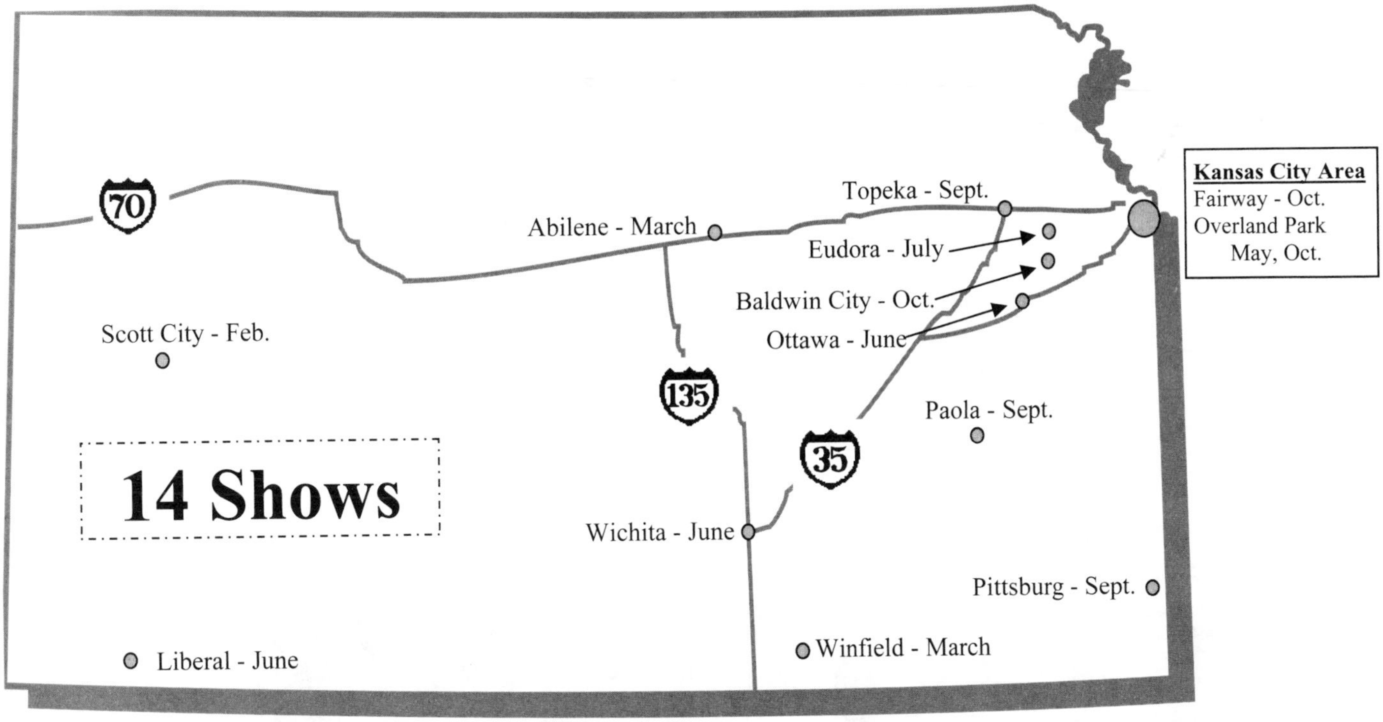

About Shows: We are listing only the very basic information about shows that happen on a regular schedule here. Please check out our website for more details on each show. Also this information tends to change quite often so please verify the event with our website or a local source before you venture far. Or if you're in the right area at the right time, give it a shot.

If you are a show organizer, please keep us updated on your event.
shows@quilterstravelcompanion.com www.quilterstravelcompanion.com

On our website you will also find:
- Exact dates (when we have them)
- Contact Information
- Events happening on a one-time basis
- Sponsor Information
- Description of Event

Month	City	Schedule	Show	Location with address
February				
	Scott City	Annual, 3rd Fri & Sat in February	Scott City Quilt Guild Show	William Carpenter 4-H Bldg - Fairgrounds, 400 E. Fair Grounds Rd.
March				
	Abilene	Annual, Last two weeks of March	Ida Stover Eisenhower Memorial Quilt Show	Dickinson County Heritage Center, 412 S. Campbell
	Winfield	Odd Years, Late March or Early April	Quilters' Heaven Quilt Show	Winfield Middle School, 130 Viking Blvd.
June				
	Overland Park	Annual, May or June	Machine Quilters Showcase	Overland Park Convention Center, 6000 College Blvd.
	Liberal	Every 3 years, 1st Fri & Sat of June, last in 2009	Affair of the Heart Quilt Show	Seward County Activity Center, 810 N. Stadium Dr.
	Ottawa	Annual, 3rd weekend of June	Sunflower Piecemakers Quilt Show	Ottawa Middle School, 13th & Ash
	Wichita	Even Years, 4th weekend of June	Common Threads Quilt Show	Bob Brown Expo Hall, 225 W. Douglas
July				
	Eudora	Annual, 2nd Fri & Sat in July	Eudora Quilt Show	Eudora Middle School, 2635 Church St.
September				
	Pittsburg	Annual, Labor Day Weekend	Little Balkans Quilt Show	Pittsburg Memorial Auditorium, 503 N. Pine
	Topeka	Annual, 3rd weekend in September	Silver Threads & Golden Memories	Topeka Women's Club, 5221 SW West Dr.
	Paola	Annual, last weekend of September	Miami County Quilt Guild Show	Paola Middle School, 405 Hospital Dr.
October				
	Fairway	Annual, 2nd weekend in October	Starlight Quilters Guild Quilt Show	Shawnee Indian Mission, 3403 W. 53rd St.
	Overland Park	Annual, 2nd weekend in October	The Blue Valley Quilters Guild Show	Presbyterian Church of Stanley, 14895 Antioch Road
	Baldwin City	Annual, 3rd weekend in October	Maple Leaf Festival Quilt Show	Elementary School, 7th & Chapel Sts.

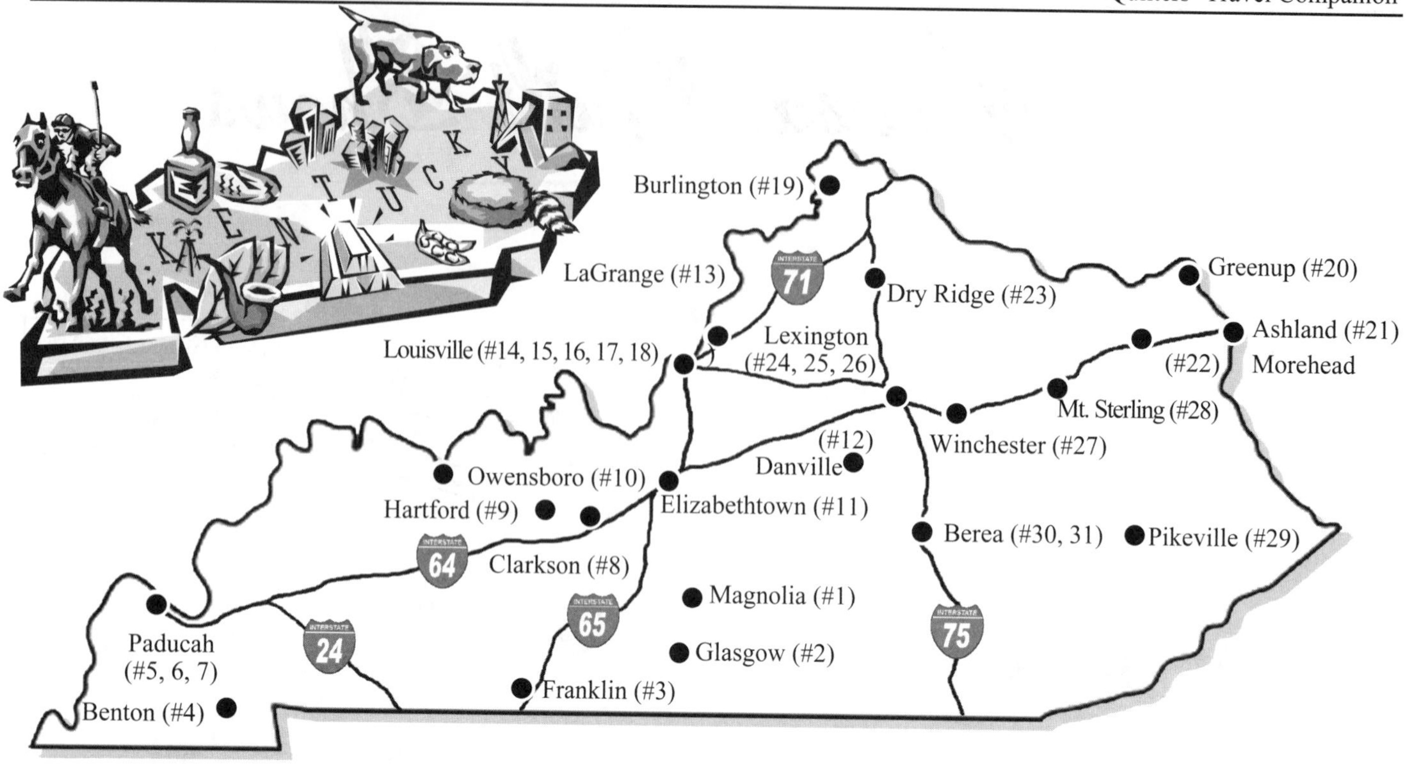

KENTUCKY

31 Featured Shops

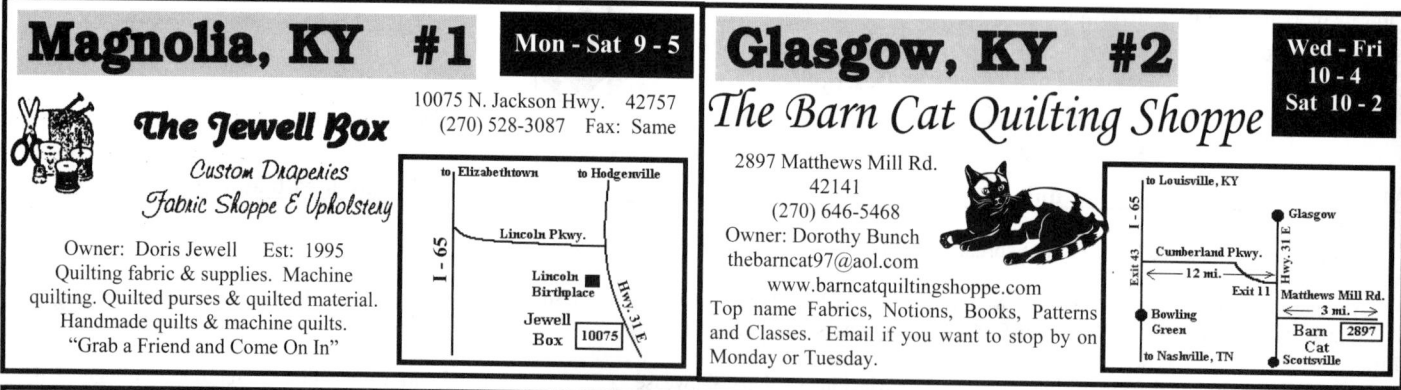

Magnolia, KY #1

Mon - Sat 9 - 5

The Jewell Box

Custom Draperies
Fabric Shoppe & Upholstery

10075 N. Jackson Hwy. 42757
(270) 528-3087 Fax: Same

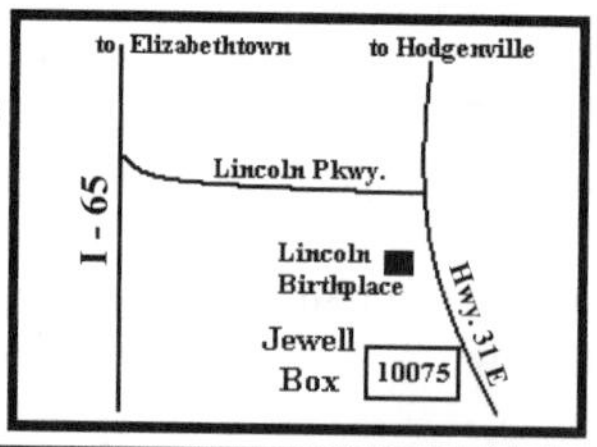

Owner: Doris Jewell Est: 1995
Quilting fabric & supplies. Machine quilting. Quilted purses & quilted material. Handmade quilts & machine quilts.
"Grab a Friend and Come On In"

Glasgow, KY #2

Wed - Fri 10 - 4
Sat 10 - 2

The Barn Cat Quilting Shoppe

2897 Matthews Mill Rd.
42141
(270) 646-5468
Owner: Dorothy Bunch
thebarncat97@aol.com
www.barncatquiltingshoppe.com

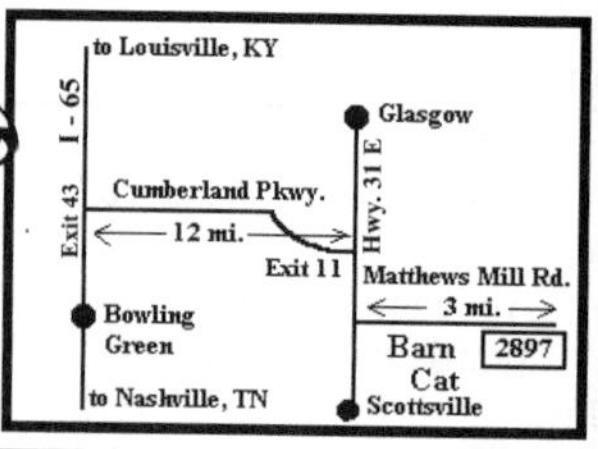

Top name Fabrics, Notions, Books, Patterns and Classes. Email if you want to stop by on Monday or Tuesday.

Franklin, KY #3

Tues - Fri 10 - 5
Sat 10 - 4

A Quilter's Fabric Garden

107 W. Cedar St. 42134
(270) 598-7767 Est: 2004 2000+ sq.ft.
djsew@aol.com Newsletter
www.quiltersfabricgarden.com

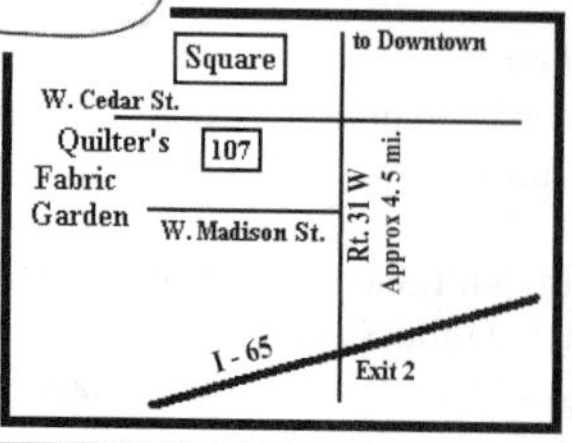

Good Selection of Thimbleberries, MODA, Reproduction Fabrics, Quilting Supplies, Books, Patterns & Kits. Wool & Wool Felt. Classes.

Benton, KY #4

Tues - Fri 10 - 5
Sat 9 - 2

Piece of Mind Quilting & Crafts

1209 Poplar St. 42025
(270) 527-2487
Owner: Bev Barrett

Owner: Bev Barrett
info@pieceofmindky.com
www.pieceofmindky.com

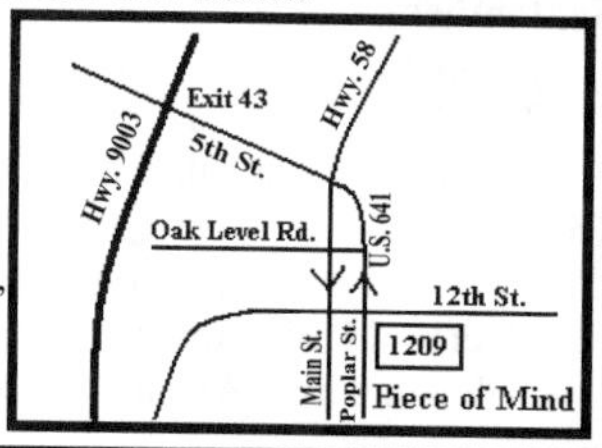

See us for your quilting and crafting needs. We have fabric, notions, embroidery supplies, patterns, Jack Dempsey Needle Arts and other craft supplies. We have a variety of classes each month that include quilt piecing and quilting, basket weaving and more.

Quilt in a Day

Home of Eleanor Burns

100% Cotton Fabric - Batiks
Reproductions - Sale Fabrics - Books
DVD's - Notions - Baby Lock - Gammill
and a Friendly Helpful Staff!

119 North 4th Street
Paducah, KY · 42001
(270)-442-2155
www.quiltinaday.com

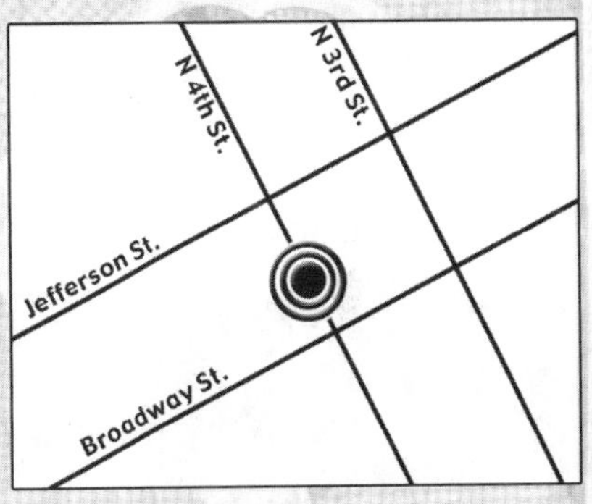

Paducah, KY #5

"The Little House with the Big Quilt Shop Inside"

Paducah, KY #6

(270) 443-5673
420 North 4th St. 42001
Owner: Pat English
Est: 1989

Designer Fabrics - Patterns - Classes - Books
Newest Notions - Brazilian Embroidery Supplies
Lace Making - Fabric Painting
Quilter's Jewelry - Tools or Gadgets
We do mail order on all those Hard-To-Finds
Janome Sewing and
Quilting Machines.

Quilters Alley

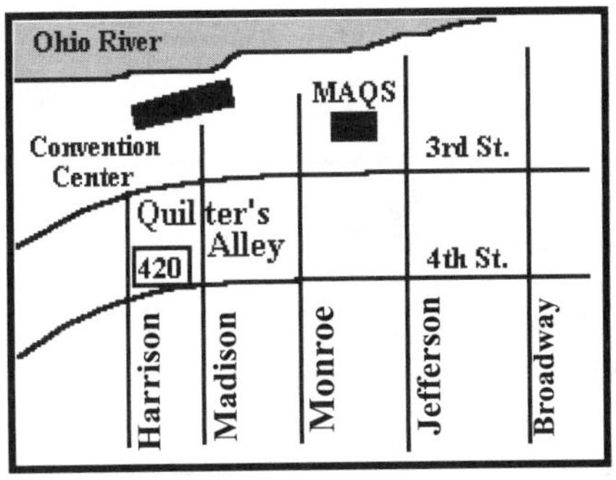

www.quiltersalleypaducah.com

Entrance on 3rd St. at 419
New Parking Area—Right across from Convention Center

Mon - Sat 10 - 5

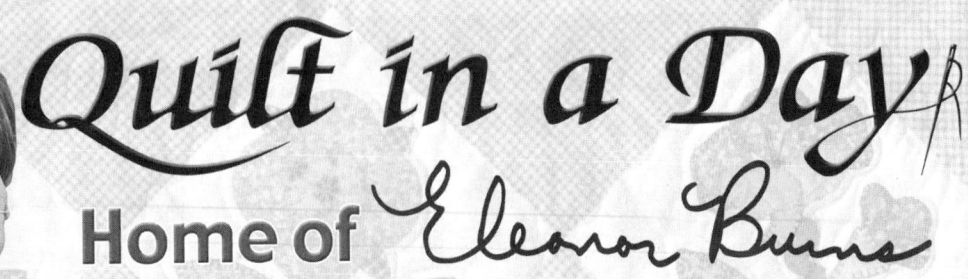

THE NATIONAL QUILT MUSEUM

Expanding the Vision, Advancing the Art

#7

Shadows of Umbria, Diane Gaudynski

Vibrant art exhibits
150 superb contemporary and traditional quilts

Museum Shop with regionally and nationally fine crafted pottery, glass, jewelry and gifts

215 Jefferson St • Paducah, KY • 270.442.8856
Open Year-round: Mon-Sat 10-5. Also, Apr-Oct Sun 1-5

VISIT US!
For a complete calendar of exhibits and workshops, go to NationalQuiltMuseum.org!

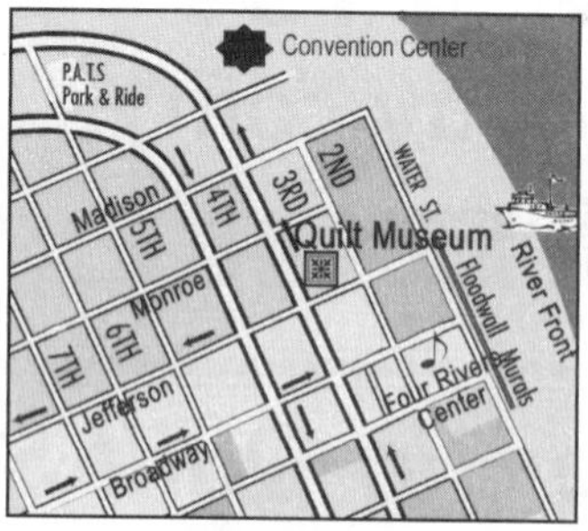

KENTUCKY Arts COUNCIL

The Kentucky Arts Council, the state arts agency, supports The National Quilt Museum with state tax dollars and federal funding from the National Endowment for the Arts.

Clarkson, KY #8

Mon - Fri 10 - 5
Sat 10 - 2

Sew Much More Sewing Center

120 W. Main St. 42726
(270) 242-3349
Owner: Dixie Franklin Est: 2005
sewmuchmore@windstream.net

Come in and join all the fun. We're a full service quilt shop here to help with all your quilting needs. We'd be happy to help you plan your next quilt.

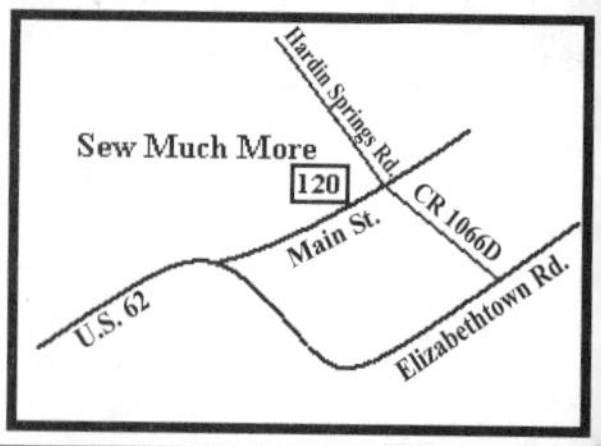

Hartford, KY #9

Mon - Fri 10 - 6
Sat 10 - 4

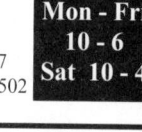

Quilts -R- Jewel's

2260 Country Club Lane 42347
(270) 298-3507 Fax: (270) 298-3502
Est: 2007 600+ bolts
Online ordering thru website.

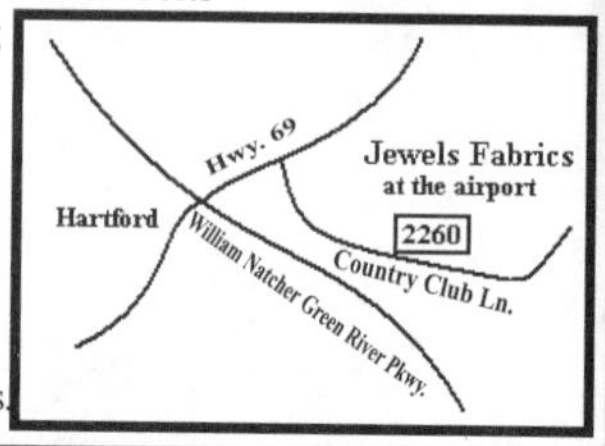

jdfortener@quiltsrjewels.com
www.quiltsrjewels.com
Located at Ohio County Airport. We offer Civil War, 30's, 108" Backing, Longarm Quilting at affordable prices. Full line of Notions.

Owensboro, KY #10

Stychee Woman Studio

219 Williamsburg Square
Owensboro, KY 42303
270-686-7777
paula@stycheewoman.com
www.stycheewoman.com

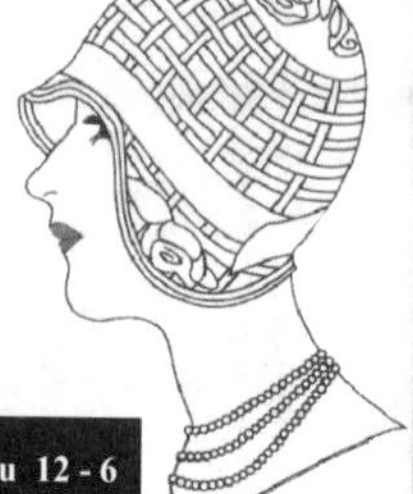

Quilt & Fabric Studio with boutique style projects and samples. An exquisitely decorated Studio that you'll not want to miss. TOP Notch Customer Service.

Tues & Thu 12 - 6
Wed & Fri 10 - 5
Sat 11 - 3

We're between US 231 and Veach Rd on the Owensboro Christian Church Campus/ Williamsburg Shopping Center in Owensboro, 1 mile North of Hwy 60 bypass.

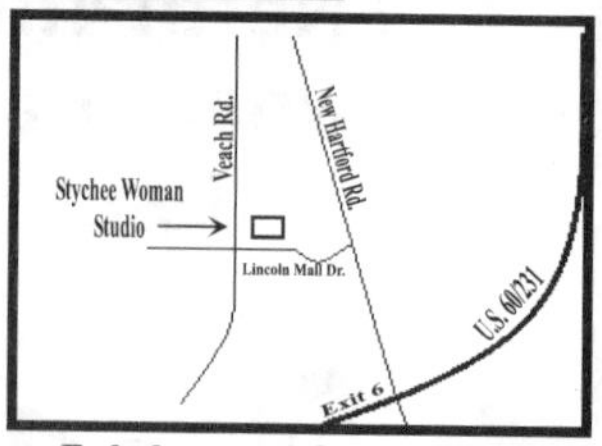

Machine Embroidered Quilts, Fabulous Fabrics and Sassy Projects.

Elizabethtown, KY #11

Mon by Chance
Tues 3 - 9, Wed 9 - 6,
Thur 9 - 9, Fri 9 - 6
Sat 9 - 3
Sun Closed

Uniquely Yours Quilt Shop

2973 Rineyville Rd.
42701
(270) 766-1456

uniquequilts@live.com
Owner: Mary Sennott

Over 4000 bolts of 100% Cotton Fabrics. Books, patterns, notions and classes. Friendly, professional advice. Quilts for sale.

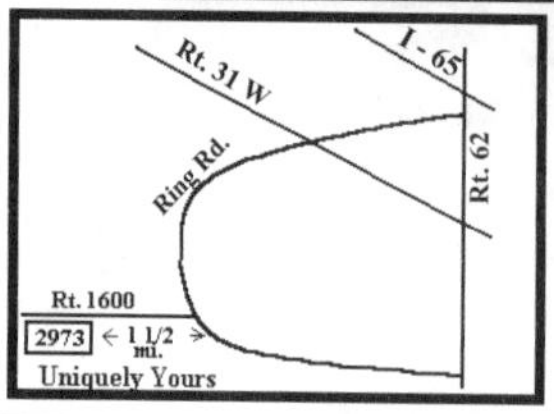

Danville, KY #12

Mon - Fri 10 - 6
Thur til 9
Sat 10 - 4

WILDERNESS ROAD QUILT COMPANY

215 W. Main St. 40422
(859) 236-1175
We're your full line Quilt Shop & Bernina Sewing Center.
Great selection of fine Quilting Cottons, Books, Patterns, Quilting Necessities.
www.wrqcd.com

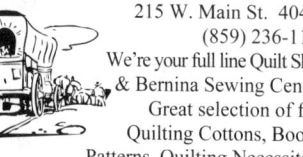

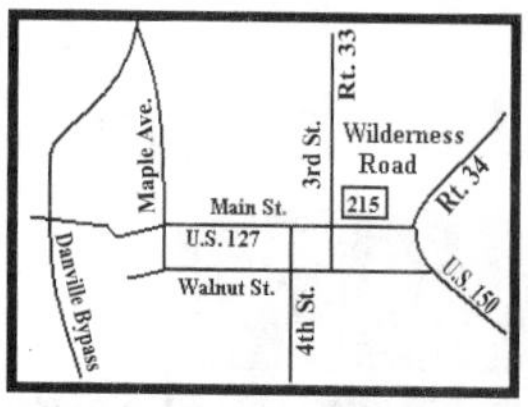

LaGrange, KY #13

Tues - Sat 10 - 5

The Gathering Room

109 E. Washington St. 40031
(502) 222-1044
www.gatheringroomquiltshop.com

Located in Historic LaGrange. Specializing in Civil War Reproduction & Fabrics in a warm color palette.
"Where Quilters Feel at Home"

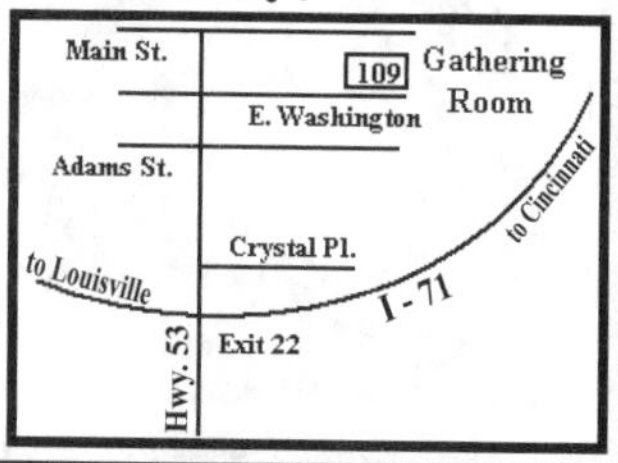

Among Friends Quilt Shop

Louisville, KY #14

9537 Taylorsville Rd.
40299

Est: 2003
6000 sq.ft.

Handi Quilter®
The Undisputed Leader in Home Machine Quilting Systems.

502-261-7377

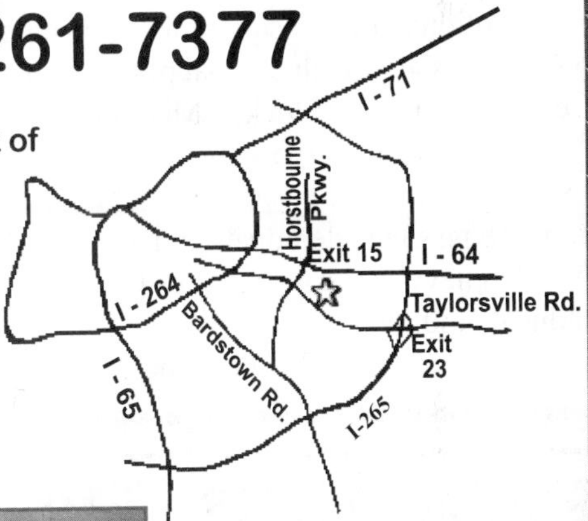

Among Friends Quilt Shop is a must see shop with 6,000 square feet of space and over 6,000 bolts of 100% cotton fabrics, as well as a complete line of quilting notions and thousands of books, patterns and gift items from which to choose. Our shop is not only spacious, it is well-lit to enhance your shopping experience and fabric selection. The full-spectrum lighting offers excellent color-rendering. We offer over 100 classes a year.

Among Friends Quilt Shop is a family-friendly quilt shop with something for everyone. Enjoy a cup of complimentary coffee, while watching TV or reading the newspaper in the café area. There are children's books and toys to entertain the little ones while mom shops.

Mon-Fri 9:30-6:00
Thurs 9:30-8:00
Sat 9:30-3:00

While here, ask for a demonstration of the Handi Quilter quilting machines and see for yourself that quality and affordability is available to you. Handi Quilter quilting machines are user-friendly and stitch like a dream!

We look forward to seeing you on your travels. The rest of the time, you can shop at Among Friends Quilt Shop on-line 24 hours a day. We are continually adding new products weekly.

Come visit us and discover that while here you are among friends.

www.amongfriendsquiltshop.com

Louisville, KY #15

Happy Heart Quilt Shop

Mon - Fri 10 - 5 Sat 10 - 4

7913 3rd. St. Rd. 40214
(502) 363-1171
Owner: Yvonne Fritze
Est: 1985
3500 sq. ft.

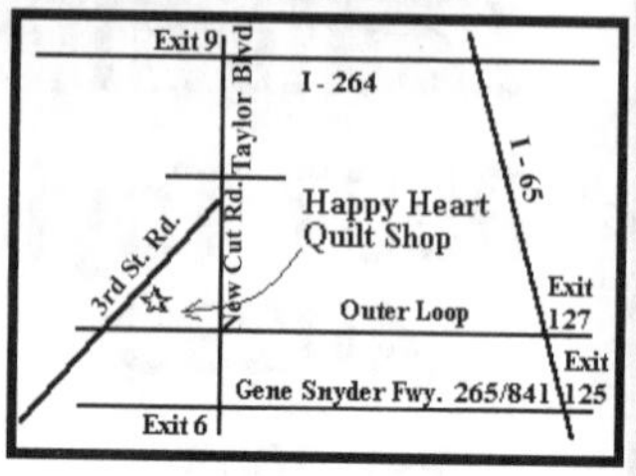

Happy Heart Quilt Shop is located ten minutes from I - 264, exit 9; or I - 65 exit 127, Kentucky Fair & Exposition Center and Louisville International Airport. There is a vast array of fabrics, 5000 bolts, in most major fabric lines, hundreds of books, patterns, stencils and notions in 3500 square feet of shopping space. Quilt kits are available—applique, cross-stitch, whole cloth, and pieced blocks. Merchandise is displayed on spacious shelving and antique pieces. Special features for customers include newsletters, classes, retreats, sales, demonstrations and problem solving. We also have two day-long bus trips to the AQS Shows in Paducah and Knoxville, TN each year. We are well known for our friendly service and our love of quilting.

Louisville, KY #16 & 17

The Smocking Shoppe

2 Great Locations

3829 Staebler Ave.
St. Matthews 40207
(502) 893-3503

169 S. English Station
Landis Lakes 40245
(502) 409-9664

We are Louisville's exclusive dealer for BERNINA, BROTHER and HUSQVARNA VIKING sewing machines, sergers and accessories. We retail the finest quality fabrics, trims, notions, books and patterns. We have the latest software to support all brands of embroidery machines. Our specialties include English smocking, heirloom and other fine sewing as well as quilting and wearable art. We offer a full range of classes.

info@smockingshop.com Online newsletter

www.smockingshop.com

HOURS:
Both Shops
Mon - Thurs 9:30 - 5:30
Fri 9:30 - 5
Sat 9:30 - 4

Est: 1981

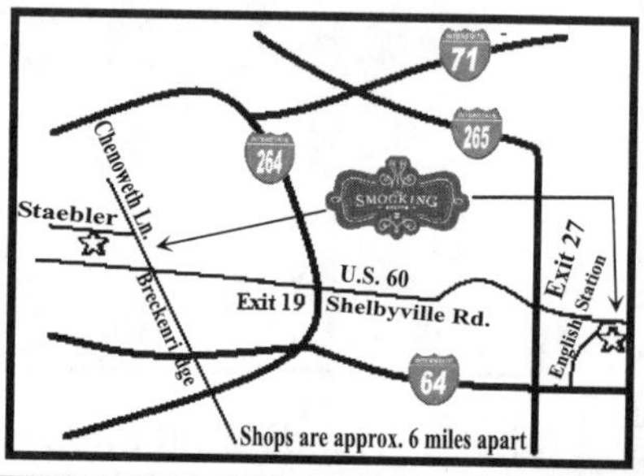

Louisville, KY #18

Mon - Thur 10 - 6
Fri - Sat 10 - 4

Forget Me Knot Quilt Shoppe
Classes • Quilting Fabric

1250 Bardstown Rd. 40204
Inside the Mid-City Mall
(502) 458-6868
Owners: Sue Clark, Darlene Roby & Carol Heil
Est: 2003
quiltshoppe@bellsouth.net

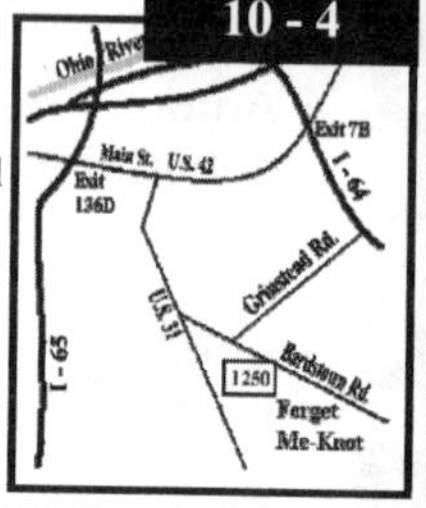

Central location with 5000 bolts of fabric.
Books, notions, patterns classes, block-of-the-month.
Friendly help plus National teachers.
"Jingle Bell Shop Hop" every July

Burlington, KY #19

Mon - Fri 10 - 6
Sat 10 - 4

Cabin Arts

5878 N. Jefferson St. 41005
(859) 586-8021
Owner: Linda Whittenburg
Est: 1992 2200 sq.ft. 5000 Bolts
Linda@cabinarts.com
www.cabinarts.com

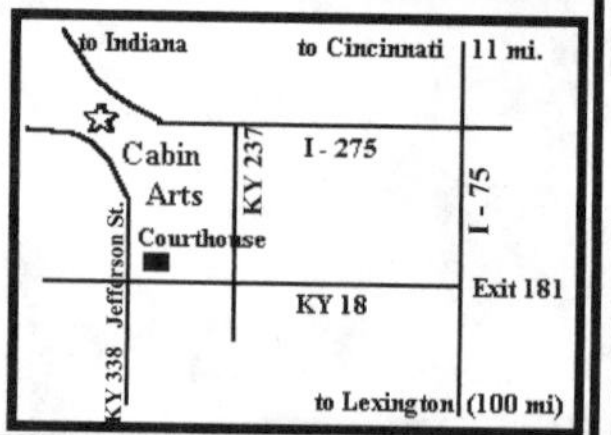

Quality Quilt Fabrics plus notions, books & more. Local Handcrafted Treasures. Classes available. Located in the Historic District in an 1850's Log Cabin.

Greenup, KY #20

Tues - Sat 10 - 5

Mom's Cotton Shop

2035 Ashland Rd. 41144
(606) 473-2164
Owner: Sue Branham

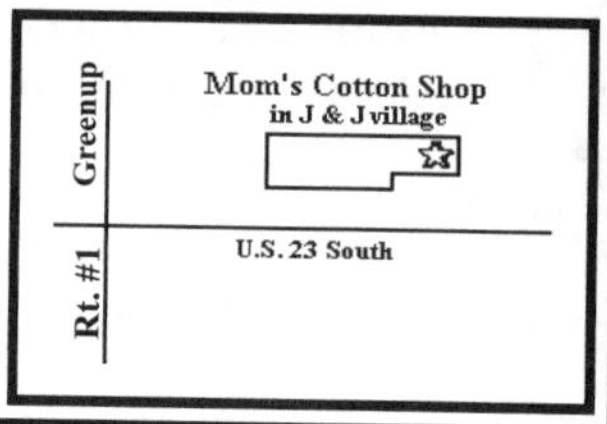

Over 1200 Bolts
Notions, Books, Patterns, Classes & Kits.

Ashland, KY #21

Mon - Fri 10 - 4:30
Closed Wed & Sun
Sat 10 - 12

Craft Attic Quilt Shop

2027 Hoods Creek Pike 41102
(606) 325-1212
Owner: Donnie Maggard
Est: 1982 1500 sq.ft. 1000 Bolts
dmag999893@aol.com

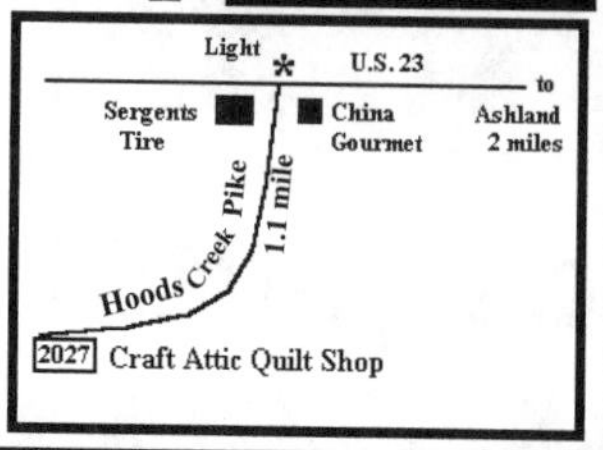

100% Cotton Fabrics.
Full Line of Quilting Supplies.
Books , Stencils , Classes

Calico Patch Quilt Shop

155 Bluebank Road
Morehead, KY 40351
(606) 784-7235
www.calicopatch.net

TUE-FRI
10 - 5
SAT
9 - 2

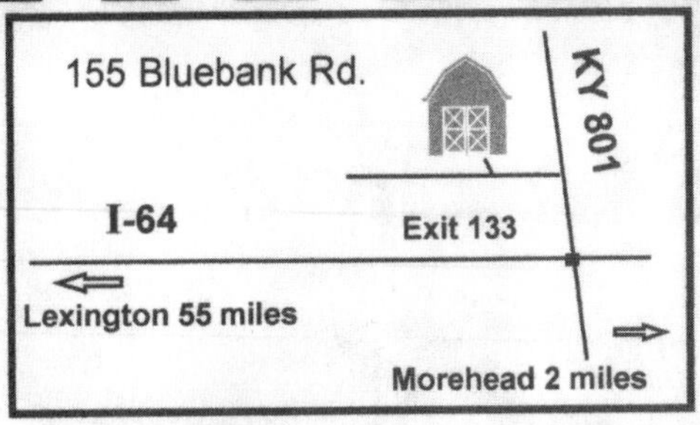

1.5 Miles From I-64

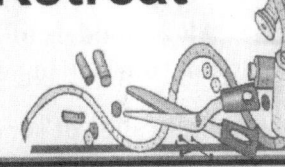

Check out our
SEWED INN
Quilting Retreat
Vacation
Home

BERNINA
Nothing Sews Like A Bernina. Nothing.

Morehead, KY #22

The Quilt Box

#23

Est. 1983

Just 3 miles from I-75 - Exit 159 (Hwy. 467 W) Dry Ridge KY 41035 (859)824-4007

- A Better Homes & Garden Top 10 Quilt Shop. One of Kentucky's best

Come Visit!!

Unique Country Atmosphere 5,000 bolts of fabric, books, patterns, notions & gifts. Knowledgeable & Friendly staff

You'll be glad you came & weather permitting are welcome to enjoy the patio & deck or stroll the gardens.

Monday-Saturday 9:30am 5:00pm Closed on Sunday
PO Box 9 Dry Ridge KY 41035 E Mail: thequiltbox @ wkybb.net

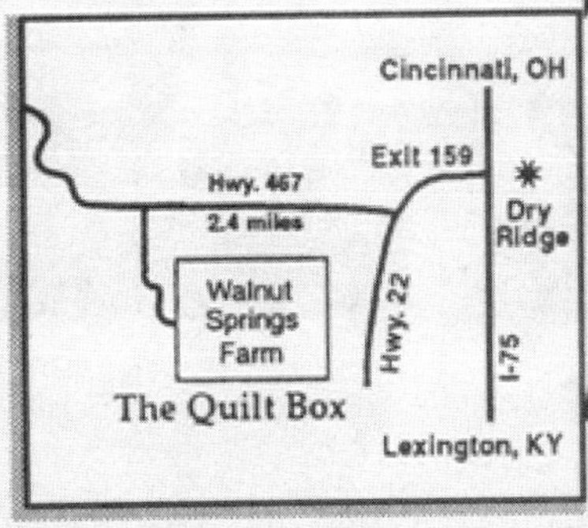

Q-first in quilting

4383 Harrodsburg Road, Suite 130, Lexington, Kentucky 40513 (859) 554-5800

- **4,000 + bolts of top quality cotton including complete collections, batiks, blenders and civil war.**
- **All 23 models of Bernina machines/sergers available for your sewing experience.**
- **Full range of services, hand and machine quilting, all models of machines repaired, scissors sharpened.**
- **Over 100 years of Quilting/Sewing experience.**
- **Two walls of latest books and patterns.**
- **Arrow and Kangaroo Cabinets: Bernina and Arrow Chairs.**
- **Isacord, Presencia, Gütermann, YLI, King Tut, Weeks Dye Works, and Hand Dyed Twist Threads**

STORE HOURS
Mon-Sat 9:30-5:00

#24

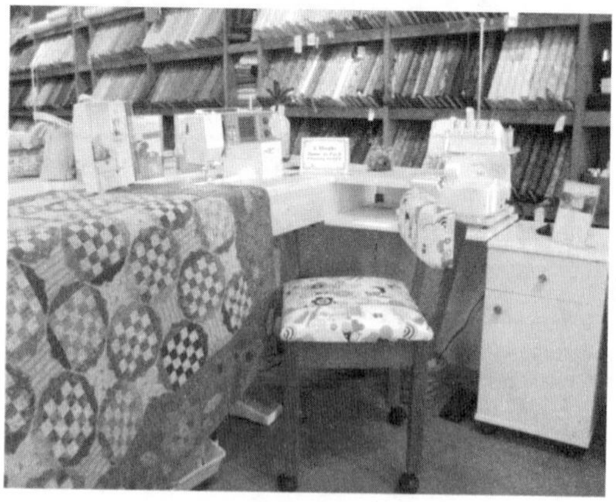

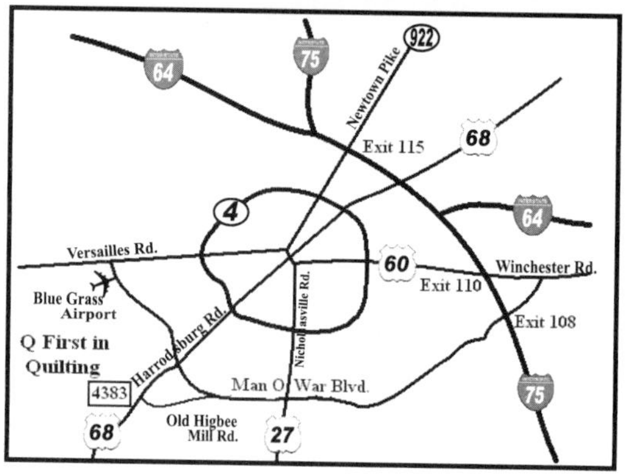

From Bluegrass airport - turn right out of Terminal. First major intersection is Harrodsburg Rd. (US 68). Turn right. Travel to first light, turn Right onto Old Harrodsburg, bear left to stay on main road and travel to the last row of shops in The South Elkhorn Village.

Look for the big Q.

From the 64/75 merge take the Newtown Pike, Bluegrass Pkwy. exit. Travel toward downtown. Travel on Newtown Pike to Circle 4. Exit on right, travel around circle 4 until you can exit right onto Harrodsburg Rd. (US68) bear right and travel across Man-O-War and turn right at First Light, Old Harrodsburg Rd., bear left to come to the back of The South Elkhorn Village.

www.qfirstky.com

Sew-A-Lot
Creative Sewing Centers

Two Store Locations

2160 Sir Barton Way
Lexington, Kentucky 40509
859-264-7472
sewliz@earthlink.net

232 N. Main St.
Centerville, Ohio 45459
937-433-7474
sewalot@erinet.com

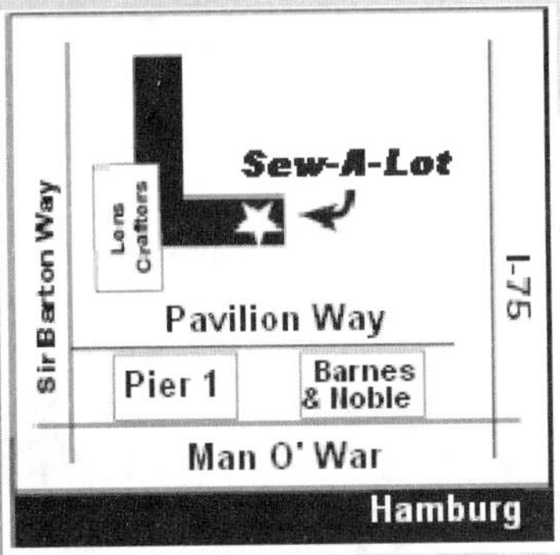

Lexington, Kentucky #25

Centerville, Ohio

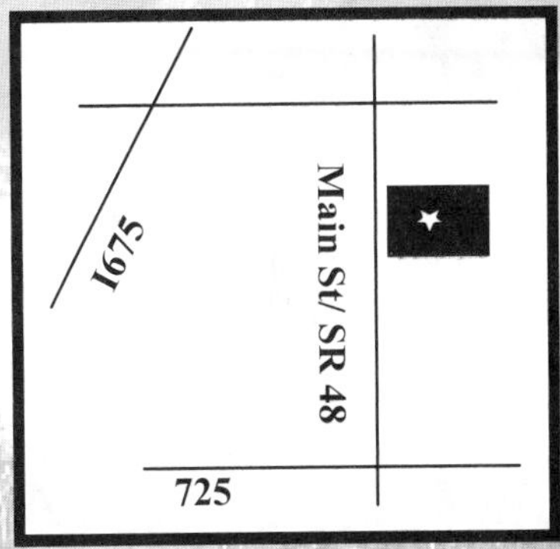

Authorized **PFAFF** Machine Dealer
Husqvarna Viking Dealer (Ohio only)
Specializing in **machine embroidery** and **quilting**.
Embroidery Designs, Patterns, Books, Threads, & Notions in stock!
FREE Newsletter and Classes are also available!

Our **Ohio** shop is located in a Historic Building built in 1874, less than half a mile off of I-675 and has
OVER 4500 BOLTS of FABRIC!
Our **Kentucky** shop is easily accessible off of interstate 75 and has
OVER 3000 BOLTS of FABRIC!

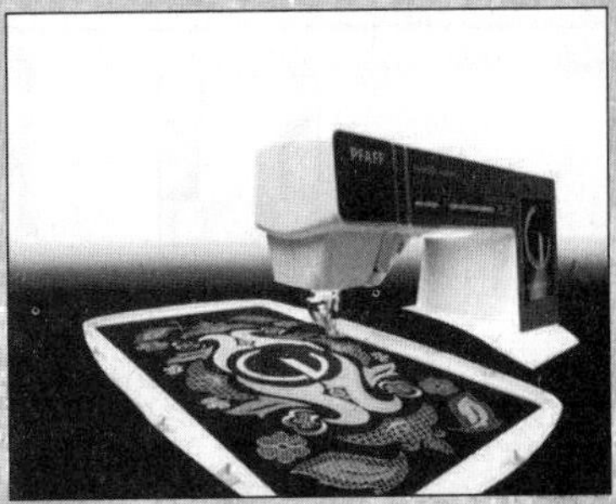

www.sewalotonline.com

Lexington, KY #26

Mon - Fri 10 - 6
Thur til 9
Sat 10 - 5:30

140 Moore Dr. 40503
(859) 278-5010
quilterssquare@insightbb.com
www.quilterssq.com

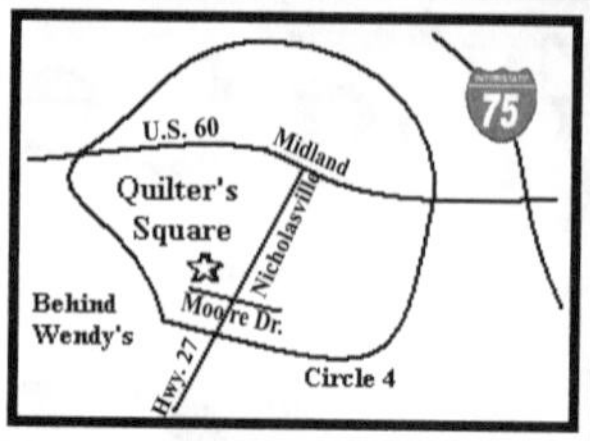

BERNINA

Friendly Service, Exceptional Selection of
FABRIC - BOOKS - PATTERNS - NOTIONS
Check out our classes and gift items
Authorized Bernina Dealer for 20 years & Service

Winchester, KY #27

Judy's Stitch in Time Quilt Shop
Fabrics • Notions • Yarns

67 S. Main St. 40391
859-744-7404
Est: 2006 1200 sq.ft. 1000+ bolts
www.judys-stitch-in-time.com

Mon - Fri 10 - 6
Sat 11 - 7

Tin Lizzie 18 Your Affordable Long Arm Quilters

Located in Historic Downtown Winchester 20 minutes southeast of Lexington. A wide selection of 100% cotton fabrics, books and notions along with needlepoint, cross stitch and DMC floss. Also carrying specialty yarns and needles.

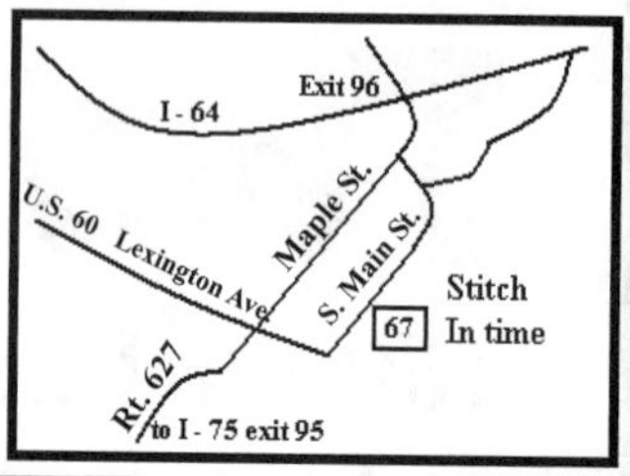

Mt. Sterling, KY 28

Tues - Fri 9 - 5
Sat 9 - 3

Sterling Thimble Quilt Shop

5060 Maysville Rd.
40353
(859) 498-0860

Owner: Becky Hill
beckyhill@roadrunner.com

A full line quilt shop featuring 100% cotton fabrics, books, notions, gifts, quilting supplies and classes.

Conveniently located just 4 miles from I - 64 at Exit 110. Follow Route 11 North away from town. Watch for the sign!

Pikeville, KY #29

Tues - Fri 10 - 6
Sat 10 - 3

Blue Bee Quilting and Fabric Shop

101 Hibbard St.
#200 41501
(606) 432-8616

Owner: Becky Preece
Est: 2009 becky.preece@suddenlink.net
www.bluebeequiltfabric.com

Your source for excellent fabrics, home-made quilts, gifts and more! Our goal is always to provide exceptional service and top-quality goods. Service will be quick and friendly.

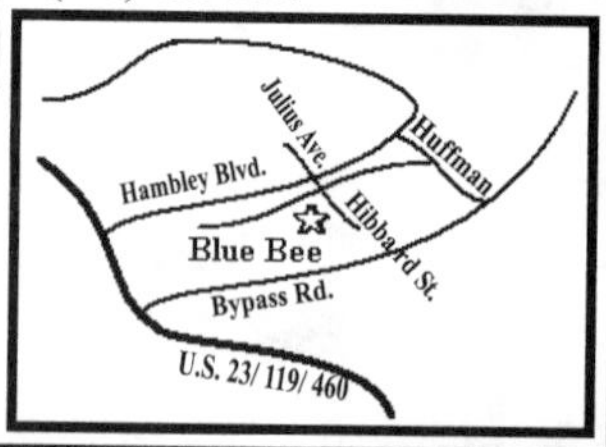

Berea, KY #30

Mon - Sat 10 - 6
Sun 1 - 6

Quilt Shop at Appalachian Arts

102 Center St. 40403
(859) 986-1239
Owners: J. Donald & Nancy Graham
Est: 1976 500 Bolts
aacshop@windstream.net

The Quilt Shop offers regional handmade quilts, fabric, quilting supplies, quilt books, braided baskets, placemats, quilted purses & much more.

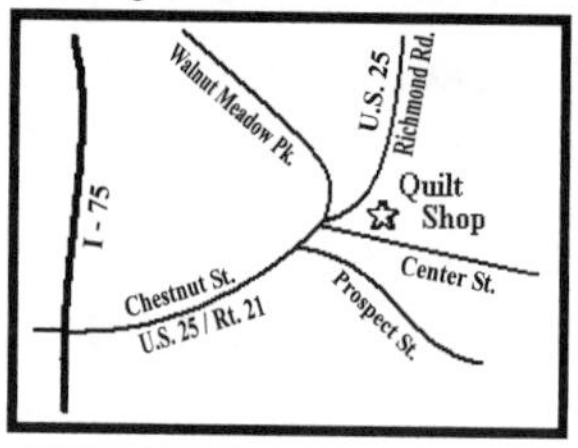

Berea, KY #31

Mon - Sat 10 - 5

Cotton Patch Quilts

210 N. Broadway #1 (Old Town) 40403
(859) 986-1080 Fax: Same
cottonpatchquilts@windstream.net
website: www.cottonpatchky.com
Simple Pantograph's (Machine Quilting) edge-to-edge all over $0.01 per sq. inch.
Specialty fabrics - Moda, Blank, Lakehouse, RJR, David Textiles. Notions, JDempsey Needle Art/Crafts and affordable quilts from $79.99 w/ shams.

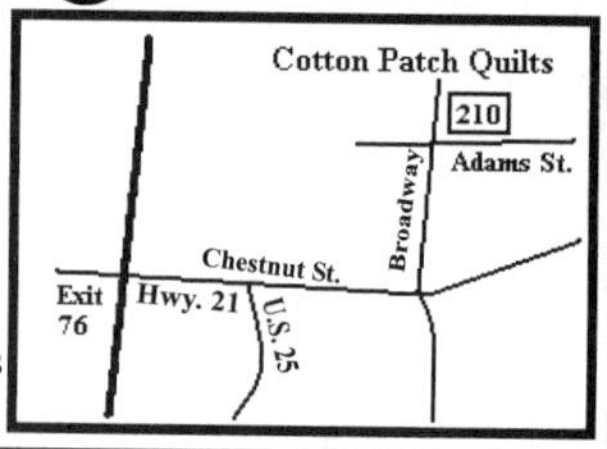

Kentucky Quilt Shops

Ashland	**Craft Attic Quilt Shop, 2027 Hoods Creek Pike**	**606-325-1212**	**See ad #21, page 226**
Ashland	Little Red Hen Quilt Shop, 1901 Central Ave	606-329-2400	
Beaver Dam	Middle of the Woods Fibers, 1391 N Main	270-274-5800	
Benton	**Piece of Mind Quilting & Crafts, 1209 Poplar**	**270-527-2487**	**See ad #2, page 222**
Berea	**Cotton Patch Quilts & Gifts, 210 N. Broadway**	**859-986-1080**	**See ad #31, this page**
Berea	**The Quilt Shop, 102 Center St.**	**859-986-1239**	**See ad #30, this page**
Boaz	Quilting Kaleidoscope, 8510 Old Mayfield	270-534-4808	
Bowling Green	The Kentucky Quilt Co., 1575 Campbell Rd.	270-842-2434	
Burlington	**Cabin Arts 5878 N. Jefferson St.**	**859-586-8021**	**See ad #19, page 226**
Clarkson	**Sew Much More Sewing Center, 120 W. Main S**	**270-242-3349**	**See ad #8, page 224**
Danville	**Wilderness Road Quilt Co., 215 W Main St.**	**859-236-1175**	**See ad #12, page 224**
David	David Appalachian Crafts, 6369 Hwy. 404	606-886-2377	
Drodhead	Quilters' Haven, 262 Bryant Ridge Rd.	606-256-1617	

Dry Ridge **The Quilt Box, 490 E Flynn Rd.** **859-824-4007** **See ad #23, page 227**
Elizabethtown **Uniquely Yours Quilt Shop, 2973 Rineyville** **270-766-1456** **See ad #11, page 224**
Flemingsburg Apron Strings, 2515 Bypass Rd. 606-845-6208
Franklin **A Quilter's Fabric Garden, 107 W. Cedar St.** **270-598-7767** **See ad #3, page 222**
Glasgow **The Barn Cat Quilting, 2897 Matthews-Mill Rd.** **270-646-5468** **See ad #2, page 222**
Greenup **Mom's Cotton Shop, 2035 Ashland Rd.** **606-473-2164** **See ad #20, page 226**
Harlan Berry Patch Quilt Shop, 159 Albert Lane 606-837-2236
Hartford **Jewels Fabrics, 2260 Country Club Ln.** **270-298-3507** **See ad #9, page 224**
Horse Cave Granny's Quilts & More, 481 Flint Ridge Rd. 270-786-4255
Jenkins Fabric Shoppe, 12976 Hwy 805 276-328-4470
LaGrange **The Gathering Room, 109 E. Washington St.** **502- 222-1044** **See ad #13 page 224**
Lexington **Sew-A-Lot Lexington, 2160 Sir Barton Way** **859-264-7472** **See ad #25, page 229 & 411**
Lexington **Q-First in Quilting, 4383 Old Harrodsburg Rd.** **859-554-5800** **See ad #24, page 228**
Lexington **Quilter's Square, 140 Moore Dr.** **859-278-5010** **See ad #26, page 230**
Louisville **Forget-Me-Knot Quilt Shop, 1250 Bardstown** **502-458-6868** **See ad #18, page 226**
Louisville **Happy Heart Quilt Shop, 7913 3rd St. Rd.** **502-363-1171** **See ad #15, page 226**
Louisville **Among Friends Quilt Shop, 9537 Taylorsville** **502-261-7377** **See ad #14, page 225 & 401**
Louisville **The Smocking Shoppe, 3829 Staebler Ave.** **502-893-3503** **See ad #16, page 226**
Louisville **The Smocking Shoppe, 169 S English Station** **502-409-9664** **See ad #17, page 226**
Louisville Austins Sewing Center, 2239 Taylorsville 502-451-9999
Louisville Sew Vintage LLC, 10278 Shelbyville 502-365-2003
Magnolia **The Jewel Box, 10075 N. Jackson Hwy.** **270-528-3087** **See ad #1, page 222**
McKee Carroll's Quilts, 2144 KY Hwy. 2004 606-287-7018
Morehead **Calico Patch Quilt Shop, 155 Bluebank Rd.** **603-784-7235** **See ad #22, page 227**
Mt. Sterling **Sterling Thimble Quilt Shop, 5060 Maysville Rd** **859-498-0860** **See ad #28, page 230**
Murray Murray Sewing Center, 942A S. 12th St 270-759-8400
Newport Beaches Sew and Vac, 700 Monmouth 859-431-1040
Owensboro **Stychee Woman Studio, 219 Williamsburg Sq.** **270-686-7777** **See ad #10, page 224**
Paducah **National Quilt Museum, 215 Jefferson St.** **270-442-8856** **See ad #7, page 224**
Paducah **Quilt in a Day, 119 N. 4th St.** **270-442-2155** **See ad #5, page 223**
Paducah **Quilters Alley, 420 N. 4th St.** **270-443-5673** **See ad #6, page 223**
Paducah Hancocks of Paducah, 3841 Hinkleville 270-443-4410
Paducah English's Sewing Machines, 7001 US Hwy. 68 502-898-7301
Paducah Bryerpatch Studio, 502 N. 5th St. 270-444-8040
Paducah The Guild LLC, 420 Broadway 270-538-0475
Pikeville **Blue Bee Quilting, 101 Hibbard St. #200** **606-432-8616** **See ad #29, page 230**
Pineville Kathy's Needle & Thread, Route #2 606-337-6753
Scottsville Sew Fine Fabrics & Quilts, 460 Rediger 270-237-4883
Smith's Grove Whittle's Fabrics, 3858 Chalybeate Rd. 270-597-2987
Somerset Pauls Surplus, 2286 N US 27 PO Box 751 606-678-4405
Somerset Back Porch Quilt Shop, 211 S. Main 606-676-0636
Whitesburg Cozy Corner, 127 E. Main St. 606-633-9637
Whittley City Agnes Fabric Shop, 66 N Main St. 606-376-8773
Winchester **Judy's Stitch In Time, 67 S. Main St** **859-744-7404** **See ad #27, page 230**

Kentucky Quilt Shows

About Shows: We are listing only the very basic information about shows that happen on a regular schedule here. Please check out our website for more details on each show. Also this information tends to change quite often so please verify the event with our website or a local source before you venture far. Or if you're in the right area at the right time, give it a shot.

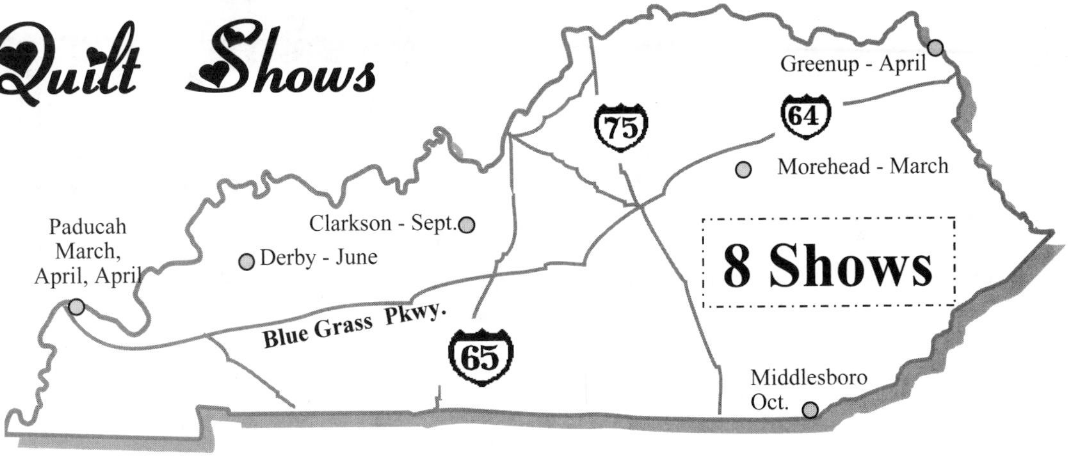

If you are a show organizer, please keep us updated on your event.
shows@quilterstravelcompanion.com www.quilterstravelcompanion.com

Month	City	Schedule	Show	Location with address
March				
	Paducah	Annual, 2nd Sat of March	Quilters Day Out	
	Morehead	Annual, 3rd weekend in March	The Rowan Country Quilt Show	Morehead Conference Center, 111 E. First St.
April				
	Greenup	Annual, 3rd week of April	Greenup County Quilt Club Show	Greenbo Lake State Park Meeting Room, Exit I-64 at Grayson, Left on Rt. 1, 15 miles
	Paducah	Annual, 3rd week in April	Rotary Club of Paducah Show	Paducah Civic Center, 2701 Park Ave.
	Paducah	Annual, Last Wed - Sat of April	American Quilter's Society Quilt Show & Contest	Paducah Expo Center, 1 Executive Blvd.
June				
	Derby	Annual, 1st weekend of June	Derby Days Quilt Show	Derby High School, 920 N. Rock Rd.
September				
	Clarkson	Annual, last weekend of September	Clarkson Quilt Show	Sew Much More, 120 W. Main
October				
	Middlesboro	Annual, 1st weekend of October	Cumberland Mountain Fall Festival	Downtown

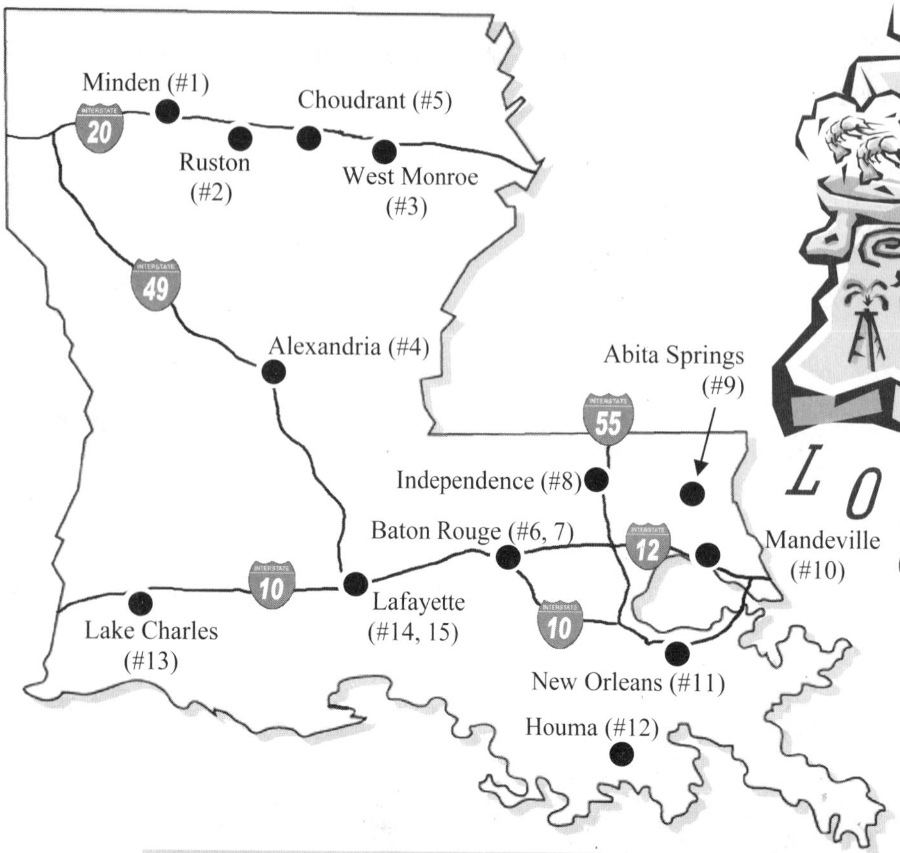

15 Featured Shops

LOUISIANA

Minden, LA #1

Tues - Fri 10 - 5

The Little Country Quilt Shop

534 Old Arcadia Rd. 71055
(318) 377-2462
Owner: Nona Sale Est: 1983

We have approx. 1000 bolts. Plus we have old and new quilts for sale. Please drop by for our group meeting every Thursday.

From I - 20 take Exit 49. Go North 3½ miles to the 3rd traffic light. Turn right & stay in exit lane for 1/4 mile. Lane turns into Old Arcadia Rd. Shop is 1 mile on left.

Ruston, LA #2

Mon - Fri 10 - 5:30 Sat 10 - 4

The Fabric Shop

100 Park Ave. 71270
(318) 251-2400
Owners: Ron & Louise Adams
Est: 1984 3000 sq.ft.
LouiseAdams@suddenlinkmail.com
www.PFAFFCreativeSewing.com

Quilting Fabrics, PFAFF & Baby Lock Sewing and Embroidery Machines.
Jewelry - Notions - Bridal Fabrics & Accessories.

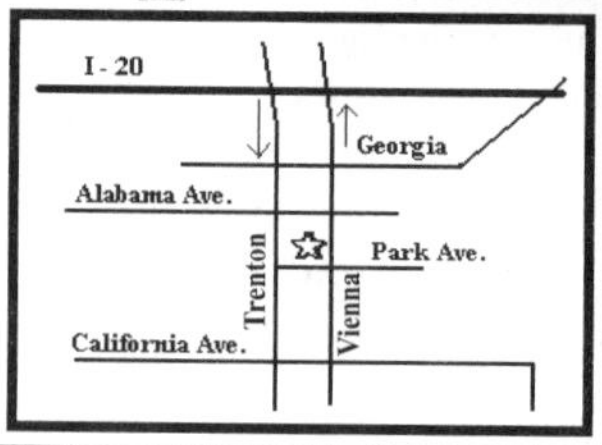

West Monroe, LA #3

Mon - Fri 9 - 5 Sat 10 - 4

Quilt 'N Stitch

6049 Cypress St. 71291
(318) 396-6020
2000+ Bolts
www.quiltnstitch.com

The store is located in a house where antiques nestle among the many fabrics, books, and notions. Authorized Bernina Dealer

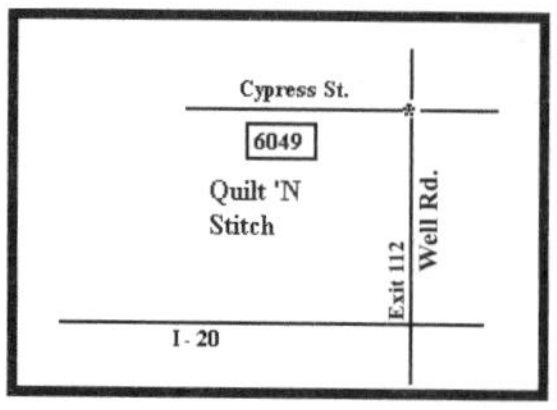

Alexandria, LA #4

Mon - Fri 9 - 5:30 Sat 9 - 2

Quilter's Delight

5412 Masonic Drive 71301
(318) 441 - 9900
quilterdelight@bellsouth.net

Full service quilt shop.
100% Cotton Fabrics, patterns, books, notions, classes, longarm quilting and custom made quilts too!

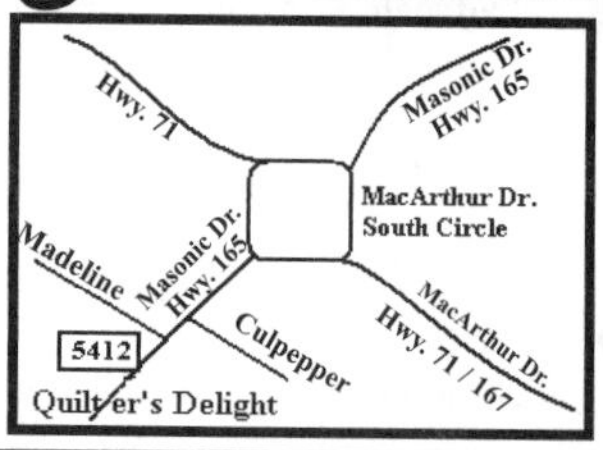

Hannah's Quilts

Mon - Fri
8 - 5
Sat 8 - 2

Fabrics, Blank Textiles.
Notions, 100% Cotton Batting
- Kaffe Fassett
- Michael Miller
- Fusions by Robert Kaufman

Long-Arm Quilting on Gammill Machines
Xtra Wide Backing in Batiks and Other Fabrics.

www.hannahsquilts.com

402 St. Peter Rd.
Choudrant, LA
71227
(318) 251-0314

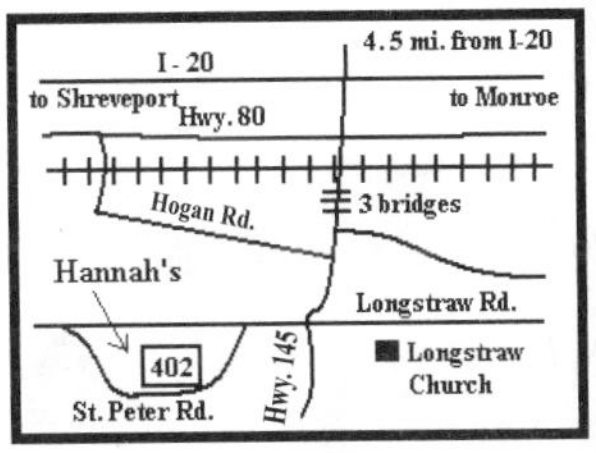

Exit 93 South, 4 miles from the Interstate.

Choudrant, LA #5

Baton Rouge, LA #6

The Quilt Corner

Louisiana's Premier Quilt Shop

Hours:
Monday - Saturday
10 am till 5 pm
Special hours on request

"Where your heart comes home to quilt"

13847 Coursey Blvd., Suite 1
Baton Rouge, LA 70817
(225) 756-0542
www.quiltcorneronline.com
info@quiltcorneronline.com

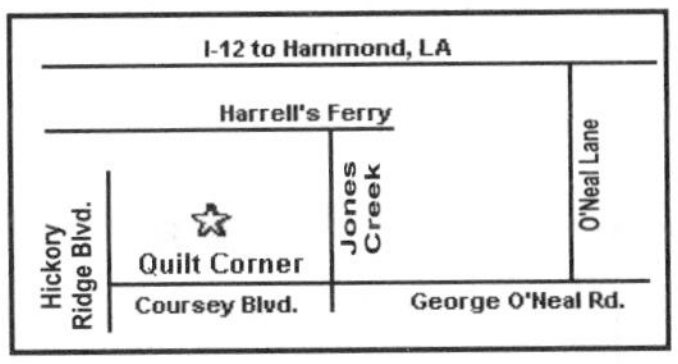

Over 1500 bolts of top quality 100% cotton fabrics: books, patterns, notions and gifts: variety of classes taught in our large classroom: we promote our local pattern and fabric designers.

Baton Rouge, LA #7

Fabric Krazy Quilt Shop

2116 S. Sherwood Forest Blvd.
Baton Rouge, LA 70816
225-272-6602
www.fabrickrazy.com
e-mail: fabrickrazy@bellsouth.net
Est: 2003 2500 sq.ft. 2500 bolts

Mon-Fri: 9:30 - 5
Sat: 9:30 - 3

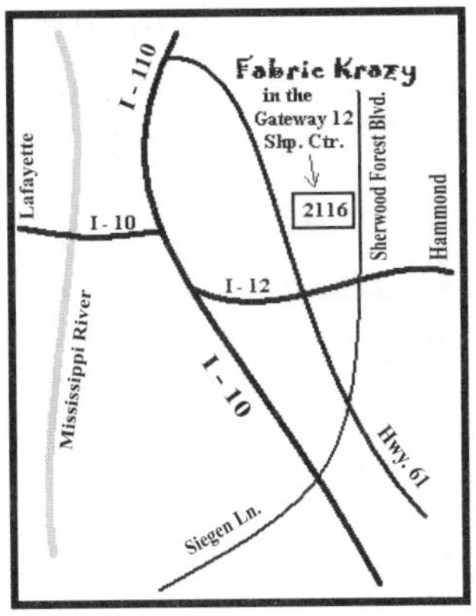

Take Exit #4
Located one block north of I - 12

Menu of services

- Where every customer is greeted as they come in
- Helpful staff
- Many samples hanging for your enjoyment
- Over 2500 bolts of the highest quality quilting fabrics from many of the major designers.
- You will find lots of bright, wild and fun fabrics along with a very good selection of batiks and oriental fabrics. There is even a little of the traditional.
- Large selection of books, notions and threads
- Tin Lizzie 18 Long arm dealer
- Sewing machines
- Sign up to receive our newsletter by email
- Block of the month and clubs (you can receive by mail)
- Long arm quilting services
- Groups and buses welcome. If you call in advance and let us know that you have a group coming, we will have welcome bags for everyone.

Independence, LA #8

Mama's Quilt Shop

15111 Catfish Farm Road 70443

985-878-6396

mamasquiltshop@yahoo.com

www.mamasquiltshop.com

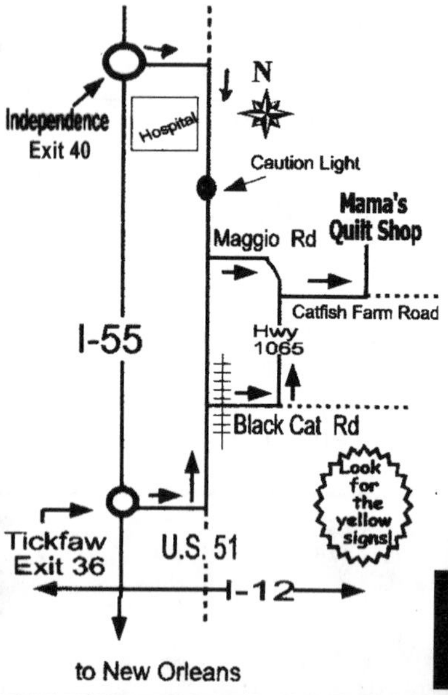

We carry over 3000 Bolts of fabric including RJR, Benatex, Marcus Brothers, Timeless Treasures, P&B, and many, many more.
Best prices around!

Fabrics, notions, books, classes and lots of inspiration at the "quilt shop in the country."

Hours: 9 am - 5 pm
Mon-Sat

Abita Springs, LA #9

Tues - Fri 10 - 5
Sat 10 - 2

Sew This

70117 Hwy. 59, Suite O 70420
(985) 871-1491
Owner: Mona Jones
Est: 2008 4800 sq.ft. Online Newsletter
sewmanyquiltsla@yahoo.com

Fabric, Patterns, BOM's
Bernina Sewing & Embroidery Machines
We teach all types of sewing classes.
Gammill Sales and Rentals.

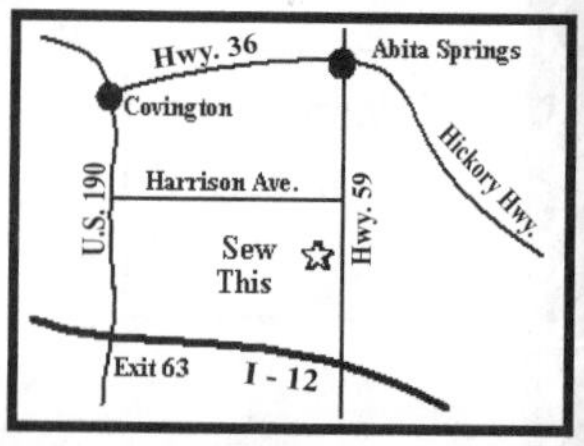

Mandeville, LA #10

Bright Hopes Quilting

Where quilters gather!

We carry a wide variety of fabrics brights, orientals, batiks, florals, plus classes, books & notions.

Mon - Fri 9:30 - 4
Sat 9:30 - 2

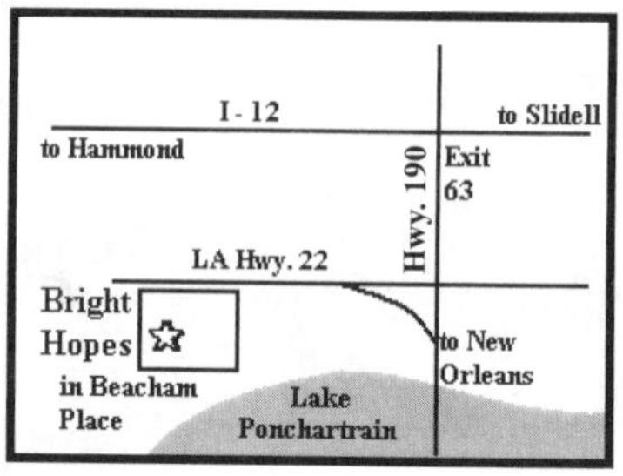

5150 Hwy. 22, Suite C1 70471
(985) 845-9554 Fax: (985) 845-9599
brighthopes@bellsouth.net
www.brighthopesquilting.blogspot.com
Owner: Pearl Squires
Est: 2003 2200 sq.ft. 3000 Bolts

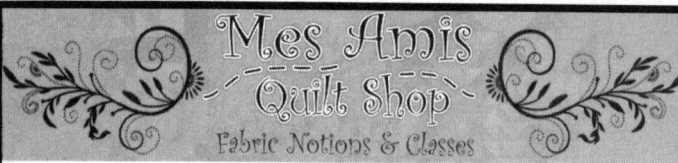

Mes Amis Quilt Shop

Fabric Notions & Classes

"Mes Amis" translates to "My Friends" and that's what our shop strives to be -- a place where friends, who just happen to quilt, come togehter to sit and sew and catch up or plan a new event, maybe even learn a new block pattern.
We have an eclectic assortment of fabrics from Granny's Treasures & 30's reproductions, Batiks, Moda, Black & Whites, to Landscape Fabrics. Come see what's new.

www.mesamisquiltshop.com

Mon - Fri 9:30 - 4 Sat 10 - 4

6505 Spanish Fort Blvd. 70121
Lake Vista Shopping Center
504-284-3455
Owner: Denise Taylor
Est: 2010
denise@mesamisquiltshop.com

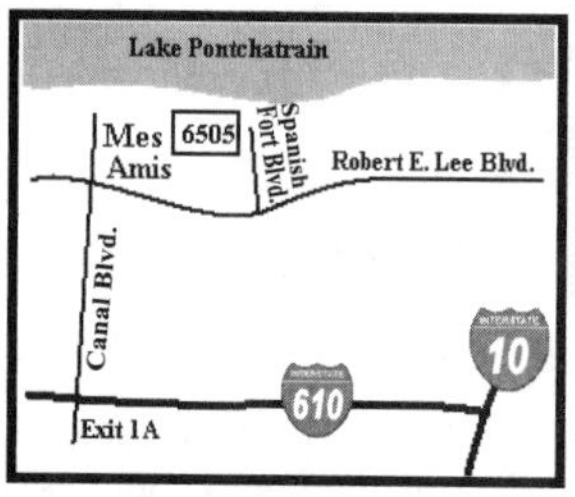

New Orleans, LA #11

Houma, LA #12

Mon - Fri 10 - 5
Sat 9 - 3

The Quilting Niche, LLC

1220 St. Charles St. 70360
(985) 876-9077 Fax: (985) 876-9078
quiltingnichellc@bellsouth.net
Owner: Debra Frank

Est: 2004 2000 sq.ft. 2000 Bolts & Growing
A complete collection of fabrics for your quilting needs.
A large selection of books, patterns and notions. Also offering classes from basic to advanced and wearables.
Bernina Dealer and Long Arm Quilting available.

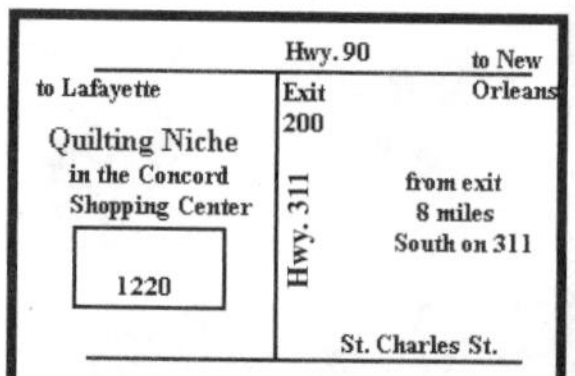

Lake Charles, LA #13

Mon - Fri
9:30 - 5
Sat 9:30 - 3

Quilts Bayou

Southwest Louisiana's premier quilt shop where stitching and laughter go hand in hand.

327 W. Prien Lake Rd.
Lake Charles, Louisiana 70601
(across the street from Prien Lake Mall)

(337) 477-9322
www.quiltsbayou.com

quiltsbayou@bellsouth.net
Owners: Vonda Wright & Sandee Golla

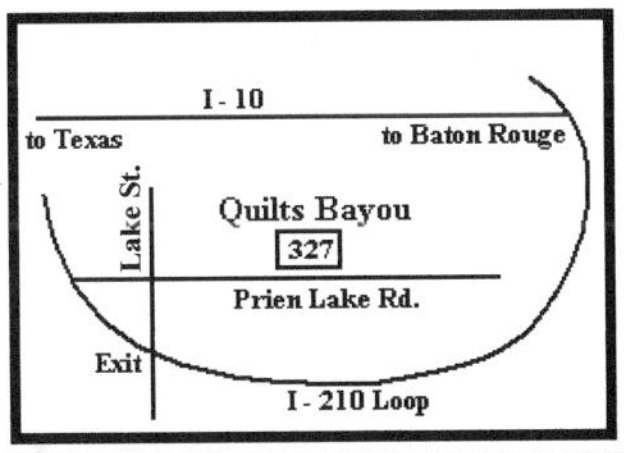

Lafayette, LA #14

The Borne Quilter
Sew + Quilt = Create!

Tues - Sat
10 - 5

Free Newsletter

1507 Kaliste Saloom Rd. Suite A 70508
(337) 408-3730 Fax: (337) 456-4754
Owners: Renée-Claire & Keith Borne
info@thebornequilter.com
www.thebornequilter.com

Specializing in fine 100% cotton fabrics. We have everything you need to inspire your quilting and creative sewing spirit, plus kits, classes and unique gift items.

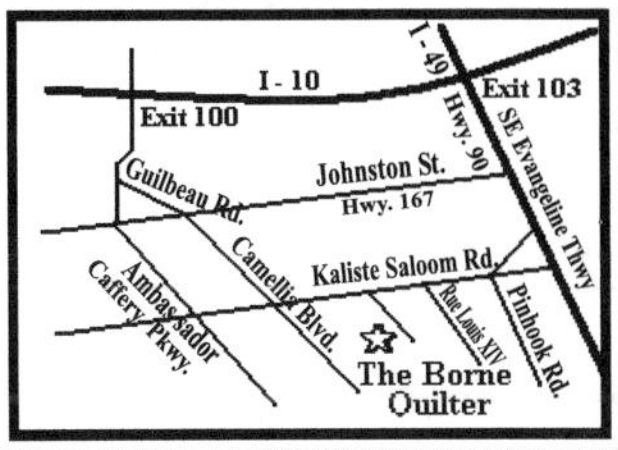

GINGER'S NEEDLEWORKS & QUILTING

www.quiltknit.com

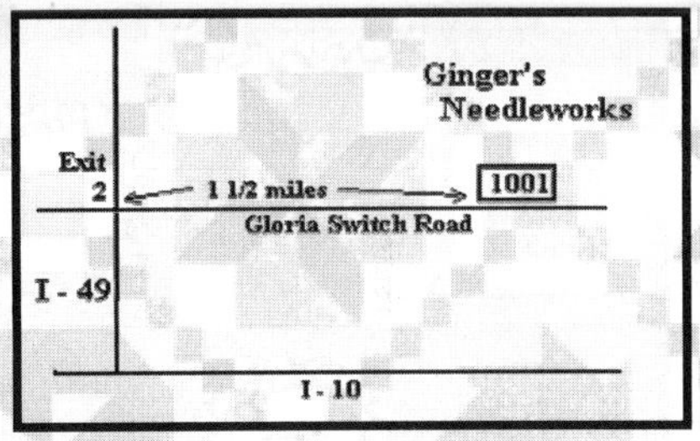

Store Hours: Monday - Friday 9 - 4

1001 East Gloria Switch Road 70507 (337) 232-7847
Owner: Ginger Moore Est:1985 2400 sq.ft.

9000 Bolts of Fabrics
Specializing in Civil War and 1930's Reproductions and Oriental Fabrics. We also have a large selection of Novelty Prints.
Lots of Notions, Patterns, and Books.

Make www.quiltknit.com your one-stop online quilt store for all your quilting fabrics, notions, books and patterns. Secure online ordering and fast service.

Lafayette, LA #15

Louisiana Quilt Shops

Abita Springs **Sew This, 70117 Hwy. 59, Suite O**
985-871-1491 **See ad #9, page 234**

Alexandria **Quilters' Delight, 5412 Masonic Drive**
318-441-9900 **See ad #4, page 232**

Baton Rouge **Fabric Krazy Quilt Shop, 2116 S. Sherwood Forest**
225-272-6602 **See ad #7, page 233**

Baton Rouge **The Quilt Corner, 13847 Coursey Blvd. #1**
225-756-0542 **See ad #6, page 233**

Bossier City Fabric Boutique, 1701 Old Minden Rd. #11 318-742-0047

Choudrant **Hannah's Quilts & Crafts, 402 St. Peter Loop Rd.**
318-251-0314 **See ad #5, page 233**

Covington Annie's Sewing Center, 2256 Phillip Dr. 985-867-8067

Houma **The Quilting Niche', LLC, 1220 St. Charles St.**
985-876-9077 **See ad #12, page 234**

Independence **Mama's Quilt Shop, 15111 Catfish Farm Rd.**
985-878-6396 **See ad #8, page 234**

Lafayette **Ginger's Needleworks, 1001 E. Gloria Switch Rd.**
337-232-7847 **See ad #15, page 235 & 194**

Lafayette **The Borne Quilter, 1507 Kaliste Saloom Rd. #A**
337-408-3730 **See ad #14, page 235**

Lafayette Bayou Stitchin' LLC, 2100 Verot School Rd., Suite 7 337-216-9118

Lake Charles **Quilts Bayou, 327 W. Prien Lake Rd.**
337-477-9322 **See ad #13, page 235**

Mandeville **Bright Hopes Quilting, 5150 Hwy. 22 Suite C-1**
985-845-9554 **See ad #10, page 234**

Metairie Fabrixx, 755 Veterans Memorial Blvd. 504-831-1118

Minden **The Little Country Quilt Shop, 534 Old Arcadia Rd.**
318-377-2462 **See ad #1, page 232**

New Orleans **Mes Amis Quilt Shop, 6505 Spanish Fort Blvd.**
504-284-3455 **See ad #11, page 234**

Pineville Aunt Nell's Quilt Shop, 1632 A Hyland Park Dr. 318-640-5294

Ruston **The Fabric Shop, 100 Park Ave.**
318-251-2400 **See ad #2, page 232**

Ruston Louisiana Quilt N More, 1800 Trade Dr. 318-768-2662
Shreveport Cottage Quilts, 9377 Mansfield Rd. 318-671-0331
Sulphur Terry's Fabric Cottage, 1840 Ruth St. 337-528-9190

West Monroe **Quilt 'N Stitch, 6049 Cypress St.**
318-396-6020 **See ad #3, page 232**

Louisiana Quilt Shows

About Shows: We are listing only the very basic information about shows that happen on a regular schedule here. Please check out our website for more details on each show. Also this information tends to change quite often so please verify the event with our website or a local source before you venture far. Or if you're in the right area at the right time, give it a shot.

If you are a show organizer, please keep us updated on your event.
shows@quilterstravelcompanion.com
www.quilterstravelcompanion.com

On our website you will also find:
- Exact dates (when we have them)
- Sponsor Information
- Contact Information
- Description of Event
- Events happening on a one-time basis

Month	City	Schedule	Show	Location with address
March				
	DeRidder	Even Years, 1st Sat. in March	Common Threads Quilters' Guild Show	War Memorial Center, Corner of 7th & S. Pine St.
April				
	Lake Charles	Even Years, 2nd weekend in April	Timeless Traditions	Lake Charles Civic Center, 900 Lakeshore Dr.
June				
	Slidell	Even Years, third weekend in June	Gulf State Quilting Association Show	Oak Harbor Center
September				
	Shreveport	Annual, late September or early October	Red River Quilters Quilt Show	Riverview Hall, 600 Clyde Fant Pkwy.
October				
	St. Martinville	Annual, 1st weekend in October	Quilters' Guild Acadienne Show	Historic Downtown
	Ponchatoula	Odd Years, 2nd Sat. in October	Berry Patch Quilt and Art Expo	Berry Patch Quilt & Art Expo, 54 W. Pine Street

MAINE

22 Featured Shops

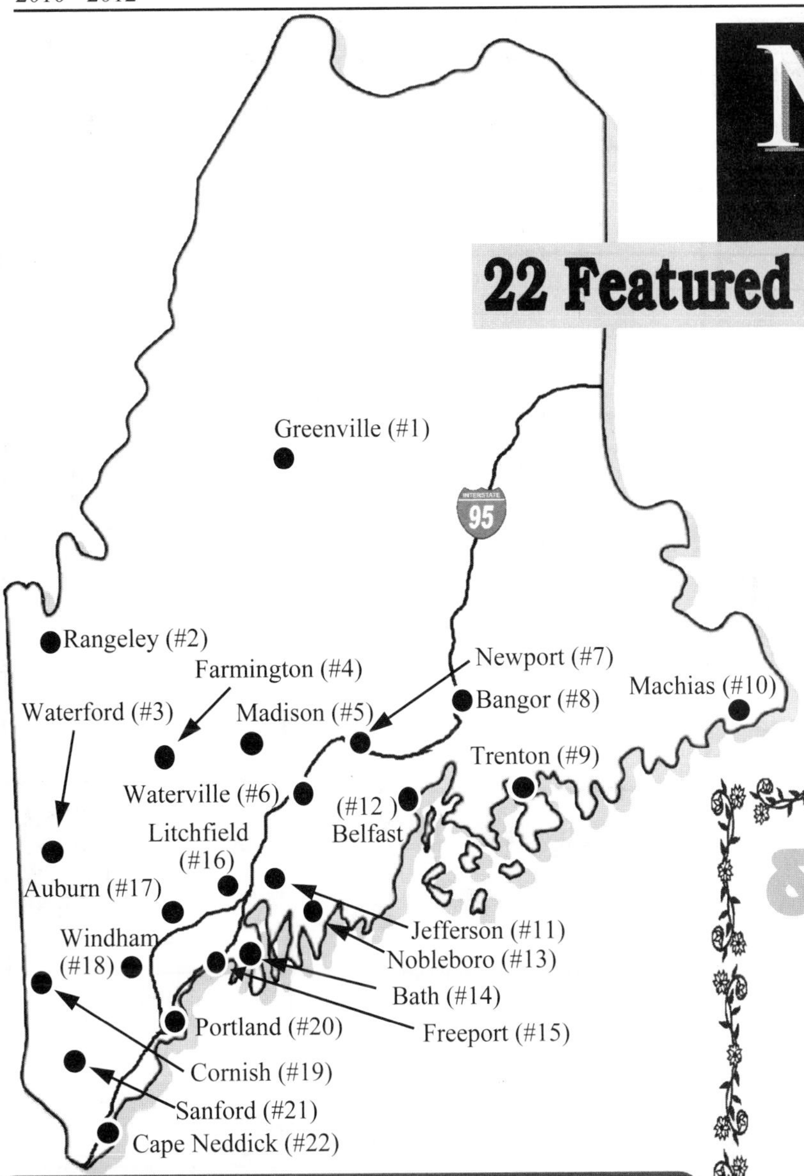

& Threads Galore Quilt Shop

Quilt Inn Rangeley Retreat Center

Store Hours: Tues thru Sat 10 - 5 Closed in March

- Over 1000 Bolts of Quality Fabric
- 150 Book Titles
- 100 Patterns
- Gadgets & Notions
- Samples to Inspire Your Creativity
- Quilts for Sale Made by Local Quilters
- Gifts for Quilters & Non-Quilters
- Fall Quilt Camps

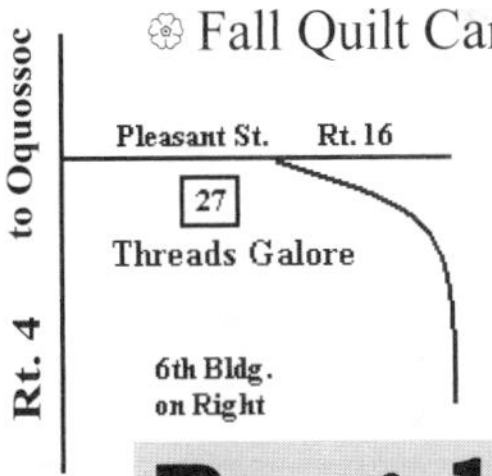

27 Pleasant St.
P.O. Box 219 04970
(207) 864-5752
carol@threadsgalore.com
www.threadsgalore.com

Rangeley, ME #2

Crazy Moose Fabrics

- 700+ bolts of Quilting Fabric
- Books, Patterns, and Samples
- Notions
- Class Offerings
- Maine Made Quilted Products
- Unique Australian Cane Toad Leather Products

Open: 10-4, Mon-Sat

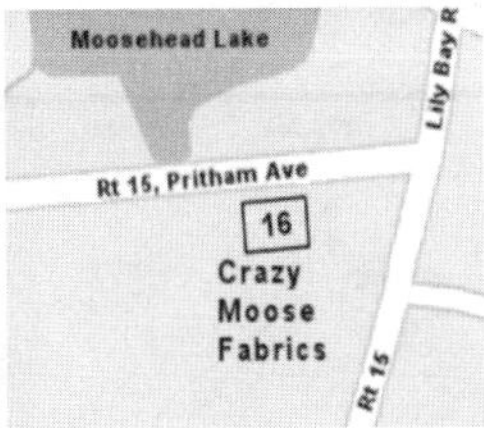

Marilyn Goodwin
www.crazymoosefabrics.com
info@crazymoosefabics.com
16 Pritham Ave., PO Box 1233
(207) 695-3600

Greenville, ME #1

Zip Code: 04441

Fabrics, Quilts, Toads, 'n More

Waterford, ME #3

Mon - Sat 9:30 - 5:30 Sun 10 - 4

Kedar Quilts

18 Valley Rd, Rt. 35 04088
(207) 583-6182
Fax: (207) 583-6424
kedar@kedarquilts.com
www.kedarquilts.com Est: 1989
Owner: Margaret Gibson 4000 Bolts
Fine 100% Cotton Fabrics, Notions, Classes, Books. FOR SALE: New Quilts, Wallhangings and much more. Quilt Weekends and Retreats. Located at Kedarburn Inn.

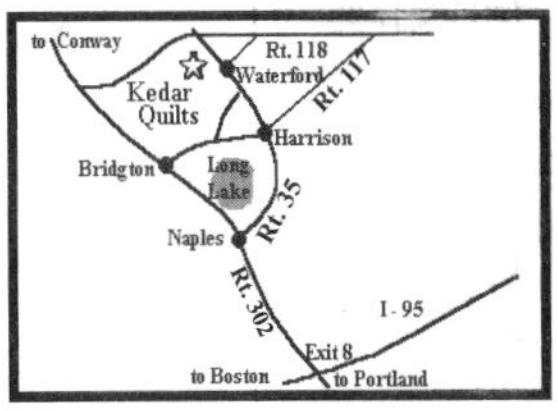

Farmington, ME #4

Mon - Sat 9 - 5
Most Sun 11 - 3

Fabric Inn
Established 1976

413 Wilton Rd. 04938
(207) 778-4288
Est: 1976 2000 sq.ft.

info@fabricinn.com
www.FabricInn.com

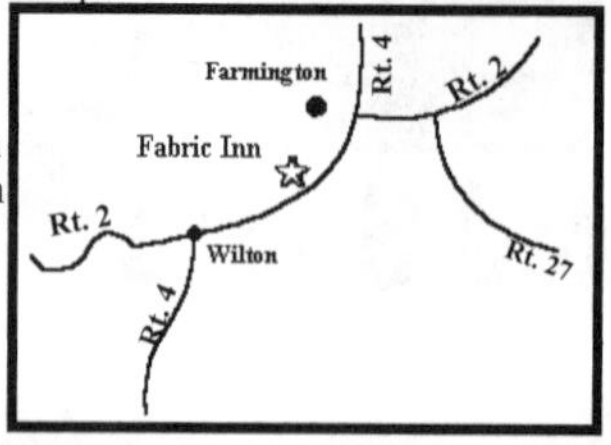

The store for all your sewing, quilting and knitting needs. Name brand fabrics, books, patterns & notions. Fine Yarns and knitting supplies. Janome sewing machines sales and service. Easy to find.

Madison, ME #5

Mon - Fri 9 - 6
Sat 9 - 5
Sun 12 - 5

The Fabric Garden

167 Lakewood Rd. 04950
(207) 474-9628
Owner: Michaela Murphy
Est: 1978 2400 sq.ft.
www.fabricgarden.com

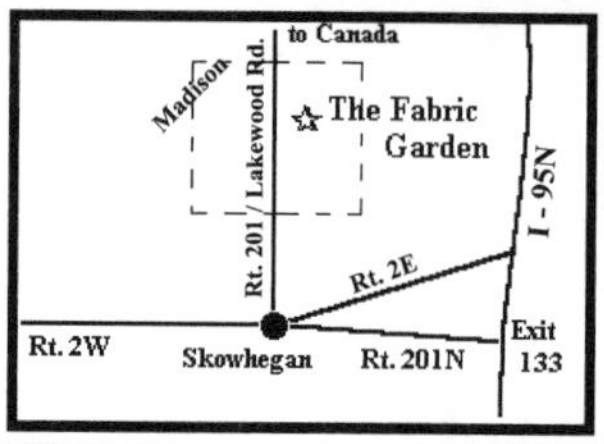

Come see why people travel far and wide. Over 8000 bolts of Quilting Cottons, Books, Patterns, Yarn and more. Janome sewing machines sales & service. "A Quilters must stop shop!"

Waterville, ME #6

Yardgoods Center
Since 1949

MAINE'S CREATIVITY SUPER STORE
10 STORES IN ONE

- *Designer / Fashion Fabrics*
- *Quilting*
- *Decorator Fabrics*
- *Home Designs*
- *Rubber Stamps*
- *Craft Supplies*
- *Needlework*
- *Fashion Yarns*
- *Sewing Machines*

DOWNTOWN SHOPPING CENTER • WATERVILLE, MAINE 04901

• FOUR FLOORS TO EXPLORE •
Friendly service and unique offerings since 1949

Visit Our QUILTERS GALLERY

~ For all your quilting needs ~

* Thousands of the newest fabrics
* Hundreds of books
* Quilters potpourri section
* Quilt in a Day Shop
* Long-arm Quilting systems

207-872-5403
Est: 1949
10,400 sq.ft.

E-mail:
vlodek@yardgoods.com
Website:
www.yardgoods.com
Fax: 207-872-2118

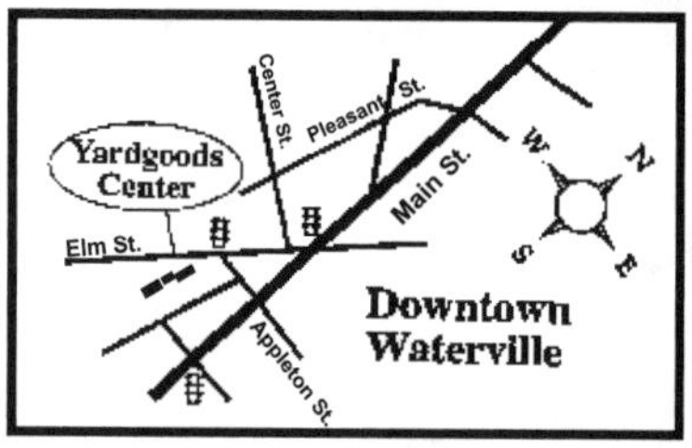

Mon - Sat 9:30 - 5

Just 4 Minutes from Exit 130 off I-95

Waterville, ME #6

Newport, ME #7

Tues - Fri 9:30 - 5
Sat 9:30 - 4

Stitches Fabrics & Yarn

162 Elm St. #2 04953
(207) 368-3340 Fax: (207) 355-0033
Owner: Jan Frost
Est: 2004 Newsletter
frostingonthequilt@msn.com

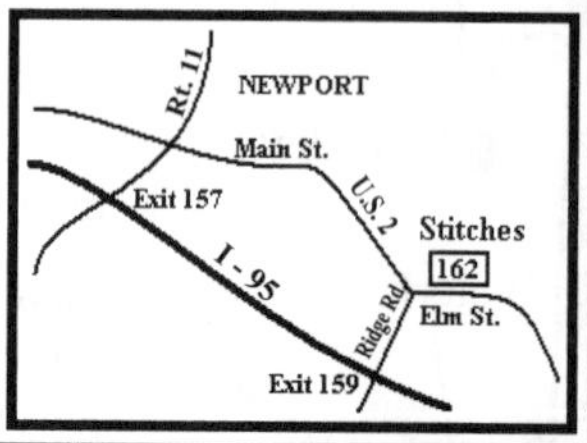

The Cutest Little Quilt Shop on Route 2 & Newport. Everything you need for your quilting. Fine Cottons, Patterns, Accessories, Knitting & Yarn Department

Bangor, ME #8

Mon - Fri 9:30 - 5:30
Sat 9:30 - 4

The Cotton Cupboard
QUILT SHOP

1213 Broadway 04401
(207) 941-8900 Fax: Same
Est: 2007 3000 sq.ft. 3000 bolts
info@cottoncupboardquilt.com
www.cottoncupboardquilt.com

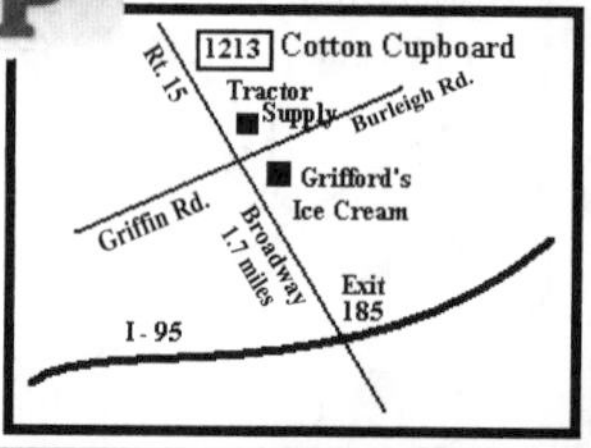

Spacious and bright, the Cotton Cupboard is your one-stop shop for fabric, books, patterns, notions, classes and fun! Newsletter available.

Trenton, ME #9

Mon - Fri 9:30 - 6
Sat 9:30 - 5
Sun 12:30-4:30

Sewing by the Sea

11 Periwinkle Lane 04605
(207) 664-2558
Fax: (207) 664-2560

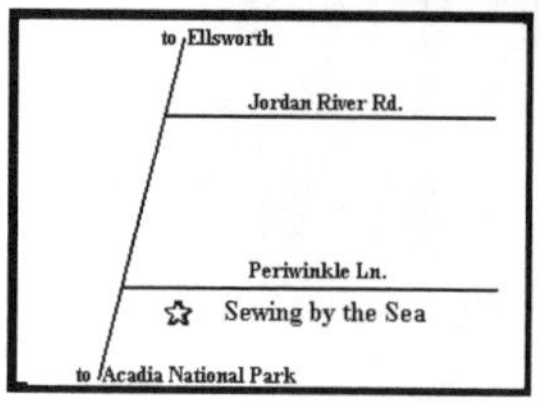

info@sewmaine.com 2000 sq.ft.
www.sewingbythesea.com
Bar Harbor area's only Quilt Shop.
Quilt Cottons, Polartec™, Kwik Sew Patterns, Maine themed kits. Pfaff Dealer.

Machias, ME #10

Tues - Sat 10 - 4

Gingham Fabrics

Route 1 East
Mail: Box 286, Cutler, ME 04626
(207) 255-8238
Owner: Linda M. Throckmorton
Est: 1977 1700 sq.ft.

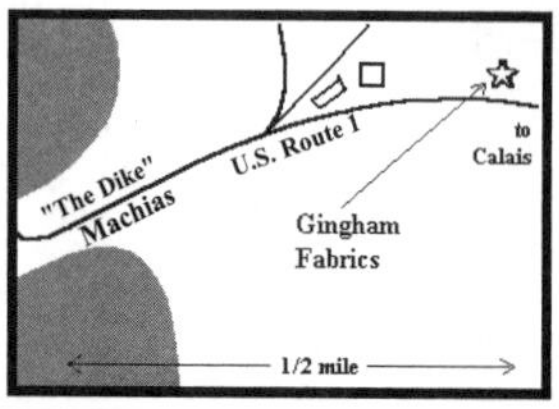

Eastern most quilt shop in the USA. Look for the geodesic dome midway between Ellsworth and Calais.

Jefferson, ME #11

Tues - Sat 10 - 4

Country Creations

696 Waldoboro Rd. 04348
(207) 549-7424 Fax: (207) 549-4734
Owner: Karon Reed Est: 1992

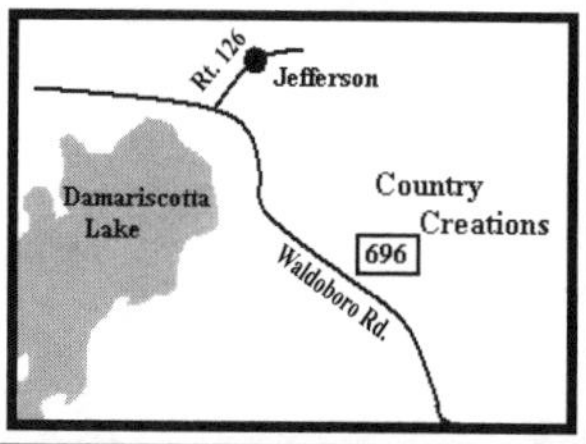

A quilters' and crafters' paradise. We offer a wide range of quilting fabrics, wools and wool felt, kits, many books and patterns, and an extensive selection of punch needle embroidery supplies. The shop is always filled with samples and kits to inspire.

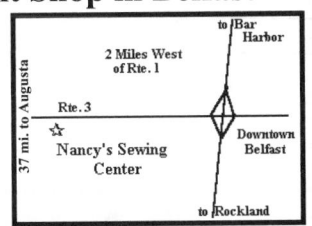

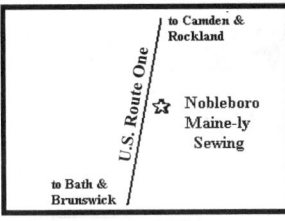

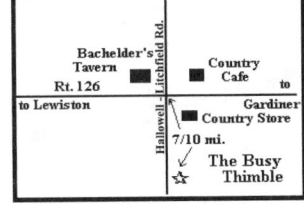

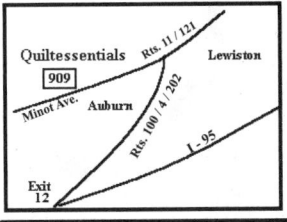

Windham, ME #18

Mon - Fri 9:30 - 4:30
Tues til 7
Sat 9:30 - 4
Sun 11 - 3

Calico Basket Quilt Shop

31 Page Road 04062
(207) 892-5606
Owner: JoAnne Hill
Est: 1982 1300 sq.ft.

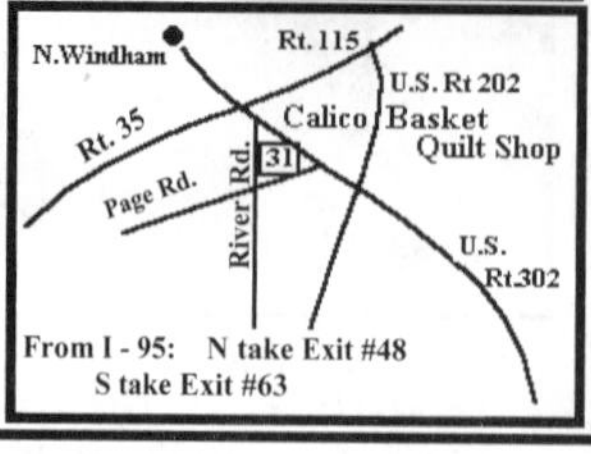

Over 8000 Top Quality Fabrics.
The Latest Books, Notions, Craft Patterns, and Quilting Supplies.

Cornish, ME #19

Wed - Sat 10 -5

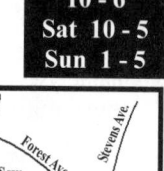

Barking Rose QUILT BARN

3 Old School St. 04020
(207) 625-8856
barkingrose@roadrunner.com
Fax: (207) 625-8856
Owner:
Judy MacIntyre
Est: 2004

We offer a wide selection of carefully selected fabrics, books, notions, old quilts, whimsical gifts, sewing related memorabilia.

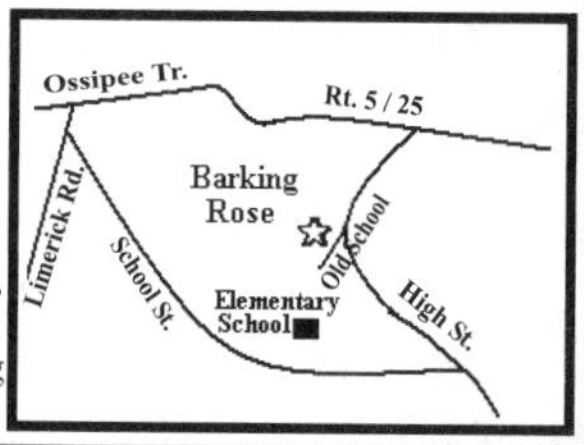

Portland, ME #20

Mon - Fri 10 - 6
Sat 10 - 5
Sun 1 - 5

Sew Portland

306 Warren Ave. 04103
(207) 797-6700
info@sewmaine.com
www.sewportland.com

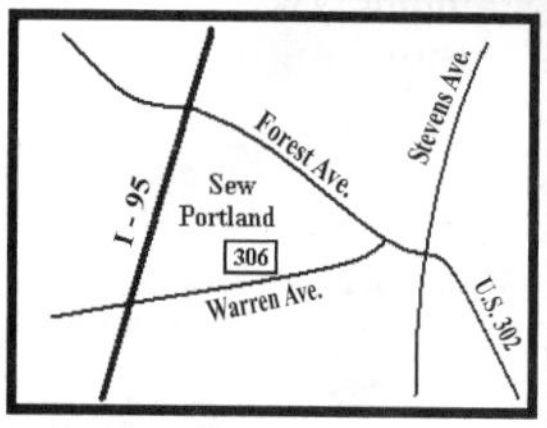

We stock a collection of contemporary, designer quilting fabrics and a few garment fabrics such as PolartecTM from Malden Mills and Bali rayon batiks. We also have patterns for quilts and bags, as well as specialty thread, battings, sewing and quilting notions, books and magazines.

Sanford, ME #21

Mon - Fri 8 - 5
Sat 9 - 4

Sanford Sewing

1923 Main St. 04073
(207) 324-8375 Fax: (207) 324-1702
Online Newsletter
sales@sanfordsewing.com
www.sanfordsewing.com

Notions galore for quilters. Long-arm supplies, authorized dealer for Bernina, Baby Lock, Juki and Handi-Quilter. Fabric, Books, Patterns and Software.

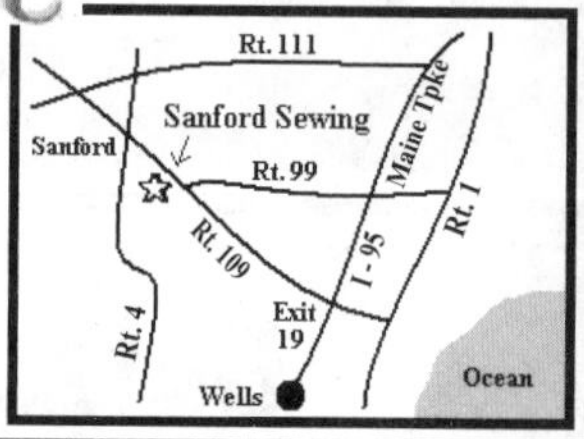

#22

KNIGHT'S QUILT SHOP

Better Homes and Gardens Quilt Sampler FEATURED SHOP 2009

Established 1999
1901 U.S. Route One, Cape Neddick, ME
207-361-2500
www.mainequiltshop.com

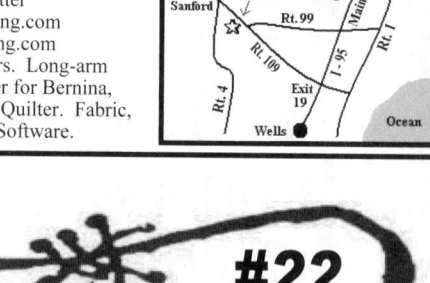

We are proud to be a *Quilt Sampler* Top 10 Shop for 2009!

- 500 + Books and Patterns
- 4,000 Bolts of Fabric
- Kits and Notions
- Ready-Made Quilts
- Tim Janis Music
- Unique Gifts for Quilters

From the north on Maine I-95, take **Exit 19 (Wells)**, left at toll, take a right onto Route 1. We are 7 miles on the left.

From the south on Maine I-95, **Exit 7 (York)**, bear right, take left onto Route 1. We are 6 miles on the right.

Maine Quilt Shops

Auburn — **Quiltessentials, 909 Minot Ave.** **207-784-4486** **See ad #17, page 239**

Bangor — **The Cotton Cupboard Quilt Shop, 1213 Broadway** **207-941-8900** **See ad #8, page 238**

Bath — **Mariner's Compass Quilt Shop, 190 Front St.** **207-443-2900** **See ad #14, page 239**

Belfast — **Nancy's Sewing Center, Route 3 West, Augusta Rd.** **207-338-1205** **See ad #12, page 239**

Biddeford — Tony's Sewing Machines, 20 Edwards Ave. 207-283-3033

Brewer — A Straight Stitch, 401 N. Maine St. 207-989-1234

Cape Neddick — **Knight's Quilt Shop, 1901 U.S. Route One** **207-361-2500** **See ad #22, page 240**

Chapman — Garden Gate Fabrics, 2184 Chapman Rd. 207-764-3800

Cornish — **Barking Rose Quilt Barn, 3 Old School St.** **207-625-8856** **See ad #19, page 240**

Cutler — **Gingham Fabrics, P.O. Box 286** **207-255-8238** **See ad #10, page 238**

Farmington — **Fabric Inn, 413 Wilton Rd** **207-778-4288** **See ad #4, page 238**

Farmington — Pins & Needles, 157 Main St. 207-779-9060

Freeport — **Cotton Weeds Quilt Shop, 541 U.S. Rt. 1, Suite 12** **207-865-4600** **See ad #15, page 239**

Gardiner — Mystic Maine Quilts, 287 Water St. 207-582-0312

Greenville — **Crazy Moose Fabrics, 16 Pritham Ave.** **207-695-3600** **See ad #1, page 237**

Hallowell — Whipper Snappers, 98 Second St. 207-622-3458

Jefferson — **Country Creations, 696 Waldoboro Rd.** **207-549-7424** **See ad #11, page 238**

Litchfield — **The Busy Thimble, 2040 Hallowell Rd.** **207-268-4581** **See ad #16, page 239**

Madison — **The Fabric Garden, 167 Lakewood Rd.** **207-474-9628** **See ad #5, page 238**

Millinocket — Jandseau's Greenhouse, 220 Iron Bridge Rd. 207-723-6332

New Harbor — Duck's, 2634 Bristol Rd. 207-677-3741

New Sharon — Imelda's Fabric & Designs, 5 Starks Rd. #134 207-778-0665

Newport — **Stitches Fabric & Yarn, 162 Elm St. #2** **207-368-3340** **See ad #7, page 238**

Nobleboro — **Maine-ly Sewing, 48 Atlantic Hwy., U.S. Rt. 1** **207-563-8445** **See ad #13, page 239**

Nobleboro — Alewives Fabrics, 10 Main St. 207-563-5002

North Edgecomb — On Board, Rte. 27, Booth Bay Rd. 207-882-7536

Portland — **Sew Portland, 306 Warren Ave.** **207-797-6700** **See ad #20, page 240**

Rangeley — **Threads Galore Quilt Shop, 27 Pleasant St.** **207-864-5752** **See ad #2, page 237**

Rockland — Quilt Divas, 607 Main St. 207-594-9447

Sanford — **Sanford Sewing Machines, 1923 Main St.** **207-324-8375** **See ad #21, page 240**

Sanford — Kathie's Quilt Shoppe, 41 Shaw's Ridge Rd. 207-490-6887

Skowhegan — Pinwheels Quilting, 95 W. Front St. 207-474-1233

Trenton — **Sewing by the Sea, 11 Periwinkle Ln.** **207-664-2558** **See ad #9, page 238**

Troy — Sew Many Things, 571 Detroit Rd. 207-948-3084

Wales — Quiltworks Unlimited, 99 Ave. Rd. 207-375-8221

Waterford — **Kedar Quilts, 18 Valley Rd., Rt. 35** **207-583-6182** **See ad #3, page 237**

Waterville — **Yardgoods Center, Inc.,60 W Concourse** **207-872-5403** **See ad #6, page 238**

West Forks — Cabin Fever Treasurers, RR 201 207-663-2268

Windham — **Calico Basket Quilt Shop, 31 Page Rd.** **207-892-5606** **See ad #18, page 240**

Wiscasset — The Marston House, PO Box 517 207-882-6010

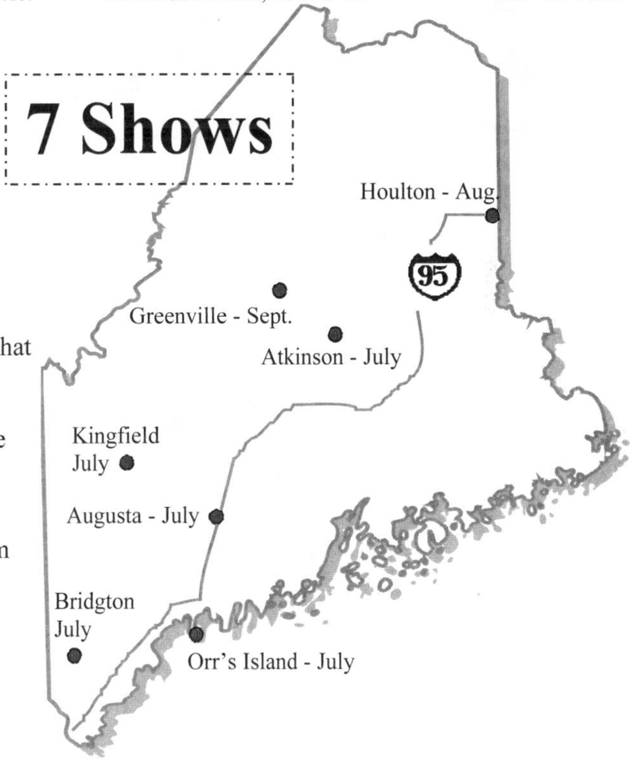

Maine Quilt Shows

About Shows: We are listing only the very basic information about shows that happen on a regular schedule here. Please check out our website for more details on each show. Also this information tends to change quite often so please verify the event with our website or a local source before you venture far. Or if you're in the right area at the right time, give it a shot.

If you are a show organizer, please keep us updated on your event.
shows@quilterstravelcompanion.com www.quilterstravelcompanion.com

On our website you will also find:

- Exact dates (when we have them)
- Sponsor Information
- Contact Information
- Description of Event
- Events happening on a one-time basis

Month	City	Schedule	Show	Location with address
July				
	Bridgton	Annual, 2nd weekend in July	Chickadee Quilt Show	Stevens Brook Elementary School, Rte. #302
	Orr's Island	Annual, 2nd weekend in July	Ocean Waves Quilters	Show Orr's Island Union Church, Rt. 24
	Atkinson	Annual, 3rd Sat. of July	Atkinson Lady Quilters	Atkinson Methodist Church, 141 S. Stagecoach Rd.
	Kingfield	Annual, 3rd weekend in July	Stitchers in the Snow	Baptist Church, Church St.
	Augusta	Annual, Last weekend of July	Maine Quilts	Augusta Civic Center, 76 Community Dr.
August				
	Houlton	Annual, 3rd weekend in August	Friends & Needles Quilt Guild Show	Houlton Lodge of Elks, 86 Main St.
September				
	Greenville	Odd Years, 1st Saturday in September	Moosehead Quilters Annual Quilt Show	Di's Kitchen and Beyond, Pleasant & Shaw St.

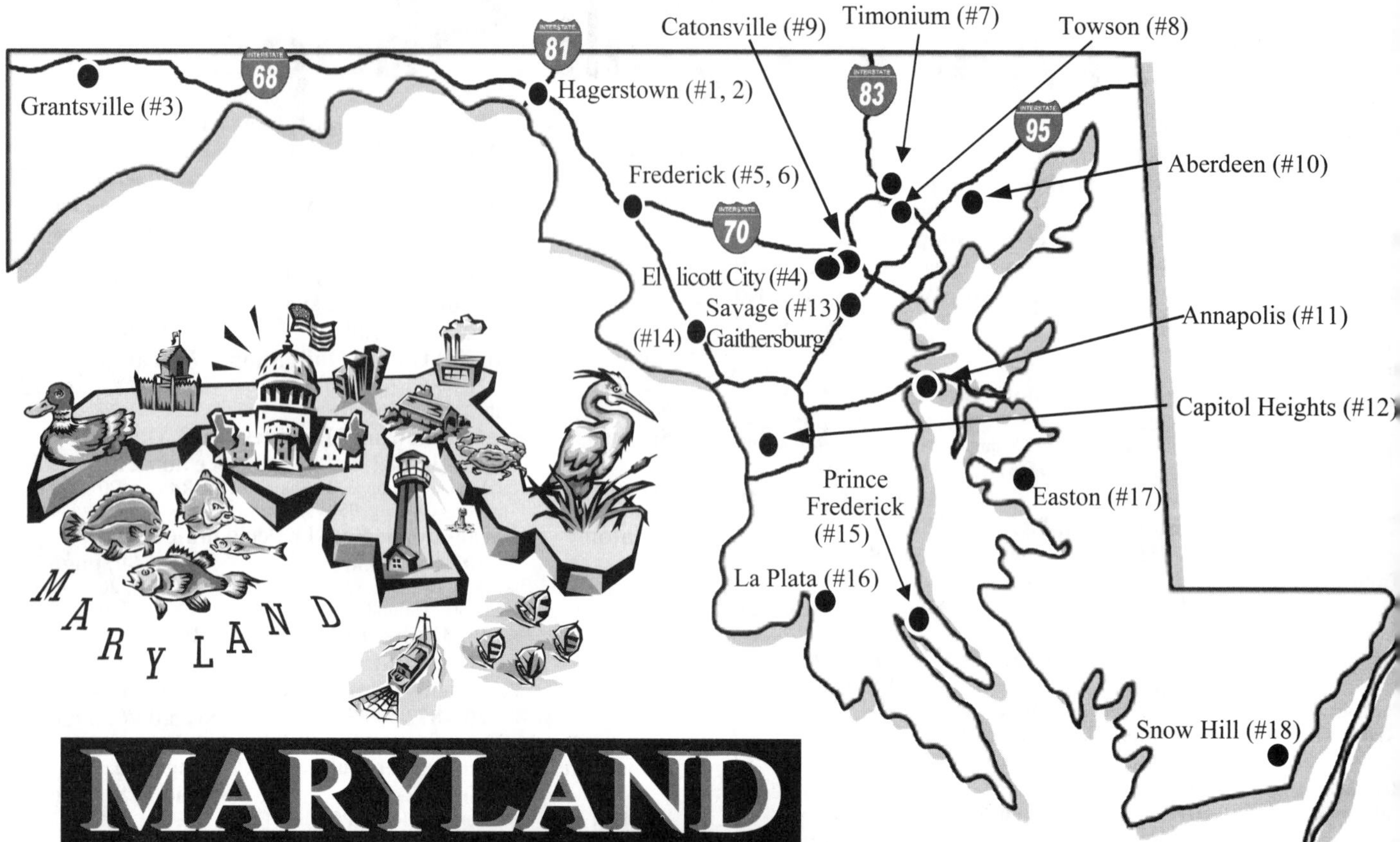

MARYLAND

18 Featured Shops

Hagerstown, MD #1

Traditions at the White Swan

Est: 1985

1700 sq.ft.

Largest Quilt Shop in the area with everything for the quilter— beginner thru advanced. 4000 bolts of fabric including— Hoffman, RJR, P&B, Benartex, Moda, Maywood, Andover & Marcus Brothers. Notions, Books, Patterns, Stencils, & Classes

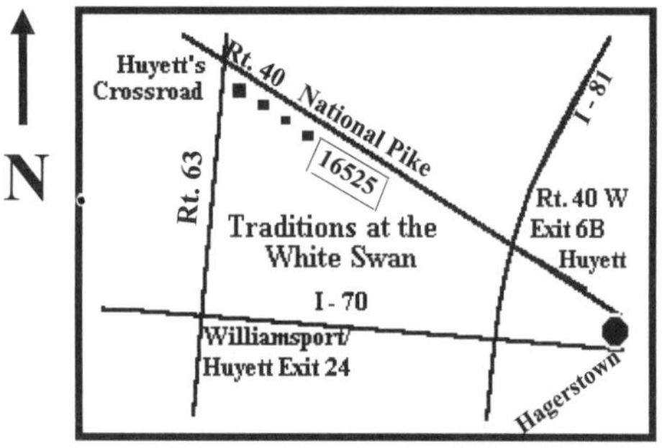

3½ miles West of town

www.whiteswanquilt.com

16525 National Pike 21740
(301) 733-9130 Owners: Dick & Wendy Shank
Fax: (301) 733-2071 whiteswan@myactv.net

Monday - Friday 10 - 5
Saturday 10 - 3
Sunday 1 - 4

The Prettiest Quilt Shop in Western Maryland!

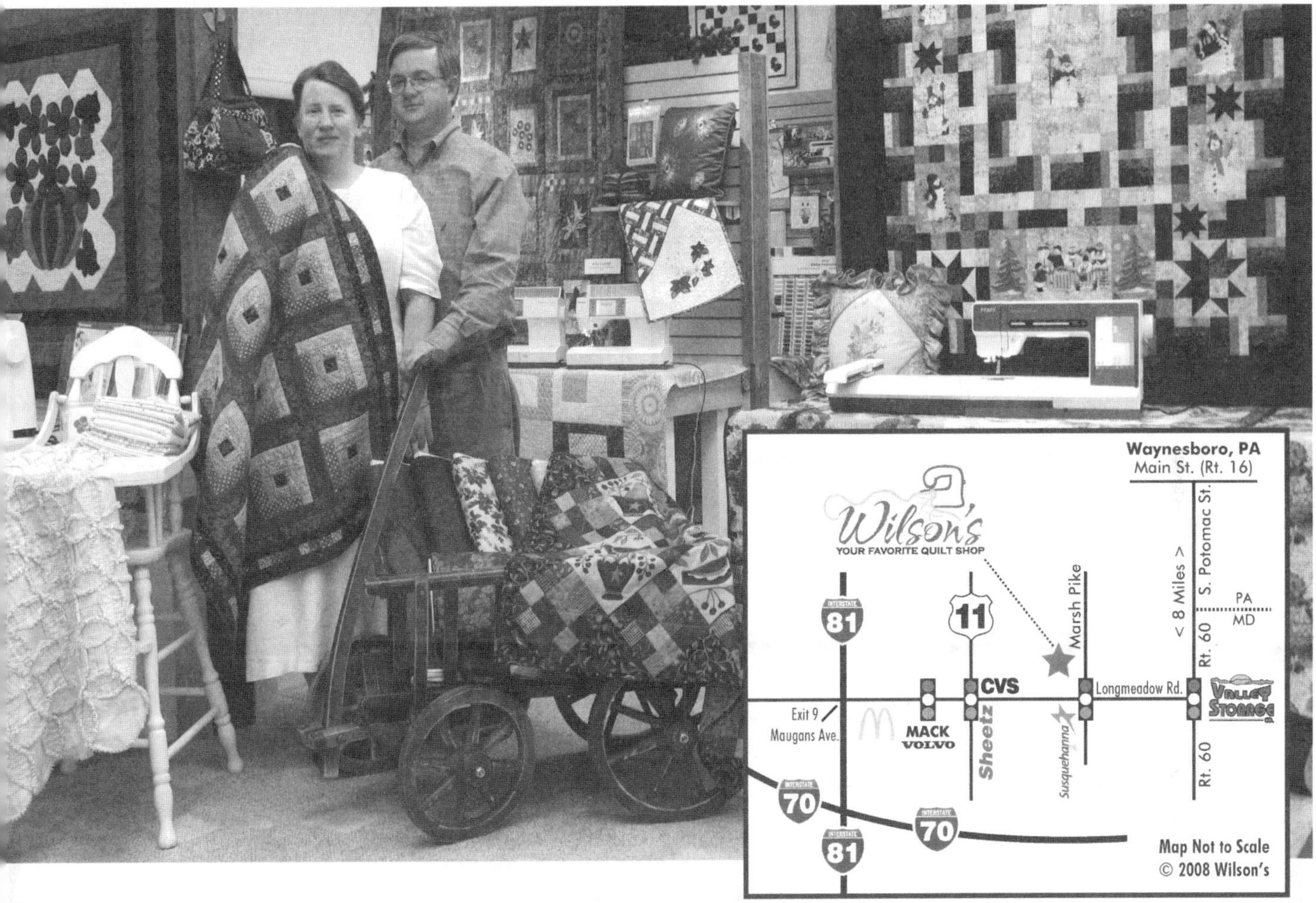

Wilson's Your Favorite Quilt Shop, offers:

- Over 3,000 bolts of "only the prettiest" fine, quality fabrics by suppliers including Moda, Hoffman and many more.
- Check out our Book Nook containing a large selection of books and patterns.
- Get great inspiration from our finished samples and grab a kit to take home!

Pfaff & Viking Sewing Machine Dealer
Country Setting • Buses Welcome
Close to the Interstate • Easy-Off / Easy-On

Visit our website at: ILuv2Quilt.com

#2

Wilson's
YOUR FAVORITE QUILT SHOP
13516 Marsh Pike
Hagerstown, Maryland 21742
301.790.3526

Store Hours
Mon., Tues., Thurs., & Fri. 9 a.m. - 5 p.m.
Sat. 9 a.m. - 2 p.m. • Wed. CLOSED

Don't go home without being able to say you were at Wilson's in Hagerstown!

Grantsville, MD #3

Mon - Sat 9 - 5

FOUR SEASONS STITCHERY

The place to go for calico and "sew" much more

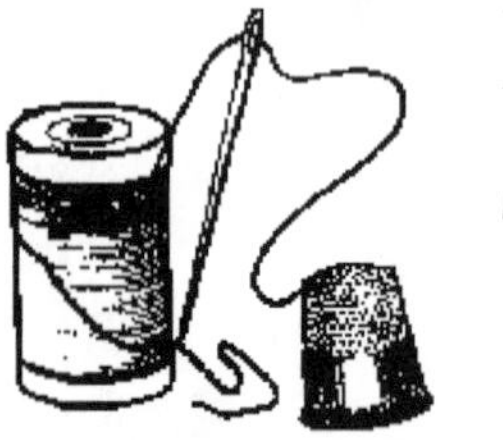

116 Main Street
Grantsville, MD 21536
www.4seasonsstitchery.com
301-895-5958

A VERY SPECIAL FABRIC SHOP with 1500 bolts of cotton quilting fabrics as well as WAVERLY decorator fabrics and apparel fabrics. Special threads, ribbons and fabrics for counted cross stitch, silk ribbon and Brazilian embroidery and other needlework. Instruction books and patterns.

Just minutes from I - 68

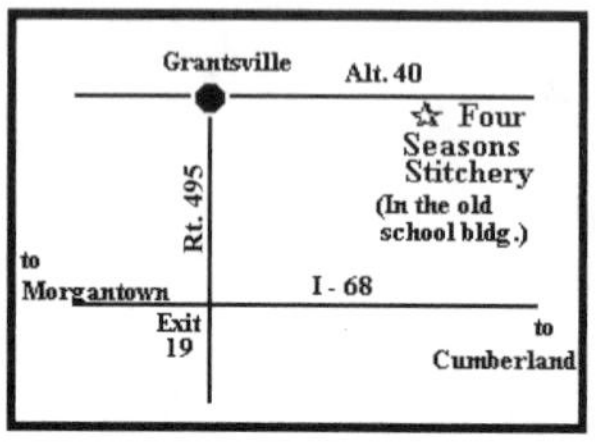

Ellicott City, MD #4

M, W, F 10 - 6
T & Th 10-8
Sat 10 - 4
Sun 12 - 4

8480 Baltimore National Pike
21043

Est: 1989 150 bolts Online newsletter
elliottcitysewvac@msn.com
www.sewfair.com

BabyLock Sewing Machines & Sergers
Horn & Koala Cabinets
Quilting & Sewing Classes
Books, notions, accessories, fabrics.

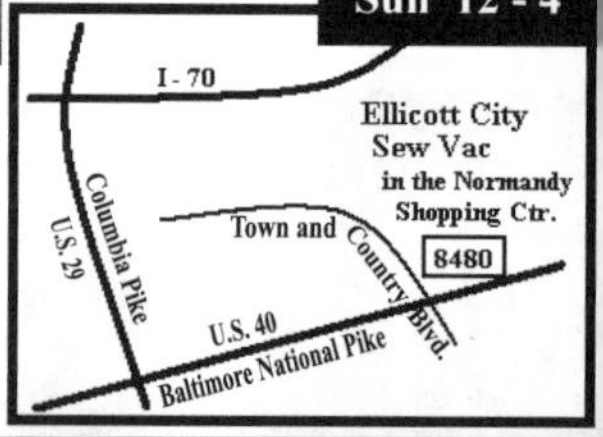

Frederick, MD #5

Mon - Fri 9 - 5
2nd Thur til 8
Sat 10 - 5

Sisto's Sewing & Quilting

1911 N. Market 21701
(301) 695-0643 Fax: (301) 695-1653
5,200 sq.ft. 5,000+ Bolts
www.sistosquilting.com
Fabrics, Patterns, Books, Notions. Brand names: RJR, Hoffman, Moda, Kauffman. Authorized dealer for Bernina, Brother, Janome and Singer Sewing Machines. Guild Day show your card and get 20% off non sale items.

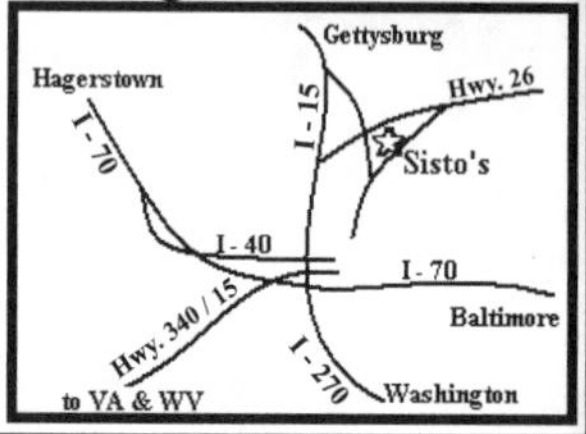

Needles & Pins

FREDERICK MARYLAND'S PREMIER QUILTING & STITCHERY SHOP

310 East Church Street, Frederick, MD 21701
Located in the Everedy Square/Shab Row Shopping Complex in historic downtown Frederick.
Shop with us online! Go to our website www.needles-n-pins.com and click on Visit Our Online Store.

Many models on display throughout the year!

Online Newsletter

Open 7 Days a Week
Call for shop hours and directions!
877-695-7199 Toll Free
or 301-695-7199

An independent shop specializing in top quality fabrics, including flannels, batiks and 19th century reproduction prints.

Full selection of National Nonwovens' Woolfelt, Hobbs Batting & Dunroven House Homespun Towels.

All Major Credit Cards Accepted

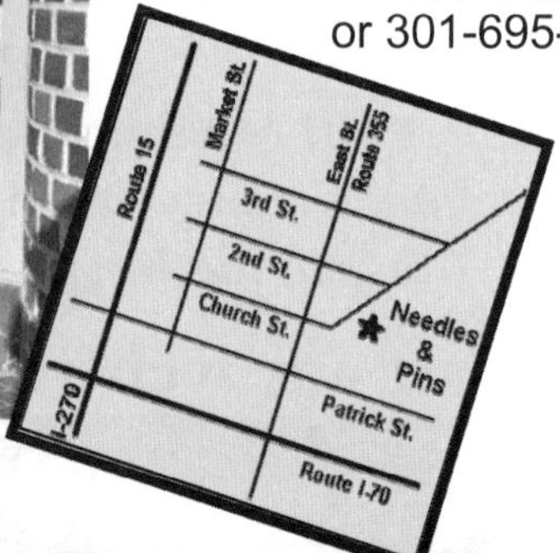

Frederick, MD #6

Stitches Etc. Home Center

Just North of Baltimore!

Store hours:
Tuesday - Friday
10:00 am--6 pm
Saturday & Sunday
11 am--4 pm
Evening hours by appointment for your convenience!

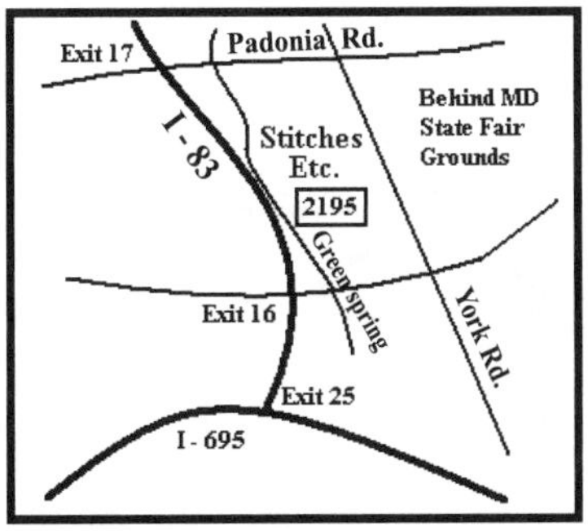

Timonium, MD #7

2195 Greenspring Dr.
(Mail: P.O. Box 266,
Phoenix, MD 21131)

mail@stitchesetc.biz
410-561-3101

4,000 bolts of quality quilting fabrics, specializing in novelties.

Believe in Your Creativity JANOME
Authorized Janome Sales and Service.

www.stitchesetc.biz

A Different Sewing, Quilting & Embroidery Experience
We hope you can take the time to visit our conviently located shop

We welcome you to the world of Bear's Paw Fabrics and Bernina.

- Over 1800 beautiful cotton fabrics for the quilter or home sewer
- Books, notions, and patterns. Loads of samples.
- Authorized Bernina Dealer with the latest sewing and embroidery machines, software and accessories.

Est: 1996

Towson, MD #8

BERNINA

8812 Orchard Tree Lane 21286
410-321-6730
Owners: Doug and Judy Munro

Mon - Fri 10 - 5
Sat 9:30 - 4
Sun 12 - 4

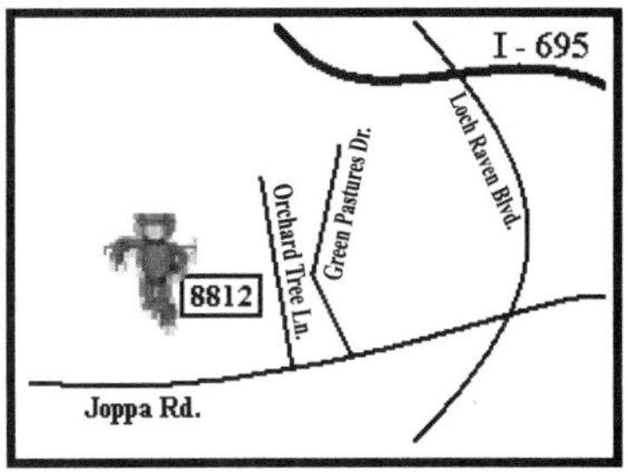

695 to Exit 29B (Loch Raven Blvd.)
right on Joppa Rd.
right on Orchard Tree Lane
5th store on left

www.bearspawfabrics.com

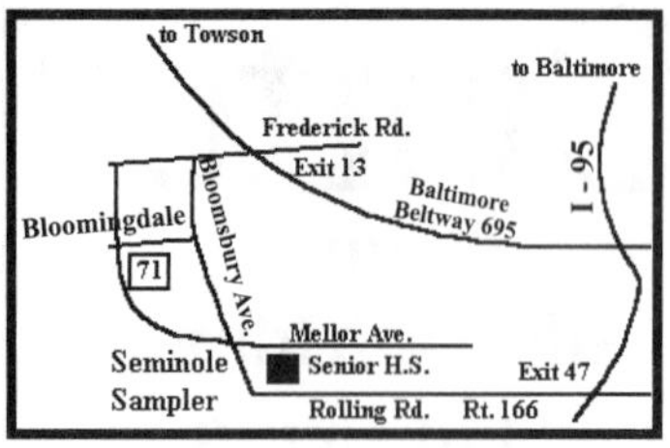

- Fine Cotton Fabrics
- Quilting Books and Patterns
- Quilting and Sewing Notions
- Batting and Supplies
- Unique Block of the Month Patterns
- Wearable Art Patterns
- Classes for Every Level

SEMINOLE SAMPLER

71 Mellor Ave. 21228
(410) 788-1720
info@seminolesampler.com
www.seminolesampler.com

Mon & Thur: 10 - 8
Tue, Fri, Sat: 10 - 5
Sun: 1 - 5
Closed Wed

3600+ sq.ft. of quilt store featuring more than 4000 bolts of fine cotton fabrics; especially known for extensive collections of batik, contemporary, Baltimore Album and Oriental fabrics. Excellent offering of books and patterns, notions and supplies. Regularly scheduled classes in every aspect of quilting, for all levels of experience. Service oriented staff cheerfully willing to assist with all quilt project needs. Guild discount on Mondays.

Catonsville, MD #9

Aberdeen, MD #10

Hoppin Bobbin

411 W. Bel Air Ave. 21001
(410) 272-2226

Tues & Thur 10 - 8
Wed & Fri 10 - 5
Sat 10 - 4

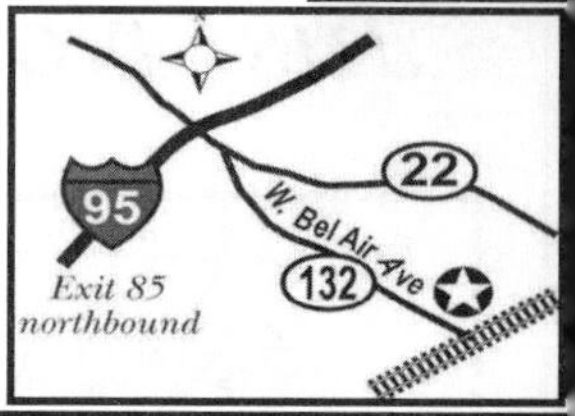

hoppinbobbin2@yahoo.com
Opening September 2010
3 minutes off I-95
Classes, Fabric, Notions, Books, Patterns, Longarm Quilting & Embroidery Services.
"When you needle little inspiration."

Annapolis, MD #11

Est: 1978

Cottonseed Glory

4 Annapolis St. 21401
(410) 263-3897
Owner: Pat Steiner
www.cottonseedglory.com

***6000 bolts** from over 50 manufacturers.*
Books, Gourmet Notions, Classes year round
Friendly, knowledgeable help, free parking.
Patterns including Cottonseed Glory's own pattern line--Plus local designers' patterns.

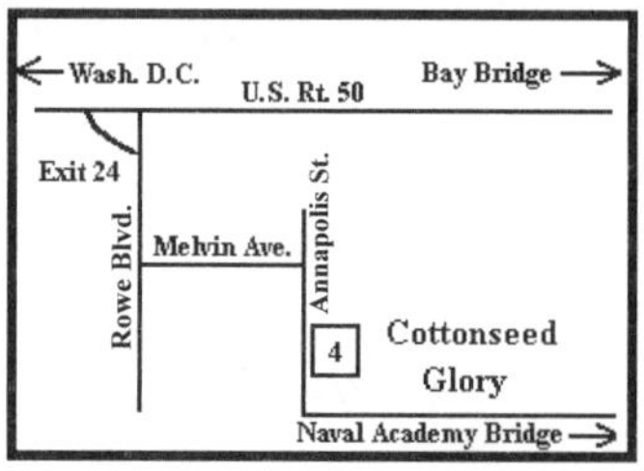

1/2 miles from U.S. Naval Academy & Historic area of Annapolis
1 mile and 2 traffic lights from Rt. 50
Free parking on our lot

Mon - Sat 10 - 5 Sun 1 - 4
(No Sun hours June - Aug)

Capitol Heights, MD #12

Mon - Sat 10 - 6

The Fabric Peddler

704 Ritchie Rd. 20743
(301) 336-3646 Est: 2005
3000 sq.ft. Online newsletter
thefabricpeddler@yahoo.com
www.thefabricpeddler.com
Quilt Fabrics, Notions, Batting, Books & Patterns, Quilt Panels.
Juki Sewing Machines.

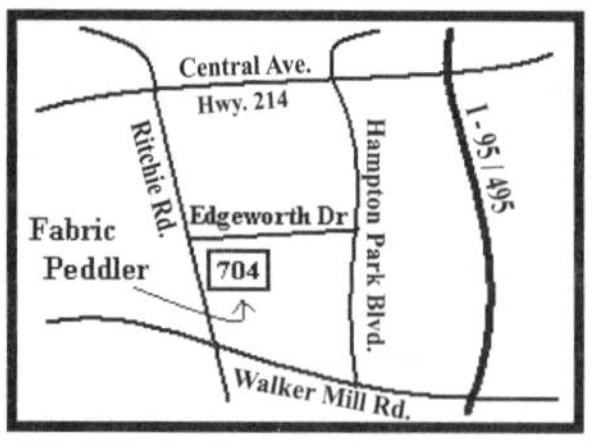

Savage, MD #13

And Sew it Goes ~ Quilting

Historic Savage Mill
8600 Foundry St, PO Box 2057
Savage, MD 20763
301.725.5548

Mon-Wed 10-6, Thurs-Sat 10-9
Sundays 11-6

andsewitgoes1@comcast.net
andsewitgoes.net

Handi Quilter

- Fabric
- Books
- Patterns
- Notions
- Classes
- Clubs

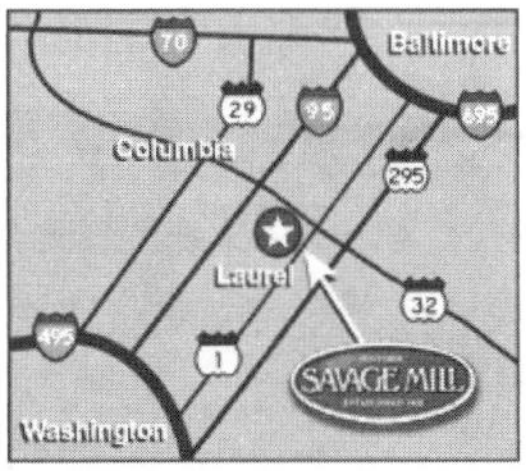

Gaithersburg, MD #14

Mon - Sat
10 - 6
Fri til 9
Sun 12 - 5
Class Eve.

15926 Luanne Dr. 20877
(301) 527-0598 Est: 1995 4000 sq.ft.
Owners: Susan & Gary McLaughlin
www.capitalquilts.com

CAPITAL QUILTS

Great selection of high quality fabric and a full range of necessities and niceties for the quilter. The largest selection of books in the area, we feature patterns by local artists. We're proud of our many classes. Service is friendly & helpful. Bring in your 'Problem Pieces'. Authorized Pfaff & Janome dealer. Easy Access by Public Trans.

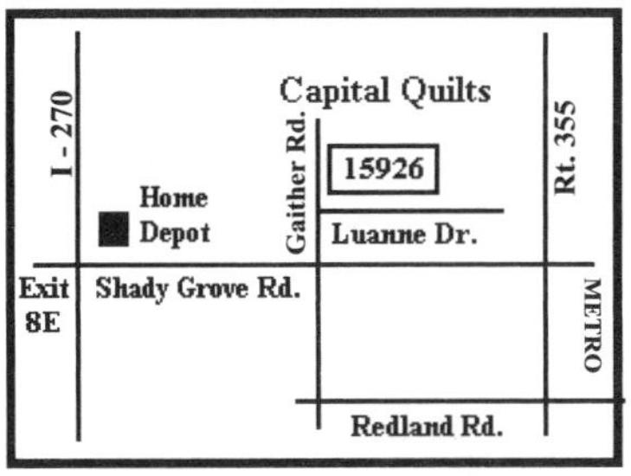

We Are Very Easy to Find!

Calvert Quilt Shop #15

"Traditional Quilting - Today's Techniques"

Maryland Route 4 at 20 Industry Lane, Prince Frederick, Maryland 20678

Serving Southern Maryland for 44 Years www.calvertquiltshop.com

Phone 410-535-0576 * 800-728-4213

We carry major manufacturers of Quilting Products.

7000 Bolts of 100 % Cotton Fabrics

Quilting & Craft Classes

Janome Sewing Machines
Sales & Service

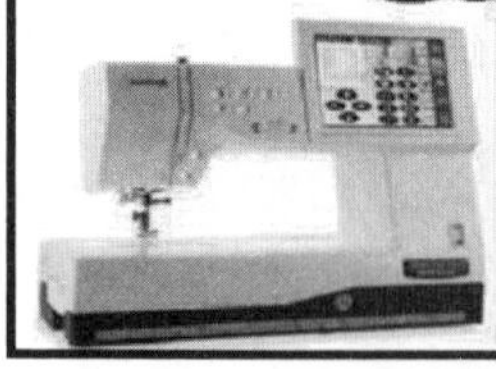

Monday - Friday
9:30am - 6pm
Sat. 10am - 4pm

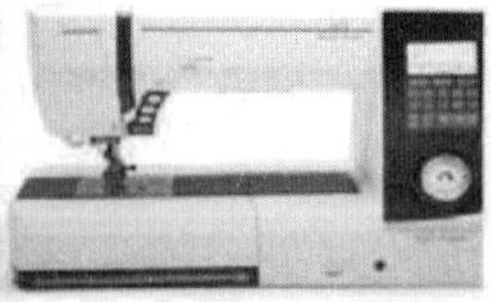

La Plata, MD #16

Material Girls Quilt Boutique

6750 Crain Hwy.,
Suites B/C
LaPlata, MD 20646
301-392-9575
Fax: 301-392-9576
Est: 2003 5000 sq.ft.
4000 bolts and ever growing
materialgirl@verizon.net
www.materialgirlsquilt.com

Material Girls is filled to the brim with 100% cotton and flannel fabrics, books, patterns, notions and so much more. We offer year round classes, lots of samples, and plenty of great ideas.

Monday - Friday 9:30 - 6:00
Wednesday 9:30 - 8:00
Saturday 9:30 - 5:00

- Southern Maryland's Authorized Bernina Dealer
- Authorized dealer of HORN cabinets

Nothing Sews Like A Bernina. Nothing
BERNINA®

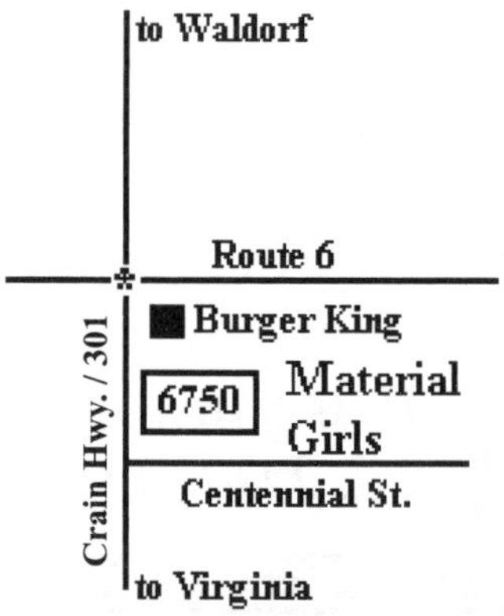

"Your sewing room away from home!"

Lilies of the Field

335 N. Aurora St., Easton, MD 21601
410-822-9117
www.liliesofthefield.biz

Mon, Wed, Fri & Sat 10 - 5
Tues & Thur 10 - 6
Mem. Day to Labor Day
Sat 10 - 3

Fine Fabrics, notions, equipment and classes for the discriminating woman who sews.
Celebrating over 20 years in business.

Easton, MD #17

Snow Hill, MD #18

Thur - Fri 10 - 5
Sat 10 - 3

The Fine Needle

121 South Dr. 21863
(410) 632-0772

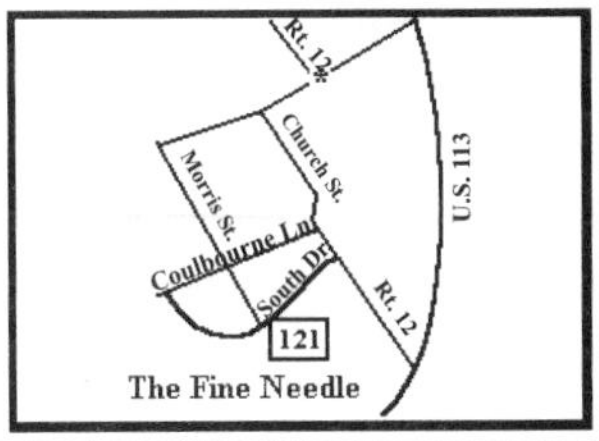

quilts@fineneedle.com
www.fineneedle.com
Owner: Stacy Mitchell
Fine fabric, fine yarns and friendly service!

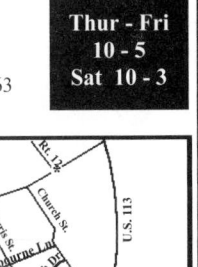

Maryland Quilt Shops

Aberdeen — **Hoppin Bobbin, 411 W. Bel Air Ave.**
410-272-2226 — **See ad #10, page 246**

Annapolis — **Cottonseed Glory, Inc., 4 Annapolis St.**
410-263-3897 — **See ad #11, page 246**

Bel Air — Sew Unique, 2202 Conowingo Rd. — 410-838-2633

Capitol Heights — **The Fabric Peddler, 704 Ritchie Rd.**
301-336-3646 — **See ad #12, page 246**

Catonsville — **Seminole Sampler, 71 Mellor Ave.**
410-788-1720 — **See ad #9, page 246**

Centreville — Peggy's Sewing Center, 210 Pennsylvania — 410-758-3827

Crofton — Tomorrow's Treasures, 2110 Priest Bridge — 410-451-0400

Easton — **Lilies of the Field, 335 N. Aurora St.**
410-822-9117 — **See ad #17, this page**

Ellicott City — **Ellicott City Sew, 8480 Baltimore National Pike**
410-465-6366 — **See ad #41, page 244**

Frederick — **Needles & Pins, 310 E. Church St.**
301-695-7199 — **See ad #6, page 244**

Frederick — **Sisto's Sewing & Quilting, 1911 N. Market St.**
301-695-0643 — **See ad #5, page 244**

Fruitland — The Dusty Attic, 301 S. Division St. — 410-546-1656

Gaithersburg — **Capital Quilts, 15926 Louanne Dr.**
301-527-0598 — **See ad #14, page 247**

Grantsville — **Four Seasons Stitchery, 116 Main St.**
301-895-5958 — **See ad #3, page 244**

Hagerstown — **Wilson's Your Favorite Quilt Shop**
13516 Marsh Pike
301-790-3526 — **See ad #2, page 243 & 403**

Hagerstown — **Traditions at the White Swan,**
16525 National Pike
301-733-9130 — **See ad #1, page 242**

Hughesville — Michelle's Quilts, 8132 Old Leonardtown Rd. — 301-274-1919

La Plata — **Material Girls Quilt Boutique,**
6750 Crain Hwy. Suites B/C
301-392-9575 — **See ad #16, page 248**

Mount Airy — Patches Quilting & Sewing, 308 S. Main St. — 301-831-0366

Pocomoke City — Robinanne's Quilting Service, 145C Market St. — 410-957-4766

Prince Frederick — **Calvert Quilt Shop, 20 Industry Lane**
410-535-0576 — **See ad #15, page 248**

Rockville — All Sewn Up, 14001 Parkvale Rd. — 301-460-2681

Salisbury — Sew Sew, Quilting Fabrics, 116 South Blvd. — 410-912-4788

Savage — **And Sew It Goes - Quilting,**
Historic Savage Mill, 8600 Foundry St.
301-725-5548 — **See ad #13, page 247**

Snow Hill — **The Fine Needle, 121 South Dr.**
410-632-0772 — **See ad #18, this page**

St. Michaels — Sewing Factory, 609 S. Talbot St. — 410-745-3178

Timonium — **Stitches Etc. Home Center, 2195 Greenspring Dr.**
410-561-3101 — **See ad #7, page 245**

Towson — **Bear's Paw Fabrics, 8812 Orchard Tree Lane**
410-321-6730 — **See ad #8, page 245**

Westminster — A Piece of My Heart Quilt, 63 East Main Street Rear — 410-751-5552

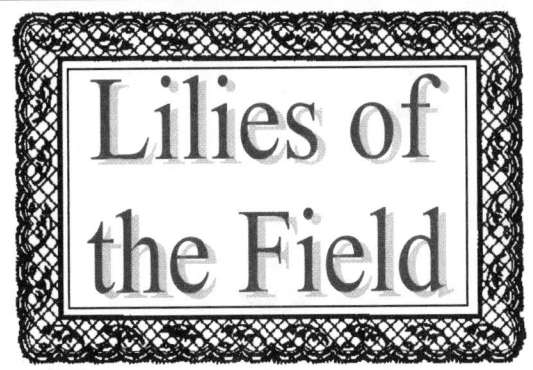

Maryland Quilt Shows

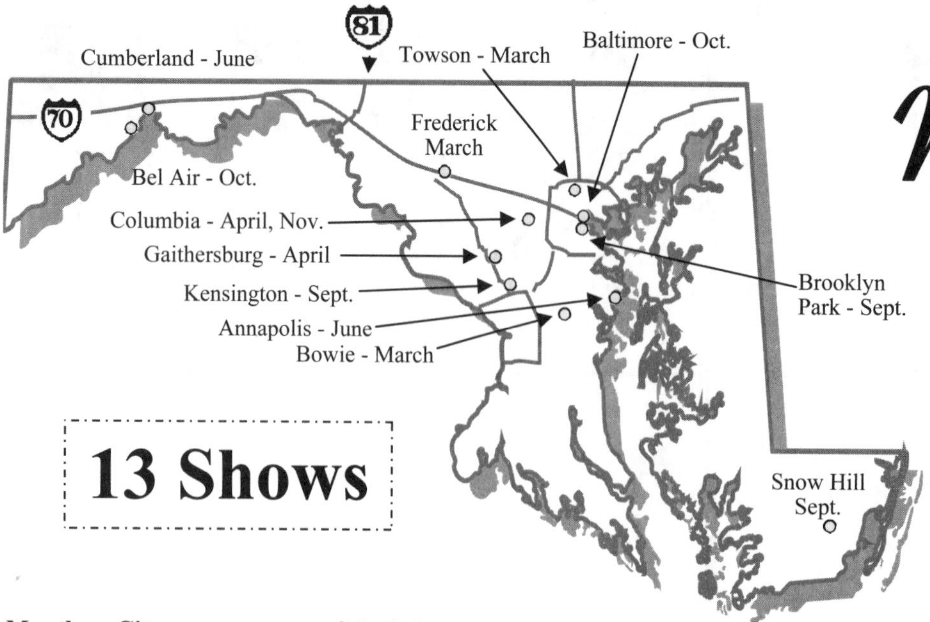

13 Shows

Month	City	Schedule	Show	Location with address
March				
	Frederick	Odd years, 1st & 2nd Weekend in March	Rose Hill Quilt Show	Rose Hill Manor Park, 1611 N. Market St.
	Bowie	Annual, 2nd weekend in March	Southern Comforters Quilt Show	C. Elizabeth Rieg School, 15542 Peach Walker Dr.
	Towson	Odd Years, 2nd weekend of March	Quilt Expo	Goucher College Sports & Rec. Center, 1021 Dulaney Valley Rd.
April				
	Columbia	Even Years, 3rd weekend in April	Fairthful Circle Quilters	First Presbyterian Church, 9325 Presbyterian Cir.
	Gaithersburg	Annual, last weekend of April	Friendship Star Quilters Show	Montgomery County Fairgrounds--Home Arts Bldg, 16 Chestnut St.
June				
	Annapolis	Annual, 2nd weekend in June	Annapolis Quilt Guild Show	Annapolis Senior High School, 2700 Riva Rd.
	Cumberland	Odd Years, 3rd weekend of June	Schoolhouse Quilt Show	Allegany County Fairgrounds, Moss Ave.
September				
	Kensington	Odd years, 3rd weekend in September	Bethesda Quilters Show	Holy Redeemer Church, 9705 Summit Ave.
	Snow Hill	Odd Years, 3rd weekend in September	Nassawango Outdoor Quilt Show	Furnace Town Living Museum, 3816 Furnace Rd.
	Brooklyn Park	Odd Years, 4th weekend in September	Friendship and Eternal Quilters Show	Brooklyn Park Middle School, 200 Hammonds Ln.
October				
	Baltimore	Even Years, 1st weekend of October	African American Quilters of Baltimore Show	Waldorf School--Children's Garden Bldg, 4701 Yellowwood Ave.
	Bel Air	Even years, 3rd weekend in October	Flying Geese Quilt Guild Show	Harford Technical High School, 200 Thomas Run
November				
	Columbia	Annual, 2nd Sat in November	Locust Quilt and Craft	Hilton Columbia, 5485 Twin Knolls Rd.

Notes

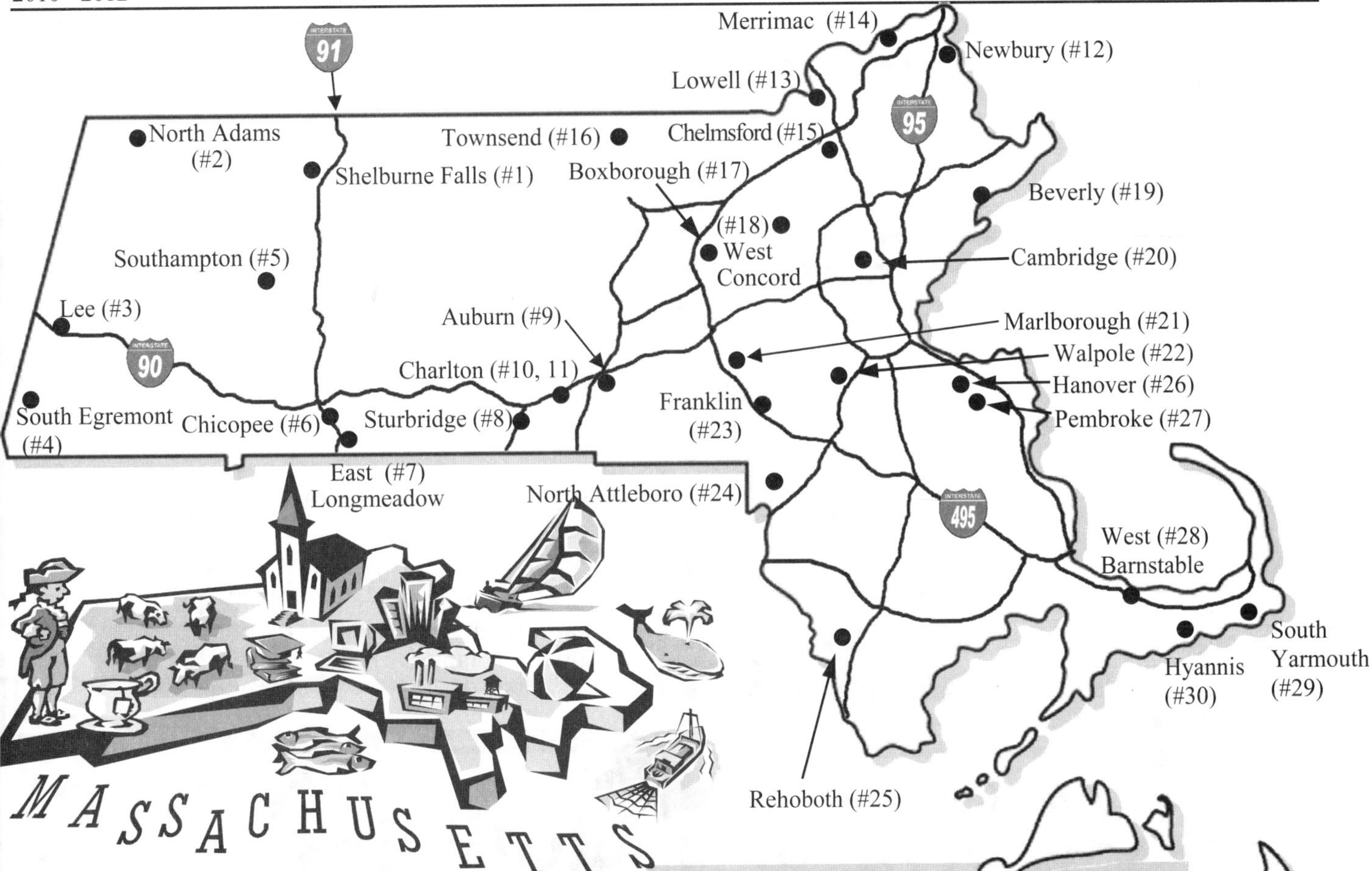

30 Featured Shops

MASSACHUSETTS

Shelburne Falls, MA #1

Tues - Sat 10 - 5
Sun 12 - 5
Thur 6:30 - 8:30
Open Mon. Holidays

A Notion to Quilt

623 Mohawk Tr. 01370
(413) 625-9644
Owners: Becki & Lenny Stratton
Est: 2003 & Nancy Hazen
www.anotiontoquilt.com
"On the Scenic Mohawk Trail"
A Notion to Quilt offers Fabric, Supplies, Notions, Quilted Products and Classes.
HandiQuilter & Janome Dealer

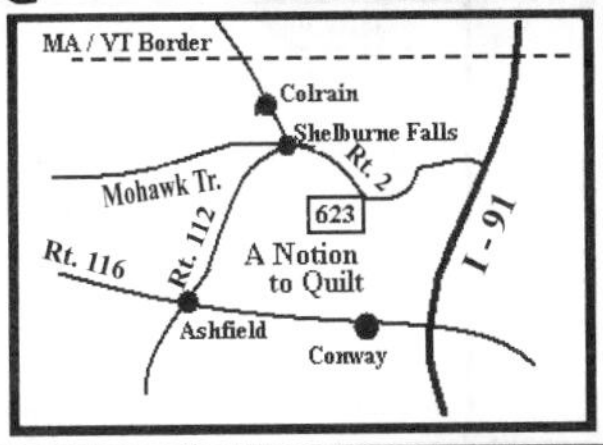

North Adams #2

Mon - Sat
10 - 4:30
Closed Wed
Sun 12 - 4

Tala's Quilt Shop

Heritage State Park-Furnace St. 01247
(413) 664-8200
Owner: Tala Neathawk Est: 2001
Over 4000+ Bolts - 1000 Flannels.
tquilting@hotmail.com
www.talasquiltshop.tripod.com/
Featured in "Quilt Samplers" 2004 magazine as one of the top ten shops in the U.S. & Canada.

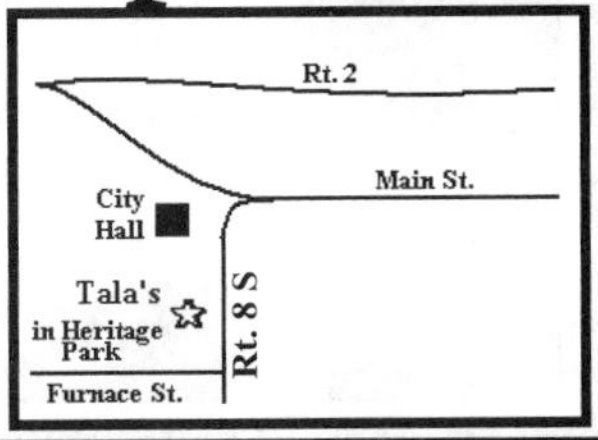

Lee, MA #3

Mon - Sat
10 - 6
Sun 12 - 5

Pumpkin Patch

58 W. Center St. (Rt. 20)
(413) 243-1635 01238
Owners: Susan & Dan Sullivan
Est: 1985 800 sq.ft.
www.pumpkinpatchquilts.com
Located in the beautiful Berkshires!
Cotton fabrics, books, patterns, etc. . . .
Classes, machine quilting . . . .
Bernina Sewing Machines

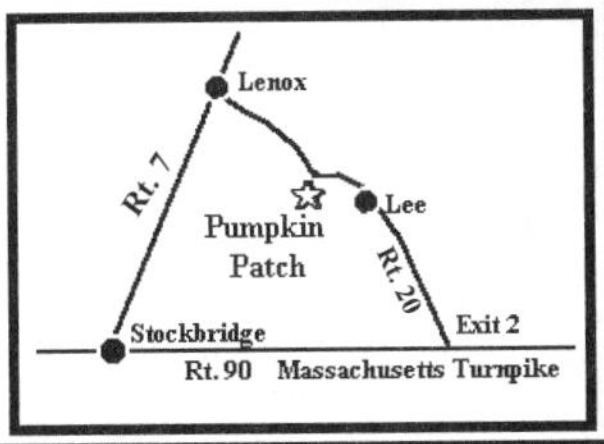

South Egremont, MA #4

Mon - Fri
10 - 5
Sat 9 - 3
Sun 12 - 3

Brookside Quiltworks

2 Egremont Sheffield Rd. PO Box 441 01258
(413) 528-0445
Owner: Catherine Kane
www.brooksidequiltworks.com
Fabric shop & Quilt Gallery
Located in the picturesque Berkshire Mountains.
Patterns, notions, batiks & batting
Long arm quilting. Friendly Service.

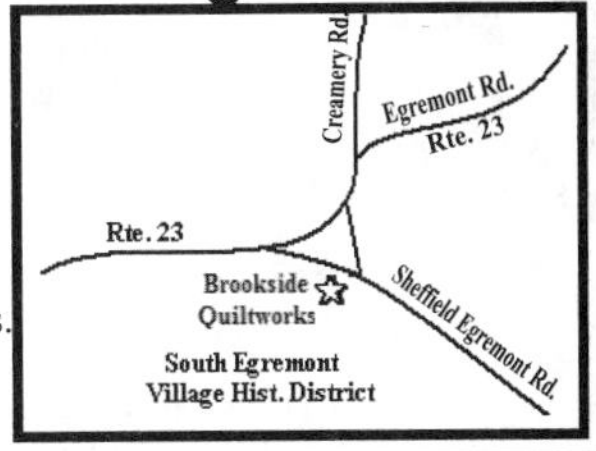

Southhampton, MA #5

Southampton Quilts

Quilting Supplies

6 Parc Place 01073
(413) 529-9641
info@southamptonquilts.com

www.southamptonquilts.com

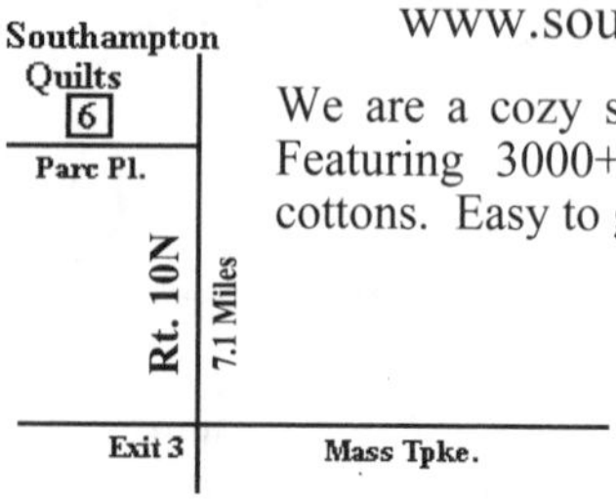

We are a cozy shop dedicated to all quilters. Featuring 3000+ bolts of the latest quality cottons. Easy to get to, friendly atmosphere.

Tues - Thur 10 - 5
Fri & Sat 10 - 4
Sun 12 - 4

Chicopee, MA #6

Bayberry Quilt & Gift Shoppe

- Full line of quilting fabrics, supplies, books & patterns displayed in a 10 room Victorian farm house.
- We offer quilting classes ….
- We also offer a CUSTOM MACHINE QUILTING SERVICE Visit us online for available patterns and price list...9 years experience….currently a 2 to 3 week turnaround time.
- 10 rooms FILLED with QUILT SAMPLES, fabrics, supplies etc...GUARANTEED TO INSPIRE YOU !!
- Handcrafted gifts and Quilts for Sale in our Gift Shoppe
- UNIQUE SHOPPE

Hours: Tues 10-4…Wed & Thurs 10-4 and 5:30-8…Sat 10-3

137 Sheridan St.
Chicopee, MA 01020
(413) 592-9653
www.bayberryquilts.com
Laura J. Knapp/Owner
Est: 1999

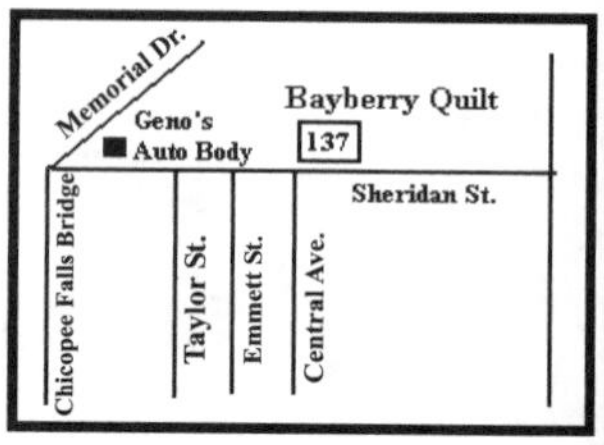

East Longmeadow, MA #7

Quilts & Treasures Inc.

Mon - Thur 10 - 8:30
Fri & Sat 10 - 5

56 Shaker Rd. 01028
(413) 525-4789
www.quiltsandtreasuresinc.com

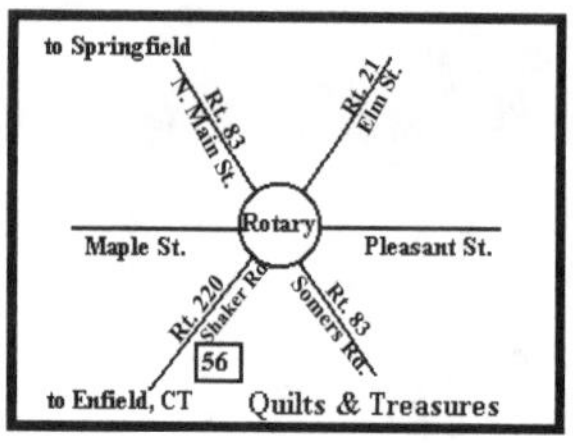

3000+ bolts of 100% Cotton Fabrics, Books, Patterns & Quilting Supplies. Authorized Pfaff dealer.

The Quilt and Cabbage

Enter a relaxing & warm atmosphere of 2000 bolts - select cottons, homespun, batiks, flannels, wool, fleece & wool yarn. Best array of books, patterns, stencils. Custom quilts & gifts. Leave with inspiration, treasures & a smile!

P.O. Box 534 01566
538 Main St. (Rt. 20)
(508) 347-3023
Owner: Jeanne Molitoris

Sturbridge, MA #8

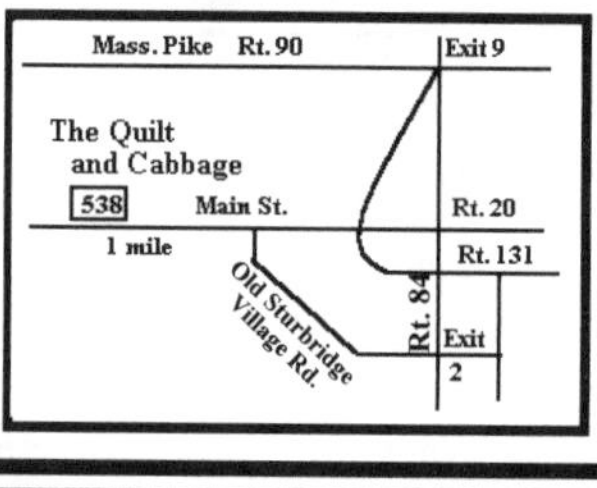

Mon & Wed - Sat
9:30 - 4:30
Sun 11 - 4
Closed Tuesday

Est: 1991

Auburn, MA #9

Mon - Wed 10 - 6
Thur - Sat 10 - 5
Sun 12 - 3
(Oct-May)

Appletree Fabrics

850 Southbridge St. 01501
Rts 12/20, Westside Plaza
(508) 832-5562
Est: 1991
Owner: Lois Therrien

Over 2500 bolts of fine quality quilting cottons. Hundreds of books & patterns.

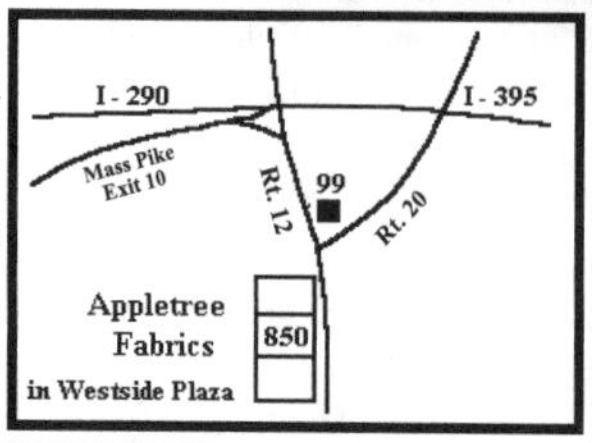

Charlton, MA #10

Mon - Thur
9:30 - 6:30
Fri 9:30 - 8
Sat 9:30 - 5
Sun 12:30 - 4

The Fabric Stash

45a Sturbridge Rd. 01507
(508) 248-0600
laurel@fabstash.com
www.fabstash.com

Worcester county's largest independent fabric store. We are more than just quilting. Come see for yourself.

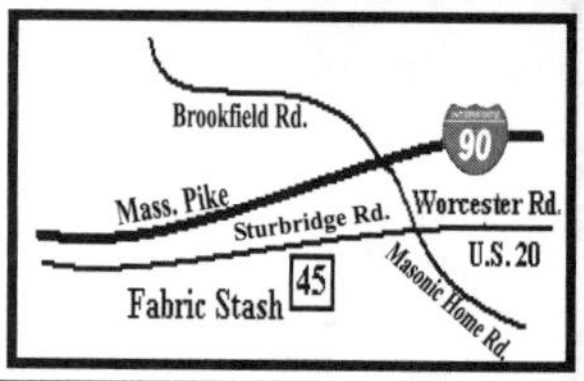

Charlton, MA #11

Charlton Sewing Center
New England's Sewing Sanctuary

We are located in a 110 year old New England church. The main floor of this building offers customers a gift shop, seating area near the fireplace and antique sewing machines within its 2100 square feet. Each month a different sewing exhibit is on display set among the stained glass windows and the original pipe organ. Large selection of fabrics, threads, fiber embellishments, sewing notions and more. Classes.

"Without a doubt we'll know that we have been renewed when we shall leave this place."

Mon - Fri 10 - 6 Sat 9 - 5

sewingmachines@charterinternet.com
www.charltonsewingcenter.com

Bernina, Pfaff, Elna, Necchi, HandiQuilter
12 Stafford St. 01507
508-248-6632
Owner: Cathy Racine Est: 1979
Selected for American Quilt Magazine in 2010.

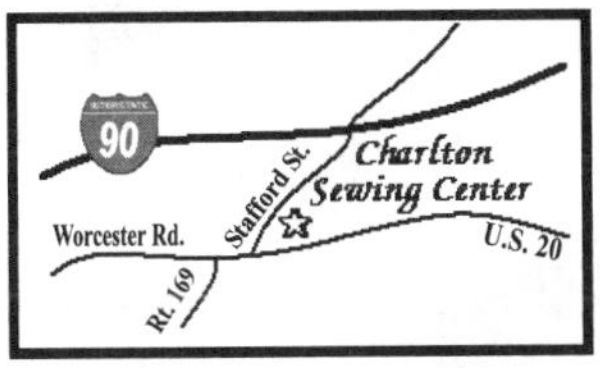

Newbury, MA #12

Tues - Sat 9:30 - 4:30

THE QUILTED ACORN SHOPPE

72 Newburyport Tpk. (Rt 1) 01951
(978) 462-0974 Est: 1983
Schedule of Classes & Sales
www.QuiltedAcorn.com
Owners: Cynthia Erekson & Sandra Schauer
Unique combination of Quilting, Folk Art Painting and Vintage Needle Arts: supplies and classes.
We specialize in Homespuns & Antique Reproduction Fabrics. Also flannels and wool felts.

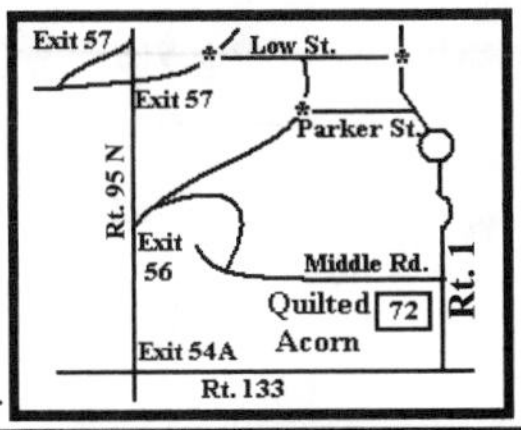

Lowell, MA #13

Tues - Sat 10 - 4
May - Oct. Sun 12 - 4

The New England Quilt Museum

18 Shattuck St. 01852
(978) 452-4207 Free to Members
www.nequiltmuseum.org
Adm: $7, $5 Seniors & Students, Members Free, 2 for 1 for AAA & WGBH.
We are the only museum in New England dedicated solely to the preservation, education and interpretation of American quiltmaking past and present. Exhibitions, workshops, programs and our library are a wonderful resource for quilters and collectors.

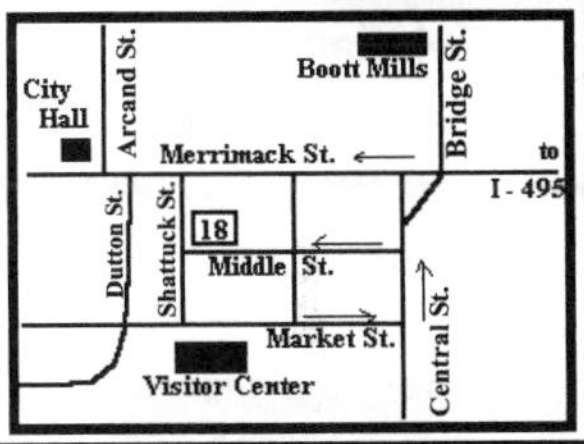

Merrimac, MA #14

Red Barn Sewing & Yarn Center
Est. 1978

116 West Main Street
Merrimac, MA 01860
978-346-9292

www.redbarnonline.com
redbarn@redbarnonline.com
Owner: Helen Gosselin

- Over 4000 bolts of quality cotton fabric.
- Books, Patterns, Notions, Classes
- Authorized Janome Sewing Machine Dealer
- 2000 Sq. Ft.

Mon-Fri 9-5 Sat 9-4

Stop by and become inspired to create your own work of art!

Follow I-495 to Exit 52. Take Rte 110 East. Go 2.3 Miles. We are on the right.

"Your Home Away From Home"

This 300 year old house has been transformed into a beautiful shop for Quilters!
Fabrics / Notions / Kits / Classes
Daily Demos / Exclusive Patterns
Fun, Friendly Staff and the Inspiration a Quilter Needs!

Welcome to

Candlelite Quilts

Chelmsford, MA #15

24 Central Square
Chelmsford, MA 01824
(978) 256-0025
Owner: Cathy Ruggiero

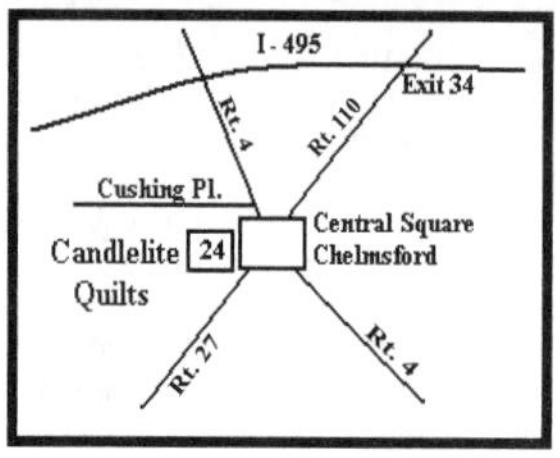

Tues - Sat 10-4
Thur til 6

www.candlelitequilts.com

Townsend, MA #16

Tues - Sat 10 - 5
Sun 12 - 4

Cobblestone Quilts

10 Elm St. (Rt. 13) 01469
(978) 597-0091 Est: 2003

Owner: Maureen Blanchard
CobblestoneQuilts@yahoo.com
www.CobblestoneQuilts.com

Fabrics, books, original patterns, long-arm machine quilting, classes and clubs.
Largest Selection of 1930's Fabric in the Area!

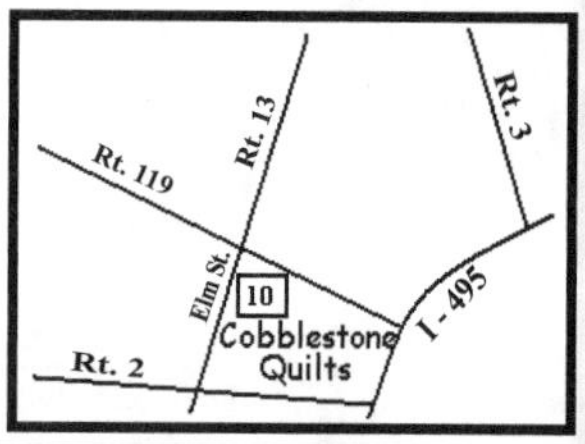

Boxborough, MA #17

Tues - Fri 10 - 5
Thurs til 7
Sat 10 - 4

The Quilted Crow

61 Stow Rd. 01719
(866) 266-9104 or (978) 266-9102
Est: 2002 1500 sq.ft.
Online Newsletter
info@thequiltedcrow.com
www.thequiltedcrow.com

Our quilt shop offers cotton and wool fabrics & supplies for quilting, wool applique, needle felting, punchneedle as well as notions and folk-art gifts.

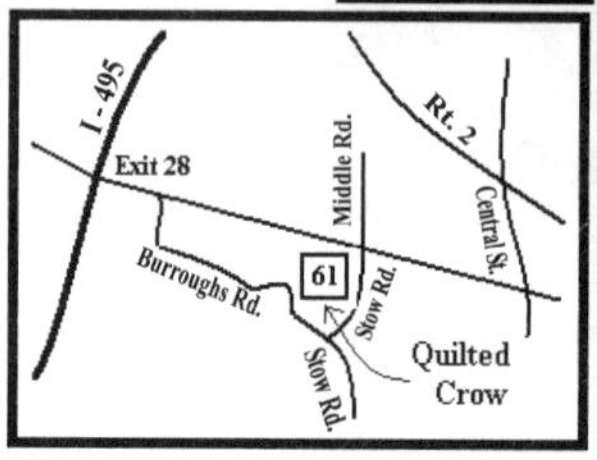

#18

the sewing cafe and Quilter's Way

Our sunny shop is located in the artisan village of West Concord. We are widely known for our friendly, knowledgable staff, our large, eye-catching selection of the latest in contemporary fabrics and the inspiration we provide to novice and experienced sewing enthusiasts alike.

Drop-in to sew or throw a party in our Sewing Cafe -- browse through over 3000 bolts and one of the largest collections of Amy Butler, Kaffe Fassett, and other designer lines in the area -- plan your next project while relaxing in our book nook -- we're confident that you'll be glad you came!

After shopping with us, you can enjoy great food and other boutique shops in the village -- unique handmade gifts, two famous local bakeries and a Five & Ten Cent Store that retains its vintage charm year after year.

75 Commonwealth Ave · Concord, MA 01742 · 978-371-1177 · www.quiltersway.com

STORE HOURS: CLOSED MONDAY • TUES&THURS 10AM-8PM • WED&FRI&SAT 10AM-6PM • SUNDAY NOON-5PM
DIRECTIONS: FOLLOW RTE 2 WEST OR EAST TO RTE 62 WEST. FOLLOW RTE 62 FOR 2 MILES, THEN TAKE THE RIGHT FORK AT THE 99 RESTAURANT. TAKE A RIGHT FORK AGAIN TO CROSS THE RAILROAD TRACKS. QUILTER'S WAY IS THE FIRST SHOP IN A RED BUILDING ON THE LEFT.

Beverly, MA #19

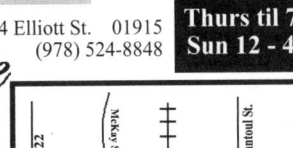

Tues - Sat 9:30 - 5:30 Thurs til 7 Sun 12 - 4

Sew Creative

14 Elliott St. 01915
(978) 524-8848

Est: 2004 2000 sq.ft. 2000 Bolts
www.sewcreativebeverly.com

Authorized PFAFF & Husqvarna Dealer. 100% cotton fabrics, books, patterns, threads, machine embroidery supplies. Classes for all ages.
"A fun place to shop where customers are friends"

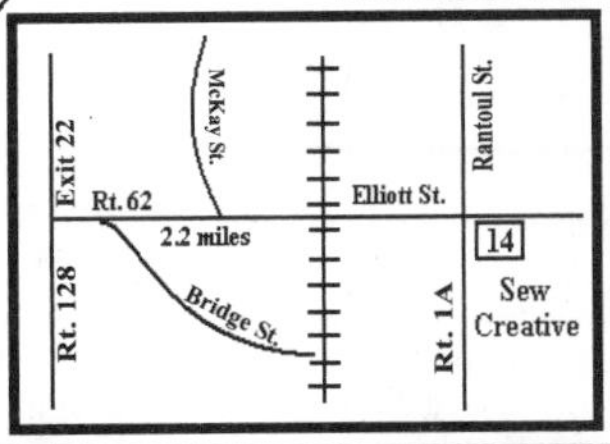

Cambridge, MA #20

Mon - Sat 10 - 6 Thurs 10-8:30 Sun 12 - 5

Cambridge Quilt Shop

95 Blanchard Rd. 02138
(617) 492-3279
Owners: Lynn Gorst, & Monique Thompson
Est: 1996 1100 sq.ft.

Our shop maintains 1750 bolts of fabric and over 200 current quilt books, plus the latest in quilting supplies and classes!

quilters@cambridgequilts.com www.cambridgequilts.com

Marlborough, MA #21

Tues 10 - 8 Wed - Fri 10 - 6 Sat 10 - 4 Sun 10 - 2

Wayside Sewing

1021 Boston Post Rd. E (Rt 20)
(508) 481-2088
Fax: (508) 481-2188
Owners: Jill & Mike
Est: 2007
2500 sq.ft.

info@waysidesewing.com
www.waysidesewing.com

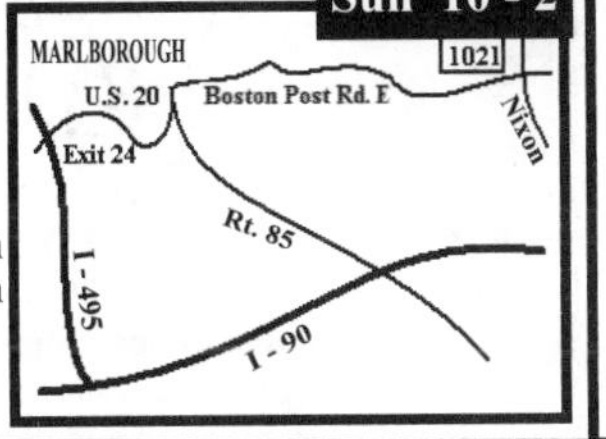

A full service sewing machine sales and service center, quilt shop, and learning center.

Walpole, MA #22

Mon - Fri 10 - 5 Sat 10 - 4

All About Quilts

958 Main St. 02081
(508) 668-0145
Owner: Margaret, Marge, Marilyn, Judy, & Linda
www.allaboutquilts.com

Quilting fabric, supplies, classes for all levels.

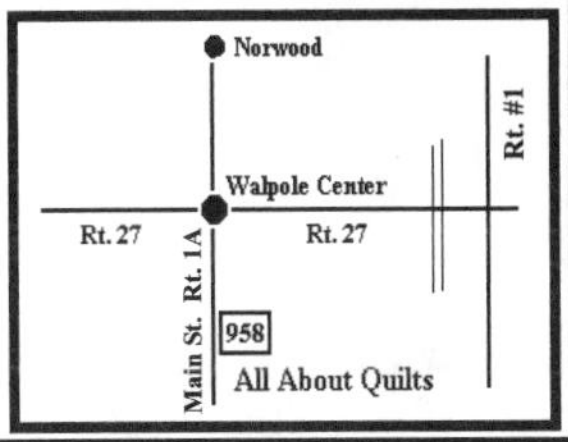

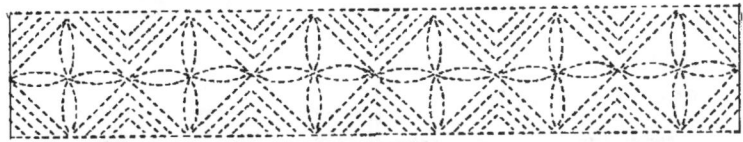

Husqvarna VIKING

Emma's QUILT CUPBOARD & SEWING MACHINES

**12 Main St.
Franklin, MA 02038
508-520-0234
www.emmasquiltcupboard.com**

*Owner: Cyndi Rich Est: 2004 3,800 sq. ft.
4,000 Bolts & growing*

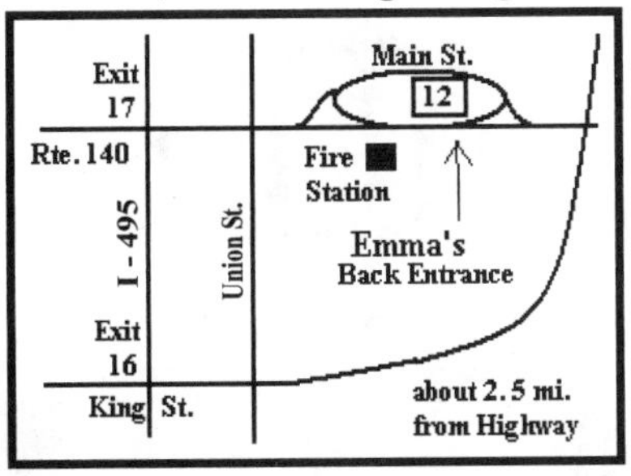

- Warm, inviting shop that makes you feel at home the minute you step in
- Full line of Husqvarna-Viking sewing machines and sergers
- Onsite sewing machine repair services by factory-authorized personnel
- Samples galore to inspire your next project
- Over 4,000 bolts of the highest quality quilting fabrics from all of the major fabric designers: Moda, RJR, Hoffman, P&B, Robert Kaufman, Northcott, Timeless Treasures, Kona Bay, Island Batik, Benartex, In the Beginning, Thimbleberries, Wilmington, Clothworks, Maywood Studios, Marcus Brothers, and more.
- Large selection of batiks, thirties, Thimbleberries, flannels, florals, reproduction, Asian fabrics, novelties, children's prints, tone-on-tone – there's something for everyone!
- Largest selection of kits, books, patterns, notions, stencils, and thread in the area
- Spacious, well-lit classroom for year-round classes and events
- Many clubs, including Saturday Samplers, Buck-A-Block, embroidery, BOMs
- Friendly, knowledgeable staff
- Long-arm quilting services available on-site
- Monthly Quilters Anonymous dinners
- Guilds/groups and buses welcomed anytime

Mon-Sat 10-6 Thurs til 8

Franklin, MA #23

Creating Tomorrow's Treasures Today!

North Attleboro, MA #24

Tues - Sat 10 - 6
Sun 12 - 5

Quilter's Stash

560 Francis J. Kelley Blvd. (Rte 152), 02760
(508) 699-3010 Owner: Sue Kassler
qstash@msn.com www.quilters-stash.com

A fun and friendly shop filled with over 3000 bolts of bright, contemporary fabric.
Largest selection of batiks in the area
Exciting displays to spark your creativity
Visit our website for classes and events, new product news, and directions to the shop.

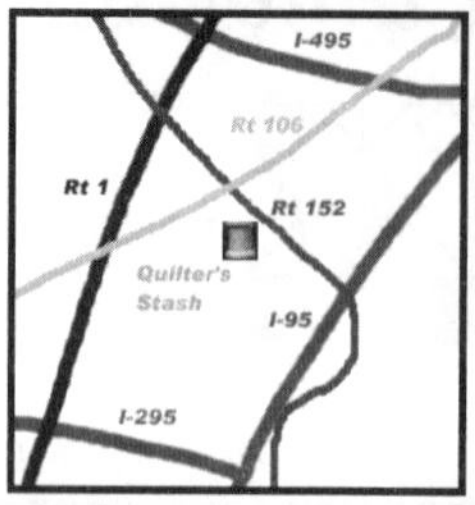

Rehoboth, MA #25

Tues - Sat
11 - 5
Or by Appt.

Loraine's Stitch 'n' Crafts

224 Winthrop St. 02769
(508) 252-5640
Est: 1989 2000 sq.ft. Online Newsletter
loraine@stitchandcrafts.com
www.stitchandcrafts.com

We have a wide assortment of handmade quilts and quilted items, quilt patterns, gifts, fabric, yarn and books. Classes available too.

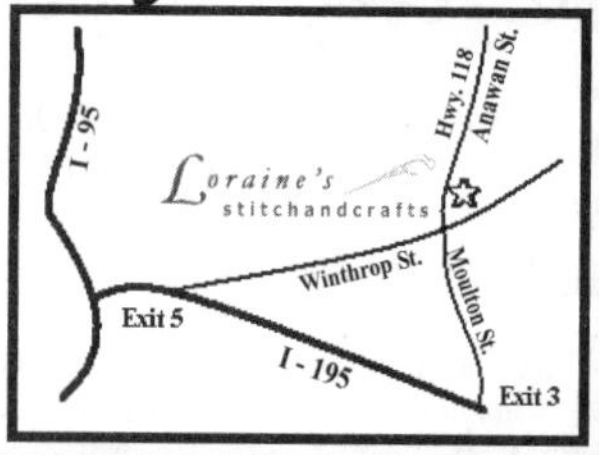

Hanover, MA #26

American Folk Art & Craft Supply

1415 Hanover St. (Rt 139)
Hanover, MA 02339
(781) 871-7277

Retail Store and Studio
Classes Available

Open: Tuesday – Saturday 10:30-7:00
www.AmericanFolkArtOnline.com

Your supplier of: Quilting, Rug Braiding and Rug Hooking Patterns and Supplies. Hand Dyed Wool, Designer Quilting Cottons, and sewing machines.

Supreme PFAFF Dealer

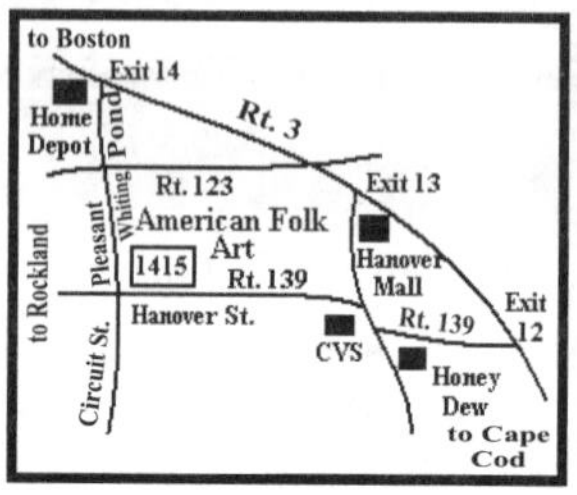

Pembroke, MA #27

Mon - Sat
10 - 5:15
Thur Eves.

Tumbleweed

158 Center St. 02359
(781) 293-6400
Est: 1973 1000 sq.ft.
www.tumbleweedquilts.com

Large selection of fabrics, hundreds of books, notions, batting & more. In a pre-civil war house. Classroom in barn.

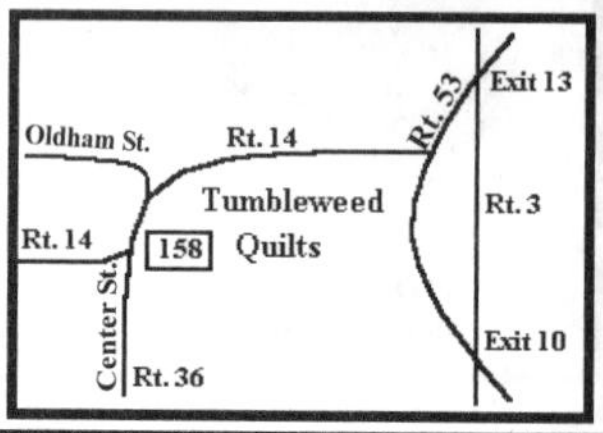

West Barnstable, MA #28

Mon - Sat
10 - 5:30
Sun 12 - 5

Tumbleweed™

Corner of Rt. 6A & Rt. 132
(508) 362-8700 02668
Est: 1973 5000 sq.ft.
www.tumbleweedquilts.com

Wonderful fabric gathered from the best mills for quilts, clothing and home decorations. Where the contemporary mixes with the traditional.

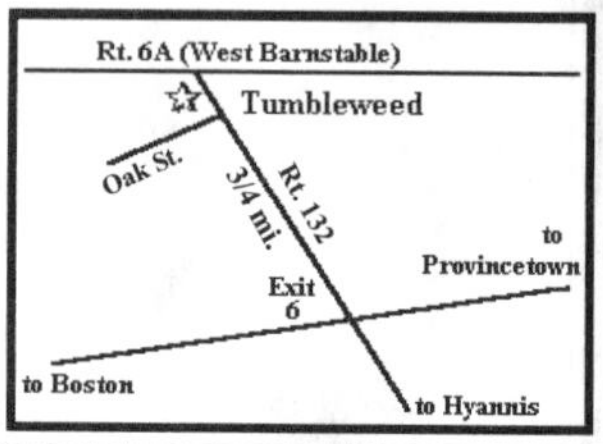

South Yarmouth, MA #29

M, T, Th, F
10 - 5
Sat 10 - 4
Sun 12 - 4

Cozy Home

9 N. Main St. 02664
(508) 394-4001
Fax: (508) 394-4007
Owner: Ellen Peterson
Est: 2006 Online Newsletter
cozyhomefabrics@gmail.com
www.cozyhomefabrics.com

Visit us for personalized, friendly service. We offer bright and unusual fabrics, classes and all quilting supplies.

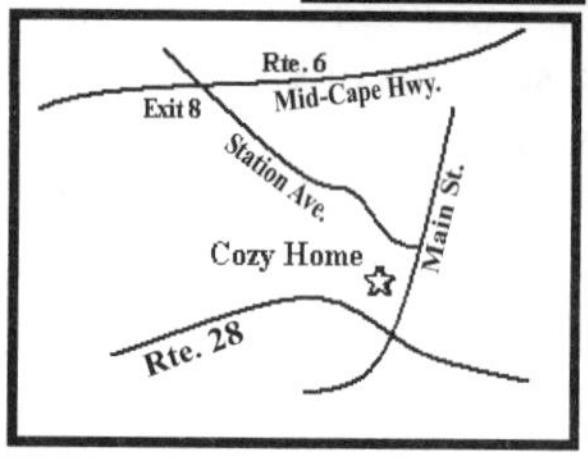

Massachusetts Quilt Shops

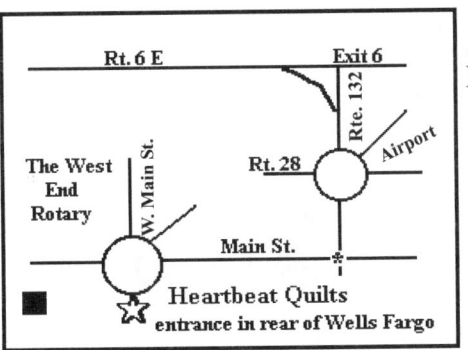

Acushnet	Perry Farm Patchworks, 196 Perryhill Rd.	508-995-1555	
Adams	A Stitch In Time, 45 Commercial St.	413-743-7174	
Arlington	Fabric Corner, 783 Massachusetts Ave.	781-643-4040	
Auburn	**Appletree Fabrics, 850 Southbridge St.**	**508-832-5562**	**See ad #9, page 252**
Belchertown	Quabbin Quilts, 561 Warren Wright Rd	413-253-3824	
Beverly	**Sew Creative, 14 Elliott St.**	**978-524-8848**	**See ad #19, page 255**
Boxborough	**The Quilted Crow, 61 Stow Rd.**	**978-266-9102**	**See ad #17, page 254**
Cambridge	**Cambridge Quilt Shop, 95 Blanchard Rd.**	**617-492-3279**	**See ad #20, page 255**
Canton	Ann's Fabrics, 235 Turnpike St.	781-828-2201	
Charlton	**The Fabric Stash, Inc., 45 A Sturbridge (Rt. 20)**	**508-248-0600**	**See ad #10, page 252**
Charlton	**Charlton Sewing Center, 12 Stafford St.**	**508-248-6632**	**See ad #11, page 253**
Chelmsford	**Candlelite Quilts, 24 Central Square**	**978-256-0025**	**See ad #15, page 254**
Chicopee	**Bayberry Quilt & Gift Shoppe, 137 Sheridan**	**413-592-9653**	**See ad #6, page 252**
Dudley	The Quilters Loft, 26 Mill Rd	508-949-9095	
East Longmeadow	**Quilts & Treasures, Inc., 56 Shaker Rd.**	**413-525-4789**	**See ad #5, page 252**
Falmouth	Fabric Corner, 12 Spring Bars Rd.	508-548-6482	
Franklin	**Emma's Quilt Cupboard, 12 Main St.**	**508-520-0234**	**See ad #23, page 255**
Franklin	Franklin Mill Store, 305 Union St.	508-528-3301	
Great Barrington	The Sewing Shop, 323 Main St. #3	413-528-0118	
Greenfield	The Textile Co., Inc., 21 Power Square	413-773-7516	
Hanover	**American Folk Art & Craft Supply, 1415 Hanover St., (Rt. 139)**	**781-871-7277**	**See ad #26, page 256**
Holden	Black Cat Quilt Shop, 1085A Main St.	508-829-6411	
Hyannis	**Heartbeat Quilts, 765 Main St.**	**508-771-0011**	**See ad #30, this page**
Ipswich	Loom N' Shuttle, 190 High St.	978-356-5551	
Lawrence	Mill Direct Textiles, 53 D Broadway St.	978-686-7700	
Lee	**Pumpkin Patch, 58 W. Center St.**	**413-243-1635**	**See ad #3, page 251**
Leominster	Terry's A Little Quilt Shop, 232 Central St Apt 2	978-840-8597	
Leominster	Quilter's Studio, 101 Prospect St.	978-537-2870	
Lowell	**The New England Quilt Museum, 18 Shattuck St.**	**978-452-4207**	**See ad #13, page 253**
Marlborough	**Wayside Sewing, 1021 Boston Post Rd. E**	**508-481-2088**	**See ad #21, page 255**
Merrimac	**Red Barn Sewing & Yarn Center, 116 W. Main St.**	**978-346-9292**	**See ad #14, page 253**
Middleboro	Pieceful Quilters, 88 E Grove St	508-946-0643	
Newbury	**The Quilted Acorn Shoppe, 72 Newburyport Turnpike**	**978-462-0974**	**See ad #12, page 253**
North Adams	**Tala's Quilt Shop, Heritage State Park**	**413-664-8200**	**See ad #2, page 251**

North Attleboro Quilter's Stash, 560 Kelley Blvd. Rte. 152
508-699-3010 **See ad #24, page 256**
Orleans Murray's Fabrics, 11 Rte. 28 508-255-0653
Pembroke Tumbleweed, 158 Center St., Box 633
781-293-6400 **See ad #27, page 256**
Reading Mary Rose's Quilts & Treasures, 10 Brande Ct. 781-942-9497
Rehoboth Loraine's Stitch 'n' Crafts, 224 Winthrop St.
508-252-5640 **See ad #25, page 256**
S. Yarmouth Cozy Home Fabrics, 9 N Main St
508-394-4001 **See ad #29, page 256**
Salem Marketplace Quilts, 6 Front St. 978-740-3890
Sandwich Scissors & Spool, 5 Rectangle Way 508-888-5669
Shelburne Falls A Notion to Quilt, LLC, 623 Mohawk Tr.
413-625-9644 **See ad #1, page 251**
South Egremont Brookside Quiltworks, 2 Egremont Sheffield
413-528-0445 **See ad #4, page 251**
Southampton Southampton Quilts, 6 Parc Place #D
413-529-9641 **See ad #5, page 252**
Sterling Willow Tree Fabrics, PO Box 483 978-424-6060
Sturbridge The Quilt and Cabbage, 538 Main St.
508-347-3023 **See ad #8, page 252**
Templeton Heather Croft Quilt Shack, 633 Patriots Rd. 978-939-1207
Townsend Cobblestone Quilts, 10 Elm St.
978-597-0091 **See ad #16, page 254**
Vineyard Haven The Heath Hen Yarn & Quilt Shop, 79 Beach Rd., Tisbury Market Place 508-693-6730
Wales Meeting House Fabric and Trim, Route 19 413-245-1235
Walpole All About Quilts, 958 Main St.
508-668-0145 **See ad #22, page 255**
Wellesley The Button Box Quilt Shop & Sewing Center, 5 Overbrook Dr. 781-489-6515
West Barnstable Tumbleweed, 1919 Rt. 6A
508-362-8700 **See ad #28, page 256**
West Concord Quilter's Way, Inc., 75 Commonwealth Ave.
978-371-1177 **See ad #18, page 254**
West Springfield Osgood Textile Co., 333 Park St. 413-737-6488
Whitman Saftler's, Inc., 342 Bedford St. 617-447-4451

Massachusetts Quilt Shows

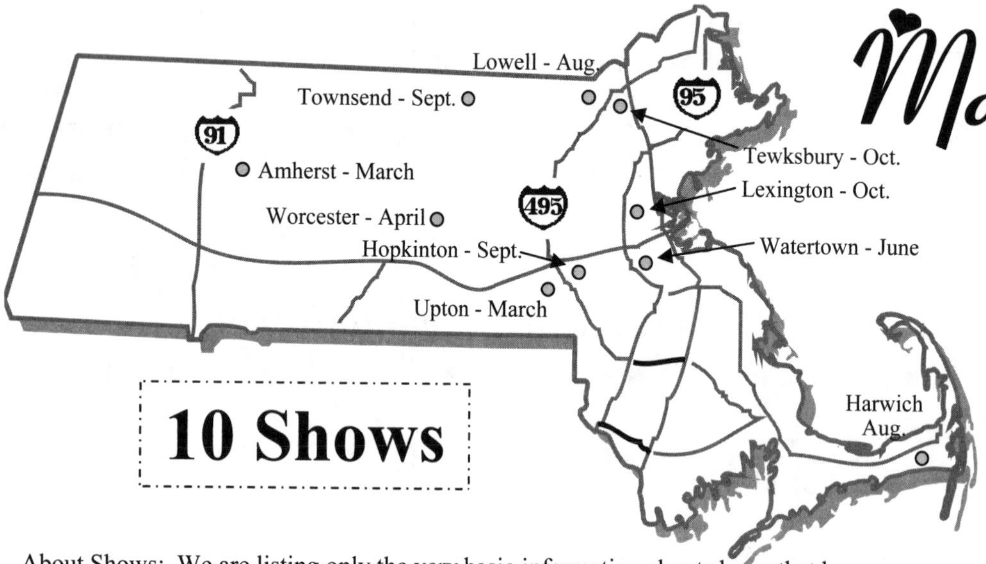

About Shows: We are listing only the very basic information about shows that happen on a regular schedule here. Please check out our website for more details on each show. Also this information tends to change quite often so please verify the event with our website or a local source before you venture far. Or if you're in the right area at the right time, give it a shot.

If you are a show organizer, please keep us updated on your event.
shows@quilterstravelcompanion.com www.quilterstravelcompanion.com

Month	City	Schedule	Show	Location with address
March				
	Amherst	Odd years 4th weekend in March	Hands Across the Valley Quilters Guild Show	Amherst College
	Upton	Even, last weekend of March	Thimble Pleasures Quilt Guild Show	Nipmuc Regional High School, 90 Pleasant St.
April				
	Worcester	Annual, 2nd Thur - Sat of April	Original Sewing & Quilt Expo	DCU Center, 50 Foster St.
June				
	Watertown	Annual, 1st weekend in June	Quilters' Connection Quilt Show and Sale	Arsenal Center for the Arts, 322 Arsenal St
August				
	Lowell	Annual, 1st weekend of August	Lowell Quilt Festival	Lowell memorial Auditorium, 50 E. Merrimack St.
	Harwich	Annual, 2nd weekend in August	Bayberry Quilters of Cape Cod Guild Quilt Show	Cape Cod Regional Technical High School, Exit 10, Mid Cape Hwy. (Rt. 6)
September				
	Townsend	Odd Years, 3rd weekend of September	Autumn Festival of Quilts	North Middlesex High School, Main St. (Rt. 119)
	Hopkinton	Odd Years, 4th weekend in September	Marathon Quilter's Guild Quilt Show	Hopkinton Cultural Arts Alliance, 98 Hayden Rowe St.
October				
	Lexington	Annual, 2nd weekend in October	Rising Star Quilters Guild Show	Cary Memorial Hall, 1605 Massachusetts Ave.
	Tewksbury	Annual, 4th weekend in October	Tewksbury Piecemakers Show	Tewksbury Senior Center, 175 Chandler St.

For the Upper Peninsula Shops #84 - 94 See Page 279
Cheboygan (#1)
Indian River (#2)
Charlevoix (#3)
75
Bellaire (#7)
Williamsburg (#8)
Cedar (#5)
Traverse City (#4)
Grayling (#6)
Harrisville (#65)
Oscoda (#64)
Bear Lake (#9)
Cadillac (#10, 11)
East Tawas (#63)
Au Gres (#62)
Gladwin (#14)
75
Custer (#12)
Reed City (#13)
Farwell (#15)
Baldwin (#16)
Midland (#59)
Bay City (#61)
Hemlock (#60)
Montague (#17)
Whitehall (#18)
127
East Lansing (#47)
Millington (#56)
Ovid (#57)
Imlay City (#54)
Port Huron (#55)
96
Comstock Park (#19)
Flushing (#58)
Wyoming (#23)
Grand Rapids (#21, 22)
Hadley (#52)
Portland (#20)
69
Richmond (#53)
Ortonville (#49)
196
Byron Center (#24)
Fenton (#48)
Lake Orion (#50)
75
Holland (#26)
96
Hastings (#25)
Charlotte (#44)
Howell
Fennville (#28)
Allegan (#27)
Bellevue (#38)
St. Clair (#51)
Battle Creek (#37)
Pinckney (#41)
South Haven (#32)
Kalamazoo (#29, 30, 31)
Southeastern Michigan (Shops # 66-83) See Page 273
Marshall (#36)
Jackson (#40)
94
East Leroy (#39)
Holt (#43)
Schoolcraft (#33)
Mason (#42)
Tecumseh (#35)
69
(#34) Stevensville
23

MICHIGAN

94 Featured Shops

Cheboygan, MI #1

Mon - Fri 10 - 6
Sat 10 - 2

THE FABRIC STASH

218 N. Main St. #102 49721
(231) 597-9551 Fax: (231) 597-9556
Owners: Peggy & Dave Gervais
Est: 2008 1400 sq.ft.
www.fabricstashquilting.com

Come enjoy our wonderful natural lighting and large work area. We have a very nice variety of fabrics. We cater to quilters, smockers and general sewing interests.

Indian River, MI #2

Mon - Fri 10 - 5
Sat 10 - 2

the Quilt House
WHERE QUILTING IS FUN

4819 S. Straits Hwy.
49749
(231) 238-4339

Owners: Barbara Richmond & Pat Miles

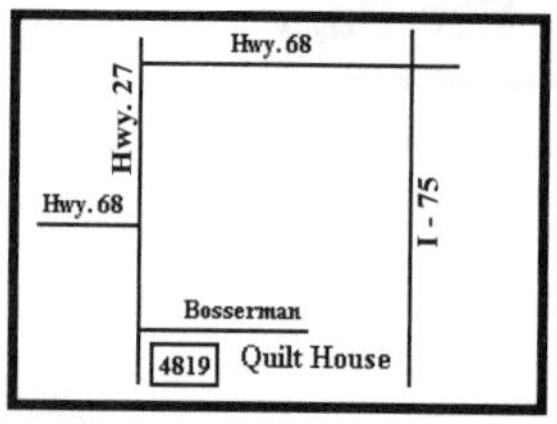

www.indianriverquilts.com
Quality Fabrics and Notions Etc. at affordable Prices.
Classes * Janome Sewing Machines

Charlevoix, MI #3

Hearts to Holly

Fabrics by Moda, Benartex, Marcus Brothers, Kaufman and more. Classes, notions, quilting supplies and gifts - something for everyone. Finished custom quilts and longarm quilting services available. Located in a beautiful cottage in the heart of downtown Charlevoix, MI.

Monday-Friday 10:00 - 6:00 Saturday 10:00 - 4:00

107 Mason St. 49720
231-547-2729
www.heartstoholly.com

Est: 2007 1000 sq.ft.
2500 Bolts Online Newsletter
heartstoholly@yahoo.com

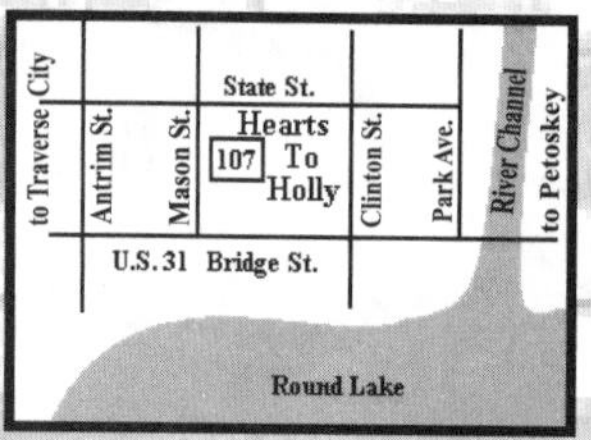

"Stop In And See What The Buzz Is All About"

Quilt-n-Bee

- Over 1,500 bolts of high quality quilting fabrics; Civil War, Reproduction, 30's, Windham, Batiks and current collections
- Smocking & Silk Ribbon Embroidery
- Hand Embroideries from Crabapple Hill
- Unique Machine Embroidery Designs
- Inspirational Samples
- Adorable Children's Patterns
- Gifts for the Quilter
- Wool Fabric & Roving
- Specialty Threads

Experienced and friendly staff ready to serve you!

Mon - Fri 9:30 - 6:00 Sat 9:30 - 5:00

1425-C
S. Airport Rd. West
(231) 922-6766
www.quiltnbee.com
Est: 2003 2,000 sq. ft.
Owners: Sharon Kaiser & Laura Hazen

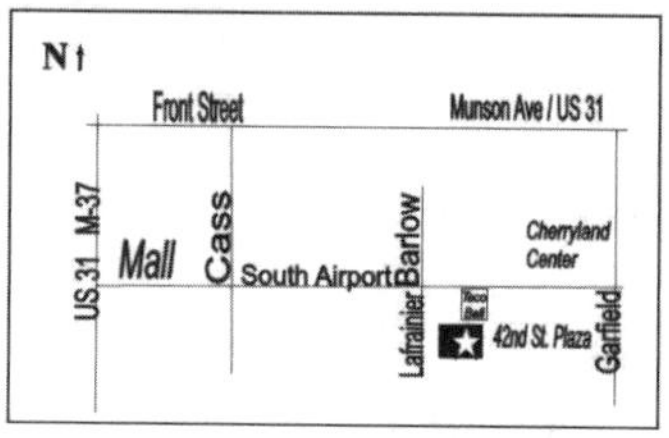

Look for us behind Taco Bell

Traverse City, MI #4

Cedar, MI #5

Mon - Sat 11 - 6

Liberty Bell Quilts

9027 S. Kasson St., P.O. Box 123 49621
(231) 228-6689 Fax: (231) 228-6677
Est: 2008 1500 sq.ft. 1000 Bolts
libertybellquilts@charterinternet.com
www.libertybellquilts.com

A charming Quilt Shop set in a scenic area that carries all the fabric & notions for Quilters!

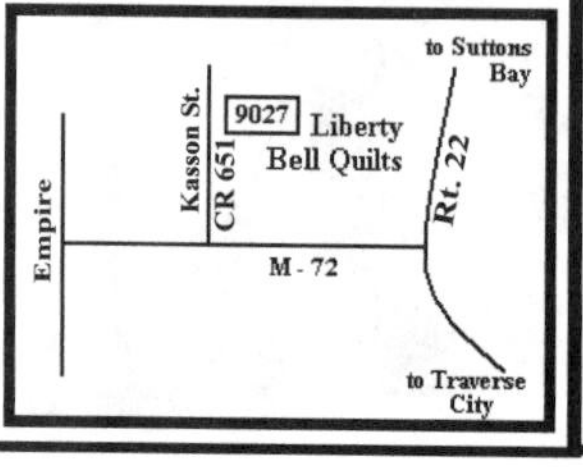

Grayling, MI #6

Mon - Sat 10 - 5

The Icehouse Quilt Shop

509 Norway St.
49738
(989) 348-4821
Est: 1980
Owner: Ali Baynham
icehouse@freeway.net
www.theicehousequiltshop.com
A unique shop for the person seeking quality in quilting and gifts.
An Authorized Bernina Dealer.

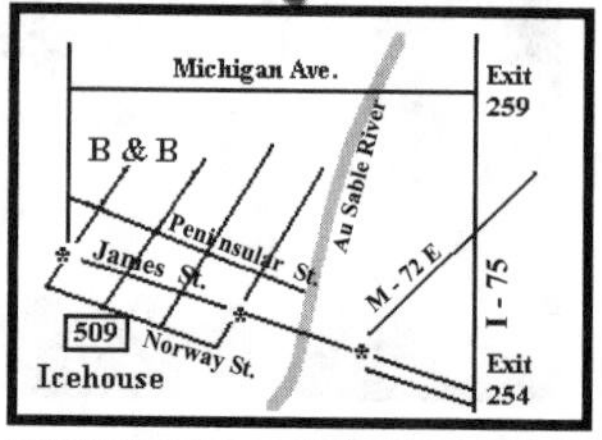

Cousin's Quilt Shop

"The little shop with a big heart."

Area's Largest Selection of Batiks by Hoffman and Bali. A good selection of fabrics by other designers. We offer classes and weekend sewing events.

www.cousinsquiltshop.com

732 E. Cayuga St.
Bellaire, MI 49615
(231) 533-4661
hartwig@torchlake.com
Owner: Carmen Hartwig

Est: 2001

Bellaire, MI #7

BERNINA

Mon - Fri 10 - 5 Sat 10 - 4

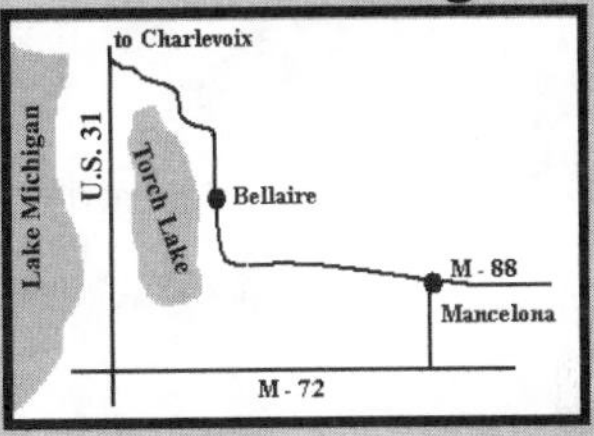

Renée's House of Quilting, Inc

Est: 2004

A Quilter's Dream

Owner:
Renee Savage

8995 M 72 East 49690 (231) 267-5895

Renee's House of Quilting is situated in a 1912 farm house where every room is filled with wonderful fabrics, patterns and books.
We carry beautiful glass buttons to accent quilted designer jackets and purses.
Asians and batiks are Renee's personal favorite so you can imagine the vast selection.

Mon - Fri 9:30 - 6 Sat 9:30 - 4

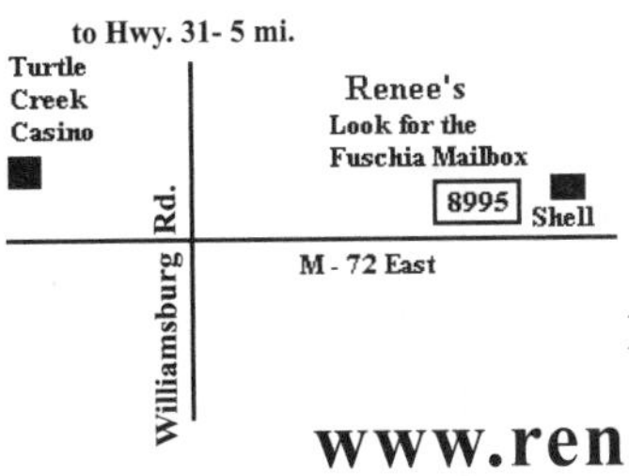

We also carry gorgeous florals and terrific bright children designs. The kitchen is just that, a kitchen, a place where we can meet and the men folk can have a cup of coffee and a cookie. Renee's husband Glenn does all the homemade cookies and cuts fat quarters too! We are open year around & love to meet quilters from all over the country.

Williamsburg, MI #8

www.reneeshouseofquilting.net

Bear Lake, MI #9

Mon - Sat 10 - 5

Two Sisters Quilting

9178 Chippewa Hwy. 49614
(231) 889-4005
Est: 2008
2sistersquilting@att.net

Complete Quilt Shop
Fabrics • Notions • Gifts
Long Arm Quilting

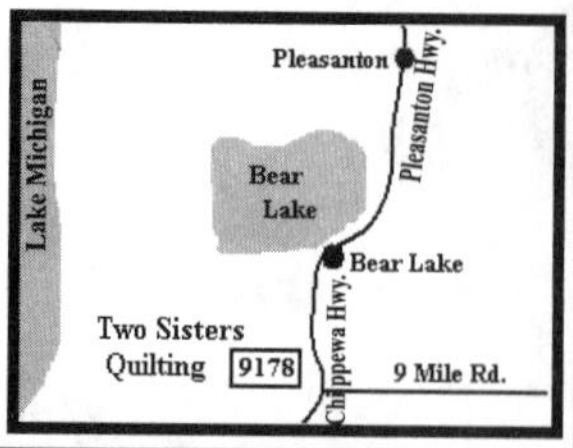

Cadillac, MI #10

Mon - Fri 9:30 - 5:30 Sat 9:30 - 4

Julie Ann's Quilting and More

117 N. Mitchell St. 49601
(231) 775-8301
Fax: 231-775-8221 3100 sq.ft. 1000 Bolts
Owners: Rick & Pamela Stokes
jfabric@att.net
Janome Authorized Dealer
Fabrics, fabrics, fabrics!!! Notions
Dakota Collectibles. Embroidery
Supplies. Classes. Needle Arts
"Create Something Sew Beautiful"

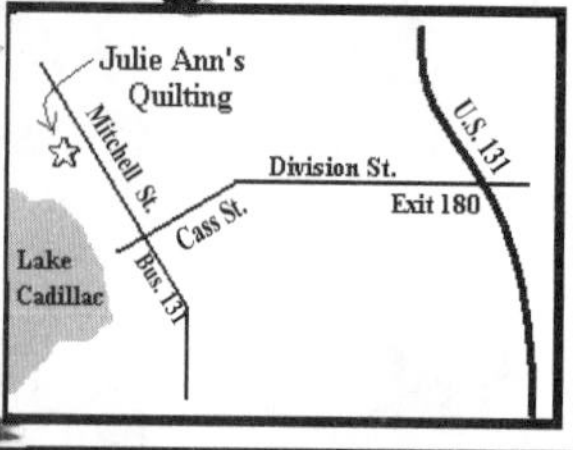

Custer, MI #12

1200+ bolts of 100% cotton fabric plus patterns, books and notions all located in a 100 year old brick farm house

Mon - Sat 10 - 5

Put a little country into your day!

3007 E. Hansen Rd.
49405
(231) 757-2812
Owner: Sue Riffle
Est: 1998

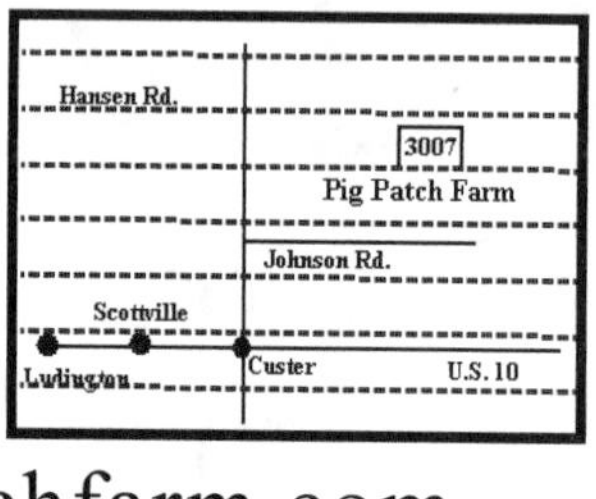

www.pigpatchfarm.com

Cadillac, MI #11

Mon, Thur, Fri 10 - 5 Tues 10 - 7 Wed 12 - 5 Sat 10 - 3

11978 W. Watergate Rd. 49601
(231) 775-8780 Est: 2008
1000 sq.ft. 1000+ bolts Newsletter

Come to Patches and Petals for all your quilting needs. Cotton Fabrics, Notions & Patterns.

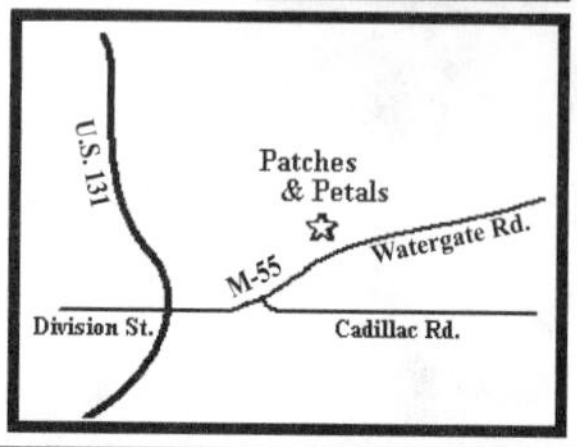

Reed City, MI #13

Mon - Fri 10 - 5 Sat 10 - 2

Crossroads QUILT Shop LLC

111-B S. Higbee St. 49677
(231) 465-4144 Fax: (231) 465-4145
Est: 2009 1500 sq.ft. Online Newsletter
crossroadsquiltshop@gmail.com
www.crossroadsquiltshop.com
We carry a broad line of fabric including Moda.
Plus a large selection of notions, books & patterns.

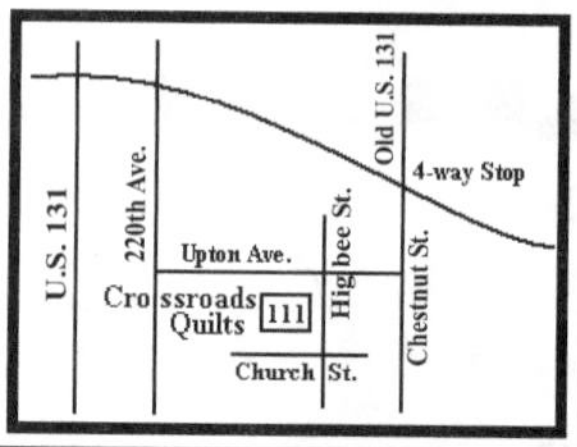

Gladwin, MI #14

Mon - Fri 10 - 5 Sat 10 - 3

Heritage Quilt Shoppe

411 E. Cedar Ave. 48624
(989) 426-5577
heritage.shoppe@att.net

Visit our old Victorian home filled with loads of fabric, notions, kits and classes!

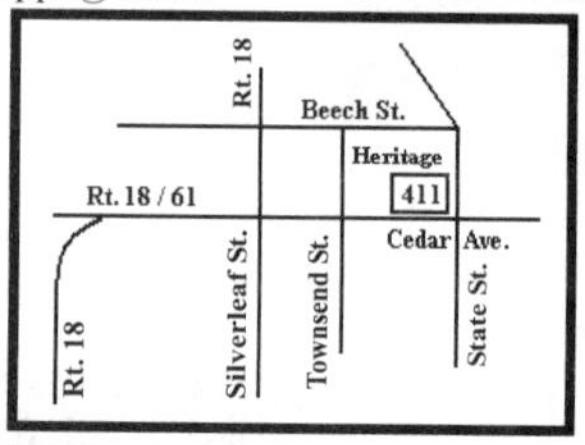

www.heritagequiltshoppe.com

Farwell, MI #15

Open 7 Days

Elm Creek

2609 W. Surrey Rd. 48622
(989) 588-6061 Fax: 588-3562
Est: 1988 10,000 sq.ft.

janice@elmcreekltd.com
www.elmcreekltd.com
Mid Michigan's Largest Fabric, Craft, Gifts & Garden Store! 6000 Bolts of Fabrics. Moda, Batiks, flannels and more. Specializing in Up North fabrics and gifts.

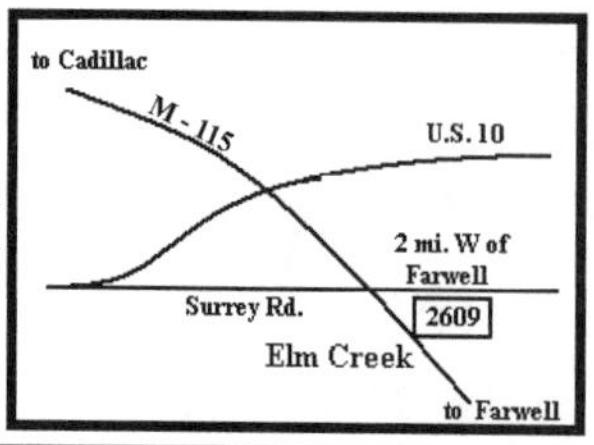

Baldwin, MI #16

Mon - Sat 9 - 6

Fabric Peddler

Est: 2009
3500 sq.ft. 1100+ bolts

815 Michigan Ave. 49304
(231) 745-4500
Fax: (231) 745-4508
Owner: Lee Ann Russell

Lee_Russell46@yahoo.com
www.fabric-peddler.com
Lots of batiks and cheery colors. Blacks & Whites. Wide variety of brand name fabrics.

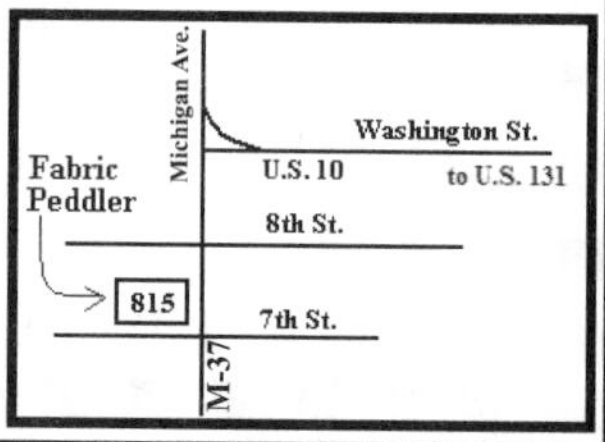

Montague, MI #17

**Mon - Sat 10 - 5
Sun 1 - 5**

Quilted Memories Inc

9919 U.S. 31 49437
(231) 893-0096 Fax: Same
Est: 2003 2500 Bolts Online Newsletter
jill@quiltedmemoriesmi.com
www.quiltedmemoriesmi.com
Full service quilt shop. Great Fabric Selection, PFAFF Authorized Dealer, Classes, Professional Long-arm Machine Quilting.

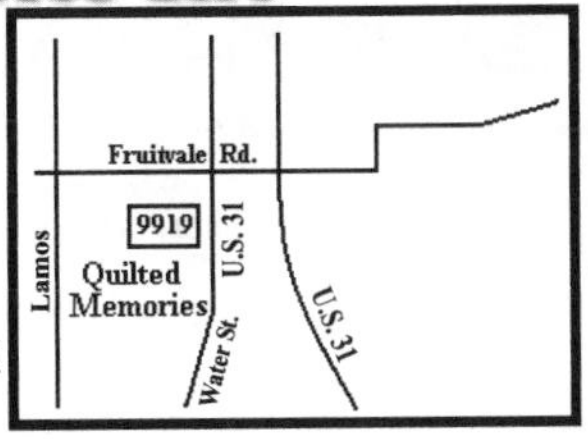

Comstock Park, MI #19

**Mon 10 - 8
Tues - Fri 10 - 6
Sat 10 - 5**

Attic Window Quilt Shop

5307 Alpine NW 49321
(616) 785-3357
Owner: Christine Brown
Est: 1997 2400 sq.ft
(new bigger classroom)
brownattic@aol.com

Nice selection of fabric, books, patterns, and notions. Specializing in reproduction fabrics 1800's - 1940's, and lots of others -- Batiks, Modas, Benartex etc. Special order and hard-to-find items. Classes, mail order and more.

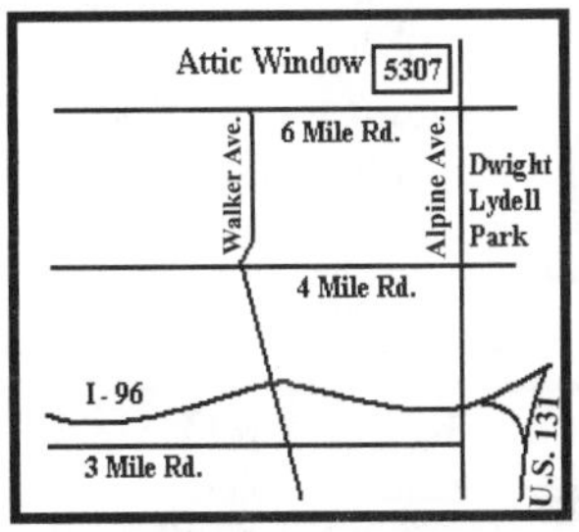

Whitehall, MI #18

Mon - Sat 10 - 5:30

The General Store

103 E. Colby St. 49461
(231) 894-2164

Two floors of unique merchandise. The finest quality quilting fabrics and notions.

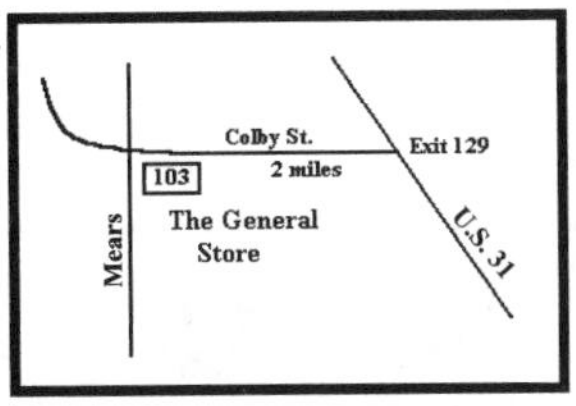

Portland, MI #20

Around the Block Quilt Shop

**Mon, Wed, Fri, & Sat 10 - 5
Tues & Thurs 10 - 8**

120 Maple St. 48875
(517) 647-5430
aroundblockquilt@aol.com
Owners: Cathy & Tom Norton
Cathy & Steve McCann
Est: 1999 3500 sq.ft.

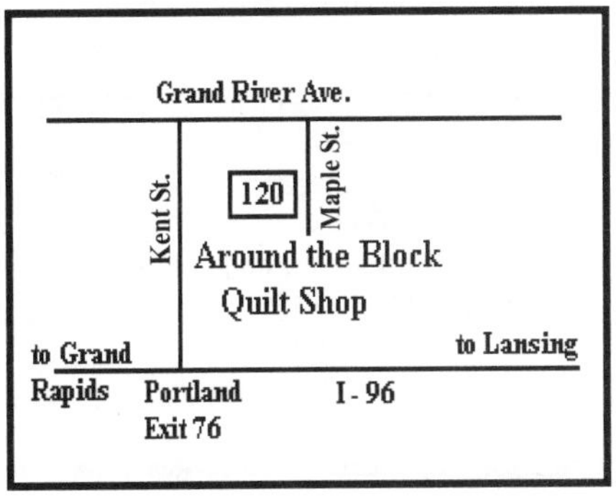

www.aroundtheblockquiltshop.com

100% Cotton Fabrics by Hoffman, Benartex, Thimbleberries, Debbie Mumm & RJR.
Classes, Books, Patterns, & Notions.
Machine Embroidery Supplies from OESD
Lansing Area Bernina Dealer. Machine Service—All Brands.

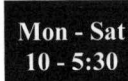

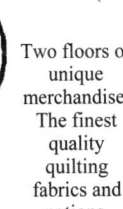

FREE FAT QUARTER

We would love to see you while you are traveling. Stop by our beautiful shop and see all the latest fabric, notion, books, patterns and accessories. *Show us your book* for a free fat quarter from our large selection. You'll find Smith-Owen has:

- Over 3800 Bolts of Quality Cotton Fabric.
- Hundreds of Books and Patterns to Choose From.
- Friendly, Knowledgeable Staff.
- The Best Machines from Pfaff and Viking
- An Experienced Service Department
- Classes from Beginner to Expert
- Nationally Known Speakers and Teachers

Smith-Owen Sewing & Quilt
4051 Plainfield NE
Grand Rapids, MI 49525
800-383-3238
616-361-5484
www.smithowensew.com

Directions: From I-96 take exit 33. Turn west on Plainfield, go two miles and we are on the left. Across the street from Kentucky Fried Chicken.

Mon-Thursday 9-8
Friday 9-5
Saturday 10-4

Grand Rapids, MI #21

Fat quarter given on ___/___

Grand Rapids, MI #22

Mon - Thur 9 - 6
Fri 9 - 6
Sat 9 - 4

Lakeshore Sewing

1971 E. Beltline NE 49525
(616) 365-8282
www.lakeshore-sewing.com

Quilting - Accessories - Fiber Arts
Babylock - Bernina - Husqvarna Viking
Be sure to visit our Wyoming, MI shop also.

Wyoming, MI #23

Mon - Thur 9 - 8
Fri 9 - 6
Sat 9 - 4

Lakeshore Sewing

1011 Gezon Pkwy. SW 49509
(616) 531-5561
www.lakeshore-sewing.com

Quilting - Accessories - Fiber Arts
Babylock - Bernina - Husqvarna Viking
Be sure to visit our Grand Rapids shop also.

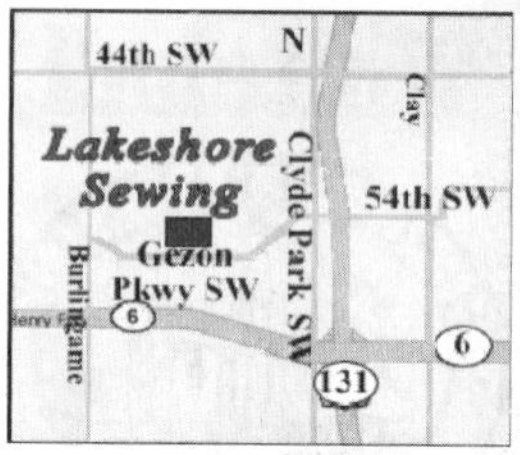

Byron Center, MI #24

We are a full service quilt shop filled with books, patterns, notions and, of course, fabrics with just a splash of antiques.

7760 Clyde Park SW,
Byron Center, MI 49315
(616) 878-9335

Mon 10-7
Tues - Sat 10 - 5

Est: 2006 2200 sq.ft. Joyce & Eric Puckett

- Located just south of Grand Rapids right off of US 131
- Specialize in Thimbleberries and hand-dye/batik fabrics
- Variety of thread including machine quilting and silk
- Custom made quilt racks
- Clubs and blocks of the month
- Large classroom

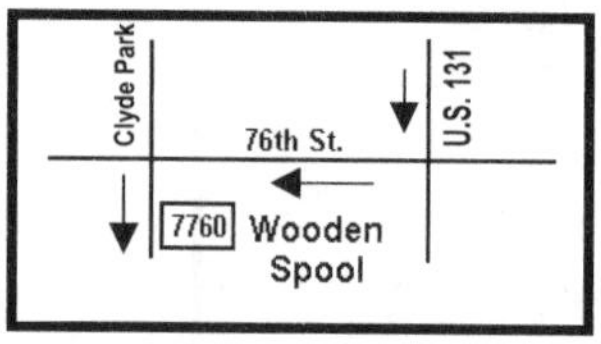

Located on Clyde Park just south of 76th St. in white building with blue awnings, across from Spartan Warehouse.

Hastings, MI #25

Mon - Thur 8 - 5:30
Fri 8 - 7
Sat 9 - 5:30

Sisters Fabrics

218 E. State St. 49058
(269) 945-9673

Large selection of calico, books, patterns, quilting supplies, fleece, dress fabrics, JHB and Streamline buttons, etc.

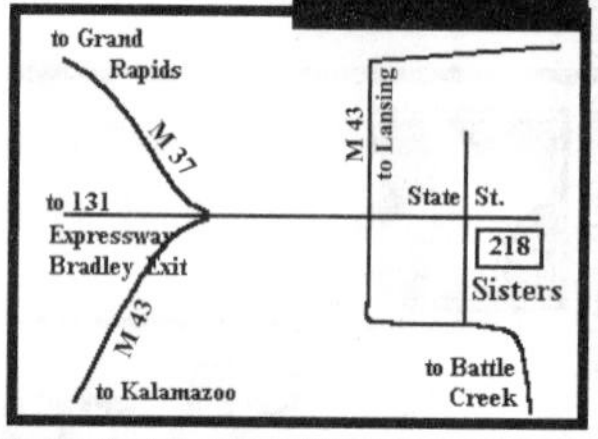

Holland, MI #26

Field's Fabrics
www.fieldsfabrics.com
Open 9-9
Mon.-Sat., Closed Sunday

Packed with Fabrics & Supplies
10,000+ Bolts,
Many Unique Prints.

281 East 8th Street
Holland, MI 49423

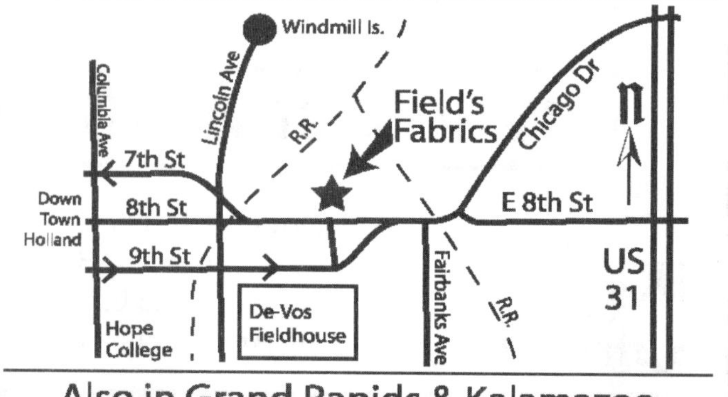

Also in Grand Rapids & Kalamazoo

Allegan, MI #27

Mon - Fri 9 - 6
Sat 9 - 4

Sharon's Quilts & More

224 Trowbridge St. 49010
(269) 686-9579
Est: 2005 1900 sq.ft.
2000+ Bolts Online Newsletter
sharonsquilts@charterinternet.com
www.sharonsquiltsandmore.com
Top quality fabrics, notions and classes. Free coffee and treats, warm and friendly atmosphere.

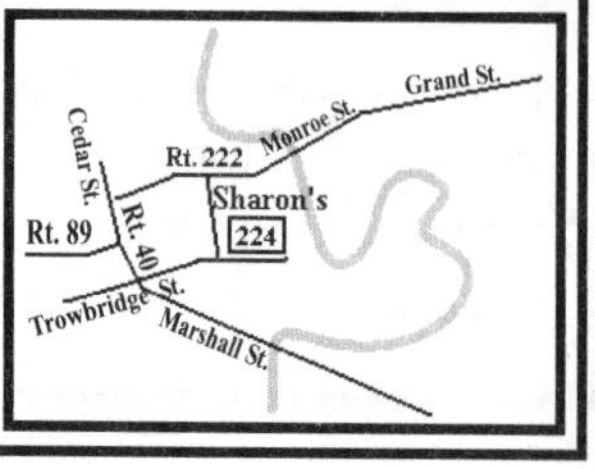

Fennville, MI #28

Custom Quilts Unlimited

Nov - April
W, TH, F, S 11-5
May - Oct.
M, TH, F, S 10-5
Wed 10-7
Always Sun 12 - 5

6184 Quilters Ct. 49408
(866) 561-6214
Est: 2007 1500 sq.ft.
Owner: Mary Smallegan

customquiltsunlimited@yahoo.com
www.customquiltsunlimited.com
Gifts for Quilters, Quality Quilting Fabrics, Notions, Completed Quilts for Sale, Custom Quilts made for You.

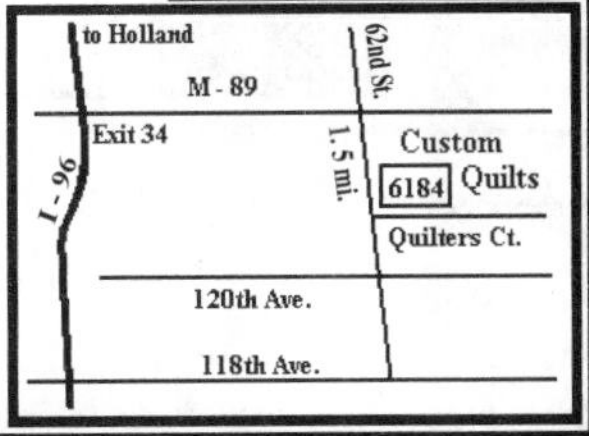

Kalamazoo, MI #29

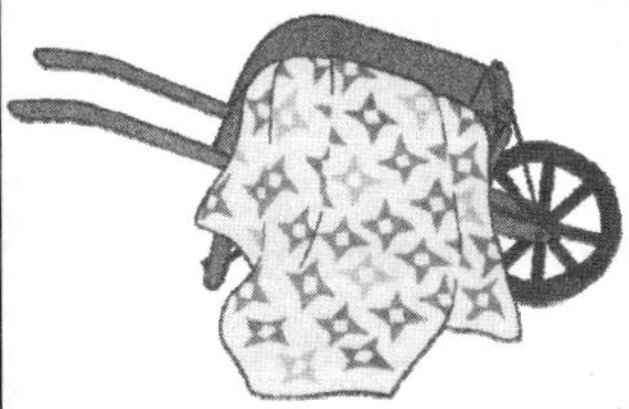

Quilts Plus

- Over 3500 Bolts of Fabric
- Classes (day & evening)
- Quilting Supplies
- Quilt Frames
- Gift Items
- Gift Certificates
- 100's of Quilt Samples & Kits
- Fabric bundles

BUSES WELCOME

Mon - Fri
10 - 6
Sat 10 - 4

FEATURING:

- Empty a Bolt - 20% OFF last Saturday of each month (will mail)
- NEW Blocks of the Month
- Hand & Machine Quilting Services Available
- Machine Cleaning & Repair Service
- FEATHERWEIGHTS & PARTS FOR SALE

3314 Stadium Dr.
Kalamazoo, MI 49008
Tel: (269) 383-1790
Fax: (269) 383-2182
quiltspluskazoo@hotmail.com
Owner: Kathleen Edwards Est: 1996

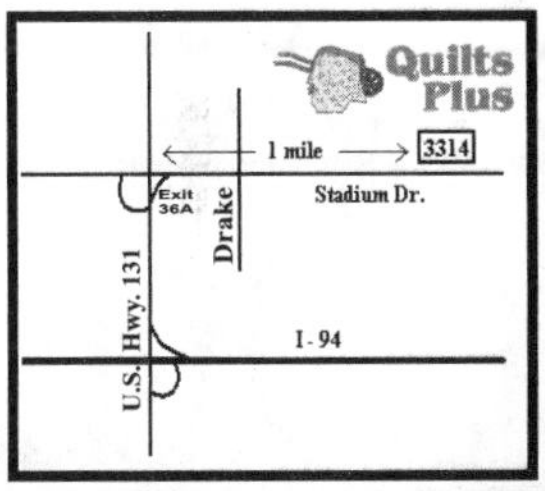

Kalamazoo, MI #30

Bernina Sewing Center & Quilt Shop

Owners:
Karen & Gary Kortman

4205 Portage Rd. 49001
(269) 383-1244 or (800) 606-1244
karen@berninakalamazoo.com
www.berninakalamazoo.com
and www.patches-n-petticoats.com

Mon - Fri
9:30 - 5:30
Wed til 7
Sat 9:30 - 4

Est: 1992
5600 sq.ft.

Quilt notions, books, and sewing supplies.
3000+ Bolts
Authorized Bernina & Baby Lock Dealer.
Long arm quilting onsite on our Gammill Quilting Machine with a Statler Stitcher.

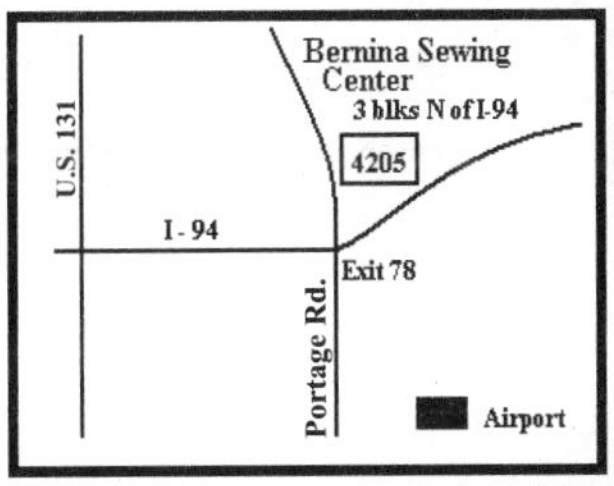

South Haven, MI #32

So South Haven

Quilts and More by the Shore

70920 CR 388 49090
269-637-0603
Owners: Carter & Marie Maxwell 1200+ bolts
www.aquiltfarm.com

Feb 15th - Dec 21st
Tues-Sat 11am-5pm
July & Aug
Mon-Sat 11am-5pm

A friendly country shop in a restored mill from the 1860s with easy highway accessibility.
We buy in full collections.
Restored 1910 cottage available for quilt retreats with full sewing facilities.
Come and visit the Lakeshore Harvest Country Barn Quilt Trail.

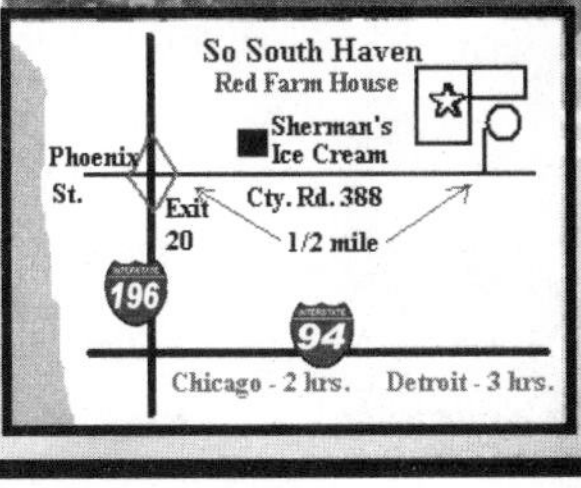

Kalamazoo, MI #31

Viking Sewing Center

Mon - Fri
9 - 5:30
Wed til 7
Sat 9 - 4

5401 Portage Rd. 49002
(269) 342-5808
Owners: Phil & Julie Rotzien
2500 sq.ft.

1000+ bolts of 100% cotton fabric. Quilting, heirloom, garment and specialty sewing classes. Viking sewing machine sales & service.

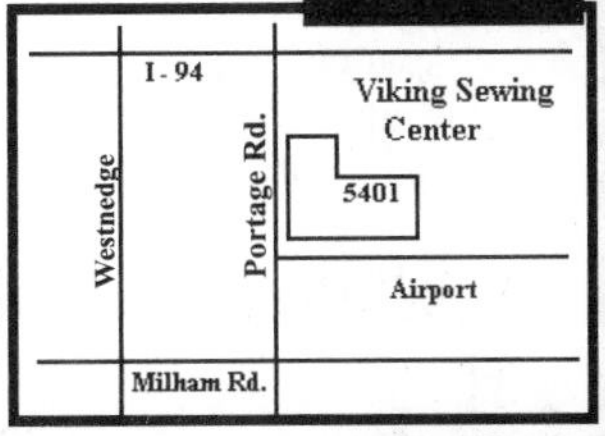

Schoolcraft, MI #33

Tues - Fri
10 - 6
Sat 10 - 4

Big Island Quilt Co.

13210 North U.S. 131 49087
(269) 679-3101 Fax: (269) 679-3123
Owner: Cynthia Prosser Est: 2006
1800 sq.ft. 1200 Bolts
Newsletter
rcpro55555@aol.com
Great fabrics, many samples and small town friendliness. The newest books, patterns & notions. Machine repair and machine quilting available.

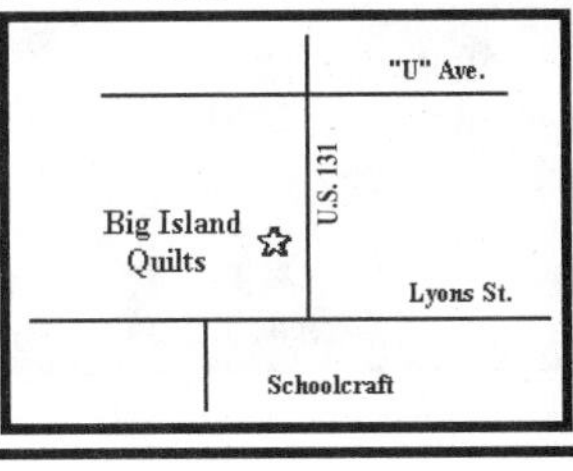

Est: 1996

Loving Stitches QUILT SHOP LLC

Owner: Holly Martin

100% cotton fabrics to choose from!!

Patterns, Books, Supplies

See our perennial garden in season.

7291 Red Arrow Hwy.
Stevensville, MI 49127
(269) 465-3795
www.lsquiltshop.com

Wed. thru Fri. 10-5
Sat. 10-3

Contact us for machine quilting with Heather & Hollyhocks Quilting
heatherbroehm@hotmail.com
www.heatherhollyhocks.com

Stevensville, MI #34

The Quilt Patch

517-423-0053 112 N. EVANS St.
www.thequiltpatch.com Tecumseh, MI 49286

Tecumseh, MI #35

HOURS
Monday & Wednesday
9:00 am - 5:00 pm
Tuesday, Thursday & Friday
9:00 am - 8:00 pm
Saturday 10:00 am - 4:00 pm
Sunday Noon - 4:00 pm

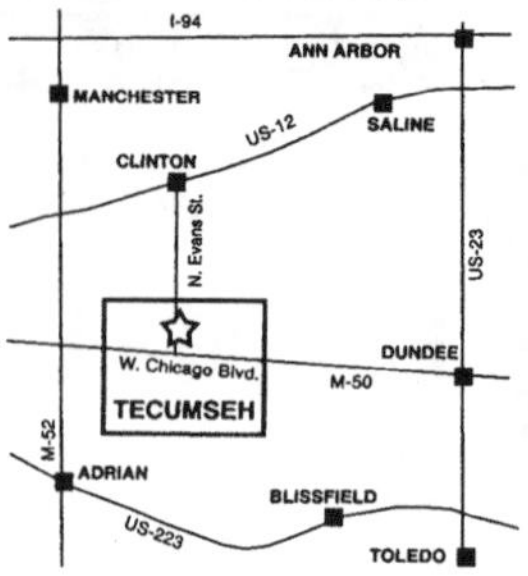

- ENJOY 9000 SQ. FT. OF QUILTER'S PARADISE
- THOUSANDS OF BOLTS, BOOKS & PATTERNS
- CLASSES FOR EVERY SKILL LEVEL
- FULL SEWING MACHINE REPAIR & SERVICE
- SCISSOR & KNIFE SHARPENING

Quilts at the Marshall House

100 Exchange St.
49068
269-781-9450

Marshall, MI #36

karen@karenquilts.com
Est. 2003 3500 sq.ft. 4000+ bolts

Open 7 Days Sun 12 - 4 Mon - Sat 10 - 5

www.QuiltsattheMarshallHouse.com

Quilting supplies and antiques in one of the oldest buildings in historic Marshall, MI.
Huge selection of books and patterns. Large selection of Asian, Batik, and 19th Century reproduction fabric.

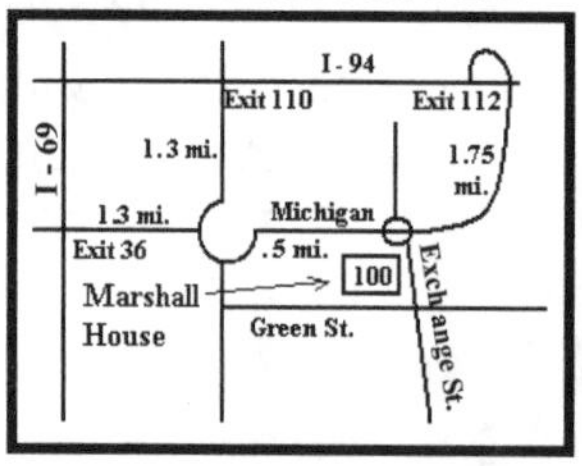

Parking in front of the building on Green St. & in the city lot directly to the west.

Sew Unique Threads

A sewing boutique specializing in contemporary Cottons.

7175 Tower Rd. #F, Battle Creek, MI 49014
269-317-3022 www.sewuniquethreads.com

- Silk dupioni, Rayons, Batiks
- Embroidery Designs & Supplies
- Great selection of unique buttons
- Books & Patterns
- Purse supplies
- Weeks dye wool
- Upholstery weight fabrics

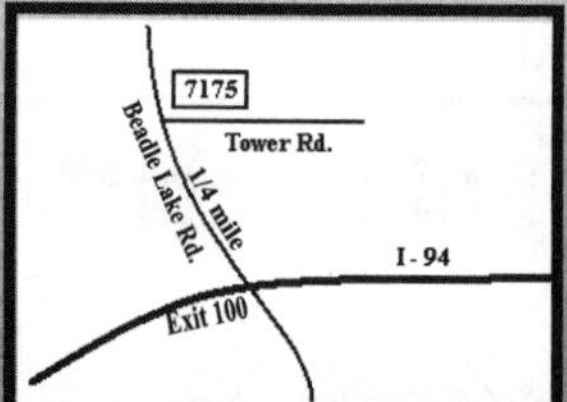

Mon - Fri
10 - 5
Thurs til 7
Sat 10 - 1

sue@sewuniquethreads.com
fax: 269-969-8917
1000 sq.ft. 1000 bolts

Battle Creek, MI #37

Bellevue, MI #38

Bellevue Barn Quilters

Mon - Fri
10 - 5
Sat 9 - 2

104 W. Capital 49021
(269) 763-2276
Est: 2008
bbqs1567@att.net
100% Cottons, Flannels, & Batiks.
Books, Patterns, Notions, Cross Stitch supplies.
Relaxing atmosphere.

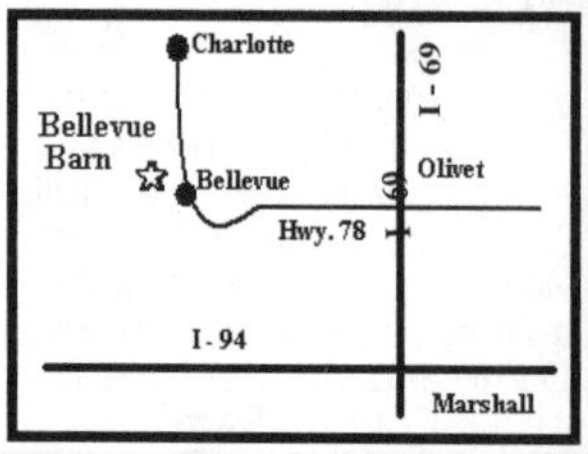

Quilt N Go

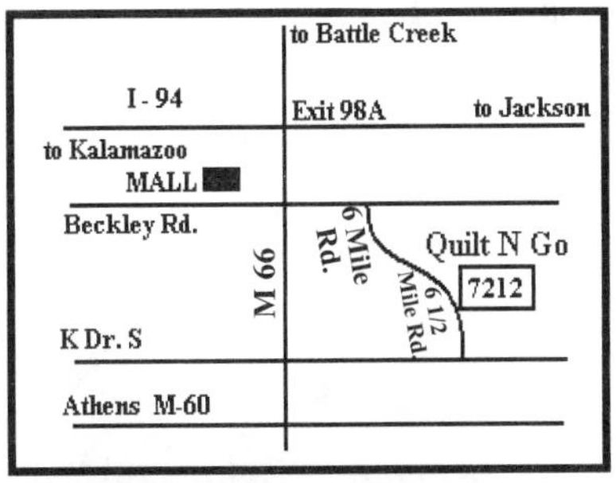

East Leroy, MI #39

"Your quilt shop in the country"
7212 6-1/2 Mile Rd
East Leroy, MI 49051
(south of Battle Creek)
269-979-2347 ruth@quiltngo.com
Owner: Ruth Dean

Receive 10% off your purchase when you show us your QTC!

M - Tu - W - F 10 - 6
Th 10 - 7
Sat 10 - 3
Closed Sunday

www.quiltngo.com

We offer classes from beginning to advanced with all the notions, books, and patterns that you need.

Over 3,000 bolts of fabric from Thimbleberries, Moda, 1930's reproductions, South Seas, Benartex, homespuns and more.

Country Stitches

Over 200 Bolts
of 100% Cotton Fabric
$4.99/yd or less!

Great Quality Fabric, Books, Patterns, Notions PLUS... Pfaff, Husqvarna Viking, Baby Lock & Singer

Hours:
Mon, Wed, Thurs
10 am - 7 pm
Tues & Fri
10 am -6 pm
Sat
10 am - 5 pm
First Sun of the Month
12 pm - 4 pm

Call **517-782-7100**
or **1-800-782-3830**
for more information

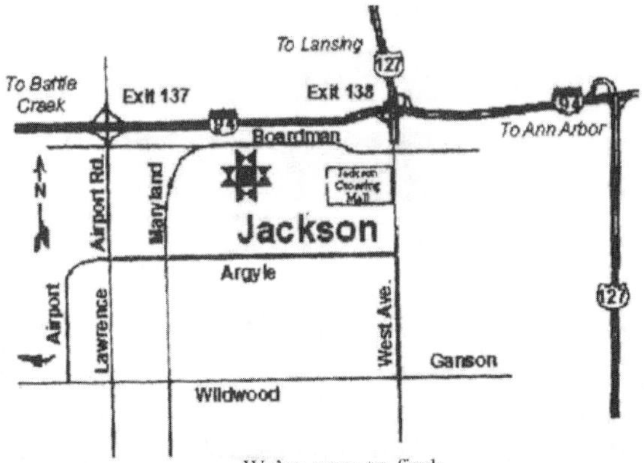

We're easy to find:
I-94 at exit 138 (US-127) Go 1 block south on West Ave then 2 blocks west (right) on Boardman Rd. (just past Lowe's)

Jackson, MI #40
Web Site: www.countrystitches.com

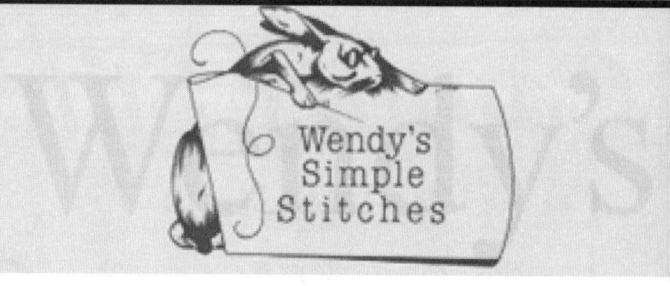

Pinckney, MI #41

jennifer's
"the shop where friends meet"
QUILT SHOP

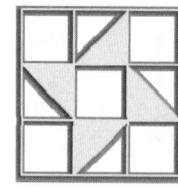

149 North Howell, Pinckney, MI 48169
734.878.6188
Est: 2005 2600+ Bolts

www.jennifersquiltshop.com

our hours are: Tuesday thru Friday 10-6
Saturday 10-3 closed Sunday and Monday

Located in beautiful downtown Pinckney "just around the corner" from Pinckney Hardware north of M-36 (Main St.)

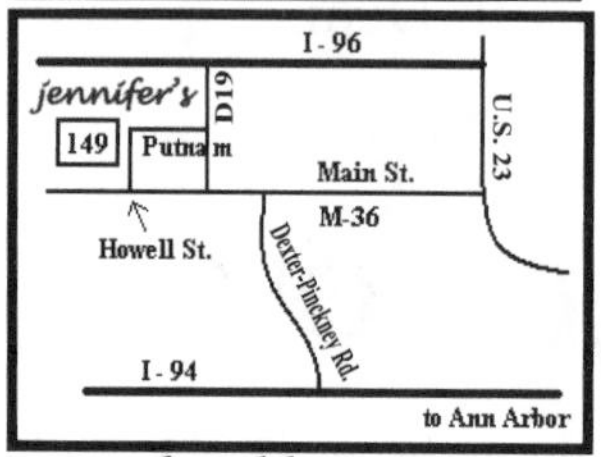

come in and say hello at jennifer's

Mason, MI #42

Mon - Sat 9:30 - 5 Thurs til 7

Yards of Fabric

116 E. Ash St. 48854
(517) 676-2973
Est: 1980 1000 sq.ft.

Quilt shop quality cottons: Moda, Timeless Treasures, Robert Kauffman, Lakehouse, Marcus Brothers, Maywood Studios and more. Charm packs, Jelly rolls, Layer Cakes and kits available. 108" wide backing, wired ribbon.

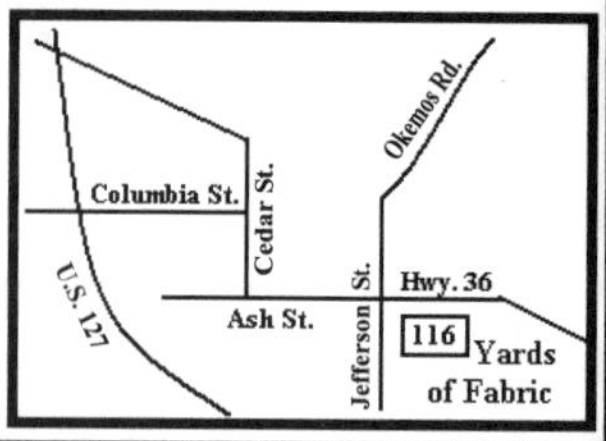

Holt, MI #43

Mon - Fri 9:30 - 6 Thur til 8 Sat 9:30 - 4 Sun 11 - 3

Everlasting Stitches, Inc.

2040 N. Aurelius Rd. 48842
(517) 699-1120 Fax: (517) 699-1122
Owner: Pam Henrys
Est: 2002 1500 sq.ft. 2500+ Bolts
High Quality Cottons from Top Companies.
Rug hooking and Supplies.
Long-arm machine rental
Handcrafted Sewing Collectables.
Friendly, helpful customer service. Coffee's On.

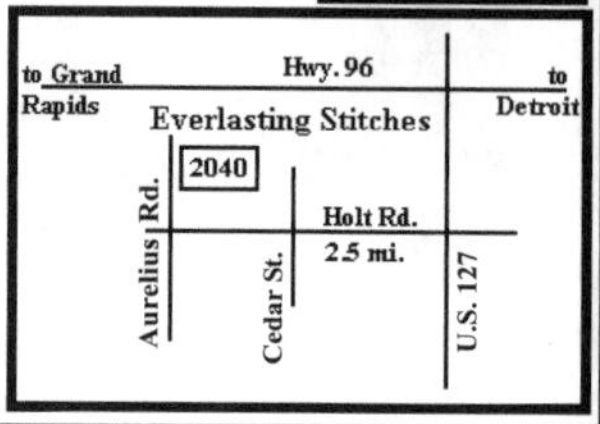

Charlotte, MI #44

Mon - Sat 10 - 5:30

The Hen House

211 S. Cochran Ave. 48813
(517) 543-6454 www.thehenhousemi.com
Specializing in the Primitive Look with: Homespuns, Reproduction Fabrics, Quilting Supplies, Rug Hooking Supplies, 100% Wools, Penny Rug Patterns, Floor Canvas, Stencils & Painting Supplies, Basket Weaving Materials, Needle Punch Embroidery Kits and Needles. Needle Felting Patterns and Supplies.

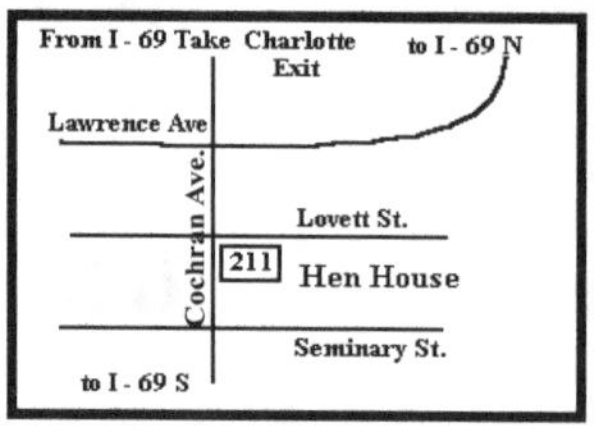

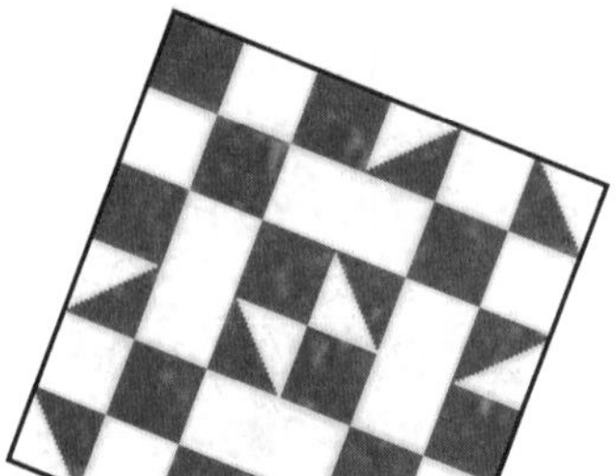

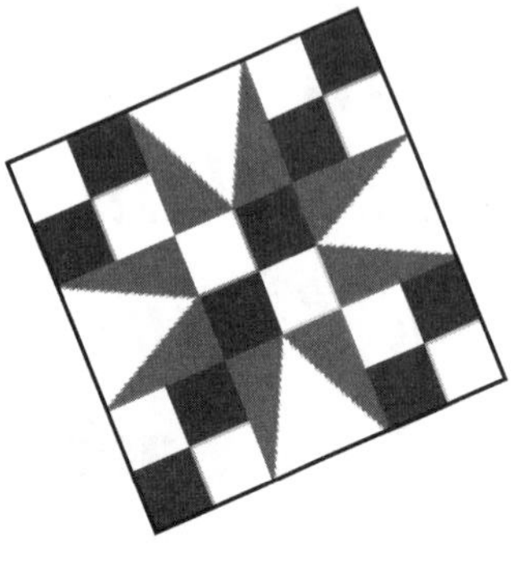

Wendy's Simple Stitches

We specialize in reproduction and children prints. We offer quality fabric such as Moda, Andover, Benartex, Wilmington Prints and many more. We also carry Presencia and Cosmo Embroidery Thread. Look for us in the little yellow house.

Howell, MI #45

Est: 2008

1500 bolts

Mon - Fri 10 - 6 Sat 10 - 4

1122 S. Michigan Ave.
Howell, MI 48843
517-545-0555
Owner: Wendy Ward
wendyward1969@sbcglobal.net

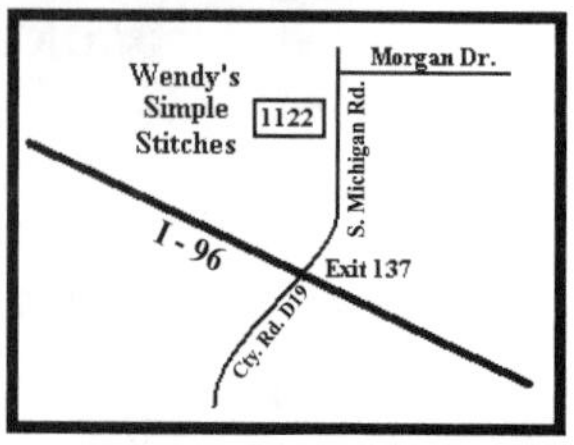

www.wendyssimplestitches.com

The Stitchery

1129 E. Grand River Ave - Howell, MI 48843 - (517)548-1731
E-Mail:st1tchery@sbcglobal.net - www.thestitcheryonline.com
Owner: Susan Reid

Howell, MI #46

Friendly, knowledgable staff ready to give you personalized service. Over 4000 bolts of fabric from major manufactures including quality cotton, flannels, wools and batiste. Quilting Supplies, Heirloom Sewing Supplies, Books, Patterns, Notions and Classes for all skill levels. Servicing all makes and models of sewing machines and sergers.

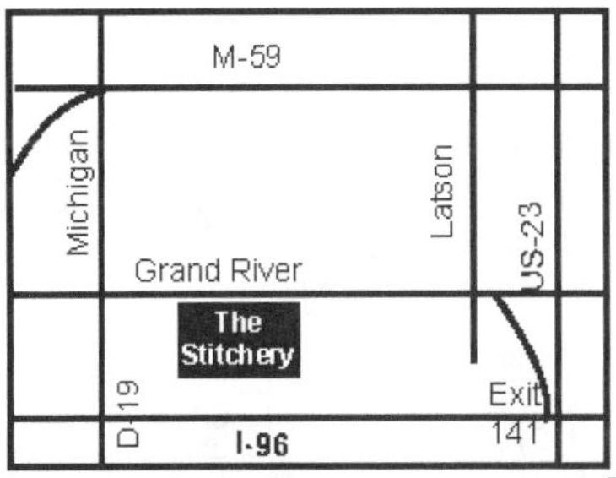

Authorized **JANOME** Sewing Machine Dealer

Mon-Fri 9 A.M.-6 P.M. Sat 9 A.M.-4 P.M.

Country Stitches

Featured in Quilt Sampler Magazine in 1996

Our Destination Store

- Over 6000 bolts of both traditional and contemporary cotton fabric line the shelves.
- A continuous quilt show of over 100 quilts offers ideas and inspiration.
- Pfaff, Baby Lock and Husqvarna Viking Sewing Machines

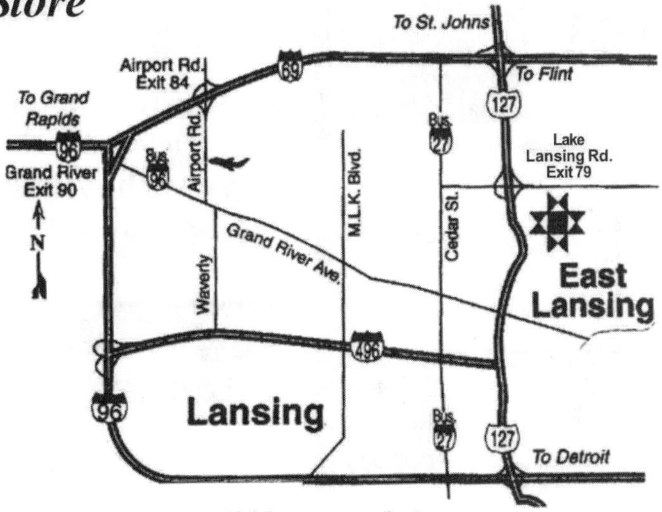

We're easy to find:
One block east of US 127
on Lake Lansing Rd.
across from Meijer

Hours:
Monday - Friday
10 am - 8 pm
Saturday
10 am - 5 pm
Sunday
Closed

Call **517-351-2416**
or **1-800-572-2031**
for more information

East Lansing, MI #47

Web Site: www.countrystitches.com

Treat yourself to Country Stitches, truly a unique quilt shop.

Fenton, MI #48

The Quilters Garden

Shop Online

Providing a variety of high quality 100% cotton quilting fabric, books, patterns, quilting supplies, wool, hand dyed wool, wool roving and classes for all.

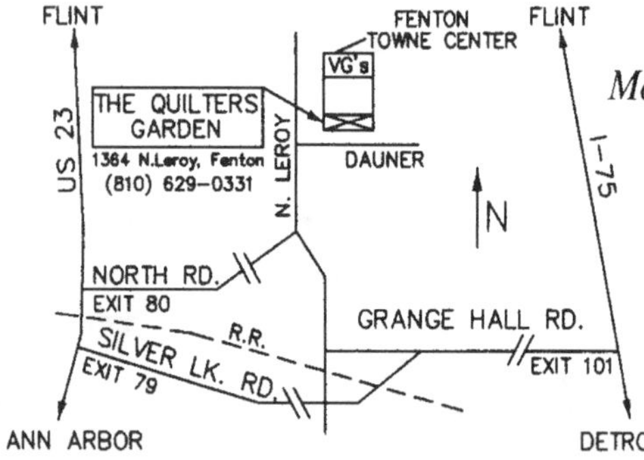

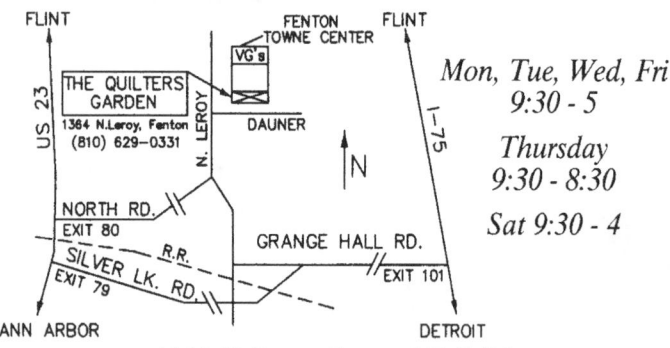

Mon, Tue, Wed, Fri 9:30 - 5
Thursday 9:30 - 8:30
Sat 9:30 - 4

1364 N. Leroy, Fenton, MI 48430
810-629-0331
quilt@thequiltersgarden.com
www.thequiltersgarden.com

mabelena

quilting supplies and comforts

470 Mill Street
Ortonville, MI 48462
248-627-9100
mabelenas@aol.com
Owner: Brenda Heffernan
Est: 2002 2000 sq.ft. 3500+ bolts

Mon - Fri 10 - 5
Thur til 8
Sat 10 - 3

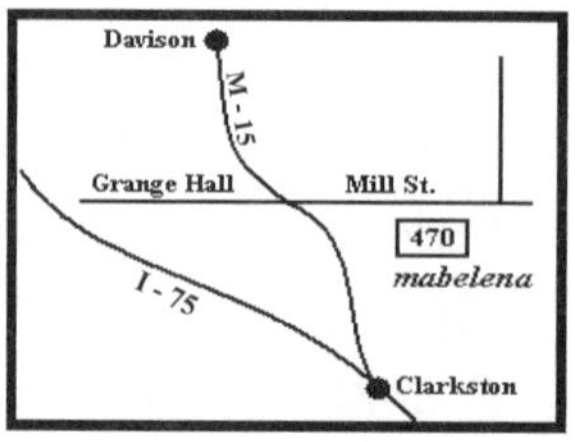

Brenda's shop is named after her grandmothers, Mabel and Lena. The shop's dedicated, friendly staff will be happy to assist you in selecting fabric for your next quilting project.

Ortonville, MI #49

Lake Orion, MI #50

Est: 2004
3000 sq.ft.

The Village Quilt Shoppe

2369 Joslyn Ct. Lake Orion, MI 48360
info@thevillagequiltshoppe.com
www.thevillagequiltshoppe.com
(248) 391-5727

Mon - Sat 10 - 5:30
Sun 11 - 5:30

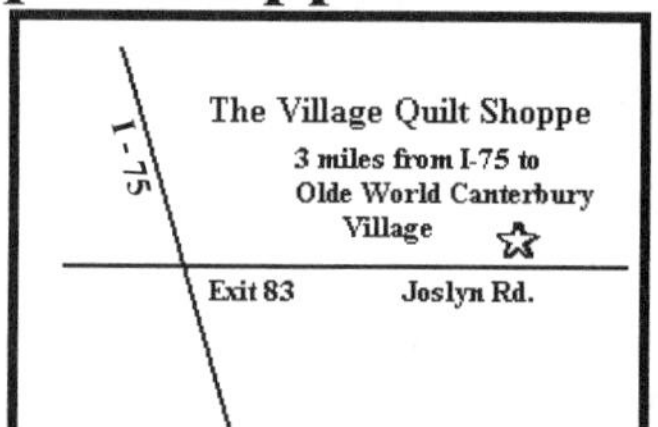

- Located at Olde World Canterbury Village.
- 3,500 bolts of fabric including RJR, Moda, Benartex, Hoffman, Michael Miller & More
- Exclusive Blocks-of-the-month
- Lots & lots of Books and Patterns
- Classes - Notions - Gifts
- Open 361 days a year
- Home of *"The Village Pattern Co."*

St. Clair, MI #51

Mon - Fri 10 - 5
Thurs til 8
Sat 10 - 4

River Place Mercantile

201 N. Riverside Ave. 48079
(810) 329-9300 Est: 2006
Owner: Margaret Hall Fax: (810) 329-9400
1800 sq.ft. 1100 bolts Online Newsletter
margarethall@riverplacemercantile.com
www.riverplacemercantile.com
Full line of Maywood's Shadow Play, Stitch Connection patterns & CD's and HoopSisters; Janome sewing machines sales & service.

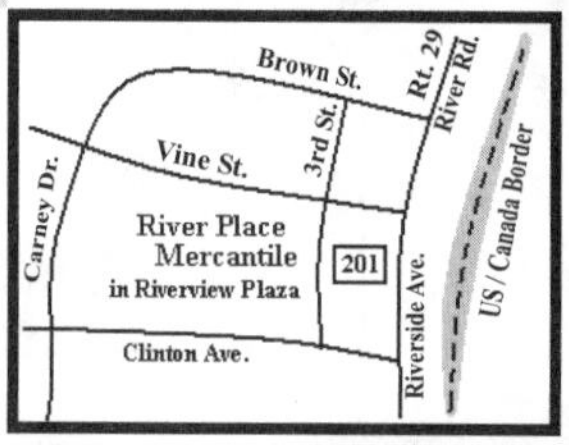

Hadley, MI #52

Mon - Sat 10 - 4

Elaine's Quilty Shop

4600 Pratt Rd. P.O. Box 194 48440
(810) 797-2242
Owner: Elaine Matznick
Est: 2003 2000 Bolts
www.angelfire.com/art3/elainesquiltyshop/

It's worth the drive to Hadley. We are a full service quilt shop that offers discounts on most notions and quilting fabrics. We carry Hoffman, Moda, Kaufman, Marcus and a lot more.

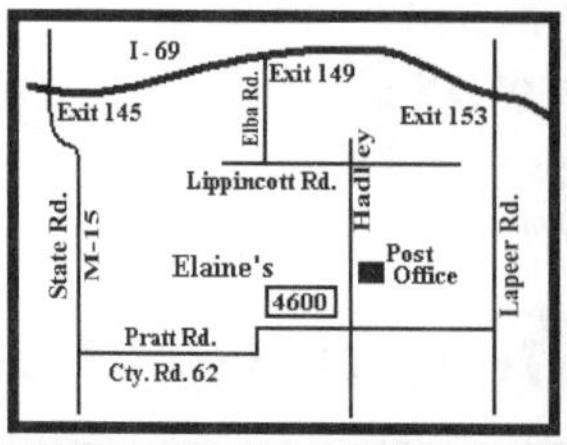

Richmond, MI #53

Tues - Thur 10 - 5
Fri 10 - 7
Sat 10 - 4

Sew Together

69295 Main St. 48062
(586) 727-1555
Owners: Gina Kaszynski & Susan Weinert
quilting@sewtogether.com
www.sewtogether.com

HandiQuilter sales and service. A large selection of cotton and wool fabrics, threads, embellishments, books, patterns, quality yarns and notions. Quilting and Knitting classes.

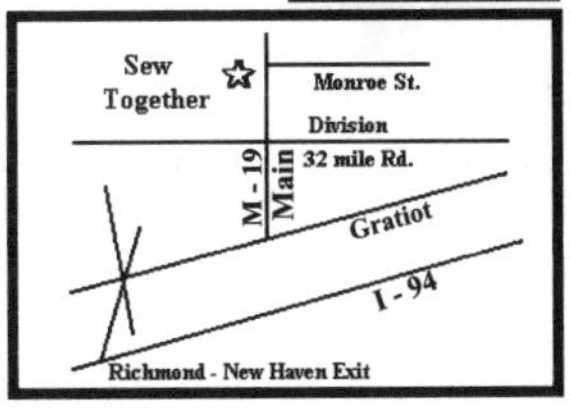

Imlay City, MI #54

Mon - Fri 9:30 - 5
Sat 9:30 - 4

The Pincushion

113 East Third Street 48444
(810) 724-7065
2 Miles North of I - 69 & M-53
Owner: Joyce Schihl Est: 1971
www.pincushionimlaycity.com

Everything For The Quilter.
Quality Quilting Fabric & Supplies.
An Extensive Book Inventory.
Small Town Friendly service.

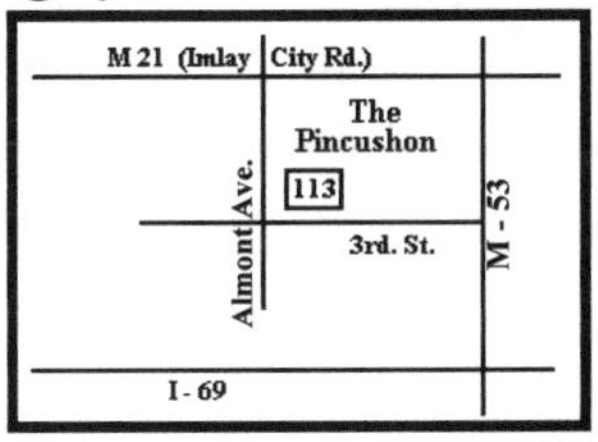

Port Huron, MI #55

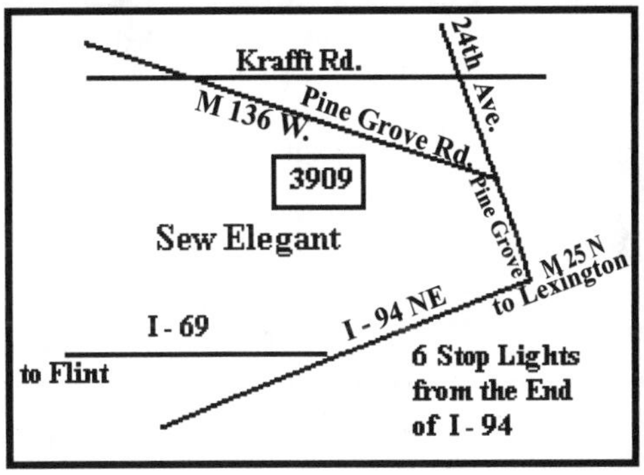

Sew Elegant
Quilt Shoppe

VAST SELECTION OF
BOOKS, PATTERNS AND SEWING
NOTIONS FOR QUILTERS.

3909 Pine Grove Rd. 48059
(810) 982-6556
Fax: (810) 982-6996
E-Mail: elsew@aol.com

Supreme Dealer of **PFAFF** Quality Machines
Est: 1986

Mon - Sat 10 - 5
Sun 12 - 4:30

www.sewelegant.com
Owner: Linda Anderson
4880 sq.ft.

Eastern Michigan's Largest Quilt Shop!
Our Shop is full of 100% cotton Fabrics--over 8,000 bolts
The place where all the pieces come together!

Millington, MI #56

Tues - Fri 10 - 5
Sat 10 - 3

My Lil' Quilt Shop

4729 Main St. 48746
(989) 871-6426
Owner: Connie Titsworth
www.mylilquiltshop.com

Servicing All Your Quilting and Machine Repair Needs

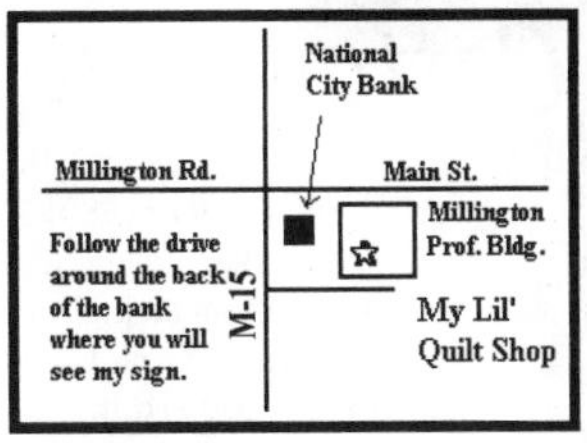

Ovid, MI #57

Mon - Sat 10 - 5

Elaine's Too

122 S. Main St.
P.O. Box 12 48866
(989) 834-2538
Owner: Elaine Matznick
Est: 2008 2000 Bolts

It's worth the drive to Ovid.
We're a full-line quilt shop.

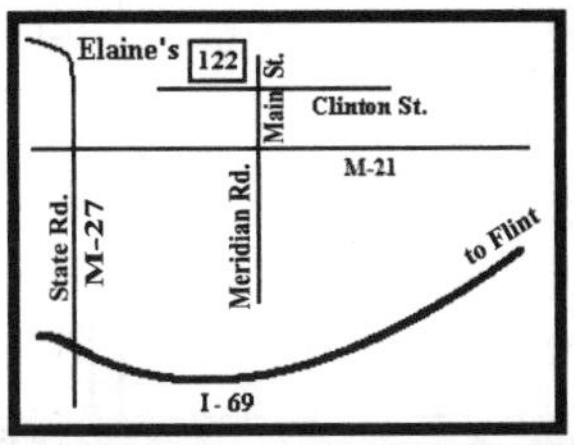

Flushing, MI #58

Mon - Sat 10 - 5
Tues til 8 Sun 1 - 4

100% Cotton fabrics.
Quilting . Notions.
Lots of classes.
Warm and personal service.
Quaint setting.

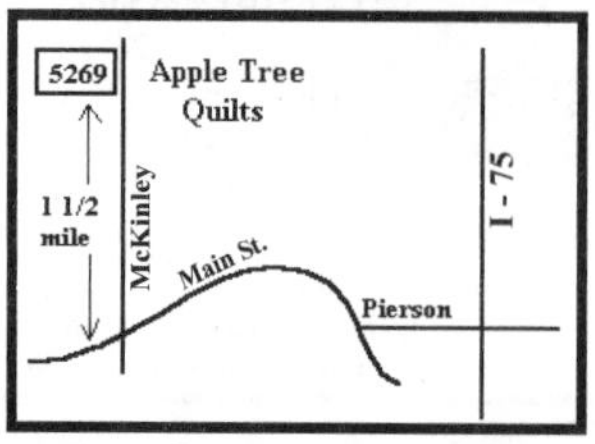

APPLE TREE QUILTS

5269 McKinley Rd. 48433
(810) 659- 4190
Owner: Judie Martin
atquilts@sbcglobal.net
Est: 1996
2000 sq.ft. 1000+ Bolts

Material Mart
Fabric & Yarns

Midland, MI #59

86 Ashman Circle 48640
989-835-8761 Fax: 989-835-9820
materialmart@sbcglobal.net
Est: 1972 4300 sq.ft. 3500 bolts Online Catalog
www.materialmart.com

Mon - Fri 9:30 - 9:00
Sat 9:30-5:00 Sun 12:00-5:00

Fabric - Yarns - Classes
Husqvarna-Viking
Sewing Machines
Professional Machine Quilting

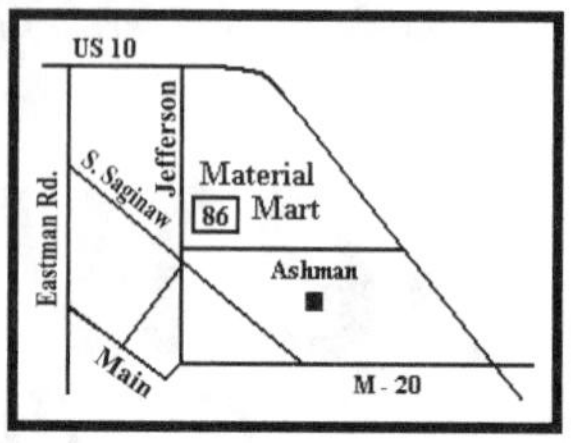

Bay City, MI #61

Mon - Fri 9:30 - 6
Wed til 8
Sat 9:30 - 5

THE FABRIC FAIR

Authorized BERNINA Dealer

206 Fifth St. 48708
(989) 893-8971 Fax: (989) 922-4230
Est: 1954 Online Newsletter
cel@thefabricfair.com
www.thefabricfair.com
Great selections of Reproduction-Civil War & 30's, Batiks, Hand Dye, Oriental, childrens, novelty, Moda marbles & Bridal fabric.

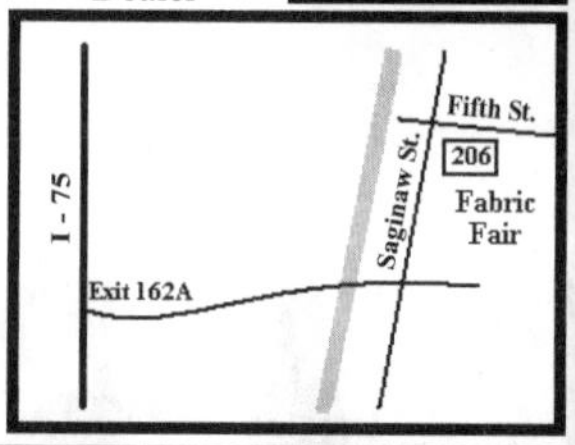

Hemlock, MI #60

Miles of Stitches

136 W. Saginaw 48626
(989) 642-2756
Est: 2008
2000+ Bolts
Fax: (989) 642-2856
milesofstitches@verizon.net

Mon - Fri 10 - 6
Sat 9 - 4

Show us this ad for 15% off your purchases.

www.milesofstitches.com

We specialize in batiks, wide backing fabrics, brights and children's. Long Arm quilting services available with over 1000 Statler designs.

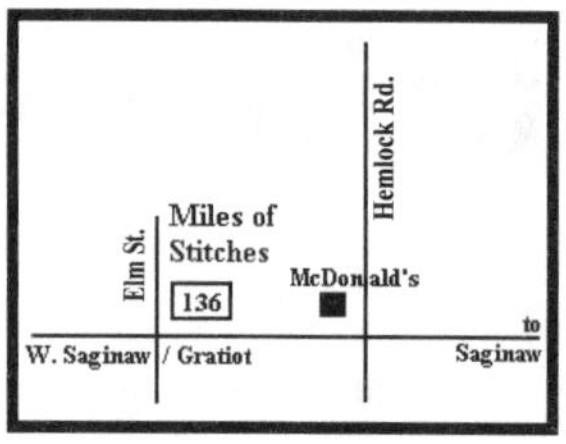

Au Gres, MI #62

Tues - Fri 10 - 4:30
Sat 10 - 2

Bayview Calicos

3631 E. Huron (U.S. 23) 48703
(989) 876-6933
Owner: Evelyn Griffore
Est: 1988
Quilt fabric, Books, Patterns, Notions & Classes. Wool & Wool Kits.
"Where Friendly Quilters Meet"

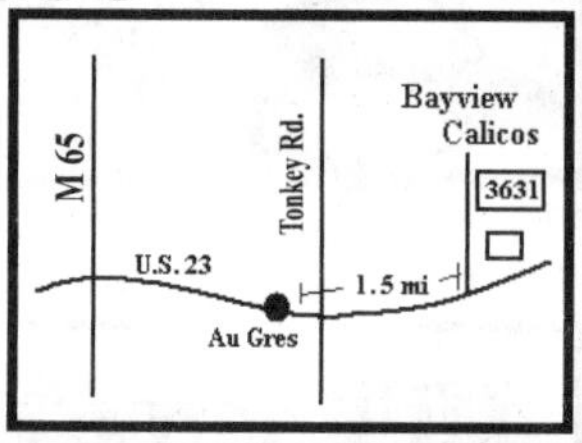

East Tawas, MI #63

Mon - Sat 10 - 5

Cotton Patch Quilt Shop

302 Newman St. 48730
(877) 362-6779 or (989) 362-6779
cottonpatch@hughes.net
www.cottonpatchfabrics.com
Owner: Doni Butzin
Est: 1996 3000 sq.ft. 3000+ Bolts
Full Service Quilt Shop.
Block of the Month Clubs.
Machine Quilting Services.

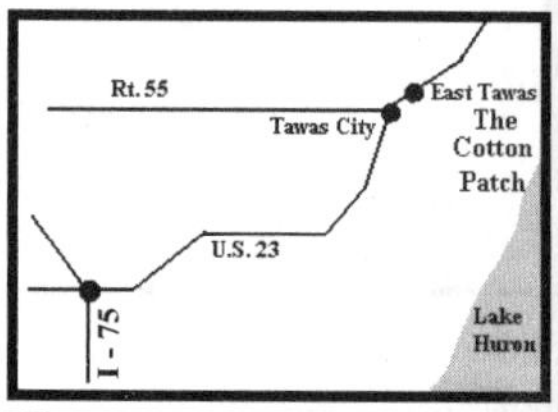

Oscoda, MI #64

Mon - Sat 10:30 - 5:30

Sunshine Quilt Shop

233 S. State (U.S. 23)
48750
(989) 739-7030

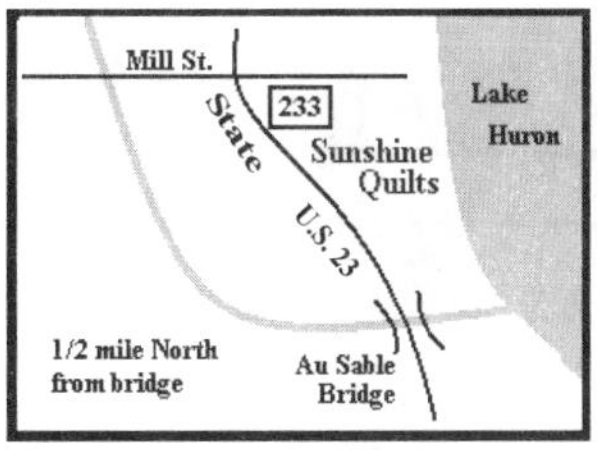

Owner: Sherrie Jaqua Free Newsletter
sunshinequiltshop@sbcglobal.net

Home of Time to Shine Patterns.
We carry Brights, Batiks, Orientals, Civil War and Thimbleberries.
Many exciting samples with kits!

Harrisville, MI #65

Mon - Sat 10 - 5

301 E. Main St., P.O. Box 75 48740
(989) 724-7788 Est: 2002 1100 sq.ft. 1000+ Bolts
hollyhockquiltshoppe@hotmail.com

We offer 100% high quality cotton, books, patterns, notions, classes. Block-a-month clubs as well as fun and inspiration.

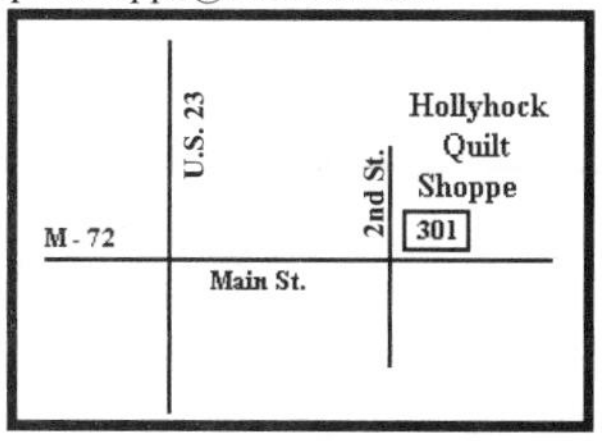

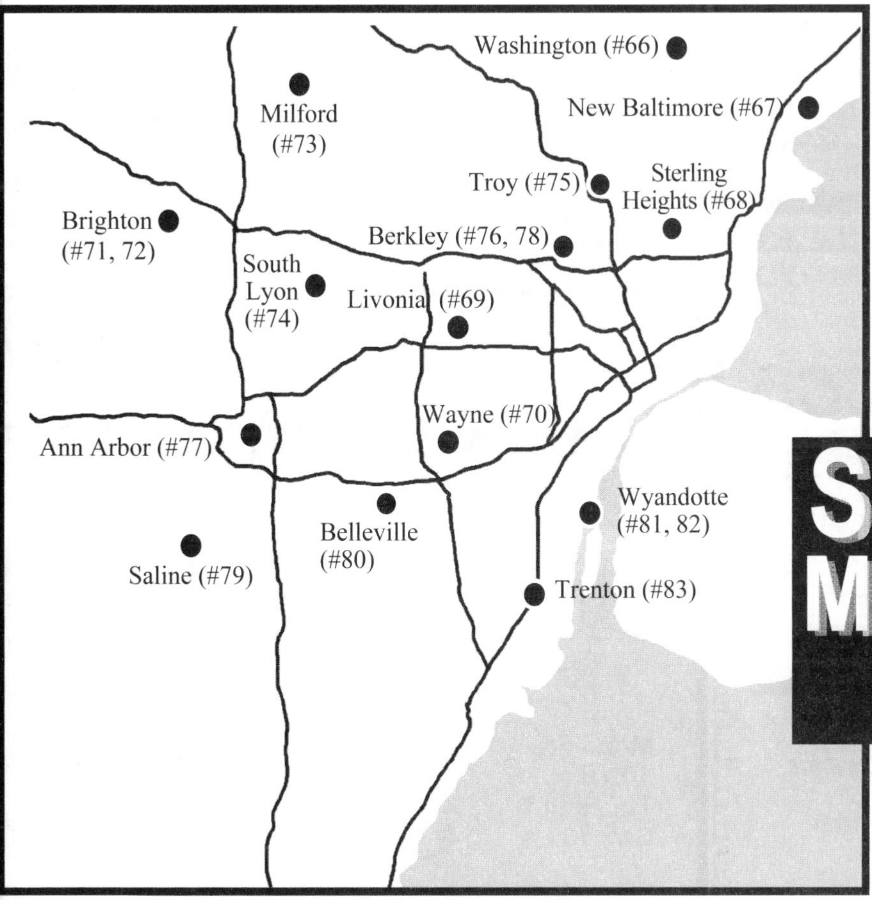

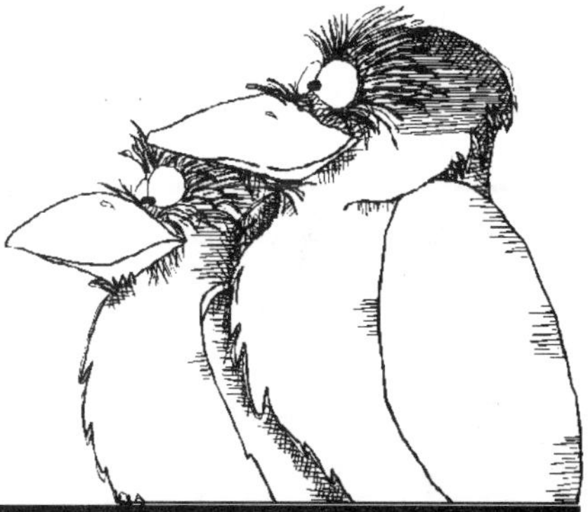

Southeastern Michigan Area

Shops #66 - 83

18 Featured Shops

Washington, MI #66

Mon - Sat 10 - 6 Mon & Thur til 8

Creative Corner of Romeo

66800 Van Dyke 48095
(586) 752-7444
Est: 1979 4500 sq.ft. 1700 Bolts
creativecornerofromeo.com

Quilt Fabrics & Supplies in one third of the store. Custom Picture Framing and Artist's supplies in the remainder.

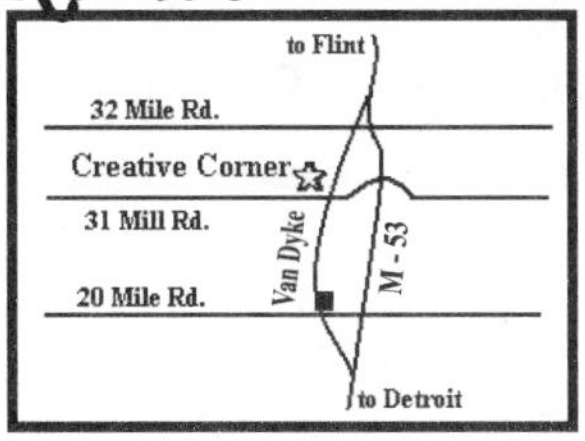

New Baltimore, MI #67

Tues - Fri 10 - 5 Sat 10 - 4

Tomorrow's Treasures Quilting

35228 23 Mile Rd. 48047
(586) 716-1334
quiltedtreasures@ymail.com
Est: 2009

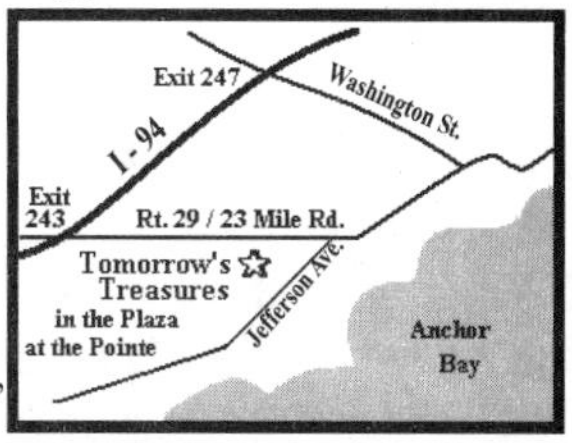

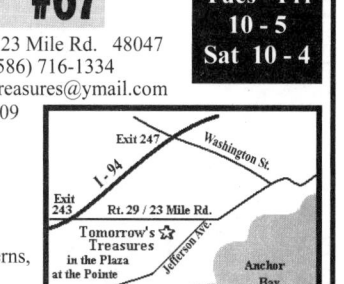

100% Quality Cotton Fabrics, Books, Patterns, Notions, Classes. Long-Arm Quilting.
"Quilts of today are truly Tomorrow's Treasures"

Sterling Heights, MI #68

Quilt-n Friends

4090 17 Mile Road 48310
(586) 979-7422
Gretchen L. Tatge
Est: 1983
www.quiltnfriends.com

2500 bolts of 100% Cotton Fabrics
Notions ... Books ... Patterns
Gifts ... Machine Quilting
Newsletter every 2 months ... Friendly Staff
Classes Year Round ... Michigan's Finest Teachers

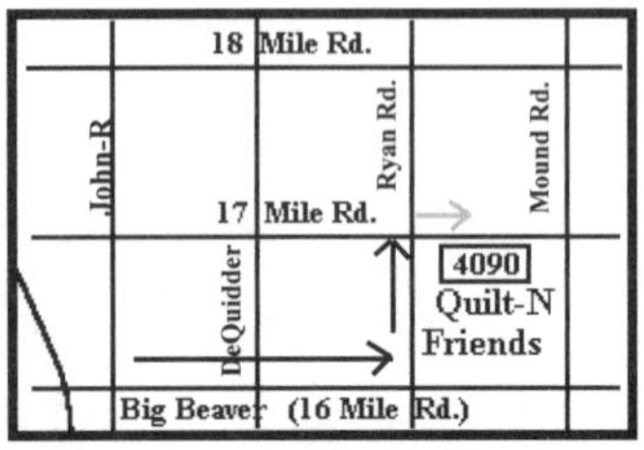

Mon - Fri 9 - 5
Sat 9 - 3
Thurs Eve til 8
(Call ahead for hours)

Livonia, MI #69

Please Call for an Appt.

Creative Quilting

36749 Angeline Cir. 48150
(734) 425-6385
Owner: Jean Coleman Est: 1990

The Finishing Touch

A MACHINE QUILTING SERVICE

Custom machine quilting. Quilts accepted from UPS, FedEx and U.S.P.S. Design choices by mutual agreement per letter or phone. Call for a flyer.

Brighton, MI #71

Mon - Fri 10 - 5
Sat 10 - 4

Creative Quilt Kits
QUILTING MADE SIMPLE AND FUN

8599 W. Grand River #8 48116
(810) 225-2849
Fax: (810) 225-2850
Est: 2007
1350 sq.ft.

creativequiltkits@att.net
www.creativequiltkits.com
Extensive selection of fabrics (4000 bolts) and kits from all major manufacturers.
Your source for quilting accessories and more!
From I-96 take exit 145 to Davis Office Center, 2 drives past Taco Bell.

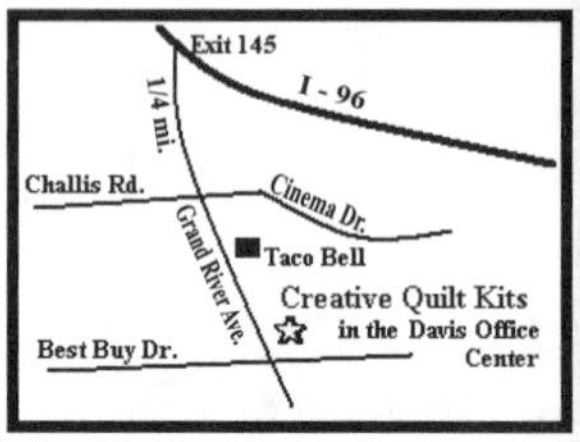

Bits 'n Pieces

Serving quilters since 1979!

34629 W. Michigan Ave.
Wayne, MI 48184
(734) 641-4970

Better Homes and Gardens Quilt Sampler FEATURED SHOP 2009

www.bitsnpieces.net

Quilting Fabrics & Patterns
Custom Kits • Original Patterns • Unique Designs

BERNINA Sewing Machines
Authorized Dealer since 1987
Sales • Service • Repair

Classes & Workshops
Quilting • Creative Clothing • Embroidery

Mon to Sat 10 - 5 Tues until 7
(closed Mondays during July and August)

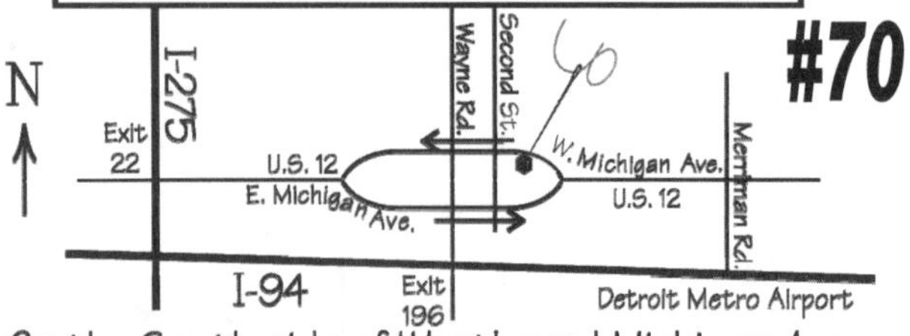

#70

On the South side of Westbound Michigan Ave.
Approximately 3 ½ miles east of I-275,
1 ½ miles west of Merriman Rd. and 4 miles north of I-94.

Monarch Quilts

2100 Grand River Annex #200
Brighton, MI 48114
810-225-7005
www.monarchquilts.com
monarchquilts@sbcglobal.net

Mon - Fri 10 - 6
Thurs til 7
Sat 10 - 4

*Friendly Assistance - we have kisses (chocolate) waiting for you!
*Complete Quilt Shop
*Long Arm Rental
*Professional Machine Quilting On-site. Speak with our quilter!
*Classes & Kits
*Over 3000 bolts including Bali * Amy Butler * Loralie * Hoffman * Art Gallery * Kaffe Fassett and many more

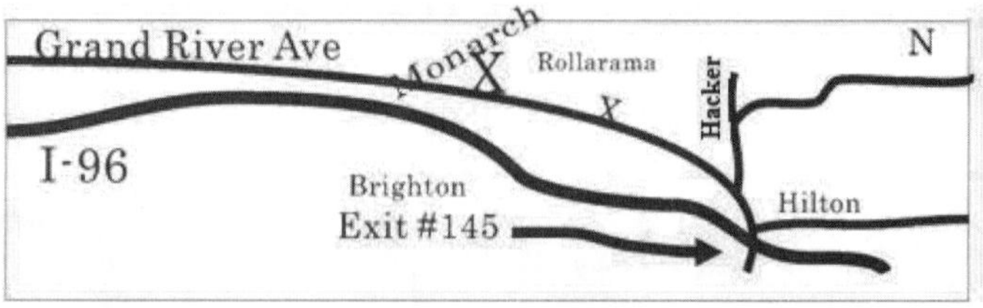

Brighton, MI #72

Where Fabrics and Quilts Come Together

Huron River Quilts

"A place to create memories with fabric and friends"

Located in the quaint town of Milford. We stock over 1500 bolts of top quality quilting fabric, hundreds of notions, books, patterns and other quilting supplies.

431 N. Main Street Milford, MI 48381
947-570-1129
Subscribe to our newsletter at: huronriverquilts@yahoo.com
Owners: Kathy Fournier & Ann Fisher
www.huronriverquilts.com

Mon - Fri 10 - 6
Thurs til 7 Sat 10 - 5

Milford, MI #73

Est: Feb. 2009

Lake St. Mercantile
Your Source for Quilting Projects Lessons & Supplies
Better Homes and Gardens
Quilt Sampler
FEATURED SHOP
2008
Located in a beautifully restored
123 year old Bank Building in Downtown South Lyon.

Gifts Cards Available • Credit Cards Accepted
115 E. Lake St. South Lyon, MI 48178
248-486-4410 Online Shopping Available
www.lakestmercantile.com

HOURS: Mon - Fri 10-6 • Sat 10-4
Sun 12-3 (except July and August)

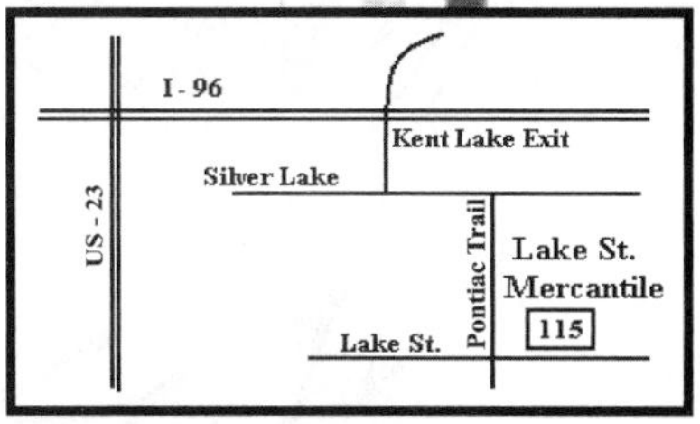

We now have two floors filled with the finest 100% cotton quilting fabric representing: Moda, Benartex, Andover & More. Also over 100 Bolts of Wool and hand-dyeds for Rug Hooking and many other projects. Of course, lets not forget our books, patterns and kits made to order.

South Lyon, MI #74

#75

The Quilted Goose

The Quilted Goose ~ Custom Machine Quilting

Award winning quilter with design imagination can make the most of your creation. We offer four levels of quilting, from simple all-over designs to heirloom quality. Your quilts will be treated with loving care in our smoke-free studio.

Be sure to ask for a copy of our brochure **"What Our Customers Have to Say About The Quilted Goose"** and find out what our customers already know!

Visit our website, call or email today for current turn-around time or to **request a copy of our free brochure**.

Custom Machine Quilting Services

Gammill Quilting Systems — Authorized **Gammill & Statler Stitcher** Sales Representative — Call today to set up your free demo! **248-740-8867**

Already own a longarm? Longarm Machine Quilting Classes forming now — call or visit our website for information and upcoming dates & locations.

For your convenience we stock several types of **batting** and **backing fabrics** to make completing your quilt even easier!

The Quilted Goose

646 East Long Lake Road, Troy, MI 48085
248-740-8867 ~ 248-740-8869 FAX
www.thequiltedgoose.com
Email: info@thequiltedgoose.com

Linda M. Thielfoldt, Designer
Hours By Appointment Only please call.
Member of IMQA

ATTN: Guilds ~ Linda is available for speaking and teaching engagements and was named as a Top Teacher of the Year 2009 Finalist by The Professional Quilter Magazine.

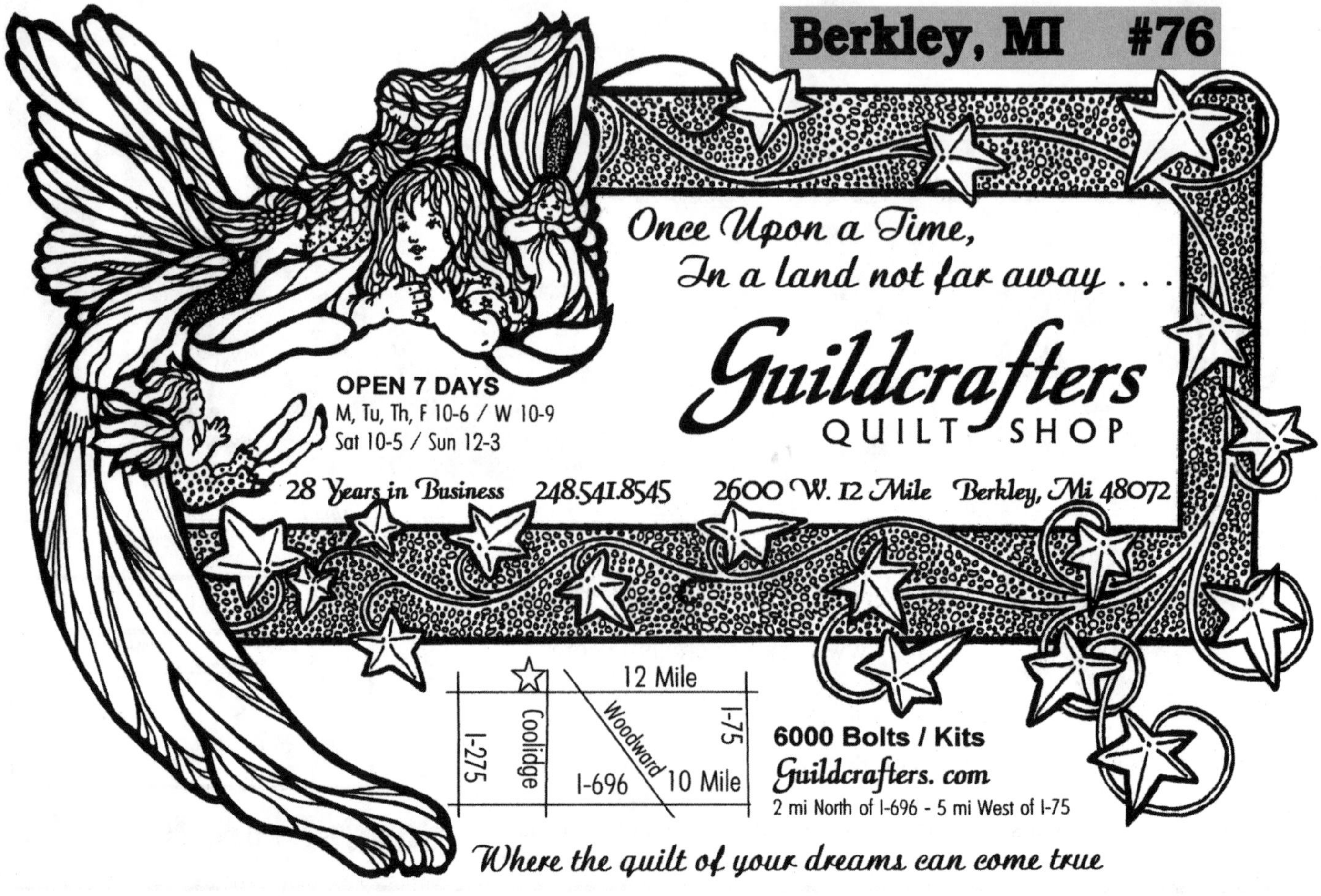
Berkley, MI #76
Once Upon a Time,
In a land not far away . . .
Guildcrafters
QUILT SHOP
OPEN 7 DAYS
M, Tu, Th, F 10-6 / W 10-9
Sat 10-5 / Sun 12-3
28 Years in Business 248.541.8545 2600 W. 12 Mile Berkley, Mi 48072
12 Mile
Coolidge
Woodward
I-75
I-275
I-696
10 Mile
6000 Bolts / Kits
Guildcrafters.com
2 mi North of I-696 - 5 mi West of I-75
Where the quilt of your dreams can come true

Ann Arbor Sewing and Quilting Center

5235 Jackson Road, Ann Arbor, MI 48103

www.annarborsewing.com

(734) 761-3094

#77

Hours: Mon-Fri 10am-6pm, Thurs 10am-8pm, Sat 10am-4pm, Sun 12pm-4pm

Ann Arbor Sewing & Quilting Center

42 years in business

- Over 6000 bolts of exciting fabrics from top manufactures: brights, batiks, novelty, oriental, traditional, flannels and more.
- Fabulous fabric room with wonderful lighting and lots of space.
- Newest and coolest Quilting & Sewing notions
- Huge assortment of thread for machine quilting & embroidery
- Buses welcome

Authorized Dealer for:

BERNINA

Husqvarna VIKING

SINGER

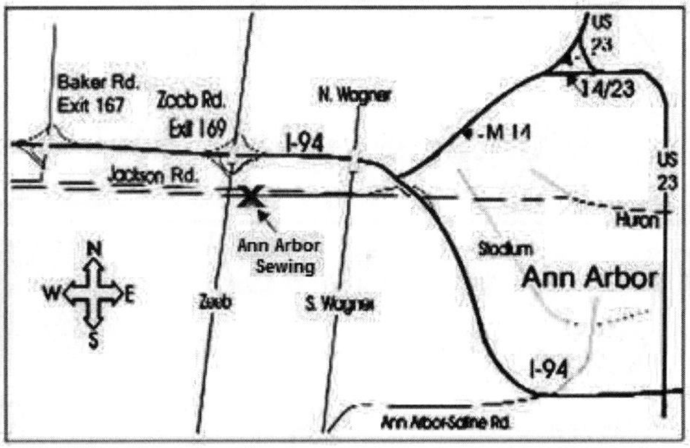

Award Winning Factory Trained Service Technicians for All Makes and Models-FREE Estimates. 24 hour Service Available

Berkley, MI #78

By Appt.

Cheryl's Heirloom Quilting

(248) 544-1113
Owner: Cheryl Mathe—designer

Please Call for Directions

Experienced long-arm machine quilting.
100's of designs or custom design available.
Excellent service. Call for information.

Belleville, MI #80

Mon - Fri 10 - 6
Sat 10 - 4
Sun 12 - 3

Threads 'N Treasures Quilt Shop, Inc.

129 South St. (Behind House) 48111
(734) 697-9376 Est: 1996
threadsntreasures@sbcglobal.net

Fabric • Notions
Classes
25% OFF all bolts
1/2 yard cut or more.
4000+ bolts of fabric.
Large 50% off Section

Computerized Gammill Quilting Machine.

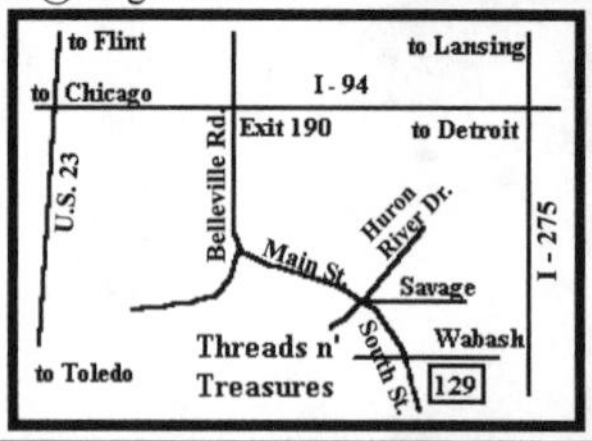

SEW FUN FABRICS, INC

664 OAK STREET, WYANDOTTE, MI 48192
Phone: 734-284-1405
www.sewfunfabrics.com

Over 2500 Bolts of Fabrics
Dealer For Tin Lizzie 18 Long arm

Hours:
Tue & Wed 10-5,
Thurs 10-8,
Fri & Sat 10-4
Closed Sun & Mon

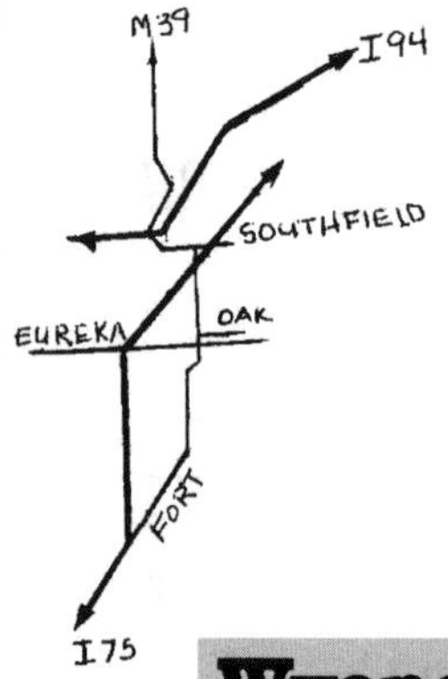

DRIVING DIRECTIONS

From South: I 75 North to Exit 28, M 85 (Fort Street). Fort Street north 9 miles turn right on Oak Street.

From north or west Interstate 75 or M39 or Interstate 94 to Southfield Road east to Fort Street Turn right on Fort Street 3.2 miles south stay in left lane. Turn left at light onto Oak Street .

Take Oak 1.1 miles cross the four sets railroad tracks. Turn left on 7th street. House on NE corner after tracks.

Wyandotte, MI #81

The Quilting Season

7025 E. Michigan Ave., Suite A3
Saline, MI 48176
(734) 429-2900
info@thequiltingseason.com
www.thequiltingseason.com
Est: 2001 2400 sq.ft.

Saline, MI #79

1500 Quilting Fabrics that Enchant and Inspire

RJR Fabrics, Moda Fabrics, Hoffman California, Benartex, Bali Fabrics & more.

Quilting Books, Patterns, Supplies and Classes

Mon 10 - 8
Tues - Fri 10 - 5
Sat 10 - 4

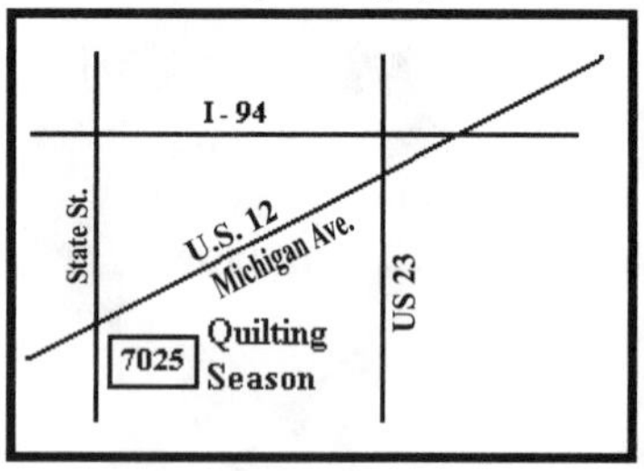

Wyandotte, MI #82

Mon - Fri 10 - 5
Sat 10 - 4

Sew What

144 Sycamore St. 48192
(734) 281-1344
Est: 1997 4000 sq.ft. 3500+ bolts
sewwhat59@aol.com

100% cotton fabrics, quilting supplies, books & patterns.
Special orders welcome.

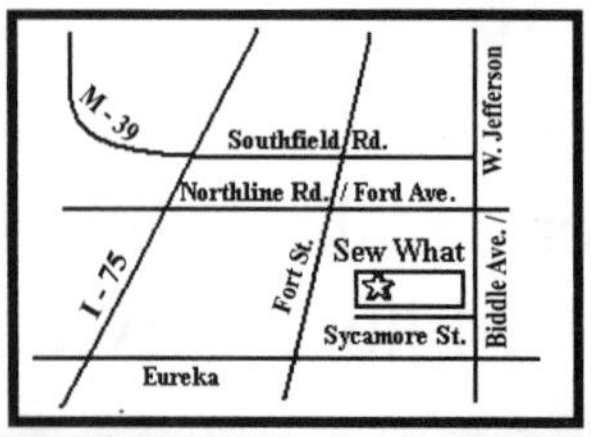

Trenton, MI #83

Mon - Sat 10 - 5

Pieceful Traditions Quilt Shop

3010 Van Horn Rd., Suite D
48183
(734) 692-1333 Online Newsletter
Fax: Same
Est: 2006
3000 sq.ft
3000 Bolts
piecefultraditions@sbcglobal.net
www.piecefultraditions.net

Quality quilting fabrics, silk, heirloom supplies, lace, silk ribbon, classes in quilting, garment construction, beginning and heirloom sewing.

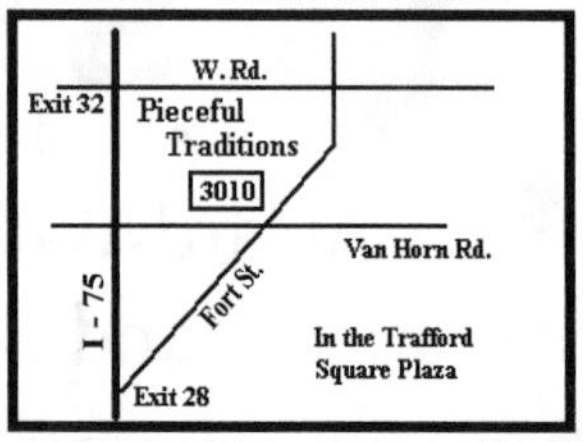

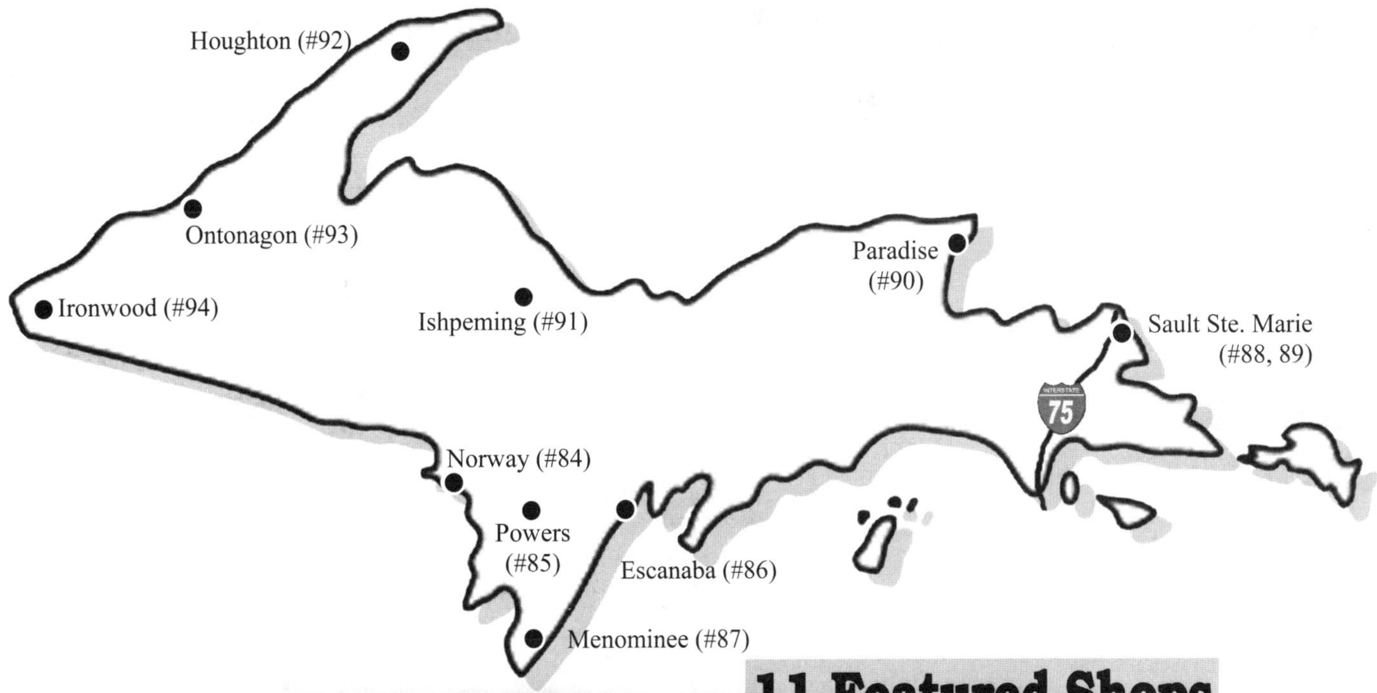

11 Featured Shops

UPPER PENINSULA

Shops #84 - 94

Norway, MI #84

JERI'S QUILT PATCH AND GIFTS

Mon-Sat 10-5, Sun 12-4 CST
Closed Holidays
703 Brown St, Norway, MI 906-563-9620
Established 1982, 4500 Sq Ft

Come and See how we pass our Savings on toYou!

Quilt Gallery

- View our Many original quilts displayed with available kits, Many Pre-cut & ready to sew.
- Enjoy Our Finished Models, See Many Possibilities.
- We have Quilts For Sale too!

Major Sale Events

- Four Day Superbowl Sunday Sale
- May Marathon Sale
- Sept Anniversary Sale
- Dec Quilter's Gift Sale

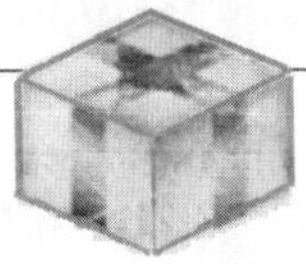

Come See !

- 1920's-1960's Vintage Apron Display
- Vintage Hot Pad Display
- Vintage Quilts For Sale

Shopping is TWICE the FUN. If you can't get to our shop- check out our ON LINE Specials too at www.jerisquiltpatch.com
We Accept All Credit Cards

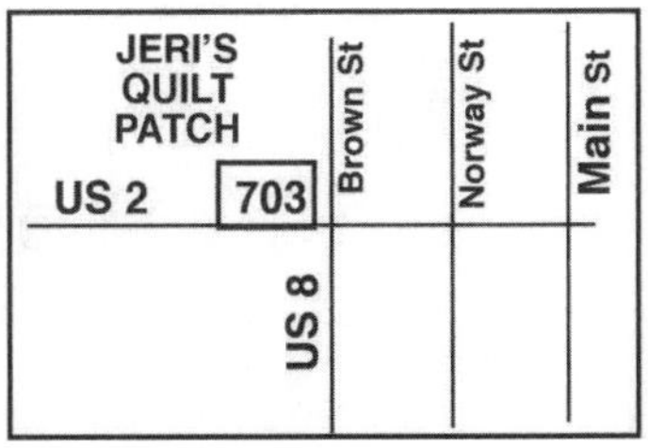

Powers, MI #85

Mon, Tues Thur, Fri 9 - 4 or By Appt.

Heirloom Quilting

N15926 High St. 49874
(906) 497-5142
Owner: Sally Gustafson Est: 2004
heirloomquilting@dsnet.us

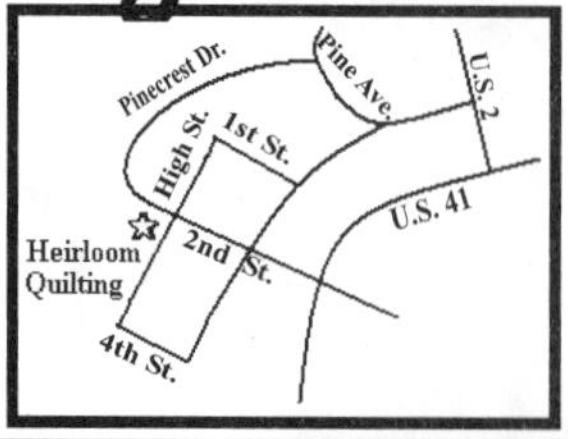

Classes on quilt construction, quality **long-arm machining** on your quilt top. Lots of samples to see and get great ideas.

Escanaba, MI #86

Mon - Fri 10 - 5 Sat & Sun by Appt.

Quilts 'n Stuff by Glenna

608 S. 14th St. 49829
(906) 786-3436 Fax: (906) 789-1483
Owner: Glenna Arkens Est: 1992
garkens@quiltsnstuff.net
www.quiltsnstuff.net

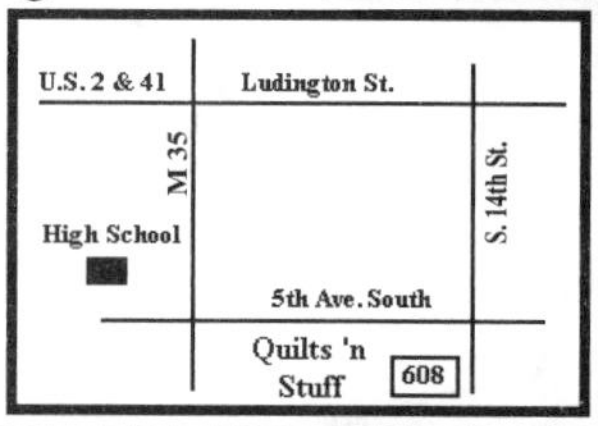

Featuring: 300 batiks, 100 patterns by Glenna, porcelain, fimo, hand painted big buttons & 1/2#'s of color family buttons. See "perfect binding miter" video on web site.

Menominee, MI #87

Mon - Fri 9:30 - 5:30 Thur til 8 Sat 10 - 4 Sun 1 - 4

Quilter's Haven, Ltd.

447 1st St. 49858
(906) 864-3078
Owner: Chris Caselton
Est: 1996 2000 sq.ft. 4000 Bolts
c_caselton@hotmail.com

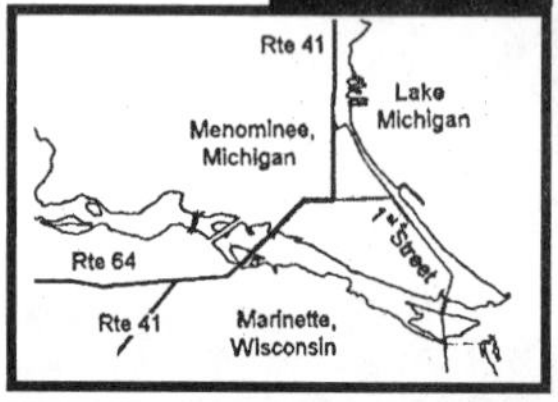

A friendly quaint quilt shop along the beautiful shore of Lake Michigan. Notions, books, patterns galore!! Bernina Sewing Machine Dealer

Sault Ste. Marie, MI #88

Tues - Fri 10 - 5 Sat 10 -3

The Quilted Moose

1812 Ashmun St. 49783
(906) 253-9886
quiltedmoose@sbcglobal.net
www.quiltedmooseshop.com

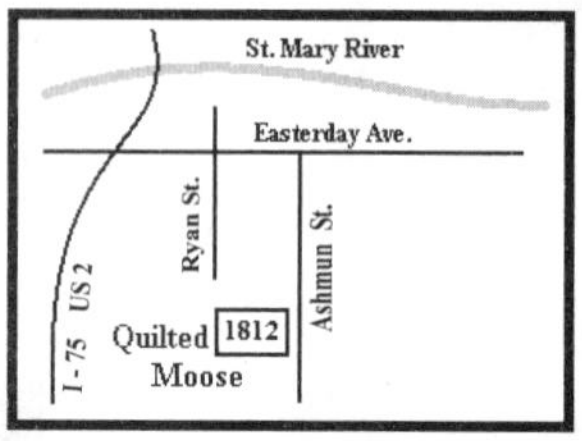

Fabrics, patterns, classes and longarm quilting with lots of northern hospitality.

Sault Ste. Marie, MI #89

May 1 - Oct 15 Mon - Sat 9 - 5 Oct 16 - Apr 30 Tues - Sat 9 - 5

Gloria's Happy Hooker

Quilting & Knitting Supplies

M - 129 (2733 Ashmun St.) 49783
(906) 635-9937
gloria@gloriasquilts.com
www.gloriasquilts.com
Owner: Gloria Larke
Quality Quilting Fabrics, Knitting Yarns.
Books, Patterns & Notions.
Home of the Famous Soo Locks

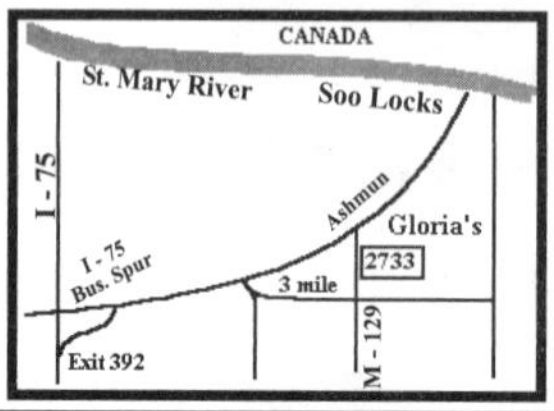

Paradise, MI #90

Open 7 Days Summer 10-7 Winter 10 - 5

Village Fabrics & Crafts

32702 W. Hwy. M-123 P.O. Box 254
(906) 492-3803 49768
villagefab@jamadots.com
www.VillageFabricsAndCrafts.com
Owner: Vicki Hallaxs Est: 1986

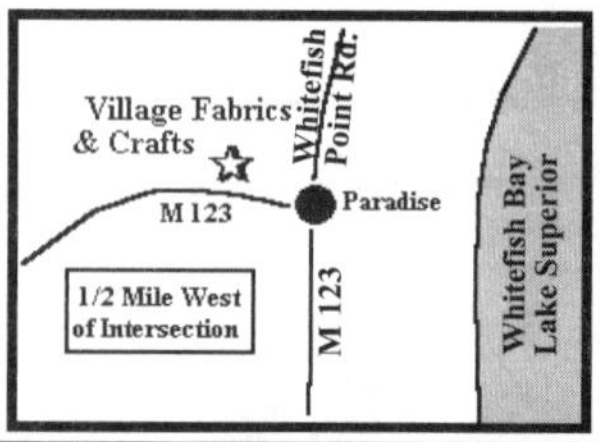

Quilting, Knitting, Crocheting, Counted Cross Stitch, Embroidery, Kid's Crafts, and Gifts. Year round classes and retreats. Buses welcome.

Ishpeming, MI #91

Mon - Fri 10 - 5 Sat 10 - 3

Country Garden Quilts & More

1335 U.S. Hwy. 41 W 49849
(906) 485-5006
Owner: Roy (Bud) & Mary Poirier
Est: 2003 1600 Bolts

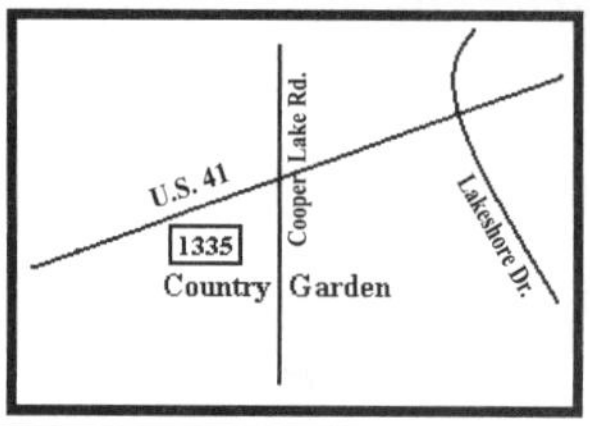

Fabrics, patterns, books, notions & classes.
Friendly, helpful customer service.

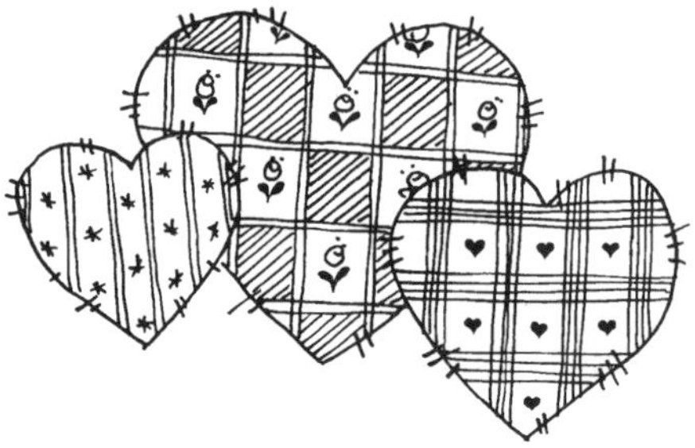

Houghton, MI #92

Mon - Fri 10:30 - 5:30
Sat 10:30 - 3

The "Copper Country's" only Full-Service Quilt Shop. Located between Chassell and Michigan Tech University in the big yellow house.

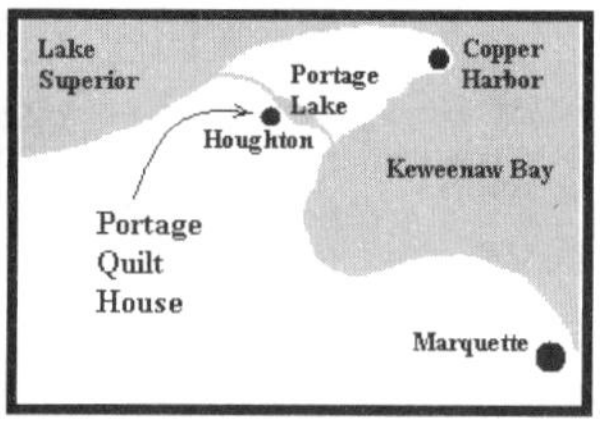

46509 U.S. Hwy. 41
Houghton, MI 49931
906-487-5500
www.portagequilthouse.com
Est: 2002 1500 sq. ft.

Portage Quilt House

Fabrics & Gifts

Ontonagon, MI #93

By Appt. Only

Polar Bear Production

35854 U.S. Hwy. 45 49953
(906) 884-2597
Owner: Barb Csmarich Est: 1998
barbcsmarich@charter.net

Quilting and Sewing Supplies
Brother Sewing Machines

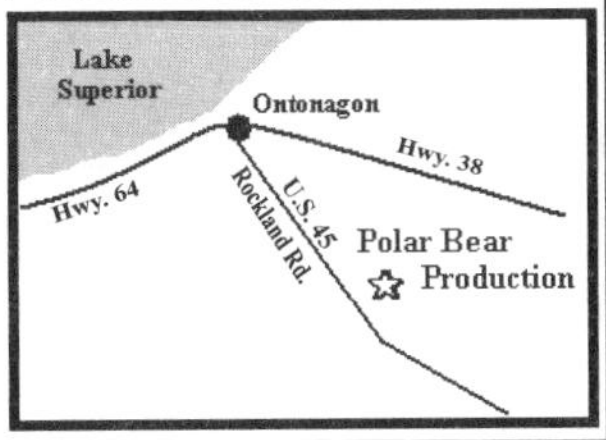

Ironwood, MI #94

Mon - Fri 9:30 - 5
Sat 9:30 - 4

The Fabric Patch

100 W. McLeod Ave 49938
(906) 932-5260 Est: 1981
Owner: Joanne Kuula
fabricpatch@sbcglobal.net
www.fabricpatch.com
Quilting Headquarters of the North. Largest Selection of quilt fabric in the UP and Northern WI. Over 3500 Bolts of Quilting Fabrics. Huge Selection of Quilting Books and Patterns. Authorized Husqvarna Viking Dealer.

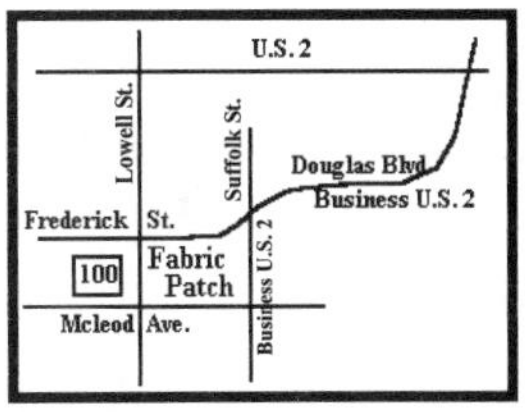

Michigan Quilt Shops

Allegan — **Sharon's Quilts & More, 224 Trowbridge St.** 269-686-9579 See ad #27, page 264
Ann Arbor — **Ann Arbor Quilting Center, 5235 Jackson Rd.** 734-761-3094 See ad #77, page 277
Au Gres — **Bayview Calicos and Ceramics, 3631 E. Huron Rd.** 989-876-6933 See ad #62, page 272
Baldwin — **Fabric Peddler, 815 N. Michigan Ave.** 231-745-4500 See ad #16, page 262
Battle Creek — **Sew Unique Threads, 7175 Tower Rd. #F** 269-317-3022 See ad #37, page 266
Bay City — **The Fabric Fair, 206 Fifth St.** 989-893-8971 See ad #61, page 272
Bear Lake — **Two Sisters Quilting, 9178 Chippewa Hwy.** 231-889-4005 See ad #9, page 262
Bellaire — **Cousin's Quilt Shop Bernina, 732 E. Cayuga St.** 231-533-4661 See ad #7, page 261
Belleville — **Threads 'N Treasures Quilt Shop, 129 South St.** 734-697-9376 See ad #80, page 278
Belleville — Sue's Quilt Shop, 48120 Harris Rd. 313-461-6540
Bellevue — **Bellevue Barn Quilter's, 104 W. Capital** 269-763-2276 See ad #38, page 266
Benton Harbor — Quilters Joy, 1041 Emerson Ave 269-757-3036
Berkley — **Guildcrafters Quilt Shop, 2600 W. 12-Mile Rd.** 248-541-8545 See ad #76, page 276
Berkley — **Cheryl's Heirloom Quilting, 2797 Oakshire** 248-544-1113 See ad #78, page 278
Brighton — **Monarch Quilts, 2100 Grand River Annex,** 810-225-7005 See ad #72, page 274
Brighton — **Creative Quilt Kits, 8599 W. Grand River #B** 810-225-2849 See ad #71, page 274
Byron Center — **Wooden Spool Quilt Shop, 7760 Clyde Park SW** 616-878-9335 See ad #24, page 264
Cadillac — **Julie Ann's Quilting, 117 N. Mitchell St.** 231-775-8301 See ad #10, page 262
Cadillac — **Patches & Petals, 11978 W. Watergate Rd.** 231-775-8780 See ad #11, page 262
Cedar — **Liberty Bell Quilts, 9027 S. Kasson Rd.** 231-228-6689 See ad #5, page 260
Charlevoix — **Hearts To Holly Quilt, 107 Mason St.** 231-547-2729 See ad #3, page 260
Charlotte — **The Hen House, 211 S. Cochran Ave.** 517-543-6454 See ad #44, page 268
Cheboygan — **The Fabric Stash, 218 N. Main St. #102** 231-597-9551 See ad #1, page 260
Comstock Park — **Attic Window Quilt Shop, 5307 Alpine NW** 616-785-3357 See ad #19, page 263
Coopersville — Quilter's Stitch, 1145 W. Randall St. 616-997-8366
Custer — **Pig Patch Farm Quilts, 3007 E. Hansen Rd.** 231-757-2812 See ad #12, page 262
Davison — Linda's Country Quilt Shop, 3058 N. State 810-658-9051
Dearborn — The Material Girls, 1850 Grindley Park St. 313-561-1111
East Lansing — **Country Stitches, Ltd., 2200 Coolidge Rd.** 517-351-2416 See ad #47, page 269
East Leroy — **Quilt N Go, 7212 6 1/2 Mile Rd.** 269-979-2347 See ad #39, page 267
East Tawas — **Cotton Patch Quilt Shop, 302 Newman St.** 989-362-6779 See ad #63, page 272
Edwardsburg — Robin's Nest: Quilts, 26848 US Hwy 12 269-663-3303
Elk Rapids — Now & Then, 126 River St., P.O. Box 727 231-264-5560
Elkton — The Backstreet Quilt Shop, 4910 York St. 989-375-4620
Escanaba — **Quilts 'N Stuff by Glenna, 608 S. 14th St.** 906-786-3436 See ad #86, page 280
Ewen — Brambleberry, Inc., 134 Pine M-28 E 906-988-2230
Farwell — **Elm Creek Ltd., 2609 W. Surrey Rd.** 989-588-6061 See ad #15, page 262
Fennville — **Custom Quilts Unlimited, 6184 Quilters Court** 269-561-6214 See ad #28, page 265
Fenton — **The Quilter's Garden, 1364 N. Leroy** 810-629-0331 See ad #48, page 270
Flushing — **Apple Tree Quilts, 5269 McKinley Rd.** 810-659-4190 See ad #58, page 272
Frankenmuth — Frankenmuth Woolen Mills, 570 S. Main St. 517-652-8121
Frankenmuth — Front Porch Quilt Shop, 305 S. Franklin St. 989-652-8050
Fremont — Quilt Something!, 48 W. Main St. 231-924-8557
Gaylord — Delphine's Quilt Shop, 114 N. Otsego Ave. 989-732-1252
Gaylord — Ben Franklin Crafts, 317 W. Main St. 989-732-2034
Gladwin — **Heritage Quilt Shoppe, 411 E. Cedar Ave.** 989-426-5577 See ad #14, page 262
Grand Rapids — **Lakeshore Sewing, 1971 E. Beltline NE** 616-365-8282 See ad #22, page 264
Grand Rapids — **Smith Owen Sewing & Quilting Center, 4051 Plainfield NE** 616-361-5484 See ad #21, page 264
Grand Rapids — Gall Sewing & Vac Center, 3861 Plainfield 616-363-1911
Grayling — **The Icehouse Quilt Shop, 509 Norway St.** 989-348-4821 See ad #6, page 260
Greenville — Forever Fabrics, 117 W. Cass St. 616-225-8486
Hadley — **Elaine's Quilty Shop, 4600 Pratt Rd.** 810-797-2242 See ad #52, page 270
Harbor Springs — Quilt Temptations, 1020 Arbor St 231-526-1999
Harrisville — **Hollyhock Quilt Shop, 310 E. Main St.** 989-724-7788 See ad #65, page 273
Hart — Quilters Patch, 5438 West Polk Rd. 231-873-0308
Hastings — **Sisters Fabrics, 218 E. State St.** 269-945-9673 See ad #25, page 264
Hastings — Quilting Passions, 214 N Jefferson 269-945-6238
Hemlock — **Miles of Stitches, 136 W. Saginaw** 989-642-2756 See ad #60, page 272
Hesperia — Fanna's Mercantile,151 Spruce 231-854-0612
Hillman — Sandy Dee's Sewing, 1015 Hawley Rd. 989-379-2406
Hillsdale — Laurie's Farmhouse Quilting, 6551 Cambria Rd. 517-357-4478
Holland — **Field's Fabrics, 281 E. 8th** 616-392-4806 See ad #26, page 264
Holt — **Everlasting Stitches Inc., 2040 N. Aurelius Rd.** 517-699-1120 See ad #43, page 268
Houghton — **Portage Quilt House, 46509 US Hwy 41** 906-487-5500 See ad #92, page 280

Houghton Lake — AJ's Quiltery & Gifts, 4532 W. Houghton Lake 989-422-5276
Houghton Lake — Suze's Stitch'n, 6230 W. Houghton Lake Dr. 989-422-6200
Howard City — Patchwork Dreams, 7675 Maple Hill Rd. 231-937-4627
Howell — Wendy's Simple Stitches, 1122 S. Michigan Rd.
517-545-0555 See ad #45, page 268
Howell — The Stitchery, 1129 E. Grand River
517-548-1731 See ad #46, page 269
Hudson — Bean Creek Quilts, 3840 South Meridian Rd. 517-448-3840
Imlay City — The Pincushion, 113 E. Third
810-724-7065 See ad #54, page 271
Indian River — The Quilt House, 4819 S. Straits Hwy.
231-238-4339 See ad #2, page 260
Interlochen — InterQuilten, 2386 M137, Suite B 231-276-9100
Iron River — Wardo's, 215 W. Genesee St. 906-265-2812
Ironwood — The Fabric Patch Limited, 100 W. McLeod Ave.
906-932-5260 See ad #94, page 281
Ishpeming — Country Garden Quilts, 1335 US Hwy. 41 W
906-485-5006 See ad #91, page 280
Jackson — Country Stitches, 1965 Boardman Rd.
517-782-7100 See ad #40, page 267
Jenison — Country Needleworks, Inc., 584 Chicago Ave. 616-457-9410
Johannesburg — The Apple Tree…more than quilts, 1026 M-32 989-786-3729
Kalamazoo — Quilts Plus, 3314 Stadium Dr.
269-383-1790 See ad #29, page 265
Kalamazoo — Bernina Sewing Quilt Shop, 4205 Portage Rd.
269-383-1244 See ad #30, page 265
Kalamazoo — Viking Sewing Center, 5401 Portage Rd.
269-342-5808 See ad #31, page 265
Kingsley — Whispering Needles, 107 Blair St. 231-263-5902
Lake Orion — The Village Quilt Shoppe, 2369 Joslyn Ct.
248-391-5727 See ad #50, page 270
Lansing — Gall Sewing & Vac, 520 Frandor Mall 517-333-0500
Levering — The Flower Lady's Farm, 5440 E Lovering 231-537-2622
Lewiston — Pine Tree Quilt Shoppe, 3060 Kneeland St. 989-786-2804
Livonia — Creative Quilting, 36749 Angeline Cir.
734-425-6385 See ad #69, page 274
Manistee — Sunrise Fabrics, 354 River St. 231-398-3795
Marine City — Quilting Dreams, 160 S Water St. 810-420-0105
Marlette — Sisters In Quilting, 6407 Morris St. 989-635-0300
Marquette — Merricks & Ben Franklin, 100 Coles Dr. 906-226-9613
Marquette — Alley Kat's Quilt Shop, 1015 N. 3rd St. 906-315-0050
Marshall — Quilts at the Marshall House, 100 Exchange St.
269-781-9450 See ad #36, page 266
Mason — Yards of Fabric, 116 E. Ash
517-676-2973 See ad #42, page 268
Mason — Keans Hallmark & Variety, 406 S. Jefferson 517-676-5144
Menominee — Quilter's Haven Ltd., 447 1st St.
906-864-3078 See ad #87, page 280
Michigamme — Country Garden Quilts and More, 103 Main St. 906-323-6203
Midland — Material Mart, 86 Ashman Cir.
989-835-8761 See ad #59, page 272
Milford — Huron River Quilts, 431 N. Main St.
947-570-1129 See ad #73, page 275
Milford — Quilter's Shoppe, 4458 Country View Ln.
Millington — My Lil' Quilt Shop, 4729 Main St.
989-871-6426 See ad #56, page 271
Mio — Stitches For You, 422 S. Morenci Ave. 989-826-1890
Montague — Quilted Memories, 9919 US Hwy 31
231-893-0096 See ad #17, page 263
Mt. Pleasant — Mt. Pleasant Sewing Center, 1024 S Mission 989-773-7403
Muskegon — Gall Sewing & Vac Center, 1930 Apple Ave. 231-773-8494
New Baltimore — Tomorrow's Treasures Quilting, 35228 23 Mile Rd.
586-716-1334 See ad #67, page 273
Newaygo — The New Ewe, 59 W. State Rd. 231-652-5262
Norton Shores — Stitched Heart, 186 E. Mount Garfield Rd. 231-798-3987
Norway — Jeri's Quilt Patch, 703 Brown, U.S. #2
906-563-9620 See ad #84, page 279
Omer — Quilt Patch Antiques, 429 E. Center St. 517-653-2332
Ontonagon — Polar Bear Production, 35854 U.S. Hwy. 45
906-884-2597 See ad #93, page 281
Ortonville — Mabelena Quilting Supplies, 470 Mill St.
248-627-9100 See ad #49, page 270
Oscoda — Sunshine Quilt Shop, 233 S. State (US 23)
989-739-7030 See ad #64, page 273
Ovid — Elaine's Too, 122 S. Main St.
989-834-2538 See ad #57, page 271

Paradise — Village Fabrics & Crafts, 32702 Hwy M-123 W
906-492-3803 See ad #90, page 280
Paris — Creative Loop, 1241 Northland Dr. 231-629-8228
Perrinton — Calico Cupboard, 4625 MacArthur 989-236-7728
Pinckney — Jennifer's Quilt Shop, 149 N. Howell
734-878-6188 See ad #41, page 268
Plainwell — Dancing Dogs Quilt Shop, 119 N Main St 517-803-3777
Port Huron — Sew Elegant Quilt Shoppe, 3909 Pine Grove
810-982-6556 See ad #55, page 271
Port Huron — Mary Maxim, Inc., 2001 Holland Ave. 810-987-2000
Port Huron — Victoria's Sewing, 2708 14th Ave 810-966-9600
Portland — Around the Block Quilt Shop, 120 Maple St.
517-647-5430 See ad #20, page 263
Powers — Heirloom Quilting, N15926 High St
906-497-5142 See ad #85, page 280
Reed City — Crossroads Quilt Shop, 111 B S. Higbee St
231-465-4144 See ad #13, page 262
Richmond — Sew Together, 69295 Main St.
586-727-1555 See ad #53, page 271
Riverdale — Sheila's Fabrics, 11995 W. Monroe Rd. 989-833-7147
Rochester — Cristina's Quilt Shoppe, 116 W 2nd St 248-601-6565
Saginaw — Quilted Cottage, 166 N Center Rd. 989-790-3123
Saginaw — Speedy Sew, 3210 Tittabawassee Rd. 989-790-9048
Saline — The Quilting Season, 7025 E. Michigan Ave.
734-429-2900 See ad #79, page 278
Sault Ste. Marie — Gloria's Happy Hooker, 2733 Ashmun (M-129)
906-635-9937 See ad #89, page 280
Sault Ste. Marie — The Quilted Moose, 1812 Ashmun St.
906-253-9886 See ad #88, page 280
Schoolcraft — Big Island Quilt Co., 13210 North U.S. 131
269-679-3101 See ad #33, page 265
Shelby Twp. — Sewing Products Co. Inc., 50304 Schoenherr 586-566-4500
Snover — Country Treasures, 2509 Ubly Rd 810-672-9422
South Haven — So South Haven, 70920 CR 388
269-637-0603 See ad #32, page 265 & 406
South Lyon — Lake Street Mercantile, 115 E. Lake St.
248-486-4410 See ad #74, page 275
St. Clair — River Place Mercantile LLC, 201 N. Riverside
810-329-9300 See ad #51, page 270
St. Louis — Common Threads Quilt Shop, 109 N. Mill St. 989-681-5082
Sterling Heights — Quilt - n - Friends, 4090 17-Mile Rd.
586-979-7422 See ad #68, page 274
Stevensville — Loving Stitches Quilt Shop, 7291 Red Arrow Hwy
269-465-3795 See ad #34, page 266
Stevensville — Accomplish Quilting.com, 2797 Kimmel St. 269-556-2552
Tecumseh — The Quilt Patch, 112 N Evans St.
517-423-0053 See ad #35, page 266
Three Rivers — Karen's Fabric Shop, 514 Walnut St. 269-279-9391
Traverse City — Quilt-n-Bee Company, 1425-C S. Airport Rd. W
231-922-6766 See ad #4, page 260
Trenton — Pieceful Traditions Quilt Shop,
3010 Van Horn Rd., Suite D
734-692-1333 See ad #83, page 278
Troy — The Quilted Goose, 646 East Long Lake Rd.
248-740-8867 See ad #75, page 276
Washington — Creative Corner Of Romeo, 66800 Van Dyke
586-752-7444 See ad #66, page 273
Wayne — Bits 'N Pieces, 34629 Michigan Ave.
734-641-4970 See ad #70, page 274
West Branch — Caroline's Sewing Room, 3100 W. Houghton Ave. 989-345-9180
West Branch — Crocker's Attic, 3156 W. M-55 989-345-1780
Whitehall — The General Store, 103 E. Colby St.
231-894-2164 See ad #18, page 263
Williamsburg — Renee's House of Quilting, 8995 M 72 East
231-267-5895 See ad #8, page 261
Wolverine Lake — Grandma Honey's Quilts, 1925 Shankin Dr. 248-624-4677
Wyandotte — Sew Fun Fabrics, Inc., 664 Oak St.
734-284-1405 See ad #81, page 278
Wyandotte — Sew What, 144 Sycamore
734-281-1344 See ad #82, page 278
Wyoming — Lakeshore Sewing, 1011 Gezon Pkwy. SW
616-531-5561 See ad #23, page 264
Wyoming — Gall Sewing Ctr, 5316 Clyde Park Ave SW 616-531-4373

Michigan Quilt Shows

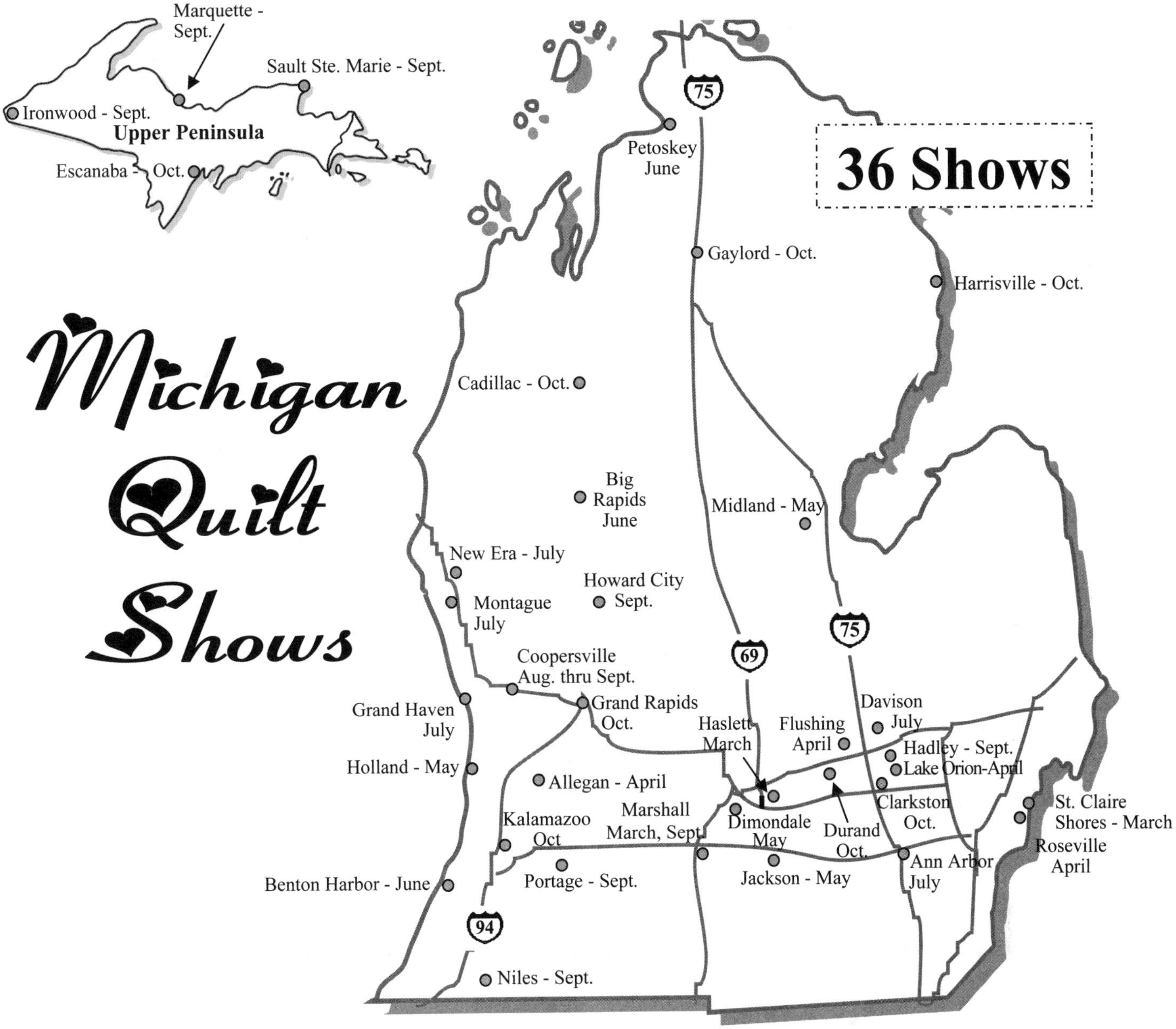

About Shows: We are listing only the very basic information about shows that happen on a regular schedule here. Please check out our website for more details on each show. Also this information tends to change quite often so please verify the event with our website or a local source before you venture far. Or if you're in the right area at the right time, give it a shot.

If you are a show organizer, please keep us updated on your event.
shows@quilterstravelcompanion.com www.quilterstravelcompanion.com

On our website you will also find:
- Exact dates (when we have them)
- Contact Information
- Events happening on a one-time basis
- Sponsor Information
- Description of Event

Month	City	Schedule	Show	Location with address
March				
	Marshall	Annual, Late Sat in March	Heritage in Fabric	First Presbyterian Church 200 W. Mansion St.
	Haslett	Odd Years, end of March or early April	Capitol City Quilt Guild Show	Haslett High School 5450 Marsh Rd.
	St. Claire Shores	Odd Years, Last week of March	Quilts from the Heart	Assumption Cultural Center 21800 Marter Rd.
April				
	Lake Orion	Even Years, Fri & Sat after Easter, April	Oakland County Quilt Guild	First Baptist Church of Lake Orion 255 E. Scripps Rd.
	Allegan	Odd Years, 3rd Sat. in April	The Iron Bridge Quilters Show	Allegan Community Center 330 Trowbridge St.
	Flushing	Odd Years, last Fri & Sat of April	Genesee Star Quilters Show	Flushing United Methodist Church 413 Main St.
	Roseville	Odd Years, last Fri & Sat of April	Quilts from the Heart	Roseville Parks & Recreation Center 18185 Sycamore

Month	City	Schedule	Show	Location with address
May				
	Holland	Annual, 1st full week in May	Tulip Time Quilt Show	Holland Area Arts Council, 150 E. 8th St.
	Midland	Odd Years, 2nd weekend in May	Vintage Memories Quilt Show	Valley Plaza, 5221 Bay City Rd.
	Dimondale	Even Years - Late May	Lansing Area Patchers Quilt Show	The Summit, 9410 Davis Highway
	Jackson	Even Years, 3rd weekend in May	Pieces & Patches Quilt Guild	Show Jackson Catholic Middle School, 915 Cooper St.
June				
	Big Rapids	Odd Years, 1st weekend in June	Big Rapids Quilt Show	Big Rapids Middle School, 500 N. Warren Ave.
	Petoskey	Odd Years, 3rd Fri & Sat in June	Quilts By The Bay	Knights of Columbus Hall, 1106 Charlevoix Ave.
	Benton Harbor	Even Years, Late June	Berrien Towne & Country Quilt Show	Lake Michigan College Mendel Center--Upton Hall, 2755 E. Napier Ave.
July				
	New Era	Odd Years, 2nd Fri & Sat in July	Friendship Ring Quilt Guild Show	New Era Christian School, 1901 Oak
	Davison	Even Years, 4th weekend in July	Evening Star Quilt Guild Show	Downtown and First Baptist Church, 208 4th St.
	Ann Arbor	Even Years, last weekend of July	Celebrating the Quilt	Washtenaw Community College, 4800 Huron River Dr.
	Grand Haven	Annual, last Fri & Sat in July	Lighthouse Quilt Guild Coast Guard Festival Show	St. Patrick's Catholic Church, 901 Columbus
	Montague	Annual, last Fri & Sat in July	Quilted Memories Quilt Show	Quilted Memories, 9919 US 31
August				
	Coopersville	Annual, August and September	Coopersville Farm Museum Quilt Show	Coopersville Farm Museum, 375 Main St.
September				
	Hadley	Annual, Late September	The Gathering Ladies Quilt Show	Town Hall, Downtown
	Marshall	Annual, 2nd weekend of September	Cal-co Quilters' Guild Show	The Mac, 15325 W. Michigan Ave.
	Niles	Odd Years, 2nd weekend in September	Niles Piecemakers Quilt Guild Show	Merritt Elementary School, 1620 LaSalle
	Howard City	Annual, 3rd Sat. of September	Patchwork Dreams Quilt Show	Edgerton Upper Elementary Gym, Shaw St.
	Ironwood	Even Years, 3rd Saturday in September	Northern Lights Quilting Guild Show	Ironwood Memorial Bldg, 213 S. Marquette
	Sault Ste. Marie	Odd Years, usually 3rd weekend in September	Keeping the Piece Quilter's Guild Show	Sault Area Middle School, 684 Marquette Ave.
	Portage	Odd Years, late September	Kalamazoo Log Cabin Quilters Show	Kingdon Indoor Center, 8151 Merchants Place
	Harrisville	Odd Years, September or October	Harrisville Harvest of Quilts	Harrisville, All over Town
October				
	Clarkston	Odd Years, 1st Fri & Sat in October	Town Hall Quilt Guild Show	First Congregational Church, 5449 Clarkston Rd.
	Durand	Annual, 1st Fri & Sat of October	Durand Quilt Show	First United Methodist Church, 10016 E. Newburg Rd.
	Grand Rapids	Even Years, 1st full weekend in October	West Michigan Quilter's Guild Show	DeltaPlex. 2500 Turner Ave. NW
	Cadillac	Annual, 2nd Saturday in October	North Star Quilt Show	Baker College Student Center, 9600 E 13th St.
	Escanaba	Odd Years, 3rd Fri & Sat of October	Rapid River Quilt Guild Show	Bay de Noc Comm. College (Joseph Heirman Bldg), 2001 N. Lincoln Rd.
	Kalamazoo	Odd Years, 3rd weekend in October	Quilts Kalamazoo	Kalamazoo County Fair-Hazel Gray Bldg., 2900 Lake St.
	Gaylord	Even Years, Fri & Sat in late Oct. or early Nov.	Heart of The Pines Quilt Guild	Treetops Convention Center, 3962 Wilkerson Rd.
	Marquette	Even Years, Fall	Marquette County Quilters Show	Northern Michigan University

Notes

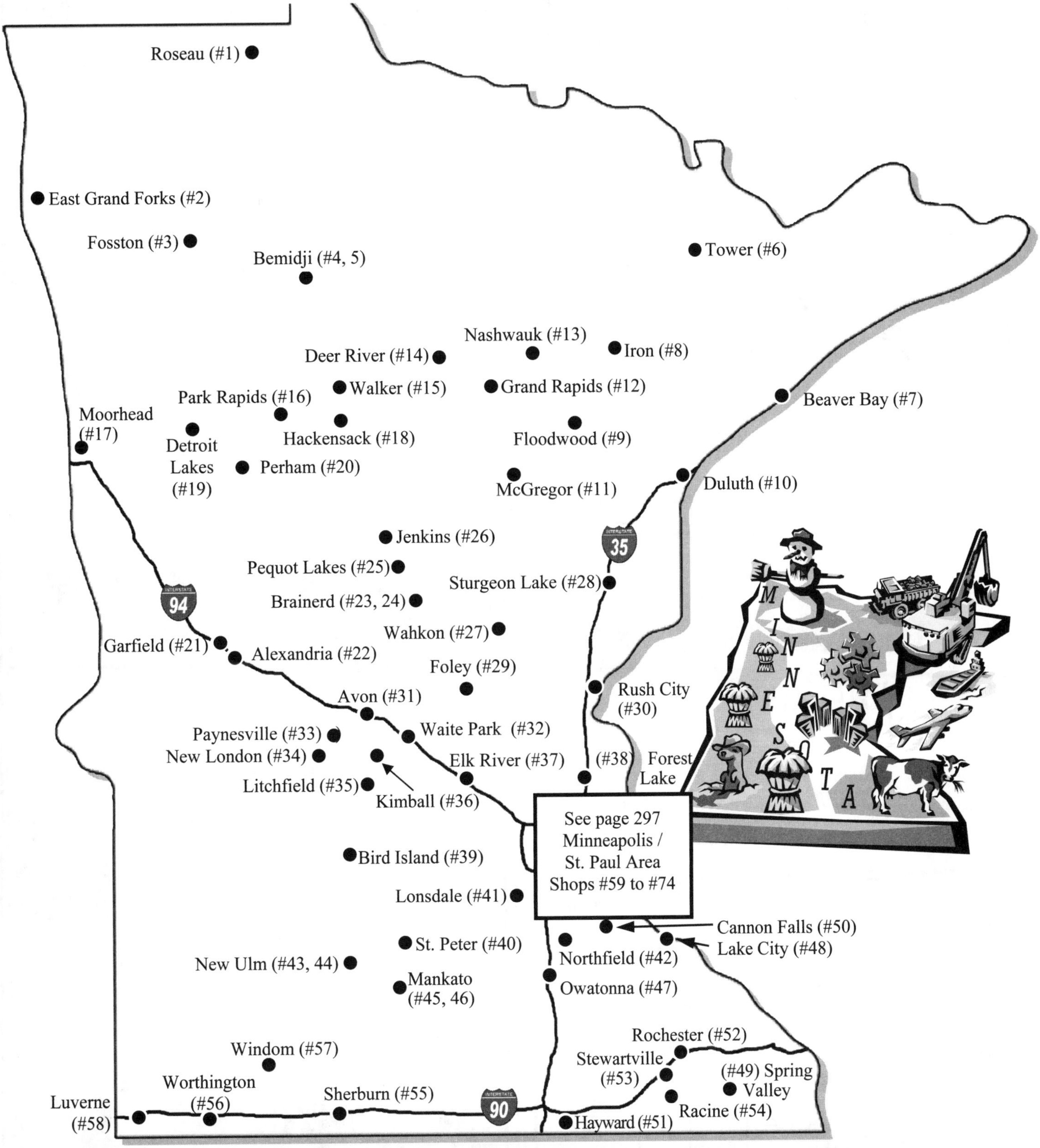

MINNESOTA

74 Featured Shops

Roseau, MN #1

Mon - Fri 10 - 6
Sat 10 - 4

Quilt S'more

209 2nd Ave. NE 56751
(218) 463-3867 Fax: Same
Owner: Judy Magnusson
Est: 2000

Quilt S'more located on Hwy. 11 downtown Roseau. Fabrics - Notions - Janome Sewing Machines - Quilts - Horn Cabinets

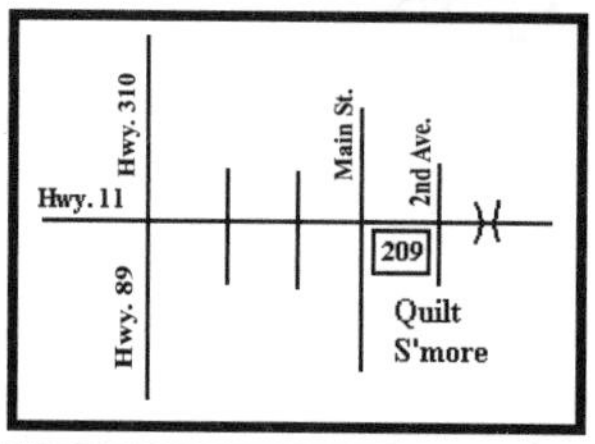

East Grand Forks, MN #2

Mon - Fri 10 - 5:30
Sat 10 - 5
Sun 12 - 4

QUILTER'S EDEN

223 DeMers Ave. 56721
(218) 773-0773
www.quilterseden.com

Your friendly hometown quilt store offers:
- 100% Cotton Fabric • Books • Patterns
- Notions • Kits • Classes • Longarm Services
- Janome Sewing Machines

We look forward to serving you! Quilter's Eden is conveniently located across from Cabela's.

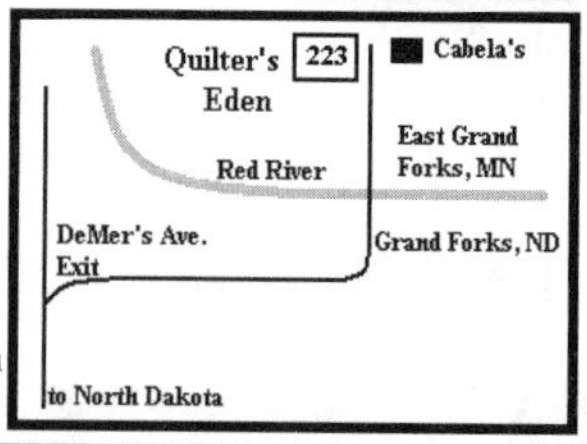

Fosston, MN #3

Tues - Fri 10 - 6
Sat 10 - 4

Red Rooster Quilts

209 2nd St. NW #5 56542
(218) 435-1662
Owner: Deb Ballard
Est: 2010 1200 Online Newsletter
redroosterquilt@gvtel.com

Bright and welcoming.
We have a variety of fabrics, notions, patterns and much more.
Stop, have a cup of coffee and check us out!

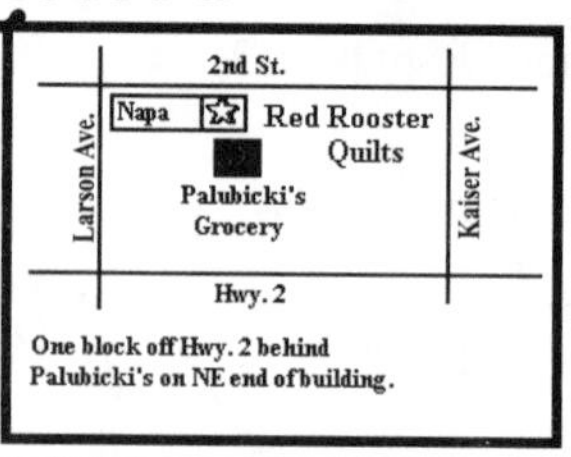

Bemidji, MN #4

By Chance Or Appt.

Willow Wood Market

23621 Cty. Rd. 9 56601
(218) 759-2310 Est: 1997
bonnie@willowwoodmarketdesigns.com
www.willowwoodmarketdesigns.com

Tucked in the woods, our shop / studio offers a variety of wools and quality fabric, as well as unique wool, needlefelting and stitchery patterns, kits, supplies and inspiration.
Mail order Available.

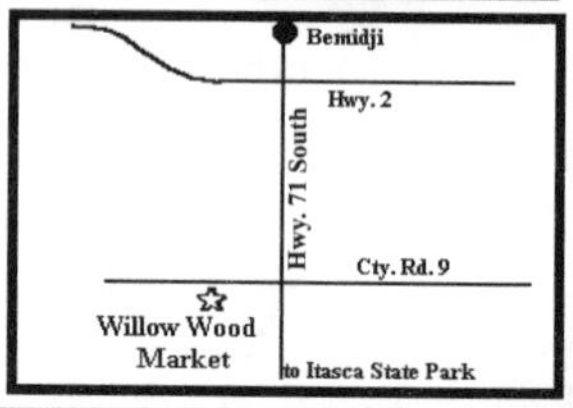

Bemidji, MN #5

Emily's Country Cottage

www.emilyscountrycottage.com

Welcome to our beautiful quilt shop & gift store with many displays, kits & samples to inspire you. With our focus on the traditional we offer lots of florals, flannels & reproduction fabrics.

We look forward to your visit!

705 Washington Ave. S,
Bemidji, MN
218-444-6387
Owner: Emily Hardwig

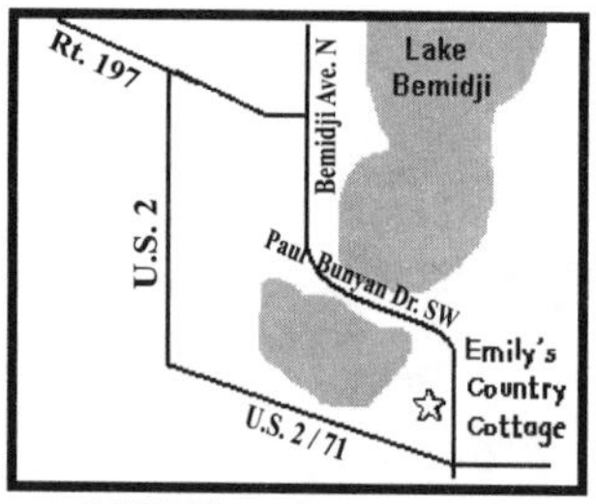

Tower, MN #6

Oct - May
Tues - Sat 10 - 4
June - Sept
Mon - Sat 10 - 5

North Country Quilts

303 Main St. 55790
(218) 753-4600
Owners: Dan & Corrine Hill Est: 1999
www.northcountryquiltshop.com

You will know you have arrived at North Country Quilts when you see all the quilts placed over the railings of our beautiful porch. We are quietly tucked at the end of town, housed in a quaint bungalow. For quilters the shop offers lots of samples to admire and inspire. The shop also entices non-quilters with its selection of already made quilts or custom quilts to be made.

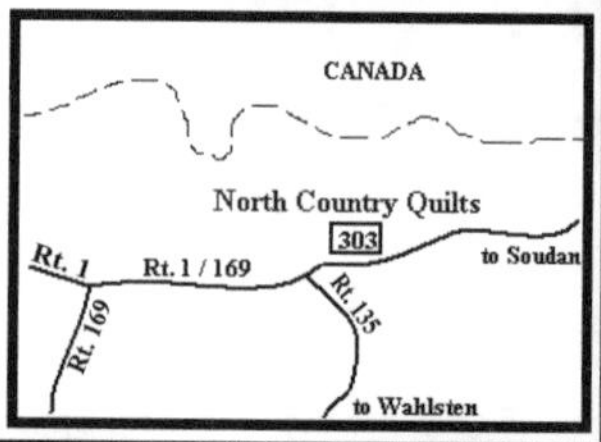

Beaver Bay, MN #7

Mon - Sat 10 - 4
Sun 12 - 4

Quilt Corner

Your Northwoods Specialist in Outdoor Nature and Wildlife Fabric and Patterns

Beaver Bay Mini Mall, 1007 Main St.
P.O. Box 304 55601
(218) 226-6406 Est: 1990
Owner: Roxanne Johnson 800 sq.ft.
www.quiltcorner.com
Over 3000 Bolts of Cotton Fabric.
Books, Notions, Patterns, & Yarn.
Many Quilts for sale. Gifts too.

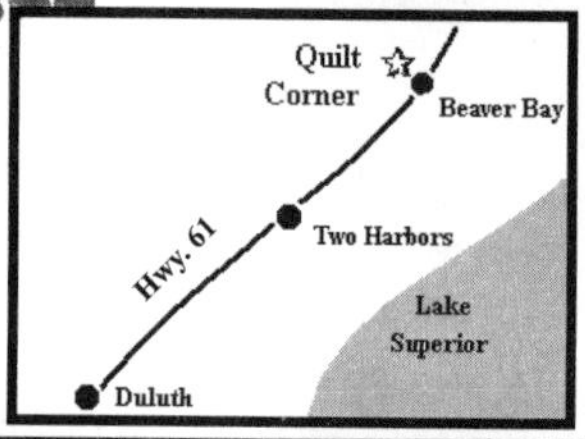

Iron, MN #8

Tues - Sat 10 - 5
Thur til 7

Terri's Treasures
Quilt Shop

8679 S. Iron Bowl Ln. 55751
(218) 744-1935
Est: 2007 900 sq.ft.

A cozy quilt shop with a variety of fabrics, notions, patterns and books. Several samples to inspire you. Classes available.

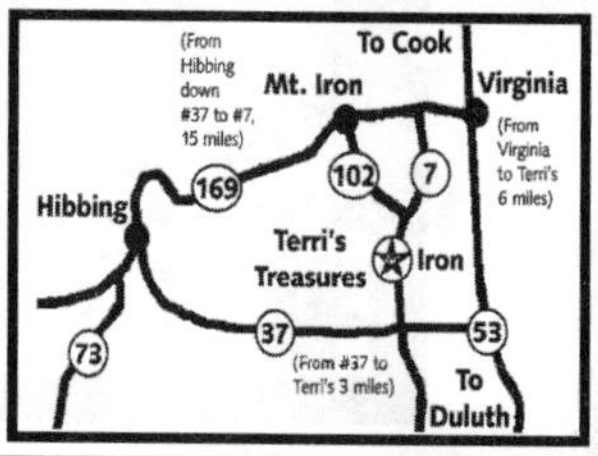

HINGELEY ROAD QUILT SHOP · FLOODWOOD, MN

HINGELEY ROAD Quilt Shop

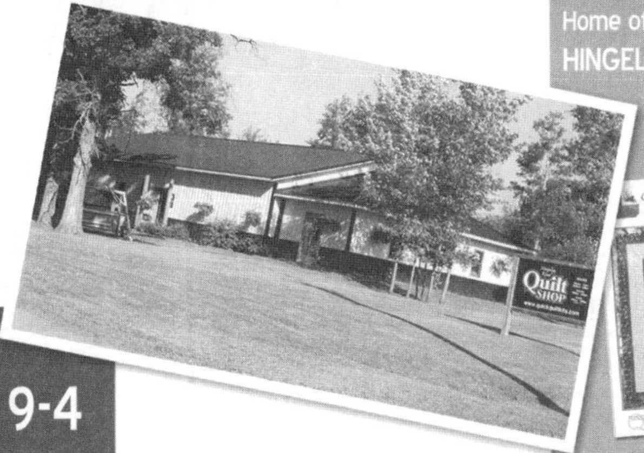

Home of :
HINGELEY ROAD QUILT DESIGNS

.... PATTERNS

Store Hours:
MON-FRI 10-5, SAT 9-4

Only the Best: Top Quality, Quilt Shop Only Quilt Fabric

* Over 6,000 bolts, including all the Moda/Holly Taylor Groups and **Minnesota Charms Hoffman Exclusive Batiks**
* Huge selection of charms, bali pops, jelly rolls, layer cakes, turnovers and custom cuts/combinations.
* Northwoods Room dedicated to Northwoods Themed Fabrics
* Year-round selection of Holiday fabrics (Christmas, Halloween), 100's of baby prints and textures. 100's of northwoods prints in the Northwoods Room. Over 1,000 batiks and over 1,000 flannels.
* All products available with our **full-service online shopping cart!**

MinnesotaCharms.com Quilt Show 1st weekend of Oct. 2010
Visit our website for details. www.MinnesotaCharms.com

BOOKS ....

Store Map:
HOW TO FIND US...

Conveniently located right on Hwy 2 - 4 miles East of Floodwood, MN

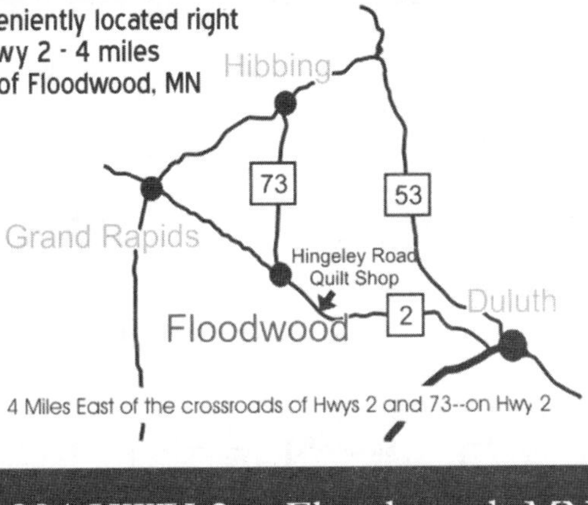

4 Miles East of the crossroads of Hwys 2 and 73--on Hwy 2

HOME OF
10,000 Charms & Hingeley Road Quilt Designs!
VISIT OUR WEBSITE:
MinnesotaCharms.com
PARTICIPATING SHOP
quiltminnesota.com

11284 HWY 2 · Floodwood, MN · 55736
4 Miles East of the HWY 2/73 Crossroads · 218-476-3139

www.HingeleyRoadQuiltShop.com
www.MinnesotaCharms.com

Kelly J's Sewing Center & Quilt Shop

- 3000+ Bolts of Quilt Shop Only Fabrics
- Lots of Batiks, Wool, Chenille & Unique Fabrics
- Gift Items
- Samples For Sale
- Custom Patterns & Kits
- Genuine Malden Mills Fleece
- Permanent & Evolving Clearance Room
- Quarterly Newsletter & Classes
- Award Winning Customer Service!

6140 Jean Duluth Rd. 55803
218-724-8781 800-638-1911

Year 'Round Hours:
Mon-Fri 9am-6pm

We're Easy To Find!
Call or Email for Simple Directions!

Take the Short Drive to Two Floors of Fun!

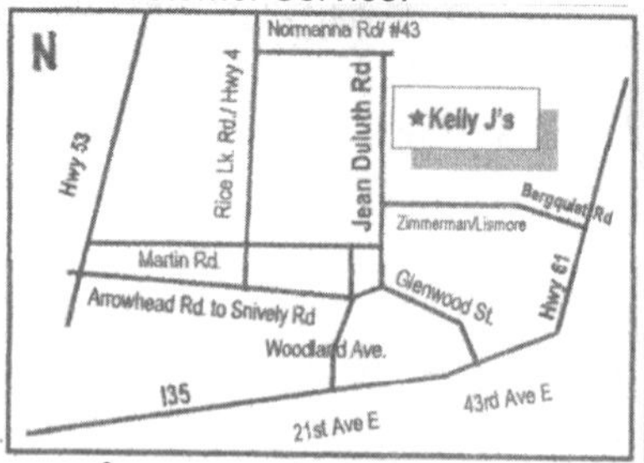

www.kellyissewingcenter.com

Duluth, MN #10

McGregor, MN #11

Timeless Treasures Quilt Shop of McGregor

Hours:
Monday - Friday
10 - 5
Saturday 10 - 4

218.768.2556

371 E. State
Hwy. 210
55760

timelesstreasures@frontiernet.net

Come Visit Us:
February ~ "Quilt Across the Stage" Quilt Show and Expo
Stars of the North Shop Hop

April ~ Loon Country Shop Hop
August ~ Quilt MN Shop Hop
November ~ Holiday Extravaganza

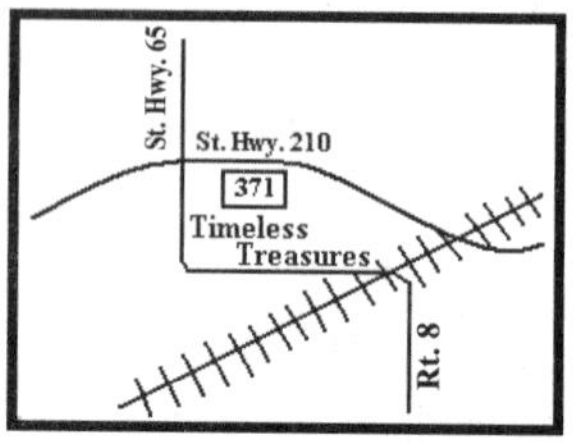

Grand Rapids, MN #12

Mon - Sat 9:30 - 5
Sun 11 - 4

ABC's of Quilting

10 NW 5th St. 55744
Junction of Hwy. 2 & 169
(218) 326-9661

Est: 2000
Located downtown in the Old Central School, built in 1898.

Over 3000 bolts of "Quilt Shop Only" fabrics.
Books, Patterns, Notions & Kits Available.
www.abcsofquilting.com

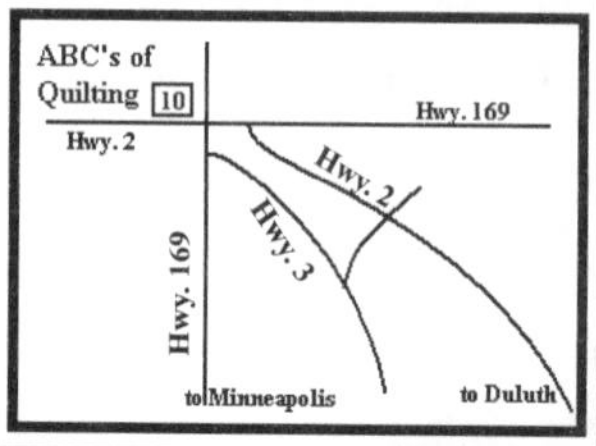

Nashwauk, MN #13

Mon - Fri 10 - 5:30
Sat 10 - 4

The Quilting Patch

602 4th St. 55769
(218) 885-3200
Owner: Janet Stram Est: 2007
quiltingpatch@mchsi.com
www.quiltingpatchonline.com

Fabrics, Books, Patterns, Quilting Supplies, Custom Quilts, Classes and Quilt Finishing. Finished Quilts, Bags & Kits

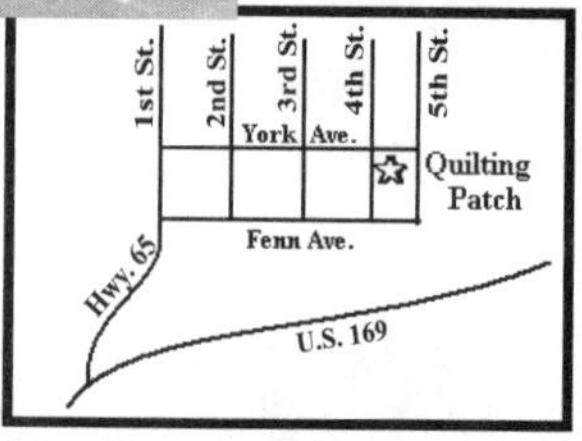

Deer River, MN #14

Mon - Fri 9 - 5
Sat 9 - 3

Heart to Hands Quilt Shop

509 Division St. 56636
(218) 246-2555 Fax: (218) 246-2066
Owner: Karen Holloway Est: 2003

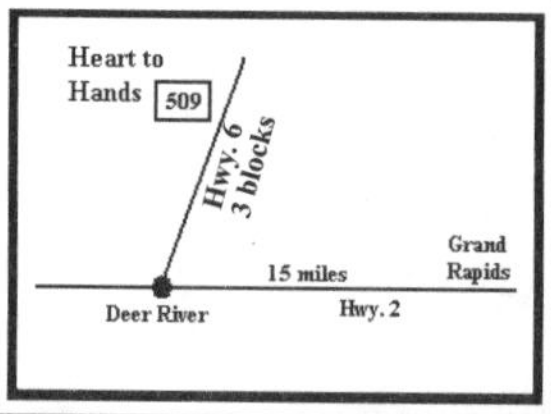

holloway@paulbunyan.net
www.hearttohandsquiltshop.com
3000+ bolts of 100% cotton fabrics from top manufacturers. Large selection of books, patterns and notions. Machine quilting available. Finished quilts for sale.

Walker, MN #15

Mon - Sat 9 - 5
Sun 11 - 4

FRONT PORCH QUILTS
613 Michigan Ave, PO Box 1316
Walker MN 56484
Jan Cyr * Jana Weise

218-547-1122

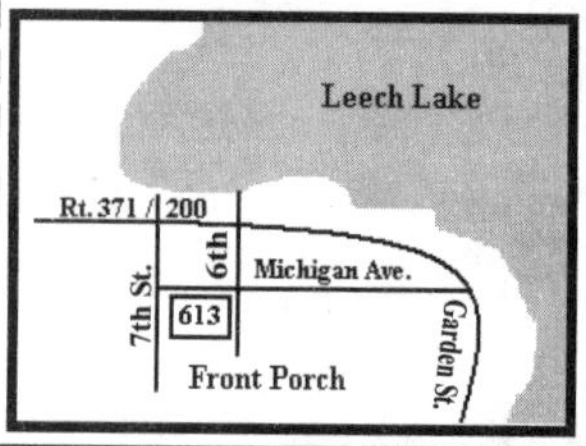

frontporchquilts@arvig.net
www.frontporchquiltshop.com
Your quilting resource near the shores of Leech Lake. Colorful selection of fabrics, patterns, books, notions, kits and many quilts on display.

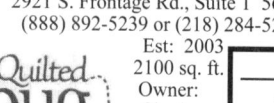

Park Rapids, MN #16

Mon - Sat 9 - 5

Monika's

210 S. Main 56470
(218) 732-3896
Owner: Monika Wilkins
Est: 1984 5000 sq.ft. 4000 Bolts
monikas@unitelc.com
www.monikasquiltshop.com
Large Selection of name brand fabrics, quilting, needlework, patterns, books, classes, and yarn for knitting and crochet available.

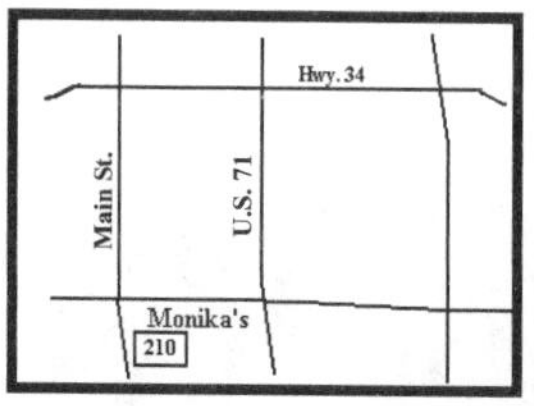

Moorhead, MN #17

Mon - Fri 10 - 6
Tu & W til 8
Sat 10 - 5
Summer Sat til 3

the Quilted Ladybug

2921 S. Frontage Rd., Suite 1 56560
(888) 892-5239 or (218) 284-5239
Est: 2003
2100 sq. ft.
Owner: Cheri Steenbock

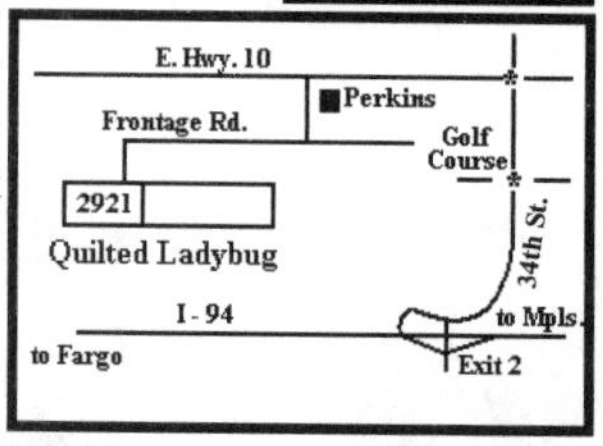

cheri@quiltedladybug.com
www.quiltedladybug.com
Look for the Red Roof!
Friendly help & advice FREE!

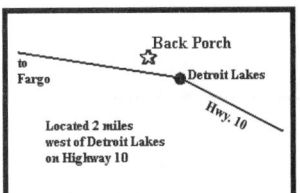

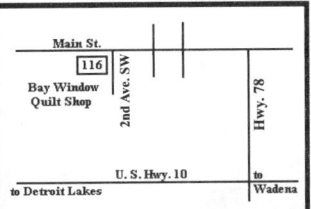

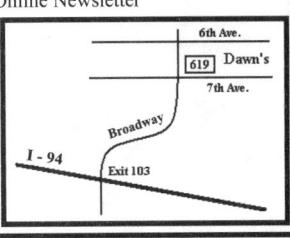

COUNTRY fabrics AND QUILTING

•We offer a wide variety of fabrics such as:

- Contemporary and Traditional fabrics
- Woven and Printed Flannels
- Batiks
- Brights
- Home Decor
- Minkee
- Baby Cottons and Flannels
- Novelties
- Seasonal
- Hand dyed Wool

baby lock · BERNINA CERTIFIED TECHNICIANS · Handi Quilter

hours:
M-F 9:30-5:30
Sa 9:30-4:00
Sun 11:00-3:00

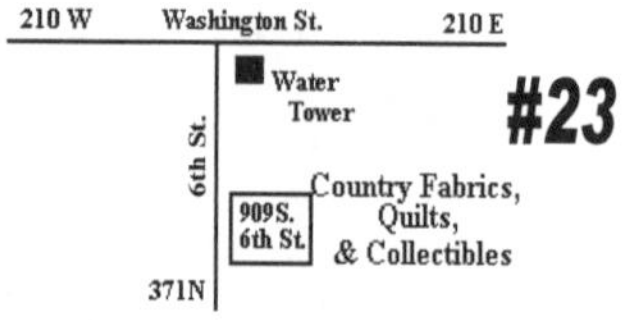

#23

909 south 6th st brainerd, mn 56401

www.countryfabricsandquilting.com phone: 218 829 7273

Colorz for Quilts

317 W. Washington St.
Brainerd, MN 56401
(218) 825-9101

Full service shop with inspiration for contemporary and traditional quilters. Large selection of batiks plus hand-dyes.

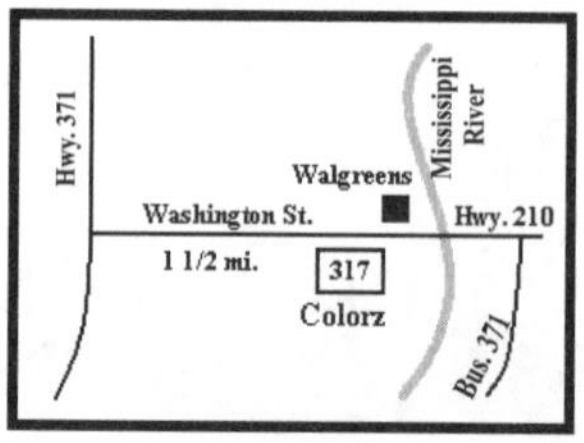

Owners: Susan Lommen & Karen DeVries
Monthly email Newsletter
colorzforquilts@gmail.com

Mon - Fri 10 - 5:30
Sat 10 - 4

Brainerd, MN #24

Pequot Lakes, MN #25

Mon - Sat 10 - 5

Mother Originals Quilt Shop

4284 Blueberrry Ln. 56472
(218) 568-6924
notheroriginals@tds.net
www.motheroriginalsquiltshop.com

We are a unique and cozy quilt shop tucked away in the beautiful Lakes Area. You'll find our shop to be filled with the finest quality quilting fabric, notions, books, ideas and inspiration. Knowledgeable staff with over 80 years of combined experience.

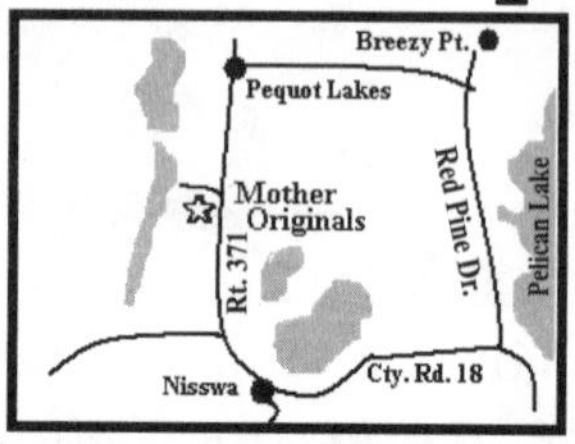

Jenkins, MN #26

Mon - Sat 10 - 5

The Quilter's Parlour QUILT SHOP 218.568.5777

34008 St. Hwy. 371
56472

Est: 2009
quiltersparlour@tds.net
www.quiltersparlourquiltshop.com
Online Newsletter with class schedule.
Everything for your quilting needs.

Wahkon, MN #27

Country Caboose Quilts
108 S. Main St.
P.O. Box 10, Wahkon, MN 56386
(320) 495-3658
ccquilting3@hotmail.com
900 sq.ft. 2500 Bolts
Online Newsletter

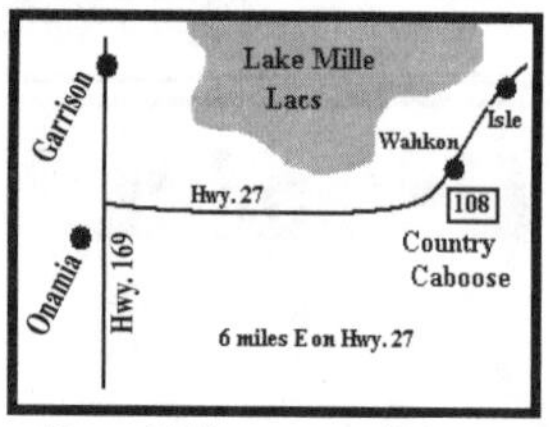

When life gives you scraps, make a quilt!

Combining small town charm and customer service, we carry a wide variety of fabrics, supplies, books and patterns.

Tues - Sun 10-5 Year Round

Sturgeon Lake, MN #28

Mon 12 - 6
Tues - Thur 10 - 6
Fri 10 - 6
Sat 9 - 4

Seams Like Home Quilt Shop

34079 Laketown Rd., Suite 6 55783
(218) 372-8886
Est: 2005 Online Newsletter
mbreegge@msn.com
www.seamslikehomequiltshop.com

Visit to see inspiring samples and displays; join a club; or take in a class in a bright, fun atmosphere.

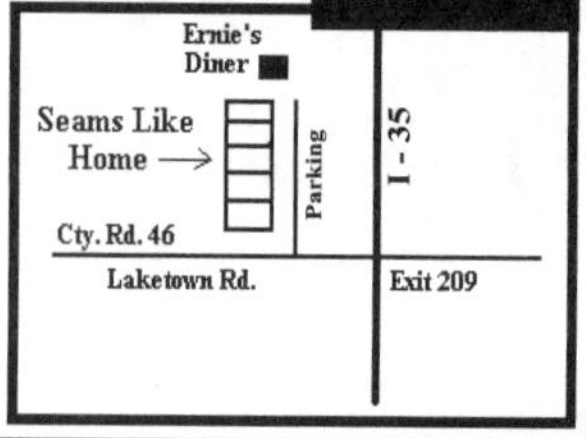

Foley, MN #29

Mon - Fri 10 - 6
Sat 10 - 3

Quilts ON BROADWAY

431 Dewey St.
P.O. Box 491 56329
(320) 968-9929

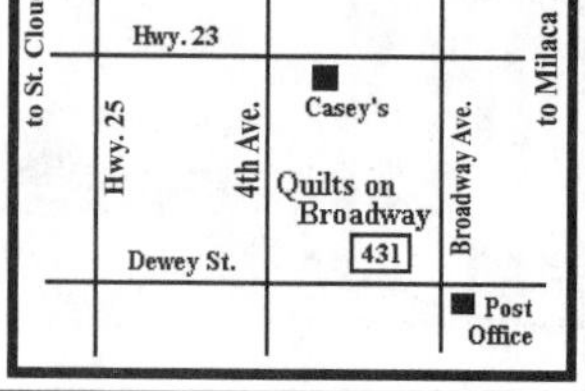

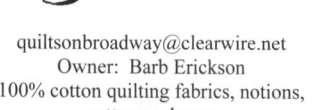

quiltsonbroadway@clearwire.net
Owner: Barb Erickson
100% cotton quilting fabrics, notions, patterns, classes

Rush City, MN #30

Mon - Fri 9 - 5
Sat 9 - 4

Fabrics Fashions and More

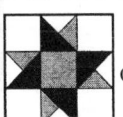

485 S. Dana, Box 21 55069
(320) 358-3693 Est: 1994
Owner: Virginia Thorn 1900 sq.ft.
vthorn@fabricfashions-more.com
www.quiltfabricandmore.com

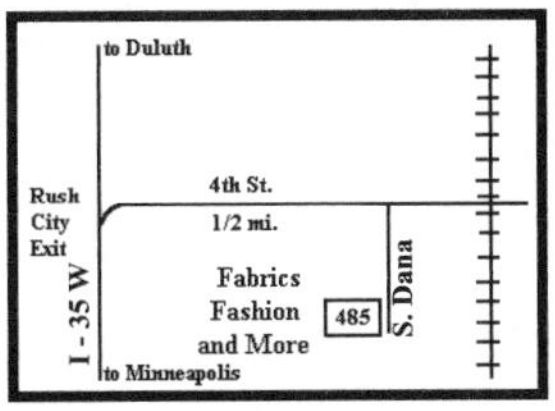

Well worth the stop! Fabrics, Books, Notions & more. Home of PFAFF Integrated Dual Feed. Authorized PFAFF Sales & Service.

Avon, MN #31

Mon - Fri 9 - 6
Sat 9 - 4

Aunt Annie's Quilts & Silks

109 Avon Ave. S, P.O. Box 359 56310
(320) 356-1061
Owner: Lucy Senstad
auntanniesquilts@aol.com
www.auntanniesquilts.com
Known for color assistance, enticing & unique fabrics, knowledgeable & helpful staff. Hand dyes, discharge dyed fabrics & gelatin prints.

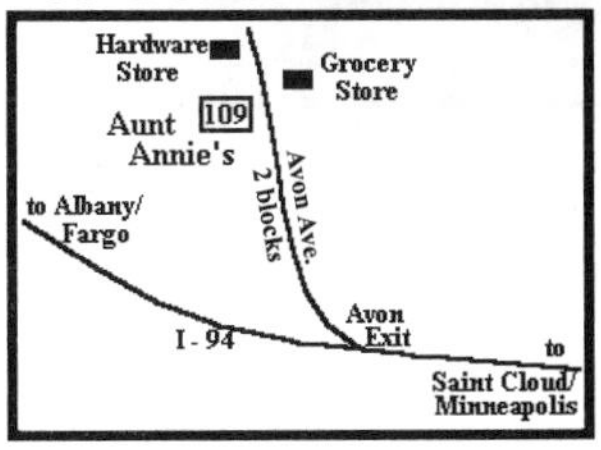

#32

Over 10,000 Bolts of Fabric

One of the largest Quilt Shops in the USA

- Over 10,000 Bolts of Cotton Fabric
- Patterns/Notions/Books
- Retreat Center — Sleeps 3-16
- Yarn

"Selected one of the top ten quilt shops in 2001by *American Patchwork & Quilting Magazine*"

Hundreds of samples and displays to Inspire You!

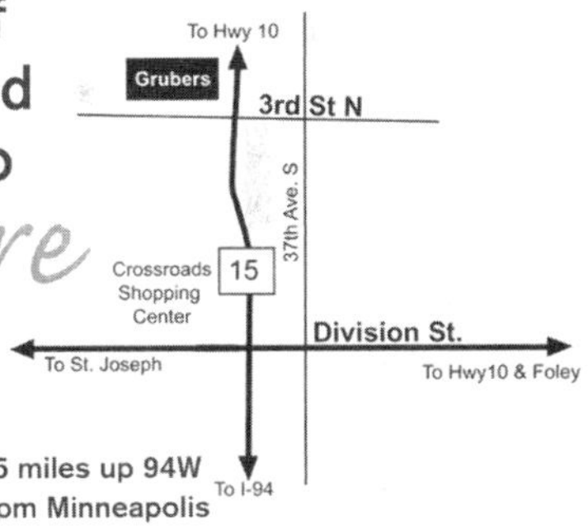

320-259-4360 or 1-877-778-7793

Only 75 miles up 94W from Minneapolis

Location: Hwy15 & 3rd St. | Waite Park, MN 56387

www.grubersquiltshop.com

Store Hours
Mon-Fri — 9:00 am-7:00 pm
Sat — 9:00 am-6:00 pm | Sun — Noon-5:00 pm

Paynesville, MN #33

Mon - Fri 10 - 5
Sat 10 - 4

Sweetwater cotton shoppe

122 W. James St. 56362
(320) 243-4436
www.sweetgirlstudio.wordpress.com
As the quilters candy store with the purple door, we have a large variety of Moda, Civil War, & reproductions.
Featured shop in Quilt Sampler 2010.

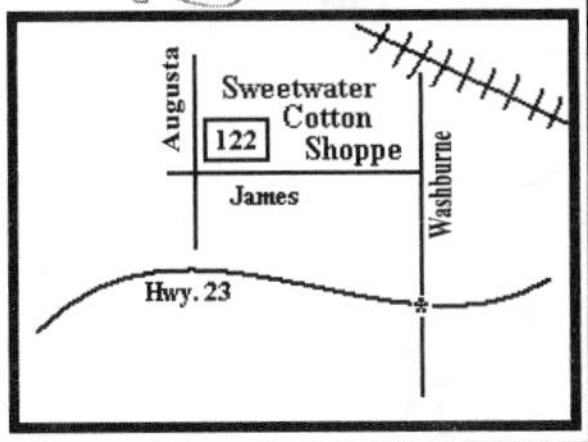

New London, MN #34

Mon - Sat 9:30 - 5

Flying Goose Quilt Shop

14 Main St. S 56273
(320) 354-3535
www.flyinggoosequiltshop.com

Vintage building with samples to inspire.
Handi-Quilter and BabyLock sewing machines.
Great gift, yarn and bead shops nearby.

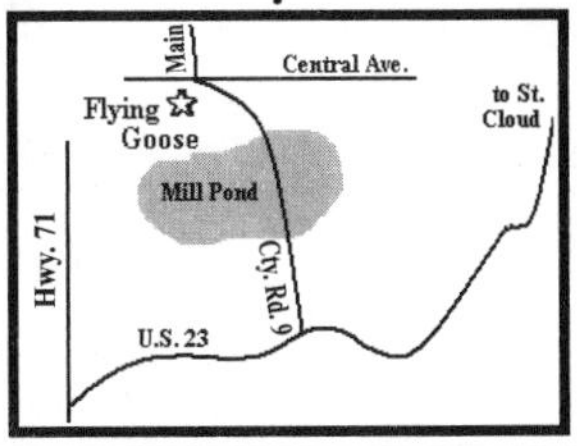

Litchfield, MN #35

Mon - Fri 9:30 - 5:30
Thur til 7
Sat 9 - 5
Sun 12:30 - 4

DeAnn's Country Village Shoppe, Inc.

115 N. Sibley Ave.
55355
(320) 693-9113
Owners: Jiggs & DeAnn Rothstein
Est: 1991

Quaint Quality Quilt Shop tucked inside a 5500 sq. ft. Gift and Home Décor Shop. Specializing in Moda Fabrics. Something for everyone --- everyday!!!

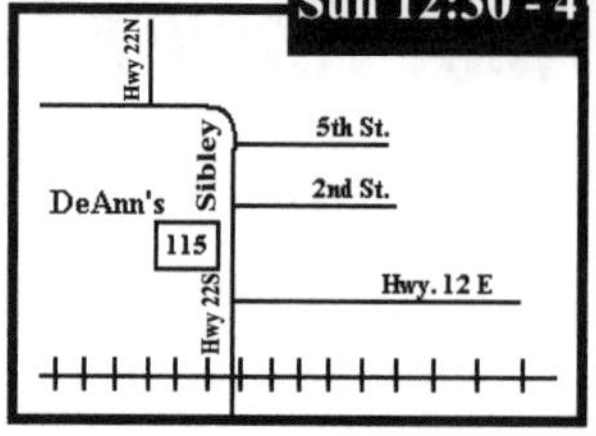

Kimball, MN #36

Mon - Fri 9 - 5
Sat 9 - 3

Gone to Pieces Quilt Shop

70 S. Main St., P.O. Box 186 55353
(320) 398-5300
Owner: Penny Callander Est: 2002
gonetopieces@meltel.net
www.gonetopiecesquiltshop.com

Carefully selected 100% cotton quilting fabric along with the latest books, patterns, notions and classes.
Machine quilting services available.

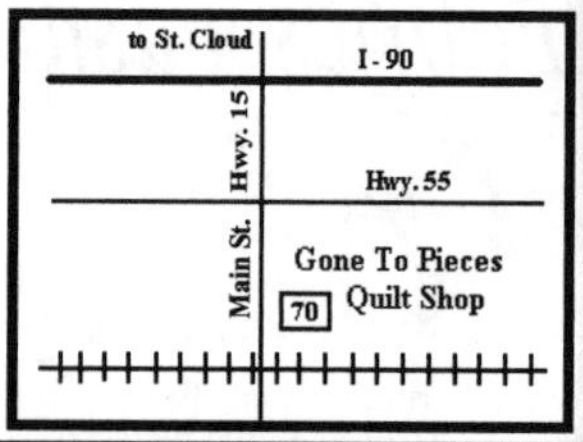

Elk River, MN #37

The Noble Quilter

Fabrics Books Notions Patterns Classes

19570 Holt Street NW
Elk River, MN 55330
763-633-4669
www.thenoblequilter.com

Come visit our warm and friendly shop that hosts something for everyone. Enjoy browsing through 1500 bolts of thoughtfully selected fabrics.
We also have a fine selection of notions, patterns and books. Customer service is our number one priority!

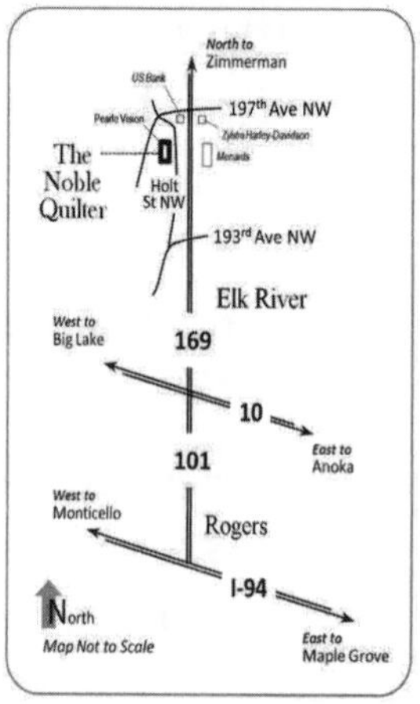

REGULAR STORE HOURS
Mon, Tue, Wed, Fri : 10am-5pm
Thu : 10am-7pm
Sat : 10am-4pm
Sun : Noon-4pm

Driving Directions:
Travel north on **169** to **Elk River.**
Turn left on **197th Ave NW.**
(Menards is on your right.)
We're located right next to Pearle Vision, which is next to Aldi grocery.

Forest Lake, MN #38

Silver Lane Quilting, Inc.

www.silverlanequilting.com

Exceptional Selection of
- ***Quality Quilting Cottons***
- ***Batiks - Flannels***
- ***Books - Patterns***
- ***Pre-packaged Kits***
- ***Essential Notions***
- ***Classes - Open Sewing***
- ***Clubs - Retreats***
- ***Gift Cards Available!***

Our shop also features:

Theresa's Quilt Studio

We offer **Classes and Hourly Rental** on our APQS Longarm.

Home of
Antler Quilt Design

quilt pattern company of an amazing young male designer, Doug Leko. Each pattern is an original creation by this high school student who has grown up quilting.

www.antlerquiltdesign.com

Our store is handicap accessible.

Spring Brooke Plaza
4869 - 208th Street North
Suite 102 and 104
Forest Lake, MN 55025
(651) 639-8800

Store Hours
* Sun Noon-4PM *
Mon 9-7
Tue, Wed & Thurs 9-6:30
Fri 9-7, Sat 9-6

Happy to open other hours for you, just call ahead!
Busses welcome.

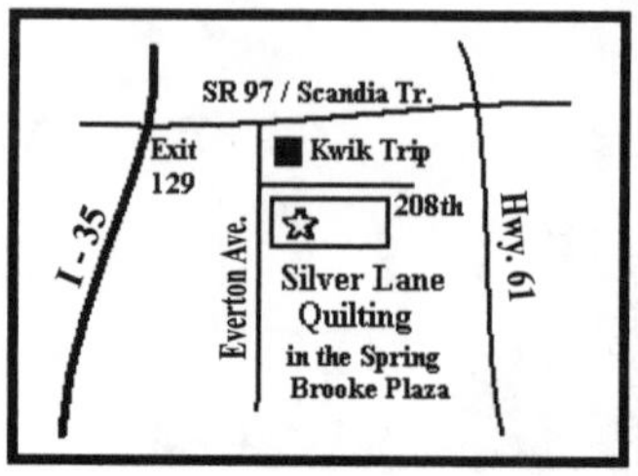

From I-35 take exit 129, drive east on SR97/Scandia Trail one-half mile to Everton Ave.

From Hwy 61 drive west on SR97/ Scandia Trail one and a half miles to Everton Ave.

GPS Coordinates to SLQ
N45°15.065' W93°00.507'

Bird Island, MN #39

Mon - Fri 9 - 5
Sat 9 - 3

Gathering Friends Quilt & Gift Shop

101 S. Main
P.O. Box 189 55310
(320) 365-4670

Owners: Deb Jacobs & Kathy Squibb
Est: 1998 3500 bolts
info@gatheringfriendsquiltshop.com
www.GatheringFriendsQuiltShop.com
Large selection of 100% cotton fabrics & flannels, gift items, quilting kits, original books and patterns.

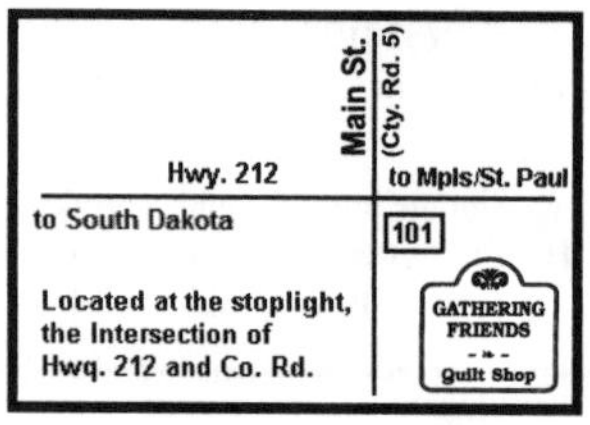

St. Peter, MN #40

Mon - Fri 9 - 5

St. Peter Woolen Mill

101 W. Broadway 56082
(507) 934-3734
spwoolen@hickorytech.net
www.woolenmill.com

Fabrics
Wool Processing & Batting
Machine Quilting

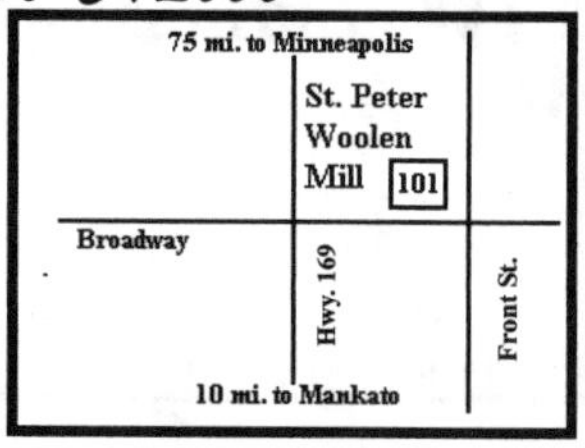

Quilting by the Hearth

**Tues - Fri 9 - 5
Sat 10 - 4**

Lisa Strawhacker
Proprietor
Est: 2004
Located in the 100 year old telephone building

This charming shop offers five rooms filled with over 3,000 bolts of quality 100% cotton fabric. We specialize in batiks and traditional cottons along with a large selection of flannel, Asian & 30's fabrics.

Our 'small town friendly' staff is always available to help. Relax in the fireplace room with coffee or tea.

208 Main St. South 55046
507-744-4284
lisa@quiltingbythehearth.com
www.quiltingbythehearth.com

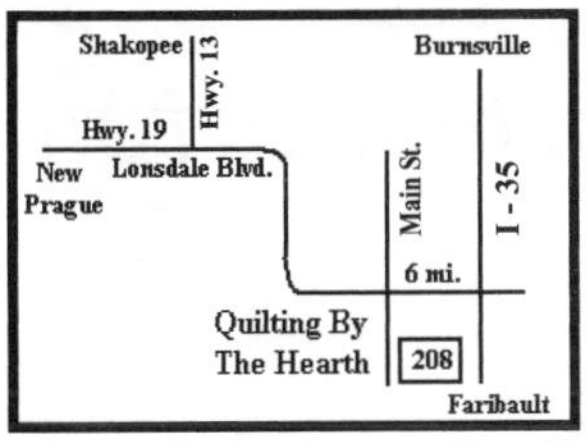

Exit I-35 for New Prague: Hwy 19

Lonsdale, MN #41

Northfield, MN #42

**Mon - Fri 9 - 5:30
Sat 9 - 4
Sun 12 - 4**

PJ's Fabric and Crafts

660 Professional Dr. 55057
(507) 301-3323 Fax: (507) 301-3324
Owner: Penny Roy Est: 2008
pjs@charterinternet.com
www.pjsfabricandcrafts.com
We carry quilting and apparel fabrics, fleece yarns, sewing notions and patterns.
We offer classes in sewing, knitting, quilting , hardanger and crocheting.
Our discount fleece is the best price anywhere.

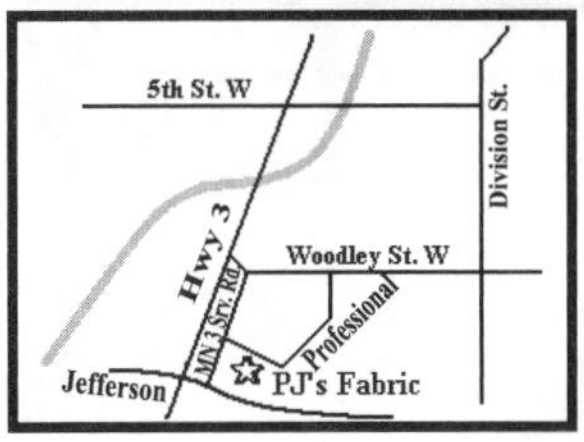

New Ulm, MN #43

**Mon - Fri 10 - 5
Sat 10 - 4**

106 S. Minnesota 56073
(507) 359-2896
www.spinningspoolsquiltshop.com
Owner:
Val Besser
Est: 2008
1200 bolts
Free Newsletter

Our trellised garden welcomes you into the ultimate of quilt shops. Let us help you 'spin' the creative quilter in you.

The Thimble Box

New Ulm, MN #44

10 N. Minnesota St. 56073
(507) 354-6721
www.thethimblebox.com

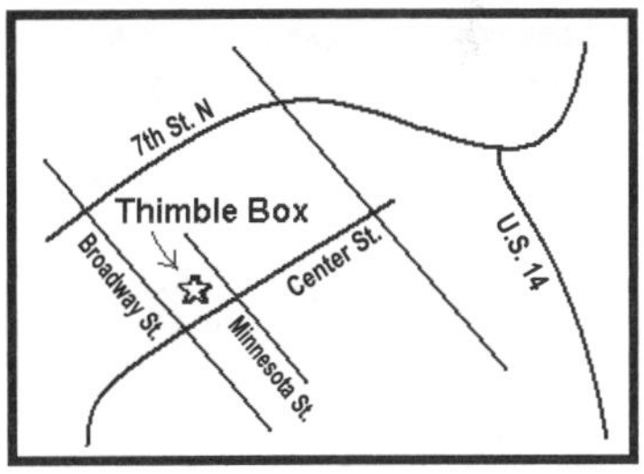

thimblebox@newulmtel.net
Owners: Maurice & Brenda Seidl

Mon - Fri
10 - 5
Sat 10 - 4

Visit the Thimble Box in Historic New Ulm with Friendly Staff and FUN events.

A large supply of flannels, homespuns, Batiks, 30's, Thimbleberries and 100% cotton fabrics are available.

RIVER CITY QUILTS

500 Raintree Rd. #35 At the Raintree Mall
(507) 625-8135
Owner: Sally Trask Est: 2000 2700 sq.ft. Over 4000 Bolts
www.rivercityquilts.com
Shop online 24/7
over 4,000 fabrics and 70+ Kits on our website

Mon - Thur 10 - 7 Fri 10 - 6 Sat 10 - 5 Sun 12 - 5

Our specialty is Kits!! Our friendly, Knowledgeable staff can help you with your next quilting project. We carry high quality quilting fabrics from Moda, RJR, Maywood, Timeless Treasures, Red Rooster, Hoffman, Quilting Treasures and more.

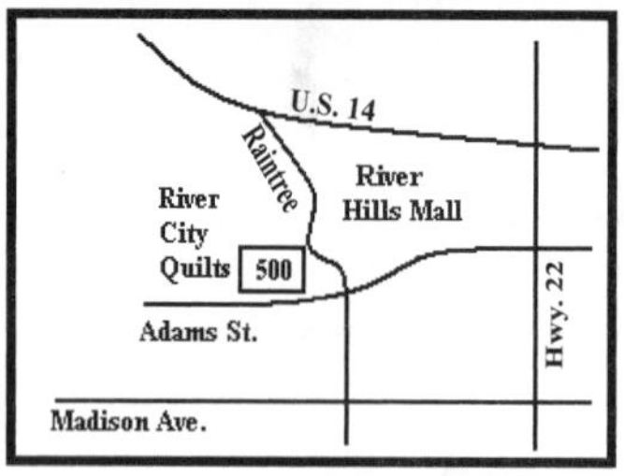

We love buses and have plenty of parking and shopping space.

Mankato, MN #45

Mankato, MN #46

Mon - Fri 10 - 6 Sat 9 - 4

FireFly Quilt Shop, Inc

1219 Caledonia St. 56001
(507) 344-0441
Owner: Janice Zernechel
Est: 2006 3000 sq.ft. 3000+ Bolts
www.fireflyquiltshop.com
We are known for our "Personal Friendly Service". Exceptional fabric selection! Inspiring Samples and many kits to choose from.

Owatonna, MN #47

Mon - Fri 9 - 5:30 Sat 9 - 4:30

The Cotton Patch

110 W. Broadway 55060
(507) 451-5979 Est: 1993 2000+ Bolts
Owner: Joan Correy
www.thecottonpatchquilts.com

Spacious, well-lit shop staffed by helpful, experienced quilters. An abundance of quality 100% cotton fabric & supplies for all your quilting needs. Located on downtown's charming Central Park, just 1 mile off I - 35 and 5 minutes from Cabela's.

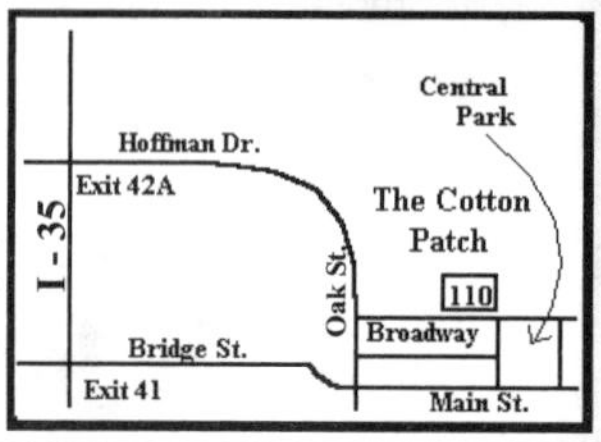

"Where all the pieces come together!"

Lake City, MN #48

RATHER BEE QUILTING

116 S. Washington
55041
(651) 345-3958
Owners: Janet Bruce & Judy Rutz
Est: 1998

Mon - Sat 9 - 5
Closed Sundays

Known for beautiful fabrics, innovative classes and friendly, knowledgeable help.

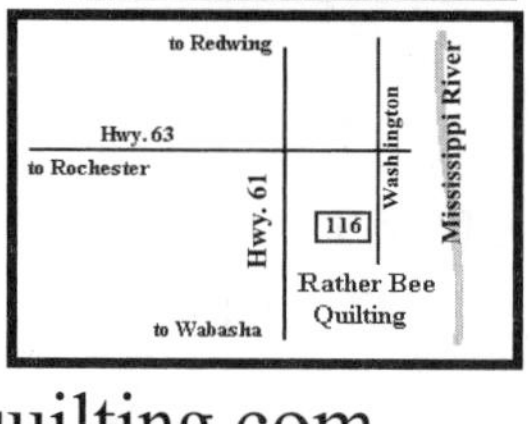

www.ratherbeequilting.com

Spring Valley, MN #49

Quilter's Quarters

616 N. Broadway
Spring Valley 55975
(507) 346-2555
cmarzolf@centurytel.net
www.quilters-quarters.net
Est: 2004 4000 sq.ft.
3500+ Bolts

Fabric, patterns, books, and notions; all to inspire beautiful new projects for you. Fun and friendly atmosphere. Great customer service.

Mon - Fri 9:00 - 5:30
Thur 9 - 7 Sat 9 - 2

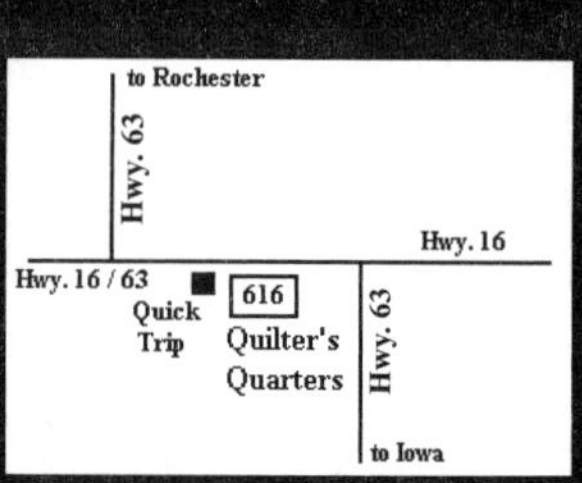

FOURTH & MAIN FABRICS

#50

HOURS

T-W 10:00-5:00
Th 10:00-7:00
F 10:00-5:00
S 10:00-4:00
Su 12:00-4:00

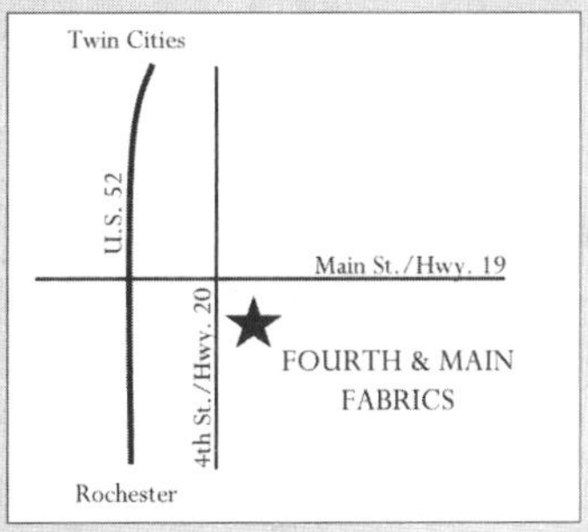

Located in a fully renovated, 19th Century, main street storefront, Fourth and Main Fabrics provides a bright and elegant setting in which to peruse a distinctive selection of fabrics, patterns, and quilting and sewing supplies and notions.

Meticulously detailed cabinets and display counters, hardwood floors, tin ceilings, chandeliers, custom lighting and expansive windows create an atmosphere that makes shopping at Fourth and Main a memorable experience.

The quality of the selection is equal to the atmosphere. We carry:

- A wide selection of distinctive fabrics, including such lines as Free Spirit, Moda and Civil War;
- Designs from such leading companies as Amy Butler, Perkins Dry Goods and Atkinson;
- A full line of DMC embroidery floss; and
- A great selection of sewing supplies and notions, including just what you are looking for in zippers, buttons and ribbons.

103 S. Fourth Street • Cannon Falls, Minnesota 55009 • 507.263.7000
WWW.FOURTHANDMAINFABRICS.COM

SINCE 1982

CALICO HUTCH

A UNIQUE QUILTING EXPERIENCE

20520 810th Ave.
Hayward, MN 56043
(507) 377-1163
ckmatson@smig.net

www.calicohutchquiltshop.com

Mon - Thur 9-5,
Fri 9-9 Sat 9-5

Hayward, MN #51

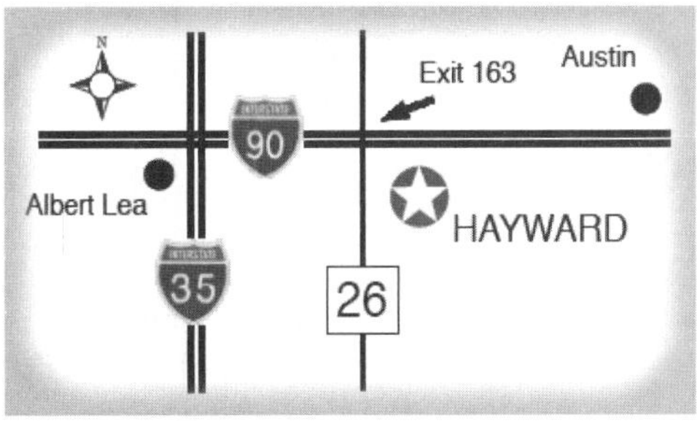

- 4000 bolts of top-quality fabric
- Hand-dyed wool
- Books, patterns and notions
- Hundreds of gorgeous samples
- Friendly, knowledgeable staff
- Abundant parking just outside the door

The Quilting Cupboard

DREAM. CREATE. INSPIRE.

1627 N Broadway Rochester, MN 55906
507-281-9988

Mon-Fri: 9am-5pm Sat: 9am-2pm

Let us inspire you with our beautiful & unique fabrics & kits! Also, check out our large selection of quilting gifts! We are located 1 mile north of downtown in River Center Shopping Mall (next to Wendy's) on the west side of Broadway. Home of designers & authors Ann Kisro & Susan Kisro! See you soon!

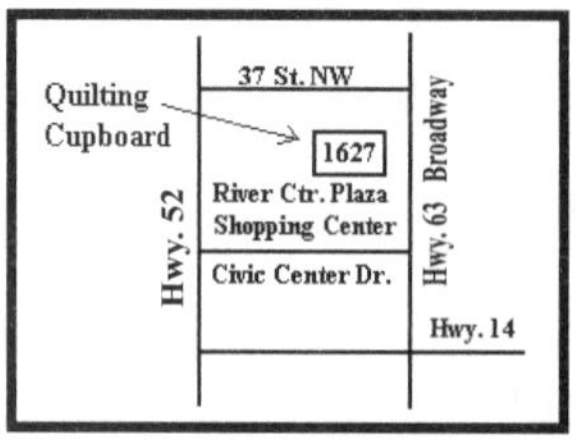

FREE FRONT DOOR PARKING!

SHOP ONLINE 24/7...

www.thequiltingcupboard.com

Stewartville, MN #53

All in Stitches

Quilting & Fiber Arts

Mon - Fri 9:30 - 6
Thur til 8 Sat 9:30 - 4

Lots of batiks and Civil War era prints, traditional fabrics, beautiful florals, flannels and children's prints. Wonderful hand-dyed wools and embellishments. PFAFF sewing machines and Tin Lizzie long-arm machines. Check our website for current class lists.

501 N. Main St. 55976
(507) 533-8897
sandy@allinstitchesmn.com
Owner: Sandy Evans
Est: 2007
2500 sq.ft. 3000 bolts
Free Online Newsletter

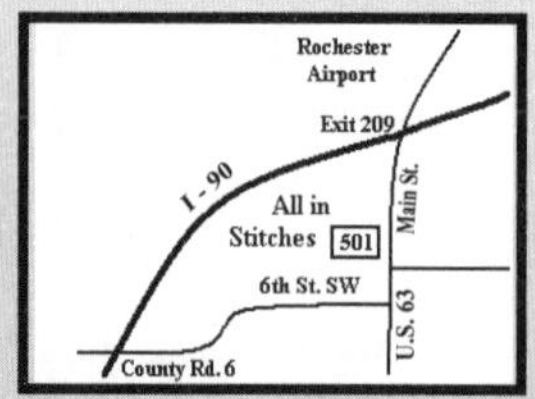

Located just 1 1/2 miles off I-90 on Hwy. 63

www.allinstitchesmn.com

Racine, MN #54

Mon - Fri 10 - 5
Sat 10 - 4

301 Hwy. 63 South 55967
(507) 378-7677
Fax: (507) 378-7678

Pine Needles

sew good for your life

Owners: Marcia Nagel & Suzie Diemer
Est: 2007 3600 sq.ft. 4000 bolts
info@pnqs.net www.pnqs.net
Bernina, APQ, Accuquilt, loads of fabric & publications and the best customer service around! 2 locations! The area's largest quilt shop!

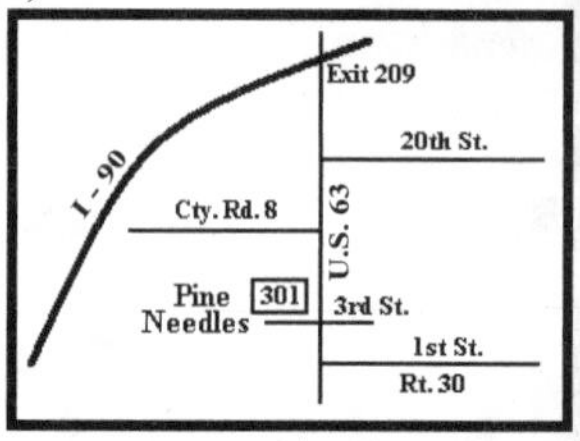

Sherburn, MN #55

Mon - Fri 10 - 5
Wed til 7
Sat 9 - 4
Sun Nov. - Palm Sun 1 - 4

Old Alley Quilt Shop

115 N. Main St. (Hwy. 4) P.O. Box 143
(507) 764-4088 56171
oldalleyquiltshop@frontiernet.net
www.oldalleyquiltshop.com
Over 2500 bolts of fabric (including great flannels & batiks!), patterns, notions, classes, long arm quilting service. Located in a renovated bowling alley on the main street of Sherburn, south of the I-90 Hwy. 4 exit!! See store or website to sign up for our classes!

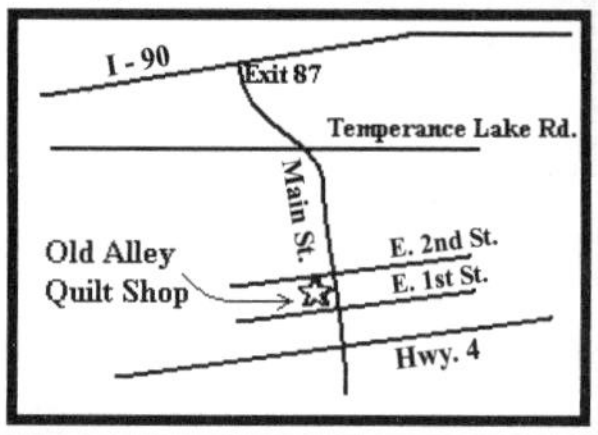

CRAFTY CORNER

Quilt & Sewing Shoppe

Est. 1982 Owners: Ken & Zuby Jansen
Hours: Mon-Thurs 9am - 5:30pm • Fri. 9am - 7pm • Sat 9am - 4pm
1820 Oxford St. Worthington, MN 56187
507-372-2707 • 1-800-SEW-MORE
craftycorner@iw.net • www.craftycornerquiltandsewingshoppe.com

We sell 100% Cotton Fabrics
7,221 Bolts in Stock
Patterns • Notions • Classes

Worthington, MN #56

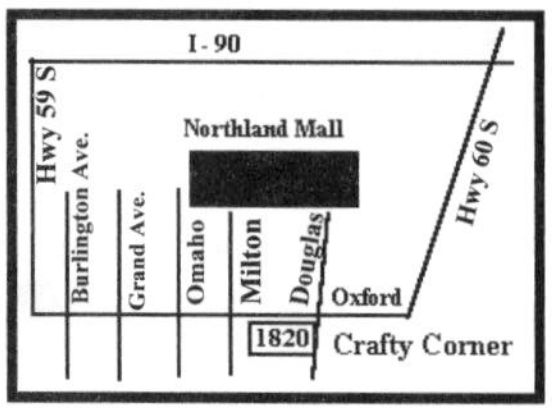

BERNINA Authorized Sales & Service
Singer Featherweights in Stock
Vacuums: Oreck • Lindhaus • Fuller

Windom, MN #57

Mon - Fri 9 - 5
Sat 9 - 3

Prairie Quilting

1293 Hale Place 56101
(507) 831-2740
Owner: Kay Peterson
prairiequilting@windomnet.com

Unique Quilt Shop location next to feed store. Great selection of 100% cotton fabrics, books, patterns, and notions. Quilts for sale.

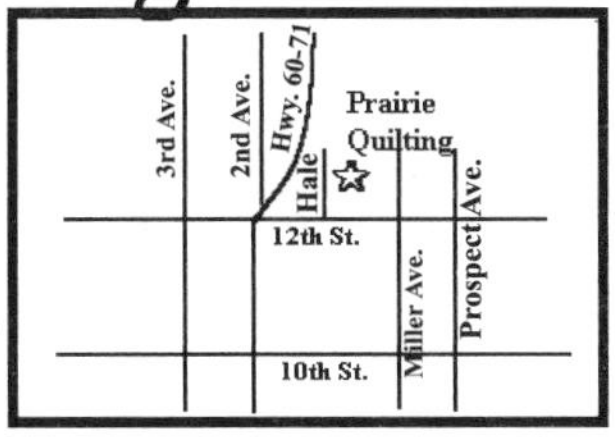

Luverne, MN #58

Mon - Fri 9 - 5
Thur til 7
Sat 9 - 12

The Sewing Basket
Husqvarna VIKING

204 E. Main St. 56156
(507) 283-9769
Owner: Barbara Bork Est: 1979
info@luvsewingbasket.com
www.luvsewingbasket.com

We carry a beautiful variety of quilting fabrics, plus books and supplies.
Authorized Husqvarna Viking sales & service.

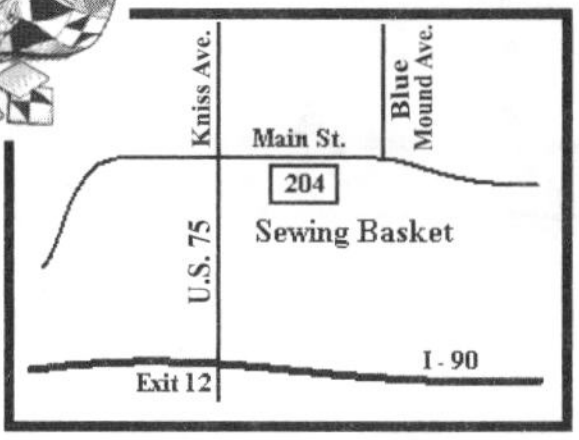

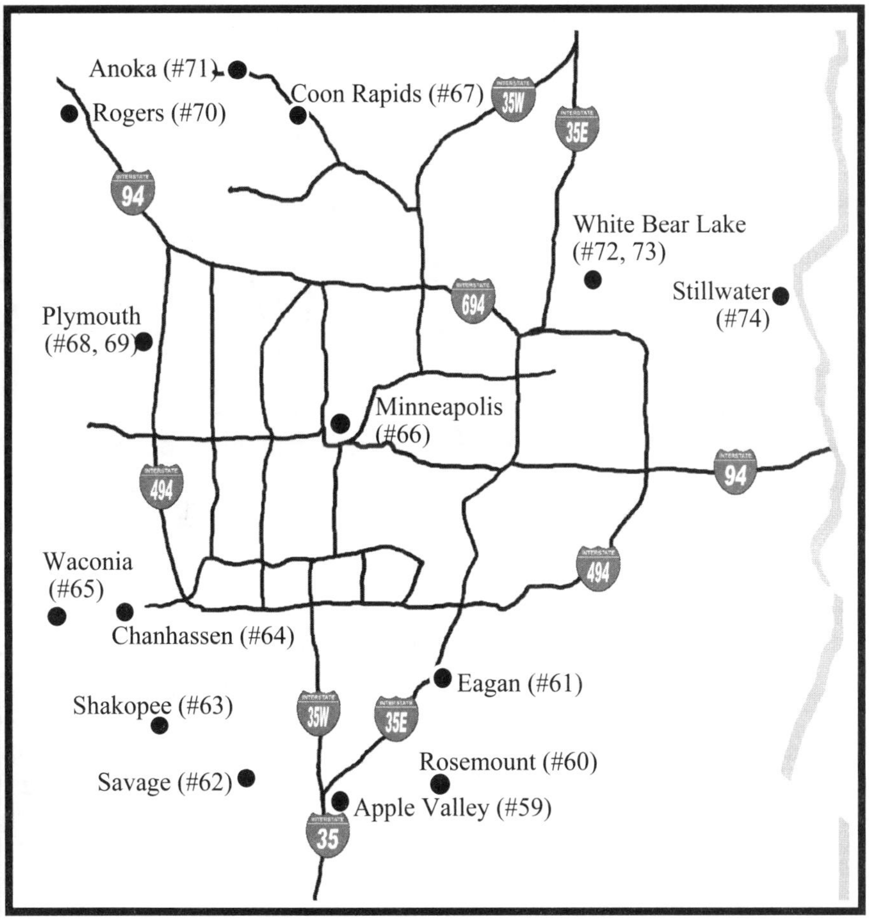

MINNEAPOLIS ST PAUL AREA

Shops #59 - 74

16 Featured Shops

Apple Valley, MN #59

Mon - Thur 10 - 8
Fri 10 - 6
Sat 10 - 5
Sun 12 - 4

Fabric Town

7655 W. 148th St. 55124
(952) 432-1827
Owner: Patti Donahue-Peltz

fabrictown2@aol.com
www.fabrictown.com
We are your friendly neighborhood quilt shop. Located in the Time Square Shopping Center. Large selection of 100% cottons, 100's of books and patterns, quilting related gifts, 100's of finished sample to inspire. Friendly and knowledgeable staff to help you.

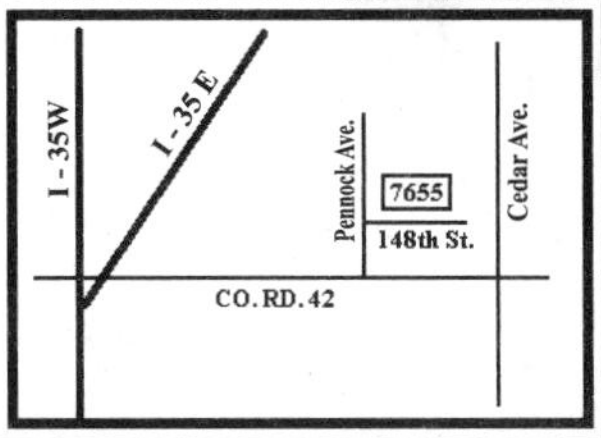

Rosemount, MN #60

Mon - Fri 10 - 8
Sat 10 - 6
Sun 12 - 5

Quilter's Haven — For All Your Quilting Needs

14760 S. Robert Tr. Ste. C 55068
(651) 322-7071 Est: 2002
www.quiltershavenmn.com
quilthav@frontiernet.net
Jean Graham
2000 sq. ft.
2000+ Bolts
Bernina Dealer

Come visit our new location, you will find a unique fabric selection including reproduction prints and florals from the 1800's, batiks, novelties, brights and flannels. Quilter's Haven also has an extensive selection of wool and patterns for rug hooking, etc.

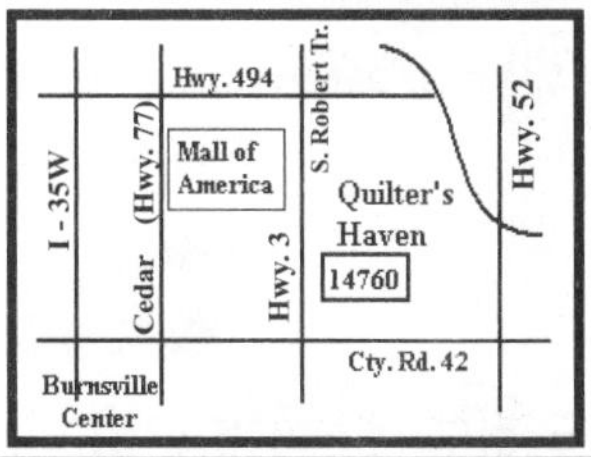

EAGAN, MINNESOTA

#61

QUILT COVE

1960 Cliff Lake Road, Suite 134 • Eagan, MN 55122

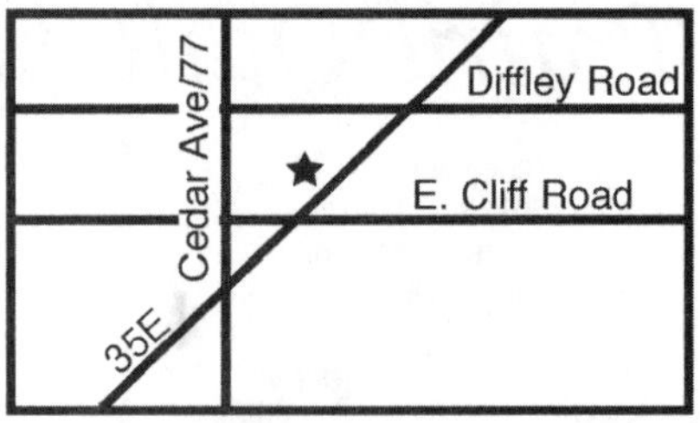

Est: 1989 | 3800 sq. ft. | 4000 bolts

Located just 5 miles south of the Mall of America (off 35E and Cliff Road between Target and Cub)

Bus Parking Available

Close to airport

A Quilt Shop offering the finest in cotton fabrics, books, patterns and quilting supplies. Classes and Gift Certificates Available.

Contact us at mail@quiltcove.com with questions

Visit our website at quiltcove.com

651-452-8891

Hours:
Mon - Fri • 10:00-8:30
Saturday • 10:00-5:00
Sunday • 1:00-5:00

Specializing in computer assisted quilting for the next generation of quilters.

Quilt Yourself

Gammill® QUILTING SYSTEMS

Creative Studio

5733 Egan Dr. (Co. Rd. 42)
(One block east of Savage Water Tower)
O'Connell Square, Savage, MN 55378
(952) 440-3321 info@quiltyourself.com

Est: 2006
2250 sq.ft.

Savage, MN #62

www.quiltyourself.com

Stitch perfect designs using our in-store Gammill. You choose to complete your quilts or we can do it for you. Completing them yourself is easy once you have taken our required Certification Class. In this class you will receive one-on-one instruction so that you will be ready to quilt your own quilts. Once certified you can rent our machines by the hour. Our Quilt For You Service is priced per square inch based on the type and density of quilting. We also carry a large selection of wide backing material & Quilters Dream Batting. Free Newsletter

Tues - Fri 10 - 5 Sat 10 - 2

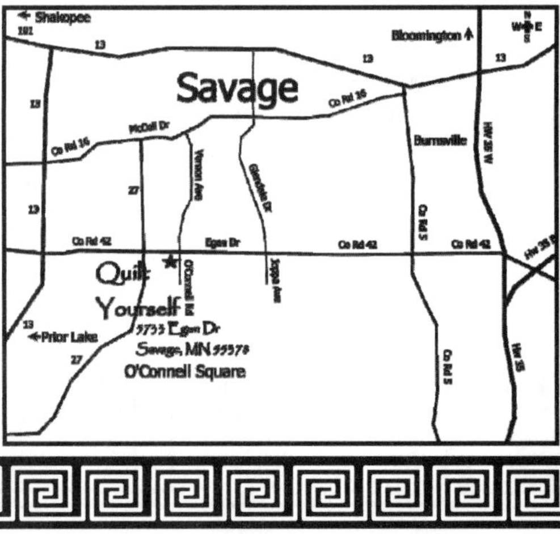

Eagle Creek Quilt Shop

A Top Ten Shop ~ Quilt Sampler Magazine 2003 Best of Quilt Sampler Magazine 2007

Located in an enchanting turn of the century railroad depot. We feature a wide array of fabric from traditional to batiks. Eagle Creek is also a paradise for wool connoisseurs and punch needle enthusiasts.

Just 20 min. from the Mall of America

Hours:
Mon. to Sat. 10~5
Tues. 10~8

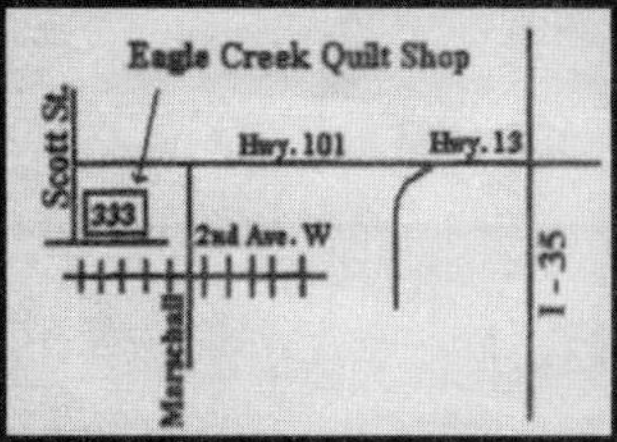

333 2nd Ave. W, Shakopee, MN 55379 ~ 952-233-3774 www.eaglecreekquiltshop.com

Chanhassen, MN #64

The Sampler
a quilt shop and more...

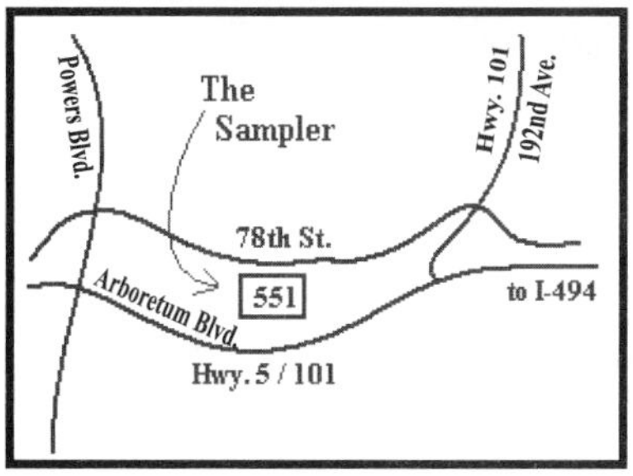

America's headquarters for
KAFFE FASSETT
fabrics!!

We are colorful, trendy, full of inspiration which you see when you come in the door. Gorgeous quilts hung everywhere!

Located in the metro area & easy to find!
You are always welcome. COME SEE US!

Also.....
Phillip Jacobs
Brandon Mably
Amy Butler
Alexander Henry
Art Gallery
Free Spirit
Heather Bailey
Bali Batiks
Beautiful Hand dyes, and so much more!!!

HOURS:

M-W-Fri-Sat. 10-5pm
Tue & Thur 10-8pm
Sun.-12-4pm

BERNINA

952-934-5307
551 W. 78th St.

866-994-8318
PO Box 532

www.the-sampler.com
Chanhassen, MN 55317

Waconia, MN #65

Mon - Fri 10 - 5
Thurs til 7 Sat 10-4

Heavenly Patchwork Quilt Shop

109 S. Elm St., Suite 200 55387
(952) 442-8677

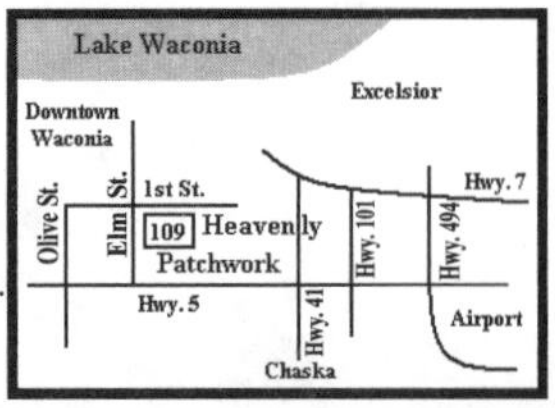

www.heavenlypatchworkquiltshop.com
Owner: Kay R. Derner Est: 2003
Located in downtown Waconia; Corner of Elm St. and 1st St. - across from St. Joseph Catholic Church in the brick building.

Minneapolis, MN #66

Mon - Sat
9:30 - 5

Glad Creations, Inc.

3400 Bloomington Ave. S 55407
(612) 724-1079 Fax: (612) 276-0275
Est: 1976 1500 sq.ft. 3000 Bolts
nancy@gladcreationsquilts.com
www.gladcreationsquilts.com

Great selection of fabrics, books and quilting supplies. Original line of patterns for rotary cut machine pieced quilts.

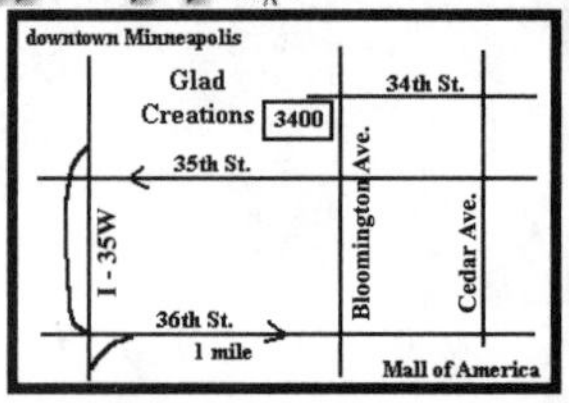

Coon Rapids, MN #67

Coming through the Twin Cities?
Take a 15-mile detour north...

Whatever you're looking for, you'll find yourself at home.

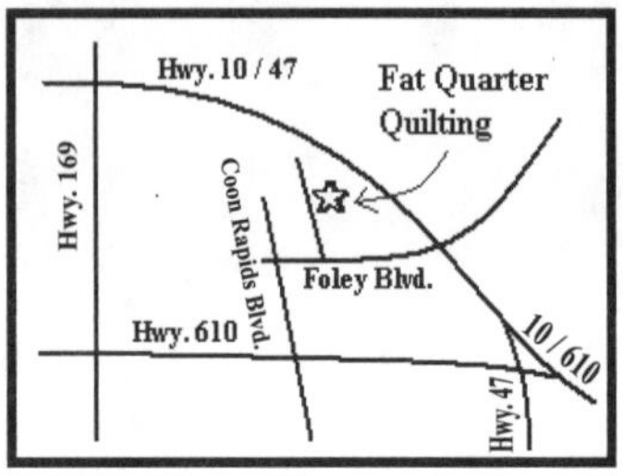

FAT QUARTER QUILTING

455 99th Avenue NW Coon Rapids, MN 55433
Phone: 763-576-8809
Mon-Fri 9-8; Sat 9-5; Sun 12-5

Check out our website for color photos, driving directions and new fabric lines!

Don't miss our fun, bright shop with a friendly staff and 3500 bolts of girly, sophisticated, funky, batik, 1930's fabric and more in cotton and flannel!

WWW. FATQUARTER.NET

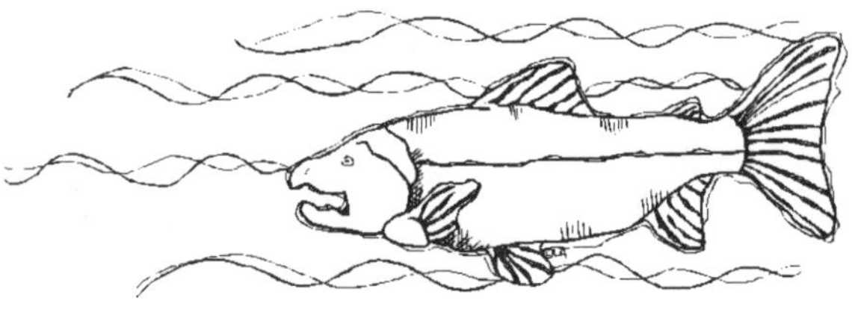

Plymouth, MN #68

FOUR SEASONS QUILTS

4172 Lancaster Ln. 55441
(763) 557-5899
www.fourseasonsquiltsmn.com
Owner: JoAnn Atkins
Est: 2003 2600 sq.ft. 5000+ Bolts

Mon - Thur 10 - 9
Fri 10 - 5:30
Sat 9 - 5 Sun 12 - 5

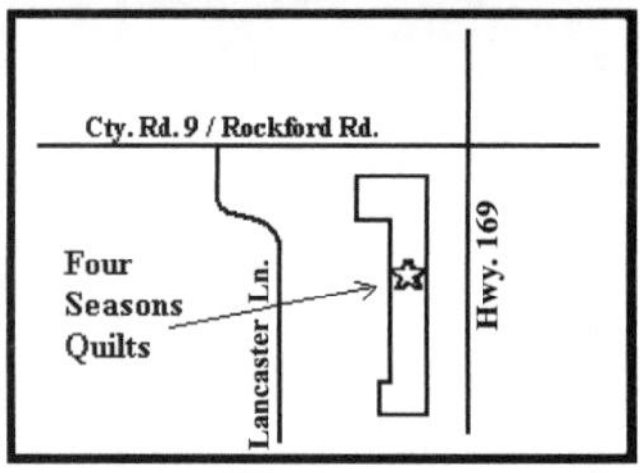

A warm & friendly quilt shop providing a wide variety of 100% cottons including reproductions and Batiks, Thimbleberries, Moda, Robert Kaufman, Michael Miller, Benartex and a large selection of books, patterns, kits & notions.

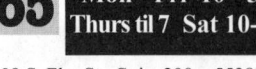

Blue Bamboo

Quality Quilting Supplies
myBlueBamboo.com

Specializing in Japanese fabrics, Bali Batiks, One Block Wonder fabrics, Paper Piecing kits and patterns by Jacqueline de Jong of Be Colourful (Holland)

763-744-1105
or 800-323-1105
5,000 bolts in coordinated groupings

- Unique Kits
- Asian
- Moda
- Japanese Obi
- Obi Samples
- Yukata Fabric
- Hoffman
- Kona Bay
- Kaufman
- Lakehouse
- Clothworks
- In The Beginning

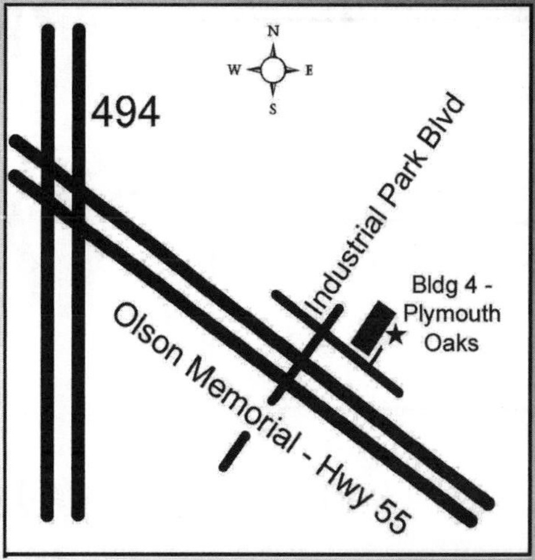

12865 Industrial Park Blvd
Plymouth, MN 55441

Directions: From 494 going north or south, exit at Hwy 55. Go east 0.7 mile to Industrial Park Blvd. Turn left. Take immediate right on frontage road. Take left at #4 Plymouth Oaks.

Plymouth, MN #69

Quilted Treasures

A Fresh Look at Traditional Quilting

Est. 1998 • 4500 bolts
Owner: Mary Wilberg
Busses Welcome

Better Homes and Gardens Quilt Sampler Featured Shop

QT Blogs
Pieces of Work
Sew Domestic
Classroom Chatter

*We specialize in **quilt kits of all styles**, over 100 beautiful quilt samples, and inspirational displays throughout the shop*

www.quiltedtreasures.net

Shop Hours:

M - F	10 - 5
Th	10 - 8
Sat	10 - 4
Sun	12 - 4

Just 2.2 miles from Cabelas!

TO CABELAS FROM SHOP: Cross Hwy. 101 on 141st Ave. Right on Rogers Drive (near Walgreens). Left on South Diamond Lake Road. Right on George Weber Drive.

Quilted Treasures of Rogers
14178 Northdale Blvd.,Rogers, MN 55374
763.428.1952
info@quiltedtreasures.net
www.quiltedtreasures.net

Rogers, MN #70

Anoka, MN #71

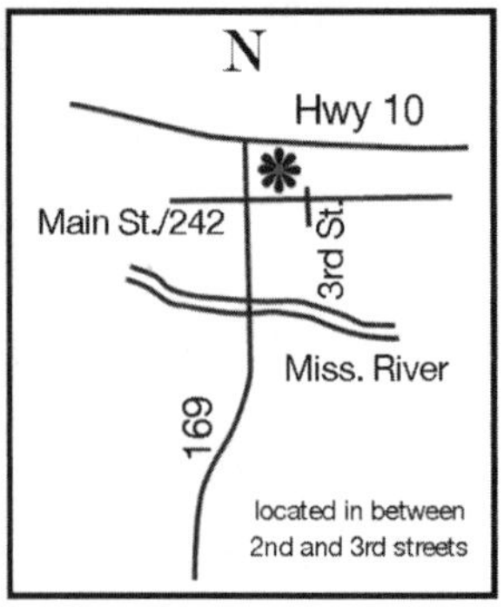

Millie P's Quilt Shop

Hours:
Mon - Fri :
9 am - 7 pm
Sat : 9 am - 5 pm
Sun : 11 am - 4 pm

✱ 3,800 square feet ✱ 2,800 bolts of fabric and growing ✱ Gammill Long Arm

A unique quilt store located in the heart of historic Downtown Anoka. Millie P's Quilt Shop was founded in January of 2010. We have fabric that will please all quilters, including brights, batiks, children's fabrics, and 30's prints. In addition to fabric, notions and classes, we offer Gammill Statler long-arm certification and rental. Stop in and get inspired. Our goal is to "continue the creative education started many generations before us ". Our customer-focused staff will help make your experience positive – you will definitely want to stop back.

219 E. Main Street • Anoka, MN 55303 • www.MilliePs.com • 763.421.0367

White Bear Lake, MN #72

Bear Patch Quilting Co.

2001 TOP TEN QUILT SHOP

A Quilter's Heaven filled with 100% cotton fabrics, patterns, books, notions, and lots of samples and great ideas to inspire your creativity. Meeting all your quilting needs with year-round classes, stitchery clubs and a friendly, knowledgeable staff.

651-429-1039
2199 Fourth St. 55110
e-mail: bearpqc@aol.com
Est: May 1997
4600 sq.ft. 5000+ Bolts

Mon - Thurs 9 - 9
Fri & Sat 9 - 5
Sun 12 - 4
call for summer hours

www.bearpatchquilting.com

Be sure to visit our Bernina sewing center across the street!

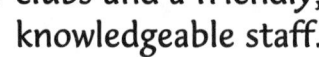

Nothing Sews Like A Bernina. Nothing.
BERNINA®

Sewing center phone 651-429-6500

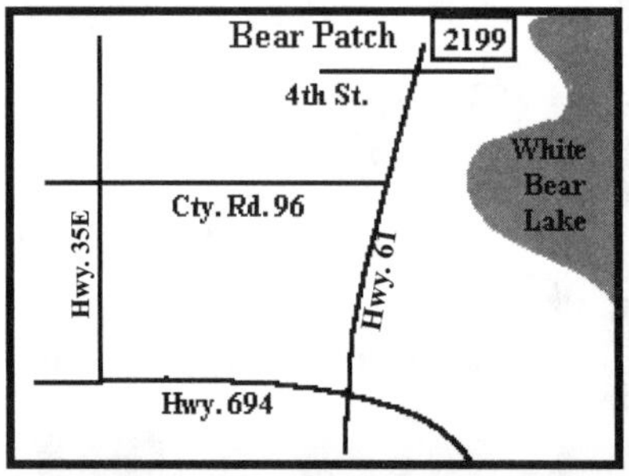

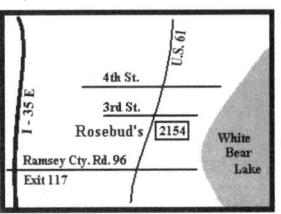

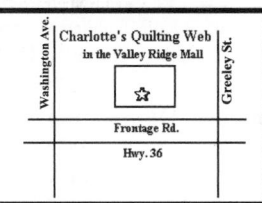

Minnesota Quilt Shops

Alexandria **Dawn's Quilt Shop, 619 Broadway St**
320-763-7011 **See ad #22, page 289**
Alexandria Heartland Sewing Co., 1804 S. Broadway 320-763-6739
Alexandria Stitchin' Post, 612 Broadway 320-763-3400
Alexandria Community Vacuum & Sewing, 1321 Broadway St. 320-762-1412
Anoka **Millie P's Quilt Shop, 219 E Main St**
763-421-0367 **See ad #71, page 302**
Apple Valley **Fabric Town, 7655 W. 148th St.**
952-432-1827 **See ad #59, page 297**
Avon **Aunt Annie's Quilts & Silks, 109 Avon Ave. South**
320-356-1061 **See ad #31, page 291**
Bagley Gram's House Of Quilts, 22906 320th St. 218-694-3000
Barrett Quilting Etc., 308 2nd St. 320-528-2620
Beaver Bay **Quilt Corner,**
Beaver Bay Mini Mall, 1007 Main St.
218-226-6406 **See ad #7, page 286**
Bemidji **Emily's Country Cottage, 705 Washington Ave. S**
218-444-6387 **See ad #5, page 286**
Bemidji **Willow Wood Market, 23621 County Rd 9**
218-759-2310 **See ad #4, page 286**
Bemidji Quilting Keepsakes, 8732 Country Club NE 218-751-5954
Bemidji J & B Sewing, 26070 County 9 218-751-2475
Bird Island **Gathering Friends Quilt Shop, 101 S. Main St.**
320-365-4670 **See ad #39, page 292**
Blaine Calla Lily Quilt Shop, 10904 Baltimore St. NE 763-784-7166
Blue Earth Quilts on First, 205 E. 1st St. 507-526-3666
Brainerd **Colorz for Quilts, 317 W. Washington St.**
218-825-9101 **See ad #24, page 290**
Brainerd **Country Fabrics and Quilting, 909 S. 6th St.**
218-829-7273 **See ad #23, page 290**
Cannon Falls **Fourth & Main Fabrics, 103 S. Fourth St.**
507-263-7000 **See ad #50, page 295**
Chanhassen **The Sampler, 551 W. 78th St.**
952-934-5307 **See ad #64, page 299 & 414**
Chisholm Quilt Shop of Chisholm, 116 W. Lake St. 218-254-1700
Clara City Shades of the Past Quilt Shop, 211 SE 1st 320-847-4040
Coon Rapids **Fat Quarter Quilting, 455 99th Ave NW Ste 240**
763-576-8809 **See ad #67, page 300**
Dawson A Simpler Thyme, 669 6th St. 320-769-2656
Deer River **Heart to Hands Quilt Shop, 509 Division St.**
218-246-2555 **See ad #14, page 288**
Deer River Needle Nook, 37584 County Road 129 218-246-2794
Detroit Lakes **Back Porch Quilts, 24047 US Hwy. 10 W**
218-844-6540 **See ad #19, page 289**
Duluth **Kelly J's Sewing Center & Quilt Shop**
6140 Jean Duluth Rd.
218-724-8781 **See ad #10, page 288**
Duluth Creations Quilt Shop, 2904 W 3rd St 218-628-1687
Duluth Quilters Coop, 319 N. Central Ave. 218-628-2900
Duluth Hannah Johnson Fabrics, 5825 E. Superior St. 218-464-0339
Eagan **Quilt Cove, 1960 Cliff Lake Rd., Suite 134**
651-452-8891 **See ad #61, page 298**
East Grand Forks **Quilter's Eden, 223 DeMers Ave**
218-773-0773 **See ad #2, page 286**
Elk River **The Noble Quilter, 19576 Holt St NW**
763-633-4669 **See ad #37, page 292**
Elk River Cottage Quilts & Fabrics, 16860 Hwy. 10 NE 763-241-1490
Fergus Falls The Quilter's Cottage, 1701 W. Lincoln Ave. 218-739-9652
Floodwood **Hingeley Road Quilting, 11284 Hwy. 2**
218-476-3139 **See ad #9, page 287 & 193**
Foley **Quilts on Broadway, 431 Dewey St.**
320-968-9929 **See ad #29, page 290**
Forest Lake **Silver Lane Quilting, 4869 - 208th St. N.**
651-639-8800 **See ad #38, page 292**
Fosston **Red Rooster Quilts, 209 2nd St. NW Ste 5**
218-435-1662 **See ad #3, page 286**
Fosston Best Friends Quilting, 808 Mark Ave N 218-435-2087
Garfield **Common Threads Quilt Shop, 101 Sanstead E**
320-834-2563 **See ad #21, page 289**

Grand Marais Crystal's Log Cabin Quilts, 1100 W. Hwy. 61 218-387-3177

Grand Rapids ABCs of Quilting, 10 NW 5th St. Ste 103
218-326-9661 See ad #12, page 288

Hackensack Piecemakers Quilt Shop, 313 Hwy. 371
218-675-6271 See ad #18, page 289

Hayward Calico Hutch, 20520 810th Ave.
507-377-1163 See ad #51, page 295

Hibbing Quilts Around the Corner, 12150 W Hwy. 169 218-263-9078

Hoffman Nuts & Bolts Quilt Shop, 213 1st St. N 320-986-2447

Hollandale The Seed Room, 103 Central Ave. S 507-889-6351

International Falls Quilters Corner & Gift Shop, 309 3rd St. 218-285-2080

Iron Terri's Treasures, 8679 S. Iron Bowl Ln.
218-744-1935 See ad #8, page 286

Jenkins Quilters Parlour Quilt Shop, 34008 State Hwy 371
218-568-5777 See ad #26, page 290

Kimball Gone To Pieces Quilt Shop, 70 S. Main St.
320-398-5300 See ad #36, page 292

Lake City Rather Bee Quilting, 116 S. Washington
651-345-3958 See ad #48, page 294

Lake Crystal Northern Treasures Quilt Supply, 133 S Main 507-317-5229

Litchfield DeAnn's Country Village Shoppe,
115 N. Sibley Ave.
320-693-9113 See ad #35, page 292

Lonsdale Quilting By The Hearth, 208 Main St. South
507-744-4284 See ad #41, page 293

Luverne The Sewing Basket, 204 E Main
507-283-9769 See ad #58, page 297

Mankato River City Quilts, 500 Raintree Rd., Ste 35
507-625-8135 See ad #45, page 294

Mankato Firefly Quilt Shop, 1219 Caledonia St.
507-344-0441 See ad #46, page 294

Marshall Fabrics Plus, 307 W. Main St. 507-537-0835

McGregor Timeless Treasures, 371 E. State Hwy. 210
218-768-2556 See ad #11, page 288

Merrifield K Dee Quilt Shop, 21755 Cty. Rd. 3 218-833-0176

Minneapolis Glad Creations Inc., 3400 Bloomington Ave. S.
612-724-1079 See ad #66, page 300

Minneapolis SR Harris Fabric Outlet, 8865 Zealand Ave. N 763-424-3500

Minneapolis Cia's Palette, 4155 Grand Ave S. 612-823-5558

Minnesota Lake Heart's Desire, Inc. 206 4th Ave. 507-462-3810

Montgomery Quilter's Dream, 116 1st St. S. 507-364-5130

Monticello Little Mountain Quilt Shop, 219 W. Broadway 763-295-3777

Moorhead The Quilted Ladybug, 2921 S. Frontage Rd.
218-284-5239 See ad #17, page 288

Nashwauk The Quilting Patch, 602 4th St.
218-885-3200 See ad #13, page 288

New London Flying Goose Quilt Shop, 14 N. Main St. South
320-354-3535 See ad #34, page 291

New Ulm The Thimble Box, 10 N. Minnesota St.
507-354-6721 See ad #44, page 293

New Ulm Spinning Spools Quilt Shop, 106 S. Minnesota
507-359-2896 See ad #43, page 293

Northfield PJ's Fabric and Crafts, 660 Professional Dr.
507-301-3323 See ad #42, page 293

Oklee The Oklee Quilt Supply, 205 Main St. 218-796-5151

Owatonna The Cotton Patch, 110 W. Broadway
507-451-5979 See ad #47, page 294

Park Rapids Monika's, 210 S. Main
218-732-3896 See ad #16, page 288

Paynesville Sweetwater Cotton Shoppe, 122 W. James St.
320-243-4436 See ad #33, page 291

Pequot Lakes Mother Originals, 4284 Blueberry Ln.
218-568-6924 See ad #25, page 290

Perham Bay Window Quilt Shop, 116 2nd Ave. SW
218-346-7272 See ad #20, page 289

Pine River JJ's Trading Post, 218 Barclay Ave. 218-587-2369

Pipestone Downtown Hobby Shop, 115-117 West Main 507-825-4309

Plymouth Four Seasons Quilts, 4172 Lancaster Ln.
763-557-5899 See ad #68, page 300

Plymouth Blue Bamboo, 12865 Industrial Park Blvd.
763-744-1105 See ad #69, page 301

Princeton Cole's Country Treasures, 105 N. Rum River 763-389-0680

Racine Pine Needles Quilt Shop, 301 Hwy. 63 S
507-378-7677 See ad #54, page 296

Rochert Cotton Hive, 33075 S. Cotton Lake Rd. 218-847-7080

Rochester The Quilting Cupboard, 1627 N. Broadway
507-281-9988 See ad #52, page 296

Rochester Quilts Galore, 357 Elton Hills Dr. NW 507-288-2220

Rochester Westbrock Quilting, 1815 75th St. Northwest 507-289-8219

Rogers Quilted Treasures, 14178 Northdale Blvd.
763-428-1952 See ad #70, page 301 & 204

Roseau Quilt S'more, 209 2nd Avenue NE
218-463-3867 See ad #1, page 286

Rosemount Quilter's Haven, 14680 S. Robert Trail
651-322-7071 See ad #60, page 297

Rush City Fabric, Fashions & More, 485 S. Dana
320-358-3693 See ad #30, page 291

Savage Quilt Yourself, 5733 Eagan Dr. Co Rd. 42
952-440-3321 See ad #62, page 298

Shakopee Eagle Creek Quilt Shop, 333 2nd Ave W.
952-233-3774 See ad #63, page 299

Sherburn Old Alley Quilt Shop, 115 N. Main St., Hwy 4
507-764-4088 See ad #55, page 296

Silver Bay Behind the Seams Quilt Shop, 5715 Hwy. 1 218-226-3390

Spring Valley Quilter's Quarters, 616 N. Broadway
507-346-2555 See ad #49, page 294

St. Charles Amish Market Sq., I - 90 & Hwy 74, 507-932-5907

St. Paul Treadle Yard Goods, 1338 Grand Ave. 651-698-9690

St. Peter St. Peter Woolen Mill, 101 West Broadway
507-934-3702 See ad #40, page 292

Stewartville All In Stitches, Inc., 501 N. Main St.
507-533-8897 See ad #53, page 296

Stillwater Charlotte's Quilting Web, 1330 W. Frontage Rd.
651-430-1333 See ad #74, page 303

Sturgeon Lake Seams Like Home Quilt Shop,
34079 Laketown Rd.
218-372-8886 See ad #28, page 290

Thief River Falls Quiltingly Yours, 212 Parkview St. 218-681-6780

Tower North Country Quilts, 303 Main St.
218-753-4600 See ad #6, page 286

Virginia Woodward's, 1425 S. 12th Ave. 218-741-1744

Waconia Heavenly Patchwork Quilt Shop, 109 S. Elm St.
952-442-8677 See ad #65, page 300

Wahkon Country Caboose Quilts, 108 S. Main St.
320-495-3658 See ad #27, page 290

Waite Park Gruber's Quilt Shop, 310 4th Ave. NE
320-259-4360 See ad #32, page 291

Walker Front Porch Quilts of Walker, INC,
613 Michigan Ave. W.
218-547-1122 See ad #15, page 288

Warroad Northern Exposure Quilts, 210 Main Ave. NE 218-386-4809

White Bear Lake Bear Patch Quilting Co., 2199 4th St.
651-429-1039 See ad #72, page 302

White Bear Lake Rosebud's Cottage, 2154 3rd St
651-426-1885 See ad #73, page 303

Windom Prairie Quilting, 1293 Hale Pl.
507-831-2740 See ad #57, page 297

Worthington Crafty Corner Quilt & Sewing Shoppe,
1820 Oxford St.
507-372-2707 See ad #56, page 296

Minnesota Quilt Shows

15 Shows

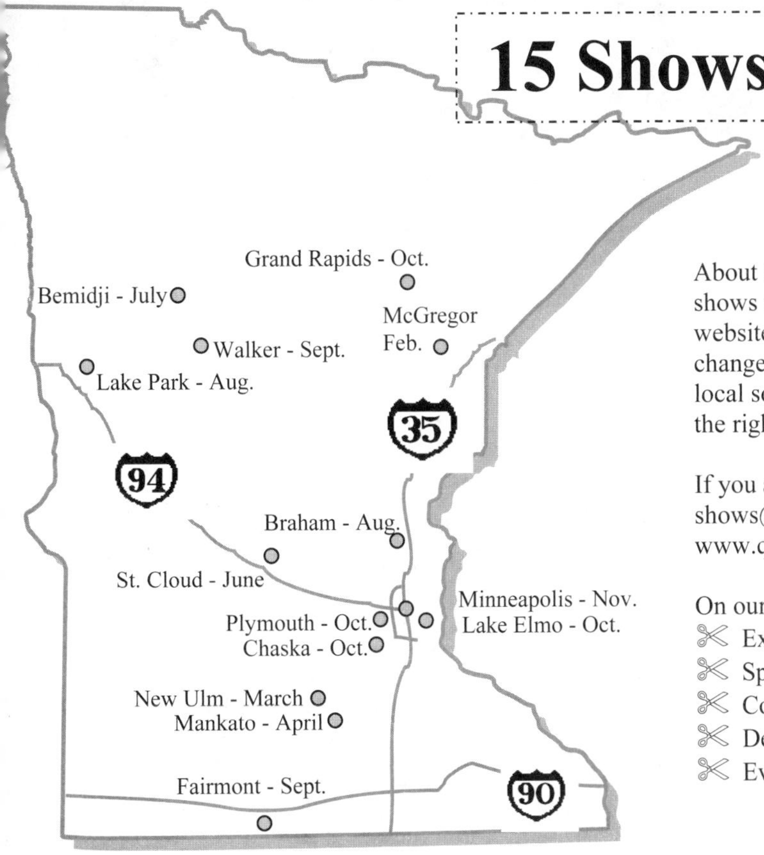

About Shows: We are listing only the very basic information about shows that happen on a regular schedule here. Please check out our website for more details on each show. Also this information tends to change quite often so please verify the event with our website or a local source before you venture far. Or if you're in the right area at the right time, give it a shot.

If you are a show organizer, please keep us updated on your event.
shows@quilterstravelcompanion.com
www.quilterstravelcompanion.com

On our website you will also find:
- Exact dates (when we have them)
- Sponsor Information
- Contact Information
- Description of Event
- Events happening on a one-time basis

Month	City	Schedule	Show	Location with address
February				
	McGregor	Annual, 2nd Sat. in February	Timeless Treasures	McGregor High School Auditorium, 148 S. 2nd St.
March				
	New Ulm	Even Years, 4th Fri & Sat in March	Prairie Piecemakers Quilt Guild	DAC, 15 N. State St.
April				
	Mankato	Odd Years, 3rd weekend in April	Deep Valley Quilters Guild Show	National Guard Armory, 100 Martin Luther King
June				
	St. Cloud	Annual, 2nd weekend in June	Minnesota Quilters Inc. Show & Conference	St. Cloud Civic Center, 10 Fourth Avenue N.
July				
	Bemidji	Odd Years, 3rd Fri & Sat in July	Quilts on Lake Bemidji Quilt Show	Evangelical Free Church, 115 Carr Lake Rd. (N. of Hwy. 2/71 on Washington)
August				
	Braham	Annual, 1st Friday in August	Hands All Around Quilters Show	Braham City Hall, 320 S. Broadway
	Lake Park	Annual, 3rd Saturday in August	Garden Quilt Show and Tea	Private Gardens, 4020 4th St.
September				
	Fairmont	Odd Years, 3rd Fri & Sat of September	Prairie Star Quilt Guild Show Bethel	Evangelical Free Church, 1125 S. State St.
	Walker	Even Years, 3rd Fri & Sat in September	Harvest Gatherings Schoolhouse for Quilters	Northern Lights Casino Hotel & Event Center, Junction of Hwy. 200 & 371
	Walker	Odd Years, 3rd Fri & Sat in September	North Woods Quilters Show	Northern Lights Casino Events Ctr, Hwy. 200 & 371 S
October				
	Chaska	Even Years, usually 2nd Fri & Sat of October	Fall Splendor of Quilts	Chaska Community Center, 1661 Park Ridge Dr.
	Plymouth	Odd Years, 1st Saturday in October	Women of the West Quilt Guild Show	Plymouth Creek Center, 14800 34th Ave. N
	Lake Elmo	Even Years, 2nd weekend in October	Quilted Treasures Quilt Show	Hooley Hall, Washington Cty. Fairgrounds, 40th St. - CO 14
	Grand Rapids	Even Years, 3rd Fri & Sat in October	Loon Country Quilter's Quilt Show	Itasca Community College Gym, 1851 E. Hwy. 69
November				
	Minneapolis	Annual, 4th Thur - Sat of November	Original Sewing & Quilt Expo	Minneapolis Convention Center, 1301 2nd Ave. S

MISSISSIPPI

5 Featured Shops

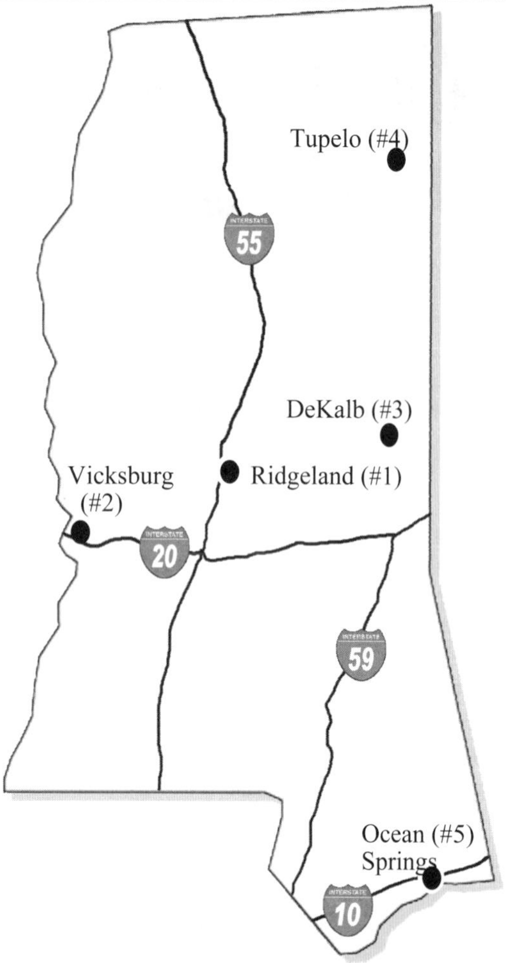

Phone: 601-991-2120
Fax: 601-991-2123
ann@berninasewingetc.com
www.berninasewingetc.com

Ridgeland, MS #1

Bernina Sewing, Etc.

665 Pear Orchard Rd., Ste. 104
Ridgeland, MS 39157

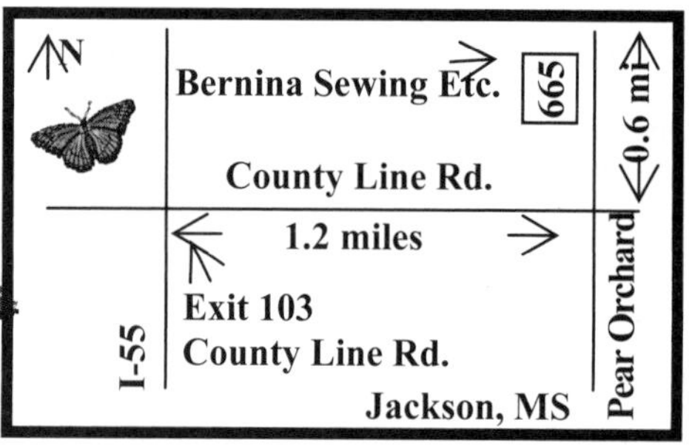

- **Authorized Bernina Dealer**
- **Quilting fabric**
- **Quilting classes**
- **Quilting books and patterns**
- **Notions**
- **Embroidery supplies & designs**
- **Threads & embellishments**

BERNINA

Mon-Fri 9 - 5
Sat 9 - 3
Sun Closed

Directions to BSE:
From I-55: Head east on County Line to Pear Orchard and turn left (north). BSE is located 0.6 miles from County Line Rd. on the left at the corner of Pear Orchard and Towne Center Road.
From the Spillway: Come across the spillway onto Lake Harbor Rd. Turn left at Pear Orchard Rd. (south). BSE is in the second building from the Ridgeland post office, on the right at the light.

Stitch-N-Frame

Established 1983

A Quilter's Paradise

The largest quilting shop in Mississippi makes it worth your trip to come to Vicksburg!

Come visit us in our new 6000 sq. ft. location.

Owners Kay & Mark Elliot invite you to stop by and take a test drive on any or all of the Gammill longarm machines, you'll be glad you did!

We carry a full line of long arm supplies in addition to Jim Shore collectables and Laurel Burch fashion accessories. All the major fabric manufacturers are represented among our 10,000 bolts of 100% cotton fabrics. We have a large selection of 30's Reproductions and Civil War Collections, along with patterns, kits, Blocks of the Month, notions and ideas galore!

Custom machine quilting, machine sales and service; quilting classes are available as well as quilting machine time rental. Join the on-line newsletter to learn about our Thursday Specials.

Gammill® QUILTING SYSTEMS

Statler Stitcher

Authorized Independent Gammill Dealer

Husbands, come play on our machines or enjoy our cozy husband waiting area.

Bus Tours Welcome

Vicksburg, MS #2

Mon - Sat 9 - 5:30

31 Willow Creek Dr.
Vicksburg, MS 39183
Toll Free: (877) 634-1462
Phone: (601) 634-0243
Fax: (601) 634-0287
stitch-n-frame@att.net

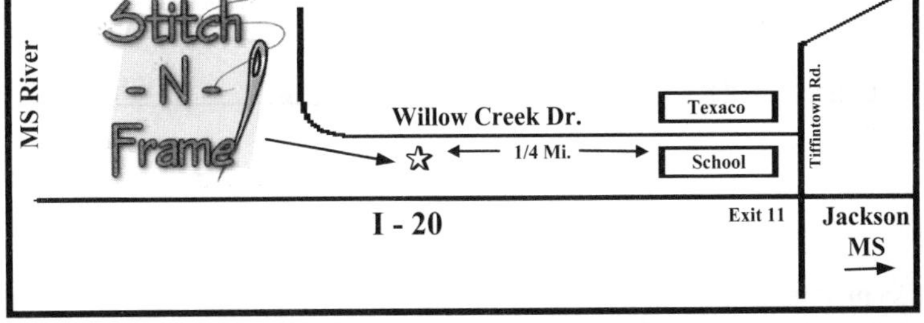

www.stitch-n-frame.net

Dekalb, MS #3

Mon, Tues, Wed, Fri 9:30- 5
Sat 9:30 - 1

Village Cloth Shoppe

302 Main Ave. 39328
(601) 743-5638
Owner: Carolyn Hobgood Est: 1971
villageclothshoppe@yahoo.com

Fabrics for Quilting, Apparel, Smocking and Heirlooms. Books, Patterns, Notions and Accessories.

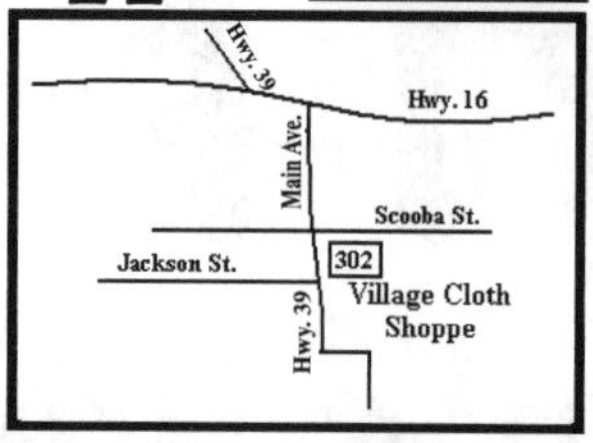

Tupelo, MS #4

Mon - Sat 10 - 5

Heirlooms Forever

3112 Cliff Gookin Blvd. 38801
(662) 842-4275 or (800) 840-4275
Fax: (662) 842-2284 Est: 1983
kathy@sews.com 7000 sq.ft.
www.sews.com

Over 2000 bolts of fabrics, quilting supplies, books, notions, threads, heirloom sewing supplies. Bernina, Brother, & Viking Machines Sales & Service. Helpful & Friendly.

Ocean Springs, MS #5

Mon - Fri 10 - 6
Sat 10 - 5

Janet's Quilting Bee

1001 Bowen Ave 39564
(228) 818-9560
Owner: Janet Bryant
Est: 2003 3000 sq.ft.
www.janetsquiltingbee.net

Large selection of brand name fabrics, books, patterns, kits and notions. Located in historic downtown Ocean Springs.
A quilter's destination on the Gulf Coast!

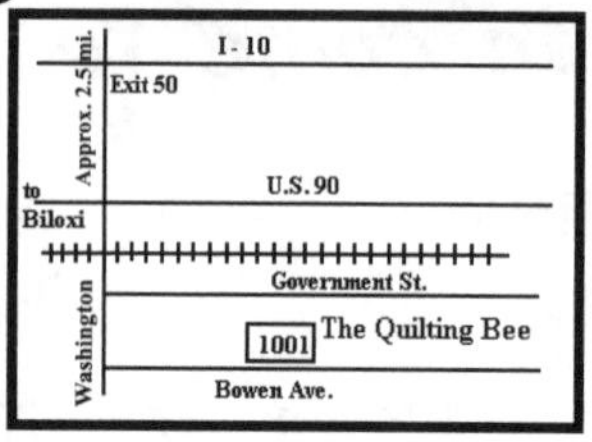

Mississippi Quilt Shops

Ackerman	Main Street Fabrics, 93 East Main St	662-285-6241
Booneville	Quilt Gallery, 1114 E. Hwy. 4 Bypass	662-728-3302
Dekalb	**Village Cloth Shoppe, 302 Main Ave.**	
	601-743-5638	**See ad #3, this page**
French Camp	Glenda's Quilt Shop, 1588 Hwy. 413	877-319-7407
Hattiesburg	Kelley's Pins & Needles, 6140 US Hwy. 98	601-268-5545
Hattiesburg	Thorstore, 52 Stonegate Drive	601-447-2281
Ocean Springs	**Janet's Quilting Bee, 1001 Bowen Ave.**	
	228-818-9560	**See ad #5, this page**
Ridgeland	**Bernina Sewing Etc., 665 Pear Orchard Rd.**	
	601-991-2120	**See ad #1, page 306**
Starkville	Golden Triangle, 401 E. Lampkin St.	662-323-2378
Tupelo	**Heirlooms Forever, 3112 Cliff Gookin Blvd.**	
	662-842-4275	**See ad #4, this page**
Vicksburg	**Stitch - N - Frame, 2222 S. Frontage Rd. #D**	
	601-634-0243	**See ad #2, page 307 & 195**

Mississippi Quilt Shows

About Shows: We are listing only the very basic information about shows that happen on a regular schedule here. Please check out our website for more details on each show. Also this information tends to change quite often so please verify the event with our website or a local source before you venture far. Or if you're in the right area at the right time, give it a shot.

5 Shows

If you are a show organizer, please keep us updated on your event.
shows@quilterstravelcompanion.com www.quilterstravelcompanion.com

On our website you will also find:
- Exact dates (when we have them)
- Contact Information
- Events happening on a one-time basis
- Sponsor Information
- Description of Event

Month	City	Schedule	Show	Location with address
April				
	Diamondhead	Even Years, 2nd weekend in April	Bay Oaks Quilt Show	Diamondhard Community Center, 5300 Diamondhead Cir.
	Long Beach	Annual, Spring	Senior Citizen's Center Quilt Show	Senior Citizen Center, 20257 Daugherty Rd.
	Kosciusko	Even Years, Last Sat. in April	Kosciusko Quilters' Show	Mary Ricks Thornton Cultural Center, Corner of Huntington & Washington Sts.
September				
	Iuka	Even years, 2nd or 3rd weekend in Sept.	Needle Chasers Quilt Show	Iuka Baptist Church, 105 W. Eastport St.
October				
	Hattiesburg	Even Years, 2nd weekend of October	Pine Belt Quilters Fiber Art and Quilt Show	Lake Terrace Convention Center, 1 Convention Center Plaza--I-59 at Exit 67A

57 Featured Shops

MISSOURI

MISSOURI

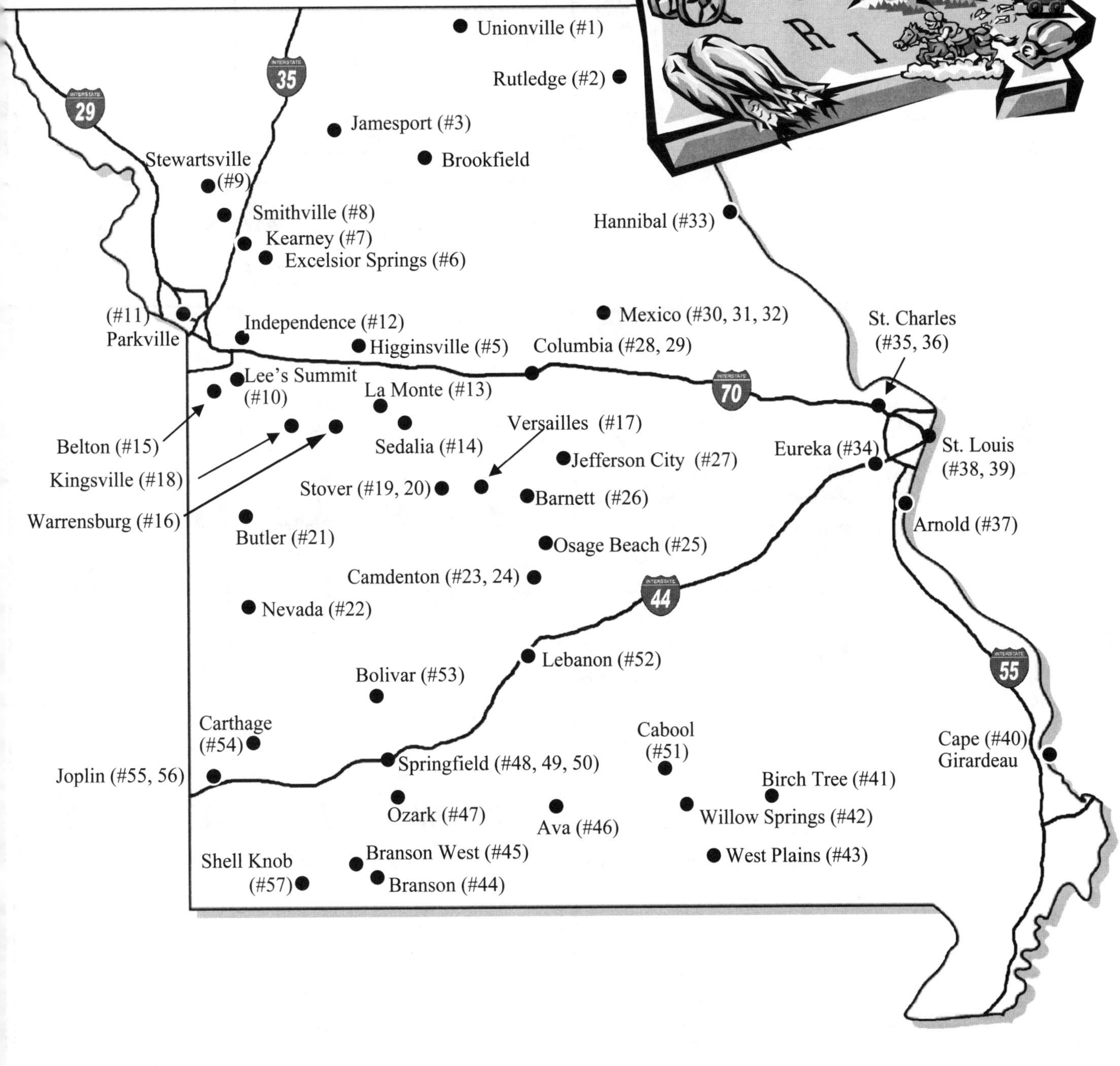
Unionville (#1)
Rutledge (#2)
Jamesport (#3)
Brookfield
Stewartsville (#9)
Smithville (#8)
Kearney (#7)
Excelsior Springs (#6)
Hannibal (#33)
(#11) Parkville
Independence (#12)
Higginsville (#5)
Mexico (#30, 31, 32)
Columbia (#28, 29)
St. Charles (#35, 36)
Lee's Summit (#10)
La Monte (#13)
Sedalia (#14)
Versailles (#17)
Belton (#15)
Kingsville (#18)
Warrensburg (#16)
Jefferson City (#27)
Eureka (#34)
St. Louis (#38, 39)
Stover (#19, 20)
Barnett (#26)
Butler (#21)
Arnold (#37)
Osage Beach (#25)
Camdenton (#23, 24)
Nevada (#22)
Lebanon (#52)
Bolivar (#53)
Carthage (#54)
Cabool (#51)
Cape (#40) Girardeau
Joplin (#55, 56)
Springfield (#48, 49, 50)
Birch Tree (#41)
Ozark (#47)
Ava (#46)
Willow Springs (#42)
Branson West (#45)
West Plains (#43)
Shell Knob (#57)
Branson (#44)
29
35
70
44
55

Unionville, MO #1

Mon - Fri 9 - 5 Sat 9 - 3

Stitch-N-Tyme

1613 Grant 63565
(660) 947-2202
Owners: Deb Smith & Janet Rowland
Est: 2009 1000 sq.ft. 1500 bolts
stitchntyme1613@yahoo.com

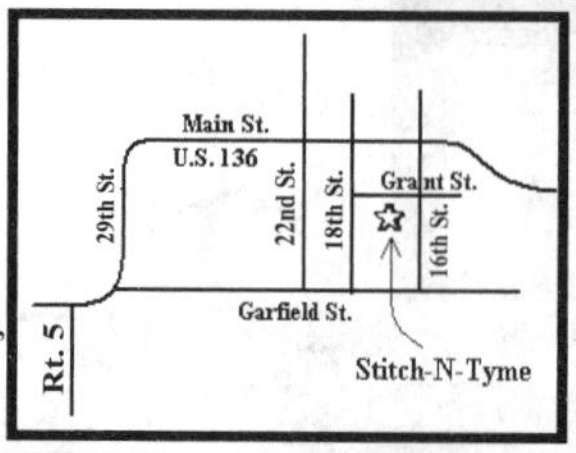

One-stop quilting shop - quilting fabrics, notions, books, patterns, classes. BOM's, Moda, Batiks, Benartex, etc. Fall retreat - call for details.

Rutledge, MO #2

Mon - Sat 8 - 5

Zimmerman's Store

Main St., Box 1 63563
(660) 883-5766 Est: 1974
Owners: Paul & Lydia Zimmerman
Mgr: Ellanor Zimmerman

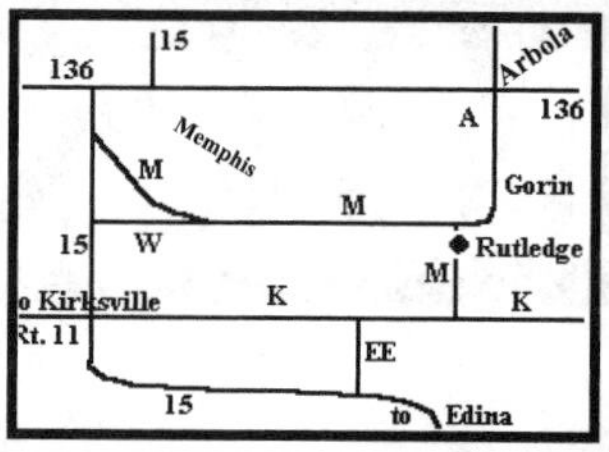

3000 bolts of 100% cotton fabrics at reasonable prices. Batting, quilt patterns & books, sewing notions, hand quilted quilts, pillows, aprons etc.

Jamesport, MO #3

Mon - Sat 8:30 - 5

Fabric Barn

21914 St. Hwy. 190 64648
No Phone

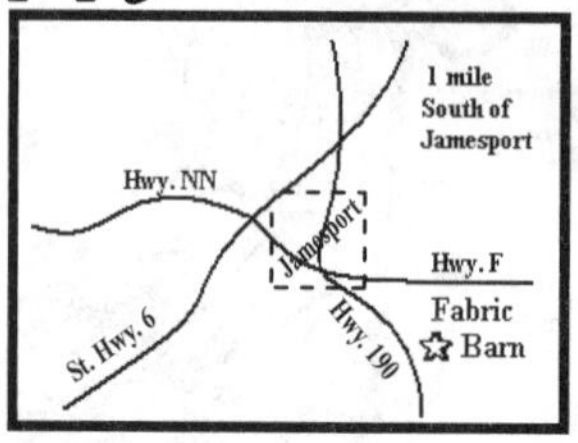

Over 2000 bolts of 100% cotton fabrics.
Specializing in Thimbleberries.
Large selection of books, patterns, templates, notions & stamped quilt blocks.

Brookfield, MO #4

Tues - Fri 10 - 5 Sat 10 - 1

Hueffmeier's Fine Pines

27905 Hwy. FF 64628
(660) 258-3244
Owner: Jeanita Hueffmeier
2500 bolts
gjhueffmeier@juno.com

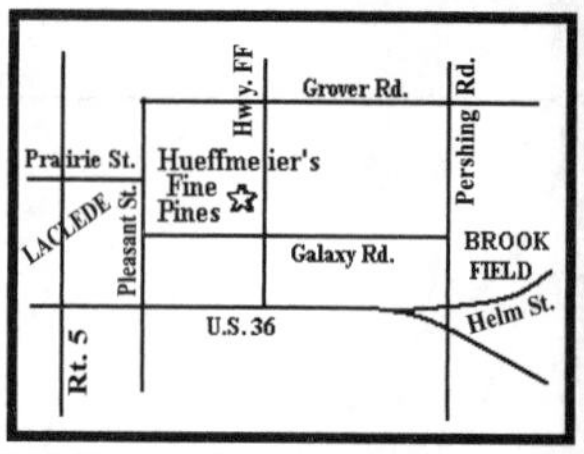

We take the difficulty out of matching fabrics with great kits and friendly help.
Also we have unique pieced quilt backs.

Excelsior Springs, MO #6

Mon - Fri 10 - 5 Sat 10 - 4

The Wooden Spool

233 E. Broadway 64024
(816) 630-5063
Owner: Jamie Fondren

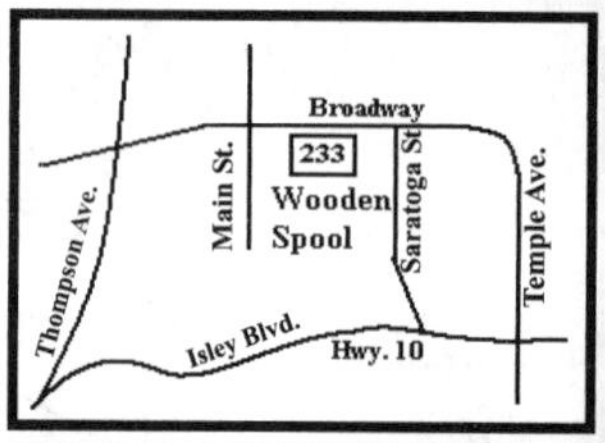

Great Quilt shop opened in May 2002.
For all of your quilting needs: Fabric, Notions, Books, Patterns, Kits, Thimbleberries Club & more.

Kearney, MO #7

Mon - Fri 10 - 5 Sat 10 - 4

and Sew Bee It! A Honey of a Quilt Shop

108 W. Washington 64060
(816) 903-2739 Est: 2007
Fax: (816) 628-7948

Owner: Darla Ebernroth 3000 Bolts 1300 sq.ft.
www.andsewbeeit.com Free Newsletter

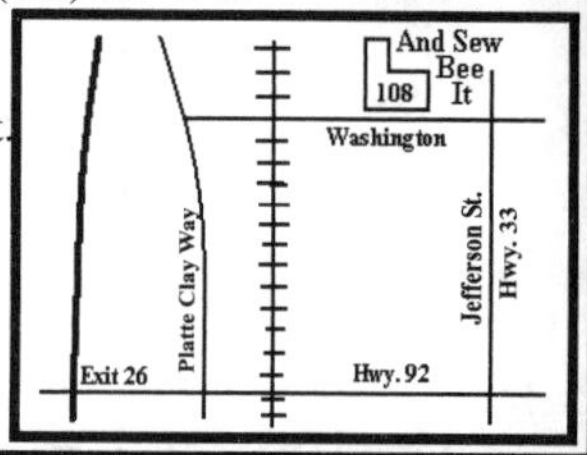

and Sew Bee It! A Honey of a Quilt Shop. Fabric, Notions, Patterns and Embroidery Designs. Pfaff, Husqvarna Viking sewing machines; service; software and accessories.

Quilter's Harvest

Celebrating 10 Years!

www.quiltersharvest.com

Everything a quilter needs! Quality fabrics, notions, books, patterns and kits. Always ready to help with friendly service.

Mon - Fri 9:30 - 6 Thur til 8 Sat 9:30 - 4

(660) 584-3399
quilter@ctcis.net
Owner: Pam Fisher
Est:2000 1300 sq.ft.
5500+ Bolts

1913 Main St. Higginsville, MO 64037

If coming from I - 70, go North on Hwy. 13 to the 2nd stoplight (by McDonalds), turn right, go to the second stop sign, turn right, we are the 2nd shop on the left hand side on Main Street just past the bank.

Higginsville, MO #5

Smithville, MO #8

Mon & Fri 10-3 Tues & Thur 10-6 Wed & Sat 10-4

Cornerstone Fabric

108 S. Bridge St. 64089
(816) 873-0005
Owner: Connie Hevalow

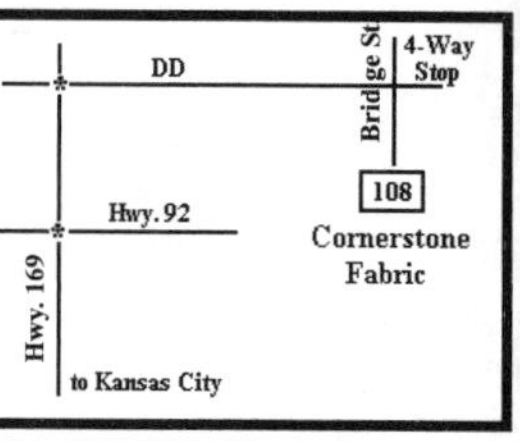

Unique, friendly shop: Sewing / Quilting supplies. Fabrics - Moda, Fabriquilt, P&B Textiles and more. Yarns, zippers, threads, trims, books, patterns and buttons.

Country Expressions
QUILT SHOPPE

The Home of Tula Pink and
"THE TULA PINK PATTERN CO."

Something for everyone from Unique Gifts to All Your Quilting Needs. We carry full lines of fabric. Gammill Quilting on Site.

NW MISSOURI'S LARGEST QUILT SHOPPE!

www.countryexpressionsquiltshoppe.com

Better Homes and Gardens Quilt Sampler FEATURED SHOP 2009

Hwy. 36, 118 Hill Rd.
Stewartsville, Missouri 64490
816-669-3490

OPEN: MONDAY - SATURDAY
10:00 TO 5:00
TUESDAY 10:00 to 8:00

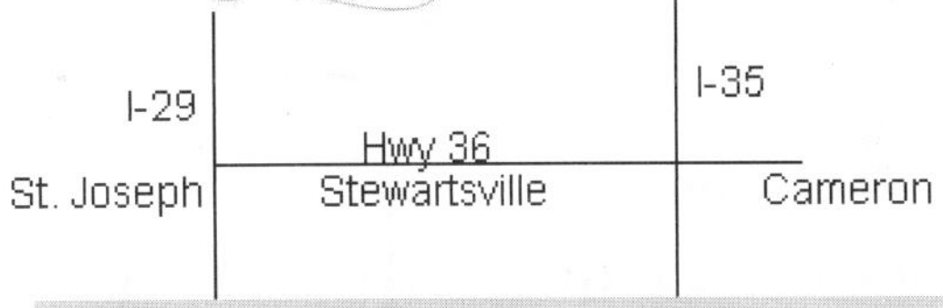

Owners: Kathy Runyan ~ Marie Saunders

Stewartsville, MO #9

QUILTER'S STATION

Fabrics
Quilting Supplies

Selected as one of the Top Ten Shops in *American Patchwork and Quilting, Quilt Sampler Magazine, Spring 2006.* A full line quilt store with over 10,000 bolts of the latest in fabrics including, Benartex, Moda, Hoffman, RJR, Kona Bay, Indo and others. Lots of hand dyed wools. Also punch needle supplies. Primitives of the Midwest each summer, a gathering of primitive teachers and students. Classes available.

3680 NE Akin Dr.
Lee's Summit, MO 64064

Toll Free 1-866-649-8024

Lee's Summit, MO #10

Mon, Tues, Wed 9:30 - 5:30
Thur 9:30 - 7, Fri 9:30 - 5
Sat 9:30 - 4

(816) 525-8955
quiltersstation@prodigy.net

- I-470 / MO-291 to Woods Chapel Rd. (Exit 12).
- Go west on Woods Chapel to second stop light (Ralph Powell Rd.).
- Turn south (left) on Ralph Powell Rd. to Chapel Ridge Shopping Center on the right.

www.quiltersstation.com

Parkville, MO #11

Peddler's Wagon

115 Main
Parkville, MO
64152
816-741-0225
Est: 1982
3400 sq.ft.

**Everything a Quilter "NEEDS" Plus Friendly Smiles and Expert Help.
Huge Collection of Models
Hours: Tues - Sat 10 - 4**

Featured in 1996 Quilt Sampler Magazine

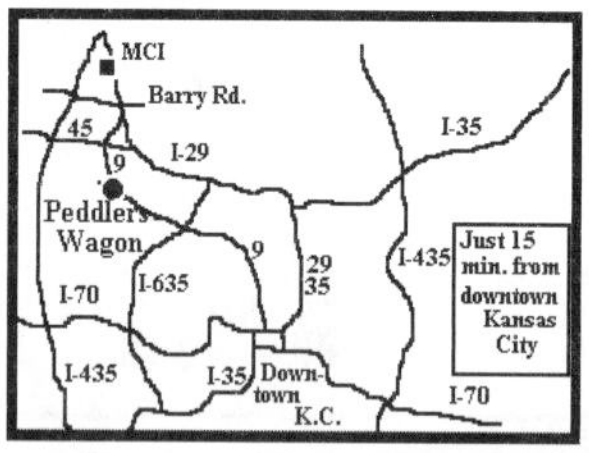

Independence, MO #12

www.rusticyearnings.com

Located in the Apple Tree Center
4621 S. Shrank Dr. 64055
(816) 373-2423
rusticy@aol.com
Est: 1993 3000 sq.ft. 5000+ Bolts

Mon - Sat 10 - 5 Sun 1 - 5

Large Selection of Books, Notions, Patterns & Fabrics for Quilting. Featuring Reproductions, 30's and batiks.

La Monte, MO #13

**Mon - Fri 9 - 5
Sat 9 - 4**

Patches Place

Hwy. 50 & Pleasant Green Rd.
P.O. Box 68 65337
(660) 347-5150 Fax: Same
Owners: Valerie & Jim Studer
www.patchesplacequiltshop.com

Large selection of Quilting Fabrics, Notions, Books, Patterns, Embroidery CD's, Jack Dempsey Quilt Blocks. Everyday Low prices! Authorized Husqvarna Viking Dealer Sales & Service.

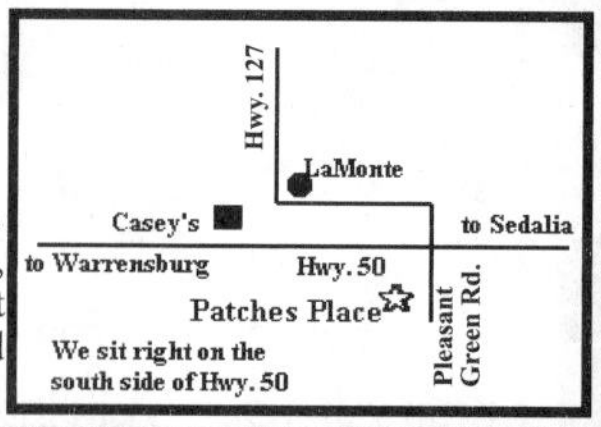

Sedalia, MO #14

**Mon - Fri 9 - 5
Sat 9 - 4**

D & T Quilt Shop

3620 S. Marshall 65301
(660) 826-4788 Fax: (660) 826-4788
Owner: Theresa Gerber
Est: 1991 1200 sq.ft.
dandt_1@charter.net

Fabrics, Notions, Embroidery Blocks. 5700+ Bolts. DMC Floss.
Happy to ship orders. Hand & Machine Quilting. We'll also sew your tops together. Friendly Country Atmosphere.

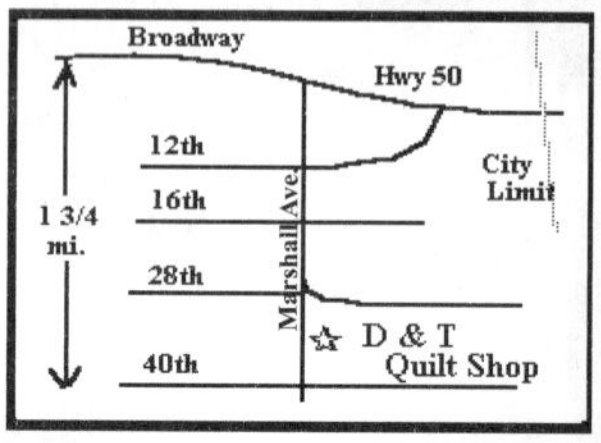

Belton, MO #15

**Tues 10 - 7
Wed - Fri 10 - 5
Sat 10 - 4**

Heritage Fine Fabrics

120 Main St. 64012
(816) 331-1992 Fax: (816) 331-3168
Owner: Connie Read
Est: 2004 865 sq.ft. 1700 bolts
Free online newsletter or $5 if mailed
nickquenum@sbcglobal.net
www.heritagefinefabrics.net

Great selection of 100% quilting cottons. Asians, Blenders, Batiks, Fairy Frost, Flannels, Kansas Troubles, Thimbleberries in a quaint 1890's cottage.

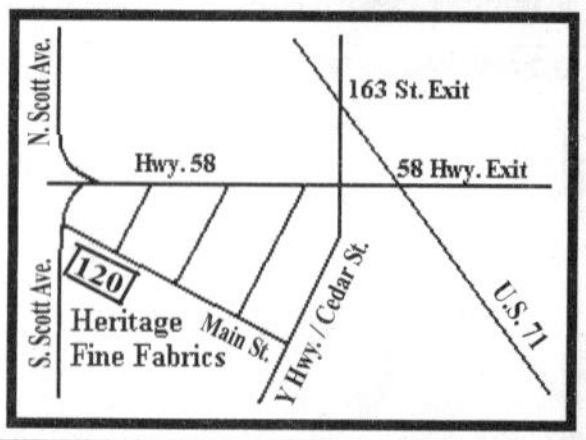

Warrensburg, MO #16

**Tues - Sat 10 - 5
Thur til 7**

Primitive Stitches

136 SW Hwy. 13 64093
(660) 747-7787
Owner: Melissa Towne
Est: 2004
1000 sq.ft.

primitivestitch@earthlink.net

Cozy shop filled with antiques and friendly service. Includes quilting items, large selection of wool felt, stitchery, needlepunch, plus much more!

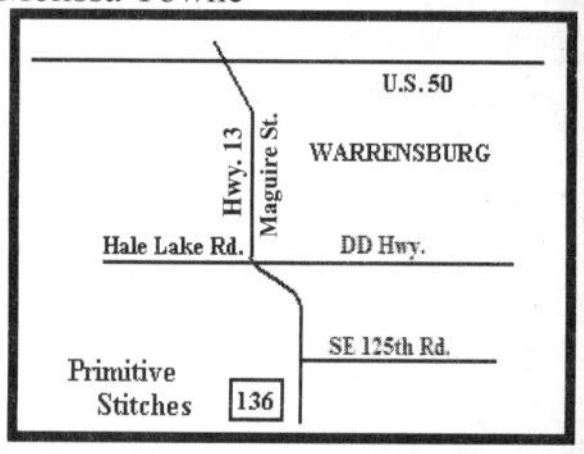

Versailles, MO #17

**Tues - Fri 10 - 5
Sat 10 - 2**

Bestitched

10206 Hwy. 52 65084
(573) 378-6832 Fax: (573) 378-5244
Owner: Rosslyn Steinmeyer
Est: 2004 1000 sq.ft. 800+ Bolts
bestitched@netscapes.com

Quilting supplies, fabric, threads, patterns, books Classes by Appointment. 2 miles west of Versailles on Hwy. 52. MC / Visa accepted.

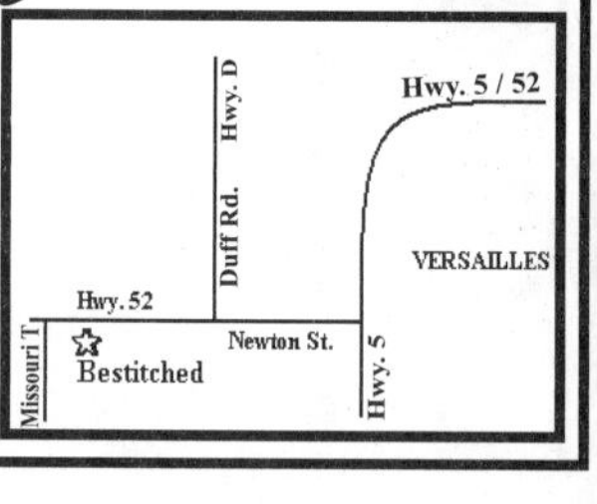

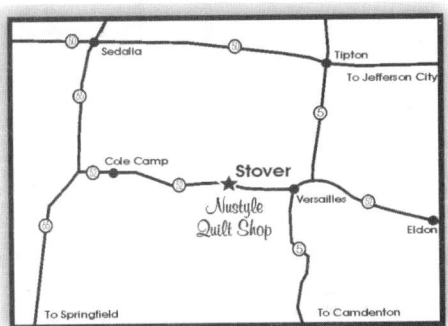

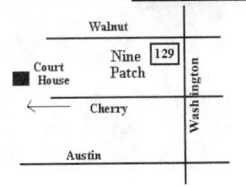

Camdenton, MO #23

Mon - Fri 10 - 5 Sat 10 - 2

Fabrics & Friends

94 N. Bus. Hwy. 5
65020
(573) 346-5036 Fax: Same

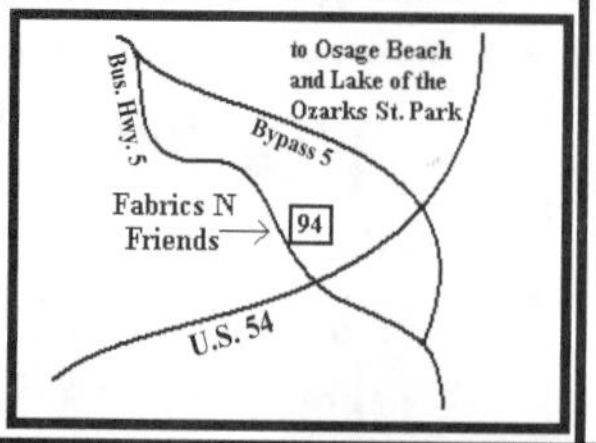

Owner: Rita & Laura Toombs Est: 2007
2600 sq.ft. fabricsandfriends@att.net
www.fabricsandfriends.com
We are located at the beautiful Lake of the Ozarks. A charming selection of Quality Quilting Fabrics and Embroidery Supplies.

Camdenton, MO #24

Mon - Fri 10 -5 Sat 10 - 3

Greenview Vac & Sew

89 Sorrento Dr. 65020
(573) 873-5411
Owners: Duane & Gertrude Beede
Est: 2003 1250 sq.ft.
850 flat folds and fat quarters
Sales & Service Sewing Machine & Vacuum Dealer for Elna, Juki and Singer. Classes, Fabric, Notions. Your complete sewing center.

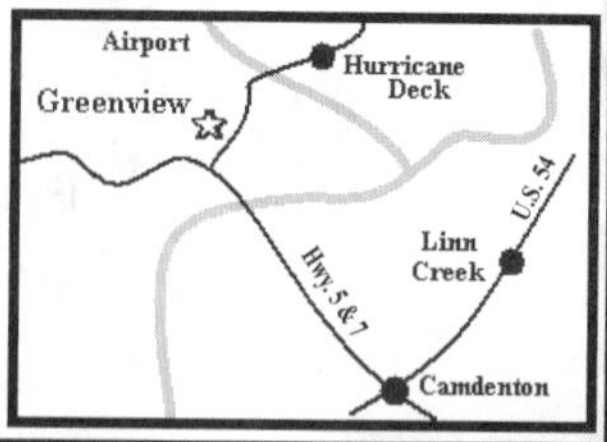

Osage Beach, MO #25

Mon - Fri 10 - 5 Sat 10 - 2

Love to Sew Boutique

877 Hwy. 42, Suite B 65065
(575) 348-1972
tamara@lovetosewboutique.com
Est: 2001
Online Newsletter

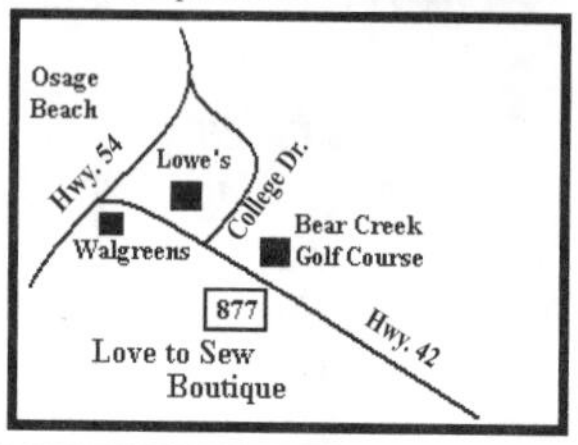

www.lovetosewboutique.com
"Your Hometown Sewing Shop"

- authorized Janome Machine Dealer
- 100% cotton Fabrics / Quilting supplies
- Machine Embroidery / Sewing Notions
- DMC Floss / Patterns · Classes

Barnett, MO #26

Mon - Sat 8 - 5

Pleasant Valley Quilts

15050 Hopewell Rd. 65011
(573) 378-4447 Fax: (573) 378-7317
Owner: Ervin & Lucille Martin
Est: 1987 2700 sq.ft. 4000 Bolts

Large selection of hand quilted quilts - crafts fabric - embroidery blocks custom quilting - wholesale available.

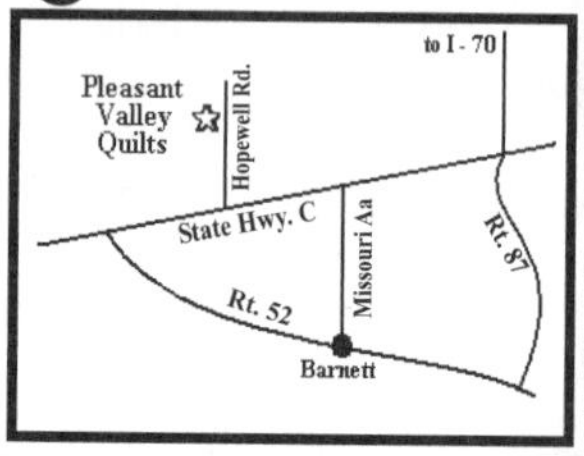

Special Quilts for Special People

Specialty Quilts

Jefferson City, MO #27

Monday - Friday
9:00 - 5:00
Saturday
10:00 - 2:00

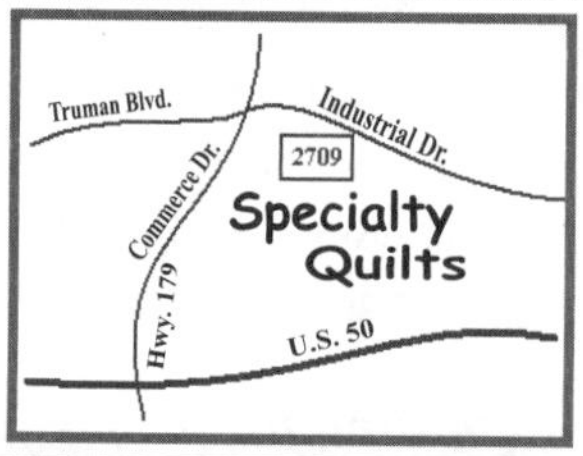

www.specialtyquilts.com

2709 D Industrial Dr.
(Rear Entrance from Metro Dr.)
Jefferson City 65109
573-761-7313
Owner:
Linda Foulk

Huge selection of Jelly Rolls, Honey Buns, Layer Cakes, Charms, Fat Quarter Bundles, Kits, Wide linings, embroidery blocks, etc.
Moda, Timeless Treasures, Benartex, Thimbleberries and much more. Books and patterns.
Custom Machine Quilting & Piecing Service.

Husqvarna VIKING

Appletree Quilting Center

www.AppletreeQuilting.com

- Super-Friendly, Professional Staff to help you! Over 350 years of combined sewing expertise!
- 5,000 square feet of Quilting Paradise - including 5000+ bolts. It's sew easy to pull a quilt at Appletree Quilting Center!
- Great selection of books, patterns, & notions.
- Heirloom sewing & smocking supplies.
- Classes, Classes, Classes! The largest selection of hands-on sewing classes in the Mid-Missouri area.
- Full line of quality built Husqvarna Viking sewing machines from Sweden. The same company that also builds Husqvarna chain saws!
- Open 7 days a week for your convenience.
- Lots of parking available. Buses and large groups are always welcome!

Directions to Our Shop:

Appletree Quilting Center is located in the heart of Missouri quilting country half way between St. Louis and Kansas City on **Interstate 70**. **Take exit #124** - Stadium Blvd. **Turn south on Stadium, then turn right on to Bernadette Dr.** (second stop light at Wendy's Restaurant). We are located in Bernadette Square, a shopping center on your right, just across from the Columbia Mall.

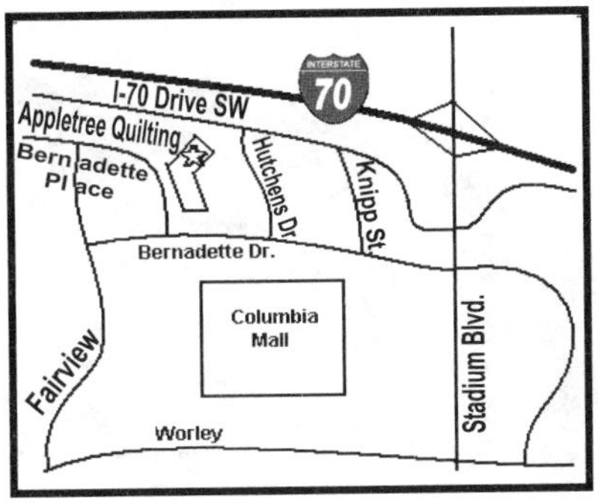

Appletree Quilting Center

#28

2541 Bernadette Drive
Columbia, MO 65203
sewing@appletreequilting.com
(573) 446-2655 1-800-269-2655

__HOURS__: OPEN 7 Days a Week for Your Convenience!

10 – 5:30 Mon. – Thr.
10 – 5 Fri. & Sat.
1 – 4 Sunday

Established 1985
Millie & Floyd Kaiser, Owners

Satin Stitches

Columbia, MO #29

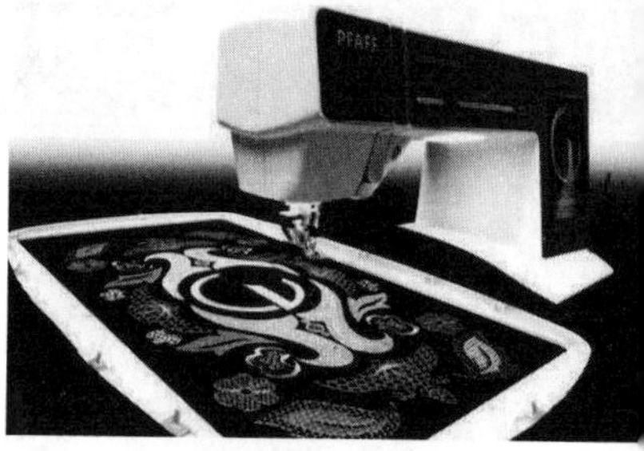

FABRICS

705 D VANDIVER DR.
COLUMBIA, MO 65202

573-817-0006 1-800-463-2483

www.marcysewing.com satinstitches@mchsi.com

PFAFF

Authorized Dealer

brother at your side

We're open Monday thru Thursday from 10:00 to 5:30
And Friday & Saturday from 9:30-3:00

We carry over 3,000 bolts of quality cotton and other fine fabrics, Pfaff & Brother sewing, embroidery machines and Sergers, Software for all machines, and supplies, notions, books, patterns, Samples, Samples, Samples and *our friendly and knowledgeable staff to help you in any way they can!*
ALWAYS A SALE ON FABRICS

Celebrating 12 years in business

Est. 1998

Where Sewing Fun Begins

Mexico, MO #30

Mid-Missouri's largest quilt store:

- Over 5000 bolts of fabric including the largest selection of 1800's reproductions in the area
- Thousands of fat quarters
- Rug hooking and needle punch supplies
- Your Block of the Month headquarters with unique monthly programs - we ship worldwide!
- Hand-dyed wool
- Candles & pottery
- Gift items
- Gourmet food section

Better Homes and Gardens Quilt Sampler FEATURED SHOP

Monday 10 - 5
Tues - Thur 10 - 6
Friday 10 - 5
Saturday 10 - 3

HOMESTEAD HEARTH™

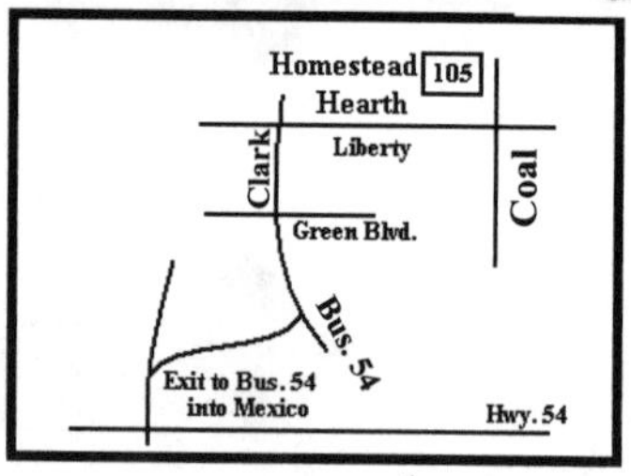

105 N. Coal 65265
(573) 581-1966
info@homesteadhearth.com
Est: 2002 8000 sq.ft

www.homesteadhearth.com

Mexico, MO #31

Mon - Sat
9 - 5

Mexico Sewing Center

123 W. Monroe 65265 (573) 581-2047
Northwest Corner of Mexico Square
www.mexicosewingcenter.com

Est: 1978

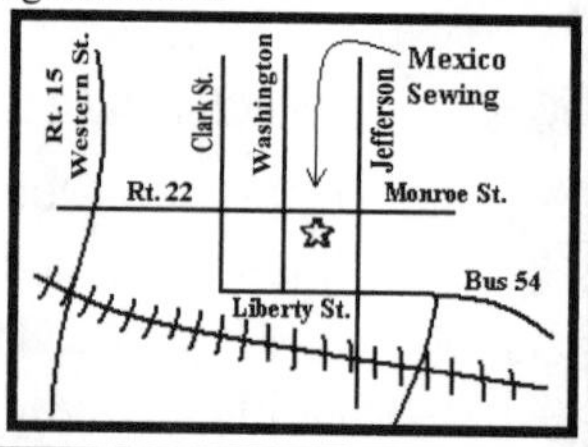

mexicosew@sbcglobal.net
Elna sewing machines. Fabrics - Hoffman, Timeless Treasures, Red Rooster and lots more. Quilting supplies, Books, Patterns, Classes, Gift Items, Fat Qtrs $2 Everyday.

Mexico, MO #32

Wed - Sat
10 - 5:30

Sticky Wicket

"Shopping at Sticky Wicket is like coming home."

104 N. Jefferson St. 65265
(573) 581-6262
www.stickywicketquilt.com
Owner: Mona Leonard
Quilt Fabric, Patterns and Supplies. Stamped Embroidery Blocks, DMC Floss, Gifts, Teas and Coffees.

Mexico exit off I-70, Highway 54 North (East) to first Mexico exit. Straight on S. Clark to Jackson. Right on Jackson to N. Jefferson, turn left, ½ block on right.

HICKORY STICK

QUILT & GIFT SHOP

Celebrating 33 years of quilting & gifts in
Historic Downtown Hannibal

- Extensive collection of quilts & redwork displayed in 3 buildings for your inspiration
- 3000 bolts of cotton, batiks & flannels
- Quilt kits & fat quarters
- Stamped embroidery kits & floss
- Books, patterns, threads & supplies

Better Homes and Gardens
Quilt Sampler
FEATURED SHOP
2009

Located across from Mark Twain's Home

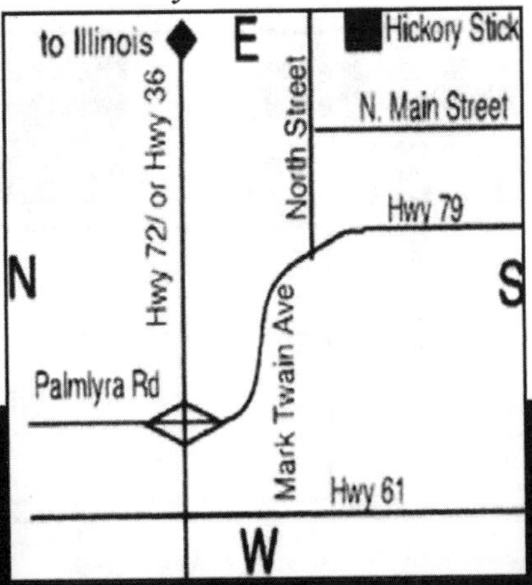

Host of

"Hometown Stitches"

Fall Quilting Symposium
Sept. 24 & 25, 2010

#33

www.hickorystickquiltshop.com • hickorystickquilts@yahoo.com
326 N. Main, Hannibal, MO 63401
573-221-4538 • Fax: 573-248-0396 • Open Daily

Susie Q Quilting

Mon - Fri 9 - 4
Wed til 8
Sat 9 - 3

131 South Central Ave.
Eureka, MO 63025
636-587-2772

Est: 2004 1500 sq. ft. 3000 Bolts

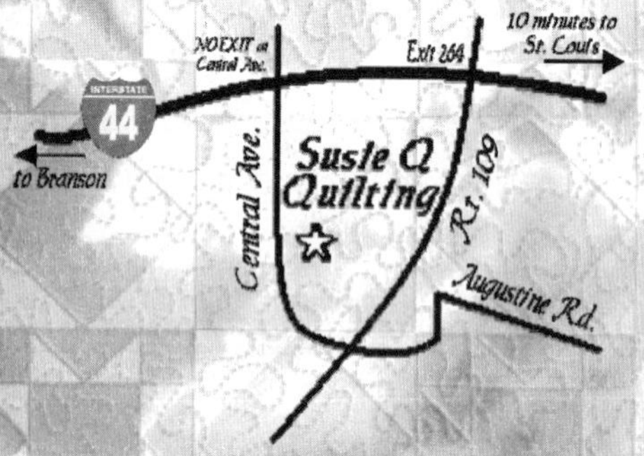

In the heart of old town Eureka only 3 minutes, and two turns, from I-44 and 10 minutes to Six Flags.

Contemporary Quilt Shop Over 300 Bolts of Batiks with lots of Brights.

Eureka, MO #34 **www.susieqquilting.com**

Patches etc.

Quilts, Fabric and Patterns -- Home of 'Redwork'.

www.patches3.com

Mon - Sat 10 - 5 Sun 11 - 5

Voted one of the 10 Best Quilt Shops in the 1st edition of Better Homes and Gardens Quilt Magazine.

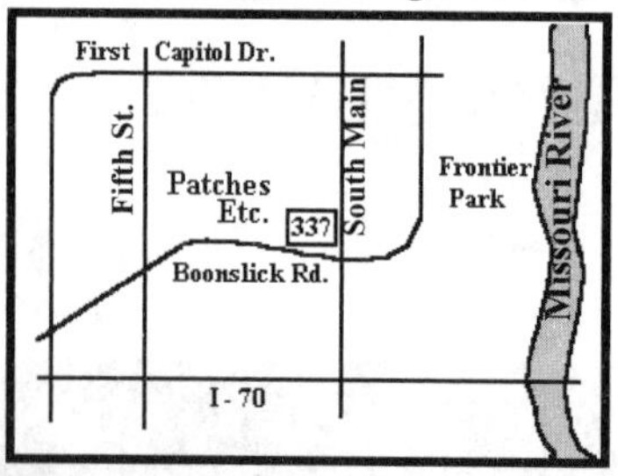

337 South Main 63301
(636) 946-6004
Onwer: Chris Stergos
Est: 1979 1500 Bolts
3patches@prodigy.net

Historic St. Charles, MO #35

St. Charles, MO #36

Mon 12 - 5
Tues - Fri 10 - 5
Sat 10 - 3

Bindings, Borders & Squares Quilt Shop

325 Droste Rd. 63301
(636) 949-2077 Fax: Same
Owner: Paula Morrow
Est: 2006 2200 sq.ft. 1700 Bolts
bbsquiltshop@sbcglobal.net
Fabrics, patterns, books, notions, preprinted embroidery, threads. Classes and sewing groups.
Long arm quilting and quilt making services.
Enter parking off Raymond St. behind Johnny Mac's.

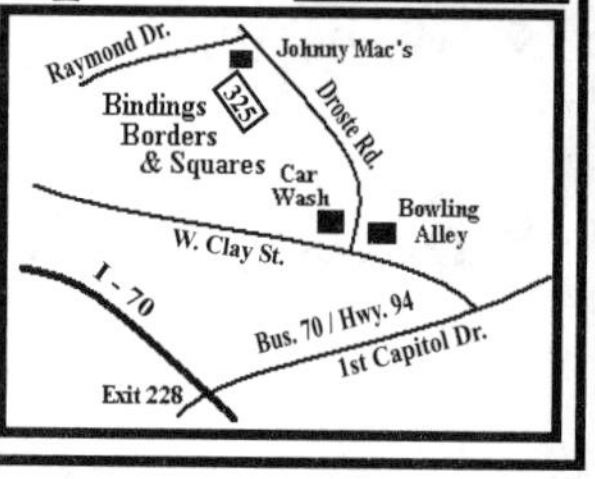

Arnold, MO #37

Tues - Fri 10 - 6
Sat 9 - 5

Your Quilt Shop

2051 Southway Dr. 63010
(866) 520-3764 or (636) 464-2929
Fax: (636) 467-5336
Owners: Rich & Sherry Sheldon
Est: 2007 3000 sq.ft. Online newsletter
sherrysquilts@ffquilts.com
www.YourQuiltShop.net
1200+ bolts of fabric. Known for Thimbleberries and over 150 quilt backings.
Award-winning, published longarm quilters!

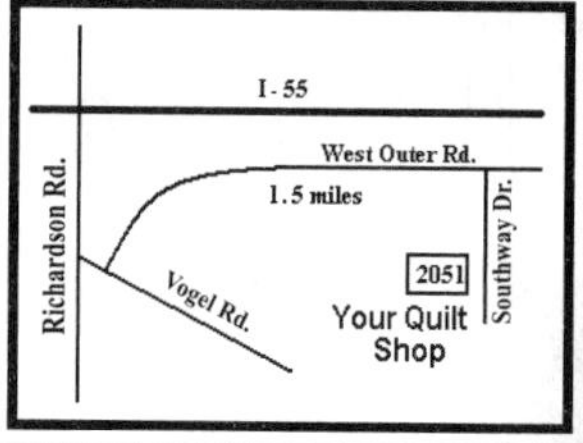

St. Louis, MO #38

M, W 9:30 - 5
T, Th 9:30 - 6:30
Fri & Sat
9:30 - 4:30
Sun 12 - 4

THE QUILTED FOX

SELECTED AS ONE OF THE TOP TEN FEATURED SHOPS
2001 QUILT SAMPLER MAGAZINE
BY BETTER HOMES AND GARDENS

6000 bolts of unique quilting fabrics
International, Asian, Australian, African and more.
Large selection of Kaffe Fassett and Amy Butler fabrics.
Fox Fabric Club for the out-of Towner.

Easy Access off & on the highway
Mail Orders always welcome
Handicap Accessible

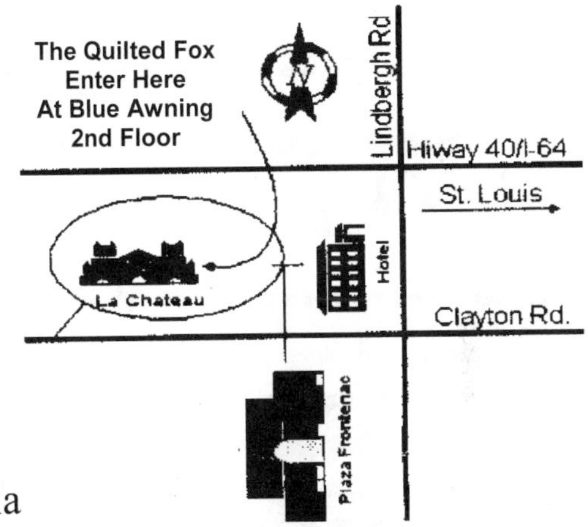

10403 Clayton Rd., St. Louis, MO 63131
(314) 993-1181
info@quiltedfox.com www.quiltedfox.com
Established 1994; 2500 sq. ft. Owner: Louise L. Georgia

Jackman's Fabrics

Since 1903

www.jackmansfabrics.com

Quilt Superstore - St. Louis, Missouri

Tin Lizzie 18 Long Arm Quilting

Babylock Sergers, Embroidery & Sewing Machines

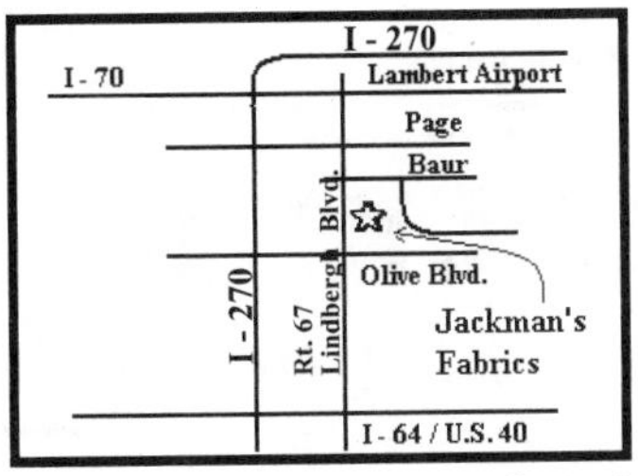

314-994-1060 • 1234 North Lindbergh, 63132

Mon. & Thurs. 10:00 - 9:00 • Tues., Wed., Fri. 10:00 - 6:00
Sat. 10:00 - 5:30 Sun. noon - 5:00

St. Louis, MO #39

Over 100,000 yards of quilting cottons!
Hoffman, Moda, Timeless Treasures, Benartex, P&B, Lakehouse, Art Gallery, Wilmington, Blank and more ...

Fabrics designed by French General, Amy Butler, Nancy Halvorson, Urban Grey, etc.

Huge collection of batiks, marbles, novelties, patterns, books, etc.

Tremendous displays! Great new ideas!

Show us this ad and you will receive a 1 time 15% discount on your entire non-sale purchase.
Bus Groups Welcome! Please Call.

The Golden Needle Sew & Vac Center

Quilting by the Mississippi River — The Sewing Basket

Hinterberg Design
Janome ...Dream. Inspire. Create.
brother at your side
Nolting® Longarm Quilting Machines
Husqvarna Viking

Quilt Fabrics ★ Notions
★ Books ★ Classes ★ Sewing Furniture ★

MENTION THIS AD FOR A FREE GIFT

HOURS:
Mon. - Fri. 9:30 - 5:30 Sat. 9:30 - 4

Moda • Hoffman • RJR • Marcus Bros • Kona Bay
Thimbleberries • Balis • Batiks • Timeless Treasures
Over 3300 bolts

573 - 339 - 0494 thegoldenneedleinc.com

330 Kingshighway • Cape Girardeau, MO #40

The Hideaway QUILT SHOP

3217 W. First St.
P.O. Box 57 65438
hideawayquilt@centurytel.net

High quality cotton fabric from top companies. Patterns and books for all levels of quilting. Kits for quilters on the go. Everything you need to complete your projects.

9 am - 5 pm
Tuesdays - Saturdays

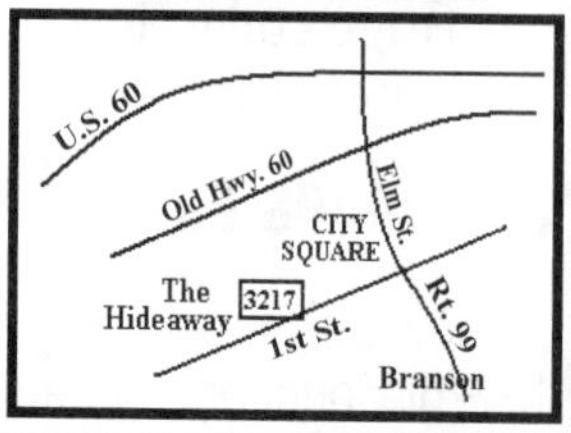

Birch Tree, MO #41

Willow Springs, MO #42

Tues - Sat
10 - 5

The Stitchin' Post

224 E. Main St. 65793
(417) 469-5806
Owner: Joan Pierce
joan@joanslinenbasket.com
Fabrics • Patterns • Books • Fat Quarters
Home Décor • Handmade Amish Baskets

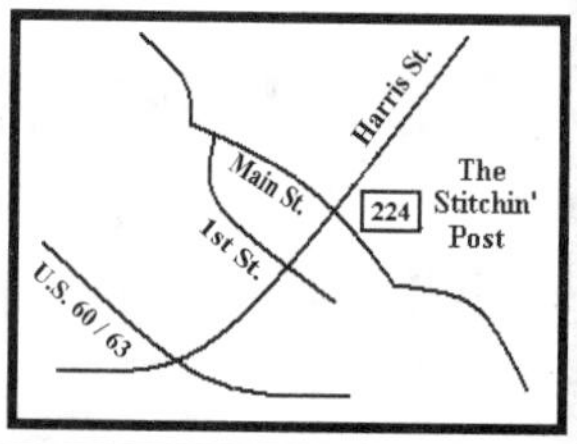

West Plains, MO #43

Mon - Fri
10 - 5
Sat 10 - 2

Viv's Sewing Connection

2124 St. Rt. CC 65775
(417) 256-8532
www.sewconnection.com Est: 2000
1500 sq.ft. 1000 Bolts Free Newsletter

We offer sewing and embroidery machines, embroidery supplies, cotton fabrics, books, notions, thread, classes and custom machine quilting.

Husqvarna VIKING

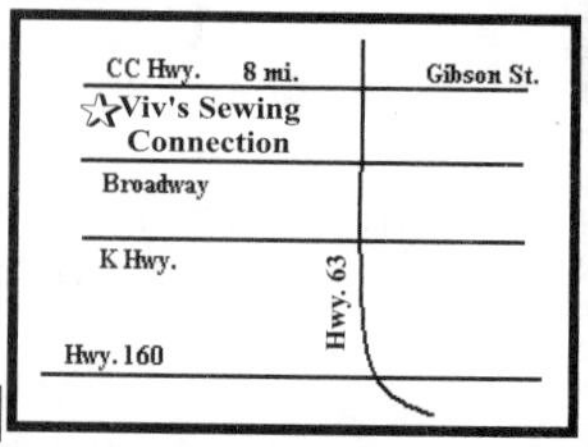

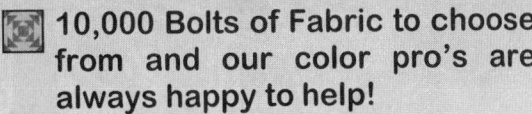

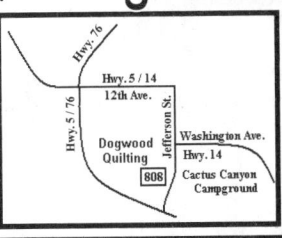

QUILT SAMPLER

www.quiltsampler.com
1802A South Glenstone Ave.
"On The Plaza" • Springfield, MO 65804
Mon - Wed: 10 - 5 • Thurs: 10 - 7
Fri: 10 - 5 • Sat: 10 - 4 • Sun: 12:30 - 4
417-886-5750 Fax: 417-886-1194
Owner: Cristen Jones Est: 1994
Bernina, Pfaff, Tin Lizzie and Handi Quilter
onsite service department

A full service quilt shop offering classes and expert advice. We have many kits, blocks of the month in a bright roomy atmosphere.

PFAFF BERNINA Tin Lizzie 18 Handi Quilter

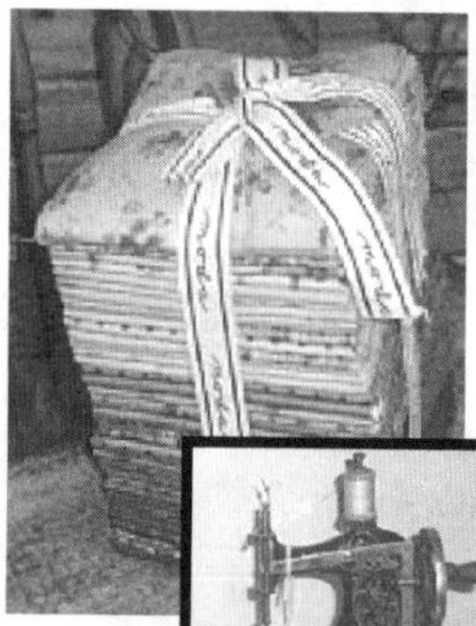

Books and Notions Software
embroidery designs and more!
Friendly, knowledgeable staff
7200 square feet
5000 bolts of fabric
Contact us at:
info@quiltsampler.com
Please visit our sister store in
Tulsa, Oklahoma.

In the Queen City of the Ozarks

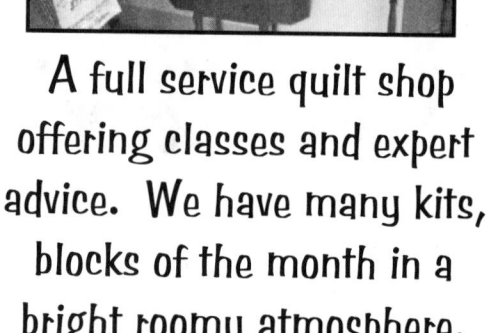

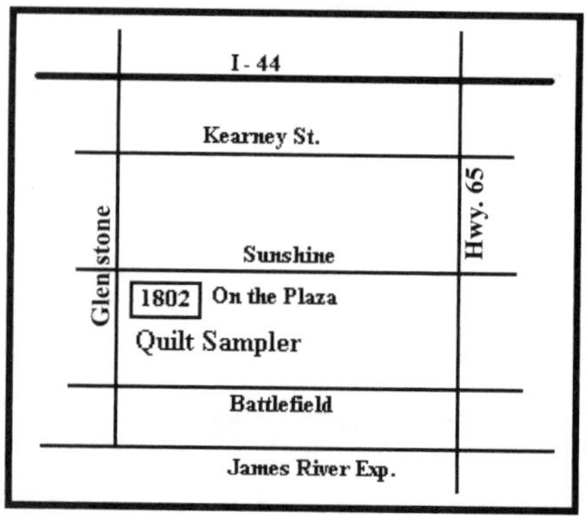

Springfield, MO #48

"The next Generation in Quilting"

Visit our "Fat Quarter Tea Room" for lunch and the BEST desserts!

- Over 1000 different book titles
- Classes for all levels of quilters.
- Authorized Gammill Longarm Showroom
- Bernina Sewing Machines
- Bring in your QTC for a 10% discount.

The "Sunshine" Store

On the northwest corner of Hwy. 65 and Sunshine.

866-MERRILY

866-637-7459

Springfield, MO #49

Merrily We Quilt Along

busy hands - happy ♥'s

Mon - Fri 10 - 5
Tues 10 - 6 Sat 10 - 4

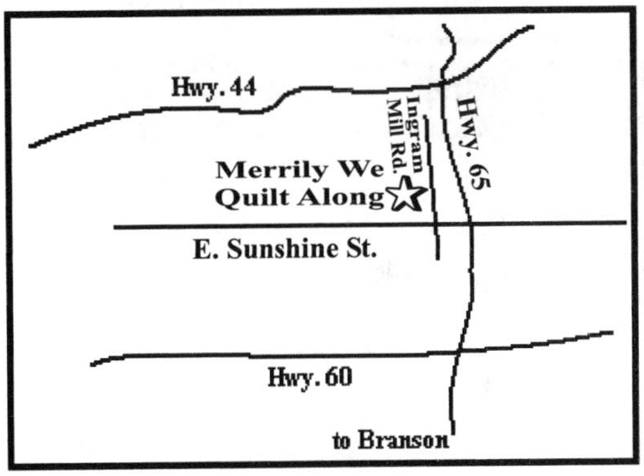

1718 S. Ingram Mill Rd.
Springfield, MO 65804
(417) 890-9000
Fax: (417) 890-9131
Owner: Merrily Parker
Est: 2001
4800 sq.ft. 4000+ Bolts

www.merrilywequiltalong.com

Springfield, MO #50

Mon - Sat 10 -5

Fabric Outlet

1333 S. Glenstone Ave. 65804
(417) 881-4966 Fax: (417) 881-4966
Est: 2005 5500 sq.ft. 5000 bolts
www.alleyfabrics.com

Huge Selection! Best Prices!
We also carry thousands of new pieces of fashion and home décor fabrics.

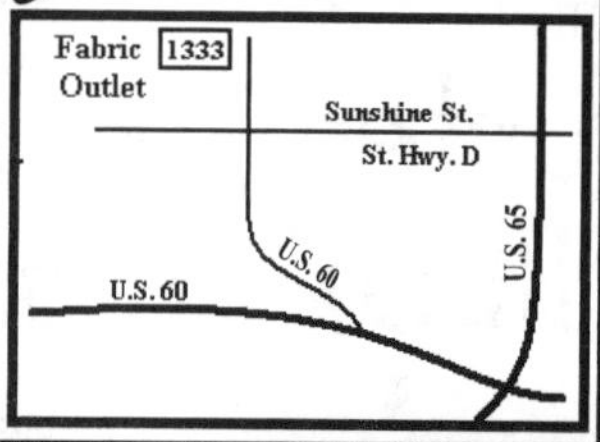

Cabool, MO #51

Mon- Sat 10 - 5:30 Sun 12 - 4 Closed Wed

Ozarks Patchwork Peddler
Fabric & Notions

536 Main St., P.O. Box 608 65689
(417) 962-0494
Owner: Dawn Plomteaux
Est: 2008
2000+ Bolts

patchworkpeddler@hotmail.com
www.ozarkspatchworkpeddler.com

Quality Quilt Fabric - Large Selection of Notions, Books, Patterns, Threads, Puzzles, Gifts and Classes. Come join in the Fun!

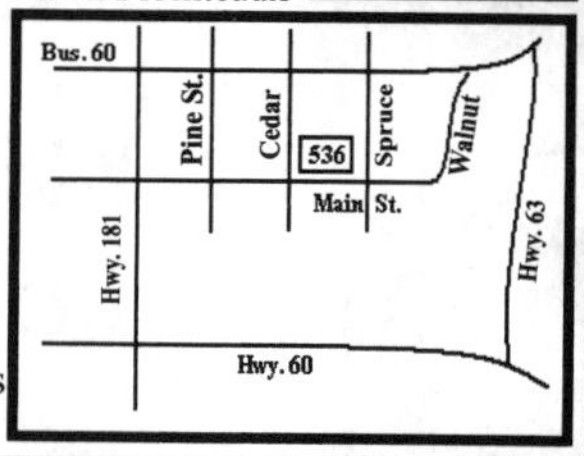

Lebanon, MO #52

Mon - Fri 9 - 5 Sat 9 - 3 Winter Weekdays til 4

The Fabric Store

844 E. Hwy. 32 65536
(417) 588-2324
Owner: Twyla Savage Est: 2007
the-fabric-store@yahoo.com

Fabrics, notions, quilting supplies, classes, DMC Floss and linens. Customized hand crafted purses. 100% cotton name-brand fabrics.

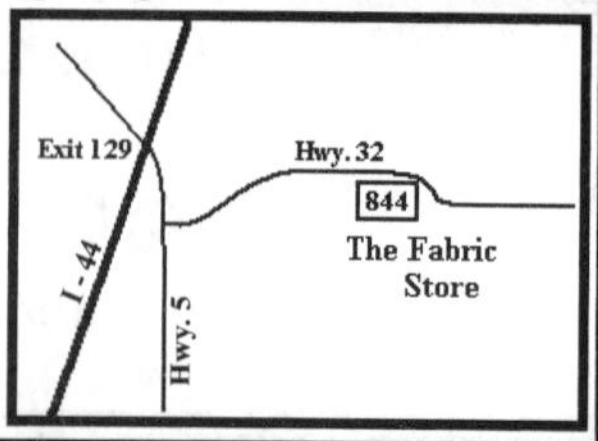

Bolivar, MO #53

Mon - Sat 10 - 5

Margie Pearl's House of Fabrics

4743 S. 131st Rd. 65613
(417) 777-4913 Fax: (417) 777-2808
Owners: Lloyd & Margie Keith
Est: 2000 4000 sq.ft. 2000+ bolts
margiep@windstream.net Free Newsletter

Large selection of fabric, notions, patterns, books, Jack Dempsey needleart, DMC, Weeks Threads, machine embroidery supplies, lace and trims.

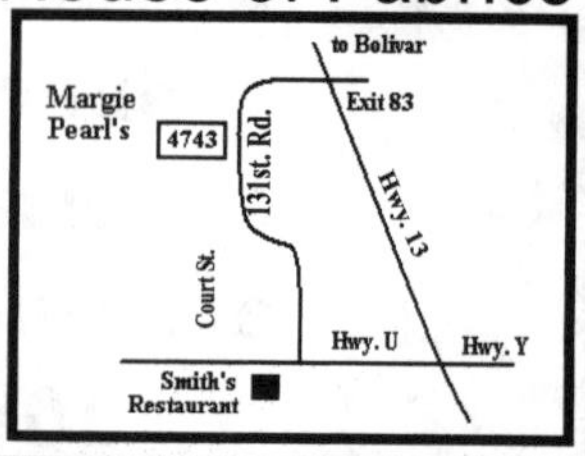

Block-BY-Block

QUILT SHOP

In the rock house across the street from Lowe's.

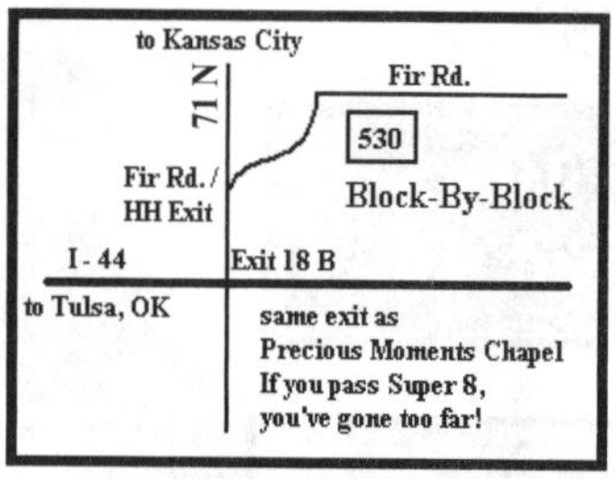

530 W. Fir Rd.
Carthage, MO
64836
amy@blockbyblock.net
Est: 2005 1800 sq. ft.
2200+ bolts

Only 5 Min. from I-44 EXIT 18B

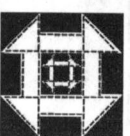

Fabrics ✱ Notions
Books ✱ More

Mon - Sat 10 - 5 Sun 1 - 5

Scream Until Your Husband Stops the Car!

(417) 358-2009
www.blockbyblock.net

Carthage, MO #54

Joplin, MO #55

Mon - Fri 9 - 6 Sat 9 - 4

Sew Neat

1603 E. 20th 64804
(417) 782-4242
Owner: Brenda Orban

Quilt fabric & supplies, sewing supplies.
Quilt Classes, beginner & advanced.
Specializing in Thimbleberries and Moda fabrics. Many items not available anywhere else. Come visit our qualified staff.

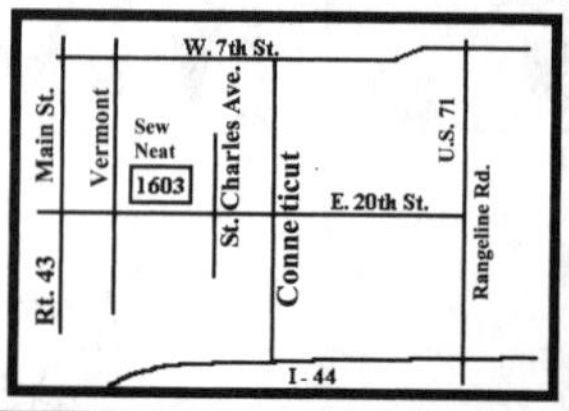

Joplin, MO #56

Mon - Sat 10 - 5:30

Bittersweet Quilts

8133 W Hwy. 86 64804
(417) 627-9555
www.bittersweetquilts.com
I-44 to exit #6, south 6.2 miles on Hwy. 86 to the Junction with P Hwy.

Over 2000 bolts of fabric.
BSQ is well worth the scenic drive through the country. What can we do for your at BSQ?

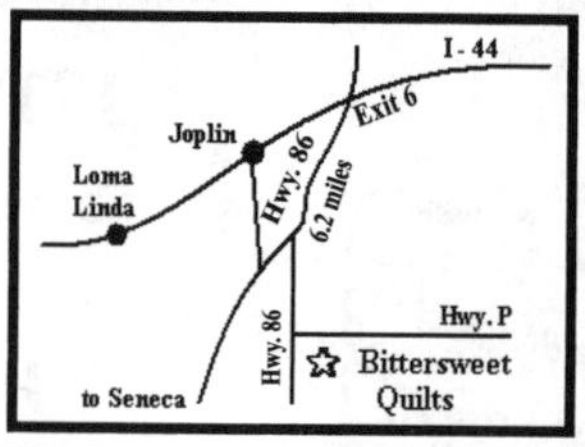

Shell Knob, MO #57

Mon - Fri 9:30 - 5 Sat 9:30 - 4

Stitches

Hwy. 39 & YY TimbeRoc Village #8
(417) 858-2990

Owner: Sharon Smith
Est: 2002 1800 sq.ft. 2000+ bolts
sstitches@centurytel.net
Located on Table Rock Lake.
Fine Fabrics & Sewing Notions
Long Arm Quilting,
Custom Sewing & Embroidery.
Custom Tailoring & Alterations.

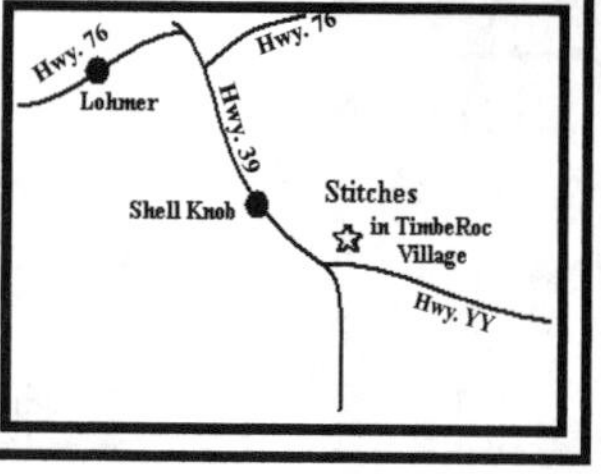

Missouri Quilt Shops

Arnold — **Your Quilt Shop, 2051 Southway Dr.**
866-520-3764 See ad #37, page 318

Ava — **Dogwood Quilting, 808 S Jefferson Ste 1**
417-683-4700 See ad #46, page 321

Ballwin — In Stitches Quilt Shop, 14664 Manchester Rd. 636-394-4471

Barnett — **Pleasant Valley Quilts, 15050 Hopewell Rd.**
573-378-4447 See ad #26, page 314

Beaufort — Quilt N Time Quilt Station, 4149 Hwy. 50 573-484-3120

Belton — **Heritage Fine Fabrics, 120 Main St.**
816-331-1992 See ad #15, page 312

Birch Tree — **The Hideaway Quilt Shop, 3217 W. 1st St.**
573-292-1008 See ad #41, page 320

Bolivar — **Margie Pearl's Fabrics, 4743 South 131st Rd.**
417-777-4913 See ad #53, page 324

Branson — **Quilts & Quilts, 1137 West Hwy. 76**
417-334-3243 See ad #44, page 321 & 198

Branson — Silver Dollar City, 399 Indian Point Rd. 417-338-8262

Branson West — **The Fabric & Décor Shoppe, 11016 St. Hwy 76**
417-272-0322 See ad #45, page 321

Brookfield — **Hueffmeier's Fine Pines, 27905 Hwy. FF**
660-258-3244 See ad #4, page 310

Brunswick — Sew Sweet Quilt Shop, 207 E. Broadway St. 660-548-3056

Buffalo — Maw & Paw Fabrics, 800 S. Ash 417-345-4414

Butler — **Rocking Chair Quilts, 21 North Main St**
660-200-2226 See ad #21, page 313

Cabool — **Ozark Patchwork Peddler, 536 Main St**
417-962-0494 See ad #51, page 324

Camdenton — **Greenview Vac & Sew, 89 Sorrento Dr.**
573-873-5411 See ad #24, page 314

Camdenton — **Fabrics & Friends, 94 N. State Hwy. 5**
573-346-5036 See ad #23, page 314

Cape Girardeau — **The Sewing Basket, 330 S. Kingshighway**
573-339-0494 See ad #40, page 320

Cape Girardeau — Quilting Shop, 134 Dena Ln. 573-335-0761

Carthage — **Block-By-Block Quilt Shop, 530 West Fir Rd.**
417-358-2009 See ad #54, page 324

Carthage — Country Store Quilt Shop, 14426 Burr Oak Rd. 417-358-9385

Cassville — Nannie Mini Bee, RR 1 Box 1877 417-652-3272

Centerview — Country Cottage Fabrics, 537 SW BB Hwy. 660-747-5368

Centralia — Material Girl Quilt Shop, 213 W Sneed St 573-682-1320

Columbia — **Appletree Quilting Center, 2541 Bernadette Dr.**
573-446-2655 See ad #28, page 315 & 203

Columbia — **Satin Stitches Sewing, 705 D Van Diver Dr.**
573-817-0006 See ad #29, page 316

Cottleville — Raspberry Patch Quilt Shop, 5377 Hwy. N 636-928-6949

Ellington — Pin Cushion, 150 Hwy. 106 573-663-2921

Eureka — **Susie Q Quilting, 131 B S. Central Ave.**
636-587-2772 See ad #34, page 318

Excelsior Springs — **The Wooden Spool, 233 E Broadway**
816-630-5063 See ad #6, page 310

Florissant — Helen's Hen House, 180 W. Dunn Rd. 314-837-7661

Hannibal — **The Hickory Stick, 326 N. Main St.**
573-221-4538 See ad #33, page 317

Hannibal — Yore Quilts, 403 Broadway 573-221-2480

Higginsville — **Quilters Harvest, 1913 Main St.**
660-584-3399 See ad #5, page 310 & 408

Independence — **Rustic Yearnings, 4621 S. Shrank Dr**
816-373-2423 See ad #12, page 312

Jamesport — **Fabric Barn, 21914 St. Hwy. 190**
no phone See ad #3, page 310

Jamesport — Ropp's Country Variety, Rt. 2, Box 173 no phone

Jamesport — Sherwood Quilt & Crafts, 1091 Hwy. U no phone

Jefferson City — **Specialty Quilts, 2709 D Industrial Dr.**
573-761-7313 See ad #27, page 314 & 202

Joplin — **Bittersweet Quilts, 8133 West Hwy. 86**
417-627-9555 See ad #56, page 324

Joplin — **Sew Neat, 1603 E. 20th**
417-782-4242 See ad #55, page 324

Kahoka — DBS Quilter & Supplies, 115 West Main St 660-727-1208

Kearney — **And Sew Bee It, 108 W. Washington**
816-903-2739 See ad #7, page 310

Kingsville — **Liberty Homestead, 115 S.W. 1991 Rd.**
816-597-9402 See ad #18, page 313

Kirksville — Quilted Square, 511 S. Baltimore St. #1 660-665-7533

LaMonte — **Patches Place, Hwy. 50 & Pleasant Green Road**
660-347-5150 See ad #13, page 312

Leadington — Country Home Quilters, 120 Union St 573-518-1981

Lebanon — **The Fabric Store, 844 E Hwy 32**
417-588-2324 See ad #52, page 324

Lee's Summit — **Quilter's Station, 3680 NE Akin Dr.**
816-525-8955 See ad #10, page 311

Lees Summit — Zoelee's Fabrics, 1329 NE Deer Valley Dr. 816-524-7217

Liberty — Quilt N Down Home, 10 W Kansas 816-206-4281

Lincoln — A Little Bit Country, 445 Cedar Lane 660-547-2867

Linn — Quilts & More, 102 S. 3rd St. 573-897-3933

Mexico — **Homestead Hearth, 105 N. Coal St.**
573-581-1966 See ad #30, page 316

Mexico — **Mexico Sewing Center, 123 W. Monroe St.**
573-581-2047 See ad #31, page 316

Mexico — **Sticky Wicket, 104 N. Jefferson St.**
573-581-6262 See ad #32, page 316

Mountain View — Calico Cupboard Quilt Shop, 116 N. Oak St. 417-934-6330

Nevada — **Nine Patch Quilt & Fabrics, 129 E. Walnut St.**
417-667-7100 See ad #22, page 313

O'Fallon — Blessings Quilt Shop, 1676 Bryan Rd. 636-474-3007

Osage Beach — **Love to Sew Boutique, 877 St. Hwy. 42-8**
573-348-1972 See ad #25, page 314

Osceola — Brenda's Quilt Stop & More, 785 SW Hwy. 54 417-876-9997

Owensville — In the Niche, 106 E. Peters Ave. 573-437-6124

Ozark — **Sew Simple Quilt Shoppe, 5241 N. 17th St.**
417-582-8383 See ad #47, page 321

Parkville — **Peddler's Wagon, 115 Main St.**
816-741-0225 See ad #11, page 312

Pierce City — Quilter's Delight Nook, 102 W. Commercial 417-476-5844

Pleasant Hill — Kathy's Quilts Plus, 32001 East State Rt. P 913-486-2822

Pleasant Hill — Quilt Stop, 431 N Hwy. 7 816-987-2541

Poplar Bluff — Country Fabrics, 796 County Rd. 605 573-785-0821

Potosi — Quilter's Corner, 201 E. High St. 573-438-6718

Rich Hill — Kountry Kin Fabrics, 113 N. 13th St. 417-395-4797

Rockville — DbarJ Quilts etc., 405 1st St 660-598-2222

Rolla — Uniquely Yours, 404 E. St. Rt. 72 573-364-2070

Rolla — Fabric Plus, 14520 State Rd. "O" 573-364-7134

Rutledge — **Zimmerman's Store, Main St.**
660-883-5766 See ad #2, page 310

Salem — Melear Fabrics, 215 West 4th St. 573-729-8900

Salisbury — Sew Creative, 407 E. Patterson 660-388-6287

Sedalia — **D & T Quilt Shop, 3620 S. Marshall**
660-826-4788 See ad #14, page 312

Sedalia — Kaye's Fabrics, 218 South Ohio Ave. 660-827-5297

Seymour — Jan's Fabric & Quilt Shop 201 Commercial St. 417-935-4440

Shell Knob — **Stitches, Hwy. 39 & YY Hwys.**
417-858-2990 See ad #57, page 324

Sikeston — Quilting Fabrics, 620 S Kingshighway St. 573-475-9393

Smithville — **Cornerstone Fabric, 108 S. Bridge**
816-873-0005 See ad #8, page 310

Springfield — **Fabric Outlet, 1333 S. Glenstone Ave.**
417-881-4966 See ad #50, page 324

Springfield — **The Quilt Sampler, 1802A S. Glenstone Ave.**
417-886-5750 See ad #48, page 322

Springfield — **Merrily We Quilt Along, 1718 S. Ingram Mill**
417-890-9000 See ad #49, page 323

Springfield — F.M. Stores, 1368 E. Sunshine St. 417-882-9244

St. Charles — **Patches Etc. Quilt Shop, 337 S. Main St.**
636-946-6004 See ad #35, page 318

St. Charles — **Bindings, Borders & Squares, 325 Droste Rd.**
636-949-2077 See ad #36, page 318

St. Charles — Stitches Etc., 341 S Main St 636-946-8016

St. Elizabeth — Country Calicos, 428 Oak Ridge Rd. 573-493-2529

St. Louis **The Quilted Fox, 10403 Clayton Rd.**
314-993-1181 **See ad #38, page 319**

St. Louis **Jackman's Fabrics, 1234 N. Lindburgh**
314-994-1060 **See ad #39, page 319**

St. Louis Make It Sew, 10206 Watson Rd. 314-966-4446
St. Louis Thimble & Thread, 2629 Yeager Rd.
St. Peters Eunice Farmer Fabrics, 1284 Jungerman Rd. 636-926-7530

Stewartsville **Country Expressions Quilt Shoppe, 118 Hill St.**
816-669-3490 **See ad #9, page 311**

Stockton Creative Notions, 211 East St. 417-276-4216

Stover **Nustyle Quilt Shop, 309 W 4th St. Hwy. 52**
573-377-2244 **See ad #19, page 313**

Stover **Stover Quality Quilting, 606 N. Ash St.**
800-521-4171 **See ad #20, page 313**

Tarkio Crafters Barn & Sel Storage, 310 S 10th St. 660-736-4854

Unionville **Stitch-N-Tyme, 1613 Grant St.**
660-947-2202 **See ad #1, page 310**

Versailles **Be Stitched, 10206 Hwy. 52**
573-378-6832 **See ad #17, page 312**

Versailles Excelsior Fabrics, 13217 Hopewell Rd. 573-378-7448
Versailles Clark's Fabrics, 813 W. Newton 573-378-5696
Versailles Linda's Cottonpatch, 13501 Hwy. 52 E 573-378-6191
Viburnum Seams Sew Sweet, 60 Walnut St 573-244-3176
Vienna Leisure Time Sewing, 410 8th St. 573-422-3500

Warrensburg **Primitive Stitches, 136 SW 13 Hwy.**
660-747-7787 **See ad #16, page 312**

Warrenton Corner Quilt Fabrics,
1000 Warrenton Outlet Center #B042 636-456-5666
Washington The Fabric Shop, 125 W. Main 636-239-9911
Waynesville The Thread Peddler, 23470 Sage Rd 573-774-2658

West Plains **Viv's Sewing Connection, 2124 State Route CC**
417-256-8532 **See ad #43, page 320**

West Plains Ozark Sampler Quilt Shop, 1364 Bill Virdon 417-255-0024

Willow Springs **The Stitchin Post, 224 E. Main St.**
417-469-5806 **See ad #42, page 320**

22 Shows Missouri Quilt Shows

About Shows: We are listing only the very basic information about shows tha happen on a regular schedule here. Please check out our website for more details on each show. Also this information tends to change quite often so please verify the event with our website or a local source before you venture f Or if you're in the right area at the right time, give it a shot.

If you are a show organizer, please keep us updated on your event.
shows@quilterstravelcompanion.com www.quilterstravelcompanion.com

On our website you will also find:

- Exact dates (when we have them)
- Sponsor Information
- Contact Information
- Description of Event
- Events happening on a one-time basis

Month	City	Schedule	Show	Location with address
February				
	Independence	Annual, 3rd Fri & Sat in February	Calico Cutups Quilt Show	Salvation Army Community Center, 14700 S. Truman Rd.
March				
	Ballwin	Odd Years, 3rd weekend in March	Thimble & Thread Quilt Guild Show	Queeny Park, 550 Weidman Rd.
	Ballwin	Even Years, Late March	Fanfare of Quilts Show	Queeny Park, 550 Weidman Rd.
	Stover	Annual, Last Fri & Sat of March	It's A Gatherin'	Stover Community Building, Legion Dr.
April				
	Springfield	Annual, 2nd weekend in April	Round Bobbin Quilting & Sewing Expo	Springfield Exposition Center, 635 E. St. Louis St.
May				
	Perryville	Annual, 2nd Sat in May	Memory Makers Quilt Shop	Perryville Elementary School, Schindler Rd.
June				
	Kirksville	Annual, 1st weekend in June	Momma's Garden Quilt Show	YMCA, 1708 S. Jamison
	Mexico	Annual, 1st full week of June	Prairie Pine Quilt Guild Show	St. John's Lutheran Church, Dorcas St. & Hendricks
	Stover	Annual, 3rd weekend of June	Stover Fair Quilt Show	Stover Community Building, 600 Legion Dr.
July				
	Rich Hill	Annual, on the 4th of July	A Stitch in Time Quilt Guild	Baptist Church, 3rd & Maple St.
September				
	Independence	Annual, Month of September	Nimble Thimbles Quilt Guild Show	Bingham Waggoner Estate, 313 W. Pacific
	Houston	Odd Years, Late Sat in September	Piney River Quilt Guild Show	Houston United Methodist Church, 422 Hawthorne St.
	Kansas City	Annual, 3rd Fri & Sat of September	Northland Needlers Quilt Show	Gashland Presbyterian Church, 8029 N. Oak Trafficway
	Springfield	Even Years, 3rd weekend in September	Ozark Piecemakers Quilt Guild Show	Springfield Expo Center, 635 E. St. Louis
	Cape Girardeau	Even Years, Late September or early October	River Heritage Quilt Show	AC Brase Arena Building, Kiwanis Dr. & Kings Hwy.
	Marshall	Annual, last weekend in September	Country Patchwork Quilt Guild Show	Salt Fork YMCA, 740 E. Yerby
	Shell Knob	Odd Years, September or October	Discovery Quilters Show	Shell Knob Elementary, Hwy. 39
October				
	University City	Odd Years, Most of October	Circle in the Square Quilters Show	University City Library, 6701 Delmar Blvd.
	Sedalia	Annual, 3rd Saturday of October	Festival of Sharing Quilt Auction	State Fairgrounds, Mathewson Ctr, 2503 W. 16th
	Kansas City	Annual, 4th Thur - Sat in October	Original Sewing & Quilt Expo	KCI Expo Center, 11730 N. Ambassador Dr.
November				
	Columbia	Even Years, 3rd weekend in November	Booneslick Trail Quilters' Guild Show	Stony Creek Inn
	Higginsville	Annual, 3rd Fri & Sat in November	Partners in Patchwork Quilt Guild Show	American Legion Building, 1001 W. 22nd St. (East of Hwy. 13 on 22nd St.)

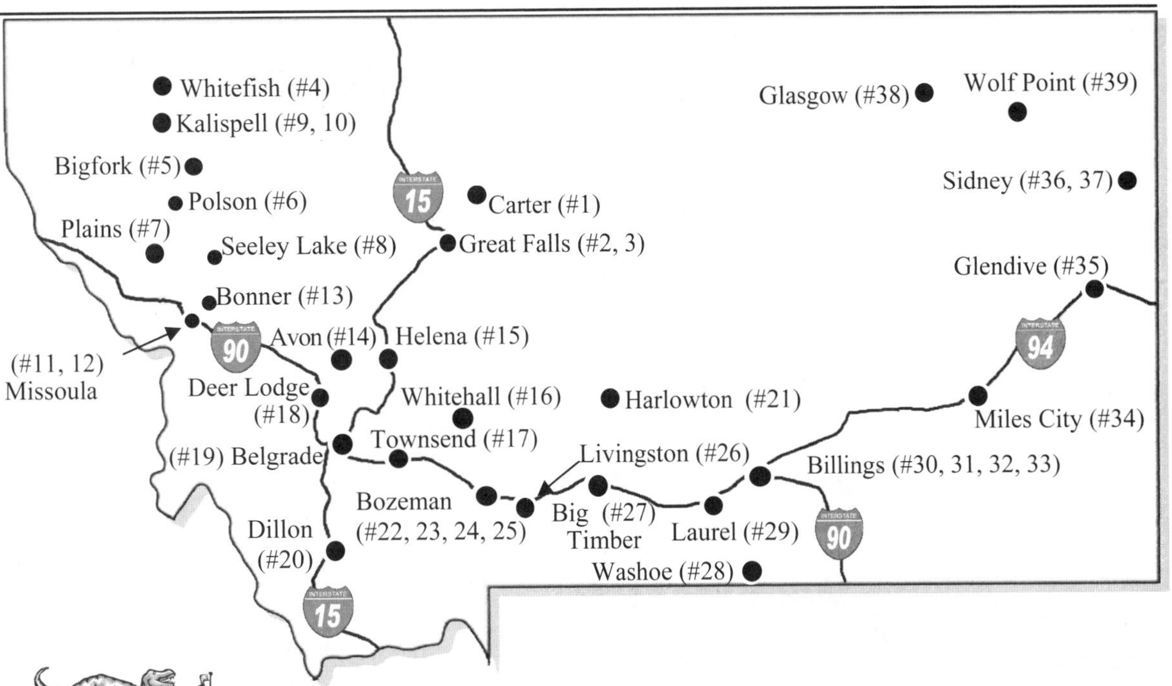

Carter, MT #1

THE QUILTING HEN

1156 Buck Bridge Rd. 59420
(406) 734-5297 P.O. Box 239
Owners: Gary & Diane Arganbright

Tues - Sat 9 - 5

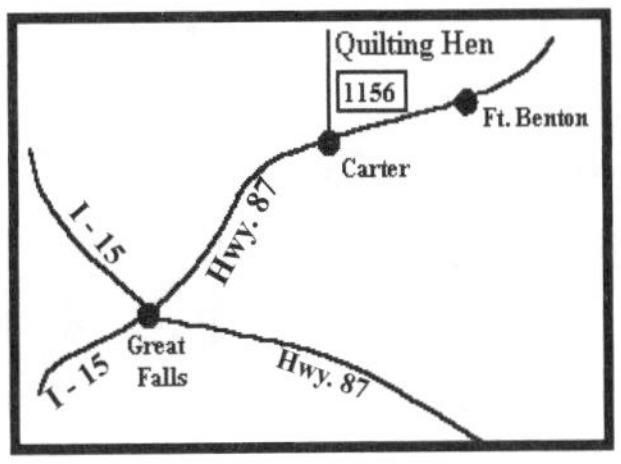

Best Prices on the Prairie!
Featured Quilt Store

Only 25 miles north of Great Falls, MT
PFAFF Supreme Dealer
for Great Falls since 1999
www.quiltinghen.com

The Quilt-a-Way

We are a Full-Service Quilt Shop. Over 3000 bolts of 100% designer Cottons. Friendly, expert staff.

Mon - Fri 10 - 6
Sat 10 - 5 Sun 11 - 4

Great Falls, MT #2

www.montanasquiltaway.com

222 13th St. S 59405
(406) 453-2788
Owner: Toni Echart
quiltaway2@bresnan.net

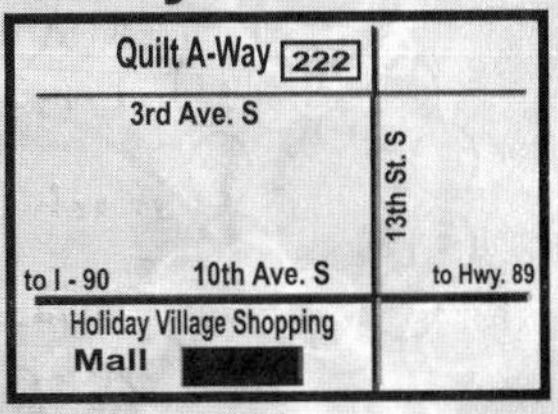

Quilt Sampler Featured Shop

Selected by American Patchwork and Quilting as one of the Top Ten Quilt Shops for Fall 2010.

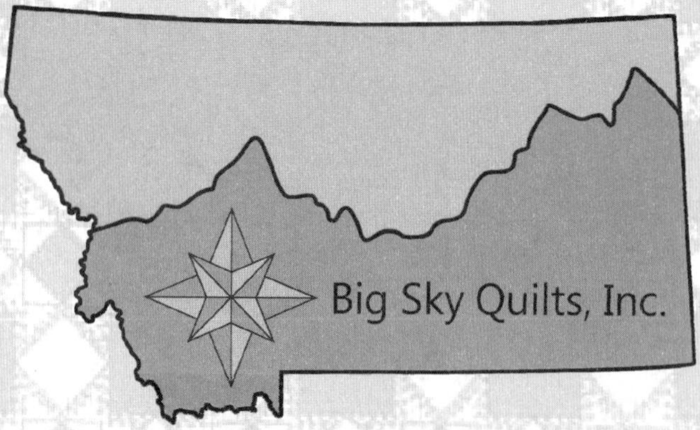

Handi Quilter 18
Representative

Sewing Machines:
Brother
elná
JANOME

406-727-1757
Joyce & Joe Watson
www.bigskyquilts.com

Large selection of Montana Made Quilts. You will always find friendly service plus a huge variety of quilting fabrics, supplies, books and patterns. We are known for our unique selection of kits and happy husband waiting area.

#3
101 A Central Avenue
Great Falls, MT 59401
Monday - Friday
10:30 a.m. - 5:30 p.m.
Saturday 10 a.m. - 5 p.m.

Whitefish, MT #4

Mon - Sat 10 - 6
Sun 11:30 - 5

BACKDOOR GENERAL STORE

131 Central Ave. 59937
(877) 702-1992
Est: 2004 2400 sq.ft.
We are a full service Quilt Shop with classes! Fabric lines such as Moda, Hoffman, Benatex and McKenna Ryan Boutique. Local Gifts, Gourmet Food and Art.
gwencarreon@bresnan.net
www.backdoorgeneralstore.com

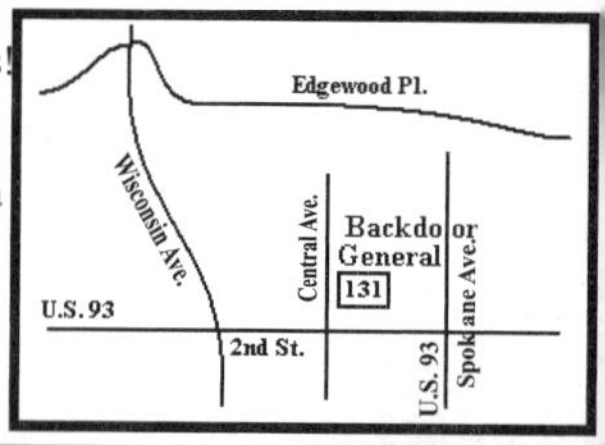

Bigfork, MT #5

Mon - Fri 10 - 5
Sat 10 - 4

Bigfork Bay Cotton Company LLC
Where Quilters Gather

8560 MT Hwy. 35 59911
(866) 245-5718 or (406) 420-1003
www.bigforkbaycottonco.com
Full Service Quilt Shop
Batiks • Flannels • Homespuns
Rayons • Wools • Hand Dyed
Designers of Original Quilt Patterns

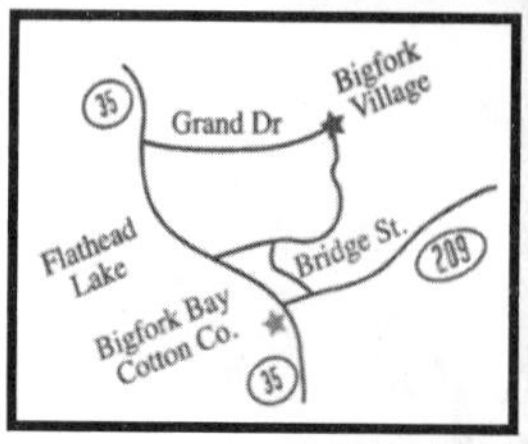

Polson, MT #6

Mon - Sat 9:30 - 5:30

All in Stitches
Montana's Premier Quilt Shop on Flathead Lake

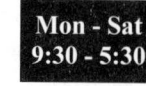

210 Main St. 59860
(406) 883-3643
Est: 2000 2000 sq. ft. 2000 Bolts
allinstitches@centurytel.net
www.polsonquiltsore.com
All In Stitches carries a wide selection of batiks, orientals, brights, books, patterns & kits. We offer a variety of classes year round.

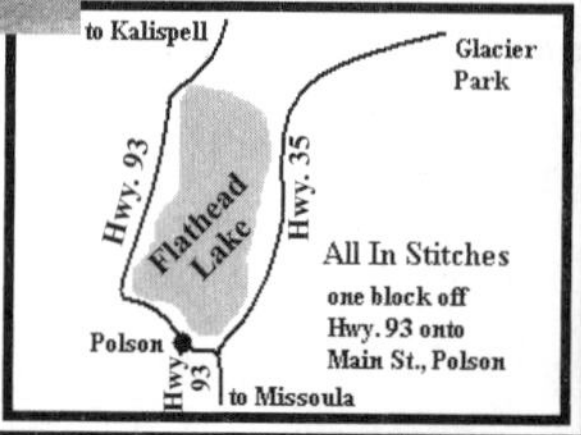

Plains, MT #7

Tues - Fri 1 - 5
Sat 11 - 3

Mary Anne's Fabrics INC.

100 Farmers St. #102 59859
(406) 826-3495
Est: 2006 1500 sq.ft. 2000 bolts
peterson@blackfoot.net
Quilting notions and sewing supplies.
Nice selection of Batiks, Flannels, Western & Wildlife themed fabrics.

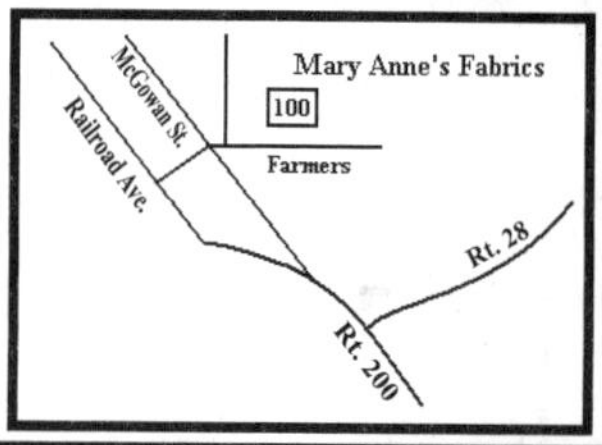

Seeley Lake, MT #8

Mon - Sat 10 - 5
Sun 12 - 4

Deer Country Quilts

Hwy. 83, P.O. Box 808 59868
(The log store in the center of town)
(406) 677-2730
www.deercountryquilts.com
Owner: Pam Rose
Est: 1996 4200 sq.ft. 4000+ Bolts
Selected by American Patchwork and Quilting as an outstanding store in North America.
Everything you need including inspiration

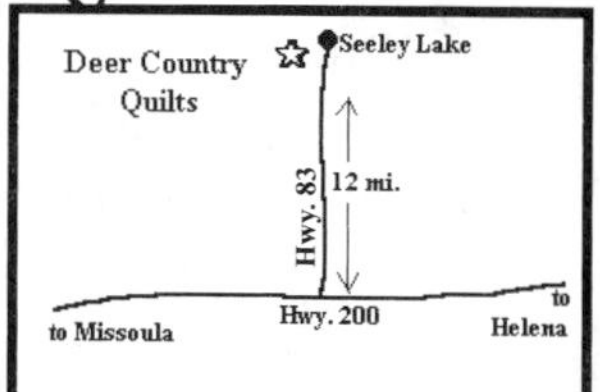

Kalispell, MT #9

Largest selection of antique, hand-quilted, novelty, and machine quilted quilts in the Northwest. Online and mail orders welcome.

Quilts • Fabrics • Supplies
Unique Patterns
Gifts • Embellishments

1710 Hwy. 93 S. 59901 (406) 257-5799

Owner: Joan Hodgeboom

Est: 1983 6000 sq.ft. plus a large class room

qg@quiltgallery.net

Across from Outlaw Inn

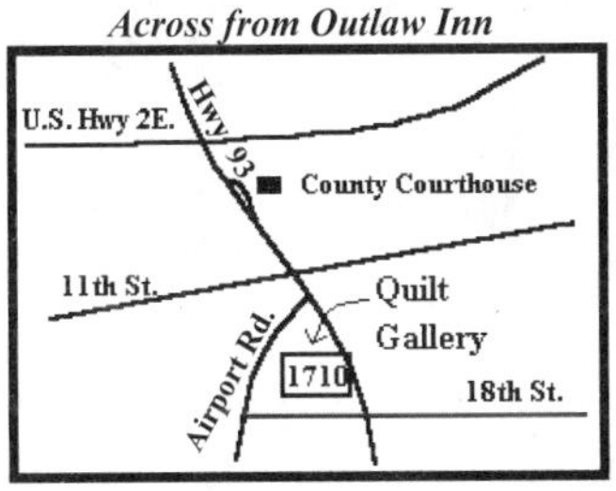

Mon - Fri 9:30 - 5:30
Sat 9:30 - 5

Selected by American Patchwork & Quilting magazine readers as one of the Top 10 quilt shops in the nation.

www.quiltgallery.net

Kalispell, MT #10

Glacier Quilts

125 Hutton Ranch Rd.
Kalispell, MT 59901
(406) 257-6966
Mgr: Coni Bjelland
Owner: Susan Gilman
info@glacierquilts.com

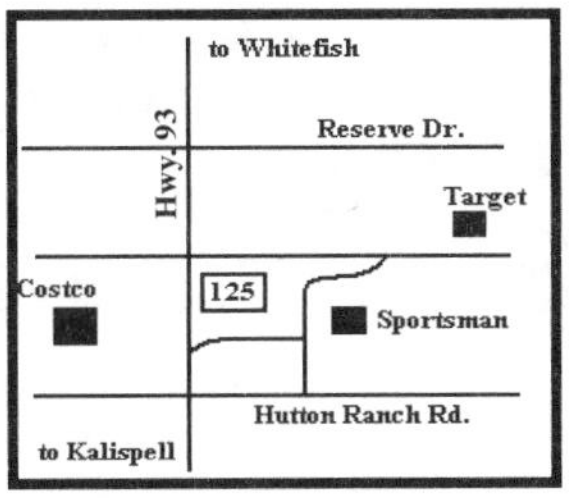

Mon - Fri 10 - 5:30
Sat 10 - 4

Authorized Dealer
Elna and Babylock

elna babylock

www.glacierquilts.com

11,000 bolts of Fabrics, Kits, Books, Patterns, Notions, Classes and Finished Quilts. Online Newsletter.

Missoula, MT #11

Timeless Quilts & Friends Quilt Shop/BERNINA

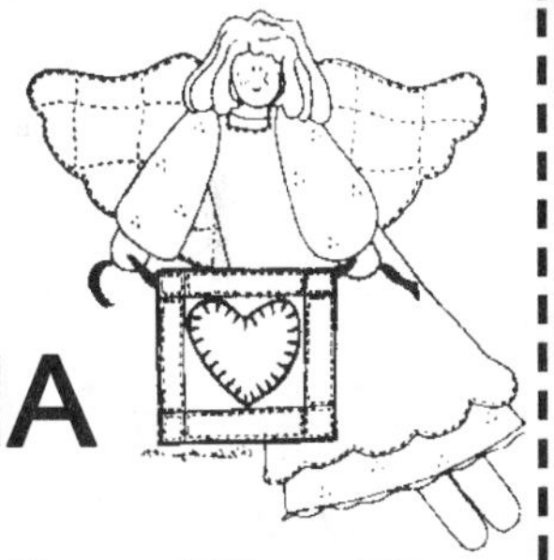

Located in the Towne Court at Reserve St.

2412 River Rd. 59804
(406) 542-6566 Fax: (406) 327-0742

www.tqandf.com

info@tqandf.com

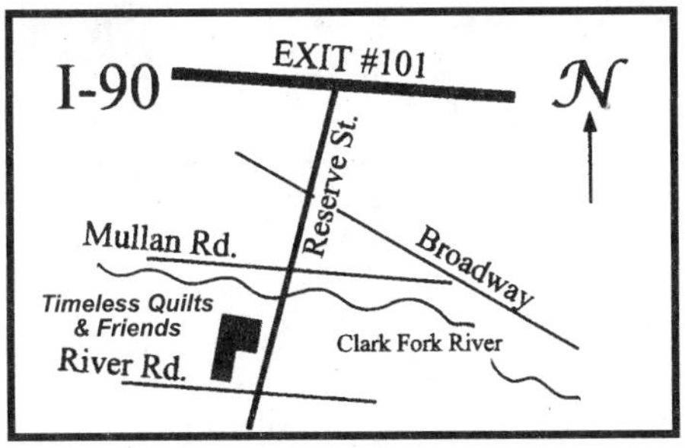

*** Featuring Fine Cotton Fabrics ***
*** Books, Patterns, Notions & Classes ***
*** Quilts for Sale ***

Custom Hand-Guided Machine Quilting
Bring your finished quilt tops along - we'll quilt them and then ship them back to you!

Mon - Fri
10 - 5
Sat 10 - 4

We sell all BERNINA sewing machines and sergers. We are an authorized BERNINA Repair shop. We service all makes & models of machines and sergers.

Missoula, MT #12

Mon - Sat 10 - 5:30 Sun 11 - 4

Quilter's Quarry

1122 S. Russell St. 59801
(406) 549-3630
Est: 2005 2000+ bolts
quiltersquarry@live.com
www.quiltersquarry.com
The best selection of batiks, flannels and patterns in town.
We're a HandiQuilter Rep.

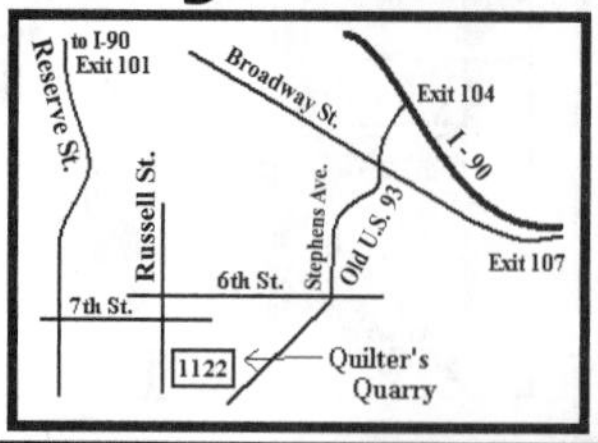

Bonner, MT #13

Mon - Sat 10 - 5

Blackfoot Trading Post

11690 E. US Hwy. 200 59823
(406) 258-6895
Est: 2000 3400 sq.ft. 2000 Bolts
blackfootquilting@montana.com
www.blackfootquilting.com
We are a quilt shop selling quality Cotton, Flannel and Batik fabrics, specializing in western and wildlife prints and patterns.
Made in Montana Quilts and Gifts.
Gammill Classic longarm quilting available.

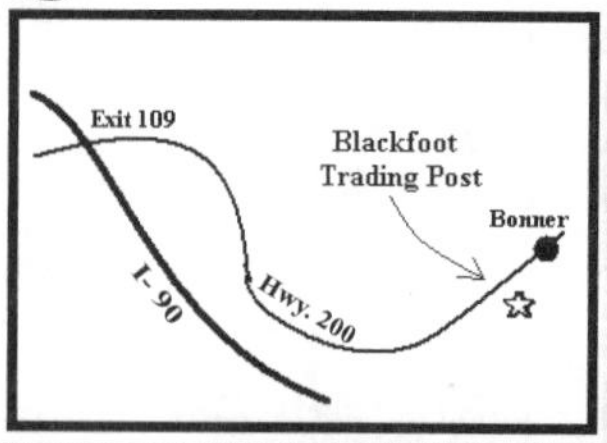

Avon, MT #14

Fri & Sat 10 - 5 Sun 12 - 4

Birdseye Mercantile

105 Main St. w 59713
(406) 492-7070
Owner: Jill McIntosh Newsletter Available
birdseyemercantile@gmail.com
Specializing in Moda Quilting fabrics and Brown's Sheep Co. Wool Yarn, patterns, gifts, beautiful antiques, and much more!
Custom Long arm and embroidery service.

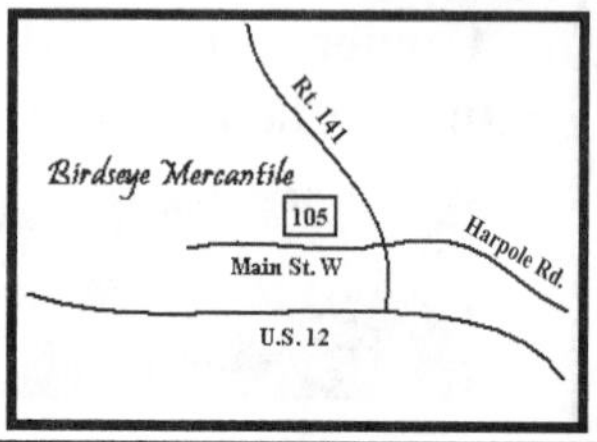

Helena, MT #15

Mon - Fri 10 - 6 Sat 10 - 5 Sun 12 - 4

The Sewing Palace

1103 Helena Ave. 59601
(406) 443-5724
Fax: (406) 443-3924
www.thesewingpalacebernina.com

Largest in-town selection of quality 100% cottons, specializing in batiks, flannels and brights. Large selection of specialty threads, books, patterns, and classes. Award winning Bernina dealer.

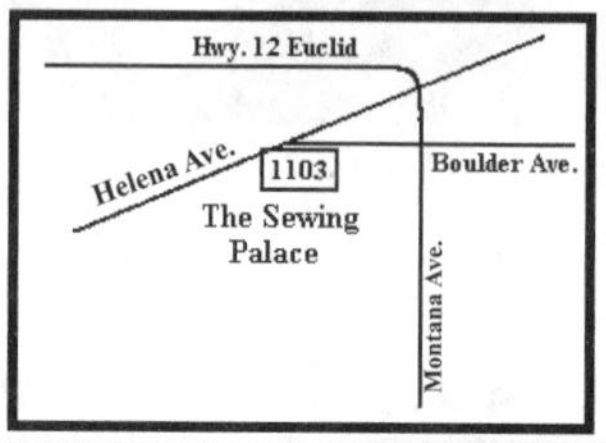

Whitehall, MT #16

Tues - Sat 10 - 5 Wed til 9 or call as the shop is at my home and I'd be happy to open.

7 Sowden Ln. 59759
(406) 287-9237
chris@dysfunctionalquilter.com
Est: 2009
Traditional Quilts & Patterns, Reproduction Fabrics, Daiwabos
Kits & Gifts
Quilt Restoration

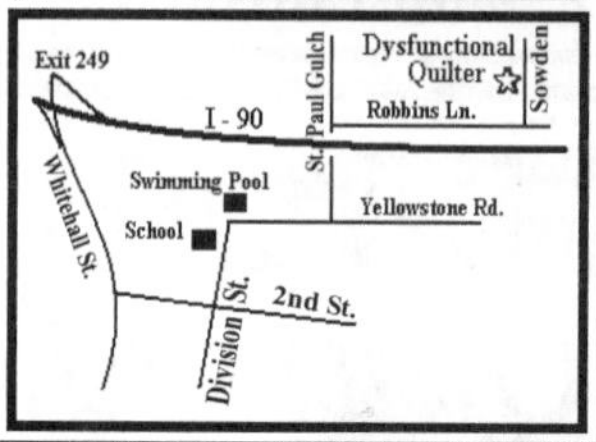

Come sneak a peek @ "2010" Ugly Fabric Quilt
www.DysfunctionalQuilter.com

Townsend, MT #17

Tues, Wed, Fri, Sat 10 - 5 Thur 12 - 6

Creative Closet

222 Broadway 59644
(406) 266-4555
Owners: Shirley & Bob Wilson
Est: 2004 2500 sq.ft. 1500 bolts

Western Wildlife fabrics. Good selection of Fairy Frost fabrics & flannels. Extraordinarily large selection of Panels and Quilting Kits.
Annual Sale - last 2 weeks of February
40% off fabric & kits.

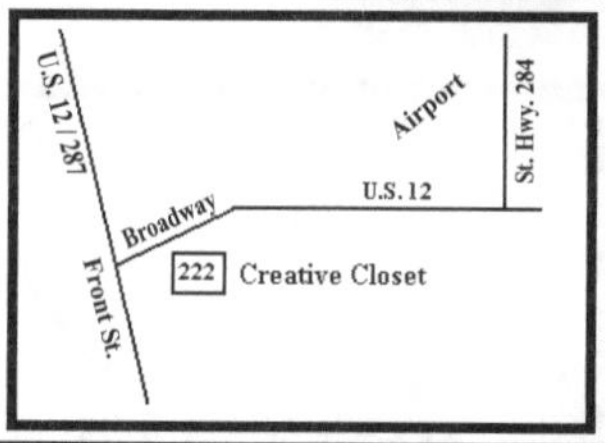

Deer Lodge, MT #18

Mon - Sat 9 - 5:30 Sun 12 - 5

Quilter's Corner, Etc.

401 Main St. 59722
(406) 846-3096
Fax: (406) 846-2298
Owner: Donna McCarthy
donnamaccpt@aol.com
www.quiltsinmontana.com
A bank built in 1912 is the home of 3000 Bolts of fabric, patterns, books and quilting ideas.

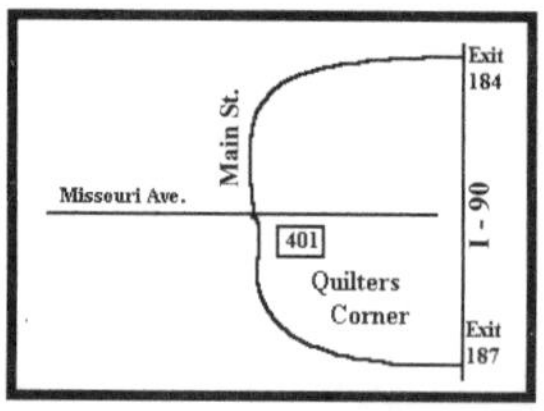

Belgrade, MT #19

Mon - Fri 10 - 5:30 Sat 10 - 4

Quilts on Broadway

206 S. Broadway 59714
(406) 388-4600 Fax: Same
Owners: Peggy & Sue Est: 2006
2500 sq.ft. 2000+ Bolts Newsletter
quiltsonbroadway@yahoo.com
www.quiltsonbroadway.com
We welcome you to our full service quilt store in our beautiful turn of the century blue house.

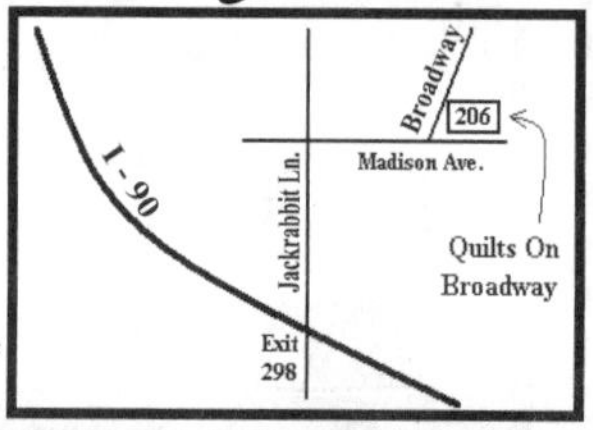

Dillon, MT #20

Mon - Sat 10 - 5:30

The No. 1 Ladies Quilt Shop

104 N. Montana St. 59725
(406) 683-5884
Fax: (406) 276-3750
Owner: Cynthia Ayers
Est: 2007 3000 sq.ft.
2500+ Bolts Online Newsletter
cynthiaayers@3riversdbs.net
www.no1ladiesquiltshop.com
Beautiful selection of Fabrics, Patterns, Books and Notions in an historic 1883 Building. Fully stocked SALE room. Formerly Crafty Quilter.

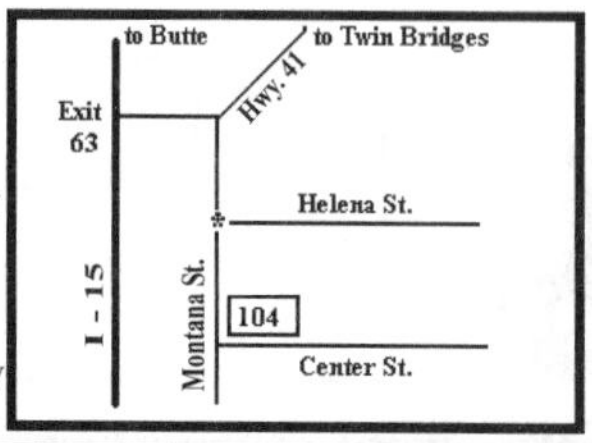

Harlowton, MT #21

Mon - Fri 9:30 - 5:30 Sat 9:30 - 5

Diana's Quilts-n-Things

101 First SE 59036
(406) 632-4861
Est: 2003 2000 sq.ft. 1000 Bolts
drday@itstriangle.com
www.dianasquiltsnthings.com

Unique quilt and gift shop with gift items handcrafted by Montana artists.
Specialize in Hoffman and Moda fabrics.

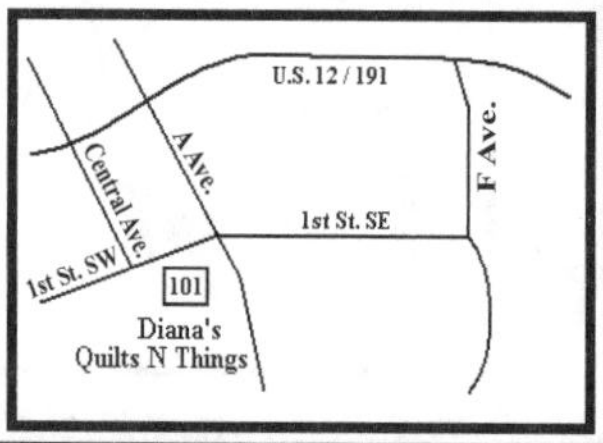

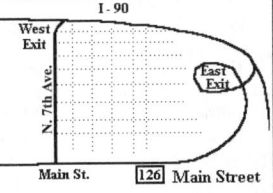

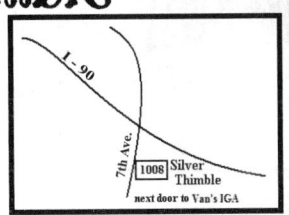

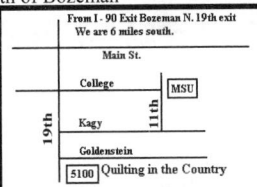

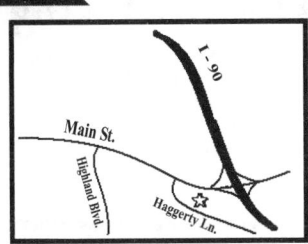

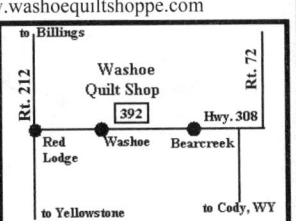

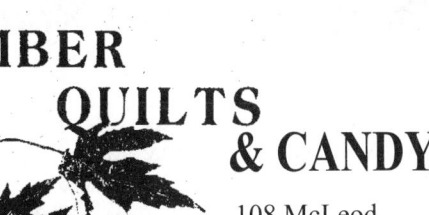

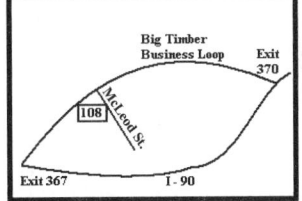

Laurel, MT #29

Mon - Fri 10 - 6
Sat 10 - 5

Trackside Quilting

401 E. Main 59044
(406) 628-7051
Fax: (406) 628-6451
Owner: Sue Hanson
tracksidequilting@msn.com Est: 2008
www.tracksidequilting.com 1400 sq.ft.
Great assortment of new fabrics, patterns, notions and kits. Just 12 miles west of Billings.

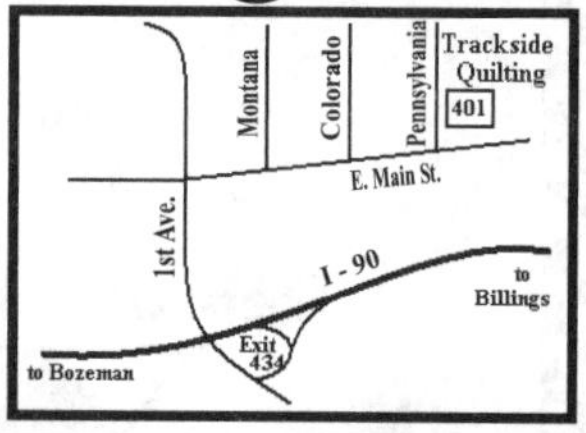

Billings, MT #30

Mon - Fri 10 - 5:30
Sat 10 - 5

Fiberworks

3213 Henesta Dr. 59102
(406) 656-6663 Fax: (406) 656-3363
www.fiberworks-heine.com Est: 1994
Owner Laura Heine invites you to her 6100 sq.ft. building to see the largest selection of fabrics, books, notions and quilt patterns around. Also see Laura's newest line of fabrics, have her sign one of her many book selections or take a long-arm quilting class. Fiberworks is touted as the "quilters haven".

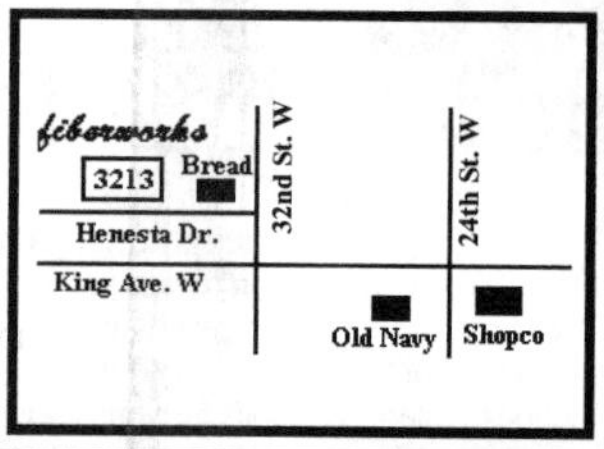

Billings, MT #31

Mon - Sat 9:30 - 5:30

Bernina Sewing Center

Friendly & Helpful.

1505 Rehberg Ln. 59102
(800) 598-8976 or (406) 656-4999
Owner: Doris Holzer
www.berninabillings.com
Authorized Bernina Dealer.
HandiQuilter Dealer.
Horn Cabinet Dealer.
Quilting books, patterns, supplies.
Large selection of quilting fabrics. Classes.

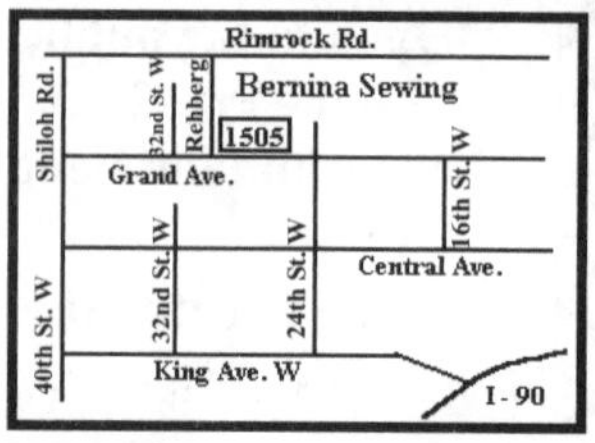

Billings, MT #32

Thurs - Sat 10 - 5
Or by Appt.

Four Winds Quilting
family, friends, faith, fabric

2311 Pine St. 59101
(406) 860-4529
Owner: Nancy Sasse
Est: 2008
Online Newsletter
Great selection of quilting cottons, quilt kits & patterns.
nancy@4windsquilting.com
www.4windsquilting.com

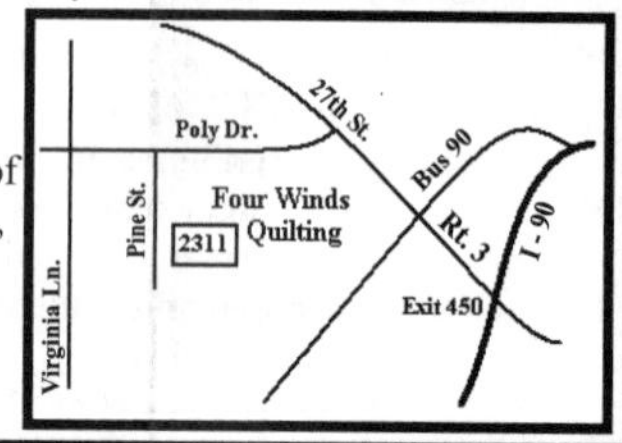

Billings, MT #33

Mon - Sat 9 - 6
Sun 12 - 5

Backdoor Quilt Shoppe

712 Carbon St. #A,
P.O. Box 80833 59102
Off 20th & King behind Perkins
(406) 655-1001 Est: 2002
(Fax: (406) 655-0009
5000 sq.ft. 4000+ Bolts
www.backdoorquiltshoppe.com
Full Service Quilt Shop.
Classes. Antique Machines.
Authorized Brother Pacesetter dealer.

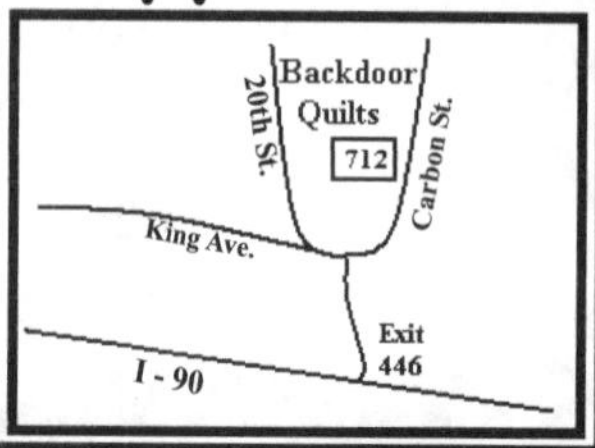

Mile City, MT #34

Mon - Sat 9 - 5:30

Fabrications

3010 Stower 59301
(406) 234-1008

Fabrics, notions, books.
Moda, Hoffman, Benartex and gifts.
Next door to Unique Creations.
6 blocks from interstate 1st stop light.

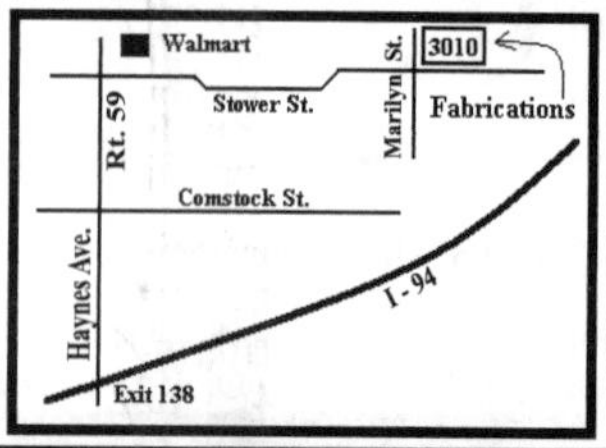

Glendive, MT #35

Mon - Sat 10 - 5
Tues til 8

The Enchanted Room

222 W. Towne St. 59330
(406) 377-4745 or (866) 377-4745
Fax: (406) 377-4745
Owners: Myrna Quale & Laura Glueckert
www.Enchanted-Room.com
Quilt Shop located in Restored Historic Home. Excellent Selection of Quilting Fabric, Books, & Notions. Unique gifts, Custom Floral, Home Decorating Accessories.

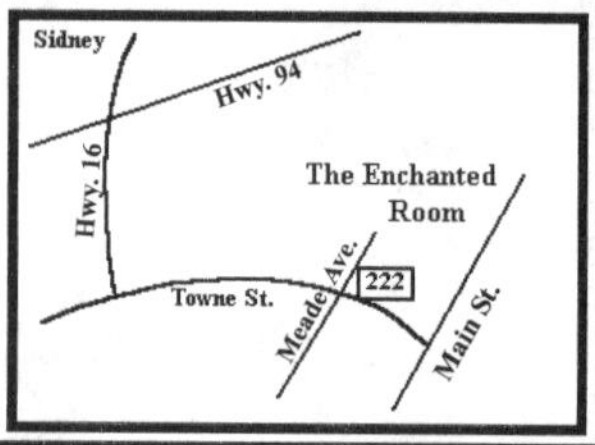

Sidney, MT #36

Summer Hrs.
Tue - Thur 10 - 5
Fri 10 - 3
Winter Hrs.
Tues - Fri 10 - 5
Sat 10 - 3

Quilts & More

12653 Cty. Rd. 352 59270
(406) 482-3366 Fax: (406) 482-6772
Est: 1999 2600 sq.ft. 3000 bolts
vanhook@midrivers.com
The best Quilt Shop in the "country" in eastern MT and western ND.
Specializing in western, flannels, batiks and jewel tones. Machine quilting available.

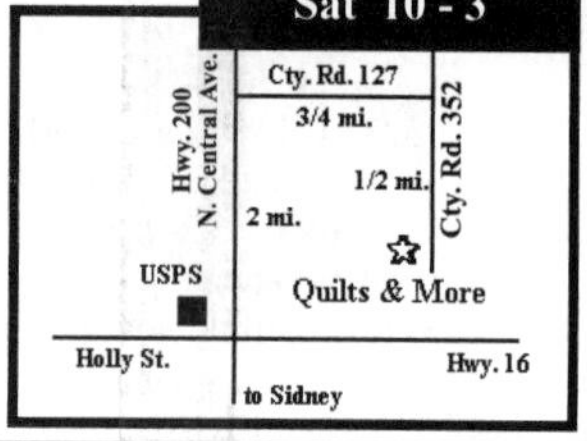

Sidney, MT #37

Mon - Fri 9 - 4:30

Quilted Treasures

609 S. Central Ave., Suite 2 59270
(406) 433-5586 Est: 2003

Custom long-arm quilting service
Average turn-around -- 4 weeks

Shop online for wide quilt back fabric at www.flipsidefabrics.com

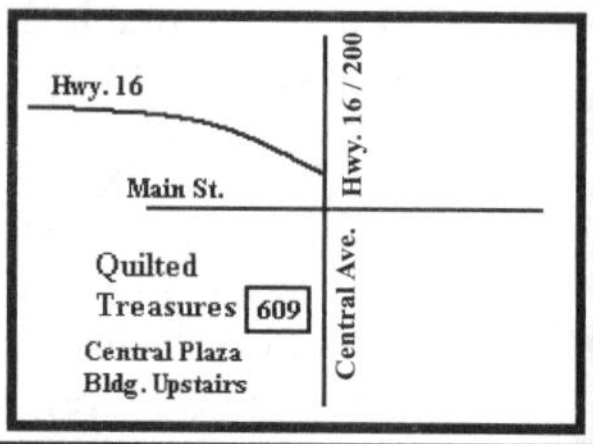

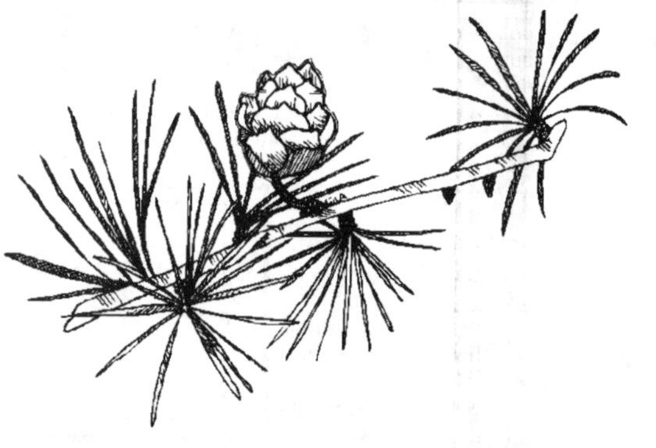

Glasgow, MT #38

Mon - Fri 9:30 - 5:30 Sept-May
Sat 10 - 4 June-Aug
Sat 10 - 3

The Plaid Square

27 US Hwy. 2 E 59230
(406) 228-9665 Est: 1999
Owner: Della Gardner 2600 sq.ft.
della@plaidsquare.com 3000+ Bolts
www.plaidsquare.com

Full line quilting shop in northeastern Montana. Many 100% cotton flannels, batiks, conversation prints and basics to choose from. Custom machine quilting available.

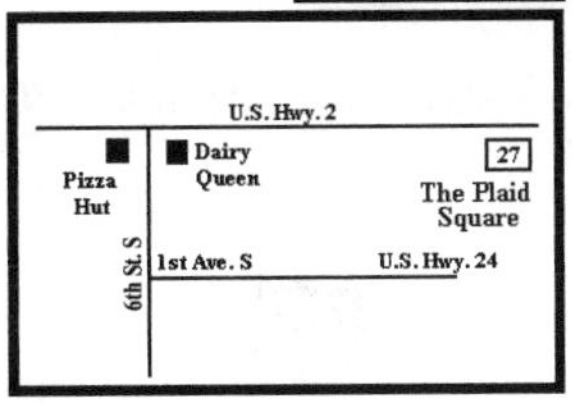

Wolf Point, MT #39

Mon - Sat 10 - 5

Fabric Attic

224 Main St. 59201
(406) 653-1506 Fax: (406) 653-1604
www.fabricattic.com

Specialties - western, wildlife cottons and flannels, 1930's, retro, and nostalgia. Full line quilting fabrics and notions. Accuquilt Go!™ retailer.

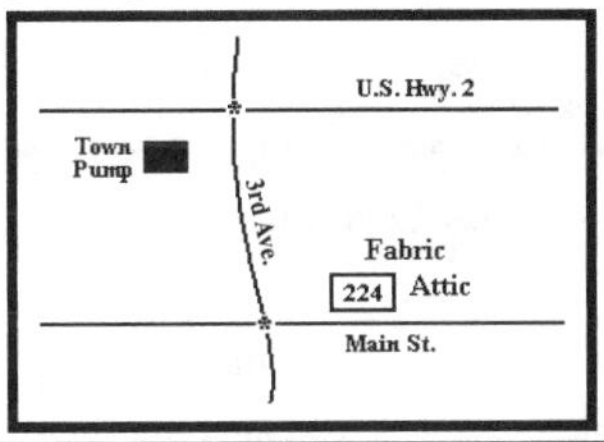

Montana Quilt Shops

Absarokee	Cloud Nine Quilts, 15 S. Woodard Ave.	406-328-4032	
Avon	**Birdseye Mercantile, 105 Main St. W**	**406-492-7070**	**See ad #14, page 330**
Belgrade	**Quilts On Broadway, 206 S. Broadway**	**406-388-4600**	**See ad #19, page 330**
Big Timber	**Little Timber Quilts, 108 McLeod St.**	**406-932-6078**	**See ad #27, page 331**
Bigfork	**Bigfork Bay Cotton Co., 310 Rocky Woods Ln.**	**406-420-1003**	**See ad #5, page 328**
Bigfork	Lynn's hip hop Shop, 1847 Hwy. 209	406-837-6634	
Billings	**Four Winds Quilting, 2311 Pine St.**	**406-860-4529**	**See ad #32, page 332**
Billings	**Bernina Sewing Center, 1505 Rehberg Ln.**	**406-656-4999**	**See ad #31, page 332**
Billings	**Fiberworks, 3213 Hensta Dr.**	**406-656-6663**	**See ad #30, page 332**
Billings	**Backdoor Quilt Shoppe, 712 Carbon St. #A**	**406-655-1001**	**See ad #33, page 332**
Billings	Billings Sewing & Vac, 1212 Grand Ave.	406-252-6989	
Billings	Pin Cushion of Billings, 828 Burlington Ave.	406-652-6328	
Billings	Mountain View Quilt Shoppe, 1106 Main St.	406-256-0475	
Bonner	**Blackfoot Trading Post, 11690 E US Hwy 200**	**406-258-6895**	**See ad #13, page 330**
Bozeman	**Main Street Quilting Company, 126 E. Main St.**	**406-586-6097**	**See ad #22, page 331**
Bozeman	**Reproduction Fabrics.com, 205 Haggerty Ln.**	**406-586-1775**	**See ad #23, page 331**
Bozeman	**Quilting in the Country, 5100 S. 19th Rd.**	**406-587-8216**	**See ad #25, page 331**
Bozeman	**The Silver Thimble, 1008 N 7th Ave.**	**406-587-0531**	**See ad #24, page 331**
Bozeman	Beverly's Bernina, 1439 W. Babcock St.	406-486-5466	
Broadus	Buffalo Land Dry Goods, 221 South Park	406-436-2899	
Butte	Top of the Hill Bernina, 66 W Park St.	406-494-6508	
Carter	**The Quilting Hen, 1156 Buck Bridge Rd.**	**406-734-5297**	**See ad #1, page 327**
Choteau	Cotton Capers Quilt Shop 425 Main S Ave.	406-466-2555	
Cut Bank	Coulee Quilts, 317 E. Railroad St.	406-873-2685	
Deer Lodge	**Quilters Corner, Etc., 401 Main St.**	**406-846-3096**	**See ad #18, page 330**
Deer Lodge	Mrs. Elliott's 608 1/2 Milwaukee Ave.	406-846-1639	
Dillon	**The No. 1 Ladies Quilt Shop, 104 N. Montana St.**	**406-683-5884**	**See ad #20, page 330**
Drummond	Cotton Patch Quilt Shoppe, 38 Front St.	406-288-3297	
Ennis	Stitches That Bind, 111 W. Main St.	406-682-3166	
Glasgow	**Plaid Square Quilting Shop, 27 US Hwy. 2 East**	**406-228-9665**	**See ad #38, this page**
Glendive	**The Enchanted Room, 222 W. Towne St.**	**406-377-4745**	**See ad #35, page 332**
Great Falls	**Big Sky Quilts, 101A Central Ave.**	**406-727-1757**	**See ad #3, page 328**
Great Falls	**The Quilt A-Way, 222 13th St. S**	**406-453-2788**	**See ad #2, page 327**
Hamilton	Fabric Country, 1593 N. 1st St.	406-363-3341	
Harlowton	**Diana's Quilts-n-Things, 101 1st SE**	**406-632-4861**	**See ad #21, page 330**
Havre	Bearly Square Quilting, 220 3rd Ave. #204	406-265-4424	
Helena	**The Sewing Palace, 1103 Helena Ave.**	**406-443-5724**	**See ad #15, page 330**
Helena	Creative Stitches, 3710 N. Montana Ave.	406-443-7540	
Kalispell	**Glacier Quilts, 125 Hutton Ranch Rd.**	**406-257-6966**	**See ad #10, page 329**
Kalispell	**Quilt Gallery, 1710 U. S. Hwy. 93 South**	**406-257-5799**	**See ad #9, page 329**
Laurel	**Trackside Quilting, 401 East Main**	**406-628-7051**	**See ad #29, page 332**
Lewistown	A Quilted Heart of Montana, 311 W. Main	406-535-4212	
Livingston	**Back Porch Quilts, 5237 US Hwy. 89 S., #14**	**406-222-0855**	**See ad #26, page 331**
Mile City	**Fabrications, 3010 Stower St.**	**406-234-1008**	**See ad #34, page 332**
Missoula	**Quilter's Quarry, 1122 S. Russell St.**	**406-549-3630**	**See ad #12, page 330**
Missoula	**Timeless Quilts & Friends Quilt Shop 2412 River Rd. #F**	**406-542-6566**	**See ad #11, page 329**
Missoula	Bobbin' & Bolts, 1900 Russell St.	406-542-0533	
Missoula	Vicki's Quilts Down Under, 2425 W. Central Ave. #B	406-728-9446	
Plains	**Mary Anne's Fabrics, LLC, 100 Farmers St.**	**406-826-3495**	**See ad #7, page 328**
Polson	**All In Stitches, 210 Main St.**	**406-883-3643**	**See ad #6, page 328**
Seeley Lake	**Deer Country Quilts, Bison & Bear Trading**	**406-677-2730**	**See ad #8, page 328**
Shelby	The Creative Needle, 325 Main St.	406-434-7106	
Sidney	**Quilted Treasures, 609 S Central Ave Suite 2**	**406-433-5586**	**See ad #37, page 332**
Sidney	**Quilts & More, 12653 Co Rd 352**	**406-482-3366**	**See ad #36, page 332**
Superior	Cabin Fever Country Quilts, 106 W. 3rd Ave.	406-822-8420	
Thompson Falls	The Quilting House, 215 Woodland St.	406-827-4700	
Townsend	**Creative Closet, 222 Broadway**	**406-266-4555**	**See ad #17, page 330**
Washoe	**Washoe Quilt Shoppe, 392 Hwy. 308 West**	**406-446-4094**	**See ad #28, page 331**
Whitefish	**Backdoor General Store, 131 Central Ave.**	**406-862-6173**	**See ad #4, page 328**
Whitehall	**The Dysfunctional Quilter, #7 Sowden Ln.**	**406-287-9237**	**See ad #16, page 330**
Wolf Point	**Fabric Attic, 224 Main St.**	**406-653-1506**	**See ad #39, this page**

Montana Quilt Shows

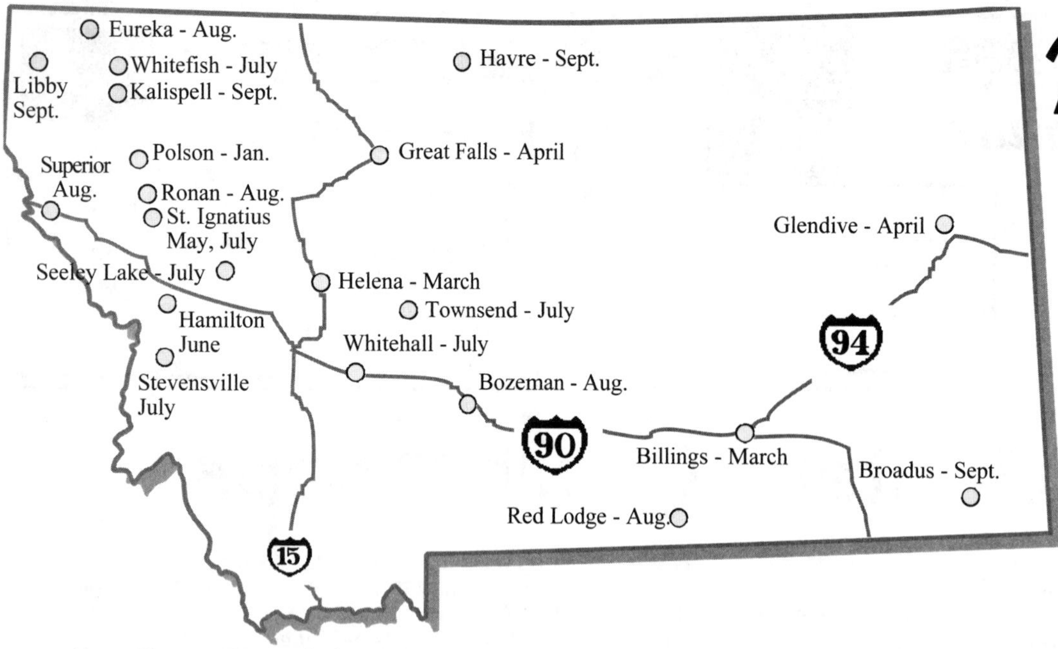

22 Shows

About Shows: We are listing only the very basic information about shows that happen on a regular schedule here. Please check out our website for more details on each show. Also this information tends to change quite often so please verify the event with our website or a local source before you venture far. Or if you're in the right area at the right time, give it a shot.

If you are a show organizer, please keep us updated on your event.
shows@quilterstravelcompanion.com www.quilterstravelcompanion.com

On our website you will also find:

- Exact dates (when we have them)
- Contact Information
- Events happening on a one-time basis
- Sponsor Information
- Description of Event

Month	City	Schedule	Show	Location with address
January				
	Polson	Annual, Last half of January	All in Stitches Quilt Show	Downtown Polson, 210 Main St.
March				
	Billings	Odd Years, 2nd weekend in March	Big Sky Quilt Retreat	Shrine Auditorium, 1125 Broadwater Ave
	Helena	Odd Years, Late March	Helena Quilters Guild Show	Helena Civic Center, 340 Neill Ave.
April				
	Great Falls	Even years, late April	Falls Quilt Guild Show	Montana ExpoPark Exhibition Hall, 400 3rd St. NW
	Glendive	Annual, 3rd or 4th weekend in April	Makoshika Quilt Show	EPEC Community Center, 315 S. Merrill Ave.
May				
	St. Ignatius	Annual, 1st weekend in May	Ayleen's Thursday Quilters Show	LDS Church, N. Main St
June				
	Hamilton	Odd Years, last weekend in June	Gems of the Bitterroot	1st Interstate Center at Fairgrounds, 409 S. First St.
July				
	Whitefish	Odd Years, 1st weekend in July	Stumptown Quilters Society Show	Whitefish Middle School, Spokane Ave & 1st St.
	St. Ignatius	Annual, 2nd Sat. in July	Quilt Auction	Big Tent by St. Ignatius, Hwy. 93 Between Missoula and Polson
	Stevensville	Even Years, 2nd Fri & Sat in July	Sapphire Quilters Show	Stevensville High School Gym, 300 Park St.
	Seeley Lake	Annual, 3rd Fri & Sat of July	Seeley Lake Quilt Festival	Seeley Elementary School, School Ln.
	Townsend	Odd Years, 3rd weekend in July	Townsend Quilt Show	Broadwater High School Gym, N. Cedar & 2nd St.
	Whitehall	Annual, 3rd weekend in July	Quilt Show & Frontier Days	Whitehall High School, 1 Yellowstone Rd.
August				
	Eureka	Annual, 1st Sat. in August	Eureka Outdoor Quilt Show	Tobacco Valley Historical Village, South end of Town
	Red Lodge	Annual, 1st weekend of August	Town & Country Quilt Guild	Carbon County Arts Center
	Ronan	Annual, 1st weekend in August	Mission Mountain Quilt Guild Show	K. William Harvey Elementary Gym, 221 4th Ave. NW
	Superior	Annual, 1st weekend of August	Cabin Fever Quilters Show	Superior High School, 410 Arizona Ave. (Exit 47 off I-90)
	Bozeman	Annual, 3rd Sat. in August	Indoor/Outdoor Quilt Show	Emerson Center for Arts & Culture, 111 S. Grand Ave.
September				
	Libby	Annual, 2nd weekend in September	Kootenai Valley Quilt Guild Show	Asa Woods School, 700 Idaho Ave.
	Broadus	Annual, 3rd Sat. in September	Stitch & Chatter Quilt Show	Broadus Community Center
	Havre	Annual, 2nd weekend in September	Hi Line Quilt Guild Show	Community Center Holiday Village Mall, Hwy. 2 West edge of Town
	Kalispell	Annual, 4th weekend in September	Flathead Quilters' Guild Show	Flathead County Fairgrounds, 265 N. Meridian Rd.

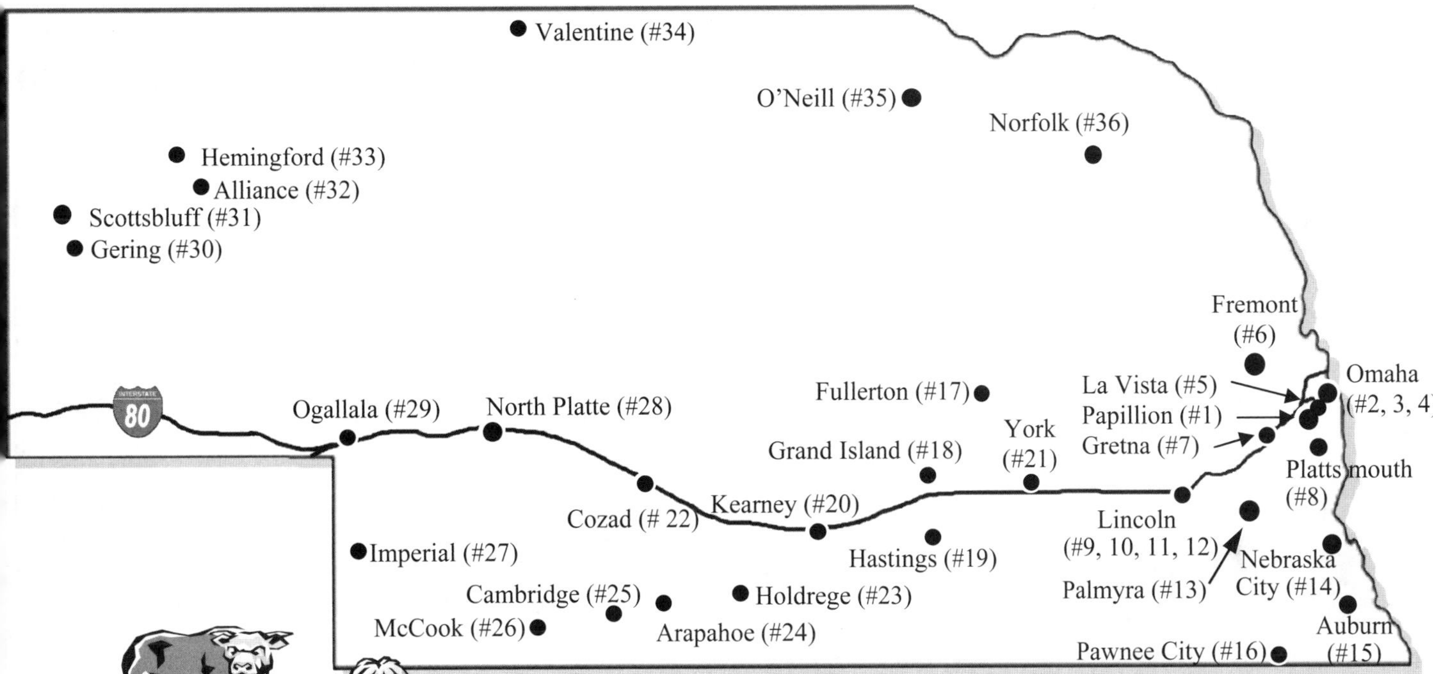

36 Featured Shops

NEBRASKA

Two Locations in the Omaha Area

Country Sampler

Mon - Fri 10:00 - 5:30 Sat 10:00 - 5:00
Thurs til 8:00 Sun 12:00 - 5:00

Omaha, NE #2

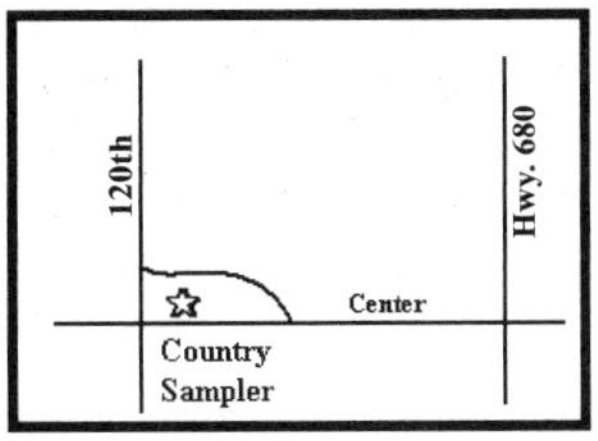

11928 W. Center Rd.
Omaha, NE 68144
(402) 333-6131
Est: 1990 5000 sq.ft.

Papillion, NE #1

841 Tara Plaza
Papillion, NE 68046
(402) 537-9515
Est: 1998 3100 sq.ft.

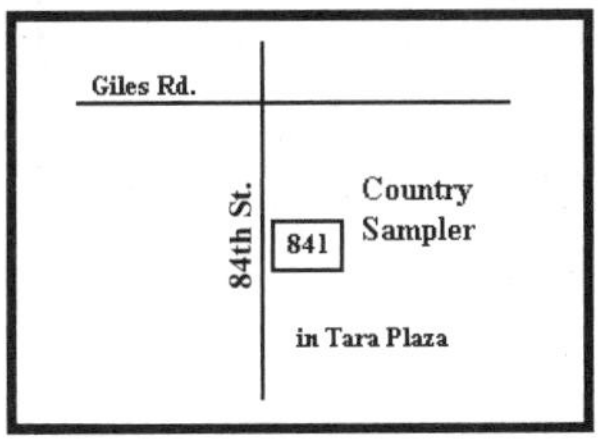

Owner: Deb Cizek

Come and see why Country Sampler was selected as a featured shop in the Better Homes & Gardens Quilt Sampler Magazine for 2002! Over 5,000 bolts of 100% cottons, flannels and homespuns! Tons of kits, patterns and books, block of the months and stitcheries.

Sunshine Stitches

525 N. 155th Plaza
Omaha, NE 68154
Pepperwood Village
(402) 504-1345
info@sunshinestitches.com
Authorized PFAFF, Brother & Juki dealer.

Over 1000 bolts of fabric to suit every taste.
Books, patterns and notions.
Largest thread selection in Omaha!
Free online Newsletter.

Mon - Sat 10 - 6
Thurs til 7 Sun 1 - 5

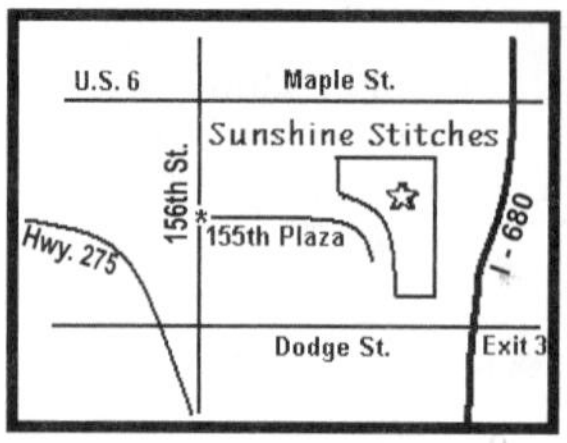

www.sunshinestitches.com

Omaha, NE #3

Omaha, NE #4

Mon - Fri 9 - 5:30
Sat 10 - 2

The Quilt Studio
The next generation in quilting

4429 S 50th St. 68117
(402) 934-4750
Owner: Carol Cisar Est: 2001 2000 sq.ft.
carol@thequiltstudio.net 2000 bolts
www.quiltstudiofabrics.net

Contemporary quilt fabrics, patterns & kits.
Longarm Quilting Specialists also!

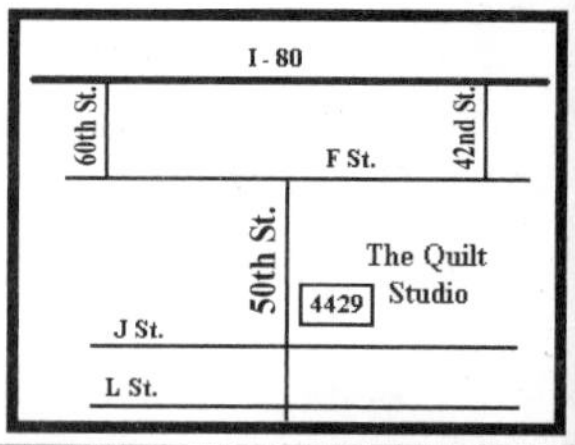

La Vista, NE #5

Mon - Fri 9:30 - 5:30
Sat 9:30 - 5

Log Cabin Quilt Shop
Serving Area Quilters since 1981

in the One Val Verde Place

9635 Giles Rd. 68128
(402) 333-5212
margie@logcabinquilts.com
www.logcabinquilts.com
Fabric from the latest designers. Patterns, books and our kit selection is extensive. We want to be your first and last stop when shopping for fabric and quilting supplies.

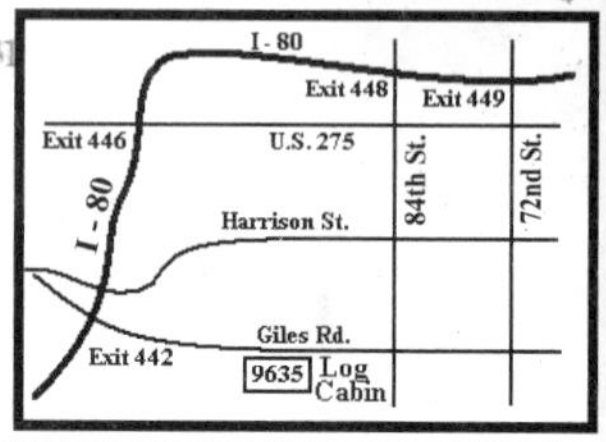

Country Traditions

330 North Main
Fremont Nebraska 68025
402-721-7752
info@countrytraditionsonline.com

Est. 1997

Better Homes Quilt Sampler Featured Shop

"Where Friendships & Quilting Traditions Begin"

Visit us online for news, mail order & newsletter!
www.countrytraditionsonline.com

- 5,000+ Bolts of Fabric
- Everything for your Quilting Needs
- Home Décor & Gift Items
- PFAFF© Sewing Machines/Accessories
- Handi-Quilter© Machines/Accessories

Handi Quilter®

PFAFF®

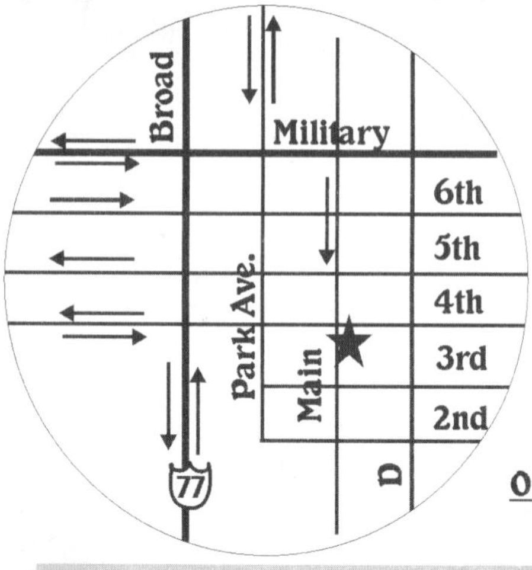

Shop Hours

Mon-Friday
10am-5:30pm

Thursdays
10am-8pm

Saturdays
10am-5pm

Online Shopping
24/7

Fremont, NE #6

Gretna, NE #7

Mon, Tues & Wed 10-5:30
Thurs 10-7
Fri & Sat 10-5

Celebrating our 10th year !

The Quilted Moose

109 Enterprise Dr., Gretna, NE 68028
(402) 332-4178 Fax: (402) 332-4757
Owner: Debbie Roberts 3000 sq.ft. 6000+ bolts
www.quiltedmooseonline.com
Minglewood Lodge Retreat Center--Accommodates up to 11 overnight guests. Call the Quilted Moose for reservations.

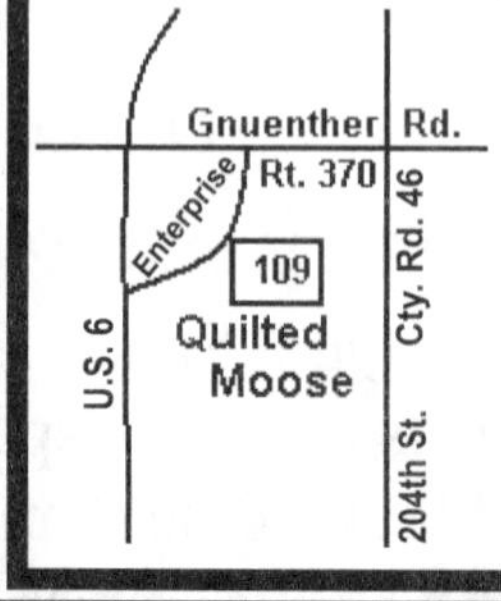

It's time to get down to the Moose! We're busy getting in new fabric and creating new kits for you. Classes. We carry the largest selection of batiks, Japanese taupes and flannels in eastern NE. Check out our exclusive designs from the Quilted Moose.

Seams To Be Quilt Shoppe

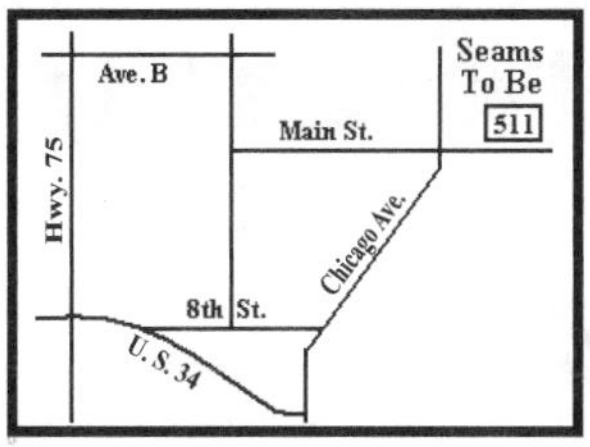

Great lighting, lots of space, great customer service. Over 6000 bolts, including 30's reproductions, batiks, flannels, Thimbleberries and brights. Only 60 miles from the International Quilt Studies Center in Lincoln, NE. "We're worth the trip"

Plattsmouth, NE #8

www.seamstobequilts.com

511 Main St. 68048
(402) 296-3360
Owner: Terri O'Brien Est: 2005
Free Newsletter 5000 sq.ft.
seams@windstream.net

Monday - Friday 10 - 6
Thursday til 7:30
Saturday 10 - 5
Sunday 1 - 5

Lincoln, NE #9

5221 S. 48th St., Suite 4
Sutter Place Mall
Lincoln, NE 68516
(402) 489-1067
calicohouse@neb.rr.com

Mon - Sat 10 - 5
Sun 1 - 4

the CALICO HOUSE

Great selection of fabrics from light and brights to dark and muddy colors.

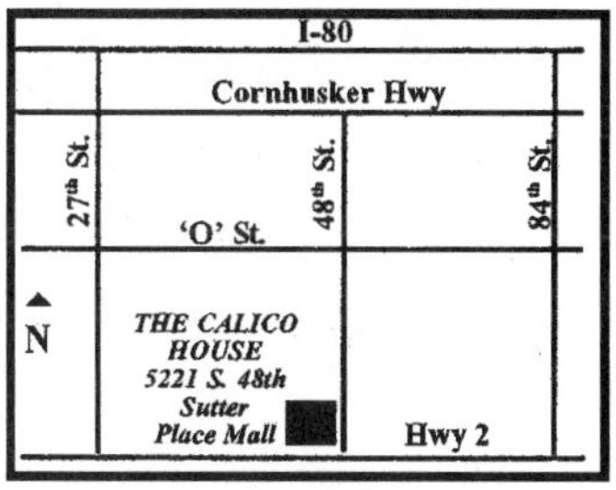

· Distances on map are not shown in accurate proportion

HOFFMAN BATIKS · MODA · FREE SPIRIT · AMY BUTLER

The Quilted Kitty®

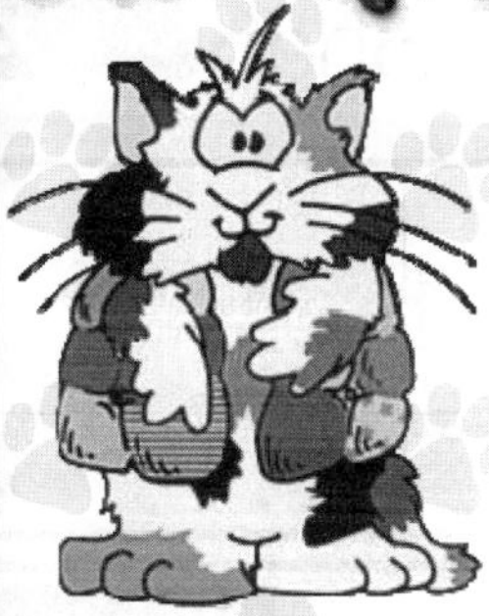

6101 S. 56th St., Ste 6
Lincoln, NE 68516
866-422-9292 or
402-420-9292
Est: 1999 2100 sq.ft.
quiltedkitty@quiltedkitty.com

A visit to the Quilted Kitty is an experience that you will not soon forget! From our beautiful 100% cotton quilting fabrics, the newest in patterns, books, notions and gifts, our great customer service and a story or two about our furry dudes, Caliber, Ople & Wally, you will leave happy and motivated to quilt!

Our quilters are not only our customers but our friends and we treat our friends special! We offer assistance from starting to finishing on your sewing projects!

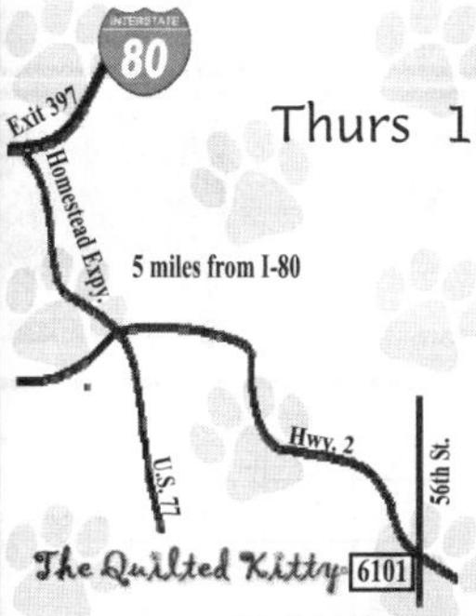

Mon - Wed 10 - 5:30
Thurs 10 - 8 Fri 12 - 5:30 Sat 10 - 4

Sign up online for our weekly newsletters to stay updated on what's new, what's happening and what's coming soon

www.quiltedkitty.com

Lincoln, NE #10

Lincoln, NE # 11

Mon - Sat 10 - 5
Thur til 8

Cosmic Cow

6136 Havelock Ave. 68507
(402) 464-4040
Owners: Roxann & Rich O'Hare
Est: 2003 5000 Bolts

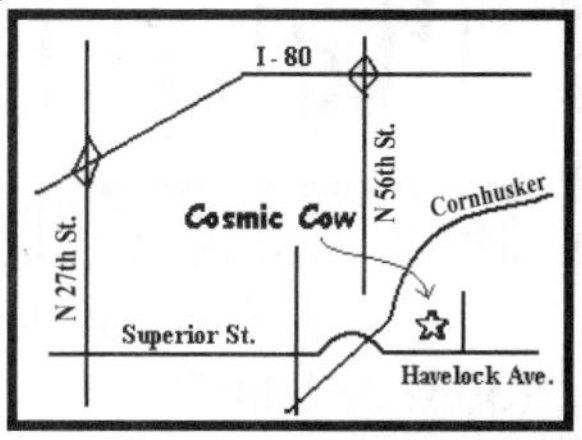

Bold, Contemporary & Fun Fabrics.
Our focus is color and lots of it.
Also hand-dyed & painted fabrics & supplies.

Lincoln, NE #12

Tues - Sat 10 - 4:30
Sun 1 - 4:30

International Quilt Study Center & Museum

1523 N. 33rd (33rd and Holdrege)
P.O. Box 830838 68583
(402) 472-6549 www.quiltstudy.org

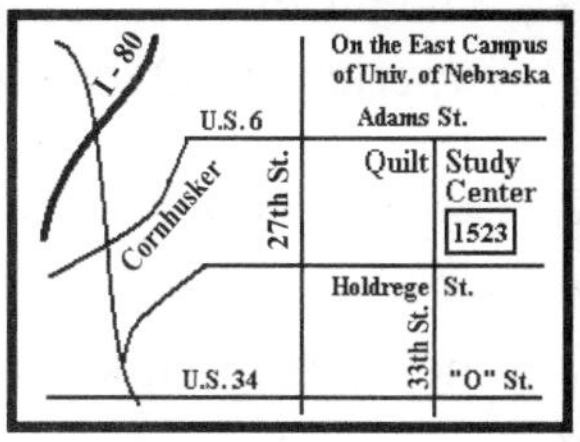

New museum features curated exhibitions (drawn from the world's largest quilt collection), virtual gallery, conservation and care tips, resource and reading room.. Visit www.quiltstudy.org for current exhibition schedule. Group tours welcome.

Palmyra, NE #13

By Appt.

Owner: Gloria Hall
Est: 1989
600 sq.ft.
(402) 780-5773
Price List Avail.

Grandma's Quilts

296 N. 10th Rd. 68418

We have over 100 quilts dating from 1870's to 1960's Vintage Fabric, Tops, Blocks, Feed Sacks & Vintage Aprons. Lectures and brochures on request.

grandma@grandmasquilts.com
www.grandmasquilts.com

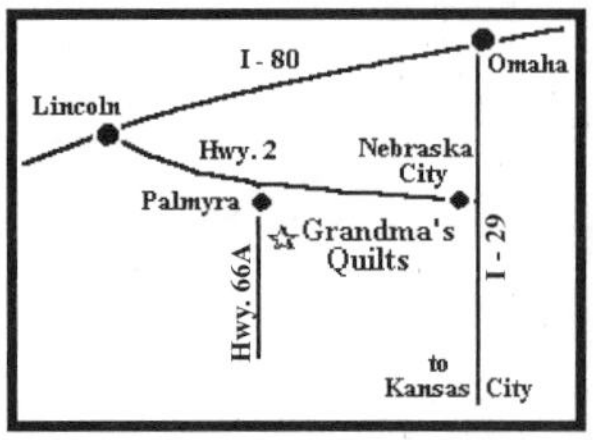

Nebraska City, NE #14

Mon - Fri 9 - 5:30
Sat 9 - 5
Sun 1 - 4

SEWING BASKET

805 Central Ave. 68410
(402) 873-3955
2700 sq.ft. 1000+ bolts
sewingbasket@windstream.net
www.thesewingbasket.biz
Traditional fabric shop since 1975. Featuring all quilting supplies; noted for varieties of novelty prints and hard to find notions.

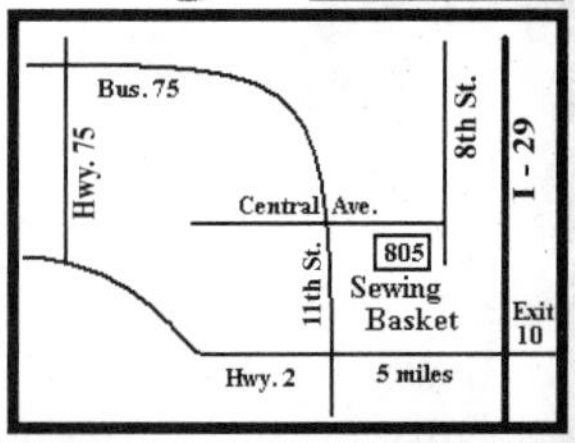

Auburn, NE #15

Tues - Fri 10:30 - 5:30
Thurs til 8
Sat 9:30-2:30

The Fabric Fairie

900 Central Ave. 68305
(402) 274-4454
Owner: Pamela Estrada
Est: 2002 1000 sq.ft. 600 Bolts
pamelasfirst@windstream.net

We love batiks!
Small town shop, big on service.
Relaxed, creative atmosphere.

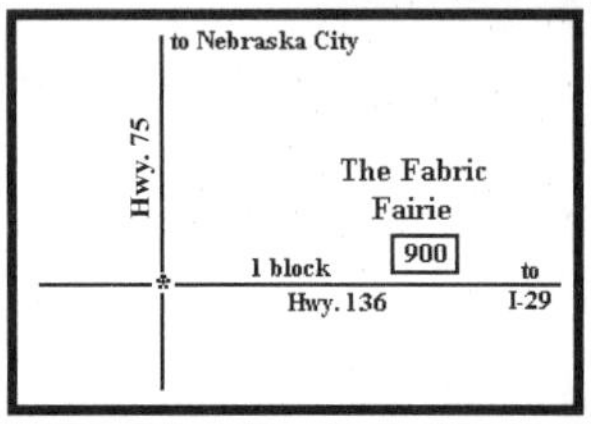

Pawnee City, NE #16

Mon - Fri 10 - 5
Sat 10 - 3

Heavenly Treasures

700 9th St. 68420
(402) 852-2270 Fax: (402) 852-2275
Owner: Marie Glenn
Est: 2004 5000 sq.ft. 3500+ bolts
heavenly4125@yahoo.com
www.heavenlytreasurespc.com
What a joyous and lively experience to visit us. You will have friendly staff to help you select fabrics or patterns. Machine quilting avail.
"The best little quilt shop this side of Heaven"

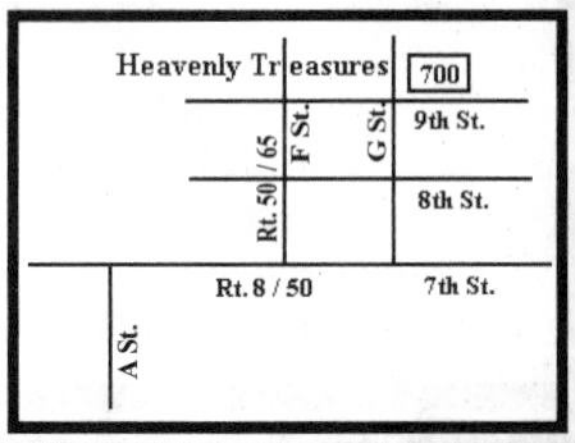

Fullerton, NE #17

Mon - Fri 9 - 5
Sat 9 - 12

Calico Annie's Quilt Shop

210 Broadway 68638
(308) 536-2925 Est: 1999
Owner: Anne Wemhoff
calicoannie@qwestoffice.net
www.calicoanniesquiltshop.com

Bolt after bolt of the newest fabrics nestled in a turn-of-the-century hardware store. 40 miles north of I - 80 exit 332 onto Hwy. 14

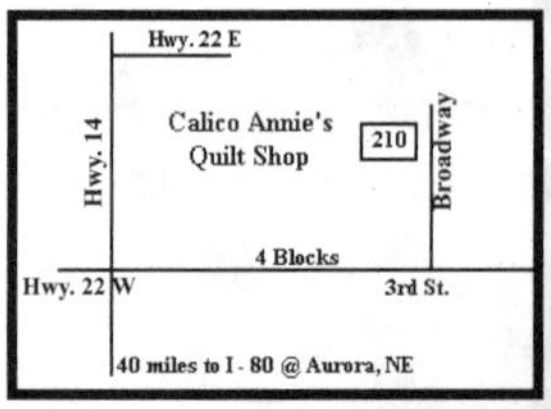

Grand Island, NE #18

Mon - Sat 9 - 6
Thurs til 8

Material Girl

FABRIC, FIBERS & QUILTING SUPPLIES

3415 W. State St. 68803
(308) 381-6675 Owner: Deb Warren
mgf@charterinternet.com

www.materialgirlfabrics.com

The ultimate shopping experience: Over 6000 bolts of bright, geometric, retro fabrics featuring many of today's famous designers, batiks and more.
Lots of Color!

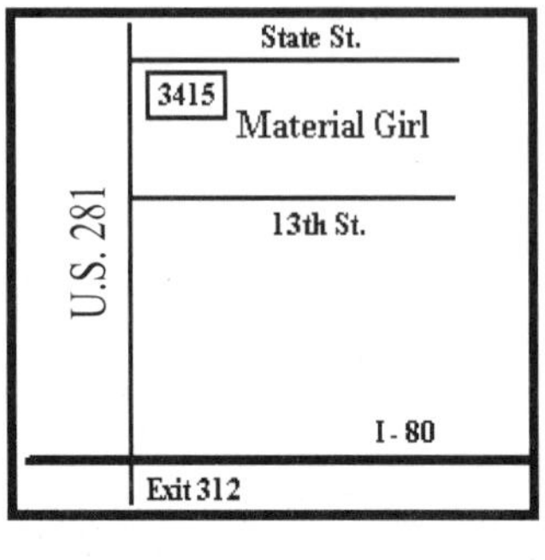

Hastings, NE #19

Mon - Fri 9:30 - 5:30
Sat 9:30 - 5
Summer Sat 9:30 - 3

Calico Cottage

731 W. 2nd St. 68901
(402) 463-6767
Owner: Sue Brown Est: 1986
calicocottage@windstream.net

Over 1500 Bolts of Cotton Fabric plus Quilting Patterns, Books and Notions.
Everything for the Quilter!

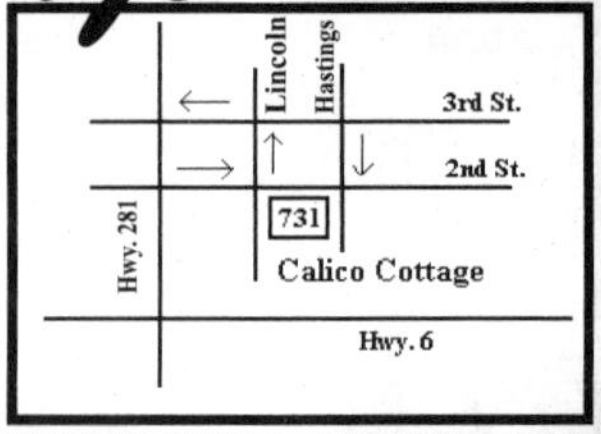

Kearney, NE #20

Mon - Sat 10 - 5
Thurs til 8

2220 Central Ave. 68847
(308) 237-2701
Owner: Phyllis Hamaker
Est: 2001
1000 sq.ft.
1000's of Bolts

A friendly atmosphere with lots of patterns, books, and kits, many Batiks and 100% cottons.
Quilt Gallery on lower level.
quilters.cottage@hotmail.com
www.quilterscottage.net

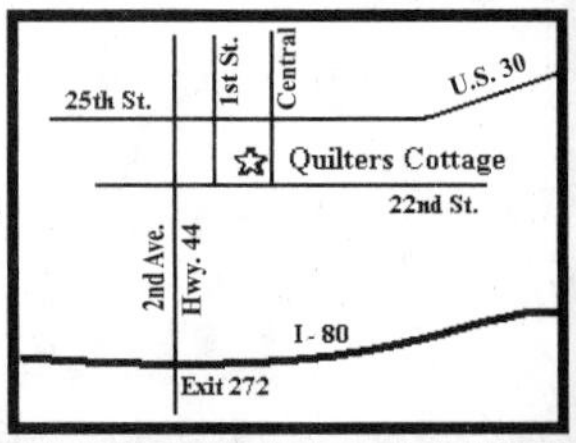

York, NE #21

www.thequiltbasket-york.com

The Quilt Basket

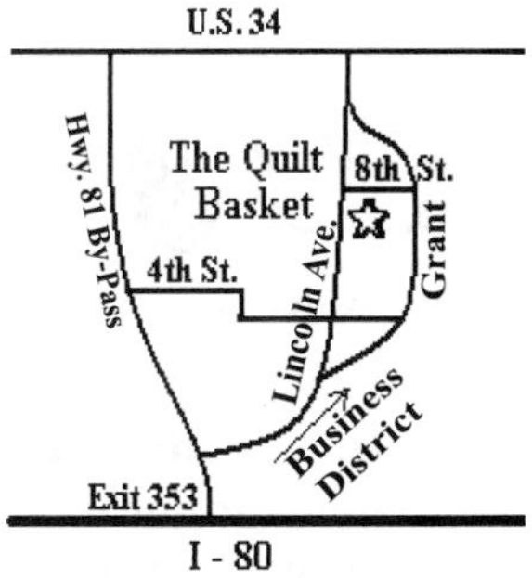

Just 3 miles north of the Junction of I-80 & 81 in Central Nebraska

- Wonderful selection of quilt supplies and fabric
- Notions, Kits & Classes
- Enjoy our Quilt Gallery
  Each month we feature a different quilt artist.
- Bernina sales & service
- Sign up for our free e-newsletter

Monday - Friday
9:30 - 5:30
Thursday til 7:00
Saturday 9:30 - 3:00

718 Lincoln Ave. 68467
402-362-5737
Fax: 402-362-5737 5000+ sq.ft.
info@thequiltbasket-york.com
3000+ Bolts of Fabric

HORN of America COLLECTION **BERNINA**

Cozad, NE #22

Prairie Point Junction

124 East 8th * Box 184 * Cozad, Nebraska 69130
308-784-2010 prairiepointjunction@yahoo.com

Proud to be a Top 10 Shop in Fall 2005 Quilt Sampler

- 2500 bolts of cotton fabrics, lots of flannels
- Tons of inspiring displays, kits, original patterns
- Home of Wool Felt Central * 78+ colors of wool felt

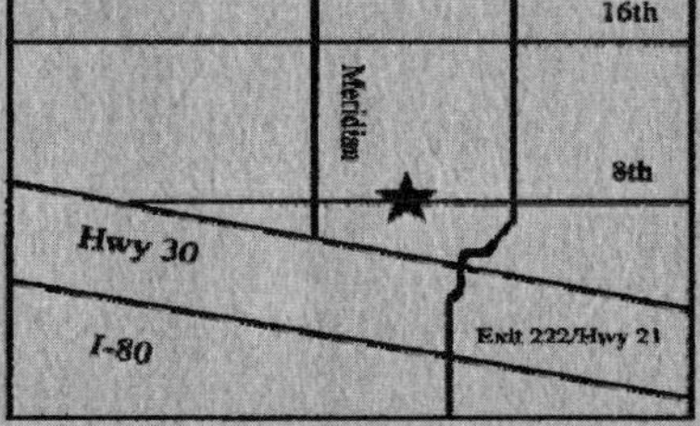

Hours:
Mon-Fri 10-5
Sat 10-4

*Just Minutes off Interstate-80

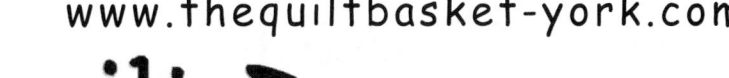

www.prairiepointjunction.com OR www.woolfeltcentral.com

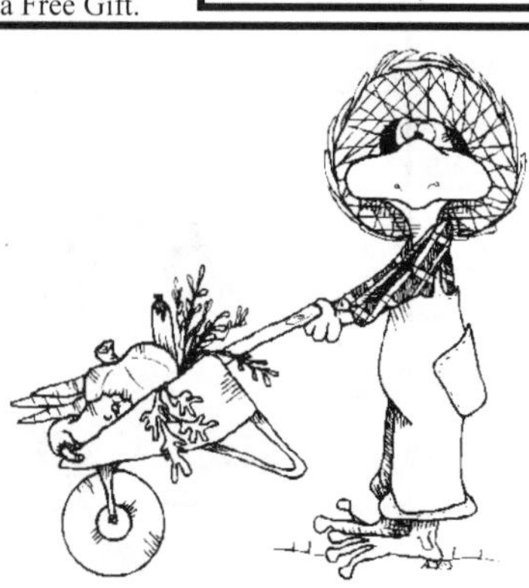

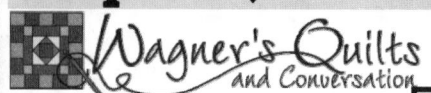

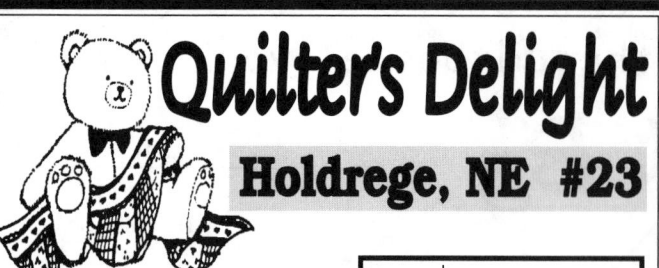

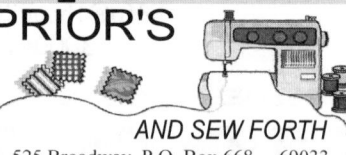

Gering, NE #30

Mon - Fri 10 - 5
Sat 10 - 4

Prairie Pines Quilt Shop

1320 Tenth St. 69341
(308) 436-5152
prairiepines@embarqmail.com
www.prairiepinesquiltshop.com

Our shop has over 2000 bolts of 100% cotton fabrics along with patterns, books, notions, and classes for all of your quilting needs. Authorized Bernina & Janome Sewing Machine Sales & Service.

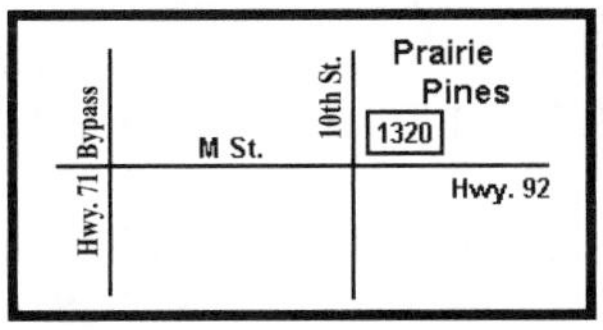

Scottsbluff, NE # 31

Mon - Fri 9:30 - 5:30
Thur til 8
Sat 9:30 - 3

Country Quilts & Fabric

15 E. 27th St. 69361
(308) 220-3622 Est: 1996
countryquilts@embarqmail.com
www.countryquiltsnfabric.com
Owner: Mary Eldridge
2000 Bolts Free Newsletter

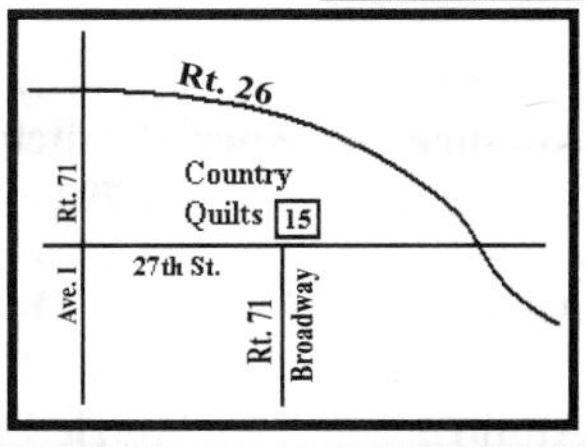

Large variety of quilting cottons, and flannels. Elna sewing machines. Books, pattern, notions, classes, and gifts. Hand made quilt hangers 8" to 28".

Alliance, NE #32

Please Call or Email for APPT.

Special Stitches Machine Quilting

Est: 1987

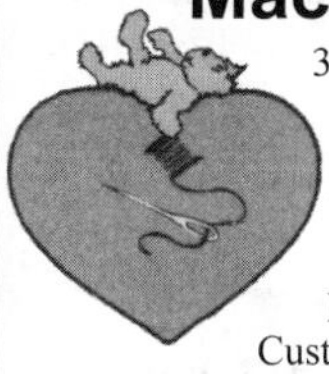

316 Box Butte Ave. 69301
(308) 762-8436
dthiems@gmail.com
www.specialstitches.com
Owner: Deb Thiems

Machine Quilting.
Custom & Memory Quilts
Drop-off Service Available.

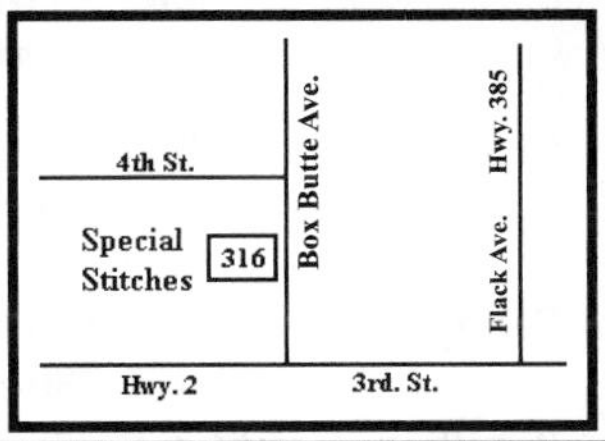

Hemingford, NE #33

Mon - Fri 10 - 5
Sat 10 - 4

PAT'S CREATIVE

7355 Gage Rd. 69348
(308) 487-3999
Fabricfun@bbc.net
www.patscreative.com
Owners: Sonya & Shelley
Est: 1975 2700 sq.ft.

Over 3000 quilting cottons - 500 Flannels Books, Patterns, Threads & Notions.
We sell Bernina & Janome Sewing Machines.
YOUR 1 STOP SEWING SHOP

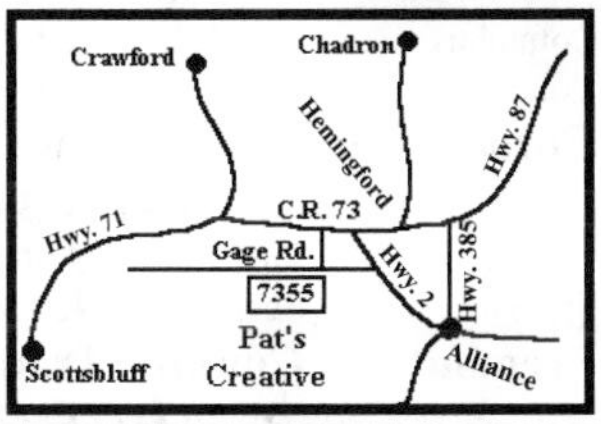

Valentine, NE #34

Mon - Sat 10 - 6

The Quilting Cupboard

130 W. Fourth St. 69201
(402) 376-3702
Owner: Susan Stec
Est: 2008 1500 sq.ft.
1000 bolts

A little shop for all your quilting needs. Fabrics, Notions, Patterns, Wool and Quilt Kits.

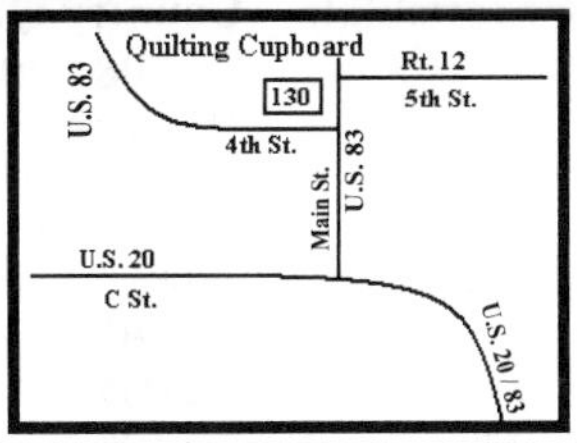

O'Neill, NE #35

Mon - Fri 9:30 - 5:30
Sat 9:30 - 3

Quilters Candy Shoppe

420 E. Douglas 68763
402-336-1953
Fax: 402-336-1957
Est: 2003

quilterscandyshoppe@msn.com
www.quiltcandy.com

Over 4000 bolts of 100% cotton & flannel, a large selection of patterns & books, a full range of quilting supplies, plus gifts for the quilter.

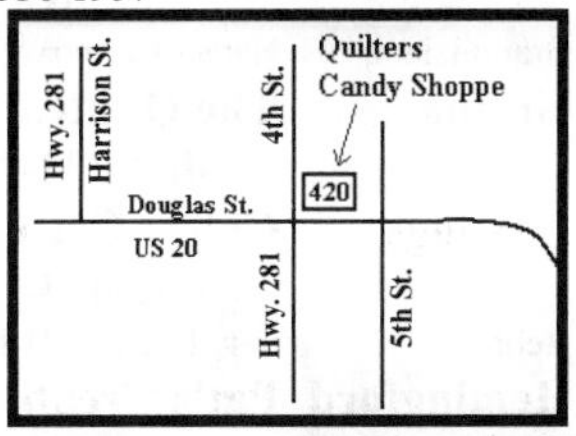

Norfolk, NE #36

Mon -Fri 9:30 - 5:30
Sat 9:30 - 3

Pieceful Pastime

322 W. Norfolk Ave. 68701
(402) 371-0045
Owner: Lea McKenna

Est: 2003 2000 bolts
piecefulpastime@conpoint.com
www.piecefulpastime.com

Our quilt shop offers fabrics, fun, classes, demonstrations, patterns, notions and walls full of samples for inspiration. Online Newsletter.

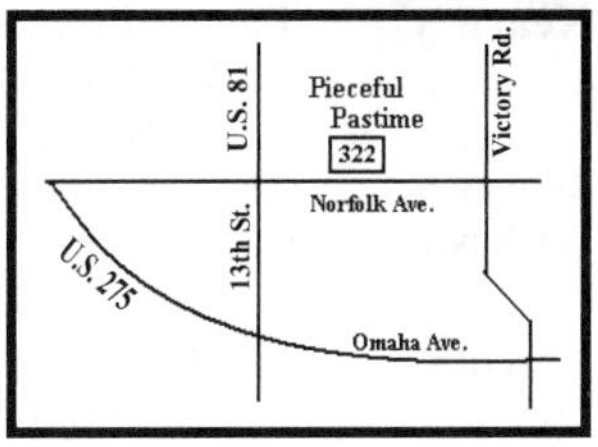

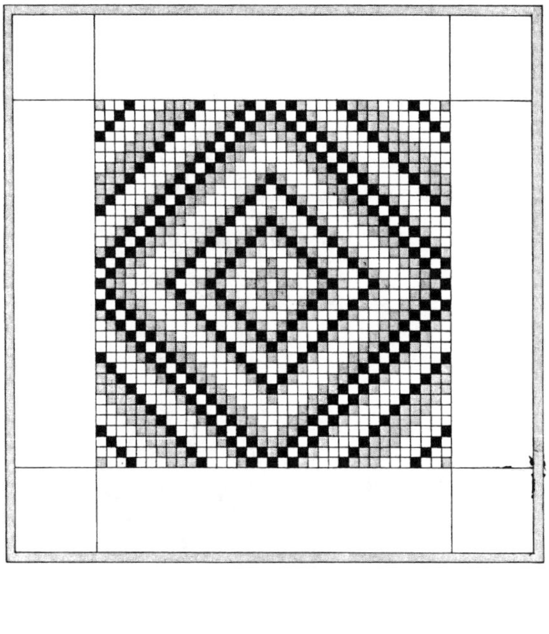

Nebraska Quilt Shops

Ainsworth — The Quilt Trail, 216 N. Main — 402-382-3282

Alliance — Special Stitches, 316 Box Butte Ave.
308-792-8436 — See ad #32, page 341

Alliance — Prairie Creations, 5611 Madison Rd. — 308-762-8365

Arapahoe — Wagner's Quilts & Conversation, 404 Chestnut
308-962-8458 — See ad #24, page 340

Auburn — The Fabric Fairie, 900 Central Ave.
402-274-4454 — See ad #15, page 338

Auburn — Needles I, 72896 638th Ave., Box 11 — 402-274-3339

Aurora — Picket Fence Quilt Shop, 1221 M St. — 402-694-6694

Bridgeport — Sew Many Friends, 912 Main St. — 308-262-0770

Cambridge — Cottage Inspirations, 710 Nasby
308-697-4000 — See ad #25, page 340

Columbus — Sew-What Needle Arts & Quilting, 3415 21st St. — 402-563-3900

Columbus — Claus'en Paus Quilt Shop, 2417 13th St. — 402-564-1618

Cozad — Prairie Point Junction, 124 East 8th
308-784-2010 — See ad #22, page 339 & 402

Crawford — Pine Needle Quilt Shop, 413 2nd St. — 308-665-1107

Franklin — Sew What's New, 629 15th Ave. — 308-425-3055

Fremont — Country Traditions, 330 N. Main
402-721-7752 — See ad #6, page 336

Fullerton — Calico Annie's Quilt Shop, 210 Broadway
308-536-2925 — See ad #17, page 338

Gering — Prairie Pines Quilt Shop, 1320 Tenth St.
308-436-5152 — See ad #30, page 341

Grand Island — Material Girl, 3415 West State St.
308-381-6675 — See ad #18, page 338

Grand Island — Nana's Country Quilt Shop, 506 W. 3rd St. — 308-382-4445

Gretna — The Quilted Moose, 109 Enterprise Dr.
402-332-4178 — See ad #7, page 336

Hastings — Calico Cottage, 731 West 2nd. St.
402-463-6767 — See ad #19, page 336

Hebron — Sew Bee It, 341 Lincoln Ave. — 402-768-6980

Hemingford — Pat's Creative, 7355 Gage Rd.
308-487-3999 — See ad #33, page 341

Holdrege — Quilter's Delight, 323 West Ave.
308-995-2728 — See ad #23, page 340

Imperial — Prior's And Sew Forth, 525 Broadway
308-882-4354 — See ad #27, page 340

Kearney — The Quilters Cottage, 2220 Central Ave.
308-237-2701 — See ad #20, page 338

Kearney — The Sewfari Quilting Co., 8 West 23rd St — 308-234-9007

Kearney — Quilt Blocks Etc., P.O. Box 63 — 308-236-8973

La Vista — Log Cabin Quilt Shop, 9635 Giles Rd
402-333-5212 — See ad #5, page 336

Lincoln — The Quilted Kitty, 6101 S. 56th St., Ste 6
402-420-9292 — See ad #10, page 337

Lincoln — The Calico House, 5221 S. 48th St. #4
402-489-1067 — See ad #9, page 337

Lincoln — Cosmic Cow, 6136 Havelock Ave.
402-464-4040 — See ad #11, page 337

Lincoln — International Quilt Study, 1523 N. 33rd
402-472-6549 — See ad #12, page 337

Lincoln — Sew Creative, 5221 S. 48th St. #17 — 402-489-6262

McCook — Sew Little Time, 213 Norris Ave.
308-345-4572 — See ad #26, page 340

Nebraska City — The Sewing Basket, 805 Central Ave.
402-873-3955 — See ad #14, page 338

Norfolk — Pieceful Pastime, 322 Norfolk Ave
402-371-0045 — See ad #36, page 341

North Platte — The Quilt Rack, 101 W. Front St
308-532-2606 — See ad #28, page 340

Ogallala — Silver Thimble Sewing Center, 108 N. Spruce St.
308-284-6838 — See ad #29, page 340

Omaha — The Quilt Studio, 4429 S. 50th St.
402-934-4750 — See ad #4, page 336

Omaha — Sunshine Stitches, 525 N. 155th Plaza
402-504-1345 — See ad #3, page 336

Omaha — Country Sampler, 11928 W. Center Rd.
402-333-6131 — See ad #2, page 335

Omaha — Personal Threads Boutique, 8600 Cass — 402-391-7733

Omaha — David M. Mangelsen's, 3457 South 84th St. — 402-391-6225

O'Neill — Quilters Candy Shoppe, 420 E. Douglas
402-336-1953 — See ad #35, page 341

Ord — Quilts N' More, 1433 M St. — 308-728-7814

Palmyra — Grandma's Quilts, 296 N. 10th Rd.
402-780-5773 — See ad #13, page 338

Papillion — Country Sampler, 841 Tara Plaza
402-537-9515 — See ad #1, page 335

Pawnee City — Heavenly Treasures, 700 9th St.
402-852-2270 — See ad #16, page 338

Plattsmouth — Seams To Be Quilt Shoppe, 511 Main St.
402-296-3360 — See ad #8, page 337

Scottsbluff — Country Quilts & Fabric, 15 E. 27th St.
308-220-3622 — See ad #31, page 341

Seward — The Fabric Fair, 636 Seward St. — 402-643-4760

Sidney — Borders Quilt Shop, 1017 Illinois St. — 308-254-2557

Syracuse — Common Threads, 325 5th St. — 402-269-2235

Valentine — The Quilting Cupboard, 130 W 4th St.
402-376-3702 — See ad #34, page 341

Wakefield — The Quilt Shop, 301 Main St. — 402-287-2325

Wayne — Just Sew, 512 E. 7th — 402-375-4697

West Point — Creative Notions, 107 N. Main St. — 402-372-2004

York — The Quilt Basket, 718 Lincoln Ave.
402-362-5737 — See ad #21, page 339

Nebraska Quilt Shows

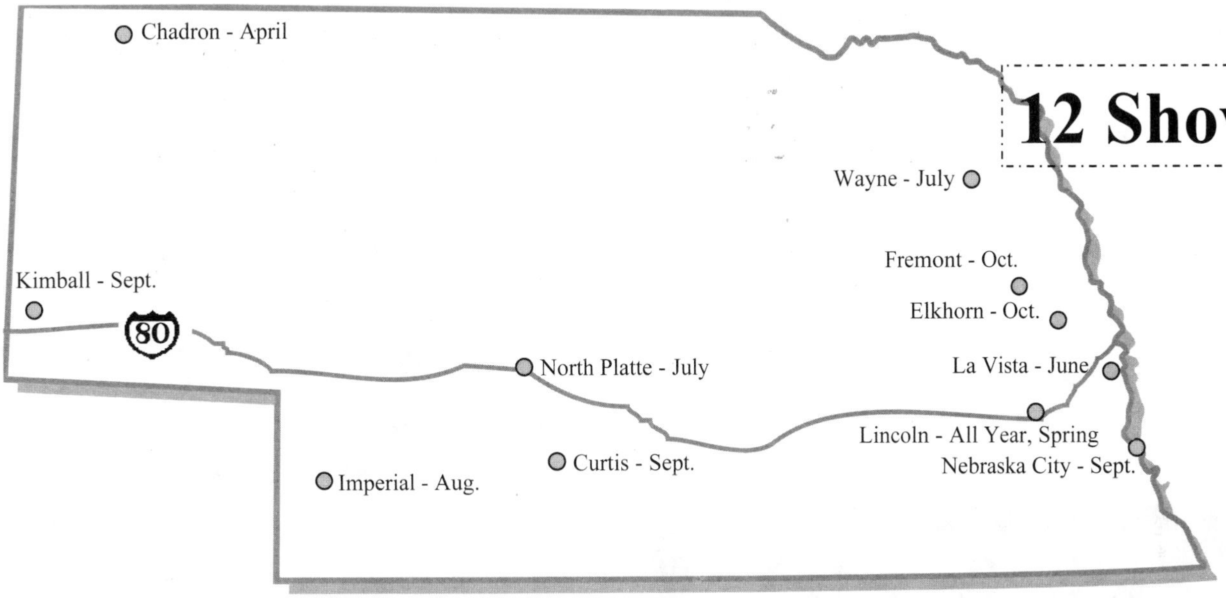

About Shows: We are listing only the very basic information about shows that happen on a regular schedule here. Please check out our website for more details on each show. Also this information tends to change quite often so please verify the event with our website or a local source before you venture far. Or if you're in the right area at the right time, give it a shot.

If you are a show organizer, please keep us updated on your event. shows@quilterstravelcompanion.com www.quilterstravelcompanion.com

On our website you will also find:

- Exact dates (when we have them)
- Sponsor Information
- Contact Information
- Description of Event

Events happening on a one-time basis

Month City	Schedule	Show	Location with address
All Year			
Lincoln	All year	Continuing Exhibitions International Quilt Study Center	University of Nebraska at Lincoln, 234 HE Bldg.
April			
Chadron	Annual, 4th weekend of April	Chadron Festival of Quilts	Assumption Arena, 4th & Spruce
Lincoln	Even Years, Spring	Lincoln Quilters Guild Show	Weary Center on NE Wesleyan Campus, N. 53rd and Huntington Ave.
June			
LaVista	Annual, 1st weekend in June	Omaha Quilters' Guild Show	LaVista Conference Center, 12520 Westport Pkwy
July			
Wayne	Annual, 2nd Sat. in July	Piecemakers Quilt Guild	Masonic Lodge, 9th & Lincoln Sts.
North Platte	Annual, 4th Thurs - Sun in July	QuiltNebraska	Sandhills Convention Center, 2102 S. Jeffers
August			
Imperial	Annual, 2nd weekend in August	Crazy Quilt Guild Quilt Show	Imperial Community Center, 1000 Wellington
September			
Curtis	Annual, 3rd Sat. in September	Frontier Stitcher Quilt Guild Show	United Methodist Church, 402 Center Ave.
Nebraska City	Annual, 3rd weekend in September	Heritage Needlework Guild Show	Bethel United Church of Christ, 2400 Central Ave. (across from Skate Park)
Kimball	Annual, last Sat. of September	Kimball Nimble Thimble Quilt Show	4-H Building, S. High School St.
October			
Fremont	Even Years, October	Prairie Piecemakers Needlework Guild Show	Fremont City Auditorium, 929 N. Broad
Elkhorn	Odd Years, Late October	Cottonwood Quilters Show	Bethany Lutheran Church, 4200 North 204th St.

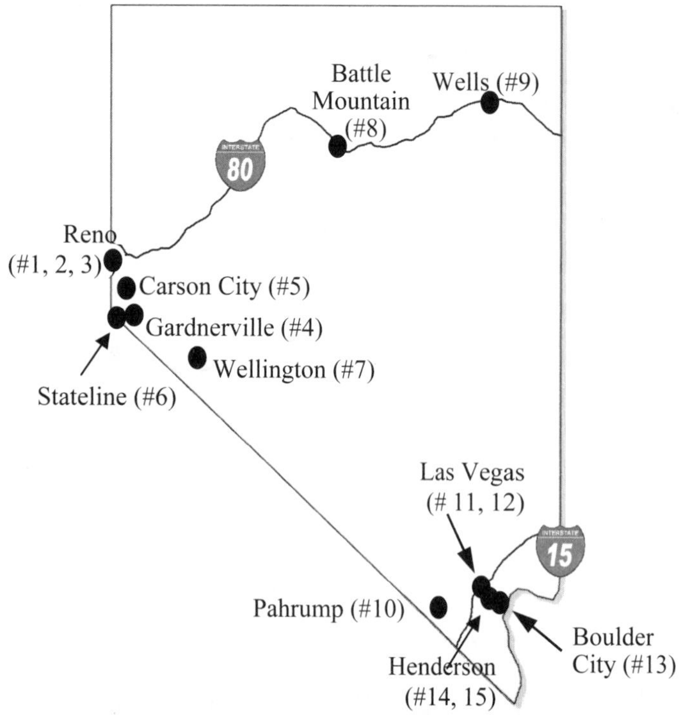

NEVADA

15 Featured Shops

Reno, NV #1

Windy Moon Quilts

440 Spokane Street 89512

800-622-8082 or 775-323-4777

"Biggest little Quilt Shop in the West"

www.windymoonquilts.com

6,000 sq. ft. of fabric, books, notions, patterns, classes, gifts, and quilting help.
Custom Long Arm Quilting
All the Quilter's Needs

Authorized Dealer of Janome & Brother Sewing Machines

Visit or Call
Monday - Saturday 10 - 5:30
Sunday 11 - 5

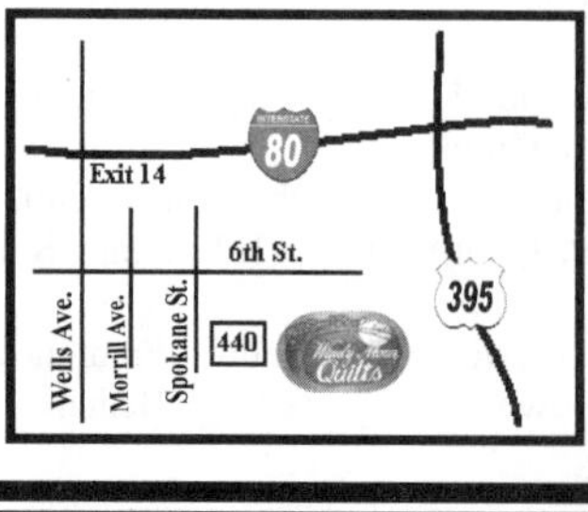

Reno, NV #2

Mon - Fri 10 - 6
Sat 10 - 5

Sew-n-Such

Your Sewing Store & Sew Much More!

Baby Lock Retailer.

2291 Kietze Ln. 89502
Franktown Corners
(775) 825-6677
www.sewnsuch.com

We offer only the finest quality first-run fabrics & goods including a wide range of threads. Our fabrics and notions are unique and our selection is inspiring.

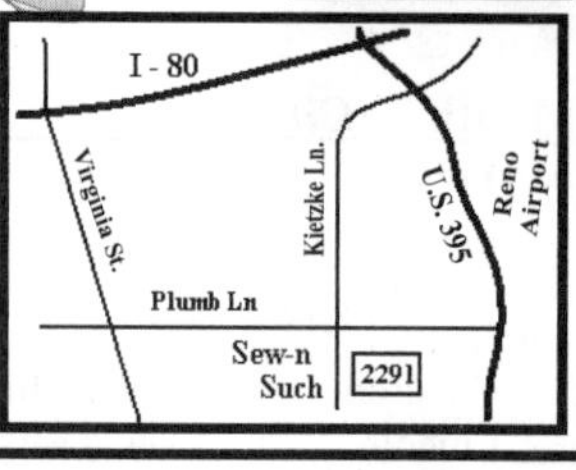

Reno, NV #3

Mon - Sat 10 - 5:30

Sierra Sewing CENTER

8056 S. Virginia St. 89511
(775) 823-9700

Great Quilt Fabrics and all the latest notions plus Viking and Pfaff Sewing Machines.

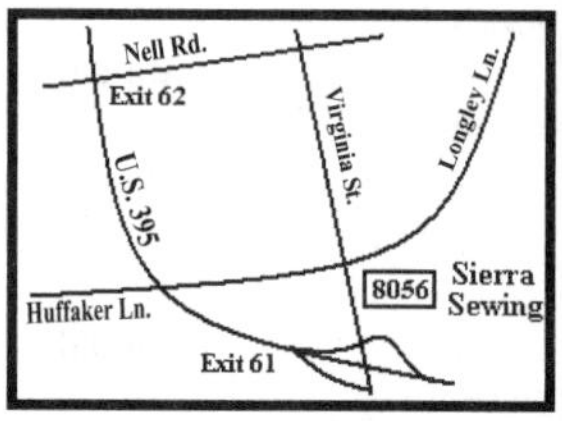

The Quilt House, Inc.

"Experience the FUN with Us!" Gardnerville, NV

Est 1999

Gardnerville, NV #4

Monday - Saturday 10am - 5pm
Closed Sundays

- 3000+ Bolts and Growing
- "Block of the Month"
- "Thimbleberries Club"
- Large selection of Quality 100% cotton fabrics
- "Kits", gift items, books, patterns, and notions
- Knowledgeable and Friendly staff
- Welcoming and Fun atmosphere.
- Quality classes and teachers
- Gift Certificates
- Bus Tours and Quilt Guilds welcome (please call ahead)
- Mail Order Available

6400+ square feet of Shopping and Creative FUN !!

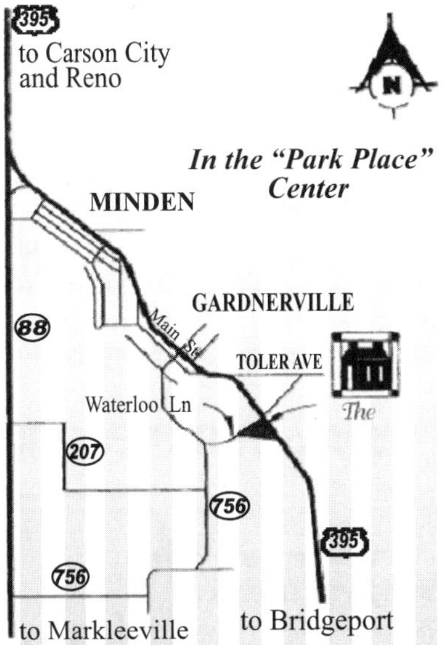

BBB Member Northern Nevada, Inc.

1328 US Hwy. 395 N. #105
Gardnerville, NV 89410
(775) 782-8845
theqlthouse@aol.com
Owners:
Gary and Janet Pierce

www.TheQuiltHouse.net

Better Homes and Gardens Quilt Sampler Featured Shop 2004 · Better Homes and Gardens Creative Collection Best of Quilt Sampler 2007 · Heavenly Seating Right Chair-Right Price · Horn of America Collection · BERNINA

Carson City, NV #5

Mon - Sat 10 - 5

Sierra Sewing Center

1000 N. Carson 89701
(775) 884-9500

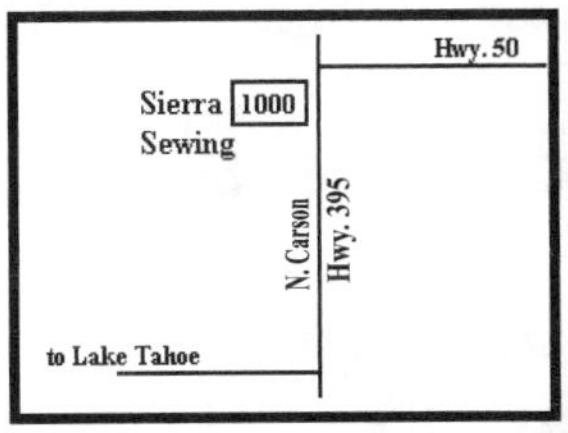

Great Quilt Fabrics and all the latest notions plus Viking and Pfaff sewing Machines.

Wellington, NV #7

Mon - Sat 10 - 4 Wed til 6

Sylvia's Quilter's Quarters

1490 Albite Rd., Suite 6 (TRE) 89444
(Located behind the Red A Frame)
(775) 266-4350
Owner: Sylvia Milam
www.quiltersquarters.topaznv.com

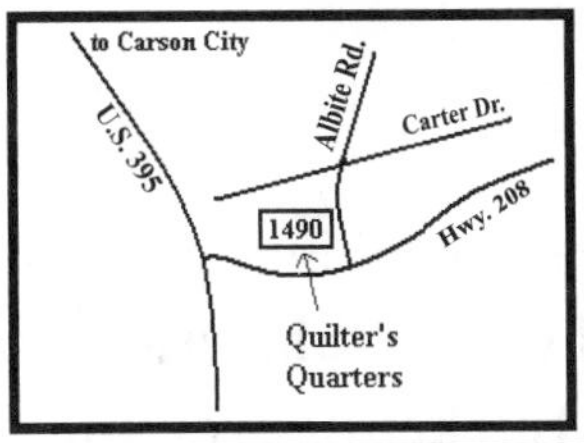

"Art from the Heart Generation to Generation"
Fabric, Notions, Books, Patterns & Quilting Classes. Specializing in Western Fabrics.

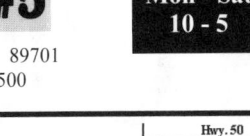

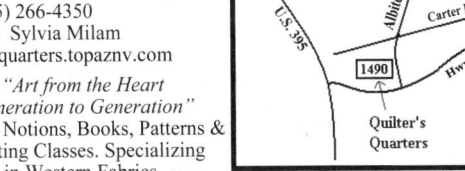

Stateline, NV #6

Fabrics Unlimited

"we're a cut above..."

155 Shady Lane /PO Box 6568
(775) 588-3211
Stateline, NV 89449-6568 Fax (775) 588-4805
Est: 2004 2300 sq. ft. Free Newsletter
fabricsunlimited@hotmail.com
www.fabricsunlimited.net

Mon - Sat 10 - 5

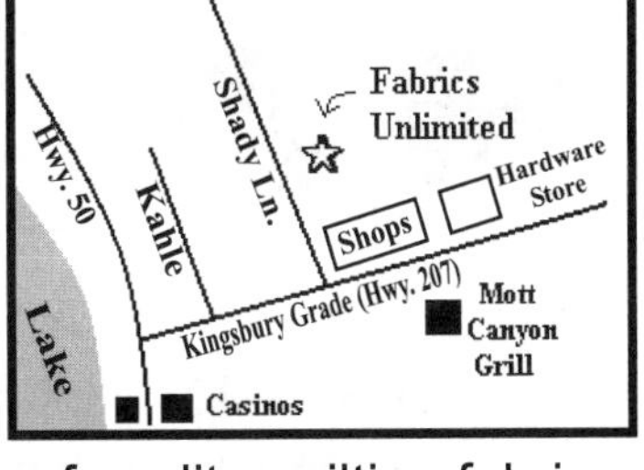

Large selection of quality quilting fabrics, notions, books, patterns, kits, embellishments.
Located on the south shore of beautiful Lake Tahoe

#8

Thimbles 'n Quilts

Samme Engelson, Owner and Fellow Fabraholic

www.thimblesandquilts.com

We carry a wonderful selection of
Fabrics • Patterns
Books • Notions
Kits • Threads

We offer classes!

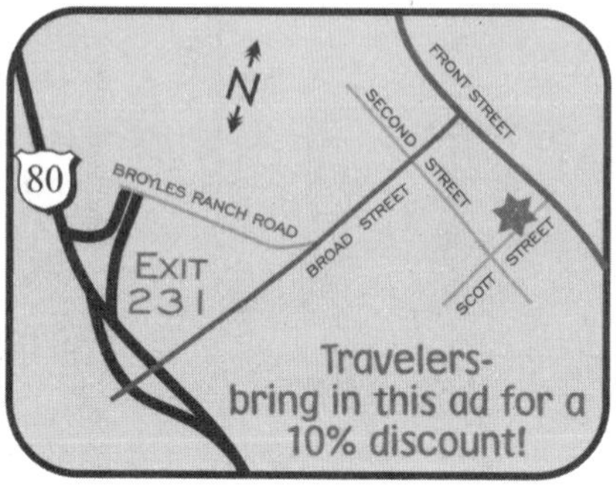

Monday-Friday 10am-6pm Saturday 10am-5pm

775.635.3110 or 1.888.262.8539

175 South Scott Street
Battle Mountain, Nevada 89820

Wells, NV #9

Tues - Sat 11 - 5

Van Thiel

436 6th St., P.O. Box 312 89835
(775) 752-3066
Owner: Yvonne VanThiel Stuart
Est: 2009 600 sq.ft.
ystuart@wrecwireless.coop

Visit our quaint quilt shop.
We offer a great variety of fabric, yarn, dmc, notions and in-home collectables.

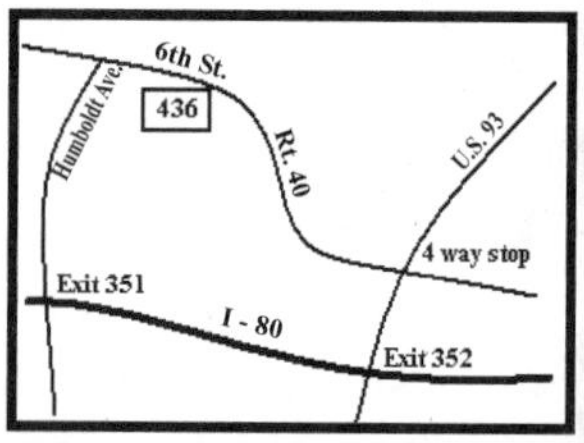

Pahrump, NV #10

Tues - Sat 9 - 5

BERNINA Sewing Center

4920 Pahrump Valley Blvd. 89048
(775) 727-3633
Owners: Bill & Trudy
Est: 2003 Newsletter
bernina4u@hotmail.com

Cotton fabrics, notions, classes scheduled every month. "Block-of-the-Month" programs.
BERNINA Sewing Machines
Repair on all brands.

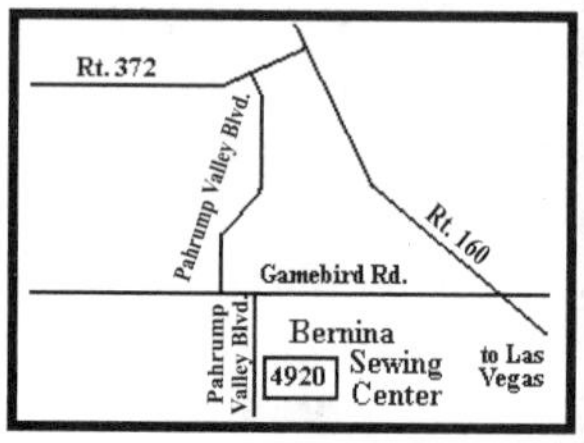

Est: 1993

3,000 sq.ft.

The Christmas Goose

**Mon - Sat 10 - 6
Sun 12 - 4**

Las Vegas, NV #11

**2988 S. Durango #109
Las Vegas, NV 89117
(702) 877-1158
E-Mail: Cmasgoose@aol.com
Owner: Jeanette Sherrick
& Andrea Marquez**

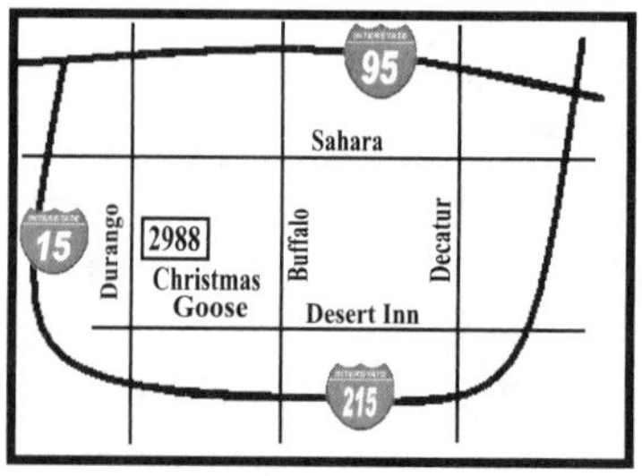

*In the Durango Edna Shopping Ctr.
Look for the Storage One sign.*

www.Christmasgoose.com

**We carry the largest selection of flannel, wool and patterns in the valley.
As well as a wonderful collection of cotton fabrics, notions and kits.
Plus country gifts such as Primdolls, Blossom Bucket figures and other unique creations.**

Las Vegas

Fabric Boutique

Quilt Shop

Closest Quilt Shop to the Strip.

4465 W. Charleston,
Las Vegas, NV 89102
(702) 878-0068
Owner: Ev Dahl

You'll find:
OVER 5,000 BOLTS OF QUILTING COTTONS
HUGE SELECTION OF PATTERNS
BOOKS ARE ALWAYS 20% OFF
CLASSES, FRIENDLY STAFF

www.fabricboutique.com

Las Vegas, NV #12

Open 7 days per week.

Check our Color of the Month 20% off Fabric Every Month a Different Color!

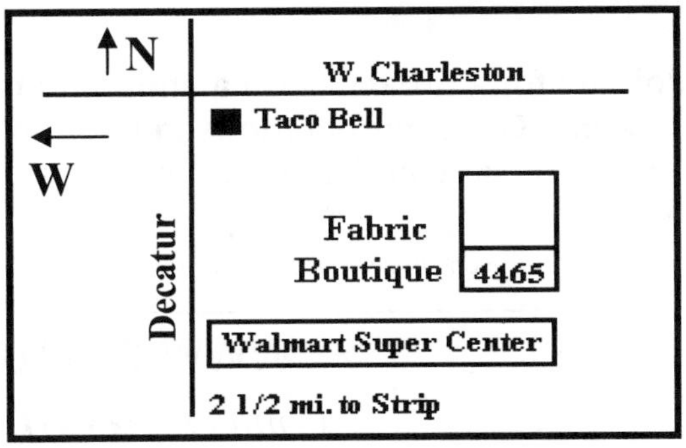

Bus Directions from the Strip:
Take Strip Bus #301 - Leaves every 8-10 minutes. Transfer to Charleston Bus #206 West - Leaves every 20 minutes.

Boulder City, NV #13

fiddlesticks QUILT SHOP

Come visit us in Historic Old Town Boulder City. We carry many fine quilt fabric lines, books, notions and patterns, as well as gifts and one of a kind treasures made by local crafts people.

1229 Arizona St. 89005
www.fiddlesticksquilts.com

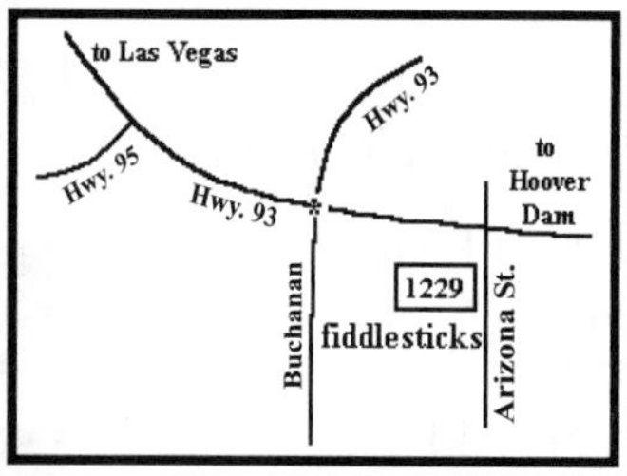

(702) 293-2979
Owner: Merry Summey

Mon - Sat 9:30 - 5
Thurs evening til 7:30

Between the Historic Boulder Dam Hotel and the Boulder Theater

We specialize in personal customer service!

VISITING LAS VEGAS? #14

Quilt Tours of Las Vegas

QUILTING Las Vegas SHOP HOP

takes you on a personalized shop hop with fellow quilters to some of the best quilt shops in the Las Vegas area.

Join us for a great day on a shopping tour to some of the best quilt shops in the Las Vegas area. Choose from thousands of bolts of fabric and outstanding selections of books, patterns, kits and notions. Increase your stash, complete a project or create a new one.

Be inspired by gorgeous shop samples!

Along the way you will experience a taste of the Las Vegas Valley where the locals live, work and shop.

www.quilttoursoflasvegas.com

Contact ***Susan Tracy*** *for more information*

❖ **lasvegasquilts@cox.net** ❖ 702-647-8458 ❖ 866-987-8458 ❖

P.O. Box 50225, Henderson, Nevada 89016 ❖ FAX: 702-437-8458 ❖ CPCN 2124

We can also arrange visits to shops that cater to those who enjoy beading, knitting, scrapbooking, model trains and woodworking. **Ask about our sewing machine rentals.**

#15

Las Vegas area's Ultimate Quilt & Sewing Shop

Just Minutes from the Las Vegas Strip

QUILTIQUE®

213 N. Stephanie Street, Suite E
Henderson, Nevada 89074

702-563-8600

info@quiltique.com
www.quiltique.com

Hours:
Monday – Saturday
10 am – 6pm

Better Homes Quilt Sampler Featured Shop 2009

BERNINA
Authorized Dealer

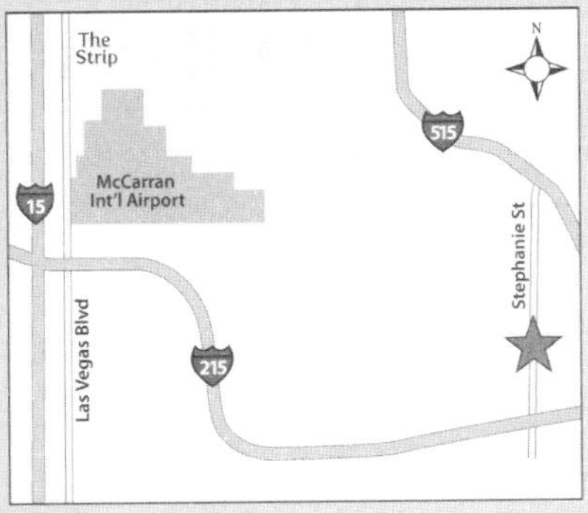

Directions:
- Take the I-215 freeway East toward Henderson
- Exit at Stephanie Street
- Travel North on Stephanie Street to American Pacific Dr.
- We are on the Northwest corner of Stephanie St. and American Pacific Dr. in the Stephanie Promenade Center

Family Owned Since 2003

Come enjoy our bright and contemporary atmosphere! Quiltique is a full service creative sewing center specializing in quilting, sewing and machine embroidery. You will find the best quilting fabrics on the market including great companies and designers such as Kaffe Fassett, Moda, Amy Butler, Hoffman Batiks, Free Spirit and Robert Kaufman, just to name a few! We also have the largest class selection in the area offering quilting, garment sewing, machine embroidery and even long-arm quilting. You will find everything you need to create the project you have been dreaming of including BERNINA Sewing Machines. *Don't miss this shop!*

2009 Better Homes and Gardens Quilt Sampler Top Shop.

- Best Selection in town! Over 6,400 sq. ft. and 6,000 bolts of designer fabrics.
- Find incredible deals on fabrics, patterns and notions in our well-stocked sale area.
- Friendly, Knowledgeable and Professional staff always ready to assist you.
- Antiques and Gifts too!

Nevada Quilt Shops

Battle Mountain Thimbles 'n Quilts, 175 S. Scott St.
775-635-3110 **See ad #8, page 346**

Boulder City Fiddlesticks Quilts & Other Works of the Heart
1229 Arizona St.
702-293-2979 **See ad #13, page 348**

Carson City Sierra Sewing, 1000 North Carson
775-884-9500 **See ad #5, page 345**

Elko Elko Floral Fabric and Gifts, 180 Idaho St. 775-738-4728
Elko Ruby Mountain Quilt Cottage, 572 5th St. 775-738-2242
Fallon Workman's Farms Crafts, 4990 Reno Hwy. 775-867-3716
Fallon The UnCommon Thread, 1525 W. Williams 775-867-4225

Gardnerville The Quilt House, 1328 Hwy. 395 #105
775-782-8845 **See ad #4, page 345 & 208**

Henderson QUILTIQUE, 213 N. Stephanie St. #E
702-563-8600 **See ad #15, page 349 & 207**

Henderson Quilt Tours of Las Vegas,
2244 Heavenly View Dr.
702-647-8458 **See ad #14, page 348**

Las Vegas Fabric Boutique Quilt Shop, 4465 W. Charleston
702-878-0068 **See ad #12, page 347**

Las Vegas The Christmas Goose, 2988 S. Durango #109
702-877-1158 **See ad #11, page 346**

Las Vegas Vac & Sew Summerlin, 2243 N. Rampart Blvd. 702-309-8787
Las Vegas Nancy's Quilt Shop, 3290 N. Buffalo Drive 702-839-2779
Minden Fabric-Chicks Creative Oasis, 1166 Annie Ct. 775-267-0204

Pahrump Bernina Sewing Center,
4920 Pahrump Valley Blvd.
775-727-3633 **See ad #10, page 346**

Pahrump The Quilted Dragon, 2890 S. Yucca Terrace Ave. 775-751-9033

Reno Windy Moon Quilts, 440 Spokane St.
800-622-8082 **See ad #1, page 344**

Reno Sierra Sewing, 8056 S. Virginia St.
775-823-9700 **See ad #3, page 344**

Reno Sew-N-Such, 2291 Kietze Ln.
775-825-6677 **See ad #2, page 344**

Reno Going Batty Quilt Shop, 9744 S. Virginia St. 775-351-2424
Sparks Ben Franklin Crafts, 530 Greenbrae Dr. 775-331-5755

Stateline Fabrics Unlimited, 155 Shady Lane
775-588-3211 **See ad #6, page 345**

Wellington Sylvia's Quilter's Quarters
1490 Albite Rd., Suite 6
775-266-4350 **See ad #7, page 345**

Wells Van Thiel, 436 6th St.
775-752-3066 **See ad #9, page 346**

Nevada Quilt Shows

About Shows: We are listing only the very basic information about shows that happen on a regular schedule here. Please check out our website for more details on each show. Also this information tends to change quite often so please verify the event with our website or a local source before you venture far. Or if you're in the right area at the right time, give it a shot.

If you are a show organizer, please keep us updated on your event. shows@quilterstravelcompanion.com
www.quilterstravelcompanion.com

On our website you will also find:
- Exact dates (when we have them)
- Sponsor Information
- Contact Information
- Description of Event
- Events happening on a one-time basis

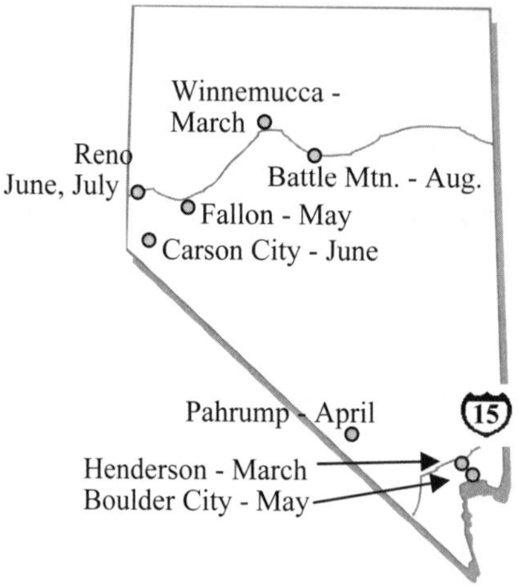

9 Shows

Month	City	Schedule	Show	Location with address
February				
	Henderson	Annual, February or March	Desert Quilters Annual Show	Henderson Convention Center 200 Water St.
March				
	Winnemucca	Odd Years, 3rd Sat of March	Winnemucca Crazy Quilters Show	Humboldt County Fairgrounds 1000 Fairgrounds Rd
April				
	Pahrump	Annual, 2nd weekend of April	Pahrump Fiber Arts and Quilt Show	Bob Ruud Community Center Hwy. 160 & Basin Rd.
May				
	Boulder City	Annual, 1st Saturday in May	Fiddlesticks Quilts and BC	Chamber of Commerce Historic Old Town
	Fallon	Annual, 3rd week in May	Nevada Quilt Guild Show	Fallon Convention Center 100 Campus Way
June				
	Reno	Annual, last weekend in June	Quilting Stitches and Crafts Expo	Grand Sierra Resort Hotel 2500 E. 2nd St.
	Carson City	Even Years, 2nd weekend in June	Carson Valley Quilt Guild Show	Carson High School 1111 N. Saliman Rd.
July				
	Reno	Annual, 3rd weekend in July	Truckee Meadows Quilters' Show	National Automobile Museum 10 S. Lake St.
August				
	Battle Mountain	Odd Years, 1st weekend in August	Battle Mountain Quilt Guild Show	Battle Mountain Civic Center 625 S. Broad St.

NEW HAMPSHIRE

25 Featured Shops

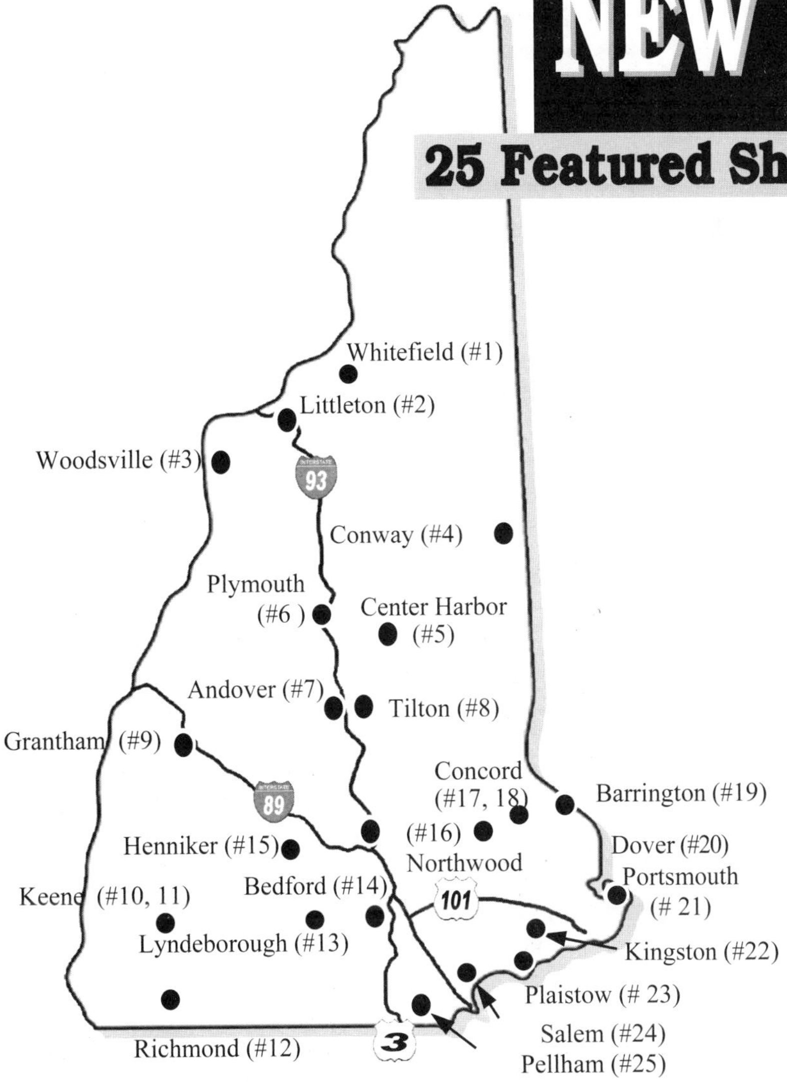

Whitefield, NH #1

Wed - Sat 10 - 6

Stitch at the Old Mill

36 Kings Square 03598
(603) 837-8778 Est: 2008
Owner: Beth Anderson
1000+ bolts 100's of patterns
beth@stitchattheoldmill.com
www.stitchattheoldmill.com

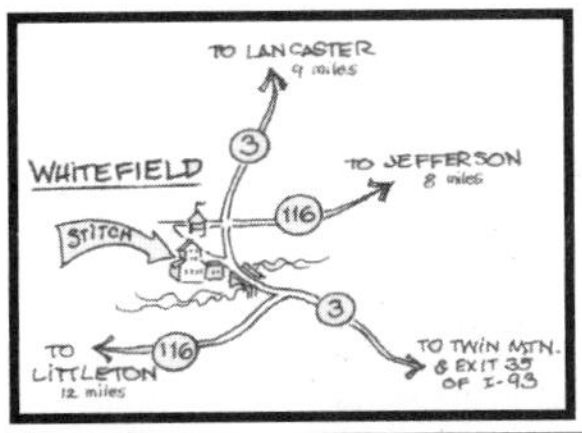

Stitch features colorful cottons, patterns, books, a homey atmosphere, classes and clubs. We even have a party plan for girlfriend groups!

Littleton, NH #2

Mon- Sat 9:30 - 6 Sun 11 - 5

Cut 'n Sew Fabrics

33 Meadow St. 03561
(603) 444-7760
Owner: Jane Ladd
Est: 1970 3200 sq.ft.

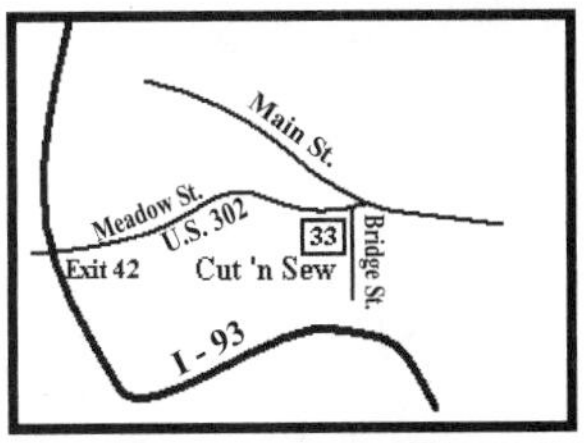

Large store filled with quilting fabrics, books and supplies. Drapery / slipcover and garment fabrics. Embroidery floss - Needlework Kits Yarn and Knitting Supplies - Sewing Machines

Woodsville, NH #3

Tues - Sat 9:30 - 5 Fri til 6

Seams Sew Easy Fabric Shoppe

65 Central St. 03785
(603) 747-3054
Owners: Chris & Lloyd Steeves

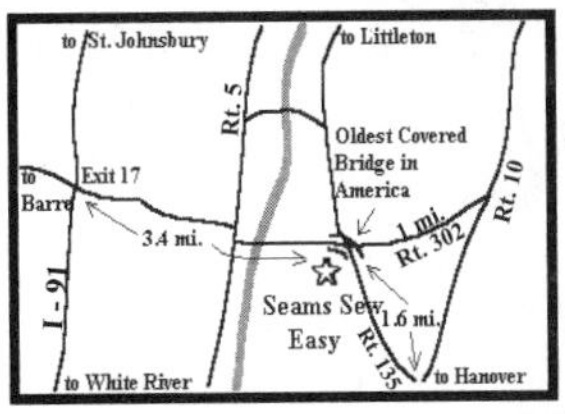

A complete fabric store featuring a large selection of quilting fabrics and supplies. Quality Paton's & Plymouth yarns.

Conway, NH #4

Mon-Sat 9-5

The Quilt Shop At VAC n' SEW

290 East Side Rd.
603-447-3470
www.quiltshopnh.com

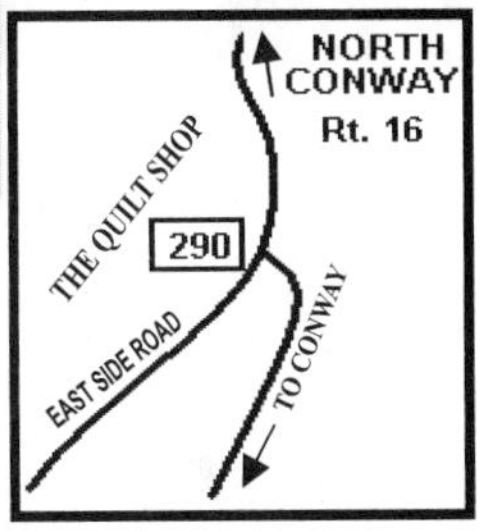

Bernina Sewing Machines
Fabrics from $3.99 / yd

Center Harbor, NH #5

Keepsake Quilting

Everything a quilter could wish for!

- A huge selection of cotton fabrics plus a vast array of books, kits and notions.
- Hundreds of handmade quilts
- Friendly, knowledgeable staff
- Annual June tent sale with incredible bargains. (Visit our web site for dates.)
- Bus tours welcome. (Please call to make arrangements)
- For a free 128-page catalog call 1-800-865-9458

Mon - Sat 9 - 5
Sun 9 - 5
Extended Summer hrs.

Route 25B
In Senters Marketplace
P.O. Box 1618
Center Harbor, NH 03226
(603) 253-4026
Est: 1988

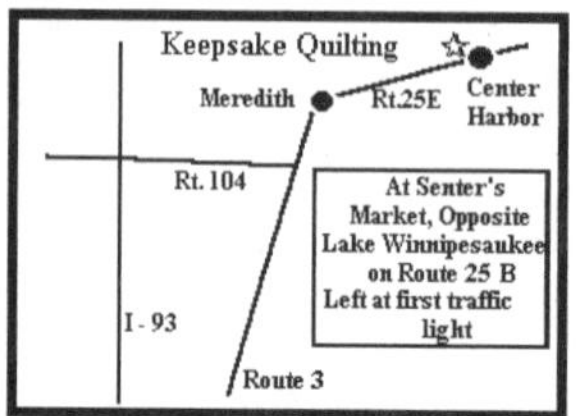

www.keepsakequilting.com

Plymouth, NH #6

Mon, Wed, Fri, Sat 9:30 - 5:30
Thur 9:30 - 8
Sun 10 - 4

The Country Heart Quilters

12 Yeaton Rd 6B / Tenney Mtn. Hwy.
(603) 536-6320 03264
www.thecountryheartquilters.com
Owner:
Loretta Botelho

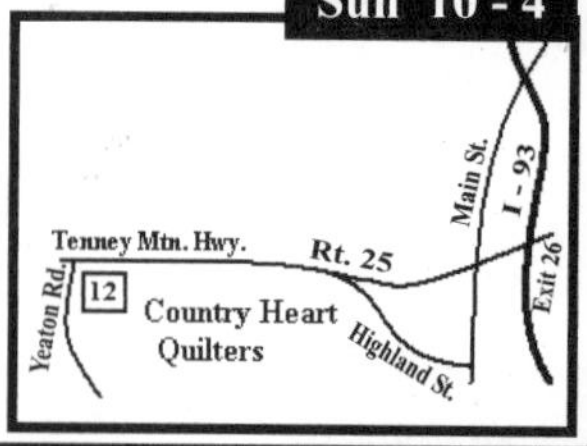

You will be greeted by a friendly smile. The shop has a country-primitive flare with lots of Thimbleberries, Whimsicals and 1800's fabrics. Loads of great books, our notion wall is full of gadgets along with many different size rulers. Kits, quilt hangers & racks plus gift items too.

Andover, NH #7

Mon - Sat 10 - 5
Sun 12 - 5

The Constant Quilter

139 Pancake Rd. 03216
(603) 735-4100
Owner: Linda Barnes
info@constantquilter.com
www.constantquilter.com

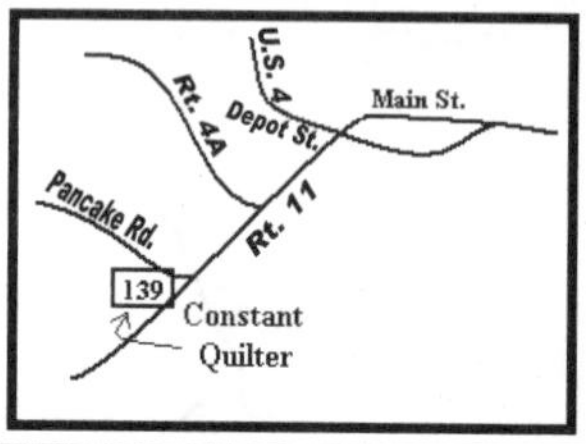

Fabrics / Books & Notions / Classes
Machine Quilting / Antiques & Collectibles
Original Patterns / Quilts for Sale
Service is our primary value, with customer satisfaction the goal for every transaction.

Tilton, NH #8

Tues - Fri 10 - 5
Sat 9 - 4

The Quilting Corner

322 W. Main St., # 110 03276
(603) 286-3437
Owner: Irene Haley
Est: 2006 1100 sq.ft.
www.quiltingcornernh.com

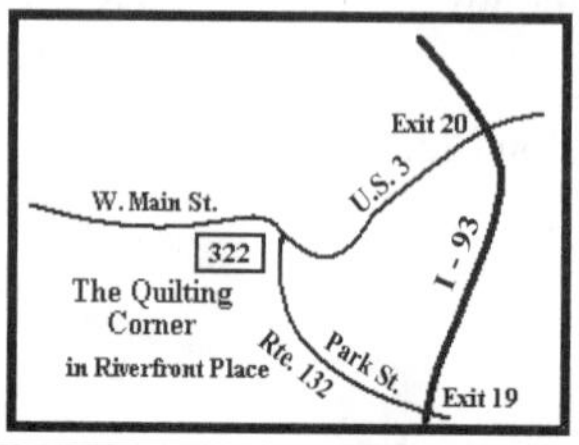

We offer Fabric, Books, Patterns, Kits, Notions, Gifts and Classes for all levels.

Grantham, NH #9

Mon - Fri 9:30 - 5
Online 24/7

Sunshine Carousel Quilt Shop

Sawyer Brook Plaza, Route 10 03753
(603) 863-5754 Est: 1990
www.scqs.com - info@scqs.com

Quilting Books, Patterns and Notions
www.qbpn.net

Quilters Auction - The Best for Less
www.quiltersauction.com

Machine Quilting Service Available.

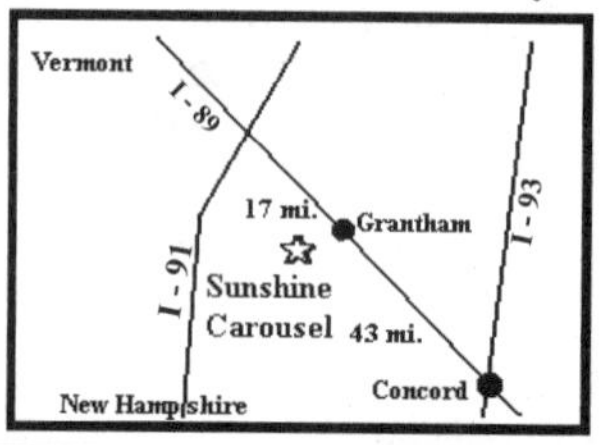

Keene, NH #10

Mon - Sat 9:30 - 5:30
Fri til 8

New England Fabrics
— & Decorating Center —

55 Ralston St., Keene, NH 03431
(603) 352-8683
www.newenglandfabrics.com
Tremendous Selection of Beautiful Fabrics for:
• Quilting • Apparel • Bridal • Draperies
• Slipcovers • Upholstery & More!
Plus Yarn & Sewing Machines
Central New England's Largest Fabric & Home Decorating Center!

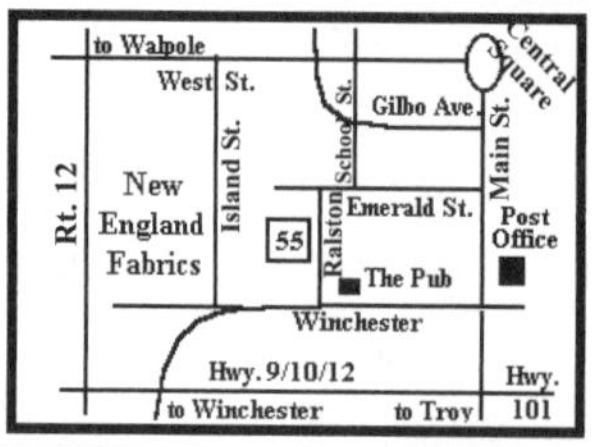

Keene, NH #11

Mon - Fri 10 - 5:30
Sat 10 - 4

The Moses House

30 Ashuelot St. 03431
Phone/Fax: (603) 352-2312
Owners: Russ Moline
Est: 1987 1800 sq.ft.
info@themoseshouse.com
www.themoseshouse.com

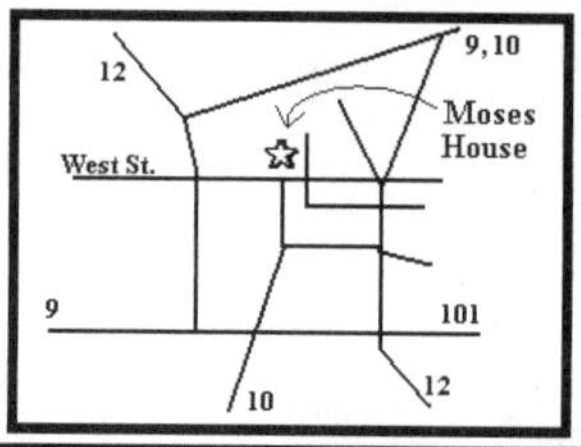

The best quilting fabrics, books, patterns, and supplies. Many reproduction fabrics. Redwork. Grace Quilting frames on display. NOLTING Longarm Quilting Machine dealer.

Richmond, NH #12

Thurs - Sun 10 - 5

Pickering Farm

19 Fitzwilliam Rd. 03470
(603) 239-7550
Owner: Diana & Steven Gallagher
Est: 1999 2000 sq.ft. 2000 bolts
www.pickeringfarmquiltshop.com
Cottage & Folk Art, Americana, Baby & 30's, 19th century reproductions. Hand dyed wools, stitchery kits and patterns.
A Quaint New England Quilt Shop with a Country Primitive Atmosphere.

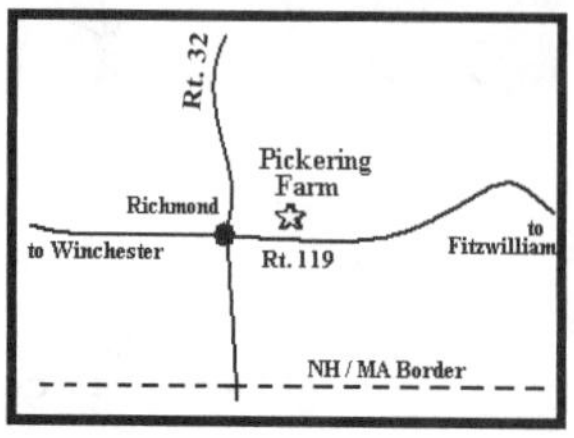

Lyndeborough, NH #13

Mon - Sat 10 - 5
Sun 12 - 5

The Bunkhouse Quilt Shop

352 Center Rd. 03082
(603) 654-6734
Over 2500 bolts of fabric
customerservice@bunkhousequiltshop.com
www.bunkhousequiltshop.com

"A FUN PLACE TO VISIT"

Bedford, NH #14

Tues - Sat
10 - 5
Thurs til 8

The Quilt Patch

133 Bedford Center Rd. 03110
(603) 472-7845
Owner: Sue Trask
Est: 2005
1200 sq.ft.
1500+ bolts
thequiltpatch@comcast.net
www.TheQuiltPatchNH.com

A quaint and friendly quilt shop in the village of Bedford. Located only 4 miles from Manchester, NH. We offer top quality famous-maker fabrics.

"Where Quilters Go To Play"

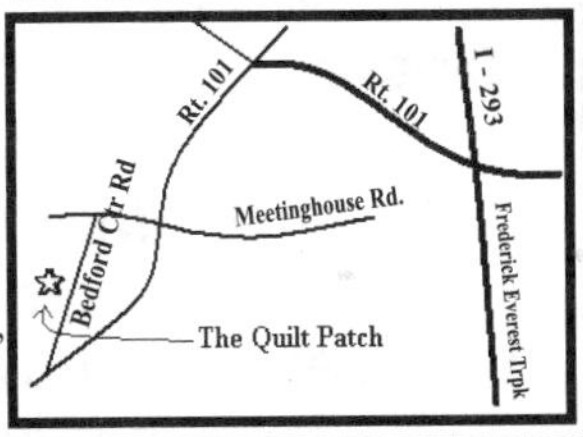

Henniker, NH #15

Tues - Sat
10 - 5
Thur til 8
Sun 1 - 4

QUILTED threads

116 Main St., P.O. Box 778 03242
(603) 428-6622
www.quiltedthreads.com

Visit our newly expanded store!
Named: "Best of NH 2005
A Quilter's Dream!"

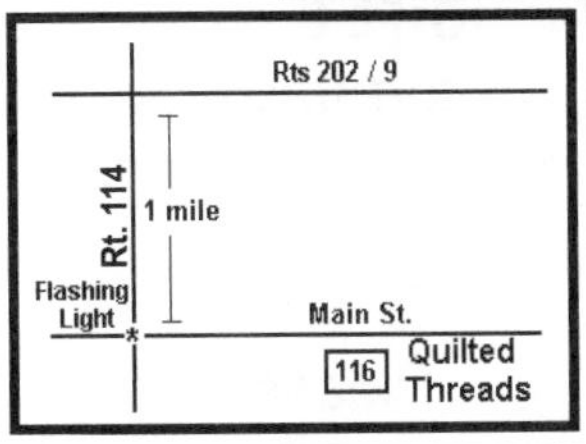

Northwood, NH # 16

CHECKERBERRIES Quilt Shop

997 First NH Turnpike, Northwood, NH 03261
603-942-5282
www.checkerberriesquiltshop.com

- ★ Reproduction and Primitive Fabrics
- ★ Quilting Patterns and Books
- ★ Wool and Rug Hooking Supplies
- ★ Penny Rug Patterns
- ★ Embroidery and Cross Stitch Supplies
- ★ Primitive Pine Furniture
- ★ Amish-made Quilts

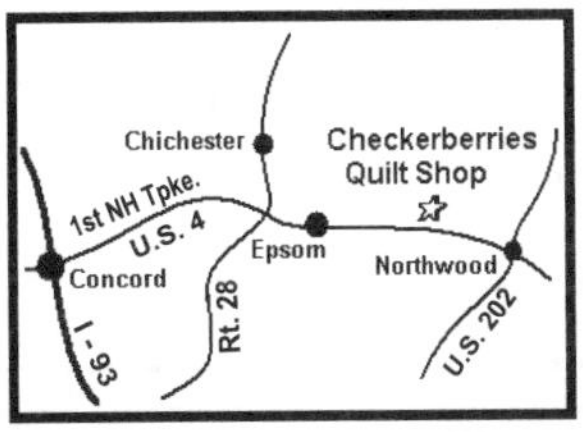

Thursday ~ Saturday
10:00 ~ 5:00
Sunday ~ 12:00 ~ 5:00

Concord, NH #18

Mon - Sat 10 - 5
June, July, Aug Mon-Fri 10 - 5 Sat 10 - 1

Golden Gese Quilt Shop

22 Liberty St. 03301
(603) 228-5540
Owner: Nancy Gesen
Est: 1987 1200 sq.ft. 2000+ Bolts
www.goldengesequilt.com

100% Cotton Fabric, Books, Patterns, Notions & Classes. Helpful Assistance.

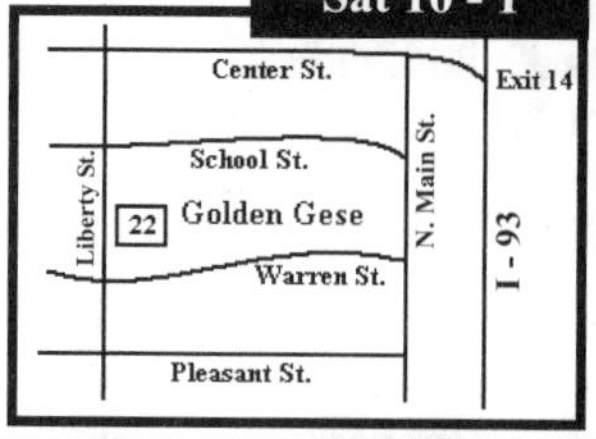

Dover, NH #20

Tues - Fri 10 - 5 Sat 10 - 4

Garrison Hill Quilt Shop

23 Floral Ave. 03820
(603) 749-9100
Owners: Tom & Donna Tetreault

Est: 2006
1500 sq.ft. 1300 bolts
dltquilts@comcast.net
Gifts, notions, books and patterns along with bright and beautiful fabrics including lots of Batiks.
www.garrisonhillquiltshop.com

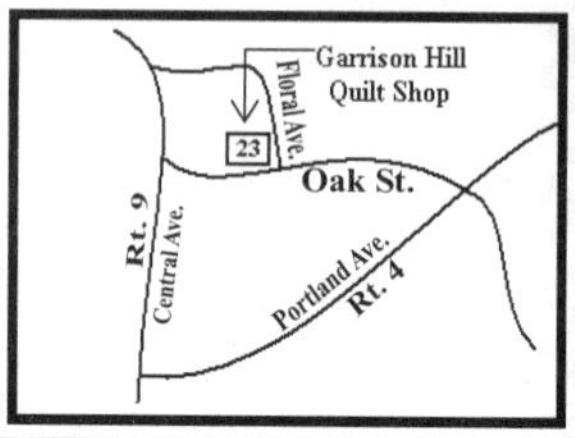

Kingston, NH #22

Stitched in Stone

53 Church St. Box 786
Kingston, NH 03848
(603) 642-4220
Owners: Glen & Tammy Romel
3900 sq.ft. 1800+ Bolts

www.stitchedinstone.com

Mon - Fri 10 - 9 Sat 10 - 5 Sun 11 - 4

We carry a large selection of Fabrics
Books ▪ Notions ▪ Patterns
Machine Embroidery Designs.

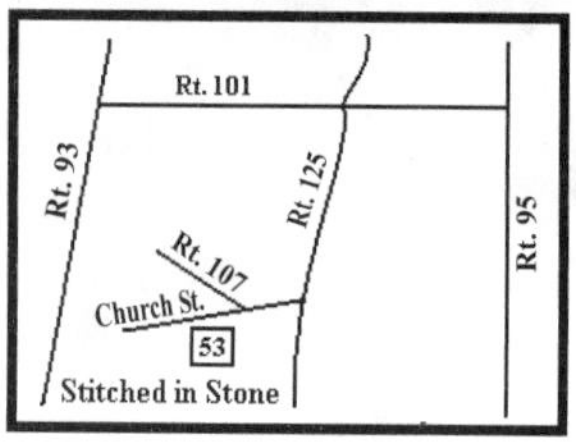

We are a full service Quilting & Knitting shop offering Classes in both. Fabrics, Notions, beads, yarn, quilting kits, patterns and books.
Authorized Horn, Elna and Baby Lock dealer

HORN of America COLLECTION
elna SWISS DESIGN
baby lock

Little Lamb Quilt Shop

The Shops at Calef's Corner
Rts 9 & 125, Barrington NH

Fabric, Wool, Notions, Books, Patterns and Classes for all your quilt making needs.

Thimbleberries® Club Shop
Fabric from Moda, RJR Fabrics, P&B Textiles, Hoffman, Northcott, Blank Textiles, Andover and more!
Expert Photo Transfer Service
Get your FREE *Friends of Little* Lamb Card
Earn Discounts!

Gift Certificates available in any amount.

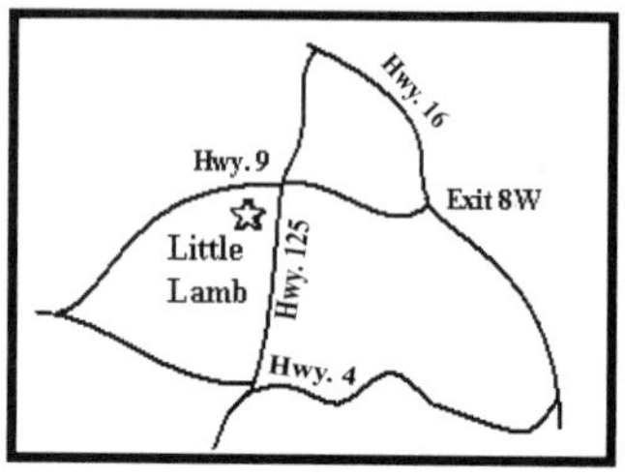

Please visit us online to see what's new!
www.littlelambquiltshop.com

Open Every Day 10 - 5

Little Lamb Quilt Shop

#19 147 Route 9, PO Box 462
Barrington NH 03825
603-664-6711 888-664-LAMB

Portsmouth, NH #21

Mon - Sat 9:30 - 5:30 Sun 12 - 5

Portsmouth FABRIC Company

112 Penhallow St. 03801
(603) 436-6343
Fax: (603) 430-2943
Est: 1979
7000 Bolts
1100 sq.ft.
BERNINA
www.portsmouthfabric.com Online Catalog
An exceptional selection of quilting cottons- designer, ethnic, batik and handpainted.
Rayons, silks and other fine garment fabrics.
Patterns, buttons, fiber art magazines & books.

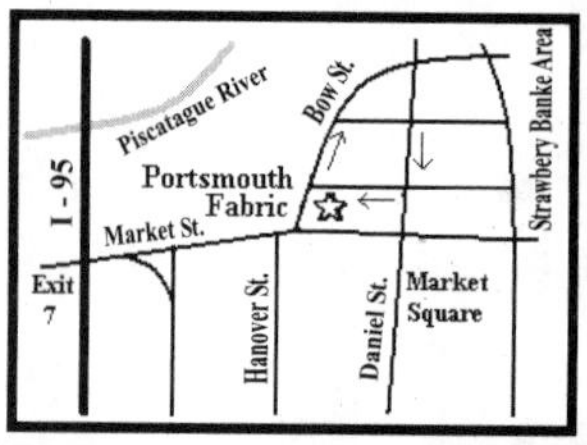

Plaistow, NH #23

Mon - Fri 10 - 5 Wed til 7 Sat 9 - 4

D&D Sewing

160 Plastow Rd., Plaistow Commons 03865
(603) 382-1122
Owners: Debbie & Dave Krauklin
Est: 2005 1600 sq.ft. 900 Bolts
mail@ddsewing.com www.ddsewing.com
Large Selection of Quilting, Sewing & Embroidery Supplies. PFAFF Sewing machines. Service on all brands. Classes.

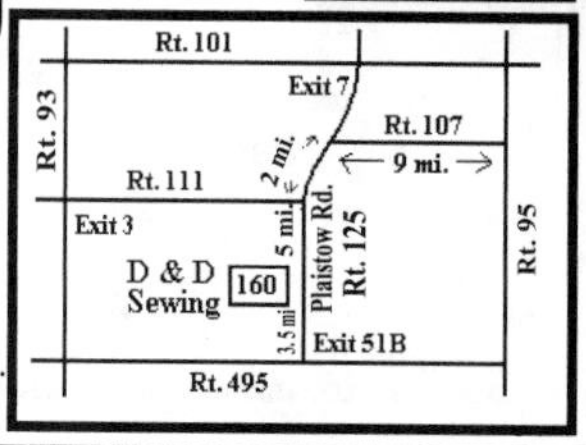

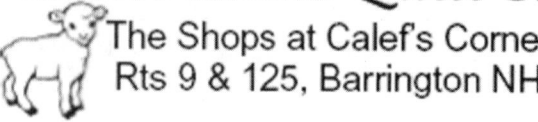

Salem, NH #24

Est: 2002 — 2400 sq. ft.

Pine Tree Quilt Shop

224 N. Broadway 03079
Salem Market Place
603-870-8100
Owner: Dina Niskala
dina@pinetreequiltshop.com

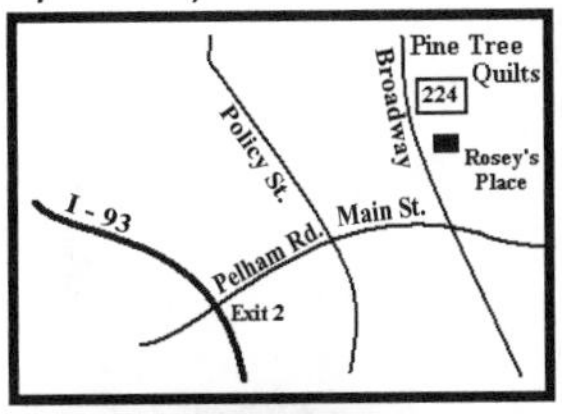

We invite you to come for a visit.
We hope to inspire you to begin your first quilt or work on your next heirloom.

- Browse through 5000 bolts of first quality fabrics
- Over 500 books and patterns
- Great selection of Workshops & Blocks-of-the-Month
- Online Newsletter
- Friendly, knowledgeable staff

Tues 10-4
Wed 10-4
Thurs 10-7
Fri 10-5
Sat 10-4

www.pinetreequiltshop.com

Pelham, NH #25

70 Bridge St. #6 03076
Stone Cottage Square
603-635-9705
www.bnpquilts.com

Hours:
Mon 10 - 6
Tues 10 - 6
Wed 10 - 9
Thur 10 - 7
Fri 10 - 6
Sat 9 - 5
Sun 10 - 5

bits 'n pieces

fax 603-635-4524
Est: 2002 2400 sq.ft.
info@bnpquilts.com

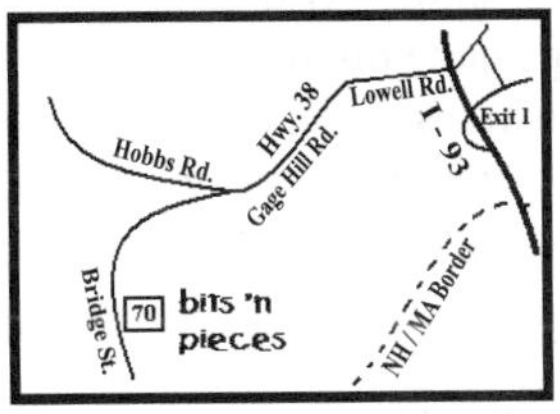

OVER 4000 BOLTS

- Batiks
- Moda
- Flannels
- Florals
- Orientals
- Hoffman
- Novelties
- Thimbleberries
- Wilderness
- Patterns
- Kits
- Fat Quarters
- Machine Quilting Services
- Newsletter
- HandiQuilter
- Much More

New Hampshire Quilt Shops

Andover **The Constant Quilter, 139 Pancake Rd.**
603-735-4100 **See ad #7, page 352**

Barrington **Little Lamb Quilt Shop, 147 Rt. 9**
603-664-6711 **See ad #19, page 354**

Barrington The Fabric Garden, 4 Rt. 125 603-868-2002

Bedford **The Quilt Patch, 133 Bedford Center Rd.**
603-472-7845 **See ad #14, page 353**

Center Harbor **Keepsake Quilting, Route 25B, Senter's Marketplace**
603-253-8148 **See ad #5, page 352**

Chocorua Patchwork House, 1808 Chocorua Mtn. Hwy. 603-367-9269

Claremont Four Pines Quilting, 38 Summer St . 603-543-3311

Concord **Peggy Anne's Quilting & Sewing Co., 57 N. Main St.**
603-223-2344 **See ad #17, page 353**

Concord **Golden Gese Quilt Shop, 22 Liberty St.**
603-228-5540 **See ad #18, page 354**

Concord In Stitches Quilting, 2 Phenix Ave. 603-224-8577

Conway **The Quilt Shop at Vac 'N Sew, 290 East Side Rd.**
603-447-3470 **See ad #4, page 351**

Derry The Amethyst Rose Quilt Shop 603-489-8161

Dover **Garrison Hill Quilt Shop, 23 Floral Ave.**
603-749-9100 **See ad #20, page 354**

Fitzwilliam The Pink Poodle Quilt Shop, 12 Old Troy Rd. 603-585-9268

Grantham **Sunshine Carousel Quilt Shop, Sawyer Brook Plaza, Route 10**
603-863-5754 **See ad #9, page 352**

Henniker **Quilted Threads, 116 Main St.**
603-428-6622 **See ad #15, page 353**

Hillsboro Apple Tree Fabrics, 282 Henniker St. 603-464-5510

Hooksett Levesque's Sew and Vac, 1261 Hooksett Rd. 603-645-1661

Hudson The Quilted Shamrock, 225 Lowel Rd. #E 603-204-5104

Keene **The Moses House, 30 Ashuelot St.**
603-352-2312 **See ad #11, page 352**

Keene **New England Fabrics & Decorating Center, 55 Ralston St.**
603-352-8683 **See ad #10, page 352**

Kingston **Stitched In Stone, 53 Church St.**
603-642-4220 **See ad #22, page 354**

Littleton **Cut 'n Sew, 33 Meadow St.**
603-444-7760 **See ad #2, page 351**

Lyndeborough **The Bunkhouse Quilt Shop, 352 Center Rd.**
603-654-6734 **See ad #13, page 352**

Newport The Quilters Workshop, 19 Main St. 603-863-7888

Northwood **Checkerberries Quilt Shop, 997 1st NH Turnpike**
603-942-5282 **See ad #16, page 353**

Pellham **Bits & Pieces Quilt Shop, 70 Bridge St Unit 6**
603-635-9705 **See at #25, this page**

Plaistow **D & D Sewing, 160 Plaistow Rd; Plaistow Commons**
603-382-1122 **See ad #23, page 354**

Plymouth **The Country Heart Quilters, 12 Yeaton Rd. #6B**
603-536-6320 **See ad #6, page 352**

Portsmouth **Portsmouth Fabric Co., 112 Penhallow St.**
603-436-6343 **See ad #21, page 354**

Portsmouth Merri Stitches, 72 Mirona Rd. #15 603-431-9922

Richmond **Pickering Farm, 19 Fitzwilliam Rd.**
603-239-7550 **See ad #12, page 352**

Salem **Pine Tree Quilt Shop, 224 N Broadway**
603-870-8100 **See ad #24, this page**

Salem Audrey's Sewing Studio & Vacuum Center, 236 N. Broadway #G 603-898-0777

Tilton **The Quilting Corner, 322 W. Main St., Ste. 110**
603-286-3437 **See ad #8, page 352**

Tilton Short Arm Café, 263 Main St. 603-286-2233

Weirs Beach The Quilted Frog 51 Endicott St. E 6033665600

Whitefield **Stitch at the Old Mill, 36 Kings Square**
603-837-8778 **See ad #1, page 351**

Woodsville **Seams Sew Easy Fabric Shoppe, 65 Central St.**
603-747-3054 **See ad #3, page 351**

New Hampshire Quilt Shows

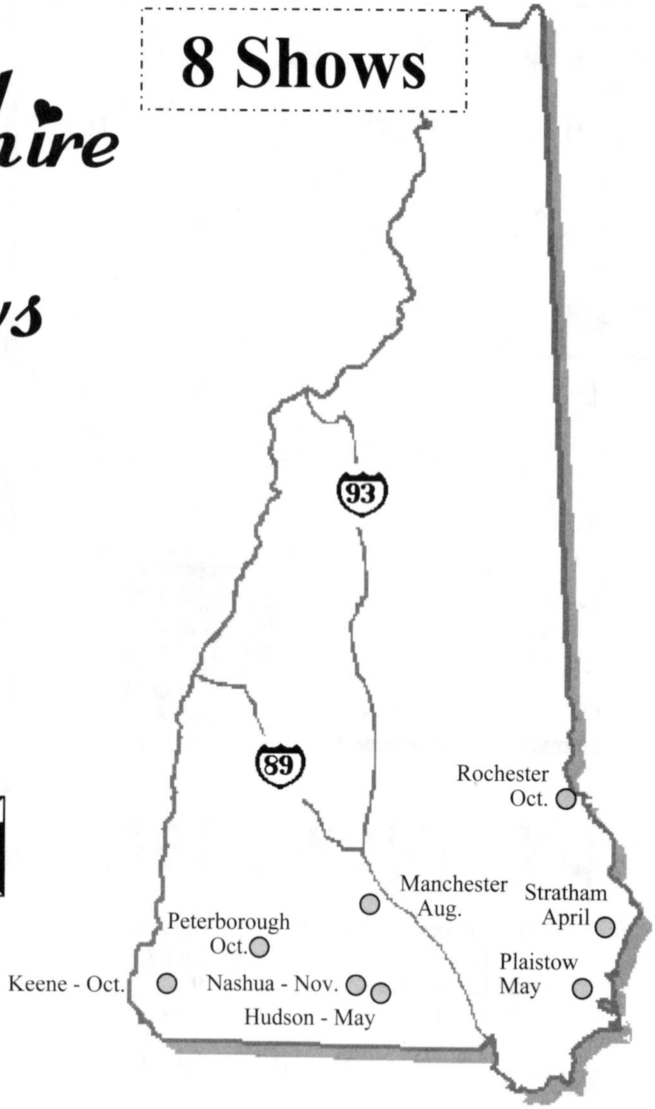

About Shows: We are listing only the very basic information about shows that happen on a regular schedule here. Please check out our website for more details on each show. Also this information tends to change quite often so please verify the event with our website or a local source before you venture far. Or if you're in the right area at the right time, give it a shot.

If you are a show organizer,
please keep us updated on your event.
shows@quilterstravelcompanion.com
www.quilterstravelcompanion.com

On our website you will also find:

- Exact dates (when we have them)
- Sponsor Information
- Contact Information
- Description of Event
- Events happening on a one-time basis

Month	City	Schedule	Show	Location with address
April				
	Stratham	Odd Years, 3rd Sat. in April	Seabreeze Quilt Guild	Co-Operative Middle School, 1 Academic Way
May				
	Plaistow	Annual, 1st Fri & Sat of May	Merrimack Valley Quilters Guild Show	Timberland Regional Middle School, 44 Greenough Rd. (4 miles from Rt. 495)
	Hudson	Annual, 1st weekend in May	Hannah Dustin Quilters Guild	Hudson Community Center, Llions Ave
August				
	Manchester	Annual, 2nd weekend in August	World Quilt Show--New England	The Radisson Center, 700 Elm St.
October				
	Keene	Odd Years, 2nd Fri & Sat in October	Cheshire Quilters' Guild	Monadnock Covenant Church, 90 Base Hill Rd.
	Peterborough	Even Years, Columbus Day Weekend in October	Monadnock Quilters' Guild Show	South Meadow School, 108 Hancock Rd.
	Rochester	Annual, 3rd weekend in October	Cocheco Quilters Guild Quilt Show	Rochester Community Center, 150 Wakefield St.
November				
	Nashua	Annual, 2nd weekend in November	A Quilters' Gathering	Radisson Hotel, 76 Northeastern Blvd. #36B

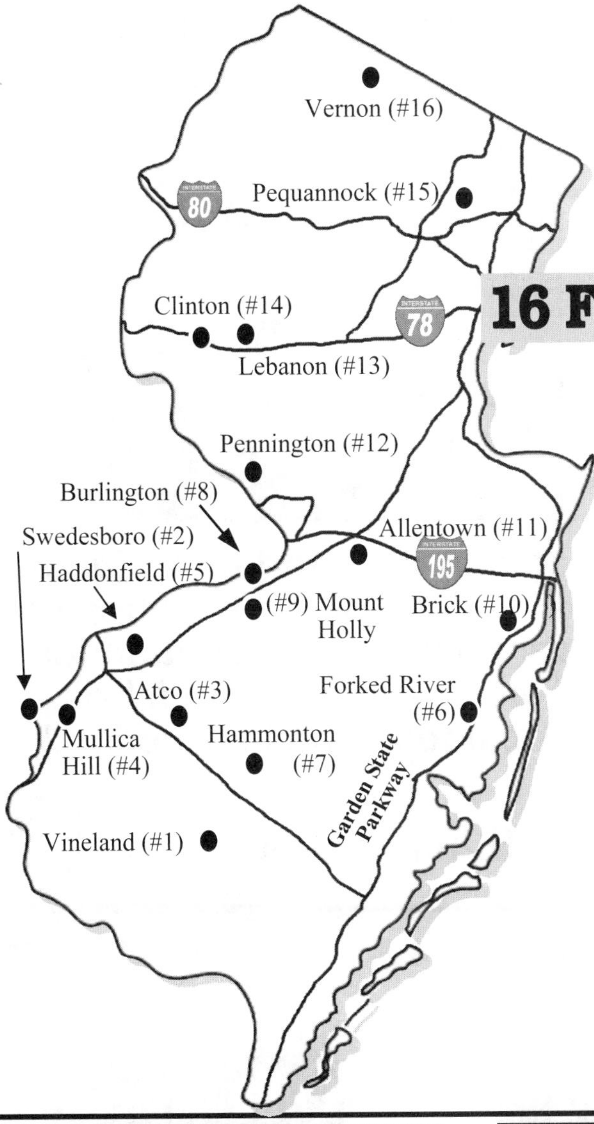

NEW JERSEY

16 Featured Shops

Vineland, NJ #1

Mon - Fri 9:30 - 6
Thur til 8
Sat 9:30 - 5:30

The Pin Cushion

22 W. Landis Ave. #1 08360
(856) 692-5460 Fax: Same
Owner: Lisa Mainiero
Est: 1972 4000 sq.ft. 3000 Bolts

Variety of fabrics includes: Quilting, Bridal, Dress, Batiks, Novelties.
Quilting Books, Notions, Patterns and Classes.

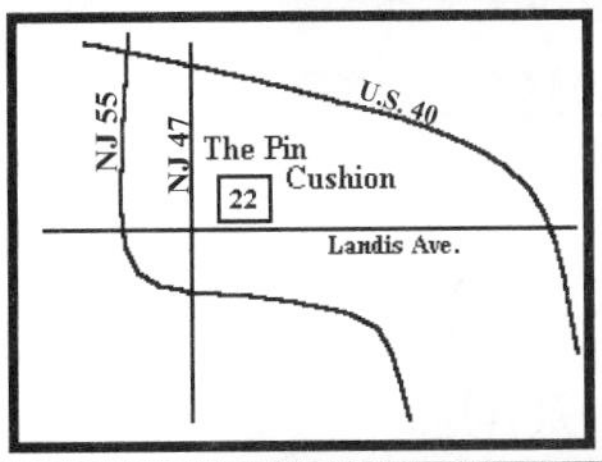

Swedesboro, NJ #2

Mon & Sat 10 - 4
Tues & Thur 10 - 8
Wed & Fri 10 - 5
Sun 12 - 4

Needles & Pins Quilt & Fabric Shop

1438 Kings Hwy. 08085
(856) 241-9977
Owner: Marie Kinsella-Diddio
Est: 2006 2000 Sq.ft. Online Newsletter
stitchinrie@comcast.net
www.needles-pins-nj.com
Large, friendly shop offering help, classes with over 4000 bolts of fabric. Large selection of books & patterns and we always have coffee & chocolate.

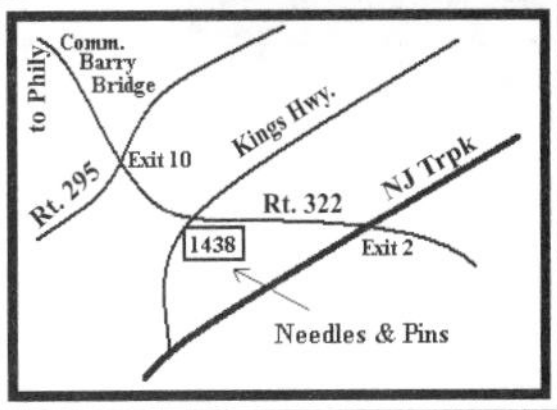

Atco, NJ #3

Tues - Fri 10 - 5
Sat 10 - 3

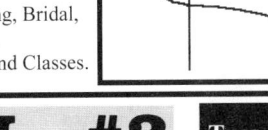

Quilted Treasures

2212 Atco Ave. 08004
(856) 768-2222
Owner: Lynn Hannigan
www.quiltedtreasuresinc.com
Small but growing Quilt Shop offering Quilting Fabric, Lessons and Supplies.
On site Long-Arm Quilting Service by Janet Eisner.

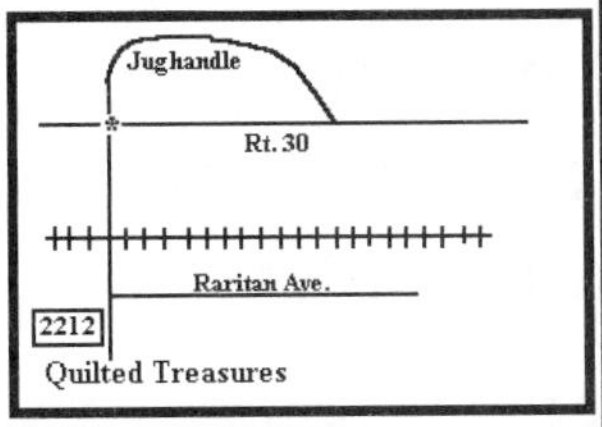

MULLICA HILL QUILT COMPANY

www.mhquiltco.com

43 S. Main St. (Courtyard Shop)
Mullica Hill, NJ 08062
856-478-2243
Fax: 856-478-2259 Free Online Newsletter
Owner: Annette Wright
awright@mhquiltco.com

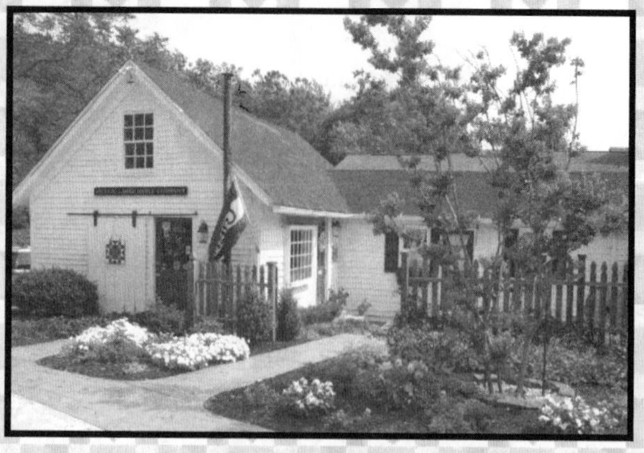

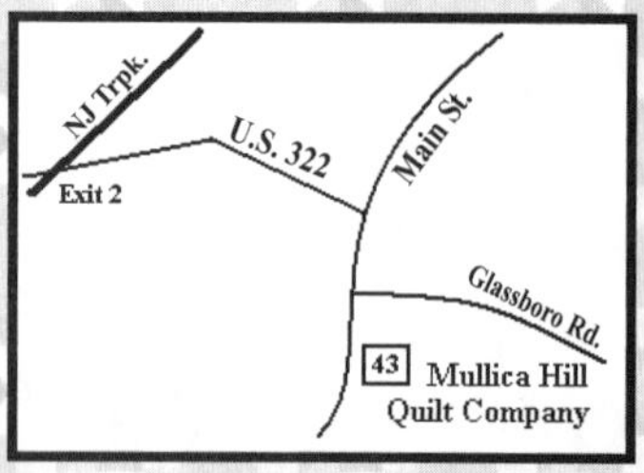

Mon - Wed
10 - 5
Thur - Fri
10 - 8
Sat 10 - 5
Sun 12 - 4

Est: 2007
1000 sq.ft
1500 bolts

"Located in the heart of Antique Country, Mullica Hill Quilt Company is Delaware Valley's destination for heirloom quality quilting fabric, patterns, books and instruction."

Mullica Hill, NJ #4

"Supplying The Fabric of Our Heritage"

Haddonfield, NJ #5

The Little Shop

Better Homes and Gardens
Quilt Sampler
FEATURED SHOP
2007

Chosen as one of the 10 featured shops in the United States & Canada for the Fall 2007 issue of Quilt Sampler magazine, published by Better Homes and Gardens.

Visit our website at:
www.thelittleshopforquilting.com
e-mail us at: LSQUILTS@aol.com

143 Kings Hwy. East 08033
(856) 429-7573 Est: 1960
Owner: Deborah Hagy Hansen 3000 bolts

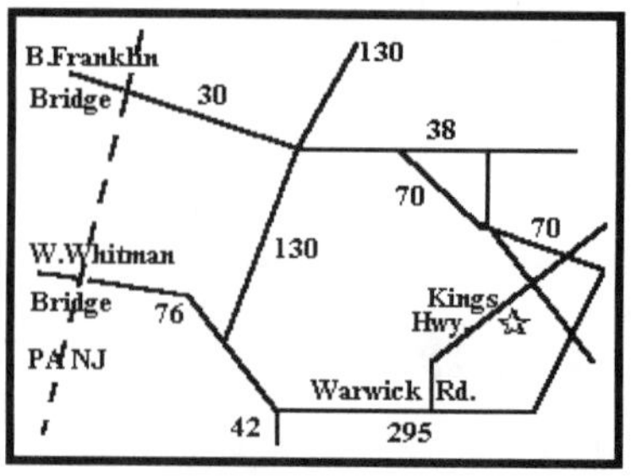

Monday - Friday 10 - 5
Saturday 10 - 4
Sunday 12:30 - 4
Class Nights 7 - 9

10 minutes from Philadelphia.
Quality cotton fabric. Instruction & Gifts.
All the latest books & notions.

Est: 1994

Forked River, NJ #6

QUILTING POSSIBILITIES
& Sewing Center

512 Rt. 9 South 08731 (609) 242-0033

5800 sq. ft. Owners: Debbie & Jim Welch qps@quiltingposs.com

www.quiltingpossibilities.net

3800+ bolts of quality quilting fabrics! We are known for our large selections of nautical prints, flannels, batiks, kits & our fat quarter section. We stock hundreds of patterns, books, kits, notions, BOMs, gifts, machine embroidery supplies & more! We are authorized Elna, Bernina, Babylock, HandiQuilter & Grace Frame dealers and do in-house service & repairs on all makes & models. Shop online or stop in to visit - our possibilities are endless!

Handi Quilter

New Jersey's Largest Quilt Shop!
We're Worth the Trip!!

Tues - Sat
10 - 4
Fri 10 - 7:30
Sun 12 - 4
Closed Mon

elna

Nothing Sews Like A Bernina. Nothing.
BERNINA®

baby lock

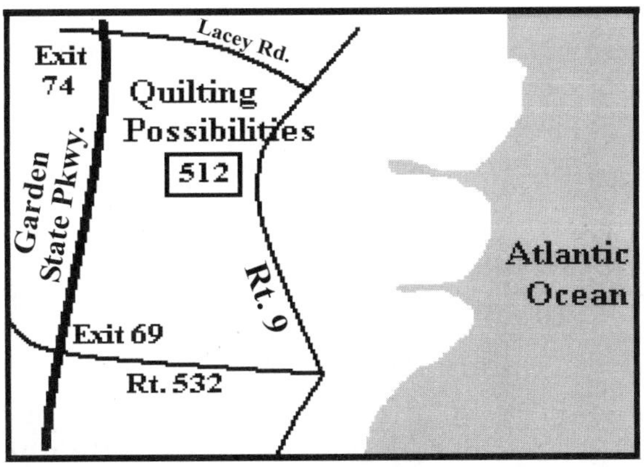

The Grace Company

Atlantic County Quilts LLC

Est: 2009

Tues-Sat 10-5
Sunday 12-4

609-704-1122

Atlantic County Quilts has over 1500 bolts of top notch cotton fabrics along with patterns, notions, and books. We have a knowledgeable staff offering year round classes and are southern New Jersey's only full service Bernina dealer. We are also a Gammill Statler Stitcher rental center with the only certified Creative Studio Trainer in the state.

BERNINA
Statler Stitcher

Hammonton, NJ #7

One Sindoni Ln. #C
Hammonton, NJ 08037
Owner: Laurie Interlante
Fax: 609-704-1142
2500 sq.ft. Online Newsletter
atlanticcountyquilts@gmail.com

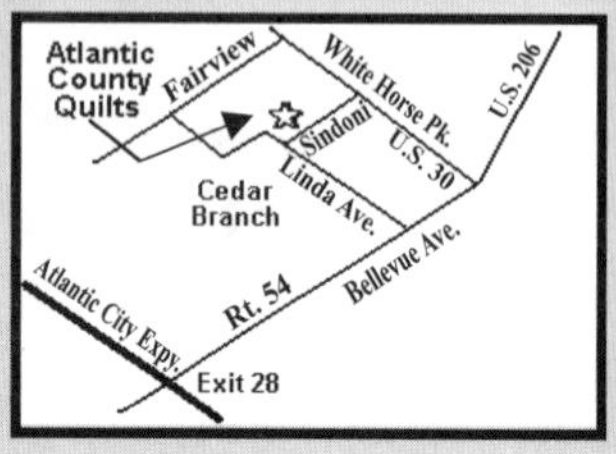

We are easily accessible to Philadelphia and the Jersey Shore.

OLDE CITY QUILTS

339 High Street, Burlington, NJ 08016
609-747-0075 www.oldecityquilts.com
Est: 2006 3000 sq.ft. 4000 bolts Online Newsletter

Mon, Tues, Thurs 10am - 7pm
Wed & Fri 10am - 8pm
Sat 10am - 6pm Sun 12pm - 5pm

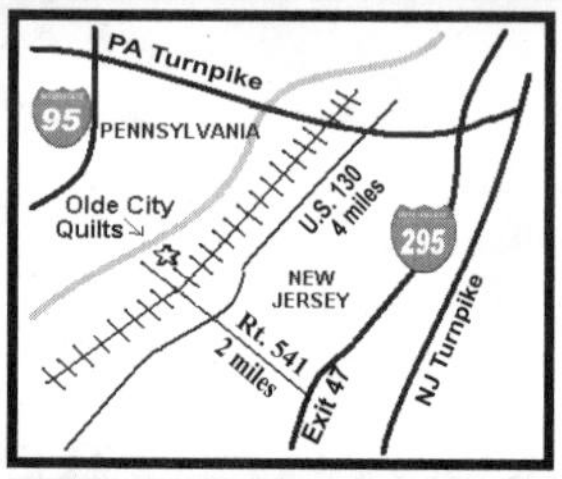

Located in Historic Burlington City is a Quilter's Paradise

- Full Service Bernina Dealership
- Over 4000 bolts of fabric
- Newest notions, books & patterns
- Innovative classes for all skill levels
- Gammill Long Arms for rental

Burlington, NJ #8

BERNINA

Mount Holly, NJ #9

The Village Quilter

Est: 2002
1700 Sq. Feet with over 3000 bolts

www.thevillagequilter.com

10 Charles St., Mt. Holly, New Jersey
08060
(The Shoppes at Mill Race Village)
(609) 265-0011
Owner: Susan Di Bartolo
Email us at: thevillagequilter@verizon.net

Mon & Tues 10-4
Wed - Sat 10-6
Thur til 8
Sun 11 - 4

8 Minutes off NJ Turnpike Exit #5

Voted one of the best fabric stores in Burlington County NJ 2006, 2008 & 2009

We are a full service shop featuring 100% quality cotton fabric, books, patterns, notions, magazines & threads.

Heavenly Seating
Right Chairs-Right Price

Premier Dealer of The Heavenly Sewing Chair

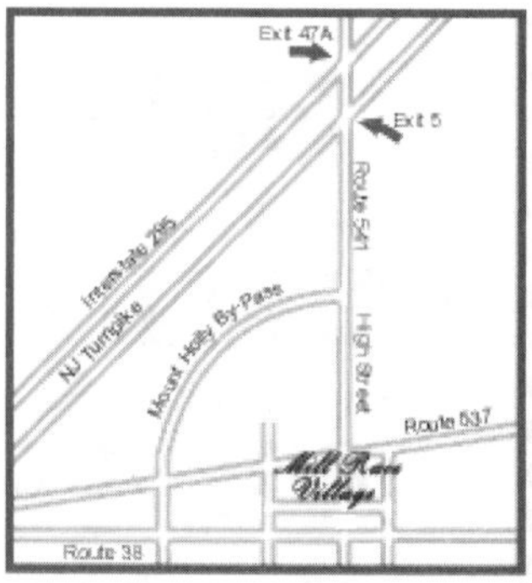

Brick, NJ #10

Crafty Fabrics

Summer
Tues - Fri 9:30 - 3
Sat 11 - 3
Winter
Tues - Fri 9:30 - 4
Sat 11 - 4

750 Mantoloking Rd. (Rt. 528) 08723
(732) 920-6220 Est: 2002
Owner: Diane McColley 1220 sq.ft.
www.craftyfabricsquilting.com

First Quality Cotton Fabrics at Discounted Prices. Books - Patterns - Notions - Gifts
Day & Evening Classes with 6 machines for your use.

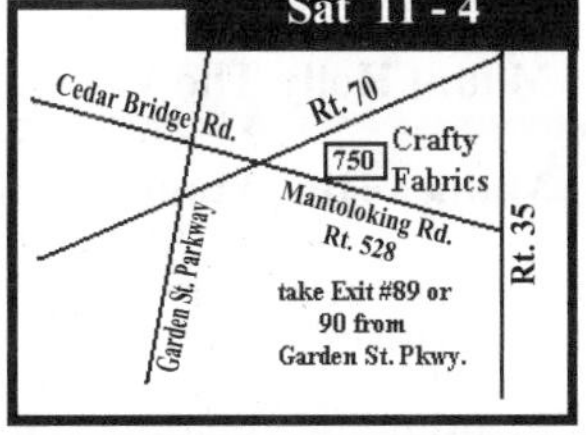

Allentown, NJ #11

The Quilters Cottage

Tues & Fri
10 - 6:30
Wed & Thur
10 - 8
Sat & Sun
10 - 4:30

34 S. Main St. 08501
(609) 259-9993
info@thequilterscottagenj.com
www.thequilterscottagenj.com

"A Quilting Haven."
A variety of classes, ample work space, Brother sewing machines and a long arm quilting machine are just the beginning of the amenities The Quilter's Cottage has to offer.

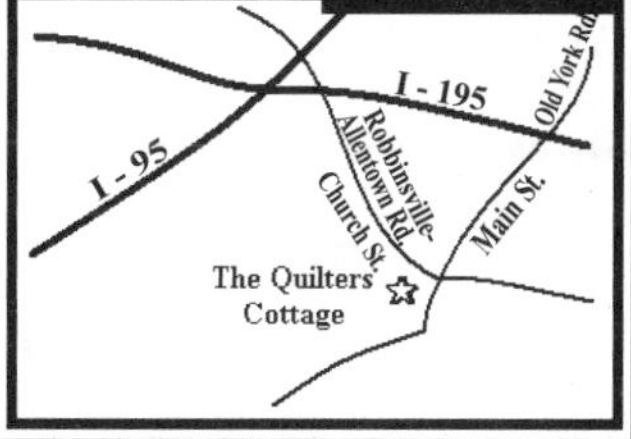

Pennington Quilt Works

Tree Farm Village
7 Tree Farm Rd. 08534
(609) 737-4321
www.penningtonquilts.com
Owner: Jan Crane
Est: 1996

Complete quilt shop with over 4000 bolts of cotton fabrics, books, patterns, notions & classes. All the basics, but always something new.

Pennington, NJ #12

Mon - Sat 10 - 5
Thurs til 8
Sun 12 - 4

BERNINA

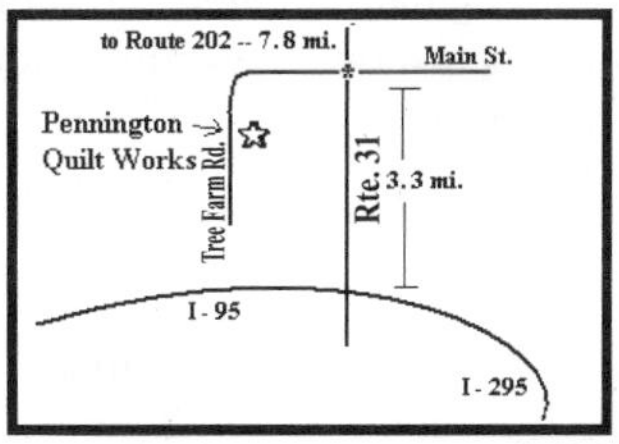

Lebanon, NJ #13

Budding Star Quilts

Mon - Sat
10 - 5:30
Sun 1 - 4

Rt. 22 E, Lebanon Plaza 08833
(908) 236-7676
www.buddingstarquilts.com
Owner: Kathy Verser Est: 1987 4000+ Bolts

We Specialize in Kits for all Levels!

Over 4000 Bolts 100% Cotton Fabric.
Large selection of flannels.
Premium selection of Yarns.
Classes in quilting and knitting for all levels.

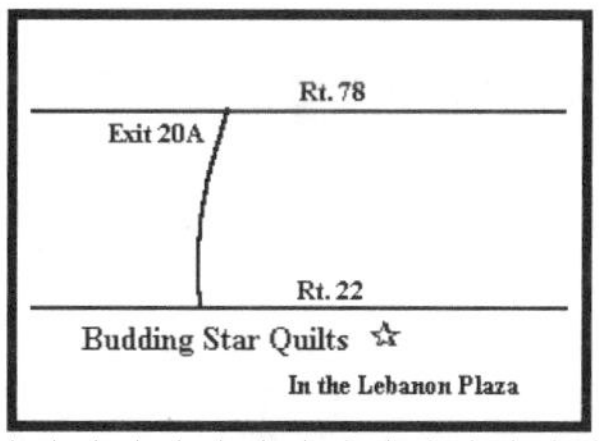

Clinton, NJ #14

Kindred Quilts

Mon - Sat
10 - 5
Thur til 7
Sun 12 - 4

21 E. Main St. 08809
(908) 730-8896
kindredquilts@gmail.com
www.kindredquilts.com
Owner: Toby Preston
Est: 1999 1500 sq.ft.

2,000 bolts of 100% cotton fabric, notions, embroidery and needle punch.

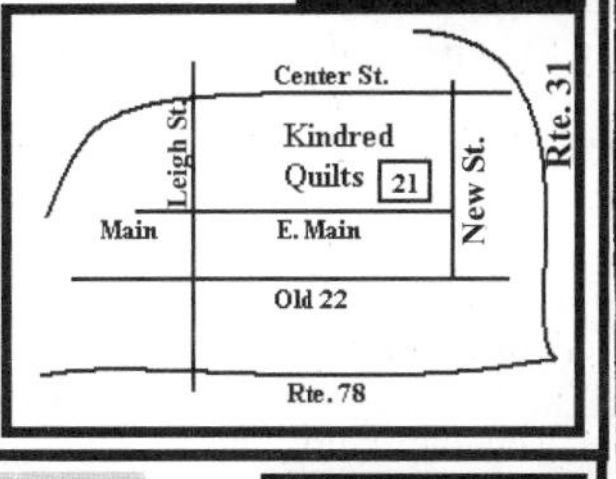

Pequannock, NJ #15

Acme COUNTRY FABRICS

BERNINA

Mon & Fri
10 - 5
and Tues &
Wed 7 - 8:30
Sat 10 - 3

24-26 Newark Pompton Tpke. 07440
(973) 696-1784 Est: 1984
Owners: Alyce Vanderstad & Janet Graimal
acmecountry@aol.com 10,000 bolts
www.acmecountryfabrics.com
Family owned and operated. We teach sewing, quilting and have a very extensive selection of 100% cotton fabrics. Large variety of threads, stabilizers, notions, books, machines and furniture.

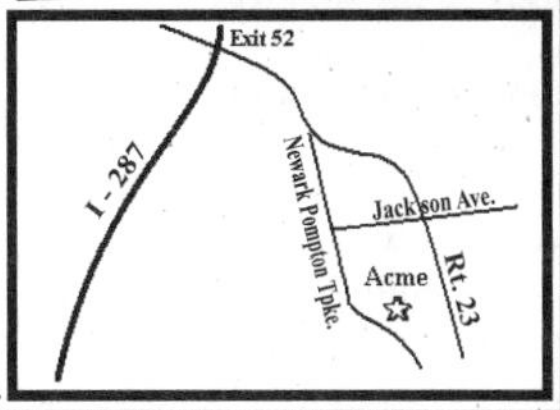

Pieceful Choices

Quilt Shop

Est: 2001

Sewing Machine Resource Center

Vernon, NJ #16

99 Route 94, Vernon, NJ 07462 ❖ (973) 823-9297
Owners: Maureen & Jon Lasslett pcqs@piecefulchoices.com

*Full Service Country Quilt Shop located in northwest NJ, minutes from NY & PA.
*Authorized JANOME Sales In-House Service and Repair on ALL Makes and Models
*Top Quality Quilting & Sewing fabric & supplies, classes, exhibits and events.
*Superior selection of 108" wide backings!
*Fat Quarter Wall

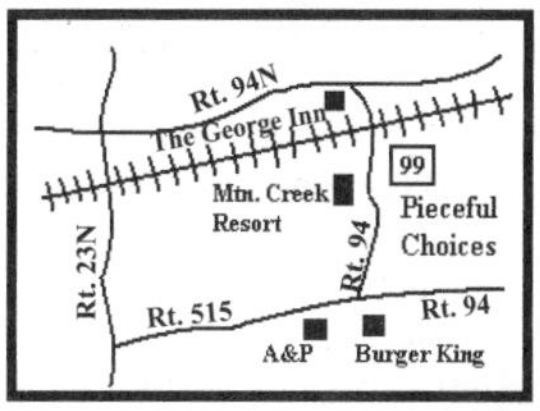

Tues, Wed,
Fri 10 - 5
Thurs 10 - 8
Sat 10 - 4
Sun 11 - 2

www.piecefulchoices.com

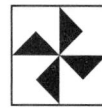

New Jersey Quilt Shops

Allentown — **The Quilters Cottage, 34 S. Main St.** **609-259-9993** **See ad #11, page 361**
Atco — **Quilted Treasures, 2212 Atco Ave.** **856-768-2222** **See ad #3, page 357**
Brick — **Crafty Fabrics, 750 Mantoloking Rd.** **732-920-6220** **See ad #10, page 361**
Bridgeton — Broad Meadows Country Fabrics, 100 Mary Elmer Dr. 856-451-2433
Browns Mills — Pastimes, 13 Trenton Rd 609-893-3311
Burlington — **Olde City Quilts, 339 High St.** **609-747-0075** **See ad #8, page 360**
Clinton — **Kindred Quilts, 21 E. Main St.** **908-730-8896** **See ad #14, page 361**
Cranford — Azimoon Fabrics, 29 Alden St. 908-996-3062
Englishtown — Fabric Inspirations, 30 Main St. 732-792-0083
Forked River — **Quilting Possibilities, 512 Rte. 9 So.** **609-242-0033** **See ad #6, page 359**
Haddonfield — **The Little Shop, 143 Kings Hwy E.** **856-429-7573** **See ad #5, page 358**
Hammonton — **Atlantic County Quilts, 1 Sindoni Ln. Ste. C** **609-704-1122** **See ad #7, page 360**
Howell — Mouse Creek Quilts, 4635 Rt. 9 North 732-534-5772
Lakewood — Stitch N'Sew Center, 123 E. County Line Rd 732-363-2220
Lebanon — **Budding Star Quilts, Rt. 22E Lebanon Plaza** **908-236-7676** **See ad #13, page 361**
Morris Plains — Aardvark & Co., 748 Speedwell Ave. 973-539-9033
Mount Holly — **The Village Quilter, 10 Charles St.** **609-265-0011** **See ad #9, page 360**
Mullica Hill — **Mullica Hill Quilt Company, 43 S. Main St.** **856-478-2243** **See ad #4, page 358**
North Plainfield — Prints Charming, 717 Greenbrook Rd. 908-769-0278
North Plainfield — Fabric Land, 855 Rte. 22 908-755-4700
Ocean City — Calico 'N Cotton, 715 Asbury Ave. 609-399-7166
Pennington — **Pennington Quilt Works, 7 Tree Farm Rd. # 104** **609-737-4321** **See ad #12, page 361**
Pequannock — **Acme Country Fabrics, 24-26 Newark Pompton** **973-696-1784** **See ad #15, page 361**
Princeton — Pins & Needles, 8 Chambers St. 609-921-9075
Princeton — American Sewing Center, 301 N. Harrison St. 609-921-2205
River Edge — The Cozy Quilt Shoppe, 466 Kinderkamack Rd. 201-483-3775
Stone Harbor — Harbor Fabric Shoppe, 346 96th St. 609-368-2831
Swedesboro — **Needles & Pins Quilt Shop, 1438 Kings Hwy.** **856-241-9977** **See ad #2, page 357**
Vernon — **Pieceful Choices Quilt Shop, 99 Route 94** **973-823-9297** **See ad #16, page 361**
Vineland — **The Pin Cushion, 22 W. Landis Ave. #1** **856-692-5460** **See ad #1 page 357**

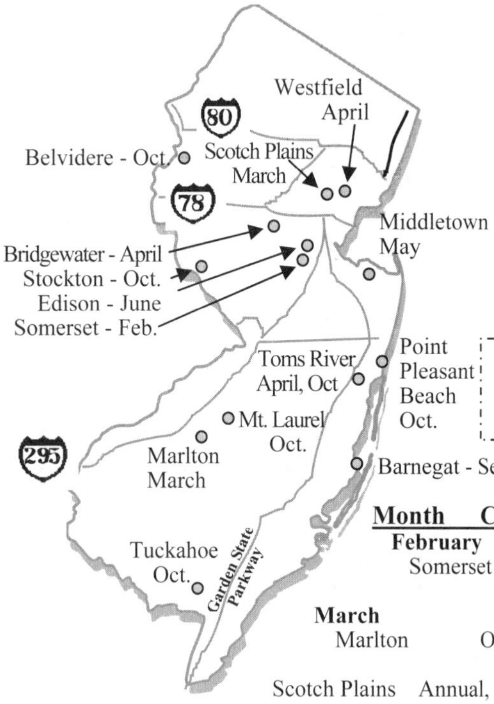

New Jersey Quilt Shows

About Shows: We are listing only the very basic information about shows that happen on a regular schedule here. Please check out our website for more details on each show. Also this information tends to change quite often so please verify the event with our website or a local source before you venture far. Or if you're in the right area at the right time, give it a shot.

15 Shows

If you are a show organizer, please keep us updated on your event.
shows@quilterstravelcompanion.com
www.quilterstravelcompanion.com

Month	City	Schedule	Show	Location with address
February				
	Somerset	Annual, late February or early March	The Quilt Fest of New Jersey	Garden State Exhibit Center, 50 Atrium Dr.
March				
	Marlton	Odd Years, 4th weekend in March	Love Apple Quilters Show	The Blue Barn (Marlton Recreation Center), 1008 Tuckerton Rd.
	Scotch Plains	Annual, Late March or early April	Harvest Quilters of Central Jersey Show	Willow Grove Presbyterian Church, 1961 Raritan Rd.
April				
	Westfield	Odd Years, April	Garden State Quilters Show	The Westfield Armory, 500 Rahway Ave.
	Toms River	Even Years, Changes around Easter	Beachplum Quilters of the Jersey Shore Show	Toms River Elks Lodge #1875, 600 Washington St.
	Bridgewater	Every 3rd Year, Last weekend of April, next 2012	Pieced Together Quilt Show	Somerset County 4-H Center, 310 Milltown Rd.
May				
	Middletown	Even Years, 2nd Fri & Sat in May	Rebecca's Reel Quilters Guild Quilt Show	Poricy Park Oak, Hill Rd.
June				
	Edison	Annual, 2nd Thurs - Sat of June	NJ Quilt Convention	NJ Convention & Expo Center--Raritan Center, 97 Sunfield Ave.
September				
	Barnegat	Annual, 2nd weekend in September	Quilts Along the Bay	Barnegat Community Center, 900 W. Bay Ave.
October				
	Point Pleasant Beach	Odd Years, Columbus Day weekend	Jersey Shore Quilters Show	St. Peter's Church - Kolbe Hall, 407 Atlantic Ave.
	Stockton	Even Years, 1st Fri - Sun in October	Quilts in the Mill	Prallsville Mills, Route 29
	Mt. Laurel	Odd Years, 3rd weekend of October	Berry Basket Quilters	Mt. Laurel Senior Center, 100 Mt. Laurel Rd.
	Tuckahoe	Odd Years, 3rd weekend in October	South Shore Quilters Show	Upper Township Community Center, 1790 Rt. 50
	Belvidere	Odd Years, 4th weekend of October	Evening Star Quilters Guild Show	Belvidere High School, 809 Oxford St.
	Toms River	Annual, fall	Quilts in Autumn	Ocean County Historical Society Museum, 26 Hadley Ave.

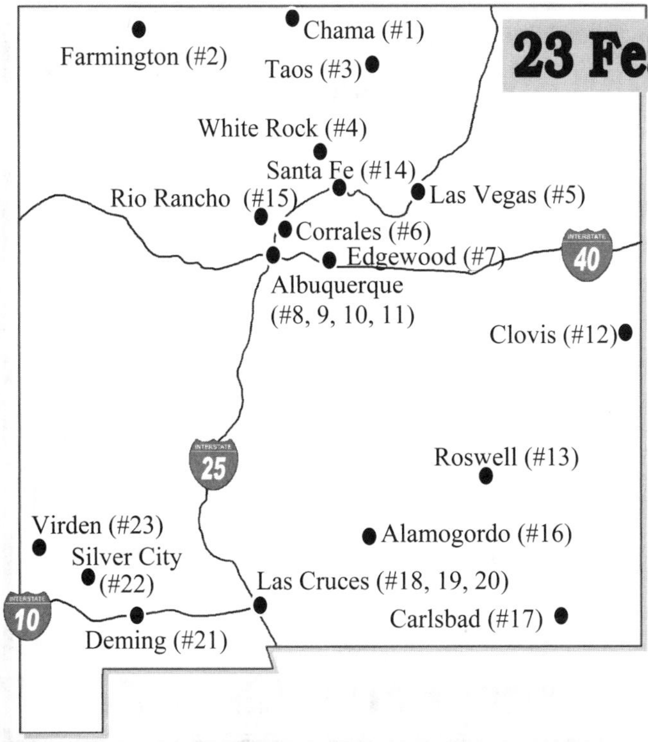

23 Featured Shops

NEW MEXICO

Little Foot Ltd.

Quilt Shop Est: 1999 Business Est: 1988

Owner: Lynn Graves

798 Terrace Avenue • Chama, NM 87520

1-800-597-7075 • 575-756-1412 • www.littlefoot.net

The Home of Little Foot®
Big Foot®
Jaws™ • That Purple Thang™
The Setting Triangle™
Notions for the Quilter
Top Piecing Foundation Sheets

Authorized Brother Sewing Machine Dealer

1100+ Bolts of 100% Cotton Fabric!!

Best selection of Flannels in the Southwest!

Mon - Fri • 10 - 3 p.m.
Closed Sat & Sun
Call ahead for winter hours.

Chama, NM #1

Farmington, NM #2

Mon - Fri 10 - 5
Thur til 6
Sat 10 - 3

Patchwork Pig

309 W. Main 87401
(505) 326-6465
Fax: (505) 326-6498
Est: 2003 6000 sq.ft.
deb@patchworkpig.biz
Owner: Deborah K. Williams
www.patchworkpig.biz

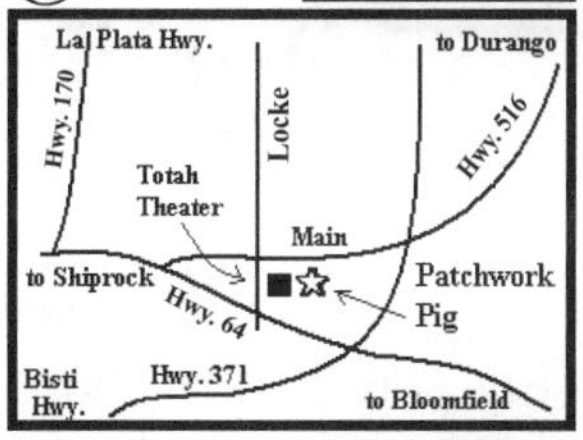

4000+ Bolts of 100% cotton, 30's, Flannel, Batiks, Thimbleberries and Wool.

Taos, NM #3

Mon - Sat 10:30 - 5
Sun 12 - 4

Taos Adobe Quilting

102 Teresina Lane 87571
(575) 751-3219 Fax: Same
Owners: Peter & Jan O'Donohue
taostogs@taosnet.com
www.TaosAdobeQuiltingandMore.com
Features Quilts, southwestern and juvenile fabrics in 100% cotton and hard to find prints.
PFAFF DEALER.

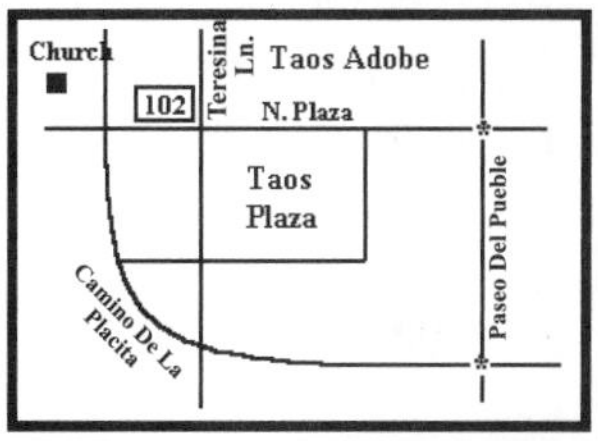

White Rock, NM #4

Tues - Sat 10 - 5

Pandy's Quilt Store

13 Sherwood Blvd. 87544
(505) 672-2004 Est: 1999
Owner: Pandy Lolos Online Newsletter
pandy@pandysquiltstore.com 1600 sq.ft.
www.pandysquiltstore.com 2000+ Bolts

We carry brights, batiks, marbles and oriental fabrics plus PFAFF sewing machines.

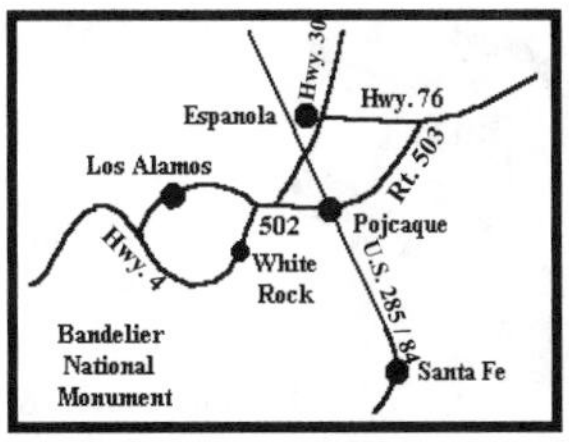

Las Vegas, NM #5

Mon - Sat 10 - 5

ThreadBear

150 Bridge St. 87701
(505) 425-6263 1500+ bolts
threadbear.nm@gmail.com

Bright, contemporary quilting fabrics, plus fine yarns, notions, and embroidery supplies. Located in historic Old Town.

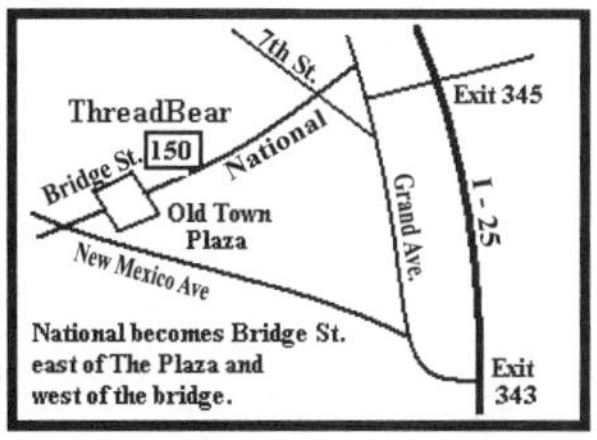

Corrales, NM #6

Mon - Fri 9:30 - 5
Sat 9 - 5

QUILTS OLÉ

3923 Corrales Rd. 87048
(505) 890-9416
Fax: (505) 890-9451
Est: 2000
2300 sq.ft.
2000 bolts

Owner: Sandra Eichenberg

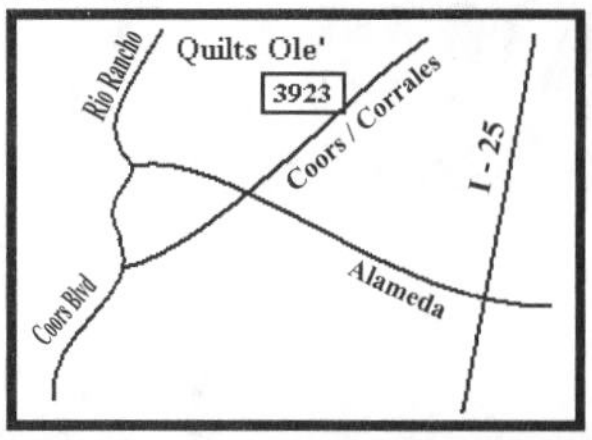

Located in a quaint village, northwest of Albuquerque. Specializing in batiks, brights & unusual prints. Notions, Books, gifts, yarn & Classes too! Featured in Quilt Sampler 2005. www.quiltsole.com

Albuquerque, NM #8

Mon - Fri 9 - 6
Sat 9 - 5
Sun 1 - 5

The Quilt Works

11117 Menaul N.E. 87112
(505) 298-8210 Est: 1985
quilt@thuntek.net 1750 sq.ft.
www.quiltworksabq.com
fax: (505) 323-8759
Owner: Shirley Brabson

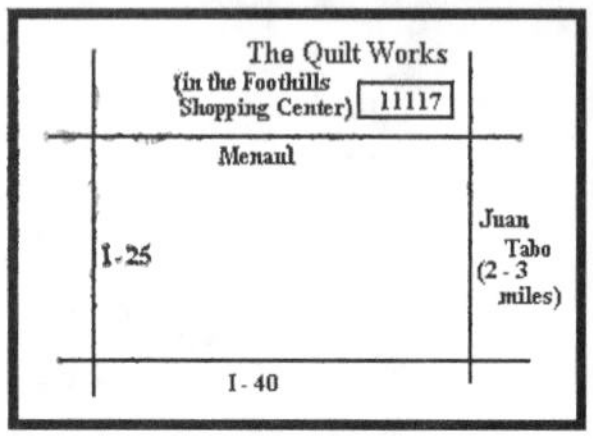

We have over 3000 bolts of cotton fabric. We're Friendly and Helpful !

Busy Bee Quilts

"Where we are never too BUSY for YOU!"
Open 9am-5pm Monday thru Saturday

- Over 1800 bolts of new fabric
- Asians, Civil War, 30's, Batiks, Southwests
- Lots of books, patterns, and kits
- All kinds of notions and supplies

Easy to find (20 miles East of Albuquerque off I-40)
Get off I-40 at Exit 187 (Edgewood) 1.5 miles North

150 State Rd. 344, Suite D
Edgewood, NM 87015
(505) 281-0195
queenbee@shopbusybee.com
www.shopbusybee.com

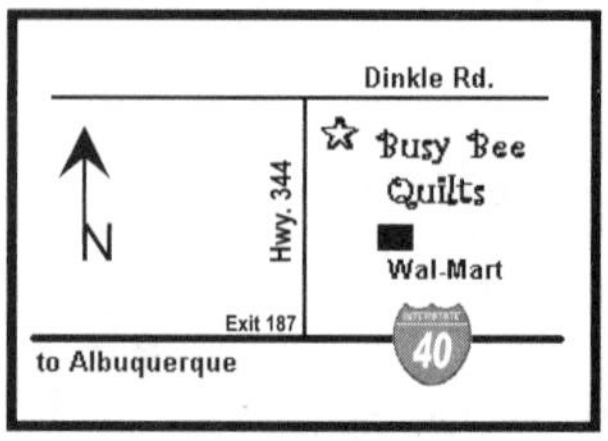

Bring this book in and receive 10% OFF your entire purchase. (sale items not included)

Edgewood, NM #7

SOUTHWEST DECORATIVES

Kokopelli Quilting Company

Hours: **Mon-Sat 9 am - 5 pm**
Sundays by appointment

You've seen our ads in national quilt magazines, come visit us!

5711 Carmel NE, Suite B
Albuquerque, NM 87113
Toll Free Credit Card Orders:
1.800.530.8995
New Mexico/Foreign call:
505.821.7400
Mary-Jo McCarthy / owner

Full service quilt shop. 4000 bolts of 100% cotton fabrics. Beautiful selection of Southwest theme fabrics. Over 300 Quilt patterns and kits.

#9

Hundreds of samples on display. Classes, Notions, Accessories. 150+ Cross Stitch charts and kits.
Long Arm Quilting Available.

Visit our website at
www.swdecoratives.com

Only 3 miles North of I-40 off I-25!

Albuquerque, NM #10

Mon - Thurs 9 - 8
Fri & Sat 9 - 5

Ann Silva's
BERNINA®
Sewing Center

American Crossing Shopping Center
3101 Menaul Blvd. NE 87107
505-881-5253
www.annsilva.com
Quality Bernina and Baby Lock Sewing Machines, Sergers and Embroidery Systems.
Sewing Classes, 2000+ Bolts of Fabric, Books, Patterns, and Notions

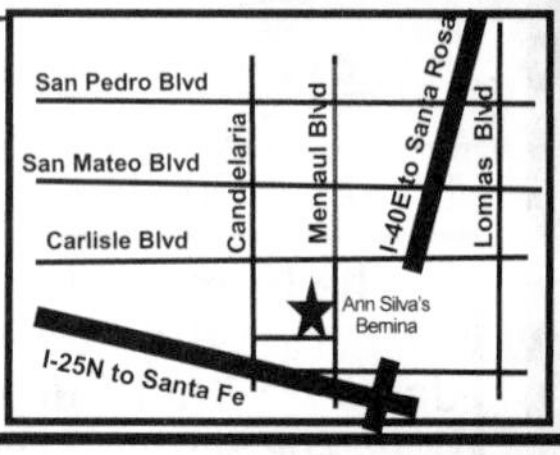

Albuquerque, NM #11

Mon - Sat 10 - 5
Thurs til 9

Quilts from the ♥

417 Tramway NE #1 87123
(505) 292-8560
Owner: Leta Brazell

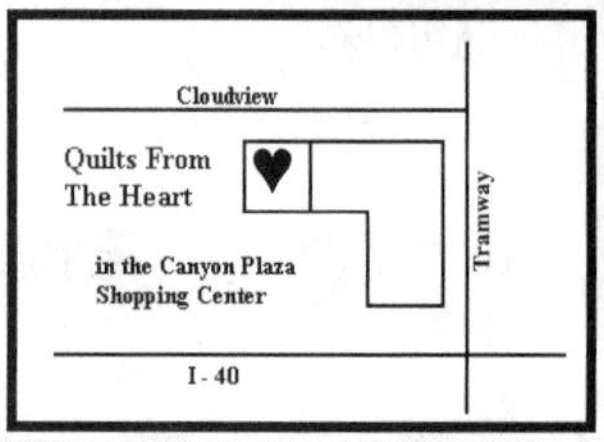

A Full Service Quilt Shop !
Quilts for Sale, Custom Quilts, Finishing, Classes, Fabric, Books, Notions & More.

Clovis, NM #12

Mon - Sat 10 -5

The Patchwork House

519 Main St. 88101
(575) 769-8072
Owner: Judy Matthews
judym1945@yahoo.com
www.thepatchworkhouse.com

Best Selection of Quality Quilting Fabrics, Books, Patterns, Notions for 100 miles.
Classes

Roswell, NM #13

Mon - Fri 10 - 5
Sat 10 - 3

Calico Cow Quilt Shop

311 N. Main 88201
(575) 623-8647 Est: 2001
Owner: Carolyn Pollard Noling
Carolynnoling@aol.com
www.calicocowquiltshop.com

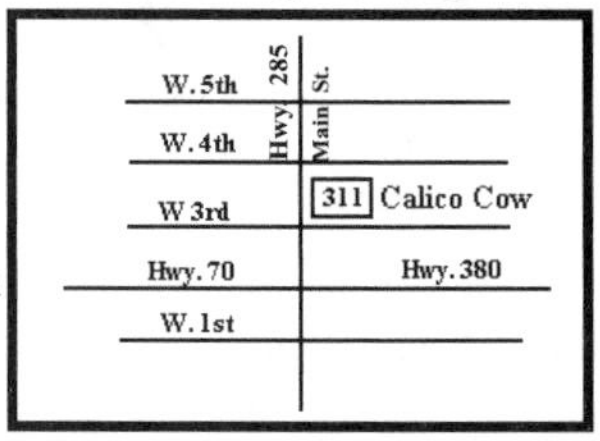

Cotton Fabrics, Flannels, Notions, Books & Patterns.

Santa Fe Quilting, Inc.

3018-A Cielo Court, Santa Fe, NM 87507
(505) 473-3747
info@santafequilting.com
Owners: Mary McCusker & Allen Winchester
Est: 2000 2400 sq.ft. Over 4500 Bolts
www.santafequilting.com

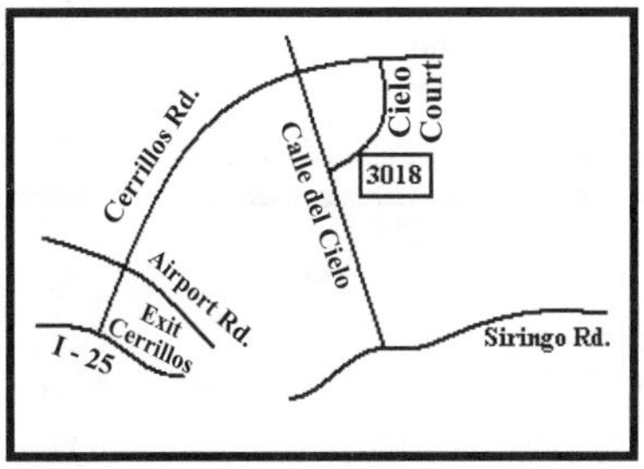

Mon - Sat 10 - 5:30 Thur til 7 Sun 1 - 5

Bright cottons, including a wide selection of Batiks. Cottons from Japan. Oriental and Southwest Fabrics and Patterns. Sashiko Supplies, Numerous Flannels. Books & Time Saving Notions. Block of the Month Kits & Classes. Sewing Machines available for class use by travelers. Fabrics from most major fabric companies are available in our store.

Santa Fe, NM #14

Quilt Bugs

3301 Southern Blvd Suite 102
(505) 994-0269 julie@quiltbugs.com

- Over 2,000 Bolts of 100% Cotton
- Small Classes
- Children's Classes
- Kits & Batting
- Books & Patterns
- Thread & Notions
- Family Owned and Operated

Visit Us At
www.quiltbugs.com

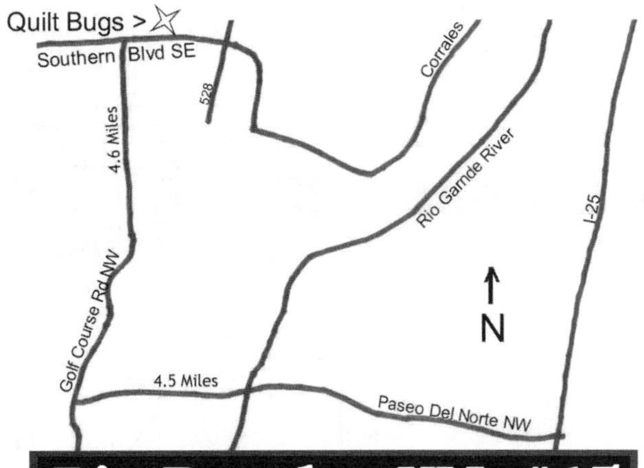

Rio Rancho, NM #15

Alamogordo, NM #16

Mon - Fri 10 - 4
Mon & Wed til 8
Sat 10 - 1

Homestead Quilting

800 Maryland Ave. 88310
(575) 434-2009
Owner: Barbara Howard
Est: 2006 3800 sq.ft.
homesteadquilting@gmail.com
www.homesteadquilting.net

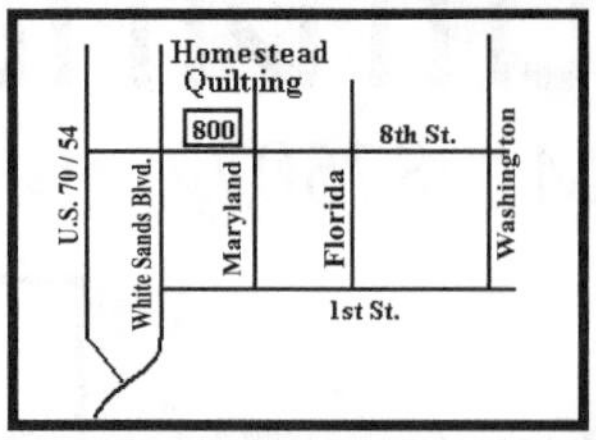

Quilting fabrics, notions, classes, long arm & Hand quilting services, tatting, weaving, spinning, knitting & crochet.

Carlsbad, NM #17

Mon - Fri
10 - 5:30
Sat 10 - 4

Jill's Fabric & Design

121 S. Canyon 88220
(575) 885-1184
Owners: Jill Balderrama & Sherry Bowman
Est: 1994 4000 sq.ft.

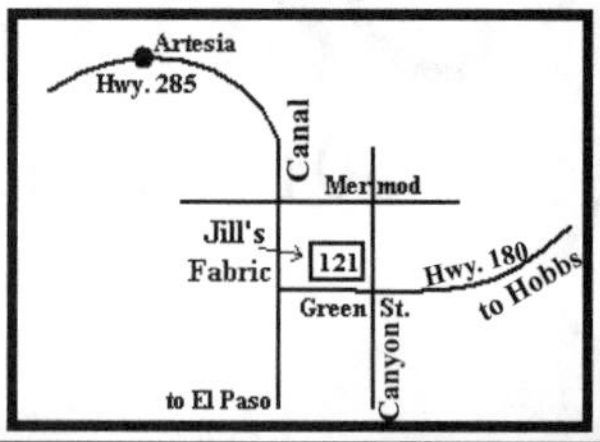

Over 3000 bolts of fabrics - cotton, flannels, wedding & dress. Also books, notions, patterns for all your sewing & quilting needs.

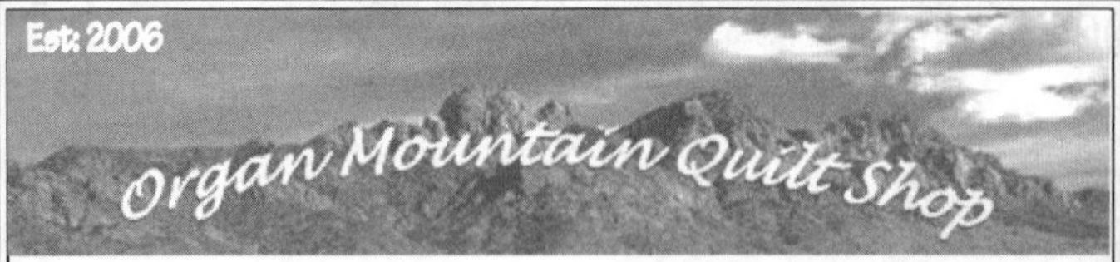

Satisfying your itch to stitch

Organ Mountain Quilt Shop is a cozy shop located in an historic building situated in Las Cruces' Downtown Mall. Stop in and visit all our great fabrics, kits and classes.

www.omqs.com

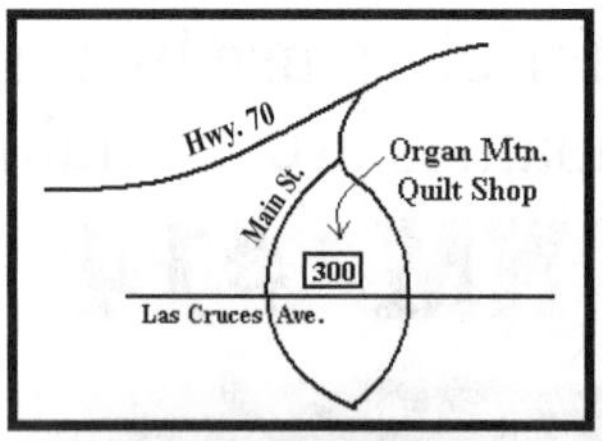

300 N. Downtown Mall
Las Cruces, NM 88001
(575) 525-8025
Owners: Vicki Rall & Elizabeth Oliver
staff@omqs.com
Free online newsletter

Mon - Fri 9 - 5
Sat 9 - 4

Las Cruces, NM #18

Las Cruces, NM #19

Mon - Sat
10 - 5
Tues 12 - 5

SEW WHAT'S NEW

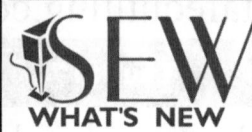

3961 E. Lohman Ave. #9 88011
(575) 524-1739
sew@lascruces.com

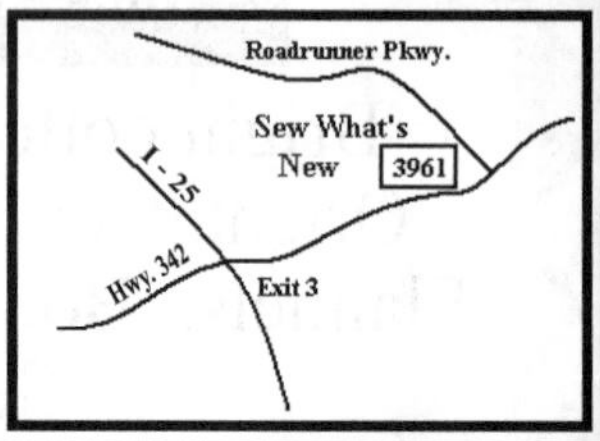

www.sewwhatsnewlascruces.com
Fabrics for Quilters
Notions, Classes & Services
Authorized Husqvarna Viking, Pfaff & Singer Dealer.
"THE Fun Place to SEWcialize"

Las Cruces, NM #20

Tues - Fri
9:30 - 5:30
Sat 9:30 -

BERNINA SEWING & DESIGN CENTER

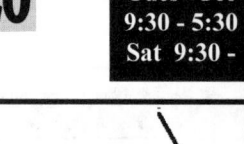

1601 E.Lohman Ave. 88001
(575) 523-2000 Fax: (575) 523-2016
Est: 2005 3200 sq.ft. 700 bolts
berninalascruces@yahoo.com
www.bernina-lascruces.com

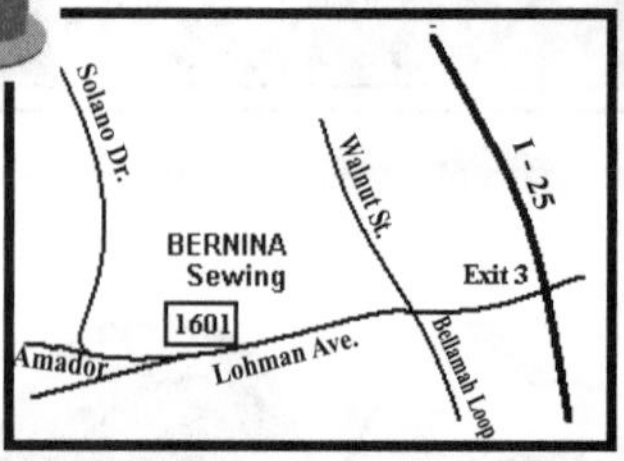

"Wonderful fabrics and classes"
"BERNINA and HandiQuilter dealer"
"Fabric Addiction Specialists"

Deming, NM #21

Mon - Fri
9 - 5:30
Sat 9:30 - 3

Sew-n-Sew

609 E. Florida, P.O. Box 493 88031
(505) 546-8085
Fax: (505) 546-8081
sewnsew@swnm.com
Owner: Janet Offutt
Est: 1990 2400 sq. ft.

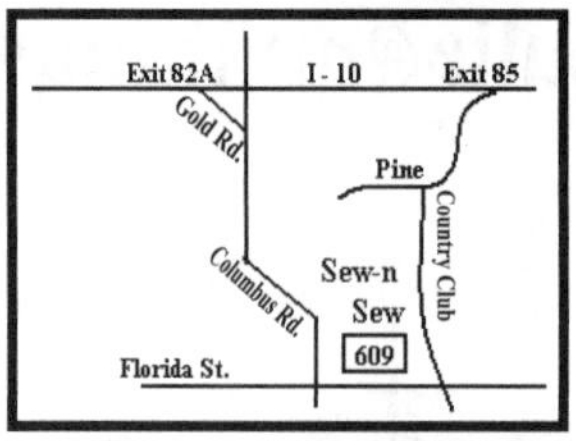

S.W. Designs, Wedding Fabrics, Patterns, Notions, Quilting Cottons, Books, etc. Quilting Fabrics, will order for special occasions. All my Fabrics are Quality.

Silver City, NM #22

Mon - Fri
9 - 5
Sat 9 - 4

Thunder Creek Quilt Company

703 N. Bullard St. 88061
(575) 538-2284
Owners: Nancy Coryell & Cindy Ugarte
Est: 1995 3000+ Bolts
sneezweeds@zianet.com

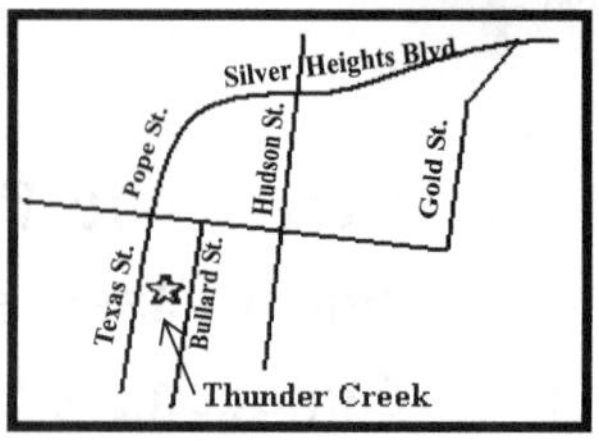

Specializing in Southwestern Fabrics & Patterns. Cotton Fabric. Notions, Sulky & Gutermann Threads. Gingher Scissors. Gifts. Long Arm Quilting. Sewing Machine Repair.

Virden, NM #23

Mon, Wed
Fri 1:30 - 6
Thur 9 - 7

Nelda's Quilt Shop

309 Richmond Ave. 88045
(575) 358-2184 Fax: (575) 358-1000
Owner: Nelda Potter
Est: 2002 1200 sq.ft. 1300+ Bolts
neldapotter@aznex.net

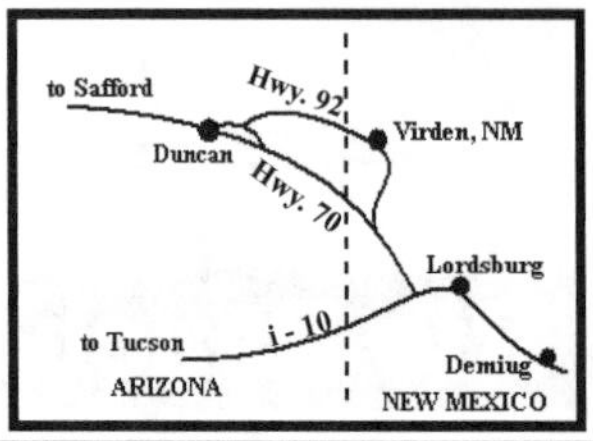

1300 Bolts of Fabric, Notions, College Classes, Hemstitching, Receiving Blankets, Long-arm Quilting and More.

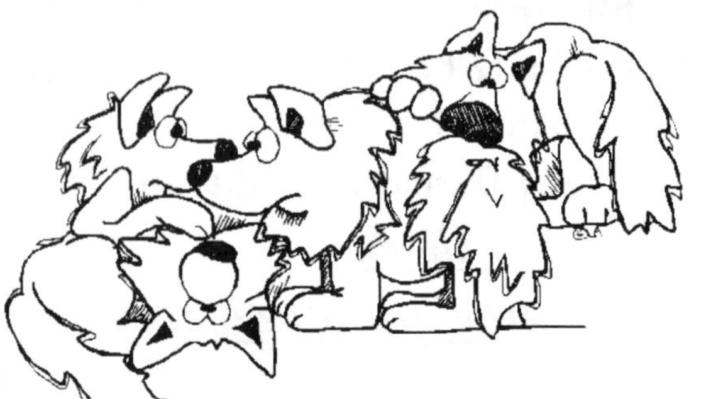

New Mexico Quilt Shops

Alamogordo **Homestead Quilting, 800 Maryland Ave.**
575-434-2009 **See ad #16, page 366**

Albuquerque **Southwest Decorative, 5711 Carmel Ave. NE #B**
505-821-7400 **See ad #9, page 364**

Albuquerque **Ann Silva's Bernina Sewing Center, 3101 Menaul NE**
505-881-5253 **See ad #10, page 364**

Albuquerque **The Quilt Works, 11117 Menaul Blvd. NE**
505-298-8210 **See ad #8, page 364**

Albuquerque **Quilts from the Heart, 417 Tramway Blvd. NE #1**
505-292-8560 **See ad #11, page 364**

Artesia Martha's Fabric Shop, 316 W. Main St. 575-748-2231
Aztec Quilt it! Ya Ya Fabric and Quilt Store, 201 S Church Ave 505-334-9566
Carlsbad Granny's Quilt Barn, 1811 Jewel St. 575-885-5276

Carlsbad **Jill's Fabric & Design, 121 S Canyon**
575-885-1184 **See ad #17, page 366**

Chama **Little Foot Ltd., 798 Terrace Ave.**
575-756-1412 **See ad #1, page 363**

Clovis **The Patchwork House, 519 N. Main St.**
575-769-8072 **See ad #12, page 364**

Corrales **Quilts Ole, 3923 Corrales Rd.**
505-890-9416 **See ad #6, page 364**

Deming **Sew-N-Sew, 609 E. Florida**
575-546-8085 **See ad #21, page 366**

Edgewood **Busy Bee Quilts, 150 State Rd. 344 #D**
505-281-0195 **See ad #7, page 364**

Farmington **Patchwork Pig, 309 W. Main St.**
505-326-6465 **See ad #2, page 363**

Farmington Quilted Threads, 5501 Evergreen Dr. 505-325-4490
Farmington Bernina Sewing Center, 3030 East Main, Suite.Y-1 505-327-9911

Las Cruces **Sew What's New, 3961 East Lohman Ave. # 9**
575-524-1739 **See ad #19, page 366**

Las Cruces **Organ Mountain Quilt Shop, 300 N. Downtown Mall**
575-525-8025 **See ad #18, page 366**

Las Cruces **Bernina Sewing & Design Center, 1601 E. Lohman Ave.**
575-523-2000 **See ad 320, apge 366**

Las Vegas **Thread Bear, 150 Bridge St.**
505-425-6263 **See ad #5, page 363**

Lovington Country Store Quilt Shop, 115 N. Main 575-396-4914

Rio Rancho **Quilt Bugs, 3301 Southern Blvd. #102**
505-994-0269 **See ad #15, page 365**

Rodeo Rodeo Country Quilters, 73 Portal Rd. 575-557-6833

Roswell **Calico Cow Quilt Shop, 311 N. Main**
575-623-8647 **See ad #13, page 364**

Ruidoso Martha's Fabric Shop, 101 Vision Dr. 575-630-2231

Santa Fe **Santa Fe Quilting, 3018 A Cielo Ct.**
505-473-3747 **See ad #14, page 365**

Silver City **Thunder Creek Quilt Company,703 N. Bullard St.**
575-538-2284 **See ad #22, page 366**

Taos **Taos Adobe Quilting, 102 Teresina Lane**
575-751-3219 **See ad #3, page 363**

Tijeras A Quilter's Affaire, P.O. Box 1719 505-292-8925
Tucumcari Desert Rose Center LLC, 212 E. Main 575-461-2342

Virden **Nelda's Quilt Shop, 309 Richmond Ave.**
575-358-2184 **See ad #23, page 366**

White Rock **Pandy's Quilt Store, 13 Sherwood Blvd.**
505-672-2004 **See ad #4, page 363**

New Mexico Quilt Shows

About Shows: We are listing only the very basic information about shows that happen on a regular schedule here. Please check out our website for more details on each show. Also this information tends to change quite often so please verify the event with our website or a local source before you venture far. Or if you're in the right area at the right time, give it a shot.

11 Shows

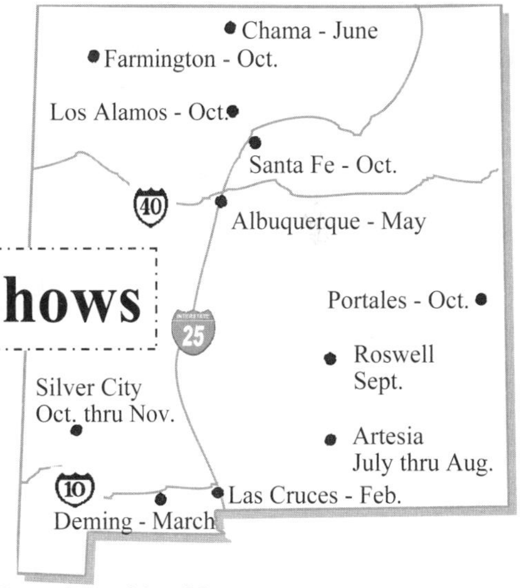

If you are a show organizer,
please keep us updated on your event.
shows@quilterstravelcompanion.com
www.quilterstravelcompanion.com

Month	City	Schedule	Show	Location with address
February				
	Las Cruces	Even Years, usually last weekend of February	Las Colcheras Quilt Guild Show	Corbett Center--NM State University Campus
March				
	Deming	Annual, 2nd Saturday in March	Desert Stitchers Quilt Show	United Methodist Church, 1010 Granite
May				
	Albuquerque	Odd Years, Thurs - Sat of Memorial Day Weekend	Albuquerque Fiber Arts Fiesta	Expo NM fairgrounds
June				
	Chama	Annual, 2nd Saturday in June	Chama Outdoor Quilt Show	Downtown Chama
August				
	Artesia	Annual, From the 3rd Tues. in July thru August	Artesia Quilters Guild's Show	Artesia Historical Museum, 505 W. Richardson
September				
	Roswell	Even Years, last Fri & Sat of September	Chili and Cheese Quilt Festival	Roswell Civic Center, 912 N. Main
October				
	Santa Fe	Even Years, 1st weekend in October	NNMQG Quilt Fiesta	Santa Fe Country Fairgrounds, 3229 Rodeo Rd.
	Silver City	Odd Years, Fall	Southwest Enchantment Quilt Show	Silver City Museum, 312 W. Broadway
	Farmington	Annual, 2nd weekend in October	San Juan Quilters Guild	Farmington Civic Center, 200 W. Arrington St.
	Los Alamos	Odd Years, Late Sat. in October	Los Alamos Quilt Guild Market	United Church, 2525 Canyon Rd.
	Portales	Annual, 3rd Fri & Sat in October	High Plains Quilt Festival	Memorial Building, 200 W. 7th St.

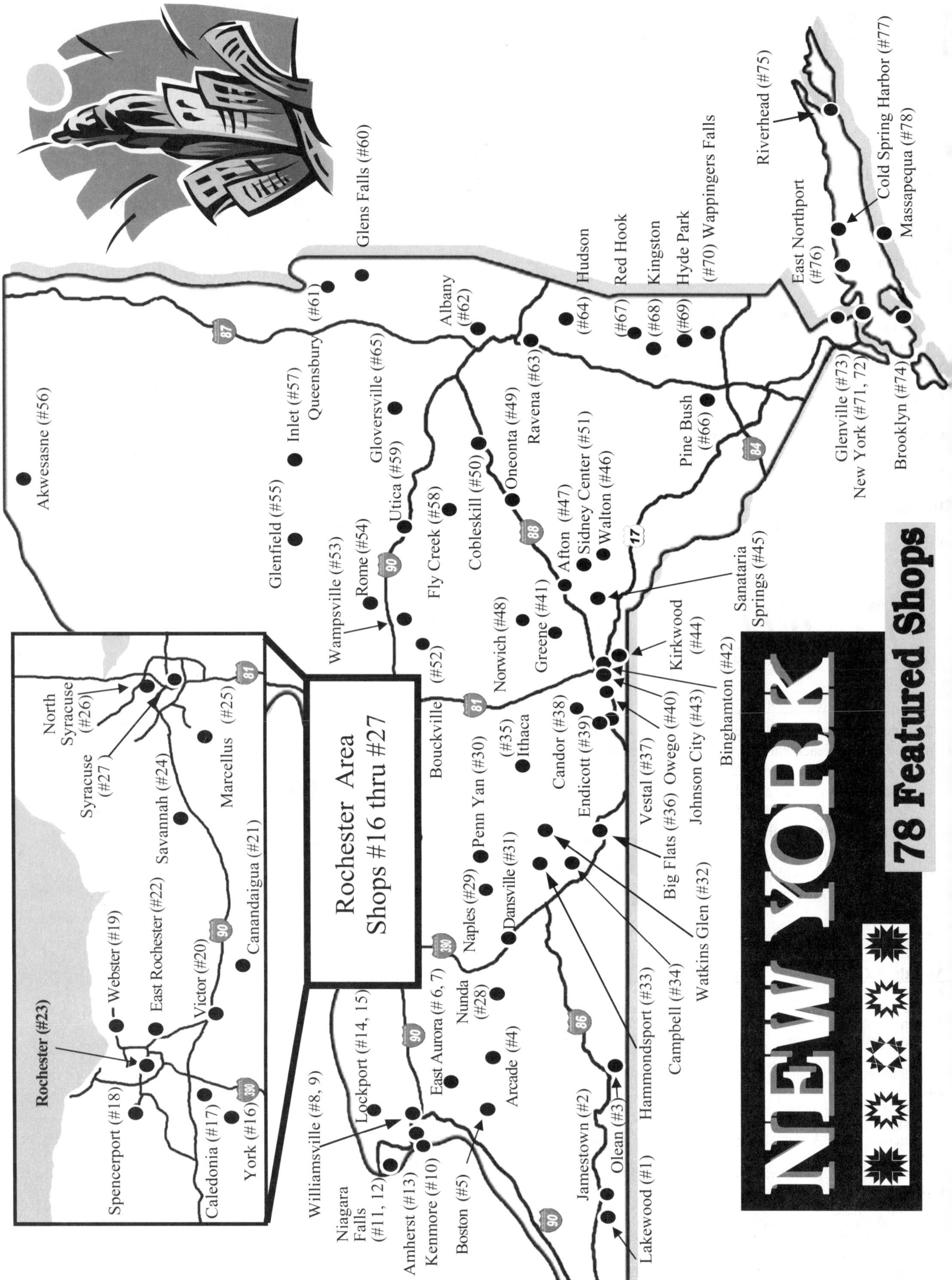
NEW YORK
78 Featured Shops
Rochester Area
Shops #16 thru #27
Rochester (#23)
Webster (#19)
East Rochester (#22)
Victor (#20)
Spencerport (#18)
Caledonia (#17)
York (#16)
Canandaigua (#21)
Savannah (#24)
Marcellus (#25)
Syracuse (#27)
North Syracuse (#26)
Akwesasne (#56)
Glenfield (#55)
Inlet (#57)
Queensbury (#61)
Glens Falls (#60)
Gloversville (#65)
Albany (#62)
Utica (#59)
Rome (#54)
Wampsville (#53)
Fly Creek (#58)
Cobleskill (#50)
Oneonta (#49)
Ravena (#63)
Hudson (#64)
Red Hook (#67)
Kingston (#68)
Hyde Park (#69)
(#70) Wappingers Falls
Pine Bush (#66)
Sidney Center (#51)
Walton (#46)
Afton (#47)
Bouckville (#52)
Norwich (#48)
Greene (#41)
Sanataria Springs (#45)
Kirkwood (#44)
Binghamton (#42)
Johnson City (#43)
Owego (#40)
Vestal (#37)
Endicott (#39)
Candor (#38)
Ithaca (#35)
Penn Yan (#30)
Naples (#29)
Dansville (#31)
Big Flats (#36)
Watkins Glen (#32)
Campbell (#34)
Hammondsport (#33)
Nunda (#28)
East Aurora (# 6, 7)
Arcade (#4)
Lockport (#14, 15)
Williamsville (#8, 9)
Niagara Falls (#11, 12)
Amherst (#13)
Kenmore (#10)
Boston (#5)
Jamestown (#2)
Olean (#3)
Lakewood (#1)
Riverhead (#75)
Cold Spring Harbor (#77)
Massapequa (#78)
East Northport (#76)
Glenville (#73)
New York (#71, 72)
Brooklyn (#74)
87
90
81
88
17
84
86
390

Lakewood, NY #1

Mon - Fri 10 - 5
Sat 10 - 4

The Calico Cat

4451 W. Fairmount Ave. (Rte. 394) 14750
(716) 763-8167 Est: 1981
Owner: Mynet Feinburg 1500 sq.ft.
calicocatny@netsync.net

Cotton fabrics, quilting supplies, classes, patterns, books & notions. Custom made T-shirt quilts. Authorized Bernina Location.

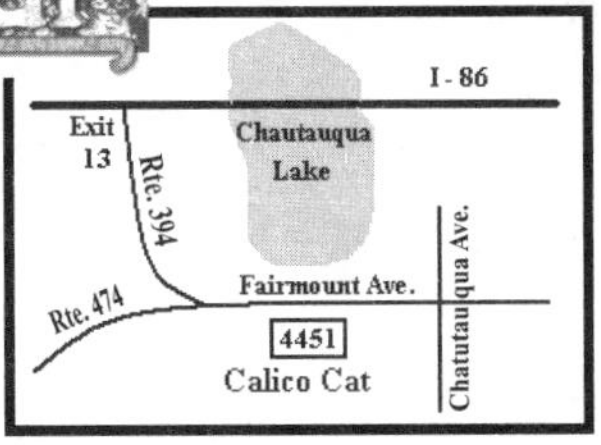

Jamestown, NY #2

Mon & Tues 12 - 9
Wed - Sat 10 - 5

Quilters' Haven

115 McDaniel Ave. 14701
(716) 665-6524 Fax: (716) 763-0070
Owner: Janice Shoup
Est: 2007 2000 sq.ft. 1000+ Bolts
quiltershavenny@yahoo.com

Custom longarm quilting available. Everything for the avid quilter's needs. Located in Lucille Ball's hometown.

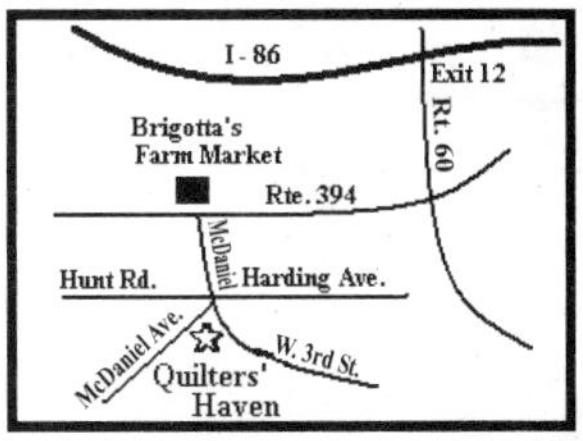

Olean, NY #3

Tues - Fri 10 - 6
Sat 10 - 4

Enchanted Mountain Quilting

324 W. State St. 14760
(716) 372-2327
Owners: Kathy, Lanna, Chris & Betsy
Est: 2009 2700 sq.ft. 800+ bolts
EMQ1@verizon.net Online Newsletter
www.enchantedmountainquilting.com
Fabrics, Notions, Books & Patterns.
Cookies & Candy made in the store.
Handcrafted gifts. Long arm quilting available.
Large variety of quilt kits and classes.

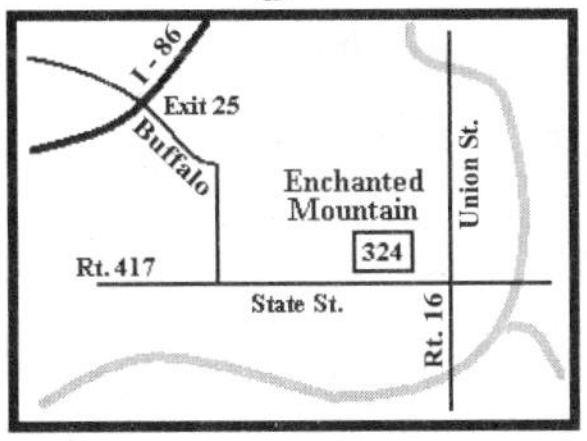

Arcade, NY #4

Mon - Fri 9:30 - 5:30
Thur til 7
Sat 9 - 3

Creekside Fabrics • Quilts & Yarn

Hand-made makes memories

237 Main St. 14009
(585) 492-4226
Owner: Sandy Pirdy
www.creeksidefabrics.com

Creekside is home to Baby Lock Sewing Machines, 1500 bolts of fabrics and bins & bins of yarns! You won't be disappointed - stop soon.

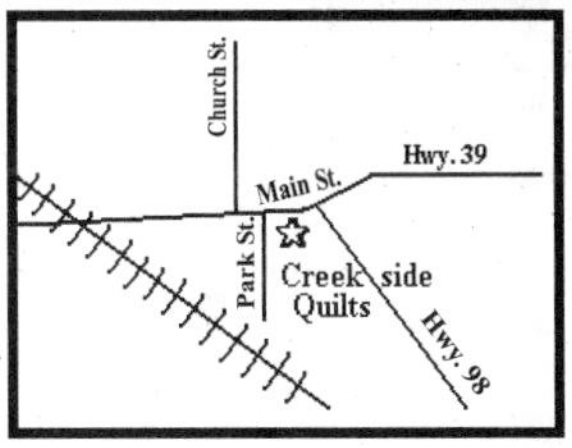

Boston, NY #5

The Quilt FARM

Tues - Sat 11 - 5
Tues & Thurs evenings til 7
Closed Sun & Mon

est. 1989 3600 sq.ft. quilt_farm&yahoo.com
www.quiltfarm.net

"WORTH THE DRIVE"

The Answer to a Quilter's Prayers in God's Country

5623 South Feddick Road 14025
(716) 941-3140
Owner: Isabell Schmit
Staffed by Family and Friends

DIRECTIONS: (a scenic country drive 30 minutes South of Buffalo)
I - 90 to Route 219 South, Exit at Rice Road
Off exit ramp turn west & go (up hill) to first intersection, left on Zimmerman, then right on South Feddick Road
Call for specifics . . . It's a challenge.

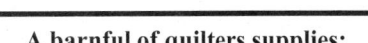

A barnful of quilters supplies:
- ... 6,000+ bolts of 100% cotton
- ... large selection of notions
- ... 450+ books & patterns plus kits
- ... Finished and Custom order Quilts
- ... Origin of "Quilt Farm" Patterns
- ... Classes

"Shop 'til the Cows come home."

East Aurora, NY #6

THE CARRIAGE QUILT SHOPPE

593 Main St. (by viaduct)
716-655-4561

Enjoy the warmth & charm of Our cozy shoppe packed full of Inspiring ideas, NEW patterns, Books, gifts & lots of fabrics and ready made quilts! We specialize in custom orders.

Join us for lots of giggles!

ALWAYS IN STORE SPECIALS

Professional long-arm machine quilting in our loft along with classes for all levels.

All Books All The time 20% off !!

Ask about our FREE pattern

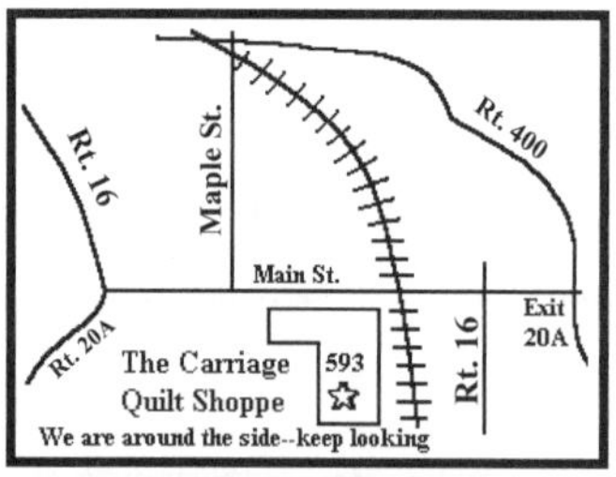

www.carriagequiltshoppe.com

Tues - Fri 10 - 5 Sat 10 - 4

East Aurora, NY #7

659 Main St. 14052
(716) 652-2811
Est: 1978
3500 sq.ft.

Williamsville, NY #8

8575 Main St. 14221
(716) 204-8350
Est: 1996
2500 sq.ft.

Aurora Sewing Center

baby lock

Store Hours:
Mon - Fri 10:00 - 5:30
Thursday til 7:00
Sat 10:00 - 4:00
Williamsville Only:
Sun 12:00 - 4:00

Owner: Barb Perry
www.Aurorasewingcenter.com
ASCBARB@aol.com

- *We have over a 1000 Bolts of fabric to choose from.*
- *Books, Patterns and more.*
- *Lots of displayed samples!*
- *We have over 90 different classes offered each semester.*
- BERNINA *sewing machines and Embroidery Systems.*
- *12 Needle Happy Embroidery system at Aurora Location.*
- *Visit our large showroom floor of Horn Cabinets in both locations.*
- *Come see our HandiQuilter at the Clarence location*
- *Largest service department on all makes and models in Western New York.*

BERNINA®

2 Great Locations ! !

Williamsville, NY #9

Mon - Fri 10 - 5
Tues til 7
Sat 10 - 4

Sew What?

6816 Main Street 14221
(716) 632-8801
Owner: Ann Shaw
Est: 1990 1500 Bolts 1900 sq.ft.
sewwhat@sewwhatquiltshop.com
www.sewwhatquiltshop.com
Large selection of unique and unusual quilting fabrics, the newest books and notions. Quilting classes and professional quilting service available.

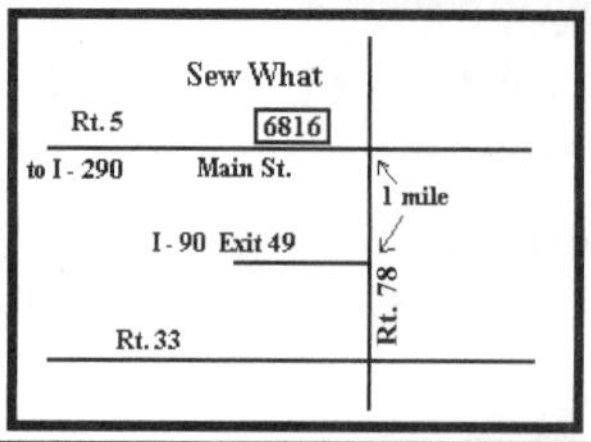

Kenmore, NY #10

Tues - Sat
10 - 4:30

Pine Grove Quilt Shop

2962 Delaware Ave. 14217
(716) 873-0774
Owners: Sue Dray and Sue Doyle
Est: 2007 4000+ bolts
pinegrovequiltshop@yahoo.com
www.pinegrovequiltshop.com
We carry 4000+ bolts of quilting fabrics including a huge selection of Batiks, Civil War Reproductions and Wide Backing.

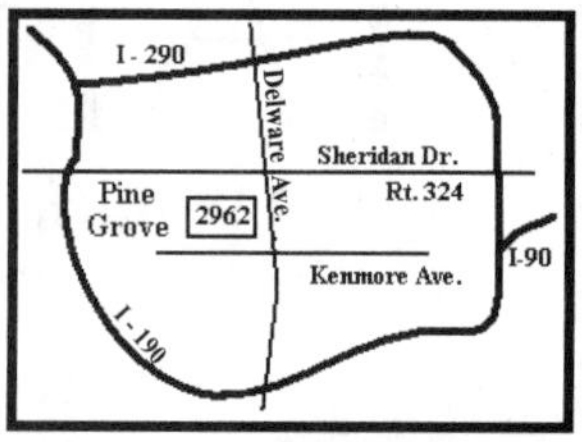

Niagara Falls, NY #11

Tues 10 - 2:30
Wed & Fri 10 - 8:30
Thur 10 - 4:30
Sat 10 - 3

Quiltmakers & Friends

4716 Military Rd. 14304
(716) 297-4067
Owner: Florence M. Rhodes

Hundreds of bolts — 100% cotton fabrics. Large selection of quilt books, notions, patterns & gifts. Classes offered.

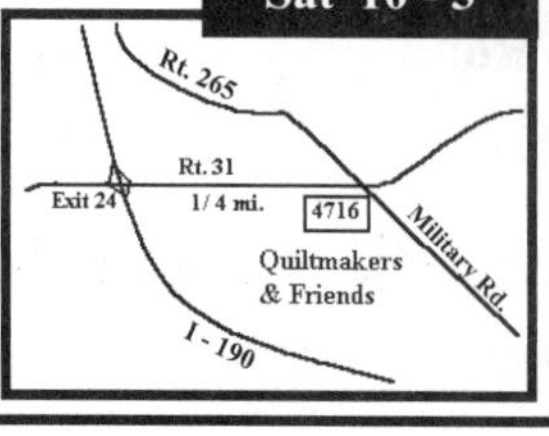

Niagara Falls, NY #12

Tues - Sat
10 - 5
Wed 10 - 8

Auntie's Attic Quilt Shop

2043 Military Rd. 14304-1724
(716) 297-3636
Owner: Denise LaMarca Est: 2005

aaqs@auntiesatticquiltshop.com
www.auntiesatticquiltshop.com

3 miles from Niagara Falls & Canada.
For all of Your Quilting Needs
Across from Fashion Outlet Mall

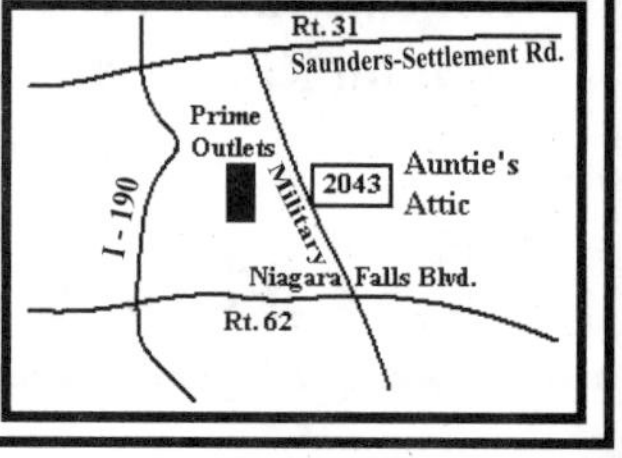

Threads of Time

Mon - Thurs 10 - 8
Fri & Sat 10 - 5

Northtown Plaza,
3133 Sheridan Dr.
Amherst, NY 14226
(716) 837-1372
totsewing@verizon.net

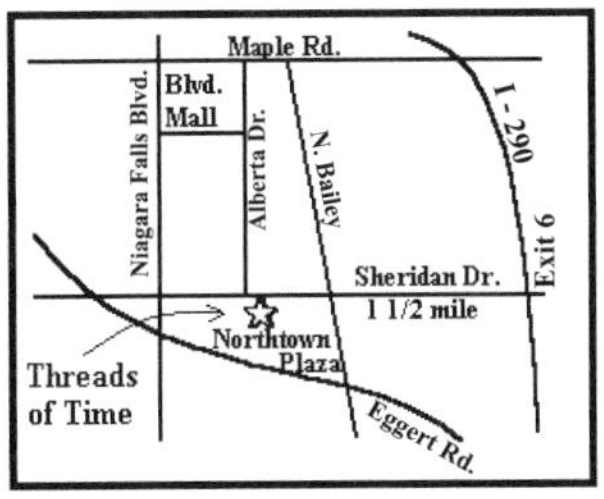

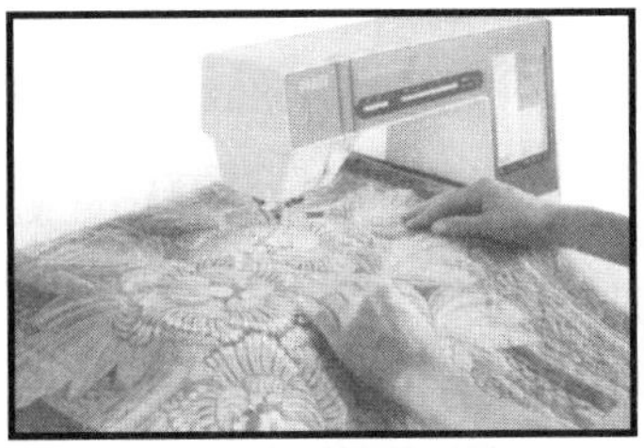

We carry over 2000 bolts of fine quilting cottons. Classes, books, patterns, a great variety of threads, notions & . . . lots of ideas.
PFAFF Authorized Sales & Service
www.totsewing.com

Amherst, NY #13

Lockport, NY #14

Mon - Fri 10 - 5
Sat 10 - 4

Heartland Quilt Shop

7121 Ridge Rd. 14094
(716) 433-3188 Fax: Same
Est: 2007
1500+ Bolts
Free Newsletter

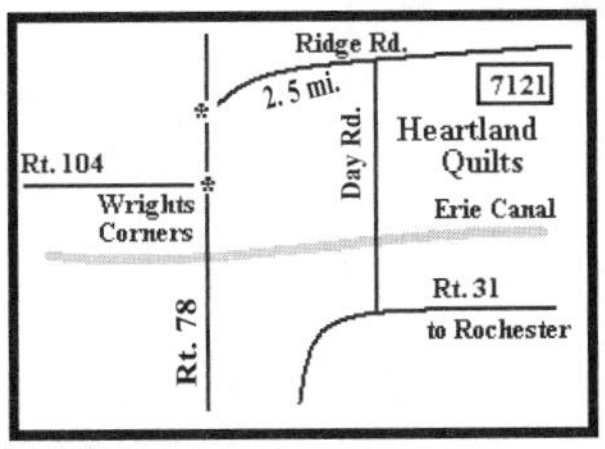

www.heartlandquiltshop.com

Great selection of fabric, books and patterns. Famous for our "Inspirations in a Bag".

Lockport, NY #15

Mon - Fri 10 - 5
Sat 10 - 3
Call for evening hrs.

MARIE'S SEWING CENTER
"We Keep You In Stitches"

6322 Robinson Rd. 14094
(716) 434-2583
Toll Free: (866) 237-9113

Est: 1998 3500 sq.ft. 3000 Bolts
Online Newsletter
mariessewingcenter@rocherter.rr.com
www.mariessewingcenter.com

Our products include Janome, New Joy, Horn Cabinets, Great Fabric, Lots of Thread, Notions and Software. Come Visit Us!

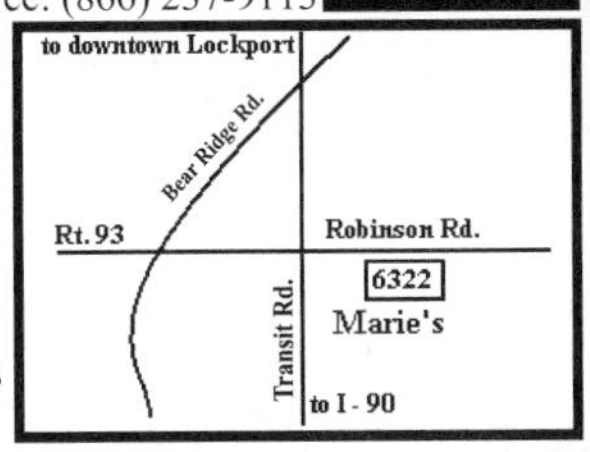

Est: 2002 Barbara J. Miller

Mt. Pleasant Quilting Company

100% cotton fabrics
including batiks and flannels.

Large selection of books, patterns, notions, supplies, kits & gift items.

Classes for all levels
~ from beginner through advanced ~

Longarm Machine Quilting Services

www.mtpleasantquiltingcompany.com

30 min. SW of Rochester
75 min. SE of Buffalo
30 min. S of Batavia
60 min. NW of Corning

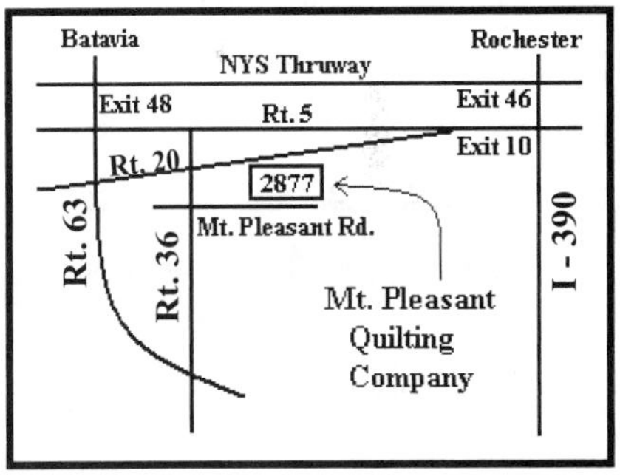

2877 Mt. Pleasant Rd.
York, NY 14592
585-243-0767
mtpquilt@rochester.rr.com

Our friendly & knowledgeable staff invites you to visit soon!

Tuesday-Friday
10-5:00
Wednesday
Evening 'til 8:00
Saturday 10-3:00
CLOSED
Sunday & Monday

York, NY #16

Over 3,500 bolts of 100% cotton fabrics from Andover, Benartex, Clothworks, Kaufman, Henry Glass, Hoffman, Kona Bay, Marcus Brothers, Michael Miller, Moda, Maywood, Northcott, P&B Textiles, RJR, Red Rooster, South Seas, Thimbleberries, Timeless Treasures, & many more.

Chestnut Bay Quilting

Caledonia, NY #17

3128 Main St., Caledonia, NY 14423
585-538-4420 pattyCBQ@aol.com
www.chestnutbayquilting.com

15 miles south of Rochester in historic Caledonia. Specializing in batiks and Civil War Reproductions. Classes and Clubs.

Wednesday - Saturday 10 - 5

Owner: Patty Cline
Est: 2008 1000 sq.ft.
Online Newsletter

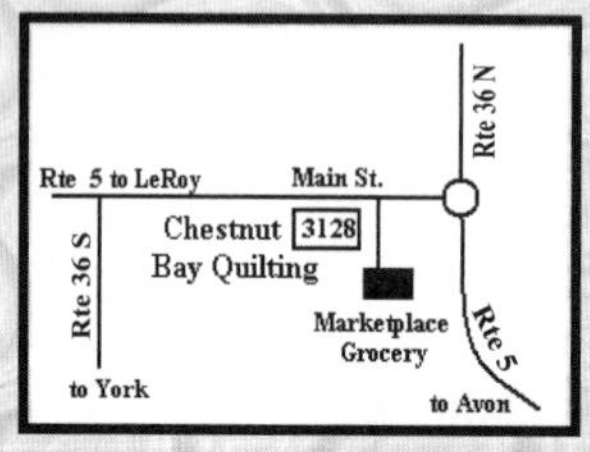

Betty's Quilting etc.

42 Nichols St. (Rt. 31)
Spencerport, NY 14559
Behind McDonald's (585) 352-9362
bettysquiltingetc@gmail.com

Est: 2006 2000 sq.ft. Free Newsletter.
Over 2000 bolts of fabric, notions, classes.
Bernina authorized dealer BERNINA

Spencerport, NY #18

www.bettysquiltingetc.com

Open 7 Days a Week
Call for Hours

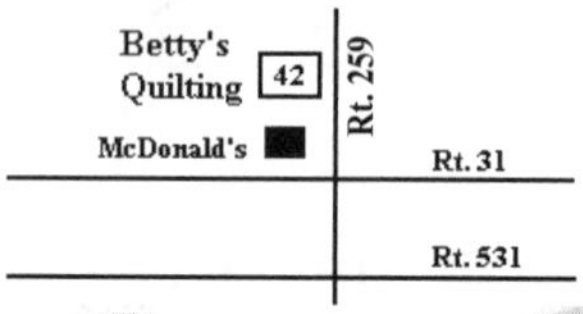

Everything a quilter needs!

Webster, NY #19

Mon - Fri 10 - 5
Wed til 8
Sat 10 - 4

The Scarlet Thread

38 E. Main St. 14580
(585) 265-4910
Fax: (585) 265-2406

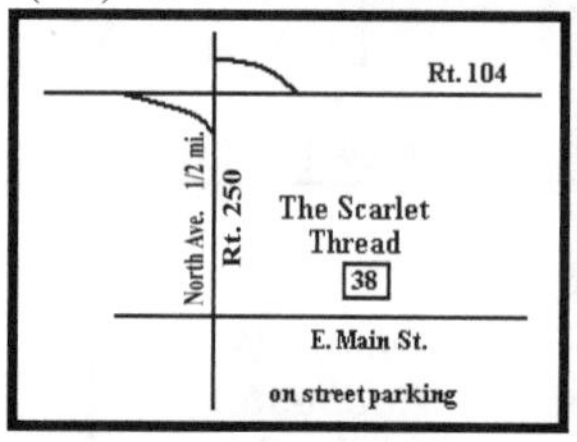

Owner: Ruth Sacco Est: 2007
thescarletthread@hotmail.com
www.scarletthreadquilts.com
A 2010/11 season Quilting Football League Store
We offer quality fabrics from Moda, Blank, Island Batiks and more. We strive to promote creativity, friendship and community.

Canandaigua, NY #21

Liberty Cottage
primitive wares, country goods, folk art & stitchery supplies

116 S. Main St.
14424
585-393-1070
Owner:
Suzanne Moulton
Est: 2000

HOURS
Mon 1 - 6
Tues 9:30 - 5:30
Wed 9:30 - 3
Thurs 9:30 - 8
Fri 9:30 - 8
Sat 9:30 - 4

A unique shop located in the heart of New York's Finger Lakes wine country. We specialize in teaching and supplying all your primitive needlework project needs using hand-dyed wool fabrics, yarns, cotton homespuns, flannels and thousands of patterns. Also home décor and gift items.

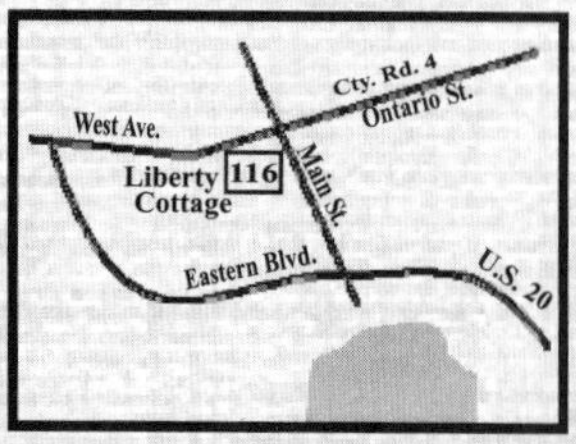

www.libertycottage.com

Ivy Thimble

QUILT & GIFT SHOP

5 Railroad St.
Victor, NY 14564
(585) 742-2680
www.ivythimble.com

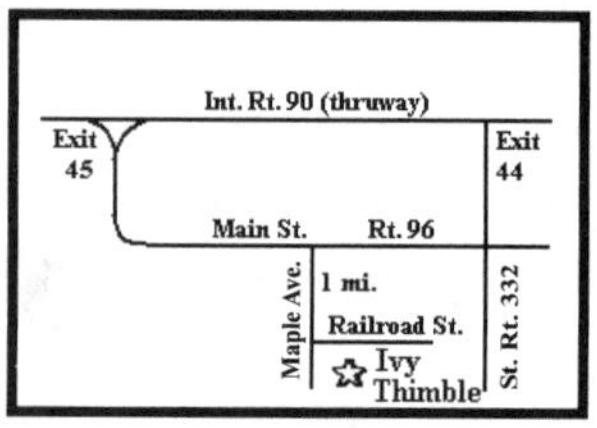

Hours:
Mon - Wed 9:30 - 5 pm
Thur 9:30 - 7 pm
Fri & Sat 9:30 - 4 pm

Victor, NY #20

We're not just a Quilt Shop!

We're your hometown full-service quilt shop! Our fun-loving and knowledgeable staff invites you to stop in and visit us soon. We offer you over 3,500 bolts of high quality fabric, a great selection of patterns and books and we now offer Longarm Quilting Services.

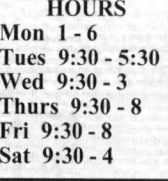

East Rochester, NY #22

patricias' fabric house

333 W. Commercial St. 14445
585-248-2362
Monday-Thursday 10-8, Friday & Saturday 10-5

33 Years in Business 1977 to 2010

WE'VE GOT YOUR QUILTING NEEDS ALL SEWED UP!

5400 sq.ft. 4000+ Bolts Bus Tours Welcome

- Outstanding collection of fine quilting cottons: Kona Bay, Moda, Hoffman, Kaufman, etc.
- Also Batiks, Orientals, Novelty Prints, Florals & Civil War
- Threads, Unusual Buttons, Books, Notions, Classes & Patterns
- Bridal & Special Occasion & Fine Dress Fabrics.
- Complete Line of *elna* Sewing Machines & Sergers.

Visit our Website patriciasfabrichouse.com *for Coupons*

We're Easy to Find! Come Visit Us!

Rochester, NY #23

Mon - Fri 10 - 5:30
Thur til 8
Sat 10 - 3

BERNINA

The Bobbin Case Inc.

1784 Monroe Ave. 14618
(585) 244-7780
thebobbincase@aol.com
Rochester's Bernina Dealership
Sales & Service. Loads of classes, threads, sewing machine cabinets, machine embroidery supplies and designs, but no fabric.

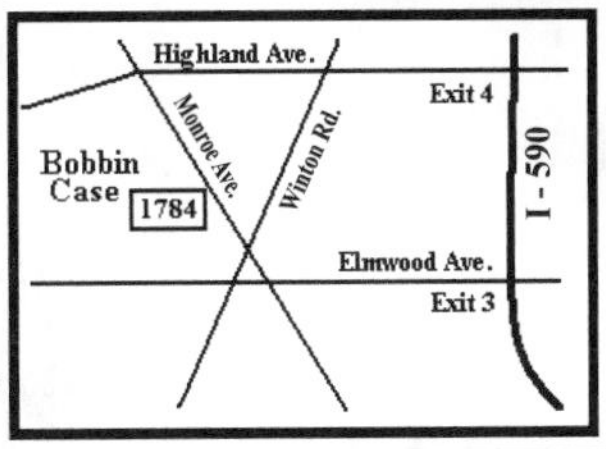

Savannah, NY #24

Mon, Tues, Wed 9 - 6
Thur & Fri 9 - 8
Sat 9 - 5

Springlake Market & Fabrics

4250 Wolcott-Spring Lake Rd. 13146
(315) 594-8485
Fax: (315) 594-1650

Owner: Arlene Zimmerman

Est: 1932 4800 sq.ft. 4000 bolts
springlakefabrics@hotmail.com
Great prices on quality pieces.
Yarns, puzzles, books, embroidery kits.
Bulk food store.

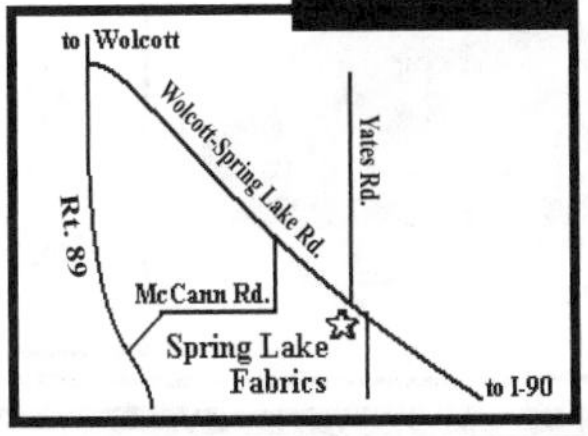

Marcellus, NY #25

Patchwork Plus

2532 Cherry Valley Tpke. (Rt. 20)
(315) 673-2208 13108
Owner: Judi West Est: 1987
judi@patchworkplus.com

Over 7500 bolts of fabric.
Come visit us in our beautiful new store located just 4 miles from Skaneateles on the scenic Cherry Valley Turnpike.

Better Homes Quilt Sampler Featured Shop

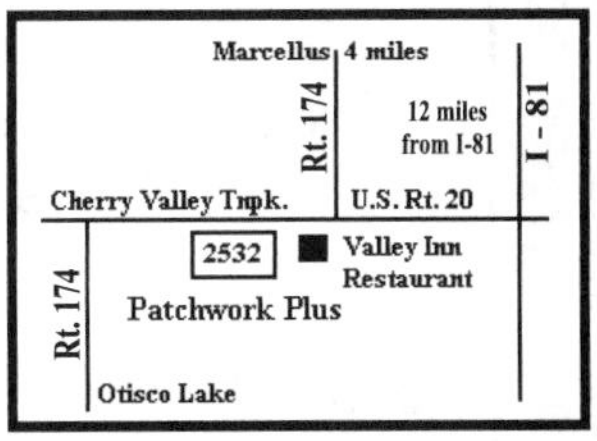

Mon - Sat 10 - 5
Sun 12 - 4

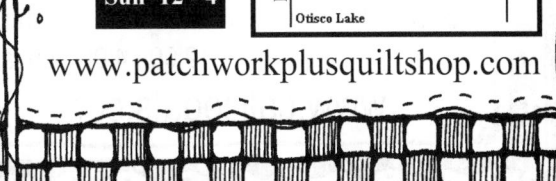

www.patchworkplusquiltshop.com

Mission Rose where friends gather to quilt, knit & create in Central New York's most unique shop.

Mission Rose Quiltery

...everything for the gourmet quilter & knitter

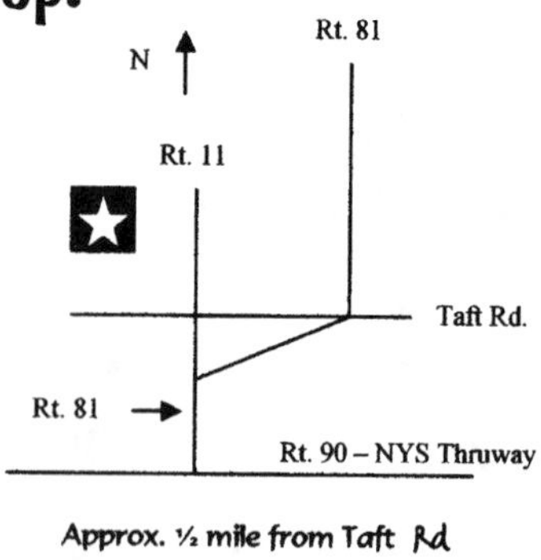

Approx. ½ mile from Taft Rd

The Quiltery offers 5,000+ bolts of high quality quilting fabric by today's hottest designers.

The Knittery offers a wide selection of the finest hand knitting yarns.

Books & patterns, gadgets & tools, needles & knick-knacks, buttons & baubles, these are just a few of our favorite things.

Year round quilting & knitting classes.

456 South Main Street
North Syracuse, NY 13212
(315) 452-3247
www.missionrosequiltery.com

Store Hours:
Monday, Wednesday, Friday, Saturday 9:30-4:30 pm
Tuesday & Thursday 9:30- 6:30 pm
Sunday 11:00-4:00 pm

North Syracuse, NY #26

Syracuse, NY #27

all kinds of fun stuff for quiltin' and stitchin'

Stop in to meet Janet and all the gals!

Great fabric store, quilt shop and sewing center! Calico Gals recently moved into a brand new building. You gotta see it! Featuring Elna sewing machines, Babylock sewing machines, fun classes and a bazillion bolts of beautiful fabrics.

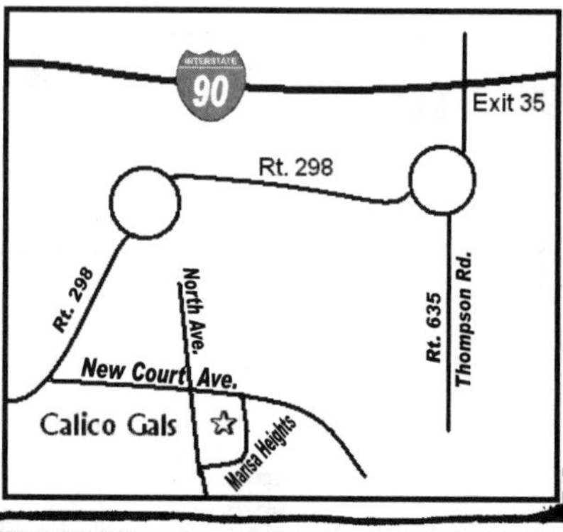

3906 New Court Ave., Syracuse, NY 13206
315-445-0617 10:00 - 5:00 Mon thru Sat
12:00 - 4:00 Sunday
www.calicogals.com

Nunda, NY #28

Mon - Fri 8 - 4
Sat 8 - 2

THE JOURNEY QUILT COMPANY

3 N. State St.
P.O. Box 713 14517
(585) 468-2320

Owner: Cindy Welch
Est: 2002 1900 sq.ft. 2500+ Bolts
Online Newsletter

journeyquilt@frontiernet.net
www.journeyquiltcompany.com

A small store filled with wonderful cottons, flannels, Batiks - over 2500 Bolts. Also a wonderful gift shop including Sterling Silver Jewelry.

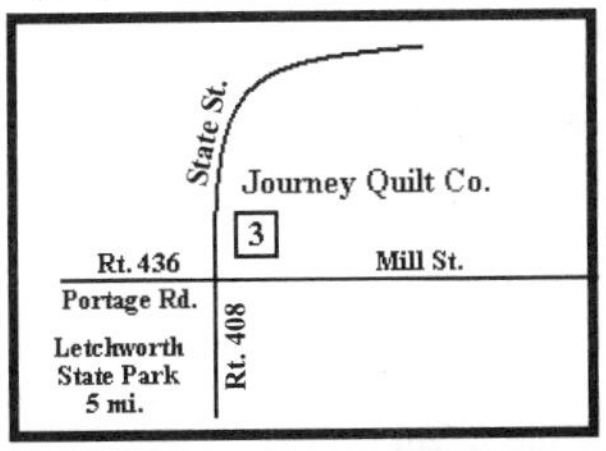

Naples, NY #29

M & W 1:30 - 5
T, T, F, S 10 - 5

Carriage House Quilts

201 N. Main St. 14512
(585) 374-9580 Fax: (585) 374-9257
CHQNaples@aol.com
Carriagehousequiltsnaples.com
Est: 2005 2000 sq. ft. 2000 Bolts
Free Newsletter
Featuring: quilting fabrics (lots of batik and flannels), books, notions, hand-dyed wools. Warm, friendly atmosphere located in a quaint village. Gammill dealer. Long arm rental.

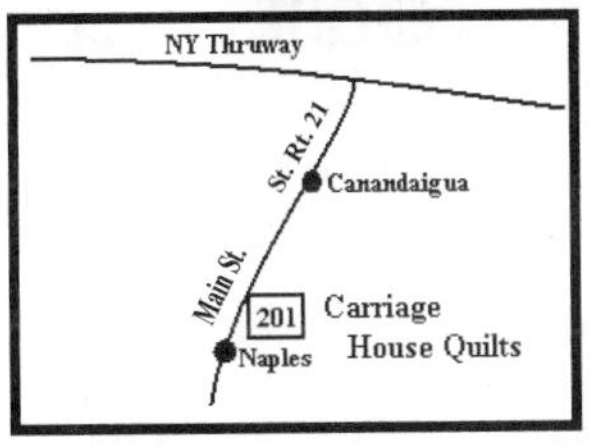

Dansville, NY #31

Material Rewards

10160 Sandy Hill Rd. 14437
(585) 335-2050
quilts@materialrewards.com
www.materialrewards.com

Tues - Fri 9:30 - 5:30
Sat 9:30 - 5

* Full service quilt shop where you'll always feel welcome!
* Over 6000 bolts of fabric
* Up to date supply of books, notions and patterns
* Long arm machine quilting. We have 20 years of experience with long arm machines!!

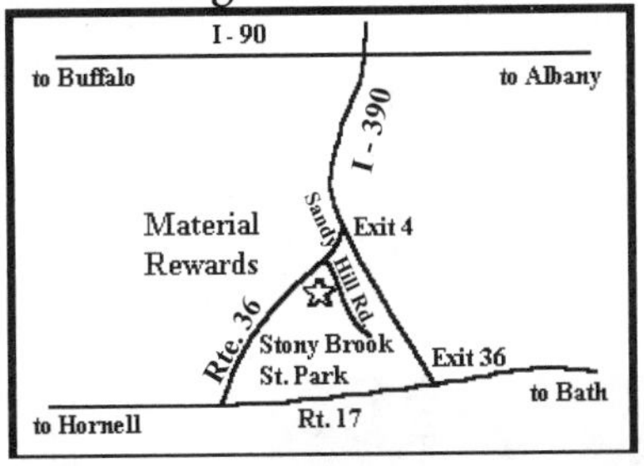

All the Creative Comforts for Quilters.

Weaver-View Farms

Amish Country Store

1190 Earls Hills Road • Penn Yan, NY 14527
Open Year 'Round -- Closed Sundays & Religious Holidays
1-315-781-2571
www.weaverviewfarms.com

With over 4,500 sq.ft. there is something for everyone!

Our Amish quilts are made by friends and family, over 300 Handstitched Quilts.
QUALITY COTTON FABRICS
BATIKS - PATTERNS
KITS

Famous Annual Fabric Sale

10,000 yards of top quality fabric from all major manufactures $2.98 per yard every winter Nov. 1 - March 31

Magical history abounds in the Finger Lakes region, never more so than on this 1800's working dairy farm.

6 miles south of Geneva, look for our signs. - Off Rt. 14 - a scenic drive along Seneca Lake.

Penn Yan, NY #30

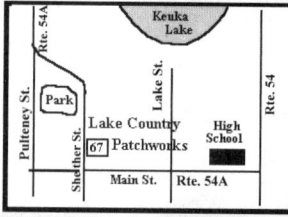

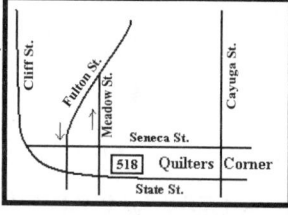

THE VILLAGE S·A·M·P·L·E·R

Come... and enjoy a unique shopping experience in the ambiance of our renovated nineteenth century country church.

18 Canal St., Big Flats, NY 14814
(607) 562-7596
Owner: Jody Kravec Est: 1986 4500 sq.ft.

Big Flats, NY #36

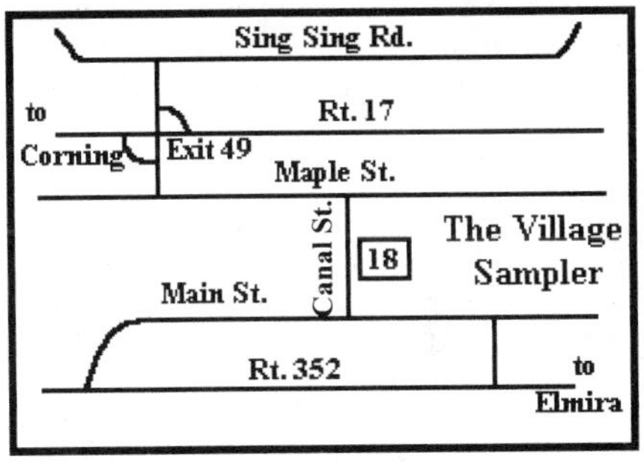

The Village Sampler is easily accessible from Exit 49, Route 17 / I-86

- The Finest 100% Cotton Fabrics Available, Quilting Books, Notions, Gadgets & Gifts
- Models & Samples to Inspire Creativity
- Counted Cross Stitch Patterns, Threads & Accessories
- Gifts—Candles, Boyds Bears, Cards
- Christmas Throughout the Year

Mon - Sat 10 - 5
Thur til 7

www.villagesampler.net

Vestal, NY #37

Grandmother's Thimble

Quilt Shop and Sewing Machines

Authorized **BERNINA**® Sales and Service

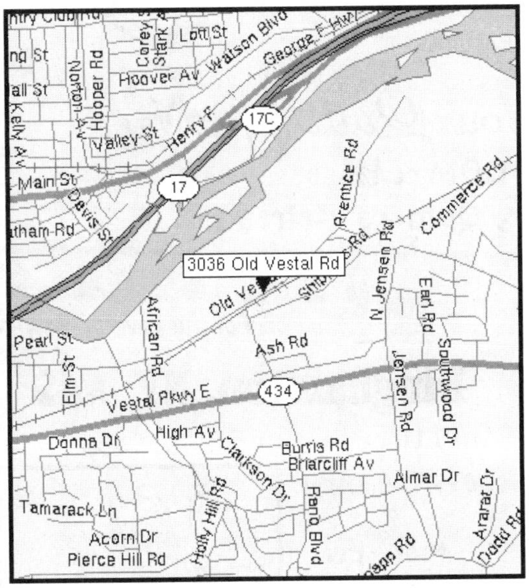

www.grandmothersthimble.net
grandmothersthimble@yahoo.com

Store Hours:
M,T,W,F 10-5:30
Thurs. 10-7, Sat. 10-4

Owner: Justine Layman
Bernina Tech: Jim Layman

3036 Old Vestal Rd.
Vestal, NY 13850
607-797-7022

We have 2000 bolts of 100% cotton fabric, quilting notions, books, classes, an on line store, custom embroidery and quilting services and a full line of Bernina sewing machines.

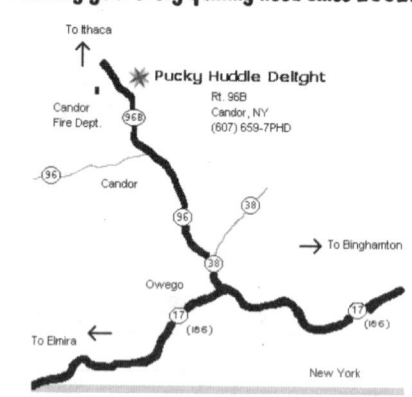

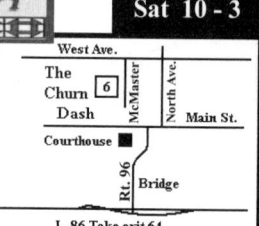

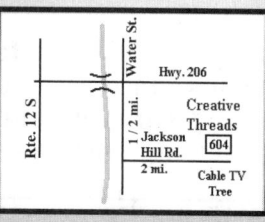

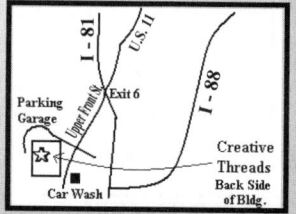

Johnson City, NY **#43**

Indulge your passion for QUILTING! Come to shop, leave *inspired!*

- Broad selection of quality quilting fabrics, including hard-to-find specials
- Premier Husqvarna Viking dealer
- Books, Patterns, Notions, Supplies
- Beginning to Advanced Classes
- Friendly Service

Visit us online at www.smquilts.com to learn more!

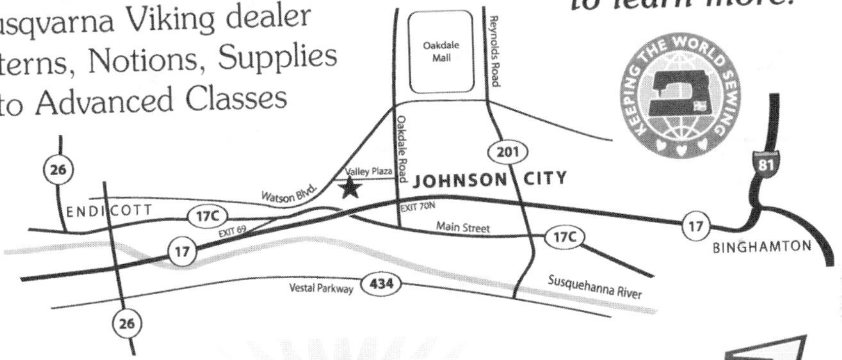

KEEPING THE WORLD SEWING

The Premier Quilt Shop in the Southern Tier!

Husqvarna VIKING

SEW MANY Quilts

"... so little time..."

800 Valley Plaza, Johnson City, NY 13790 Phone **607-797-1796** **www.smquilts.com**

Monday–Saturday 10:00am–6:00pm MASTERCARD • VISA • DISCOVER • AMERICAN EXPRESS

2335 U.S. Rt. 11
Kirkwood, NY 13795
(607) 238-7182

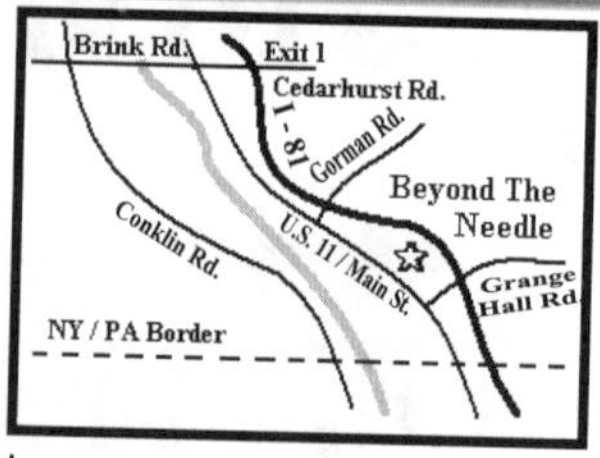

- Your Quilting Inspiration Headquarters
- We carry the newest quality fabrics, books, patterns, notions.
- Block of the Month programs
- Visit our 2nd location in Scranton, PA, just 45 minutes down I-81

Kirkwood, NY #44

Mon - Sat 10 - 5
Sun Noon - 5

Owner: Lisa Wilson
Est: 2007 2000+ Bolts
lisa@beyondtheneedle.com

www.beyondtheneedle.com

Sanitaria Springs, NY #45

Tues - F 10 - 5
Sat 10 -

Quilted Crow
Fabric & Quilt Shop

54 Cafferty Rd. 13787
(607) 648-8956 Fax: Same
Owner: Peg Springstead
quiltedcrow@frontiernet .net
Quality Cottons, Flannels, Hand-dyed Wool
Long Arm Quilting
www.quiltedcrow.net

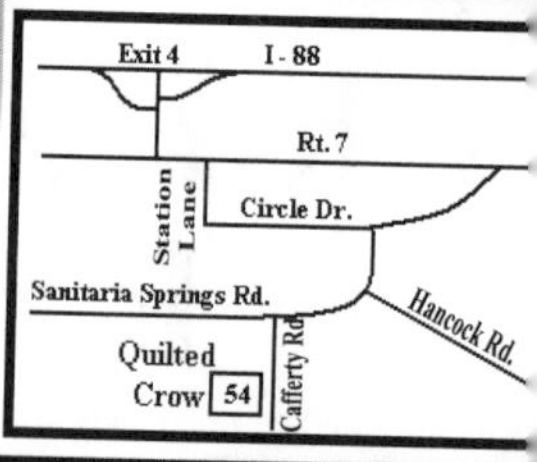

Walton, NY #46

Mon - Sat 10 -
Thurs also 6 -
Closed
Wed & Sun

Where Quilters Gather

137 Stockton Ave. 13856
(607) 865-8550
Owner: Amy Govern
wherequiltersgather@stny.rr.com
www.wherequiltersgather.com

We have over 2000 bolts of quality cottons, flannels, batiks. Books, Patterns & Notions. Plus lots of great classes.

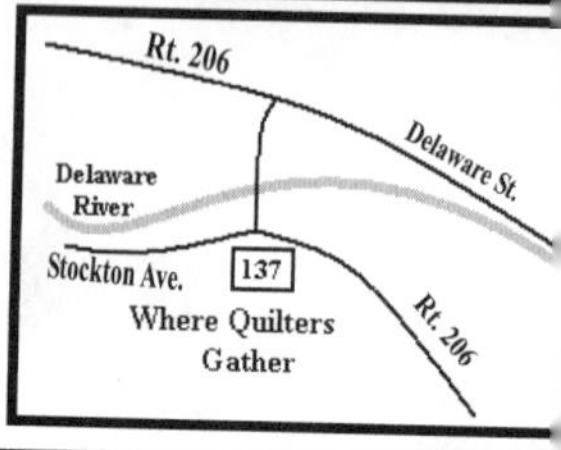

Afton, NY #47

Mon, Wed
Thur, Fri
9 - 5
Tues 9 - 2
Sat 9 - 3

Sew Clever

195 Hwy. 41 S, P.O. Box 303 13730
(607) 639-2460 Fax: (607) 639-3436
Est: 1979 2000 sq.ft. 3000 Bolts
sewclever@gmail.com

Husqvarna Viking, Brother, & Tin Lizzie 18 Sewing Machines.
Thousands of Bolts of Fine Cottons, Batiks, Homespuns; Books Galore, Many Notions.

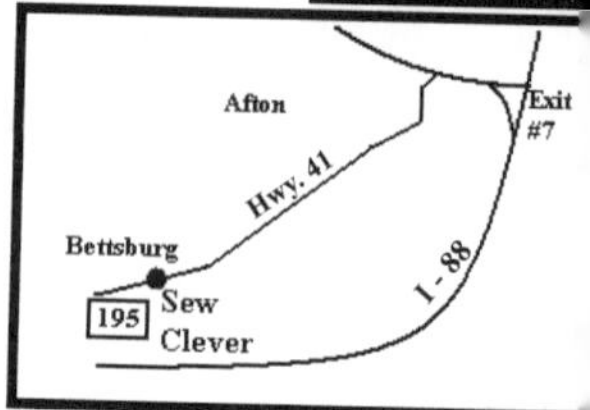

Norwich, NY #48

Mon - Sat
10 - 6
Thur til 9

Sew Nice

6142 St. Hwy. 12 (North Plaza) 13815
(607) 334-2477
Fax: (607) 334-2481
sewnice@frontiernet.net

Looking for a great selection of fabrics and quilting supplies? We have them!
Plenty of parking and easy access.

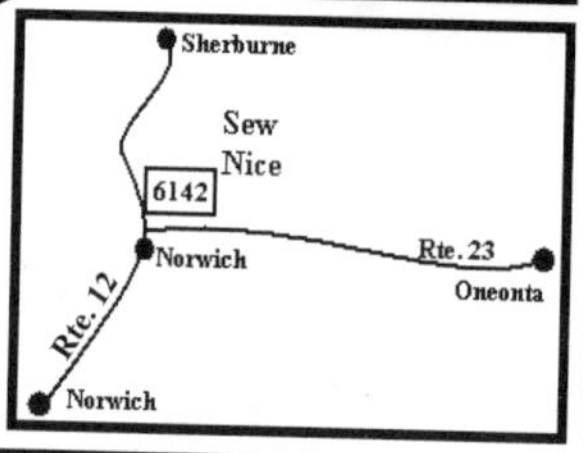

Oneonta, NY #49

Mon - Fri
9:30 - 4
Tues til 7
Sat 9:30 - 3

Country Fabrics & Quilts

5252 St. Hwy. 23 13820
(607) 432-9726
Est: 1990 2000 sq. ft.

Over 4000 bolts of cotton fabrics plus notions, books, & patterns. Also fleece, knits, corduroy, & denim.
Custom machine and hand quilting.
2 miles off of I -88

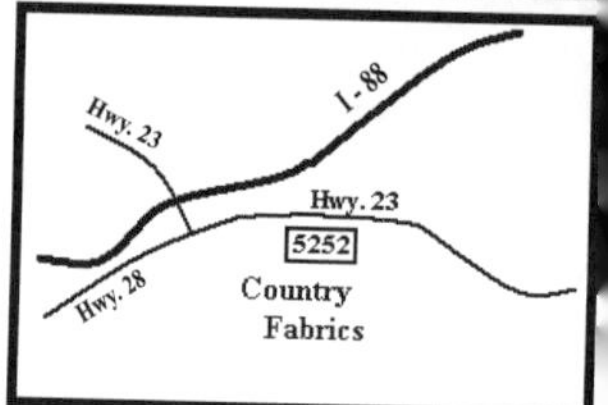

Cobleskill, NY #50

Tues - Fri
10 - 6
Sat 10 - 5
Sun 11 - 5

The Yardstick

147 Barnerville Rd. #1 12043
(518)234-2179 Est: 1975
Owner: Merilyn Ludwig 5000 sq.ft.
yardstic@telenet.net
www.yardstickny.com

Husqvarna Viking sewing machines sales & service. Over 2000 bolts of 100% cotton fabrics, books, notions, patterns, & classes. Friendly Knowledgeable Staff.

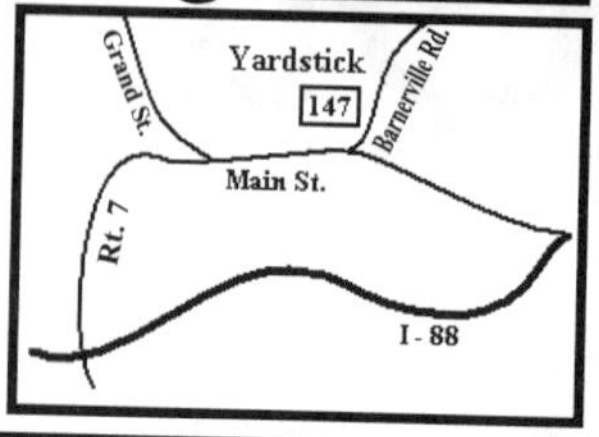

The Fieldstone House

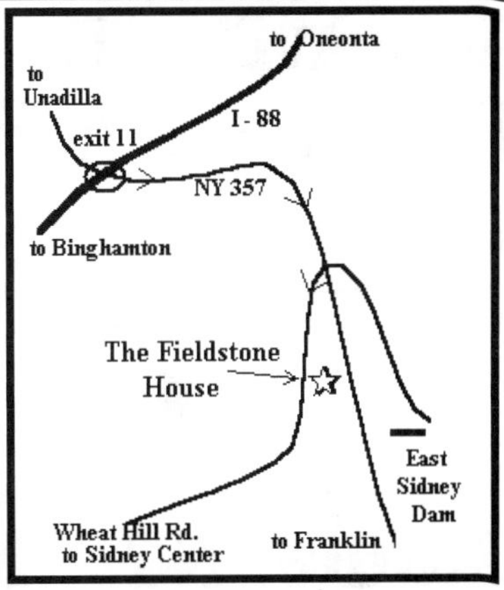

1884 Wheat Hill Rd. 13839
(607) 369-9177
Proprietors: Jane & Allan Kirby
fieldstonehouse@frontiernet.net
www.fieldstonehousefabrics.com

Sidney Center, NY #51

Featuring :
Fabric Shop
Country Tea Room

The Fabric Shop

Shop is filled to capacity with more than 20,000 bolts of current favorites & past treasures

This outstanding selection includes all of your favorite designs from . . .

Andover • Alexander Henry • Bali Fabrications • Clothworks • Debbie Mumm • Hoffman • Indo-Sales In the Beginning • Kaffe Fassett • Kona Bay • Makower • Marcus Brothers • Michael Miller Moda • Northcott • P&B • Robert Kaufman • RJR • Timeless Treasures .... and more.

Books, Threads, Needles, Muslin, Battings,
Templates, Buttons, Cutting Tools, Flannels, Clothing Patterns

"A quilter's dream come true"

Hours: 7 days a week 11 - 5
Closed Occasionally for Quilt Shows
and Family Events
We recommend calling in advance.

The Country Tea Room

A delightful lunch is served by
reservation only.

Relax and enjoy with friends and family.

Visit our website for a list of quilt shows we vend…
or contact us for a list of quilt show dates/locations.

Bouckville, NY #52

Thur - Sat 11 - 5
Sun 12 - 4
Other Days by Chance

The Gingham Patch

3490 Pratts Rd. 13310
(315) 893-7750 Est: 2003 Newsletter
Owner: Jennifer Scharman 1500 sq.ft.
jennscharman@yahoo.com
www.ginghampatch.com
Antiques & Primitive Country Gifts presented in a home studio setting. We carry homespun fabrics & handmade quilters baskets.

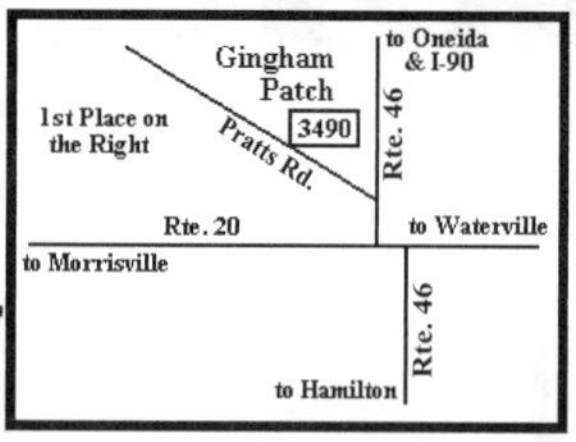

Wampsville, NY #53

Mon - Sat 10 - 5
Thur til 8
Sun 12 - 4

101 Genesee St.
13163
(315) 363-6834

Owner: Paula Schultz 1700 sq.ft.
Est: 1980 Celebrating 30 Years in business!
cottonsetc@verizon.net
www.cottonsetcquiltshop.com
Our motto is "You Can Never Have Too Much Fabric!" A Pot-pourri of Quilting & Fashion Fabrics, Notions, Books & Patterns. Ask for your free gift!

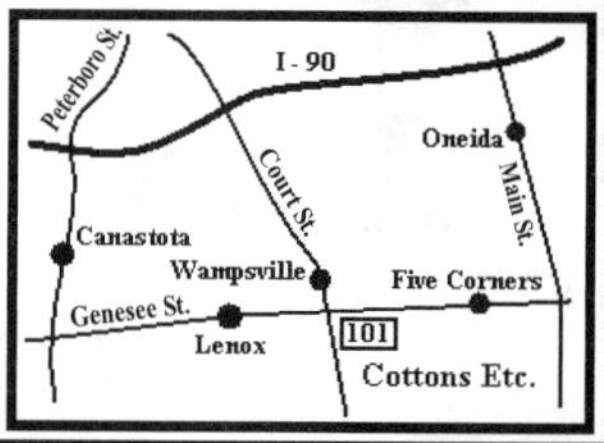

Rome, NY #54

Tues - Sat 10 - 6
Thurs 3 - 7:30
Sun 11 - 5

Stash Away Quilt Shoppe

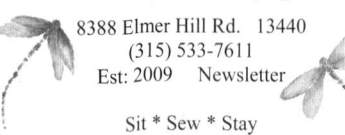

8388 Elmer Hill Rd. 13440
(315) 533-7611
Est: 2009 Newsletter

Sit * Sew * Stay
Open Sewing Classes.

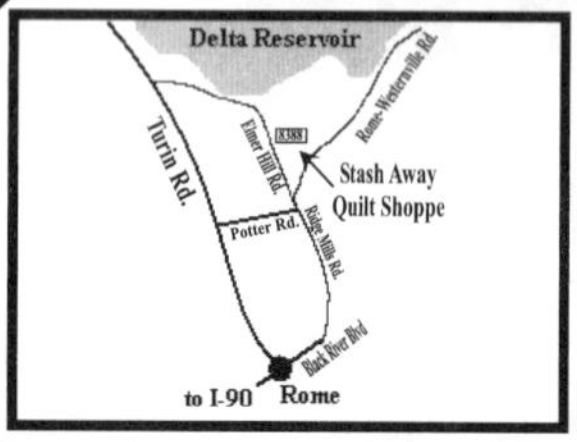

Glenfield, NY #55

Mon & Thur 9 - 5
Tues, Wed, Fri 1 - 6
Sat 10 - 3

Sew Crazy Fabric Shop

5146 State Route 12 13343
(315) 376-7630
Owners: Bonnie & Dustin Roes
Est: 2006 1800 sq.ft. 1000+ bolts
sewcrazy06@hotmail.com

Great selection of top quality quilting fabric.
Notions, patterns and books.
Lots of fat quarters and kits.

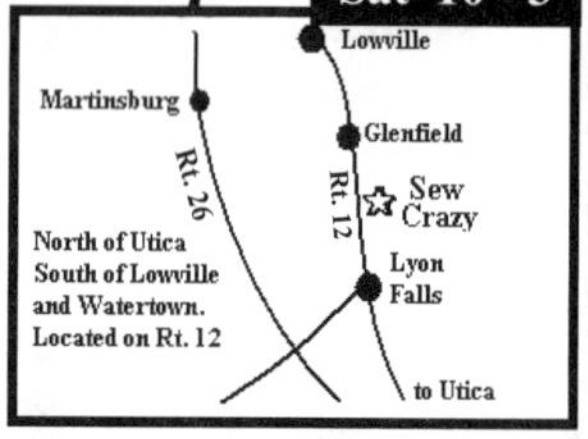

6 miles from Canadian Border

Dreamcrafters Quilt Shop

Akwesasne, NY #56

Located at the Wolf Pack Gift Shop on Rte. 37
1422 State Route 37, Hogansburg, NY 13655
(518) 358-4285 Owner: Dyan Swamp
E-Mail: dreamquilt@aol.com

Store Hours
Mon - Fri
9am - 7pm
Sat & Sun
10am - 6pm

LARGEST QUILT SHOP IN NORTHERN NY SUPPLIES FOR ALL YOUR "DREAM" CREATIONS

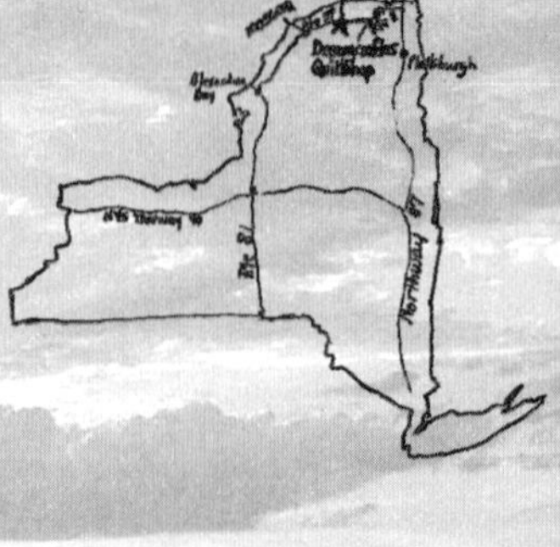

- 6000+ Bolts of 100% Cottons, Hoffman, Kaufman, Batiks
- Notions: Batting, Thread & Stencils
- Huge Selection of Books & Patterns
- Quilts For Sale
- Fat Quarters Galore!!!
- Yard Cuts & 1/2 Yard Cuts
- Kits
- Quilter's Gifts
- All purchases are tax-free

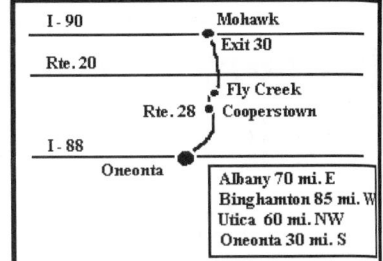

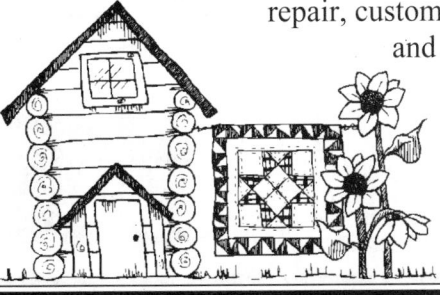

Utica, NY #59

Tiger Lily Quilt Co.

in The Shoppes At The Finish Line
809 Court St. 13502
(315) 735-5328
Owner: Donna Papaleo
www.tigerlilyquiltco.com

A unique quilt shop located in a historic cotton mill, at the finish line for the Boilermaker Rd. Race, in the Brewery District. We specialize in top quality fabrics, notions, books & patterns. Our teaching staff includes several award winning quilters. Stop in, get inspired, sign up for a class our newsletter and email list.

Mon - Fri 9:30 - 5
Sat 10 - 4

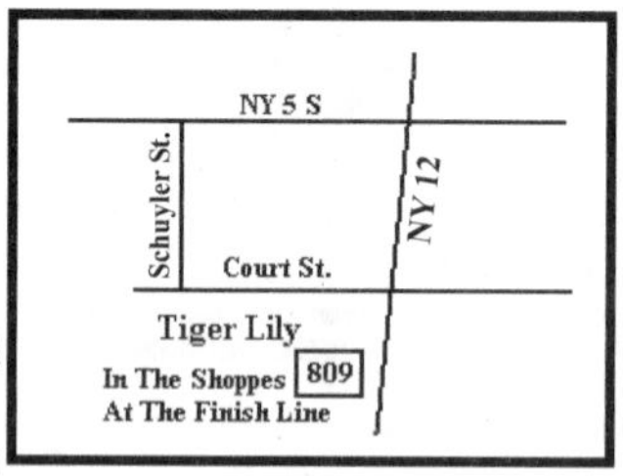

Directions to Tiger Lily:
From NYS Thruway Exit 31:
Follow signs to Rte 12, Take Rte 12 South To the first traffic light, turn right onto Court Street. Go through the next light at intersection of Court St and Sunset Ave.. The Shoppes at the Finish Line driveway is on the left. The building sits back from the street on the left side of the large parking lot.

Patchwork Passion QUILT SHOP

VISIT OUR NEW LOCATION

206 GLEN ST.
GLENS FALLS, NY 12001

Fabrics • Books • Patterns • Notions
Classes • Machine Quilting Service

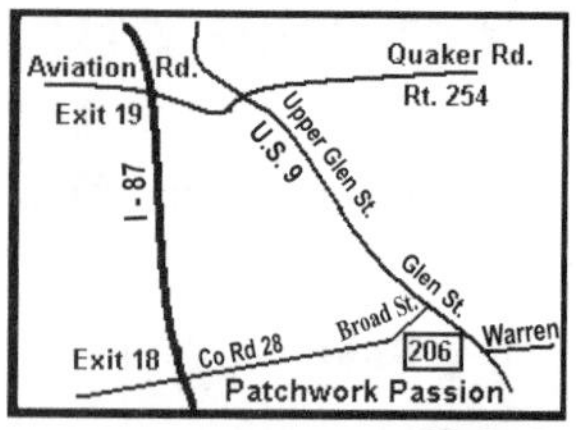

#60

AND OUR NEWEST ADDITION
THE QUILT LOFT
Featuring Handcrafted Quilts and Fiber Art Gifts!

Authorized Dealer of Nolting Longarm Quilting Machines

Open 7 Days a Week!
518.798.0644
www.PatchworkPassion.biz

Queensbury, NY #61

Mon - Fri 10 - 6
Sat 10 - 4

Heirloom Sewing Center & Quilt Shop

820 St. Rt. 9, Northway Plaza #1310 12804
518-761-6619
Owner: Jackie Smith Est: 2001
jacsmi18@aol.com 3800 sq. ft.
www.heirloomsewingcenter.com

Brother Dealer

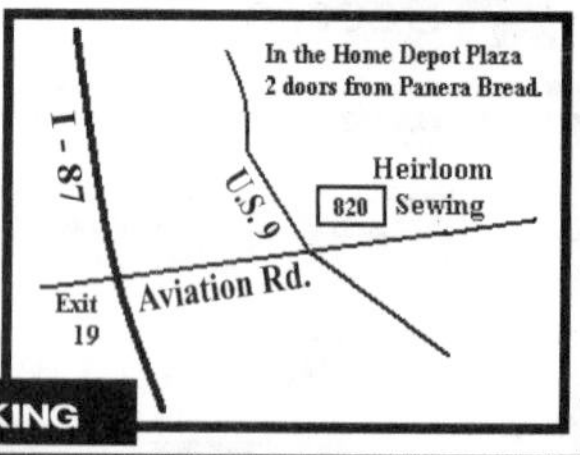

Husqvarna VIKING

Albany, NY #62

Mon - Sat 10 - 5
Thur til 8
Labor Day to Mem. Day Sun 11-4

Flying Geese Fabrics

Rosewood Plaza
501 New Karner Rd. 12205
(518) 456-8885
Est: 1996 2000 Bolts
flyinggeesenews@yahoo.com
Owner: Tara Conlon

We offer the finest fabrics, books and patterns with great classes. We'll be the quilt shop where you will be inspired to get creative to make your projects special. Just 4 miles west of I-87.

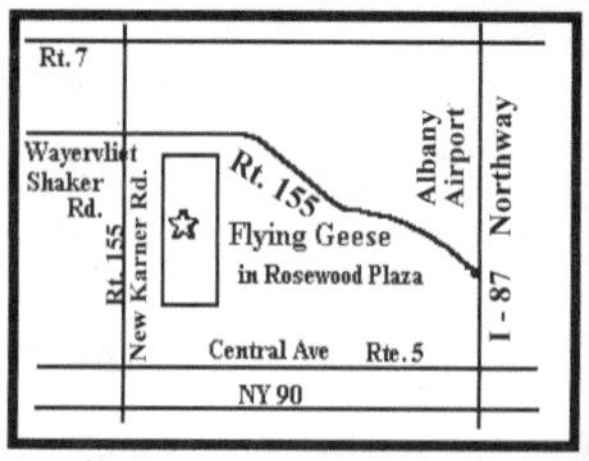

Hudson, NY #64

Thur - Mon 10 - 5:30
Sun 12 - 5

FABRICations Quilt Shop

558 Warren St. 12534
(518) 822-0772

Over 3000 bolts of 100% cotton quilting fabric, featuring international & contemporary fabrics along with traditional.
Books, notions, supplies & Classes.

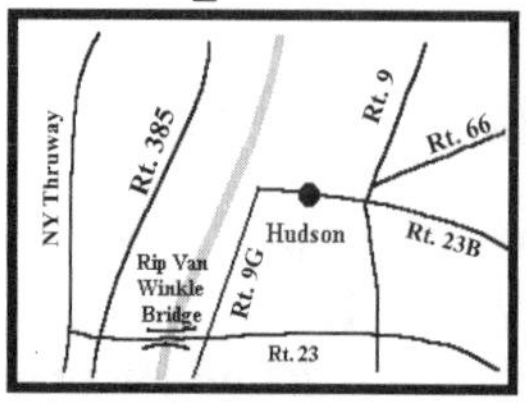

Ravena, NY #63

Log Cabin Fabrics

702 Starr Rd. 12143 (518) 767-9236
Owner: Londa VanDerzee Est: 1987

Visit a country quilt shop, 15 minutes south of Albany.
Over 2500 bolts, classes, books & patterns.

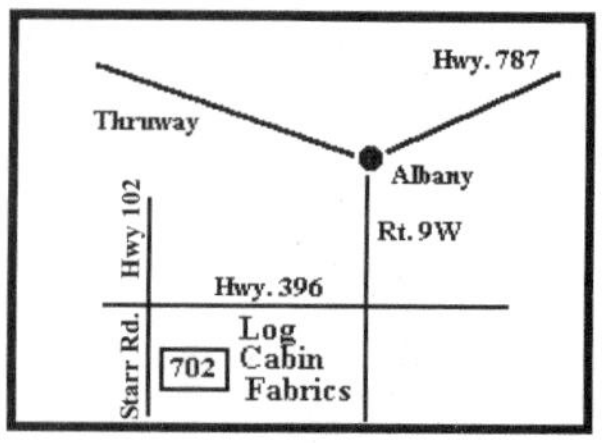

www.logcabinfabrics.net

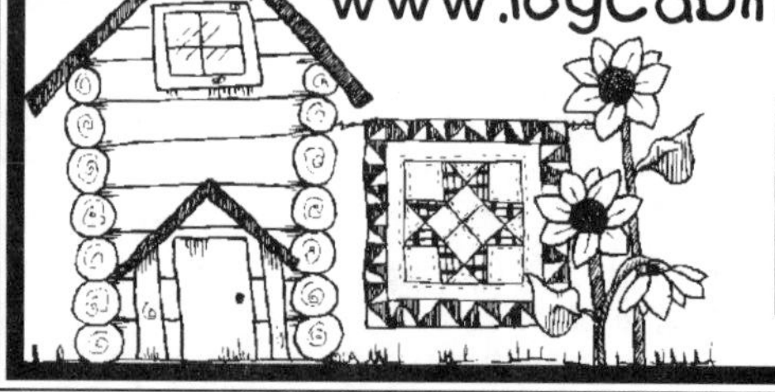

Tue 10 - 9
Wed - Fri 10 - 5
Sat 10 - 4

385 S. Main St.
Gloversville, NY 12078
(518) 725-4919
Fax: (518) 773-4166
gsc@nycap.rr.com
www.gloversvillesewingcenter.com
Mon-Fri 9-5:30, Thurs til 8, Sat 9-5

Owners: Diana & John Marshall
Est: 1981 5000 sq.ft. 4000+ Bolts

Gloversville, NY #65

Specializing in Sales and Service of

Bernina • Brother

Including Bernina 8 Series

Over 4000 Broadcloths in Stock

Including Hoffman • Andover

Robert Kaufman • Michael Miller • Marcus

Area's Largest Selection of

Quilting Books & Patterns

Large Assortment of

Decorative Threads
Silk Ribbons
Specialty Needles
Sewing Machine
Attachments.

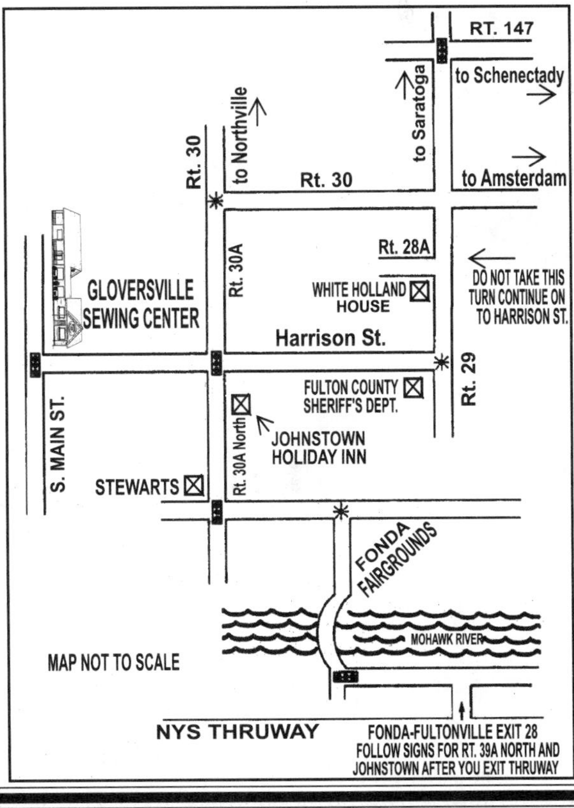

From A to Z -- It's all here!

"Where Creativity Comes to Life"

Quilter's Attic Sewing Center

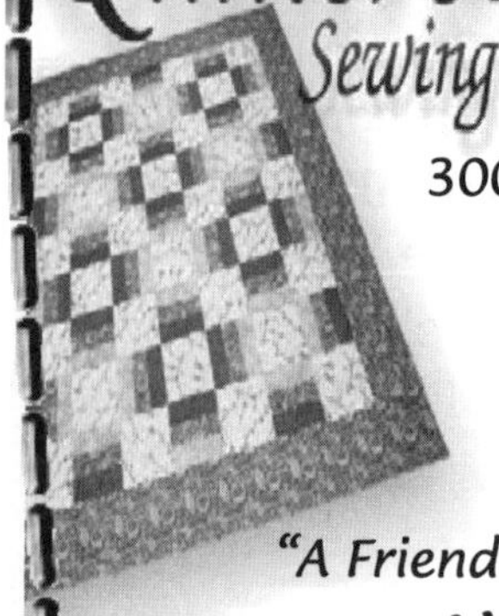

Est. 1994

3000 bolts, quilting supplies, machine embroidery supplies, classes.
PFAFF & Baby lock Sewing Machines.

"A Friendly Full Service Quilt Shop"

www.quiltersattic.com

Tues-Sat 10:00-4:30
Wed eve til 7:00
Sometimes on Sunday- call ahead

118 Maple Ave.
(Route 302)
845-744-5888

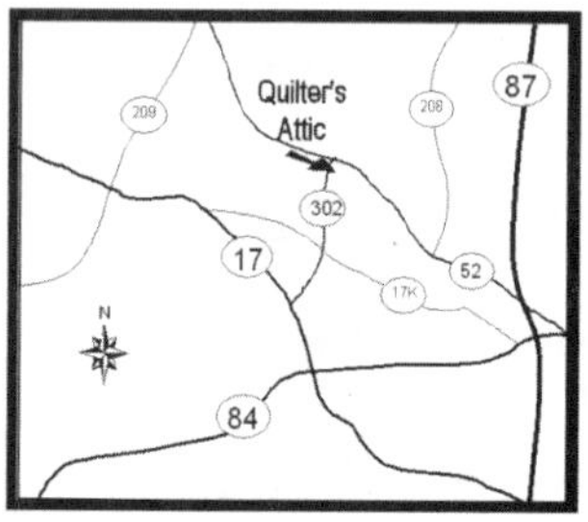

From Route 84: Exit 8 (Route 52W) 15 miles to Pine Bush. Left on Rt. 302
From Route 17: Exit 119 (Route 302N) to Pine Bush, 10 miles on right
Bus tours welcome - please call ahead.

Pine Bush, NY #66

Red Hook, NY #67

Tues - Sat 10 - 5

The Village Fabric Shoppe

33 W. Market St. 12571
(845) 758-8541 Est: 1981
villagefabricshoppe@gmail.com
www.villagefabricshoppe.com
We specialize in fine, quilting fabrics - Quilter's Reproductions, Batiks, Embellishments and more.
year round classes, supplies, books, patterns, gifts, kits - Friendly Service.

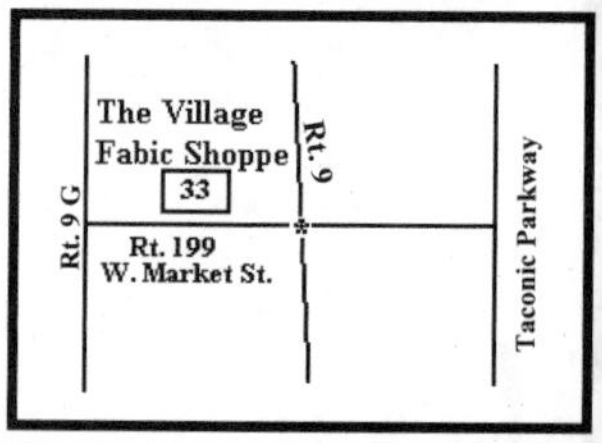

Kingston, NY #68

**Mon - Sat 10 - 6
Suns 12 - 5
Sept. - May**

Style Fabrics

Kingston Plaza, 222 Plaza Rd. 12401
(845) 338-1793 Fax: (845) 338-2659
Eileen.Style.Fab@juno.com
www.style-fabrics.com

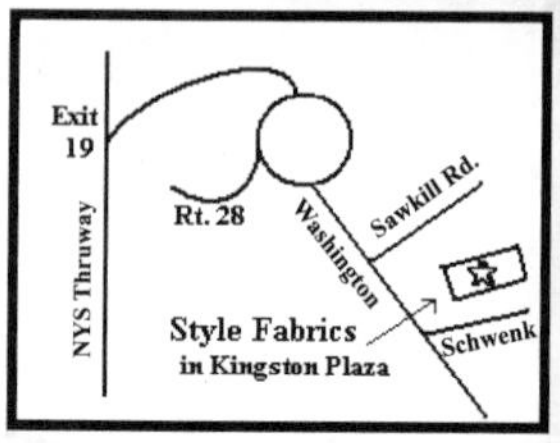

Est: 1995 3000 sq.ft. 2000 Bolts of Cottons
Quality quilting cottons - lots of novelty prints, batiks, Oriental prints and More!
Plus: great dress fabrics! We're easy to get to!

New York, NY #71

**Tues - Fri 11 - 7
Sat 10 - 6
Sun 11 - 5**

**133 West 25th St. 10001
(212) 807-0390**
Owner: Cathy Izzo
info@cityquilter.com
www.cityquilter.com

THE CITY QUILTER

A "Best of Quilt Sampler" Shop

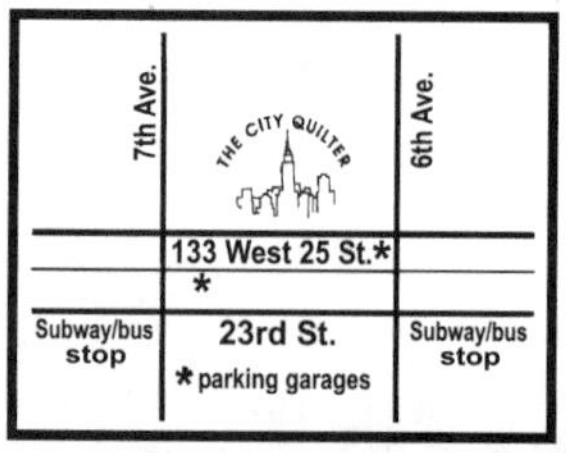

Wide selection of sophisticated, contemporary & exotic cotton prints. Exclusive New York themed fabrics.

Hyde Park, NY #69

**Mon - Sat 10 - 5
Sun 12 - 4
Summer Mon-Sat til 6**

Quilted Bear Den

4260 Albany Post Rd. #1
12538
(845) 233-4858
Owner: John Scibran
info@quiltedbearden.com
www.quiltedbearden.com

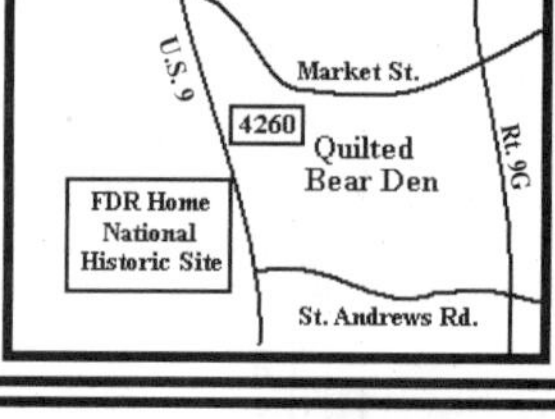

"A Beary Different Quilt Shop"

Wappingers Falls, NY #70

**Tues, Wed, Fri 10 - 5
Thur 10 - 8
Sat 10 - 4
Sun 12 - 4**

Quilt Basket

939 Route 376 12590
(845) 227-7606
Owners: Cathy & Allan Anderson
Est: 1989 1800 sq.ft. 3000 Bolts
www.quiltbasket.com

Handi Quilter & JANOME
Sales, Service & Classes.

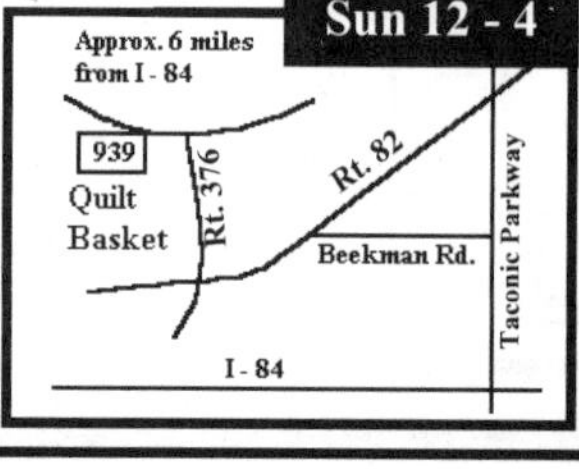

New York, NY #72

Paron Fabrics.

Mon - Thur 8:30 - 7
Fri 8:30 - 5:45
Sat 9 - 5
Sun 11 - 4

206 W. 40th St. 10018
(212) 768-3266 Fax: (212) 768-3260
Owners: Mark Glenn & Gary Babyatzky
mgrparon@aol.com
Online store: www.manhattenfabrics.com
www.paronfabrics.com

We are two stores in one - one full price, one half price. We feature the finest designer fabrics among our diverse and always changing inventory. Full line of patterns. We ship worldwide.

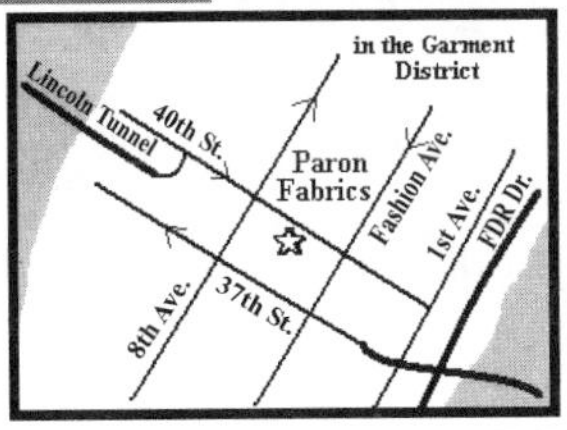

Glenville, NY #73

The Joyful Quilter

Mon - Fri 10 - 5
Wed til 8
Sat 10 - 4

19 Glenridge Rd., Unit A 12302
(518) 399-0128
Owner: Susan Pettengill Est: 2007
1500 sq.ft. 1000+ Bolts Newsletter
spettengill@msn.com

Hundreds of batiks, the latest patterns and books, excellent customer service, a warm welcome and the best coffee in town!

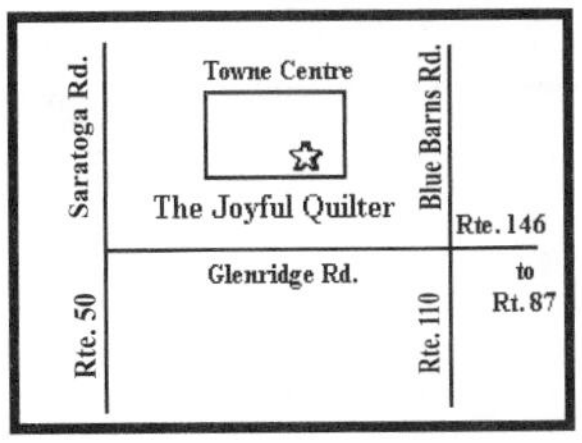

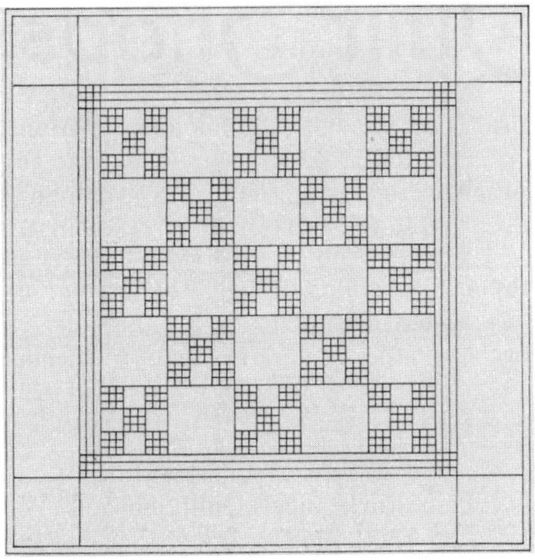

Brooklyn, NY #74

SEW BEARY SPECIAL

By Appt. Only

1025 E. 28th St. 11210
(718) 951-3973
Est: 1993
Owner:
Marcie Brenner

A Shoppe for Quilters! Large selection of 100% cotton Fabrics, Books, Patterns, Tools, Supplies, Battings, Gifts & Classes.

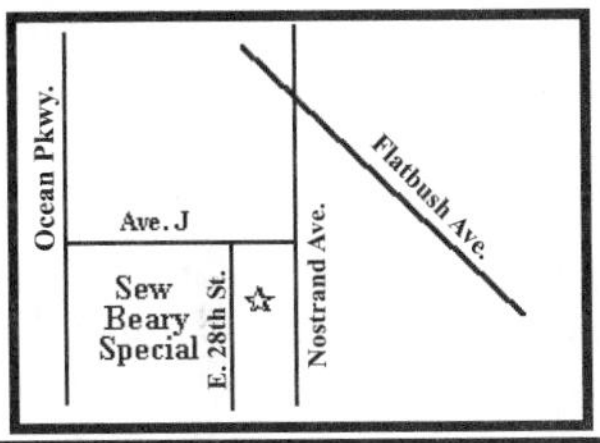

PIECEFUL QUILTING

Creative Inspiration One Block at a Time

Riverhead, NY #75

31 McDermott St. 11901
631-727-5909
Mon - Fri 10am - 6pm
Sat. 10am - 5pm

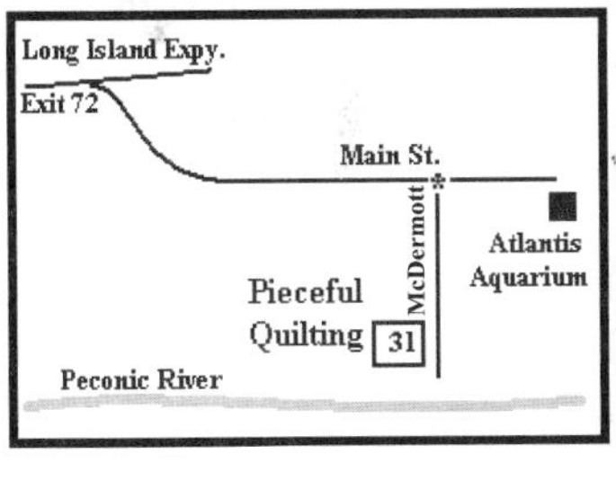

Two Shops to Serve You

BERNINA baby lock

East Northport, NY #76

3027 Jericho Trpk. 11731
631-670-6254
Mon - Fri 10am - 6pm
Sat 10am - 5pm
Sun 11am - 4pm

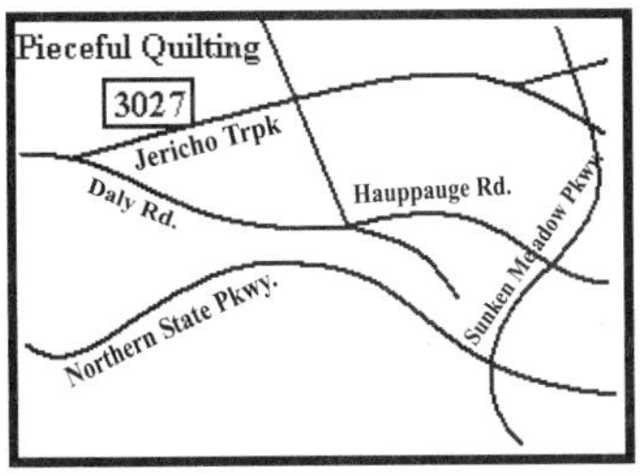

Classes
Special Events
Frequent Buyers Club
Thousands of bolts of your favorite fabrics.
The best place for unique and affordable gifts with a quilty theme.

www.piecefulquilting.com

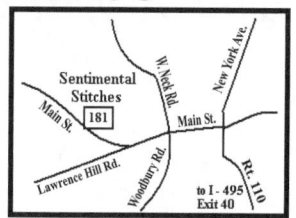

New York Quilt Shops

Afton **Sew Clever, 195 Hwy 41 South**
607-639-2460 **See ad #47, page 380**
Akwesasne **Dreamcrafter Quilt Shop, 1422 St. Rte. 37**
518-358-4285 **See ad #56, page 382 & 194**
Albany **Flying Geese Fabrics, 501 New Karner Rd.**
518-456-8885 **See ad #62, page 384**
Altona Maw & Paw's Fabrics, 4954 Military Tpke. 518-236-5762
Amherst **Threads of Time, 3133 Sheridan Dr.**
716-837-1372 **See ad #13, page 371**
Arcade **Creekside Fabrics & Quilts, 237 Main St.**
585-492-4226 **See ad #4, page 369**
Bayside Sew Time Sewing, 7835 Springfield Blvd. 718-776-1900
Big Flats **The Village Sampler, 18 Canal St.**
607-562-7596 **See ad #36, page 377**
Binghamton **Creative Threads, 1115 Upper Front St.**
607-724-2151 **See ad #42, page 378**
Boston **Quilt Farm, 5623 S. Feddick Rd.**
716-941-3140 **See ad #5, page 369**
Bouckville **The Gingham Patch, 3490 Pratts Rd.**
315-893-7750 **See ad #52, page 382**
Brooklyn **Sew Beary Special, 1025 E. 28th St.**
718-951-3973 **See ad #74, page 387**
Brockport Country Treasures Quilt Shop, 61 Main St. 585-637-5148
Brooklyn Sew Materialistic, 1310 Coney Island Ave. 718-338-6104
Buffalo Elmwood Village Fabrics, 982 Elmwood Ave. 716-881-2866
Caledonia **Chestnut Bay Quilting, 3128 Main St.**
585-538-4420 **See ad #17, page 372**
Campbell **Sew Pieceful, 5541 County Rte. 125**
607-583-4968 **See ad #34, page 376**
Canandaigua **Liberty Cottage, 116 S. Main St.**
585-393-1070 **See ad #21, page 372**
Candor **Pucky Huddle Delight, 71 Owego Rd.**
607-659-7743 **See ad #38, page 378**
Cazenovia Cazenovia Fabrics, 45 Albany St. 315-655-8500
Chatham Foofsique Quilting Emporium, 437 Route 295 518-392-3111
Clarksville Quilter's Studio, Etc., 1967 Delaware Turnpike 518-768-8091
Cobleskill **The Yardstick, 147 Barnerville Rd. #1**
518-234-2179 **See ad #50, page 380**
Cold Spring Harbor **Sentimental Stitches, 181 Main St.**
631-692-4145 **See ad #60, this page**
Corning Corning Stitch Works, 15 W. Market St. 607-377-5376
Cortland Dye Lot Quilting, 201 McLean Rd. 607-753-6068
Croton-on-Hudson Pinwheels, 2006 Albany Post Rd 914-271-1045
Dansville **Material Rewards, 10160 Sandy Hill Rd.**
585-335-2050 **See ad #31, page 375**
Depew Sew on -Sew Forth, 6152 Transit Rd. 716-684-4880
Dundee The Fabric Shop, 12 Main St. 607-243-7052
Dunkirk Mauzy's Sewing Center, 1170 Central Ave. 716-366-3630
East Aurora **The Carriage Quilt Shoppe, 593 Main St.**
716-655-4561 **See ad #6, page 370**
East Aurora **Aurora Sewing Center, 659 Main St.**
716-652-2811 **See ad #7, page 370**
East Aurora Vidler's 5 & 10 Store, 690 Main St. 716-652-0481
East Northport **Pieceful Quilting, 3027 Jericho Turnpike**
631-670-6254 **See ad #76, page 387**
East Rochester **Patricia's Fabric House, 333 W. Commerical St.**
585-248-2362 **See ad #22, page 373**
East Syracuse Knechts Sewing Inc., 6701 Manlius Center 315-437-0963
Ellicottville Ellicottville Quilt Shop, 19 Jefferson St. 716-699-2065
Elmira Nancy's Bunny Hutch, 964B Pennsylvania Ave. 607-732-2480
Endicott **Patchwork Angels Quilt Shop, 307 W Main St**
607-748-0682 **See ad #39, page 378**
Esperance Quiltbug.com, 169 Main St. 888-817-6577
Fairport Sew Creative, 23 N. Main 585-388-0230
Floral Park Patchwork Patch, 32 Hemlock St. 516-326-0774
Fly Creek **Heartworks Quilts & Fabrics, 6237 Rt. #28**
607-547-2501 **See ad #58, page 383**
Fulton Herron's Fabric Center, 121 Cayuga St. 315-592-4031
Glenfield **Sew Crazy Fabric Shop, 5146 State Rte. 12**
315-376-7630 **See ad #55, page 382**
Glens Falls **Patchwork Passion Quilt Shop, 206 Glen St.**
518-798-0644 **See ad #60, page 384**
Glens Falls Patti's Quilting & Fabric, 485 Glen St. 518-683-7107
Glens Falls Adirondack Quilts, 21 Cooper St. 518-615-0134
Glenville **The Joyful Quilter, 19 Glenridge Rd., Unit A**
518-399-0128 **See ad #73, page 387**
Gloversville **Gloversville Sewing Center, 385 S. Main St.**
518-725-4919 **See ad #65, page 385**
Grand Island Mooselodge Fabrics, 33 Brandywine Drive 716-773-3174
Greene **Creative Threads, 604 Jackson Hill Rd.**
607-656-8883 **See ad #41, page 378**
Hammondsport **Lake Country Patchworks, 67 Shether St.**
607-569-3530 **See ad #33, page 376**
Hartsdale Hartsdale Fabrics, 275 S. Central Ave. 914-428-7780
Hicksville Gone Sewin, 107-11 Stewart Ave 516-342-1127
Himrod Golden Lane Fabrics, 3252 Penn Yan Himrod 315-536-8342
Hornell Sally's Bright Ideas, 24 A Park Dr. #101 607-324-2161
Hudson **Fabrications Quilt Shop, 558 Warren St.**
518-822-0772 **See ad #64, page 384**
Hurleyville Chris-Sans Nubian Quilt House, 278 Meyerhoff Rd. 914-434-6667
Hyde Park **Quilted Bear Den, 4260 Albany Post Rd. #1**
845-233-4858 **See ad #69, page 386**
Inlet **Black Bear Trading Post, 115 Rt. 28**
315-357-5092 **See ad #57, page 383**
Islip Sew What's New, 400 Main St 631-277-4215
Ithaca **Quilters Corner, 518 W. State St.**
607-266-0850 **See ad #35, page 376**

Ithaca Homespun Boutique, 314 E. State St. 607-277-0954

Jamestown Quilters' Haven, 115 McDaniel Ave.
716-665-6524 See ad #2, page 369

Johnson City Sew Many Quilts, 800 Valley Plaza Drive
607-797-1796 See ad #43, page 379 & 409

Kenmore Pine Grove Quilt Shop, 2962 Delaware Ave
716-873-0774 See ad #10, page 370

Kingston Style Fabrics 222 Plaza Rd.
845-338-1793 See ad #68, page 386

Kirkwood Beyond the Needle, LLC, 2335 U.S. Rt. 11
607-238-7182 See ad #44, page 380

Lake Grove Sew Time Sewing Center, 2793 Middle Country 631-737-3944

Lakewood Calico Cat, 4451 W. Fairmount Ave.
716-763-8167 See ad #1, page 369

Lockport Marie's Sewing Center, 6322 Robinson Rd
716-434-2583 See ad #15, page 371

Lockport Heartland Quilt Shop, 7121 Ridge Rd.
716-433-3188 See ad #14, page 371

Mamaroneck The Quilt Cottage, 414 Mamamaroneck Ave. 914-777-1333

Marcellus Patchwork Plus, 2532 Cherry Valley Turnpike
315-673-2208 See ad #25, page 373

Maryland Smitty's Stitchery, 208 Lake Shore Dr. N. 607-433-5292

Massapequa The Quilting Bug, 30E Broadway
516-541-8600 See ad #75, page 388

Medina The Whole Nine Yards, 513 Main St. 585-798-1309
Monsey Patchwork Sampler, 7 Fieldcrest St. 845-354-1011
Mt. Kisco Pins & Needles, 161 Main St. 914-666-0824
Munnsville Running with Scissors, 5550 West Rd 315-495-7255

Naples Carriage House Quilts, 201 N. Main St.
585-374-9580 See ad #29, page 375

New York The City Quilter, 133 W. 25th St.
212-807-0390 See ad #71, page 386

New York Paron Fabrics, 206 W. 40th St.
212-768-3266 See ad #72, page 387

New York Purl Patchwork, 147 Sullivan St. 212-420-8798
New York Andover Fabrics, 1384 Broadway - 15th Floor 212-710-1000
New York Laura Fisher Antique Quilts, 305 East 61st St. 212-838-2596
New York B&J Fabrics, 525 7th Ave., 2nd Floor 212-354-8150
Newcomb Aunt Polly's Material Girls, 5795 St. Rt. 28N 518-582-2260

Niagara Falls Auntie's Attic Quilt Shop, 2043 Military Rd.
716-297-3636 See ad #12, page 370

Niagara Falls Quiltmakers and Friends, 4716 Military Rd.
716-297-4067 See ad #11, page 370

North Syracuse Mission Rose Quiltery and Knittery, 456 S. Main St.
315-452-3247 See ad #26, page 374

North Tonawanda Teddy Bear Fabrics, 64 Webster St. 716-692-4756

Norwich Sew Nice, 6142 State Hwy 12 (North Plaza)
607-334-2477 See ad #48, page 380

Nunda The Journey Quilt Co., 3 N. State St.
585-468-2320 See ad #28, page 375

Olean Enchanted Mountain Quilting, 324 W. State St.
716-372-2327 See ad #3, page 369

Oneonta Country Fabrics & Quilts, 5252 St. Hwy. 23
607-432-9726 See ad #49, page 380

Oneonta Piecework Fabrics, 75 Chestnut St. 607-431-9675
Ontario WOWK Quilt Embroidery, 5409 Fosdick Rd. 352-357-3669
Oswego The Quilter's Nook, 193 W 1st St. #12 315-343-0029

Owego The Churn Dash, 6 McMaster St. Suite 4
607-687-6811 See ad #40, page 378

Patchogue 112 Sewing Supplies, Inc., 142 Route 112 631-475-8282

Penn Yan Weaver View Farms, 1190 Earls Hill Rd
315-781-2571 See ad #30, page 375 & 406

Pine Bush Quilter's Attic, 118 Maple Ave.(Rt. 302)
845-744-5888 See ad #66, page 386

Plattsburgh Loose Threads, 164 Boynton Ave. #304 518-825-0268
Port Chester Nimble Thimble, 21 Putnam Ave. 914-934-2934
Potsdam Misty Hollow, 22 Market St. 315-265-1660
Pulaski Lil Tot-N-Craft Shop, 4749 Salina St. 315-298-5214

Queensbury Heirloom Sewing Center & Quilt Shop, 820 St. Rt. 9 #1310
518-761-6619 See ad #61, page 384

Ravena Log Cabin Fabrics, 702 Starr Rd.
518-767-9236 See ad #63, page 384

Red Hook The Village Fabric Shoppe, 33 W. Market St.
845-758-8541 See ad #67, page 386

Richville Hart Country Fabrics, 115 County Rt. 20 315-287-3250

Riverhead Pieceful Quilting, 31 McDermott Ave
631-727-5909 See ad #75, page 387

Rochester The Bobbin Case, Inc., 1784 Monroe Ave.
585-244-7780 See ad #23, page 373

Rome Stash Away Quilt Shoppe, 8388 Elmer Hill Rd
315-533-7611 See ad #54, page 382

Sanitaria Springs Quilted Crow, 54 Cafferty Rd.
607-648-8956 See ad #45, page 380

Saranac Lake Mountain Gift & Powder Co., Inc., 13 Broadway 518-891-4206

Savannah Spring Lake Fabrics, 4250 Wolcott Spring Lake
315-594-8485 See ad #24, page 373

Sidney Center The Fieldstone House, 1884 Wheat Hill Rd.
607-369-9177 See ad #51, page 381

South Hampton Hildreth's Dept. Store, 51 Main St. 800-462-1842
Southold Old Country Charm, Inc.,53995 Rte 25 631-765-3940

Spencerport Betty's Quilting Etc., 42 Nichols St. (Rte. 31)
585-352-9362 See ad #18, page 372

Stanley From the Heart, 1725 Rt. 245 585-526-4429
Sweet Valley 118 Fabrics & More, 1205 St. Rt. 118 570-477-3166

Syracuse Calico Gals, 3906 New Court Ave.
315-445-0617 See ad #27, page 374

Utica Tiger Lily Quilt Company, 809 Court St.
315-735-5328 See ad #59, page 384

Valley Cottage The Happy Quilter, 3 Lake Ridge Plaza (Rt. 303)845-268-8744

Vestal Grandmother's Thimble, 3036 Old Vestal Rd.
607-797-7022 See ad #37, page 377

Victor Ivy Thimble Quilt & Gift Shop, 5 Railroad St.
585-742-2680 See ad #20, page 372

Walton Where Quilters Gather, 137 Stockton Ave.
607-865-8550 See ad #46, page 380

Wampsville Cottons Etc., 101 Genesee St.
315-363-6834 See ad #53, page 382

Wappingers Falls The Quilt Basket, Cambridge Commons; 939 Rte. 376 Suite 4
845-227-7606 See ad #70, page 386

Watkins Glen O'Susannah's Quilts & Gifts, 111 W Fourth St.
607-535-6550 See ad #32, page 376

Webster The Scarlet Thread, 38 E. Main St.
585-265-4910 See ad #19, page 372

West Nyack Quilter's Crossing, 12 Strawtown Rd. 845-348-8840
White Plains White Plains Sewing, 200 Hamilton Ave. 914-682-0595

Williamsville Aurora Sewing Center, 8575 Main St.
716-204-8350 See ad #8, page 370

Williamsville Sew What ?, 6816 Main St.
716-632-8801 See ad #9, page 370

York Mt. Pleasant Quilting Company 2877 Mt. Pleasant Rd.
585-243-0767 See ad #16, page 371

Yorktown Heights Fabric Mart-NY, 2019 Crompond Rd. 914-962-3328

New York Quilt Shows

43 Shows

About Shows: We are listing only the very basic information about shows that happen on a regular schedule here. Please check out our website for more details on each show. Also this information tends to change quite often so please verify the event with our website or a local source before you venture far. Or if you're in the right area at the right time, give it a shot.

If you are a show organizer, please keep us updated on your event.
shows@quilterstravelcompanion.com
www.quilterstravelcompanion.com

On our website you will also find:
- Exact dates (when we have them)
- Sponsor Information
- Contact Information
- Description of Event
- Events happening on a one-time basis

February
Cooperstown Annual, 2nd two weeks in February
Cooperstown Fenimore Quilt Club Show
Cooperstown Art Association Galleries, 22 Main St.

March
East Rochester Annual, 3rd Sat in March
Patricias' Fabric House, 333 W. Commercial St.
Garden City Even Years, 3rd weekend of March
Long Island Quilters' Society Show
Garden City Field House, 295 Stewart Ave
New York Odd Years, 3rd weekend of March
Urban Inspirations Quilt Show Fashion Institute of Technology 27th St. & 7th Ave.
Sackets Harbor Annual, 3rd weekend in March Great Lakes Seaway Trail Quilt Show Seaway Trail Discovery Center, Corner of Ray & West Main

April
Amherst Even Years, 3rd weekend in April Amherst Museum Quilters Guild Show Amherst Museum, 3755 Tonawanda Creek Rd.
Cairo Annual, 3rd weekend in April Piecemaker's Open House Quilt Show Cairo Town Hall, Main St. & Railroad Ave.
Fayetteville Odd years, 3rd weekend in April Towpath Quilt Guild Show Mott Road Elementary School, 7173 Mott Rd.
Grand Island Even Years, Spring River Lea Quilt Guild Show Whitehaven Road Baptist Church, 1290 Whitehaven Rd.
Ravena Odd years, 3rd weekend in April Quilters United in Learning Together Show Ravena-Coeymans-Selkirk High School, 2025 US-9W
North Tonawanda Odd Years, last weekend in April Twin City Quilters Guild Show Wheatfield Community Senior Center, 2800 Church Rd

May
Somers Annual, 1st weekend of May Northern Star Quilter's Guild John F. Kennedy High School, Rt. 138
Fairport Odd Years, 2nd Sat of May Perinton Quilt guild Quilt Show St. Johns of Rochester Gym Building, 18 Wickford Way
Warwick Even Years, May Stars of the Valley Quilt Show Sanfordville Elementary School, 144 Sanfordville Rd.
Malone Even Years, 3rd weekend in May Adirondack Quilters Guild Spring Show Holy Family School, 12 Homstead Park

June
Glens Falls Odd Years, 1st weekend of June Wings Falls Quilters Guild Show Venue Changes
Stone Ridge Annual, First Sat & Sun in June Wiltwyck Quilter's Guild Show Ulster County Community College, Cottekill Rd.
North Blenheim Annual Lansing Manor Quilt Show Lansing Manor, 1378 SR 30
Riverhead Annual, 1st weekend in June Peconic Quilt Show Suffolk Community College, 121 Speonk-Riverhead Rd.
Staten Island Even Years, 1st Sunday of June Quilting on the Courthouse Steps Historic Richmond Town, 441 Clarke Ave.

August
Syracuse Annual, Late July into August Quilting by the Lake Quilt Show Onondaga Community College
East Rochester Annual, 3rd Sat in August Patricias' Fabric House Quilt Show Patricias' Fabric House, 333 W. Commercial St.
Hunter Annual, 3rd weekend in August The Great Catskill Mountain Quilt Show CMF Performing Arts Center, Main St., Rt. 23A

September
Newcomb Annual, 2nd weekend in September Newcomb's Mt. Quilters Show Newcomb Central School, Rt. 28 N
Rochester Even Years, 3rd weekend in September Quilt and Needlework Expo Show United Methodist Church of North Chili, 2200 Westside
Chautauqua Annual, 4th weekend in September Chautauqua Fall Festival Chautauqua Institution, Rt. 394
Whitesboro Odd Years, Last weekend of September Mohawk Valley Quilt Show Utica Curling Club, 8300 Clark Mills Rd.

October
Dryden Odd Years, 1st weekend in October Tompkins County Quilters Guild Show Tompkins Cortland Comm. College, 170 North St.
East Aurora Even Years,first Fri & Sat in October Morningstar Quilt Guild Show St. Matthias Episcopal Church, 374 Main St.
Gilbertsville Annual, 1st weekend in October Heirlooms, Past and Present The Major's Inn, State Hwy. 51
Poughkeepsie Odd Years, Columbus Day Weekend Dutchess Heritage Quilt Show Dutchess Community College--Falcon Hall, Pendell Rd.
Arcade Odd Years, 1st weekend after Columbus Day Hope Lutheran Church Quilt Show Hope Lutheran Church, 2 E. Main St.
Old Forge Annual, early October to early November The Arts Guild Show Arts Center of Old Forge, 3260 St. Rt. 28
Oxford Odd Years, Columbus Day weekend, October Chenango Piecemakers Show Oxford Academy High School, 50 S. Washington Ave.
Clifton Park Odd Years, October Empire QuiltFest Shenendohowa High School East

Baldwinsville Odd Years, 4th weekend in October Candlelight Quilters Guild Show Van Buren School, 14 Ford St.
Henrietta Odd Years, 4th weekend of October Henrietta Quilt Club Show Henrietta Public Library, 455 Calkins Rd.
Rochester Even Years, 4th Fri & Sat in October Irondequoit Quilt Club Show Lutheran Church of the Resurrection, 3736 St. Paul

November
Lockport Odd Years, 1st weekend in November Kenan Quilters' Guild Quilt Show Kenan Arena 433 Locust St.
Auburn Annual, Early November thru early January Schweinfurth Memorial Art Center Show Schweinfurth Mem. Art Ctr, 205 Genessee St.

46 Featured Shops

NORTH CAROLINA

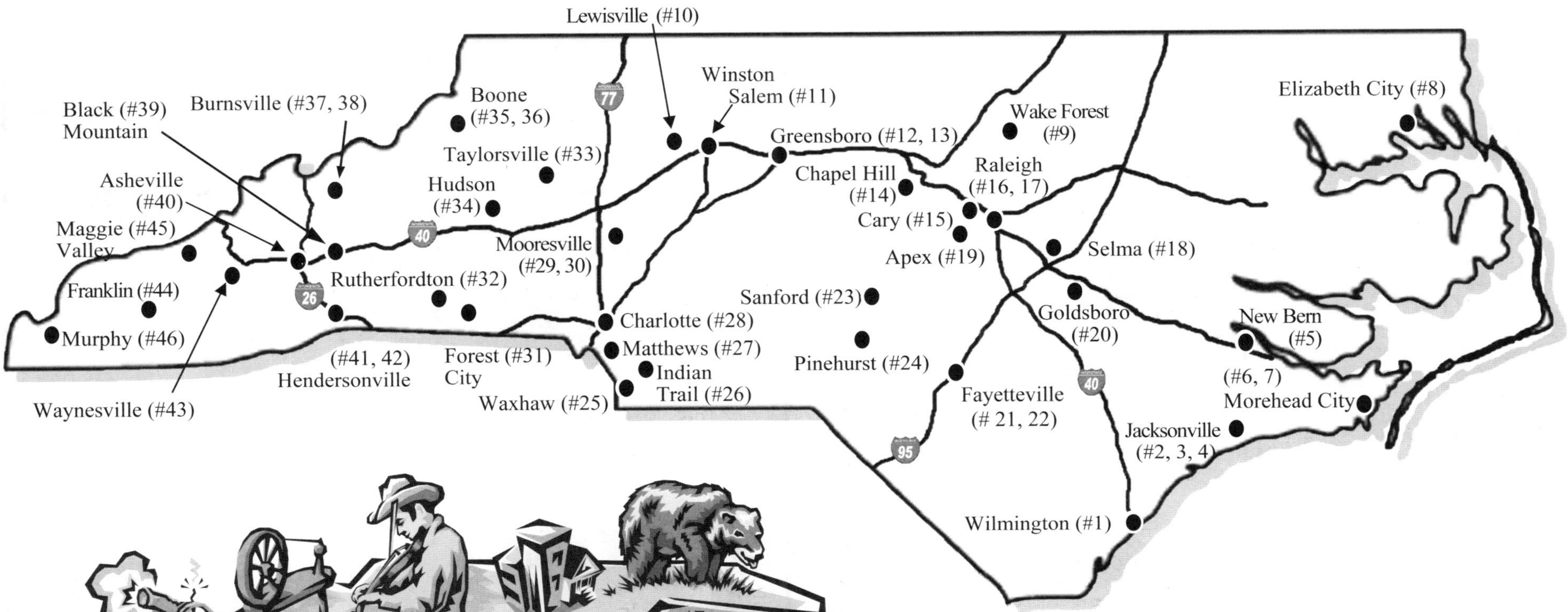

Wilmington, NC #1

Mon - Fri 10 - 5
Sat 10 - 3

Fran's Sewing Circle

5751 Oleander Dr. Unit 5 28403
(910) 397-9399 Fax: Same
Est: 1996 2600 sq. ft
franssc@aol.com
www.franssewingcircle.com.

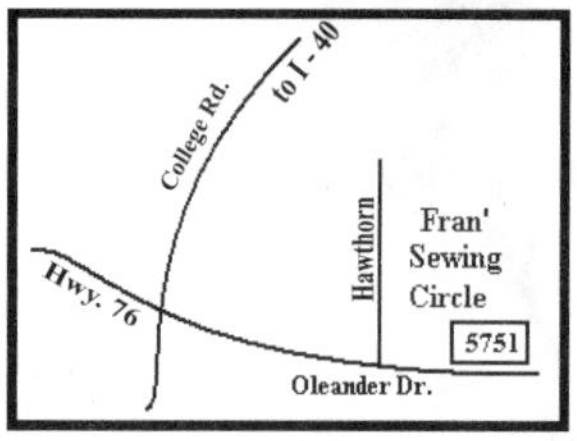

Great Fabrics - cottons, silk, linen & more:
Notions - Books - Buttons - Many Classes

Jacksonville, NC #2

Tues - Fri 10 - 4
Sat 10 - 2

The Country Collection

2864 Wilmington Hwy (Hwy 17 S) 28540
(910) 347-1960 Fax: Same
countrycollection@ec.rr.com
Owner: Frances Cauley
Est: 1994 1800+ sq. ft. 3000 Bolts

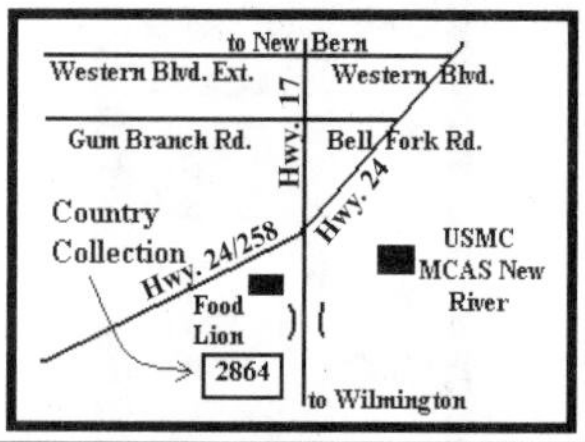

100% cotton designer fabrics. Books, patterns, notions & classes. Moda, Jinny Beyer & Thimbleberries Quilt kits. Friendly professional guidance. Mail order.

Jacksonville, NC #3

Tues - Fri 10 - 5
Sat 10 - 4

The Cotton Patch Quilt Shoppe

112 Phillips Rd. (Hwy. 17) 28540
(910) 938-1395
Fax: (910) 938-7543
Owner: Sharon C. Turner
Est: 1993
2750 sq.ft. 7000 Bolts

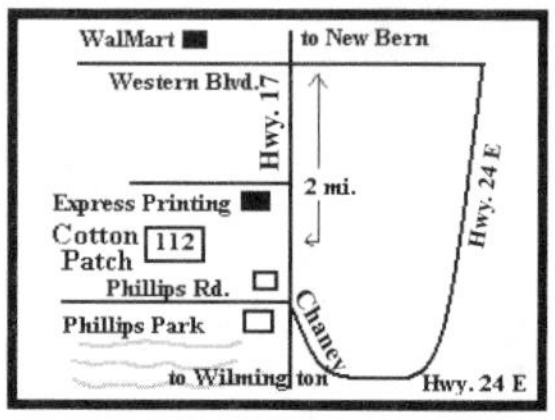

Large selection Fabrics, Books & Patterns, Kits, Notions, Classes.
"A Really Great Quilt Store."

Jacksonville, NC #4

Mon - Fri 10 - 5
Thur til 7
Sat 10 - 4

All About Quilting

3736 Henderson Dr. 28546
(910) 577-9200 Fax: (910) 577-9300
Operator: Kirsta Meadows
Est: 2003
www.allaboutquilting.net

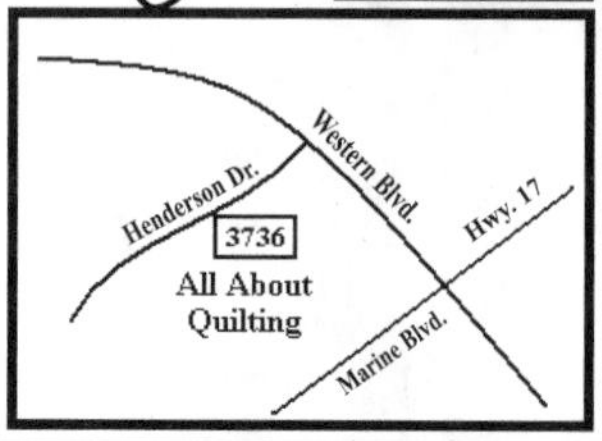

Fabric, Books, Classes with certified teachers, Gift Items and friendly service. Authorized Elna Sewing Machine Dealership. Sales & Service. Financing Available.

BERNINA

The Ultimate Sewing Experience

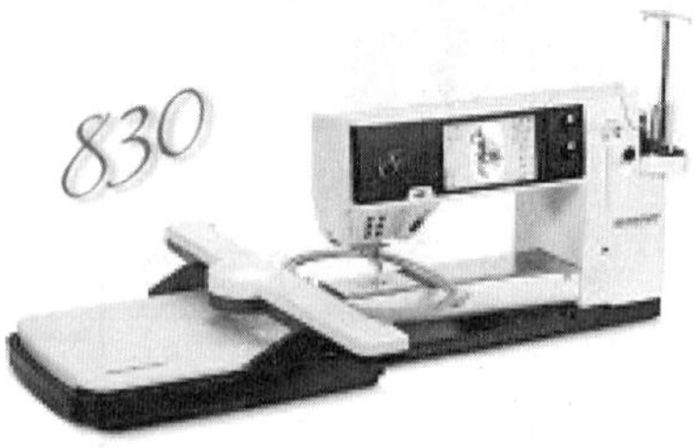

Unleash your creative aspirations with the BERNINA 8 Series

Experience the Difference

Large Selection of Fabrics, Notions and Supplies for Fashion, Quilting, Smocking, Heirloom & Embroidery. Sewing Classes & Events

New Bern Fabric Center

1218 S Glenburnie Rd, New Bern NC 28562
252 633-4780 Visit: www.nbfabric.com
Hours: 9-5:30 M-F; 9-5 Sat. - Est. 1974

Embroidery & Cutwork Software

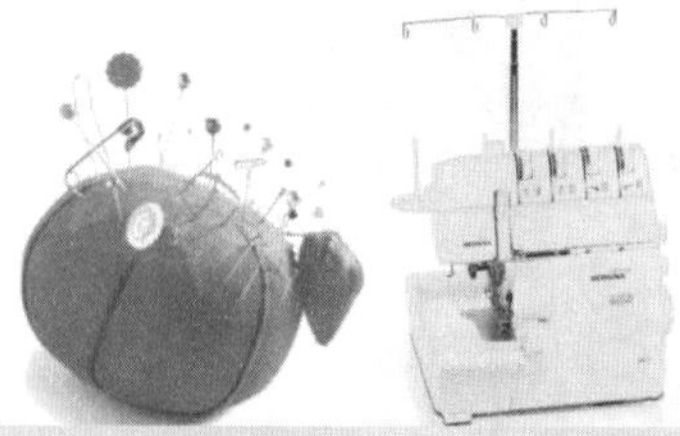

Sewing Notions Bernina Sergers

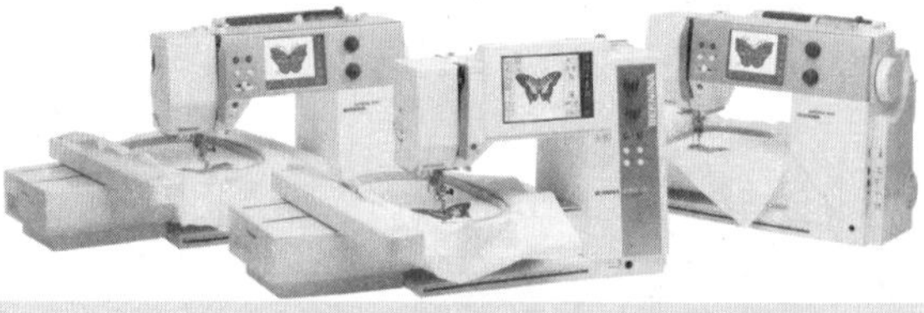

Bernina Artista Models 730, 640 & 630

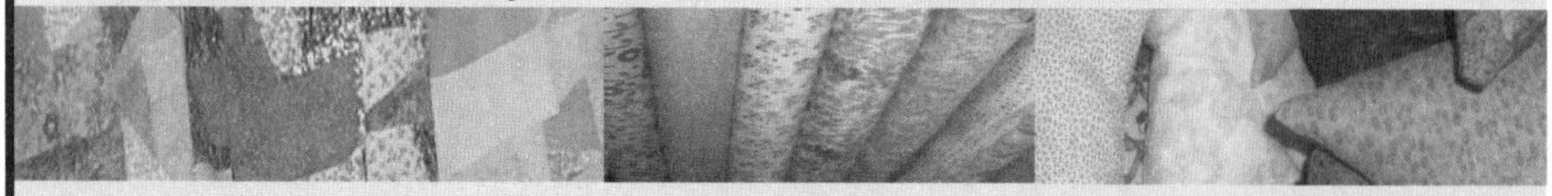

Quilted Bags from a Quilting Class Bolts of Fabric Donated Comfort Pillows

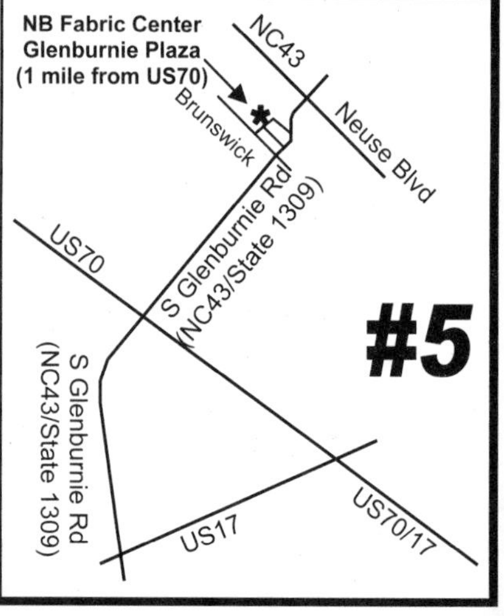

#5

Morehead City, NC #6

Tues - Fri 10 - 6
Sat 10 - 4

The Quilted

110 Little 9 Rd. 28557
(252) 222-0787
contact@albfabrics.com
www.quiltedbutterfly.com
Est: 1999 3000 sq. ft. Free Newsletter
Carteret County's Largest In-stock Decorator Fabric Store & Quilt Shop. Original Patterns & Designs, Oriental & Batik Fabrics & More!

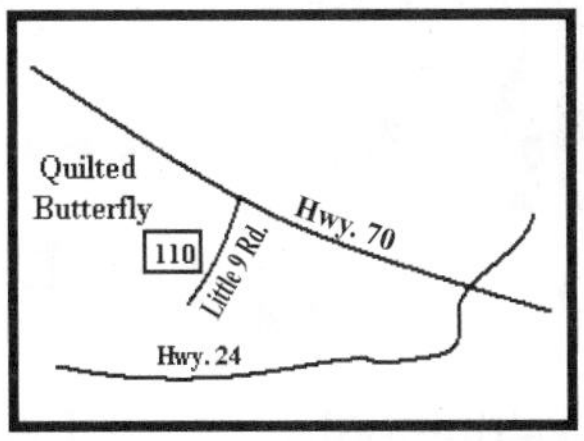

Morehead City, NC #7

Tues - Sat 10 - 4

Sew It Seams

905 Arendell St. 28557
(252) 247-2114
sewitseams@embarqmail.com
www.sewitseamsquiltshop.com

Personal Service and
Southern Hospitality.
Great Selection of 100% cotton fabrics, books, patterns, notions and classes.

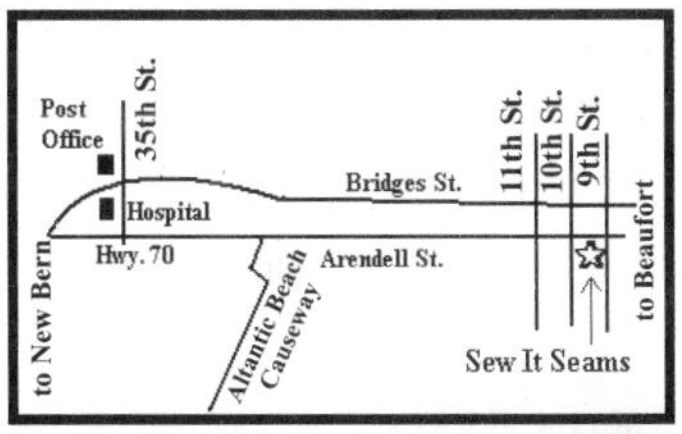

Elizabeth City, NC #8

Tues - Sat 10 - 5

Quilts & More

1092 Commissary Rd. 27909
(252) 338-9500
Est: 1999 1300 sq.ft. 1000 bolts

"Where you always feel at home."
Hugs and cookies for every customer
Wide variety of high quality fabrics.

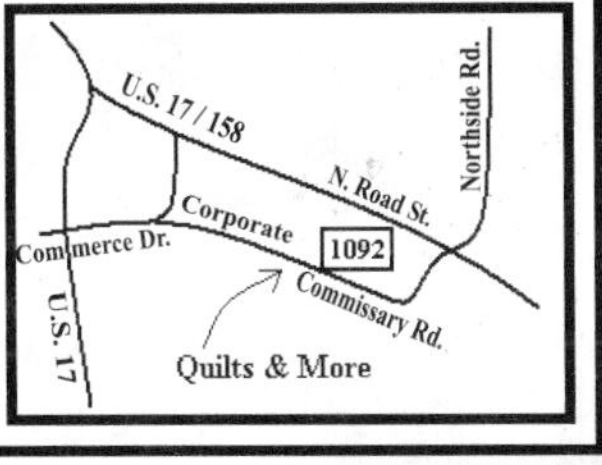

Wake Forest, NC #9

Tues - Fri 10 - 6:30
Sat 9 - 2:30

Quilts Like Crazy

Fabric, Notions & Janome Machines
1241 S. Main St. #8 27587
(919) 562-3425 Est: 2003
Owner: Betsy Jebe 3000 sq.ft.
betsy@quiltslikecrazy.com 1700 bolts
www.quiltslikecrazy.com
When you walk in the front door you will be inspired by the many quilts, embroidery projects displayed all over the shop.

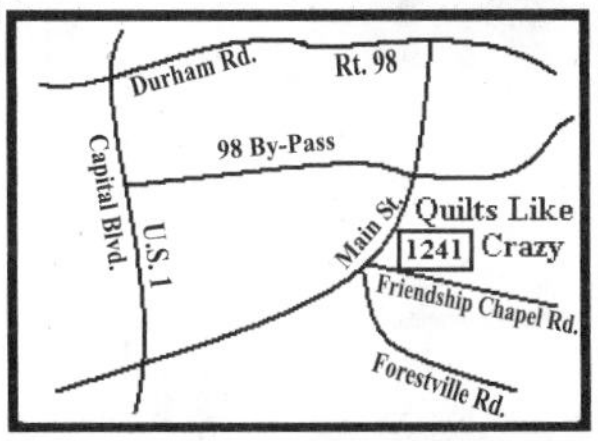

Lewisville, NC #10

Mon - Fri 10 - 5
Sat 10 - 3

Sewingly Yours

1329 Lewisville-Clemmons Rd.
(336) 766-8271
We specialize in quality quilt fabrics, notions, classes. Quilt threads, batting, quality fabrics, Great Prices. Expert repairs and tune ups are also available. Husqvarna-Viking and Babylock dealer. We offer friendly service and share our love of sewing & quilting.

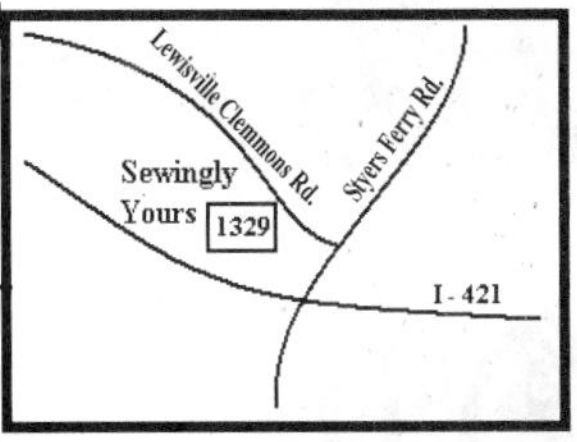

Winston-Salem, NC #11

Mon, Tues, Wed 10 - 6
Thur 10 - 7
Fri 10 - 5
Sat 10 - 4

Sew Original

3358 Robinhood Rd. 27106
(336) 760-1121
Owners: Shirley Bailey & Melinda Rose
seworiginal@bellsouth.net
www.seworiginal.org
Large selection of Fabrics - Latest Patterns
Books - Notions - Classes
We even offer a "Kids Can Sew" Camp and a Teen Camp. Bernina Dealer.

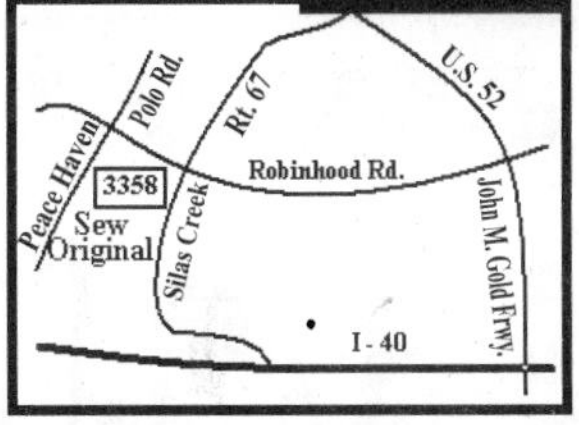

Greensboro, NC #12

Mon - Sat 10 - 6
Sun 1 - 5

Ye Olde Forest Quilters

3706 - 102 Elmsley Ct. 27406
(336) 339-5190
joanne@yeoldeforest.com
www.yeoldeforest.com
We sell quality quilting fabrics, Superior Threads, quilting books, gadgets, rulers and longarm supplies. We also offer quilt classes, personal quilting training, quilting and sewing space available for groups and sew much more!

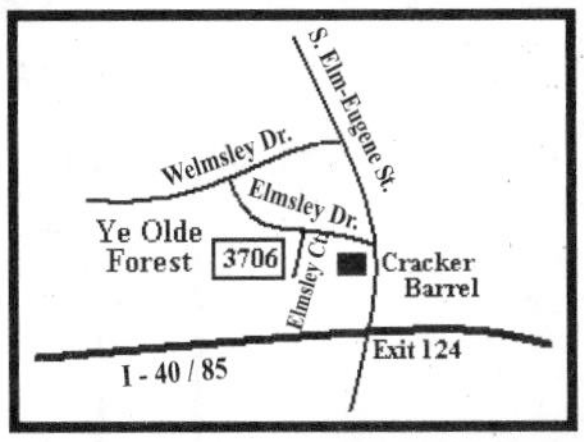

Greensboro, NC #13

Mon - Sat 10 - 5:30
Sun 1 - 5

Randy's Quilt Shop

2417-C Lawndale Dr. 27408
(336) 545-5558 Fax: (336) 545-5805
Owner: Randy Silvers
randysquiltshop@triad.rr.com
www.randysquiltshop.com
Over 8500 bolts of fabric, Thousands of Batiks, Notions, Books, & Patterns
Classes from Beginner to Advanced
Professional, Knowledgeable Staff
Authorized Bernina & Babylock.

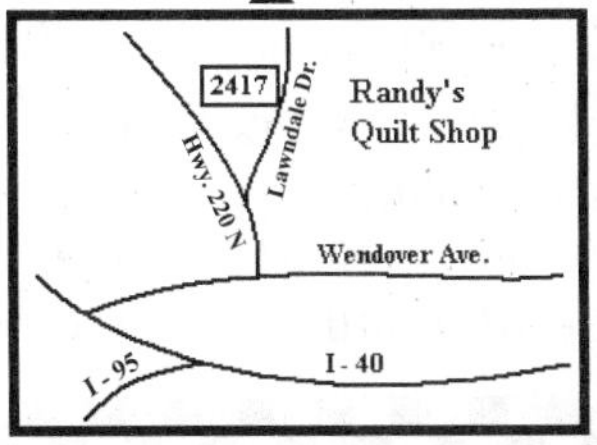

Quilting: one of life's...

THIMBLE PLEASURES

225 S. Elliott Rd. 27514
(919) 968-6050
www.thimblepleasures.com

Mon - Sat 10 - 6
Tues 10 - 9 Sun 1 - 5

thimblepleasures@bellsouth.net
Owner: Julie Holbrook
Quarterly Newsletter
Bernina Sales & On-Site Service

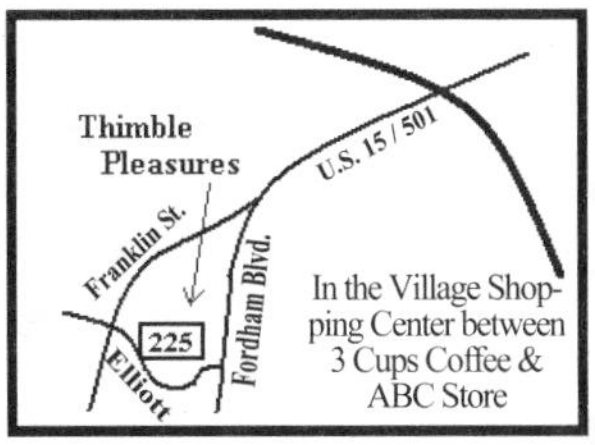

Over 5000 Bolts of 100% Cotton Designer Fabrics.
Specializing in Batiks, Asian and Novelties.
Books, Patterns, Notions. Wide variety of classes.

Chapel Hill, NC #14

Cary, NC #15

Mon - Fri 10 - 6
Sat 10 - 5

Etc. Crafts

226 E. Chatham St. 27511
(919) 467-7636
Owner: Jean Petersen

Large selection of 100% Cotton Quilting Fabrics. Books and Notions.

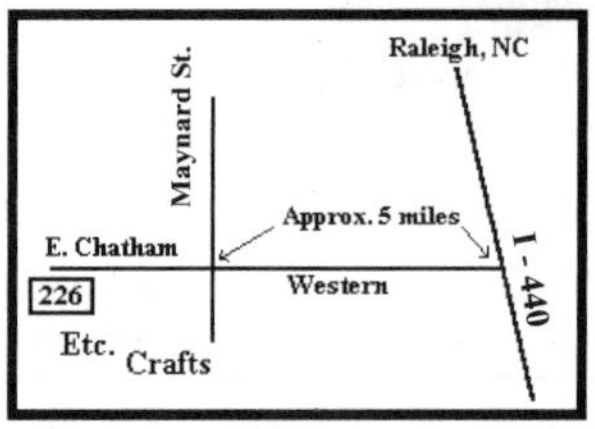

Raleigh, NC #16

Mon - Fri 10 - 2
Thur til 7
Sat 10 - 4

Wish Upon a Quilt!

8817 Westgate Park Dr. #104
(919) 782-6363 27617
www.wishuponaquilt.com

We offer you Wonderful Fabrics at lower than retail prices.

Patterns • Books • Notions • Threads
Batting • Classes

"Wish Upon A Quilt Where all Your Quilting Dreams Come True."

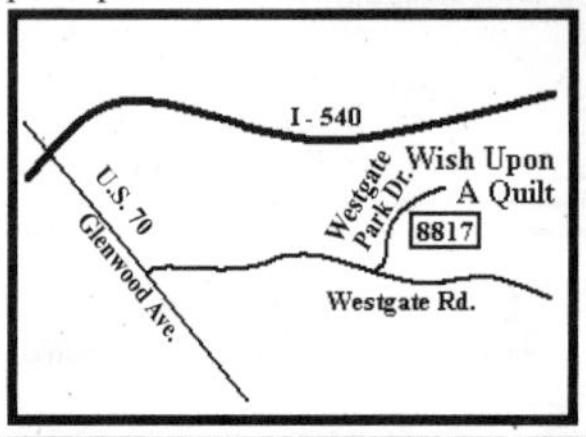

Raleigh, NC #17

Bernina World of Sewing

4000 bolts of 100% cotton fabric. Authorized Bernina Dealer. Wide variety of specialty patterns, threads, notions and sewing accessories.
Large selection of sewing cabinets and work tables.
"Come Visit Us and be a part of the excitement"

Mon - Sat 10 - 5
Thur til 6

6013 Glenwood Ave. 27612
(919) 782-2945
Visit Us on the internet:
www.bernina worldofsewing.com

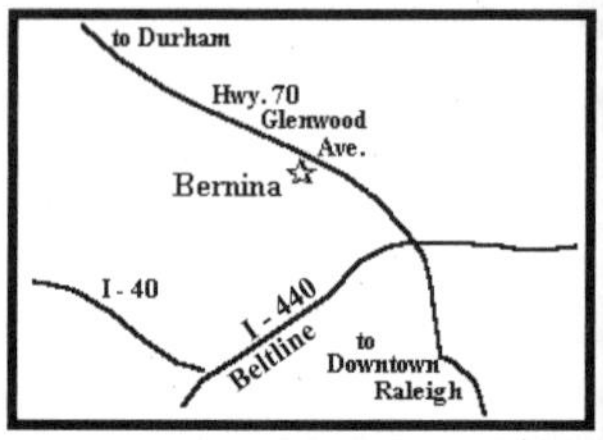

Located 1- 1/4 miles West of Crabtree Valley Mall on Hwy. 70 in Oak Park Shopping Center.

Selma, NC #18

WHISTLE STOP Quilt Shop

A destination for quilters & friends.

104 E. Anderson St. ✧ Selma, NC ✧ 27576
919/975-0404

Bolts & Bolts of Fabric

Mon - Sat 10:00 - 4:30 Closed Wed
1st Sunday of each Month 1 - 4

Better Homes and Gardens Quilt Sampler FEATURED SHOP

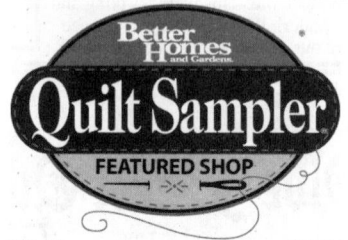

Connie Walker, Owner Est: 2001
www.whistlestopquiltshop.com

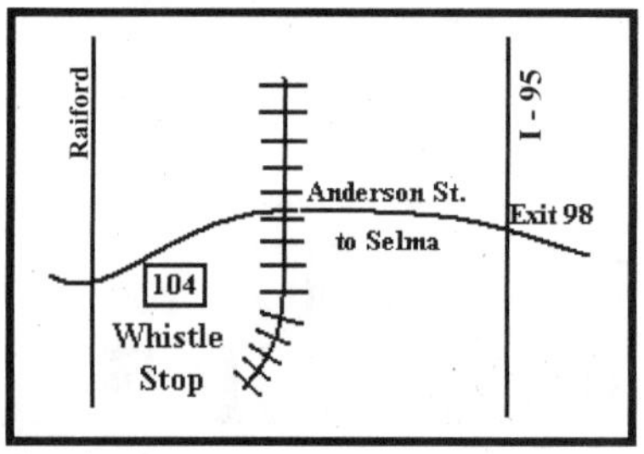

Conveniently located less than 1 mile off I - 95, exit 98.

Over 2400 bolts of 100% designer cottons, books, patterns, notions & more including batiks, homespuns, novelties, 30s & Civil War reproductions. Kits are our specialty!
Plan a trip to the Whistle Stop and discover Uptown Selma, home to over 20 shops and more than 100 antique dealers -- all within walking distance!

Apex, NC #19

Tues - Sat 10 - 6

Plain and Simple Quilt Shop

1510 N. Salem St. 27502
(919) 303-6176
Owner: Sharon Reilly
plainandsimplequ@nc.rr.com
www.plainandsimplequiltshop.net

We specialize in Folk Art & Homespuns
also Vintage - Romantic - Cottage Themes
"Doing Ordinary Things in an Extraordinary Way"

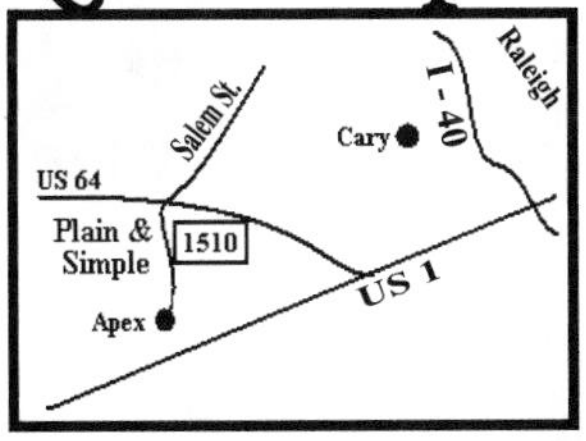

Goldsboro, NC #20

Tues - Fri 10 -5
Sat 10 - 3

Thistle Bee Quilt Shoppe

2707-E Royall Ave. 27534
(919) 778-2277 Est: 2005
Fax: (919) 778-7722

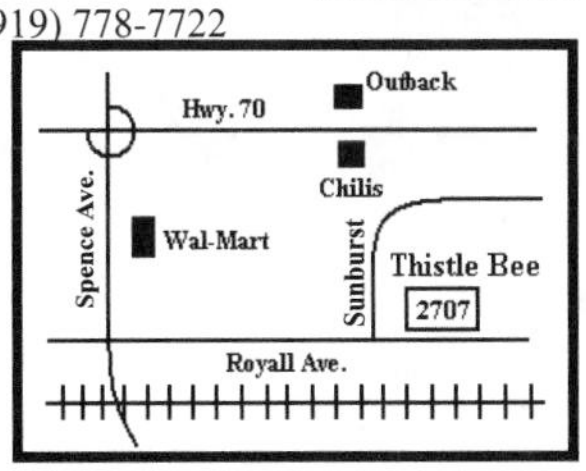

thistlebeebuzz@bellsouth.net
www.thistlebeequiltshoppe.com
1000+ Bolts Free Newsletter
A place for gathering, inspiration, quilt classes, quality 100% cotton, books, patterns, notions, batting, woolfelt and redwork.

Statler Stitcher

Loving Stitches

BERNINA

Sewing, Quilting & Fabric Center

www.lovingstitches.net

- ***Eastern NC's largest quilting store (10,000 sq ft)***
- ***Authorized Gammill & Statler Stitcher dealer for NC, SC, & VA***
- ***Hundreds of classes in sewing, quilting, clothing construction embroidery for all skill levels. Special events by world masters***
- ***Over 5000 bolts of 100% cotton fabrics***
- ***Large selection of books, notions & patterns***
- ***Certified service technician - all brands***
- ***Specially made quilt kits & BOMs***
- ***Expert quilting services***
- ***Quilt guild member discounts***

7076 Ramsey St / Hwy 401
Fayetteville, NC 28311
(910) 630-3912

Mon-Sat 10 am-6 pm

Fayetteville, NC #21

We're only 10 minutes from I-95. Take exit 58 & follow the signs for Hwy. 401N. Call for help with directions. Busses always welcomed!

Gammill® QUILTING SYSTEMS

Fayetteville, NC #22

Tues - Sat 10 - 4

Quilts 'n tiques

122 Anderson St. P.O. Box 83 28301
(910) 486-0074
Owner: Gail Dowling
Est: 2004 1700 sq.ft. 3500 Bolts
gaildow@msn.com
In Historical downtown Fayetteville.
Little shop packed with charm.
Fabrics, notions, patterns and gifts.

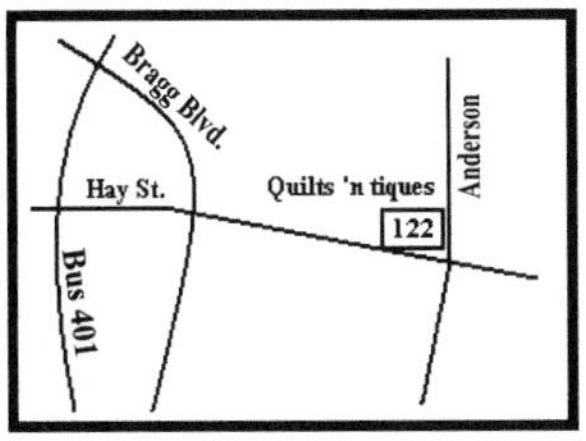

Sanford, NC #23

By Appt. Only

Imagination Quilt Shoppe

We are in the midst of a move, please call first for address & hours.
P.O. Box 2805 27331
(919) 721-0444 Est: 2006
sales@imaginationquiltshoppe.com
www.imaginationquiltshoppe.com

Visit us for quilting fabrics and supplies and we will help you to *"Use you imagination and let your quilts soar."*

PINEHURST, NC #24

Linderella's Quilt Works

- Bright, happy fabrics to inspire you!
- Home of Linderella's whimsical patterns!
- Moda, Kaffe Fassett, Amy Butler & more!
- Fast & friendly customer service always!
- Classes & workshops for all skills!

910-215-5981
Mon-Sat 10a-6p www.linderellas.com
Olmsted Village-Camellia Parke Shoppes
246-D Olmsted Boulevard ~ Pinehurst, NC

The Quilting Nook

Hours:
Mon-Sat 10 to 5
Closed Sunday

Historic Downtown Waxhaw, NC
103 W. South Main Street
704-243-0044

Your one stop for quality Quilting Fabrics, Books, Patterns, Notions, Gifts and More! We offer one of the largest selection of Batiks in the area.
All Major Credit Cards accepted.

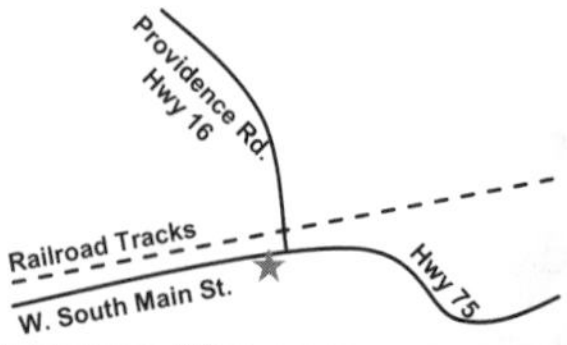

www.TheQuiltingNook.com

Waxhaw, NC #25

Indian Trail, NC #26

Mon - Sat 10 - 6
Sun 1 - 6

overall QUILTER

6580-A Old Monroe Rd. 28079
(704) 296-0206 Fax: 288-1629
Owner: Aimee Griffin Est: 2006
shop@overallquilter.com 1500 sq.ft
www.overallquilter.com Free Newsletter

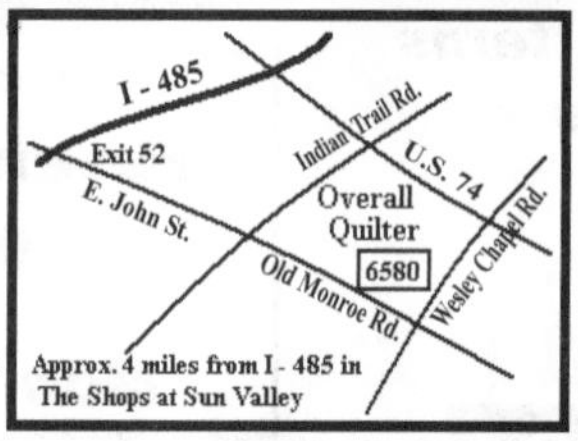

Our goal is to create an exciting and comfortable environment full of ideas and inspiration.

Matthews, NC #27

Mon - Thur 10 - 4:30
Fri & Sat 10 - 4

QUILT PATCH FABRICS

1017 Stallings Rd. 28104 (704) 821-7554
Owners: Charlotte Harkey, Bryan Gregory, Janice Cooper Est: 1996
www.quiltpatchfabrics.com
Full color range of 100% cotton fabrics (3000+ bolts), books & patterns, notions, hand & machine technique classes, machine quilting service available.

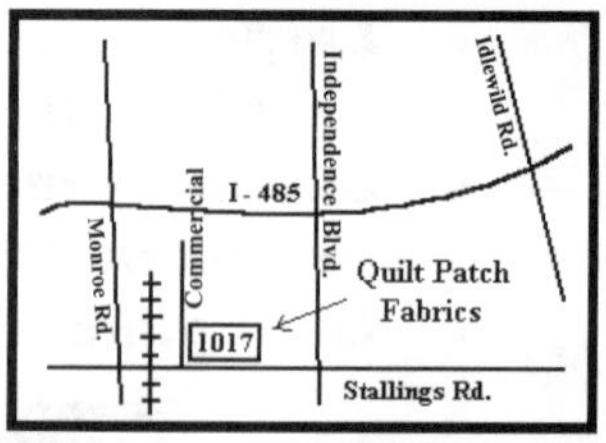

Charlotte, NC #28

Mon & Wed - Sat 10 - 5
Tues 1:30 - 8
Sun 1 - 5

QBee Quilts, LLC
"a place to gather"
10720 S. Tryon St., # F 28273
(704) 588-2225
Owner: Diane K. Plunkett Est: 2008
1500 sq.ft. 1200+ bolts Free Newsletter
diane@thequiltingbee.net
www.thequiltingbee.net
Full Service Shop - Fabulous Fabrics - Notions
Books - Patterns - Longarm Service - Classes
Charlotte's one & only quilt shop. - Great Staff.

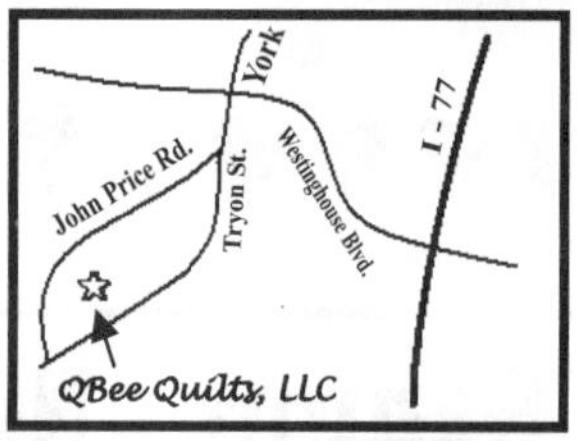

Mooresville, NC #29

Tues - Sat 10 - 5

Quilters Loft Company

PFAFF Sewing Machines

188 N. Main St. 28115
(704) 662-8660
Owner: Erica Ransom
http://quiltersloftcompany.blogspot.com
Fabrics, patterns, books, notions, classes, and embroidery supplies.
Corner of N Main & W Moore Sts.

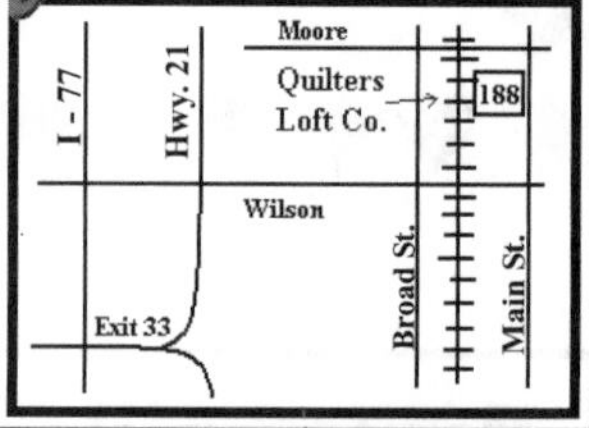

Mooresville, NC #30

Mon - Fri 10 - 5:30
Sat 9:30 - 3:30

Rene's Quilt Shop

195 W. Statesville Ave. 28115
(704) 799-2829
Owner: René Crowder
Est: 2001 1600 sq.ft. 1000 Bolts
www.renesquiltshop.com

Fabrics, Books, Patterns, Notions, Classes.
Helpful, friendly staff.
Hand and machine quilting services.

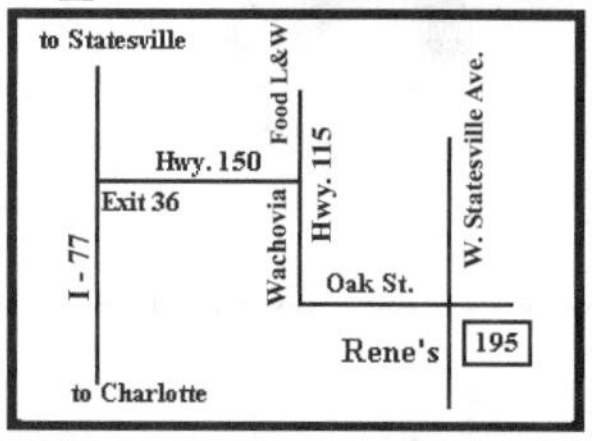

Forest City, NC #31

Mon, Wed, Thur, & Fri 9 - 5 Sat 9 - 2
Summer Hours
Mon - Fri 9 - 5
Sat 9 - 2

Schoolhouse Quilts

399 Sunset Memorial Rd. 28043
(828) 245-9774
Owner: Brenda Arrowood
Est: 1995 3500 sq.ft. 3000+ Bolts
shquilts@nctv.com
www.schoolhousequiltsnc.com
Special Books (1000 titles) & Unique Notions.
DVD's, tools, fabric, mats and more.

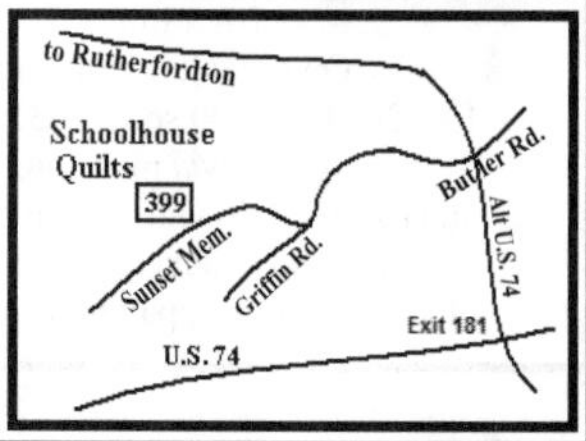

Rutherfordton, NC #32

Tues - Thur 10 - 6
Fri 10 - 5
Sat 10 - 3

Ann's Cozy Quilts & Fabrics

412 Charlotte Rd. 28139
(828) 286-9997
Est: 2007 2000 sq.ft.
2000+ Bolts
info@quiltfabricstore.com
www.quiltfabricstore.com
A truly friendly, helpful, beautiful, "comfy" shop to browse in rooms of fabrics, patterns, books and notions-so many sewing and quilting goodies! Classes. Authorized HandiQuilter Representative

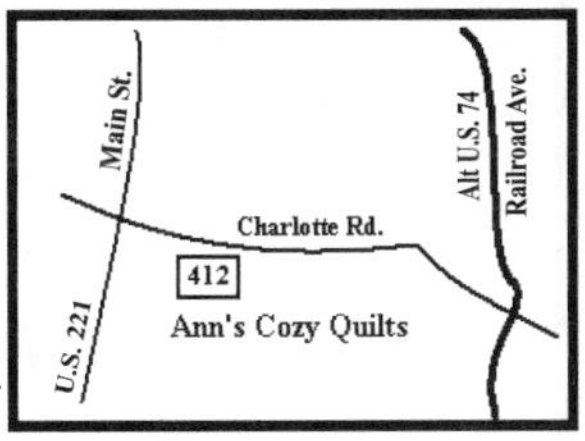

Taylorsville, NC #33

Tues - Fri 10 - 5
Sat 10 - 3

The Cottage Quilt Shop

100 S. Center St. 28681
(828) 632-1660 Fax: (828) 352-9382
Owner: Cynthia & Bill Shatzel
Est: 2008 2800 sq.ft. 1400 bolts
Cynthia@thecottagequiltshop.com
www.TheCottageQuiltShop.com
Good selection, reasonable prices, classes, Handi-Quilter dealer, Notions and Gifts. Online Newsletter. *Worth the Trip!*

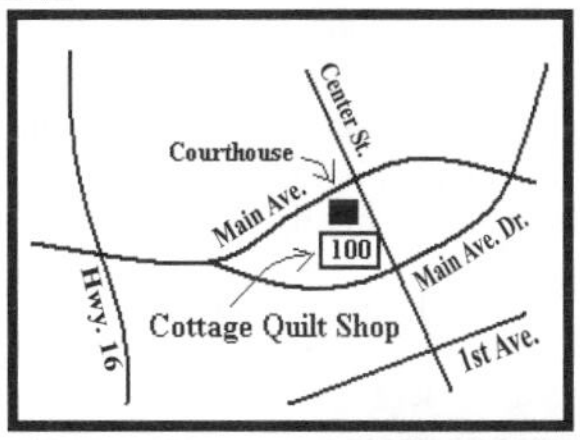

Hudson, NC #34

Nana's Quiltin' Place

115-B Hickman Ave., Hudson, NC 28638

828-728-4473
Est: 2009
Dixie Stoltz

Tues & Thur 10 - 7
Wed 9 - 4
Fri & Sat 9 - 3

dixiesquilting@charter.net
www.dixiesquilting.com

Lots of fabric to choose from for your quilts starting at $6 per yard. Plenty of patterns to choose from. Books, patterns, kits, gifts and classes. We have rocking chairs to bring in your hand-work and sit and visit. We'd love to meet you.

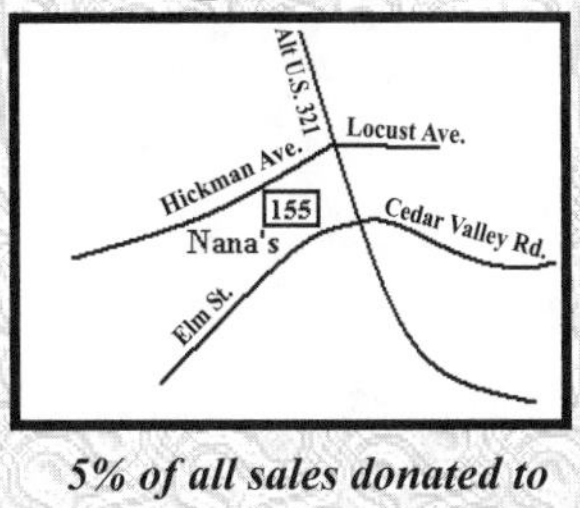

5% of all sales donated to the No-Kill Animal Shelter in Hickory, NC

Boone, NC #35

Mon - Fri 10 - 5
Sat 10 - 4

Sew Original

1586-C U.S. 421 South 28607
(828) 264-1049
Owners: Shirley Bailey & Melinda Rose
seworiginalnc@bellsouth.net
www.seworiginal.org
Large selection of Fabrics - Latest Patterns Books - Notions - Classes. We even offer a "Kids Can Sew" Camp a Teen Camp.
BERNINA Dealer.

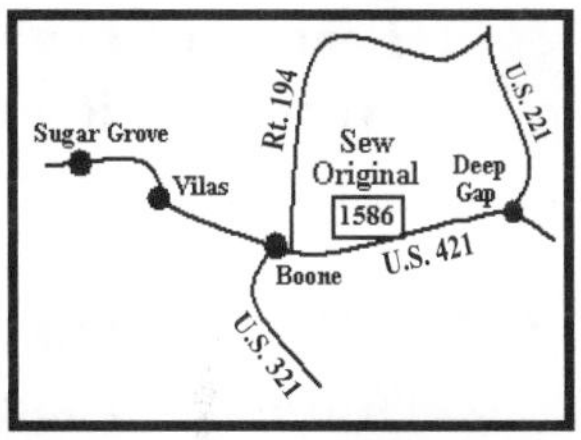

Boone, NC #36

Tues - Sat 10 - 5:30

The Quilt Shop inc.

199 New Market Center 28607
thequiltshop@bellsouth.net
(828) 263-8691
Fax: (828) 263-8718
Est: 2003 1400 sq.ft.
The friendliest quilt shop in the High Country. We carry a great selection of Kaffe Fassett and other designer fabrics.

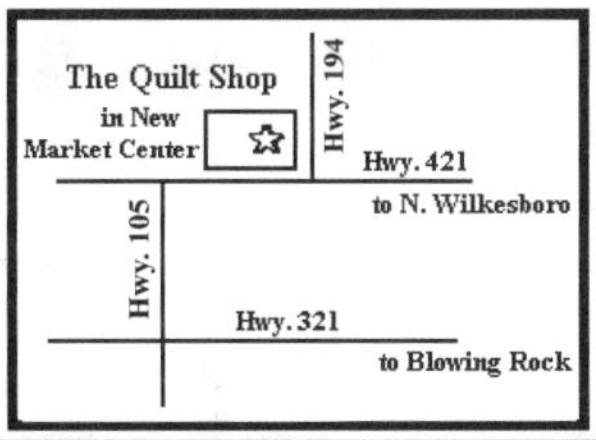

Burnsville, NC #37

Mon - Fri 9 - 5
Sat 9 - 2

The Country Peddler

3 Town Square 28714
(828) 682-7810
Owners: Barbara & Tommy Pittman
Est: 1980
tpittman5@verizon.net
Great selection of quilts, fabrics, & notions. Custom quilts made to order. Quilted and fabric gifts.

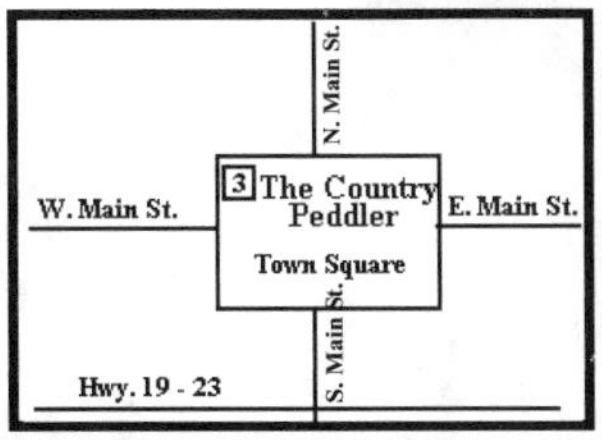

Burnsville, NC #38

Needle Me This

www.needle-me-this.com

- Fabric
- Books
- Patterns
- Notions
- Classes
- Janome Dealer
- HandiQuilter Dealer

Better Homes Quilt Sampler Featured Shop 2008

Mon - Sat 10 - 5
Thurs til 8

230 E. Main St. 28714
888-218-0881
828-682-9462
Est: 2006 2300 sq.ft.
1800 bolts email newsletter
needlemethis@earthlink.net

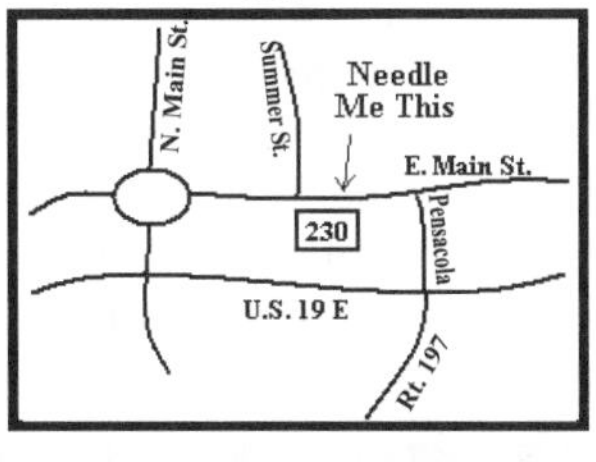

Black Mountain, NC #39

Mon - Fri 10 - 5
Sat 11 - 4

Marti's Patchwork Cottage

206 Sutton Ave. 28711
(828) 669-9005
Owner: Marti Cummins
Est: 1996 950 sq.ft. 1200 Bolts
www.martispatchworkcottage.com

Best little quilt shop anywhere dedicated to helping you make a wonderful, unique masterpiece.

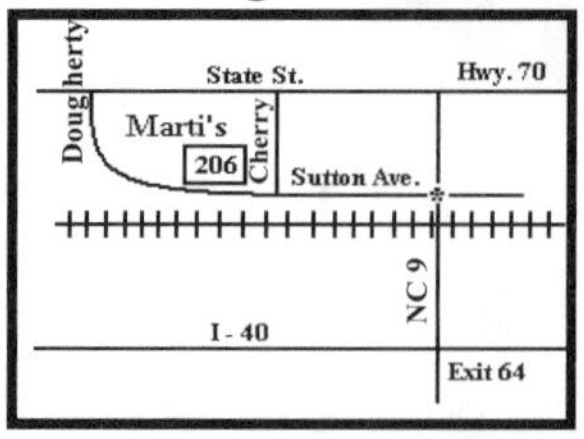

Asheville, NC #40

Mon - Sat 10 - 5:30

Asheville Cotton Co.

1378 Hendersonville Rd. 28803
828-277-4100 ~ ashevillecottonco.com

Come see our large selection of beautiful quilting fabric, patterns, notions & books. We love machine embroidery, too!

We're conveniently located in the Parkway Center, more commonly known as the Harris Teeter Shopping Center. Go 2.3 miles south of I-40, we're on the left. It's across the street from Carolina Day School You'll also see a Starbucks Coffee Shop in the center. We are located next to Eddie Spaghetti.

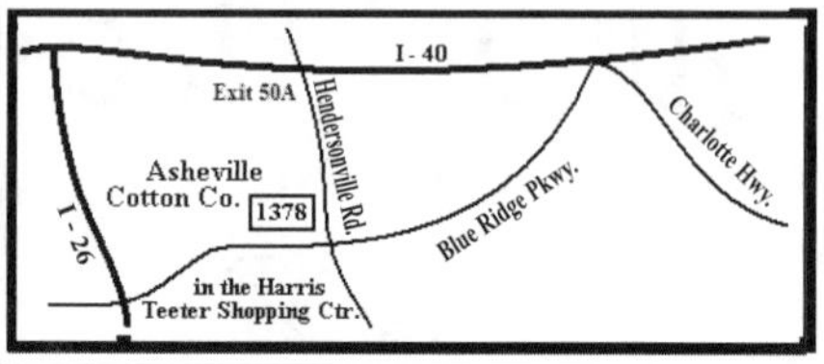

3800 sq. ft.
6000+ bolts of Quilting Cotton!

BERNINA
baby lock

Material Things Quilt Shop

2021 Asheville Hwy.
Hendersonville, NC 28791
(828) 698-5556

Featuring a variety of fabrics including Civil War, 30's Reproductions, Wool, Wool Felt, Punchneedle and Rug Hooking Supplies.
Books • Patterns • Notions • Classes
We are here to meet your quilting needs!
Authorized Janome Sewing Machine Dealer
www.materialthingsquiltshop.com

Hendersonville, NC #41

Mon - Sat 10 - 5

Fax: (828) 698-5513
mthings@bellsouth.net
Owner: Andi Edwards
Est: 2001 2000 sq.ft.

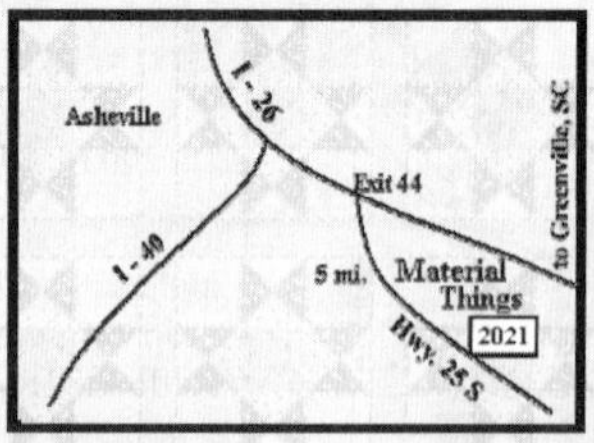

One Stop Quilt Shoppe

Authorized Dealer Bernina and Pfaff Sewing Machines & Sergers,

Sales • Service • Education • Classes Fabric • Books Notions • Gifts

BERNINA USA HORN of America Collection PFAFF USA

My Quilt Shoppe

25% OFF* ONE DAY SHOPPING SPREE
* some restrictions apply

Located in Historic Hendersonville, NC
828.692.8870
www.MyQuiltShoppe.com

We've Moved!
New Location!

1032 C Greenville Hwy.
Hendersonville
NC 28792

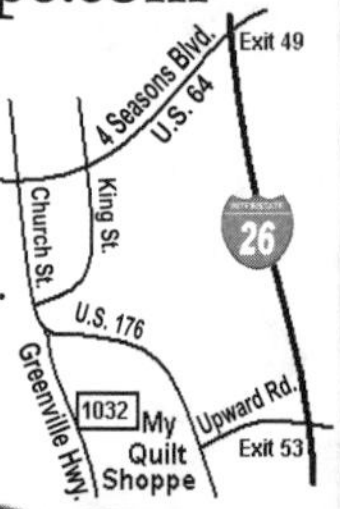

#42

QUILTERS QUARTERS

... A QUILT SHOP

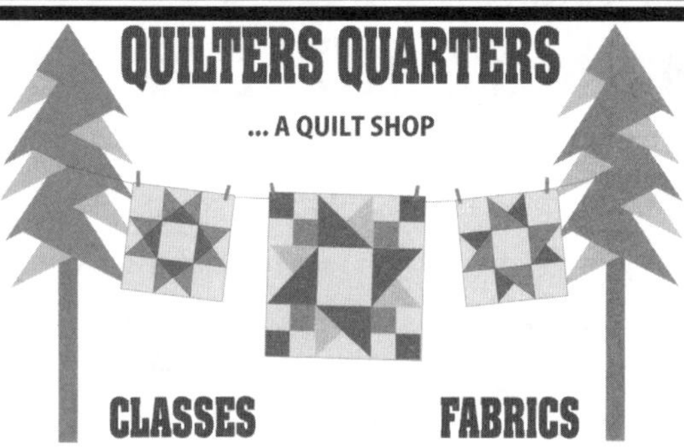

Mon - Sat 10 - 5:30

Est: 2008
2000 sq.ft.
3000+ Bolts
e-newsletter

2020 Dellwood Rd. 28786
(828) 926-0803 quiltersquarters@bellsouth.net
Visit us online at www.quiltersquartersnc.com

Waynesville, NC #43

Rustic free-standing quilt shop nestled in the Smoky Mountains.
Great atmosphere - friendly service - big selection of kits - supplies - classes.

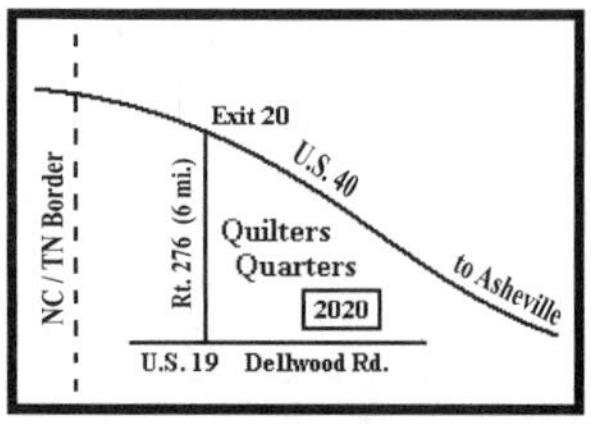

A Stitch in Time

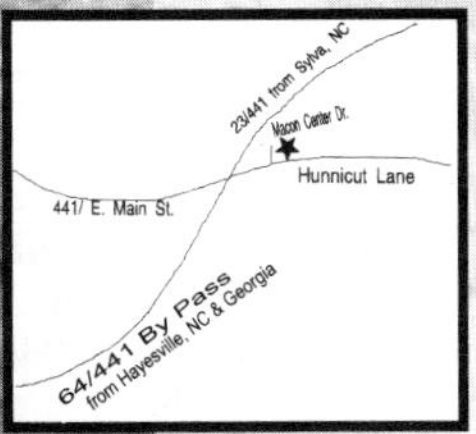

Fine Quilting, Heirloom & Smocking Supplies
23 Macon Center Dr. 28734
828.524.3300
Maxine Ramey

Mon - Fri 10 - 5 Sat 10 - 1

Franklin, NC #44

Please visit our bright & cheerful shop and enjoy:

- Friendly, personalized service from our knowledgeable staff
- 2000+ bolts of fine quilting fabrics & supplies
- Heirloom sewing supplies
- Specializing in beautiful quilt kits
- Wool felt
- Latest & greatest notions, books & patterns
- Loads of samples to inspire!
- Classes & e-newsletter

Visit us online at www.astitchintimenc.com

Husqvarna VIKING

Maggie Valley, NC #45

Summit Sew and Quilt Retreat Center

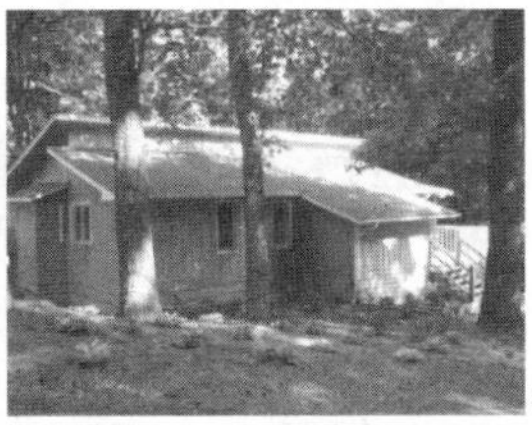

(704) 682-9567
www.summitquiltretreat.com

Hosts: Kim & Becca Polson Sleeps 6.
The ultimate girl friends getaway! Quilt and sew to your little hearts content. Relax and work on your next family heirloom. If any husbands tag along, there are plenty of trout streams in the area.

Murphy, NC #46

Mon - Sat 10 - 5

Bless My Stitches Quilt Shop

104 Tennessee St. 28906
(828) 835-4900
www.blessmystitches.com
1000+ bolts of fabrics, notions, books, patterns, hand & machine embroidery supplies, Authorized Janome Dealer, Accuquilt Machines, lots of classes.
Online Newsletter.

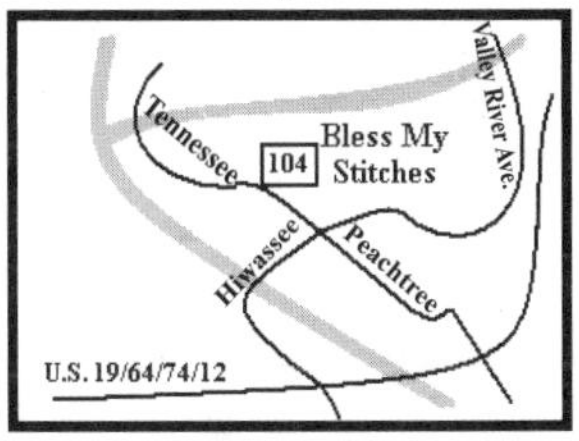

North Carolina Quilt Shops

Andrews In Nonnie's Attic, 84 Chestnut St. 828-321-2800
Apex Plain and Simple Quilt Shop, 1510 N. Salem St.
919-303-6176 See ad #19, page 395
Asheboro Quilting Coop, 312 Sunset Ave Ste C 336-625-1468
Asheville Asheville Cotton Co., 1378 Hendersonville Rd.
828-277-4100 See ad #40, page 398
Ayden Quilt Shop, 4159 Emma Cannon Road 252-746-7900
Black Mountain Marti's Patchwork Cottage, 206 Sutton Ave.
828-669-9005 See ad #39, page 398
Boone The Quilt Shop, Inc., 199 New Market Center
828-263-8691 See ad #36, page 397
Boone Sew Original, 1586-C 421 South
828-264-1049 See ad #35, page 397
Burnsville The Country Peddler Quilt Shop, 3 Town Square
828-682-7810 See ad #37, page 397
Burnsville Needle Me This, 230 E Main St.
828-682-9462 See ad #38, page 397
Cary Etc. Crafts, 226 E. Chatham St.
919-467-7636 See ad #15, page 394
Chapel Hill Thimble Pleasures, 225 S. Elliott Rd.
919-968-6050 See ad #14, page 393
Charlotte QBee Quilts, 10720 S. Tryon St. #F
704-588-2225 See ad #28, page 396
Charlotte Lee's Sewing Center, 7888-D Rea Rd. 704-542-8760
Columbus Elaine's Attic, 280 Landrum Rd. 828-863-4036
Concord Sew Much Fun!, 8653 Concord Mills Blvd. 704-867-7397
Denver Quilters Haven, 4732 N. Hwy. 16 704-483-5999
Elizabeth City Quilts & More, 1092 Commissary Rd.
252-338-9500 See ad #8, page 393
Fayetteville Loving Stitches, 7076 Ramsey St.
910-630-3912 See ad #21, page 395 & 412
Fayetteville Quilts 'n Tiques, 122 Anderson St.
910-486-0074 See ad #22, page 395
Fayetteville Crafts, Frames & Things, Inc., 108 Owen Dr. 910-485-4833
Fletcher Foam & Fabrics Outlet, 3049 Hendersonville Rd. 828-684-0801
Forest City Schoolhouse Quilts, 399 Sunset Memorial Rd.
828-245-9774 See ad #31, page 396
Franklin A Stitch in Time, 23 Macon Center Dr.
828-524-3300 See ad #44, this page
Franklin Sew Creative, 91 Highlands Rd. 828-524-5221
Gastonia Mary Jo's Cloth Store, Inc., 401 Cox Rd. 704-861-9100
Goldsboro Thistle Bee Quilt Shoppe, 2707-E Royall Ave.
919-778-2277 See ad #20, page 395
Granite Falls The Cotton Quilt, 4900 Troy Rd. 828-728-4386
Greensboro Ye Olde Forest Quilters, 5315 Liberty Rd. #E
336-339-5190 See ad #12, page 393
Greensboro Randy's Quilt Shop, 2417-C Lawndale Dr.
336-545-5558 See ad #13, page 393
Greensboro McKinney Sewing, 1710 Battleground Ave. 336-274-6793
Hendersonville My Quilt Shoppe, 1032C Greenville Hwy.
828-692-8870 See ad #42, page 398
Hendersonville Material Things Quilt Shop, 2021 Asheville Hwy.
828-698-5556 See ad #41, page 398
Hickory Lee Sewing Center, 2361 US Hwy. 70 SE 828-327-6888
Hudson Nana's Quiltin' Place, 155-B Hickman Ave.
828-728-4473 See ad #34, page 397
Indian Trail Overall Quilter, 6580-A Old Monroe Rd.
704-296-0206 See ad #26, page 396
Jacksonville All About Quilting, 3736 Henderson Rd.
910-577-9200 See ad #4, page 392
Jacksonville The Country Collection, 2864 Wilmington Hwy.
910-347-1960 See ad #2, page 392
Jacksonville The Cotton Patch Quilt Shoppe, 112 Phillips Rd.
910-938-1395 See ad #3, page 392
Lewisville Sewingly Yours, 1329 Lewisville Clemmons Rd
336-766-8271 See ad #10, page 393
Maggie Valley Summit Sew & Quilt Retreat, 388 Summit
704-682-9567 See ad #45, this page
Matthews Quilt Patch Fabrics, 1017 Stallings Rd.
704-821-7554 See ad #27, page 396
Mooresville Rene's Quilt Shop, 195 W. Statesville Ave.
704-799-2829 See ad #30, page 396
Mooresville Quilters Loft Co., 188 N. Main St.
704-662-8660 See ad #29, page 396
Morehead City The Quilted Butterfly, 110 Little 9 Rd.
252-222-0787 See ad #6, page 393
Morehead City Sew It Seams, 905 Arendell St.
252-247-2114 See ad #7, page 393
Morganton Morganton Sewing Center, 128 N. Sterling St. 828-439-8050
Murphy Bless My Stitches Quilt Shop, 104 Tennessee St
828-835-4900 See ad #46, this page
New Bern New Bern Fabric Center, 1218 S. Glenburnie Rd.
252-633-4780 See ad #5, page 392 & 410
New Bern Sewing Solutions, 1505 S. Glenburnie Rd. #G 252-633-1799

Pinehurst	**Linderella's Quilt Works, 246-D Olmsted Blvd.**	**910-215-5981**	**See ad #24, page 396**
Raleigh	**Bernina World of Sewing, 6013 Glenwood Ave.**	**919-782-2945**	**See ad #17, page 394**
Raleigh	**Wish Upon A Quilt, 8817 Westgate Park Dr. #104**	**919-782-6363**	**See ad #16, page 394**
Raleigh	Sew Unique Fabrics, 8800 Harvest Oaks Dr.	919-845-8802	
Raleigh	Carolina Sew N Vac Center, 1249 Buck Jones	919-469-4730	
Rockwell	Andersons Sew & So, 10104 Old Beatty Ford	704-279-3647	
Rutherfordton	**Ann's Cozy Quilts & Fabrics, 412 Charlotte Rd.**	**828-286-9997**	**See ad #32, page 397**
Sanford	**Imagination Quilt Shoppe, 711 Carthage St.**	**919-721-0444**	**See ad #23, page 395**
Selma	**Whistle Stop Quilt Shop, 104 E. Anderson St.**	**919-975-0404**	**See ad #18, page 394**
Shelby	Lee's Sewing Center, 114 W. Graham St.	704-487-5224	
Southport	Angelwing Needleworks, 507 N. Howe St.	910-454-9163	
Statesville	Needle and Thread, 236 W Broad St	704-838-1100	
Taylorsville	**The Cottage Quilt Shop, 100 S Center St**	**828-632-1660**	**See ad #33, page 397**
Wake Forest	**Quilts Like Crazy, 1241 S Main St. Ste 8**	**919-562-3425**	**See ad #9, page 393**
Waxhaw	**The Quilting Nook, 103 W. South Main St.**	**704-243-0044**	**See ad #25, page 396**
Waynesville	**Quilters Quarters, 2020 Dellwood Rd.**	**828-926-0803**	**See ad #43, page 398**
Wilmington	**Fran's Sewing Circle, 5751 Oleander Dr. Unit 5**	**910-397-9399**	**See ad #1, page 392**
Wilson	Four Sisters Quilt Works, 3710 C Peppermill Dr.	252-399-0030	
Winston-Salem	**Sew Original, 3358 Robinhood Rd.**	**336-760-1121**	**See ad #11, page 393**
Woodleaf	Little Country Quilt Shop, 840 Parks Rd.	704-278-1773	

North Carolina Quilt Shows

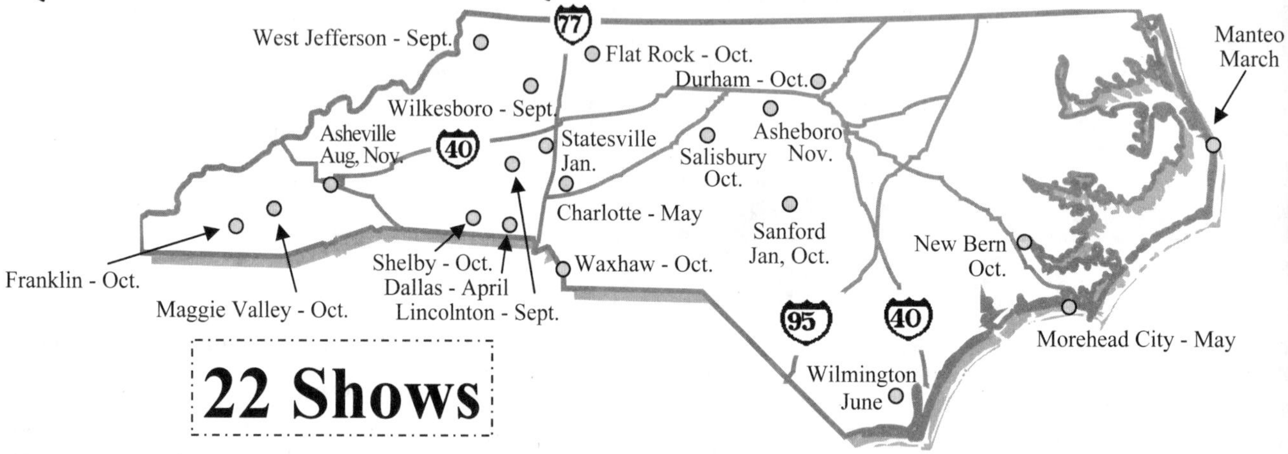

About Shows: We are listing only the very basic information about shows that happen on a regular schedule here. Please check out our website for more details on each show. Also this information tends to change quite often so please verify the event with our website or a local source before you venture far. Or if you're in the right area at the right time, give it a shot.
If you are a show organizer, please keep us updated on your event.
shows@quilterstravelcompanion.com www.quilterstravelcompanion.com

Month	City	Schedule	Show	Location with address
January				
	Sanford	Annual, 2nd Fri & Sat in January	The Quilting and Fiber Art Marketplace	Dennis Wicker Civic Center, 1801 Nash St.
	Statesville	Annual, 2nd Fri & Sat in January	The Quilting and Needle Art Extravaganza	Statesville Civic Center, 300 S. Center St.
March				
	Manteo	Annual, Most of March	Priceless Pieces Past & Present	The Art Gallery -- Roanoke Island Festival Park
April				
	Dallas	Odd Years, 4th Saturday in April	Community Quilt Show	Gaston County Citizens Resource Center, 1303 Dallas-Cherryville Hwy.
May				
	Morehead City	Annual, Fri & Sat following Mother's Day	Coastal Stars Quilt Show	Crystal Coast Civic Center, 3505 Arendell St.
June				
	Charlotte	Annual, Late May or Early June	North Carolina Quilt Symposium	Johnson & Wales University, 801 W. Trade St.
	Wilmington	Annual, last weekend in June	Quilters By The Sea Quilt Show	Temple Baptist Church, 709 George Anderson Dr.
August				
	Asheville	Annual, 1st weekend of August	Asheville Quilt Show	North Carolina Arboretum, 100 Frederick Law Olmsted Way
September				
	Wilkesboro	Annual, first full weekend of September	Wilkes County Quilters Show	Holiday Inn Express, 1700 Winkler St.
	West Jefferson	Annual, 3rd Weekend in September	Ashe Piecemakers Quilt Guild Show	Jefferson Station, 230 Hice Ave.
	Lincolnton	Odd Years, FallPiecemakers	Quilt Guild Show	First Baptist Church, 201 Robin Rd.
October				
	Maggie Valley	Annual, 1st full weekend in October	High Country Quilters' Guild Show	Town Hall & Community Center, 3987 Soco Rd.
	Shelby	Odd Years, 2nd week in October	Foothills Quilters Guild Show	Cleveland County Arts Council, 111 S. Washington St.
	Waxhaw	Annual, 2nd Sat. of October	Barnful of Quilts	Fox Farms, 7505 Sims Rd.
	Durham	Even Years, 3rd weekend in October	Durham Orange Quilters Show American	Tobacco Campus, 324 Blackwell St., Bay 7
	Flat Rock	Even Years, 3rd weekend in October	Western North Carolina Quilt Guild Show	Blue Ridge Community College, E. Campus Dr.
	Salisbury	Odd Years, 3rd weekend in October	Salisbury-Rowan Quilters' Guild	Salisbury Civic Center, 315 S. Boundary St.
	Sanford	Odd Years, 3rd weekend of October	Hearts & Hands ECA Quilt Guild Show	McCain Agricultural Center, 2420 Tramway Rd.
	Franklin	Annual, 4th Fri & Sat in October	Pumpkin Fest	Downtown Franklin
	New Bern	Even Years, Late October	Twin Rivers Quilters Guild Show	New Bern Riverfront Convention Center, 203 S. Front
November				
	Asheboro	Odd Years, 2nd Fri & Sat in November	Randolph Quilters Guild Show	Central Carolina Comm. Church, 1128 N. Fayetteville
	Asheville	Annual, 2nd Saturday in November	Asheville One Stop Shop Hop	Western NC Ag Centers, Expo Bldg, Exit 40 off I - 26

Among Friends Quilt Shop

Louisville, KY

9537 Taylorsville Rd.
40299

Est: 2003
6000 sq.ft.

Handi Quilter®

The Undisputed Leader in Home Machine Quilting Systems.

502-261-7377

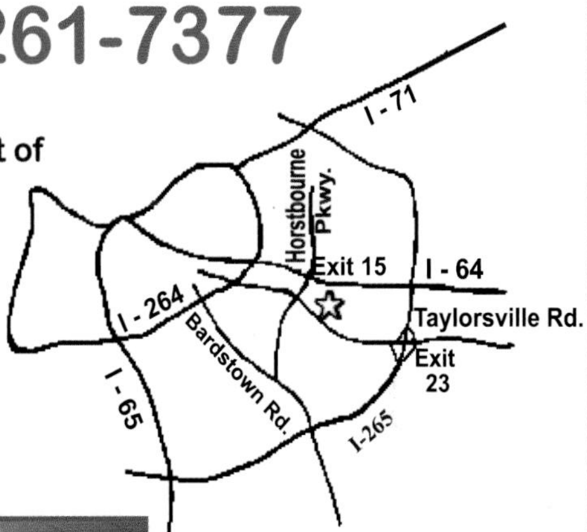

Among Friends Quilt Shop is a must see shop with 6,000 square feet of space and over 6,000 bolts of 100% cotton fabrics, as well as a complete line of quilting notions and thousands of books, patterns and gift items from which to choose. Our shop is not only spacious, it is well-lit to enhance your shopping experience and fabric selection. The full-spectrum lighting offers excellent color-rendering. We offer over 100 classes a year.

Among Friends Quilt Shop is a family-friendly quilt shop with something for everyone. Enjoy a cup of complimentary coffee, while watching TV or reading the newspaper in the café area. There are children's books and toys to entertain the little ones while mom shops.

Mon-Fri 9:30-6:00
Thurs 9:30-8:00
Sat 9:30-3:00

While here, ask for a demonstration of the Handi Quilter quilting machines and see for yourself that quality and affordability is available to you. Handi Quilter quilting machines are user-friendly and stitch like a dream!

We look forward to seeing you on your travels. The rest of the time, you can shop at Among Friends Quilt Shop on-line 24 hours a day. We are continually adding new products weekly.

Come visit us and discover that while here you are among friends.

www.amongfriendsquiltshop.com

Cozad, NE

Prairie Point Junction

124 East 8th * Box 184 * Cozad, Nebraska 69130
308-784-2010 prairiepointjunction@yahoo.com

Proud to be a Top 10 Shop in Fall 2005 Quilt Sampler

- 2500 bolts of cotton fabrics, lots of flannels
- Tons of inspiring displays, kits, original patterns
- Home of Wool Felt Central * 78+ colors of wool felt

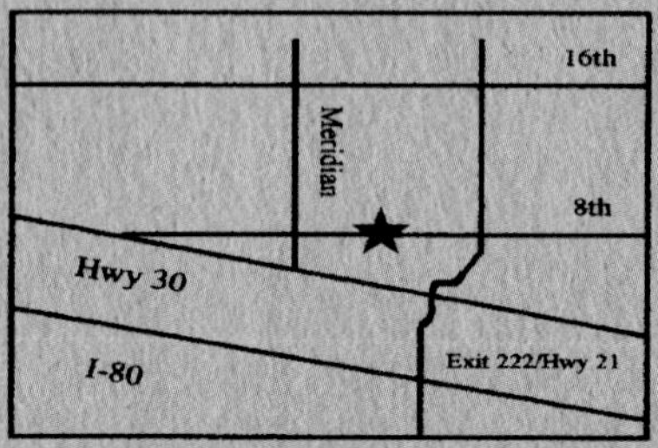

Hours:
Mon-Fri 10-5
Sat 10-4

**Just Minutes off Interstate-80*

www.prairiepointjunction.com OR www.woolfeltcentral.com

There's only one . . .

YODER DEPARTMENT STORE

- Quilting
- Fashion
- Bridal

Every Major Manufacturer and More Represented.

12,000+ Bolts of Fabric In Stock

Silk • Velvet • Wool • Linen • Denim

Quilting Supplies & Kits
Notions Patterns Books

260-768-4887

Yoder's Shopping Center
300 S. Van Buren St. (SR 5)
Shipshewana, IN

M-Sat 8a-5:30p

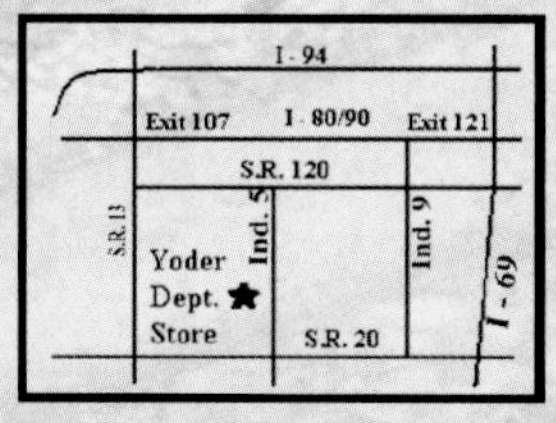

Shipshewana, IN

www.YoderDepartmentStore.com

Cannon Beach, OR

CENTER DIAMOND

1065 S. Hemlock
Cannon Beach, OR 97110
(503) 436-0833
Fax: (503) 436-2540
www.centerdiamond.com
Owner: Julie Walker
Est: 1994 1500 sq.ft.
centerdiamond@aol.com

Over 2000 bolts of the most gorgeous 100% cotton fabrics. Books, patterns, notions & gifts.

7 Days a Week 10 - 5

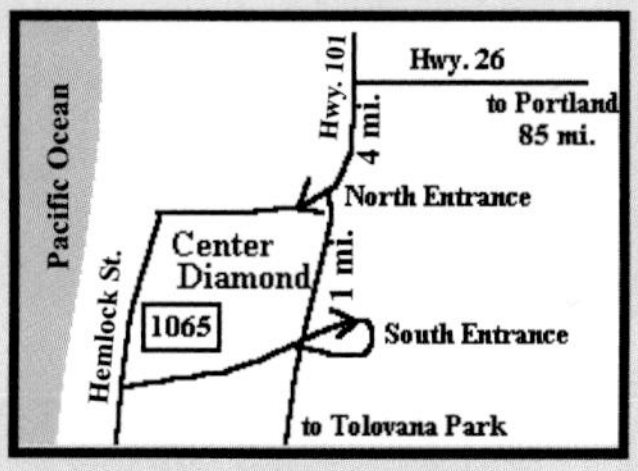

Located 1 block from the beach.

The Prettiest Quilt Shop in Western Maryland!

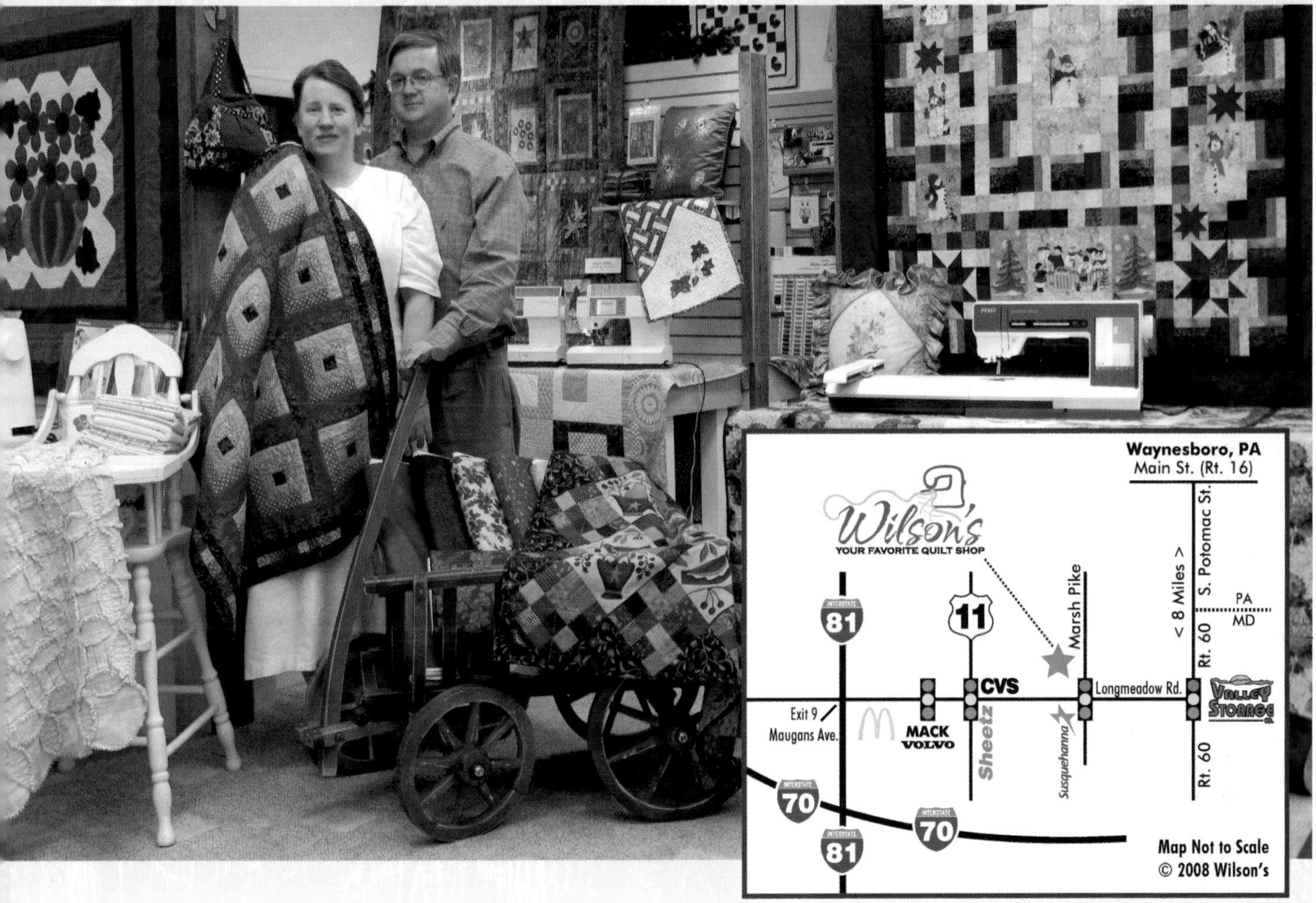

Wilson's Your Favorite Quilt Shop, offers:

- Over 3,000 bolts of "only the prettiest" fine, quality fabrics by suppliers including Moda, Hoffman and many more.
- Check out our Book Nook containing a large selection of books and patterns.
- Get great inspiration from our finished samples and grab a kit to take home!

Pfaff & Viking Sewing Machine Dealer
Country Setting • Buses Welcome
Close to the Interstate • Easy-Off / Easy-On

Visit our website at: ILuv2Quilt.com

Wilson's
YOUR FAVORITE QUILT SHOP
13516 Marsh Pike
Hagerstown, Maryland 21742
301.790.3526

Store Hours
Mon., Tues., Thurs., & Fri. 9 a.m. - 5 p.m.
Sat. 9 a.m. - 2 p.m. • Wed. CLOSED

Don't go home without being able to say you were at Wilson's in Hagerstown!

Tennessee Quilts

Jonesborough, TN

Over 8,000 Quality Quilting Fabrics Online and in the Shop. Featuring a large selection of Kaffe Fassett fabrics.

Frequent Workshops by National Instructors

114 Boone St. in Historic Jonesborough
Tennessee 37659

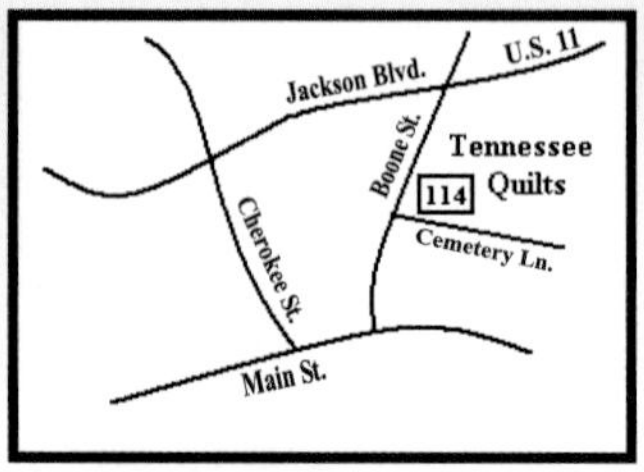

Across from the Visitors Center

423/753-6644

fax: 423/610-0681
linda@tennesseequilts.com

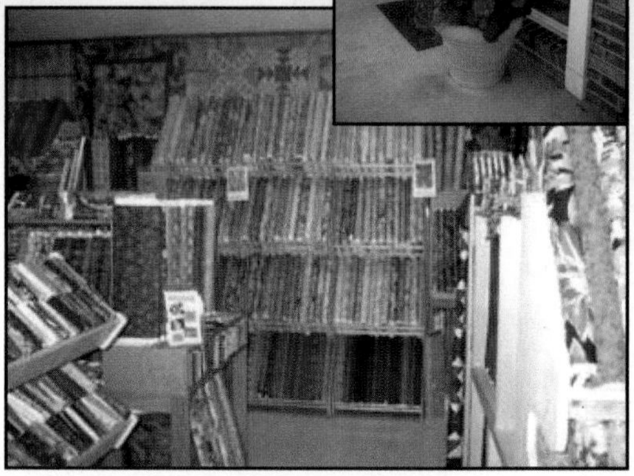

www.tennesseequilts.com
Monday - Saturday 9:30 - 5:30

QUILTING FABRIC

Name Brand Coordinating 100% Cotton Fabric at Outlet Prices!

FREE! FREE! FREE!
1 Fat Quarter of Your Choice

Pinnacle Fabrics
RJR
Jacob's Ladder
Michael Miller
moda Fabrics
South Seas Imports
Concord House

ADDITIONAL FABRIC
25% DISCOUNT
WITH THIS AD

Mon - Sat
10 - 6:30

Rose & Hubble
Chanteclaire
Red Rooster
Maywood Studios

Thomas Sewing Center, Inc.

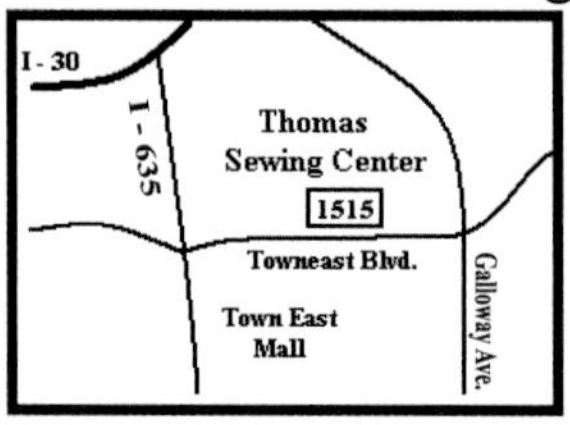

1515 N. Towneast Blvd. #133
Mesquite, TX
75150
972-681-3996
Est: 1987 3069 sq.ft.
4000+ Bolts

www.thomassewing.com for online fabric

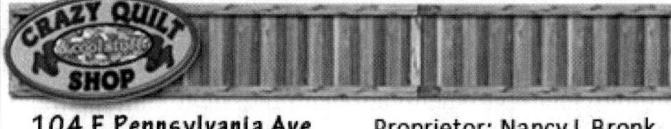

Crazy Quilt Shop

104 E Pennsylvania Ave
Roslyn, WA 98941-237
509-649-3777

Proprietor: Nancy L Bronk
crazyquiltshop@hotmail.com

Explore Historic Roslyn and The Crazy Quilt Shop

Tues - Sat
11 - 5

The Crazy Quilt Shop embodies the Roslyn experience, where the famous televison show Northern Exposure was filmed. Not only do we provide a relaxed and friendly shopping experience, we specialize in retreats. Retreat guests have 24hour access to the Shop workspace and the adjacent Hummingbird Inn.

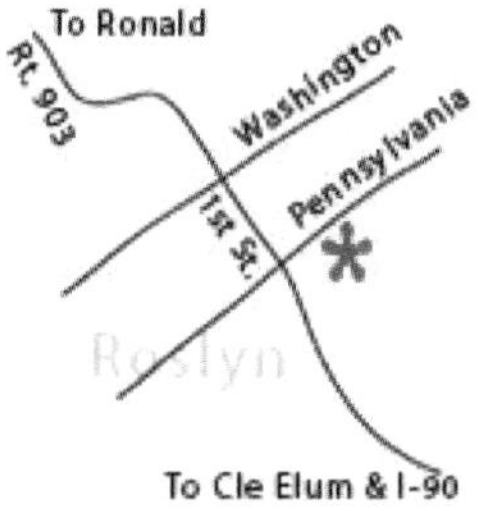

Visit our website:
www.thecrazyquiltshop.com

Attend our Annual "Crazy for Quilts Show"

The weekend before Labor Day weekend.

And Always a Friendly Northwest Welcome

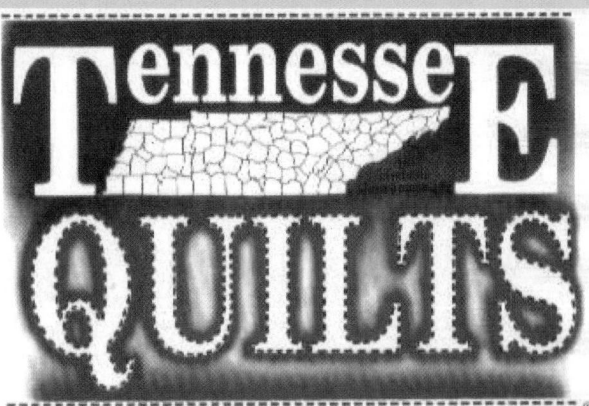

West Linn, OR

Tues - Fri 10 - 6
Sat 10 - 5

* Over 8000 Fabrics to choose from
* Large selection of Hand-Dyed wools
* Large selection of books, patterns, threads and notions
* Home décor-gifts for every room of your house, inside & out!
* Complete website including our entire fabric collection, classes and events!
* Check out the "Shoppe's" blog, "Boughs of Holly!"

1914 Willamette Falls Dr
West Linn, OR 97068

www.hollyhillquiltshoppe.com
hollyhillquiltshoppe@comcast.net
503-607-0600

Don't forget to visit our brand new gift and home décor shop, Pickleweed Hill

Debbie Busby Wools

Selected as one of 2010's Top Ten Shops by Better Homes and Gardens Quilt Sampler Magazine, *Hollyhill Quilt Shoppe & Mercantile* is considered to be one of Oregon's most celebrated quilting destinations. Nestled in the historic Willamette section of West Linn, the Shoppe opened in September 2005 and is family owned by Jan Hill and her son, Brian. The "Shoppe" carries complete collections from your favorite designers! But the real charm can be found in the many enchanting displays that bring the fabric to life! During the holidays the Shoppe becomes a winter wonderland! Strong attention to detail along with a very friendly and knowledgeable staff make this a must-see on any quilting adventure!

Moda
Andover
Clothworks
Lakehouse
Michael Miller
Westminster Fibers
Alexander Henry
Northcott, P&B
and many more!

It's the kind of shop where inspiration lives and creativity begins.

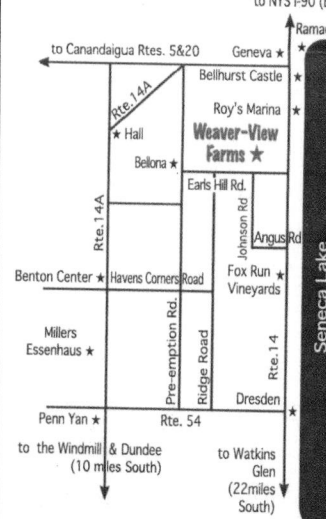

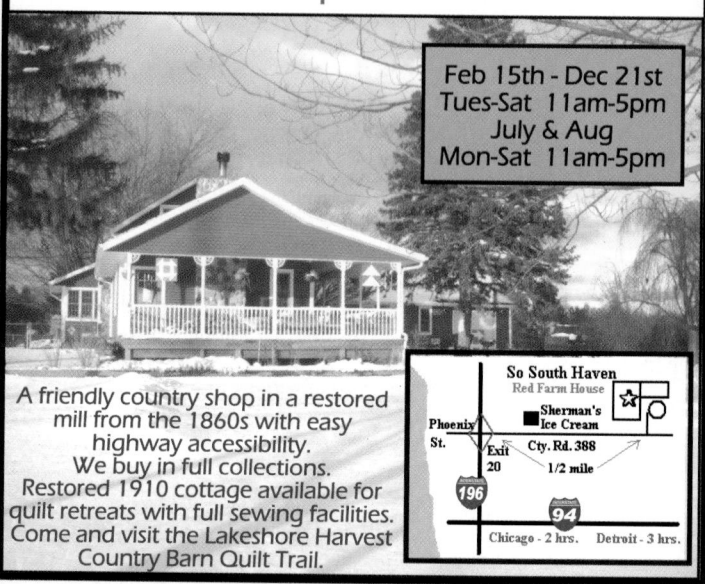

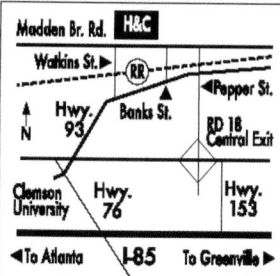

Quilter's Corner

In the Red Barn

Meet Q.C. our shop dog

312 Danbury Rd. (Rt. 7)
New Milford, CT 06776
(860) 355-4516

Est: 1999

Owner: Becky Frazer
Fax: (860) 355-9510
2300 sq.ft. 3000+ Bolts

Mon - Sat 10 - 5
Wed til 8 on class nights

Your source for fabrics, supplies, classes and unique gifts.

New Milford, CT

Spacious, well lit shop filled with 100% cotton fabrics, books, patterns, notions, gift items and a friendly, helpful staff.

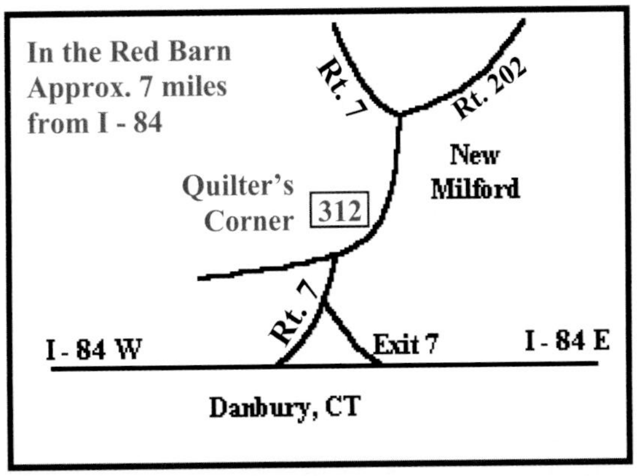

www.quilterscorneronline.com

Material matters Quilt Shop & Training Center

We carry a huge selection of longarm and machine quilting supplies.
Longarm quilting machines available for rent.
Longarm Quilting Training and Demonstrations.
Large selection of Books and Classes
We carry a wide variety of Batiks , Basics, Backings and Batting.
Stop in to try a wide variety of machines and frames.

Just North of Milwaukee off Hwy 45 or I43.
www.material-matters.com
1-800-443-5800

Open most days, hours by appointment
Call for hours and location.

West Bend, WI

Quilter's Harvest

Celebrating 10 Years!

www.quiltersharvest.com

Everything a quilter needs! Quality fabrics, notions, books, patterns and kits. Always ready to help with friendly service.

Mon - Fri 9:30 - 6 Thur til 8 Sat 9:30 - 4

(660) 584-3399
quilter@ctcis.net
Owner: Pam Fisher
Est:2000 1300 sq.ft.
5500+ Bolts

1913 Main St. Higginsville, MO 64037

If coming from I - 70, go North on Hwy. 13 to the 2nd stoplight (by McDonalds), turn right, go to the second stop sign, turn right, we are the 2nd shop on the left hand side on Main Street just past the bank.

Higginsville, MO

Erie, PA

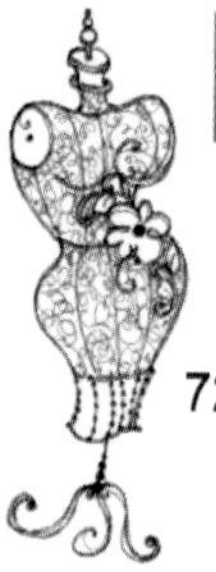

Millcreek Sewing & Fabric

Summit Towne Centre
7200 Peach St. #460 Erie, PA 16509
814-866-8227
Est: 1998 5500 sq.ft. 4000+ Bolts
www.millcreeksew.com

"Just to see the Marvelous Samples It's Worth the Trip!"

Tri State Leader in Batiks and Flannels

Hundreds of Books and Patterns
Friendly, Knowledgeable Staff

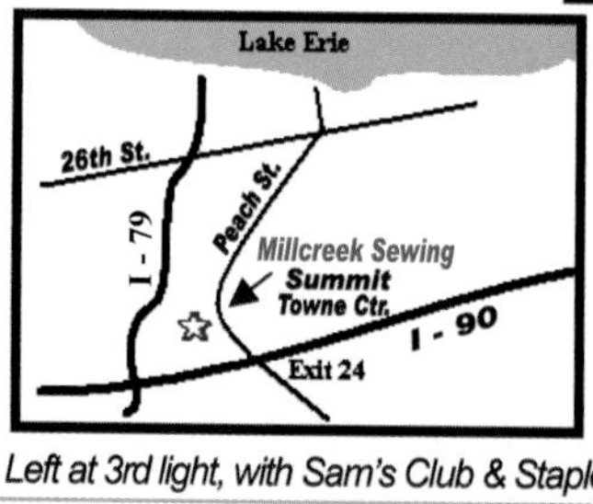

Left at 3rd light, with Sam's Club & Staples

Mon - Sat 10 - 7

baby lock
FOR THE LOVE OF SEWING
TinLizzie 18

Johnson City, NY

Indulge your passion for QUILTING! Come to shop, leave *inspired!*

- Broad selection of quality quilting fabrics, including hard-to-find specials
- Premier Husqvarna Viking dealer
- Books, Patterns, Notions, Supplies
- Beginning to Advanced Classes
- Friendly Service

Visit us online at www.smquilts.com to learn more!

Keeping the World Sewing

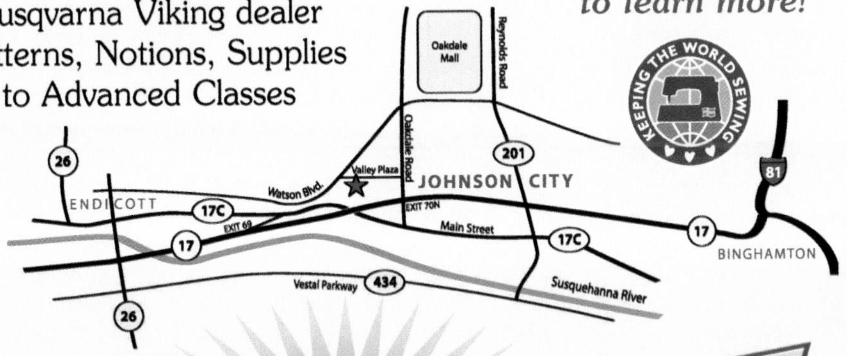

The Premier Quilt Shop in the Southern Tier!

Husqvarna VIKING

SEW MANY Quilts

"... so little time..."

800 Valley Plaza, Johnson City, NY 13790 Phone **607-797-1796** www.smquilts.com
Monday–Saturday 10:00am–6:00pm MASTERCARD • VISA • DISCOVER • AMERICAN EXPRESS

BERNINA

The Ultimate Sewing Experience

Unleash your creative aspirations with the **BERNINA 8 Series**

Experience the Difference

Embroidery & Cutwork Software

Large Selection of Fabrics, Notions and Supplies for Fashion, Quilting, Smocking, Heirloom & Embroidery. Sewing Classes & Events

New Bern Fabric Center

1218 S Glenburnie Rd, New Bern NC 28562
252 633-4780 Visit: www.nbfabric.com
Hours: 9-5:30 M-F; 9-5 Sat. - Est. 1974

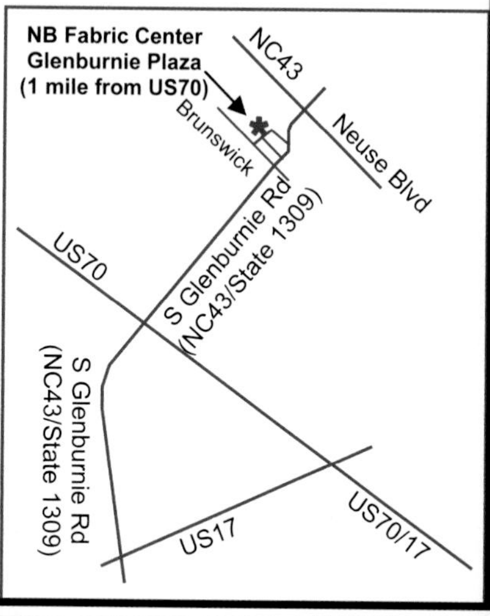

Sewing Notions Bernina Sergers

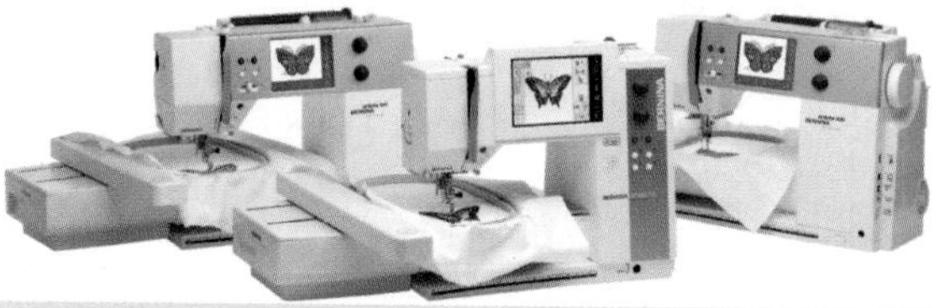

Bernina Artista Models 730, 640 & 630

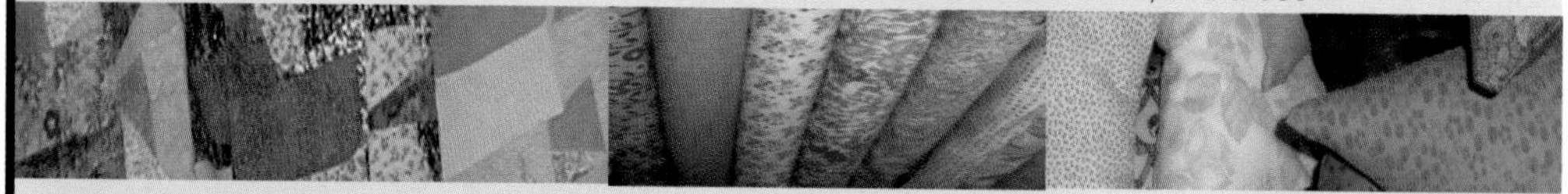

Quilted Bags from a Quilting Class Bolts of Fabric Donated Comfort Pillows

3500 bolts of fabric!

Over 3700 SQ FT packed with inspiration!

FABRIC • YARN • CRAFTS • GIFTS • CARDS • LOCAL ARTS

the Treasure Hunt

Your destination quilt shop

919 Maple Ave, Carpinteria
m-sat 10-5, sun 11-4
www.CarpinteriaQuilts.com
805.684.3360

Your local creative outlet

WILD ROSE

Quilt Shop & Retreat

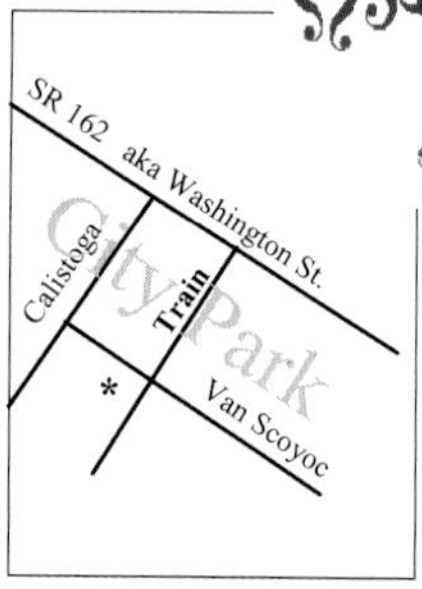

Nestled in a picturesque little town with a stunning view of Mt. Rainier, you'll find a gorgeous quilt shop and 10-person Retreat Center.

Built to look like an 1880's saloon, our modern shop has over 3200 bolts and a huge selection of reproduction, florals, "go-withs," contemporaries and flannels. We have a wide and current range of books, patterns and notions. Our fully equipped Retreat Center is like no other...AND we have an elevator so you don't have to carry your machine and other equipment up the stairs. Sew upstairs, shop downstairs....it just doesn't get any better than that!

www.thewildrosequiltshop.com

Orting, WA

Mon-Sat 9-5
Sun 11-4

125 Van Scoyoc Ave SW
~ Orting, WA 98360 ~
360-893-0202

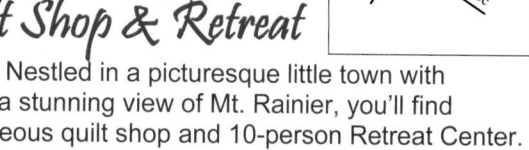

Sew-A-Lot
Creative Sewing Centers

Two Store Locations

232 N. Main St.
Centerville, Ohio 45459
937-433-7474
sewalot@erinet.com

2160 Sir Barton Way
Lexington, Kentucky 40509
859-264-7472
sewliz@earthlink.net

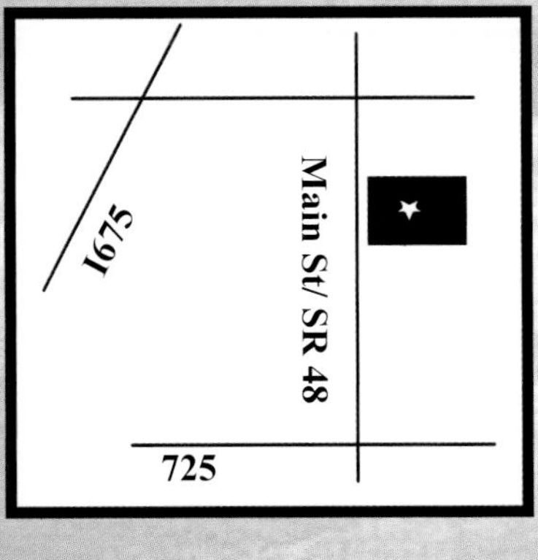

Centerville, Ohio

Lexington, Kentucky

Authorized **PFAFF** Machine Dealer
Husqvarna Viking Dealer (Ohio only)
Specializing in **machine embroidery** and **quilting**.
Embroidery Designs, Patterns, Books, Threads, & Notions in stock!
FREE Newsletter and Classes are also available!

Our **Ohio** shop is located in a Historic Building built in 1874, less than half a mile off of I-675 and has
OVER 4500 BOLTS of FABRIC!
Our **Kentucky** shop is easily accessible off of interstate 75 and has
OVER 3000 BOLTS of FABRIC!

www.sewalotonline.com

The place to go when you want to sew! Largest Selection! We have it all!

California's cutting edge quilt store!

The most quilting and sewing supplies under one roof!

We give out-of-state fabric discounts

- ❖ classes
- ❖ books
- ❖ furniture
- ❖ fabric
- ❖ buttons
- ❖ zippers
- ❖ knits
- ❖ batiks
- ❖ minkee
- ❖ rayon
- ❖ wool
- ❖ flannel
- ❖ notions galore
- ❖ thread haven
- ❖ sashiko supplies
- ❖ angelina fibers
- ❖ 12+ batting varieties
- ❖ embroidery machines
- ❖ 49+ sewing machines
- ❖ world's best sergers
- ❖ friendly fabric finders
- ❖ over 4500 bolts of fabric
- ❖ award-winning quilts
- ❖ free abundant parking

www.eddiesquiltingbee.com

Open 7 Days a Week
Mon-Fri 9am-8:30pm
Sat 9am-5:30pm
Sun 11am-5:00pm

Eddie's Quilting Bee

Toll free: 1-888-QUILTER

Local: (408) 830-9595 (1-888-784-5837)

480 S. Mathilda Ave., Sunnyvale

1 block north of El Camino, next to BofA

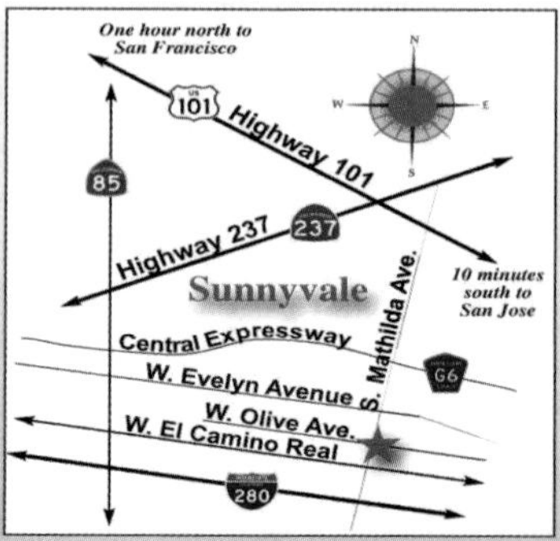

Factory Authorized Dealer!

Husqvarna VIKING | baby lock | BERNINA Nothing Sews Like A Bernina. Nothing. | JANOME | KOALA CABINETS | Tin Lizzie 18 Your Affordable Longarm quilter | HORN of America COLLECTION

Statler Stitcher

Loving Stitches

BERNINA

Sewing, Quilting & Fabric Center

www.lovingstitches.net

- *Eastern NC's largest quilting store (10,000 sq ft)*
- *Authorized Gammill & Statler Stitcher dealer for NC, SC, & VA*
- *Hundreds of classes in sewing, quilting, clothing construction embroidery for all skill levels. Special events by world masters*
- *Over 5000 bolts of 100% cotton fabrics*
- *Large selection of books, notions & patterns*
- *Certified service technician - all brands*
- *Specially made quilt kits & BOMs*
- *Expert quilting services*
- *Quilt guild member discounts*

7076 Ramsey St / Hwy 401
Fayetteville, NC 28311
(910) 630-3912

Mon-Sat 10 am-6 pm

Fayetteville, NC

We're only 10 minutes from I-95. Take exit 58 & follow the signs for Hwy. 401N. Call for help with directions. Busses always welcomed!

Gammill® QUILTING SYSTEMS

QUILT CORRAL

IS NOW BACK AT

Mistletoe Ranch

The Ultimate Christmas & Gift Store

605-574-4197
Email: info@mistletoeranch.com
www.mistletoeranch.com

Thousands of bolts of gorgeous fabrics. The latest books and patterns from the most innovative designers!

WE ARE IN THE BUSINESS OF SELLING FUN FABULOUS FABRIC TO MAKE ALL YOUR QUILTING DREAMS BECOME A REALITY!

23835 Hwy 385
Hill City, SD 57745

Home of Gutzy Geisha Designs™

Unique patterns that utilize large scale prints, simply layered and cut to create exquisite kaleidoscoping blocks...

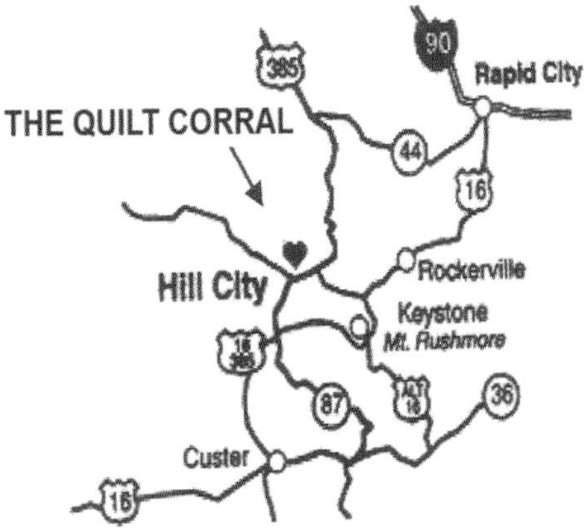

- *Books*
- *Patterns*
- *Notions*
- *Ideas*
- *Personal Service*

Email: quiltcorraltoo@ll.net
www.quiltcorral.com
605-574-9044

Chanhassen, MN

The Sampler

a quilt shop and more...

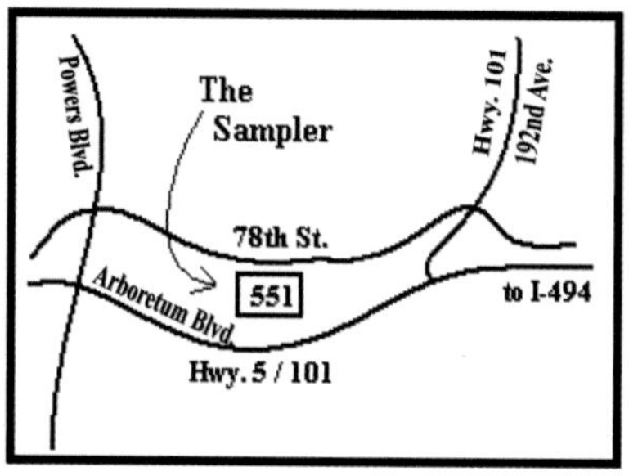

America's headquarters for
KAFFE FASSETT
fabrics!!

We are colorful, trendy, full of inspiration which you see when you come in the door. Gorgeous quilts hung everywhere!

Located in the metro area & easy to find!
You are always welcome. COME SEE US!

Also.....
Phillip Jacobs
Brandon Mably
Amy Butler
Alexander Henry
Art Gallery
Free Spirit
Heather Bailey
Bali Batiks
Beautiful Hand dyes,
and so much more!!!

HOURS:

M-W-Fri-Sat. 10-5pm
Tue & Thur 10-8pm
Sun.-12-4pm

952-934-5307
551 W. 78th St.

866-994-8318
PO Box 532

BERNINA

www.the-sampler.com
Chanhassen, MN 55317

Dunedin, FL

RAINBOWS END QUILT SHOPPE

941 BROADWAY STREET (ALT 19)
DUNEDIN, FLORIDA 34698

(727)733-8572 (800) 353-1928 FAX (727)736-0235

LARGEST COMPLETE QUILT SHOPPE IN FLORIDA

OVER 18,000 BOLTS OF 100% COTTON FABRIC
QUILT, WALLHANGING & BLOCK OF THE MONTH KITS

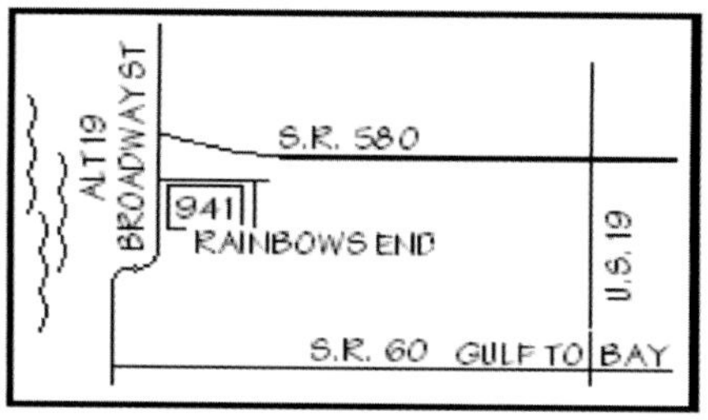

EST. 1982 7200 SQ. FT.

HOURS -
MON- SAT 10 AM TO 5 PM
WED 10 AM - 8 PM

WWW.RAINBOWS-END.COM
WWW.RAINBOWSENDQUILTSHOPPE.COM
WWW.RAINBOWSENDQUILTSHOPPE.BLOGSPOT.COM

HUNDREDS OF BOOKS, PATTERNS, NOTIONS, STENCILS, GIFT ITEMS, QUILTING SOFTWARE
LARGE COLLECTION OF SAMPLES OF CLASSES, PATTERNS, BOOKS & KITS
AUTHORIZED ELNA & PFAFF SALES & SERVICE
SEWING MACHINE CENTER

A Quilters Dream
INSPIRED QUILTING
INDULGE YOUR PASSION FOR QUILTING & SEWING
Take a class, join a club, shop online or take part in one of the many different featured events at The Quilt Store!
For all of the latest updates sign up for our newsletter at www.thequiltstore.ca.
Over 60,000 Metres Instock!
Current Fabrics, Patterns, Books and Notions
Warm and Friendly Atmosphere
elna
JANOME
BERNINA
brother
Husqvarna
Handi Quilter
VIKING
We Service What We Sell!
VISA
MasterCard
Store Hours: Mon - Fri: 9-6 Saturday: 9-5 Sunday: Closed
Service Shop Hours: Mon - Fri: 9-5 Sat & Sun: Closed
The Quilt Store.ca
Quilt
EVELYN'S SEWING CENTRE
17817 Leslie St. Unit 40, Newmarket, ON L3Y 8C6
905-853-7001
www.thequiltstore.ca

where winning things happen when you step through our doors...

Est: 2008

Wylie, TX

DFW's Most Talked About Block of the Month Headquarters

We are located in the historic downtown district of Wylie, TX. We offer all the nostalgia of quilting history and all the style of quilting trends.

blueribbonquiltshoppe@gmail.com
www.blueribbonquiltshoppe.co

M, Tu, W, F 10-6 Th 10-7
Sat 9-5 1st & 3rd Sun 1-5

Blue Ribbon Quilt Shoppe

Alexander Henry
Batiks
Benartex
Blank Quilting
Clothworks
David Textiles
Elizabeth's Studio
Free Spirit
Galaxy
Henry Glass
Hoffman
Kona Bay
Marcus Brothers
Maywood Studios
Moda
Northcott
P&B Textiles
Quilting Treasures
Red Rooster Fabrics
RJR
Shannon Fabrics/Cuddle
Thimbleberries
Timeless Treasures
Troy
Wilmington Prints
Windham Fabrics

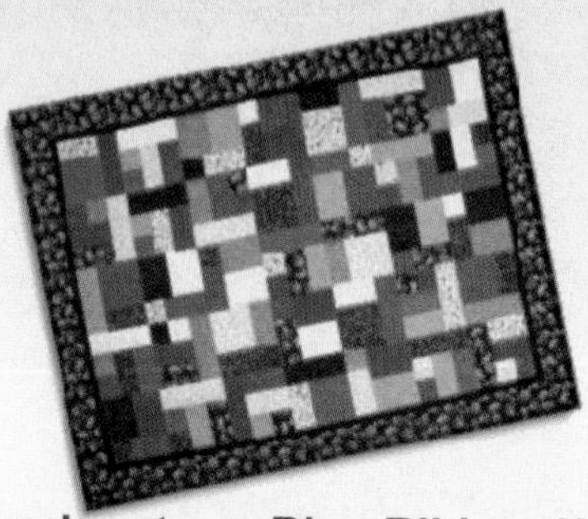

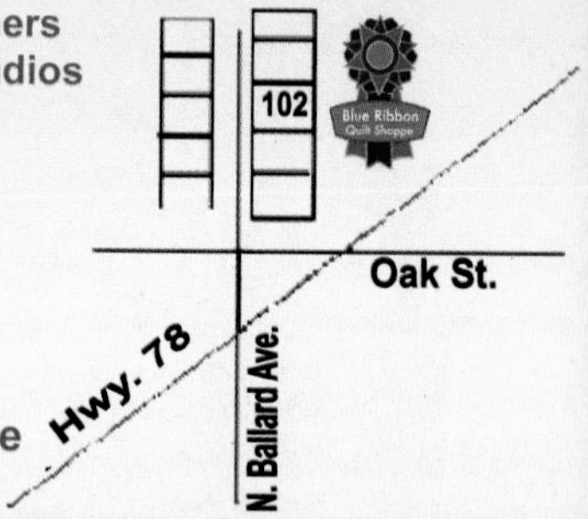

102 C North Ballard Ave.
Wylie, TX 75098
972-941-0777
4600 sq.ft. 2700+ Bolts

Check out our Blue Ribbon University
A collection of quilt classes for beginner and intermediate quilters: Learn a new skill with each new quilt.

Gillette, WY

Northeastern Wyoming's One Stop Quilt Shop!

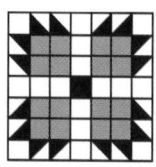

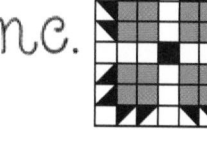

Quilt Nook, Inc.

211 West 2nd Street
Gillette, WY 82716
(307) 682-9196 (888) 268-3381

Over 5000 square feet of Quilter's Heaven!

* Koala Cabinets
* Kits, Books, Patterns
* Janome Sewing Machines
* Quilting Notions, Stablizers, Needles
* Guterman, YLI, Star, Mettler, Quilting Threads
* Over 8,000 Bolts of 100% Cotton Quilting Fabrics

SHOP HOURS
Tuesday 9:00am to 7:00pm
Wednesday - Friday 9:00am to 5:00 pm
Saturday 9:00am to 3:00pm
CLOSED Sunday - Monday

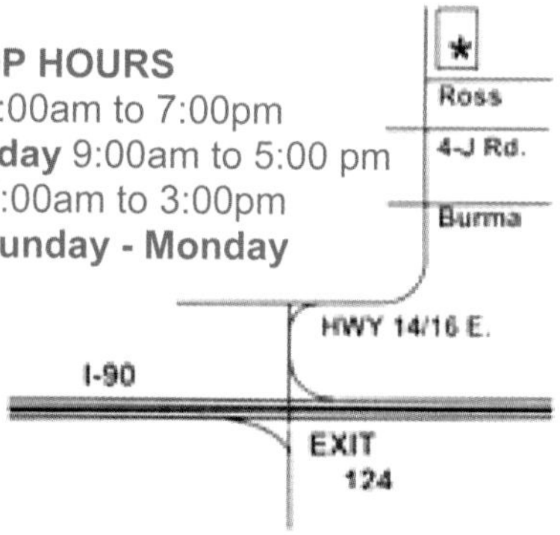

JANOME
Authorized Dealer, Sales and Service Center!

QTC History continued from page 74.

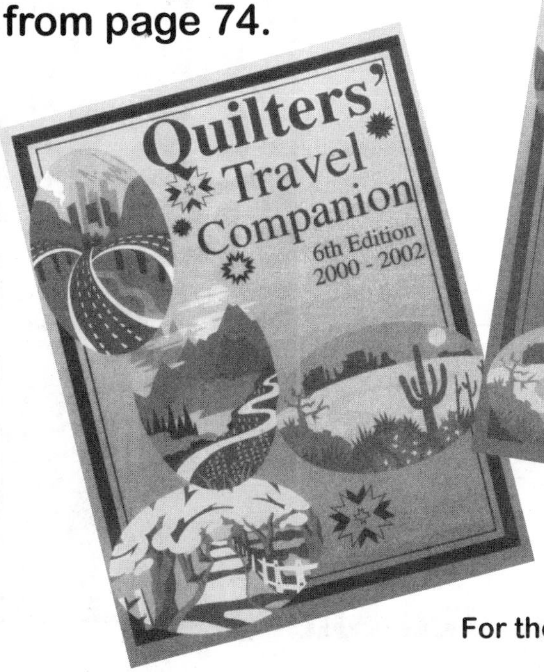

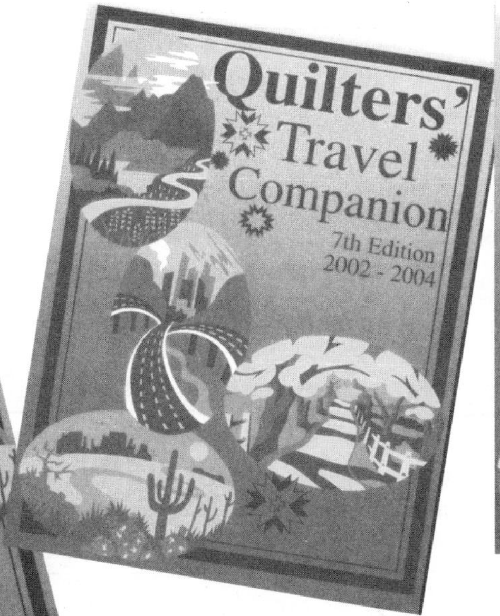

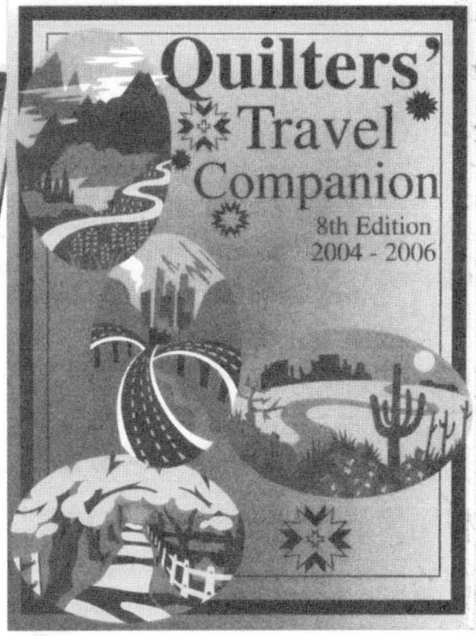

In 2000 with the 6th edition the QTC grew to 1600 featured shops in 416 pages.
2002 featured over 1750 great shops and was 432 pages.
For the 8th edition in 2004 we had over 2000 shops and 560 pages.

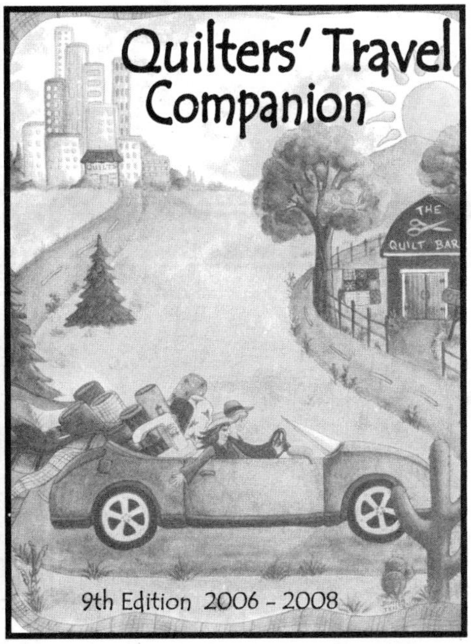

In 2006, finally the picture of the cover that had always been in my mind's eye came to life by artist Donna Jensen. With each subsequent cover she has been able to make each better than the last.

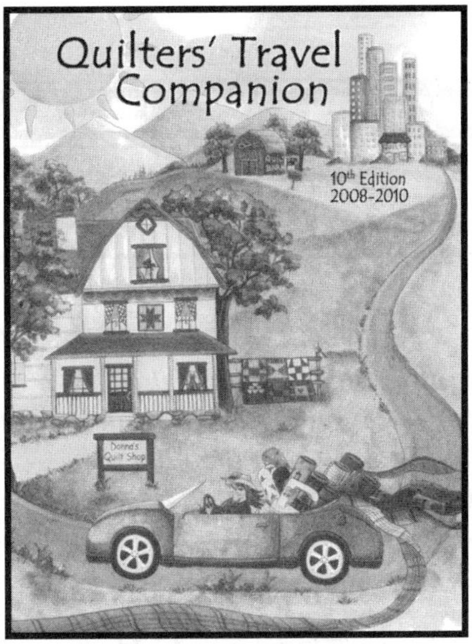

With the 9th edition we added full color pages and Shop Hops. We had 1937 featured stores and 576 pages.

Then with the 10th edition we added quilt shows along with maps showing the show locations.
It had 1931 featured shops, over 1000 shows and was 704 pages.

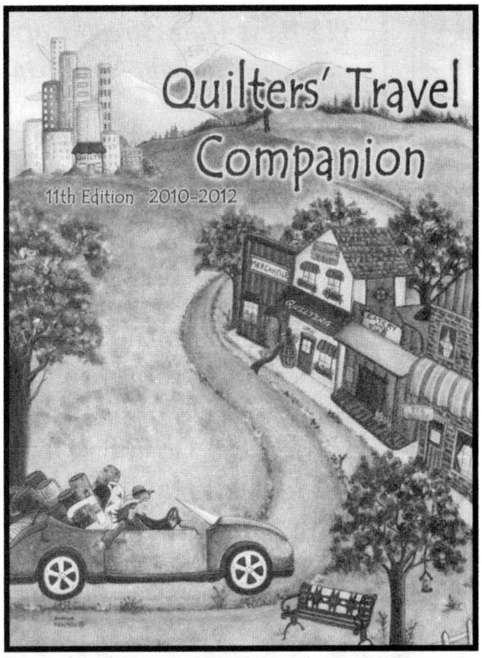

As the QTC has continued to grow we remain proud of the support we offer to independent, locally owned quilt stores.
For the highest quality fabrics, unique notions and above all, ideas and inspiration for your quilting projects, please give these stores your patronage and support.

Our new 11th edition has 640 pages and 2050 featured shops. We added over 400 'new' shops to our family (this is more than in any single edition to date). There are over 1200 shows included.

Over the years our website has also grown by leaps and bounds.
Check there for shop changes and additions. We list guilds, shop hops, more show information, retreat facilities and more.
www.quilterstravelcompanion.com

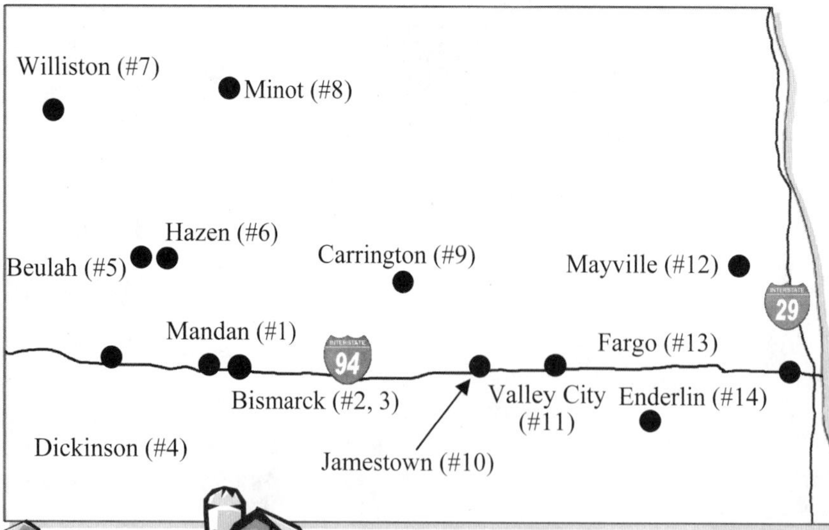

NORTH DAKOTA

14 Featured Shops

Mandan, ND #1

Sewing Machines Plus!

Your Friendly Sewing & Quilting Place - Established 1998
322 West Main Street (Corner of 3rd Avenue NW & Main Street)
Mandan, North Dakota 58554 - (701) 663-9025
sewing_art@hotmail.com

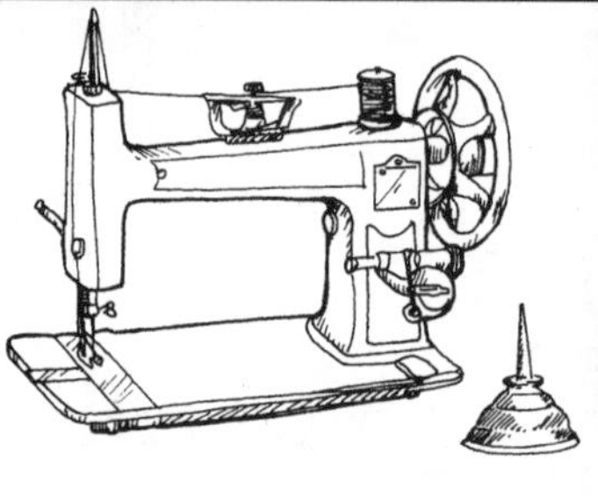

Monday 9-8
Tues-Fri 9-5:30
Saturday 9-4

- 100% Cotton Quilt Fabrics
- Threads & Notions
- Quilting Supplies
- Patterns & Books
- Machine Embroidery Designs
- Software & Supplies
- Classes
- Authorized Bernina Dealer
- Authorized Handi Quilter Representative
- Guaranteed Repair & Service on all Brands.

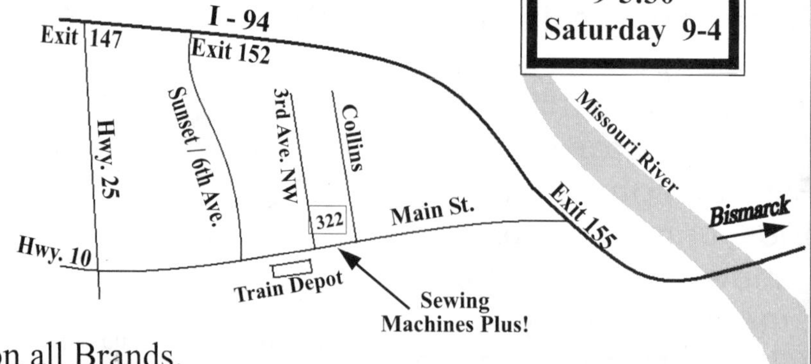

Bismarck, ND #2

Bismarck Sewing & Quilting

www.bismarcksewingandquilting.com

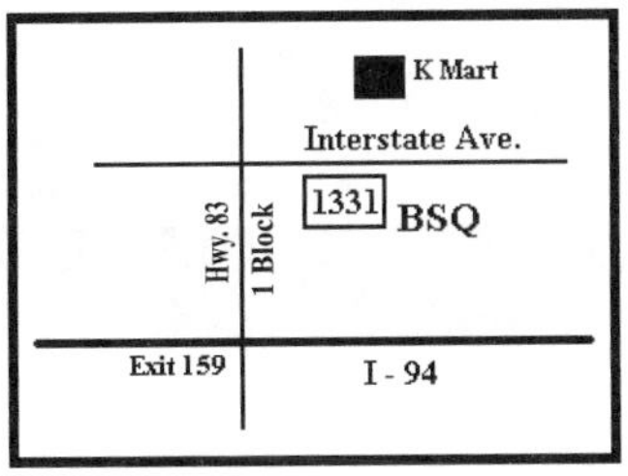

1331 E. Interstate Ave. 58503
(701) 258-5139
Fax: (701) 223-2116
joy@bismarcksewingandquilting.com
www.bismarcksewingandquilting.com

- Large variety of quilting cottons: 1930's, Brights, Reproduction, Batiks, Wool
- Kits Available
- Notions
- Books
- Patterns
- Embellishments
- Quilt Jewelry
- Gift Items
- Sewing & Embroidery Supplies
- Authorized Babylock® & Janome Dealer

Mon 10 - 6 Tues 10 - 8
Wed & Thurs 10 - 6
Fri 10 - 5 Sat 9:30 - 4

baby lock
JANOME ...Dream. Inspire. Create.

Bismarck, ND #3

Mon 9 - 8
Tues - Fri 9 - 6
Sat 9 - 5

The Quilt Shoppe

Inside J & R Vacuum & Sewing
223 E. Main 58501
(701) 258-5619
(800) 371-5515
www.jrsewfun.com

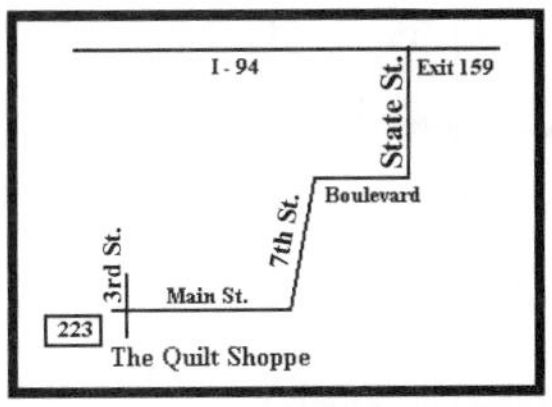

Quilt supplies, classes, name brand 100% cotton quilting fabrics, books, patterns, notions, cabinets, PFAFF, BabyLock & Singer sewing machines.

Dickinson, ND #4

Mon - Sat
9:30 - 5:30

Dakota Sew and So

2797 3rd Ave. W 58601
(701) 225-1408
Owners: Holly Martinson
dakotasewandso@ndsupernet.com
www.dakotasewandso.com
Over 4000 bolts of Quilt, Bridal, Fashion, Wools and Yarns too. Mail order and newsletter available upon request.
Bernina and Janome Dealer.

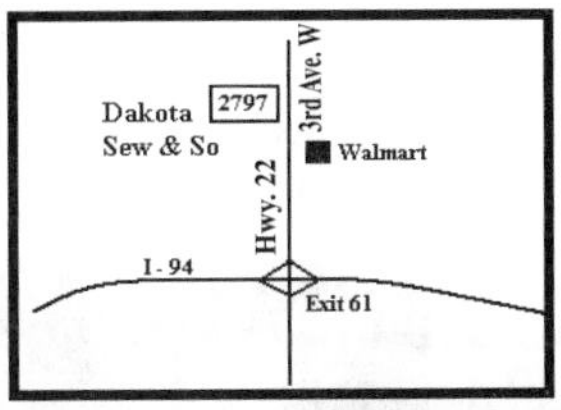

Beulah, ND #5

Tue - Sat
9:30 - 5:30

Dakota Sew and So

105 W. Main St. 58523
(701) 873-2727
Owners: Holly Martinson
dakotasewandso@ndsupernet.com
www.dakotasewandso.com

Nice selection of Quilting Cottons.
Bernina and Janome Dealer.

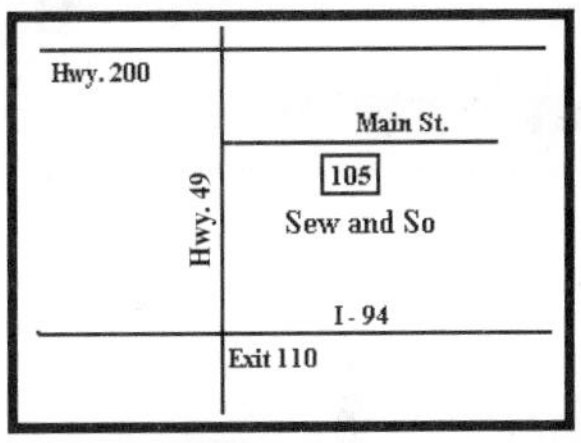

Hazen, ND #6

Mon - Fri
9:30 - 5
Sat by Appt.

Quilts from the Heart and More!

748-3999

213 1st Ave. NW
P.O. Box 756 58545

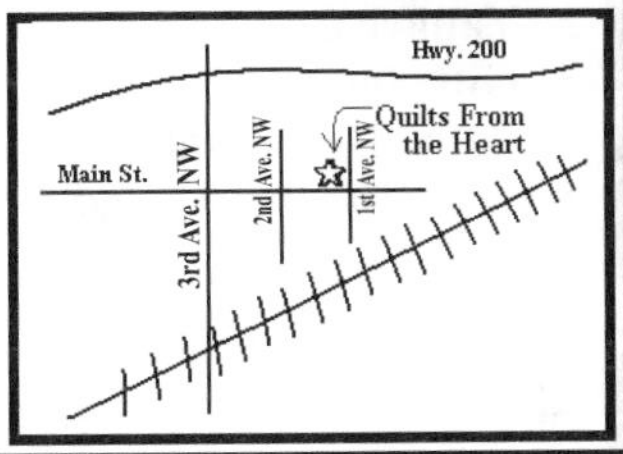

quiltsfromtheheart@westriv.com
Owner: Toni Hagel

Williston, ND #7

Mon - Fri
10 - 5
Sat 10 - 4

the Bent Pin Quilter's Supply

222 Main St. 58801
(800) 246-0718 or (701) 572-0718
thebentpin@nemontel.net

Est: 1988
3500 Bolts

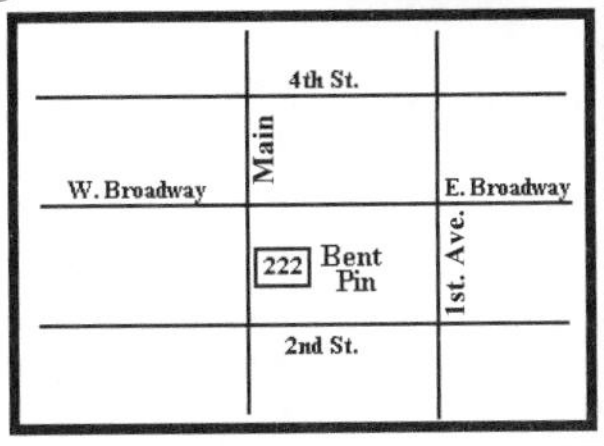

www.thebentpin.net

100% cottons including Hoffman, Moda, RJR & many others. Large selection of books, patterns & notions. Authorized Bernina Dealer & HandiQuilter representative.

Minot, ND #8

Prairie Rose Quilt Shop

(701) 852-2835
1500 53rd Ave. SW 58701
www.prairierosequiltshop.com

Owner: Carmen R. Haugen
Est: 1998 1750 sq.ft.
2500 Bolts

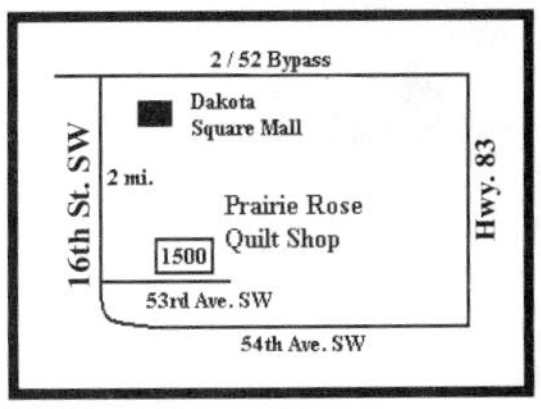

Mon - Fri 10 - 5:30
Sat 10 - 2
Summer Sat, Please Call First

Full service quilt shop offering quality quilting fabric and machine quilting. Specializing in florals, plaids, batiks, flannels & wool.

Designer Fabrics

929 Main St. 58421
(701) 652-3535 Est: 1992
dfabqlt@daktel.com

Complete quilt shop located in a historical building, specializing in traditional quilting. Many books, patterns, notions & classes. Friendly, helpful staff.

Owner:
Jackie Jones

Mon - Fri 10 - 5
Sunday 12 - 5
Closed Saturday

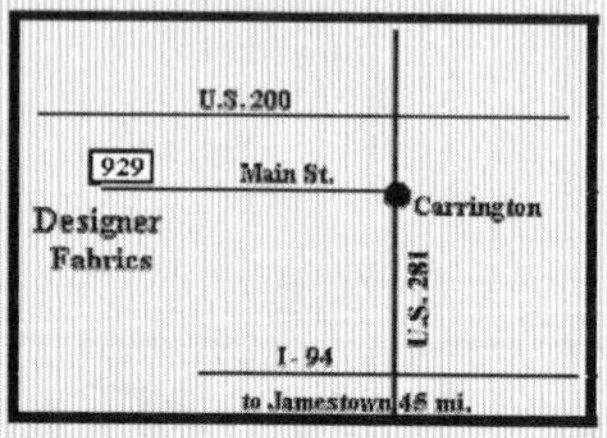

www.quiltdesignerfabrics.com

Carrington, ND #9

Comforts of Home

112 17th St. SE 58401
(701) 252-5691
comforts@daktel.com
www.comfortsofhome.blogspot.com
Est: 2003 Free Newsletter

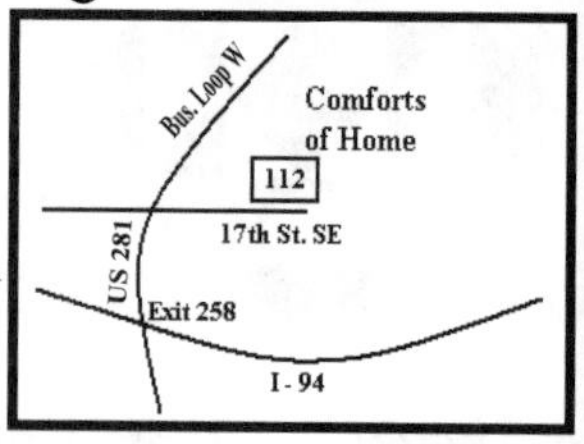

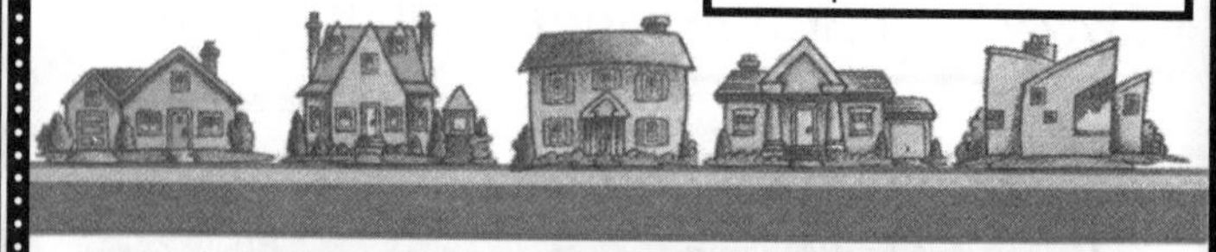

Mon - Fri 9:30 - 5:30 Thurs til 8 Sat 9:30 - 4:30

A touch of Quilting . . . . Fabric, Notions, Books, Patterns & Classes on the road to the Buffalo

Jamestown, ND #10

Valley City, ND #11

Quilted Ceiling

A Destination Shop!

* **Over 3000 bolts of top quality fabric**
* **Kits in a variety of sizes**
* **Books, patterns and a large selection of notions**
* **Hand knitting yarn, books, patterns and notions**
* **Large quilt display to inspire you**
* **Yankee Candles**
* **Gifts for all occasions**
* **Baby, Bridal and Gift registry**
* **Friendly, knowledgeable staff**

Monday - Saturday
9:30 - 5:30

316 Central Ave. N 58072
Phone/Fax: (701) 845-4926
info@quiltedceiling.com
Est: 2005

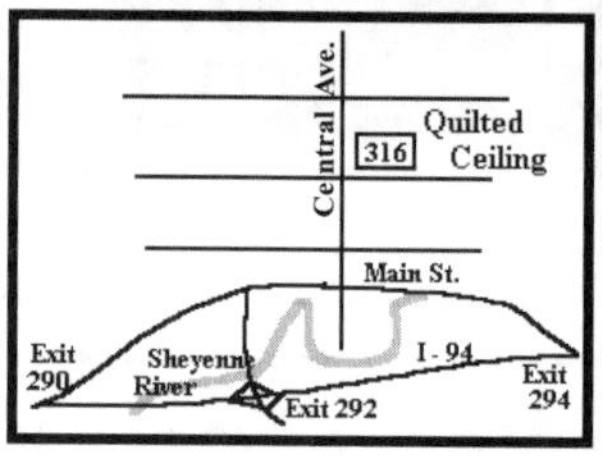

Visit our website: www.quiltedceiling.com

Mayville, ND #12

Faye's Henhouse Quilts

Mon - Sat
9 - 5:30
Tues til 9

37 Center Ave. North, Mayville, ND 58257
(701) 786-3790
www.fayesquiltshop.com
Owner: Faye Grandalen
Est: 1996 3200 sq.ft. 5000+ Bolts

Fine cotton fabrics, quilting supplies, books, patterns, notions, and custom machine quilting, classes, gift items, and quilt racks.

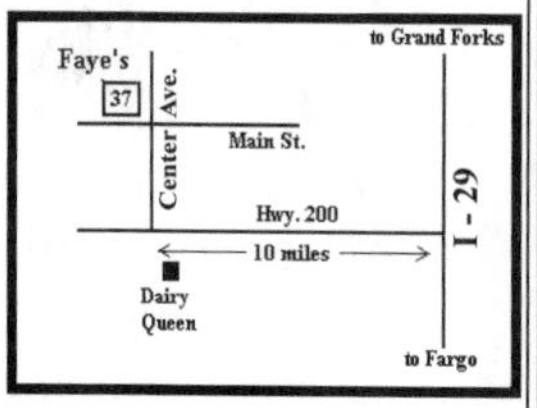

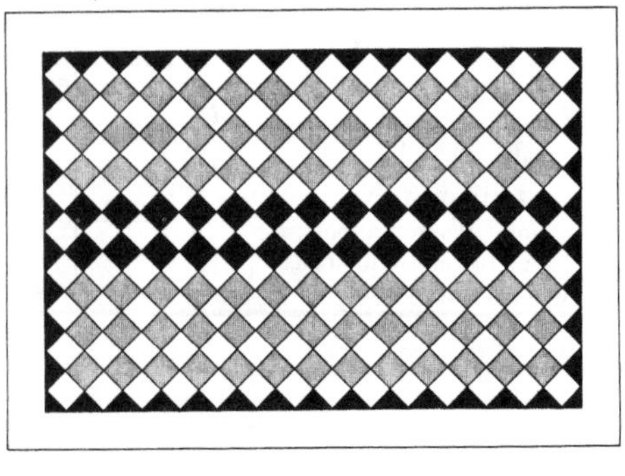

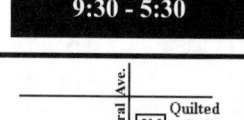

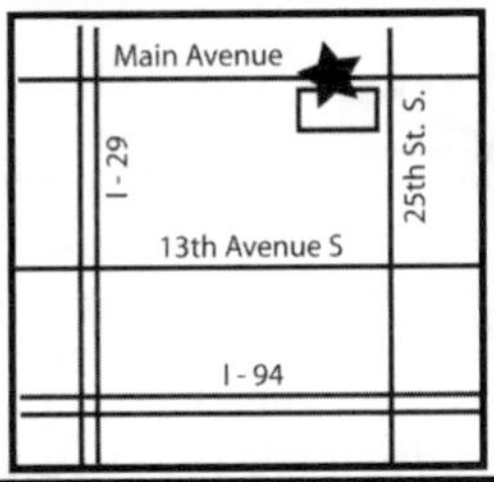

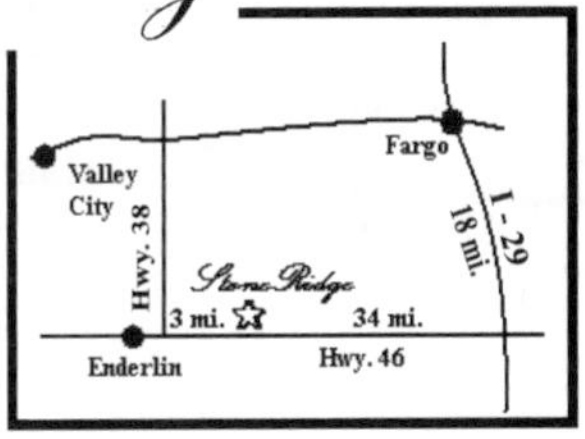

North Dakota Quilt Shops

Beach Sip - n - Sew, 22 Central Ave., Suite 2 701-872-4226
Beulah Dakota Sew and So, 105 West Main St.
701-873-2727 See ad #5, page 419
Bismarck Bismarck Quilting, 1331 E. Interstate Ave.
701-258-5139 See ad #2, page 419
Bismarck The Quilt Shoppe, 223 E. Main Ave.
800-371-5515 See ad #3, page 419
Bismarck The Quilt Haus, 515 N. 4th St.
Bottineau Simple Threads, 120 11th Ave. #A 701-228-2180
Carrington Designer Fabrics, 929 Main St.
701-652-3535 See ad #9, page 420
Devils Lake Quilt Essential, 316 4th Street NE 701-262-4783
Dickinson Dakota Sew and So, 2797 3rd Ave. West
701-225-1408 See ad #4, page 419
Enderlin Stone Ridge Quilting, 13991 54th St. SE
701-437-2013 See ad #14, this page
Fargo Rae-Bon Quilt & Sewing Center, 2590 Main Ave.
701-433-7203 See ad #13, this page
Fargo Starflower Fabrics, 2113 27th Ave. S. 701-232-8597
Fargo Stitch It Quilts, 2502 S. University Dr. 701-277-1899
Hazen Quilts From the Heart & More, 213 1st Ave. NW
701-748-3999 See ad #6, page 419
Hettinger Dakota Cabin Quilts, 218 S. Main St. 701-567-4772
Jamestown Comforts of Home, 112 17th St. SE
701-252-5691 See ad #10, page 420
Mandan Sewing Machines Plus!, 322 West Main St.
701-663-9025 See ad #1, page 418
Mayville Faye's Henhouse Quilts, 37 Center Ave. N
701-786-3790 See ad #12, page 420
Mayville Lyda's Scrappy Quilters Haven, 340 W. Main St. 701-788-8777
Mayville SewBatik, 879 W. Main 877-235-5025
Minot Prairie Rose Quilt Shop, 1500 53rd Ave. SW
701-852-2835 See ad #8, page 419
Minot Carol's Etc., 112 S. Main St. 701-839-6183
Minot Bernina Plus, 104 S. Main St. 701-837-5638
New Rockford 3 Sisters Quilt And Gift Shop, 813 1st Ave N. 701-947-2307
Oakes The Waltzing Quilter, 503 Main St. 701-742-2813
Valley City Quilted Ceiling, 316 Central North
701-845-4926 See ad #11, page 420
Williston The Bent Pin, 222 Main St.
701-572-0718 See ad #7, page 419

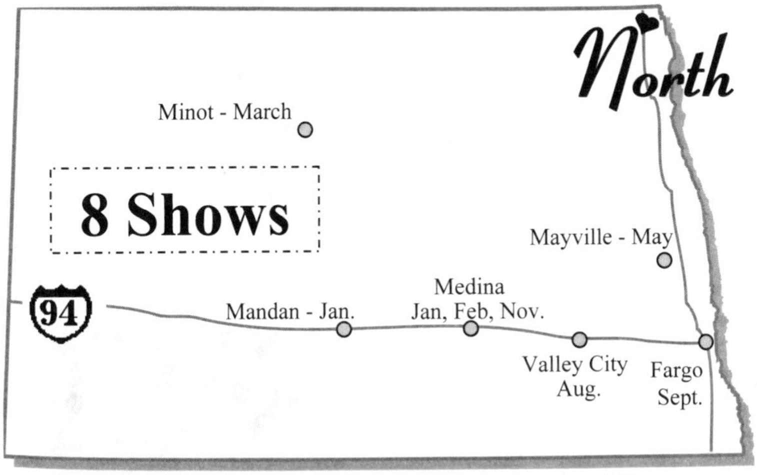

North Dakota Quilt Shows

About Shows: We are listing only the very basic information about shows that happen on a regular schedule here. Please check out our website for more details on each show. Also this information tends to change quite often so please verify the event with our website or a local source before you venture far. Or if you're in the right area at the right time, give it a shot.

If you are a show organizer, please keep us updated on your event. shows@quilterstravelcompanion.com www.quilterstravelcompanion.com

Month	City	Schedule	Show	Location with address
January				
	Medina	Annual, 2nd weekend in January	Crystal Springs Retreat	Crystal Springs Baptist Camp, 4848 36th St. SE
	Mandan	Annual, last Fri & Sat of January	North Dakota State Quilters' Showcase	Mandan Community Center, 901 Division St.
February				
	Medina	Annual, 3rd weekend in February	Crystal Springs Retreat	Crystal Springs Baptist Camp, 4848 36th St. SE
March				
	Minot	Annual, 3rd weekend of March	Minot Prairie Quilt Festival	Grand International Hotel, 1505 N. Broadway
May				
	Mayville	Annual, Saturday before Mother's Day	Mother's Day Tea	Faye's Henhouse Quilts, 37 Center Ave. N
August				
	Valley City	Annual, 1st weekend of August	Quilter's Jubilee	Barnes County Courthouse, 230 4th St. NW
September				
	Fargo	Annual, last weekend in September	Quilters' Guild of North Dakota Show	Holiday Inn, 3803 13th Ave. S
November				
	Medina	Annual, 3rd Weekend in November	Crystal Springs Retreat	Crystal Springs Baptist Camp, 4848 36th St. SE

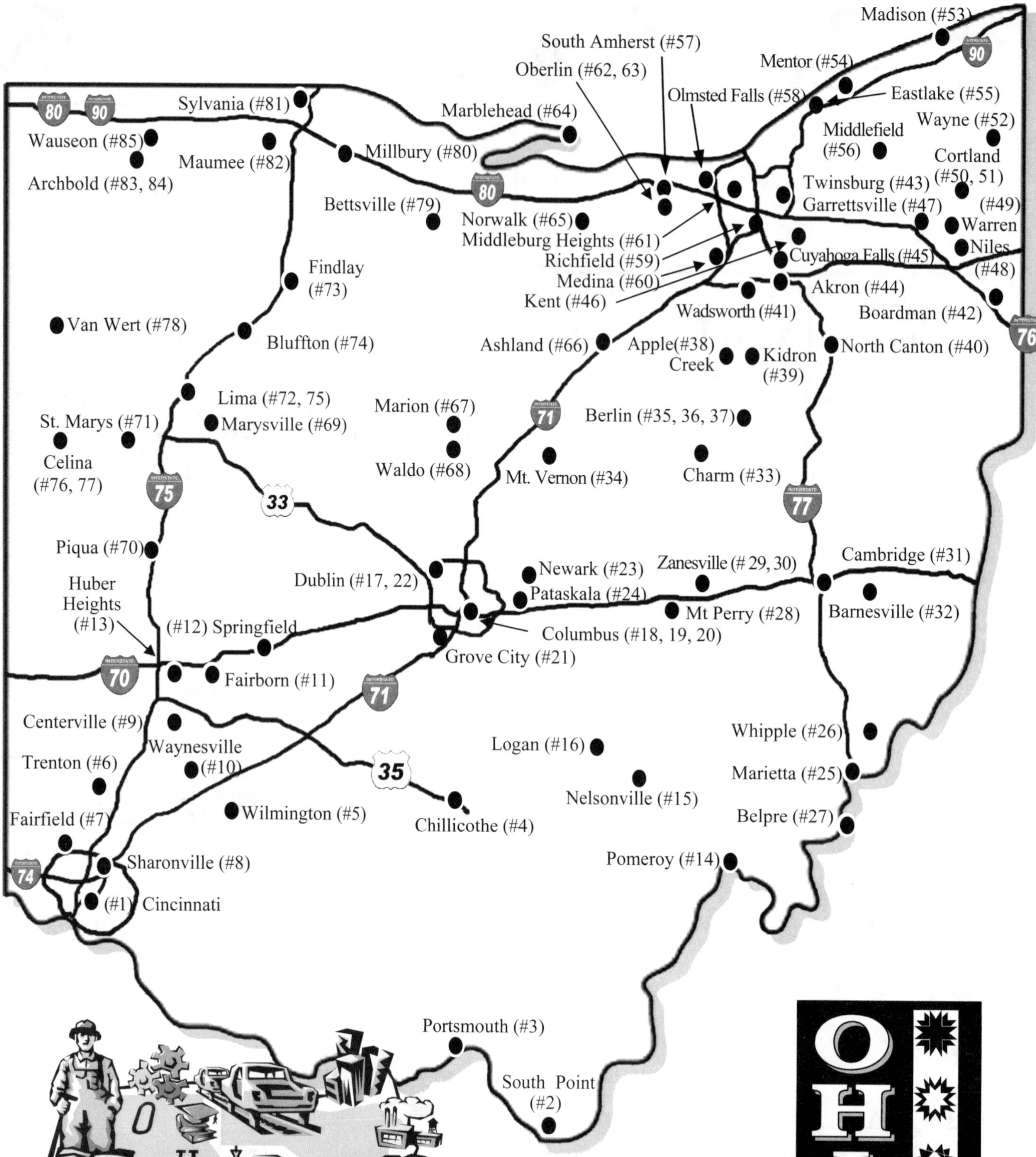
Madison (#53)
South Amherst (#57)
Oberlin (#62, 63)
Mentor (#54)
Olmsted Falls (#58)
Eastlake (#55)
Sylvania (#81)
Marblehead (#64)
Wayne (#52)
Middlefield (#56)
Wauseon (#85)
Maumee (#82)
Millbury (#80)
Cortland (#50, 51)
Archbold (#83, 84)
Twinsburg (#43)
Garrettsville (#47)
(#49)
Bettsville (#79)
Norwalk (#65)
Warren
Middleburg Heights (#61)
Niles (#48)
Richfield (#59)
Cuyahoga Falls (#45)
Medina (#60)
Findlay (#73)
Kent (#46)
Akron (#44)
Wadsworth (#41)
Boardman (#42)
Van Wert (#78)
Bluffton (#74)
Ashland (#66)
Apple Creek (#38)
Kidron (#39)
North Canton (#40)
Lima (#72, 75)
Marion (#67)
Berlin (#35, 36, 37)
St. Marys (#71)
Marysville (#69)
Celina (#76, 77)
Waldo (#68)
Mt. Vernon (#34)
Charm (#33)
Piqua (#70)
Newark (#23)
Zanesville (# 29, 30)
Cambridge (#31)
Huber Heights (#13)
Dublin (#17, 22)
Pataskala (#24)
Barnesville (#32)
Mt Perry (#28)
(#12) Springfield
Columbus (#18, 19, 20)
Grove City (#21)
Fairborn (#11)
Centerville (#9)
Waynesville (#10)
Logan (#16)
Whipple (#26)
Trenton (#6)
Marietta (#25)
Nelsonville (#15)
Wilmington (#5)
Chillicothe (#4)
Belpre (#27)
Fairfield (#7)
Sharonville (#8)
Pomeroy (#14)
(#1) Cincinnati
Portsmouth (#3)
South Point (#2)
80
90
76
71
75
33
77
70
35
74

O
H
I
O

OHIO

85 Featured Shops

www.bestfriendsquilts.com

OPEN SUNDAY

BEST FRIENDS QUILT SHOPPE

Your *friendly* neighborhood quilt shoppe!

513-385-2200

BEAUTIFUL FABRICS

FAT QUARTERS
of every fabric!

home of the famous
BRAND X PURSE

plus TOTE, BACKPACK, AND MORE...

You'll want them all *Very Badley!*

Full color patterns available now!

ELECTRIC QUILT 6.0
try it live at Best Friends!

CUSTOM Machine Quilting

VISIT us online

www.bestfriendsquilts.com

Best Friends Quilt Shoppe
8782 Colerain Ave
Cincinnati, Ohio 45251
513-385-2200
quilts@fuse.net

#1

Directions: from I-275, exit # 33 South on Colerain. We are on the left with Furniture Fair & Golden Corral.

HOURS: M-F 10-7, Sa 10-5, Su 12-4

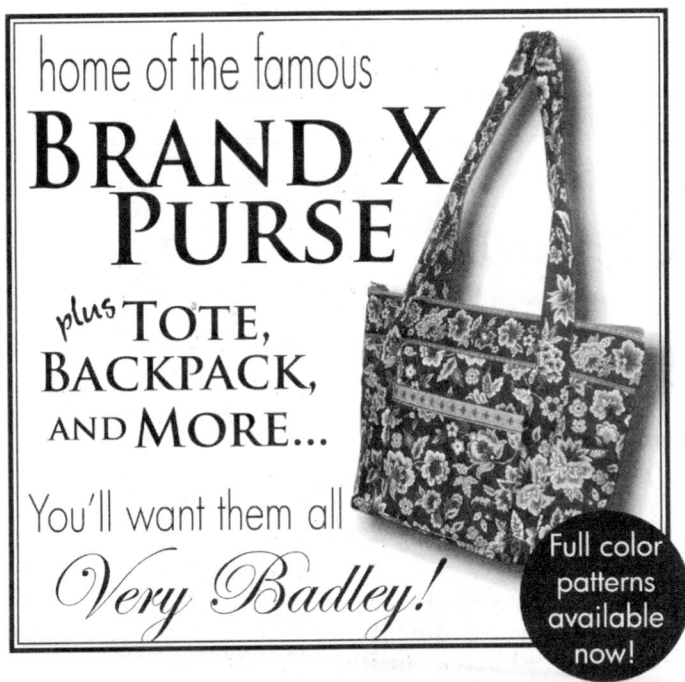

South Point, OH #2

Quilts and Things

Tues - Thurs 10 - 5
Fri & Sat 11 - 4
Thurs eve. by appt.

207 A Solida Rd. 45680
(740) 377-4551
Owners: Jesus Our Savior & Suzie Burck
www.quiltsandthings.us

Fabric & Quilt Shop
We carry Moda - Thimbleberries - Maywood
Pat Sloan - Civil War
30's & 40's Reproductions.
"Wisemen still seek him"

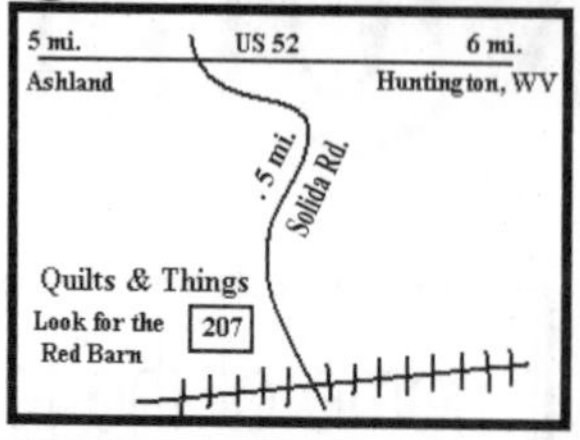

Portsmouth, OH #3

Lil's Quilt Shop

Mon - Fri 9 - 5
Sat 9 - 3

210 Market St. 45662
(740) 353-4570
Est: 1983 Owner: Lillian McKenzie
lil@lilsquiltshoppe.com
www.lilsquiltshoppe.com

Fabric Lines Galore -- Thimbleberries, Moda, Benartex, Roc-lon, Homespuns, Blank and many more. Lots of Notions & Books Classes. Always a friendly smile.

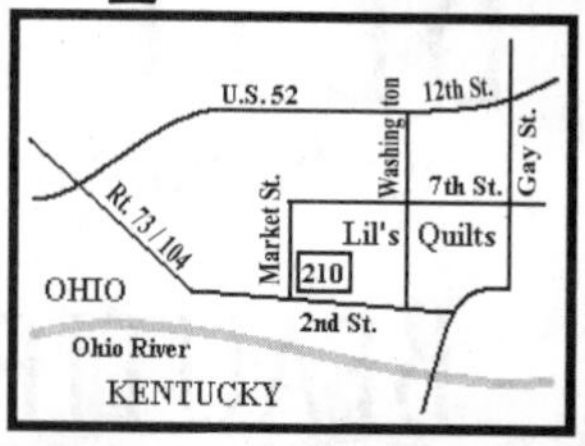

#4

Creations SewClever Quilt Shop

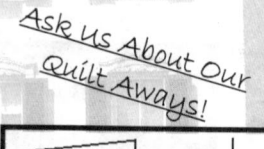

MON-SAT 10AM-5PM

192 S. Paint St. Chillicothe, OH 45601
Rita Fishel - Goddess, Queen Mother
(740) 775-1957 or
Toll Free 1-888-SEW-CLVR
Fax: (740) 773-2390
E-Mail: Sewclevr@bright.net

- Fine Fabrics
- Classes
- Kits
- Creative Grids Rulers
- Machine Quilting Services

Creations SewClever is a friendly, full-line quilt shop found in a beautiful 1800's Greek Revival home in the historic district of downtown Chillicothe. Call, write, or visit us online for class schedules, or a free quarterly newsletter.

Ask us About Our Quilt Aways!

Shop Online!
On our secure server

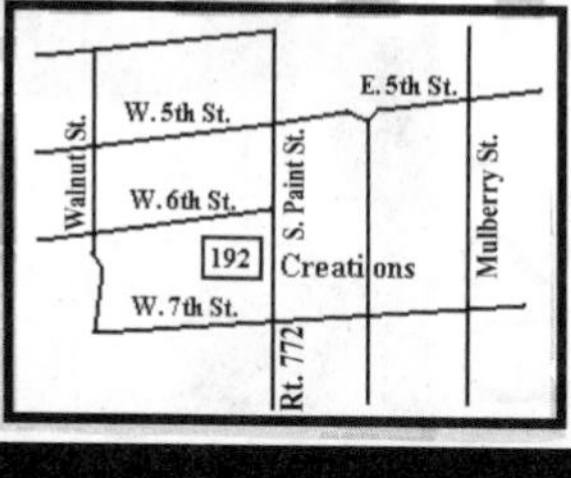

www.creationssewclever.com

Wilmington, OH #5

Cotton Junky Quilt Shop

Mon - Thur 9 - 6
Fri & Sat 9 - 4

199 N. Spring St. 45177
(937) 366-6302
Owners: Kevin & Carol Earhart
Est: 2008 1500 sq.ft. 600 bolts
cottonjunky@yahoo.com Online Newsletter
Fabric, Quilting Accessories. Notions, Books, Patterns, Quilting Novelties, DMC Floss, Classes, Stitchery Supplies.
Needlepoint & Cross stitch also.

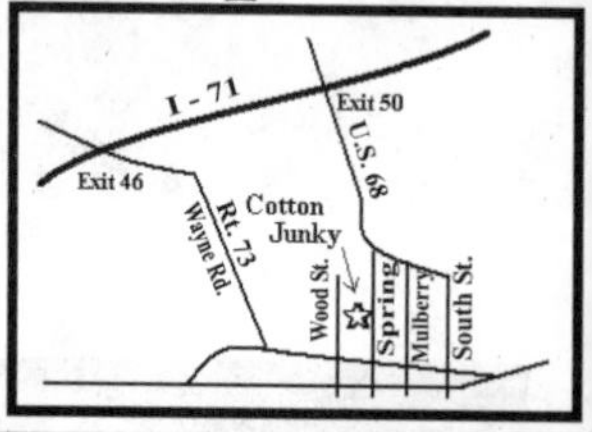

Trenton, OH #6

Valley Quilts

Mon - Fri 10 - 5
Sat 10 - 3

104 E. State St. 45067
(513) 988-2560
Est: 2006

2400 sq.ft. 2500 bolts Online newsletter
valleyquilts@cinci.rr.com
www.valleyquiltsonline.com
Wonderful service. Lots of notions, books, patterns and beautiful fabrics.
Quilter's Dream batting. Great classes.
Husqvarna/Viking sales and service.

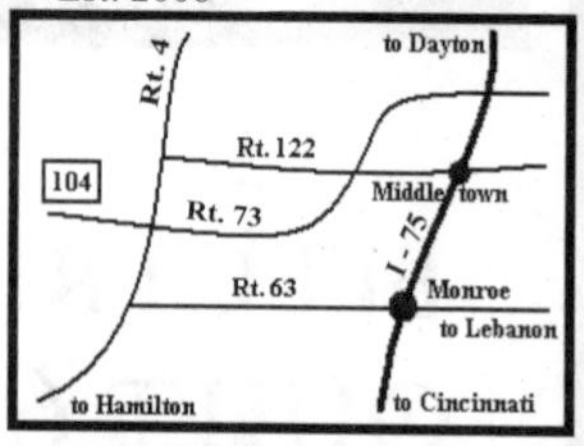

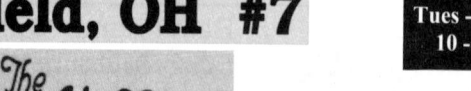

Sew-Ezy sewing studio

Mon - Fri 10 - 5:30
Sat 10 - 5

11427 Lebanon Rd. (US 42)
Sharonville, OH 45241
513-563-7474
www.sewezy.com

Cincinnati, OH #8

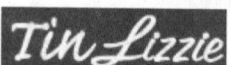

Tin Lizzie

Janome Sew-Ezy

Sharonville, OH

Cozy, intimate shop with fun and surprises tucked in every "nook and cranny" of our old house. You'll find beautiful fabric, countless patterns, wonderful books and notions along with lots of great samples and ideas.
You'll love your visit.

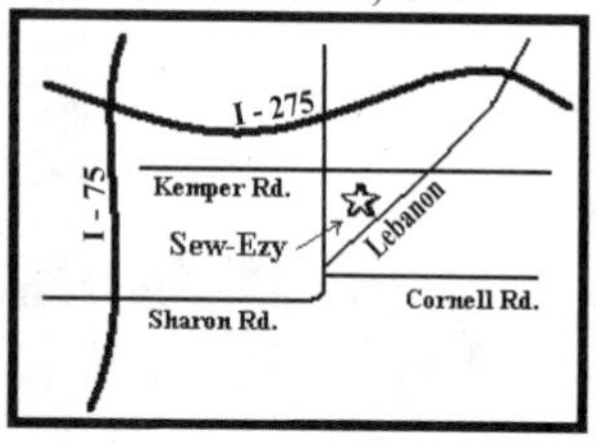

Fairfield, OH #7

The Bramble Patch

Tues - Sat 10 - 4

690 A Nilles Rd. 45014
(513) 829-0283
Est: 2005 1100 sq.ft. 500+ Bolts
www.bpquilts.com

Fabrics, Patterns, Notions, Classes
Thimbleberries Quilt Club
Machine Quilting on our Gammill Longarm

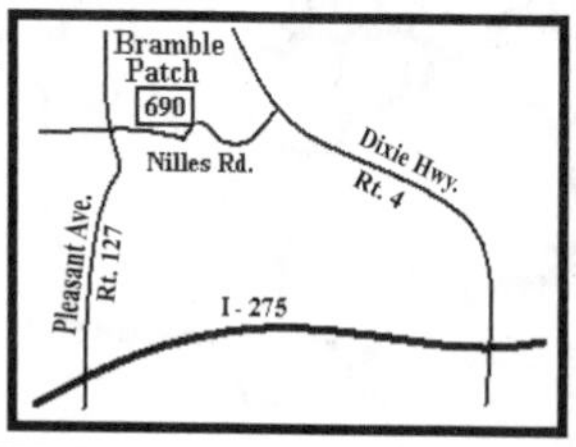

Sew-A-Lot
Creative Sewing Centers

Two Store Locations

232 N. Main St.
Centerville, Ohio 45459
937-433-7474
sewalot@erinet.com

2160 Sir Barton Way
Lexington, Kentucky 40509
859-264-7472
sewliz@earthlink.net

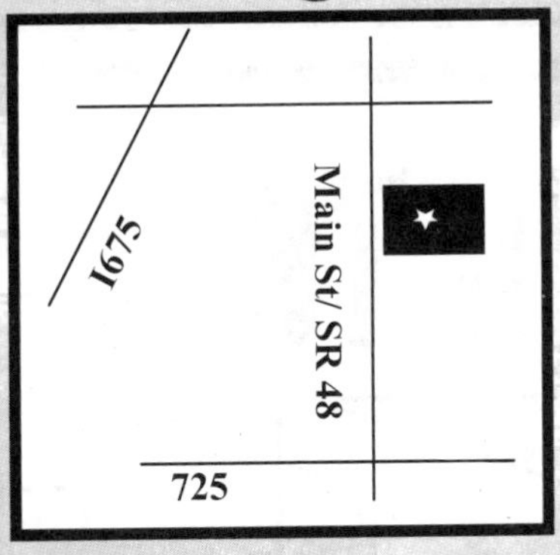

Centerville, Ohio # 9

Lexington, Kentucky

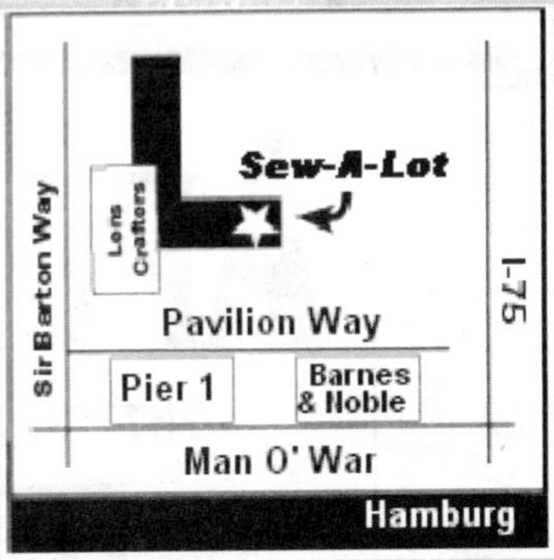

Authorized **PFAFF** Machine Dealer
Husqvarna Viking Dealer (Ohio only)
Specializing in **machine embroidery** and **quilting**.
Embroidery Designs, Patterns, Books, Threads, & Notions in stock!
FREE Newsletter and Classes are also available!

Our **Ohio** shop is located in a Historic Building built in 1874, less than half a mile off of I-675 and has
OVER 4500 BOLTS of FABRIC!
Our **Kentucky** shop is easily accessible off of interstate 75 and has
OVER 3000 BOLTS of FABRIC!

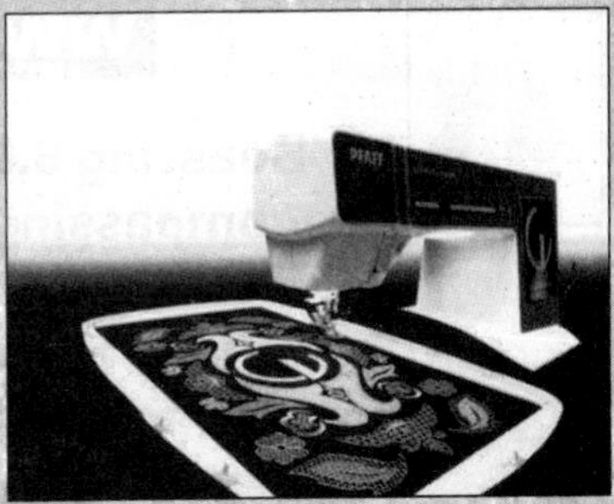

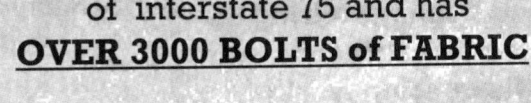

www.sewalotonline.com

Fabric Shack

Mon - Sat 10 - 5
Thur til 8 Sun 12 - 5

Waynesville, OH #10

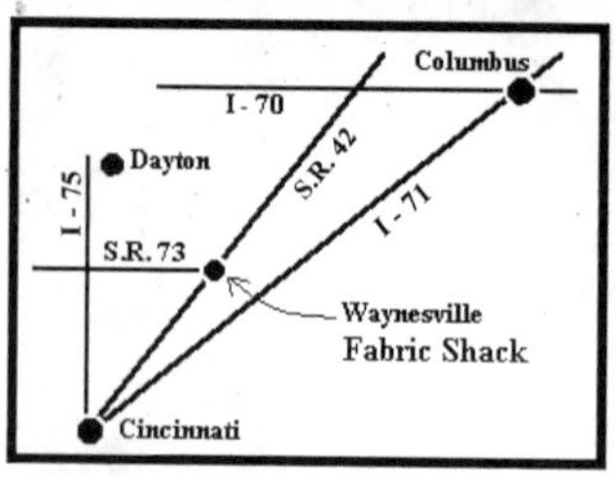

99 S. Marvin Ln. & Miami St. 45068
(877) 666-4245 or (513) 897-0092 Fax: (513) 897-7175
info@fabricshack.com www.fabricshack.com
Owner: Maxine Young Est: 1986 3000 sq.ft. 10,000+ Bolts

The ultimate quilt shop . . .
All the fabrics, colors, designers, the biggest in the midwest . . .
Notions, patterns, and books too!
Exclusive online supplier for Mountain Mist patterns and supplies.

Mountain Mist

Visit our website at www.fabricshack.com

We have over 20,000 fabrics online and in stock!
Click on Sale-A-bratioN to see 1,000's of beautiful fabrics at great prices!

The Fabric Shack, P.O. Box 517, Waynesville, OH 45068
(513) 897-0092 or (877) 666-4245 info@fabricshack.com

Order Form
Catalog

Please Print

Name ____________
Address ____________
City ____________
State ________ Zip ________
Telephone (   )____________

APPALACHIAN QUILTS

7577 Dayton Springfield Rd. 45324

Fairborn, OH #11

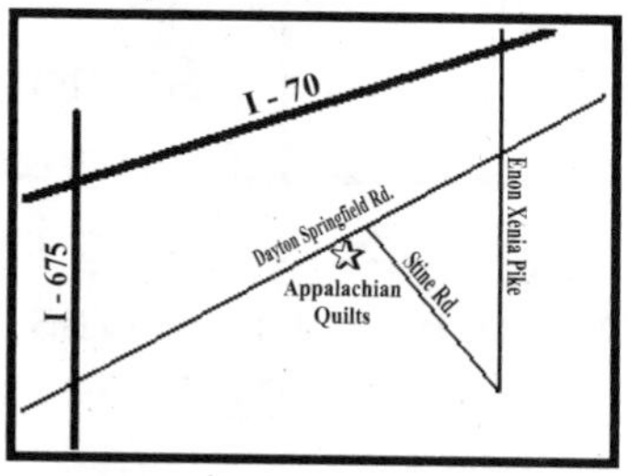

(937) 863-0070
appalachian@copper.net
Owner: Cynthia Faccenda
6000+ Bolts

www.quiltweb.net

Boasting 6,000 s.f., our shop has a full-encompassing inventory of notions, books, patterns, batting and quality quilting supplies, focusing on the latest trends and techniques in today's quilting world.

- **Thimbleberries**
- **Kansas Troubles**
- **Moda**
- **Jo Morton**
- **Kaffe Fasset**
- **The area's largest selection of backings and batiks**

Believe in Your Creativity
JANOME
Authorized Dealer

There is something for everyone!

Mon, Tues, Wed, Fri 10 - 5
Thurs 10 - 7 Sat 10 - 4

Springfield, OH #12

Creative Fires LLC

- Just minutes off I - 70
- Authorized BERNINA Dealer
- Authorized Tin Lizzie 18 Dealer
- Area's largest selection of Flannel
- Wide variety of Threads, Notions, Patterns, Design Cards, Fat Quarters, Quality Quilting Fabrics, Quilt Kits & Classes
- Online Store
- Excellent Service & Weekly Sales

1525 Progress Drive
Springfield, OH 45505
(937) 327-9420
Creativefires@sbcglobal.net
www.creativefires.net
Owners: Robert & Kathryn Fowler
Est. 2001 3,000 Sq. Ft.

BERNINA
Tin Lizzie 18
Your Affordable Longarm quilter

Normal Business Hours:
Tues, Wed, Fri 11 - 5
Thurs 11 - 7 Sat 11 - 3

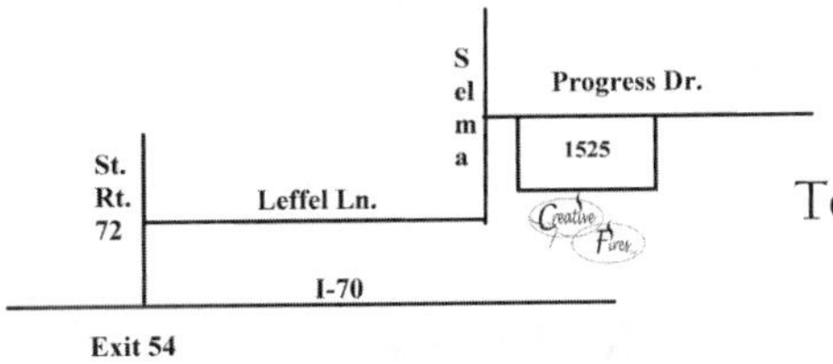

To sign up for our newsletter & weekly e-mail specials, please visit us at:
www.creativefires.net

Huber Heights, OH #13

Sulphur Grove Quilt Shop

Tues - Fri 10 - 5
Sat 10 - 4
Last Sun 12 - 4

7340 Taylorsville Rd. 45424
(866) 922-7021 or (937) 233-7021
Est: 2005 2000 bolts Online Newsletter
SulphurGroveQuiltShop@gmail.com
www.sulphurgrovequiltshop.com
The shop is quaint, friendly and prides itself on its customer service. We carry quality fabric, hard to find notions and a large selection of unusual patterns. Special Orders Welcome. Authorized HandiQuilter Dealer.

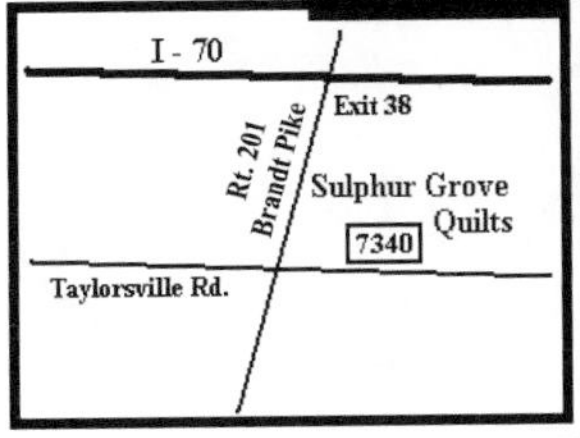

Pomeroy, OH #14

The Fabric Shop

Mon - Sat 9 - 5

110 W. Main St. 45769
(740) 992-2284 Fax: (740) 992-4189
Owner: Becky Anderson Est: 1959
becky@thefabricshop.net
www.thefabricshop.net

We specialize in QUILT FABRIC, NOTIONS AND MACHINE QUILTING. Biggest quilt shop in the area. Stop by, it will be worth your trip.

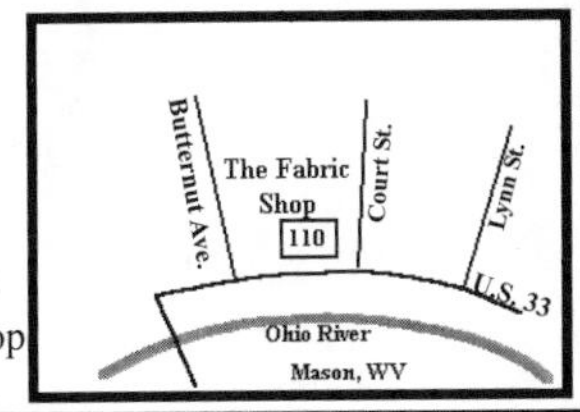

Nelsonville, OH #15

Nelsonville Quilt Co.

Tues - Sat 9:30 - 5:30
Last Fri of the Month 9:30 - 10
Sun - Mon appt. or by chance

52 W. Washington St. 45764
(740) 753-3343
Est: 2005 3300 sq. ft.
www.nelsonvillequilts.com

Located in the Historic Art District of Nelsonville. Fine quilting fabrics - great books, patterns & notions. Longarm quilting services available. Janome Dealer.

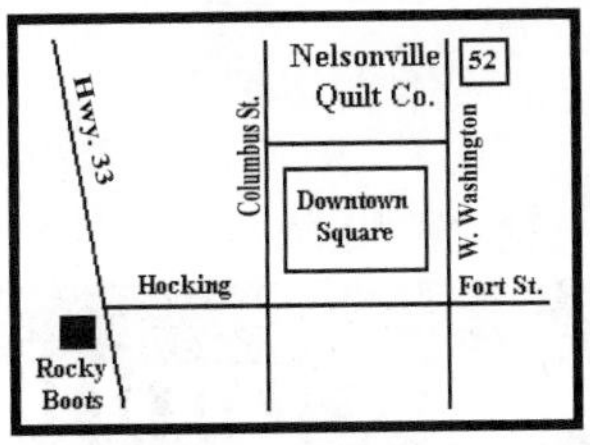

Logan, OH #16

Honey Fork Fabrics

Mon - Sat 10 - 6

19151 Goat Run-Honey Fork Rd. 43138
(740) 385-6072
Est: 1998 1000 sq.ft. Free Newsletter
questions@honeyforkfabrics.com
www.honeyforkfabrics.com
Quaint, full service shop in the country. Super selection of Hoffman Batiks, Moda Marbles, and many current fabric collections.

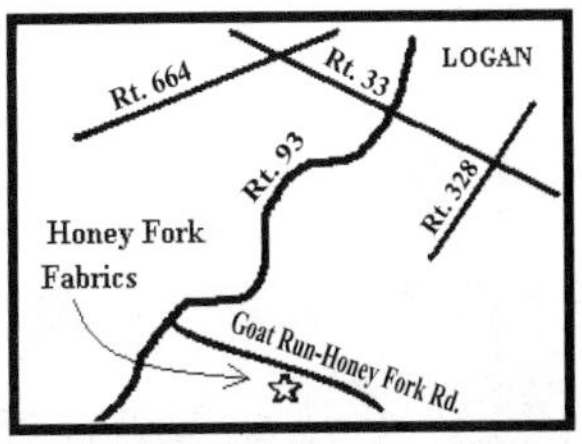

Quilt Beginnings

Thousands of Bolts • 2 Great Locations

Why visit Quilt Beginnings?

- Great selection of fabrics
- Inspiring samples
- Friendly and helpful staff
- Lots of kits ready to go
- Top tier Pfaff & Baby Lock dealer
- A fun place to shop

baby lock PFAFF

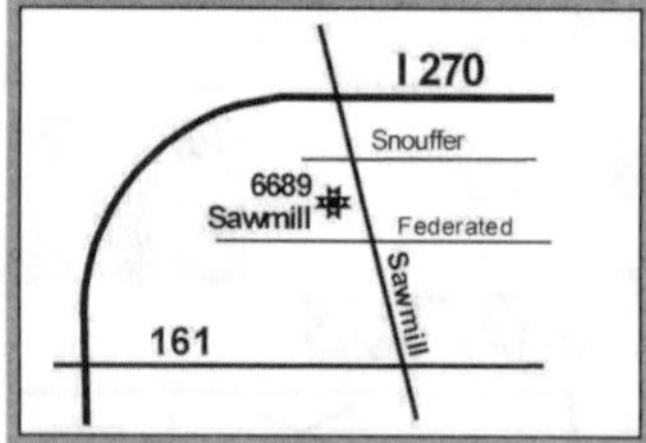

#17

NORTHWEST
6689 Sawmill Rd.
Dublin 43017
614.799.2688
Just south of I-270
Store Hours:
Mon & Wed 10-8 • Tue & Thu 10-6
Fri & Sat 10-5 • Sun Noon-5

EAST
3409 E. Broad St.
Columbus 43213
614.237.1322
Just east of James Rd.
Store Hours:
Mon & Wed 10-6 • Tue & Thu 10-8
Fri & Sat 10-5 • Sun Noon-5

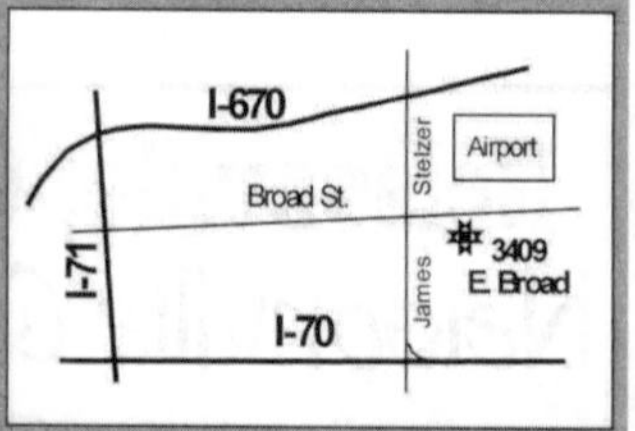

#18

Visit us at www.QuiltBeginnings.com

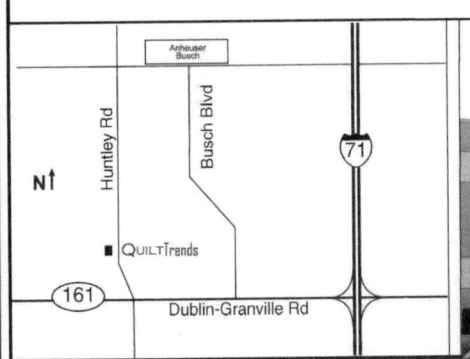

Columbus, OH #20

The Glass Thimble Quilt Shop

"New Ownership in August 2006"

3434 N. High St. 43214
800-323-1725 or 614-267-9566
Fax: 614-267-1795
Owners: Justine & Jamie McKenna
Est: 1979 5000 sq.ft.
customerservice@glassthimble.com
Free online newsletter

Mon - Sat 10 - 5 Tues & Thur til 8

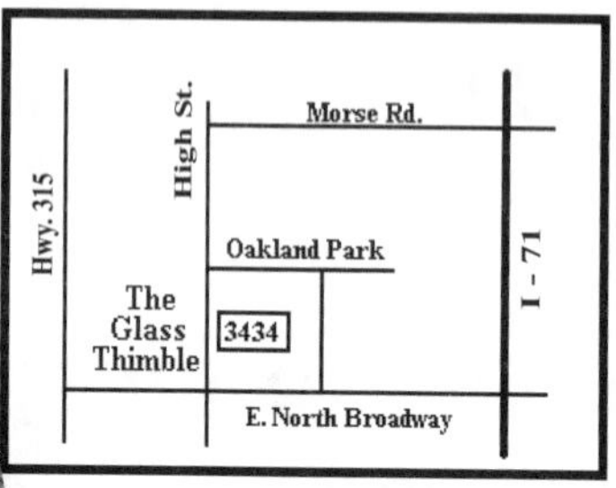

COME SHOP AT CENTRAL OHIO'S OLDEST AND MOST LOVED QUILT SHOP WITH THE LARGEST AND BEST SELECTION OF TOP QUALITY QUILTING FABRICS RANGING FROM CIVIL WAR REPRODUCTIONS TO BATIKS.

WWW.GLASSTHIMBLE.COM

Grove City, OH #21

Always In Stitches

**Mon, Wed & Fri 10 - 5
Tu & Th 10 - 8
Sat 10-4 Sun 12-4**

3937 Broadway St. #B 43123
(614) 539-7845 Fax: (614) 539-7846
maryclark1203@yahoo.com
www.alwaysinstitchesohio.com
Est: 2005 3800 sq.ft. 2000+ Bolts
Situated in a Beautifully Renovated Feed Store & Grainery. Housed with Scrapbook Shop and Day Spa. Shop Selection includes Batiks, Brights, Primitives & Flannels. Great Patterns & Books

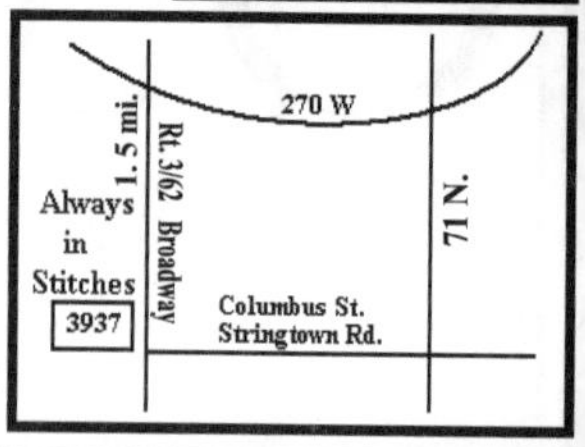

Your New Favorite Quilt Shop

Red Rooster Quilts

100+ Samples and Kits
Over 3,000 bolts of Fabric.
1000's of Fat Quarters
4500 sq.ft.

**Mon - Sat 10 - 5
Tues & Thur til 8**

48 Corbins Mill Dr. 43017
www.redroosterquilts.com
(614) 734-9007
Janome Sewing Machines

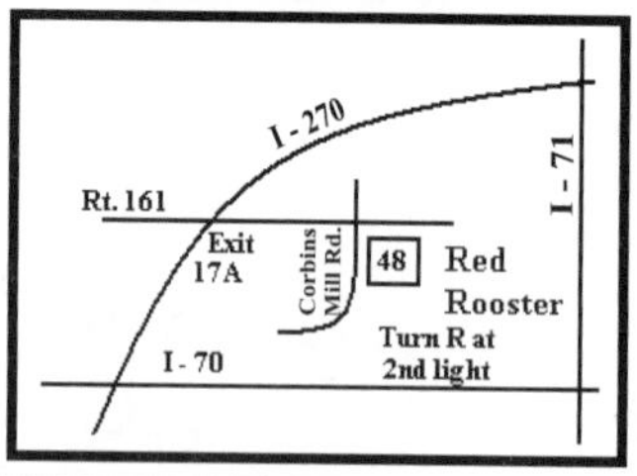

Dublin, OH #22

Newark, OH #23

Bunny's Sew Fine Fabrics

Mon - Sat 10 - 5:30 Wed til 7

28 Price Rd. 43055
(740) 366-1433 Est: 1999
sewfinefabrics@hotmail.com
www.bunnys-sewfinefabrics.com
Owner: Linda Schofield 2000 sq.ft.
Full service quilt shop. 2500 Bolts. Machine quilting service done in house. Notions, books, patterns and classes. Thimbleberries Club.

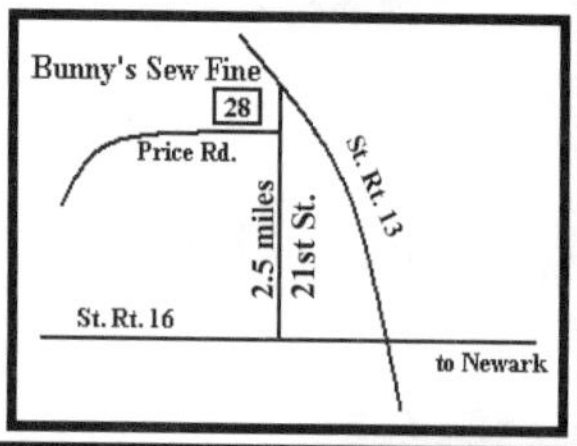

Pataskala, OH #24

Calico Cupboard

Mon - Sat 10 - 5 Thur til 8

74 Oak Meadow Dr.
43062
(740) 927-2636
Est: 2003
2000 sq.ft.
3000 bolts
calicocup@earthlink.net
www.calico-cupboard.com
Located in Pataskala Square.
We have 100% cotton, wool, flannel, homespuns, wool felt, books, patterns, notions.

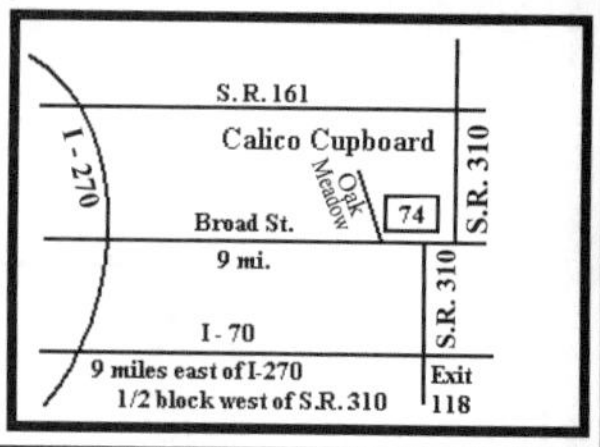

Marietta, OH #25

Quilter's Corner

Mon - Sat 9 - 5 Mon til 7

400 Tennis Center Dr. 45750
(740) 373-6150
Owner: Jenice Miller Est: 1985
info@mariettaquilts.com
www.mariettaquilts.com
Cotton Fabric * Stencils * Quilting Supplies
Batting * Patterns * Books * New Larger Showroom * Authorized Bernina® Dealer
Long-arm services available.

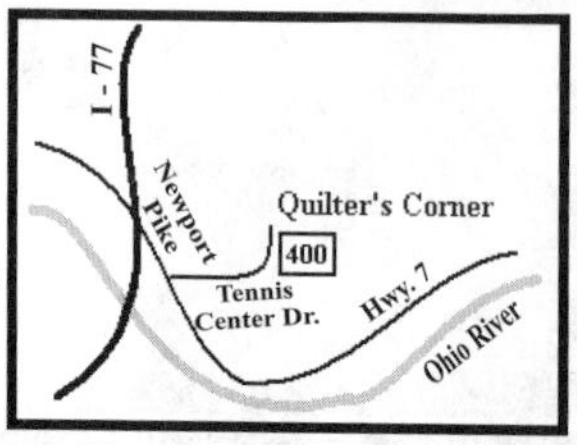

The Quilted Work

Marietta, OH #26

320 Stanleyville Narrows Rd.
mailing: Whipple, OH
45788
(740) 373-0579
Owners: Larry & Marla Work
workml@earthlink.net

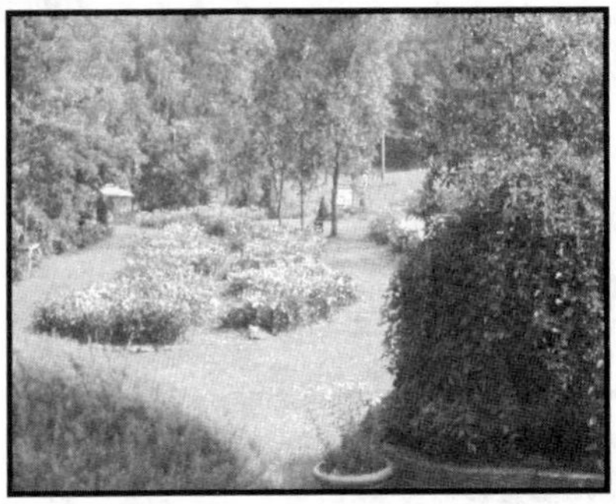

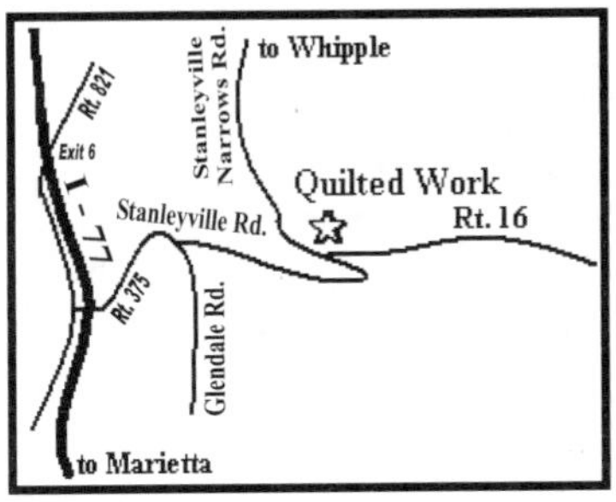

Located 10 minutes from Marietta, 4 miles off I - 77

www.thequiltedwork.net

7 Days a Week 10 - 6

- Fabric
- Accucut studio 200+ dies
- Go.Accucut Cutter Accessories
- Quilting Kits
- Longarm Quilting
- Plants for Sale
- Daylily Outings

We also have retreat facilities with a private kitchen, full bath & sleeping area.
"A Home away from Home."

Neff's Country Loft

Hinterberg Dealer
Rowe Pottery
Certified Dealer
Custom Framing

Two Shops in One: Country Store and Quilt Shop

Create your quilt from a selection of over 2000 Bolts. Specializing in the country look to a primitive Folk art feel. Enjoy our great collection of Moda designer fabrics, wools, primitive stitchery, quilt patterns, collectable books and wool rug hooking. Punch Needle embroidery is all the rage. Stop in and let us show you how to begin your project.

Browse and enjoy shopping in our unique Country atmosphere where you will be inspired by our country accents and displays to help complete your homespun lifestyle.

2514 Washington Blvd.
Belpre, OH 45714
Phone/Fax: (740) 423-1965
neffscountryloft@sbcglobal.net

Celebrating our 16th year in business!

Belpre, OH #27

We host sewing retreats, rug hooking workshops, and classes for all Levels. Member of Mystery Shop Hop in October.

Mon - Fri
10 - 6
Sat 10 - 5
Sun's Seasonal

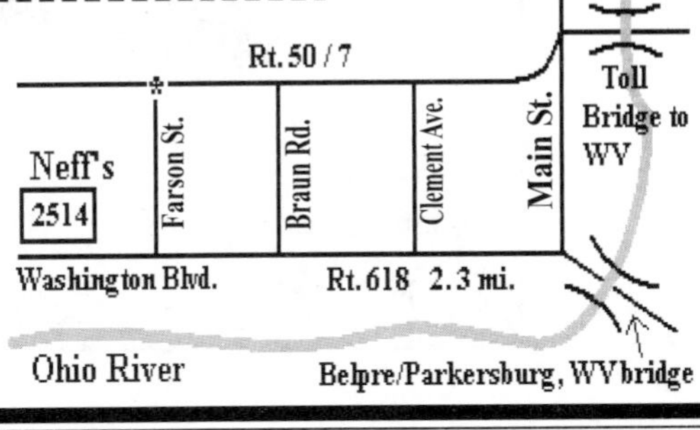

www.neffscountryloft.com

Mt. Perry, OH #28

Mon, Wed, & Thur 9 - 5
Tues 9 - 9

Snip N Stitch

8845 Bagley Rd. 43760
(740) 849-2413 Fax: (740) 849-2911
Owners: Bernadine Swingle & Paula Frank
Est: 1976 800+ Bolts Online newsletter
snipnstitch@hughes.net
www.snipnstitch.com
A beautiful drive in the country to our little country quilt shop. Lots of kits, notions, quilt fabric and Viking sewing machines.

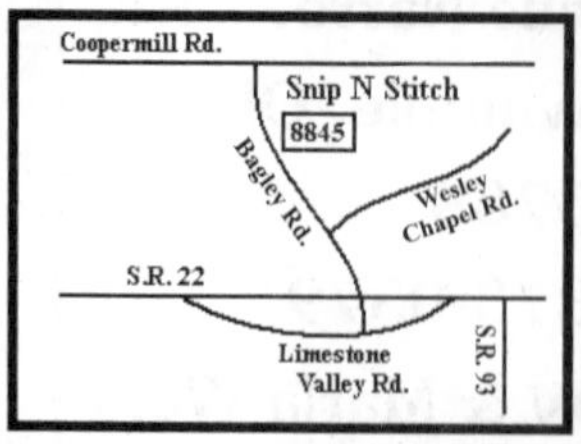

Zanesville, OH #29

A Touch of Thread Quilting Gallery

2885 E. Pike, US Rt. 40 43701
(740) 454-8372
(800) 760-7701
martha@atouchofthread.net

Mon - Fri 10 - 6
Sat 10 - 2

A Touch of Thread Quilting Gallery, where a touch of thread becomes a thing of beauty. Over 5000 square feet of Quilters' dreams. We are the authorized Gammill Quilting Machine dealer for Ohio and much of WV, KY, IN and PA. We carry the full line of BabyLock Sewing, Embroidery, and Serger Machines, as well as a large selection of quality fabrics, notions, and several lines of threads for sewing, embroidery, and machine quilting. New to sewing and quilting? We offer classes for Longarm quilters and sewers, with nationally recognized and local teachers.

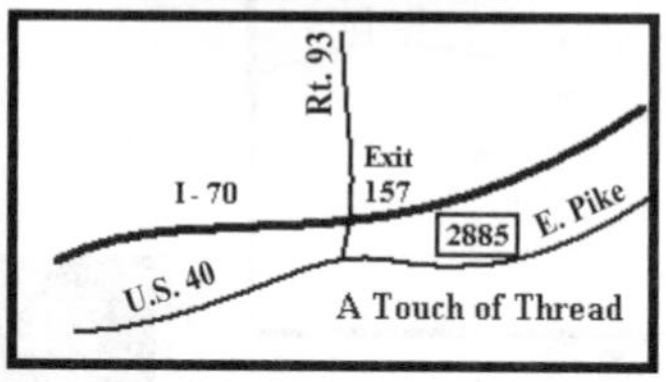

baby lock
Gammill Quilting Systems Authorized Dealer
Statler Stitcher

www.atouchofthread.net

Zanesville, OH #30

Mon - Fri 10 - 5
Tues til 7
Sat 10 - 4

Nonna's Quilting Nook

1004 Beverly Ave. 43701
(740) 450-2626 Fax: Same
Owners: Phil & Rita Lawrence
Est: 2005 3000 sq.ft. 3000 Bolts
rlawrence004@columbus.rr.com

Large selection of quality fabrics including Hoffman, Moda, RJR, Red Rooster & Benartex. PFAFF authorized sales and service dealer.

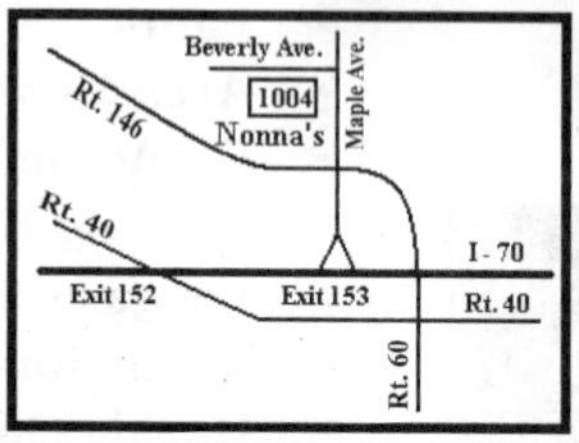

Cambridge, OH #31

Almost Sisters Quilt Shop, LLC

1996 E. Wheeling Ave.
Cambridge, OH 43725
(740) 435-9590

The friendly quilter's haven

Fabric, Classes, Patterns, Kits
& Long Arm Quilting Service
www.almostsistersquilts.com

Mon - Fri 10 - 5
Tues til 8
Sat 10 - 3

Fax: (740) 432-7043
Owners: Evelyn Smith
& Charlene Watts
evsmith@live.com
charwatts@wildblue.net

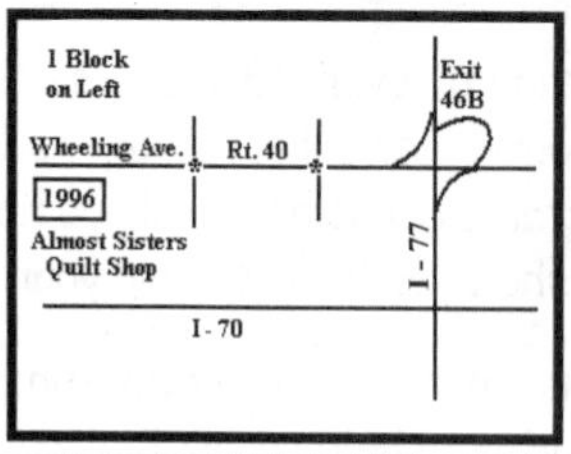

Barnesville, OH #32

Tues - Fri 10 - 5
Sat 10 - 3
Closed July 12-24 in 2010 and 2011

Karen's Quilt & Craft Connection

119 W. Main St. 43713
(740) 425-2100
Owner: Karen Deliman Est: 2003
www.zippytech.com/~karenscrafts/
The Quilt Store with More.
Quality quilting fabrics and stamped embroidery.

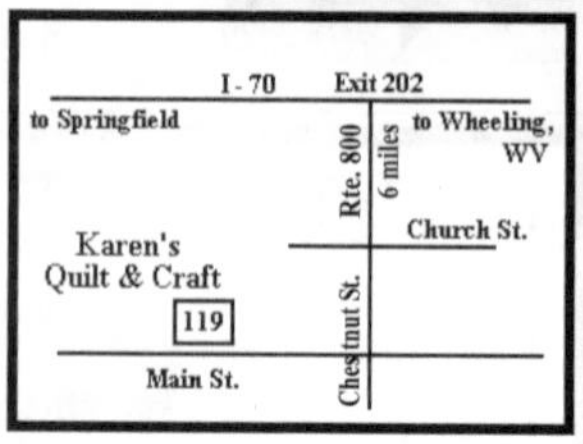

Charm, OH #33

Miller's Dry Goods

4500 S.R. 557 Est: 1965
Mail—Millersburg, OH 44654
(330) 893-9899
Owners: The Miller Family
quilts@millersdrygoods.com

Mon - Sat 8 - 5

Over 8,000 bolts of fabric, including outlet in basement. Beautiful selection of local handmade Quilts, Wall Hangings, Rugs, Tablerunners, etc. Also Quilt books, patterns, stencils and lots of notions.

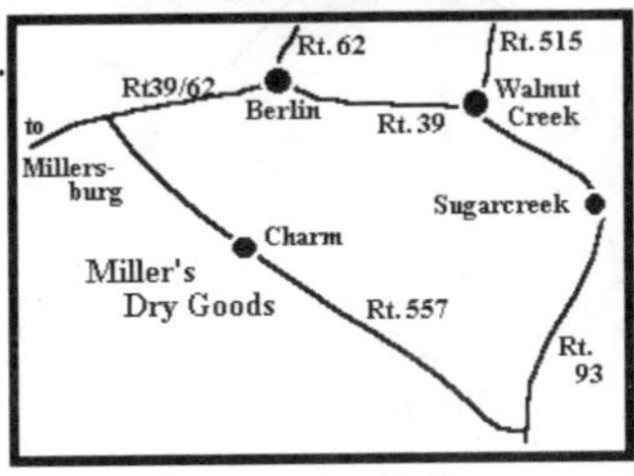

Visit our new online store **www.millersdrygoods.com**

Mt. Vernon, OH #34

Paw Patch Quilt Shop

444 Columbus Rd. Suite E
Mt. Vernon, OH 43050
(740) 397-9450

Fax: (740) 397-9450
Jean, Carol & Sam
ppqs@embarqmail.com
2000 sq.ft. 2000+ bolts

www.ppqs.net

"The shop for quilters and those who just love quilts."

Mon - Fri 10 - 5
Sat 10 - 3

JANOME
Because You Simply Love To Sew™
Authorized dealer and service center

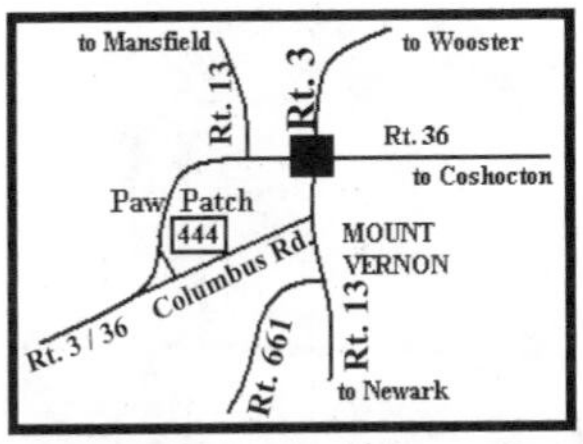

Helping Hands

Quilt Shop & Museum

- fabrics - over 3000 bolts
- books & patterns
- embroidery & quilt kits
- stencils
- notions & supplies
- quilting frames
- crafts
- quilts
- wall hangings
- 2 buildings - 2 floors
- custom orders welcome
- quarterly newsletter
- everyday sale area (50% off)

Mon - Sat 9 - 5

www.helpinghandsquilts.com
4818 St. Rt. 39 (Main St.)
P.O. Box 183 44610
(330) 893-2233 Est: 1975

Bus Tours-Please call ahead for "special" customer service and gift.
Air conditioned, MC/Visa/Discover accepted. WE SHIP.
Lodging, Restaurants and ATMs within walking distance.

Destination Quilt Shop

Berlin, OH #35

Gramma Fannie's Quilt Barn

Mon - Sat 10 - 5

Visit our unique shop specializing in:
- our own line of patterns & kits
- custom order and locally made quilts available
- top of the line quilt fabrics
- books & stencils

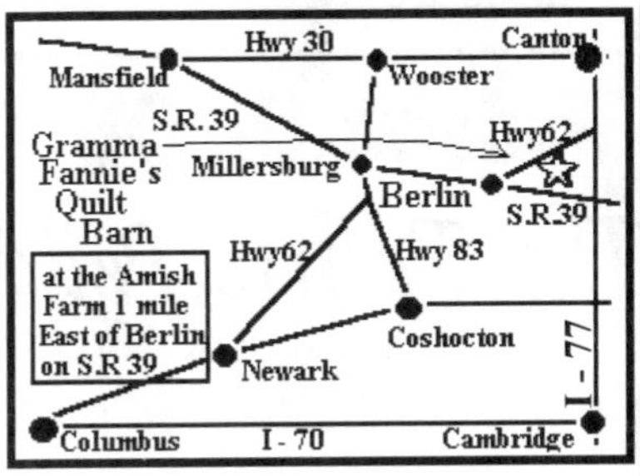

Located at Schrock's Amish Farm and Home

4363 State Route 39
P.O. Box 270
Berlin, OH 44610
(330) 893-3243
Est: 1991
1 mile east of Berlin

www.GrammaFanniesQuilts.com

Berlin, OH #36

Berlin, OH #37

Mon - Sat 10 - 5

Country Craft Cupboard

P.O. Box 419, 4813 E. Main St.
(330) 893-3163 44610
www.countrycraftcupboard.com
Owner: Karen Lamp
Est: 1984 3500 sq.ft. Moda Fabrics
1000+ bolts of specialty fabrics, including 100% wool. Supplies for rug hooking, scrapbooking, rubber stamping, counted cross stitch & punch needle! Hundreds of patterns & models. In an Old Country Store!

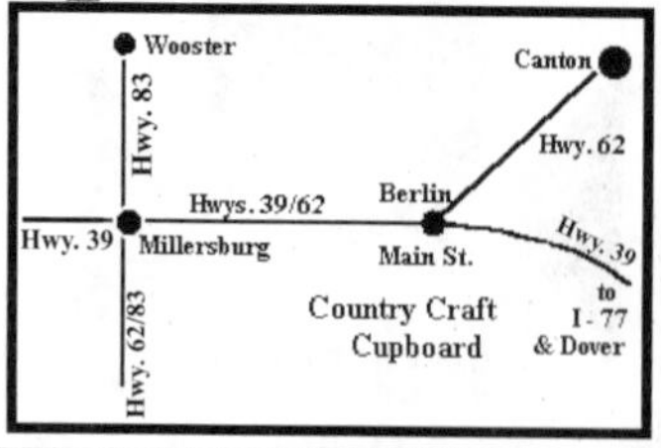

Apple Creek, OH #38

Mon 8 - 7 Tues - Fri 8 - 5 Sat 8 - 4

Pine Tree Fabric

12464 Western Rd. 44606
(330) 857-3651
We are located 1 mile south of Kidron.
¼ mi. West on Western Road
Our Shop has Top Quality Quilt Fabric, etc.

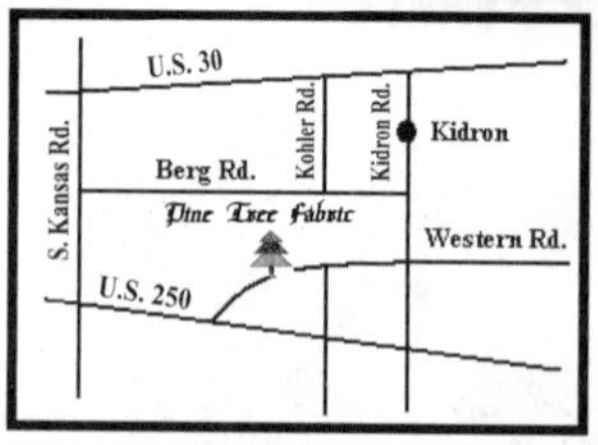

Kidron, OH #39

Hearthside Quilt Shoppe & Needle Nook

13110 Emerson Rd.
PO Box 222, Kidron, OH 44636
Located next to Lehman's Old Fashioned Hardware
(330) 857-4004
info@hearthsidequiltshoppe.com
Owner:
Glenda Lehman-Ervin
Mgr. Cheryl Gerber
Est: 1990 4800 sq.ft.

Mon - Sat 9:30 - 5

You will enjoy the warm and welcoming atmosphere among the thousands of bolts of designer fabrics, hundreds of books, patterns and quilting supplies. It will keep you looking all day!

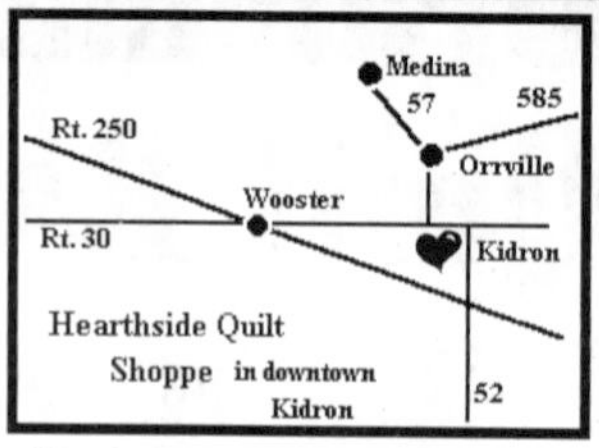

www.hearthsidequiltshoppe.com

Quilt Garden

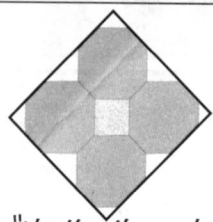

"planting the seeds of quilting"

1664 N. Main St.,
North Canton, OH 44720
(330) 966-6670

North Canton, OH #40

Est: 2004

Mon - Fri 10 - 5 Sat 10 - 4

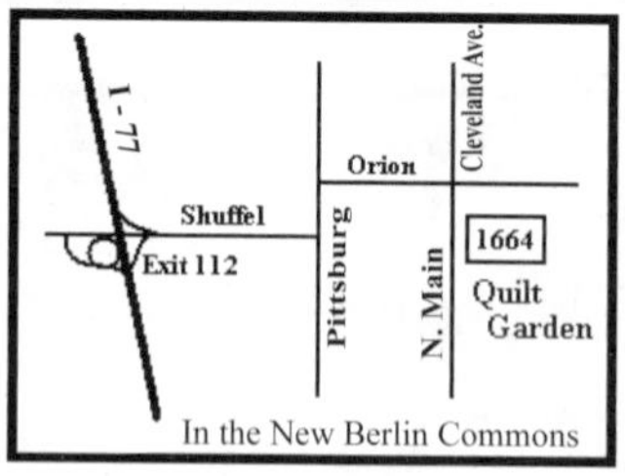

Spacious shop with friendly, knowledgeable staff.
Karen Conley, proprietor
The very latest fabrics from Moda, Hoffman, RJR, Timeless Treasures and more. Books, patterns, kits and notions.
Spacious classroom and longarm rental.

Wadsworth, OH #41

Mon - Fri 10 - 6 Sat 10 - 5

The Fabric Peddler

139 College St. 44281
(330) 336-1101
Owner: Barb Moore
Est: 1998 2000+ Bolts
fabricpeddler@yahoo.com
Over 2000 bolts of Quality Fabric, Books, Patterns, Quilting Supplies & Cross Stitch. Participant in The Ohio Amish Country Quilt Shop Hop.

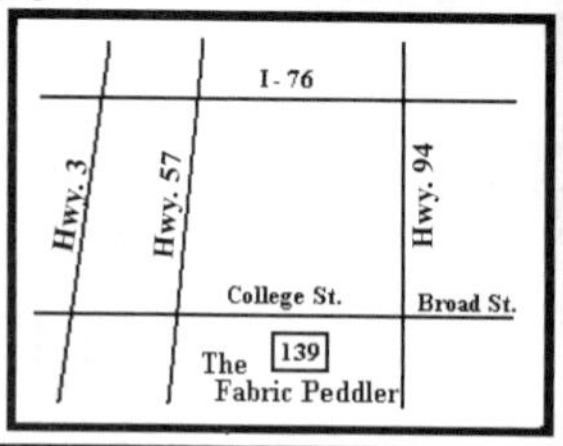

BERNINA STORE & SEW MUCH MORE

Boardman, OH #42

2 Great Locations

7081 West Blvd. 44512
(330) 726-9396

Mon, Tues, Wed 10 - 6 Thur 10-8 Fri 10-5 Sat 10-4 Sun Closed

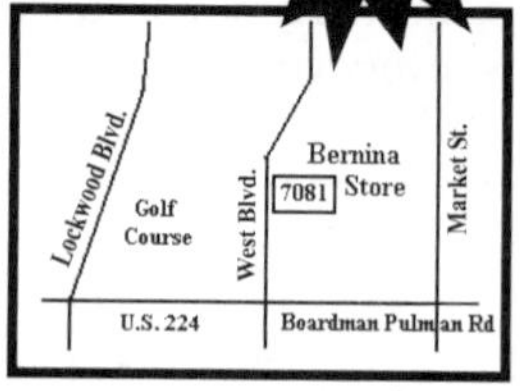

www.berninastore.com

Twinsburg, OH #43

Owner: Joyce Martin
joyce@berninastore.com

8900 H-107 Darrow Rd. 44087
(330) 487-0460

Mon, Wed, Thur 10 - 6 Tues 10 - 8 Fri 10 - 5 Sat 10 - 4 Sun Closed

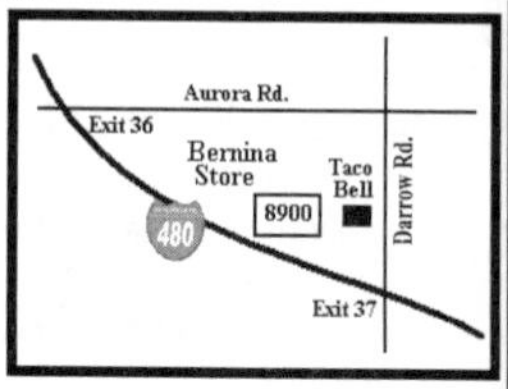

Full-Line, Full-Service BERNINA Dealer.
Sewing, Embroidery and Serging Machines & Classes, Notions, Supplies, Quilting Fabric & Supplies. Unique Sewing Furniture, Horn & Regal Cabinets.

A Piece in Time

A Piece in Time Quilt Shop & Creative Sewing Center

Your complete quilting and sewing center, featuring Bernina, Elna and Pfaff machines. Incredible selection of beautiful fabrics, books, notions, patterns and gifts.

You'll be inspired by all our beautiful quilts on display! "Wow, better than a quilt show!"

Exquisite custom machine quilting...send us your tops! Call ahead to schedule a bus tour visit!

Akron, OH #44

Open 7 Days: Mon-Thur 10-6 Fri & Sat 10-5 Sun 12-4

3963 S. Main St., Akron, OH 44319
Corner of S. Main and St. Rt. 619,
in the plaza next to Hallmark
330-644-6100 or 1-800-SANDY-98 (726-3998)

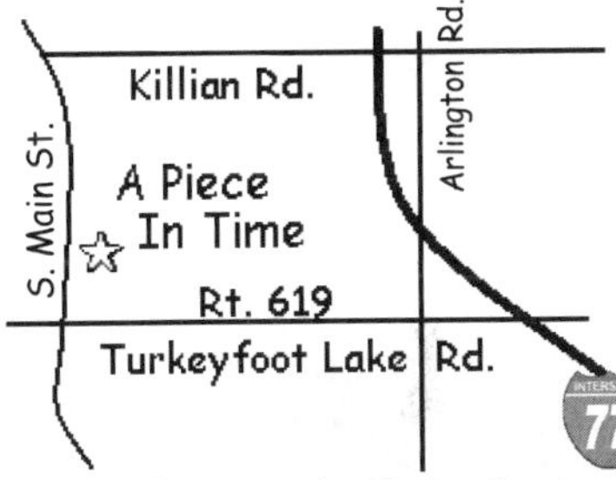

In the South Main Center
Next to Hallmark

Cuyahoga Falls, OH #45

Mon - Thur 10 - 9
Fri & Sat 10 - 4

Stitch, Piece 'n Purl

2018 State Rd. 44223
(330) 928-9097 Fax: (330) 928-4766
info@stitchpiecenpurl.com
www.stitchpiecenpurl.com
Northeast Ohio's most complete Needlework Shop. Quilting Fabric, Specialty Yarn, Cross Stitch, Needlework Supplies, Punch Needle, Hand Dyed Wool & Floss, Spinning Wheels, Notions, Books, Patterns, Classes.

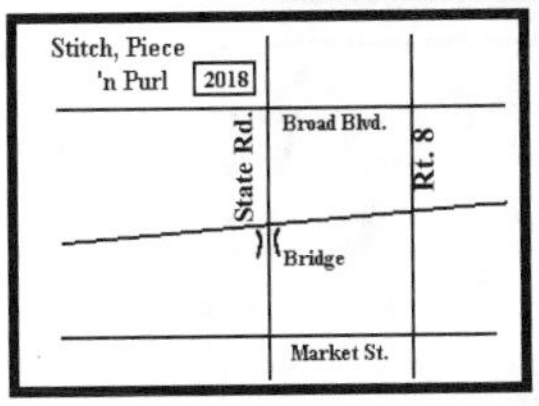

Kent, OH #46

Est: 2006 1800 sq.ft.

Katie Brooke Quilt Shop

144 E. Main St. 44240
(330) 677-1156
2000 bolts Online newsletter
ktbrookedesigns@yahoo.com
www.katiebrookequiltshop.com

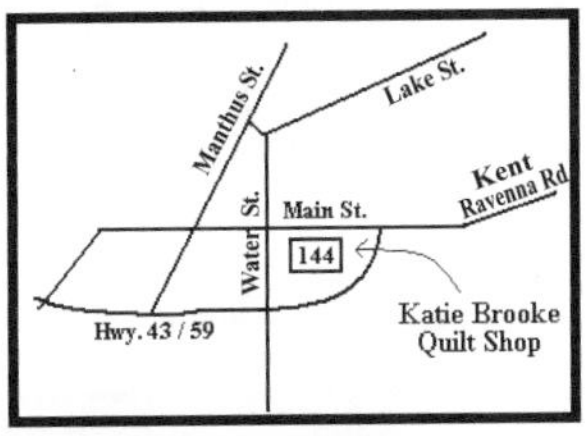

Mon - Fri 10 - 5, Thurs til 8, Sat 10 - 4

We specialize in Civil War, 30's & 40's reproductions and florals. Quilt frames and hangers. Classes & Clubs, Special Events

Located in downtown Kent at Acorn Alley and close to Kent State Fashion Museum.

Garrettsville, OH #47

Tues - Sat 10 - 5
Thur til 7

Shaker Tree

8119 Main St. 44231
(330) 527-0112
Est: 2004 3200 sq.ft. 2500+ bolts
www.shakertree.com

Come enjoy top quality quilt fabrics from Moda, RJR, Thimbleberries, Michael Miller, and others. We also carry a nice selection of homespuns and flannels. We have a wonderful selection of wool on the bolt, as well as random cuts of hand-dyes.

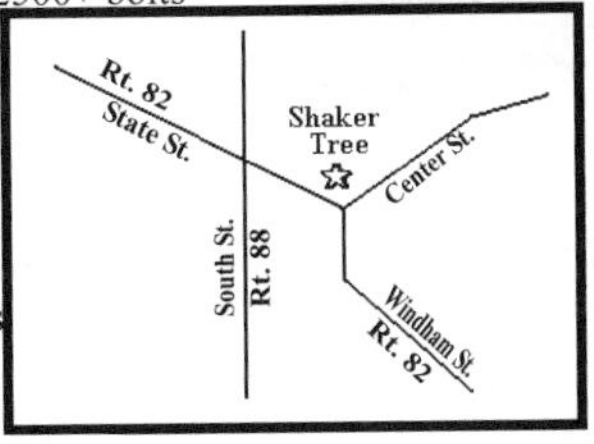

Niles, OH #48

Mon - Fri 10 - 5
Tues til 6
Sat 10 - 2

Viking and White Sewing Center

40 Youngstown Warren Rd. 44446
(330) 544-5300
Est: 1996 2800 sq.ft. 1000+ bolts
vwniles@cboss.com
www.viking-white-niles.com

Visit our spacious showroom offering quilters with top quality fabric and accessories.
Complete line of Husqvarna Viking sewing machines.

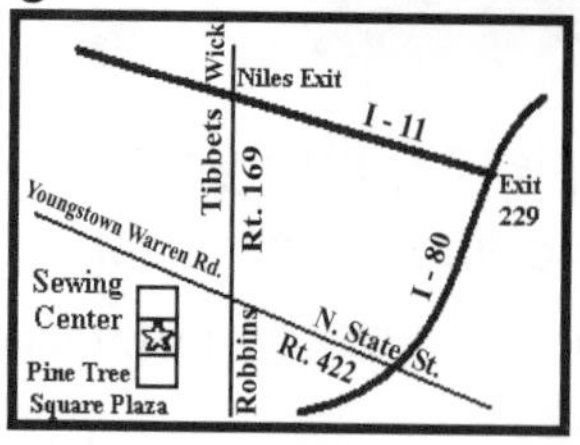

Warren, OH #49

Mon - Fri 10 - 5
Tues til 8
Sat 10 - 2

Just Quilt It
A QUILTERS MARKET

171 Folsom St. NW 44483
(330) 469-6956
Est: 2010 2500 sq.ft. 1000 bolts
info@aquiltersmarket.com
www.aquiltersmarket.com
"A Quilters Market" of supplies, fabrics, notions, books, and patterns.
Custom machine quilting.

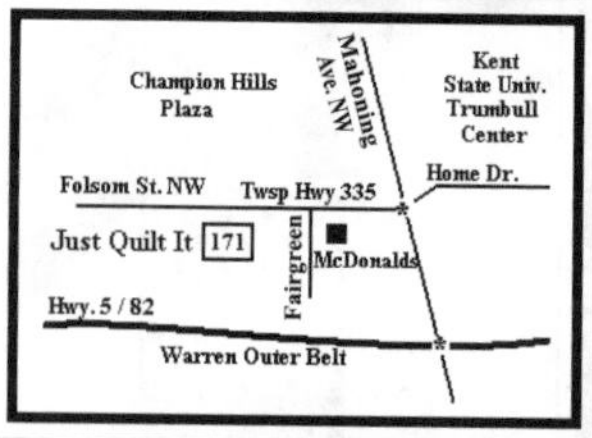

Cortland, OH #50

Designers Two
Fabrics & Sewing Machines

140 N High St. (Rt. 5) 44410
Phone & Fax 330-638-3737
Owner: Peg Viole Est: 1989

Mon - Fri 10 - 5
Sat 10 - 2

Quilting cottons to die for. The best quality, fabulous colors & prints. Lots of novelties too. Unusual notions & gadgets, fun patterns, & more!
Our shop is stuffed to the brim & well worth the trip!

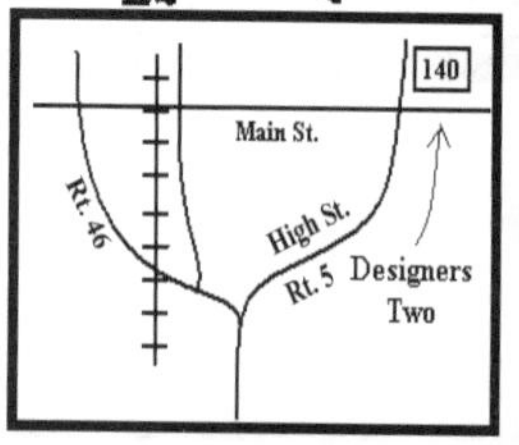

Cortland, OH #51

Tues - Fri 11 - 5
Sat 11 - 3

Quilter's Fancy LLC

124 N. High St. 44410
(866) 953-0722
Owner: Cindy Oravecz

www.quiltersfancy.com
Embellishments for Quilts, Clothing & Needle Art. Your resource for hard-to-find needles, notions, charms, gifts, 3D fabric and ribbon flowers, fabric, trim and beads.

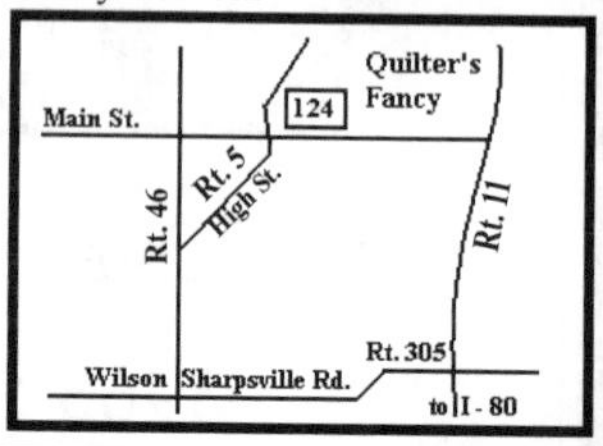

Wayne, OH #52

Tues 10 - 8
Wed - Fri 10 - 6
Sat 10 - 4
1st Sun 1 - 5

a little Touch of Heaven
Quilt Shoppe

102 E. Main St. 43466
Rte. 281, P.O. Box 373
(419) 288-2300

Owner: Cindy Reynolds
Est: 2008 1500 sq.ft. 1100 bolts
reynco55@yahoo.com
www.littletouchofheaven.org

Fabric, Notions, Longarm Services, Gifts and Classes.

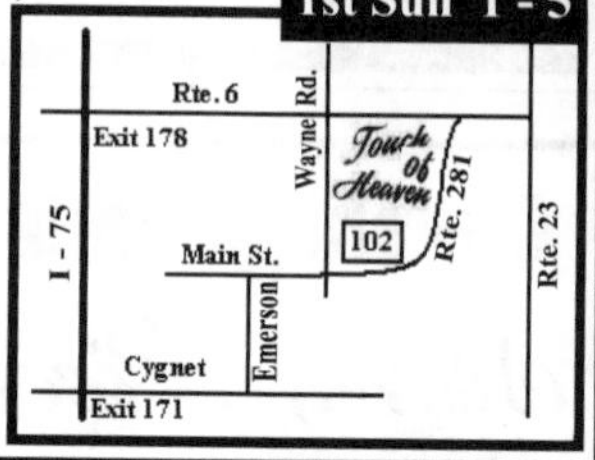

Madison, OH #53

Mon - Fri 10 - 5:30
Thur til 6:30
Sat 10 - 4

Cottonpicker's Quilt Shop

136-A W. Main St. 44057
(440) 428-6449
Owner: Beth Safick Est: 2004
1100 sq.ft. 1700 Bolts Free Newsletter
cottonpickers@ncweb.com
www.cottonpickersquiltshop.com
We specialize in Quality Quilting Fabrics, Notions & Classes for all levels. We also carry Wool, Rug Hooking supplies & Gifts.
Friendly service always available.

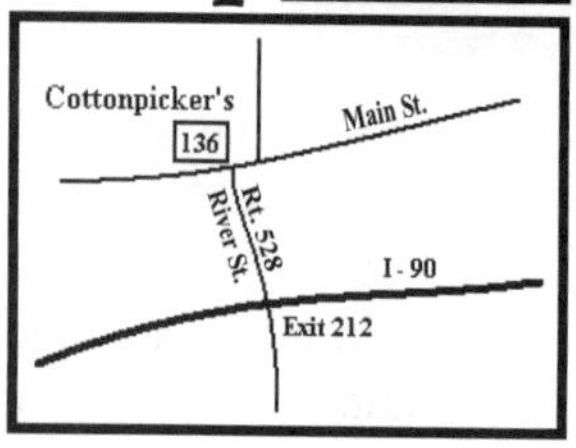

Mentor, OH #54

Mon - Fri 9 - 5
Sat 10 - 5
Eve Classes Avail.

Quilts & Sew Forth

7312 Center St. 44060
(440) 266-1601
Fax: (440) 266-1602

Owners: Monique Noonan & Hilary Cavotta
Est: 2009 1200 sq.ft. 2400 bolts
info@quiltsandsewforth.com
www.quiltsandsewforth.com
From fabric and notions to books, we offer education and service to inspire customers to explore all kinds of sewing. Free Newsletter.

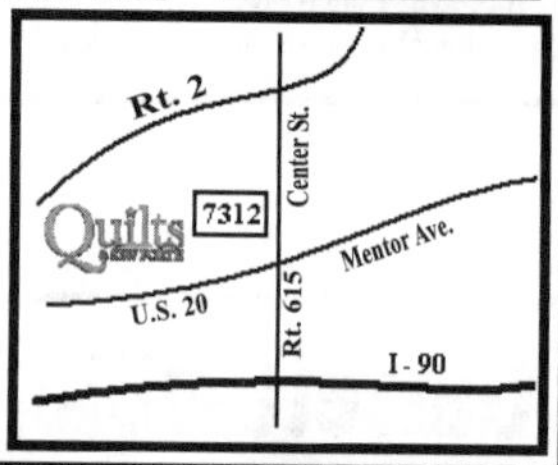

Eastlake, OH #55

Tues - Sat 10 - 6
Sun 12 - 4

Mara's Fabric & Gifts

35003 Vine St. 44095
(440) 942-7849 Est: 2006
Owner: Mara Walker
marasfabric@sbcglobal.net
www.marasfabricandgifts.com

A Quaint and Friendly Quilt Shop.
We are committed to offering quality quilting fabrics, patterns and books.

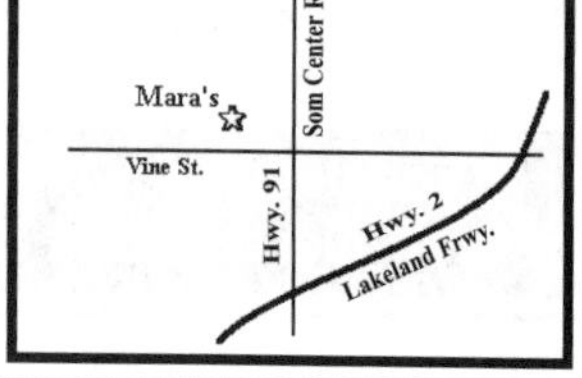

Middlefield, OH #56

Mon - Fri 10 - 5
Closed Wed
Sat 10 - 2

Tiny Stitches LLC

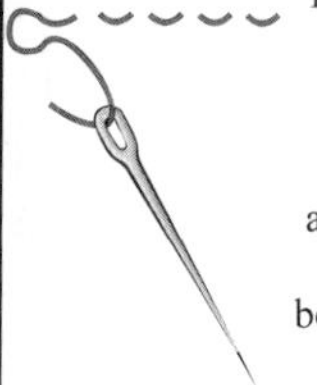

14277 Old State Rd. 44062
(440) 632-9410
Est: 2007

Located at Settler's Village among other specialty shops. Offering fabrics, notions, books, patterns, wallhangings, quilts and quilted gifts.

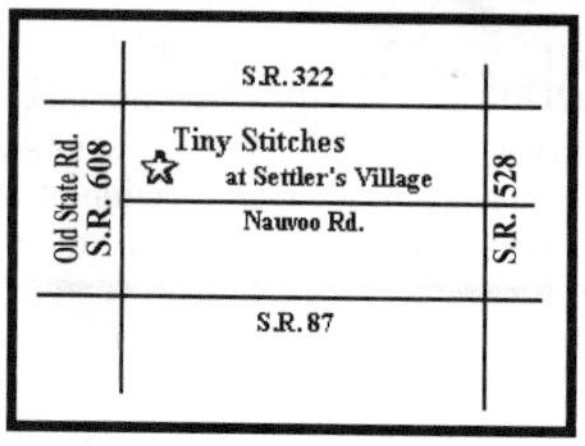

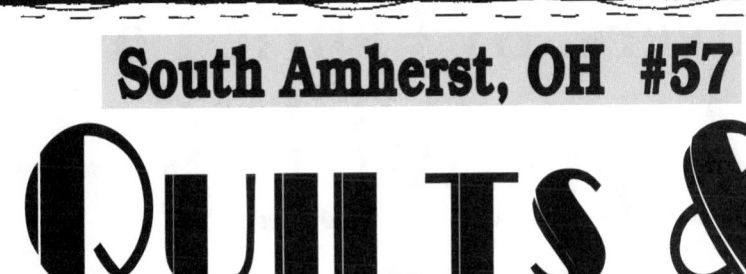

South Amherst, OH #57

QUILTS & KREATIONS

101 E. Main St. 44001
Phone / Fax (440) 986-4132
quiltskreations@centurytel.net
www.quiltskreations.com
Owner: Sandra Whitaker

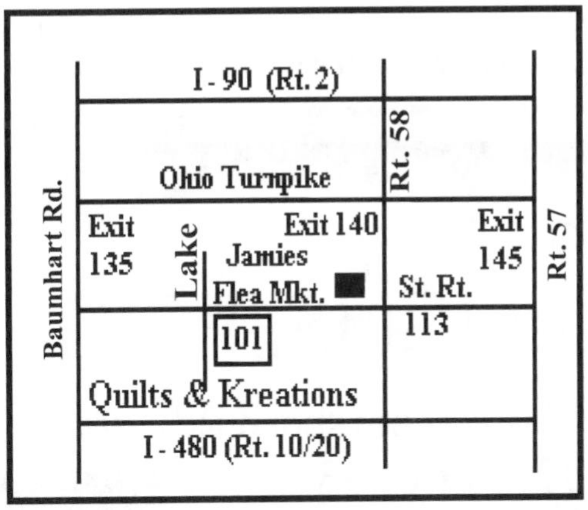

QUILTS & KREATIONS was established in 1980 and we have grown in size throughout the years. We offer you over 3600 sq.ft. of shopping area in our 100+ year old building. There are over 6000 bolts of designer fabric to choose from and one thousand of these bolts are flannels. We stock the area's largest selection of 100% cotton fabrics, patterns, and books. We are Lorain County's only authorized Bernina Dealer and Lorain County's most complete quilt shop. Authorized Happy Embroidery Machine Dealer also.

Easily accessible from either the Ohio Turnpike or Interstate Route 90. We are 1.6 miles west of State Route 58 on State Route 113 in South Amherst, Ohio. We are on the southeast corner of the street at the light.

BERNINA

Mon - Sat 10 - 5
Thur til 7
Oct to April Sun 12 - 4

For Fabric Lovers, By Fabric Lovers

ABIGAYLE'S Quiltery

Mon - Sat 10 - 5
Thur til 8
Sun 12 - 5

Olmsted Falls, OH #58

8096 Columbia Rd. 44138 (440) 235-7446
shop@abigayles.com www.abigayles.com
Owners: Beverly Morris & Nancy Bryant
Est: 1999 5000+ Bolts

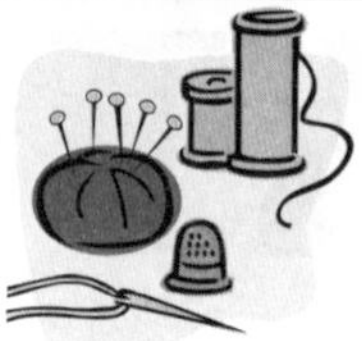

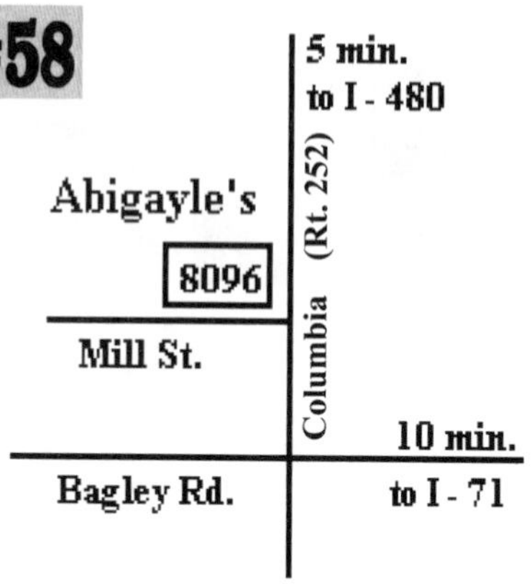

Located in Grand Pacific Junction in Historic Olmsted Falls, Ohio, Abigayle's Quiltery occupies the Simmerer Homestead; a large, charming Victorian home. Step back in time & allow yourself to stroll along the brick walkways & visit the surrounding shops.

At Abigayle's we take pride in our great selection of ever-changing samples, huge class schedule, many fun and interesting clubs, both here at the shop and by mail. We host several quilt shows and feature almost constant trunk shows. We stock books, patterns, BERNINA & Pfaff sewing machines and the newest, most wonderful 100% cotton fabrics around.

POLKA DOT pincushion inc.

4131 W. Streetsboro Rd. 44286
330-659-0233

Monday 12-5
Tuesday 10-5
Wednesday 10-5
Thursday 10-8
Friday 10-5
Saturday 10- 4
Sunday Closed

A great place to find inspiration for your next sewing or quilting project. Choose from many kits, classes and workshops for all levels. Sign up for our emails to receive news of special events and our newsletter.

www.pdpincushion.com

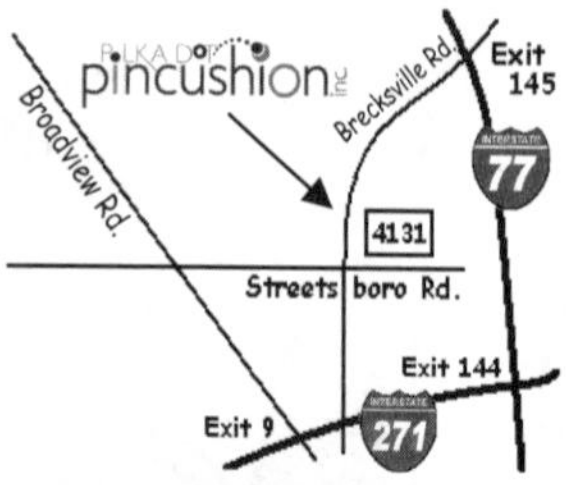

Opened: 2005 3000 bolts
2450 square feet
Owner: Ronnie Rajkovich
ronnie@pdpincushion.com

Richfield, OH #59

Medina, OH #60

Little Red Quilt House

3616 Ridge Rd. 44256
(234) 248-4492
Est: 2009 2500 sq.ft.
500+ bolts
Online Newsletter
raescott@aol.com

Mon - Wed 10 - 7
Thurs & Fri 10 - 5
Sat 9 - 4
Closed on the Lord's Day

"The House where all are welcome!"

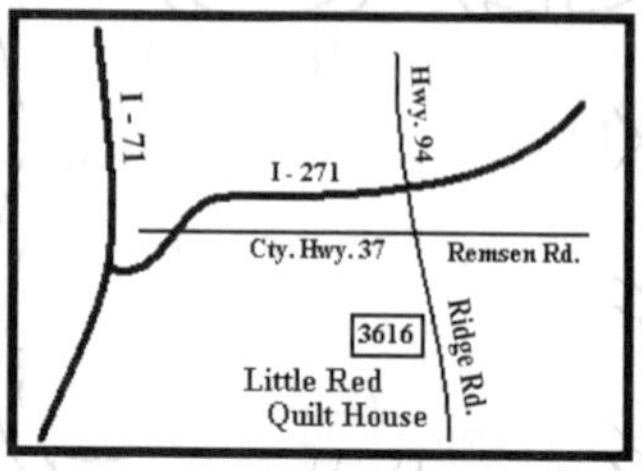

A traditional quilt shop offering traditional fabric, patterns and supplies. Long arm rental and memory quilt service.

www.littleredquilthouse.com

Middleburg Hts, OH #61

**Mon -Fri 10 - 5:30
Thur til 8
Sat 10 - 4**

PINS & NEEDLES

7535 Pearl Rd. 44130
(440) 243-6400 Fax: (440) 243-6696
Online Newsletter
middleburghts@pinsandneedles.com
www.pinsandneedles.com

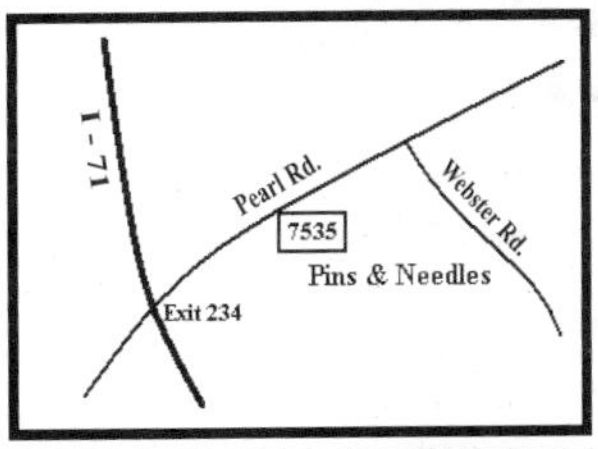

Everything for Sewing and Embroidery. Sales - new and used, service, parts, group or individual classes, clubs, fabric & notions.

Oberlin, OH #62

**Mon - Fri 10 - 5
Sat 10 - 3
Closed Wed & Sun**

Olla Mae's Drygoods

5 S. Main St. Lower Level 44074
(440) 776-0309
Owners: Roberta Lawson & Kathleen Clark
ollamaesdrygoods@yahoo.com Est: 2002
www.ollamaes.com

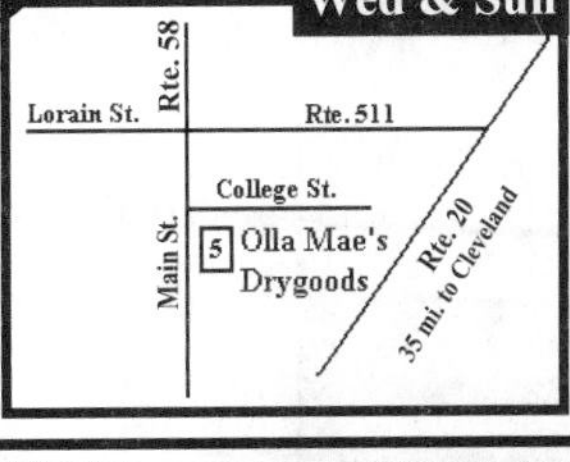

The Underground Quilt Shop
100% Cotton Fabrics, Books, Patterns, Notions, Classes and Quilts.

Oberlin, OH #63

**Tues - Sat 10 - 6
Sun 12 - 4**

ginko gallery & studio

19 S. Main St. (State Rte. 58) 44074
(440) 774-3117
Owner: Liz Burgess Est: 1997
ginkogallery@oberlin.net
www.ginkogallery.net

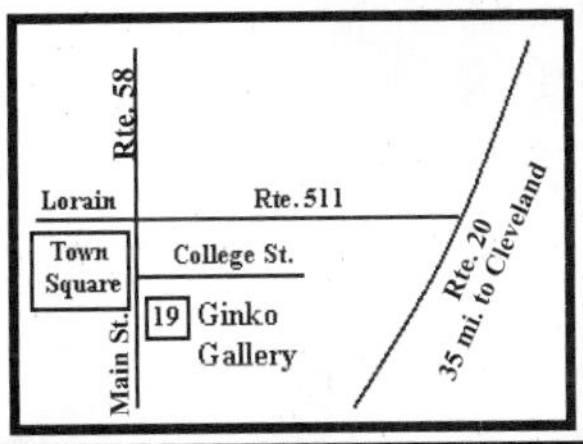

Hand-dyed fabrics, original quilts, wall hangings, wearables. Fiber art studio within one block of art museum, bead shop & restaurants.

Marblehead, OH #64

**Apr 1 - Sept 30
Mon - Sat 10 - 5
Oct 1 - Mar 31
Mon - Sat 10 - 4**

Nautical Needle Quilt Shop

199 S. Bridge Rd. (Rte 269 off Rte 2)
(419) 732-2990 Fax: (419) 732-1965
Est: 2005 2200 sq.ft. 2000 Bolts

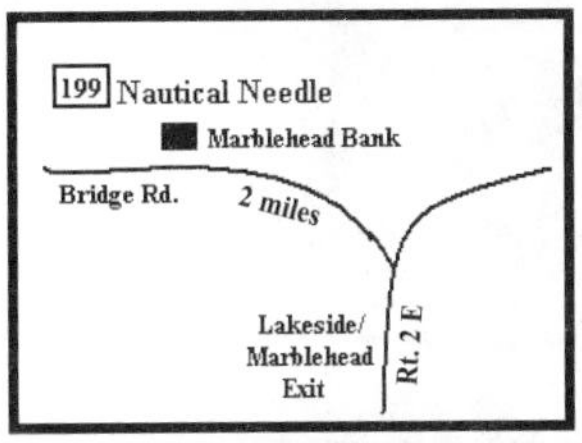

www.nauticalneedleonline.com
Full service - specializing in nautical and Lakehouse fabrics. Located on the shores of Lake Erie. Longarm quilting service, knowledgeable staff. Janome sewing machines.

Norwalk, OH #65

**M & Th 10-8
T & F 10 - 5
Sat 10 - 3**

Sew Little Time, ltd.

34 E. Main Street 44857
419-660-0200
sew_little_time@yahoo.com
www.sew-little-time.com
Sewing Machines
The Latest Fabrics! Patterns
Books Sewing Notions
Embroidery Designs
Grace Quilting Frames
Quilting Supplies Handmade
Gifts Gift Certificates
Embroidery Club Classes

Authorized JANOME Dealer

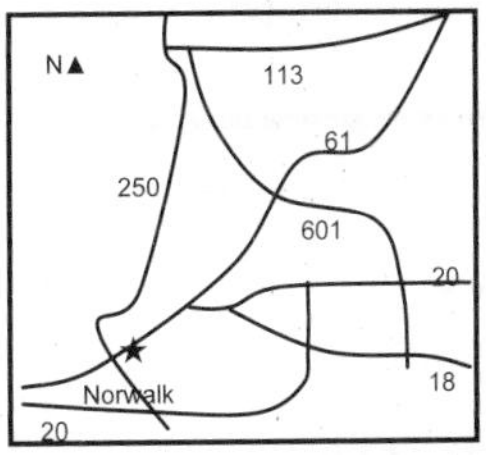

Country Charm Fabrics

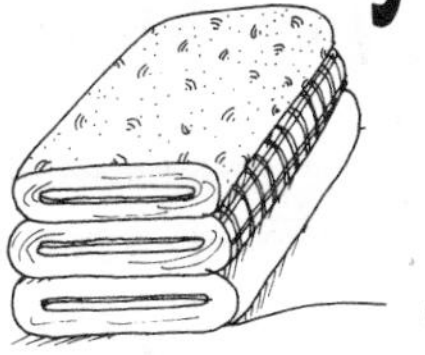

**1422 Twp. Rd. 593
Ashland, Oh 44805
(419) 281-2341
countrycharm@bright.net
Owner: Cindy Doggett Est: 1975**

**Mon, Tues, Thur & Fri 10 - 5
Sat 10 - 4
Closed Sun & Wed**

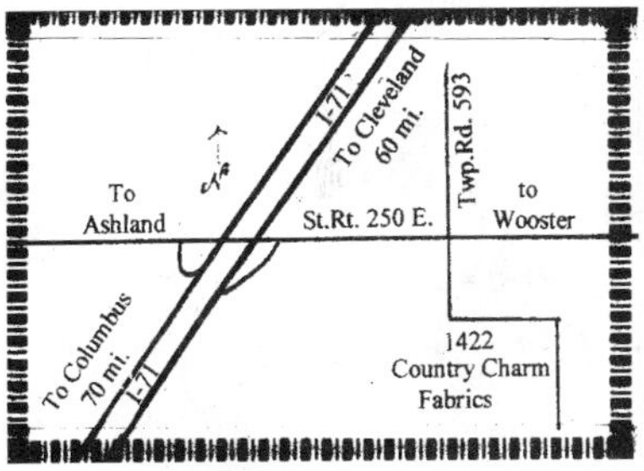

**Over 3,000+ bolts of Fabric
A Complete array of Quilting fabrics from the best mills. Notions, Quilt Frames, Classes, and all of the essentials for the Quilting Enthusiast.**

We may be moving in Summer of 2010. Please call ahead for new location.

Ashland, OH #66

Marion, OH #67

**Tues - Fri 10 - 5
Sat 10 - 3**

1569 Cascade Dr. 43302
(740) 389-5555
www.goodwivesco.com

GOOD WIVES CO.
Wares for the Household

Better Homes Quilt Sampler Featured Shop 2007

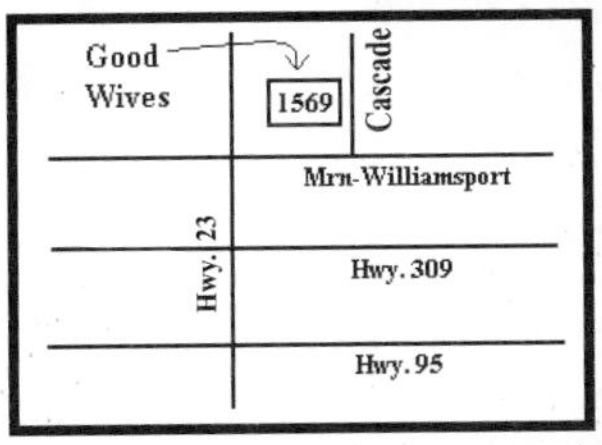

We carry Reproduction fabric of the 19th Century, homespun fabric, overdyed wool and wares for the period home. Colonial and primitive patterns/books.

Waldo, OH #68

Tues - Sat 10 - 5

Serendipitee Quilt Shop
Delightful Discoveries for Quilters

7127 Waldo Delaware Rd. 43356
(740) 726-2900 Est: 2009
www.serendipiteequiltshop.com
One mile South of Waldo, specializing in top quality quilting fabrics, books, patterns and notions. Classes available.

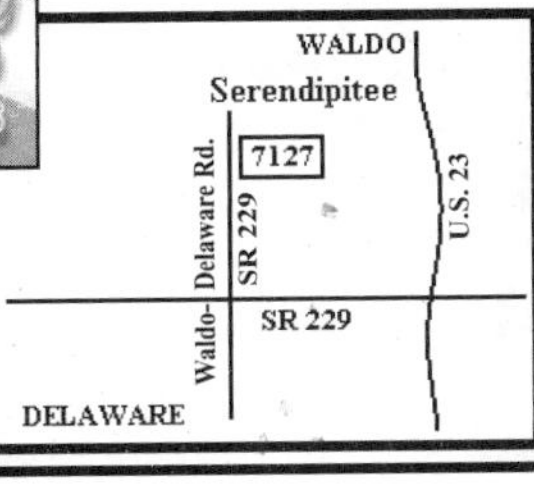

Marysville, OH #69

**Mon - Sat 10 - 5
Tues & Thur til 8**

LONESTAR QUILTING, LLC

108 S. Main St. 43040
(937) 644-1234
Owner: Debbie Wheeler
Est: 2009
1500+ bolts
Newsletter
Full service quilt shop offering quilting fabrics and notions. We also provide a wide variety of quilting, embroidery threads, books and patterns
Long arm quilting lsq@lonestarquilting.net
T-Shirt quilt-making www.lonestarquilting.net

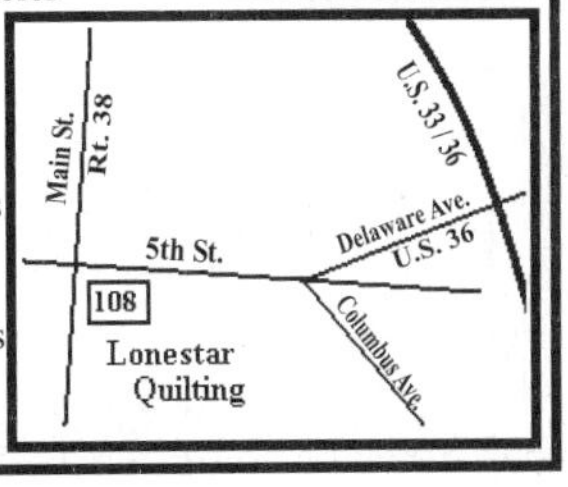

Piqua, OH #70

Blackberry Patchworks

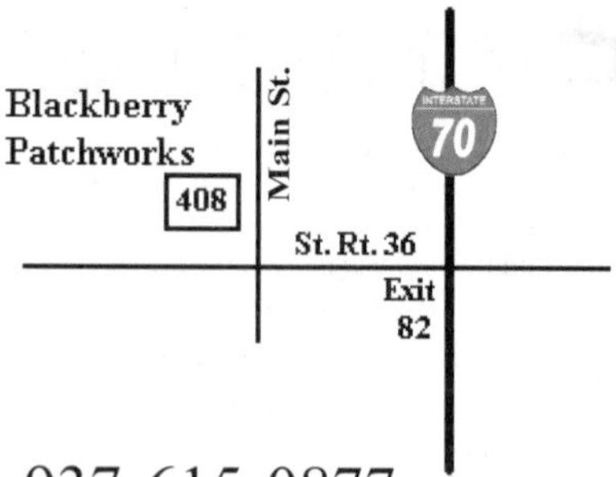

Step inside the doors of Blackberry Patchworks--
you just might be surprised at what you'll find.

Large selection of homespuns

Hand-dyed wools

Rich warm colors of quilt shop quality fabrics

Our own line of distinct patterns and kits

937-615-0877
408 N. Main St.
Piqua, OH 45356
Est: 2002 2200 sq. ft.
2300+ Bolts
Proprietor: Phyllis Meiring
info@blackberrypatchworks.com
Free Newsletter

Stop by anytime; you're always welcome.

www.blackberrypatchworks.com

Mon - Fri
10 - 5
Tues til
7:30
Sat
10 - 3

St. Marys, OH #71

Cozy cabin quilts

20331 S.R. 116 45885
(419) 394-6762
Fax: (419) 394-6762
cozycabinquilts@watchtv.net
Est: 2006 3000 sq.ft. 2000+ Bolts
Owner: Rebecca Barber

Mon 9:30 - 4
Tues - Fri 9:30 - 5
Sat 9 - 4
Or By Appointment

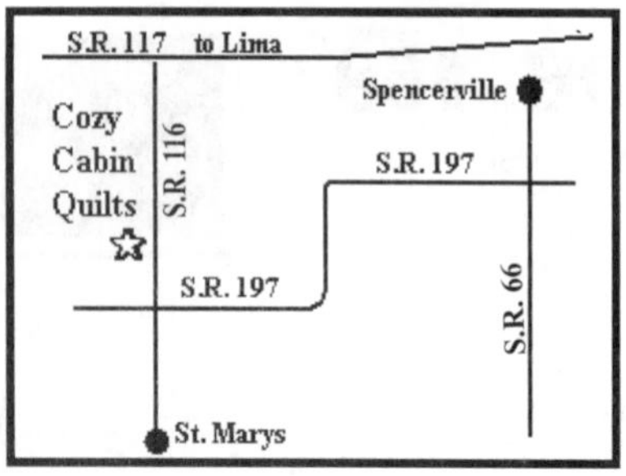

- **Top Quality, 1st run fabrics from top Manufacturers**
- **Fat Quarters**
- **Classes**
- **Award Winning Long Arm Quilting**
- **Books and Patterns**
- **Notions**

www.cozycabinquilts.net

The Sewing Centers of Lima & Findlay

Both easily accessible from I - 75 ❖ We're about 30 miles apart.

Lima, OH #72

Est:
1988
1500 sq.ft.

Findlay, OH #73

Est:
1993
1300 sq.ft.

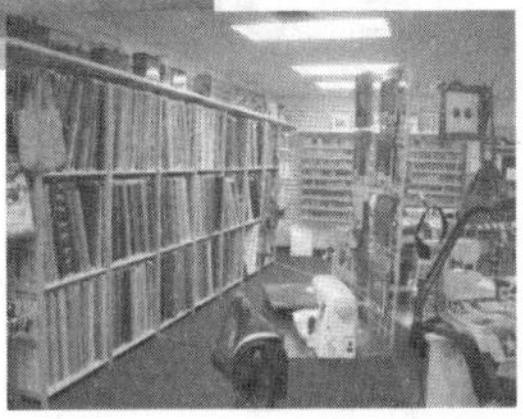

Mon - Fri 10 - 5:30 Sat 10 - 2

2100 Harding Hwy. 45804
(419) 228-8200
300+ Bolts
limasewingcenter@embarqmail.com

Quilting & Sewing Notions
Janome & BabyLock Sewing
Machine Dealers

1207 Tiffin Ave. 45840
(419) 422-5812
300+ Bolts
findlaysewingctr@att.net

Tin Lizzy Quilting Machines & Frames
Full Service Sewing Machine Stores

Believe in Your Creativity JANOME baby lock

Tin Lizzie 18 Your Affordable Long Arm Quilters

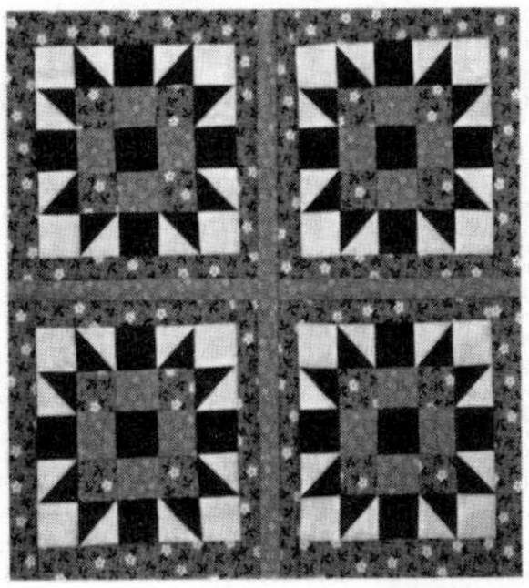

Forever In Stitches LLC

The Destination Quilt Shop™ #74

120 North Main Street
Bluffton OH 45817
1.5 Miles From I-75
Phone: (419) 358 – 0656
URL: www.fisllc.com

Hours
Open Every Day
Daily 10:00 - 5:30
Sunday 1:00 - 5:00

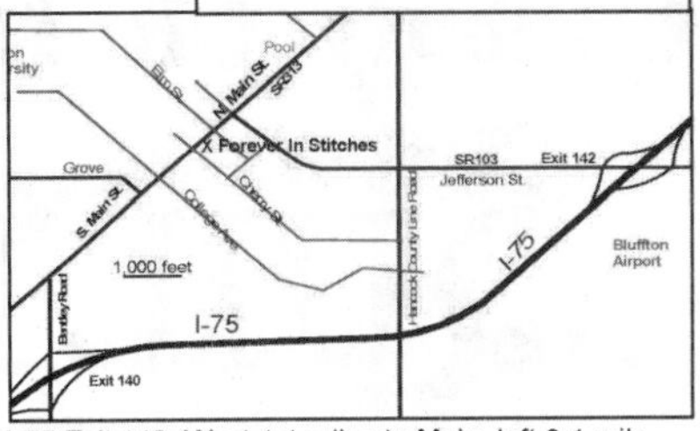

I-75 Exit 142: West 1.1 miles to Main, left 0.1 mile.
I-75 Exit 140: North 0.4 miles to Main, right 1.1 mi.

3,000 Square Feet Of Quilting

3,000 Bolts Of Fabric Displayed With Their Fat Quarters, Notions, Patterns, Books, Magazines, Gifts, Gammill Statler Stitcher Long-Arm Quilting, BOMs, Projects Of The Month, And Sew Much More....

Lima, OH #75

Mon, Wed, Fri 9 - 5
T & Th 9 - 6
Sat 8 - 1

Heavenly Stitches
Where Quilting is Divine

2696 Greely Chapel Rd. 45804
(419) 905-5950
Owners: Heather & Shana Pisle and Leslie Huber
Est: 2010
Great selection of fabrics, notions, thread & yarns. Come visit our charming country church shop.
Longarm on-site.

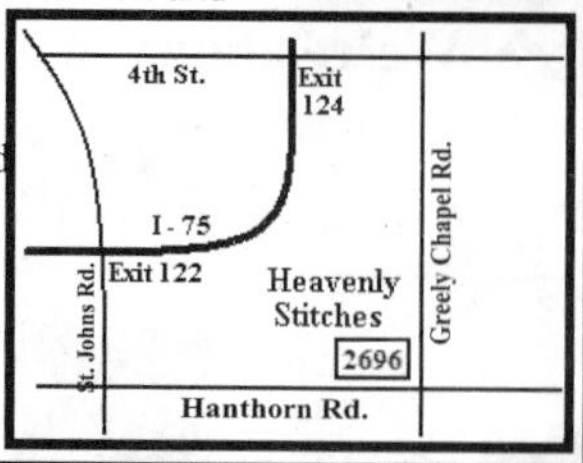

www.HeavenlyStitchesQuilts.com

Celina, OH #76

Mon 10 - 8
Tues - Fri 10 - 5
Sat 10 - 4

Linda's SEW 'N SO

Parking lot behind store

216 W. Fayette St. 45822
(419) 586-2324
Owners: Linda & David Huston Est: 1982
3600 sq.ft. Online Newsletter
Quilt Stencils (hundreds!) Janome-Brother dealer
Hinterberg Quilt frames-Voyager 17
Custom embroidery Quilt rulers-cutters-mats

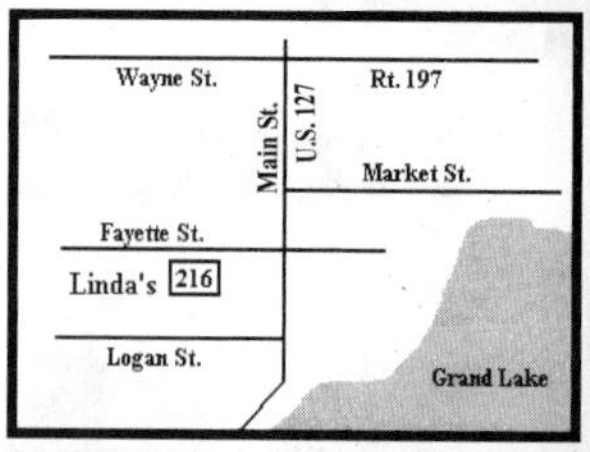

Celina, OH #77

HOURS:
Mon, Wed & Fri 10 - 6
Tues 10 - 8
Thur 4 - 8
Winter Sat 10 - 2
Summer Sat 10 - 4

The Quilterie
Fabrics ~ Kits ~ Notions ~ Gifts

126 S. Main St., Celina, OH 45822
(419) 586-0910 Owner: Valerie Vermillion
www.thequilterie.com
Freshest fabrics from top designers by Benartex, Moda and many other distinguished manufacturers.
Books, Magazines, Notions and Gifts.
Classes for all skill levels and the area's finest longarm quilting.
sales@thequilterie.com
fax: (419) 586-0910
Est: 2004 3000 sq.ft.
3000 bolts Online Newsletter

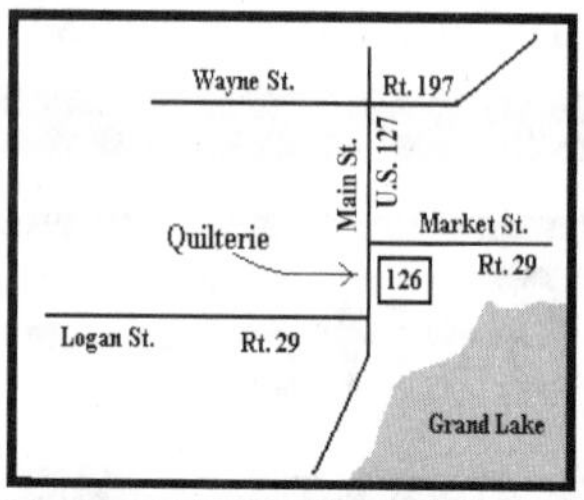

Van Wert, OH #78

Mon - Fri 9:30 - 5
Sat 9 - 3:30

The COUNTRY CUPBOARD

229 S. Washington St. 45891
(419) 238-7742
Owner: Sharon K. Cox Est: 1997
sharon@thecountrycupboard.org

Small shop but very personable.
We carry Moda - Thimbleberries and name brand fabrics. Patterns - Gifts & Classes.

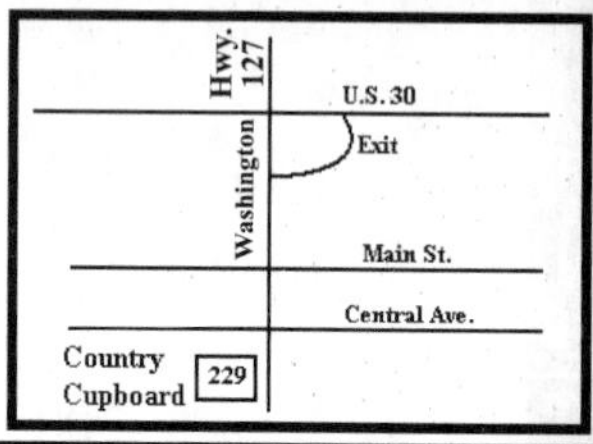

THE DOOR MOUSE

Over 15,000 bolts of cotton, patterns, and quilting supplies in a barn setting. Featuring quilts and many handcrafted memories, legends and heirlooms which capture the beauty and simplicity of rural life. Join our friendly staff for classes in the corn crib.
Mail Orders Welcome. We accept Visa/MC & Discover

5047 W. SR 12
P.O. Box 455 44815
(419) 986-5667
E-Mail:
thedoormouse@verizon.net
Web Site:
www.thedoormouse.com
Owner: Mary Ann Sorg

Mon - Sat 10 - 5
Wed til 8
Last Sunday of each month 12 - 5

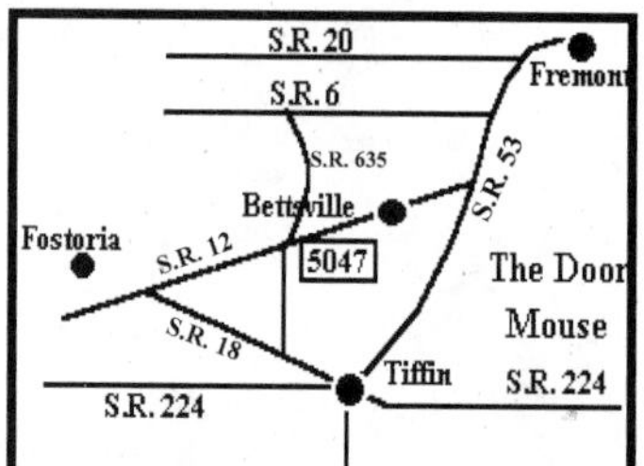

Est: 1979 3600 sq.ft.

Bettsville, OH #79

Millbury, OH #80

Tues - Fri 10 - 5
Thur til 8
Sat 10 - 4

Black Swamp QUILT Shoppe

Northwest Ohio's Bernina Sewing Dealer
BERNINA

1535 Woodville Rd. (SR 51) 43447
(419) 972-4131 3.4 miles east of I-280
Owner: Allison Gollehon
Est: 2005 3000+ sq.ft.
blackswamp@bizwoh.rr.com
www.blackswampquiltshoppe.com

Specializing in quality Quilting Fabrics, Notions, Classes, Inspiration & FUN!
Huge Selection of
Wool & Rug Hooking Supplies.
Come in and see us!

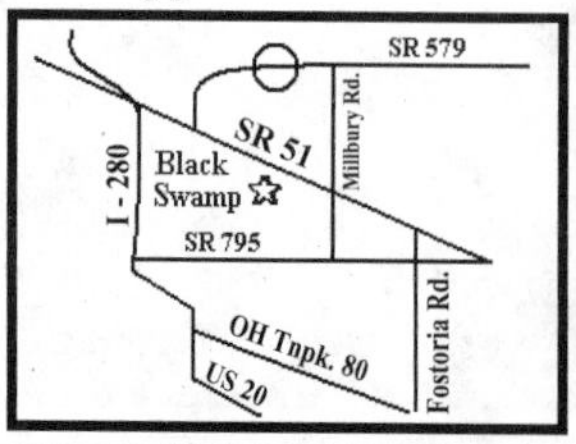

Sylvania, OH #81

Wed, Fri, & Sat 10 - 4
Tues & Thur til 7

Sonflower Quilts & Gifts

Saxon Square, 6600 Sylvania Ave. 43560
(419) 885-4438 Fax: (419) 885-4408
sonflowerquilts@sonflowerquilts.com
www.sonflowerquilts.com
Owners: Kathy Walch & Cathy Frick
Est: 2003 2100 sq.ft. 1200+ bolts

A full-service friendly quilt shop offering a wide selection of fabrics, quilting notions, patterns, and classes as well as fellowship.

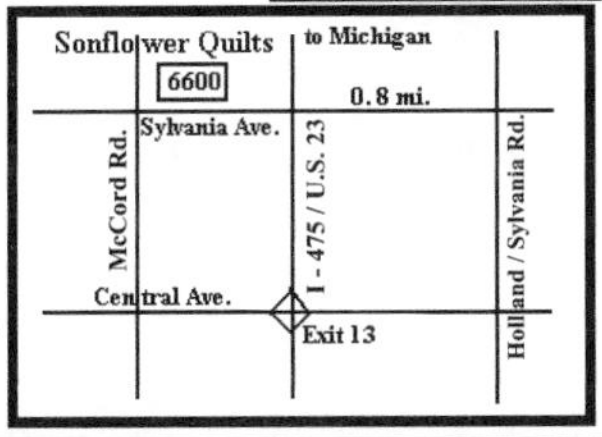

Maumee, OH #82

Mon - Sat 10 - 4
Tues eve 7 - 9

The Quilt Foundry

234 W. Wayne 43537
(419) 893-5703
www.quiltfoundry.com
Owners: Mary Beham, Margaret Okuley, Peg Sawyer, Gretchen Schultz
Est: 1981 1000 sq.ft.

The Quilt Foundry offers friendly, personalized service in your search for wonderful fabric, supplies, books and classes.

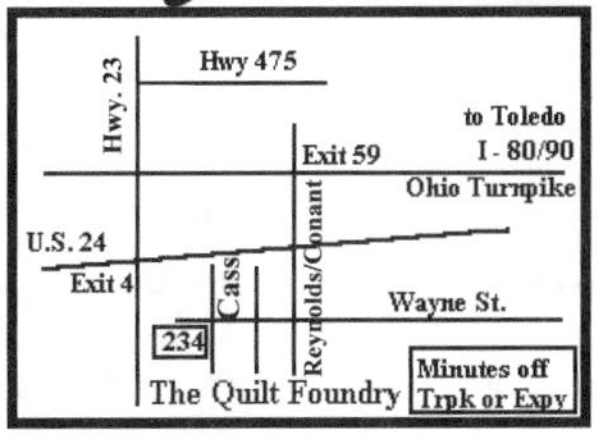

#84

Threads of Tradition
The Quilt Shop at Sauder Village

Meet our friendly and knowledgeable staff or simply enjoy browsing through our variety of...

- 3,500 bolts of top quality fabric
- Books, patterns, notions and quilting gifts
- Wool... solids and hand dyed
- Quilt kits unique to our shop
- Custom hand quilting service

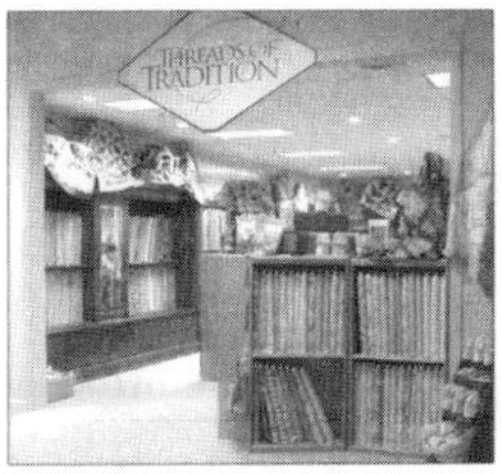

Join us for a variety of special events or take part in one of our many groups...

- Annual 6-day Quilt Show
- OH-MI Shop Hop
- Quilter's Road Show Shop Hop
- Saturday Sampler
- Monthly e-newsletter
- Lots of classes
- Spring & Fall Quilting Retreats

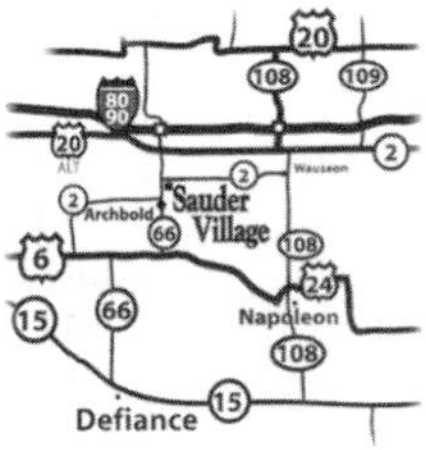

Monday-Saturday, 10 am - 5 pm, Sunday 1 - 4 pm
(Closed Sundays November - late April)

Sauder Village 22611 St. Rt. 2, Archbold, OH 43502 • 800.590.9755
lrufenacht@saudervillage.org • www.SauderVillage.org

Archbold, OH #83

Sauder Heritage Inn

Threads of Tradition Quilt Shop at Sauder Village - Spring & Fall Quilt Retreats
Or host your group anytime at the beautiful Heritage Inn
Call for Details 800-590-9755 or visit www.saudervillage.org

Corner Quilts & Gifts

2500+ Bolts of fabric, 100% cotton, large selection of flannels & homespuns, several 108" wide cotton backing. Books, Patterns and Notions. Amish Handmade Baskets, Gifts, Classes. Machine quilting services available.

14707 County Rd. J 43567
(419) 337-8458 Est: 2002
Fax: (419) 337-0600 1800 sq.ft.
sales@CornerQuilts.com
www.cornerquiltsonline.com
Owners: Kathie McClarren & Martha Bennetts

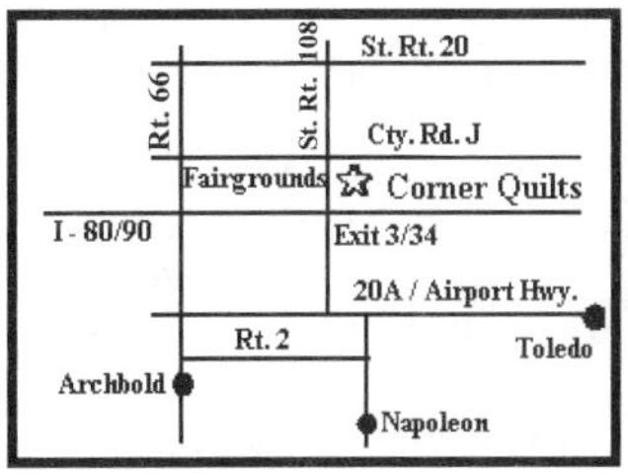

Mon - Fri 10 - 5
Sat 9 - 3
2nd Thurs til 8

Wauseon, OH #85

Ohio Quilt Shops

Akron A Piece In Time, 3963 S. Main St. 330-644-6100 See ad #44, page 435

Apple Creek Pine Tree Fabric, 12464 Western 330-857-3651 See ad #38, page 434

Archbold Sauder Heritage Inn, 22611 State Rt. 2 800-590-9755 See ad #83, page 443

Archbold Threads of Tradition, 22611 State Rt. 2 419-446-2541 See ad #84, page 443

Ashland Country Charm Fabrics, 1422 Twp. Rd. 593 419-281-2341 See ad #66, page 439

Avon Birds of a Feather, 36840 Detroit Rd. 440- 934-2374

Barnesville Karen's Quilt & Craft Connection, 119 W. Main 740-425-2100 See ad #32, page 432

Beaver Creek The Mason Jar Quilt Shop, 2169 N Fairfield Rd 937-431-4790

Belpre Neff's Country Loft, 2514 Washington Blvd. 740-423-1965 See ad #27, page 431

Berlin Helping Hands Quilt Shop, 4818 Main St. 330-893-2233 See ad #35, page 433

Berlin Gramma Fannie's Quilt Barn, 4363 St. Rt. 39 330-893-3243 See ad #36, page 433

Berlin Country Craft Cupboard, 4813 E. Main St. 330-893-3163 See ad #37, page 434

Berlin Zinck's in Berlin, 4779 E. Main St., 330-893-2071

Bettsville The Door Mouse, 5047 W. SR 12 419-986-5667 See ad #79, page 442

Bluffton Forever In Stitches, 120 N. Main St. 419-358-0656 See ad #74, page 441

Boardman Bernina Store & Sew Much More, 7081 West Blvd. 330-726-9396 See ad #42, page 434

Bremen Main Street Quilters, 111 Main St 740-569-4900

Brunswick Carol's Fabric Shop, 1325 N. Carpenter Rd. 330-225-4436

Bryan Quilt Shoppe, 06537 State Rte 15 419-636-2900

Cambridge Almost Sisters Quilt Shop, 1996 E Wheeling Ave 740-435-9590 See ad #31, page 432

Canton Angelic's A Quilters Haven, 3033 Cleveland SW 330-484-5480

Celina The Quilterie, 126 S Main St 419-586-0910 See ad #77, page 442

Celina Linda's Sew'n So, 216 W. Fayette 419-586-2324 See ad #76, page 442

Centerville Sew-A-Lot , 232 N. Main St. 937-433-7474 See ad #9, page 425 & 411

Chillicothe Creations Sew Clever, 192 S. Paint 740-775-1957 See ad #4, page 424

Chillicothe Quilted Quackers , 15 Betts Lane 740-773-3434

Cincinnati Best Friends Quilt Shoppe 8782 Colerain Ave. 513-385-2200 See ad #1, page 423

Coldwater Coldwater Ben Franklin, 840 E. Main St. 419-678-2321

Columbus Quilt Trends, 6155-J Huntley Rd. 614-841-7845 See ad #19, page 429

Columbus Quilt Beginnings, 3409 E. Broad St. 614-237-1322 See ad #18, page 428

Columbus The Glass Thimble, 3434 North High St. 614-267-9566 See ad #20, page 430

Columbus Beths Creative Stitchery, 5324 N. High St. 614-436-2611

Columbus Plantation Quilts, 2363 Somersworth Dr. 614-252-5552

Columbus Picking up the Pieces, 911 City Park Ave. 614-443-9988

Cortland Quilters Fancy LLC, 124 North High St. 330-637-3106 See ad #51, page 436

Cortland Designers Two Fabrics, 140 N. High St. (Rt. 5) 330-638-3737 See ad #50, page 436

Cuyahoga Falls Stitch, Piece 'N Purl2018 State Rd. 330-928-9097 See ad #45, page 435

Dayton Stitching Poste, 101 E. Alex Bel Rd. 937-436-9200

Dublin Quilt Beginnings North, 6689 Sawmill Rd. 614-799-2688 See ad #17, page 428

Dublin Red Rooster Quilts, 48 Corbins Mill Dr. 614- 734-9007 See ad #22, page 430

Eastlake Mara's Fabric & Gifts, 35003 Vine St. 440-942-7849 See ad #55, page 436

Fairborn Appalachian Quilts, 7577 Dayton-Springfield 937-863-0070 See ad #11, page 426

Fairfield The Bramble Patch Quilt Shop, 690A Nilles 513-829-0283 See ad #7, page 424

Findlay Findlay Sewing Center, 1207 Tiffen Ave. 419-422-5812 See ad #73, page 441

Garrettsville Shaker Tree, 8119 Main St. 330-527-0112 See ad #47, page 435

Georgetown Schoolhouse Quilts, 103 N. Main St. 937-378-4828

Glendale Stitches Quilt Shop, 16 Village Square 513-733-3999

Goshen Quilt Cabin, 1703 St Rte 28 513-722-7332

Grove City Always in Stitches, 3937 Broadway St. B 614-539-7845 See ad #21, page 430

Hebron Heavy Metal Quilting, 140 E. Main St. 740-929-3940

Huber Heights Sulphur Grove Quilt Shop, 7340 Taylorsville 937-233-7021 See ad #13, page 427

Kent Katie Brooke Quilt Shop, 144 E Main St 330-677-1156 See ad #46, page 435

Kidron Hearthside Quilt Shoppe, 13110 Emerson 330-857-4004 See ad #39, page 434

Lancaster Farmer's Country Store, 540 N. High St. 740-654-4853

Lancaster Pleasant Mtn Stitchery, 2229 W. Fair Ave. 740-652-9688

Lebanon Oh Susannah, 16 S. Broadway 513-932-8246

Lima Country Side Stitch Shop, 1207 N. McClure 419-649-1391

Lima Heavenly Stitches, 2696 Greely Chapel Rd 419-905-5950 See ad #75, page 442

Lima Lima Sewing Center, 2100 Harding Hwy. 419-228-8200 See ad #72, page 441

Little Hocking Sew Happy Quilting, 58 Franklin Dr 740-989-0040

Logan Honey Fork Fabrics, 9151 Goat Run-Honey Fork 740-385-6072 See ad #16, page 427

Louisville Empty Spools, 10087 Reeder Ave.

Louisville AnnaLouisa's NeedleArts, 1408 N. Chapel 330-875-5300

Madison Cottonpicker's Quilt Shop 136-A W. Main St. 440-428-6449 See ad #53, page 436

Mansfield Bev's Fabric Shop, 466 Melody Lane 419-589-3276

Marblehead Nautical Needle 199 S. Bridge Rd. 419-732-2990 See ad #64, page 439

Marietta Quilter's Corner, 400 Tennis Center Dr. 740-373-6150 See ad #25, page 430

Marion Good Wives Company, 1569 Cascade Dr. 740-389-5555 See ad #67, page 439

Marion The Second Sister, 1326 E. Center St. 740-382-2836

Marysville Lonestar Quilting LLC, 108 South Main St 937-644-1234 See ad #69, page 439

Maumee Quilt Foundry, 234 W. Wayne St. 419-893-5703 See ad #82, page 443

Medina Karens Quilting, 3616 Ridge Rd. 330-239-9892

Medina Little Red Quilt House, 3616 Ridge Rd. 234-248-4492 See ad #60, page 438

Mentor Quilts & Sew Forth, LLC, 7312 Center St. 440-266-1601 See ad #54, page 436

Middleburg Heights Pins & Needles Sewing Shoppes, 7535 Pearl 440-243-6400 See ad #61, page 439

Middlefield Tiny Stitches Quilt Shop, 14277 Old State Rd. 440-632-9410 See ad #56, page 436

Milan The Sewing Connection, 11001 U.S. Rt. 250 419-499-9393

Millbury Black Swamp Quilt Shoppe, 1535 Woodville 419-972-4131 See ad #80, page 442

Millersburg Miller's Dry Goods, 4500 St. Rt. 557 330-893-9899 See ad #33, page 433

Millersburg Chestnut Ridge Sewing, 3647 St. Rt. 39 330-893-3359

Mt. Hope Lone Star Quilts, 7700 CR 77, Box 32 330-674-3858

Mt. Perry Snip'n Stitch, 8845 Bagley Rd. 740-849-2413 See ad #28, page 432

Mt. Vernon Paw Patch Quilt Shop, 444 Columbus Rd. 877-397-9450 See ad #34, page 433

Mt. Vernon Aunt Bee's Quilts & More, 229 S. Main St. 740-393-3900

Nelsonville Nelsonville Quilt Co., 52 W. Washington St. 740-753-3343 See ad #15, page 427

Newark Bunny's Sew Fine Fabrics, 28 Price Rd. 740-366-1433 See ad #23, page 430

Niles Viking & White Sewing Ctr, 40 Youngstown Warren
330-544-5300 See ad #48, page 436

North Canton Quilt Garden, 1664 N. Main St.
330-966-6670 See ad #40, page 434

Northfield Memory Lane Quilting, 512 W Aurora Rd 330-468-2831

Norwalk Sew Little Time LTD., 34 East Main St.
419-660-0200 See ad #65, page 439

Oberlin Ginko Gallery & Studio, 19 S. Main St.
440-774-3117 See ad #63, page 439

Oberlin Olla Mae's Drygoods, 5 South Main St.
440-776-0309 See ad #62, page 439

Olmsted Falls Abigayle's Quiltery, 8096 Columbia Rd.
440-235-7446 See ad #58, page 438

Parma Quilter's Source, 6683 State Rd. 440-843-2464

Pataskala Calico Cupboard Quilt Shop 74 Oak Meadow
740-927-2636 See ad #24, page 430

Piqua Blackberry Patchworks, 408 N Main St.
937-615-0877 See ad #70, page 440

Pomeroy The Fabric Shop, 110 W. Main St.
740-992-2284 See ad #14, page 427

Portsmouth Lil's Quilt Shoppe, 210 Market St.
740-353-4570 See ad #3, page 424

Protorville D & B Quilt Shop, 6971 St. Rt. 775 740-886-8730

Richfield The Polka Dot Pincushion, 4131 W. Streetsboro
330- 659-0233 See ad #59, page 438 & 202

Salineville The Attic, 16060 Spring Valley Rd.

Sharonville Sew Ezy Sewing Studio, 11427 Lebanon Rd.
513-563-7474 See ad #8, page 424

Sharonville Aunt Ruth's Quilt Shop, 11041 Reading Rd. 513-733-0006

Shiloh Country Fabrics, 6142 Ganges 5 Point Rd. 419-896-3785

South Amherst Quilts & Kreations, 101 E. Main St.
440-986-4132 See ad #57, page 437

South Point Quilts And Things, 207A Solida Rd.
740-377-4551 See ad #2, page 424

Springfield Creative Fires, LLC, 1525 Progress Drive
937-327-9420 See ad #12, page 427

St. Marys Cozy Cabin Quilts, 20331 State Route 116
419- 394-6762 See ad #71, page 440

Sugarcreek Carlisle Fabric, 2310 Co. Rd. 144 330-852-2264

Sugarcreek Swiss Village Quilts & Crafts, 113 S. Broadway 330-852-4855

Sylvania Sonflower Quilts & Gifts, 6600 Sylvania,
419-885-4438 See ad #81, page 443

Trenton Valley Quilts, 104 E. State St.
513-988-2560 See ad #6, page 424

Twinsburg Bernina Store & Sew Much More, 8900 H-107 Darrow
330-487-0460 See ad #43, page 434

Van Wert The Country Cupboard, 229 S Washington St.
888-795-5751 See ad #78, page 442

Wadsworth The Fabric Peddler, 139 College St.
330-336-1101 See ad #41, page 434

Waldo Serendipitee, 7127 Waldo-Delaware Rd.
740-726-2900 See ad #68, page 439

Warren Just Quilt It Inc., 171 Folsom St. NW
330-469-6956 See ad #49, page 436

Wauseon Corner Quilts & Gifts, 14707 County Rd. J
419-337-8458 See ad #85, page 443

Wayne A Little Touch of Heaven, 102 E. Main St.
419-288-2300 See ad #52, page 436

Waynesville Fabric Shack Stores, 99 S. Marvin Lane
513-897-0092 See ad #10, page 426

Whipple The Quilted Work, 320 Stanleyville Narrows Rd.
740-373-0579 See ad #26, page 431

Wilmington Cotton Junky Quilt Shop, 199 N Spring St
937-366-6302 See ad #5, page 424

Youngstown Quilter's Quarters, 8458 Market St. 330-758-7072

Zanesville Nonna's Quilting Nook, 1004 Beverly Ave.
740-450-2626 See ad #30, page 432

Zanesville A Touch of Thread Quilting Center, 2885 E. Pike
740-454-8372 See ad #29, page 432

35 Shows

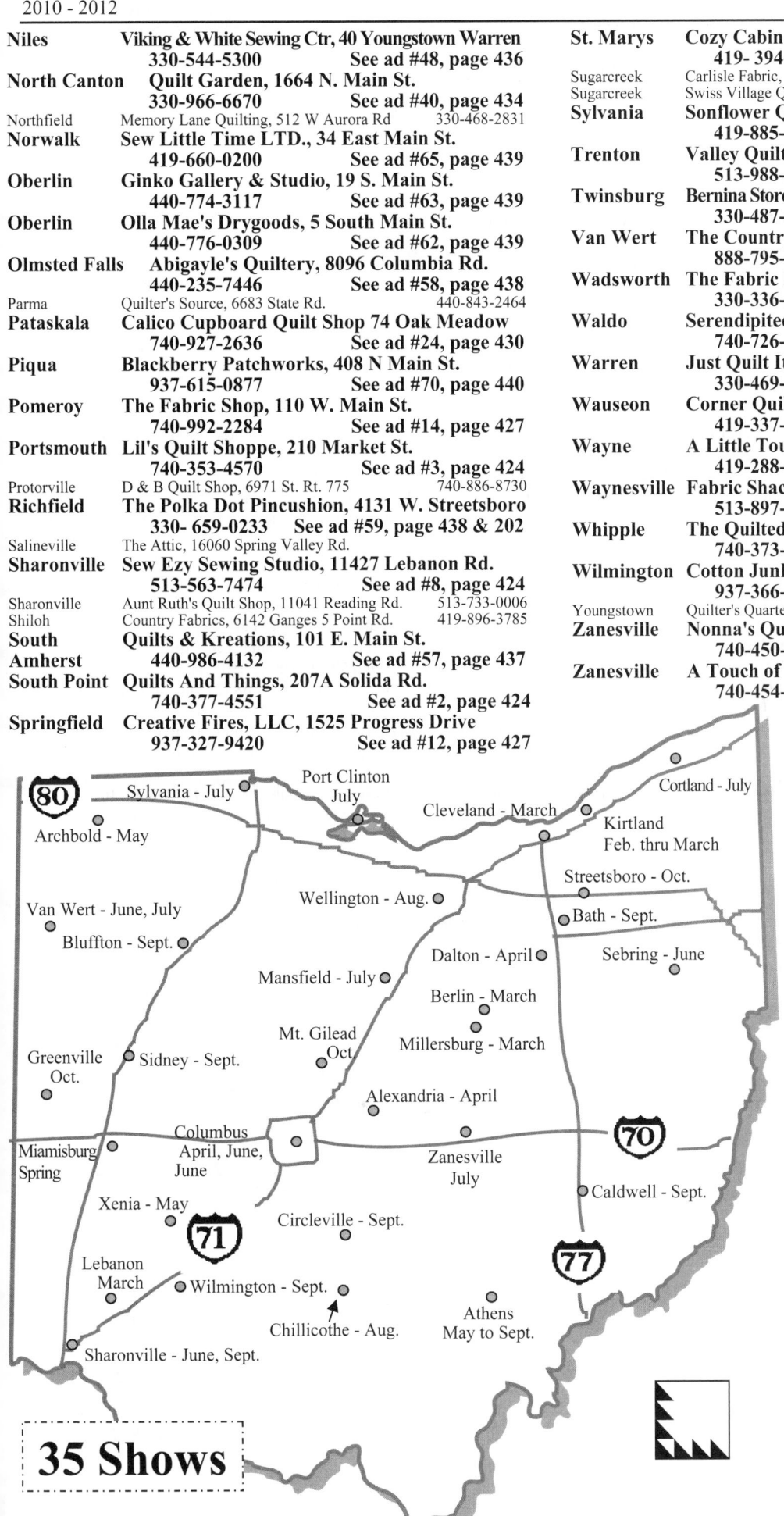

Ohio Quilt Shows

About Shows: We are listing only the very basic information about shows that happen on a regular schedule here. Please check out our website for more details on each show. Also this information tends to change quite often so please verify the event with our website or a local source before you venture far. Or if you're in the right area at the right time, give it a shot.

If you are a show organizer, please keep us updated on your event.
shows@quilterstravelcompanion.com
www.quilterstravelcompanion.com

On our website you will also find:

- Exact dates (when we have them)
- Sponsor Information
- Contact Information
- Description of Event
- Events happening on a one-time basis

Month	City	Schedule	Show	Location with address
February				
	Kirtland	Annual, Mid February to end of March	Quilts	Lake Metroparks Farmpark, 800 Chardon Rd.
March				
	Lebanon	Annual, 1st weekend in March	Lebanon Quilt & Fabric Arts Show	Warren County Historical Museum, 105 S. Broadway
	Berlin	Annual, last Wed - Sat in March	Amish Country Quilt Show Berlin	Christian Fellowship, 5382 Cty. Rd. 201
	Millersburg	Annual, 4th Wed-Sat of March	Amish Country Quilt Show & Vendors Mall	Berlin Christian Fellowship, 5382 Cty. Rd. 201
	Cleveland	Annual, last Thur-Sat of March	Original Sewing & Quilt Expo	I-X Center, 6200 Riverside Dr.
April				
	Alexandria	Annual, During the month of April	Alexandria Museum Quilt Show	Alexandria Museum, 23 W. Main St.
	Columbus	Even Years, April	CMQ Quilt Spectacular	Whitehall Community Park 402 N. Hamilton Rd.
	Dalton	Annual, 2nd weekend in April	Amish Country Quilt Show	Buckeye Event Center 624 Henry St.
	Miamisburg	Annual, Spring	Miamisburg Quilt Show	Miamisburg First Church of God 446 N. Heincke Rd.
May				
	Archbold	Annual, Tues - Sun ending on the first Sun in May	Sauder Village Quilt Fair	Founders Hall at Historic Sauder Village, 22611 St. Rt. 2
	Xenia	Even Years, 2nd Weekend in May	Miami Valley Quilter's Guild Show	Greene County FairgroundsAssembly Hall, 120 Fairgrounds Rd.
	Athens	Odd Years, Memorial Day thru Labor Day	Quilt National	Dairy Barn Cultural Arts Center, 8000 Dairy Ln.
June				
	Columbus	Annual, June	Quilt Surface Desgin Symposium	Ramada Plaza Hotel & Conference Center
	Van Wert	Annual, first full weekend in June	West Central Ohio Quilt Guild	Van Wert County Fairgrounds, 1055 S. Washington St.
	Columbus	Annual, June	National Quilting Association Show	Greater Columbus Convention Center--Hall C, 500 N. High
	Sebring	Odd years, last weekend of June	Northeast Ohio Regional Quilt Council Quilt Show	Sebring McKinley High School, 225 E. Indiana Ave.
	Sharonville	Annual, Last weekend in June	The Original Creative Festival	Sharonville Convention Center, 11355 Chester Rd.
July				
	Van Wert	Annual, 1st Fri & Sat of July	Old Fashioned Farmers Days Quilt Show	Van Wert County Fairground, 1055 S. Washington
	Cortland	Annual, 3rd or 4th Saturday in July	Party in the Parking Lot	Downtown Cortland, 124 - 140 N. High St.
	Mansfield	Odd Years, 3rd Fri & Sat in July	Mansfield Millenium Quilt Guild Show	Baku Grotto Hall, 747 S. Main St.
	Sylvania	Odd Years, 3rd weekend in July	Kaleidoscope of Quilts Show	Franciscan Center, 6832 Convent Blvd.
	Zanesville	Even Years, 3rd weekend in July	Pieceable Quilters Guild Show	Muskingum County Fairgrounds, Brighton Blvd. and Pershing Rd.
	Port Clinton	Even Years, 4th Fri & Sat in July	Ohio Star Quilters' Guild Show	Peace Lutheran Church 900 Jefferson St.
August				
	Wellington	Annual, 1st or 2nd Saturday of August	Ohio Outdoor Quilt Festival	Bonnie Brae Elk Farm, 27717 Quarry Rd.
	Chillicothe	Annual, last weekend in August	Ross County Quilters Guild Show	Tyler Methodist Church, 200 Mill St.
September				
	Circleville	Annual, first Thur - Sat in Sept. after Labor Day	Goodtime Quilters Quilt Show	The Trinity Lutheran Church, 135 E. Mound St.
	Sharonville	Annual, 2nd weekend in September	Quilting, Stitches and Crafts Expo	Sharonville Convention Center, 11355 Chester Rd.
	Sidney	Annual, 2nd weekend in September	Applefest Quilt Show	Cameo Theater, 304 S. West Ave.
	Wilmington	Annual, 2nd weekend in September	Clinton County Associations Show	Clinton County Fairgrounds, 958 W. Main St.
	Bath	Annual, 4th weekend in September	Cascade Quilt Guild Show	Bath Church Fellowship Hall, 3980 Bath Rd.
	Bluffton	Annual, last Saturday in September	Fall Festival Quilt Show	Maple Crest Senior Living Village, 700 Maple Crest Ct. (at Augsberger Rd.)
	Caldwell	Last weekend of September	Townsquare QuiltLovers Guild Show	Noble County Fairgrounds-Floral Hall, I-77 Exit 25
October				
	Mt. Gilead	Odd Years, October	Morrow County Quilting Show	Park Avenue Elementary, Park Ave.
	Streetsboro	Annual, first weekend in October	Streetsboro Quilt Guild Show	Faith Baptist Church, 9890 St. Rte. 43
	Greenville	Annual, 2nd Weekend in October	Towne Squares Quilt Club	Darke County Fairgrounds, Youth Building, St. Rt. 49

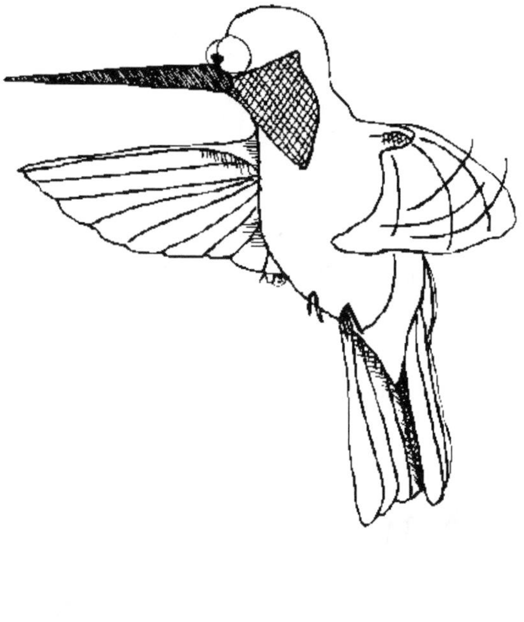

OKLAHOMA

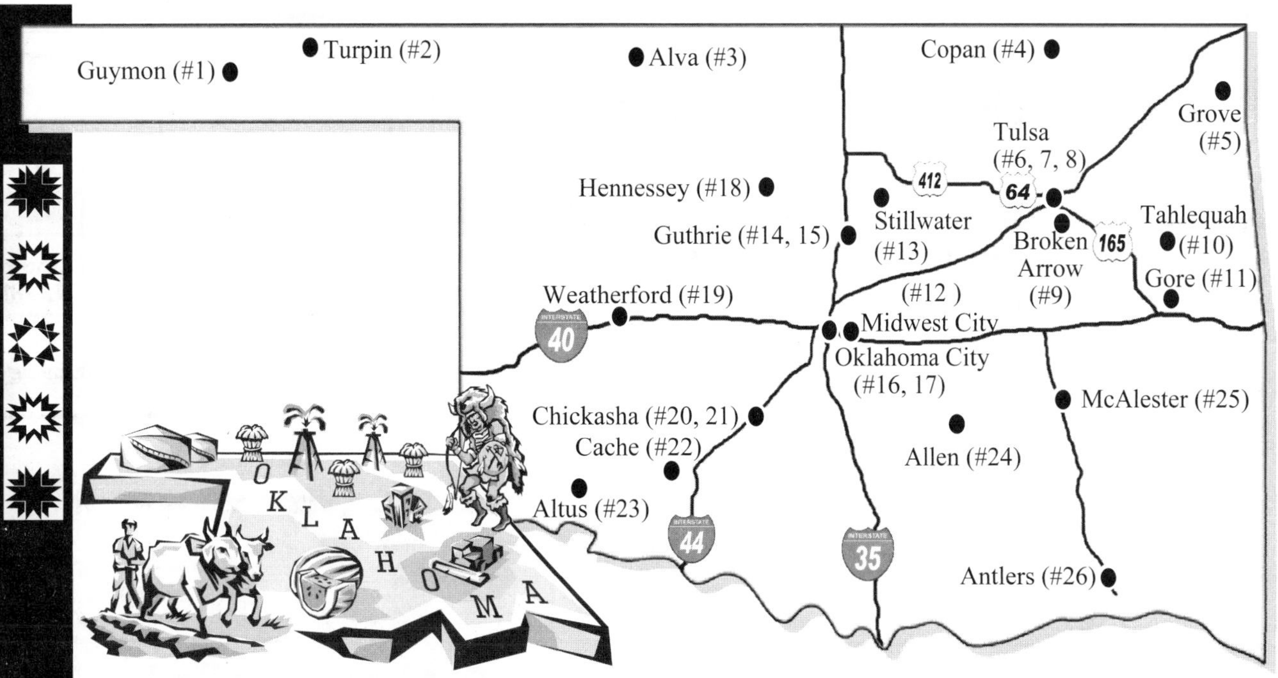

26 Featured Shops

Guymon, OK #1

Evenings and Weekends by Appt.-Please Call

Cheryl's Quilt Corner

1608 N. Ellison 73942
(580) 338-3677
Owner: Cheryl Ashpaugh
cherylas@ptsi.net
www.cherylsquiltcorner.com
Online Store open 24 / 7

Newly expanded shop meeting your quilting needs with a warm home atmosphere. Custom machine quilting, 100% top quality cotton fabrics, books, patterns, notions & battings. Classes by request.

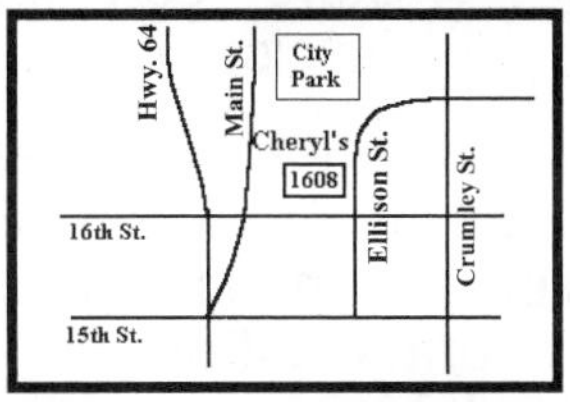

Turpin, OK #2

Mon - Fri 10 - 5 Open most Sats, but call first.

Prairie Trails Quilting

Rt. 1, Box 32-H 73950
(580) 778-3501
jdlptq@ptsi.net Owner: Janet Lewis
Country charm and friendly service - located 7 miles north of Turpin and 1 1/4 miles west of Hwy 83 (on cty. rd. EW-3)
Offering 100% Cotton Fabric, Quilting Notions & Supplies, Books, Patterns, Classes, and Custom Machine Quilting.

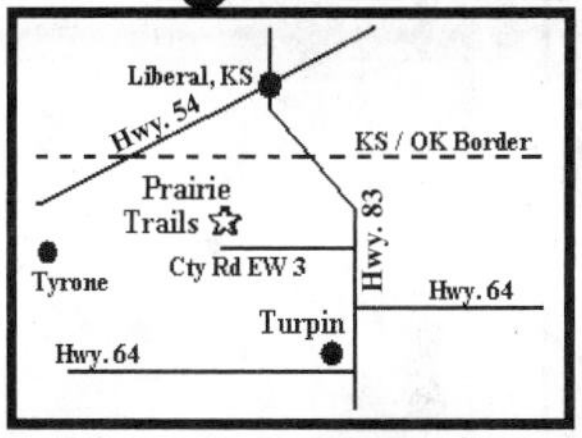

Alva, OK #3

Mon - Fri 9 - 5:30 Sat 10 - 2

Fabrics & More Etc.

428 Flynn 73717
(580) 327-0240
Est: 2004 3000 Bolts

www.fabricsandmoreetc.com
An antique tin ceiling reveals a fabulous fabric selection, unique notions, patterns, books and kits. The warmest Northwest Oklahoma hospitality.

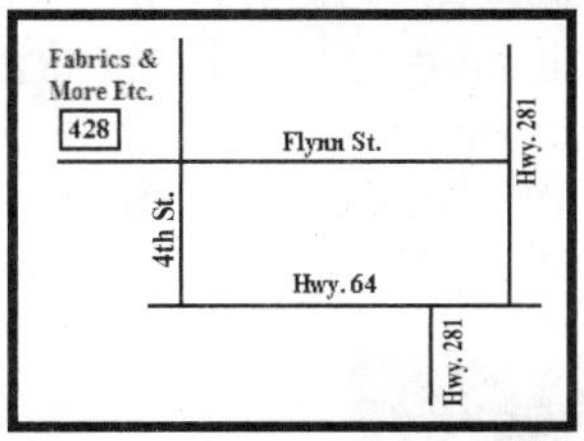

Copan, OK #4

Wed - Sat 10 - 4 Thur til 8:30

Corner Sew & So

101 S. Caney Ave. 74022
(918) 532-5533
Owner: Gwen Engelbert
Est: 2001 2000+ bolts
cornersewandso@aol.com
www.cornersewandso.com
Check out all our wonderful fabrics.
Two long arm quilting machines with 600 different patterns.

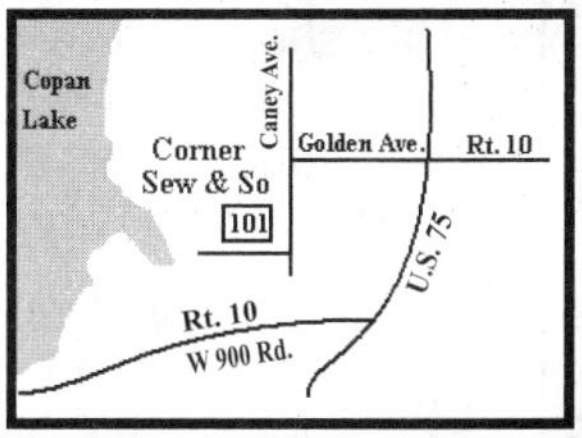

Grove, OK #5

Tues 10 - 9 Wed - Sat 10 - 4 Extended Summer Hours

Prints of Piece

25501 S 655 Rd. 74344
(918) 786-2046
quiltshop74344@sbcglobal.net

100% Quality Cotton Fabrics
Books - Patterns
Notions - Classes
Custom Long-Arm Quilting done on a Gammill Classic Plus also available for hourly rental.

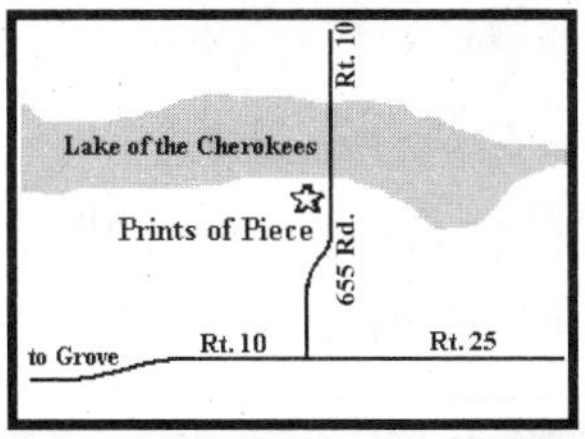

Tulsa, OK #6

Mon - Fri 10 - 5:30 Tues til 7 Sat 10 - 5

Cotton Patch

8250 East 71st St. 74133
(918) 252-1995
Fax: (918) 294-9542
Owners: Nancy & Mike Mullman
Est: 1977 1200 sq.ft.
www.ecottonpatch.com

Large quilt fabric selection, books, notions, and patterns.

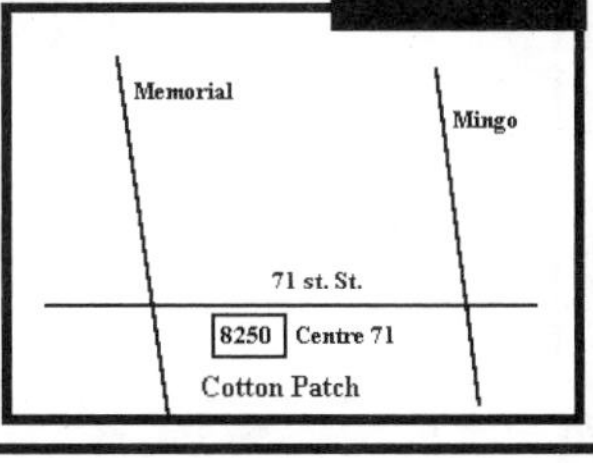

Tulsa, OK #7

6068 S. Sheridan Rd. 74145
(In the Park Plaza Shopping Center)
(888) 543-7004
(918) 493-1136 Fax: (918) 493-1933
Owner: Lindy Legener

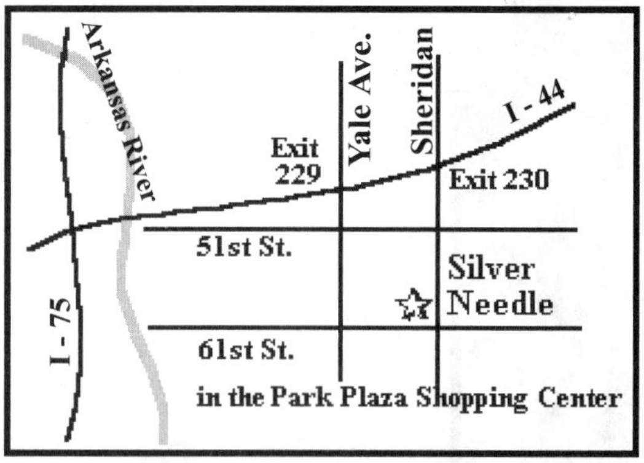

Est: 1984

THE SILVER NEEDLE®
Fine Needlework Materials

We have a unique shop specializing in counted techniques, unique accessories, and friendly service.

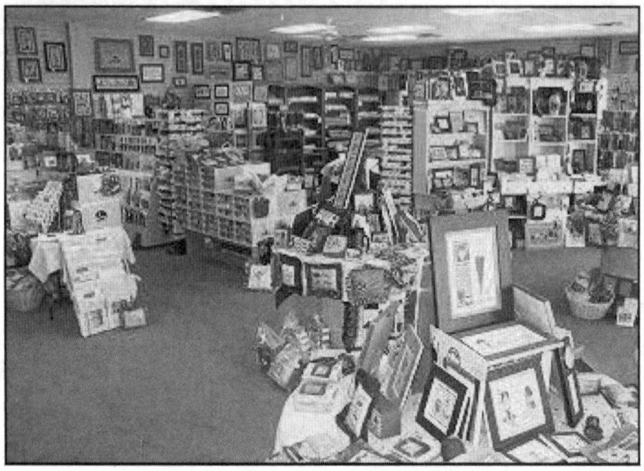

This shop picture is only a glimpse of what we feature at THE SILVER NEEDLE. The walls and tables are covered with stitched models--always so much fun to see.

We are approximately 2 miles -- 2 or 3 minutes off of I-44 in Tulsa. We hope your travels bring you to our door.

Extensive assortments of:
Shepherd's Bush, Lizzie Kate, Just Nan, Pine Mountain, Bent Creek, Mill Hill, Drawn Thread … so many cool lines, I can't list them all!

We are a Vera Bradley Retailer--a Store within a Store-- carrying the entire line of luscious bags and accessories!

Specialty threads by Weeks Dye Works, Gentle Art, Crescent Colours, DMC, Silks, and Perles, the colors are mouthwatering! Glistening beads and charms, buttons, galore, exquisite scissors, everything you need for Needlework! Along with reproduction samplers and reference books, we carry miniature punch needle embroidery with all it's trimmings, and magnifying lamps for every need.

We are 'Home' to Secret Needle Night … an exclusive monthly design that we create and stitch in novelty threads. Full details about Secret Needle Night, as well as other great automatic-ship programs, and all our wonderful offerings are on our website.

Mon - Sat
10 - 6

You can reach us at E-Mail:
lindy@thesilverneedle.com

Shop at our Two Web Sites !
thesilverneedle.com or silversites.net
Our websites are updated daily, and we offer free monthly E-mail newsletter, complete with exclusive specials.

QUILT SAMPLER

Creative Sewing Center LLC

www.quiltsampler.com
6024 S. Sheridan • Tulsa, OK 74145
Mon - Fri: 10 - 5 • Sat: 10 - 4
918-493-3388 Fax (918) 493-3387
Owner: Cristen Jones Est: 2007
Bernina, Pfaff, Tin Lizzie and Handi Quilter onsite service department

PFAFF BERNINA Tin Lizzie 18 Handi Quilter

Books and Notions Software embroidery designs and more!
Friendly, knowledgeable staff
5600 square feet
4500 bolts of fabric

Contact us at:
info@quiltsampler.com

Please visit our sister store in Springfield, Missouri.

A full service quilt shop offering classes and expert advice. We have many books, kits and blocks of the month, in a bright roomy atmosphere.

Near historic Route 66

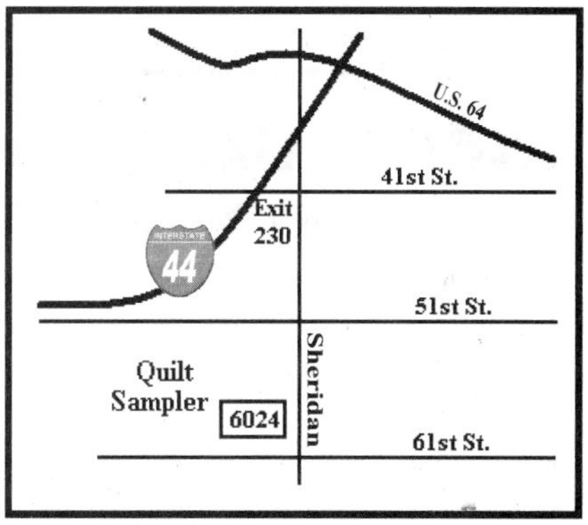

Tulsa, OK #8

"The next Generation in Quilting"

Broken Arrow, OK #9

SewFlakes
fine quilt & fashion fabrics

Christine Fornell
Est: 2004

www.sewflakesfabrics.com

- Quilt Fabric
- Fashion Fabric
- Pre-Cuts
- Block of the Months
- Patterns
- Kits
- Classes
- Events
- BERNINA

BERNINA

106 S. Main
Broken Arrow, OK
918-251-7094
sewflakes@inbox.com

Mon- Fri 10 - 5
Thur til 8 Sat 10 - 4

We strive to meet your sewing needs no matter your project preference. We offer over 3,000 bolts of high quality, 100% cotton, quilting fabrics and also silks, wools, lycras, rayons, bamboo knits, faux furs, velvets and much more.

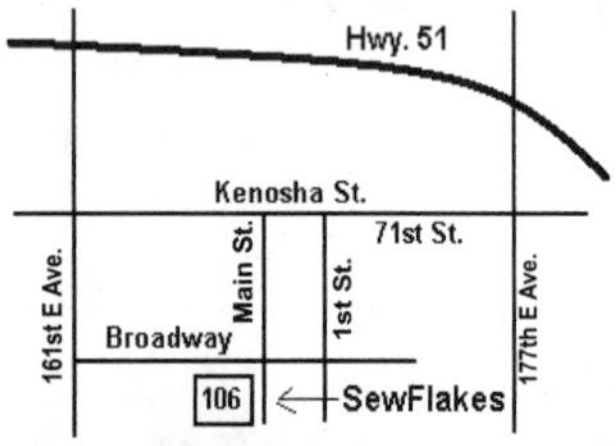

Broken Arrow, OK #9

Tahlequah, OK #10

Tues - Fri 10 - 5
Sat 10 - 2

Serendipity Quilt Shop

109 N. Muskogee Ave.
P.O. Box 294, 74465
(918) 453-2840
Est: 2002 1400 sq. ft.
1000+ Bolts

100% Cotton Fabrics, quilting supplies, patterns, books and classes.

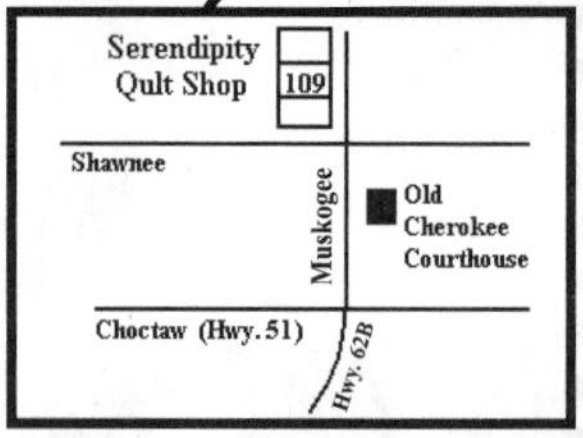

Gore, OK #11

Tues - Sat 10 - 5

Fabric Patch

305 S. Main St. 74435
(918) 489-5163 Cell (918) 208-3387
Est: 2009 2000 sq.ft. 1800 bolts
Very reasonable prices. Cotton blenders, calicos, polka dots, batiks & prints.
Large selection of 60-108" wide backings.
Batting by the yard or roll. Notions, books, patterns & classes. Janome Sewing Machines.
We service all makes and models also.

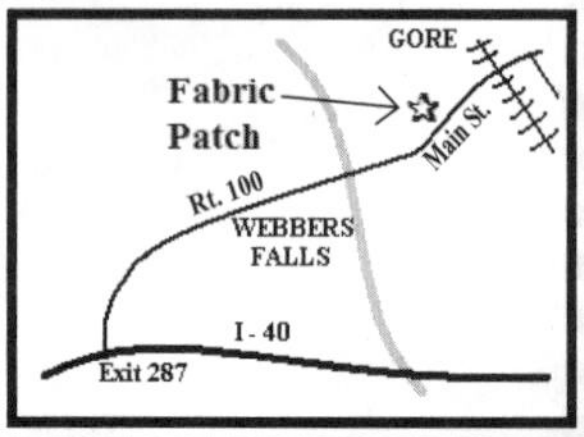

Midwest City, OK #12

Mon - Sat 10 - 6
Thurs til 8

Quilter's Corner

1110 S. Air Depot Blvd. #14 73110
(405) 455-5005
Owner: Mary Dubois Est: 2006
4000 sq.ft. 1800 bolts Newsletter
quilterscorner@coxinet.net
Quilting fabrics, supplies & notions.
Hand embroidery supplies.
Quilting & Hand embroidery classes
PFAFF sewing machines.

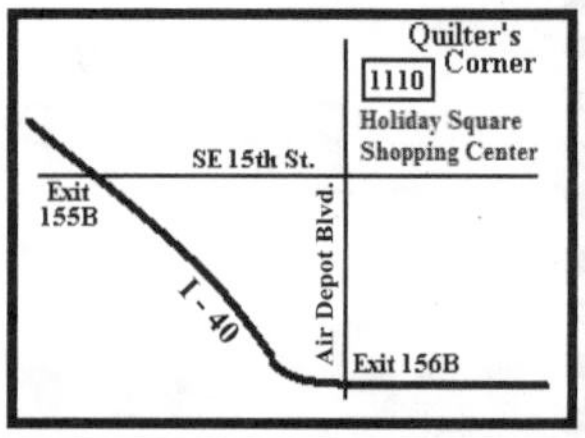

Stillwater, OK #13

Mon - Sat 10 - 6

Sew-N-Sews

217 S. Perkins Rd.
74074
(405) 707-0700

Est: 2002 2000 sq.ft. 1500 bolts
sewnsews@sbcglobla.net Online newsletter
www.sewnsews.com

Authorized Brother and Juki dealer with support classes for all levels. Large selection of DMC threads, ribbons and trims, wide variety of notions. Special order embroidery also offered.

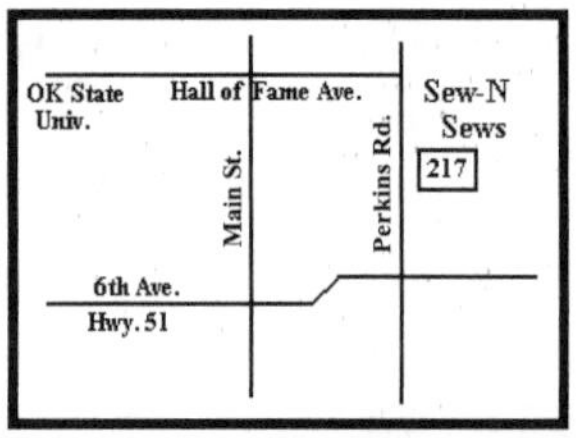

Guthrie, OK #14

Mon - Sat 10 - 5

EXTRA SPECIAL

117 W. Oklahoma Ave. 73044
(405) 282-1144 (800) 795-2844
Owner: Laurah Kilbourn
laurah@extraspecialfabric.com
www.extraspecialfabric.com
Est: 1991 2000+ Bolts
Specializing in Western Fabrics, Southwest, Novelty, Calico, Faux Fur, Fleece, Barkcloth.
Fashion to quilting.

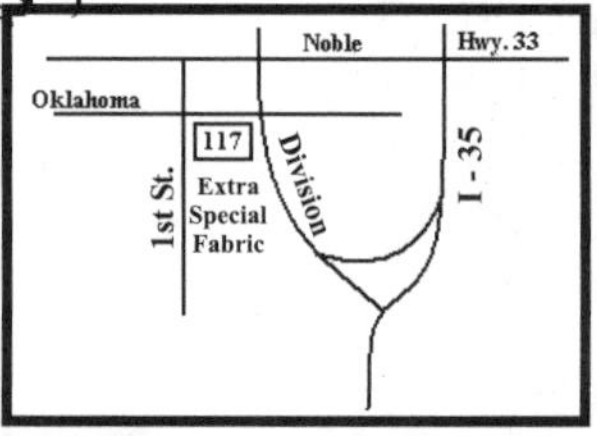

Guthrie, OK #15

Tues - Fri 9 - 5
Thur til 7
Sat 9 - 3

Sooner Quilts

7821 S. Sooner Rd. 73044
(405) 282-2070
Owner: Michelle Schroeder

4000 Bolts, Books, Patterns, Notions, Embellishments, and Classes.
Custom Longarm Quilting - Janome Dealer

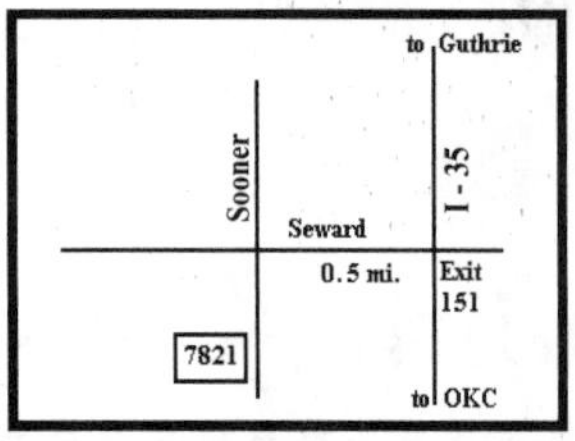

Oklahoma City, OK #16

Mon - Sat 9:30 - 5

Sew-N-Sews

5127 N. Portland
73132
(405) 942-2700

Est: 1984 2000 sq.ft. 1500 bolts
sewnsews@sbcglobla.net Online newsletter
www.sewnsews.com

Authorized Brother and Juki dealer with support classes for all levels. Large selection of DMC threads, ribbons and trims, wide variety of notions. Special order embroidery also offered.

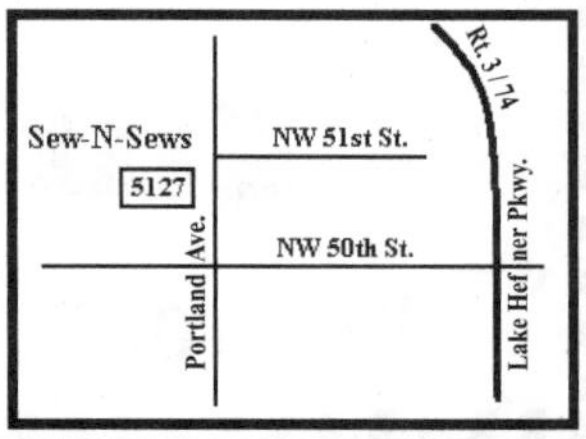

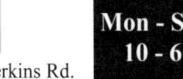

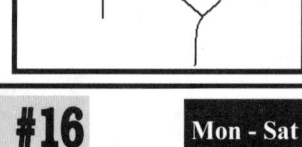

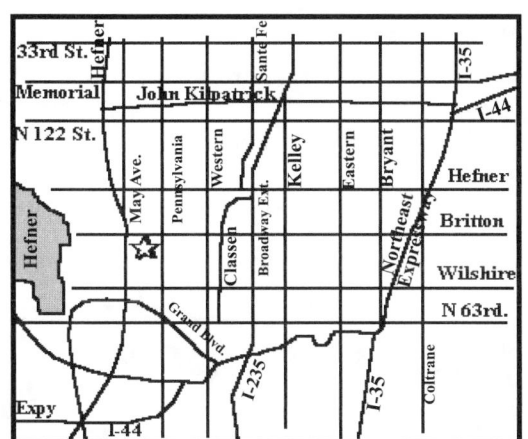

Weatherford, OK #19

Mon - Fri 10 -5
Sat 10 - 3

the Quilters Knitche
FABRIC • NOTIONS • GIFTS

111 E. Main St. 73096
(580) 774-7522
Owner: Linda Stewart

Est: 2007
2400 sq.ft.
1200 bolts

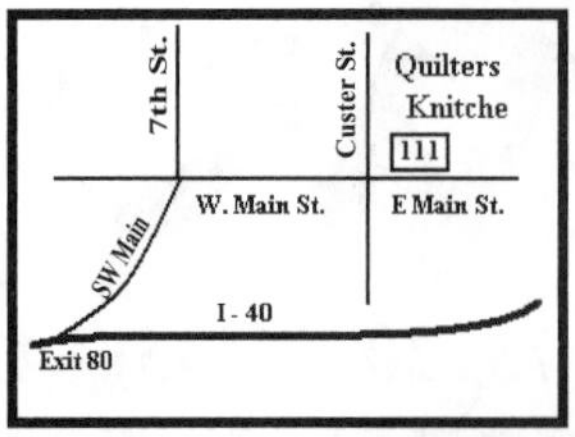

thequiltersknitche@sbcglobal.net
www.thequiltersknitche.com
Quality fabrics, the latest in notions, books and patterns. We have kits available. Locally crafted quilts. Classes for all levels of quilters.

Chickasha, OK #20

Please Call Ahead for Hours

Becky's Stitch in Time

2227 Carolina 73018
cell (405) 206-8914 (405) 224-5024
noellambert_40@yahoo.com
Owner: Noel & Becky Lambert

We carry a full line of 100% cotton fabrics specializing in Oriental Fabrics by Kona Bay. We also carry lines by Benartex, P&B & more.

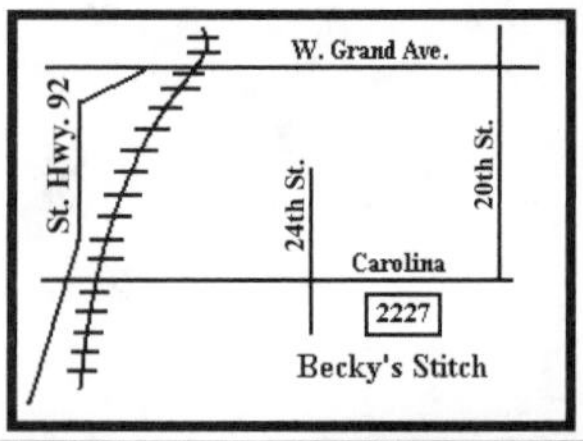

Chickasha, OK #21

Mon - Fri 10 - 5:30
Tues til 8
Sat 10 - 4

STEELMAN
Framing, Gifts & Sew Much More

410 Chickasha Ave. 73018
(405) 224-2036
grannylady@suddenlink.net

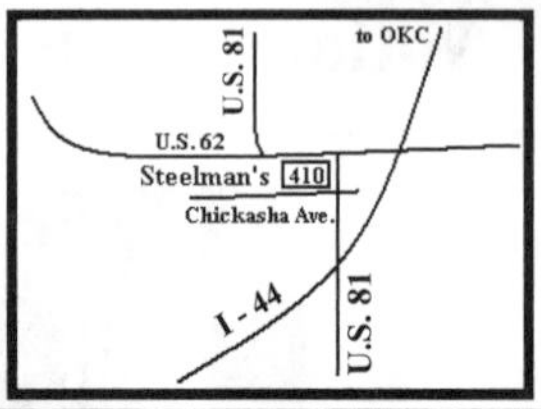

Owner: Wade & Phylis Steelman
Est: 1960 5000 sq.ft.
Step inside historic downtown's most unique building to experience a quilter's heaven. 1500+ bolts of quality 100% cotton fabric from top companies, supplies and notions.

Cache, OK #22

Tues - Fri 10 - 5
Sat 9 - 2

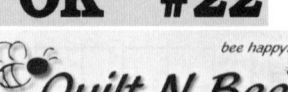

bee happy!
Quilt N Bee

506 C Ave., P.O. Box 131
73527
Phone/Fax (580) 429-2400
info@quiltnbee.biz Est: 2006 2000 sq.ft.
www.quiltnbee.biz
Inspiring quilt shop, over 1500 bolts, fun staff. Long Arm on site. Classes. Excellent web site with secure online shopping & newsletter.

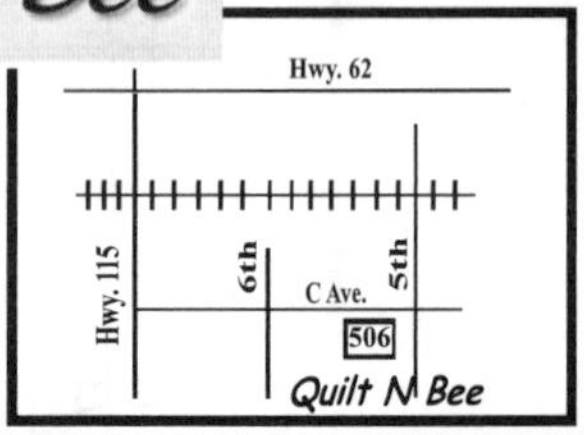

Altus, OK #23

Mon - Fri 9:30 - 5:30
Sat 9 - 5

Johnson's

105 W. Commerce 73521
(580) 477-1398 Fax: (580) 482-2248
Owner: Anita Johnson
Est: 1997 2500 sq.ft. 4000+ bolts
johnvac@sbcglobal.net

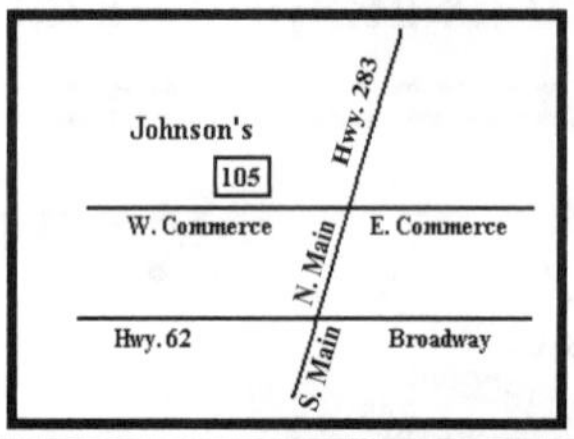

Large selection of notions, books and patterns. Huge selection of Moda, P & B, Fabriquilt, Batiks, Flannel & more. Quilting Classes & Long Arm Quilting available.

Allen, OK #24

Mon - Sat 9 - 5:30

Prairie Notions

701 E. Gilmore 74825
(580) 857-2831
Okie_page@hotmail.com
Owners: George & Pamala Price
Est: 2001

Custom Machine Quilting - Scissor Sharpening
Finished quilts
Native American Fabrics

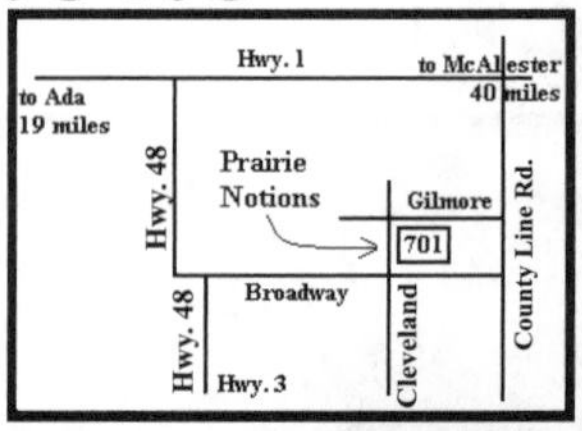

McAlester, OK #25

Mon - Fri 9 - 5:30
Wed 1 - 5:30
Sat 9 - 2

Country Fabrics & Quilts

5400 S. Hwy. 69 74501
(918) 423-0933
Owner: Louise Hoffman

1000+ Bolts of Quality Fabrics, Notions, Quilting Patterns, Books, Long Arm Machine Quilting.
We also have quilt classes.
On Hwy. 69 3 mi. S. of Wal- Mart or 1/2 mi. N of Turnpike.

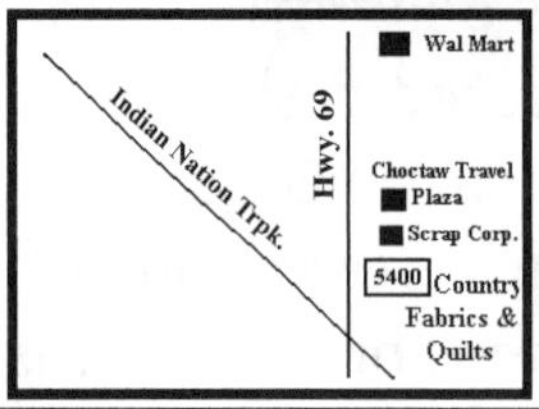

Antlers, OK #26

Mon - Fri 9 - 6
Sat 9 - 4
Evenings by Appt.

Betsy's Quilts & Fabric Shop

HC 83, Box 870, P.O. Box 947 74523
(580) 298-5821 Fax: Same
(888) 817-5821 Est: 1994
Owner: Betty Hairfield 6000 sq.ft.

Over 5000 Bolts of Name Brand Fabrics.
Quilts, Books, Patterns, Notions.
Dealer of AccuQuilt Die Cutter Machine .
Machine Quilting Pattern or Outlined.

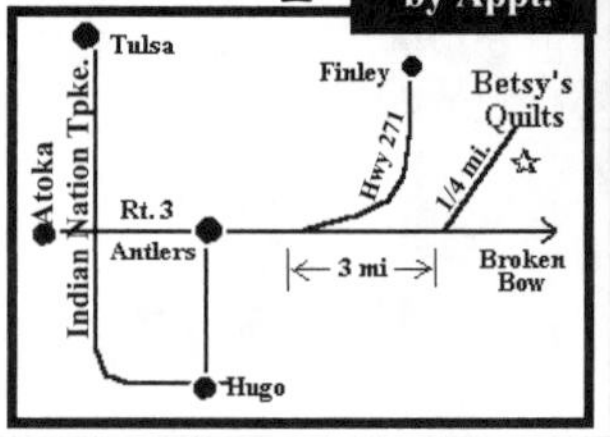

Oklahoma Quilt Shops

Allen — **Prairie Notions Fabric Shop, 701 E Gilmore**
580-857-2831 — **See ad #24, this page**

Altus — **Johnson's Sewing, 105 W. Commerce**
580-477-1398 — **See ad #23, this page**

Alva — **Fabrics & More Etc., 428 Flynn St.**
580-327-0240 — **See ad #3, page 447**

Antlers — **Betsy's Quilts & Fabric Shop, HC 83, Box 870**
580-298-5821 — **See ad #26, this page**

Bixby — The Log Cabin Quilt Shop, 14803 E. 171st — 918-366-6902

Broken Arrow — **SewFlakes, 106 S. Main**
918-251-7094 — **See ad #9, page 450 & 204**

Cache — **Quilt N Bee, 506 C Ave.**
580-429-2400 — **See ad #22, this page**

Chickasha — **Becky's Stitch in Time, 2227 Carolina**
405-224-5024 — **See ad #20, this page**

Chickasha — **Steelman Framing, Sew Much More, 410 Chickasha**
405-224-2036 — **See ad #21, this page**

Chickasha — Bush Family Affair, 401 W. Chickasha Ave. — 405-224-2280

Clinton — Cindy's Quilts, P.O. Box 1212 — 580-323-1174

Copan	**Corner Sew & So, 101 S Caney Ave.**	**918-532-5533**	**See ad #4, page 447**
Duncan	Deb's Sew Biz, 427 S. Hwy. 81	580-255-2843	
El Reno	K's Quilting Studio, 107 S. Bickford Ave.	405-422-2707	
Elk City	Circle B Quilting Ranch, 1820 N. Washington	580-225-2000	
Eufaula	Fabric Store, 130 North Main	918-689-3320	
Frederick	Thayer Rags Fabric Center, 108 W. Grand	580-335-3380	
Gore	**Fabric Patch, 305 S Main St.**	**918-489-5163**	**See ad #11, page 450**
Grove	**Prints of Piece, 25501 S 655 Rd.**	**918-786-2046**	**See ad #5, page 447**
Guthrie	**Extra Special Fabric, 117 W. Oklahoma Ave.**	**405-282-1144**	**See ad #14, page 450**
Guthrie	**Sooner Quilts, 7821 S. Sooner Rd.**	**405-282-2070**	**See ad #15, page 450**
Guymon	**Cheryl's Quilt Corner, 1608 N. Ellison**	**580-338-3677**	**See ad #1, page 447**
Harrah	Sew Awesome, 1950 N. Church Ave.	405-454-2960	
Hennessey	**Prairie Quilt, 101 S. Main St.**	**405-853-6801**	**See ad #18, page 451**
Jay	Keepin' U N Stitches, 705 N. 4th St.	918-253-2455	
Lawton	Morning Star Quiltworks, 1010 SW "E" Ave.	580-248-9200	
Mangum	Busy Bee, 120 E. Lincoln St.	580-782-3805	
McAlester	**Country Fabrics & Quilts, 5400 S. Hwy. 69**	**918-423-0933**	**See ad #25, page 452**
Midwest City	**Quilter's Corner, 1110 S. Air Depot Blvd. #14**	**405-455-5005**	**See ad #12, page 450**
Moore	Country Collections by Hart, 113 W. Main	405-799-0773	
Oklahoma City	**Sew N Sews, 5127 N. Portland**	**405-942-2700**	**See ad #16, page 450**
Oklahoma City	**Oklahoma Quiltworks, 9323 N. Pennsylvania**	**405-842-4778**	**See ad #17, page 451**
Oklahoma City	The Savage Quilter, 6815 N. May Ave.	405-840-1466	
Pauls Valley	The Quilt Shoppe, 304 W. Ridge Dr.	405-238-4098	
Pawhuska	Jody's Quilting, 602 E. Main St.	918-287-3032	
Ponca City	Completely Quilted, 315 E Grand Ave	580-718-9300	
Ringwood	Quilters Depot, 116 E. 3rd St.	580-883-4999	
Sand Springs	The Little Quilt Shop, 7 W 40th	918-245-1339	
Sapulpa	Back Home Quilt Fabric, LLC, 11 No. Water	918-224-4015	
Seminole	Country Patchwork Angel, 36151 Old Hwy. 270	405-257-3946	
Shawnee	Sue's Sewing Shoppe, 2301 N. Kickapoo	405-273-4600	
Stillwater	**Sew N Sews, 217 S. Perkins Rd.**	**405-707-0700**	**See ad #13, page 450**
Stillwater	The Quilt Box Fabric Shop, 912 S. Main St.	405-533-2867	
Tahlequah	**Serendipity Quilt Shop, 109 N. Muskogee Ave.**	**918-453-2840**	**See ad #10, page 450**
Tulsa	**Quilt Sampler Creative Sewing Center, LLC 6024 S. Sheridan**	**918-493-3388**	**See ad #8, page 449**
Tulsa	**The Silver Needle, 6068 S. Sheridan Rd.**	**918-493-1136**	**See ad #7, page 448**
Tulsa	**Cotton Patch, 8250 East 71st St.**	**918-252-1995**	**See ad #6, page 447**
Turpin	**Prairie Trails Quilting, RR1 Box 32H**	**580-778-3501**	**See ad #2, page 447**
Weatherford	**Quilter's Knitche 111 E. Main St.**	**580-774-7522**	**See ad #19, page 452**
Woodward	Quilter's Café, 821 Main St.	580-254-5732	

Oklahoma Quilt Shows

About Shows: We are listing only the very basic information about shows that happen on a regular schedule here. Please check out our website for more details on each show. Also this information tends to change quite often so please verify the event with our website or a local source before you venture far. Or if you're in the right area at the right time, give it a shot.

If you are a show organizer, please keep us updated on your event.
shows@quilterstravelcompanion.com
www.quilterstravelcompanion.com

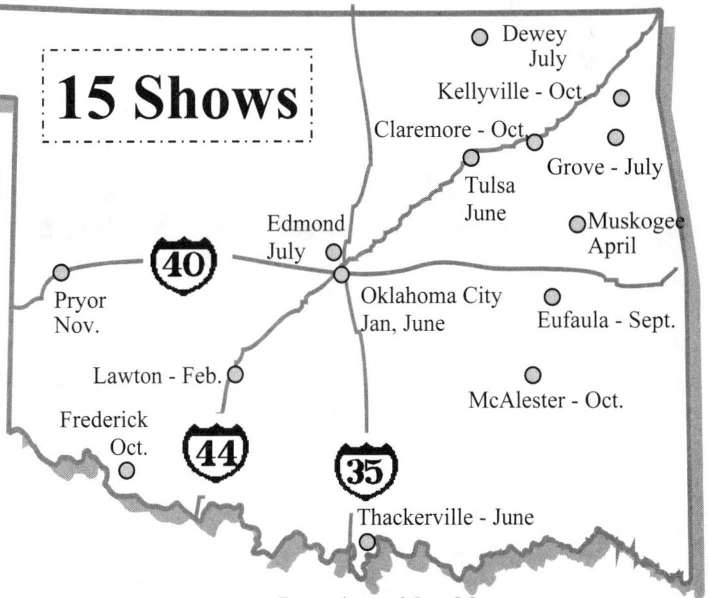

Month	City	Schedule	Show	Location with address
January				
	Oklahoma City	Annual, 2nd full Weekend in January	OKC Winter Quilt Show	Cox Convention Center, 1 Myriad Gardens
February				
	Lawton	Odd Years, 3rd Fri & Sat of February	For the Love of Quilts	Great Plains Coliseum, 920 S. Sheridan
April				
	Muskogee	Annual, 2nd Fri & Sat in April	Muskogee Area Quilters Guild Show	St. Paul United Meth. Church, 2307 W. Broadway
June				
	Thackerville	Annual, early June	Red River Quilters Showcase	Winstar World Casino Event Center
	Tulsa	Even Years, 1st Fri & Sat in June	Green Country Quilters Guild Show	Tulsa Fairgrounds, Exchange Center, 4401 E. 21st
	Oklahoma City	Odd Years, 3rd weekend in June	Central Oklahoma Quilters Guild Show	State Fair Park W I-40 / I-44
July				
	Grove	Odd Years, 1st Wed - Sat in July	Grand Lake O' the Cherokees Quilt Guild Show	Grove Community Center, 104 W. 4th St.
	Dewey	Odd Years, 2nd weekend in July	Jubilee Quilters Guild Show	Washington County Fair Bldg., 1109 N. Delaware
	Edmond	Even Years, last weekend in July	Edmond Quilt Festival Hamilton Field House	University of Central Oklahoma
September				
	Eufaula	Odd Years, Saturday of Labor Day weekend	Piecemakers Quilters Guild Show	Northfork Baptist Church, Bridgeport Access Rd.
October				
	Claremore	Annual, 3rd weekend in October	Autumn Leaves Quilt Show	Claremore Community Center, 2301 N. Sioux Ave.
	Frederick	Annual, 4th Saturday in October	Quilter's Day Quilt Show	Pioneer Townsite Museum Complex, 200 N. 9th
	McAlester	Annual, last Sat in October	Kiamichi Quilt Guild Show	St. John's Catholic Church Gym, 3rd Ave. & E. Washington St.
	Kellyville	Annual, Late October or Early November	Creek County HCE Quilt Show	Creek County Fairgrounds, 17806 W. Hwy. 66
November				
	Pryor	Odd Years, 1st Fri & Sat in November	Pryor Patchers Quilt Show	First Free Will Baptist Church, 107 S. Ora

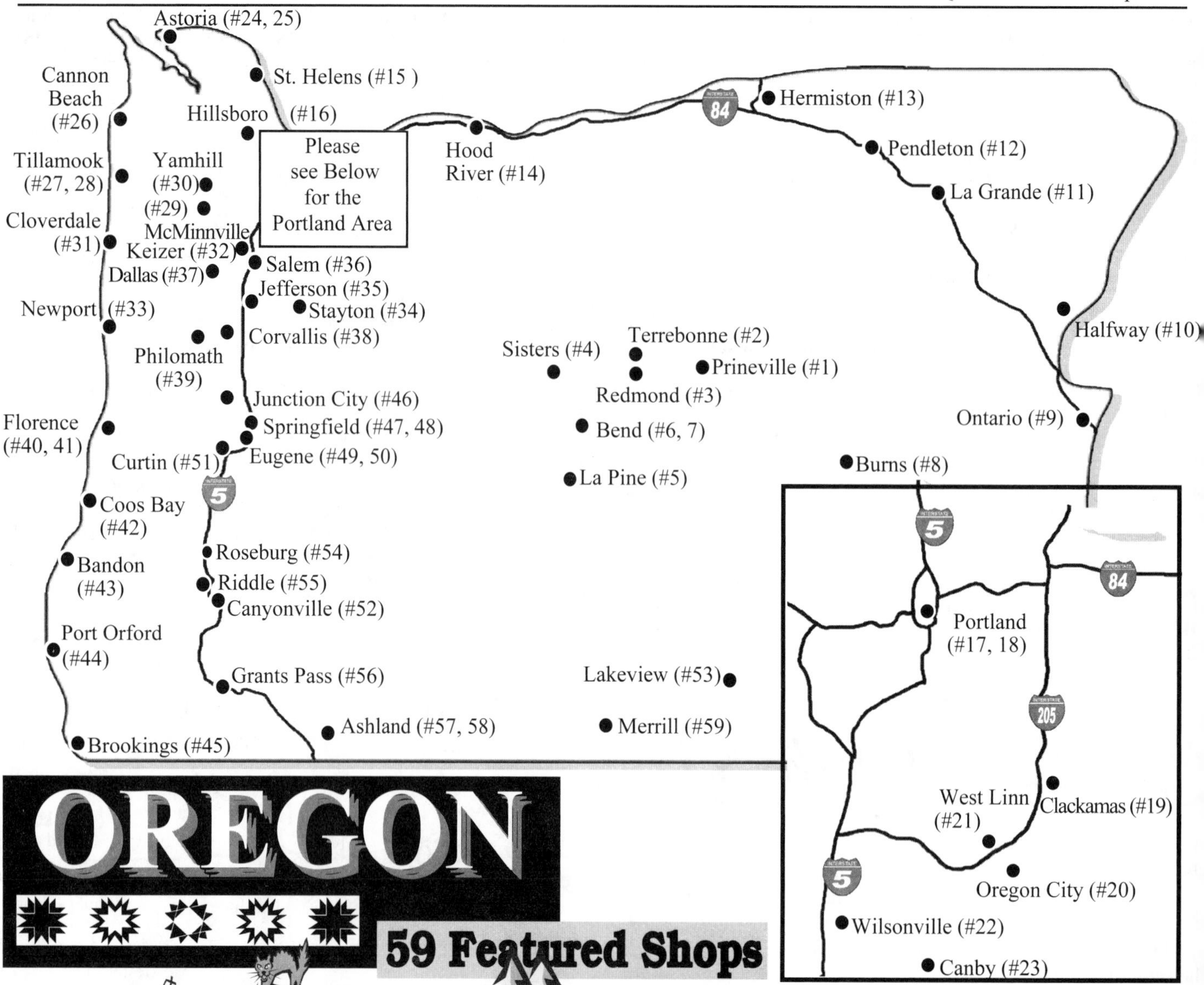

OREGON

59 Featured Shops

Prineville, OR #1

**Tues - Fri 10 - 6
Mon & Sat 10 - 4
Sunday Summer only 12 - 4**

395 N Main St. 97754
(541) 447-1338
Owner: Rhonda Krider
Est: 2008 1900 sq.ft. Online newsletter
thequiltshack@yahoo.com
www.thequiltshack.com
An excellent variety of fabrics, yarn, patterns, notions, and gifts. Flannels, westerns, batiks and many other varieties of fabrics. Classes too.

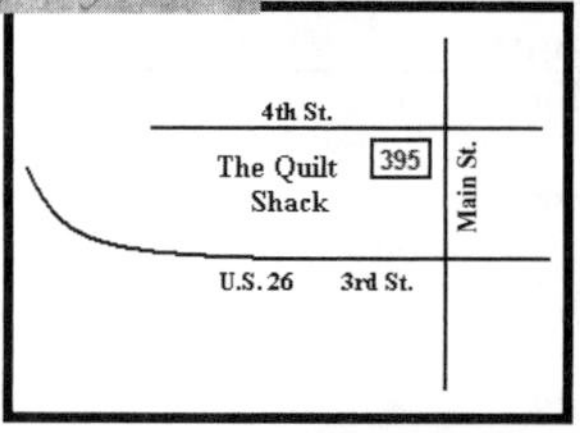

Terrebonne, OR #2

Mon - Sat 10 - 5

Quilters Attic

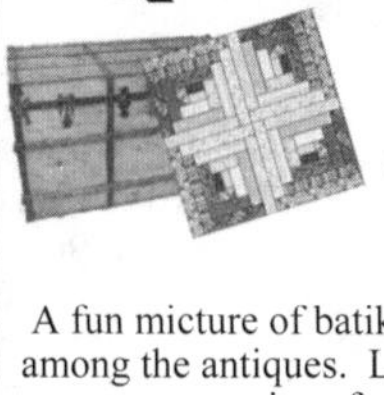

8154 11th St. #1, P.O. Box 156 97760
(541) 548-8119
Owner: Kathy Ferguson
info@quiltersattic.net
www.quiltersattic.net

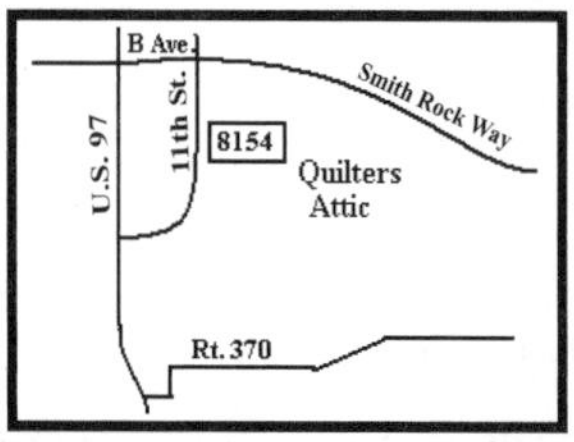

A fun micture of batiks, western, 30's, florals among the antiques. Lots of books, patterns & notions for great ideas.

Redmond, OR #3

**M, W, F 10 - 5
Tu, Th 12 - 5
Sat 10 - 4**

High Mountain Fabrics

1542 S. Hwy. 97 97756
(Behind Carpet Company)
(541) 548-6909
Est: 2002 2500 sq.ft. 2500+ Bolts

A Quilt Shop with 100% Cottons, Flannels, Books, Patterns & Notions.

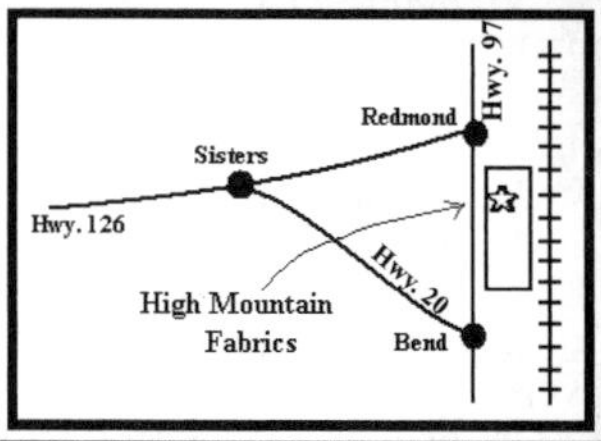

#4

Stitchin' Post

SEWING • QUILTING • KNITTING

where education & inspiration thrive

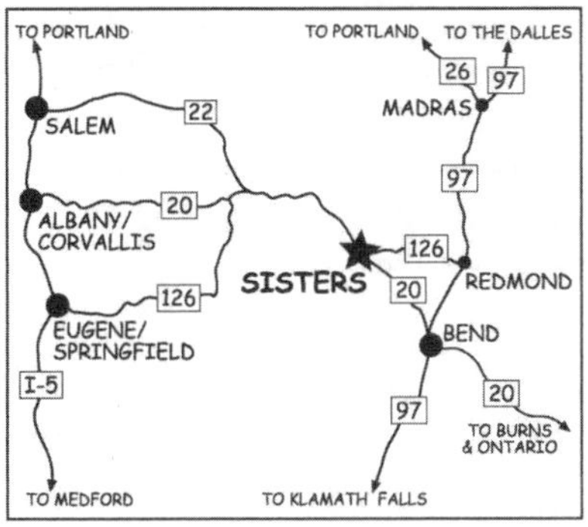

Shop online or come visit one of the finest quilt shops in America.

Store Hours: Monday - Saturday 9 - 5, Sunday 10 - 5

Home of
The Sisters Outdoor Quilt Show™
(Second Saturday in July)

311 W. Cascade/PO Box 280, Sisters, OR 97759
(541) 549-6061 • Fax (541) 549-1922 • *stitchinpost.com*

La Pine, OR #5

Homestead Quilts and Gallery

Mon - Fri 9:30 - 5
Sat 10 - 4
Spring & Sum Sun 10 - 4

51425 Hwy. 97
(La Pine Hwy. Ctr) 97739
(541) 536-2360
Owner: Cathy Buono
1500 Bolts

In an Historic 100 Year old Building in Oregon's Newest City.
Fabric; Classes; Notions; Yarn; Craft Paint Beads; Local Artists, many mediums; Gifts

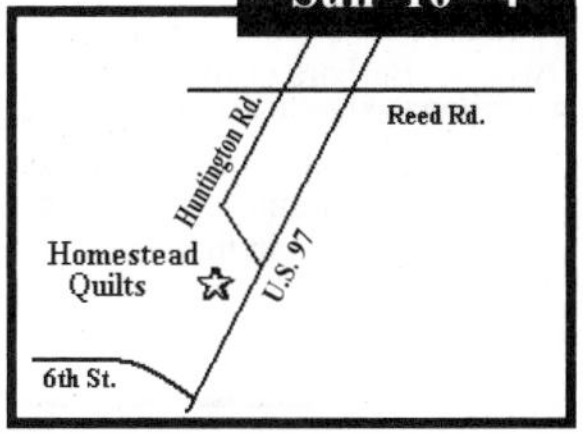

Bend, OR #6

Mon - Sat 9:30 - 5:30
Sun 12 - 4

BJ's Quilt Basket

20225 Badger Rd. 97702
(541) 383-4310 Fax: (541) 383-248
Owner:
Vicki Jensen

vicki@bjsquiltbasket.com
www.bjsquiltbasket.com
1000's of top quality cottons & specialty fabrics, classes, mail order available, Blocks of the Month, July Festival of Classes - please join us!!

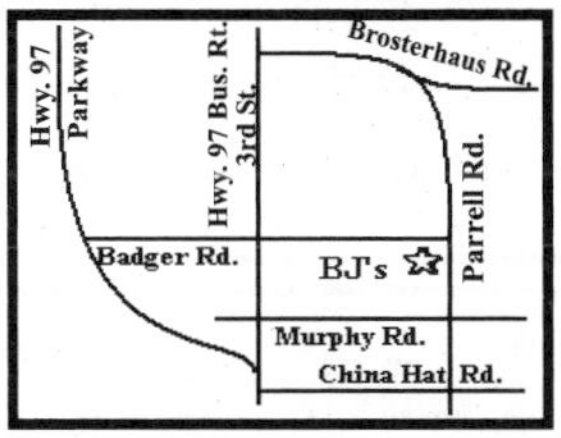

SEW MANY QUILTS "So Little Time"

Bend, OR #7

1375 SE Wilson, Suite 170
Bend, OR 97702
541-385-7166
Fax 541-385-8741
Owners: Sharon Botkins & Gail Ransdall

Better Homes and Gardens Quilt Sampler FEATURED SHOP 2008

SHOP ONLINE:
www.sewmanyquiltsinbend.com
Email: smq@qwestoffice.net

"So Many Samples, It's Like a Mini Quilt Show Each time You Visit"

Our shop is over 5000 sq. ft. of inspiration!! You're invited to Bend's finest quilt shop featuring a charming personality, the friendliest atmosphere and a great selection of fabrics, books, patterns, notions and gifts displayed among antiques. We have a large variety of machine embroidery and hand stitchery projects. Come in and try out the Bernina Stitch Regulator and see what all the excitement is about! We have a large selection of machines and software to fit each of your sewing needs.

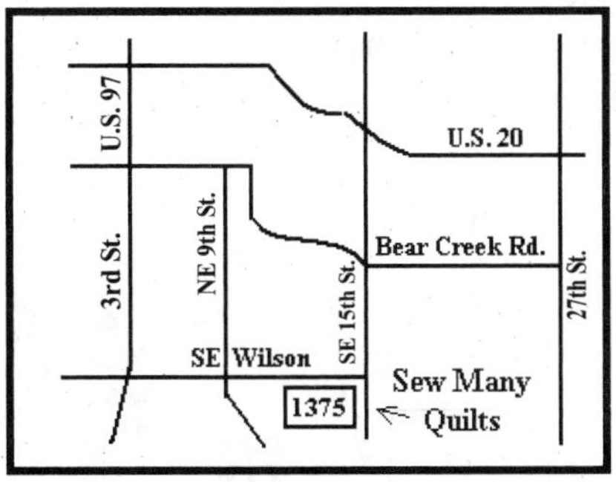

Mon - Fri 9:30 - 5:30
Sat 9:30 - 5
Sun 12 - 4

BERNINA
AUTHORIZED BERNINA DEALER - Nothing Sews Like a Bernina

Burns, OR #8

Mon - Fri 9 - 5:30
Sat 10 - 5

Country Lane Quilts

406 N. Broadway 97720
(541) 573-6406 Fax: (541) 573-6155
Owners: Barbara Ormond & LaDonna Baron
Est: 2003 5000 sq.ft. 4000 Bolts & growing
fabric@country-lane-quilts.com
www.country-lane-quilts.com
"A Quilter's oasis in the Oregon High Desert." Large selection of Western Fabric, Janome Sewing Machines, Quilters Supplies, Books, Buttons & Patterns.

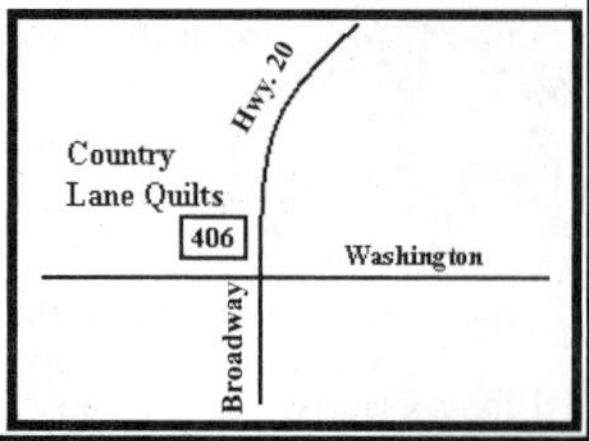

Ontario, OR #9

Mon - Fri 10 - 6
Sat 10 - 5

199 S. Oregon St. 97914
(541) 889-3085
Owner: Heather McLean
Online Newsletter

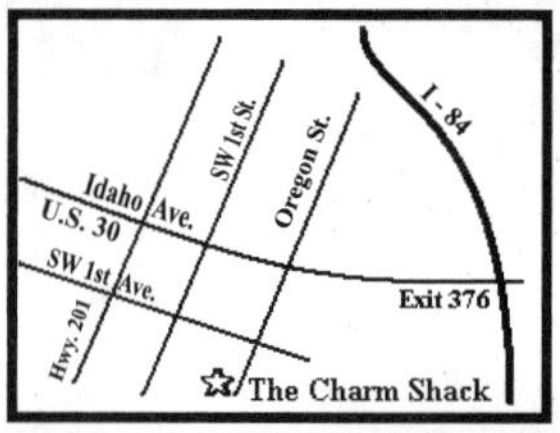

thecharmshack@me.com
A charming shop that carries a wide array of quilting patterns, notions, and fabric, with lots of samples and classes.

Halfway, OR #10

Mon - Sat 9 - 5

Quilts Plus

280 S. Main St., P.O. Box 626 97834
(541) 742-5040 Fax: (541) 742-5041
Owner: Roberta Bryan
Est: 1986 2400 sq.ft.
quiltsplus@pinetel.com

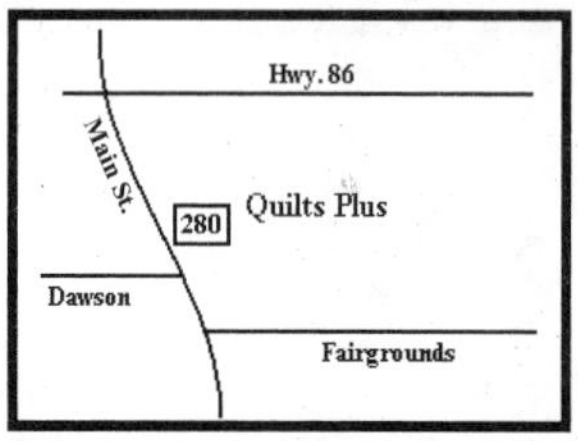

Over 2500 Bolts of Quilting Fabric
Longarm MachineQuilting - Gift Shop
Espresso Bar - Antiques & Collectibles
Notions - Craft Supplies

La Grande, OR #11

Sun 12 - 5
Mon - Thurs 10 - 5:30
Fri 10 - 4
Sat Closed

Quilt Therapy

1107 Washington 97850
(888) 663-1817 or (541) 663-1817
Fax: (541) 663-9728
Est: 2001 1900 sq.ft.
Owner: Faith Hohstadt
quilttherapy@verizon.net
www.quilt-therapy.com

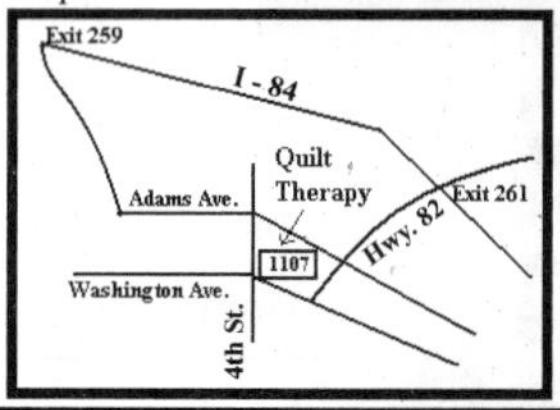

Everything for your quilting and knitting addiction! Quality fabrics, specialty yarns, notions, gifts, kits, BOM, classes and helpful advice. Machine quilting services available.

Pendleton, OR #12

Mon - Fri 10 - 6
Sat 10 - 4
Sun 12 - 4

Pendleton Quiltworks

138 SE Court 97801
(541) 276-9546
Owner: Rachelle Doherty
Est: 2003

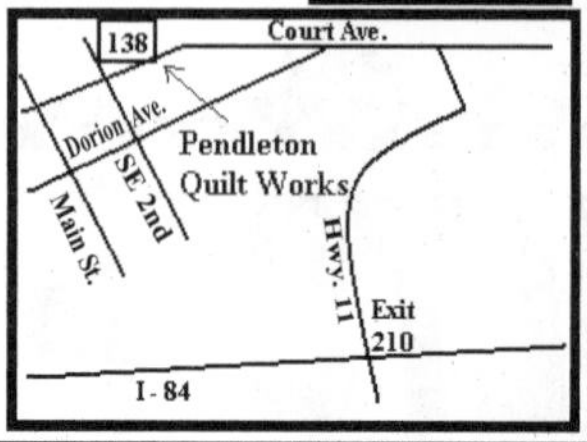

pendletonquiltworks@hotmail.com
www.pendletonquiltworks.com
New Friends, Quality Fabrics!
Color, Creativity and Customer Satisfaction.
Located in historic downtown Pendleton.

Hermiston, OR #13

Mon - Sat 10 - 5:30

Aunty Ida's Quilt Shop
& BERNINA Sewing Center

435 W. Hermiston 97838
(541) 567-2726
Owners: Idamarie & Tom Martin
www.auntyida.com
PFAFF Sewing Machines and Handiquilters HQ16 on Display! Over 2000 bolts of quality fabrics! Books, Patterns, Notions and Classes.

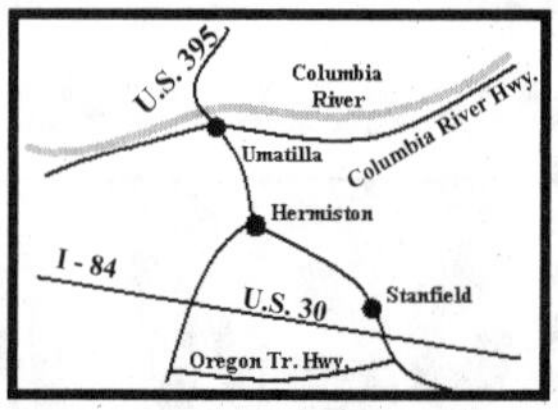

Hood River, OR #14

Mon - Sat 10 - 5

ETC - Every Thread Counts

1204 Nix Rd. #101 97031
(541) 386-5044
Est: 1987
Owner: Ann Zuehlke
etc@gorge.net
www.everythreadcounts.net

Quilting supplies, Fabric, Classes, etc.

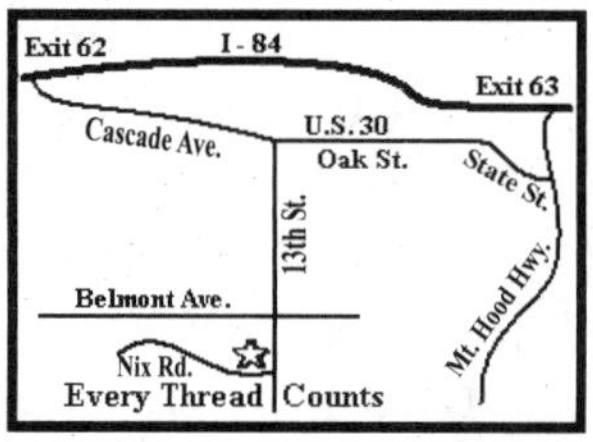

St. Helens, OR #15

Mon - Sat 10 - 5
Sun Closed

Fibers & Stitches
Fabric and Quilting Supplies

58093 Columbia River Hwy. 97053
(866) 617-8448 or (503) 397-5536
www.fibersandstitches.com

Oregon quilters have called us home since 1996. We're committed to providing you with the highest quality fabric and quilting supplies.

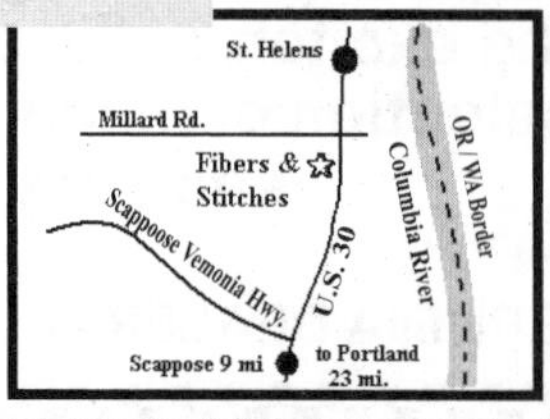

Sharon's Attic Quilt Shop

sharonsatticquiltshop.com
Fabric * Notions * Threads * Books * Patterns
Long Arm Quilting

*A bright, entertaining and sociable shop filled with 1000's of bolts of 100% cotton fabric. Batiks, Reproductions, Flannels, Kits & Thimbleberries.
*Wonderful samples displayed to inspire you.
*Visit our website for online sales and classes for all skills.
*Quilt Books, Notions, Patterns, Gadgets, Kits & Threads.
*Hand Embroidery; Patterns, Kits, Threads, & Supplies.
*Classes, Sewing machines-Bernina & Pfaff

2950 SW CORNELIUS PASS RD #D
HILLSBORO, OR 97123
503-259-3475
Fax 503-259-3469
ssrice991@integra.net

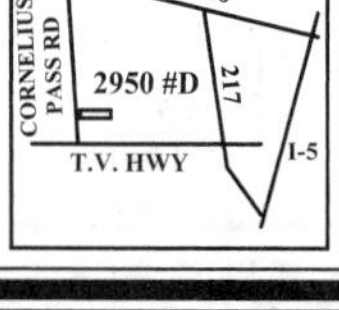

#16

FabricDepot

1½ Acres of Fabric

Retail & Wholesale *Plenty of Free Parking* *Buses & RVs Welcome*

11,000 Quilting Cottons *2,000 Home Dec Fabrics* *Fashion & Bridal Fabrics* *Notions · Crafts · Yarn*

Shop In Store

Enjoy a complete fabric shopping experience in one of the largest, most complete fabric stores in America! We have the finest inventory of fabrics, notions, books & patterns. Our quilting floor is pure joy. We offer an unrivaled selection of more than 11,000 designer quilting cottons. From the oldest names in the industry to the most recent design houses, we carry the latest offerings of more than 75 suppliers. Current designer collections are complemented with row upon row of quality solids, marbles and background fabrics. We stock more than 175 colors of Kona® Cotton solids and 600 Bali batik cottons! Ever popular is our wide variety of themed and novelty prints, quilter's flannel and children's prints.

All fabric is neatly draped and displayed at eye level under excellent lighting. New fabric is added daily and shopping carts are available for your convenience. You will find beautiful display quilts and model garments. Our customer service associates are passionate about sewing. Don't forget to visit our Batting Department for a full line of premium cotton, wool and silk batting.

EXPIRES: DECEMBER 31ST, 2012

25% off

YOUR ENTIRE FABRIC PURCHASE

ONE COUPON PER CUSTOMER. IN STORE ONLY. DISCOUNT DOES NOT APPLY TO PREVIOUSLY DISCOUNTED OR MARKED DOWN ITEMS. LIMITED TO STOCK ON HAND.

QTC

SHOP AT HOME

www.fabricdepot.com

Great online discounts and specials! All inquiries directed to **info@fabricdepot.com** will be answered, or call **1-888-896-1478** for toll-free customer support. We can ship your in store purchase home.

FROM I-205 Northbound Exit #20 (Washington & Stark). Right on Washington. Travel 1 mile east to corner of Stark & 122nd. Washington becomes Stark St.

FROM I-205 Southbound Exit #21A (Glisan & Stark). Keep to the right and follow exit to 3rd light. (Be careful not to enter I-205 again) Turn Left on Washington. Travel 1 mile east to corner of Stark & 122nd. Washington becomes Stark St.

FROM I-84 Eastbound Exit #10 (122nd Ave). Turn left at light. Travel south for 1.8 miles to corner of 122nd & Stark.

FROM I-84 Westbound Exit #9: Merge onto I-205 Southbound. From I-205 Southbound, Exit #21A as above.

Portland, OR #17

700 SE 122nd Avenue **Portland, Oregon 97233**	MON–SAT 9AM–9PM	SUN: 10AM–7PM	**(503) 252-9530** **1 (800) 392-3376**

A Common Thread

Owned and operated by women who sew
Fabrics • Quilting • Garments • Home Décor
Embroidery • Craft Sewing • Notions • Threads
Classes • Bernina • Janome • HandiQuilter
Miele • Full Service & Repairs

 # 18

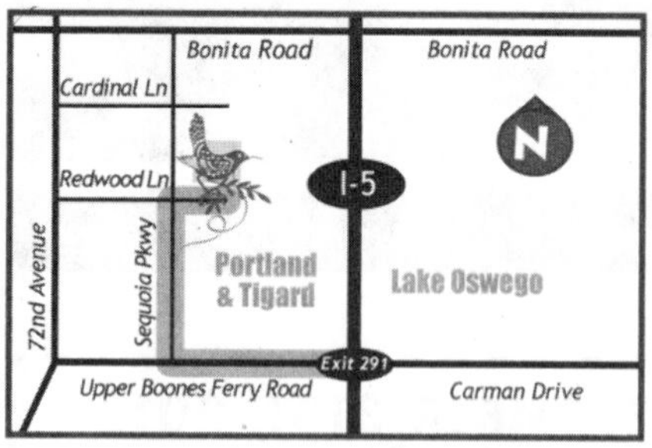

Great Location!
You'll easily find our big, beautiful location just west of I-5 off the Carman Dr. exit #291 at the corner of Sequoia Pkwy and Redwood Ln.

Store Hours
Mon-Fri 9:30-6:00 pm
Saturday 10:00-5:00pm
Sunday noon-5:00 pm

A Common Thread
15320 Sequoia Parkway, Portland, Oregon 97220
503 624-7440 or toll free 877 915-6789
www.acommonthreadsewing.com

Clackamas, OR #19

Mon - Thur 9 - 6
Fri & Sat 9 - 5

Quilting Delights LLC

"The Heart & Art of Quilting"

14863 SE Oregon Trail Dr. 97015
(503) 658-1600

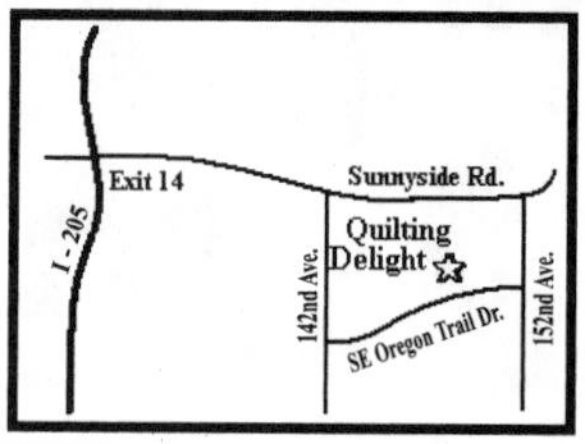

info@quiltingdelgihts.com
www.quiltingdelights.com
Autherized BERNINA dealer!
2000 bolts, block-of-the-month quilts.
Extraordinary classroom space
Great energy and a fun place to be!

Come and visit ***Let's Quilt***, an inspiring, educational and friendly quilt store in the metro area. You'll enjoy our large bright store featuring 50 or more displayed quilts. We offer 4,000 bolts of fabric including 30's and 1800 reproductions, Asians, batiks, DeGama indigos and much more. You'll also find wool felting supplies.

We offer daily and evening classes throughout the entire year. Our classroom is bright and airy with individual sewing stations for all students. In addition there are lots of fun activities, including a Mystery Book Club, Quilt Bingo and Wednesdays Intense Quilters Club.

Let's Quilt

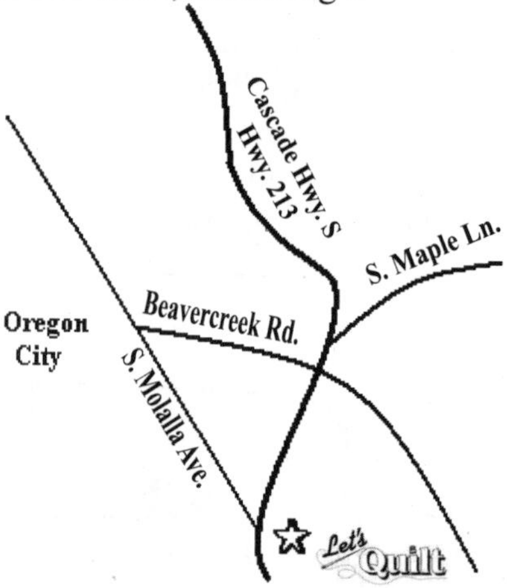

Oregon City, OR #20

503 518-4321
www.letsquiltshop.com

Store hours are:
Tues-Fri 9:30-5:00
Sat. 9:30-5:00
Sundays Please Call Ahead

19713 S. Hwy. 213, Suite 120
Oregon City, OR 97045

Our new shop is conveniently located in Oregon City on Hwy. 213, just 2.8 miles from !-205, in the Haggan shopping center.

West Linn, OR #21

Tues - Fri 10 - 6
Sat 10 - 5

- Over 8000 Fabrics to choose from
- Large selection of Hand-Dyed wools
- Large selection of books, patterns, threads and notions
- Home décor-gifts for every room of your house, inside & out!
- Complete website including our entire fabric collection, classes and events!
- Check out the "Shoppe's" blog, "Boughs of Holly!"

1914 Willamette Falls Dr
West Linn, OR 97068

www.hollyhillquiltshoppe.com
hollyhillquiltshoppe@comcast.net
503-607-0600

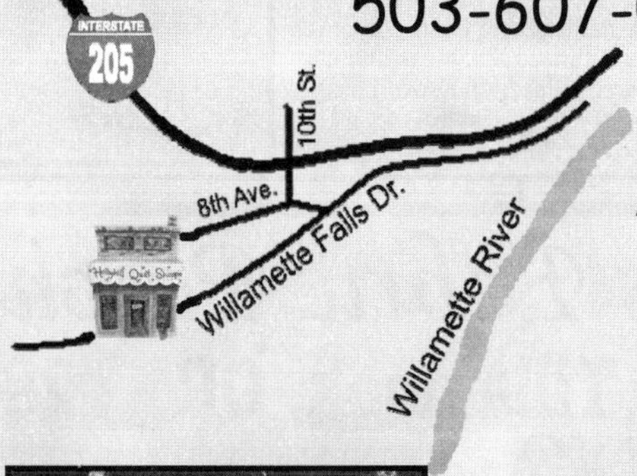

Don't forget to visit our brand new gift and home décor shop, Pickleweed Hill

Selected as one of 2010's Top Ten Shops by Better Homes and Gardens Quilt Sampler Magazine, *Hollyhill Quilt Shoppe & Mercantile* is considered to be one of Oregon's most celebrated quilting destinations. Nestled in the historic Willamette section of West Linn, the Shoppe opened in September 2005 and is family owned by Jan Hill and her son, Brian.

The "Shoppe" carries complete collections from your favorite designers! But the real charm can be found in the many enchanting displays that bring the fabric to life! During the holidays the Shoppe becomes a winter wonderland! Strong attention to detail along with a very friendly and knowledgeable staff make this a must-see on any quilting adventure!

Debbie Busby Wools

- *Moda*
- *Andover*
- *Clothworks*
- *Lakehouse*
- *Michael Miller*
- *Westminster Fibers*
- *Alexander Henry*
- *Northcott, P&B*
- *and many more!*

It's the kind of shop where inspiration lives and creativity begins.

Wilsonville, OR #22

Mon - Sat 10 - 5

Speckled Hen Quilts

www.speckledhenquilts.net

30775 SW Boone Ferry Rd. Suite F 97070
(Turn on 5th Street)
(503) 570-3368

Quilt Sampler FEATURED SHOP

Specializing in 1800's reproduction & 30's fabrics.

Spotted Roosters & Speckled Hens
This is where the FUN begins!

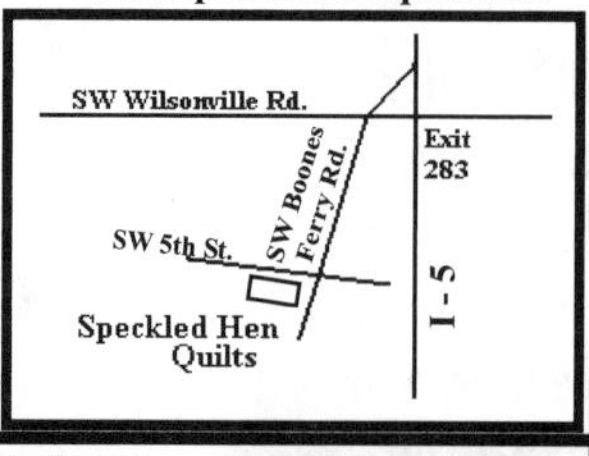

Canby, OR #23

Mon - Sat 10 - 5

Canby Quilt & Fabric

248 NW 1st Ave. 97013
(503) 263-3563
Owner: Sandy Nelson
Est: 2007 2000 sq.ft. 2000 bolts
quilts@canby.com
www.canbyquilts.com
DEDICATED TO THE QUILTER AND WOULD BE QUILTER.
We carry the latest books, patterns and 100% cotton fabrics.

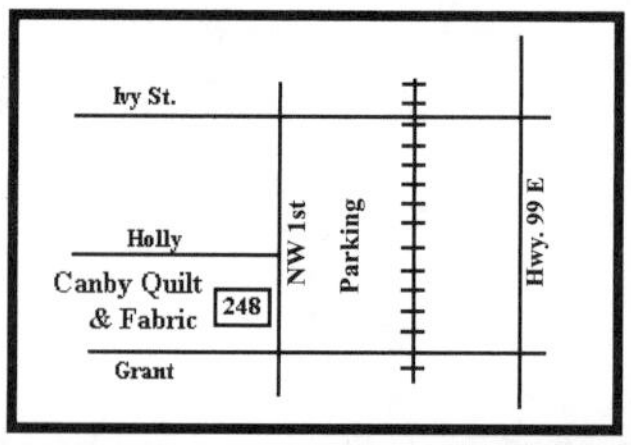

Astoria, OR #24

All Year
Tues-Fri 10-5:30
Sat 10 - 3
Summer add
Sun-Mon 12 - 3

Custom Threads

1282 Commercial St. 97103
(503) 325-7780 Fax: Same
Owner: Eda Linstrom
Est: 1989 1700 sq.ft. 1500 bolts
eda.marie@gmail.com

A full-service needlework & stitchery shop.

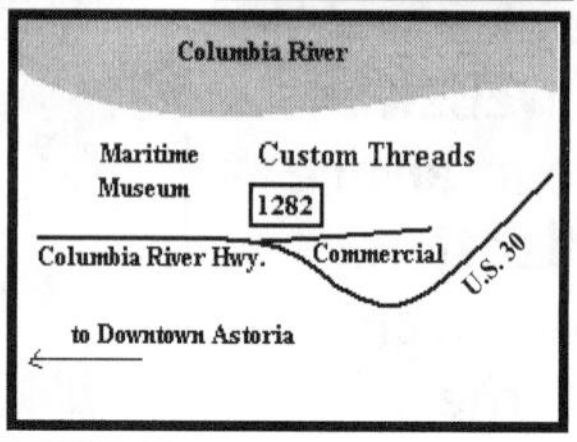

Astoria, OR #25

Open 7 Days 10 - 5

108 10th St. 97103
(800) 298-3177 or (503) 325-3300
Fax: (503) 325-9744 www.homespunquilt.com

Quality cotton fabrics for quilting and sewing Wool felt and rug hooking supplies, books, patterns, notions, and classes.

Bernina Dealer and authorized repair.

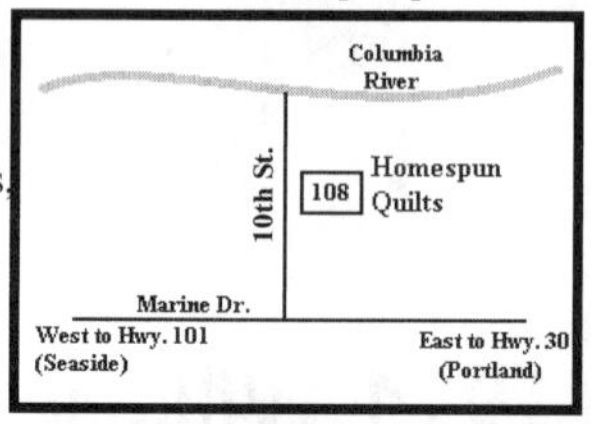

Tillamook, OR #27

April - October
Mon - Sat 10 - 5
Sun 12 - 4
November - March
Mon - Sat 10 - 4

LATIMER QUILT & TEXTILE CENTER

2105 Wilson River Loop 97141
(503) 842-8622
latimertextile@oregoncoast.com
www.latimerquiltandtextile.com

An active textile museum, dedicated to the preservation and promotion of the textile arts...weaving, spinning, quilting, history, research, education & exhibits.
Handcrafted gift items for sale.
Exhibits change every two months.

We are located one block east of Shilo Inn off Hwy. 101

Cannon Beach, OR #26

CENTER DIAMOND

1065 S. Hemlock
Cannon Beach, OR 97110
(503) 436-0833
Fax: (503) 436-2540
www.centerdiamond.com
Owner: Julie Walker
Est: 1994 1500 sq.ft.
centerdiamond@aol.com

Over 2000 bolts of the most gorgeous 100% cotton fabrics. Books, patterns, notions & gifts.

7 Days a Week 10 - 5

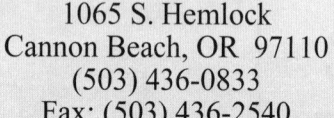

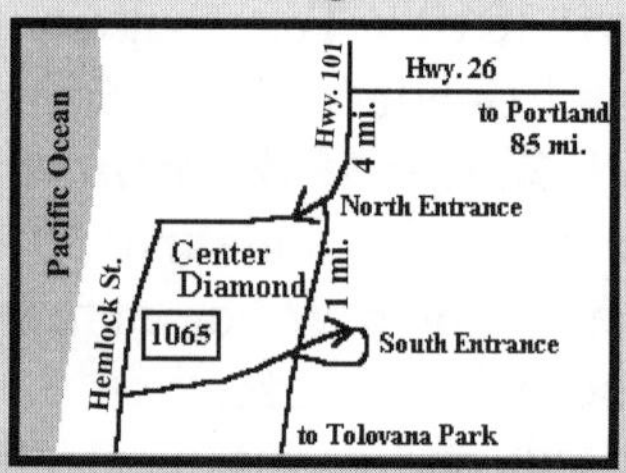

Located 1 block from the beach.

Jane's Fabric Patch

Tillamook, OR #28

1110 Main Ave. 97141
(503) 842-9392
fabric@pacifier.com
Owner: Jane Wise
Est: 1981 5000+ Bolts

Mon - Fri 9 - 5:30
Sat 10 - 4
Summer - Sundays & Holidays 11 - 3

Coastal Retreat.
Multi-faceted Quilt shop.
Large fabric selection, creative, knowledgeable and friendly ideas and assistance. Janome Dealer

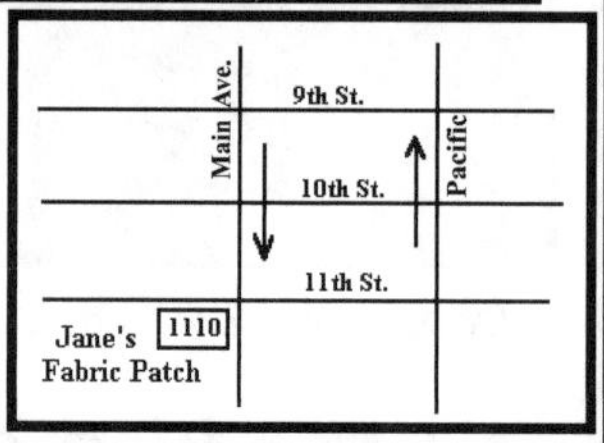

Web Site: www.janesfabricpatch.com

BOERSMA'S

It's SEW Much Better!

203 E. 3rd St. McMinnville, OR 97128
(503) 472-4611 (800) VAC-SEWS
jack@boersmas.com
Owners: Jack & Michelle Boersma Est: 1935
Located in Historic Downtown 20,000 sq.ft. 10,000 Bolts

McMinnville, OR #29

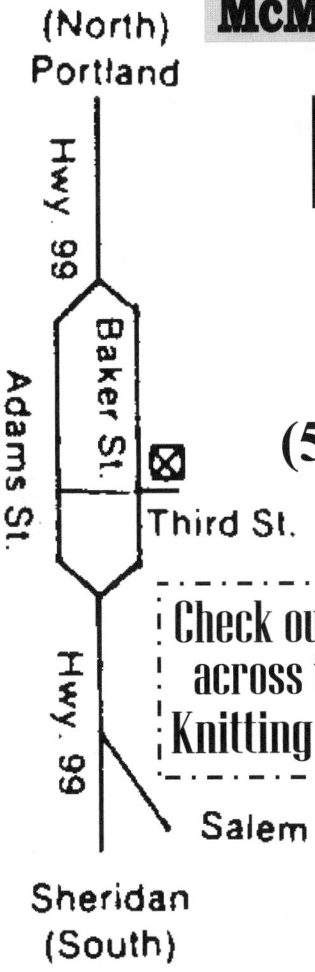

Mon - Fri 9 - 6
Sat 9 - 5

Boersma's
203 E. 3rd St.
Downtown
(503) 472-4611

Check out our "Knitting Basket" across the street for all your Knitting & Crocheting Needs!

Gammill Quilting Systems

- Sales & Service
- Hands-on Training
- Set-Up & Delivery
- Classes
- In-store Machine Rental

- Fine 100% Cottons
- Quilt Books
- Notions
- Classes
- Collectibles & Gift Items

Sewing Machine Sales & Service
Experienced Staff

www.boersmas.com

The Quilted Hill

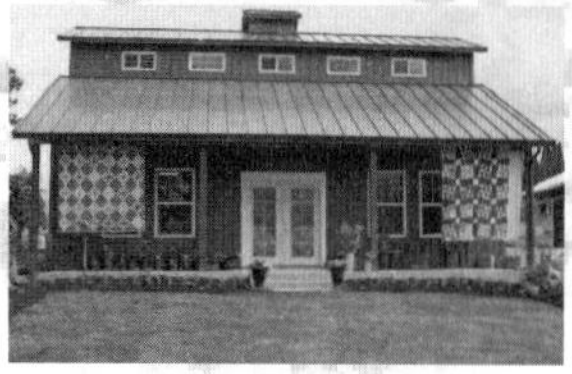

Top Quality Fabric & Supplies!
Reasonable prices!
Friendly knowledgeable service!
Undeniably the best View!

Open Tues-Sat 10-4

7601 NE Blackburn Rd.
Yamhill, OR 97148
(503) 662-4052
Owner: Bobbie Bebereia
Est: 2001 2500 Bolts

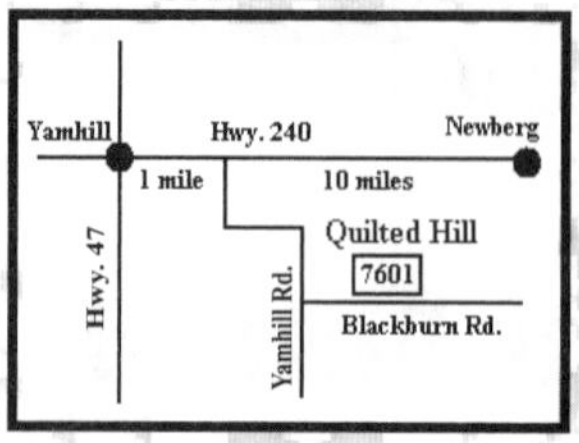

www.TheQuiltedHill.com

Better Homes and Gardens Quilt Sampler Featured Shop

Yamhill, OR #30

Cloverdale, OR #31

7 Days
10 - 5

B J's Fabrics & Quilts

38105 Hwy. 101 S, P.O. Box 215 97112
(877) 690-5267 (503) 392-6195
BJsfabrics@embarqmail.com Est: 1997
www.BJsFabricsquilts.com
Owner: Barbara Lewis Over 2000 bolts of fabric.
Hwy. 101 from the North-2 miles south of Cloverdale, turn left past the 90 mile marker, then left again at the 2nd driveway. Hwy. 101 from the South-¼ mile from the Pacific City Turn-off, turn right after BJ's Fabrics & Quilts state sign, left at 2nd driveway.

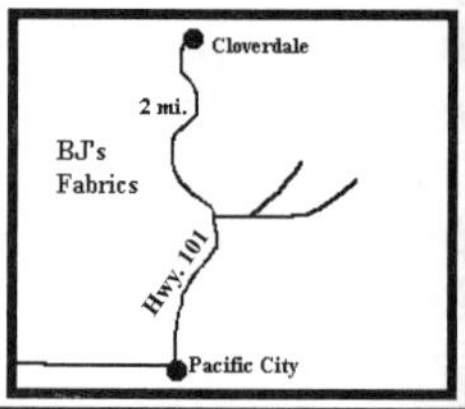

4475 River Road N - Keizer, OR 97303
503-463-1880

The Cotton Patch

...Where Creativity Grows

A warm, inviting atmosphere where quilters can gather to laugh and talk quilting. The store reflects a light and bright atmosphere, where you can choose the perfect fabrics for your quilts or projects. The staff is knowledgeable, friendly and ready to assist in the selection of any fabric, talk quilt design or just to offer friendly conversation and encouragement.

New Ownership: Diane Bowden
thecottonpatch@msn.com
www.cottonpatchoregon.com

Mon - Fri 10 - 5
Sat 10 - 4 Sun 12 - 4

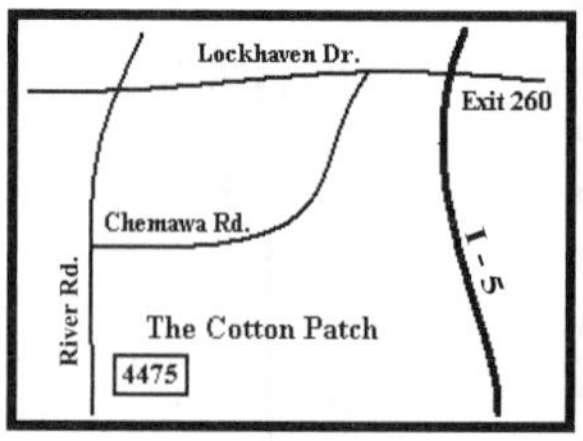

Keizer, OR #32

QUILTER'S COVE

www.quilterscove.net
"On-Line Store open 24 Hrs a day"

Where you come to be "Sew" inspired with fabric, books, patterns, notions & gifts. We feature Landscapes, Batiks, Asian, Fish, Nautical, & Beachy. We are a full Service Quilt Shop with everything you need for your first or 100th quilt. Hundreds of Patterns, Books and Notions.

Mon - Sat 10 - 5 * Sun 11 - 4

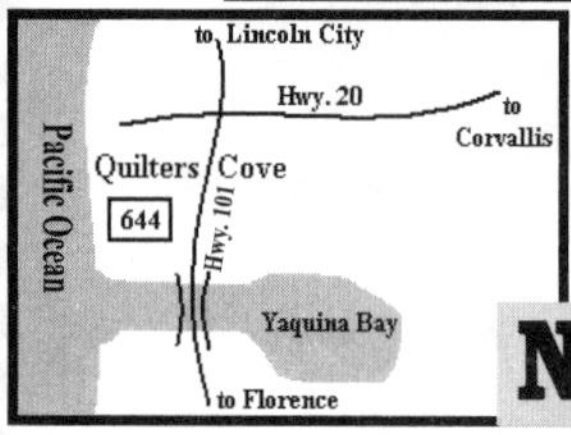

644 SW Coast Hwy. B 97365
866-43-QUILT or 541-265-2591
info@quilterscove.net
Est: 2004
Owners: Holly Nevins & Judy Muller

Newport, OR #33

Stayton, OR #34

Tues - Fri
11 - 5
Sat 10 - 4

Quilt 'n Stitch

193 N. 3rd Ave. 97383
(503) 767-4240
quiltnstitch@wvi.com
www.quiltnstitch.biz
The greatest new collections of fabric.
Authorized HQ16 Representative
Check our class schedule online.

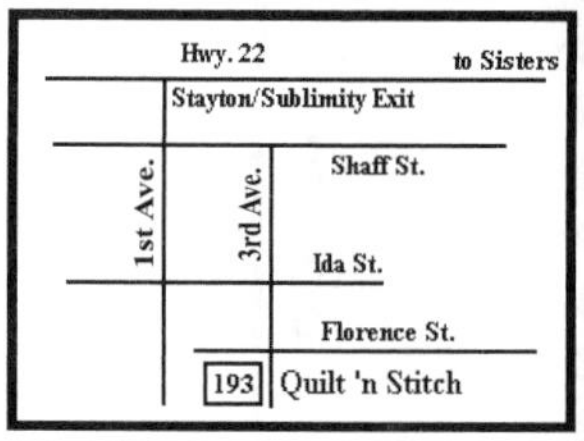

Jefferson, OR #35

Mon - Fri 9 - 5
Weekends &
Evening by Appt.

Janice Jenney Studios

13364 Marlatt Rd. S 97352
(541) 327-9886 Owner: Janice Jenney
Est: 1998 720 sq.ft. www.janicejenney.com
"I love turning your quilt tops into warm bed coverings." Quilts & custom machine quilting. Wide backings and batting available. We also sell finished quilts, table runners, wallhangings, etc.

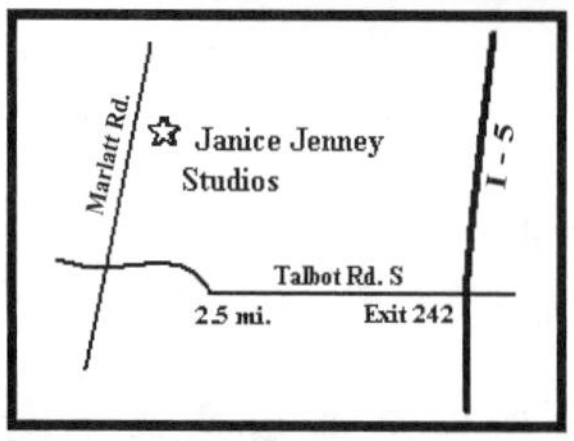

Established in 1900 as a General Store

GREENBAUM'S Quilted Forest

We Inspire Creativity

Top 10 Quilt Shop

Better Homes & Gardens' *Quilt Sampler* *& one of the 20 Best of all time!*

Salem, OR #36

- Over 3000 square feet filled with the hottest fabric, books, patterns & more!
- Friendly & knowledgeable staff
- Expert help selecting fabric. Use our carts to select from Westminster, Free Spirit, Moda, Maywood, lots of batiks and more!
- Classes & retreats
- Exclusive Oregon Thimblelady thimble dealer
- Online shopping: www.quiltedforest.com

HOURS

Mon, Fri, Sat. 9:30 am to 5:30 pm
Tues, Wed, Thurs. 9:30 am to 8:00 pm
Sunday Noon to 5:00 pm

503-363-7973 or Toll Free 1-877-700-2233

web: quiltedforest.com • e-mail: sylvia@quiltedforest.com
240 Commercial Street NE • Salem Oregon 97301

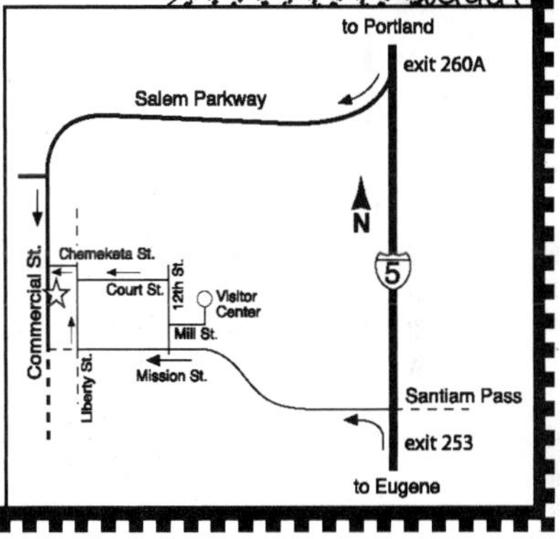

Rachel Greco, Owner

Grandma's Attic Sewing Emporium, Inc.

- 100% cotton fabrics for Quilting/Sewing
- Patterns, Books, Notions and More!
- Block of the Month/Fabric Clubs by Mail
- Join our Redwork Embroidery Club

Dallas, OR #37

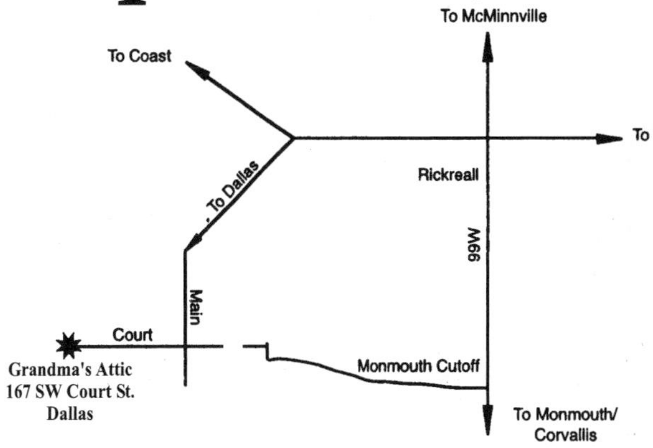

167 SW Court St. 97338
Est: 1995 4400 sq.ft.
5000+ Bolts

Mon - Fri 9:30 - 5:30
Sat 10 - 5
Sun 12 - 4

(503) 623-0451 Fax: (503) 623-0498
E-Mail: GrandmasAttic@compuserve.com
Web: www.GrandmasAtticQuilting.com

Hester's Garden©

Quiltwork Patches

Over 4000 Bolts of Quality 100% Cotton Fabric
Displayed in a Beautiful Well-Lit Store

* Indonesian Wax Batiks
* Oriental * African
* Flannels
* 1930's Reproductions
* Conversationals
* Florals
* Kaffe Fassett and Friends
* Moda Marbles
* Large SALE Section

Corvallis, OR #38

* New Fabrics Daily, Featuring Designer Collections
* Hundreds of Books & Tools * Classes for All Levels
* LOTS of Creative Ideas Displayed with Great Samples
* Est. 1979 * Helpful Staff * Neat & Well-Organized
* Mail Order Fabric Bundle-of-the-Month Clubs
* Visit our website: **www.quiltworkpatches.com**

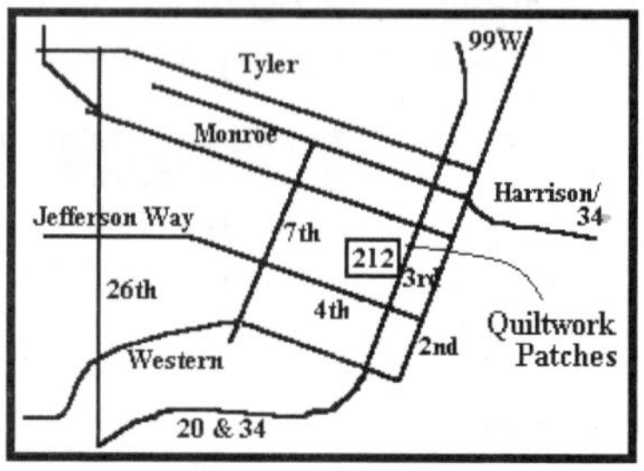

212 SW 3rd Street, Corvallis, OR 97333, 541-752-4820
Hours: Monday - Saturday 9:30 - 5:30

JanniLou Creations

1243 Main P.O. Box 333
Philomath, OR 97370-0333
(541) 929-3795; fax (541) 929-3597
www.jannilou.com

JanniLou CREATIONS

QUILT SHOP

Philomath, OR #39

* Great patterns, books, notions & more.
* Absolutely beginning to advanced classes

Next time you're in Philomath,
drop by to see us "on location" at
the old Waucomah movie theater building.

Mon, Wed and Fri 10:00a-5:30p
Tues & Thurs 10:00a-8:00p
Sat 9:30a-5:30p

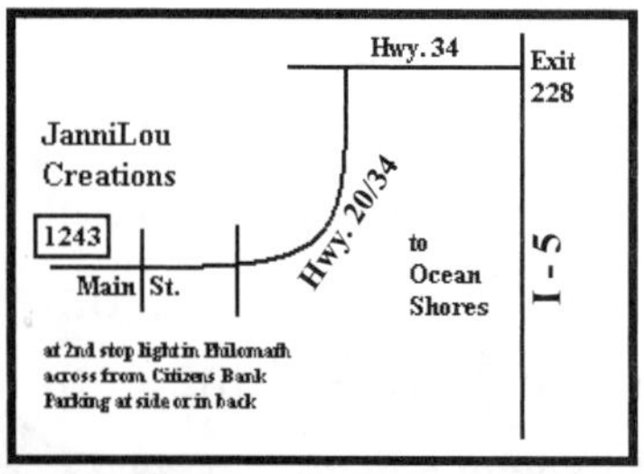

Admit One ...or many!

Florence, OR #40

wenz-dazequiltingfabric.com

Wenz-daze Quilter's Emporium

North of Fred Meyer

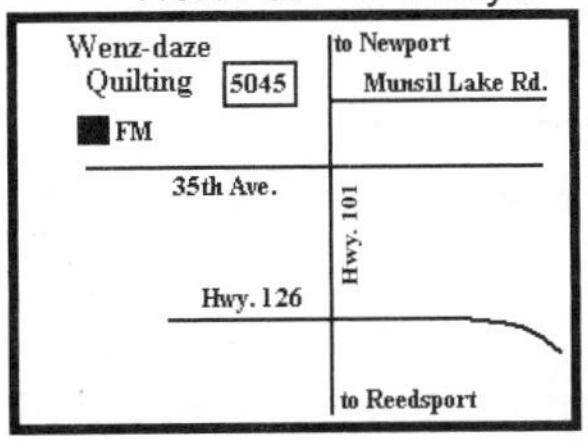

Homey atmosphere, 1800 bolts of Asian, 30's & 40's, Novelty, and Flannels, 100% Cotton. We also have Quilting Notions, Patterns, Books, Emboridery Supplies, Wool Felt and many samples to inspire you. Handi Quilter, HQ16, Avanté Sales & Service.

5045 Hwy. 101 97439
541-997-3293

Charley & Cyndie Wenz
Est: 2008 3200 sq.ft.
wenz-daze@charter.net
Online Newsletter

Nov-April Mon-Sat 10-5
May-Oct Mon-Sat 8-5, Sun 12-4

Florence, OR #41

Joy of Quilting

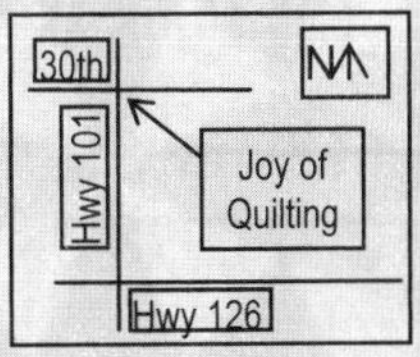

Mon - Sat 10 - 5

2970 Highway 101 ♥ PO Box 1187
Florence OR 97439
541-902-8863
joy@oregonfast.net Owner: Laverne Sanders
www.joyofquilting.net

- ♥ 2000 Bolts of Current Collections, Batiks, Blenders, Flannels & Wide Backing
- ♥ Large Selection of the Latest Notions & Gifts
- ♥ Library of the Newest Quilting Books & Patterns

Always available at Joy of Quilting — a cup of coffee, a piece of chocolate, and a warm welcome!

Coos Bay, OR #42

Mon - Fri 10 - 6
Sat 10 - 5

Threads That Bind

120 Central 97420
(541) 267-0749
threadsthatbind@verizon.net Est: 1996
www.threadsthatbind.net
Everything for the Quilter!
Fabrics, Books, Notions

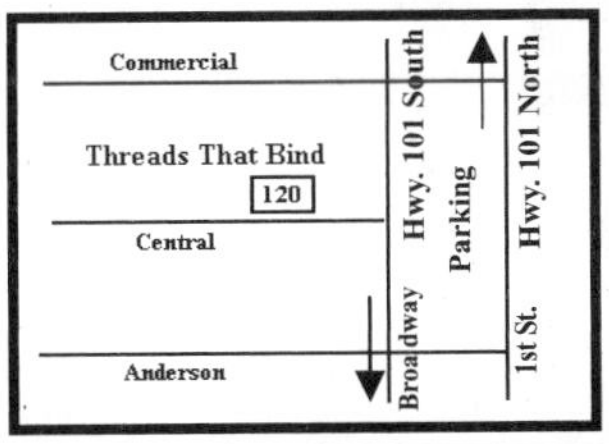

Port Orford, OR #44

Seven Days a Week 10 - 5

Quilter's Corner

335 W. 7th, P.O. Box 69
(541) 332-0502 97465
Owner: Debbie Dorman
Est: 1994 1800 sq.ft. 3000 Bolts
quilterscorner@carrollsweb.com

Fabric, Notions, Patterns and Books.
Classes and Quilts.
Friendly, Spacious and Wonderful Lighting.

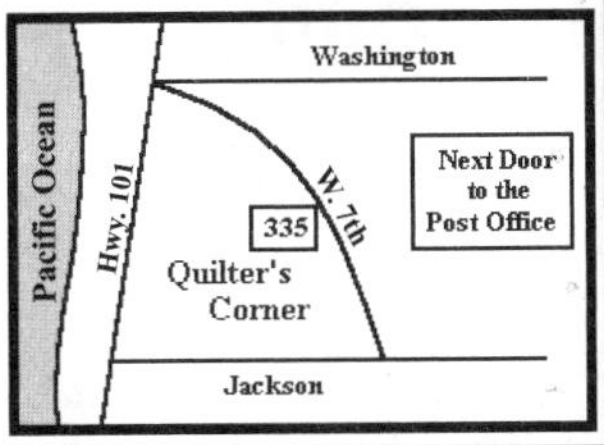

Brookings, OR #45

Mon- Sat 10 - 5

800 Chetco Ave.
P.O. Box 4012 97415
(541) 469-6117

Owners:
Michelle Fallert
& Laurie Mitts
Est: 1988
1500 sq. ft.
1000 Bolts

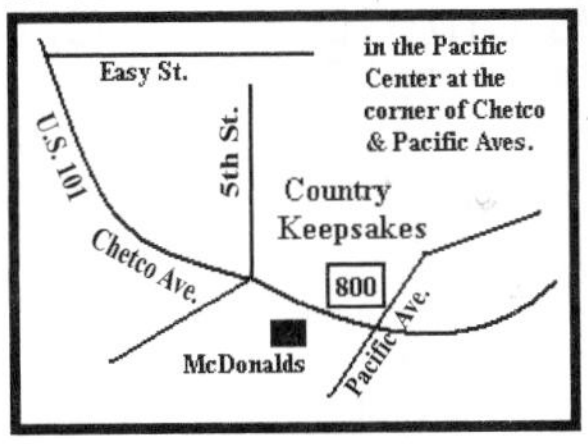

www.countrykeepsakesquiltshop.com
"The Best Little Quilt Shop on the Wild Rivers Coast."

Bandon, OR #43

Est: 1988

Winter Hours
mid Sept - mid June
Mon - Sat 10 - 5
Sun 12 - 4
Summer Hours
mid June - mid Sept
Mon - Sat 9 - 6
Sun 10 - 5

640 2nd St. SE, Hwy. 101 97411
(800) 347-9021
Owners: Michelle Hagglund michelle@forget-me-knots.net
Fax: (541) 347-9021 2700 sq.ft. 3000 Bolts

A unique & charming shop specializing in quilting, kits, embroidery supplies, silk ribbon embroidery. Supplies, patterns, books, classes & a large selection of 100% cottons.

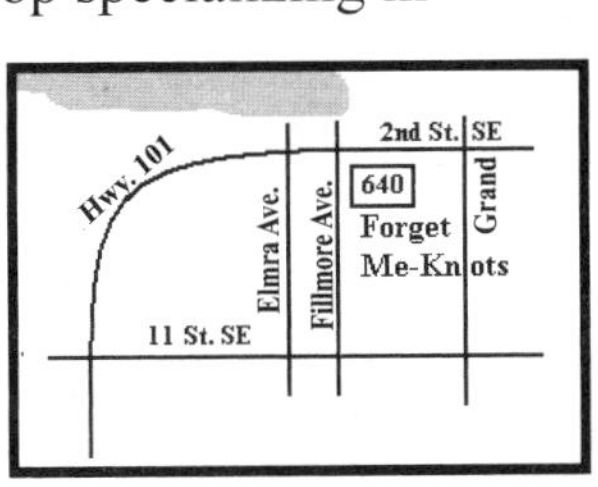

On-line store now available

www.forget-me-knots.net

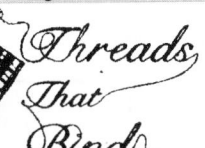

Junction City, OR #46

Thimbles & Threads

665 Ivy St. 97448
(541) 998-3312

Owner: Bobbie De Less
ththreads@qwestoffice.net
www.thimblesthreadsonline.com

Mon - Sat 10 - 5

Great shop in Oregon with all the latest fabric, patterns and notions.
Stop by and see us.
Free Newsletter

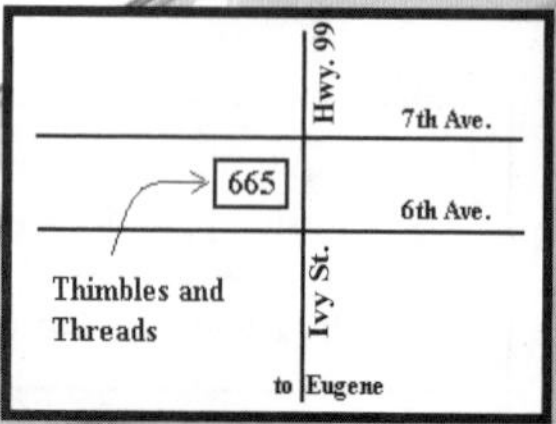

Springfield, OR #47

Mon - Fri 10 - 5 Sun 1 - 4

Jean Marie's Fabrics

637 Main St. 97477
(541) 746-0433
Owner: Winona Carlson
Est: 1975 2000 sq.ft. 1000+ bolts
jmf@jeanmariesfabrics.com
www.jeanmariesfabrics.com
Quilting fabrics, books & supplies. Supplies for weddings. Juki Sewing machines & sergers. Machine repair. Hoffman, Michael Miller and other special fabrics. Classes.

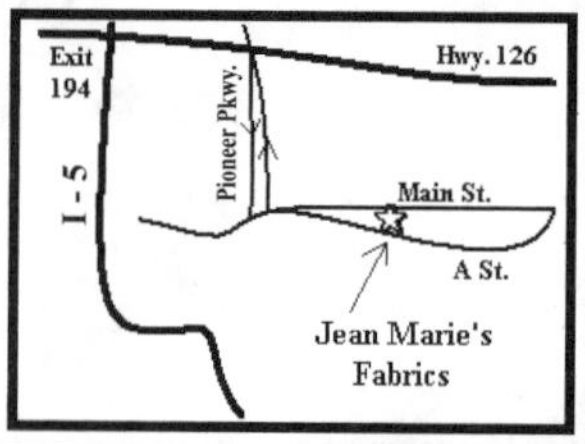

Springfield, OR #48

Mon - Sat 10 - 5:30

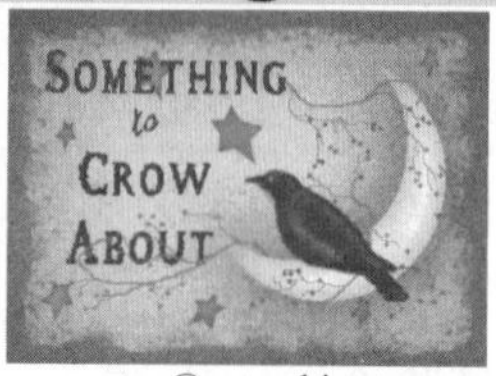

4227-C Main St. 97478
(541) 746-3256
Owner: Kennette Blotzer Est: 1993
2050 sq.ft.
3000 bolts
Online Newsletter
stca@somethingtocrowabout.com
www.somethingtocrowabout.com
We are a full service quilt shop specializing in Civil War, Homespuns, Patriotic, Primitives and 30's Reproductions. Many BOM's too!

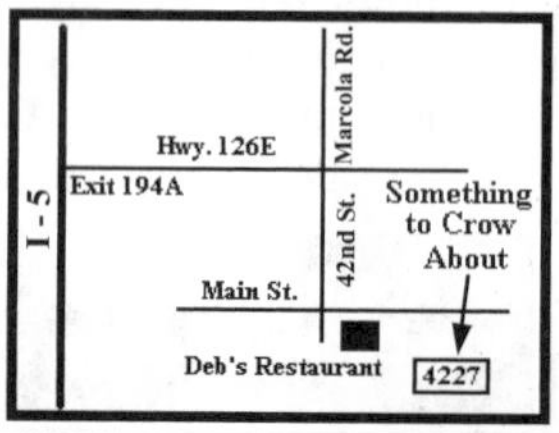

Eugene, OR #49

The Quilt Patch

448 W. 3rd Ave. 97401
541-484-1925
Helen Andrews, Owner
quiltpatch@preferredld.com
www.quiltpatch.biz

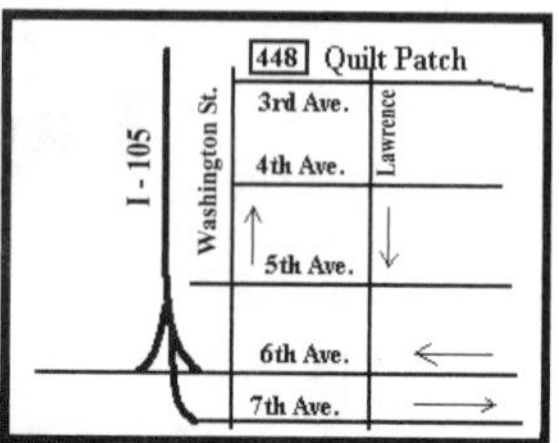

We are dedicated to bringing a variety of cotton fabrics to our customers. We feature 1800's & 1930's reproductions, batiks, and Asians. We carry the latest books and patterns. We offer classes and hold special quilting events.

Mon - Sat 10 - 5 Sun 12 - 4

Eugene, OR #50

Mon - Sat 10 - 5:30 Sun 12 - 4

Piece by Piece fabrics

62 W. 13th Ave. 97401
(541) 743-0266
becky@piecebypiecefabrics.com
www.piecebypiecefabrics.com
Specializing in high quality contemporary fabrics, books, patterns and notions for sewing and quilting.

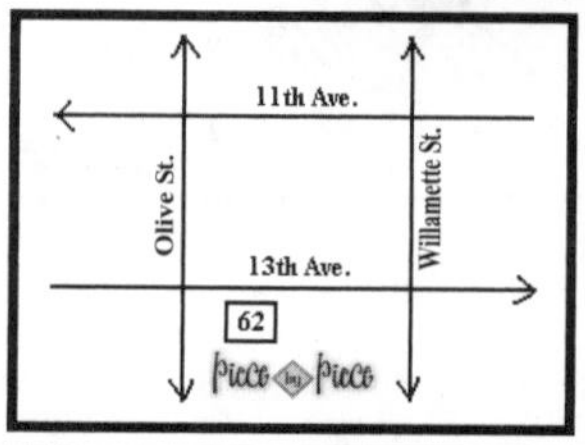

Curtin, OR #51

Mon, Thurs & Fri 9 - 5

Dee-Dee's Quilts & Fabric

241 Bear Creek Rd. 97424
(541) 942-3738
2000 Bolts

A working Fabric Shop.
If traveling I-5 it's a great place to take a break. RV parking available.

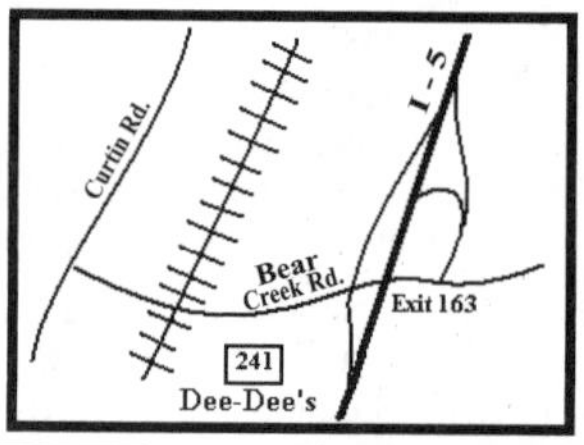

Canyonville, OR #52

Mon - Fri 10 - 5 Sat 10 - 4

J & J Fabrics

413 S. Main St., P.O. Box 549 97417
(541) 839-4319 Fax: Same
Owner: Judy Cuthbertson
Est: 1990 1840 sq.ft.
jandjfabrics@frontiernet.net
Quilters Welcome. 100% cotton fabric, flannels, books, patterns, notions. Just south of Seven Feathers Hotel & Casino Resort

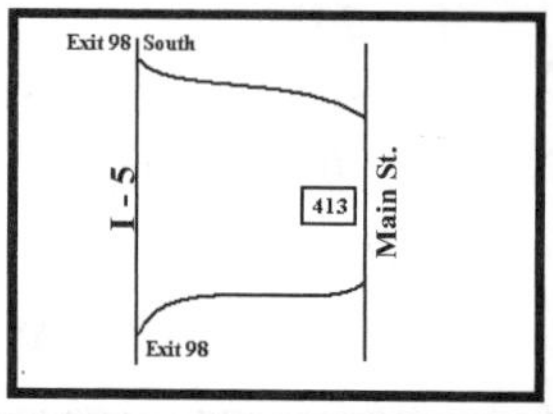

Lakeview, OR #53

Tues - Fri 11 - 5 Sat 10 - 4

Goose Tracks Quilting & Fabric Arts

728 N. 2nd St. 97630
(541) 947-0299
goose000@centurytel.net
Est: 2004

Fabric, notions, books, patterns, classes. Large selection of western and landscape fabrics. Custom designed art quilts and kits.

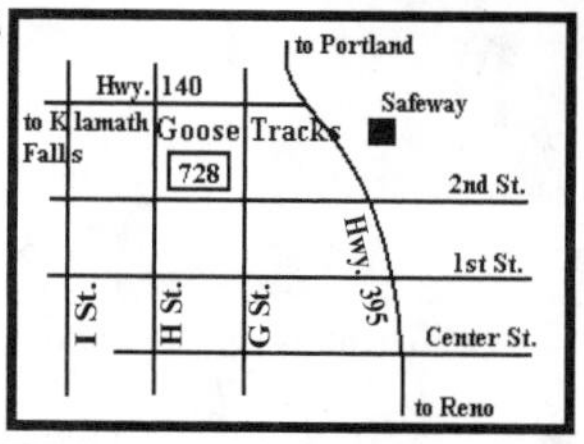

Est: 1983

Country Lady Quilt Shop and Gallery

Roseburg, OR #54

611 & 613 SE Jackson St. 97470
(541) 673-1007
cntryldy@rosenet.net

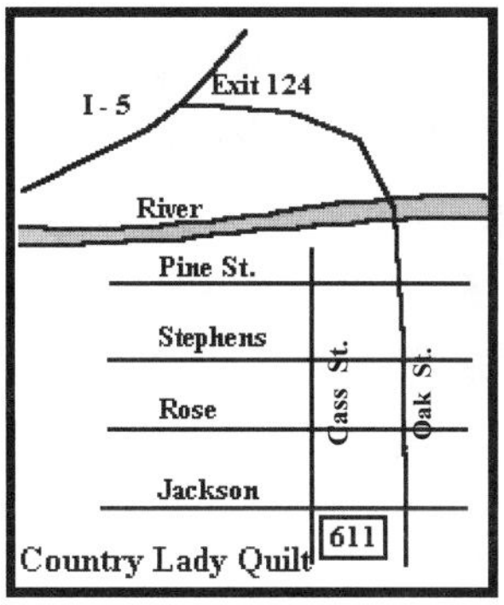

Located in Historic Downtown Roseburg, Oregon

- Stop and Pet the Fabric
- Open Sisters Weekend
- Traveling - "Call", we will stay open
- 3 Gammill Long-arm Quilting Machines
- Statler Stitcher Long-Arm Gammill

Mon - Sat 10 - 5

Owner:
Charlie Weckerle

www.countryladyquiltshop.com

* Hometown Folks * Friendly Customer Service * Where you are #1 *

Riddle, OR #55

Thistleberries

Old Town Quilt Shop

336 Main St. * Riddle, Oregon 97469
* 541-874-3200 *
Proprietors:
Ruth & Johnny Holland * Kris Evans
thistleberries@frontiernet.net

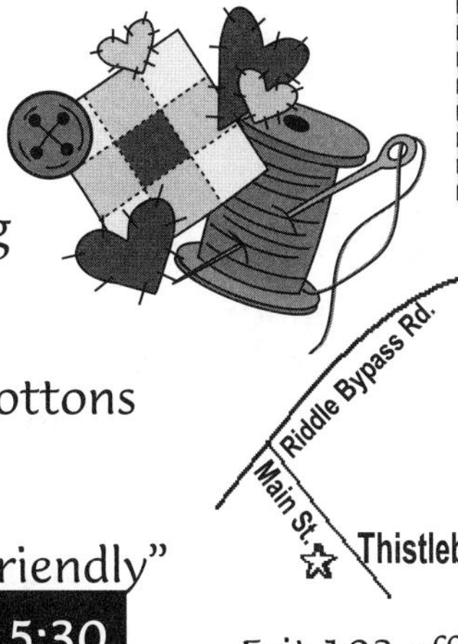

Traveling? "Call" we'll stay open! Show us your QTC for a discount on your purchase.

Something for Everyone

- Located in the old 1910 State Bank Building
- Featuring Quilter Debbie Caffrey
- 1500 plus bolts of fabric
- Specialty fabrics-U of O and OSU Fleece & Cottons
- APQS Long Arm Quilting
- Mail Orders Welcome
- "Best Buys" Coupon Book-made "Traveler Friendly"
- Soy Candles

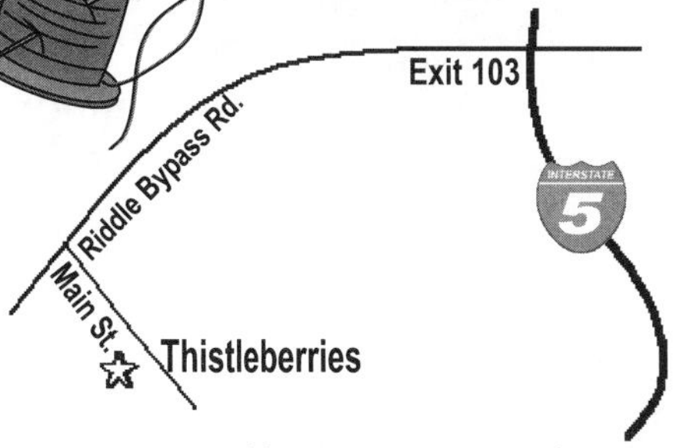

Mon - Fri 10:00 - 5:30
Sat 10 - 4

Exit 103 off I-5 * Just 3 miles * 1st Building on right after the tracks.

* Moda * Maywood * Island Batiks * Blue Hill * Avlyn * Clotheworks * Andover * Blank * Large Selection of Flannels *

PLAZA QUILTING & SEWING CENTER

A QUILTER'S HAVEN

Plaza "A QUILTER'S HAVEN"

We have a full line of high quality fabrics for the quilter.
Over 3,000 prints and over 200 solids.
A great selection of quilt and craft patterns and books.
Also a great selection of aids, notions and threads.
GREAT PRICES!

Mon. - Fri. 9:30 - 6
Sat. 9:30 - 5:30
Sun. 12 - 4

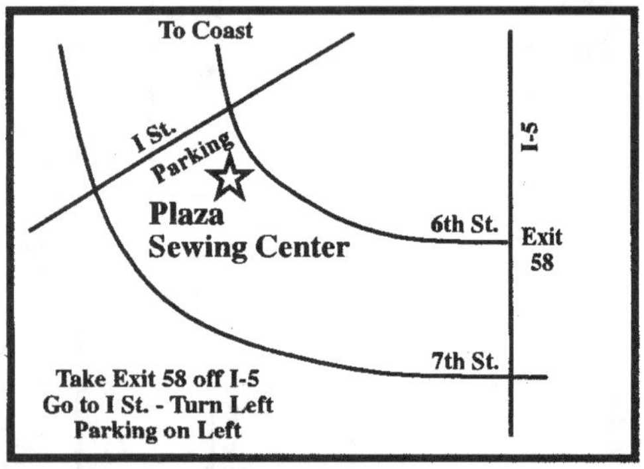

Only 8 Minutes From Freeway

311 SE 6th St. Golden Rule Plaza 97526
(541) 479-5757
Owners: Rick & Mary Chapman
Est: 1967 5000 sq. ft.

Grants Pass, OR #56

Ashland, OR #57

FABRIC of VISION

Est: 2006

10:00 - 5:00 Daily

145 East Main Street
Ashland, OR 97520
541-482-4009

www.fabricofvision.com

Quilt Shop and Fiber Art Gallery.

Contemporary, modern and retro textiles so diverse in design that it's a joy to create something wonderful with them. In addition to soft cottons, you will find a selection of silk, linen, wool, bamboo and occasionally hemp. Contemporary Japanese fabrics by echino, Kokka, and naniIRO are our specialty. Designers include Alexander Henry, Kaffe Fassett, Amy Butler, Kona Bay, Moda, Lonni Rossi, and Denyse Schmidt.

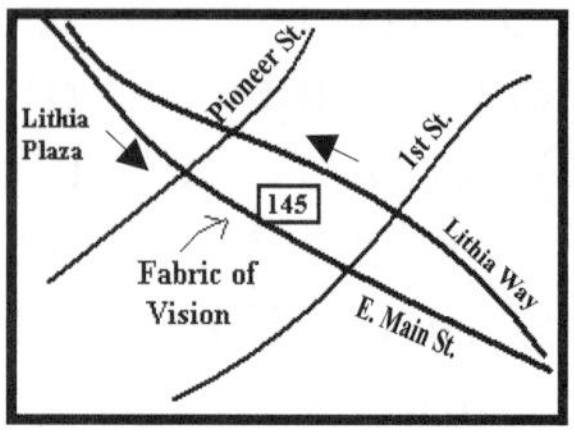

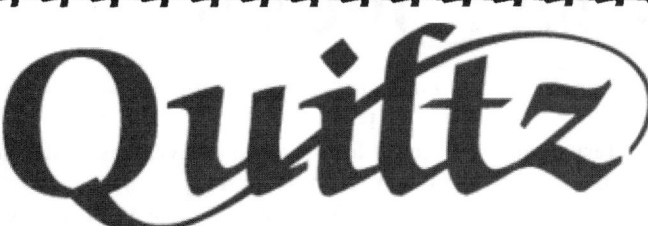

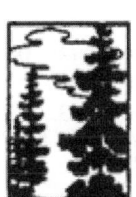

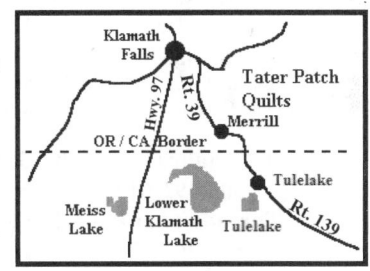

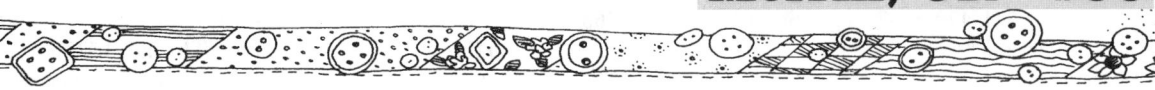

Oregon Quilt Shops

Ashland **Quiltz, 53 North 2nd St.**
541-488-1650 **See ad #58, page 469**
Ashland **Fabric of Vision, 145 E. Main St.**
541-482-4009 **See ad #57, page 468**
Astoria **Homespun Quilts, 108 10th St.**
503-325-3300 **See ad #25, page 460**
Astoria **Custom Threads, 1282 Commercial St.**
503-325-7780 **See ad #24, page 460**
Baker City LaDonna's Fiber Arts, 1833 Main St. 541-523-2693
Baker City Traditions Quilt Shop, 1630 Campbell St 541-523-4558
Bandon **Forget-Me-Knots, 640 2nd St. SE Hwy. 101**
800-347-9021 **See ad #43, page 465**
Beaverton Montavilla Sewing, 4955 SW Western 503-619-6619
Beaverton Mill End Retail Store, 4955 NW Western 503-646-3000
Bend **Sew Many Quilts, 1375 SE Wilson, #170**
541-385-7166 **See ad #7, page 455**
Bend **B J's Quilt Basket, 20225 Badger Rd.**
541-383-4310 **See ad #6, page 455**
Bend Amish House, 2620 NE Hwy. 20 #230 541-388-4651
Brookings **Country Keepsakes, 800 Chetco Ave.**
541-469-6117 **See ad #45, page 465**
Brownsville Callapooya Quilts, 402 Main St. 541-466-5777
Burns **Country Lane Quilts, 406 N. Broadway**
541-573-6406 **See ad #8, page 456**
Canby **Quilt & Fabric, 248 NW 1st Ave.**
503-263-3563 **See ad #23, page 460**
Cannon Beach **Center Diamond, 1065 S. Hemlock**
503-436-0833 **See ad #26, page 460 & 402**
Canyonville **J & J Fabrics, 413 S. Main St.**
541-839-4319 **See ad #52, page 466**
Cave Junction Picket Fence Fabrics, 379 Caves Hwy 541-592-5003
Central Point Jeanette's Fabrics, 26 E. Pine St. 541-664-5266
Clackamas **Quilting Delights, 14863 SE Oregon Trail Dr**
503-658-1600 **See ad #19, page 458**
Clatskanie Bobbin Along, 80 NE Art Steele St. 503-728-3913
Clatskanie Quilt Garden Quilt Shop, 350 W. Columbia River Hwy. 503-728-0626
Cloverdale **B J's Fabrics & Quilts, 38105 Hwy. 101 S**
503-392-6195 **See ad #31, page 462**
Coos Bay **Threads That Bind, 120 Central Ave.**
541-267-0749 **See ad #42, page 465**
Corvallis **Quiltwork Patches, 212 SW 3rd St.**
541-752-4820 **See ad #38, page 464**
Cottage Grove Pandora's Box, 602 E. Main 541-942-5194
Curtin **Dee Dee's Quilts & Fabric, 241 Bear Creek**
541-942-3738 **See ad #51, page 466**
Dallas **Grandma's Attic Sewing Emporium, 167 SW Court**
503-623-0451 **See ad #37, page 463**
Enterprise Savoies Specialties, 105 SW 1st St. 541-426-3232
Eugene **Piece by Piece Fabrics, 62 W. 13th Ave.**
541-743-0266 **See ad #50, page 466**
Eugene **The Quilt Patch, 448 W. 3rd Ave.**
541-484-1925 **See ad #49, page 466**
Eugene 27th Street Fabrics, 2710 Willamette 541-345-7221
Florence **Wenz-daze Quilter's Emporium, 5045 Hwy. 101**
541-997-3293 **See ad #40, page 465**
Florence **Joy of Quilting, 2970 Hwy. 101**
541-902-8863 **See ad #41, page 465**
Grants Pass **Plaza Quilting & Sewing Center, 311 SE 6th**
541-479-5757 **See ad #56, page 468**
Grants Pass Purple Pincushion Quilt Shop, 1580-B NE 7th St. 541-956-6857
Halfway **Quilts Plus, 280 S. Main St.**
541-742-5040 **See ad #10, page 456**
Hermiston **Aunty Ida's Country Loveables Quilt Shop**
435 W. Hermiston Ave.
541-567-2726 **See ad #13, page 456**
Hillsboro **Sharon's Attic Quilt Shop, 2950 SW Cornelius Pass**
503-259-3475 **See ad #16, page 456**
Hillsboro Crazy 4 Quilts, 3080 SE Willow Dr 503-640-4445
Hillsboro Furever Friends, 2257 NE Cornell Rd. 503-640-1907
Hood River **E.T.C.--Every Thread Counts 1204 Nix #100**
541-386-5044 **See ad #14, page 456**
Independence Ladies of Liberty Mercantile, 130 C St. 503-837-0676
Jacksonville Llamas & Llambs Boutique, 180 N. Oregon 541-899-9141
Jefferson **Janice Jenney Studios, 13364 Marlatt Rd. S**
541-327-9886 **See ad #35, page 462**
Joseph Cattle Country Quilts. 203 N. Main St. #2 541-432-6669
Junction City **Thimbles & Threads, 665 Ivy St.**
541-998-3312 **See ad #46, page 466**
Keizer **The Cotton Patch, 4475 River Rd. N**
503-463-1880 **See ad #32, page 462**
Klamath Falls Quilting Sisters, 26654 Rocky Point 541-883-3114
Klamath Falls Kate's Quilted Rooster, 2000 South 6th St. 541-850-8833
La Grande **Quilt Therapy, 1107 Washington**
541-663-1817 **See ad #11, page 456**
Lake Oswego The Pine Needle, 429 First St. 503-635-1353
Lakeview **Goose Tracks Fabric Arts, 728 N. 2nd St.**
541-947-0299 **See ad #53, page 466**
LaPine **Homestead Quilts and Gallery, 51425 Hwy 97**
541-536-2360 **See ad #5, page 455**
Lebanon Finally Together Quilt Shop, 2645 S. Main 541-258-6006
McMinnville **Boersma's Sewing Center, 203 E. Third St.**
503-472-4611 **See ad #29, page 461**
Medford Craft Warehouse, 2340 Poplar Dr. 541-779-1940
Medford Top Stitch, 1596 Biddle Rd 541-608-7722
Medford Fasturn Junction, 3859 S. Stage Rd 541-772-8430
Merrill **Tater Patch Quilts, 109 E. Front St.**
541-798-5955 **See ad #59, page 469**
Merrill Heart to Heart Quilters, 122 E. Front St. 541-798-9111
Milwaukie Mill End Store, 9701 S.E. McLoughlin 503-786-1234
Milwaukie Quilter's Corner, 15717 SE McLaughlin 503-653-1310
Molalla Country Bumpkin, 18089 S. Hwy. 211 503-829-6874
Mulino Mill Barn Mercantile, 26412 S. Hwy. 213 503-829-4746
Newberg Itchin' to Stitch, 3809 Coffey Ln.
Newport **Quilter's Cove, 644 SW Coast Hwy.Suite B**
541-265-2591 **See ad #33, page 462**
Ontario **Charm Shack Quilt Shop, 199 S. Oregon St.**
541-889-3085 **See ad #9, page 456**
Oregon City **Let's Quilt, 19713 S. Hwy. 213 Suite 120**
503-518-4321 **See ad #20, page 458**
Oregon City Heart To Hand Quilt Shop, 412 S Beavercreek Rd Suite 607 503-230-9075
Pendleton **Pendleton Quilt Works, 138 SE Court**
541-276-9546 **See ad #12, page 456**
Philomath **Janni Lou Creations, 1243 Main**
541-929-3795 **See ad #39, page 464**
Phoenix McQuilts, 4403 S. Pacific Hwy. 541-535-2573
Pleasant Hill Country Bumpkin Quilt Shop, 35817 Hwy. 58 541-736-1159
Port Orford **Quilter's Corner335 W. 7th**
541-332-0502 **See ad #44, page 465**
Portland **Fabric Depot700 SE 122nd Ave.**
503-252-9530 **See ad #17, page 457**
Portland **A Common Thread, 15230 SW Sequoia Pkwy.**
503-624-7440 **See ad #18, page 458**

Portland — Fibers in Motions, 7855 SW Capital Hwy. 503-977-2758
Portland — Montavilla Sewing Center , 326 SE Stark St 503-254-7317
Portland — Cool Cottons, 2417 SE Hawthorne Blvd. 503-232-0417
Portland — Bolt Neighborhood, 2136 NE Alberta St. 503-287-2658
Prairie City — Quilts and Beyond, 114 W. Front St. 541-820-4777

Prineville — **The Quilt Shack, 395 N Main**
541-447-1338 **See ad #1, page 454**

Redmond — **High Mountain Fabric, 1542 S. Hwy. 97**
541-548-6909 **See ad #3, page 454**

Reedsport — Quilt Shop, 679 W. Alder Pl. 541-271-2616

Riddle — **Thistleberries Old Town Quilt Shop, 336 N. Main**
541-874-3200 **See ad #55, page 467**

Riddle — Etcetera Needlework Shop, 120 Main St. 541-874-3571
Riddle — Eagle's Nest 951, Canyonville Riddle Rd. 541-839-4100

Roseburg — **Country Lady Quilt Shop, 611 S.E. Jackson St.**
541-673-1007 **See ad #54, page 467**

Salem — **Greenbaum's Quilted Forest**
240 Commercial St. N.E.
503-363-7973 **See ad #36, page 463**

Sandy — Paradise Quilts & Fabrics 38821 Proctor 503-668-3106
Silver Lake — Desert Rose Quilt Shop, 65458 Hwy. 31 541-576-3530

Sisters — **The Stitchin' Post, 311 W. Cascade St.**
541-549-6061 **See ad #4, page 455**

Springfield — **Jean Marie's Fabrics, 637 Main St.**
541-746-0433 **See ad #47, page 466**

Springfield — **Something to Crow About, 4227C Main St.**
541-746-3256 **See ad #48, page 466**

St. Helens — **Fibers & Stitches, 58093 Columbia River**
503-397-5536 **See ad #15, page 456**

Stayton — **Quilt-N-Stitch 193 N. 3rd Ave.**
503-767-4240 **See ad #34, page 462**

Sublimity — Country Classics, 480 S. Center 503-769-4645
Sweet Home — Seamingly Creative, 1245 Main St. 541-367-8934

Terrebonne — **Quilter's Attic, 8154 11th St. #1**
541-548-8119 **See ad #2, page 454**

The Dalles — The Cotton Shop, 115 E. 2nd St. 541-296-5358

Tillamook — **Latimer Quilt & Textile Center**
2105 Wilson River Loop
503-842-8622 **See ad #27, page 460**

Tillamook — **Jane's Fabric Patch 1110 Main Ave.**
503-842-9392 **See ad #28, page 460**

Waldport — Ruth's Family Fabrics, 385 Hwy. 34 #5A 541-563-3064

West Linn — **Hollyhill Quilt Shoppe & Mercantile**
1914 Willamette Falls Dr.
503-607-0600 **See ad #21, page 459 & 405**

Wheeler — Creative Fabrics, 475 Nehalem Blvd. 503-368-5900

Wilsonville — **Speckled Hen Quilts, 30775 Sw Boone Ferry**
5035703368 **See ad #22, page 460**

Yamhill — **The Quilted Hill 7601 NE Blackburn Rd.**
503-662-4052 **See ad #30, page 462**

Yoncalla — Quilt Connections 8542 Hayhurst Rd.

Oregon Quilt Shows

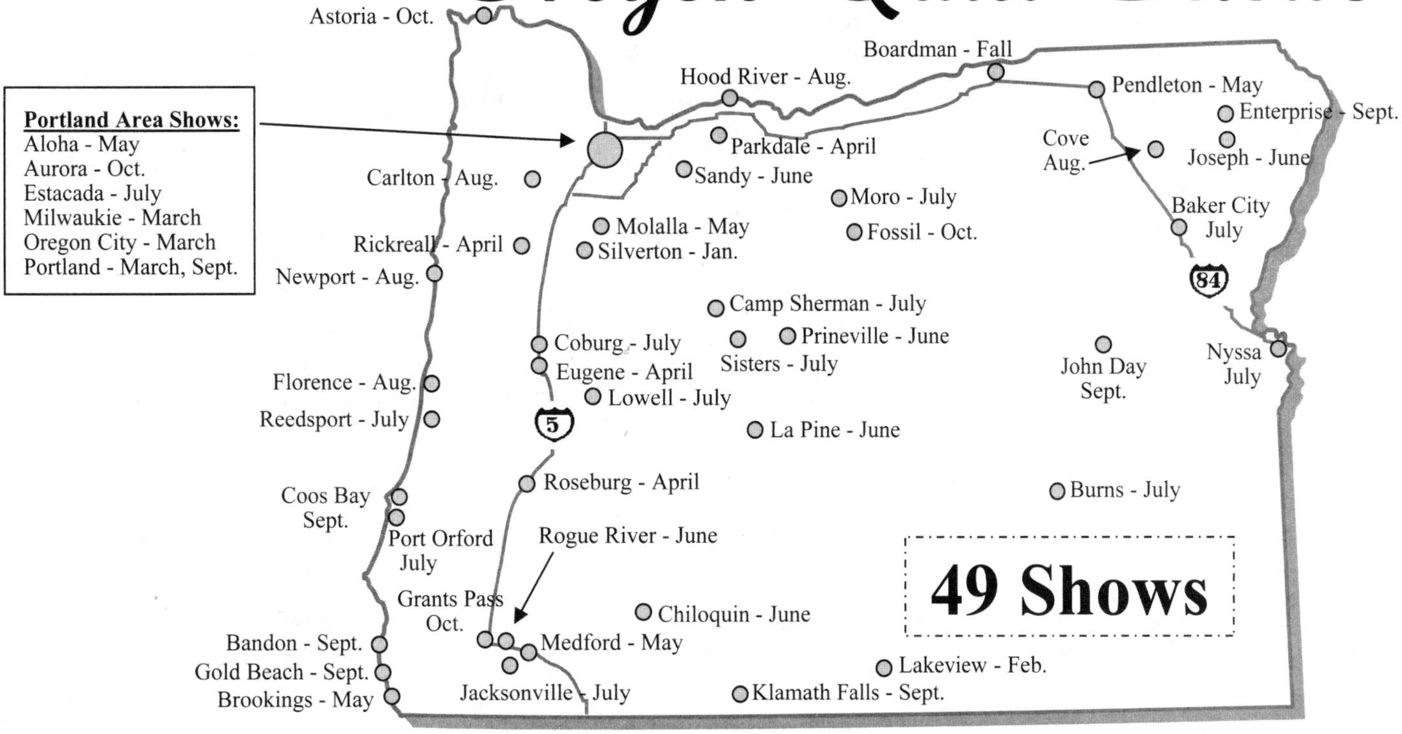

About Shows: We are listing only the very basic information about shows that happen on a regular schedule here. Please check out our website for more details on each show. Also this information tends to change quite often so please verify the event with our website or a local source before you venture far. Or if you're in the right area at the right time, give it a shot.

If you are a show organizer, please keep us updated on your event.
shows@quilterstravelcompanion.com www.quilterstravelcompanion.com

On our website you will also find:
- Exact dates (when we have them)
- Contact Information
- Events happening on a one-time basis
- Sponsor Information
- Description of Event

Month	City	Schedule	Show	Location with address
January				
	Silverton	Annual, last Fri & Sat in January	Stitches in Bloom Quilt Show	The Oregon Garden, 879 W. Main St.
February				
	Lakeview	Annual, 1st weekend of February	Winter Quilt Festival	Lake County Fairgrounds, 1900 N 4th St
March				
	Portland	Annual, 2nd weekend in March	Northwest Quilters' Quilt Show	University Place Hotel, 310 SW Lincoln St.
	Milwaukie	Annual, 4th weekend in March	Airing of the Quilts	Milwaukie Center, 5440 SE Kellogg Creek Dr.
	Oregon City	Annual, last Sat. of March	Let's Quilt and Saves Sew and Vac Show	Clackamas Community College, 19600 S Molalla Ave
April				
	Eugene	Annual, 3rd week in April	Pioneer Quilters Show	Lane County Historical Museum, 740 West 13th Ave
	Parkdale	Annual, 3rd weekend in April	Every Thread Counts Show	Parkdale Community Center, 7300 Clear Creek Rd.
	Rickreall	Odd Years, 3rd weekend in April	Mid - Valley Quilt Guild Show	Polk County Fairgrounds, 520 Pacific Hwy
	Roseburg	Annual, 3rd weekend in April	Umpqua Valley Quilters' Guild Quilt Show	Douglas County Fairgrounds - Exhibit Bldg, 211 Frear St (Exit 123 off I-5)
May				
	Pendleton	Annual, 1st weekend in May	Krazy Horse Quilters Quilt Show	Pendleton Convention Center, 1601 Westgate
	Aloha	Annual, Mother's Day weekend	Tualatin Hills Park & Recreation Show	Jenkins Estate, 8005 SW Grabhorn Rd
	Molalla	Annual, Mother's Day weekend	Molalla Historic Society Show	Dibble House & Vonder Ahe House, 650 S. Molalla Ave
	Medford	Annual, 3rd weekend in May	Mountain Stars Quilter's Guild Show	Medford Armory, 1701 S Pacific Hwy
	Brookings	Annual, Memorial Day Weekend	Azalea Quilter's Guild Show	Kalmiopsis Elementary School, 650 Easy St
June				
	Joseph	Annual, 2nd weekend in June	Wallowa Mountain Quilt Guild Show	Joseph High School, 400 E Williams
	Prineville	Annual, 4th Saturday in June	Crook County Quilt Guild Show	Crook County Elementary School, 295 NE Holly St
	Sandy	Annual, 4th weekend of June	Sandy Historical Society Quilt Show	Sandy Union High School, 17100 Bluff Rd.
	Chiloquin	Annual, last weekend of June	Chiloquilters Quilt Show	Chiloquin Community Center, 140 S. 1st St.
	La Pine	Annual, late June to early July	La Pine Needle Quilters Show	La Pine Senior Activity Center, Huntington & Victory
	Rogue River	Annual, Last Sat in June	Rogue Valley Piecemakers Quilt Guild Show	Rogue River Middle School, 301 Pine St
July				
	Moro	Annual, 1st weekend in July	Sherman County Quilt and Doll Show	Downtown & Sherman County Museum
	Port Orford	Annual, 4th of July	Jubilee Quilt Show	Community Center 11th Street (off Hwy. 101)
	Burns	Annual, 2nd Thurs - Sat in July	High Desert Quilt Show	Downtown Burns
	Camp Sherman	Annual, 2nd Fri. of July	Pine Needlers Quilt Show	Camp Sherman Community Hall, Rt. 1419, South of Hwy. 20
	Jacksonville	Annual, 2nd weekend of July	Jacksonville Museum Quilters Show	Historic U.S. Hotel, 2nd Floor 3rd & California
	Nyssa	Annual, 2nd weekend in July	Thunderegg Days Quilt Show	Nyssa Elementary School Gym 809 Bower Ave.
	Sisters	Annual, 2nd Saturday in July	Sisters Outdoor Quilt Show	All Over Town
	Baker City	Annual, 3rd weekend in July	Baker City Quilt Guild Show	The Old Armory, 2600 East St. (Exit 304 off I-84)
	Reedsport	Annual, 3rd weekend in July	Reedsport Presbyterian Women's Quilt Show	Presbyterian Church, 2360 Longwood Dr.
	Coburg	Annual, last Sat. of July	Coburg Quilt Show & Tea	All Over Town
	Estacada	Annual, last Fri & Sat of July	Skip a Week Quilt Guild Show	Estacada High School, 255 NE 6th Ave.
	Lowell	Annual, last weekend of July	Blackberry Jam Festival Quilt Show	Lowel Grange, 2nd & Moss St.
August				
	Carlton	Annual, 1st weekend in August	Carlton's Walk in the Park	Wennerberg Park, W. Main St.
	Florence	Odd Years, 1st Weekend in August	Rhododendron Quilt Guild Show	Siuslaw Middle School, 26th & Oak Streets
	Hood River	Annual, 1st weekend of August	Van Gogh Days Quilt Show	Rasmussen Farms, 3020 Thomsen Rd.
	Newport	Annual, 1st weekend in August	Oregon Coastal Quilters Guild Show	Newport Recreation Center, 225 SE Avery
	Cove	Annual, 3rd weekend of August	Quilts & Beyond	Cove Elementary School Gym, 803 Main St.
September				
	Bandon	Annual, 2nd weekend in September	Bandon Quilt Guild Show	Farwest Hall (Now Bandon Odd Fellows Hall), Rt. 42 S (East of Hwy. 101)
	Enterprise	Annual, weekend after Labor Day	Hells Canyon Mule Days Quilt Show	Wallowa County Fairgrounds, Cloverleaf Hall 668 NW 1st St. (Hwy. 3)
	Coos Bay	Annual, 3rd weekend of September	Coos Sand 'N Sea Quilt Show	Swoya Boys & Girls Club 3333 Walnut St.
	Fossil	Annual, mid September til early October	Fossil Quilt Show	Fossil General Mercantile 555 Main St.
	Gold Beach	Annual, 3rd weekend of September	Festival of Quilts	Event Center on the Beach (Fairgrounds) Hwy. 101
	John Day	Annual, 3rd weekend in September	Quilt Show	Grant County Fairgrounds 411 NW Bridge St.
	Klamath Falls	Odd Years, 3rd weekend in September	Heart of the Basin Quilt Guild Show	Klamath County Fairgrounds 3531 S. 6th St.
	Portland	Annual,4th weekend in September	Northwest Quilting Expo	Portland Oregon Expo Center 2060 N. Marine Dr.
	Boardman	Annual, Fall	Boardman Fall Quilt Show	Greenfield Grange-Pink Bldg under the Water Tower, 209 NW 1st St.
October				
	Grants Pass	Annual, 1st Fri & Sat in October	Hugo Ladies Club School House Quilters Show	Hugo Ladies Club, 6050 Hugo Rd.
	Astoria	Annual, 3rd Sat. in October Schoolhouse	Quilters' Quilt Show	Lewis & Clark Elementary School, 92179 Lewis & Clark Rd.
	Aurora	Annual, last part of OctoberOld Aurora	Colony Museum's Quilt Show	Old Aurora Colony Museum, 2nd & Liberty St.

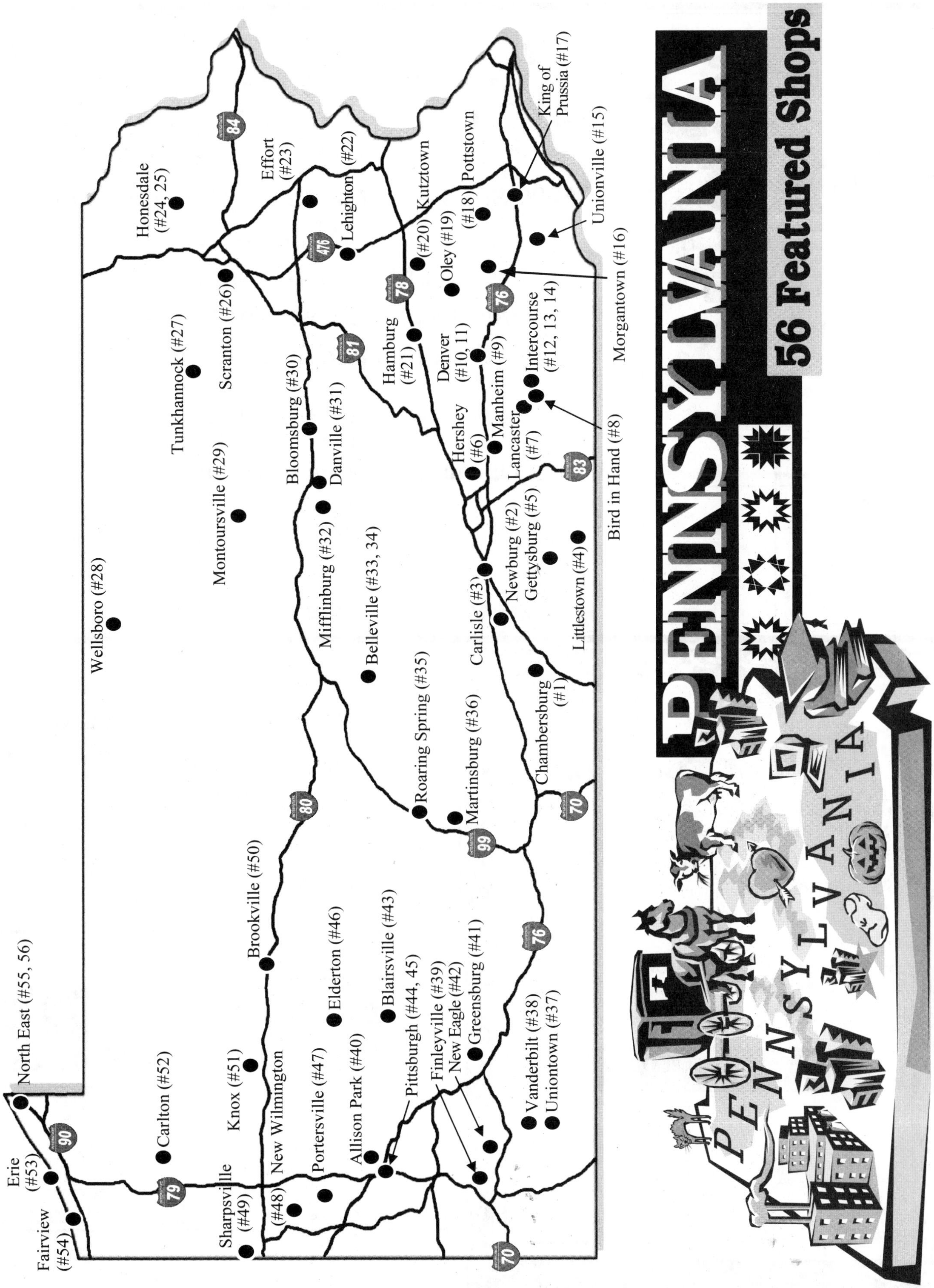
PENNSYLVANIA
56 Featured Shops
North East (#55, 56)
Erie (#53)
Fairview (#54)
Carlton (#52)
Sharpsville (#49)
Knox (#51)
New Wilmington (#48)
Portersville (#47)
Allison Park (#40)
Pittsburgh (#44, 45)
Finleyville (#39)
New Eagle (#42)
Greensburg (#41)
Vanderbilt (#38)
Uniontown (#37)
Elderton (#46)
Blairsville (#43)
Brookville (#50)
Wellsboro (#28)
Montoursville (#29)
Tunkhannock (#27)
Scranton (#26)
Honesdale (#24, 25)
Effort (#23)
Lehighton (#22)
Bloomsburg (#30)
Danville (#31)
Mifflinburg (#32)
Belleville (#33, 34)
Roaring Spring (#35)
Martinsburg (#36)
Chambersburg (#1)
Carlisle (#3)
Newburg (#2)
Gettysburg (#5)
Littlestown (#4)
Hershey (#6)
Lancaster (#7)
Bird in Hand (#8)
Manheim (#9)
Denver (#10, 11)
Intercourse (#12, 13, 14)
Hamburg (#21)
Kutztown (#20)
Oley (#19)
Pottstown (#18)
Morgantown (#16)
Unionville (#15)
King of Prussia (#17)
90
79
80
99
76
70
83
81
78
476
84
P E N N S Y L V A N I A

The Sew'n Place #1

Est. 1982

PFAFF

Husqvarna VIKING

JUKI

SINGER

5200 Square feet of sewing and quilting!
Thousands of bolts of fabrics!
Lots of books and supplies!
Friendly and knowledgeable staff!
Beautiful and inspirational!

On the corner of Walker Road and Gateway Avenue
Chambersburg, PA.

Opening at this location July 1, 2010

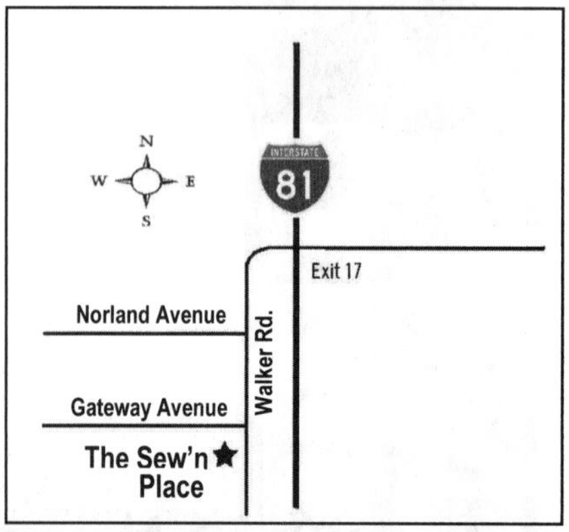

428 Gateway Avenue
Chambersburg, PA 17201
Phone: (717)263-5606

www.sewnplace.com

Newburg, PA #2

Esh's Store

- Hand Made Quilt and Wall Hangings
- VIP and Pillow Panels
- Lots of Fabric for Quilts and Crafts
- Batting
- Great Customer Service
- Great Prices
- Produce (in season) grown on our farm

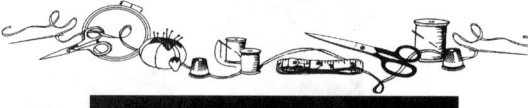

Monday - Saturday 8 to 5

16285 Cumberland Hwy.
Newburg, PA 17240
717-423-6754
Fax: 717-423-5624
Owner: Rebecca Esh
2800 sq.ft. 5000 bolts

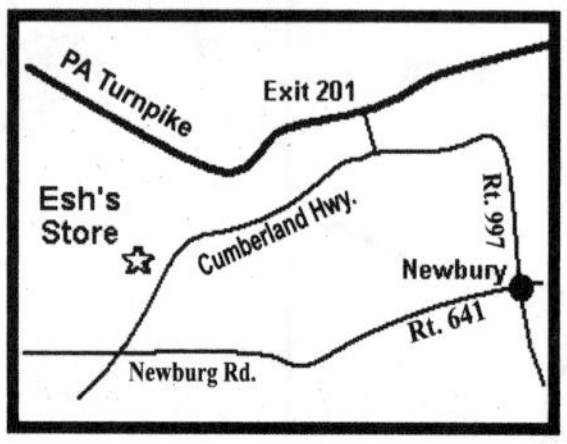

Carlisle, PA #3

Tues- Fri 9 - 4
Thurs 9 - 8
Weekends by Appointment only
Call for Summer Hrs.

Calico Corner

341 Barnstable Road 17015
(717) 249-8644
Owner: Janet Shultzabarger
Est: 1984 600+ Bolts
calicoquil@comcast.com
www.calicocorneronline.com

Personal attention to quilters needs. 100% cottons, notions, books, kits. Very reasonable prices and service with a smile.

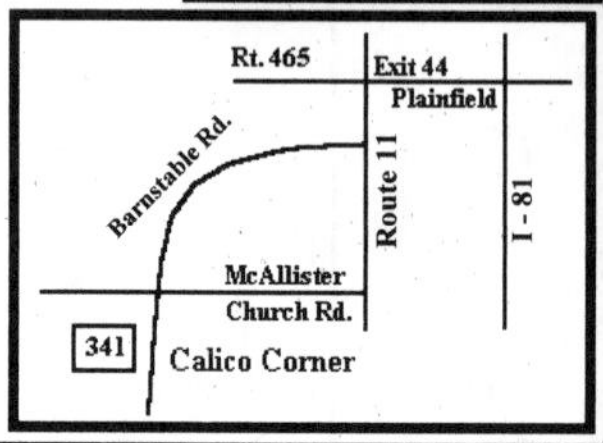

Littlestown, PA #4

Mon - Sat
9:30 - 5
Sun 1 - 5

The Finishing Stitch

1897 Hanover Pike 17340
(717) 359-4121
Owner: Jean Mirizio
Est: 2009 3600 sq.ft. 2500+ bolts
thefinishingstitch@juno.com

Batiks, RJR, Moda, Hoffman, Flannels, Homespuns, Supplies, Classes, Quilts, Gifts, Jim Shore, Heritage Lace, Marie Osmond Handbags, and Home Accents.

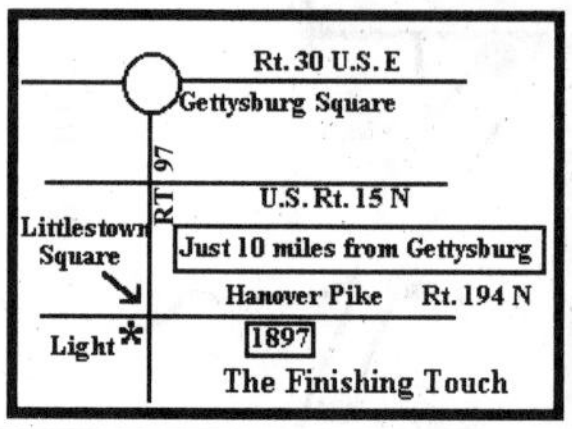

Gettysburg, PA #5

Needle & Thread

2215 Fairfield Rd. 17325
(717) 334-4011
Owner: Darlene Grube

Mon, Wed, Thur 9:30 - 6
Fri 9:30 - 8 Sat 9:30 - 5

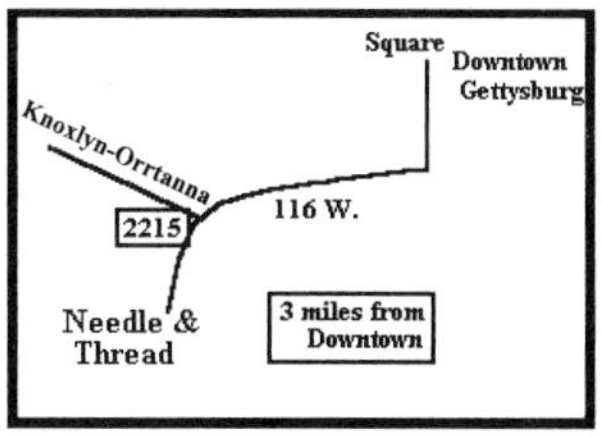

FULL LINE FABRIC STORE

We specialize in Civil War Reproduction Cottons.

Books, patterns, notions and 10,000 bolts of fabric to choose from for quilting, dressmaking, bridal, upholstery and home décor. Hundreds of reproduction fabrics for quilting and Civil War costuming -- cottons, voiles, silks, wools, shirtings, linings, even Hainesworth wool broadcloth from England.

Hershey, PA #6

Quiltmakers Cottage

Friendly, welcoming atmosphere.
Extensive selection of fabrics: batiks, flannels, orientals, brights, contemporary & traditional.
Wide selection of books, patterns, supplies and gifts. Exceptional Kits.
Featured in Spring 2010 Quilt Sampler.

Better Homes and Gardens Quilt Sampler FEATURED SHOP

Owners: Joan Fischer & Beth Reese
Opened 2003

Tues - Fri 10 - 6 Sat 10 - 5

1034 E. Chocolate Ave.
Hershey, PA 17033
(717) 534-9900
www.QuiltmakersCottage.com
quiltmakerscottage@gmail.com
Online Newsletter

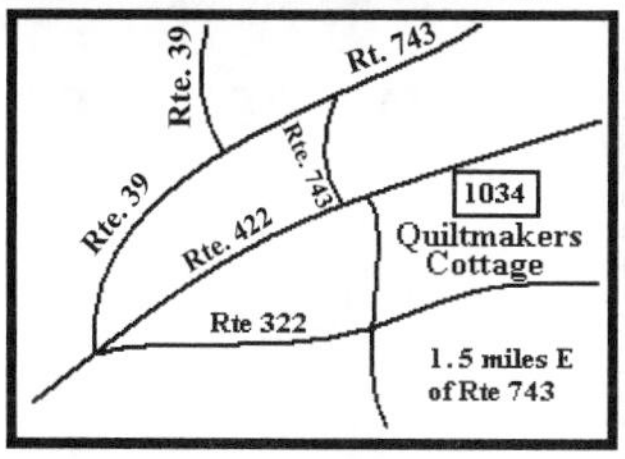

Lancaster, PA #7

Mon - Sat 9 - 5

LANCASTER Quilt & Textile MUSEUM

37 N. Market St. 17603
(717) 299-6440
www.quiltsandtextilemuseum.com

Discover Amish quilting traditions. Visit the Museum Store for Amish quilts, craft supplies and other textiles.

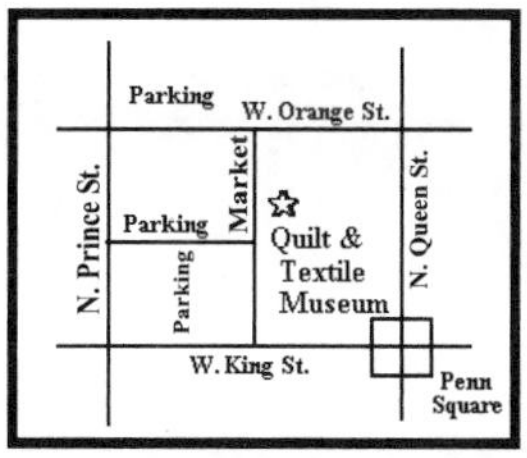

Bird in Hand, PA #8

Mon - Sat 9 - 5
Jan & Feb
Mon - Fri 10 - 4
Sat 9 - 5

Log Cabin Quilt Shop

2679 Old Philadelphia Pike
P.O. Box 297 17505
(717) 393-1702
Owners: Glenn & Ruth Miller
lcqs@verizon.net
Sale $3/yd fabrics, fat quarter sets (8 @ $14.95), Charm packs, flannels, Civil War & 30's prints.
Also a large display of the finest Amish Handmade Quilts.

STITCH & CRAFT

* **Fabric, notions & accessories**
* **Books and Patterns**
* **Sewing machines and sergers by**

baby lock FOR THE LOVE OF SEWING

Mon - Sat 9 - 5
Tues & Fri til 8

Rt. 72 at Turnpike exit 266
2957 Lebanon Rd.
Manheim, PA 17545
Phone # 717-664-4230
stitchcraft@dejazzd.com
We honor most credit cards.

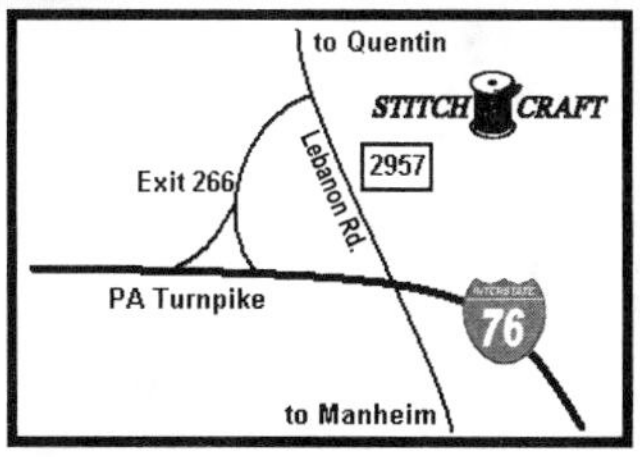

Manheim, PA #9

Burkholder Fabrics LLC

Mon, Tues, Thur 8 - 7
Wed, Fri Sat 8 - 5

Denver, PA #10

2155 West Route 897, Denver, PA 17517
(717) 336-6692 www.burkfabrics.com

Over 12,000 Bolts of First-Quality Cotton, Flannel, Homespuns & Novelties.

Show us this ad for 20% OFF your entire purchase (one-time)

- **Experienced, Helpful Staff**
- **Classes available on all levels**
- **Bus & Guild Member Discounts**
- **Close to Turnpike**
- **Plenty of Parking**

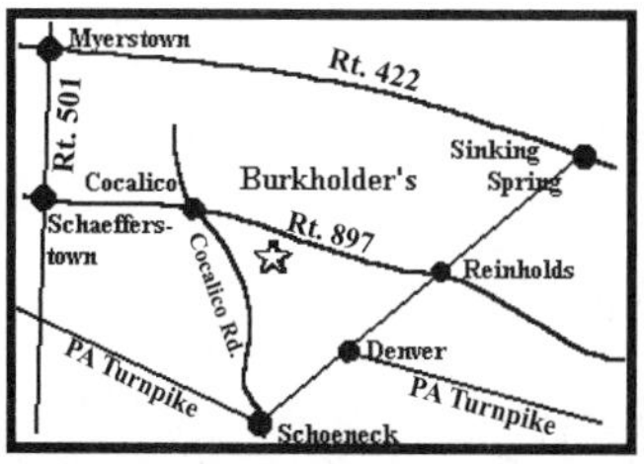

Zook's Fabrics

Intercourse, PA #12

Mon - Sat 8 - 5

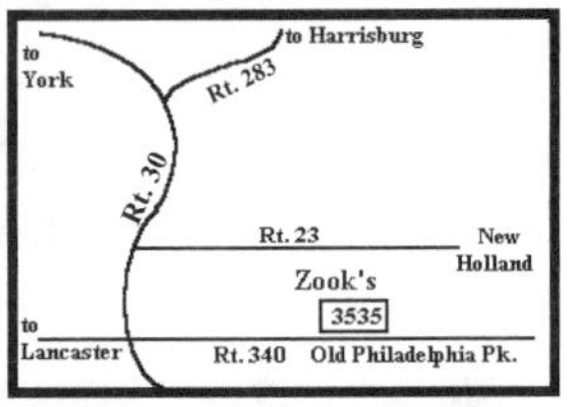

3535 Old Philadelphia Pk.
P.O. Box 514 17534
(717) 768-8153 Fax: Same

Z&S fabrics

Two Great Shops!

Sauder's Fabrics

Denver, PA #11

Mon, Tues & Thur 8 - 8
Wed, Fri & Sat 8 - 5

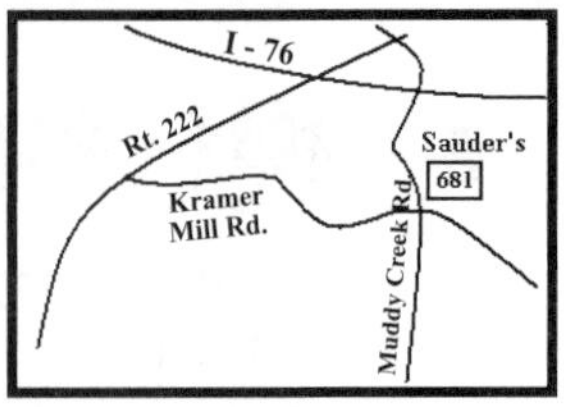

681 S. Muddy Creek Rd.
17517
(717)336-2664

Blue Hill Fabrics Aunt Lindy's Paper Dolls by Sibling Arts Studio

Marcus Fabrics Aunt Grace Conversationals by Judie Rothermel

Moda Plume by Tula Pink

Clothworks Dancing Horses by laurel Burch

One of the largest selections of fabrics, with over 25,000 Bolts!
Also available: Books, Patterns, Notions and Hand Made Gifts

www.ZandSFabrics.com

1ST QUALITY FABRICS IN THE HEART OF INTERCOURSE, PA

Opening in March 2010!

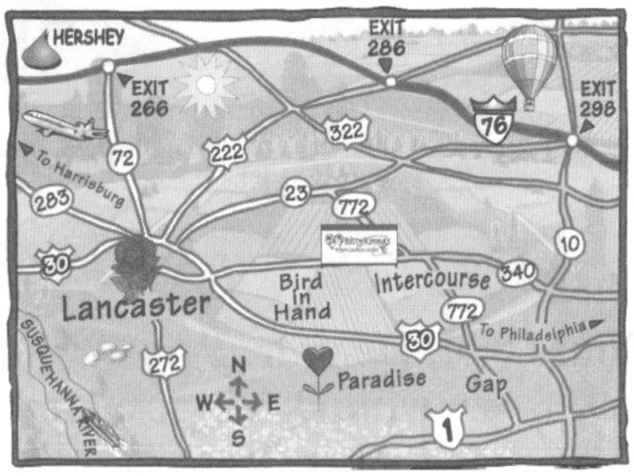

- Fabrics, Notions, Patterns, Books & Supplies For Discriminating Quilters
- Experienced, Helpful Staff
- Specializing In Fabrics: Asians, Batiks, Reproductions & Brilliant Blenders
- BittyKinna's Own Inspired Line Of Patterns
- Individual Instruction & Group Classes

HOURS: M - SA 9AM - 6PM
SU 12PM - 4 PM ◆ By Appointment

BittyKinna

Etymology: Italian dialect.

1a: A term of endearment meaning "Little Mousie" referring to someone who is always scurrying around, getting into mischief;

1b: The owner's apt nickname when she was a little girl.

QUILT SHOP
BittyKinna's
Where Quilters Gather

#13

717.768.8885 ◆ 3466 Old Philadelphia Pike ◆ P.O. Box 330 ◆ Intercourse, Pennsylvania 17534 ◆ www.bittykinna.com

The Old Country Store

QUILTS

- Finest quality quilts.
- Best prices and selection!
- More than 300 local Amish and Mennonite craftspersons!
- Hundreds of handmade dolls, pillows, table runners, toys, games, scherenschnitte and crafts.

FABRIC

- More than 60,000 yards of fabric!
- First quality goods.
- Wide assortment of solids.
- Fabric Packs of many combinations. Very popular!
- Quilting books and notions
- We do cut quarter-yards.

#14

The Old Country Store
Route 340, east of Lancaster
3510 Old Philadelphia Pike, Intercourse, PA 17534
800/828-8218 • 717/768-7101

9 a.m.–6:30 p.m. daily — June through August.
9 a.m.–5 p.m. daily — September through May.
Closed Sundays.

SHOP The Old Country Store ONLINE at www.TheOldCountryStore.com

(200 FREE PARKING SPACES RIGHT BEHIND THE STORE.)

LOCATED ON THE SECOND FLOOR OF THE HISTORIC OLD COUNTRY STORE

The People's Place QUILT MUSEUM

Founded 1988.

Visit our nationally-acclaimed Quilt Museum

- Dazzling contemporary quilts.
- Free admission.
- Hands-on exhibits.
- Beautiful Museum Shoppe.

9 a.m.–5 p.m. daily — Monday–Saturday. Closed Sunday.

www.PPQuiltMuseum.com

Roundabout Quilting

an independent quilt shop 610.347.1122

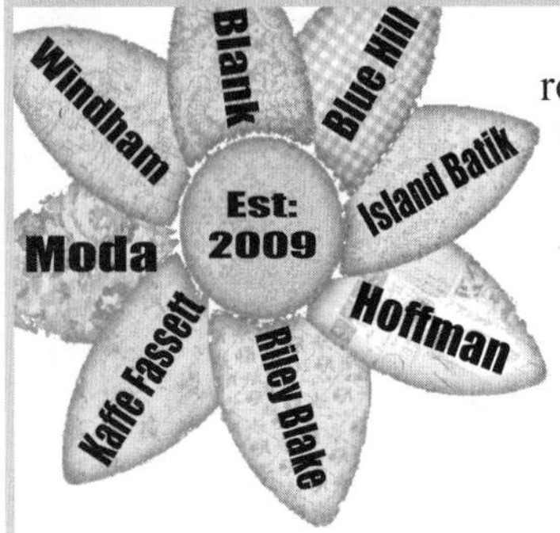

5 Cemetery Ln. 19375
roundaboutquilting@gmail.com
Owner: Andra Rudershausen

Tues - Fri 10 - 4
Sat 10 - 3 Sun 12 - 4
and during eve. classes

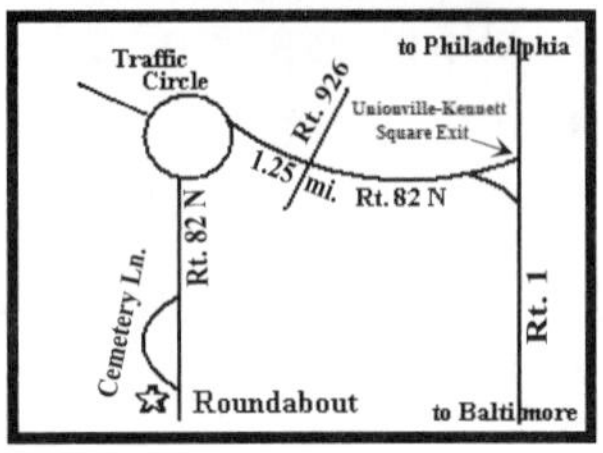

Come enjoy beautiful samples and kits in our historic building . . . plus all the latest in fabrics, notions, books and patterns.

www.roundaboutquilting.com

Unionville, PA #15

Morgantown, PA #16

Mon - Sat 9 - 7
Thur & Fri 9 - 9

Hayloft Fabrics

150 Morview Blvd. 19543
on 2nd Floor of Martin's Country Market
(610) 286-5045
Shop online at: www.hayloftfabrics.com

One Stop Fabric Shop!
A huge selection of almost 8000 bolts of quilting fabric, plus loads of quilting notions and books. Buses welcome.

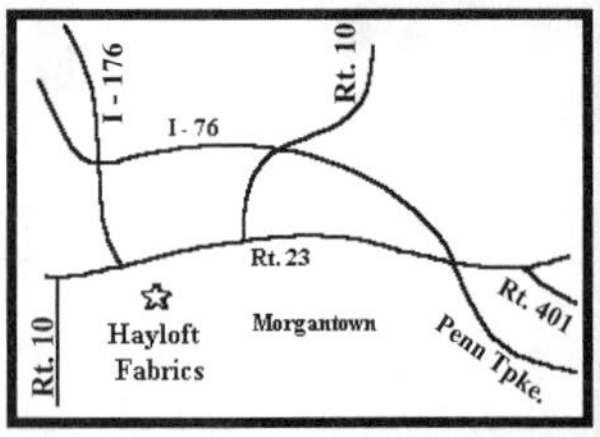

King of Prussia, PA #17

Mon - Fri 10 - 6
Sat 10 - 5
Sun 12 - 5

Steve's Sewing, Vacuum & Quilting

156 West Dekalb
19406
(610) 768-9453

Valley Forge Shopping Center, Rte 202
Owners: Steve & Karen Chubin
Est: 1992 7000 sq.ft. 2000+ bolts
steves@stevessewandvac.com
www.stevessewandvac.com
Sewing Machines • Sergers • Vacuums
Quilting Supplies • Fabrics • Sewing Notions
Accessories • Furniture • Lessons • Classes

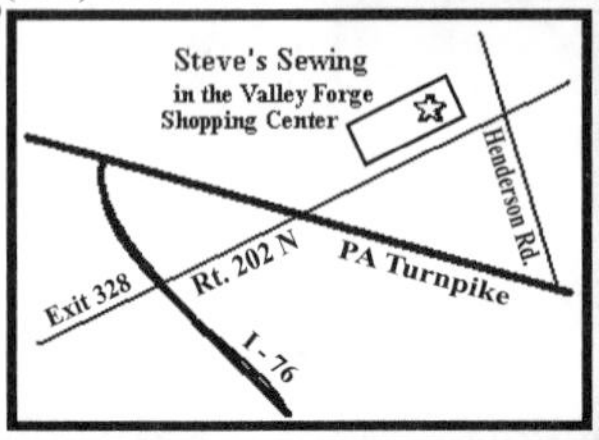

Oley, PA #19

Tues - Sat 10 - 5
Thur til 8

Ladyfingers Sewing Studio

6375 Oley Turnpike Rd. 19547
(610) 689-0068 Fax: (610) 689-0067
info@ladyfingerssewing.com
www.ladyfingerssewing.com Est: 1975
Owner: Gail Kessler 4000+ bolts
Nestled in the beautiful historic Oley Valley. Fabric designer, Gail Kessler's treasure trove of quilting delights awaits you in her 1860 historic landmark hotel location.

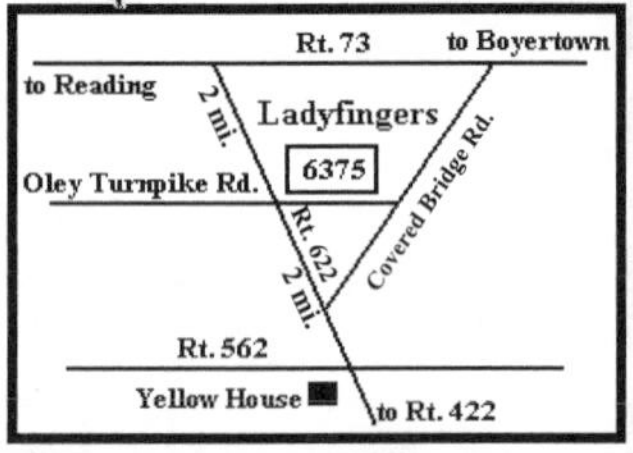

Pottstown, PA #18

Generations Quilt Shop

Wed - Sat 10 - 5
Thur til 8
Sun 12 - 5

120 Shoemaker Rd.
19464
(610) 718-5505
Est: 2001 1500 sq.ft.
Owner: Linda Mendenhall 3500+ Bolts
comments@generationsquiltshop.com
www.generationsquiltshop.com

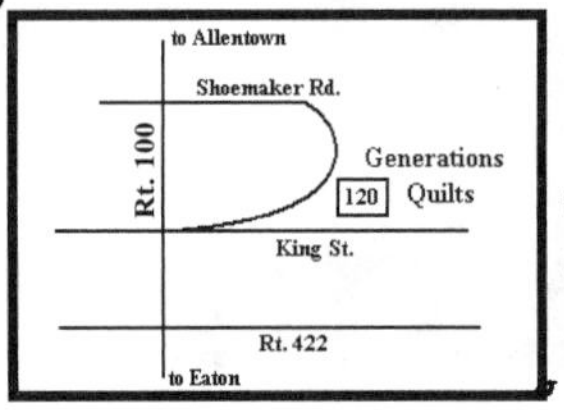

Our bright and cheery A-Frame Cottage holds Books, Patterns, Notions and a friendly staff. Our beautiful Fabrics come from all major manufacturers .

Kutztown, PA #20

Wooden Bridge Drygoods

195 Deysher Rd. 19530
(610) 683-7159

Over 8000 bolts of 100% cotton fabrics, quilting supplies, notions, Kwik-Sew patterns, quilt books and quilt tops. We accept most major credit cards.

Mon, Tues, Fri 9 - 5
Wed & Thur 9 - 7
Sat 9 - 4

Fax: (610) 683-7284
Owners: Anna Mae Martin & Louise Shirk

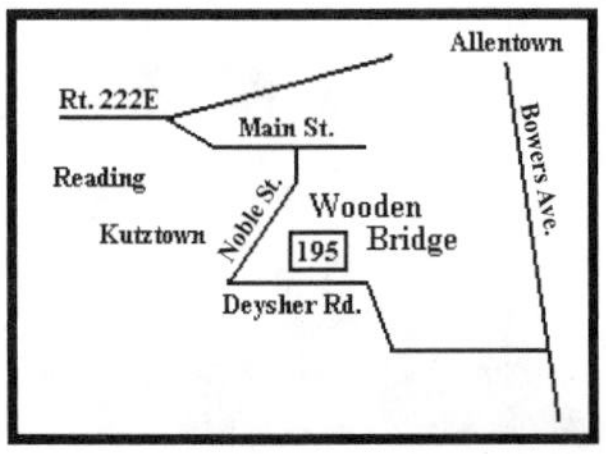

Hamburg, PA #21

260 N. Fourth St. 19526
(610) 562-7173
hapsew@comcast.net
www.happysewingroom.com
Owner: Jean Boyd
Est: 1990

Happy Sewing Room

We offer beautiful cotton fabrics, quilting supplies, patterns, books, gift items & most important the personal service every quilter deserves.

Wed & Fri 10 - 5
Thurs 10 - 7 Sat 10 - 3
Closed Sun - Tues

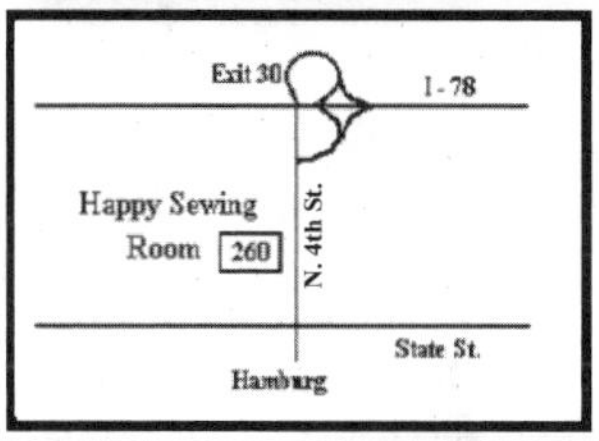

Lehighton, PA #22

Mon - Fri 10 - 6
Thur til 8
Sat 10 - 2

The Quilted Crow

"The shop where friendships grow."

179 Interchange Rd. 18235
(610) 379-4700 Fax: Same
Est:2009 1000 sq.ft. 800 bolts
qcrow@ptd.net
www.The-QuiltedCrow.com

100% Quality Cotton Fabrics
Books - Patterns - Notions - Classes

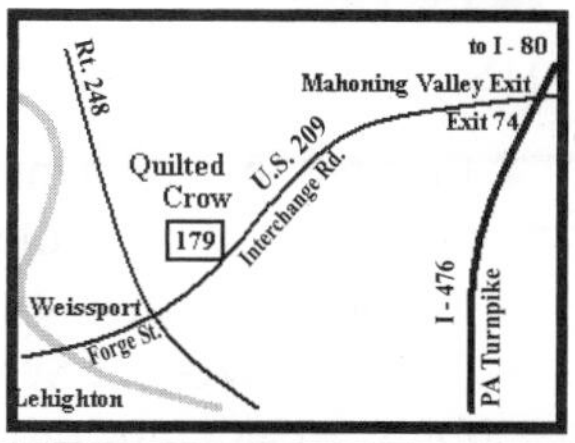

Effort, PA #23

Tues - Sun 10 - 5

The Country Quilterie

Carriage House Square
R.R. #3, Box 2482, Route 115 N,
(570) 620-9707 18330
Owner: Maryann Kwant Est: 1989
makwant@aol.com 1500 sq.ft.
www.countryquilterie.com

Over 3000 Bolts of Quilting Fabric, Books, Notions, Supplies. Largest selection of Quilts in the Poconos. Quilted Accessories and Gifts.

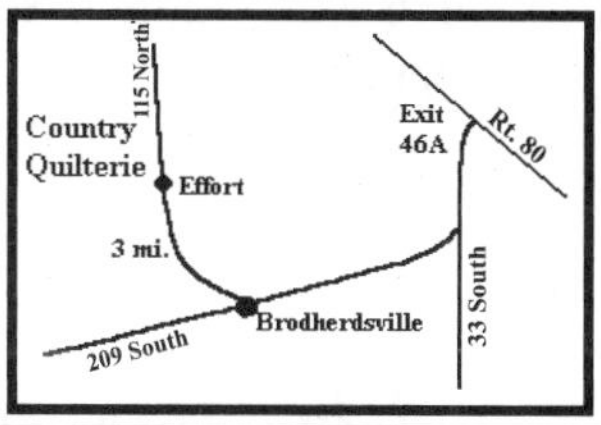

Honesdale, PA #24

Tues - Sat 10 - 5

The Mountain Quiltworks

20 Grandma's Lane 18431
(570) 253-9510 800+ Bolts .
Owner: Amy R. Dunn 1100 sq.ft
fabric@localnet.com

Custom Hand-Quilting our Specialty! Find everything you need to create tomorrow's heirlooms. From various source books, stencils & patterns to, of course, top quality cotton fabrics.

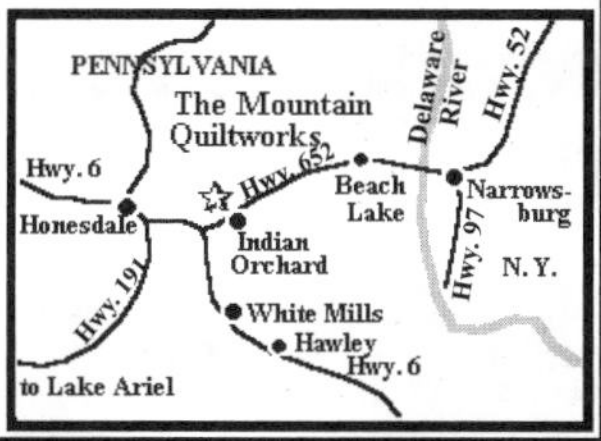

Honesdale, PA #25

Tues - Sat 10 - 6

www.astitchintimepa.com

114 7th St.. 18431
(570) 253-6864
Owner: Jackie Murphy
astitchintime2@gmail.com

A Stitch In Time provides high quality fabrics, quilting supplies and classes to the NE Pennsylvania/Delaware River Valley area.

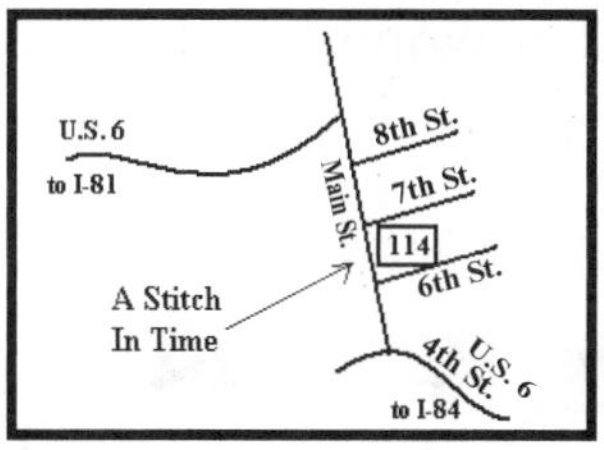

733 Oak St.
Scranton, PA 18508
(570) 955-0956

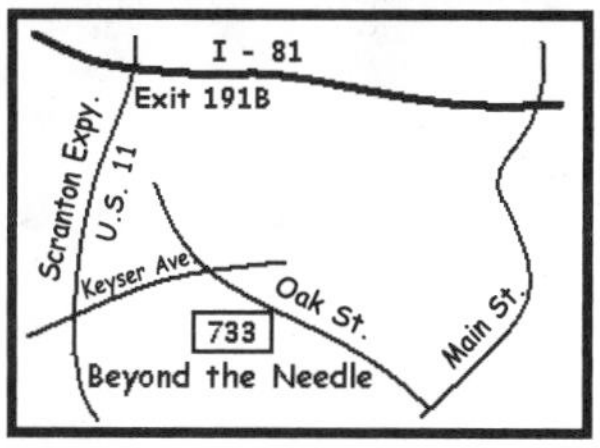

- Your Quilting Inspiration Headquarters
- We carry the newest quality fabrics, books, patterns, notions.
- Block of the Month programs
- Visit our 2nd location in Kirkwood, NY, just 45 minutes down I-81

Scranton, PA #26

Mon - Sat 10 - 5

Owner: Lisa Wilson
Est: 2009 1000+ Bolts
Fax (570) 955-0948
lisa@beyondtheneedle.com

www.beyondtheneedle.com

Endless Mountains Quiltworks

Proud to Be One of America's Top Ten Quilt Shops

- Located in Tunkhannock, Gateway to the beautiful Endless Mountains region of Northeastern PA
- 25 Miles West of Scranton and Only 20 Minutes Off I-81
- RV Accessible
- Home of the *Pennsylvania Fieldstones* Quilt Pattern
- 3000 Sq. Ft. with 4500 Bolts
- Long Arm Quilting Service
- Opened in 2001 by Owner Jeannette Kitlan

Tues-Sat 10-5,
Sun 1-5, Mon Closed

EMQuiltworks.com

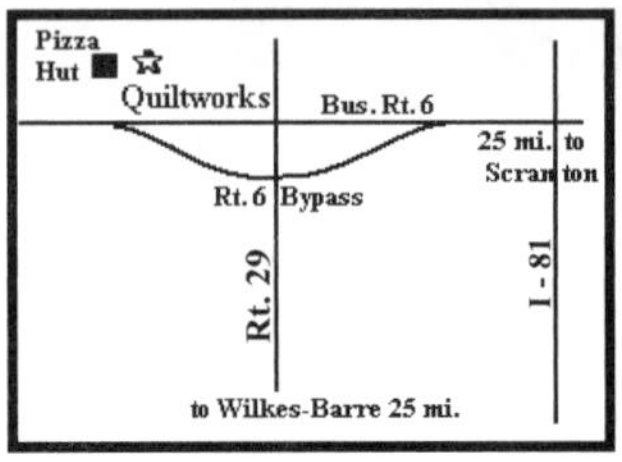

4 Towne Plaza Shopping Center Bus. Rt. 6 W next to Pizza Hut
Tunkhannock, PA 18657 570-836-7575

Tunkhannock, PA #27

Wellsboro, PA #28

Needles Quilt Shop

73 Main St. 16901
(570) 724-1616
Fax: (570) 723-8539
Owners: Katie Mader & Mary Ginn
Est: 2003

needlesquiltshop@yahoo.com
needlesquiltshop.com

Mon - Sat 10 - 5

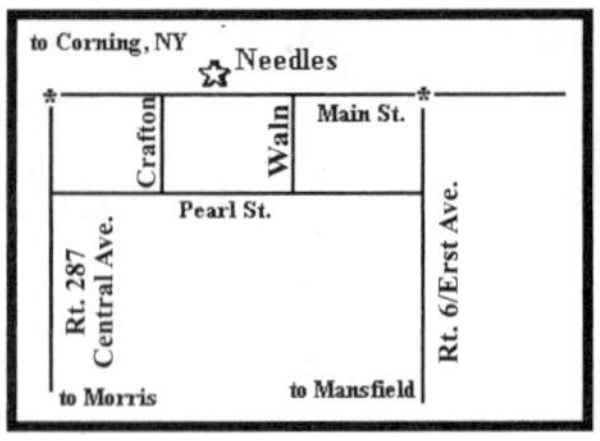

The Cozy Quilt Shop in the heart of Canyon Country

- Fabrics, Notions, & Accessories for the dedicated Quilter.
- Full array of books, patterns and gift items
- Ready-made kits and kits to order.
- Personalized service to aid in the making of your Treasured Heirlooms.

Our Gathering Place

Come spend your day with us. We offer over 4,000 bolts of fine cotton fabric, unique block of the months, wonderful quilt kits, books, patterns & more. Our classes inspire both beginners and seasoned quilters alike.

We hope to see you soon or visit our online store:

www.ogpquiltshop.com

Montoursville, PA #29

Tues, Wed, Thur 10 - 5 Fri 10 - 7 Sat 10 - 3
Call for Summer Hours

936 Plaza Dr. Savoy Plaza 17754
(570) 368-1130 Owner: Chris Kroboth
Montoursville is located about
5 mi. E of Williamsport off I - 180 / U.S. 220

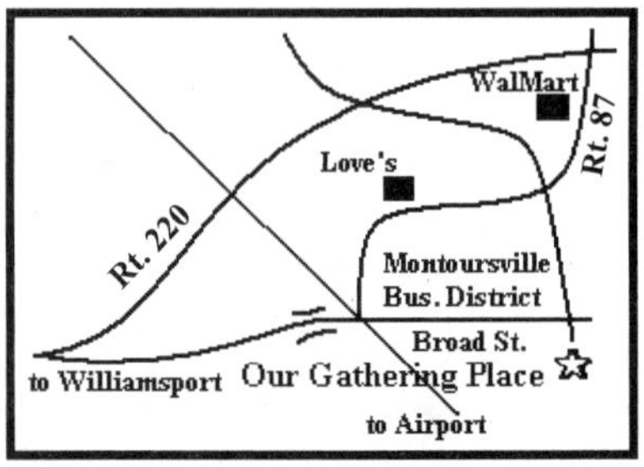

Reproduction Fabrics, Civil War Fabrics, Wools, Batiks, Flannel Fabrics, Quilt Kits

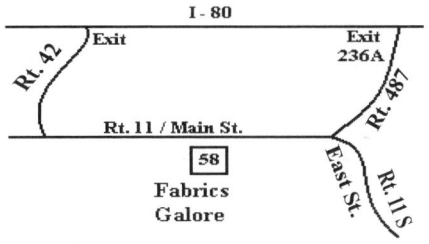

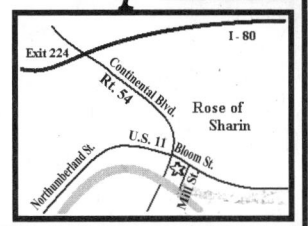

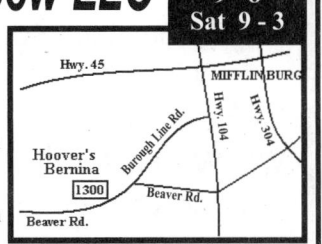

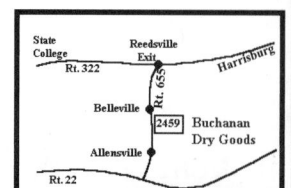

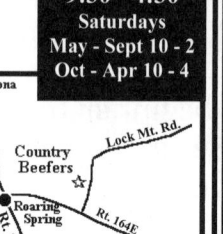

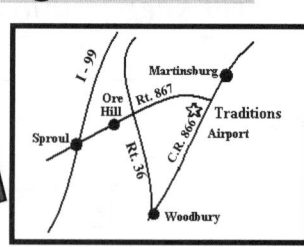

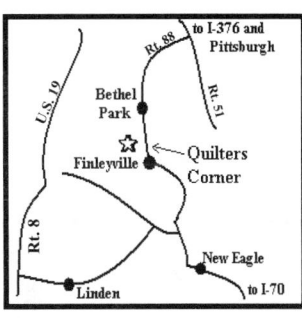

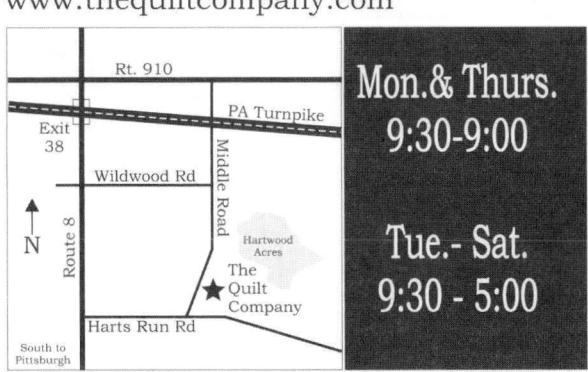

THE STITCH IN TIME SHOPPE, INC

Mon, Tues, Fri & Sat 10 - 5
Wed & Thur 10 - 8
Sun 12 - 4

801 N. Greengate Rd. #370
Gabriel Brothers Plaza
(724) 836-0611
Fax: (724) 836-1250
Est: 1995

www.thestitchintimeshoppe.com

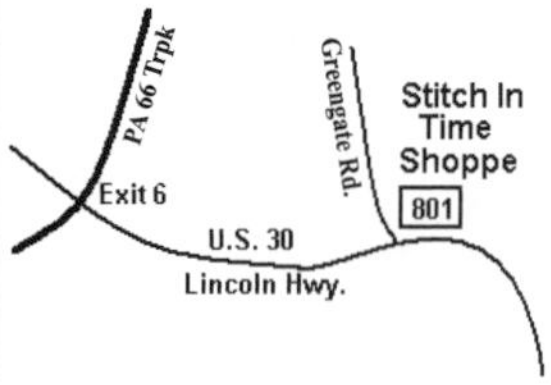

Our full service sewing center has been supplying the Greensburg Area with sewing, embroidery and quilting fabric needs for over 15 years. Some of our services include Brother Sewing and Embroidery Machine Sales and Repairs, over 900 Bolts of Quilting Fabrics, Thread Selection, Classes and Sewing Machine Cabinets.

Greensburg, PA #41

New Eagle, PA #42
Ellen Palmer Quilt Shop

Tues 10 - 8
Wed - Fri 10 - 5
Sat 10 - 3

121 Main St. 15067
(724) 258-2715
Owner: Barbara Palmer
Est: 2004 500 bolts Online newsletter
bpalmer55@comcast.net

Big quilts for order.
Notions, Patterns, Books and Classs.

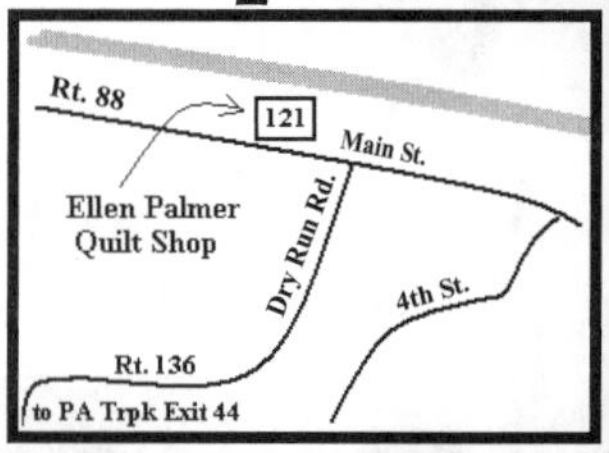

Blairsville, PA #43
Peace By Piece Quilt & Gift Shop

Tues 10 - 7
Wed - Fri 10 - 5
Sat 10 - 3

433 Old Indiana Rd. 15717
(724) 248-9777 Est: 2007
debbie@peacebypiecequilts.com
www.peacebypiecequilts.com
Have a cup of tea and browse. Many samples and kits! Moda fabric, reproductions, Civil War and more. Embroidery is our specialty.

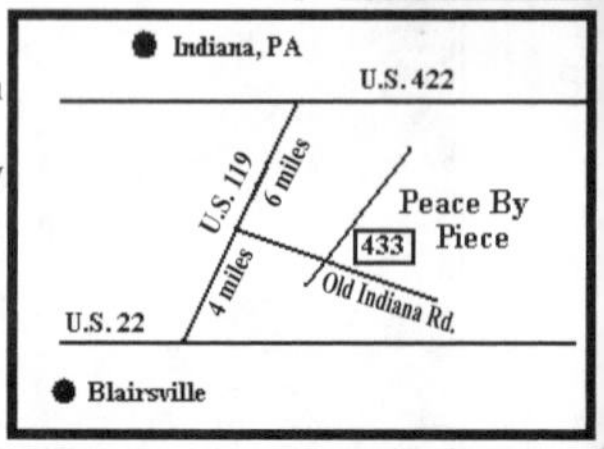

Pittsburgh, PA #44
Piecing It Together

Mon - Sat 10 - 5
Thur til 8

3458 Babcock Blvd. 15237
(412) 364-2440
Owners: Johanna Blanarik
Est: 1986 1200 sq.ft.
piecitto@fyi.net
www.fyi.net/~piecitto

Complete line of quilting supplies, 100% cotton fabrics, books, notions, patterns, and classes. Lots of samples. Personal, friendly.

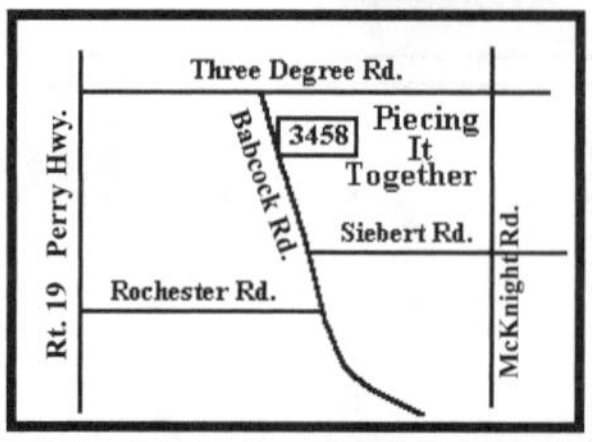

Pittsburgh, PA #45
Quilters Depot

Mon- Fri 10 - 6
Tues til 8
Sat 9 - 3

4160 Library Rd. 15234
(412) 308-6236
Est: 2009 2800 sq.ft. Online Newsletter
quiltersdepotpa@comcast.net
www.quiltersdepotpa.com

We are more than a normal Quilt Store. We are a depot! Fabrics, notions, classes, clubs, knitting, crochet and embroidery.

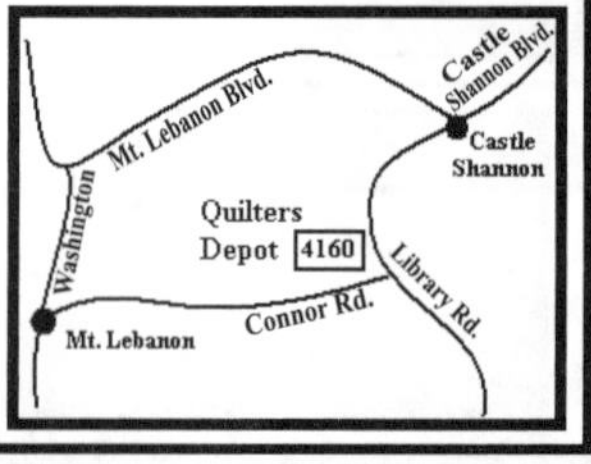

Elderton, PA #46
Judy's Quilting Center LLC

Mon - Fri 10 - 5
Wed til 8
Sat 10 - 3

11275 Rte. 422, P.O. Box 178 15736
(724) 354-3360 Fax: (724) 354-3145
judysquilts@windstream.net
Owners: Judy Kimmel

... all roads lead to Judy's Quilting Center!

5000+ Bolts 100% Cotton quilt quality Fabric.
We now do long-arm machine quilting.
Friendly Service. Fun Classes.

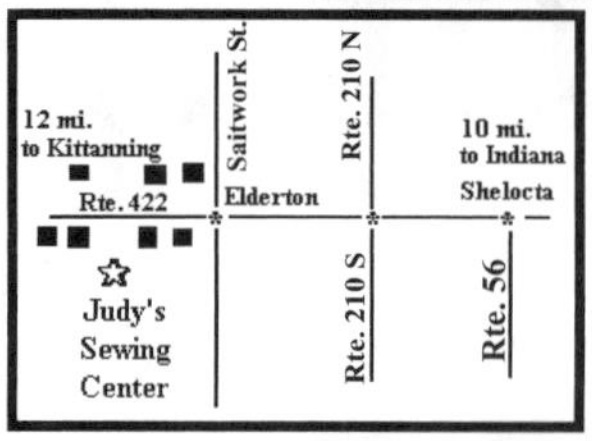

Portersville, PA #47
Muddy Creek Originals

Tues - Sat 10 - 4
Sun 12 - 4

1310 Perry Hwy. 16051
(724) 368-3772
Owner: Sheryl Robinson Est: 2002
1000 sq.ft. 2400+ Bolts Free Newsletter
muddycreekoriginals@zoominternet.net
www.muddycreekoriginals.com
We are a full-service quilt shop specializing in contemporary fabrics, batiks, Japanese prints, books, notions, classes & Two Cousins patterns.

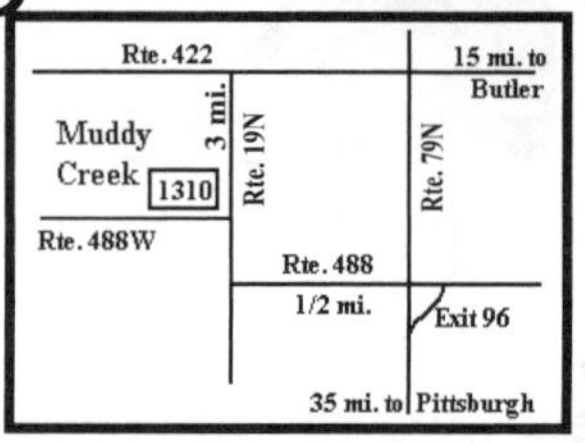

New Wilmington, PA #48
The Quilting Bee

Tues - Fri 10 - 4:30
Sat 10 - 4

126 S. Market St. 16142
(724) 946-8566
Owner: Linda Miller
TheQuiltingBee.PA@gmail.com
Est: 1981 1200+ Bolts Free Newsletter

Large selection of Quality Quilting Fabrics, Books & Patterns. Located 1 hour north of Pittsburgh in the Heart of Amish Country

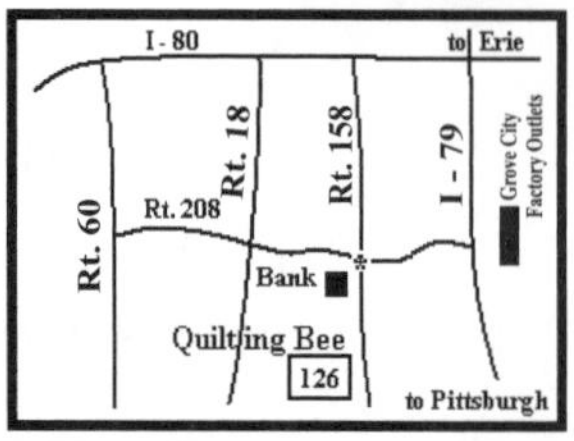

Sharpsville, PA #49
Shaffer's Countryside Quilting

Tues 10 - 5
Wed 12 - 7
Thur & Fri 10 - 5
Sat 10 - 3

2741 Winner Rd. 16150
(724) 962-9394
judyquilts@hotsheet.com Est: 1998
www.shafferscountrysidequilting.com
Owner: Judy Shaffer 2500 bolts
Best quality cotton fabrics - Moda, RJR, P&B, and more. Knowledgeable, friendly staff, special orders welcome. Visa and Mastercard.

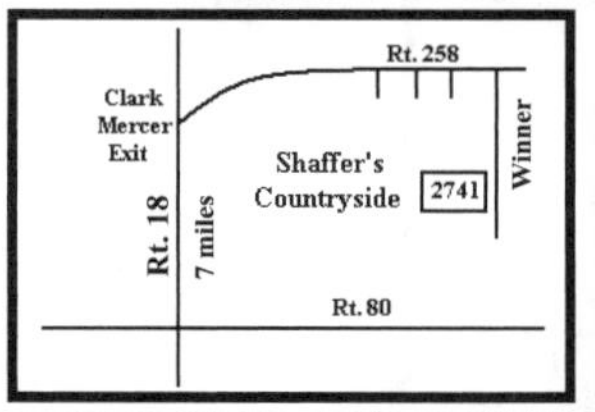

HEIRLOOM Quilting and Antiques

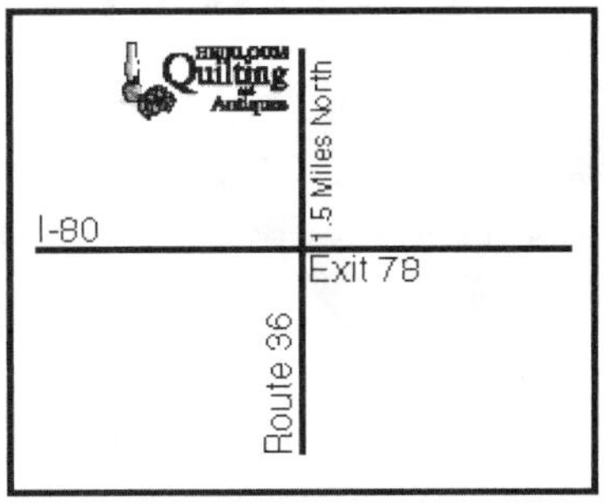

PFAFF machines, Handi Quilter, AccuQuilt & accessories
Nearly 8,000 bolts of fabric • Books • Notions • Patterns
Quilting / Sewing Classes - FUN

HOURS:
Mon-Sat 10 am - 5 pm
Call for Holiday Hours
www.heirloomquilting.com

(814) 849-8739
Durfee Burtner, Proprietor
1225 Rt. 36 BROOKVILLE, PA 15825
1.5 MILES N. OF I-80, EXIT 78

Brookville, PA #50

Knox, PA #51
Countryside Quilts

Mon - Fri 10 - 4:30
Sat 10 - 3

6361 Canoe Ripple Rd. 16232
(814) 797-2434
Exit 53 from I - 80
Owner: Sally Byers Est: 1987
In the heart of Clarion County. We are the area's Largest and Most Unique Country gift, craft and Quilting supply shop. With 100% Cottons, Books, Quilting Patterns and the area's largest supply of Craft Patterns. Homespuns and Flannels.
"Become a fan on Facebook"

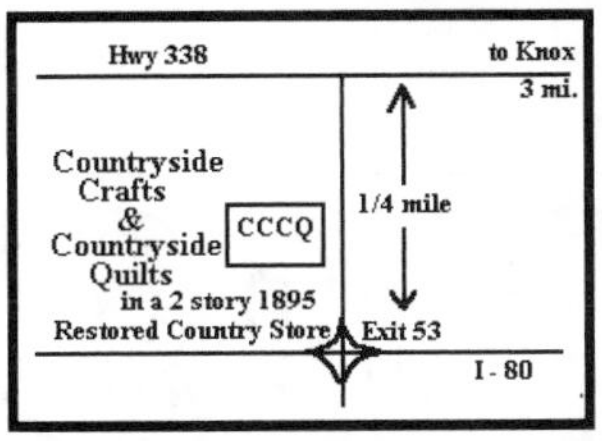

Carlton, PA #52
Homespun Treasures Quilt Shop

Mon - Sat 10 - 4

509 U.S. 322 16311
(814) 425-2889
Owner: Gail M. Baker
quiltLov@windstream.net
www.homespuntreasuresquiltshop.com

Located between Meadville & Franklin, PA. Large selection of Fabric, Books & Notions. Classes Available. Always looking to see your work. Bring it in and share.

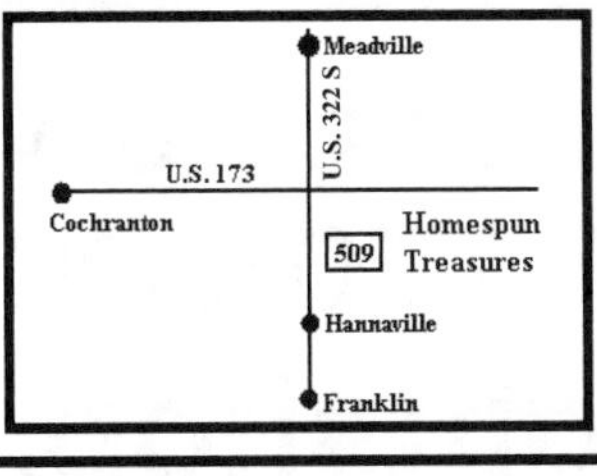

Erie, PA #53

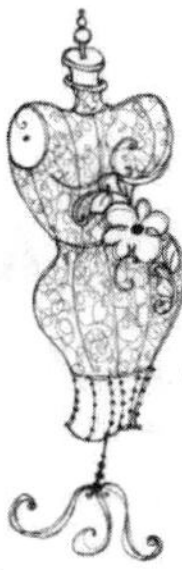

Millcreek Sewing & Fabric

Summit Towne Centre
7200 Peach St. #460 Erie, PA 16509
814-866-8227
Est: 1998 5500 sq.ft. 4000+ Bolts
www.millcreeksew.com

"Just to see the Marvelous Samples It's Worth the Trip!"

Tri State Leader in Batiks and Flannels

Hundreds of Books and Patterns Friendly, Knowledgeable Staff

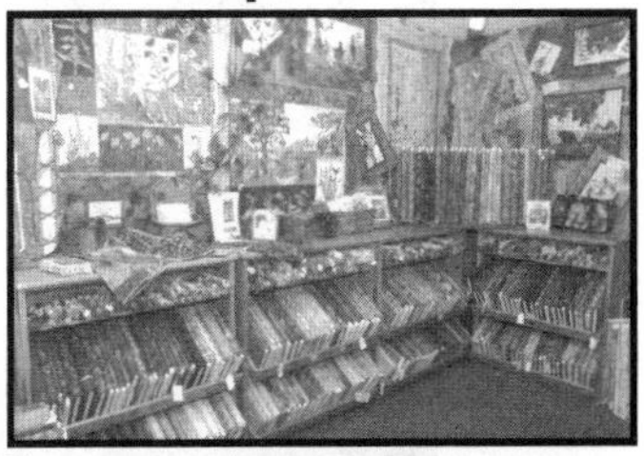

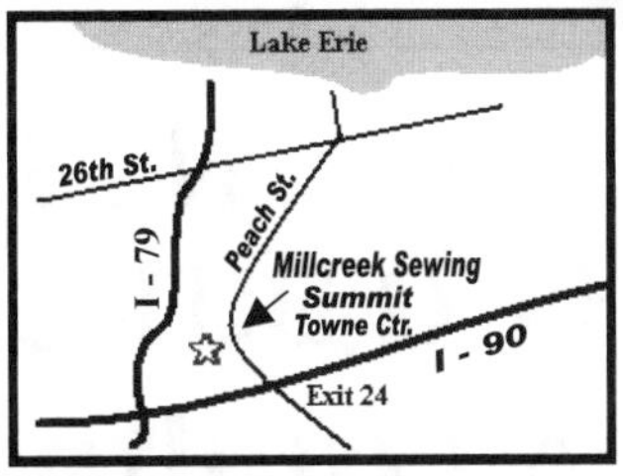

Left at 3rd light, with Sam's Club

Mon - Sat 10 - 5
Thurs til 7

baby lock
FOR THE LOVE OF SEWING

Fairview, PA #54

INTERNATIONAL FABRIC COLLECTION

Est: 1987

7870 W. Ridge Road
P.O. Box 72, Fairview, PA 16415
info@intfab.com 2500 sq.ft.
Owner: Dorothy Brown

www.intfab.com

Cottons from Africa, Alexander Henry, Australia, France, Germany, Guatemala, Holland, Italy, Japan, Kona Bay, Liberty Fabric, Dupioni Silks, Sashiko Supplies, Unusual Books and Patterns.

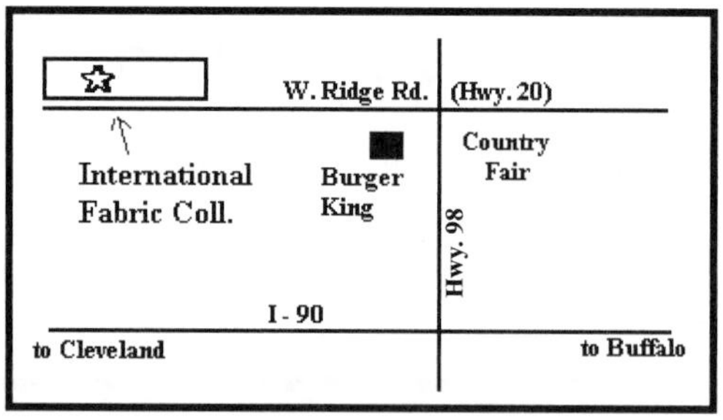

Open Monday - Friday from 9 am to 3 pm
other times by appointment.

Please call 800-462-3891 to check hours.

North East, PA #55

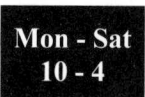

Pillowcasegram *Sending Unique Gifts*

Mon - Sat 10 - 4

We carry a very large selection of novelty fabrics, along with many other quilting fabrics.

We specialize in making fun custom-made pillowcases for every special occasion. Pillowcasegrams are personalized custom-made pillowcases that are fun for all ages. Pillowcasegrams are sent along with your personal telegram message to the recipient. Send a pillowcasegram for special occasions, holidays, sports, hobbies, bridal, school spirit, etc.

We spend one-third of our lives with our heads on our pillows… so make them fun!

3 W. Main St. 16428
(814) 725-3400
Est: 2008 1800 sq.ft.
1000 bolts Online newsletter
pillowcasegram@aol.com

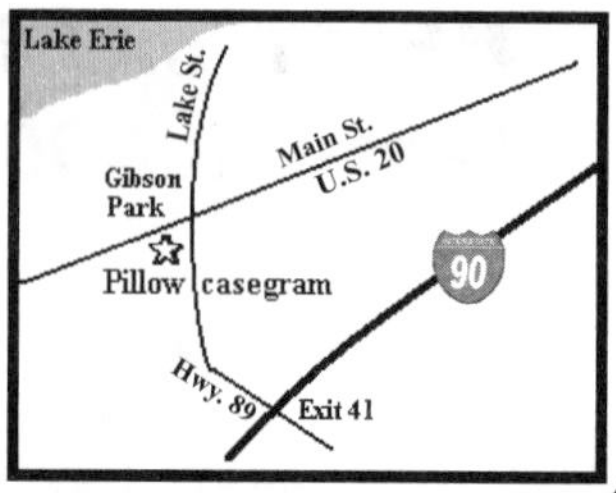

www.pcgfabricscom

North East, PA #56

CALICO PATCH Quilt Shop

Mon - Fri 10 - 5 Sat 10 - 4

107 Clay St. #3 16428
(814) 725-2275
calpatchqs@aol.com Est: 1998
www.calicopatchquiltshop.com
Owner: Joy Reich 1600 sq.ft. 1600+ Bolts
Books - Notions - Classes and the largest selection of Thimbleberries Fabric in the Tri-state area. Mail Order - Guild discount.

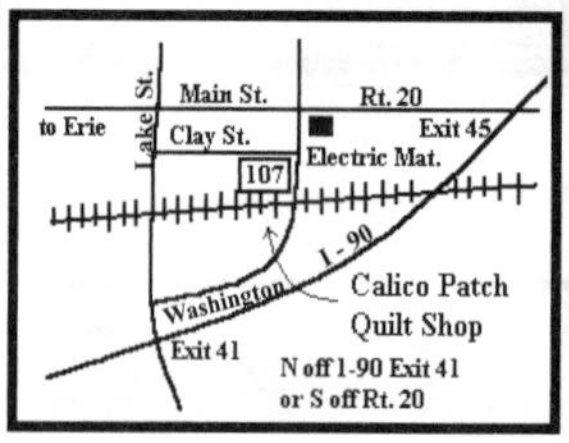

Check This Out !

Quilters' Gift Shop

2506 Robinson St.
Colorado Springs
Colorado 80904
719-685-5041
orders@quiltersgiftshop.com

No Fabric, No Patterns, No Notions
NOTHING BUT GIFTS FOR QUILTERS
www.quiltersgiftshop.com

Pennsylvania Quilt Shops

Airville	Country Variety Store, 209 Telegraph Rd.	
Allentown	Tucker Yarn Co., 950 Hamilton Mall	610-434-1846
Allentown	Springtown Textile Co., 950 West Hamilton	610-439-8811
Allison Park	**The Quilt Company, 3940 Middle Rd.**	
	412-487-9532	**See ad #40, page 483**
Altoona	Ben Franklin Crafts, 911 Logan Blvd.	814-943-2944
Bellefonte	Third Bay Quilt Shop, 105 Rapid Hill Rd	
Belleview	**Mary Lee's Fabric Shop, 3510 W Main St**	
	717-935-2691	**See ad #33, page 481**
Belleville	**A.M. Buchanan Dry Goods, 2459 St. Rt. 655**	
	717-483-6428	**See ad #34, page 482**
Bensalem	The Quilting Circle, 2625 Street Rd.	215-638-1150
Bird in Hand	**Log Cabin Quilt Shop, 2679 Old Philadelphia Pike**	
	717-393-1702	**See ad #8, page 475**
Bird in Hand	Fisher's Hand Made Quilts, 2713-A Old Philadelphia Pike	717-392-5440
Bird-in-Hand	The Quilt and Fabric Shack, 3137 Old Philadephia Pike	717-768-0338
Blairsville	**Peace by Piece Quilt and Gift Shop**	
	433 Old Indiana Rd.	
	724-248-9777	**See ad #43, page 484**
Blandon	Quilted Cat, 8500 Allentown Pike	610-916-1595
Bloomsburg	**Fabrics Galore, 58 E Main St**	
	570-784-8799	**See ad #30, page 481**
Bradford	Little Fabric Garden, 12 Northgate Dr.	814-362-6070
Brookville	**Heirloom Quilting and Antiques**	
	1225 Rt. 36N, HC07	
	814-849-8739	**See ad #50, page 485**
Camp Hill	All Sew Easy, 3300 Hartzdale Dr. #103	717-763-9120
Carlisle	**Calico Corner, 341 Barnstable Rd.**	
	717-249-8644	**See ad #3, page 474**
Carlton	**Homespun Treasures, 509 US Hwy. 322**	
	814-425-2889	**See ad #52, page 485**
Chadds Ford	Quilter's Corner, 100 Ridge Rd. #8	610-459-8993
Chambersburg	**The Sew'n Place 955 Wayne Ave**	
	717-263-5606	**See ad #1, page 474**
Clarion	Sew Elegant, 11977 Route 66	814-764-3422
Clarks-Summit	Carriage Barn Antiques, 1550 Fairview Rd.	750-587-5405
Clifton Heights	Hayes Sewing Machines, 9 E. Baltimore Pike	610-259-5959
Coudersport	Quilter's Heaven, 709 N. Main St.	814-274-8007
Curwensville	Kay's Quilters Stash, 308 Thompson St	814-236-0378
Dallas	Back Mountain Quiltworks, 52 Mill St.	717-675-4018
Danville	**Rose of Sharin, 311 Mill St.**	
	570-275-1005	**See ad #31, page 481**
Denver	**Sauder's Fabrics, 681 South Muddycreek**	
	717-336-2664	**See ad #11, page 476**
Denver	**Burkholder Fabrics, 2155 W. Route 897**	
	717-336-6692	**See ad #10, page 475**
Doylestown	Byrne Sewing Connection, 422 E. Butler	215-230-9411
Doylestown	Sew Smart Fabrics, 30 W. Oakland Ave.	215-345-7990
East Earl	Goods Store, 1338 Main St.	717-354-4026
Easton	At Piece Quiltery, 2210 Corriere Rd. #F	610-438-4630
Effort	**The Country Quilterie R. R. #3 Box 2482**	
	570-620-9707	**See ad #23, page 479**
Elderton	**Judy's Quilting Center LLC 11275 Rte 422**	
	724-354-3360	**See ad #46, page 484**
Ephrata	Piece by Piece Quilt Shop, 22 N. State #201	717-738-6983
Ephrata	Goods Store, 1686 W. Main St.	717-733-7356
Erie	**Mill Creek Sewing & Fabric Center**	
	7200 Peach St Unit 460	
	814-866-8227	**See ad #53, page 485 & 408**
Erie	Burning the Midnight Oil Quilts, 8845 Wattsburg Rd.	814-825-9000
Exton	The Quilt Block Inc., 95 E. Welsh Pool Rd.	610-363-0404
Fairview	**The International Fabric Collection**	
	7870 West Ridge Rd. Ste. 8	
	814-474-1151	**See ad #54, page 486**
Finleyville	**Quilters Corner 6101 State Rt. 88**	
	724-348-8010	**See ad #39, page 483**
Fleetwood	Quilting Friends, 1412 N. Richmond Rd.	610-944-7475
Fleetwood	Quilters Palette, 3130 Pricetown Rd. # L	610-929-3191
Gettysburg	**Needle and Thread, 2215 Fairfield Rd.**	
	717-334-4011	**See ad #5, page 475**
Gilbert	Ladybutton Fabrics, Apen Ln.	610-681-5162
Gipsy	Village Variety Store, 33 Main St.	814-845-7503
Glenside	Granny's Sewing Den, 243 Keswick Ave.	215-885-4959
Goodville	Obie's Country Store, 1585 Main St.	717-445-4616
Greencastle	Marlan's Fabrics, 15021 Molly Pitcher Hwy.	717-597-3266
Greencastle	Stitch-N-Time, 128 S. Antrim Way	717-597-0051
Greensburg	**The Stitch in Time Shoppe**	
	801 N. Greengate Rd. Ste. 370	
	724-836-0611	**See ad #41, page 484**
Hamburg	**Happy Sewing Room, 260 N. Fourth St.**	
	610-562-7173	**See ad #21, page 479**
Hegins	Quilting In The Valley, 243 Fountain Rd.	570-682-1088
Hershey	**Quiltmakers Cottage, 1034 E. Chocolate Ave.**	
	717-534-9900	**See ad #6, page 475**
Honesdale	**A Stitch In Time, 102 10th St.**	
	570-253-6864	**See ad #25, page 479**
Honesdale	**Mountain Quiltworks, 20 Grandma's Ln.**	
	570-253-9510	**See ad #24, page 479**
Intercourse	**Zook's Fabric Store**	
	3535 Old Philadelphia Pike	
	717-768-8153	**See ad #12, page 476**
Intercourse	**Bitty Kinna's - Where Quilters Gather**	
	3466 Old Philadelphia Pike	
	717-768-8885	**See ad #13, page 476 & 206**
Intercourse	**The Old Country Store**	
	3510 Old Philadelphia Pike	
	800-828-8218	**See ad #14, page 477**
Intercourse	Nancy's Corner, 3503 Old Philadelphia Pike	717-768-8790
Intercourse	Village Quilts, 3519 Old Philadelphia Pike	717-768-0783
Jersey Shore	Inspirations Quilt Shop, 701 Allegheny St.	570-398-7399
Johnstown	Quilt Peddler, 620 Lamberd Ave.	814-262-9656
King of Prussia	**Steve's Sewing, Vacuum & Quilting**	
	Route 202 156 W. Dekalb Pike	
	610-768-9453	**See ad #17, page 478**
Kingston	Touch of Eyelet, 1188 Wyoming Ave.	570-283-3048
Knox	**Countryside Quilts, 6361 Canoe Ripple Rd.**	
	814-797-2434	**See ad #51, page 485**
Kutztown	**Wooden Bridge Dry Goods, 195 Deysher Rd.**	
	610-683-7159	**See ad #20, page 478**
Kutztown	Weaver's Quilts, 29 Linsol Rd.	610-683-7156
Lancaster	**Lancaster Quilt and Textile Museum**	
	13 West King St.	
	717-299-6440	**See ad #7, page 475**
Lebanon	Tom's Quilts 15 E. High St.	717-279-6262
Lebanon	Martin's Fabric Barn, 2799 E Cumberland St	717-274-5359
Leechburg	Farmhouse Fabrics, 786 Schenley Rd	724-845-2745
Lehighton	**The Quilted Crow, 179 Interchange Rd**	
	610-379-4700	**See ad #22, page 479**
Lewisburg	The Beckoning Cat, 209 Market St.	570-523-1520

Lititz — Weaver's Dry Goods, 108 W. Brubaker Valley 717-627-1724

Littlestown — The Finishing Stitch, 1897 Hanover Pike
717-359-4121 See ad #4, page 474

Lower Burrell — The Sewing Store, 103 Macbeth Dr. 724-334-1985

Loysville — Wise Dry Goods, 5683 Sherman Valley Rd. 717-789-4308

Manheim — Stitch & Craft, 2957 Lebanon Rd.
717-664-4230 See ad #9, page 475

Martinsburg — Traditions, 2327 Curryville Rd.
814-793-3980 See ad #36, page 482

Marysville — Smile Spinners, 1975 Valley Rd. 717-957-4225

Mechanicsburg — Quaint Quilts, 500 Cocklin St. 717-766-7166

Mercer — The Gallery, 116 N. Pitt St. 724-662-0464

Midland — Create A Stitch, 17 7th St. 724-643-4833

Mifflinburg — Hoover's Bernina Sew LLC, 1300 Beaver Rd.
570-966-3822 See ad #32, page 481

Montoursville — Our Gathering Place, 936 Plaza Dr.
570-368-1130 See ad #29, page 480

Morgantown — Hayloft Fabrics, 150 Moreview Blvd
610-286-5045 See ad #16, page 478

Nescopeck — J & B Craft Supply, 650 Harter Ave. 570-752-2627

New Brighton — Amy Baughman's Sewing Center, 472 Constitution Blvd. 724-846-8140

New Eagle — Ellen Palmer Quilt Shop, 121 Main St
724-258-2715 See ad #42, page 484

New Holland — Brubaker's Sewing Center, 20 N. Robert 717-354-8332

New Holland — Good's Store, 165 Earland Dr. 717-355-0571

New Holland — Cedar Lane Dry Goods, 204 Orlan Rd. 717-354-0030

New Kensington — Olcott Cottage Quilts, 3740 Milligantown 724-334-8599

New Wilmington — The Quilting Bee, 126 S. Market St.
724-946-8566 See ad #48, page 484

Newburg — Esh's Store, 16285 Cumberland Hwy
717-423-6754 See ad #2, page 474

North East — Calico Patch Quilt Shoppe, 107 Clay St. #3
814-725-2275 See ad #56, page 486

North East — Pillowcasegram & Other Things, 3 W. Main
814-725-3400 See ad #55, page 486

Northampton — Dave Iron's Antiques, 223 Covered Bridge 610-262-9335

Oley — Ladyfingers Sewing Studio
6375 Oley Turnpike Rd
610-689-0068 See ad #19, page 478

Philadelphia — Fabrics on the Hill, 8434 Germantown Ave. 215-247-3485

Philadelphia — Kincus Fabrics, 755 South 4th St. 215-923-8836

Phoenixville — Chester County Quilting, 206 Village At Eland, Rt. 113 610-917-2527

Pittsburgh — Piecing it Together, 3458 Babcock Blvd.
412-364-2440 See ad #44, page 484

Pittsburgh — Quilters Depot, 4160 Library Rd.
412-308-6236 See ad #45, page 484

Pittsfield — Quiltessentials, 212 Main St. 814-563-9798

Portersville — Muddy Creek Originals, 1310 Perry Hwy
724-368-3772 See ad #47, page 484

Pottstown — Pottstown Sewing, 142 Shoemaker Rd. 610-326-5055

Pottstown — Generations Quilt Shop, 120 Shoemaker Rd.
610-718-5505 See ad #18, page 478

Punxsutawney — Lydia's Quilt Shop, 56 Stuchell Ln. 814-938-8488

Quarryville — Goods Store, 333 W. 4th St. 717-786-9028

Red Hill — Quilter's Remedy Fabric Boutique, 80 Gravel Pike #A 215-679-8170

Roaring Spring — The Country Beefers, 125 Lock Mt. Rd.
814-224-4818 See ad #35, page 482

Ronks — Quilt Shop at Millers, 2811 Lincoln Hwy E 717-687-8480

Ronks — Dutchland Quilt Patch, 2851A Lincoln Hwy. E 717-687-0534

Ronks — Family Farm Quilt, 3511 W. Newport Rd. 717-768-8375

Schaefferstown — Goods Store, Rte. 501 N 717-949-2663

Scranton — Beyond the Needle, 33 Oak St.
570-955-0956 See ad #26, page 479

Selinsgrove — The Sewing Shanty, Inc., 29 S. Market St. 570-372-1922

Sharpsville — Shaffer's Countryside Quilting, 2741 Winner
724-962-9394 See ad #49, page 484

Slippery Rock — Fabric Sewing Center, 537 New Castle Rd. 724-794-3076

Strasburg — Amish Country Crafts 717-687-9935

Stroudsburg — American Ribbon's Quilt Shop, 827 B Ann St. 570-421-7470

Stroudsburg — Pocono Sew & Vac, 567 Main St. 570-421-4580

Tamaqua — Caroline's Quilt Shop 109 E Broad St 570-668-3090

Tunkhannock — Endless Mountain Quiltworks, 4 Towne Plaza
570-836-7575 See ad #27, page 480

Uniontown — Sew Special, 73 W. Main St.
724-438-1765 See ad #37, page 482

Unionville — Roundabout Quilting, 5 Cemetary Ln.
610-347-1122 See ad #15, page 478

Vanderbilt — Seams Like Home Quilt Retreat
117 Numetrics Rd.
7249841399 See ad #38, page 482

Warren — Riverside Stitchin' Quilt, 317 PA Ave. W 814-723-8356

Wellsboro — Needles Quilt Shop, 73 Main St.
570-724-1616 See ad #28, page 480

White Oak — Quilters Nook Inc., 2521 Poinsettia Dr. 412-751-1356

Womelsdorf — In Stitches Quilt & Fabric, 4017 Conrad Weiser Pkwy 610-589-2625

York — Sew Unforgettable, 3605 E. Market St. 717-755-5833

Pennsylvania Quilt Shows

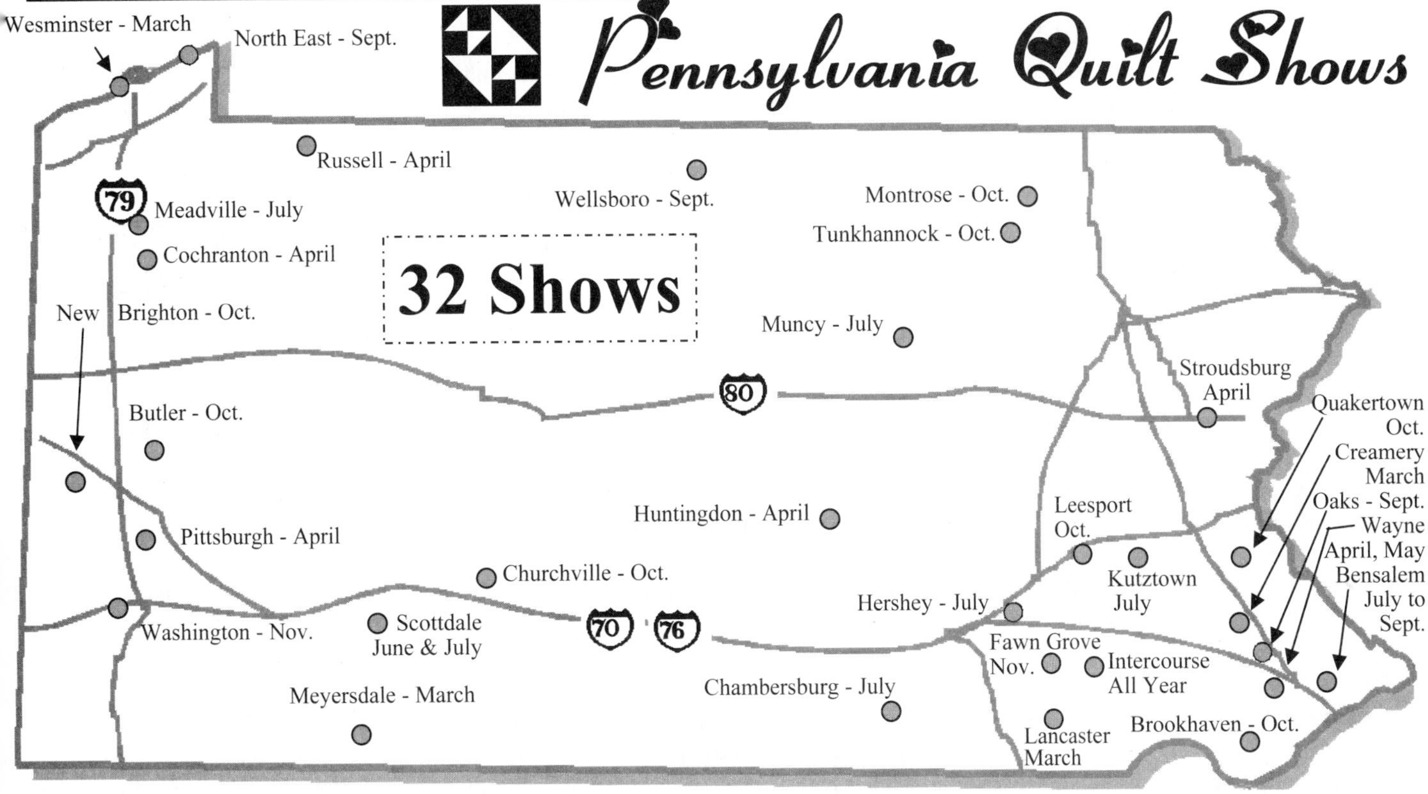

Month	City	Schedule	Show	Location with address
January				
	Intercourse	All Year	The People's Place Quilt Museum	Old Country Store--2nd Floor, 3510 Old Philadelphia Pike
March				
	Creamery	Annual, 2nd weekend in March	Homemaker's Country Quilters Show	Montgomery County 4-H Center
	Lancaster	Annual, last Wed. to Sun of March	Spring Quilt Blossom Festival	Continental Inn, 2285 Lincoln Hwy E
	Meyersdale	Annual, last two weekends of March	Pennsylvania Maple Festival Quilt Show	Meyersdale Fire Dept, Hall Main & Grant
	Wesminster	Odd years, 4th weekend in March	County Line Quilters Guild Show	Archbishop Wood High School, 655 York Rd.
April				
	Pittsburgh	Annual, 3rd weekend in April	Three Rivers Quilters Show	The Circuit Center, 5 Hot Metal St.
	Russell	Even Years, 3rd weekend in April	Quilting to the Beat	Russell Elementary School, Rte. 62
	Wayne	Annual April and May	Art Quilt Elements	Wayne Art Center, 413 Maplewood Ave.
	Stroudsburg	Odd Years, 4th Saturday in April	Pocono Mountain Quilters' Guild Show	Stroudsburg High School, 1100 W Main St
	Cochranton	Annual, Last weekend of April	Country Charm Quilt Show	Cochranton High School Gym, 105 2nd St.
	Huntingdon	Annual, Last weekend in April	Huntingdon Quilt Show	Huntingdon Community Center, 310 5th St
June				
	Scottdale	Annual, June & July	West Overton Museum Quilt Show	West Overton Museum Village
July				
	Kutztown	Annual, 1st week of July	Kutztown Festival	Kutztown Fairgrounds, 144 N. Whiteoak St.
	Bensalem	Annual, Mid-July to late September	Bucks County Quilt Show	Bucks County Visitors Center, 3207 Street Rd.
	Meadville	Annual, 2nd weekend of July	Red Door Quilters Show	Meadville Area Recreation Complex, 800 Thurston.
	Chambersburg	Odd Years, 3rd weekend in July	Chambersburg Quilt Guild Show	Falling Spring Presbyterian, 221 N. Main St.
	Muncy	Annual, 3rd week in July	Muncy Historical Society Quilt Show	Muncy High School Gym, 200 W. Penn St.
	Hershey	Annual, last weekend of July	Quilt Odyssey	Hershey Lodge & Convention Center, W. Chcolate Ave. & University
September				
	Oaks	Annual, 2nd weekend in September	Pennsylvania National Quilt Extravaganza	Greater Philadelphia Expo Center, 100 Station
	Wellsboro	Even Years, most of September	Mountain Laurel Quilt Guild Show	Gmeiner Art and Cultural Center, 134 Main St.
	North East	Odd Years, last weekend of September	North East Crazy Quilters Show	North East Elementary Center, Rt. 89 & 50 E
October				
	Butler	Odd Years, 1st weekend of October	Quilt ExplosionFamily	First Resource Center, 216 N. Washington St.
	Churchville	Odd Years, 1st weekend of October	Newtown Quilters' Guild Show	Maureen Welch Elementary School, 750 New Rd.
	Tunkhannock	Annual, first Saturday in October	Airing of the Quilts	Endless Mountains Quiltworks, 4 Towne Plaza
	Montrose	Odd Years, 2nd weekend in October	Quilts of the Endless Mountains	Several Locations, Downtown
	New Brighton	Annual, 2nd weekend in October	Beaver Valley Piecemakers	Brady's Run Lodge, Rt. 51, Constitution Blvd.
	Brookhaven	Even Years, 3rd weekend in October	Brandywine Valley Quilt Show	Brookhaven Municipal Bldg., 2 Cambridge Rd.
	Brookhaven	Odd Years, 3rd weekend in October	Undercover Quilters Show	Brookhaven Municipal Bldg. #2, Cambridge Rd.
	Leesport	Even Years, 3rd Fri & Sat in October	Berks Quilters Guild Quilt Show	Leesport Farmers Market, 312 Gernants Church Rd
	Quakertown	Annual, 2nd Fri & Sat in October	Keystone Quilters Quilt Show	Quakertown Christian School, 50 E. Paletown Rd.
November				
	Fawn Grove	Odd Years, 1st weekend of November	Fall Festival of Quilts	Fawn Grove Community Center, N. Market St. (Rt. 425)
	Washington	Odd Years, early November	Martha Washington Guild Show	Church of the Covenant, 267 E. Beau St. (Rt. 136)

HISTORY OF THE AMISH QUILT

The origin of the Amish quilt has a long and interesting history that can gives us a better understanding of the Amish people themselves. The Amish, as most people know, shun modern society in order to live a simpler life focused on god and family. As the fast-paced world carries on around them, the Amish choose to live quietly and peacefully off the land with little to no help from the outside world. What this means is no electricity, no phones, no automobiles, and as little contact with the world that goes on around them as possible. Anything to do with the outside world is shunned by the Amish, including art.

Art, for the sake of art, is looked down upon by the Amish people because it serves no real purpose. However, the art of Amish quilting was able to develop within the Amish community because the quilt itself served a purpose, so adding decorative elements to it was considered acceptable. The art of Amish quilting, however, didn't become a tradition in Amish homes until the late 1800s. Originally brought to America by British Quakers, the idea of quilting did not catch on quickly within the Amish communities. At the time, the Amish used simple coverings for their beds, much like their neighboring Mennonites and Pennsylvania Germans. While quilting caught on with these other groups, the Amish originally rejected the idea of quilting for art and didn't take on the practice until it was no longer considered fashionable by the local Mennonites and Germans.

Once the Amish did beginning quilting, they slowly began to make it their own with Amish inspired patterns that were unique and simple, yet beautiful. Between 1850 and 1870, the Amish of Pennsylvania began developing their signature quilt designs from simple one color whole cloth quilts to piecing together colored pieces of cloth into a variety of patterns. The earliest Amish designs were basic squares and rectangles, which slowly evolved into more colorful and bold patterns, such as Amish style baskets, flowers, and grapevines. These patterns began to develop slowly over time, first showing up in just the corners and the borders and eventually working their way to the centers and focal points of the Amish quilts. You can easily tell how old an Amish quilt is simply by how prominent the designs are within it. The less the embellishments, the older the Amish quilt.

Many of the Amish quilters of the time worked on their quilts alone during the cold winter months, but then got together with the other Amish quilters of the town to form Quilting Bees in the spring and summer months. These quilting gatherings gave the Amish women the opportunity to catch up on all the town news while finishing the assembly of their specially designed Amish quilts. Initially Amish quilts were crafted for dowry purposes or to be presented to important people as gifts. Eventually the Amish began selling their Amish quilts for profit.

Around the 1970s, the beauty of the Amish quilt became a must-have item for fashionable, young city folk. Amish quilts were suddenly being appreciated as works of art due to their similarities to the "pop art" styles of the time. This created an interesting problem for the Amish people due to their intense desire for separation from the modern world. As more people wanted to own one of the handmade Amish works of art, the Amish would often find that their own Amish quilts were being stolen right off their own clothes lines.

As a result, the Amish began making their quilts for the purpose of selling them at the local markets. While they greatly enjoy their privacy and solitude, the Amish people seemed to find a nice balance between their desire to live a separate and simpler life, yet still benefit through commerce by selling their handmade Amish wares to the modern buyers who desired their work. This balance between simplicity and consumerism has changed Amish quilt making in a variety of ways. In order to attract the eye of a visiting outside, the Amish women began departing from the traditional Amish quilt patterns for more updated colors and styles. Brighter colors, unique patterns, and more elaborate techniques have developed in the Amish quilting world in an effort to attract more customers by offering more updated styles.

The attraction to these beautiful Amish quilts has always been rooted in the desire to look back at our history and to appreciate all the handmade and traditional things of the past. While the Amish quilt makers retain their relative solitary existence, they have greatly impacted the way the world views quilt making. So too, in a subtle way, has the world impacted the way the Amish make their quilts. The current trends and fashions from around the world have impacted the different Amish styles and patterns that the Amish quilter makes. While the old Amish traditions of hand sewing and creating each piece still remain the cornerstone of the Amish quilt, its partnership with the world as a whole has somehow made the relationships between the Amish and the modern communities closer rather than farther apart.

While the simplicity, variety, colors, and designs may have changed over the past hundred of so years, the basic workmanship and subtleness of the Amish quilt still remains the same today. Amish quilts are so rich and full of life, yet have a history and sentimentality to them that makes you want to treasure one for years to come and eventually pass it on to a loved one near and dear to your heart. An Amish quilt is the essence of what it means to be an American today.
It expresses the hard work and determination that all Americans, Amish and non-Amish alike, have shown throughout history.

article from www.theamishquilt.com
parent website: www.amishquilter.com

3 Featured Shops

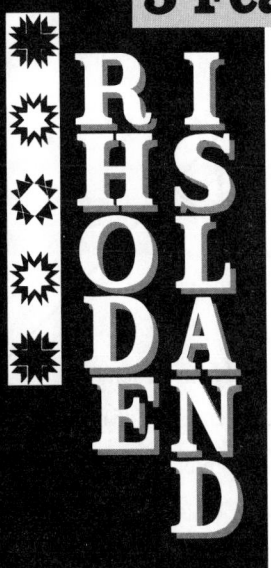

RHODE ISLAND

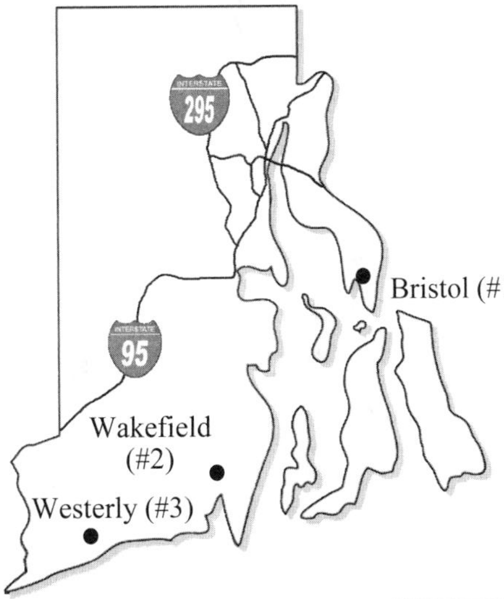

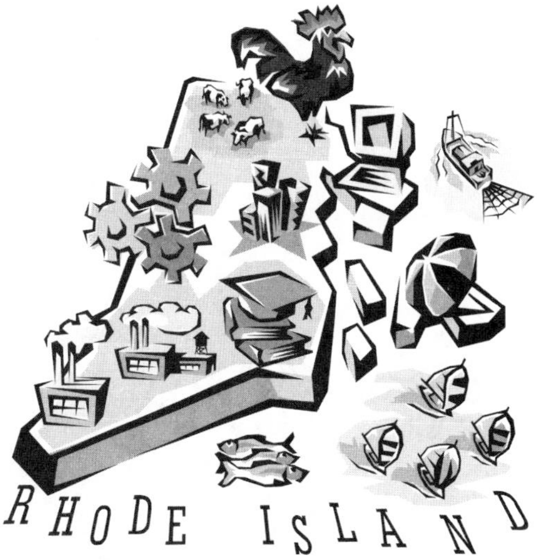

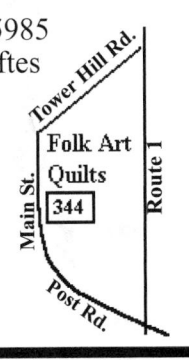

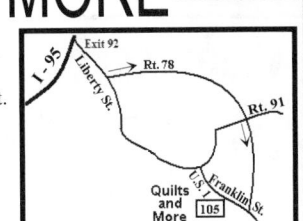

Rhode Island Quilt Shops

Barrington	Barrington Fabrics, 232 Waseca	401-245-9235
Bristol	**Just Quilts, 201 Gooding Ave**	
	401-254-1240 See ad #1, this page	
Exeter	The Sewing Room, 567 S. County Trail, Ste. 207	401-295-0083
Lincoln	Ryco's Creative Trim Center, 25 Carrington St.	401-725-1779
Pawtucket	Lorraine Fabrics, 593 Mineral Spring	401-722-9500
Wakefield	**Folk Art Quilts, 344 Main St.**	
	401-789-5985 See ad #2, this page	
Warwick	Jan Banan Co., 212 Pine St.	401-467-7978
Westerly	**Quilts And More, 105 Franklin St.**	
	401-637-4199 See ad #3, this page	

3 Shows

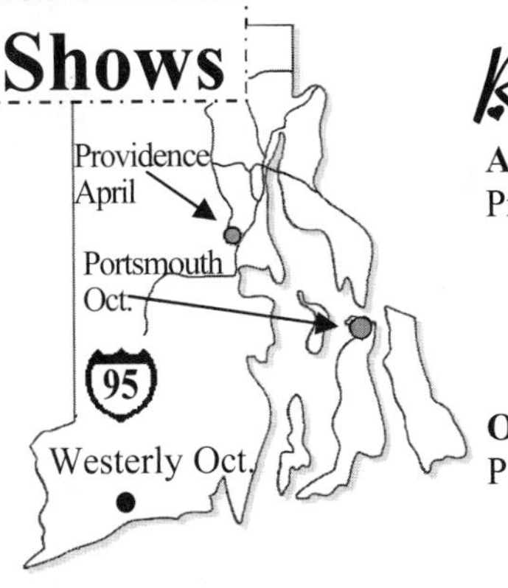

Rhode Island Shows

April
Providence
Annual, 2nd week in April
Machine Quilters Exposition
Rhode Island Convention Center
1 Sabin St.

October
Portsmouth
Even Years, 3rd weekend in Oct.
Quilters by the Sea Show
Portsmouth Middle School, Jepson Ln.

Westerly Odd Years, 4th weekend in October
Ninigret Quilters Quilt Show
Westerly Armory, 8 Dixon St.

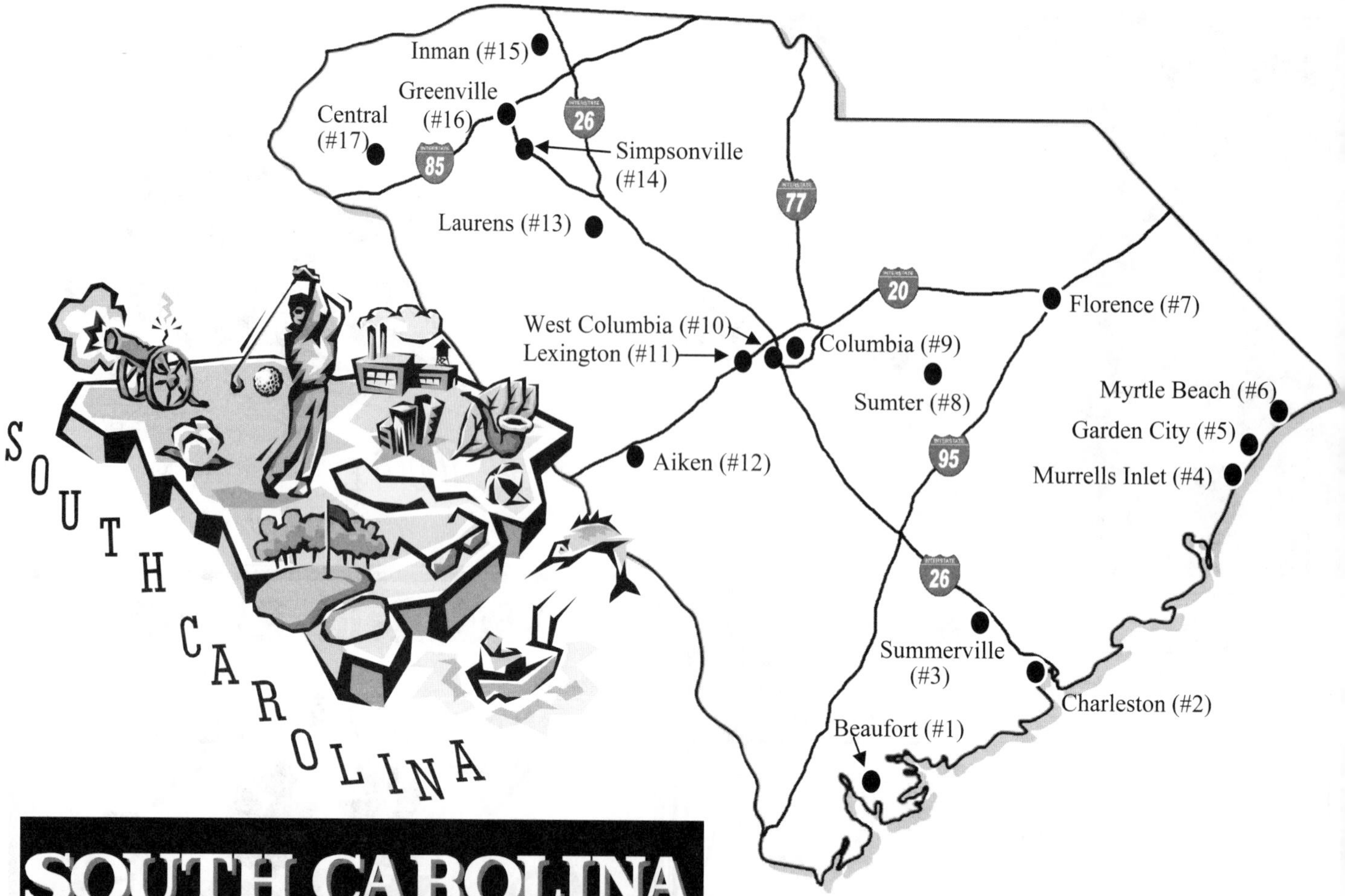

SOUTH CAROLINA

17 Featured Shops

Creative Stitches

60 B Robert Smalls Pkwy. Beaufort, SC 29906
843-524-1892 Fax: (843) 770-9922
www.creativestitchesbft.com
cstitches@hargray.com
Est: 2000 1500 sq.ft. 2000 bolts

Mon - Sat 10 - 5

Beaufort, SC #1

High Quality Fabrics from Top Companies. Notions, Books & Patterns. Friendly, helpful service with a Smile!!

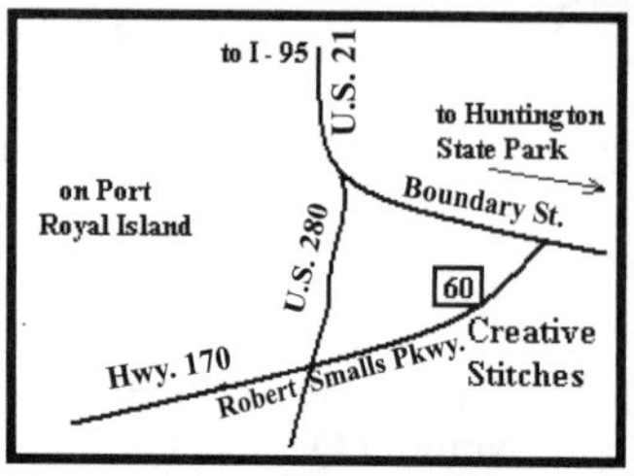

Charleston, SC #2

People, Places, & Quilts

Mon - Fri 10 - 5:30
Sat 10 - 5

1 Henrietta St. 29403
(843) 937-9333
Owner: Diane Frankenberger
email@ppquilts.com Free Newsletter
www.ppquilts.com

Located in historic downtown Charleston in an old Grocery Store, PPQ is a full service quilt/sewing shop with books, patterns, notions, and fabrics ranging from 1800's reproductions to Kaffee Fassett!

1 block off Marion Square within walking distance of the Museum, Visitors Center and Aquarium

Summerville, SC #3

People, Places, & Quilts

Mon - Fri 10 - 5:30
Sat 10 - 5
3rd Thur til 8

129 West Richardson Ave. 29483
In Cauthen's old Hardware Store
(843) 871-8872 Owner: Diane Frankenberger
email@ppquilts.com Free Newsletter
www.ppquilts.com Est: 1990

A full service quilt shop located in historic downtown Summerville, PPQ is a full service quilt/sewing shop with books, patterns, notions, Janome Sewing Machines, and fabrics ranging from 1800's to Amy Butler!

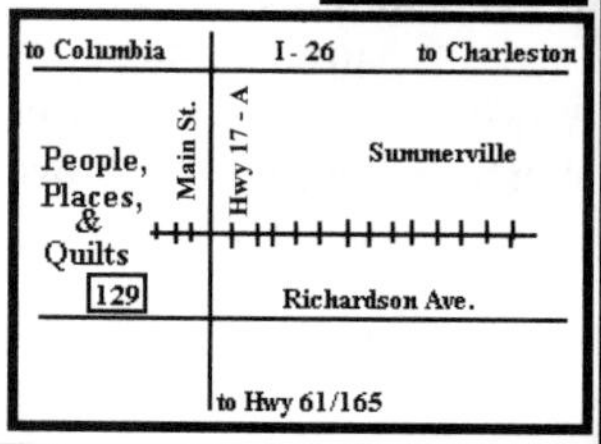

Murrells Inlet, SC #4

Mon - Sat 10 - 5

4410 Hwy. 17 Bypass S.
Unit B7 29576
(843) 357-3228
Est: 2003
4000 sq.ft.
Free Newsletter

WE LOVE TO SEW!

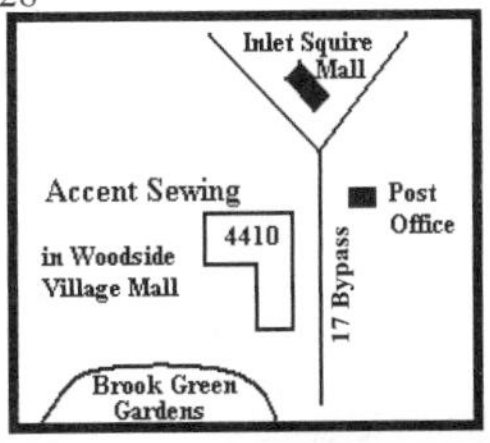

accentsewing@aol.com
www.AccentSewing.com
Bernina/Babylock/Handi-Quilter Authorized Dealer, Servicing all brands. Quilting & Garment Fabrics, All your Embroidery Supplies. Notions, Books, Zippers, Buttons etc. Lots of Fun classes!

Myrtle Beach, SC #6

Mon - Sat 9:30 - 5

Sewin' in the Carolinas

3246 Waccamaw Blvd. 29579
(843) 236-8901
www.quiltinginthecarolinas.com
"A Quilt Shop with all the Fixins"
Sales & Service - Fabric, Patterns, Notions Classes, Sewing Machines, Embroidery Machines, Embroidery Software.
Authorized Janome & Singer Dealer.
Friendly Staff to Assist You. Over 3500 bolts.

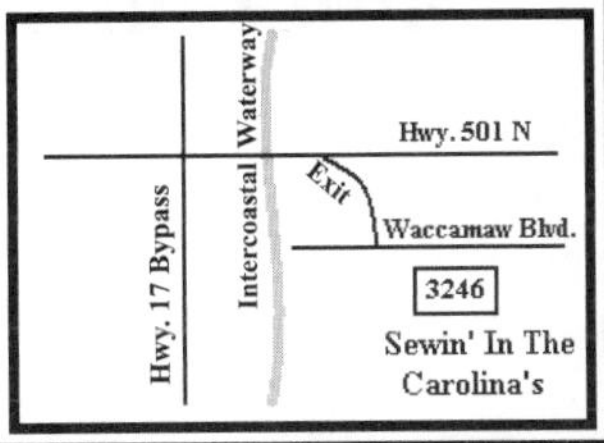

Florence, SC #7

Tues - Fri 10 - 5:30
Sat 10 - 3
Mon by Appt.

Sew Unique Quilt Shop
So Uniquely More...

Huntington Plaza
804-H Second Loop Rd. 29505
(843) 629-9633
sewunique4u@bellsouth.net
www.sewuniquequiltsandmore.com

Quilt Quality Fabrics, Smocking fabrics, Notions, Patterns and Classes.

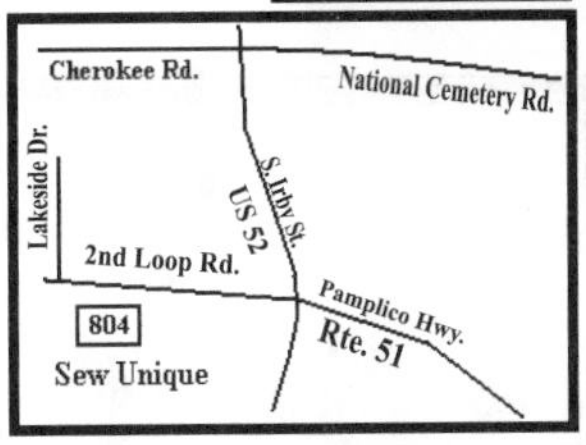

Quilters Cottage

St. Michaels Plaza
2571 Ocean Hwy. - Business 17
Garden City, SC 29576
Shop: 843-651-4004 Fax: 843-651-4033
qcottage@sccoast.net
Pat & Rhett Roman - Experienced Owners

Mon - Fri 10 - 5
Sat 10 - 4

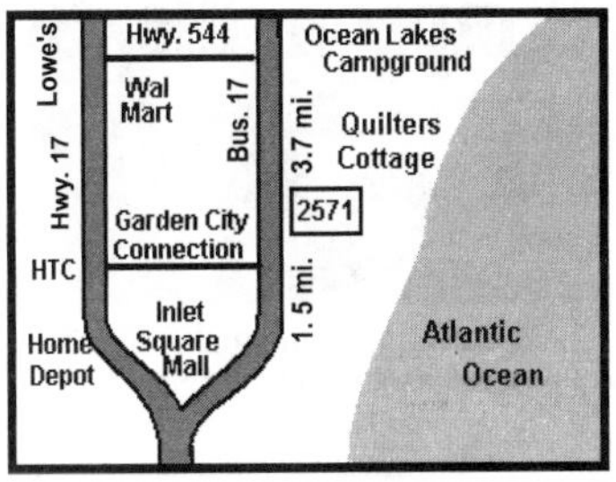

* 100% Cotton Fabrics & Batiks
* Books & Patterns
* Notions & Threads
* Classes
* Newsletter
* Mail Orders
* Long Arm Quilting
* Custom Embroidery

Specializing In

* Customer Service
* Friendly Atmosphere
* Quilting Knowledge
* Experienced Staff

(All which helps to)
Bring Ideas To Reality

Garden City, SC #5

Sumter, SC #8

Mon, Wed Fri 10 - 6
Tues & Thur 10 - 9
Sun 1:30 - 6

My Favorite Things, LLC
A Quilter's Studio

12 W. Liberty St., Suite I 29150
(803) 883-4887 Fax: Same
Est: 2009 myfavoritethingsllc@sc.rr.com
www.myfavoritethingsllc.com

Sumter's only Full Service Quilt Studio. All levels of classes, over 1000 bolts of cotton Fabric, Books, Notions & Supplies.
"We further the art of Quilting one laugh at a time."

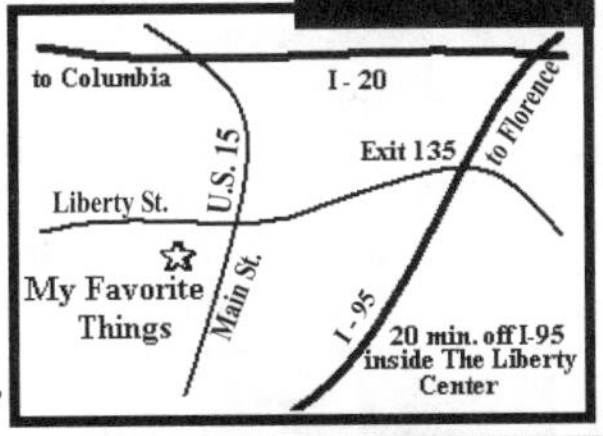

Columbia, SC #9

Mon - Sat 10 - 5
Tues til 8

The Quilted Pearl

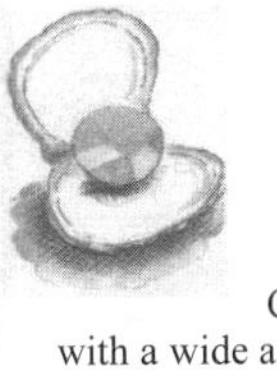

224 O'Neil Ct. #19 29223
(803) 462-6075
Est: 2005 3000 sq.ft.
3000 Bolts
quiltedpearl@sc.rr.com
www.quiltedpearl.com
Columbia's BEST quilt shop, with a wide assortment of fabrics, books & notions. Full spectrum lighting.

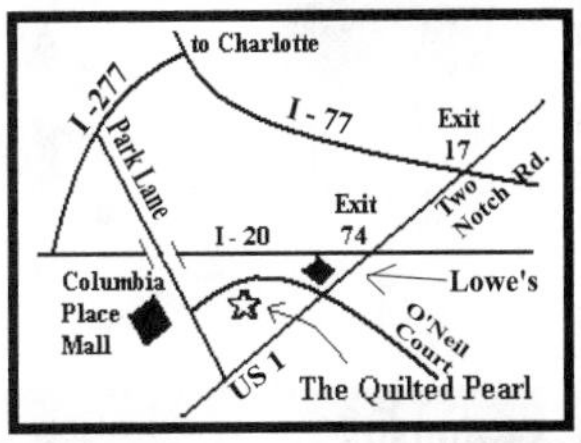

West Columbia, SC #10

Mon - Fri 9 - 6
Sat 9 - 3

Creative Sewing Machine Center

519 12th St. 29169
(803) 936-1251 Fax: (803) 936-1973
sewcreate@sc.rr.com
www.creative-sewing-machine-center.com
Est: 2001 12,000 sq.ft.
100% Cottons, Notions, Patterns, Books, Samples, Classes. 4 brands of machines, a welcoming place to get inspired.
Let's GET CREATIVE!

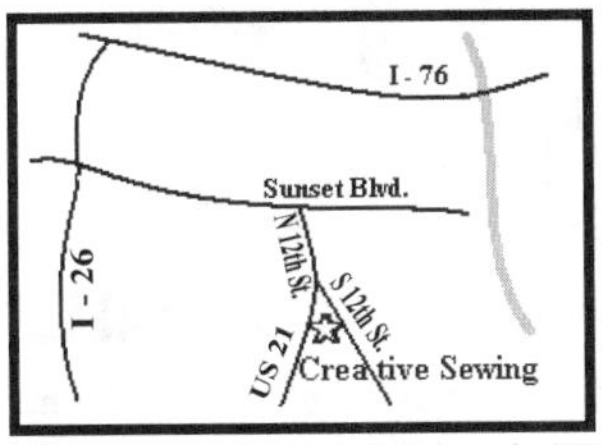

Lexington, SC #11

Tues - Fri 10 - 6
Sat 10 - 4

Pieces & Patches

711 E. Main St. #H 29072
(803) 359-3442
Owner: Audrey Liddle
Est: 2004 Newsletter
aliddle@sc.rr.com
www.piecesandpatchessc.com
A wide variety of fabrics and notions to use in sewing arts. We are known for friendly, caring services. Quilting and other fiber arts classes.

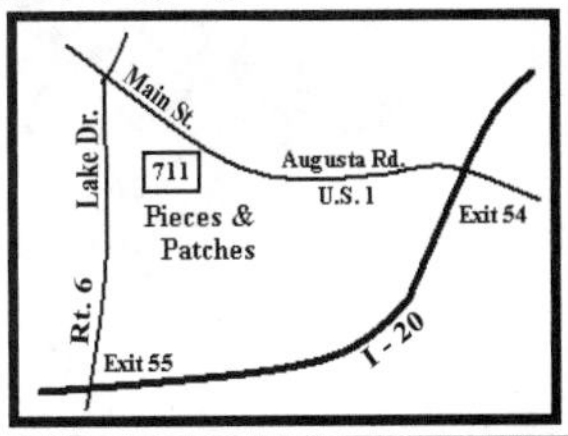

Aiken, SC #12

Mon - Fri 10 - 5
Sat 10 - 4

Aiken Quilt Shoppe

146 Laurens St. SW 29801
(803) 649-7511
Owners: Nancy & Joe Clifton
Est: 2006 2200 sq.ft.
www.aikenquiltshoppe.com
Located in historic and charming downtown Aiken, featuring quality fabrics, patterns & notions, exciting class schedule, rental time on our APQS Lenni Long arm machine so you can complete your own quilts. Friendly customer service.

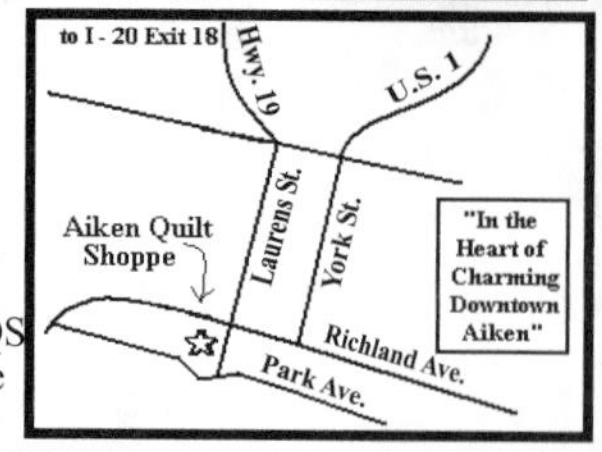

Laurens, SC #13

Tues - Fri 10 - 5:30
Sat 10 - 2

Stitches

115 E. Laurens St. 29360
(864) 681-1567
stitchesinc@prtcnet.com
www.stitchesinc.net Est: 2005
Located on the Historic Downtown Laurens Square. We have fabric, books, quilting supplies, and gift items. Long arm quilting services and custom made quilts available.

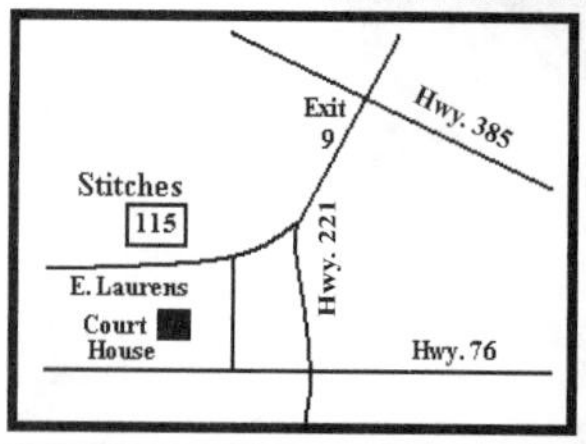

Simpsonville, SC #14

Mon - Fri 9:30 - 6
Sat 9:30 - 3

Marietta's Quilt & Sew

1004 W. Georgia Rd. #C1
29680
(864) 962-5353

Owner: Marietta Louk Est: 2009
1500 sq.ft. Online Newsletter
molson1390@aol.com
www.mariettasquiltandsew.com
BabyLock Dealer, Quilting Fabrics, Notions, Patterns, Classes, Sewing Machine Repairs (all makes), Custom Embroidery and Very Friendly Service.

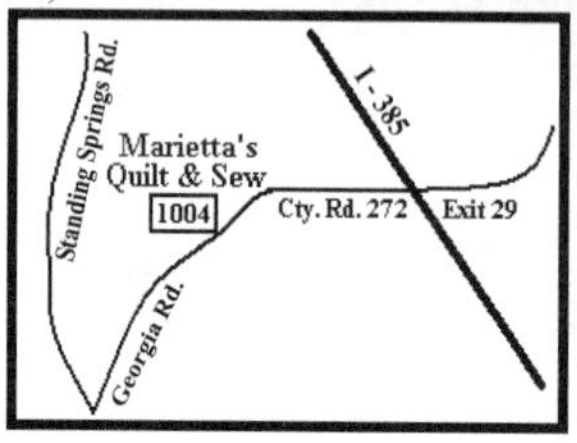

Inman, SC #15

Mon - Fri 10 - 5
Sat 10 - 4

Inman Quilt Cottage

25 S. Main St. 29349
(864) 472-0888
Owners: Becky Putnam & Jody Raines
www.inmanquiltcottage.com
inmanquiltcottage@windstream.net
Fabric, Notions, Classes, Antiques
HandiQuilter Representative

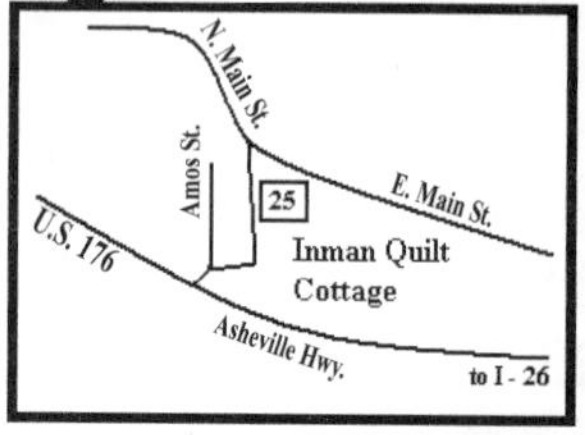

Viking Sew 'n Quilt

Offering the best of Quilting Supplies and Sewing Machines--Instruction by the best teachers

A Guild membership discount of 10% on the purchase of regular priced items applies.

Mon-Fri 10 - 5:45
Sat. 10 - 4

Greenville, SC #16

1266 Woodruff Road Behind Zaxby's
(864) 286-9507 www.vikingsewnquilt.com
vikingsewnquilt@aol.com

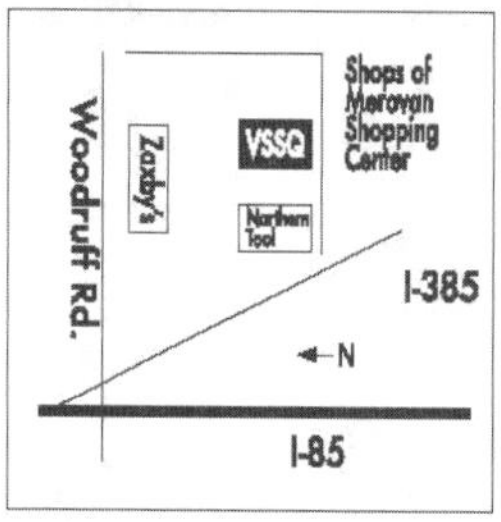

Husqvarna VIKING

Heirlooms & Comforts

104 Madden Bridge Road
Downtown Central
(864) 639-9507
www.heirloomsandcomforts.net

Celebrating 25 Years

Husqvarna VIKING

Upstate's most complete quilt shop. 2,000 sq. ft. of Fabrics, Books, Patterns, Notions, Classes, Sergers, Sewing and Embroidery Machines.
Authorized Husqvarna Viking® Dealer

Established in 1984 The Oldest Quilt Shop in South Carolina

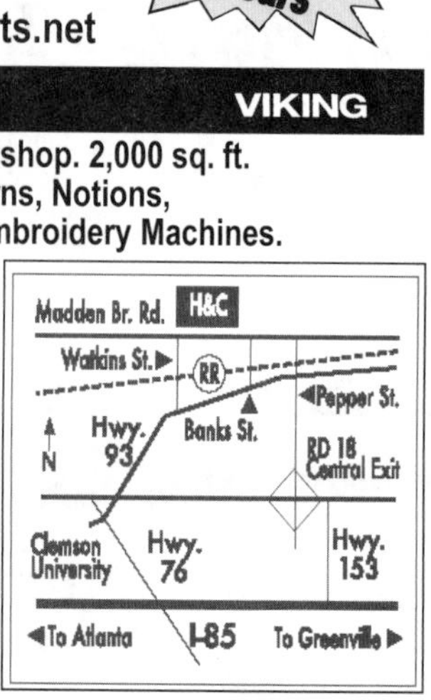

Monday - Friday 10:00 - 5 :00
Saturday 10:00 - 3:00

Central, SC #17

South Carolina Quilt Shops

Aiken	Aiken Quilt Shoppe, 146 Laurens St. SW	803-649-7511	See ad #12, page 494
Beaufort	Creative Stitches, 60B Robert Smalls Pkwy	843-524-1892	See ad #1, page 492
Central	Heirlooms & Comforts, 104 Madden Bridge	864-639-9507	See ad #17, page 494 & 406
Charleston	People, Places & Quilts, 1 Henrietta St.	843-937-9333	See ad #2, page 492
Charleston	Margiotta's Sewing Machine, 874 Orleans	843-763-7397	
Columbia	The Quilted Pearl, 224 O'Neil Court; #19	803-462-6075	See ad #9, page 493
Conway	Sew Many Common Threads, 2290 Hwy. 544	843-347-6000	
Florence	Sew Unique, 804-H Second Loop Rd.	843-629-9633	See ad #7, page 493
Garden City	Quilters' Cottage, 2571 Ocean Hwy, Bus. 17	843-651-4004	See ad #5, page 493
Greenville	Viking Sew N Quilt, 1266 Woodruff Rd.	864-286-9507	See ad #16, page 494
Hilton Head Island	Cross Stitch Junction, 33 Office Park Rd.	843-842-8878	
Inman	Inman Quilt Cottage, 25 S. Main St.	864-472-0888	See ad #15, page 494
Laurens	Stitches, 115 E. Laurens St.	864-681-1567	See ad #13, page 494
Lexington	Pieces & Patches, 711 E. Main St. #H	866-432-3424	See ad #11, page 493
Murrells Inlet	Accent Sewing, 4410 Hwy. 17 Bypass South	843-357-3228	See ad #4, page 493
Myrtle Beach	Sewin In The Carolinas, 3246 Waccamaw	843-236-8901	See ad #6, page 493
Rock Hill	Uncommon Thread, 2342 C Ebenezer Rd.	877-294-5427	
Simpsonville	Mariettas Quilt & Sew, 1004 W Georgia Rd.	864-962-5353	See ad #14, page 494
Summerton	Sparkleberry Stitchery, 4 Burgess St.	803-410-0696	
Summerville	People, Places & Quilts, 129 W. Richardson	843-871-8872	See ad #3, page 492
Summerville	Sew'n Sew, 1106 N. Main St.	843-871-7822	
Sumter	My Favorite Things, 12 West Liberty St.	803-883-4887	See ad #8, page 493
Walterboro	Calico Patches, 244 E. Washington	843-782-4267	
West Columbia	Creative Sewing Machine Center, 519 12th St.	803-936-1251	See ad #10, page 493

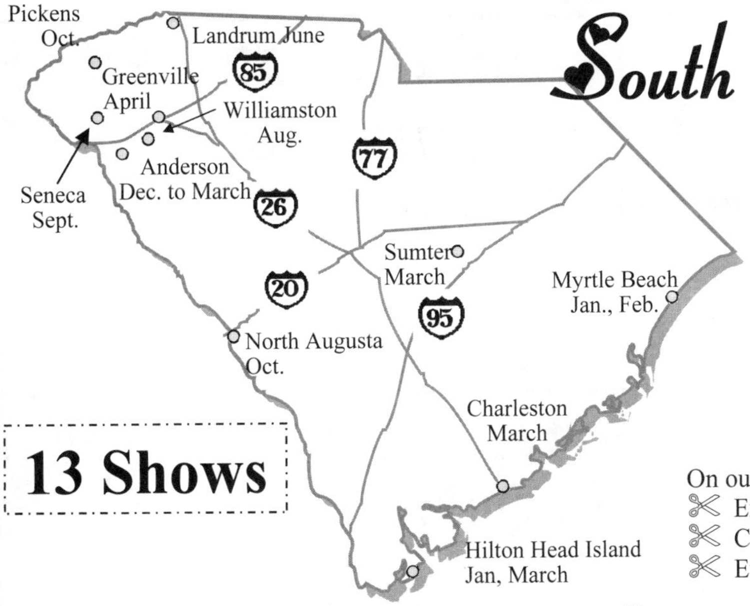

13 Shows

South Carolina Quilt Show

About Shows: We are listing only the very basic information about shows that happen on a regular schedule here. Please check out our website for more details on each show. Also this information tends to change quite often so please verify the event with our website or a local source before you venture far. Or if you're in the right area at the right time, give it a shot.

If you are a show organizer, please keep us updated on your event.
shows@quilterstravelcompanion.com
www.quilterstravelcompanion.com

On our website you will also find:
- Exact dates (when we have them)
- Contact Information
- Events happening on a one-time basis
- Sponsor Information
- Description of Event

Month	City	Schedule	Show	Location with address
January				
	Myrtle Beach	Annual, 3rd weekend in January	Myrtle Beach Quilt Party Vendor Extravaganza	Myrtle Beach Convention Center, 2101 N. Oak
	Hilton Head Island	Annual, Late January or Early February	Jinny Beyer Quilting Seminar	Marriott Beach & Golf Resort, Palmetto Dunes Plantation
February				
	Myrtle Beach	Annual, Last weekend of February	Horry County Museum Quilt Show	Ocean Lakes Family Campground, 6001 S. Kings Hwy.
March				
	Charleston	Even Years, 1st weekend of March	A Celebration of Quilts	Gaillard Auditorium, 77 Calhoun St.
	Sumter	Odd Years, 3rd weekend in March	Swan Lake Quilt Guild Show	Patriot Hall, 135 Haynesworth St.
	Hilton Head Island	Even Years, 4th weekend of March	Palmetto Quilt Guild Show	St. Andrew by the Sea United Methodist, 20 Pope Ave.
April				
	Greenville	Even Years, 3rd weekend of April	Foothills Piecemakers Quilting Guild Show	Morningside Baptist Church, 1115 Pelham .
June				
	Landrum	Odd Years, 2nd weekend in June	Landrum Quilters Quilt Show	Landrum Middle School Gymnasium, 104 Redland Rd.
August				
	Williamston	Even Years, last weekend in August	Anderson Area Quilt Show	First Baptist Church, Main St.
September				
	Seneca	Even Years, 3rd weekend in September	Lake and Mountain Quilters Guild Show	Shaver Center
October				
	North Augusta	Odd Years, October	Pieceful Hearts Quilters Quilt Show	N Augusta Activities Ctr,, 100 Riverview Park
	Pickens	Odd Years, October	Up Country Quilters Quilt Show	First Baptist Church, 406 E. Main St.
December				
	Anderson	Even Dec. to Odd March	Prickly Fingers Quilt Exhibit	Anderson County Museum, 202 E. Greenville St.

19 Featured Shops

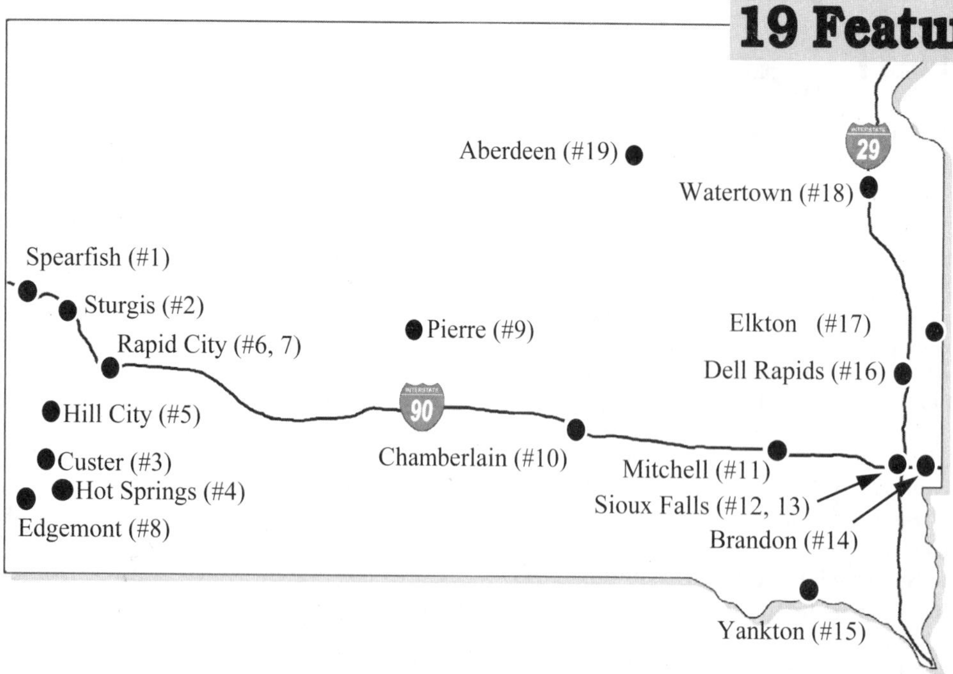

SOUTH DAKOTA

Sturgis, SD #2

Mon - Fri 10 - 5:30
Sat 10 - 1

Fabric Junction

1609 Junction 57785
(605) 347-2235 tlkoontz@rushmore.com
www.junctionfabric.com
Est: 1998 1280 sq.ft.

Home of the Junction Stripper. Check us out at the shop or online for fun and discounts.

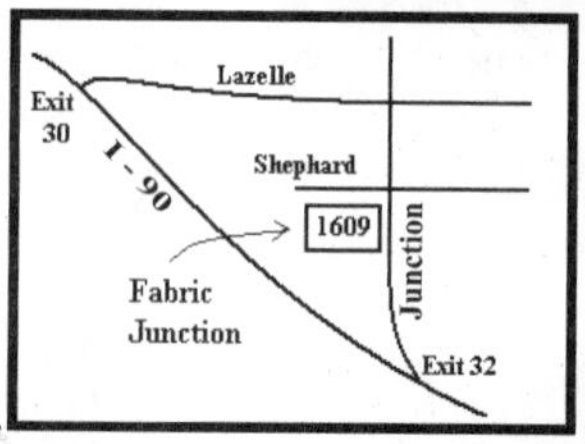

Spearfish, SD #1

Dakota Quilt Company

1004 Main St.
Spearfish, SD
57783
(605) 642-2939
or (877) 642-2939

Store Hours:
Tues - Sat 9 - 5
Closed Sun & Mon

Owner: Kim Ellis
Est: 1998 2500 sq.ft.
dakotaquilt@rushmore.com

...where hearts and hands come together to create lifetime friendships and heirlooms.

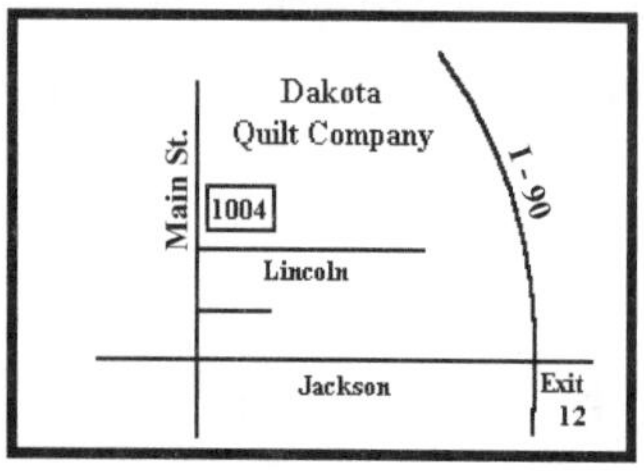

Featuring quilting fabrics, patterns, books, kits, classes and long arm machine quilting.

www.dakotaquiltcompany.com

Custer, SD #3

Mon - Sat 9 - 5

The Quilt Shop

325 Mt. Rushmore Rd. 57730
(605) 673-3606

Quilting fabric and supplies.
Next to the Dairy Queen.

Hot Springs, SD #4

Mon - Sat 10 - 6

HeartSong Quilts

345 N. River St. 57747
(605) 745-5330
Owners: Ann & Brian Powers
Est: 2008 2000 sq.ft. 1000 bolts
brian@heartsongquilts.com
www.heartsongquilts.com
Dazzling and Unique! HeartSong offers the latest bold and beautiful fabrics, books, patterns as well as traditional quilters' favorites.

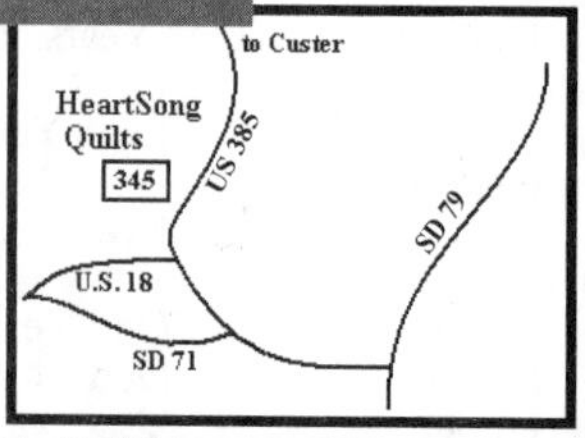

QUILT CORRAL

IS NOW BACK AT

Mistletoe Ranch

The Ultimate Christmas & Gift Store

605-574-4197
Email: info@mistletoeranch.com
www.mistletoeranch.com

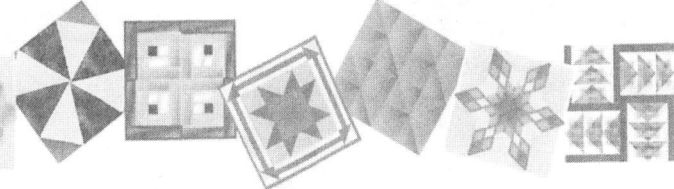

**Thousands of bolts of gorgeous fabrics.
The latest books and patterns from
the most innovative designers!**

**23835 Hwy 385
Hill City, SD 57745**

**WE ARE IN THE BUSINESS OF
SELLING FUN FABULOUS FABRIC
TO MAKE ALL YOUR QUILTING
DREAMS BECOME A REALITY!**

Home of Gutzy Geisha Designs™

*Unique patterns that utilize large scale prints, simply layered
and cut to create exquisite kaleidoscoping blocks...*

- *Books*
- *Patterns*
- *Notions*
- *Ideas*
- *Personal Service*

Email: quiltcorraltoo@ll.net
www.quiltcorral.com
605-574-9044

#5

Rapid City, SD #6

Welcome to the region's premiere quilting store. We invite you in for shopping, coffee and a friendly chat.

- **South Dakota Original Patterns**
- **Weekly Quilting Classes**
- **South Dakota Quilters Wall**
- **Authorized Husqvarna Viking Dealer**
- **Email: quilting@quiltconnectionsd.com**

Better Homes and Gardens Quilt Sampler FEATURED SHOP

Directions: From I-90 take exit 58 south. We're on the left, at the corner of Haines Ave and Lindbergh.

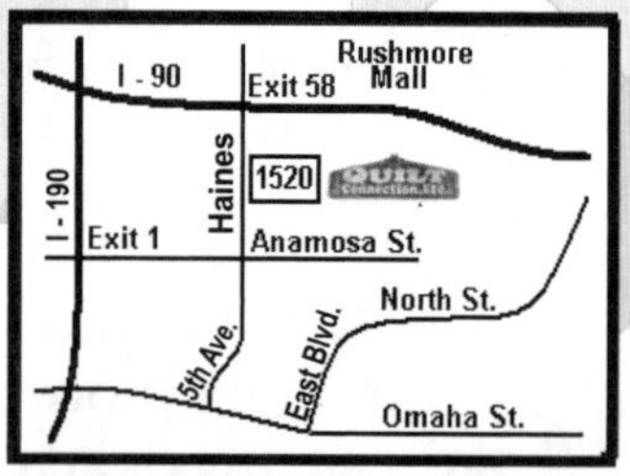

QUILT Connection, Etc.

1520 Haines Ave. #1 • Rapid City
605-355-0178

Husqvarna VIKING

When Visiting the Black Hills Come Visit Us!
We are Located 25 Miles from Mt. Rushmore

Thimble Cottage

Quilt Village

Home of Pearl Louise Designs

902 Mt. Rushmore Rd. Rapid City 57701
(605) 341-6569 www.thimblecottage.com

Mon. - Fri. 9:00 - 5:00
Saturday 10:00 - 4:00

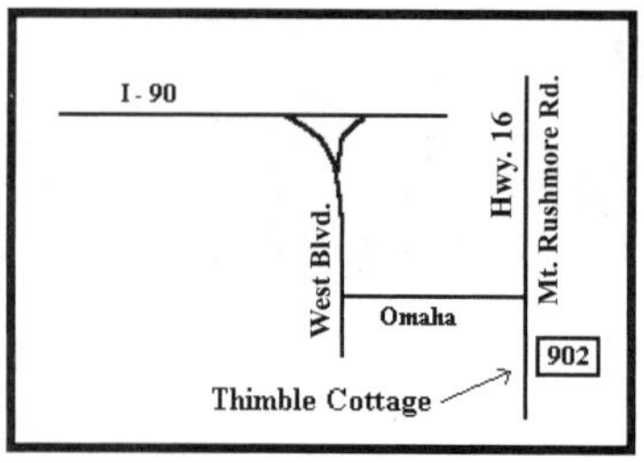

Rapid City, SD #7

Imagine yourself entering a quilt shop that looks like a group of buildings from Dickens Village. This wonderful shop is filled with the fresh aroma of newly baked cookies, assorted sweet embroidered Stitcheries and cutie pie Block of the Month Quilts. Imagine antique wardrobes, beds and cupboards overflowing with fabrics of every color. Imagine a wide assortment of easy to follow patterns and books at your fingertips. Fill your dreams here at The Thimble Cottage Quilt Village,

"Your Inspiration Destination".

Join our online club for tips. Our very own "Pearls of Wisdom".

NUTS AND BOLTS FABRICS

We're NUTS about our BOLTS!

Fabric, Books, Notions, Patterns, & Classes. Specializing in Blenders, Florals & Western Prints. Patchabilities patterns & kits. Watkins, South Dakota & Nebraska Popcorn Balls & Gift items. Home of the Porch Rabbit, makers of hoods featuring Malden Mills Polar System Fleece. We offer vintage sewing machines & repair, Long arm Quilting & Quilt Repairs. Small town charm & service.

Winter
Tues - Fri 10 - 5
Sat 9 - 2
Summer
Mon - Fri 10 - 5
Sat 9 - 2

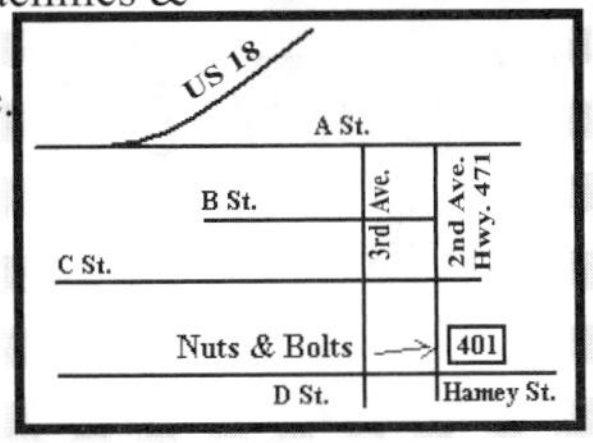

401 2nd Ave., P.O. Box 5 57735
(605) 662-5758
After Hrs # (605) 890-2300
Owners: Jerry & Earleene Kellogg
www.nutsandboltsfabric.com

Est: 2005 **Edgemont, SD #8** 2000 sq.ft.

Pierre, SD #9

Mon - Fri 9:30 - 5
Sat 9:30 - 4

Quilt Yard

209 W. Dakota, Suite 101 57501
(605) 945-1195
Owner: Nancy Galinat

100% Cotton, Books and Patterns. Classes.
Moda, RJR, Benartex, SSI, P&B.

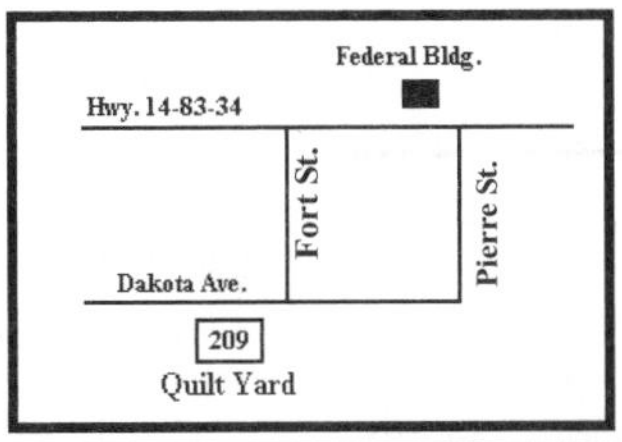

Chamberlain, SD #10

Mon - Sat 9 - 5

The Quilt Shop

315 N. Main 57325
(605) 234-5739 Sonya & Linda
thequiltshopsd@yahoo.com
www.southdakotaquiltshop.com

Quilting fabric and custom made quilts, APQS dealer and longarm quilting.

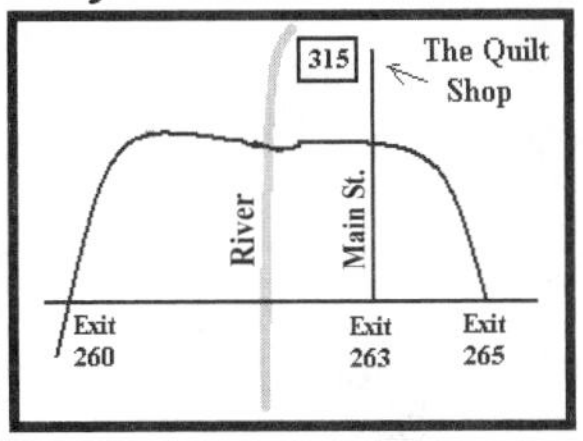

Mitchell, SD #11

Mon - Sat 9 - 5:30

The Pin Cushion

320 North Main Street
(605) 996-0947 Fax: (605) 996-0017
Owner: Carma Popp
Est: 1987 2000 sq.ft.
www.thepincushionquiltshop.com

100% Cottons, Books, and Patterns. Classes. Friendly, helpful staff. Authorized Pfaff Dealer

PFAFF

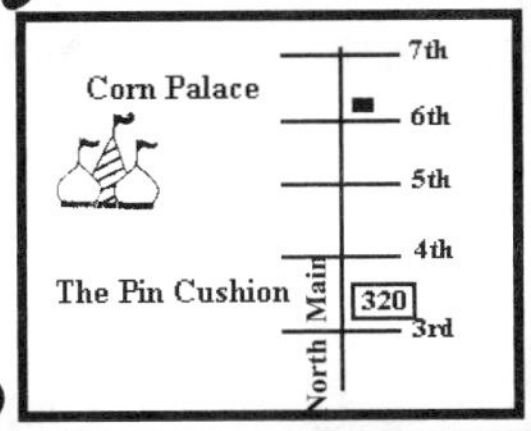

Sioux Falls, SD #13

Mon - Fri 9:30-6
Sat 9:30-4

Heirloom Creations

Where Creative People Come to Shop!

3800 S Western Ave. 57105
(605) 332-4435 4000 sq.ft.
info@heirloomcreations.net 4000 Bolts
www.heirloomcreations.net
Bernina, Janome, Husqvarna Viking, & Singer Authorized Dealer Threads, decorative zippers, huge book selection. Print off our current newsletter for all the newest products and daily classes.

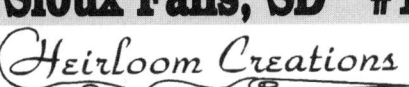

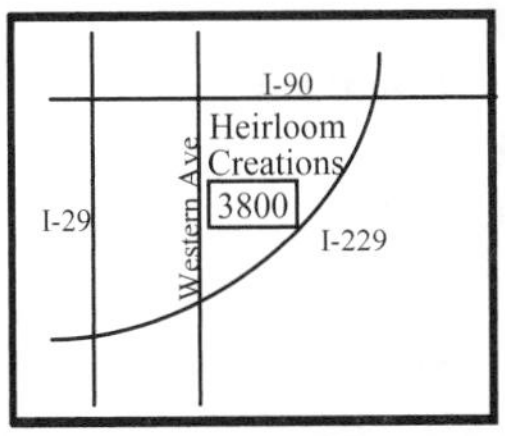

The Dutch Rose Quilt Shop

5107 W. 41st St.
Sioux Falls, SD 57106
(605) 362-1650

A full service quilt shop with a great selection of cottons, flannels, batiks, patterns, notions and kits.

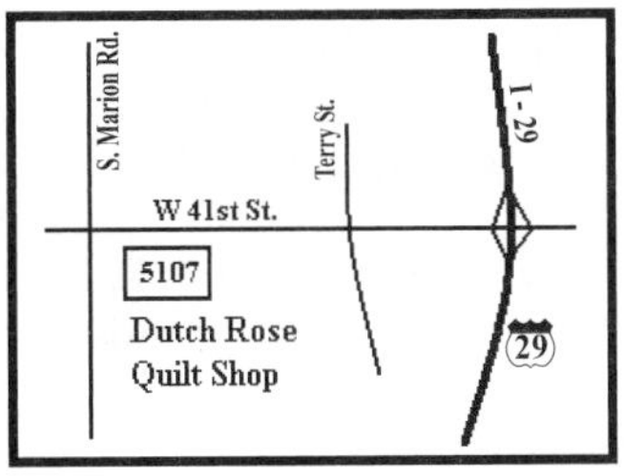

Mon - Fri 9:30 - 6
Sat 9:30 - 5 Sun Noon - 4

Located 3 Blocks West of I-29 on 41st St.
dutchrosequiltshop@gmail.com
2000 sq. ft. 3200 bolts

Sioux Falls, SD #12

Brandon, SD #14

Mon - Fri 9:30 - 5
Sat 9:30 - 3

Quilted Memories

723 N. Splitrock Blvd. 57005
(605) 582-7411 Est: 1997
Owner: Jeff & Twyla Voldseth
www.quiltedmem.com 3000+ Bolts
Great 100% cotton fabrics, patterns & books. We feature Jo Morton fabrics & Civil War reproductions.
Hand embroidery, and patterns. Homespuns, flannels, block of the month, kits & lots of samples for embroidery and quilting including reproduction quilts.

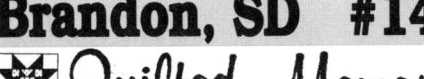

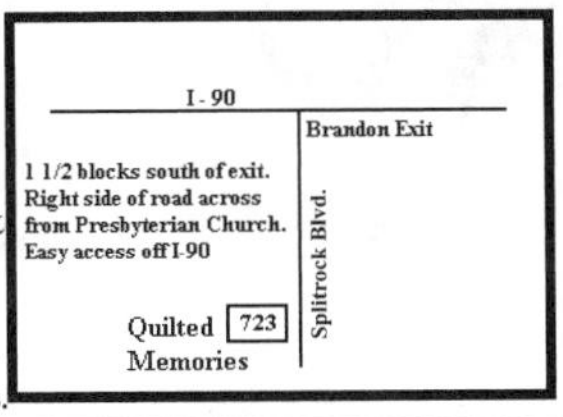

Yankton, SD #15

Mon - Fri 10 - 5:30
Thur til 8
Sat 10 - 5

Four Seasons Fabric

909 Broadway #4 57078 (605) 665-3406
www.fourseasonsfabrics.com

A great array of cottons, books, patterns, notions and other quilting goodies plus apparel fabrics and super classes! Machine embroidery supplies.

Nothing Sews Like A Bernina. Nothing.
BERNINA®

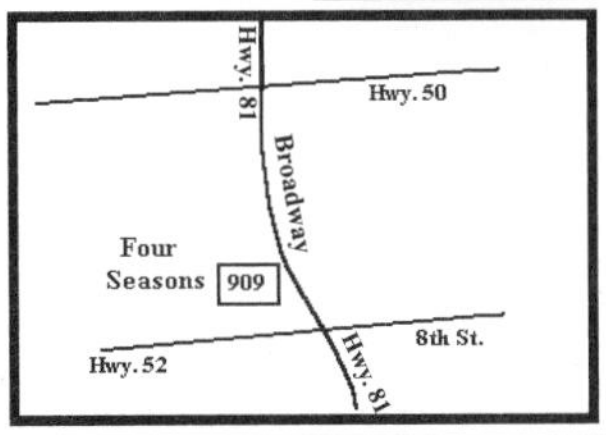

Dell Rapids, SD #16

Tues - Fri 10 - 5
Sat 9 - 2

Always Your Design

434 E. 4th, P.O. Box 144 57022
(605) 428-4545
Owners: Diane Bunkers & Deb Mergen
alwaysydesign@siouxvalley.net
www.Alwaysyourdesign.com

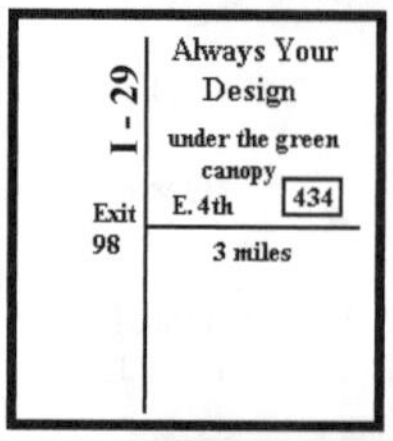

Two friendly sisters in an 1904 Quarry Rock building. 4000+ Bolts, Fat Quarters, All Wool, Flannels, Cottons, Homespuns, Batiks, & Notions.

Elkton, SD #17

Mon - Fri 9 - 5
Thur til 7
Sat 9 - 4

Ivy Lane Quilts & "Stuff"

502 E. North Dr. 57026
(605) 542-2051 Fax: (605) 542-2052
ivylane@itctel.com
Owners: Linda Louder & Bev Lytle.
Free Newsletter Est: 1998 2000 sq.ft.

Moda, Kaufman, Blank, Timeless Treasures, Hoffman, and Kona Bay. Outstanding books, patterns, notions & class offerings. Authorized Pfaff dealer. 1st in customer service.

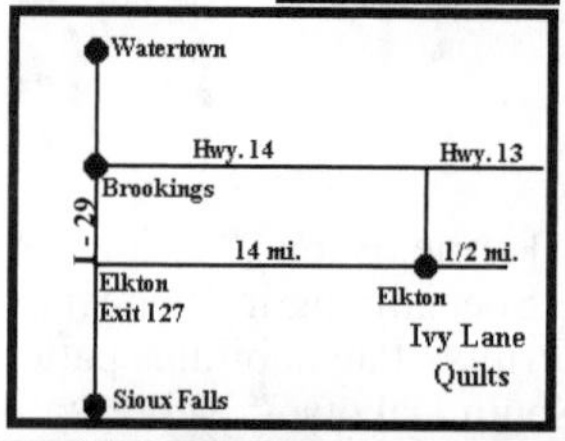

Watertown, SD #18

Mon - Fri 9 - 5
Sat 9 - 4

Dakota Quilt Shop

21 1st Ave. SE 57201
(605) 753-6922
Owner: Dorothy Spieker
dorothy@dakotaquiltshop.com
www.dakotaquiltshop.com

Providing Fabrics, Notions and Longarm Services for Quilters.

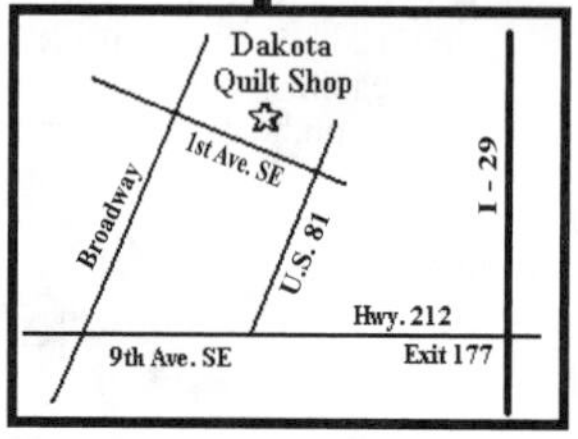

Aberdeen, SD #19

Mon - Fri 9 - 5
Sat 9 - 4
Closed Sat June - Sept

The Fabric Bin

inside Sander's Sew -N- Vac
111 & 113 S. Main 57401
(605) 225-4203 Fax: (605) 225-6707
Est: 1945 3000 bolts
sewvac@midconetwork.com
www.sanderssewnvac.com

Offering Janome and Pfaff sewing machine Sales & Service. Largest selection of fabrics, patterns, books and notions in the area.

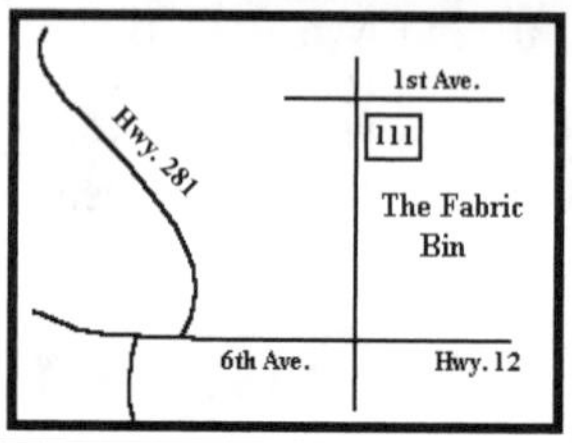

South Dakota Quilt Shops

Aberdeen — **The Fabric Bin, 111 South Main**
605-225-4203 — **See ad #19, this page**

Brandon — **Quilted Memories, 723 N. Splitrock Blvd.**
605-582-7411 — **See ad #14, page 499**

Chamberlain — **The Quilt Shop, 315 North Main**
605-234-5739 — **See ad #10, page 499**

Custer — **The Quilt Shop, 325 Mt. Rushmore Rd.**
605-673-3606 — **See ad #3, page 496**

Dell Rapids — **Always Your Design, 434 East 4th St.**
605-428-4545 — **See ad #16, this page**

Edgemont — **Nuts & Bolts Fabric Shop, 401 2nd Ave.**
605-662-5758 — **See ad #8, page 499**

Elkton — **Ivy Lane Quilts & "Stuff" Inc., 502 E. North**
605-542-2051 — **See ad #17, this page**

Gregory — Quilt Stitchery, 515 Main St. — 605-835-9050

Hill City — **The Quilt Corral, 23835 Hwy. 385**
605-574-4197 — **See ad #5, page 497 & 413**

Hot Springs — **HeartSong Quilts, 345 N. River St.**
605-745-5330 — **See ad #4, page 496**

Mitchell — **The Pin Cushion, 320 N. Main St.**
605-996-0947 — **See ad #11, page 499**

Pierre — **Quilt Yard, 209 W Dakota Ave Suite 101**
605-945-1195 — **See ad #9, page 499**

Pierre — Bears Den Quilts, 3451 Bond Pl. — 605-224-4423

Rapid City — **Thimble Cottage Quilt Village**
902 Mt. Rushmore Rd.
605-341-6569 — **See ad #7, page 498**

Rapid City — **Quilt Connection Etc., 1520 Haines Ave. #1**
605-355-0178 — **See ad #6, page 498**

Rapid City — Fabric City, 120 Knollwood Dr. #D 6053422050

Sioux Falls — **Heirloom Creations, 3800 S. Western Ave.**
605-332-4435 — **See ad #13, page 499**

Sioux Falls — **The Dutch Rose Quilt Shop, 5107 West 41st**
605-362-1650 — **See ad #12, page 499**

Spearfish — **Dakota Quilt Company, 1004 Main St.**
605-642-2939 — **See ad #1, page 496**

Sturgis — **Fabric Junction, 1609 Junction**
605-347-2235 — **See ad #2, page 496**

Tabor — Quilters Quarters, 112 Lidice Ave. — 605-463-2436

Watertown — **Dakota Quilt Shop, 21 First Ave SE**
605-753-6922 — **See ad #18, this page**

Yankton — **Four Seasons Fabrics, 909 Broadway #4**
605-665-3406 — **See ad #15, page 499**

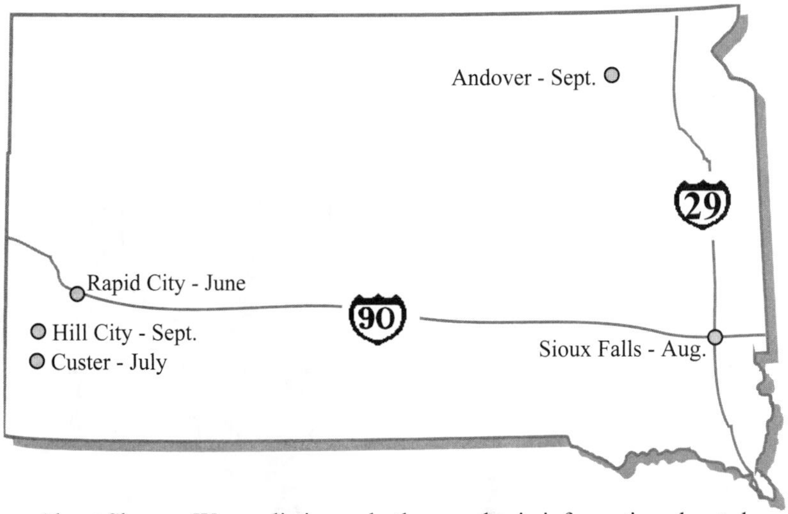

South Dakota Quilt Shows

5 Shows

About Shows: We are listing only the very basic information about shows that happen on a regular schedule here. Please check out our website for more details on each show. Also this information tends to change quite often so please verify the event with our website or a local source before you venture far. Or if you're in the right area at the right time, give it a shot.

If you are a show organizer, please keep us updated on your event.
shows@quilterstravelcompanion.com www.quilterstravelcompanion.com

On our website you will also find:
- Exact dates (when we have them)
- Sponsor Information
- Contact Information
- Description of Event
- Events happening on a one-time basis

Month	City	Schedule	Show	Location with address
June				
	Rapid City	Annual, 2nd weekend of June	Black Hills Quilters Guild Show	Rushmore Plaza Civic Center, 444 Mt. Rushmore Rd. N
July				
	Custer	Odd Years, last weekend of July	Custer Piecemakers' Quilt Show	Custer YMCA Bldg., 644 Crook St.
August				
	Sioux Falls	Annual, 2nd Sat. in August	Quilts & Vines	Strawbale Winery, 47215 257th St.
September				
	Andover	Annual, weekend after Labor Day	James Valley Threshers Quilt Show	Fairgrounds--Heritage Craft Bldg.
	Hill City	Annual, the Sunday after Labor Day in September	Outdoor Quilt Show & Sale	Downtown, Main St.

Notes

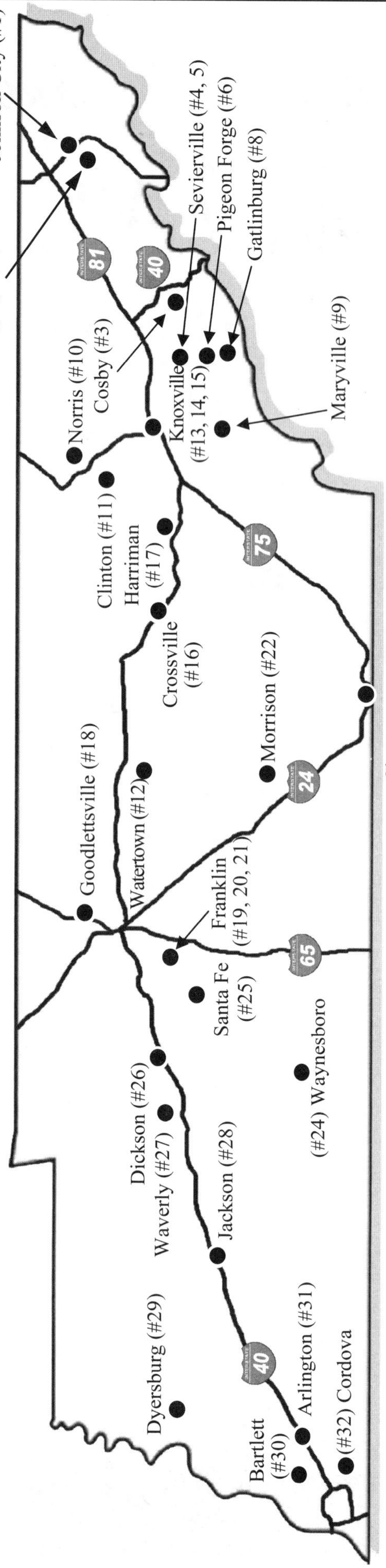

TENNESSEE

32 Featured Shops

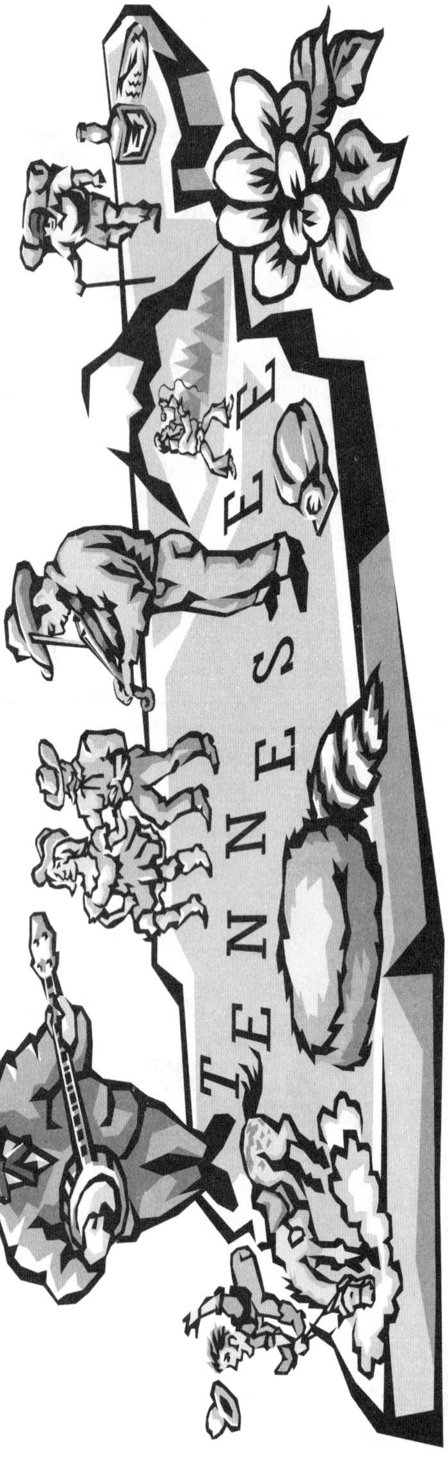

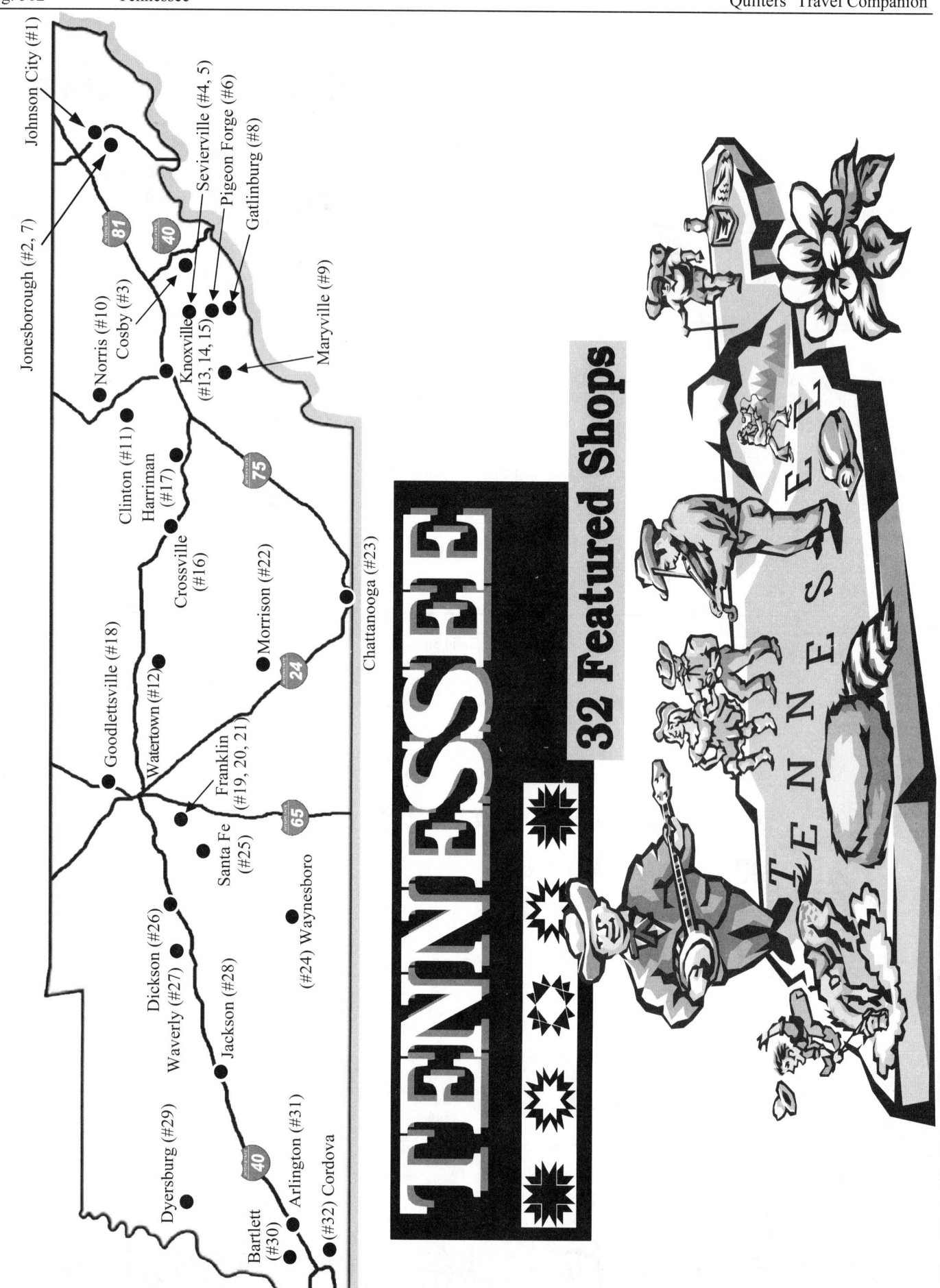

Somewhere Sewing

To God Be The Glory

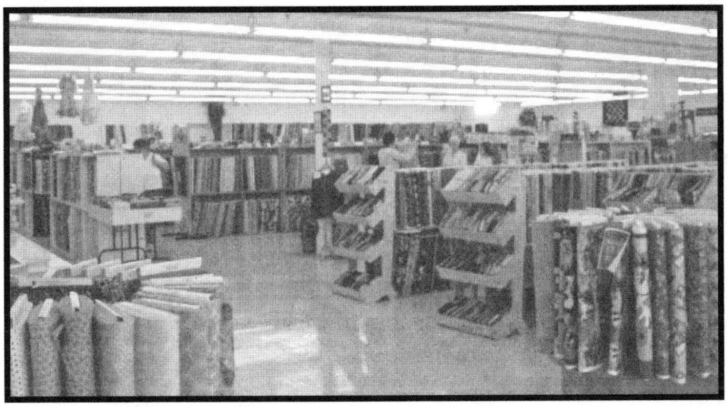

Experience 8000 bolts of quality cottons at great prices.
Books & Notions

Sewing Machine Lines:
Brother, Babylock
Janome
Voyager by Hinterberg

Hinterberg Stretch Frames

Classes Available.

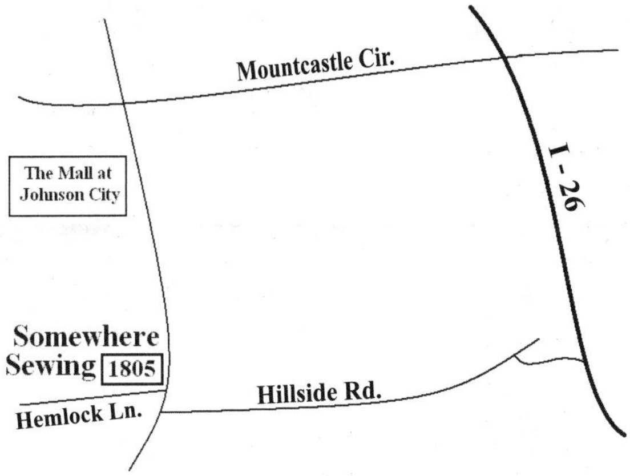

"A Quilters Paradise."

One of the largest quilt shops in the Southeast with over 8500 square feet of great stuff for quilters.

Mon - Sat
9am - 5pm

1805 N. Roan St, Suite F2 37601
423-926-1417 or 866-558-9739
www.somewheresewing.com
somewheresewing@aol.com Est: 2000
Owner: Debi Moffitt

Johnson City, TN #1

Tennessee Quilts

Jonesborough, TN #2

Over 8,000 Quality Quilting Fabrics Online and in the Shop. Featuring a large selection of Kaffe Fassett fabrics.

Frequent Workshops by National Instructors

114 Boone St. in Historic Jonesborough
Tennessee 37659

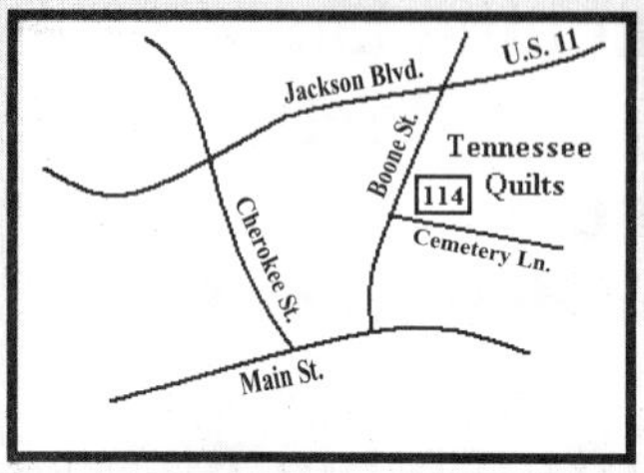

Across from the Visitors Center

423/753-6644

fax: 423/610-0681
linda@tennesseequilts.com

www.tennesseequilts.com

Monday - Saturday 9:30 - 5:30

ONE OF TENNESSEE'S LARGEST SHOPS

Cosby, TN #3

3892 Cosby Highway (Scenic Hwy. 321)
(just 19 miles from Gatlinburg)
(423) 487-3866
jamahol@mindspring.com
www.hollowaysquilts.com
Owners: Maria & John Holloway

Holloway's Country Home

Full line quilt shop featuring American made quilts, wall hangings and wearable art. Fabric - Notions - Kits.

HAND QUILTED WITH AMERICAN PRIDE

Uniquely designed quilts, wall hangings.

THE LARGEST SELECTION OF FINE VINTAGE QUILTS IN THE AREA!

If you are a collector of American Quilts or other American hand crafts, visit us in our historical log building in the quiet country atmosphere of the small TN community of Cosby.

Longarm machine quilting available. Ask for Pauline.

Our house next door is a quilters overnight getaway. We can accommodate up to twelve quilters. We have a large sewing room and all the comforts of home.

Call or email us about our Quilt Retreats

GET AWAY TO THE PEACEFUL SMOKY MOUNTAINS AND QUILT - QUILT - QUILT

Daily 9:00 - 5:00
March 1 to Dec. 15
Closed Sundays
Winter Hours Vary
Please Call Ahead

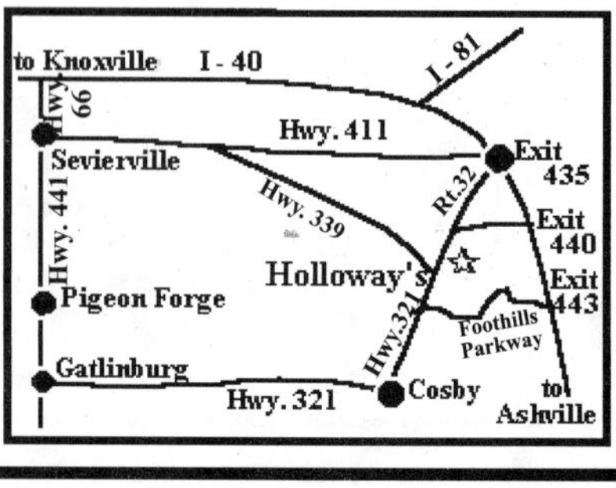

#4

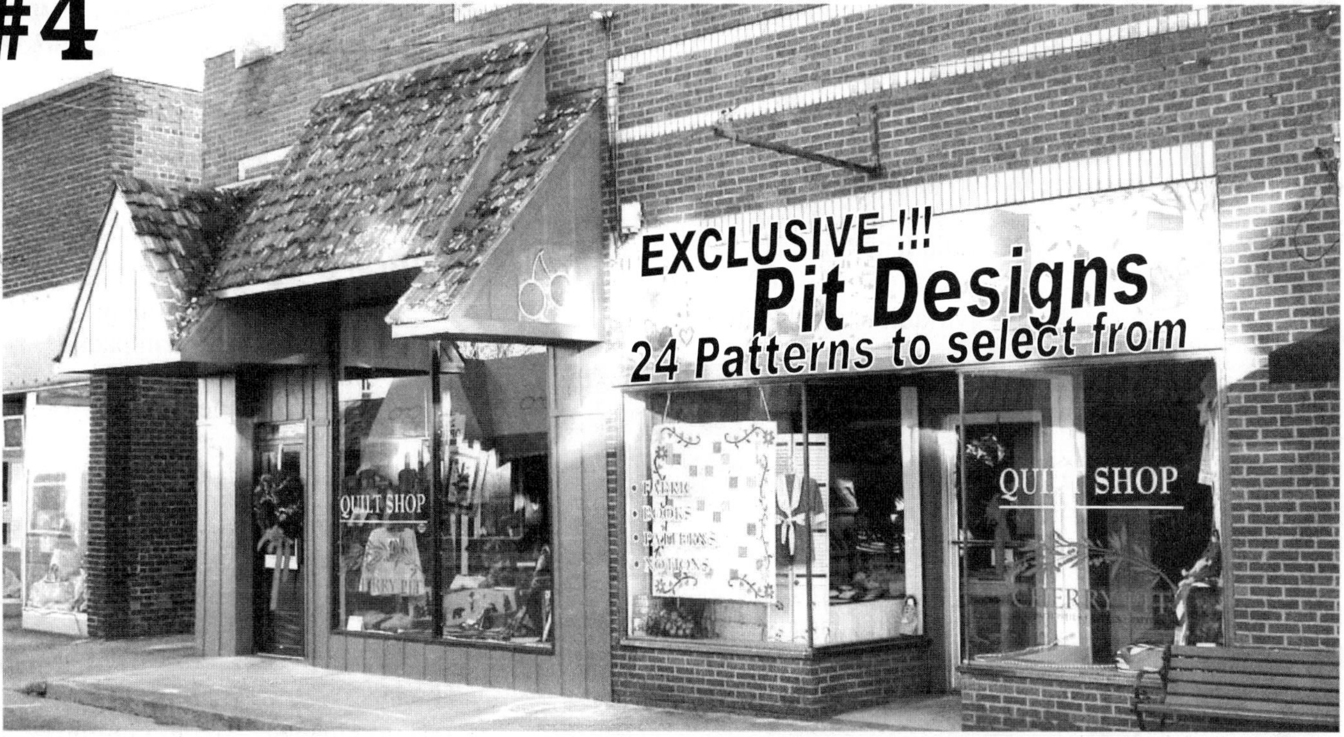

The CHERRY PIT QUILT SHOP in Historic Downtown Sevierville, TN

About Our Quilt Shop

- **Models** hang on the 1930's red brick walls
- 100% cotton **fabric** from major fabric manufacturers and designers. **You'll feel our quality.**
- Check out our clothing, wall hangings and quilt **kits.**
- Need a new quilt project? Browse through our many **books and patterns.**
- Extensive **Block of the Month** program available to fit all lifestyles. We ship. See BOMs on website.
- 3600 sq. ft. **show rooms.**
- Quilt Sampler shop Spring 2005

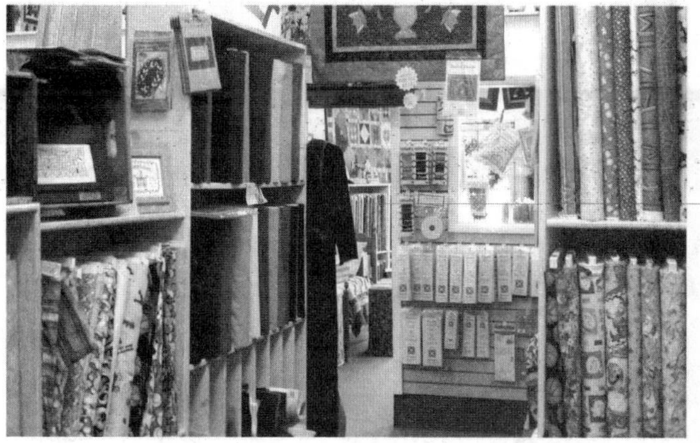

the CHERRY PIT

www.quiltingatthecherrypit.com

tcherryp@bellsouth.net

East Tennessee's
"destination quilt shop"

115 Bruce Street
Sevierville, TN 37862

OPEN
Mon.-Fri
9:30 - 5:00
Sat.
9:00 - 1:00
Phone
(865) 453-4062

Neighbors to Dollywood and the Great Smokey Mountains.

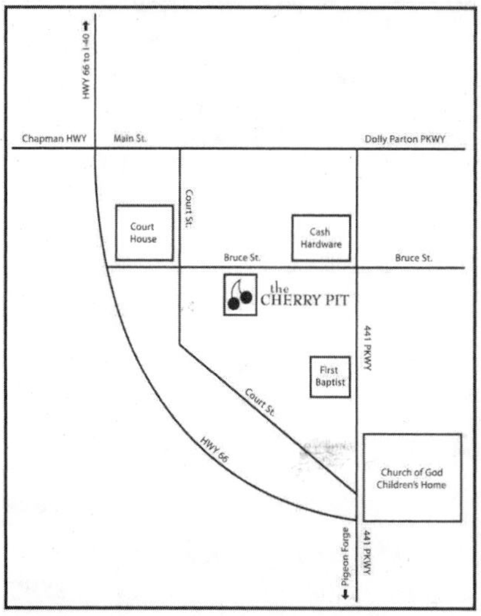

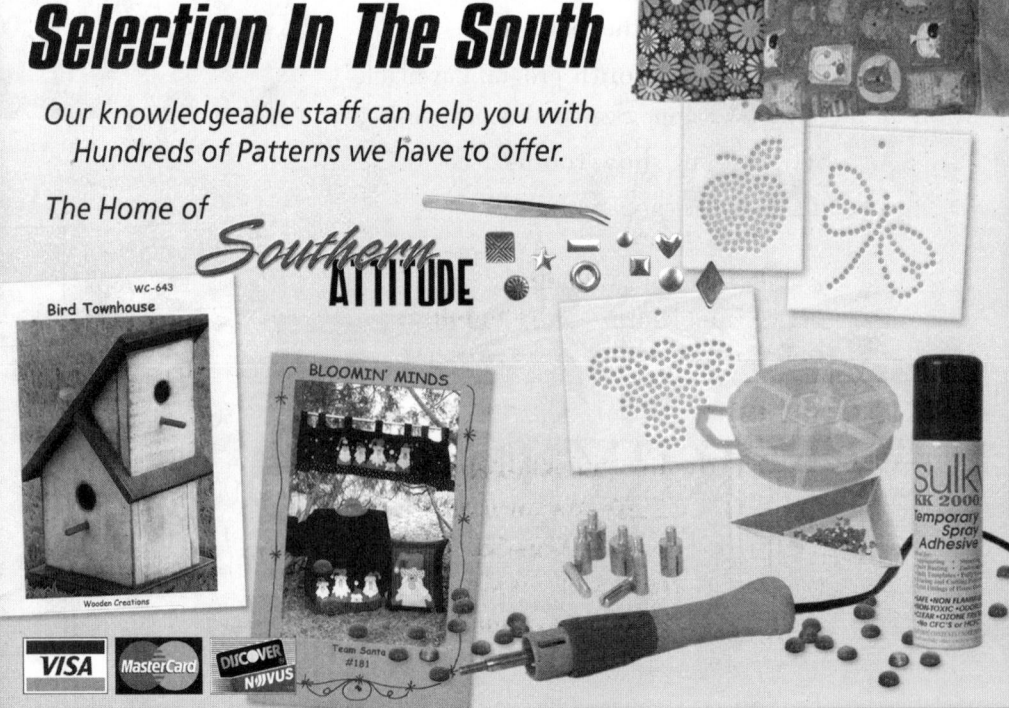

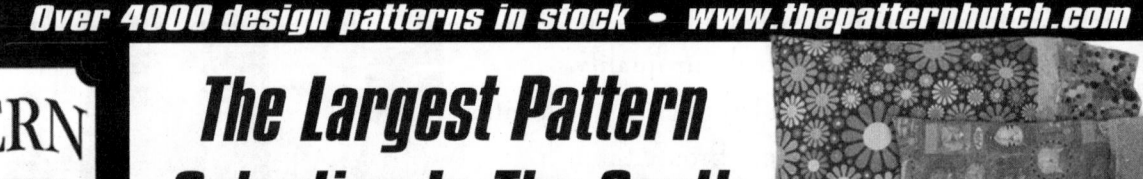

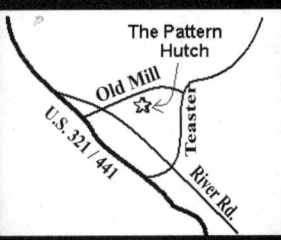

Sewing Bee

107 E. Jackson Blvd., Hwy. 11-E 37659
(423) 753-7399 Est: 1994

Jonesborough, TN #7

Located in Tennessee's Oldest Town

Tues - Fri 10 - 5
Sat 10 - 2

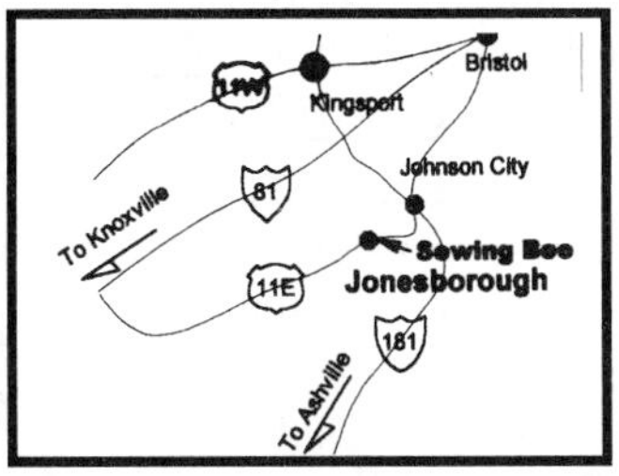

Quilting Fabrics and Notions.
Authorized Pfaff dealer.
Books, patterns & gift items.

Authorized Pfaff Dealer & HQ 16 Representative

Gatlinburg, TN #8

Mon - Sat
10 - 5

Mountain Stitches by Susan

601 Glades Rd. #13 37738
(865) 436-0077
www.mountainstitchesbysusan.com
Owner: Susan Dudley

MEMBER
Great Smoky Arts & Crafts Community

Located in the Great Smoky Arts & Crafts Community. Fine Cottons, Fat Quarters, Patterns & Kits. Friendly & Helpful.

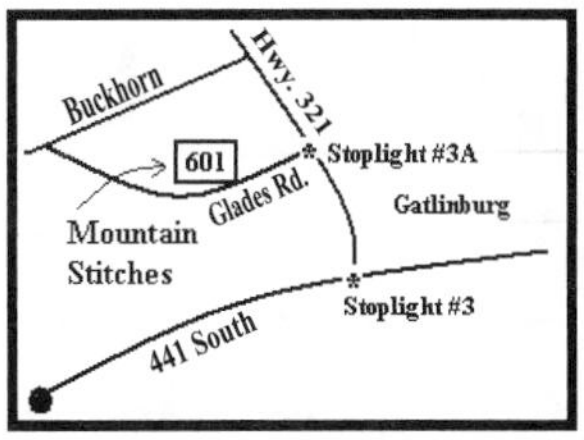

Pappy's Quilting Place

3426 Sevierville Rd.
Maryville, TN 37804
(865) 980-0950
tina@pappysquilting.com
Owners:
John & Shirley Harrison
Est: 2005

www.pappysquilting.com

Mon - Sat
9 - 5
Sun 9 - 4

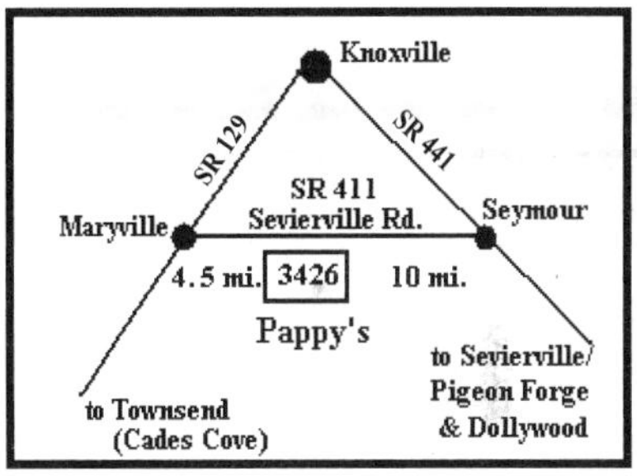

Fabric, Notions, Classes, Handi Quilter
Longarm Quilting Machine Sales, Service.
Custom Quilting
Machine embroidery supplies.

Maryville, TN #9

Norris, TN #10

Open during Daylight Hours Year Round

Museum of Appalachia

2819 Andersonville Hwy.
P.O. Box 1189 37828
(865) 494-7680 Fax: (865) 494-8957
501C3 Organization (non-profit)
museum@museumofappalachia.org
www.museumofappalachia.org
One of the nation's largest collections of authentic Appalachian artifacts & historic log structures. Large gift shop; regional crafts, handmade & vintage quilts, quilts related items.

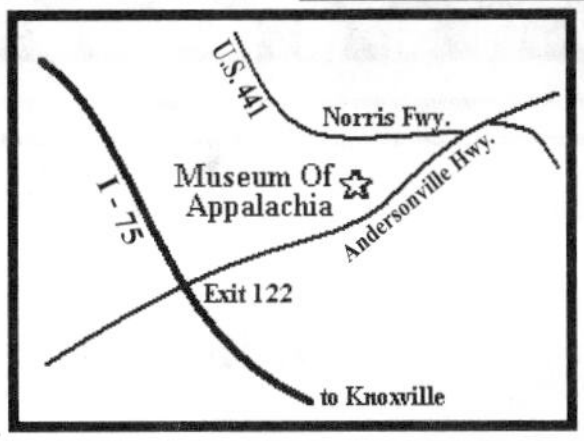

Clinton, TN #11

Mon - Fri
8 - 5
Sat 8 - 1

Sew Unique Fabric

403 Hillcrest St. 37716
(865) 457-5070 Est: 1997
sewuniquesewing@bellsouth.net
www.sewuniquefabric.com
A truly unique Machine, Fabric and Notions store. We carry a wide variety of high quality cotton quilting fabrics and supplies.
We have Cotton, TeeKnits, Fleece, Flannel, Toile and Designer fabric all at fantastic prices.
Pfaff & Brother Dealer.

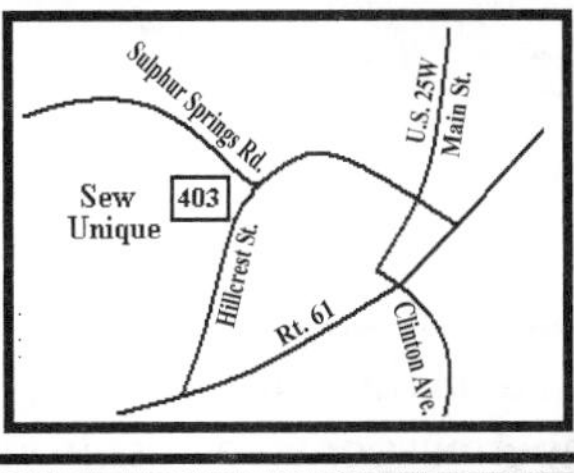

Watertown, TN #12

Tues & Thur
10 - 8
Sat 10 - 5
Sun 1 - 5

Country Store
Quilt Shop

3360 Sparta Pike
(615) 444-4228
marhartn@yahoo.com
Owner: Margie Harris

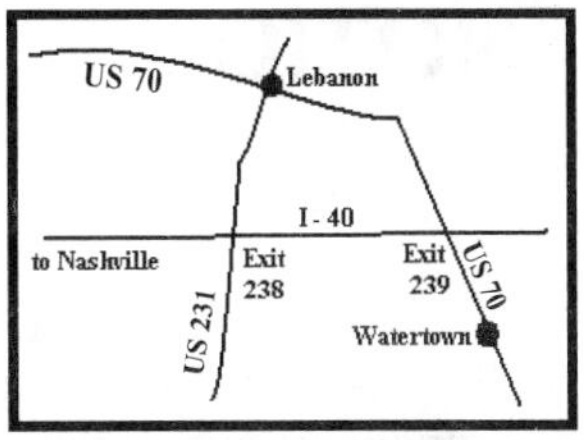

Fabrics, Quilt Supplies, Quilt Kits, Classes

Knoxville, TN #13

Mon - Fri
10 - 5
Sat 10 - 3

SEWING MACHINES ETC
SALES ✝ SERVICE *ALL* MAKES

8419 Kingston Pike 37919
(865) 690-7770
Est: 1983 4500 sq.ft.

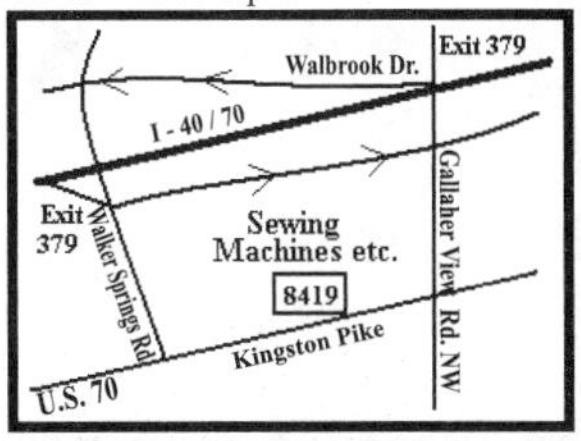

www.sewingmachinesetc.com
Over 3000 bolts of the best manufacturers fabrics.
Fat quarters, notions including the latest in Sewing,

Gina's BERNINA Sewing Center

Knoxville, TN #14

Specializing in quilting & heirloom sewing.
We have over 5000 bolts of top quality brands including Robert Kaufman, Hoffman, P&B, Bali, In the Beginning, Free Spirit, Moda, RJR, etc. In addition to our quilt shop we also carry a full line of classic children's sewing supplies including Children's Corner patterns and French laces. Gina's has been a full service sewing store for over 27 years. We would love to assist you in all of your sewing needs.

Call for our extensive class schedule.

Directions: We are just 5 minutes from the interstate. Coming from **I-40/75** take the Lovell Road **exit #374**. **Go South to Kingston Pike** (approximately 1 mile) and **take a right**. (Landmark= Walgreens on your right at this intersection). **Go 3/10's of a mile and we will be on your left in Farragut Square**. Our building is right after a nursery that changes names every few months (currently Saplings). So don't count on the name but it hasn't disappeared completely yet!
Follow these directions & you'll make it!

Gina's is the place for all your Bernina needs.

10816 Kingston Pike
Knoxville, TN 37934
(865) 966-5941 or
Toll free 1-877-236-1291

Join us on the web at
ginasbernina.com
info@ginasbernina.com

Store Hours
Monday-Friday 9:30-5:00
Saturday 9:30-4:00

Mammaw's Thimble

Monday
10 - 5
Tues - Sat
10 - 7

4028 Papermill Dr.
"Sweet 16"
Knoxville, TN 37909
(865) 588-8818

#15

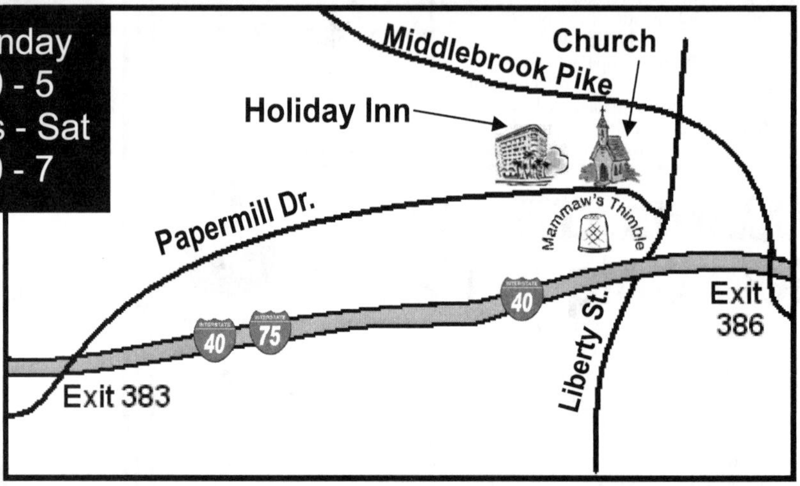

Conveniently located on the North side of I-40 just 1.3 miles east of exit 383, in the Papermill Center across from the red brick church.

OVER 8,000 Bolts & 30,000 Fat Quarters

BOOKS • PATTERNS • NOTIONS • CLASSES

Established
2001

Owned & Operated by
Vivian Ann Wright

Blessings
Little
Quilt Shop
Crossville, TN
Little Blessings
QUILT SHOP
4351 Hwy. 127 N. Crossville, TN
blessings4u@frontiernet.net
931-707-7724
#16
www.littleblessing.net
Owners: Robert & Julia Ranney
"Where we are always wrapped up in Quilting"
• Large selection of quality 100% cotton quilting fabric and growing
• Featuring the Newest Patterns & Books
• Large selection of quilting & sewing notions
• Friendly knowledgeable Staff
• Comfortable classroom
• Classes for all skill levels
• Longarm Quilting Services
an authorized PFAFF dealer
Machine Sales & Service
Mon - Fri 9:30 - 5:00
Sat 9:00 - 3:00
Little Blessings
127 North
Exit 317
I-40

Loose Threads

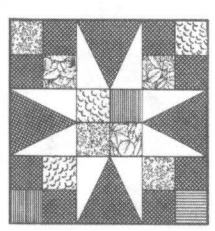

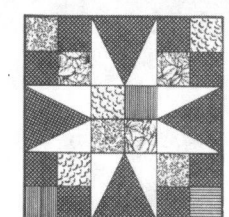

1211 S. Roane St. #5,
Harriman, TN 37748
865-882-5588
loosethreadstn@earthlink.net
Est: 2003 3600 sq.ft.

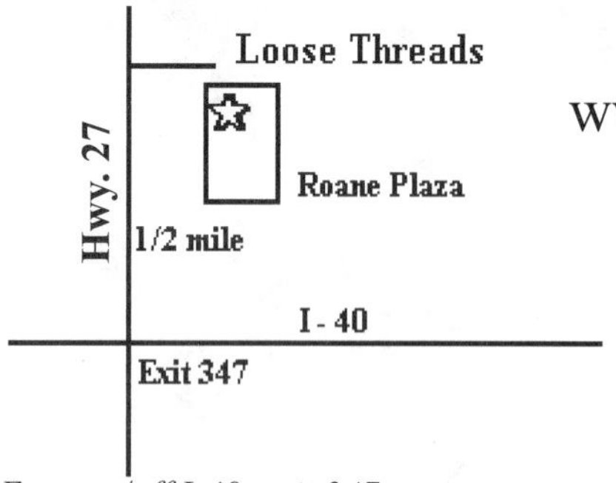

www.loosethreadsquiltshop.com

Fabric & Quilting Supplies, etc.etc.etc.

Mon & Sat 9 - 3
Tues - Fri 9:30 - 5:30

Easy on/off I-40, exit 347
2 Block North (Hwy. 27) on Right.
On the back left hand side of Roane Plaza

Come visit us and our ever-growing FIRST quality 100% cotton prints, including Batiks & Flannels.

Books, Patterns, Threads, Notions -- Sale Room

VISA MasterCard AMERICAN EXPRESS DISCOVER

Harriman, TN #17

Goodlettsville, TN #18

Quilter's Attic

Where memories are made!

Established 1987

Monday:	9 am - 4 pm
Tuesday:	9 am - 4 pm
Wednesday:	9 am - 4 pm
Thursday:	9 am - 8 pm
Friday:	9 am - 4 pm
Saturday:	10 am - 4 pm

Only one mile from Interstate I-65.

126 N. Main Street 37072
- 14 miles north of downtown Nashville –

(615) 859 – 5603

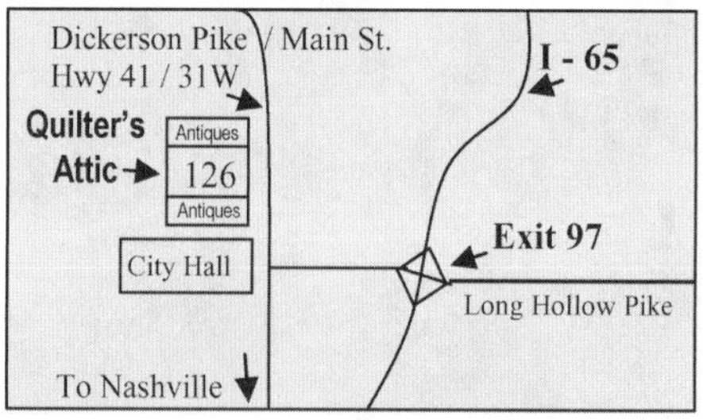

Over 100 quilts & wall hangings on display.
Classes, fabric, books, patterns & notions.
Set in the midst of an antique community.
4500 sq. ft. Over 3000 bolts
Owner: Fran Sargent
www.thequiltersattic.com

Franklin, TN #19

The Quilting Squares

Est: 2003

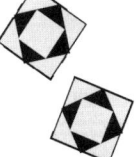

107 Confederate Dr. Suite #1 37064
615-794-4769 877-794-4769
Owners: Kay Roberts / Kathy Kuryla
www.thequiltingsquares.com

HOURS:
Mon - Fri 10 - 5
Sat 10 - 4

"A gathering place for quilters to enjoy the art of quiltmaking"

A unique quilt shop located in historic Franklin, TN carrying a full line of quilting supplies including fabrics, books, patterns & notions.

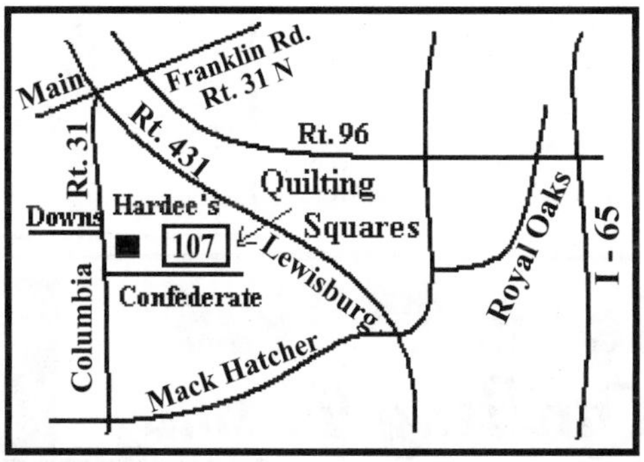

- ★ Jodi Barrows SNS Products & Fabrics
- ★ Square In A Square Products
- ★ Well stocked sale rack
- ★ Samples to inspire you
- ★ Classes - beginner to advanced
- ★ Shop our website in your PJ's
- ★ Workshops for Quilt Guilds & Shows
- ★ Vendors at Quilt Shows
- ★ Knowledgeable & friendly staff

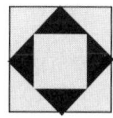

Butterfly MEADOWS

INN & FARM

We know quilters and have created a special place for you. Come relax at Butterfly Meadows Inn & Farm. We offer overnight accommodations in seven comfortable rooms and suites for you and your friends. Our spacious gathering rooms are ideal for quilting and enjoying the company of fellow quilters. Our Swallowtail room, with 1100 square feet, will be set up for your group with individual sewing tables and chairs, ironing and cutting stations. Enjoy scrumptious, home-cooked meals.

With the look and charm of a 100 year old farmhouse, surrounded by woods and meadows, you can step back in time to a simpler way of life and enjoy a special "piece-ful" retreat. Please call 877-671-4594 or email relax@butterflymeadowsinn.com to book your group stay *(up to 22 guests)*. Check our website, butterflymeadowsinn.com for our open retreats and specials.

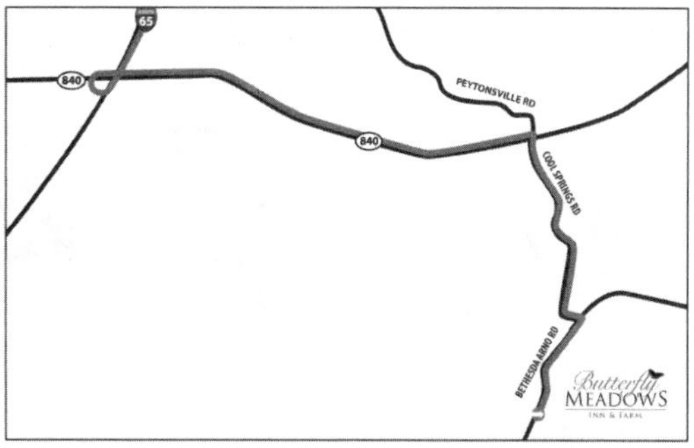

6775 Bethesda Arno Road, Franklin, Tennessee 37179
877-671-4594 ~ relax@butterflymeadowsinn.com
www.butterflymeadowsinn.com

#20

Franklin, TN #21

Mon - Sat 9:30 - 5

Stitchers Garden

209 S. Royal Oaks Blvd. #223 37064
in the Watson Glen Shopping Center
(615) 790-0603
Owner: Myra Nickolaus
Est: 1988 3000 sq.ft.
Middle Tennessee's Most Complete Quilting Shop! Over 8000 bolts of all cotton fabrics, complete Jinny Beyer palette, Q-Snap frames, stencils, books, templates, patterns, & classes.

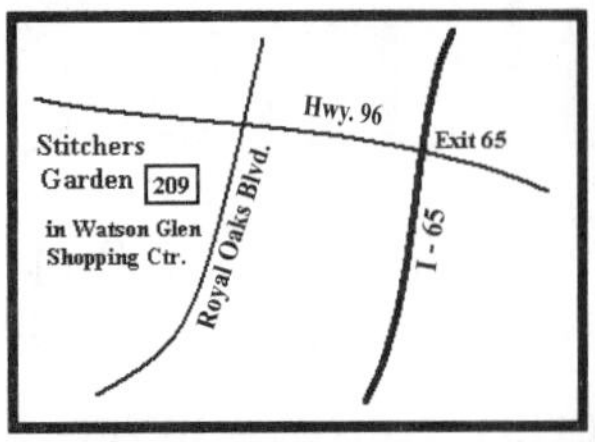

Morrison, TN #22

Call to schedule your retreat

The Cottage

Beautiful Crafting Retreat located on 100 acre lake at 879 Tom Grissom Rd. Huge work areas with 6' tables, chairs, craft lamps, lots of electrical outlets for up to 25 guests, sleeps 14 upstairs and 11 downstairs. Fully equipped kitchens for your convenience or we will cater your meals. All bed and bath linens provided.
Call 931-668-2100 or email: fredanddi@blomand.net
Approximately 1-2 hours from Knoxville, Chattanooga or Nashville.

Chattanooga, TN #23

Lavender Lime

Est. 2005

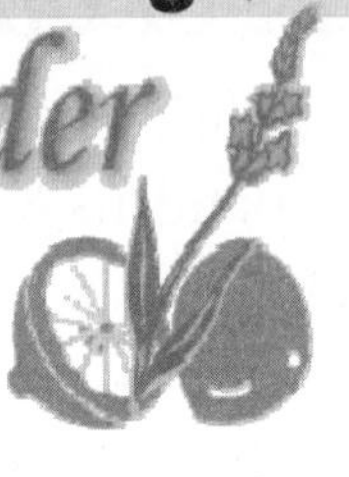

Better Homes Quilt Sampler Featured Shop

Mon - Fri 10:00 - 6:00
Sat 10:00 - 4:00

Quilting and Creative Sewing Center
"Home of Designs by Lavender Lime"
www.lavenderlimeinspires.com

5084 South Terrace,
Suite 11 37412
(423) 499-5282

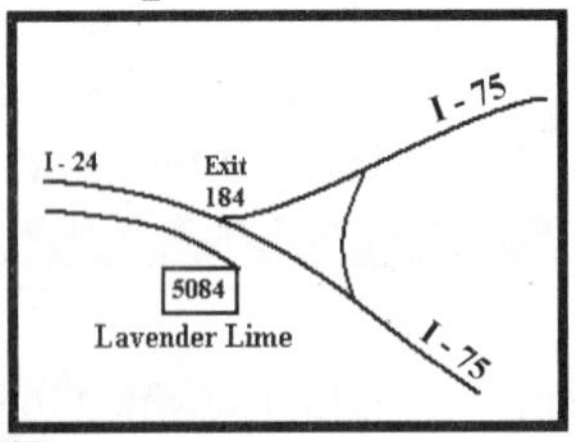

Great selection of fabrics, books, patterns & more

BERNINA
Handi Quilter

Great bus and RV parking
Easy access at the I-75 / I-24 split

Waynesboro, TN #24

Thur, Fri & Sat 11 - 5

Ms. Gracies Quilting by the creek

4499 S. 48 38485
(931) 722-7840

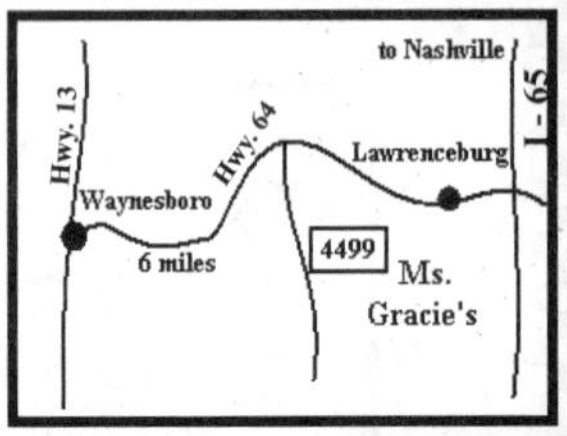

msgracie@tds.net www.msgracies.com
Custom Quilts, Quilt Repair, Long Arm Quilting, Quilts For Sale, Quilt Kits

Santa Fe, TN #25

Mon, Tues Wed 9 - 5
Fri 9 - 4
Sat 9 - 12

The Quilting Frame

5990 Leipers Creek Rd. 38482
(931) 682-3746
Owner: Sandra & Larry Adkison
Est: 2005 1500 sq.ft.
sadkison2@netzero.net
Machine quilting - 2 Gammill machines (one computerized, one manual)
Fabric & Notions, Custom Quilts, T-shirts quilts
Custom made quilts and custom picture framing.

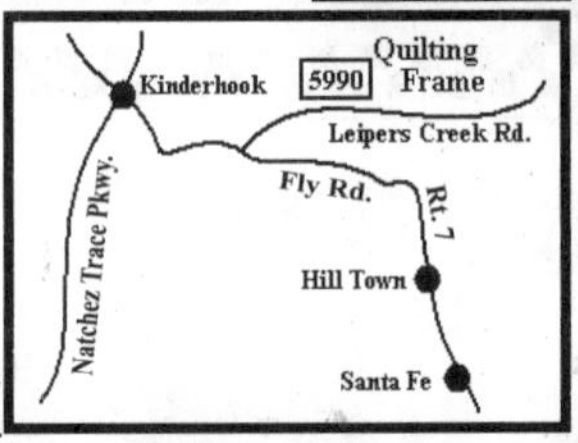

Dickson, TN #26

Mon - Sat 10 - 4

Granny B's Quilt Shop
Miss Mable's Village

301 W. College St. 37055
(615) 441-3884
tearoom@mindspring.com
www.grannyb.org
Est: 2004

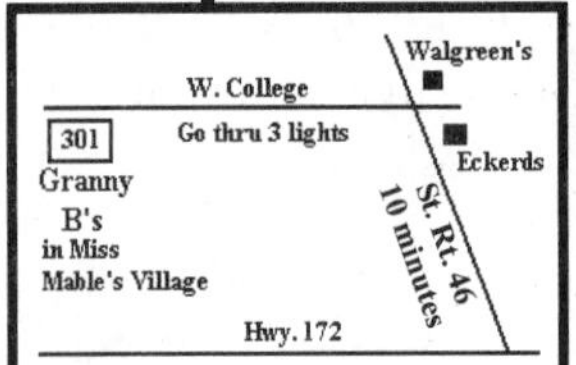

Waverly, TN #27

Tues - Fri 9 - 4
Sat 9 - 12
Call for Winter Hours

Pumpkin Creek Fabrics

178 Factory Ct. 37185
(931) 296-5022 Fax: (931) 296-5053
Owners: Diane & Gary Parks
Est: 2005 1200 sq. ft. Free Newsletter
www.pumpkincreekfabrics.com
Quality fabrics - Moda, Hoffman Batiks, Kaufman, Princess Mirah Batiks, Michael Miller, Windham, Maywood Studios, Timeless Treasures & more!
Authorized HandiQuilter Representative.

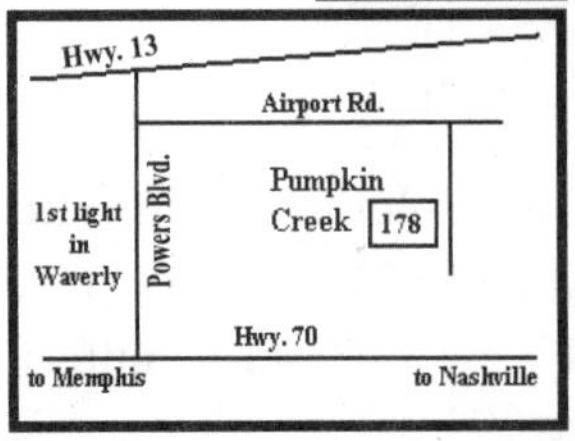

SEW MANY IDEAS

405 Vann Dr.
Jackson, TN 38305
(731) 668-8099
www.sewmanyideas.com
Est: 2002 3500 sq.ft.

Mon - Sat 10 - 5

Jackson, TN #28

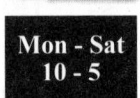

Sew Many Ideas offers a full line of **BERNINA** sewing and embroidery machines and the Avanate'18 Handi Quilter.
"Eye Candy" includes 1200 bolts of contemporary quilt fabric, books, patterns and notions!
Visit us on "Facebook" and become a fan!

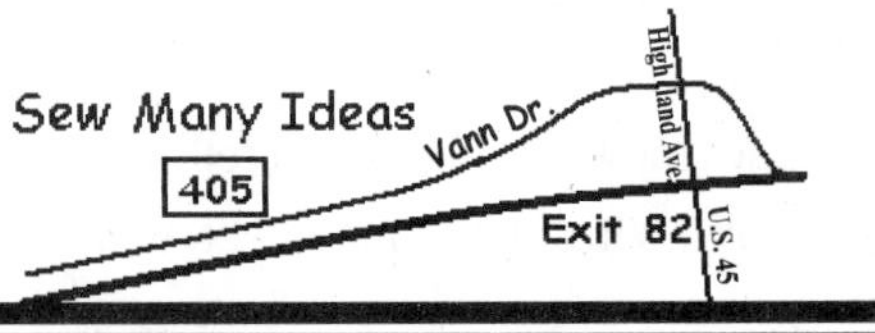

Dyersburg, TN #29

Tues - Fri 10 - 5 Sat 10 - 4

Stitchery QUILT SHOPPE

2675 Lake Rd. #D 38024
(731) 285-2332
Owners: Linda & Danny McCulloch
www.stitcheryquiltshoppe.com
We are a full service quilt shoppe offering Gammill Long-arm Quilting Services
Fabrics Books Notions

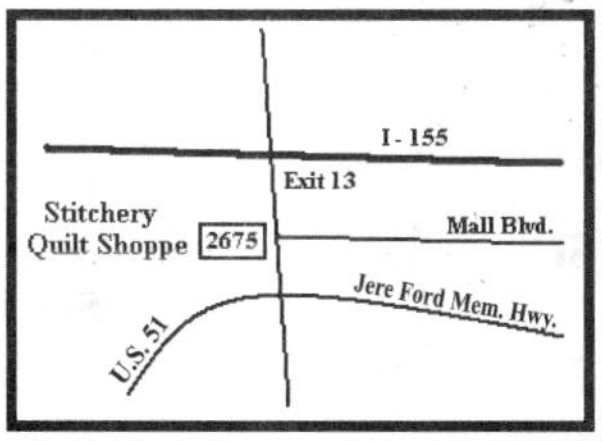

Klassy Katz

Tues - Fri 10 - 5 Sat 10 - 4:30

QUILTING & CLOTHING FABRIC

Come shop in a friendly atmosphere.
Lots of samples throughout the store.
Over 2000 bolts of name brand cottons.

2958 Elmore Park Rd.
Bartlett, TN 38134
(901) 213-0099
klassykatz@bellsouth.net
www.klassykatzfabricshop.com
Owner: Toni Katz
Est: 2001 2800 sq.ft.
Minutes from I - 40

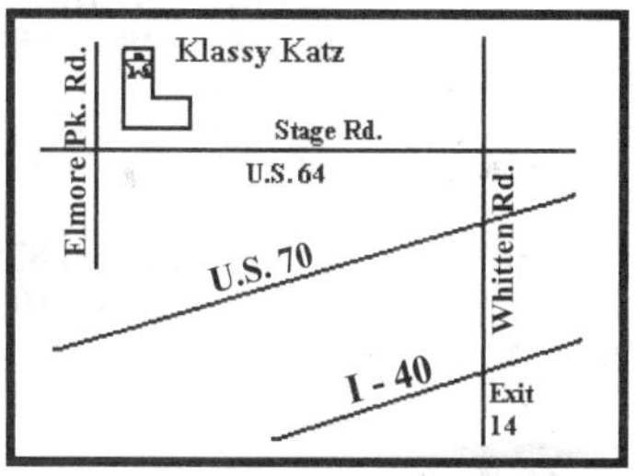

Bernina Dealership

Bartlett, TN #30

Arlington, TN #31

Tues - Sat 10 - 5

The Quilting Barn

12019 Walker St. 38002
(901) 867-4824 Fax: (901) 867-1906
quiltingbarn@bellsouth.net
www.arlingtonquiltingbarn.com
Owner: Pat Vargo
Come join us on Historic Depot Square for all your quilting needs.

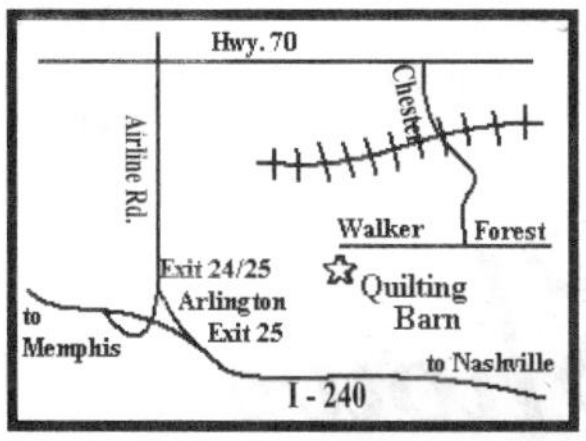

Cordova, TN #32

Mon - Sat 10 - 6

QuiltSmiths

8553 Macon Rd. #102
38018
(901) 624-9985

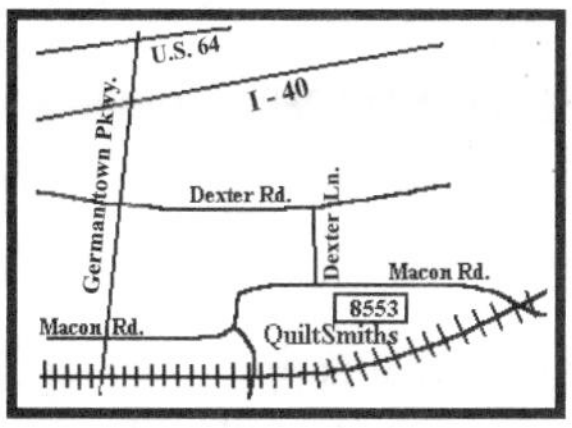

shop@quiltsmiths.com www.QuiltSmiths.com
Owners: Michael & Rita Smith
Est: 1999 1550 sq.ft. 2500 Bolts
Best lines of fabric. Large selection of batiks, children's prints, 1930's prints, Moda, Hoffman, Kona Bay-all your favorites!
Classes, notions, friendly service.

Tennessee Quilt Shops

Arlington — **The Quilting Barn, 12019 Walker St.**
901-867-4824 **See ad #31, this page**

Bartlett — **Klassy Katz, 2958 Elmore Park Rd.**
901-213-0099 **See ad #30, this page**

Camden — The Quilting Bee, 235 Hwy. 641 N. 731-584-1080

Chattanooga — **Lavender Lime Quilting, 5084 South Terrace**
423-499-5282 **See ad #23, page 512**

Clarkrange — Susan's Quilt Shop, 2712 Martha Washington 931-863-3446

Clinton — **Sew Unique Fabric Store, 403 Hillcrest St**
865-457-5070 **See ad #11, page 507**

Cookeville — The Most Amazing Quilt Shop, 739 S. Jefferson 931-526-6699

Cookeville — Country Patchworks, 283 S. Lowe Ave. 931-526-7276

Cookeville — Spring Creek Quilts, 210 Tommy Dodson Hwy. 931-498-3473

Cordova — **Quiltsmiths, 8553 Macon Rd. #102**
901-624-9985 **See ad #32, this page**

Cosby — **Holloway's Country Home, 3892 Cosby Hwy.**
423-487-3866 **See ad #3, page 504**

Crossville — **Little Blessing Quilt Shop, 4351 Hwy 127 N**
931-707-7724 **See ad #16, page 509 & 197**

Decherd — Decherd Needleworks, 300 E. Main St. 931-968-0808

Dickson — **Granny B's Quilt Shop, 301 W. College St.**
615-441-3884 **See ad #26, page 512**

Dyersburg — **Stitchery Quilt Shoppe, 2675 Lake Rd. #D**
731-285-2332 **See ad #29, this page**

Elizabethton — Ida's Place, 874 Gap Creek Rd. 423-542-0999

Fayetteville — Hooked On Quilting, 8 Elkton Pike 931-433-1886

Franklin — **The Quilting Squares, 107 Confederate**
615-794-4769 **See ad #19, page 511**

Franklin — **Butterfly Meadows Inn & Farm**
6775 Bethesda Arno Rd.
877-671-4594 **See ad #20, page 511 & 198**

Franklin — **Stitcher's Garden, 209 S. Royal Oaks Blvd.**
615-790-0603 **See ad #21, page 512**

Gatlinburg — Maple's Tree, 639 Parkway #1 865-436-4602

Gatlinburg — **Mountain Stitches by Susan, 601 Glades Rd.**
865-436-0077 **See ad #8, page 507**

Goodlettsville — **Quilter's Attic, 126 N. Main St.**
615-859-5603 **See ad #18, page 510**

Harriman — **Loose Threads, 1211 S. Roane St. #5**
865-882-5588 **See ad #17, page 510**

Harrogate — Cosby's Fabric & Crafts, 662 Patterson Rd. 423-869-5599

Jackson — The Fabric Source, 1090 U.S. Hwy. 45 Bypass 731-668-1877

Jackson — **Sew Many Ideas, 405 Vann Dr.**
731-668-8099 **See ad #28, page 512**

Jamestown — Bluetick Fabrics, 847 Old Hwy. 127 S. 931-752-7539

Johnson City — **Somewhere Sewing**
1805 North Roan St., Ste F2
423-926-1417 **See ad #1, page 503 & 199**

Jonesborough **Tennessee Quilts, 114 Boone St.**
423-753-6644 **See ad #2, page 504 & 404**

Jonesborough **Sewing Bee, 107 E. Jackson Blvd.**
423-753-7399 **See ad #7, page 507**

Jonesborough Pioneer Quilting, 732 Mill Springs Rd. 423-753-7154

Knoxville **Gina's Bernina Sewing Center**
10816 Kingston Pike
423-966-5941 **See ad #14, page 508**

Knoxville **Mammaw's Thimble Fabric & Quilt Shop**
4028 Papermill Drive, "Sweet 16"
865-588-8818 **See ad #15, page 508**

Knoxville **Sewing Machines Etc., 8419 Kingston Pike**
865-690-7770 **See ad #13, page 507**

Lebanon Lebanon Sewing Cntr, 1411 W. Main St. 615-443-7644

Maryville **Pappy's Quilting Place, 3426 Sevierville Rd.**
865-980-0950 **See ad #9, page 507**

Maryville Dorothy's, 433 Lee Lambert Rd. 423-983-4969
McMinnville B & J Quilt Shop, 1202 Sparta St. 931-473-8141
Monterey Purple Mountain Quilt Shop, 107 W Commercial Ave. 931-839-9665

Morrison **The Cottage, 879 Tom Grissom Rd.**
931-668-2100 **See ad #22, page 512**

Murfreesboro Quilt Connection , 1011 A Memorial Blvd. 615-867-0210

Nashville Textile Fabric Stores, 2717 Franklin Pike 615-297-5346
Nashville Dancing Needles, 2717 Pike Rd 615-885-0898

Norris **Museum of Appalachia, 2819 Andersonville Hwy.**
865-494-7680 **See ad #10, page 507**

Pegram Stitchin Station, P.O. Box 212 615-797-9477

Pigeon Forge **The Pattern Hutch, 172 Old Mill Ave.**
866-728-8376 **See ad #6, page 506**

Powell Elizabeth's Quilts, 2302 Bull Run Valley Rd. 865-947-5766

Santa Fe **The Quilting Frame, 5990 Leipers Creek Rd.**
931-682-3746 **See ad #25, page 512**

Sevierville **Machine Quiltin' by Ivy, 1020 Old Knoxville Hwy.**
865-428-8008 **See ad #5, page 506**

Sevierville **The Cherry Pit, 115 Bruce St.**
865-453-4062 **See ad #3, page 505**

Smithville Becky's Fabrics & More, 105 W. Main St. 615-597-8521
Smyrna Stitcher's Playhouse, 540 Rock Springs Rd. 615-355-1309
Tallahoma Quilting Dreams, 114 SW Atlantic St. 931-393-3870

Watertown **Country Store Quilt Shop, 3360 Sparta Pike**
615-444-4228 **See ad #12, page 507**

Waverly **Pumpkin Creek Fabrics, 178 Factory Court**
931-296-5022 **See ad #27, page 512**

Waynesboro **Ms. Gracie's Quilting, 4499 S 48th**
931-722-7840 **See ad #24, page 512**

Tennessee Quilt Shows

9 Shows

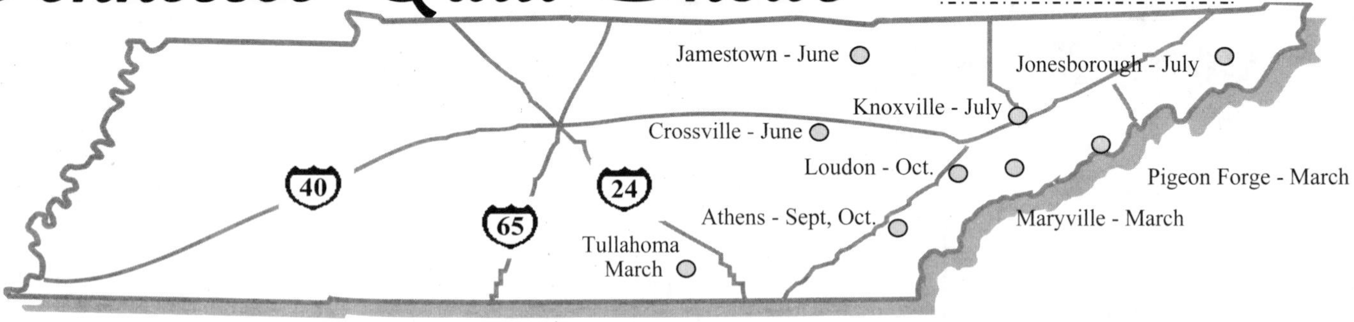

About Shows: We are listing only the very basic information about shows that happen on a regular schedule here. Please check out our website for more details on each show. Also this information tends to change quite often so please verify the event with our website or a local source before you venture far. Or if you're in the right area at the right time, give it a shot.

If you are a show organizer, please keep us updated on your event.
shows@quilterstravelcompanion.com www.quilterstravelcompanion.com

On our website you will also find:
- Exact dates (when we have them)
- Sponsor Information
- Contact Information
- Description of Event
- Events happening on a one-time basis

Month	City	Schedule	Show	Location with address
March				
	Pigeon Forge	Annual, 2nd Wed-Sun in March	A Mountain Quiltfest	Music Road Hotel & Convention Center, 314 Henderson Chapel Rd.
	Tullahoma	Annual, mid-March	Quilt Show	Church of Jesus Christ of Latter-Day Saints, 112 Old Shelbyville
	Maryville	Annual, 3rd weekend in March	Smoky Mountain Quilters Quilt Show	Cooper Athletic Center Maryville College
June				
	Jamestown	Odd years 2nd weekend in June	Sew Sweet Quilters Show	First Baptist Church, 306 E. Central Ave.
	Crossville	Odd Years, 3rd Fri & Sat in June	Mountain Memories Quilt Show	Cumberland County Comm. Complex/Fairgrounds, 1398 Livigston Rd.
July				
	Knoxville	Annual, 3rd weekend of July	AQS Quilt Expo & Contest	Knoxville Convention Center
	Jonesborough	Annual, Late July	Tennessee Quilts' QuiltFest	Tennessee Quilts, 114 Boone St.
September				
	Athens	Annual, Sept. Oct.	McMinn County Living Heritage Museum Quilt Show	McMinn County Living Heritage Museum, 422 W. Madison Ave.
October				
	Loudon	Even Years, 2nd weekend in October	The Village Quilters Show	Tellico Village-Chota Recreation Center, 145 Awohili Dr. (off Hwy. 444)

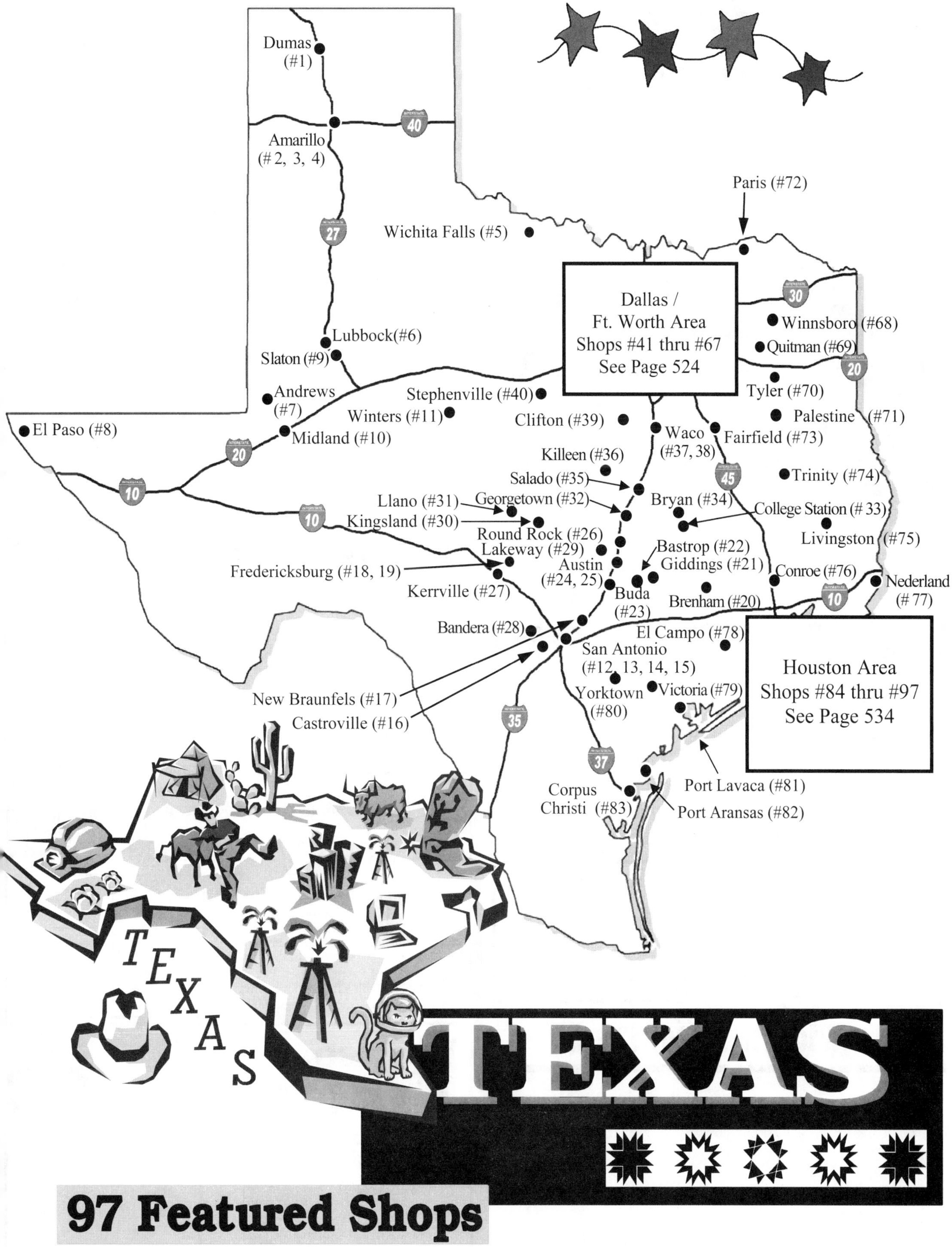
Dumas (#1)
Amarillo (# 2, 3, 4)
40
27
Wichita Falls (#5)
Paris (#72)
Dallas / Ft. Worth Area Shops #41 thru #67 See Page 524
30
Winnsboro (#68)
Quitman (#69)
20
Lubbock(#6)
Slaton (#9)
Andrews (#7)
Stephenville (#40)
Tyler (#70)
El Paso (#8)
Winters (#11)
Clifton (#39)
Palestine (#71)
Midland (#10)
Waco (#37, 38)
Fairfield (#73)
20
Killeen (#36)
45
Salado (#35)
Trinity (#74)
10
Llano (#31)
Georgetown (#32)
Bryan (#34)
College Station (# 33)
10
Kingsland (#30)
Round Rock (#26)
Livingston (#75)
Lakeway (#29)
Bastrop (#22)
Fredericksburg (#18, 19)
Austin (#24, 25)
Giddings (#21)
Conroe (#76)
Nederland (# 77)
Kerrville (#27)
Buda (#23)
Brenham (#20)
10
Bandera (#28)
El Campo (#78)
San Antonio (#12, 13, 14, 15)
Houston Area Shops #84 thru #97 See Page 534
New Braunfels (#17)
Yorktown (#80)
Victoria (#79)
Castroville (#16)
35
37
Corpus Christi (#83)
Port Lavaca (#81)
Port Aransas (#82)
TEXAS
TEXAS
97 Featured Shops

Dumas, TX #1

Mon - Fri 10 - 5
Sat 10 - 4

Down Home Quilts

102 E. 7th, Suite A 79029
(806) 934-4041 Fax: (806) 934-4042
Owner: Helen King
Est: 2001 1800 sq.ft. 2500 Bolts
downhomequilts@nts-online.net

Quilt kits for those on the go. Fabric, batting & notions for those planning their own. And Custom Quilting to help you finish your project.

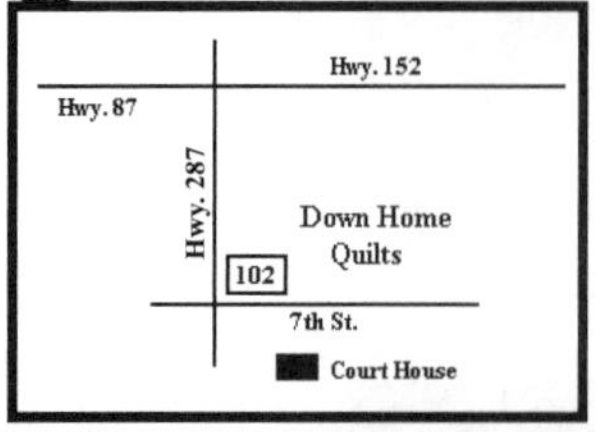

Amarillo, TX #2

Mon - Sat 10 - 5

Pam's Quilting Corner

204 S. Western St. 79106
(806) 373-7777
Owner: Pam Burkhalter
Est: 2005 7500 sq.ft. 2000 Bolts
pamsquiltcorner@hotmail.com
www.pamsquiltingcorner.com

Quilting supplies, fabric, notions, and books. Route 66 Fabric.

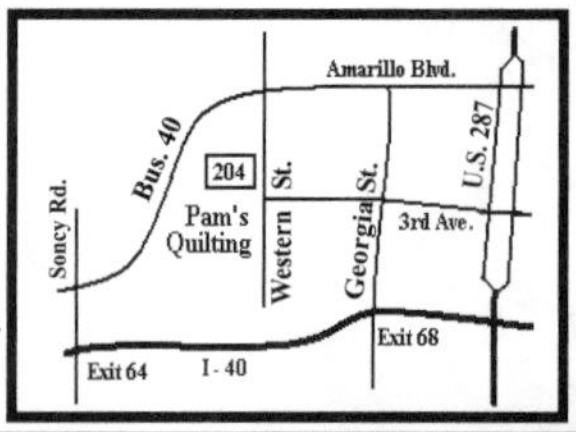

Amarillo, TX #3

Mon - Sat 10 - 5:30

SISTERS' SCRAPS *Quilt Shop*

6018 SW 33rd Ave. 79106
www.sistersscraps.com

(877) 727-8458
(806) 372-0660
Est: 2003

We offer beautiful quilting fabric, wool, stitcheries, and great, friendly service.

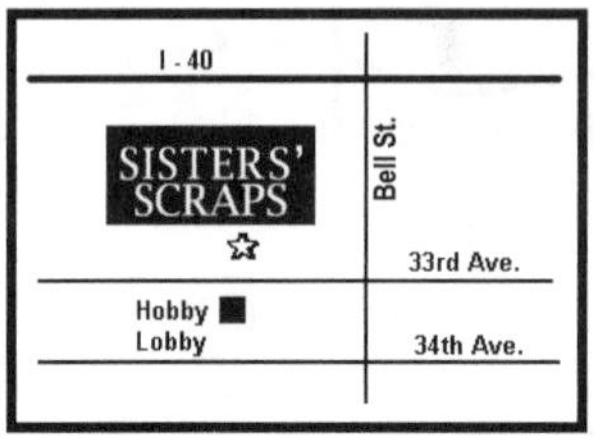

Amarillo, TX #4

Mon - Sat 9:30 - 5:30

Get the Red Carpet Treatment at

R & R Quilts and More

4332 Teckla Blvd. 79109-5422
(806) 359-6235
rrquilts@amaonline.com
www.rrquilts.com

Over 5000 Bolts of 100% cotton fabrics. Classes, Supplies, Books and Patterns.

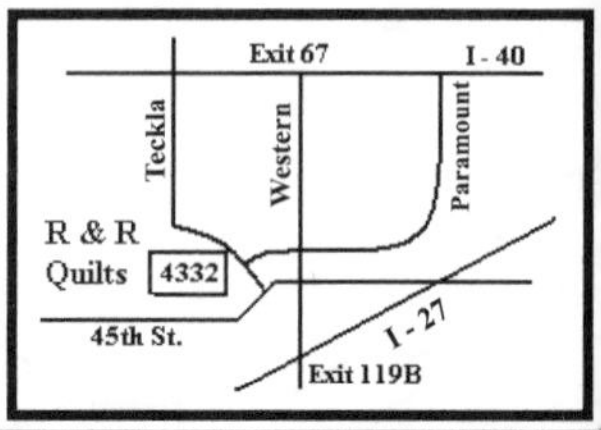

Wichita Falls, TX #5

Tues-Fri 10-5:30
Sat 10-3

The Enchanted Quilt

3401 Kemp Blvd., Suite M 76308
(940) 689-0990
Owner: Kathy Sims
info@theenchantedquilt.com
www.theenchantedquilt.com

Specializing in Western, black & whites, children's and flannels. Also books, notions, patterns & classes.

Est: 2008 1700 sq.ft.
Free Newsletter

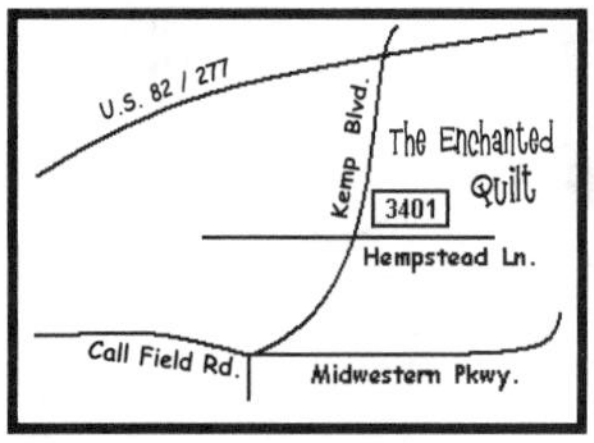

Lubbock, TX #6

Mon-Fri 10 - 6
Sat 10 - 5

Rachael's Fabrics & Quilting

4636 50th St. 79414
(806) 795-4693 or (877) 778-6167
Fax (806) 795-4408 Est: 1980
mail@rachaelsfabrics.com
www.rachaelsfabrics.com
Owner: Barbara Harris Pfaff Dealer

Newest fabrics, notions, books, patterns, and machines. Custom machine quilts. Rug hooking, punch needle & wool applique. Excellent classes, Wonderful displays and really friendly people!

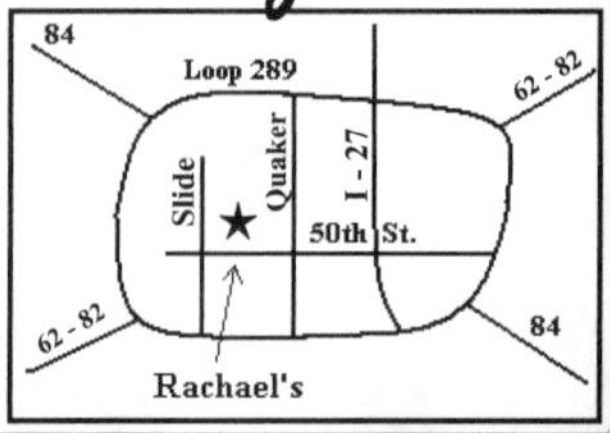

Andrews, TX #7

Tues - Fri 10 - 6
Sat 10 - 5

The Sewing Cottage

102 S. Main 79714
(432) 524-7409 Fax: (432) 524-2216
Est: 2007
sewingcottage@windstream.net

2100 bolts of Fabric, Classes, Patterns, Books. Quilt Kits, and lots more. Authorized Husqvarna Viking and Singer

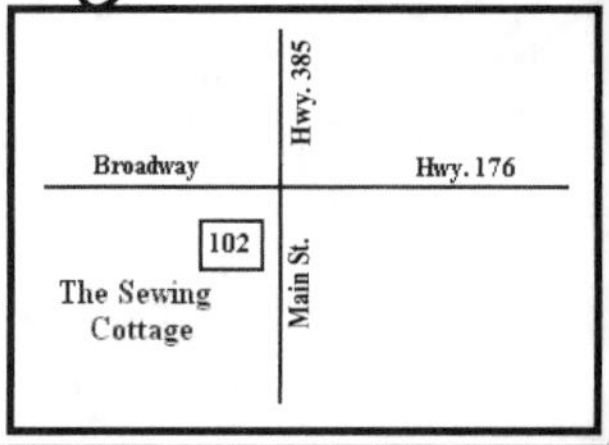

El Paso, TX #8

Mon - Sat 10 - 5
Tues 12 - 5

SEW WHAT'S NEW

7410 Remcon Circle 79912
(915) 760-5300
sew@lascruces.com

www.sewwhatsnewlascruces.com

Fabrics for Quilters
Notions, Classes & Services
Authorized Husqvarna Viking, Pfaff & Singer Dealer.
"THE Fun Place to SEWcialize"

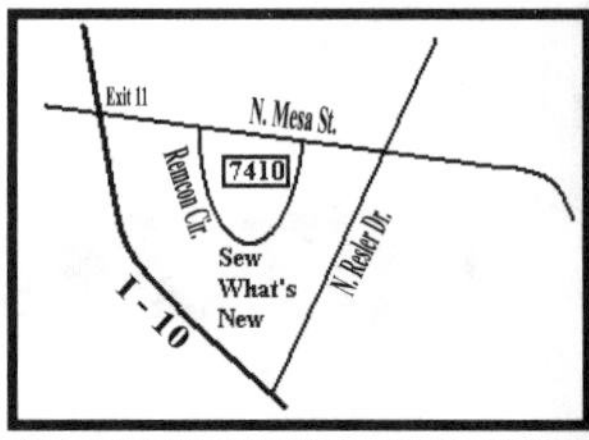

Full service, premier quilt shop

Quilts-N-More

1000+ bolts of outstanding 100% cotton fabrics
300+ quality quilt reference books
150+ unique pattern titles
Specializing in a wide array of color and reproduction; plus a tremendous selection of supplies, batiks, batting, gadgets and quilting tools. Largest Selection of Reproduction Fabrics on the South Plains.
An uptown quilt shop in a small town atmosphere.
Where Brights Are Neutrals!
Custom Quilts & T-Shirt Quilts
Gift Certificates Available

www.thelastlittlequiltshop.com

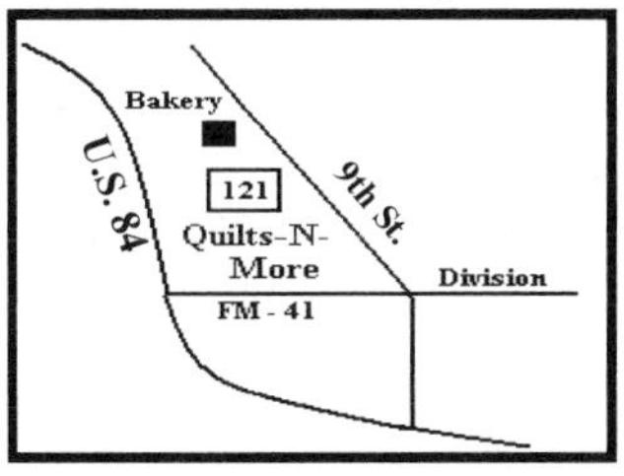

Take any Slaton Exit off Hwy. 84. Follow to downtown.

Slaton, TX #9

121 South 9th, Slaton, TX 79364
806-828-3222 Fax: 806-828-3990
quilts-n-more@clearwire.net
Owner: Nancy Pracht
Mon - Fri 9:30 - 5:30
Thurs 9:30 - 7 Sat 9:30 - 3

APQS Long Arm Quilt Machines ❖ Accu-Cut Dealer
Custom & Commercial embroidery available

APQS American Professional Quilting Systems

accuquilt better cuts make better quilts

Midland, TX #10

the quilting patch

where friendships grow and creativity flows

3323 N. Midland Dr., Suite 110 432-262-6616
Midland, TX 79707 theqp@grandecom.net
Owners: Sally Maddox and Shawnna Hoffman
www.quiltingpatchtx.com

Large selection of books, notions, accessories, gift items.
Over 4000 bolts of 100% cotton fabric.

Full line of Pfaff & Bernina sewing machines, accessories and Embroidery CD's.

We have a great staff who are very knowledgeable and friendly and willing to help you.

Mon-Fri 10am-6pm
Sat 10am-5pm
Closed Sundays

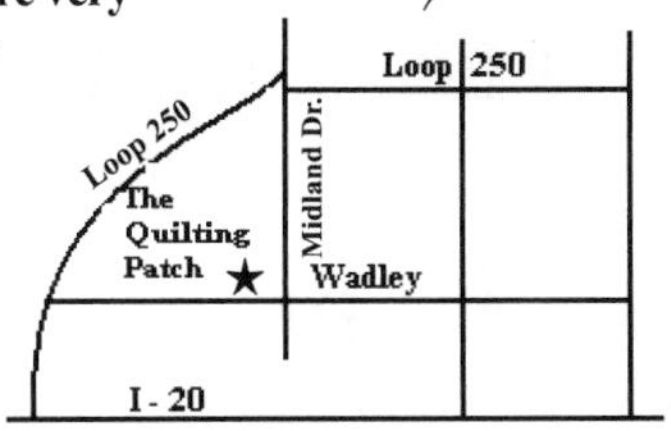

Winters, TX #11

Mon - Fri 9 - 5:30
Sat 9:30 - 2:30

Bluebonnet Mercantile

106 S. Main St. 79567
(325) 754-4057 Fax: Same
Owner: Cheryl Bryan
Est: 2004 2000+ Bolts
bluebonnet@wtxs.net
Great selection of fabrics, books, patterns and notions. Moda, RJR, P&B, Benartex, Thimbleberries, Blank, Maywood & Avlyn fabrics. Gifts too.

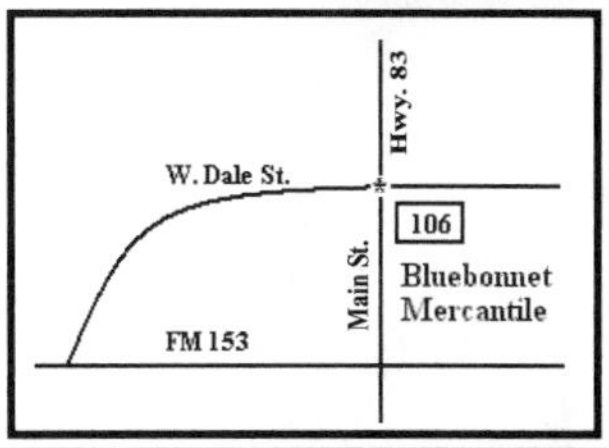

San Antonio, TX #12

Mon - Fri 9:30 - 5:30
Sat 9:30 - 3

Seventh Heaven Quilt Shop

6706 N. New Braunfels 78209
(210) 822-9980
Owner: Dixie Bradbury
quilts@seventhheavenquiltshop.com
www.seventhheavenquiltshop.com
Est: 1990 3600 sq.ft. 3000+ Bolts
Heavenly delight 100% Cotton Fabrics
RJR, P&B, Moda and more.
Patterns, Books and Supplies.
Baby Lock Sewing Machines.

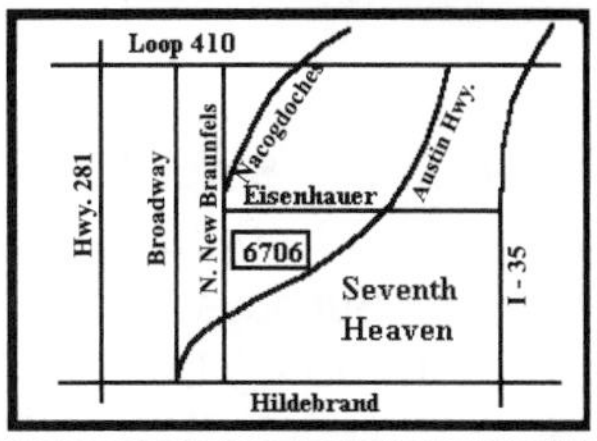

San Antonio, TX #13

Sew Special Quilts - Bernina

The Market at Leon Springs
24165 IH 10 West #421, 78257
(800) 891-8279 or (210) 698-6076
Owner: Laurie Mangold
Est: 1987 2600 sq.ft. 1800 Bolts

Open: Mon - Sat

A full service shop for all of your quilting and wearable needs. Staffed by a helpful, friendly group of dedicated employees. Come see our unique "Quilt Block Floor".

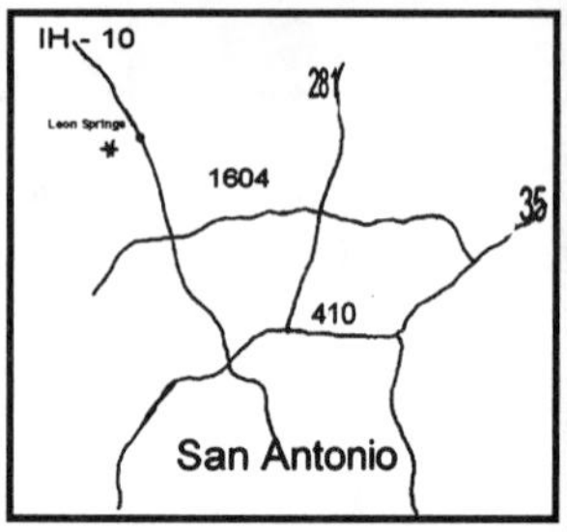

Exit 550 from Boerne
Exit 551 from San Antonio

CREATIVE SEWING CENTER

11777 West Ave. at Blanco Rd. 78216
210-344-0791 or toll free 877-331-7862
info@creativesewingonline.com

Mon - Sat
9:30 - 6:00

Come visit us when you are in the San Antonio area. Bus tours welcome and handicap parking right in front. Choose from over 8000 bolts. We have 8000 square feet filled with beautiful quilting and natural fiber fabrics, with over 3000 bolts of novelty prints. Large selection of rulers, quilting accessories and books. We carry the largest selection of threads in the area—from machine embellishment to quilting & fiber arts. Sales, service and machine instruction for Bernina, Brother and HandiQuilter. Machines from $249.00 to the most exciting embroidery machines and software on the market today. We have a large selection of sewing machine notions, accessories and cabinets.

www.creativesewingonline.com

San Antonio, TX #14

San Antonio, TX #15

Mon - Fri 10 - 7
Sat 10 - 4

MEMORIES BY THE YARD

8015 Mainland Dr. 78250
(210) 520-4833 Fax: (210) 520-6216
www.memoriesbytheyard.com
Featuring 3000+ cotton and flannel fabrics from Kaufman - Hoffman - Benartex - RJR Timeless Treasures - Moda - FabriQuilt Andover - Michael Miller - Cranston Marcus Brothers. Books, Patterns & Quilting Supplies.

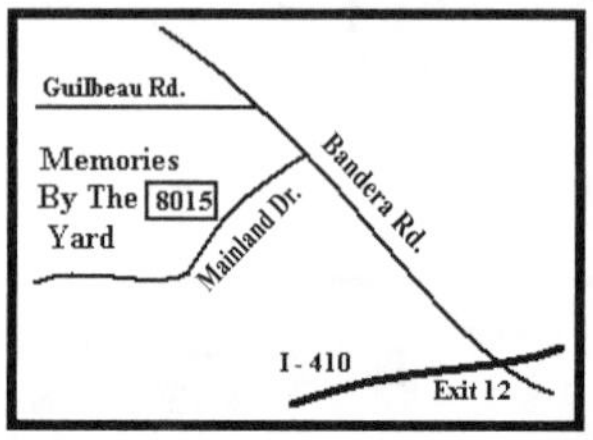

Fabric 'N Friends

Est: 2003

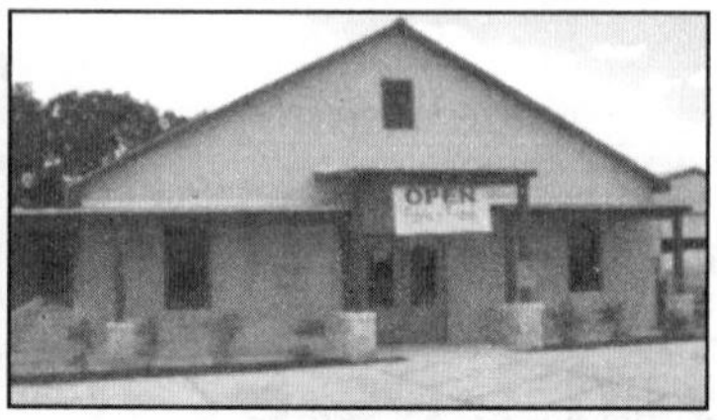

813 Paris St. 78009
(830) 931-0141
Owner: Jeanne M. Stephens
3600 sq.ft. 3000+ Bolts
fabricnfriends@msn.com
www.fabricnfriends.com

Castroville, TX #16

Mon - Sat 9:30 - 5:30 Tues til 7

Friendly Service providing top quality cotton fabrics - batiks, homespuns, brights, western, 30's and great prints. Patterns, books, notions & classes too.

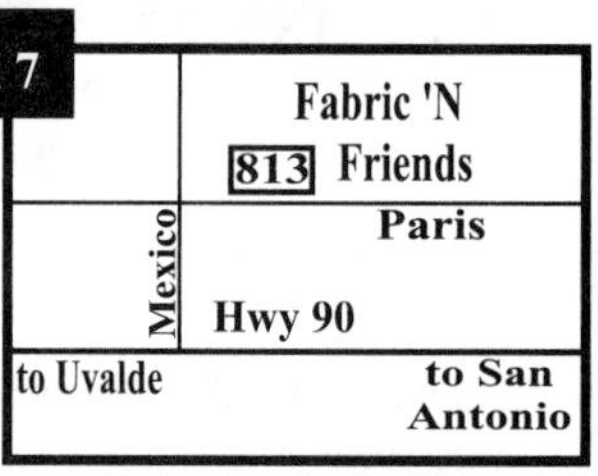

creative sewlutions @ The QUILT HAUS

651 N. Business IH35, Ste. 510
New Braunfels, TX 78130
830-620-1382
www.creativesewlutions.com

Eclectic selection of over 5000 bolts of fabric, books, patterns, notions, gifts & classes. Friendly, expert staff. Quilt Retreats.

OPEN DAILY
Monday - Saturday
9:30 - 5:30
Sundays
12:00 - 5:00

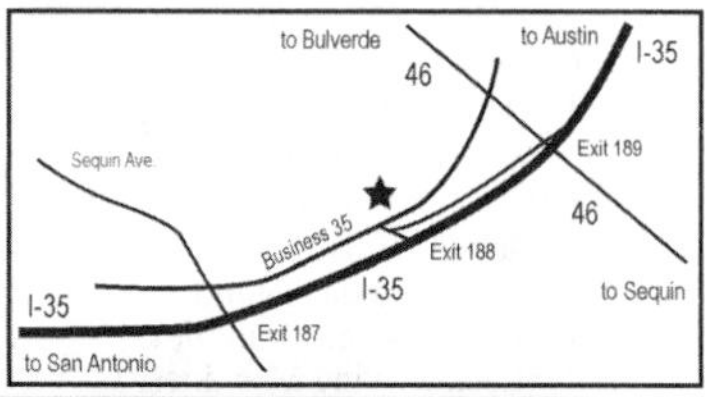

New Braunfels, TX #17

Fredericksburg, TX #18

Mon - Fri 9:30 - 5:30
Call for Sat. Hours

Pocketful of Poseys

311 East Highway St. 78624
(830) 990-4140 or (877) 427-6739
Fax: (830) 990-8221
Owner: Cynthia Laurent-Conner
Est: 1999
3600 sq.ft.
1500+ Bolts

Claurent@KTC.com
www.pocketfulofposeysquilting.com
Fun shop to relax & design your quilt project. Located in the beautiful hill country.

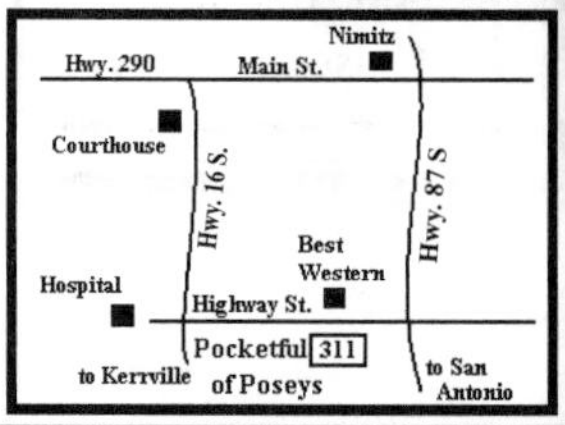

#19

Deep in the Square of Texas!

The Revolutionary Quilting System
Used by Thousands is Available in Historic Fredericksburg, Texas.

FREDERICKSBURG IS NESTLED IN THE HEART OF RICH TEXAS HISTORY *and* DISTINCTIVE CULTURE. Located in the Texas hill country–65 miles northwest of San Antonio and 70 miles west of Austin–it's the perfect setting for a quilter's paradise.

The Fredericksburg Pie Company is home to many Square in a Square™ quilting products and is located one block off Fredericksburg's renowned main street: 3.5 miles of unique shops, century-old homes, and days of enjoyment.

Jodi Barrows has developed a reputation in the quilting world of weaving her love of history into an extensive collection of custom fabric designs, as well as her historical novels. Fredericksburg is the perfect setting to experience this unique blend of quilting and history.

MEET JODI IN PERSON!

Don't miss out on your opportunity to meet Jodi Barrows in person at **The Fredericksburg Pie Company**!

Join us for book signings and lectures throughout the year. See Jodi's schedule at squareinasquare.com. We look forward to seeing you there!

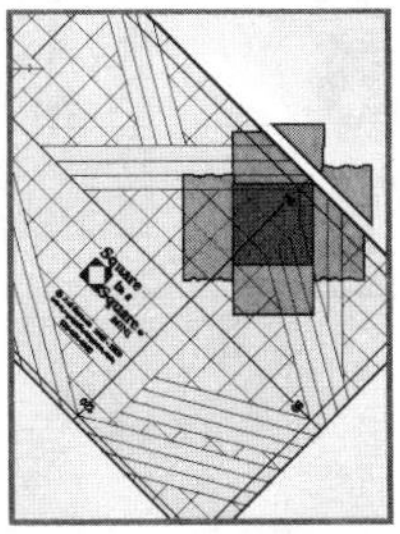

ONE SQUARE DOES IT ALL

The technique begins with a piece of fabric to which strips are attached, and then cut with a rotary cutter in a unique way. The results are entire blocks or parts of blocks quickly and accurately achieved. Learn more by watching videos on our website.

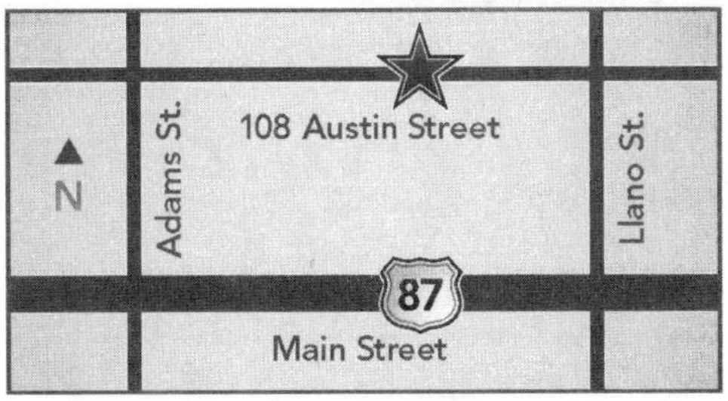

TOOLS, QUILTS, & PATTERNS

While in Fredericksburg, be sure to see the variety of products and quilts for sale at **The Fredericksburg Pie Company**, or visit squareinasquare.com.

The Fredericksburg Pie Company
108 E. Austin Street
Fredericksburg, TX 78624
1 Block Off Main Street Between Adams & Llano
Parking in the rear
(830) 990-6992
Monday - Saturday: 10 am – 6 pm
Sunday: 11 am – 4 pm | *Closed Wednesday*

SNS PUBLISHING (888) 624-6260 squareinasquare.com

Brenham, TX #20

Stitch Haven

For Those Who Love Quilting Needlework and Fine Fabrics

Tues - Fri 10 - 5:30
Sat 10 - 3

Featuring Cotton Fabrics and Supplies for Quilting, Wearable Art, Cross-Stitch, and Embroidery

1600 S. Day St. 77833
(979) 836-3200
stitchhaven@mail.com

www.stitchhaven.com

Giddings, TX #21

Mon - Fri 9 - 6
Sat 10 - 3

ALL AROUND THE BLOCK QUILT SHOP

979 N. Leon 78942
(979) 542-2782
allaroundtheblockquiltshop@verizon.net
Est: 2003

Machine Quilting
Fabric, Notions,
Books, Classes
"A Place Where Friends Gather!"

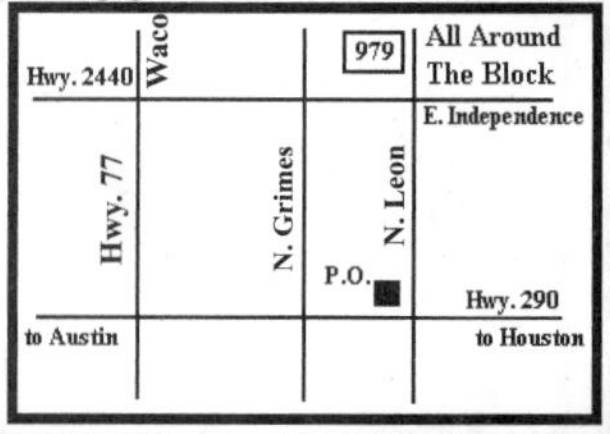

Bastrop, TX #22

Tues - Fri 10 - 6
Sat 9 - 4

Lost Pines Quilt Shop

709 Chestnut St. 78602
(512) 321-9300 Est: 2009
Owners: Linda & Duane Hudson
1700 sq.ft. Free Online Newsletter
lpqs@att.net
www.lostpinesquiltshop.com
Quaint Quilt Shop in Historic Downtown Bastrop, Texas. Just off Main Street.
The only Quilt Shop in the County!!!

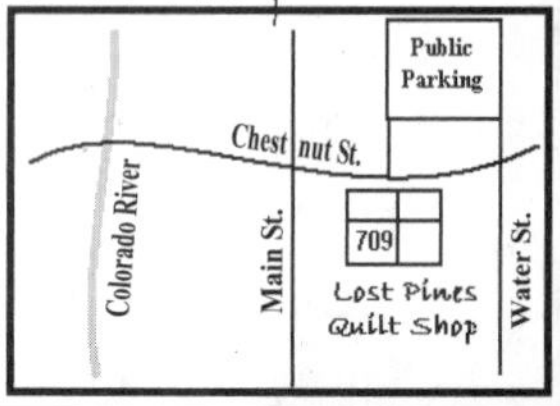

Buda, TX #23

Tues - Sat 10 - 5

B & B Quilting and Gifts

107 S. Austin St., 78610
(512) 312-2299
www.bbquilting.com Est: 2004
Owners: Nancy Brinkley & Lori Beckers

Over 3000 bolts of 100% quality cotton fabrics, patterns, books and notions for the quilter or seamstress.
Jewelry and quilt related gifts.

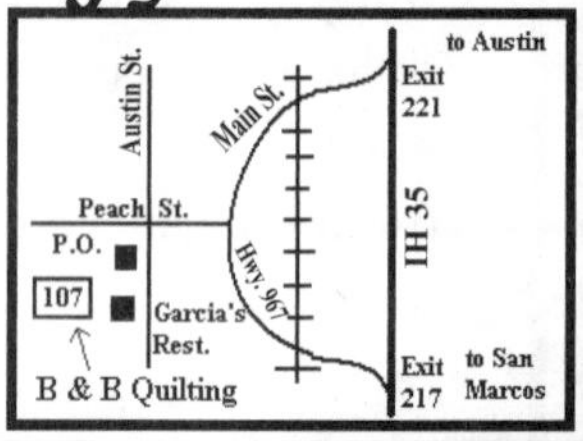

Austin, TX #25

Mon - Sat 10 - 5
Thur til 8

The Quilt Store, Inc.

2700 W. Anderson, #301 78757
(512) 453-1145
www.quiltstore.com

More than 5,000 bolts of 100% cotton fabric plus much more.

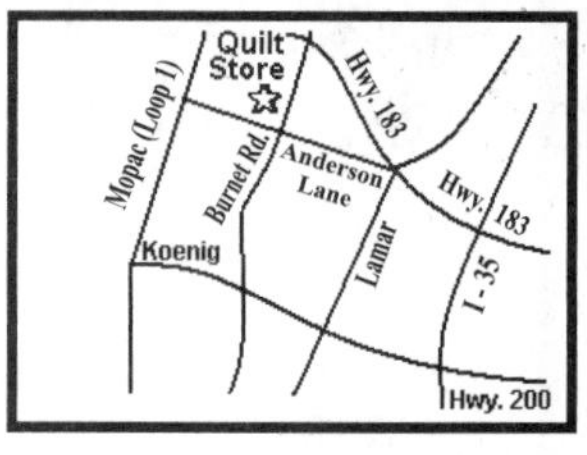

Austin, TX #24

HONEY BEE QUILT STORE

9308 Anderson Mill Rd. #300 Austin, TX 78729
(512) 257-1269

Our philosophy is customer service, customer service, customer service.

www.honeybeequiltstore.com

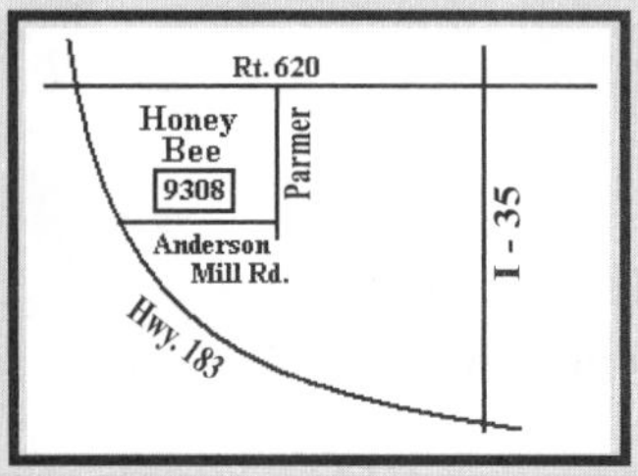

Mon - Sat 9 - 5
Tues til 8
Sun 1 - 5

Round Rock, TX #26

Evenings & Weekends By Appointment

Kim's Quilts

Call for Appointment and Location
(512) 248-8858
Owner: Kim Jones Est: 1998
www.kims-quilts.com

Custom quilt studio. Excellent quality, affordable prices. Machine quilted or hand-tied. See quilts, books & crafts that are in stock on my website.

Great Stuff for the Quilter and Sewing Enthusiast

CREATIONS

Kerrville, TX #27

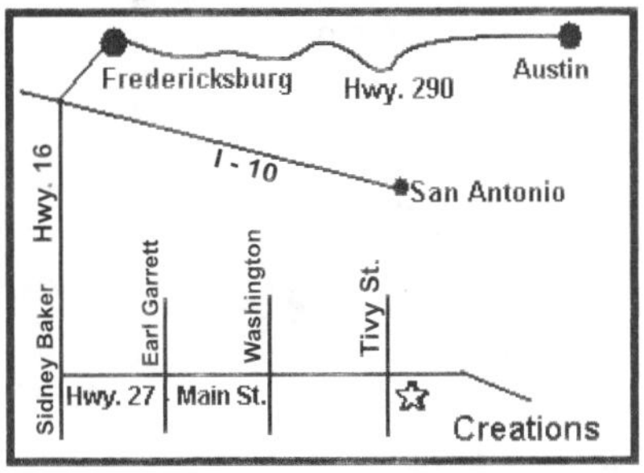

CREATIONS
1013 MAIN
KERRVILLE
830-896-8088
Est: 1978

Beautiful fabrics and inspiring displays are set in a turn of the century home. You'll find great quilting fabrics as well as linens and Bali rayons. Enjoy a cup of coffee while wandering through the shop. Take an on-line tour of our store at: www.creations-online.com

Watch for the opening of The Main House in early 2011. This is our 8,000 sq. foot retreat center located next to Creations. The latest news is always available on our website.

Monday--Saturday: 9:30--5:30
Sunday: 12:30--4:00

e-mail: creations@creations-online.com
Featured in the 1996 edition of Quilt Sampler

Bandera, TX #28

Gone Quiltin'

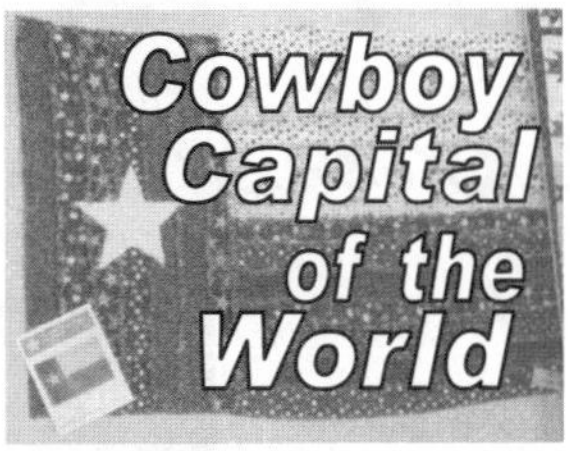

1115 Cedar St., Bandera, TX
(830) 796-4360
Mailing: 158 Old Orchard Ln.
Bandera, TX 78003
Owner: Tammy Kimmel
tammy@gonequiltin.com

Hours:
Mon - Fri 9 - 5
Sat 10 - 3

www.gonequiltin.com

- 3000 square feet of fabrics (including many flannels), notions, books and patterns.
- We specialize in Western, Southwestern, Bluebonnet, wildflower and uniquely Texas fabrics.
- On-site sewing machine service, repair and restoration.
- Long-arm quilting, most quilts finished within 7 days.
- Rent our long-arm to finish your own quilts.
- AccuQuilt Go! retailer.
- Arrow and Kangaroo Cabinets
- Tin Lizzie 18 LS retailer
- Full line of Hemingworth Embroidery Threads

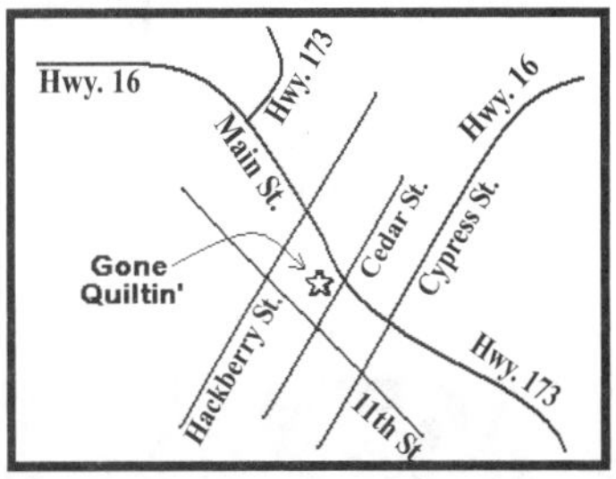

Bandera has a huge visitor community, with RV parks all over town and many winter Texans.

1503-A RR 620 N 78734
512-294-2776
Owner: Jessica Dieterle
www.thecottoncupboard.com

Lakeway, TX #29

A quilters home away from home nestled in the Texas hill country

We encourage creativity and self expression through fabric. We offer notions, Quilting and Sewing classes for all ages, sharpening, repair, and fat quarters for every fabric.

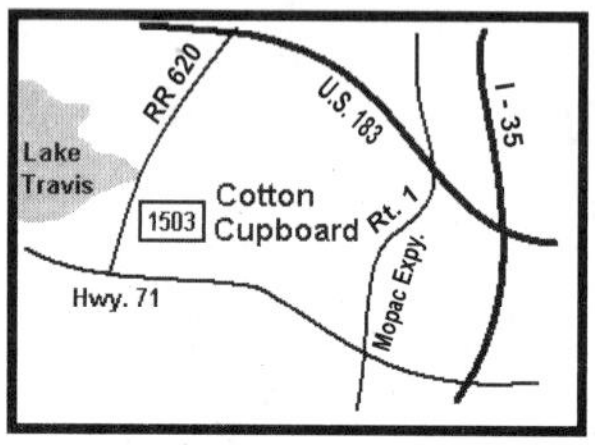

Fax: 866-231-2947
Est: 2009 2400 sq.ft.
2000+ bolts
Online newsletter
sewhappy@thecottoncupboard.com

Mon - Fri 10 - 6
Sat 10 - 6

Kingsland, TX #30

Mon - Sat 10 - 5

Barb's Quilt Nook, Etc.

120 Dan St. P.O. Box 868 78639
(325) 388-5225 Fax: (325) 388-3999
Owners: Barbara & Jon Selby Est: 2001
barbsew@verizon.net 3600 sq.ft.
www.barbsquilts.com

All Your Quilting Needs!
100% Cotton Fabrics - Books - Patterns
Notions - Classes
Come, We would Love to Meet You!

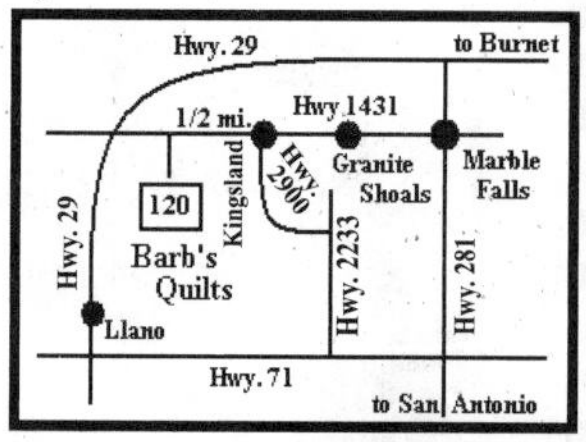

Llano, TX #31

Mon, Tues, Thurs, Fri 5:30p-7:30p
Wed 1 - 5

The Country Quilt Shop

102 Rio Oaks Lane (CR 116)
P.O. Box 996 78643
(325) 247-4247
Owner: Ann Feller Est: 2009
1100 sq.ft. Free Newsletter
thecountryquiltshop@gmail.com

We are a new shop just opened and growing fast. Carrying 30's, western, contemporary, baby & children's & lots of traditional fabrics.

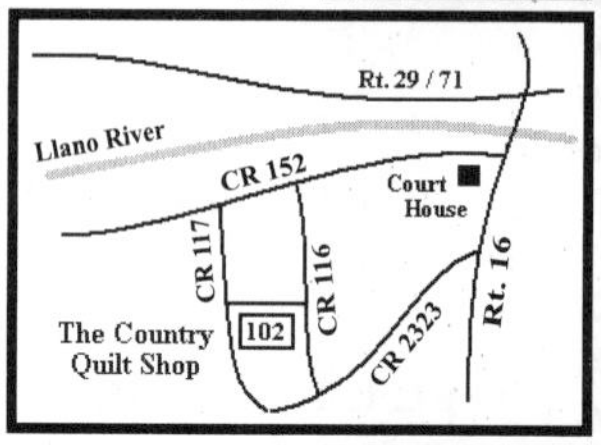

College Station, TX #33

Mon - Sat 10 - 6

Pruitt's Fabrics

318 George Bush Dr. 77840
(979) 693-9357
www.pruittsfabric.com Est: 1946

Oldest Fabric Shop in Texas.
Texas A&M Fabrics.
Quilting cottons, ribbons & trims.
Family Owned

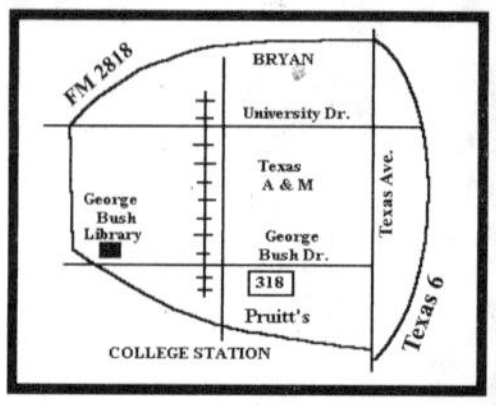

Georgetown, TX #32

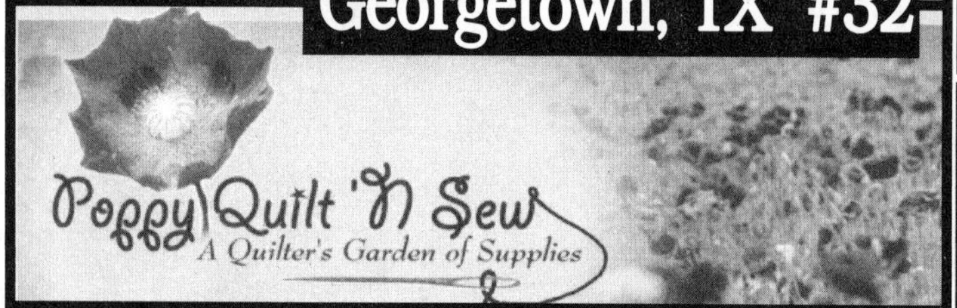

Over 3000 bolts of fabric with friendly service to assist you.

Mon - Fri 10 - 5 Sat 10 - 4

4106 Williams Dr. #102
78628
512-863-6108
Owner: Anita Brockell
Est: 2006 2000 sq.ft.
Online Newsletter
Fax: 512-863-6172
poppyquiltnsew@gmail.com

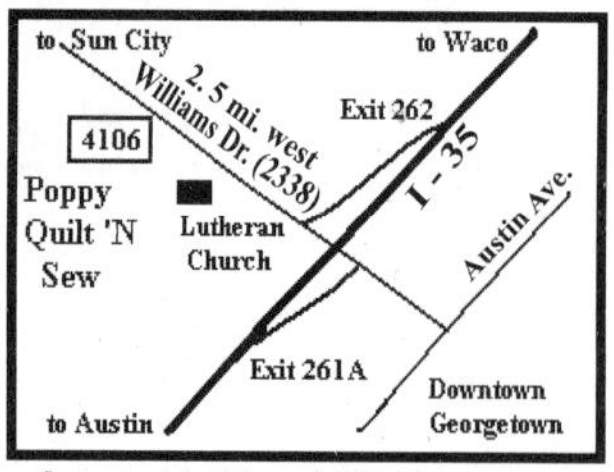

Located in historic Georgetown just 2 1/2 miles west of I - 35.

www.poppyquiltnsew.com

LONE★STAR
Quiltworks

www.lonestarquiltworks.com

4301 S. Texas Ave., Bryan, TX 77802
(979) 595-1072 Est: 2005
lonestarquiltworks@suddenlink.net 3000 sq.

Tues - Fri 10 - 6
Sat 10 - 4

Bryan, TX #34

Color Consultation

- Over 5000 Bolts of Exquisite Fabrics
- Yarn and Knitting Supplies
- Notions, Books, and Patterns
- Books & Patterns
- Longarm Machine Quilting
- Quilting, Knitting & Crochet Classes
- T-Shirt Quilts & Custom Quilts
- Authorized Babylock Dealer

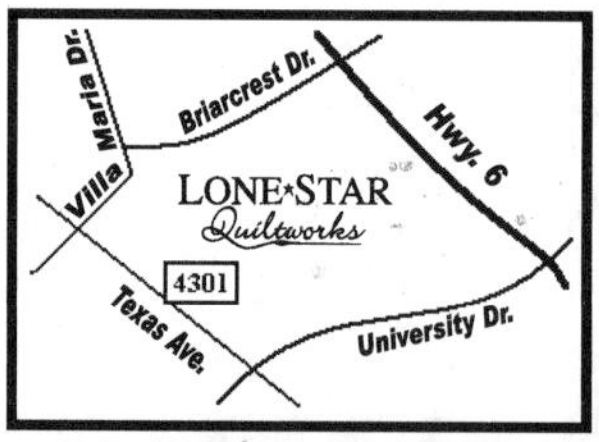

A Sewing Basket

560 N. Main Street Salado, TX 76571
1-877-244-0450 or 1-254-947-5423
sewbskt@vvm.com
www.TheSewingBasket.com

Quality fabric, quilting supplies & classes, sewing notions, books, patterns, and sew much more! Specializing in Cowboy Fabric.

Open Mon-Sat 9:30-5:30
Sundays 12-4:30

Easy on and off Interstate 35.

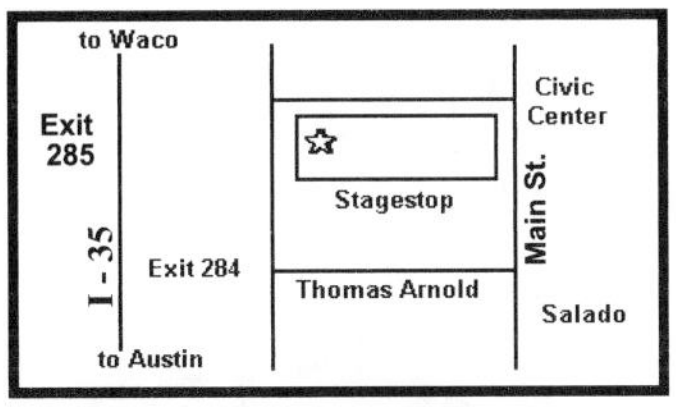

Salado, TX #35

Killeen, TX #36

Tues—Fri 9:30 — 5:30
Sat 9:30-4:30

Quiltin' Country

4904 W. Stan Schlueter 76549
(254) 554-3700
Quiltinctry2@aol.com
www.quiltincountryonline.com
Owner: Gayle S. Smith
Est: 2003 2000 sq. ft.

Beautiful 100% cotton fabrics, friendly, knowledgeable staff, spacious showroom, books, patterns, notions & classes.

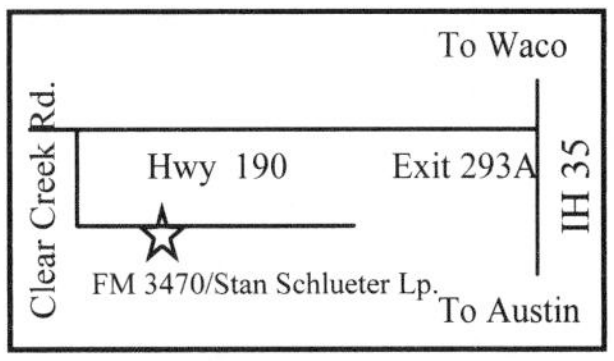

Authorized Husqvarna Viking Dealer & Certified Machine Technician

Husqvarna VIKING

Waco, TX #37

Appointments from 8 am to 8 pm

Homestead Sewing & Quilting

1012 Meixner 76705

Quilt Restoration • Custom Quilts
Finishing • Rebinding
memory quilts, pillows, woven rugs, made from "loved one's" clothing

Est. 1980 **254 829-2380**

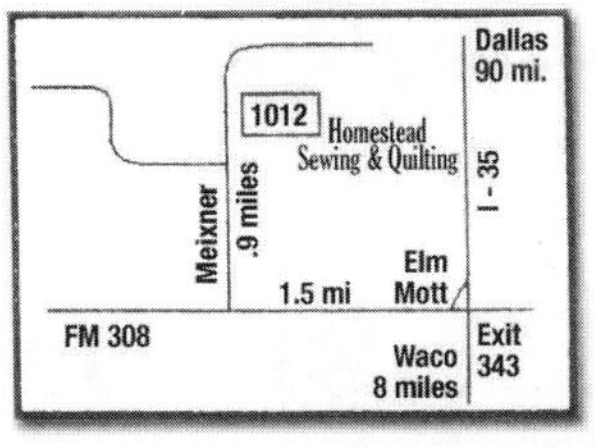

Waco, TX #38

Mon - Fri 9:30 - 5:30
Sat 9:30 - 4:30

Tomorrow's Quilts

800 Lake Air Dr. 76710
(254) 741-6988
tomorrowsquilts@sbcglobal.net
www.tomorrowsquilts.com
Owner: Linda Mather
Est: 2004 3200 sq. ft. 3000+ Bolts
A Friendly and inspiring quilt shop in the heart of Texas.
Quality Fabrics, Kits, Gifts and Classes.

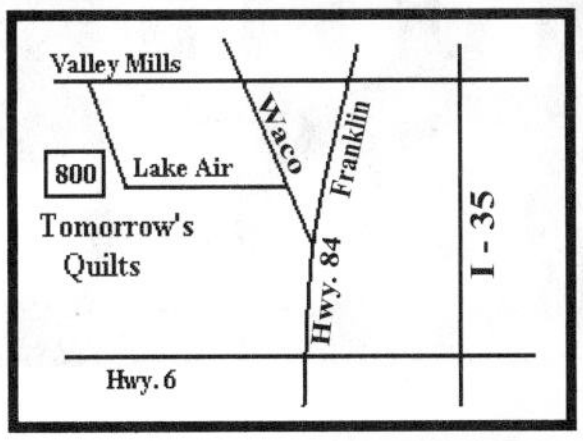

Stephenville, TX #40

Mon - Sat 9:30 - 5:30

The Flying Needle

1495 W. South Loop
76401 Est: 1971
(254) 965-7577 or (877) FNEEDLE
theflyingneeedle@htcomp.net
www.theflyingneedle.net
3000+ Bolts of Cotton from Dozens of Manufacturers, Notions New and Old, Hundreds of Books, Patterns and Supplies.

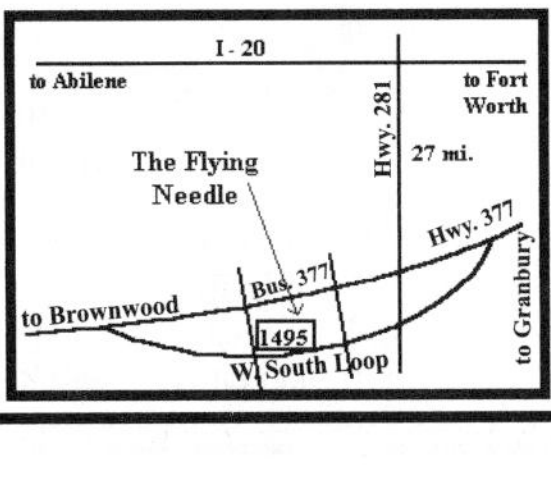

Quilting Cousins

Quilting Fabric and Notions

603 S. Avenue G (Hwy. 6)
P.O. Box 17 Clifton, TX 76634
254-675-0010 Owner: Glenda J. Sager

Come to visit our lovely shop in the hill country of Texas. The tea and coffee is always ready and the cookie basket full.

Tues - Fri 10 - 6
Sat 10 - 2

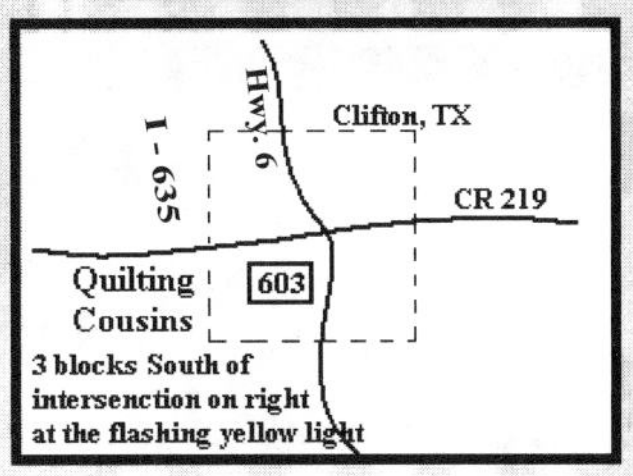

Fax: 254-675-0017
Est: 2007 1400 sq.ft.
1500 Bolts
Free Newsletter

quiltingcousins_gjsager@yahoo.com
www.quiltingcousins.net

Clifton, TX #39

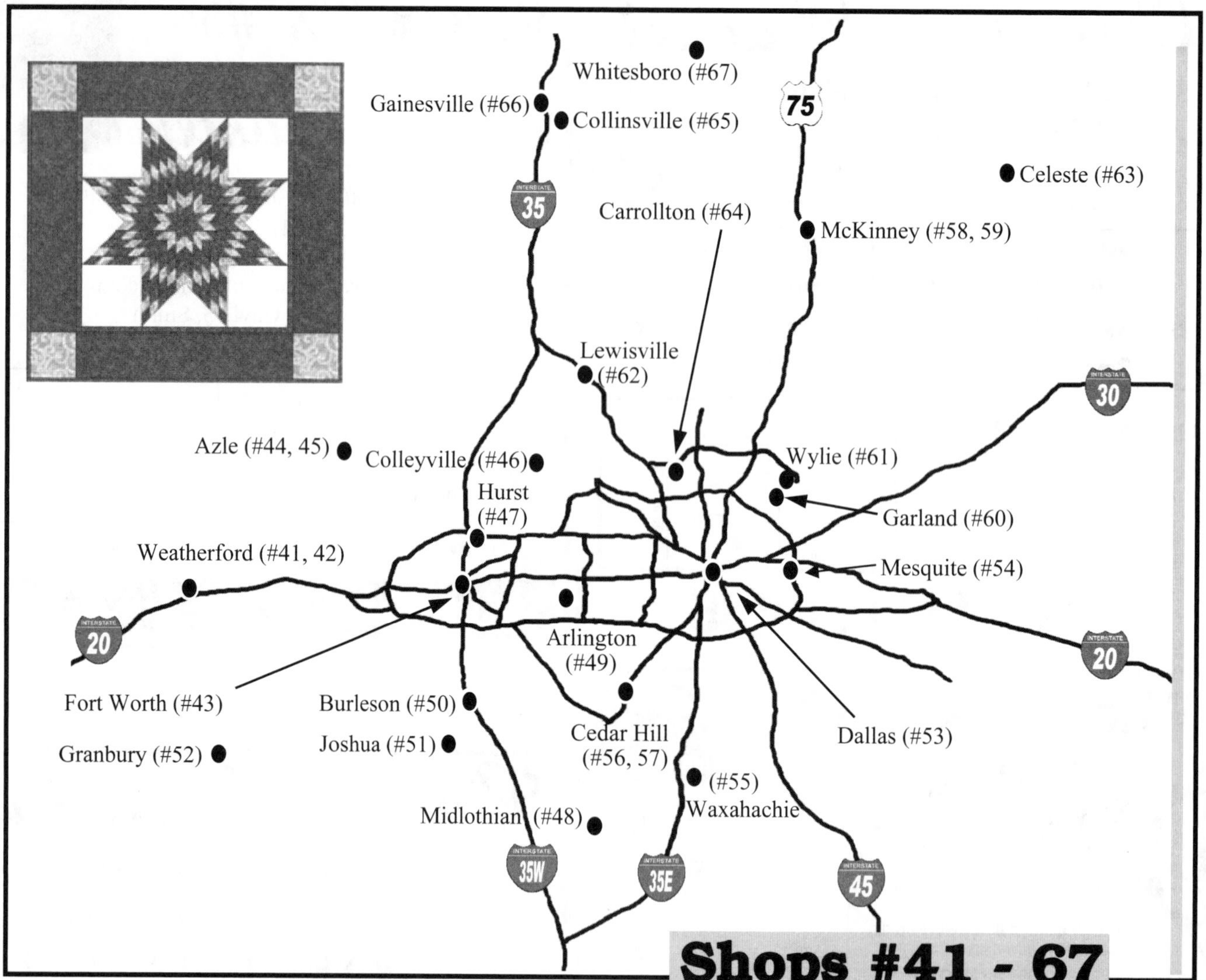

Shops #41 - 67

27 Featured Shops

Fort Worth Dallas Area

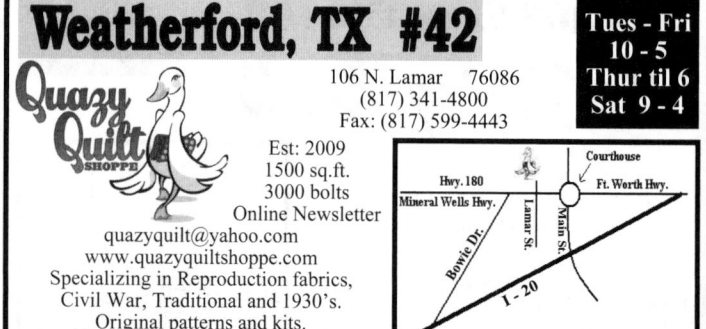

Peachtree Quilts

Weatherford, TX #41

133 N. Waco St. 76086
(817) 599-4114
Owner: Linda Payne
1800+ Bolts

Tues - Sat 10 - 5:30

Specializing in Batiks and Designer fabrics
Books, Kits, Patterns and Notions

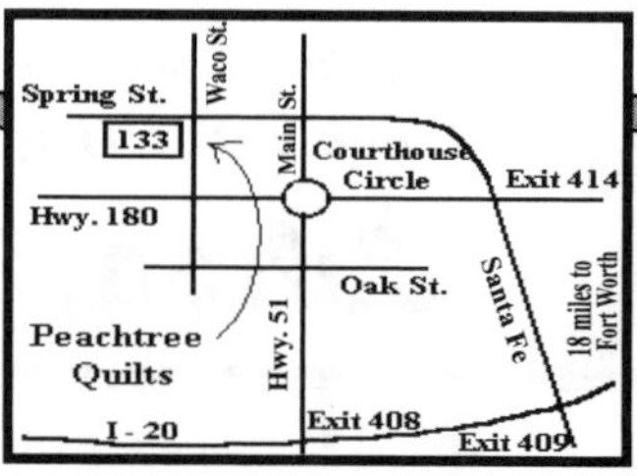

Weatherford, TX #42

Quazy Quilt Shoppe

106 N. Lamar 76086
(817) 341-4800
Fax: (817) 599-4443

Tues - Fri 10 - 5
Thur til 6
Sat 9 - 4

Est: 2009
1500 sq.ft.
3000 bolts
Online Newsletter
quazyquilt@yahoo.com
www.quazyquiltshoppe.com
Specializing in Reproduction fabrics, Civil War, Traditional and 1930's.
Original patterns and kits.
Classes, Notions, Books. Custom Quilting.

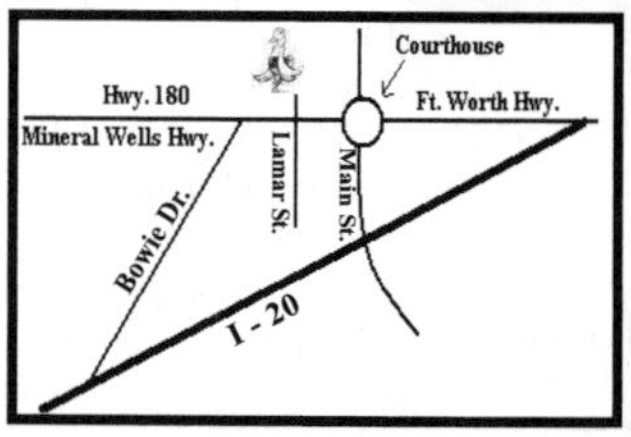

Cabbage Rose

Quilting, Fabrics and Gifts

Over 8,000 fabrics in stock,
5,000 sq. ft. of quilting paradise.

- A complete line of quilting and sewing supplies including books, notions, patterns, gifts and classes.
- Fabrics range from Florals, Western, Pastels, Novelty prints, Reproductions, Brights, Batiks, and more!!
- Michael Miller, Amy Butler, Heather Bailey, Kaffe Fassett, RJR, Marcus Brothers, Free Spirit, all the Moda Designers and more!!
- Wonderful assortment of quilting patterns, children clothing, patterns, bags, Serendipity Studios, Fig Tree & Amy Butler - and so much more!!
- Veda Wilhite original patterns and books.
- Located near Fort Worth's Cultural District.

"Come spend the day with us."

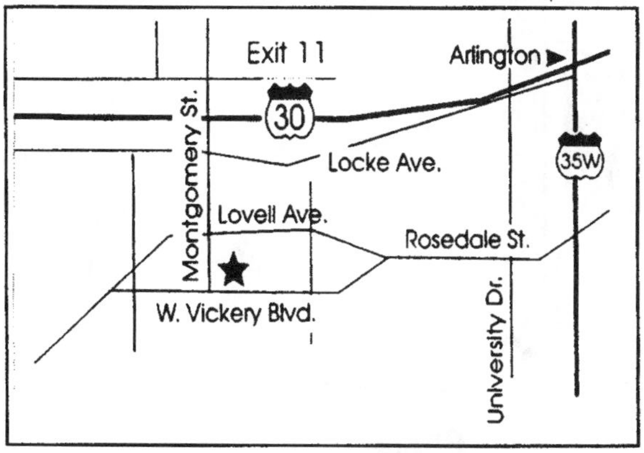

3526 W. Vickery Blvd.
Fort Worth, TX 76107
(817) 377-3993
Est: 1997
crquilts@flash.net
Owner: Karen O'Neill
Mon - Sat 10 - 5
Thurs til 7

www.CabbageRoseQuilting.com

Fort Worth, TX #43

Azle, TX #44

By Appt. Only

QUILTS by Eagle Mountain Products

1635 W. Bill B Rd. 76020
(817) 237-0881
Owner: Nadj Pankey
Est: 1996
900 sq.ft.
Online Newsletter
empquilts@skywi.com
www.empquilts.com

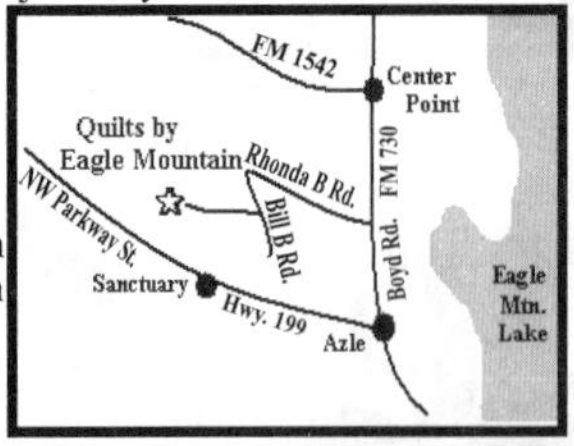

Award winning computer-guided quilting. Verrry reasonable rates. Call for quotes and availability. World-wide service.

Azle, TX #45

Tues - Fri 10 - 5 Sat 10 - 3

Quilts & Stuffs

900 NW Parkway 76020
(817) 270-0452
Owner: Anna Waghalter
Est: 1996 1300 sq.ft.

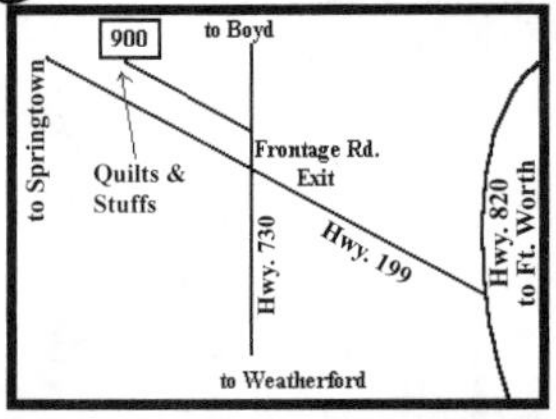

"At Home" take your shoes off atmosphere. We have machine Quilting available as well as cotton fabrics etc.

Colleyville, TX #46

Mon & Thur 9 - 6 Tues, Wed, & Fri 9 - 5 Sat 10 - 4

Quilter's Dream

6409 Colleyville Blvd. 76034
(817) 481-7105
Owner: Beverly Ingram
www.quiltersdreamtx.com

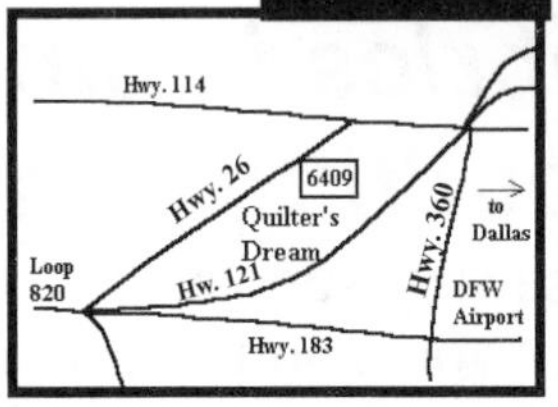

We are known for our knowledgeable, friendly staff and large selection of beautiful 100% cotton fabrics, books & notions.

Hurst, TX #47

Mon - Fri 10 - 6:30 Sat 10 - 5

Quilter's Stash/ BERNINA

848 W. Pipeline Rd. 76053
(817) 595-1778
Owner: Bill Moore
Est: 1999 10,000+ Bolts
www.quiltersstashinc.com
Best Quality 100% Cotton Fabrics, Books, Notions, Patterns and Classes.
Gift Certificates

Nothing Sews Like A Bernina. Nothing. BERNINA®

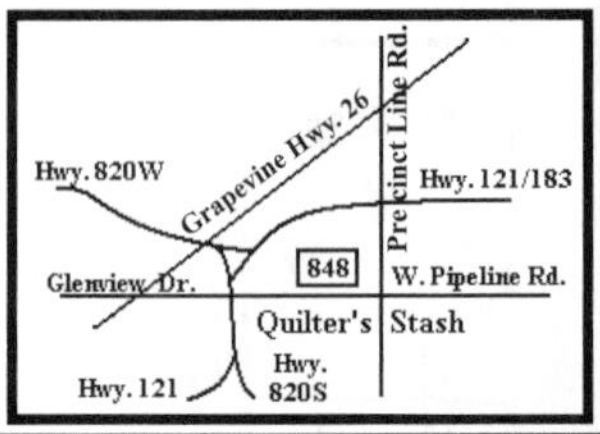

Arlington, TX #49

Mon - Sat 10 - 5

Quilt Among Friends

2081 E. Division St. 76011
(817) 795-0900
Owner: Debbie Mahanay
Est: 2007
3900 sq.ft.
quiltamongfriend@aol.com 2000+ Bolts
www.quiltamongfriends.com

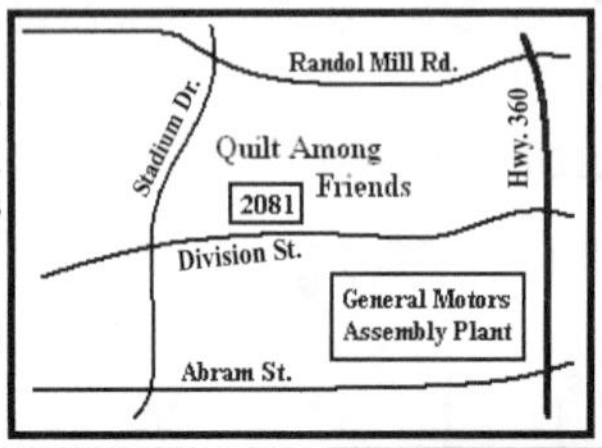

Fabric, Patterns, Kits, Notions, BOM, Classes
5 minutes from Six Flags Over Texas, Rangers Ballpark in Arlington and the new Dallas Cowboys Stadium.

Burleson, TX #50

Mon - Fri 10 - 5 Sat 10 - 3

Country Stitches quilt shop

426 SW Wilshire Blvd. 76028
(817) 426-5981
www.countrystitchesquiltshop.com
3000 sq.ft. 3600 Bolts

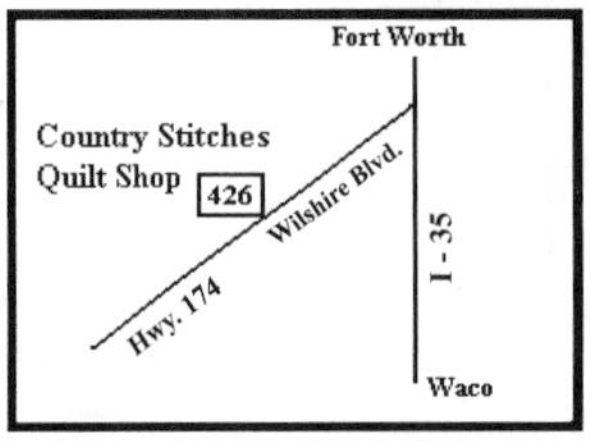

We carry only 100% High Quality Cotton Fabrics, Books, and Notions. Come see our Large Selection of Reproduction Fabrics.

Joshua, TX #51

Tues - Sat 10 - 5 Sun 10 - 2

Batiks Galore

7301 CR 912 76058
(817) 556-2200
New Retreat Coming

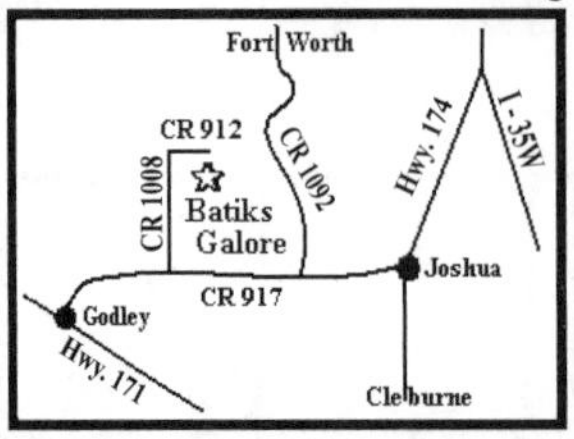

bc-tex@att. net Fax: (817) 556-5888
Owner: Barbara Clark Est: 2004
1000 Bolts of Batiks only
www.BatiksGalore.com
Off the beaten path, but worth the trip. Bold Over Batiks, Hoffman, Timeless Treasures, Island Batiks, Cotton & Rayon

Est: 2000

Quilts 'n More

Midlothian, TX #48

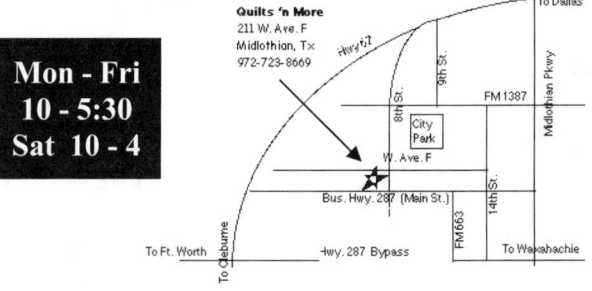

4000+ bolts of 100% cotton fabrics, notions, books, patterns, classes and long-arm quilting.

Mon - Fri 10 - 5:30 Sat 10 - 4

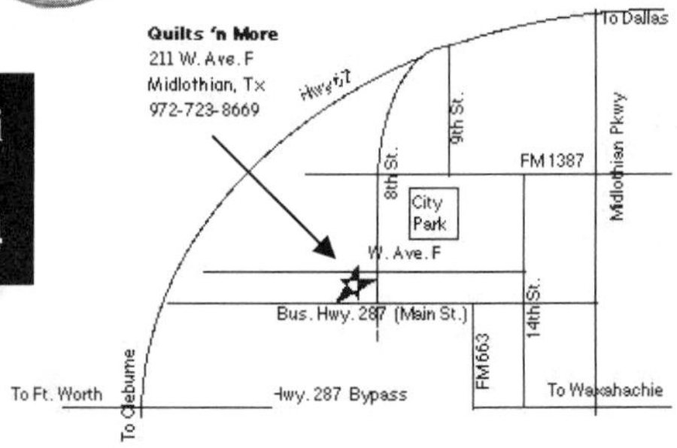

211 W. Ave. F, Midlothian, TX 76065
(972) 723-8669
www.quiltsnmore.biz
Owners: Kathleen Allen & Jean McKinney

Houston St. Mercantile

126 N. Houston St.
Granbury, TX 76048
(817) 279-0425

Owner: Glenda Westbrook
www.houstonstmercantile.com
Authorized baby lock Dealer

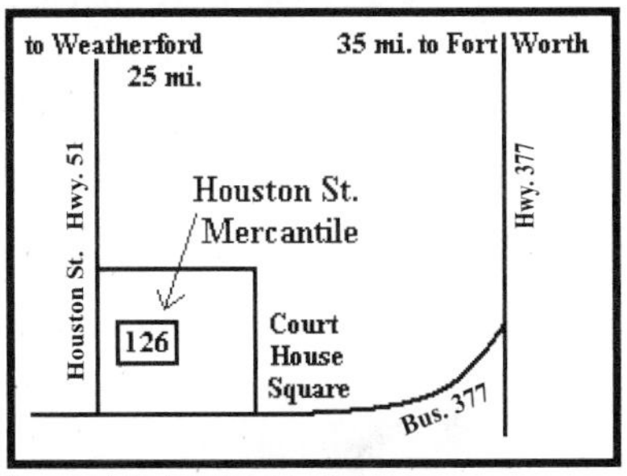

Granbury, TX #52

Mon - Fri 10 - 5
Sat 10 - 6 Sun 12 - 5

Houston St. Mercantile offers a delight to quilters with its fantastic selection of quality fabrics, (over 4,000 Bolts) patterns, books, and classes.

Also of interest is **The Quilt Inn of Granbury** a quaint and historic Bed and Breakfast especially for quilt retreats.

For information call owner, Glenda Westbrook
email - info@houstonstmercantile.com

Quilters Connection

Where Quilters Get it!

Dallas, TX #53

3000 sq. ft. of Brights, Batiks, Civil War/Traditional, 30's, Asians, and many new fabrics (3000 bolts). Lots of Notions, Books, Patterns, & Kits. We have fun classes, clubs, groups, and a Coffee Bar! Custom Quilts & Finishing. Long-arm quilting on site.

Mon-Fri 10-6, Tues til 8 PM, Sat 10-5, closed Sun
9658 Plano Road
Dallas, TX 75238
214-343-1440
888-494-0291
www.quilters-connection.com
info@quilters-connection.com

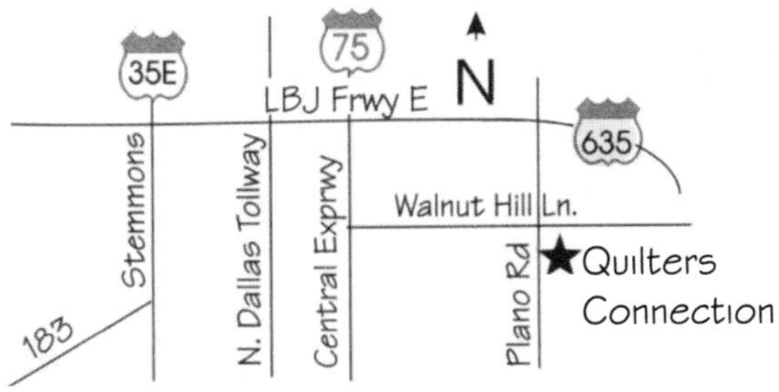

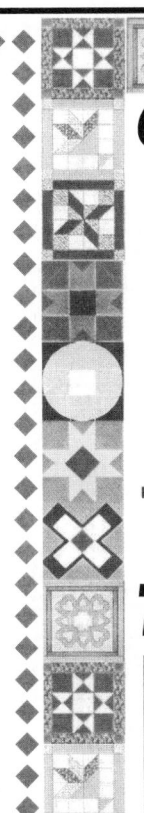

QUILTING FABRIC

Name Brand Coordinating 100% Cotton Fabric at Outlet Prices!

FREE! FREE! FREE!
1 Fat Quarter of Your Choice

ADDITIONAL FABRIC
25% DISCOUNT
WITH THIS AD

Pinnacle Fabrics
RJR
Jacob's Ladder
Michael Miller
moda FABRICS
SOUTH SEAS IMPORTS
Concord House
ROSE & HUBBLE
Jinny Beyer
Chanteclaire
RED ROOSTER
MAYWOOD STUDIOS

Mon - Sat
10 - 6:30

Thomas Sewing Center, Inc.

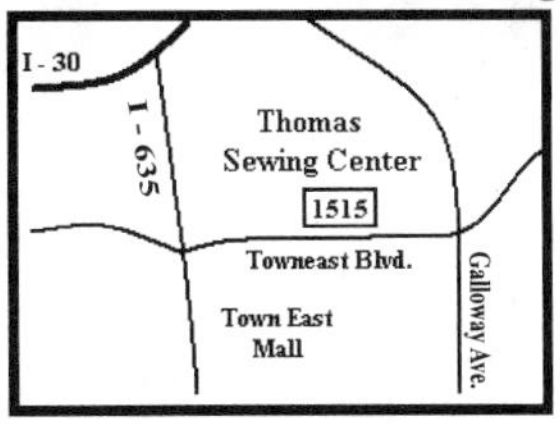

1515 N. Towneast Blvd. #133
Mesquite, TX 75150
972-681-3996
Est: 1987 3069 sq.ft.
4000+ Bolts

www.thomassewing.com for online fabric

Common Threads Quilting

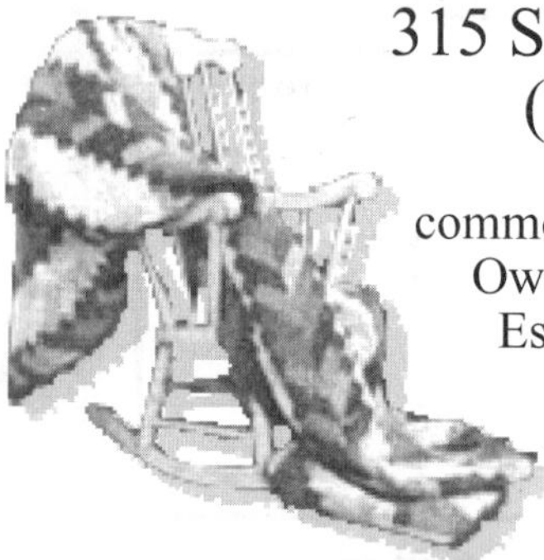

315 S. Rogers St. 75165
(972) 935-0510

commonthreads@sbcglobal.net
Owner: Denice Lipscomb
Est: 2002 3000 sq.ft.
Over 4,000 Bolts

Mon - Fri 9:30 - 5
Sat 9:30 - 4:30

Better Homes and Gardens Quilt Sampler FEATURED SHOP

www.commonthreadsquilting.com

Specializing in 19th and 20th Century Reproduction Fabrics. Large selection of Traditional Florals. Victorian building just off the Square.

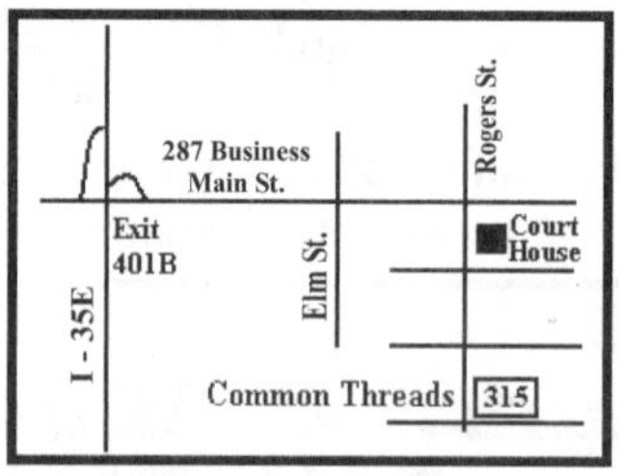

Waxahachie, TX #55

1890 House
A Quilters Retreat

398 S. Broad St.
(972) 291-0472
Mailing: 445 East F.M. 1382, Suite 3-189, 75104
info@1890quilters.com www.1890quilters.com

Cedar Hill, TX #56

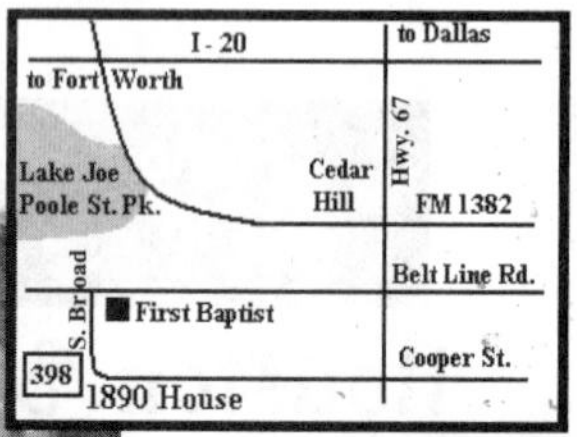

Reservations Only

"A Place for Expressing Creativity"

Only minutes from Dallas/Ft. Worth Metroplex. Set your own schedules-work as early or late as you wish. Bring your own instructor-Finish projects or begin new ones without the usual interruptions of our hectic lives. We offer that difficult to find place for small groups of friends to work, play, create and relax together. The 1890 House is a recently restored, nicely appointed Victorian style farmhouse accommodating eight in four bedrooms.

Cedar Hill, TX #57

Mon - Fri 10 - 5
Sat 10 - 4

Just Stitchin, Inc.

605 Cedar St. 75104
(972) 291-8729
Fax: (972) 291-9652
Owner: Deb Brizendine
Est: 2005 1565 sq.ft.
deborah@juststitchin.com
www.juststitchin.com
2000+ bolts featuring Jinny Beyer, batiks/ hand dyes, Oriental, florals, Moda Marbles and more. Longarm quilting available

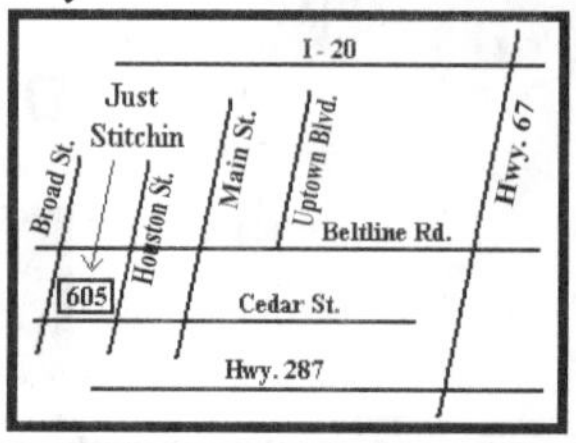

McKinney, TX #59

Mon - Sat 10 - 5
Thurs til 7

Happiness Is ... Quilting!

217 N. Kentucky St. 75069
(972) 542-8839 Fax: (972) 542-5951
Owner: Laura Kay Houser
info@happinessisquilting.com
www.happinessisquilting.com
Est: 2006 1200 sq.ft. Free Newsletter
Your full service quilt shop offering quality fabric, notions, books, patterns, classes and friendly customer service in historic downtown.

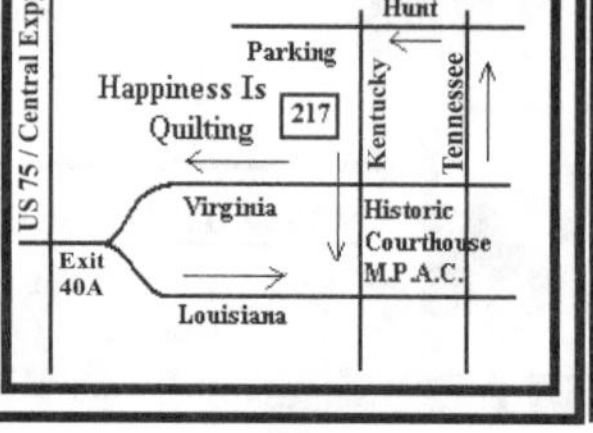

McKinney, TX #58

The Quilt Asylum

★ Featured in May 2006 edition of Quilt Sampler Magazine
★ Largest Collection of Kaffe Fassett fabrics in DFW metroplex
★ Full service quilt shop with classes, BOM's, books, patterns, notions & gifts
★Fat Quarters for every bolt in the store
★Wide selection of pre-cut charms, strips, and kits
★Conveniently located on US 75

Better Homes and Gardens Quilt Sampler FEATURED SHOP

Mon 10 - 7
Tues - Sat 10 - 5

153 S. Central Expy.
McKinney, TX 75070
(972) 562-2686
(888) ASYLUM-8
6300 sq. ft. 3000+ Bolts
thequiltasylum@sbcglobal.net
www.thequiltasylum.com

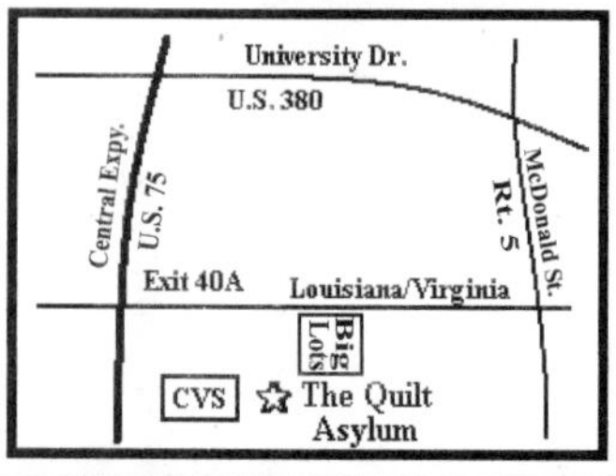

Suzy's Quilt Shop

111 N. 6th Street, Garland, Texas 75040 972-272-8180

www.suzysquilts.com suzysquilts@aol.com

You are the Heart of our Business

Store Hours:
Mon-Fri 9:30am-5:00pm
Saturday 9:30am-4:00pm

Owner: Suzanne Cook
Est 1989 4200 sq ft.

Classes Are Fun!
See our Class Schedule on our website. www.suzysquilts.com Color Pictures of each class. Sign up by phone. Plan your trip to be here for our of our classes.

"The road to Suzy's is never long."

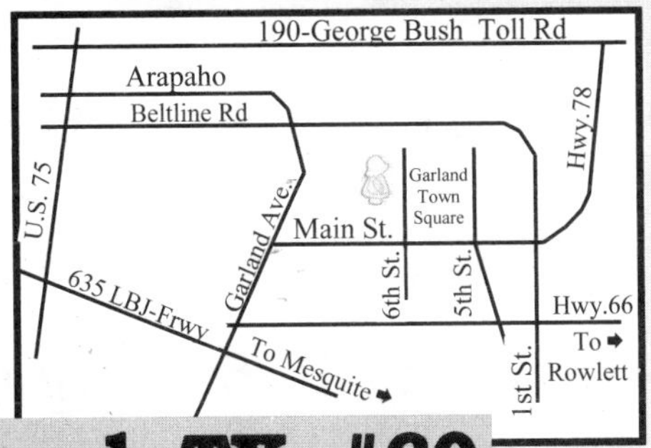

Patterns * Supplies * Books * Fabrics
Kits * Classes * Gifts * Original Patterns
Lots of Samples * 1st Sat Samplers

Clubs
Thimbleberries, 20-30's, Appliqué Lovers, Tea Party, Floss & Chocolate, Dear Jane, Scrap Swap, and Redwork/Embroidery & Fat (hind) Quarter.

Mondays Are Fun
Every Monday Is Sit-n-Sew
Bring Your Project
Bring a Friend

Garland, TX #60

where winning things happen when you step through our doors...

Est: 2008

Wylie, TX #61

DFW's Most Talked About Block of the Month Headquarters

We are located in the historic downtown district of Wylie, TX. We offer all the nostalgia of quilting history and all the style of quilting trends.

blueribbonquiltshoppe@gmail.com
www.blueribbonquiltshoppe.co

M, Tu, W, F 10-6 Th 10-7
Sat 9-5 1st & 3rd Sun 1-5

Blue Ribbon Quilt Shoppe

Alexander Henry
Batiks
Benartex
Blank Quilting
Clothworks
David Textiles
Elizabeth's Studio
Free Spirit
Galaxy
Henry Glass
Hoffman
Kona Bay
Marcus Brothers
Maywood Studios
Moda
Northcott
P&B Textiles
Quilting Treasures
Red Rooster Fabrics
RJR
Shannon Fabrics/Cuddle
Thimbleberries
Timeless Treasures
Troy
Wilmington Prints
Windham Fabrics

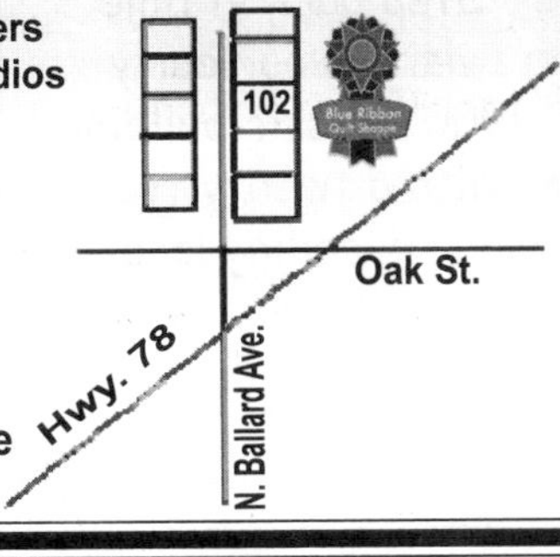

102 C North Ballard Ave.
Wylie, TX 75098
972-941-0777
4600 sq.ft. 2700+ Bolts

Check out our Blue Ribbon University
A collection of quilt classes for beginner and intermediate quilters: Learn a new skill with each new quilt.

Quilt Country

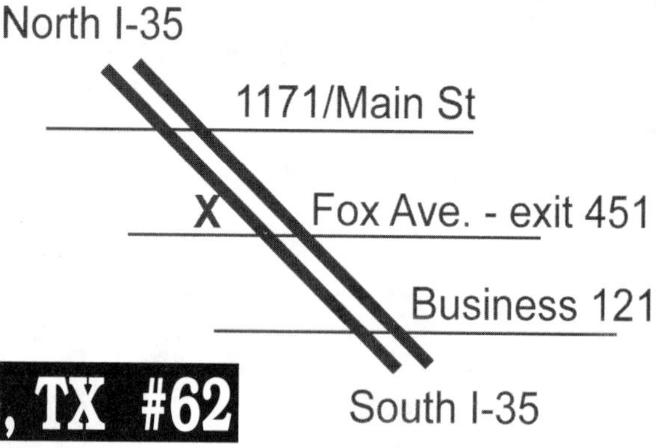

701 South Stemmons #60
Lewisville, TX 75067
972.436.7022

Lewisville, TX #62

Love Fabric? 10,000 bolts from which to choose!

Love Thread? Tons of fibers and threads!

Love Quilts? Over 250 models to inspire you!

Love Embellishments? Beads, glitter, inks, & more!

Open 7 days a week! Monday - Saturday 10-5 Sunday 1-5

Largest Quilt Store in Northeast Texas

Celeste, TX #63

Quilt Mercantile

215 Hwy. 69 N 75423
(903) 568-8739

quiltmercantile215@msn.com
Owners: Vickey Dees & Jennifer Tenney
Est: 2002 5,400 sq.ft. 3,000 Bolts

Tues 9 - 7 Wed - Fri 9 - 5 Sat 9 - 1

Step back in time visiting our early 1900's rustic building with a twenty foot high tin ceiling located 15 miles north of Greenville.

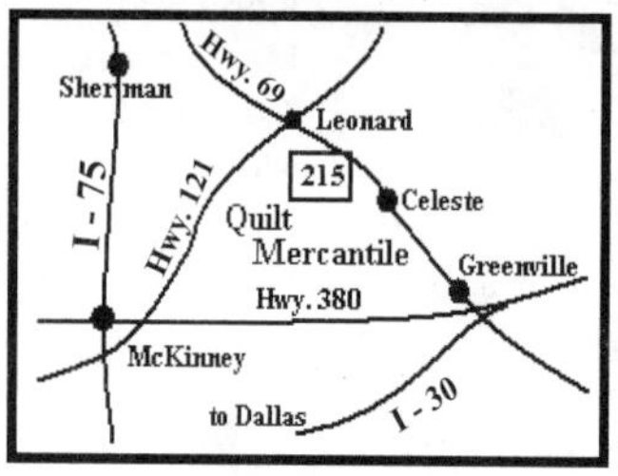

www.quiltmercantile.com

Carrollton, TX #64

The Old Craft Store

1110 W. Main Street 75006
(972) 242-9111 Fax: (972) 245-0407
oldstore@earthlink.net
www.theoldcraftstore.com
Owner: Melba Hamrick
Est: 1971 3000 sq.ft.
2500 Bolts

Mon - Sat 10 - 5
Thurs til 7

Collinsville, TX #65

Mon - Sat 10 - 5

102 N. Main St. 76233
(903) 429-3939

The Sewing Boutique

www.thesewingboutique.com

French Hand Sewing, English Hand Smocking, Quilting and Long Arm Quilting.
Fabrics, Notions, Classes.

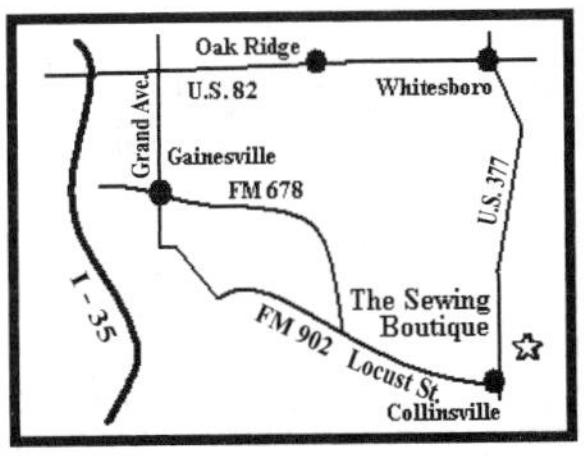

Gainesville, TX #66

Mon - Sat 10 - 5 Tues til 8

Pass Time Fabrics

105 W. California St. 76240
(940) 668-1747
Owner: Karen Brooks Est: 1986
PassTimeFabrics@sbcglobal.net
www.PassTimeFabrics.com

Full line of 100% cotton calicos and solids. Books, notions, patterns, classes - everything for quilters!

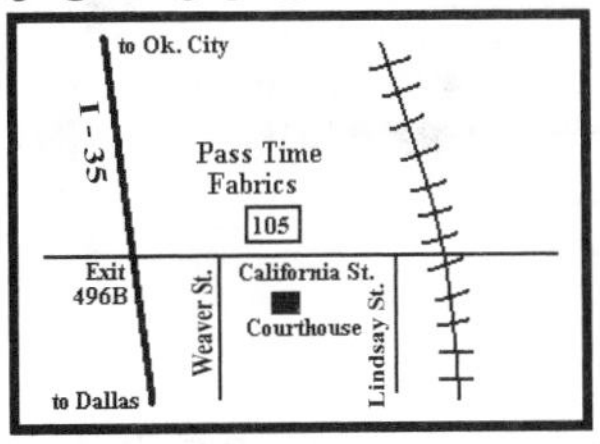

Whitesboro, TX #67

Mon - Fri 10 - 5 Sat 10 - 4

Kaleidoscope Quilt Shop

114 E. Main St. 76273
(903) 564-4681
Owner: Donna Sluder
Est: 2001 3000+ Bolts
donnasluder@msn.com
www.kaleidoscope-quilt-shop.com

Better Homes and Gardens Quilt Sampler Featured Shop

We are a quaint shop located in an early 1900's building. We have a very friendly and knowledgeable staff. Lots of 100% cotton fabrics, kits, books, notions & classes.

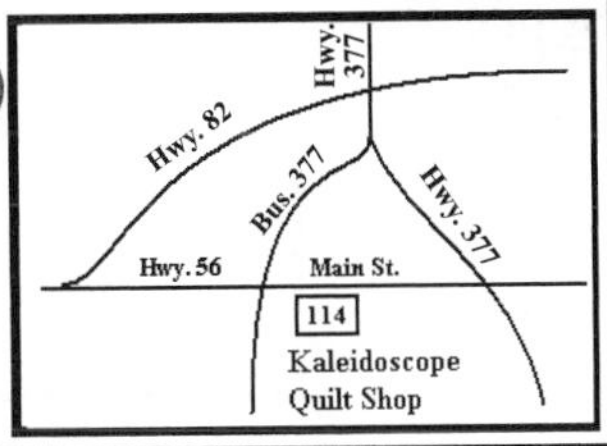

Calico Junction

www.calicojunction.net
Winnsboro, TX
(903) 342-3399
calicojquilts@aol.com

Tues, Wed, Thur 9:30 - 5
Fri & Sat 9:30 - 4

Winnsboro, TX #68

Authorized Janome Sewing Machine Dealer in East Texas for Sales and Service

Block of the Month * Flannels * Marbles
Jelly Rolls * Cakes/Charm Packs * Kits

Specializing in Roxanne products, Rada Cutlery, T-shirt quilts, and quilted concealed handgun purses.

The friendliest and most helpful shop in East Texas!

At the time of publication for the QTC, we were planning a move, please call for address and directions.

Texas Premier Quilt Shop

Stitchin' Heaven

Located in Beautiful East Texas!
Featured shop in Quilt Sampler 2000

Over 6,000 bolts of quality cotton fabrics in this 7,200 square foot "Quilter's Paradise"
The very latest in quilting tools and supplies
A complete library of books & patterns

Treat Yourself to our "Sew 'n Spa"
A sewing retreat with spa options available in a beautiful east Texas setting.
Rest, relax and enjoy!

"The Bunkhouse"
Rent our 2200 square foot log cabin built especially for quilts for your next small group retreat.

Visit our website: www.stitchinheaven.com
For a complete listing of happenings in the shop and an incredible on-line shopping experience!
Be sure and register for our "Hot Flashes" - our on-line newsletter!

Owner: Debby Luttrell
502 E. Goode
P.O. Box 1914
Quitman, Texas
75783

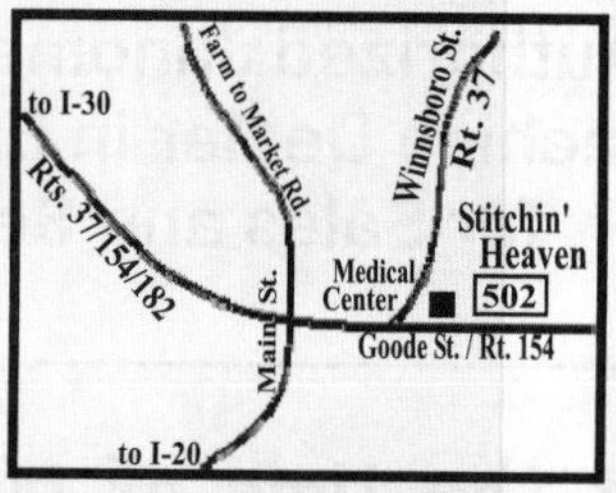

Email: info@stitchinheaven.com
Toll Free: 800 841-3901
Fax: 903 763-3117
100% Satisfactions Guaranteed!
Be sure and plan to visit when you are in the area! It's worth the drive!

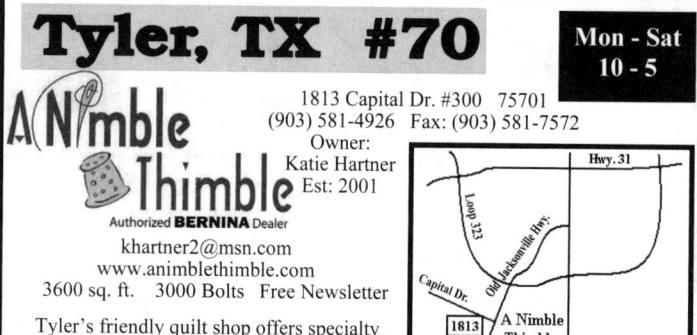

Quitman, TX #69

Tyler, TX #70

Mon - Sat
10 - 5

A Nimble Thimble

Authorized BERNINA Dealer

1813 Capital Dr. #300 75701
(903) 581-4926 Fax: (903) 581-7572
Owner:
Katie Hartner
Est: 2001

khartner2@msn.com
www.animblethimble.com
3600 sq. ft. 3000 Bolts Free Newsletter

Tyler's friendly quilt shop offers specialty classes in quilting, rughooking & punchneedle.

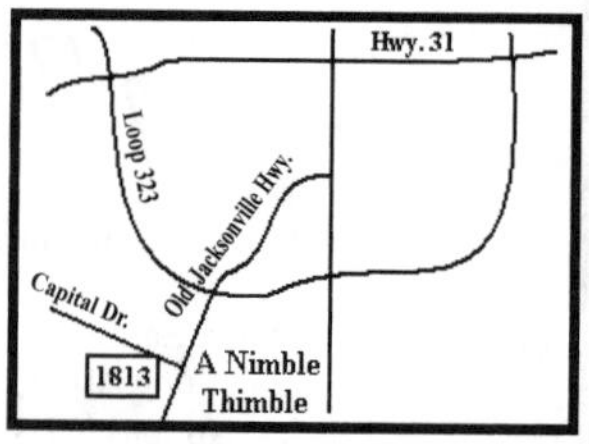

Palestine, TX #71

Tues - Fri
9 - 5
Sat 9 - 1

Grimes Sewing Center

619 W. Oak St. 75801
(903) 729-2889
Est: 1991 2600 sq.ft. 2000+ Bolts

Fabrics, Quilting Supplies, Patterns, Books, Notions, Classes

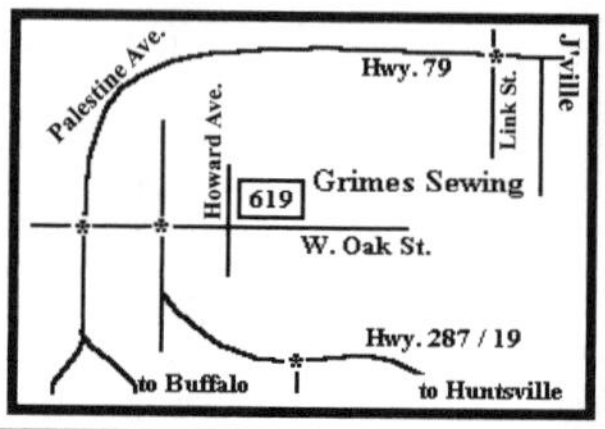

Sew Much More

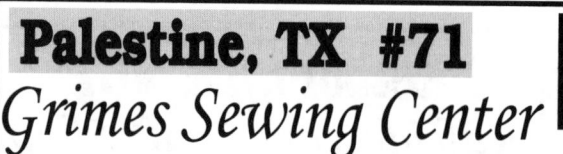

Largest Quilt Shop in NE Texas

A full service shop (5,000 sq. ft. and expanding) with a bright, inviting atmosphere to enjoy a huge (over 8,000 bolts) selection of beautiful cotton fabrics, notions, books, patterns, kits and all the wonderful items that quilters love. We specialize in flannels, Orientals, 30's reproduction & civil war prints while still offering a full complement of current quilting fabrics.

2400 Stillhouse Rd., Paris, TX 75462
(903) 784-6342
sewmuchmore@suddenlinkmail.com
Fax: (903) 784-0694
Authorized Babylock Dealer
www.sewmuchmorequilt.com

Mon - Fri
9:30 - 5:00
Sat
9:30 - 3:00

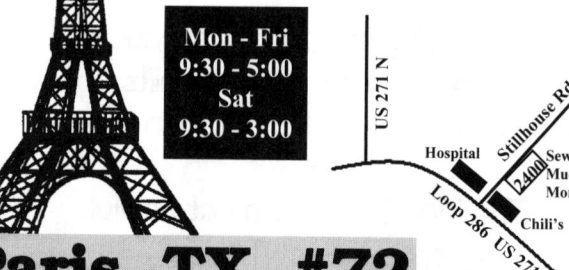

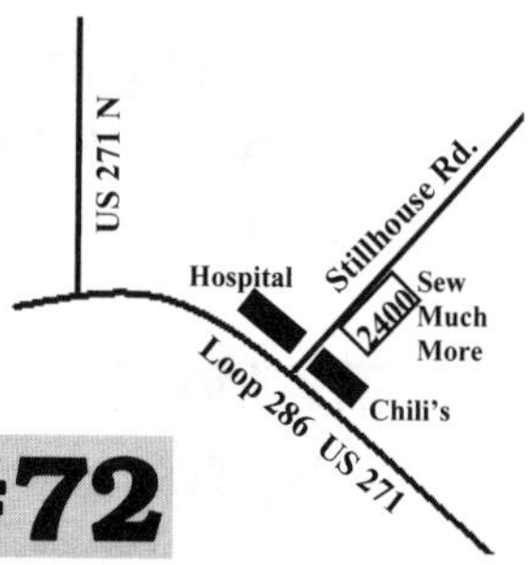

Paris, TX #72

Fairfield, TX #73

Tues - Fri 10 - 5
Sat 10 - 3

Cotton Cottage

221 E. Commerce 75840
(903) 389-6528
Owner: Pam Beene Est: 1996
contact@cottoncottagequiltshop.com
www.cottoncottagequiltshop.com
100% Cotton fabric, notions, books, patterns.
Catering to Quilters & Creative Clothing.
Classes and Friendly Service.
Custom made quilts and quilting.

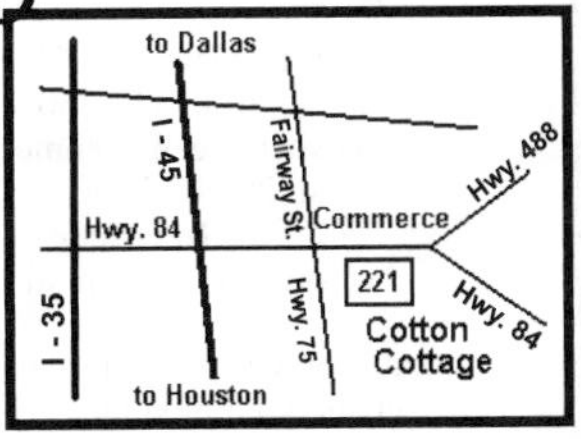

Trinity, TX #74

Tues - Fri 10 - 6
Sat 10 - 4

Heavenly Threads Quilt Shop

334 Prospect (Hwy. 19)
P.O. Box 1845 75862
(936) 594-1237 Est: 2003
Owner: Patricia McCartney 1500 sq.ft.
www.heavenlythreadsquilts.com

A full service Quilt Shop nestled in the East Texas Pines. Friendly service, classes, patterns, books, and lots of fun.

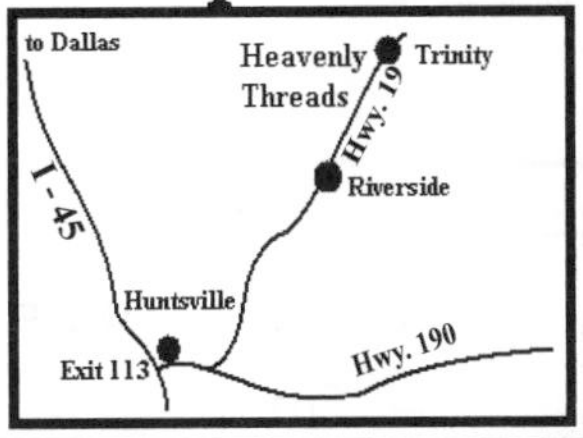

Jean's Corner

712 N. Jackson 77351
(936) 327-8817
jyarbrough@livingston.net
Owner: Jean Yarbrough

Mon - Fri 9 - 5
Sat by Appt

Brand name 100% cotton Fabrics
Books - Notions
Janome Sewing Machines
2,000 Bolts of Fabric

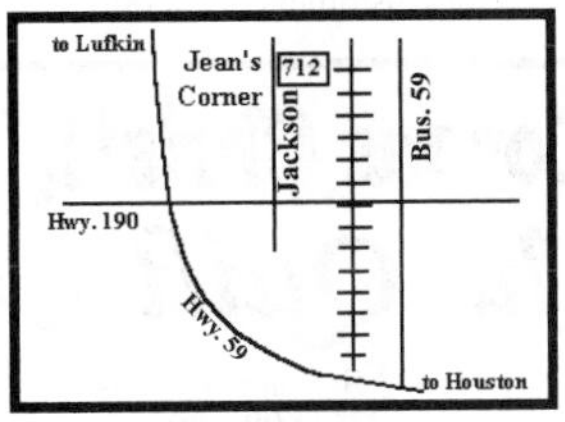

Livingston, TX #75

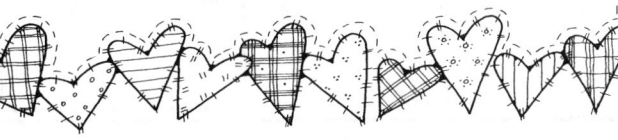

Conroe, TX #76

Tues 10 - 7
Wed - Fri 10 - 6
Sat 10 - 4

Quilter's Quarters

www.quiltersquarters-tx.com
3401 W. Davis, Suite E 77304
(936) 756-7200 Fax: (936) 756-7200
QLDY2003@yahoo.com
Est: 2005 1600 sq.ft. 1700 Bolts
Free Email Newsletter
Full Service Quilt Shop.
Books, Notions, Classes,
Fabrics. On Closed Days
Call for Appointment.

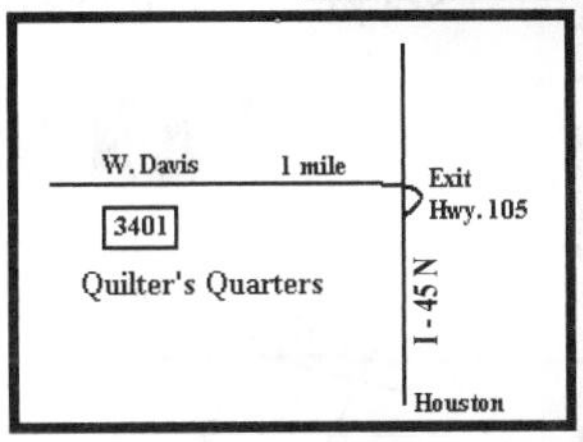

THE FABRIC STORE

and sew much more

We offer a wide selection of quality quilting fabrics, along with patterns, notions & classes.
Come see us--We love to sew and quilt as much as you do!

1605 South Hwy. 69
Nederland, TX 77627
(409) 729-5288

Tues - Fri 10 - 5:30
Sat 9:30 - 4

Nederland, TX #77

Over 5,000 bolts of fabric
3500 sq.ft.

www.thefabricstoreonline.com

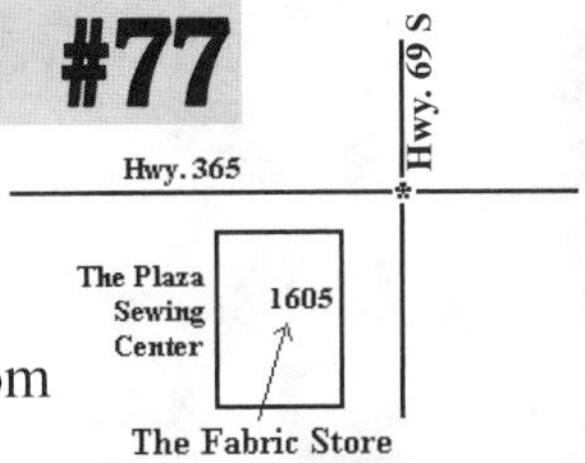

El Campo, TX #78

Cedar Chest Quilt Shoppe

121 S. Mechanic 77437
(979) 578-8929
Est: 2010 1800 sq.ft.
Online Newsletter
info@cedarchestquiltshoppe.com

Tues - Fri 10 - 5:30
Sat 10 - 3

Located in beautiful downtown El Campo, we offer quality quilt fabrics, notions, hand stitchery and friendly service.
COME VISIT US!

www.cedarchestquiltshoppe.com

Victoria, TX #79

Mon - Fri 10 - 5
Sat 10 - 2
Summer
Mon - Fri 10 - 4

Quilters Patch

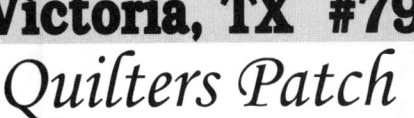

205 North Star, Suite Q 77904
Located off Hwy. 77
(361) 578-0380 or (866) 578-0380
qpatch2@suddenlinkmail.com
www.quilterspatch.com
Owners: Karen Leach & Sherry Ware
Est: 1995 2000 sq.ft. 4000 Bolts
For All Your Quilting and Sewing Necessities.

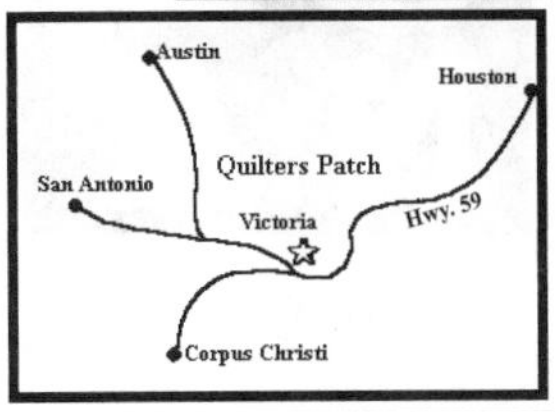

Seams like home
a little fabric store

Tues - Fri 9 - 5
Sat 9 - 12

Cotton fabrics, notions, patterns, books, etc.

Everything you need to start and finish a project.

Yorktown, TX #80

441 W. 5th 78164
(361) 564-9455
Owner: Sarah Hahn
Est: 2008 1800 sq.ft.
sarah@alittlefabricstore.com
www.alittlefabricstore.com

Port Lavaca, TX #81

Beefore It's A Quilt

Mon - Fri 10 - 5
Sat 10 - 4

119 E. Main St. 77979
(361) 552-1350
Owner: Jean Wehmeyer
Est: 2004 3500 sq.ft.
Free Newsletter
beeforeitsaquilt@gmail.com

A great shop with everything you need to create your next masterpiece.

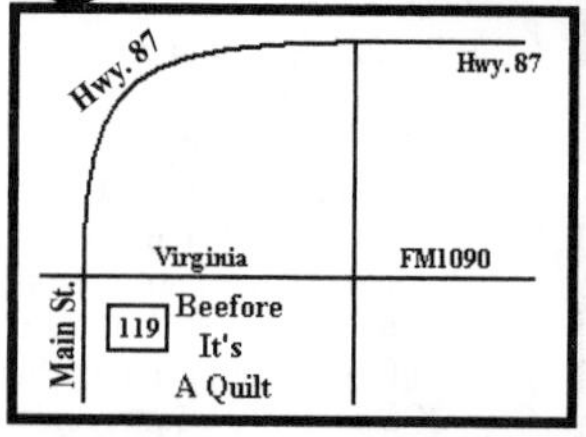

Port Aransas, TX #82

Kalico & Keepsakes

Tues - Sat 10 - 4

600 Cut Off Rd. #10 78373
(361) 739-1496
Owner: Dee Cromer
www.kalicoandkeepsakes.com

Full line of quality Fabric and Notions.
Professional finishing on Gammill Machine.
Our Customers are soon Friends.

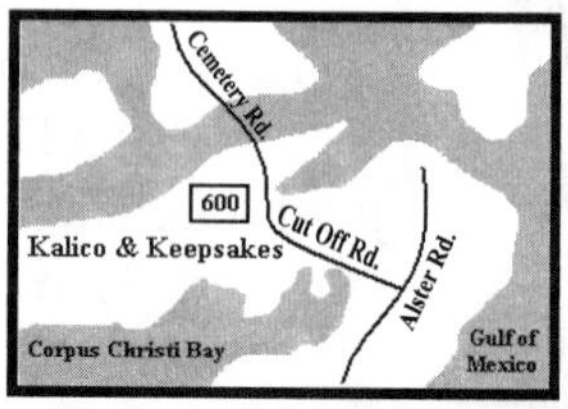

Corpus Christi, TX #83

The Quilt Cottage

Mon - Fri 10 - 5:30
Sat 10 - 5

5433 S. Staples 78411
(361) 985-0908
www.thequiltcottage.com
Owner: Lynda Butler Est: 1994 2200 sq.ft.
A very warm & friendly shop. We have over 2000 bolts all cotton fabric. Loads of Books, Patterns, Notions, Classes, etc.
Professional Machine Quilting.

Authorized Dealer **JANOME**

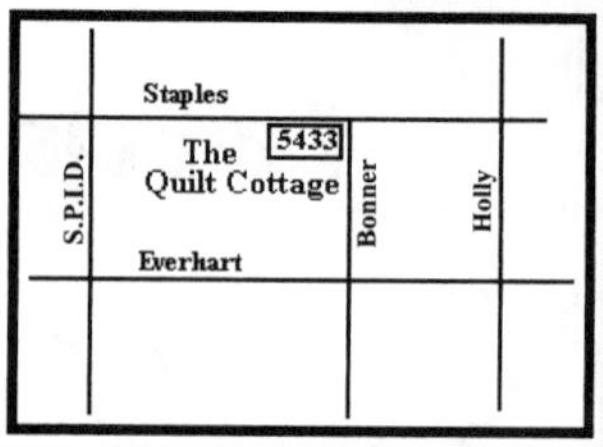

HOUSTON AREA

14 Featured Shops

Shops # 84 - 97

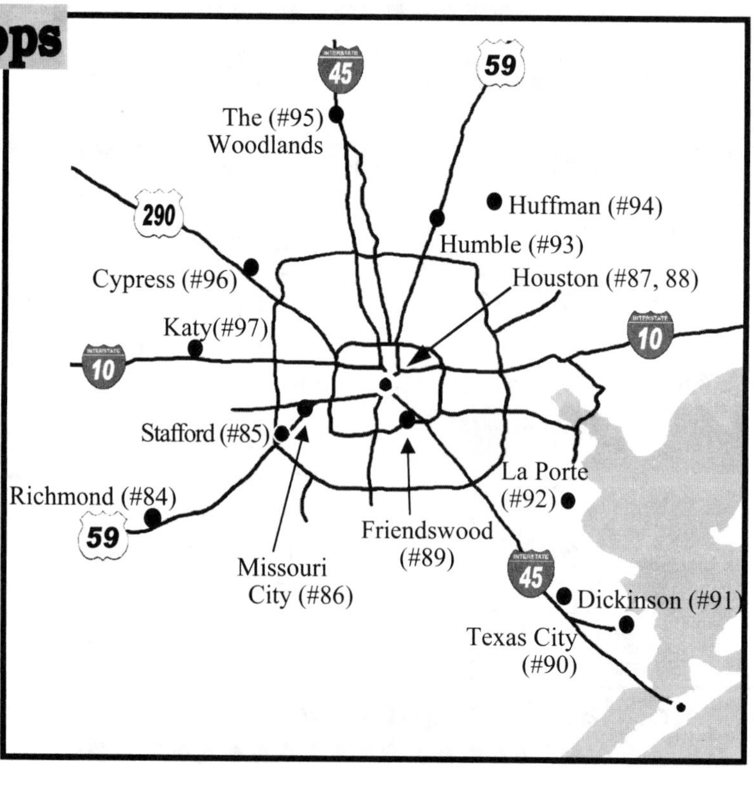

QUILTERS COTTAGE

920 FM 359 77406
(281) 633-9331
Monday - Saturday 10 - 5

Richmond, TX #84

Our store offers everything a quilter needs including thousands of bolts of fabric by P&B, Moda, Hoffman, Robert Kaufman, RJR, Bali Fabrications, Island Batiks, Red Rooster, Michael Miller, Kona Bay, Island Sea Imports, Andover, Timeless Treasures, Henry Glass and Loralie Designs. We are also an authorized Janome Sewing Machine dealer. Our notions wall is full of the latest in quilter's notions including Thangles, Fons and Porter, Omnigrid Rulers, ergonomic rotary cutters, June Tailer, Mats and pressing pads. Hundreds of the latest books and patterns are available in our Book Nook. Gifts Too!

5000 sq.ft.
6000 Bolts
Fax: 281-633-9331
(call first)
quilts@texas
quilterscottage.com

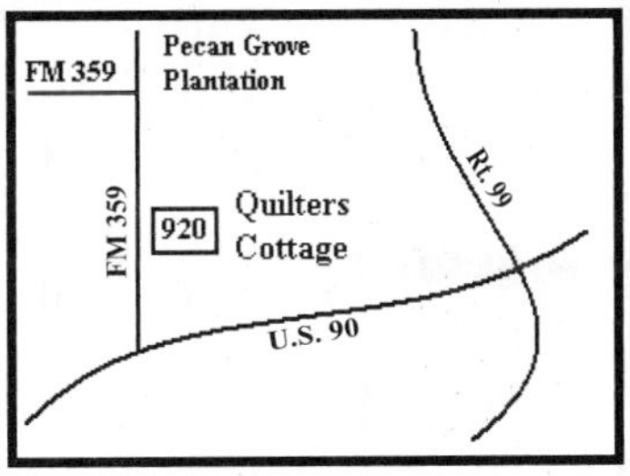

www.texasquilterscottage.com

Stafford, TX #85

Mon - Sat 10 - 5
Thurs til 6
Sun 12 - 4

"Putting the pieces together at . . . "

QUILTER'S EMPORIUM

11925 Southwest Frwy.,
Suite 11 77477
(281) 491-0016

www.quiltersemporium.com
Owner: Rose Ann Cook
Fabric, kits, patterns, books, gifts, antiques, consignments, BOMs, retreats, cruises, and classes for all skill levels. Dealer for Janome Sewing Machines and Horn Sewing Cabinetry. Authorized Tin Lizzie 18 Quilting System.

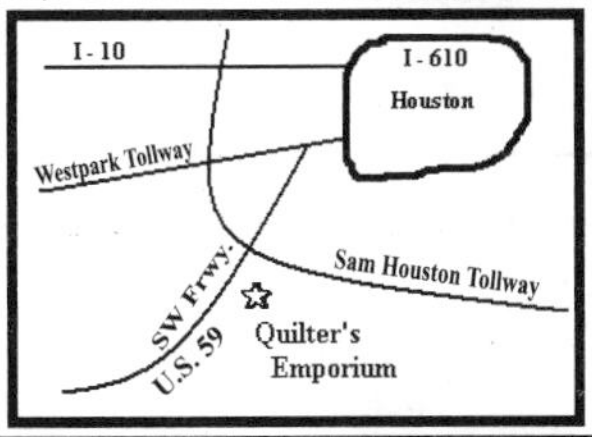

Missouri City, TX #86

Mon - Sat 10 - 5

Little Stitches SEWING CENTER

3340 FM 1092 #130 77459
(281) 403-1564 Fax: (281) 403-1714

Est: 2001 3500 sq. ft. 2500 bolts
littlestitchessewing@yahoo.com
www.littlestitchessewing.com

The friendliest quilt shop in the Houston area. Fabric, notions, threads, books, patterns, machine embroidery supplies.

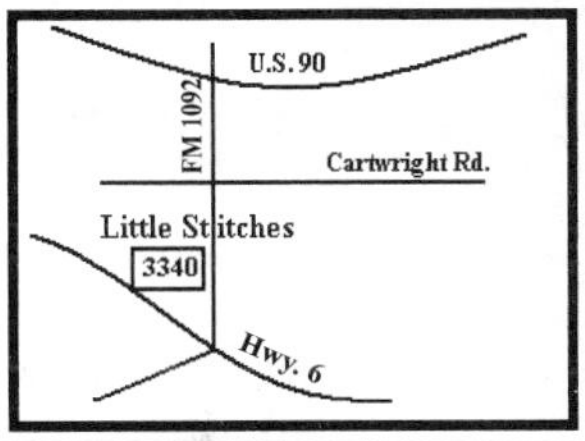

Time Treasured Quilts

A Full Service Quilt Shop

- Quilting Fabric
- Notions
- Kits
- Classes
- Patterns
- Books

Store Hours
Mon - Fri 10 - 6
Sat 10 - 5
Sun Closed

Gammill Longarm Machines

- Quilting Services
  All Over ▪ Custom
- Rental
- Sales
  - **Gammill Dealer**
  - Most models available for demonstration, call the shop for details
  - Machine maintenance

Gammill Quilting Systems

Linda's Electric Quilters LLC

Visit our web site: **www.timetreasuredquilts.com**

Address: 12916 Malcomson
Houston, TX 77070
281-370-6061

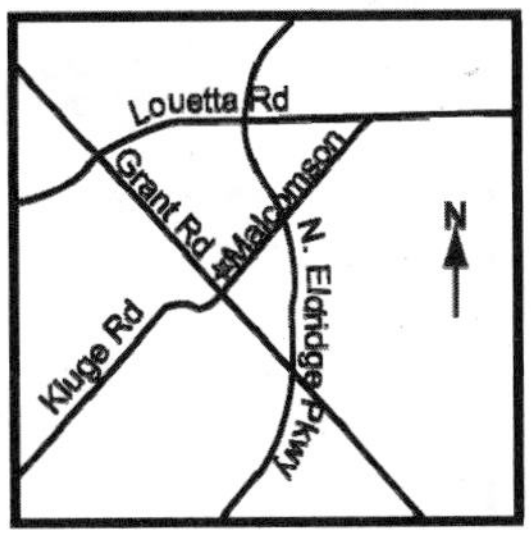

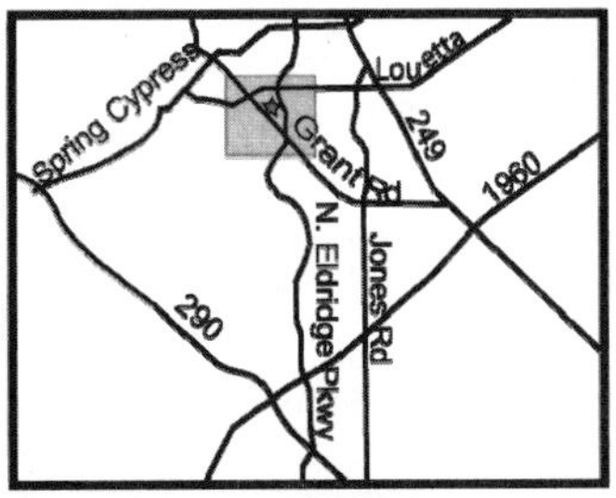

Houston, TX #87

Houston, TX #88

Mon - Sat 10 - 5

Buttons 'n' Bows

14070 Memorial Dr. 77079
(281) 496-0170
store@buttonsnbows.net
www.buttonsnbows.net
Est: 1980

Specializing in Fine Fabrics, English Smocking and Quilting Supplies.

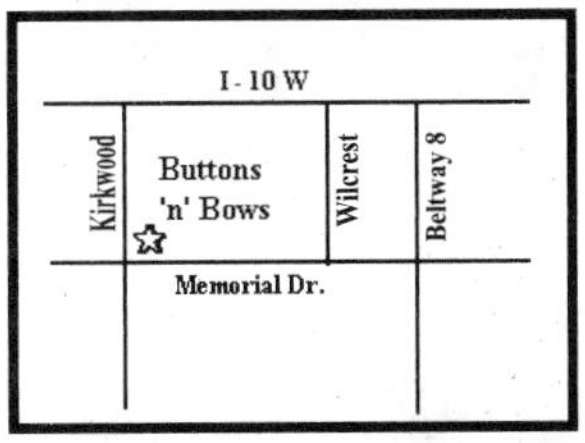

Friendswood, TX #89

Mon - Fri 10 - 5:30
Sat 10 - 4

180 S. Friendswood Dr.
77546
(281) 996-1756

Quakertown Quilts
(888) 464-7845
ramona@quakertownonline.com
www.Quakertown Quilts.com
Current fabrics, kits, books, notions, patterns, classes, Saturday sampler, blocks-of-the-month, clubs, & gifts.

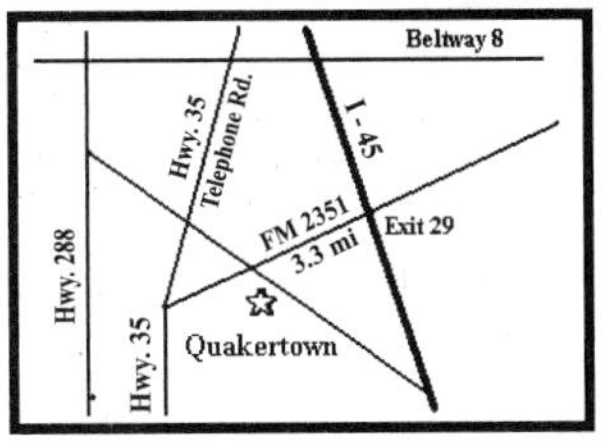

Texas City, TX #90

Mon - Fri 10 - 5:30
Sat 10 - 4

CACTUS QUILTS

1811 6th St. N 77590
(409) 965-9778 Fax: (409) 965-9779
Owner: Carla Hoff
Est: 2002 2000 sq.ft. 3000 bolts
www.cactusquilts.com
3000 bolts of 100% cotton fabrics, notions, books & patterns. Smiles always here and they are free. Come see for yourself.

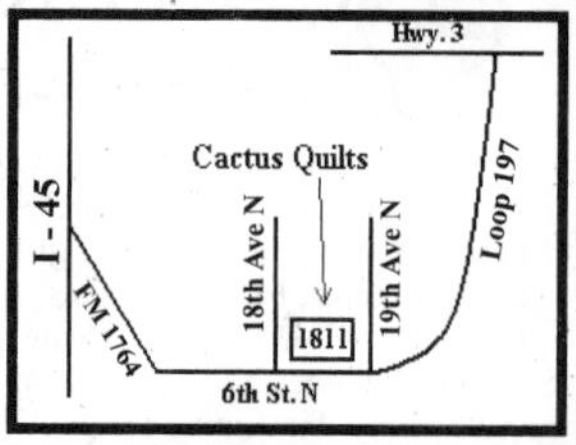

Dickinson, TX #91

Mon - Sat 10 - 5
Sun 1 - 4

Pinwheels & Posies

For all your sewing and quilting needs

3335 IH 45 77539
(281) 337-1213
Est: 2008 1800 sq.ft.

3000 bolts Online newsletter
pinwheelsandposies@verizon.net
www.pinwheelsandposies.com

Great Fabric Collections, Patterns, Books, Notions, Kits, Block-of-the-Month programs, Presensia threads.

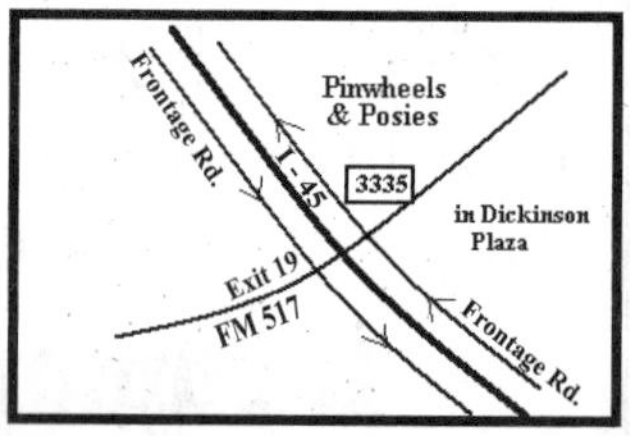

La Porte, TX #92

www.ppnq.com

Mon - Fri 10 - 5
Sat 10 - 4
Est: 1986

Painted Pony 'n Quilts

10,000+ top name quilting fabrics in contemporary, country, plaid, reproduction and oriental styles. Notions, Gifts, Janome Dealer. Friendly, knowledgeable staff to assist in all areas. Samples on display. International mail-order for: BOM's, Fabrics, Books, Patterns, Kits. Tour shop for the Houston Int. Festival.

1015 S. Broadway
77571
(281) 471-5735
ppnqstaff@ppnq.com
Owner: Sherrie S. Thomas
8600 sq. ft.

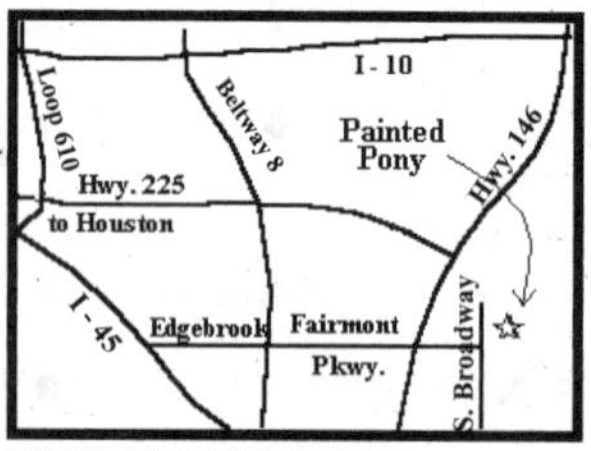

Humble, TX #93

It's A Stitch

(281) 446-4999
9574 FM 1960 Bypass
77338
Owners: Judy & John Curtis
customercare@itsastitchonline.com
Est: 1992 8350 sq.ft.

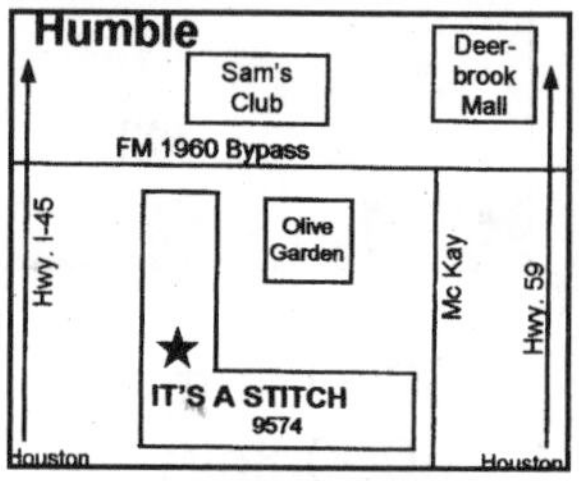

Mon - Fri 10 - 5:30
Sat 10 - 5

- **Over 6,000 Bolts of 100% Cotton Fabric**
- **Great Selection of Kits, Notions, Books, Patterns, Batting & Wool Felt.**
- **#1 Bernina Dealer in Texas**
- **Koala, Horn & Roberts Furniture**

www.itsastitchonline.com

Huffman, TX #94

Mon - Fri 10 - 6
Thur til 8
Sat 10 - 3

The Quilt Room

11515 FM 1960 Suite B 77336
(281) 324-9018
cjquiltroom@yahoo.com

www.thequiltroomhuffman.com
Full Service Quilt Shop.
We carry books, patterns & notions.
And, of course, FABRIC!

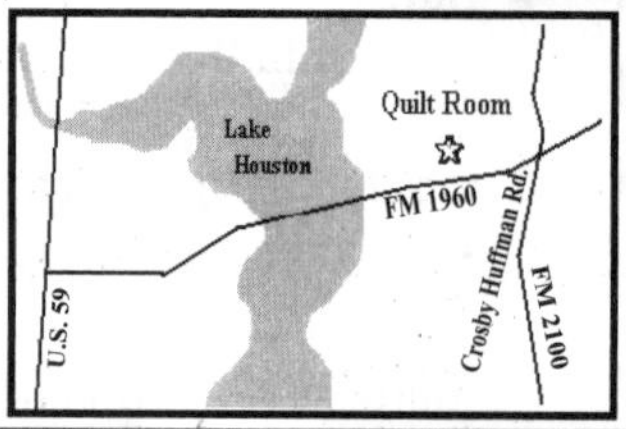

The Woodlands, TX #95

Mon - Fri 10 - 4:30
Sat 10 - 4

25823 Budde Rd.
77380
(281) 419-2800

Quakertown Quilts

(888) 419-2801
ramona@quakertownonline.com
www.Quakertown Quilts.com
Current fabrics, kits, books, notions, patterns, classes, Saturday sampler, blocks-of-the-month, clubs, & gifts.

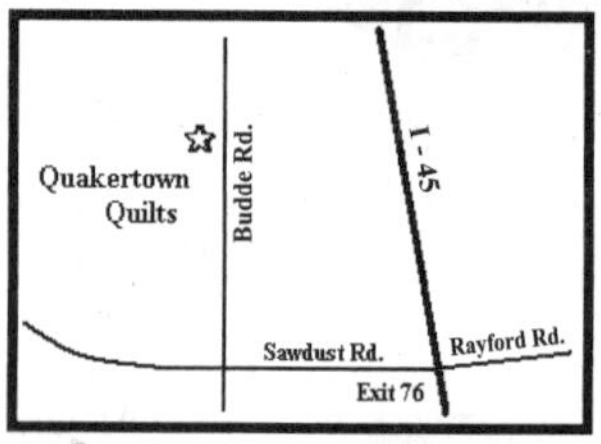

Cypress, TX #96

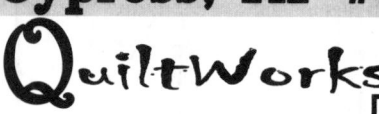

Mon & Thur 9 - 8
Wed & Fri 9 - 6
Sat 9 - 4

QuiltWorks

25250 Northwest Fwy. #140 77429
(281) 256-3550
Est: 2009 5000 sq.ft.
www.quiltworkstexas.com
Home of quilting supplies for the beginning to the advanced quilter. Pfaff dealer of sewing and embroidery machines. We also carry a wide variety of fabrics, threads, embroidery thread, notions, batting, books and templates.

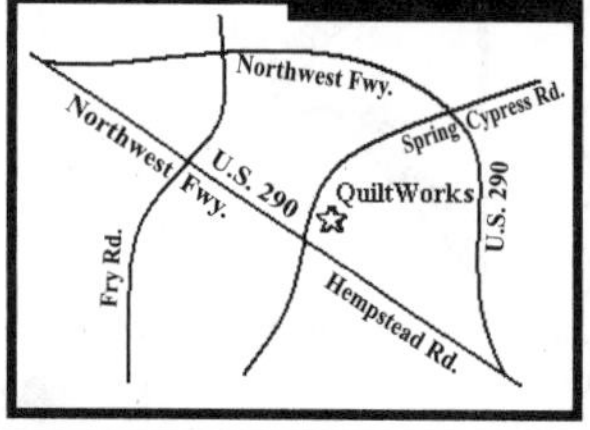

Katy, TX #97

Mon - Sat 10 - 5

Quilt 'n Sew Studio

829 S. Mason Rd. #224 77450
(281) 398-0670
Owner: Terri Burton Est: 1993
inquiry@quiltnsew.com
www.quiltnsew.com
Offering exceptional quality, service, convenience, value & education. We offer 100's of quilting & sewing supplies including notions, fabrics, kits, patterns and software.

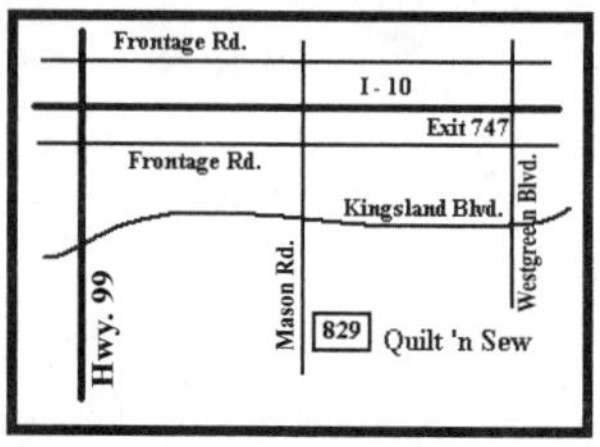

Texas Quilt Shops

Abilene Linda's Treasury, 7500 Cty. Rd. 203 325-529-3328
Amarillo Fabric Dreams and Things LLC, 1926 Civic Cir. 806-352-4458
Amarillo Pam's Quilting Corner, 204 S. Western St.
806-373-7777 See ad #2, page 516
Amarillo R & R Quilts & More, 4332 Teckla Blvd.
806-359-6235 See ad #4, page 516
Amarillo Sisters' Scraps, 6018 SW 33rd Ave.
806-372-0660 See ad #3, page 516
Amarillo Quilting Friends, 91 N. Fairmont St. 806-373-8379
Andrews The Sewing Cottage, 102 S. Main St.
432-524-7409 See ad #7, page 516
Arlington Lone Star House of Quilts, 1210 W. Abram St. 817-277-4749
Arlington Quilting Among Friends, 2081 E. Division St.
817-795-0900 See ad #49, page 526
Arlington Magnolia Quiltworks, 2224 W. Park Row #A 817-275-8515
Aubrey Fruit Jar Junction, 5848 Harmony Ranch Rd. 940-365-3158
Austin The Quilt Store, 2700 W. Anderson Ln. #301
512-453-1145 See ad #25, page 520
Austin Honey Bee Quilt Store, 9308 Anderson Mill Rd
512-257-1269 See ad #24, page 520
Austin Deb's Quilting, 3107 Foxton Cv 512-292-9864
Austin Bernina Sewing Center, 2900 W. Anderson #H 512-467-8406
Austin Austin Sewing Machines, 8213 Brodie Lane 512-899-3233
Azle Quilts & Stuffs, 900 NW Pkwy. St.
817-270-0452 See ad #45, page 526
Azle Quilts by Eagle Mountain Products
1635 W Bill B Rd
817-237-0881 See ad #44, page 526
Bandera Gone Quiltin', 1115 Cedar St.
8307964360 See ad #28, page 521
Bastrop Lost Pines Quilt Shop, 709 Chestnut St.
512-321-9300 See ad #22, page 520
Beaumont Sew What Bernina, 4310 Dowlen Rd. #8 409-892-7574
Bowie Bowie Sewing Center, 217 N. Smythe St. 940-872-6220
Brenham Stitch Haven, Inc., 1600 S. Day St.
979-836-3200 See ad #20, page 520
Bridgeport A & K Quilting & Fabric, 12103 FM 2210 E 940-748-2060
Bryan Lone Star Quiltworks, 4301 S. Texas Ave.
979-595-1072 See ad #34, page 522
Buda B & B Quilting & Gifts, 107 S. Austin St.
512-312-2299 See ad #23, page 520
Burkburnett The Stitching Depot, 316 East 3rd St. 940-569-0804
Burleson Country Stitches Quilt Shop, 426 SW Wilshire Blvd
817-426-5981 See ad #50, page 526
Burleson Sandy's Quilt Shop, 811 NE Alsbury, Ste 650 817-447-1233
Camp Wood Suzie Q Quilts, 214 S. Nueces St. 830-597-6310
Carrollton The Old Craft Store, 1110 W. Main St.
972-242-9111 See ad #64, page 530
Carrollton The Quilter's Workshop, 2540 Old Denton Rd. 972-323-6348
Castroville Fabric 'N Friends, 813 Paris St.
830-931-0141 See ad #16, page 518
Cedar Hill Just Stitchin, 605 Cedar St.
972-291-8729 See ad #57, page 528
Cedar Hill The 1890 House A Quilters Retreat
455 East F.M. 1382 Suite 3-189
972-291-0472 See ad #56, page 528
Cedar Park Ready to Sew Bernina, 2800 East Whitestone Blvd., Suite 225 512-260-4100
Cedar Park B J's Quilts & Things, 3404 Shenandoah Dr. 512-258-2852
Celeste Quilt Mercantile, 15 Hwy 69 N
903-568-8739 See ad #63, page 530

Childress Arbor Rose Quilts & Gifts, 611 Ave. F NW 940-937-2797
Clifton Quilting Cousins, 603 South Ave. G (Hwy. 6)
254-675-0010 See ad #39, page 523
College Station Pruitt's Fabric, 318 George Bush Dr.
979-693-9357 See ad #33, page 522
Colleyville Quilter's Dream, 6409 Colleyville Blvd.
817-481-7105 See ad #46, page 526
Collinsville The Sewing Boutique, 102 N Main St
9034293939 See ad #65, page 531
Conroe Quilt 'N Time Sisters, 17641 Linda Ln. 409-231-3322
Conroe Quilter's Quarters, 3401 West Davis Suite E
936-756-7200 See ad #76, page 533
Converse General Store/Quilt Studio, 305 S. Sequin 210-659-7278
Copper Canyon Patch Quilts, 670 Estates Dr
Corpus Christi Beautiful Creations Sewing Center, PO Box 271396 979-618-0537
Corpus Christi The Quilt Cottage, 5433 S. Staples, Suite H
361-985-0908 See ad #83, page 534
Crosby Quilter's Quarters, 306 Wahl 281-328-9600
Cypress QuiltWorks, 25250 NW Freeway #140
281-256-3550 See ad #96, page 536
Dallas Quilters Connection, 9658 Plano Rd.
214-343-1440 See ad #53, page 527
Dickinson Pinwheels and Posies, 3335 IH 45
281-337-1213 See ad #91, page 536
Dumas Down Home Quilts, 102 E. 7th St. Suite A
806-934-4041 See ad #1, page 516
El Campo Cedar Chest Quilt Shoppe, 121 S Mechanic
979-578-8929 See ad #78, page 533
El Paso Sew What's New, 7410 Remcon Cir.
915-760-5300 See ad #8, page 516
El Paso Bernina of El Paso, 1809 Trawood Dr. 915-599-1909
Fairfield Cotton Cottage, 221 E. Commerce St.
903-389-6528 See ad #73, page 533
Fort Worth Cherry's Quilt Shop, 4320 Wichita St. 817-531-0074
Fort Worth Berry Patch Fabrics, 4913 S. Hulen 817-346-6400
Fort Worth Cabbage Rose Quilting Fabrics & Gifts
3526 W. Vickery Blvd.
817-377-3993 See ad #43, page 525
Fredericksburg Pocketful of Poseys, 311 E. Hwy. St.
830-990-4140 See ad #18, page 518
Fredericksburg Sandy Jenkins Designs, 203 E. Austin St. 830-997-8944
Fredericksburg Fredericksburg Pie Company and Quilts
108 East Austin
830-910-6992 See ad #19, page 519 & 201
Freeport Broad Street Market, 120 W. Broad St. 979-233-6900
Friendswood Quakertown Quilts, 180 S. Friendswood Dr.
281-996-1756 See ad #89, page 535
Gainesville Pass Time Fabrics, 105 West California St.
940-668-1747 See ad #66, page 531
Garland Ruby Jane's Retro Fabric, 2940 Broadway Blvd. #114 972-278-7600
Garland Quilting Friends, 318 Saddlebrook Dr. 972-496-3753
Garland Suzy's Quilt Shop, 111 N. 6th St.
972-272-8180 See ad #60, page 529 & 200
Georgetown Poppy Quilt 'N Sew, 4106 Williams Dr., # 102
512-863-6108 See ad #32, page 522
Giddings All Around the Block Quilt Shop
979 North Leon
979-542-2782 See ad #21, page 520

Granbury The Iron Horse Inn, 616 Thorp Spring 817-579-5535

Granbury Houston St. Mercantile, 126 N. Houston St.
817-279-0425 See ad #52, page 527

Grapevine Bluebonnet Quilting, 2713 Newcastle Dr 817-251-1813
Groesbeck Quilt Patch, 442 E. Navasota 254-729-8742
Hamilton One More Stitch, 520 N. Rice 254-386-8874
Harlingen Picket Fence Quilt & Fabric Shop, 2815 S. 77 Sunshine Strip 956-412-2668
Hemphill Cedar Tree Nest Quilts, 1570 Tag Hwy. St. S 409-787-4076
Hewitt Wrapped in Quilts, 935 Vail Highlands 254-666-5226

Houston Buttons N Bows, 14070 Memorial Dr.
2814960170 See ad #88, page 535

Houston Time Treasured Quilts, 12916 Malcomson
2813706061 See ad #87, page 535

Houston Cottontail Quilts, 14781 Memorial Dr. 713-899-3884
Houston High Fashion Fabric Cntr, 3101 Louisiana 713-528-7299
Houston SunFlower Quilts, 3572 West T.C. Jester 713-290-9232

Huffman The Quilt Room, 11515 FM 1960, Suite B
281-324-9018 See ad #94, page 536

Humble It's a Stitch, 9574 FM 1960 Bypass
281-446-4999 See ad #93, page 536

Huntington Backyard Quilt Shop, 11274 US Hwy. 69 S 936-876-4758
Huntsville Fabric Carousel, 1101 12th St. 936-295-8322

Hurst Quilter's Stash Bernina, 848 W. Pipeline Rd.
817-595-1778 See ad #47, page 526

Jefferson Quilter's Corner, 1102 FM 2208 Rt. 903-665-3385

Joshua Batiks Galore, 7301 CR 912
817-556-2200 See ad #51, page 526

Katy Quilt N Sew Studio
829 S. Mason Rd., Ste 224
281-398-0670 See ad #97, page 536

Katy The Feathered Star, 1002 Avenue A 281-371-2456
Keene Quilt N Stitches, 615 Lewis Ln. 817-645-9860
Keller Sew Creative, 945 Tealwood Dr. 817-788-2407

Kerrville Creations, 1013 Main St.
830-896-8088 See ad #27, page 521

Kerrville Jasmine Heirlooms, 1308 Water St. 830-257-5440

Killeen Quiltin' Country, 4904 W Stan Schlueter Lp.
254-554-3700 See ad #36, page 523

Killeen Carol's Creations, 601 S 2nd St. 254-628-8788

Kingsland Barb's Quilt Nook Etc., 120 Dan St.
325-388-5225 See ad #30, page 522

Kountze Jae's of the Big Thicket, 7616 Old Honey Island Rd. 409-246-4462

La Porte Painted Pony N Quilts, 1015 S. Broadway St.
281-471-5735 See ad #92, page 536

Lake Jackson Calico Cat Sewing Center, 209 Parking Wy 979-285-9277

Lakeway Cotton Cupboard, 1503-A N RR 620
5122942776 See ad #29, page 522

Lewisville Quilt Country, 701 S. Stemmons #60
972-436-7022 See ad #62, page 530

Livingston Jean's Corner at Feeder's Supply
712 N. Jackson St.
936-327-8817 See ad #75, page 533

Llano The Country Quilt Shop,
102 Rio Oaks LN CR 116
325-247-4247 See ad #31, page 522

Lockhart Raney House Quilts, 3253 Williamson Rd. 512-376-5990
Longview Sharman's Sewing Ctr., 1017 McCann Rd. 903-753-8014

Lubbock Rachael's Fabrics & Quilting, 4636 50th St.
806-795-4693 See ad #6, page 516

Lubbock Moore Quilts and Fabrics, 6301 B 19th 806-799-1151
Lufkin Glenda's Sewing Studio, 1515 Blue Bonnet St 727-535-1270
Lufkin Rick's Sewing Machine Cntr, 114 E. Lufkin 936-639-9487
Lufkin Bove Sewing Center, 501 E. Lufkin Ave. 936-634-2146
Madisonville Lone Star Quilt Emporium, 201 N. Texas St 936-349-0964
McAllen Rio Bravo Fabric Store, 1510 Beaumont 956-686-0291

McKinney Happiness Is ... Quilting! 217 N. Kentucky
972-542-8839 See ad #59, page 528

Mckinney Linda's Electric Quilters, 2001 Central Cir. 972-542-4000

McKinney The Quilt Asylum, 153 S Central Expwy
972-562-2686 See ad #58, page 528

Mesquite Thomas Sewing Center, Inc.
1515 N. Town East Blvd., Ste. 133
972-681-3996 See ad #54, page 527 & 404

Midland The Quilting Patch, 3323 N. Midland Dr. 110
432-262-6616 See ad #10, page 517

Midlothian Quilts 'n More, 211 W. Ave. F
972-723-8669 See ad #48, page 526

Missouri City Little Stitches Sewing Center
3340 FM 1092 #130
281-403-1564 See ad #86, page 535

Montgomery Sew Many Things, 301 Prairie 936-597-5799
Nacogdoches Bove Sewing Center, 1122 N. University 936-569-7663
Nederland Sew-N-Sew's, 2703 Avenue H 409-729-7397

Nederland The Fabric Store & Sew Much More
1605 South Hwy 69
409-729-5288 See ad #77, page 533

New Braunfels Creative Sewlutions @ The Quilt Haus
651 N. Business 35, #510
830-620-1382 See ad #17, page 518

Palestine Grime's Sewing Center, 619 W. Oak St.
903-729-2889 See ad #71, page 532

Paris Sew Much More, 2400 Stillhouse Rd.
903-784-6342 See ad #72, page 532

Pittsburg Quilters Playhouse, 1880 FM 3384 903-855-1429
Plano Bernina Sewing Of Plano, 2400 K Ave #C 972-578-9227
Plano Pieceful Patchwork, 3417 Parkhaven Dr. 972-964-9678
Plano Plano Singer & New Home Sewing Center 2070 W. Spring Creek Pkwy. #326 972-527-7401

Port Aransas Kalico & Keepsakes Quilt Shop
600 Cut Off Rd. #10
361-739-1496 See ad #82, page 534

Port Lavaca Beefore It's A Quilt, 119 E. Main St.
361-552-1350 See ad #81, page 534

Portland Stitches Sewing Center, 801 Houston St. 361-643-1739

Quitman Stitchin' Heaven, 502 E. Goode St.
903-763-5048 See ad #69, page 532

Richardson The Fabric Affair, 101 S. Coit Rd Ste 339 972-234-1937
Richardson Kay Fabrics, 518 W. Arapaho Rd. 972-234-5111

Richmond Quilters Cottage, 920 FM 359
281-633-9331 See ad #84, page 535

Rockport Golden Needles & Quilts, 701 N. Allen St. 361-729-7873
Rockwall Texas Quiltworks, 212 E. Rusk 972-771-9952

Round Rock Kim's Quilts, 2403 Meadow Brook Dr.
512-248-8858 See ad #26, page 520

Round Rock Austin's Sewing & Vacuum, 1401 South IH 35 Suite 170 512-310-7349

Salado A Sewing Basket, 560 N. Main St. #6
254-947-5423 See ad #35, page 523

San Antonio Sew Special Quilts--Bernina
24165 IH 10 West #421
210-698-6076 See ad #13, page 518

San Antonio Creative Sewing Center, 11777 West Ave.
210-344-0791 See ad #14, page 518

San Antonio Memories By The Yard, 8015 Mainland
210-520-4833 See ad #15, page 518

San Antonio Seventh Heaven Quilt Shop
6706 N. New Braunfels Ave.
210-822-9980 See ad #12, page 517

San Antonio Las Colchas, 110 Ogden St. 210-223-2405

San Antonio Cats Meow Quilt Shop, 5890 De Zavala Rd. #103 210-561-8185
San Antonio Plain Jane's Folk Art, 9807 Fredericksburg 210-558-6223
Santa Anna Quilters Patch, 705 Wallis Ave. 325-348-3771
Sequin Quilting Gin, 286 Gin Spur 830-303-5765
Sequin You're So Crafty, 516 N. Austin 830-379-0730
Shiner Martha's Quilting Corner, 117 E. 7th St. 361-594-8286

Slaton Quilts-n-More, 121 S. 9th
806-828-3222 See ad #9, page 517

Spring Texas Quilt Machines, 2311 Sciaaca Rd 281-793-1777
Spring The Hen House, 5701 Louetta #200 281-379-7306
Spring The Needle Nest, 2219 Sawdust Rd. 281-292-3153

Stafford Quilter's Emporium
11925 Southwest Freeway, Suite 11
281-491-0016 See ad #85, page 535

Stephenville The Flying Needle, 1495 W. South Loop
254-965-7577 See ad #40, page 523

Sugar Land Astrid's Creations, 1823 Cheyenne River Cir 281-265-6429
Sunrise Beach Patches, 103 Sunrise Dr.

Texas City Cactus Quilts, 1811 6th St. N
409-965-9778 See ad #90, page 536

The Woodlands Quakertown Quilts, 25823 Budde
2814192800 See ad #95, page 536

Tomball KV Quilters, 412 W. Main 281-516-3180

Trinity Heavenly Threads Quilt Shop
334 Prospect A
936-594-1237 See ad #74, page 533

Tyler A Nimble Thimble
1813 Capital Drive #300
903-581-4926 See ad #70, page 532

Tyler Quilting Barn, 11334 St. Hwy. 64E 903-566-3518
Tyler Granny's Needle Haus, 6004 S. Broadway 903-561-4637
Tyler Sharman's Sewing Cntr., 6005 S Broadway 903-581-5470
Van Alstyne Alford Inn Quilt Shop and Retreat 101 East Marshall St. 903-482-6688

Victoria Quilters Patch, 205 N. Star Rd. #Q
361-578-0380 See ad #79, page 533

Waco Homestead Sewing & Quilting
1012 Meixner
254-829-2380 See ad #37, page 523

Waco Tomorrow's Quilts, 800 Lake Air Dr.
254-741-6988 See ad #38, page 523

Waco The Quilt Farm, 523 Wagoner Rd. 254-829-1211

Waxahachie Common Threads Quilting
315 S. Rogers St.
972-935-0510 See ad #55, page 528

Waxahachie Waxahachie Emporium, 116 N Collage #A 972-938-2262

Weatherford Quazy Quilt Shoppe, 106 N. Lamar
817-341-4800 See ad #42, page 524

Weatherford Peachtree Quilts, 133 N. Waco St.
817-599-4114 See ad #41, page 524

Webster Fabrics Etcetera, 571 W. Bay Area Blvd. 281-338-1904

Whitesboro Kaleidoscope Quilt Shop, 114 E. Main St.
903-564-4681 See ad #67, page 531

Whitney My Mini Quilt Shop, 5120 FM 933 N 254-694-4950

Wichita Falls The Enchanted Quilt, 3401 Kemp Blvd. #M
940-689-0990 See ad #5, page 516

Wills Point Country Junction Quilt Store, 124 N. 4th St. 903-873-3555
Wimberley Cella's Fabric Shoppe, 15950 Ranch Rd. 12 512-847-3313

Winnsboro Calico Junction, 107 E. Elm St.
903-342-3399 See ad #68, page 531

Winters Bluebonnet Mercantile, 106 South Main St.
325-754-4057 See ad #11, page 517

Wylie Blue Ribbon Quilt Shoppe, 102-C N. Ballard
972-941-0777 See ad #61, page 529 & 416

Yorktown Seams Like Home, 441 W. 5th
361-564-9455 See ad #80, page 534

Texas Quilt Shows

51 Shows

About Shows: We are listing only the very basic information about shows that happen on a regular schedule here. Please check out our website for more details on each show.
Also this information tends to change quite often so please verify the event with our website or a local source before you venture far. Or if you're in the right area at the right time, give it a shot.

If you are a show organizer, please keep us updated on your event.
shows@quilterstravelcompanion.com
www.quilterstravelcompanion.com

On our website you will also find:
- Exact dates (when we have them)
- Contact Information
- Events happening on a one-time basis
- Sponsor Information
- Description of Event

Month	City	Schedule	Show	Location with address
January				
	Rockport	Even Years, last weekend of January	Piecemakers by the Bay Quilt Guild Show	Rockport-Fulton High School, 1803 Omohundro
	Jefferson	Annual, last weekend in January	Jefferson Quilt Show	Cypress Valley Education Center, 120 E. Austin St.
February				
	Brenham	Even Years, 1st weekend in February	Friendship Quilters Guild Show	Washington County Fairgrounds, 1305 E. Blue Bell Rd.
	Azle	Odd Years, 2nd weekend in February	Happy Scrappers Quilt Guild Show	
	Beaumont	Even Years, 2nd weekend in February	Golden Threads Quilt Show	Beaumont Civic Center, 801 Main
	Corpus Christi	Odd Years, 2nd weekend of February	Coastal Bend Quilt Guild Show	American Bank Center, 1901 N. Shoreline Dr.
	Pharr	Annual, 3rd weekend in February	Rio Grande Valley Quilt Guild	Pharr International Convention Ctr, 3000 N. Cage Blvd.
	La Grange	Annual, last Fri & Sat in February	Best Little Quilt Show in Texas	Fayette County Fairgrounds--Commerical Exhibit Hall, Hwy. 77

Month	City	Schedule	Show	Location with address
March				
	Lampasas	Annual, 1st Fri & Sat in March	Needle Art & Quilt Show	Lampasas County Courthouse, 3rd & Pecan
	Dallas	Annual, 2nd weekend in March	Dallas Quilt Celebration	Dallas Market Hall, 1-35 & Market Center Blvd.
	Tyler	Annual, last Fri & Sat in March	Azalea Quilt Show	Harvey Convention Center, 2000 W. Front St.
April				
	Channelview	Annual, 1st Fri & Sat in April	North Channel Spring Quilt Show	Channelview FFA Fairgrounds, 16204 Wood Dr.
	Dimmitt	Annual, 1st or 2nd weekend in April	Ogallala Quilters Society Show	Expo Center, SE 4th & E. Lee
	Humble	Odd Years, 2nd weekend of April	Kingwood Area Quilt Guild Show	Humble Civic Center, 8233 Will Clayton Pkwy.
	Pearland	Odd Years, 3rd weekend in April	Bay Area Quilt Guild Show	Knights of Columbus Hall, 2320 Hatfield Rd.
	Brownwood	Annual, last weekend of April	Heart of Texas Quilt Show	Brownwood Coliseum, 500 E. Baker
May				
	Huntsville	Annual, 1st Weekend of May	Tall Pine Quilt Guild Show	Historic Downtown Huntsville
	Arlington	Annual, 2nd Fri & Sat in May	Quilters Guild of Arlington	Bob Duncan Center (in Vandergriff Park), 2800 S. Center St. (N of I-20)
	Giddings	Annual, 2nd weekend in May	Lee County Fair & Rodeo	Fireman's Park in Fireman's Hall, U.S. Hwy 290--2 mi. W. of Town
	Kerrville	Odd Years, Memorial Day Weekend	Hill Country Quilt Guild Show	Schreiner Univ. - Edington Gym, 2100 Memorial Blvd.
June				
	Keller	Annual, 1st Sat. in June	Old Town Quilts Qoutdoor Quilt Show	Downtown Keller
	Abilene	Annual, 2nd weekend in June	Abilene Quilters Guild Show	Abilene Civic Center, 1100 N. 6th (N. 6th and Pine)
July				
	Monahans	Annual, early July	Sandhills Cutups Quilt Show	Ward County Community Center, Corner of 4th and Calvin
	Weatherford	Annual, 2nd Sat. in July	Parker County Peach Festival	Historic Downtown Weatherford
	Midlothian	Annual, 3rd weekend in July	Creative Quilters Guild Show	Midlothian Conference Center, 1 Community Circle
	New Braunfels	Even year, last weekend in July	New Braunfels Area Quilt Guild Show	New Braunfels Civic Center, 380 S. Seguin St.
August				
	Fort Worth	Annual, early August	Fort Worth Quilt Guild Show	Forth Worth Academy of Fine Arts
	Plano	Odd Years, 3rd Fri & Sat in August	Quilters Guild of Plano Show	Plano Centre, 2000 E. Spring Creek Pkwy.
September				
	Conroe	Even Years, Sept. or Oct.	Golden Needles Quilt Show	Tree of Life Lutheran Church, 3402 Loop 336 W
	Fredericksburg	Even years, Labor Day weekend	Vereins Quilt Guild Of Fredericksburg	Gillespie Farm Bureau, 237 Equestrian Dr
	Bryan	Odd Years, 2nd weekend of September	Brazos Bluebonnet Quilt Show	Brazos Center, 3232 Briarcrest Dr.
	Caldwell	Annual, 2nd weekend in September	Creative Memories Quilt Guild Show	Caldwell Civic Center, 103 Presidential Corridor W
	San Antonio	Odd Years, 2nd weekend in September	San Antonio Quilters Show	Live Oak Civic Center, 8101 Pat Booker Rd.
	Sulphur Springs	Annual, 2nd weekend in September	Lone Star Heritage Quilt Guild Show	Hopkins County Civic Center, 1200 Houston St.
	Conroe	Odd Years, Sept. or Oct	Golden Needles Quilt Show and Live Auction	Lone Star Convention Center, 9055 FM 1484
	Fort Worth	Annual, 3rd weekend in September	Trinity Valley Quilters Guild Show	Will Rogers Complex--Amon Exhibit Hall, 3401 W. Lancaster Ave.
	Wichita Falls	Even Years, Fall	Red River Quilters Guild Show	Multi-Purpose Events Center, 1000 5th St.
	Austin	Even Years, Third weekend in September	Austin Area Quilt Guild Show	Lester E. Palmer Events Center, 900 Barton Springs
	Post Oak	Annual, last Fri & Sat of September	Busy Bee Quilt Show	Community Center, Schmittou Rd. & FM 2127
	Weatherford	Annual, last weekend of September	Quilter's Guild of Parker County Show	County Sherrif's Facility, 2251 Mineral Wells Hwy
October				
	Burkburnett	Annual, first Saturday in October	Friendship Display of Quilts	Burburnett Community Center, 735 Davy Dr.
	Midland	Odd Years, 1st Saturday of October	Midland Quilter's Guild Quilt Show	Midland Center, 105 N. Main St.
	Round Rock	Odd Years, first weekend of October	Chisholm Trail Quilt Guild Show	Dell Diamond, 3400 E. Palm Valley Rd.
	Stephenville	Even Years, first weekend of October	Town N Country Quilt Guild Show	Valley Grove Baptist Church, 1731 S. US Hwy. 281
	Vernon	Annual, October	Red River Valley Museum Show	Red River Valley Museum, 4600 College Dr.
	Mineola	Annual, 2nd Fri & Sat in Oct.	Quilt Celebration	Mineola League of the Arts, 200 W. Blair St.
	Onalaska	Annual, October	Greater Onalaska Heritage Quilt Show	Onalaska Elementary School Cafetorium
	Canton	Annual, 3rd weekend of October	Heritage Quilt Guild of Van Zandt Show	Canton Civic Ctr, Flea Market Rd off Hwy. 64
	Goldthwaite	Annual, 3rd Sat. in October	Courthouse Steps Quilters Show	Mills County Civic Center, 1103 Cline St.
	Granbury	Odd Years, 3rd weekend in October	Granbury Quilters Guild Show	Granbury Resort Convention Center, 621 E. Pearl St.
	Houston	Annual, late October or early November	International Quilt Festival	George Brown Convention Center, 1001 Avenida de las Americas

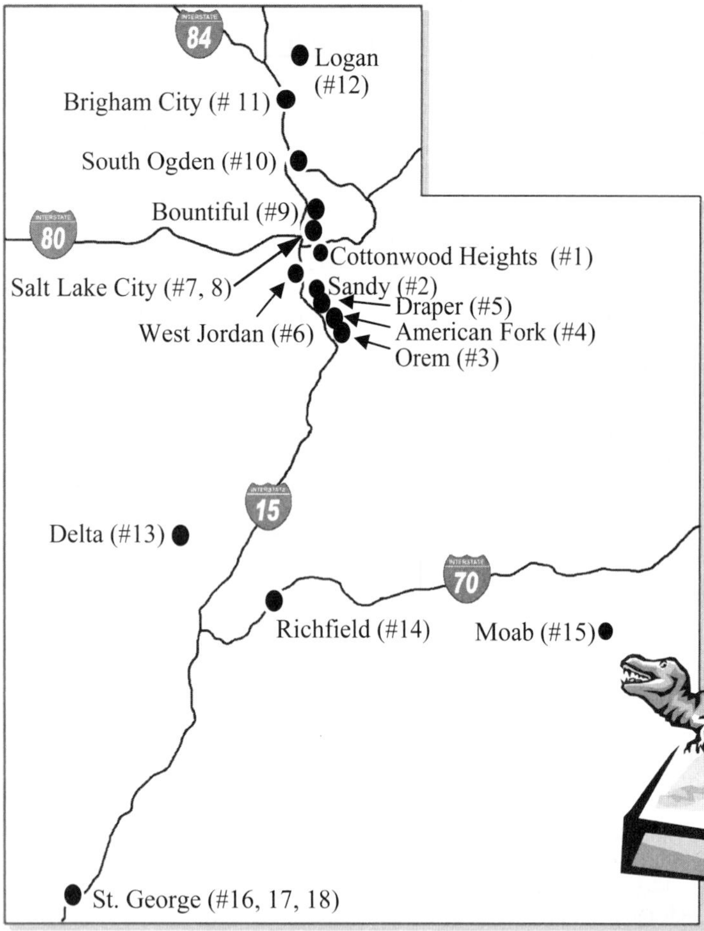

18 Featured Shops

UTAH

#1 Elaine's Quilt Block

6970 South 3000 East
Cottonwood Heights, UT 84121

801-947-9100

10-6 M,F,S 10-8 TU-TH

www.elainesquiltblock.com

Come visit our unique 19th century style building with 6,100 square feet of floor space.

Discover over 5,000 bolts of fabric including:

- Orientals
- Batiks
- Brushed Plaids
- Country
- Chenille
- Baby Flannels
- Civil War Collection
- Moda

LOCATED AT THE BASE OF UTAH'S SCENIC WASATCH MOUNTAINS

Full-service shop including Instruction, Machine Quilting and Hemstitching

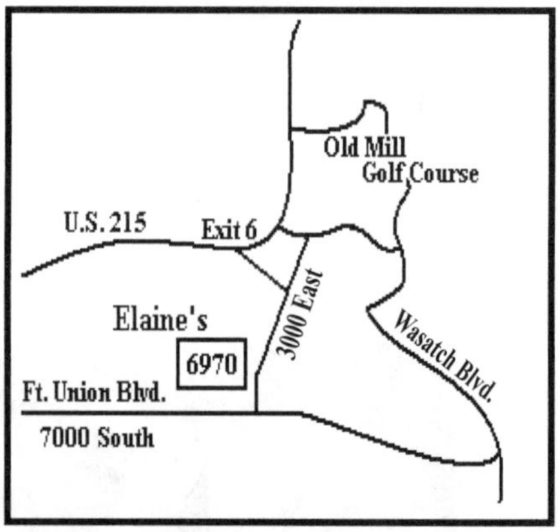

Quilt, Quilt, Quilt Etc.

Sandy, UT #2

Weekdays 10 - 9
Saturdays 10 - 5

Over 15,000 Bolts of 100% Cotton Fabric

- All the top lines including Batiks, Flannels, Civil War and 30's Reproductions
- Large selection of Patterns, Books & Notions
- Over 40 quilts on display
- Custom machine quilting

11 East Main Street - Sandy Utah 84070
801-255-2666 or Toll Free 877-422-6765
www.quilt-etc.com

10 Minutes South of Salt Lake City

3 Blocks from Historic Sandy, TRAX station

Owner: Dorthey Chase
Established: 1988

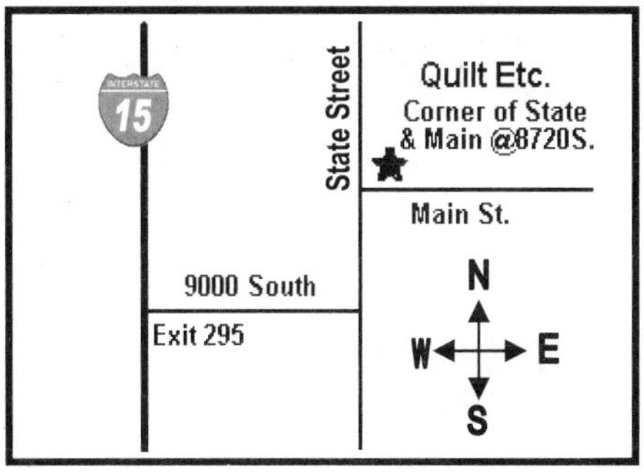

Orem, UT #3

Mon - Sat 10 - 6

The Stitching Corner

631 E 1700 S 84097
(801) 426-6900
Owner: Scott Blackham

Est: 1990
5400 sq.ft.
4000+ bolts

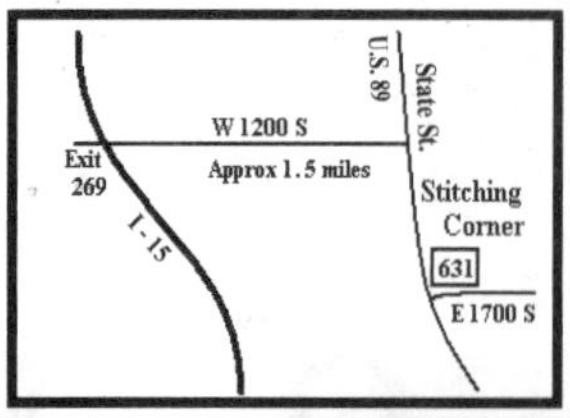

blackham@juno.com Newsletter
www.stitchingcornerinc.com
Utah's Exclusive Wool & Silk Headquarters.
We're fully stocked for all your project needs.
Your one stop shop -- quilting, heirloom sewing.
Batiks, Patterns, Classes & Machine Quilting.

American Fork, UT #4

Mon - Fri 10 - 6
Sat 10 - 5

The Quilting Cottage

35 S 100 E St. 84003
(801) 492-6119

www.thequiltingcottage.net

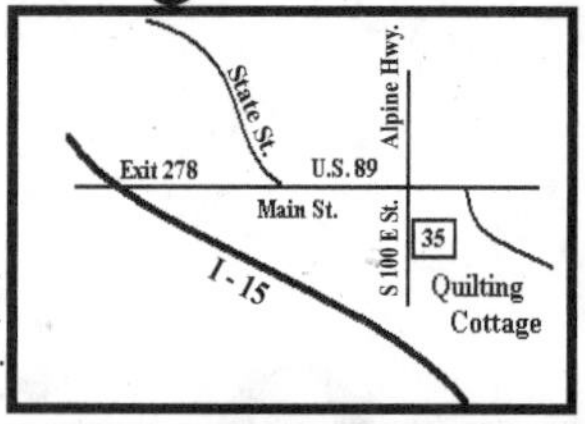

Large selection of 1800's and Civil War fabrics.
Fabrics that appeal to every age group: Michael Miller, Free Spirit, Amy Butler, Moda and more.
Long arm quilting available.

Draper, UT #5

Mon - Thur 10 - 6
Fri & Sat 10 - 5

Thimbles and Threads

12215 S 900 E 84020
(801) 576-0390
Owner: Cathie Zimmerman
Est: 1995
3000+ bolts
Newsletter

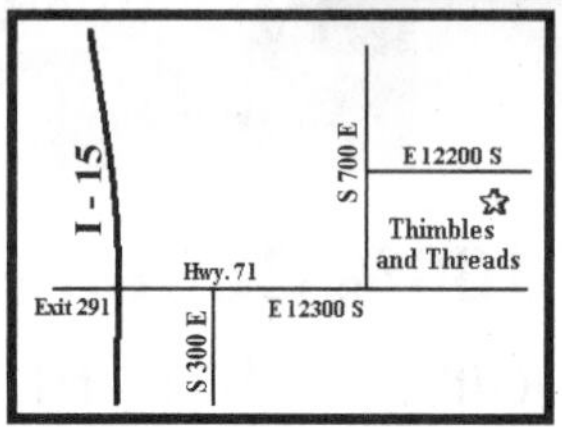

cathie@thimblesandthreads.com
www.thimblesandthreads.com
Built in 1910 by Utah Egg as a poultry and egg distribution center, our unique building retains its original character, hardwood maple flooring, and plantation style porch.

West Jordan, UT #6

Mon - Sat 10 - 8

Pine Needles

1100 W 7800 S #3 84088
(801) 233-0551
Owner: Sandy Workman

www.pineneedlesonline.com

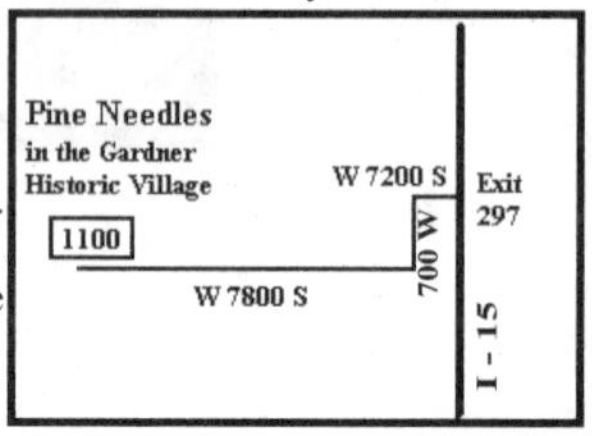

Est: 1996 1800 sq.ft.
We are proud to carry all the wonderful necessities for quilting, cross stitch, primitive embroidery and Russian punch needle. Many of the items we offer are by local artisans whose work appeals to shoppers and tourists alike. Our walls are brimming with the promise of projects to be done.

Salt Lake City, UT #8

Mon - Sat 10 - 5

Whimsy Cottage

4647 S 2300 E 84117
(801) 274-1443
Est: 2005 1500 sq.ft. 1500 bolts
www.whimsycottage.net

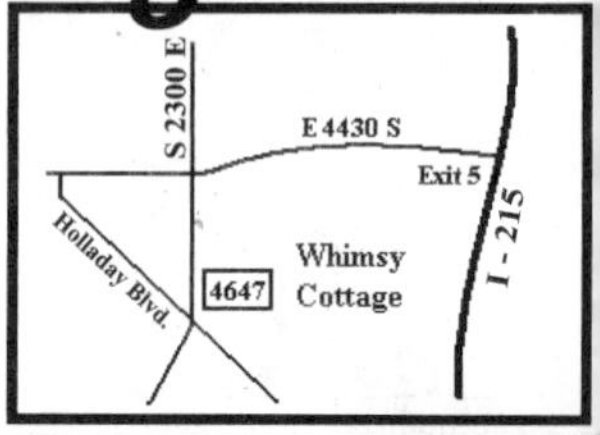

Fresh fabrics, inspiration, books & notions for the art of quilting.

Pipers Quilts & Comforts

Your Local Everything Knitting & Quilting Store
801-484-5890
www.pipersquilts.com
1944 S 1100 E
Salt Lake City, UT 84106

American Patchwork & Quilting Top 10 Quilt Shop 2004

Salt Lake City, UT #7

Quilting, Applique, Wool Projects and Children's items.
Crochet, Knitting, Needle Punch & Embroidery.
We strive to reflect the joy these arts bring to us & our customers.

Tues - Sat 11 - 7

www.pipersquilts.com
Est: 1998
3500 sq. ft. 1500 Bolts.
Moda * Alexander Henry
Debbie Bliss * Rowan
Amy Butler * Art Gallery
Freespirit * and More

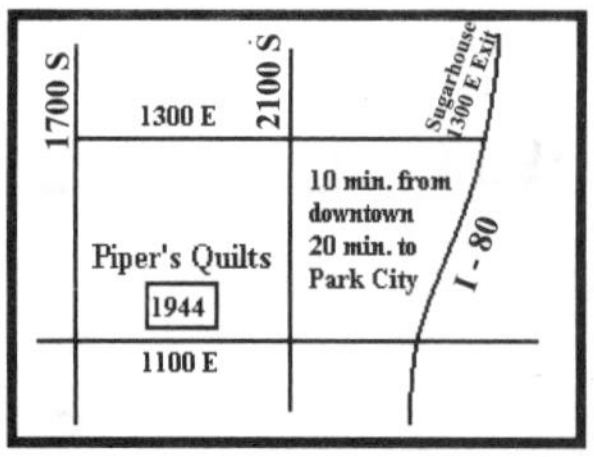

Across from the Sugarhouse Post Office. 5 Minutes from downtown Salt Lake City

Bountiful, UT #9

Mon - Fri 10 - 6
Sat 10 - 5

Quilter's Haven
Fabrics & Gifts

583 W 2600 S 84010
(801) 292-1846
Est: 1996

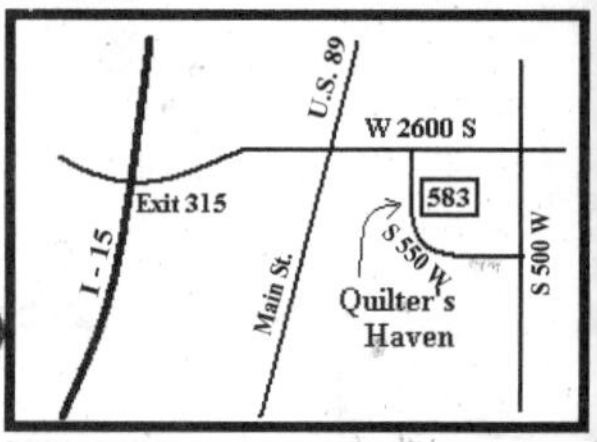

3500 sq.ft. 3000+ bolts Online newsletter
quiltershaven.utah@yahoo.com
www.quiltershaven-ut.com
Large selection of fine fabrics.
Better Homes & Garden Quilt Sampler Featured Shop-Spring 2010

South Ogden, UT #10

Mon - Sat 10 - 6

Gardiners Sew & Quilt

3789 Wall Ave. 84405
(801) 394-4466
Owners: Curt & Irene Gardiner
Est: 1975 3000 sq.ft.

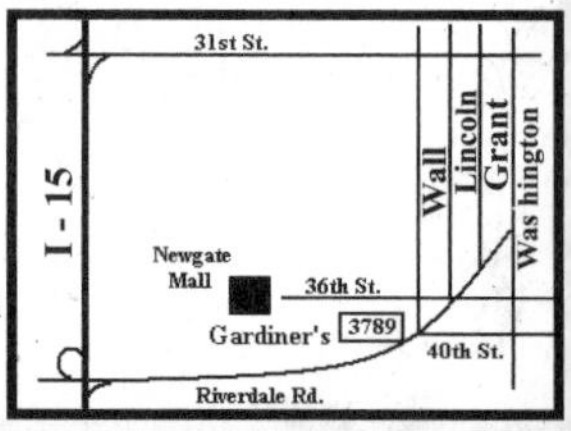

- Northern Utah's Premier Quilt Shop -
10,000+ bolts of 100% cotton, Largest selection of Flannels, Notions, Books, Patterns, Hemstitching, expert machine quilting & classes.

Brigham City, UT #11

Mon - Sat 10 - 6

Village Dry Goods

96 S. Main 84302
(435) 723-1315
www.villagedrygoods.com
Owners: RoLayne & Fran

On Historic Main Street.
Specializing in quilt fabric, tons of kits, stitchery, and Block of the Months.

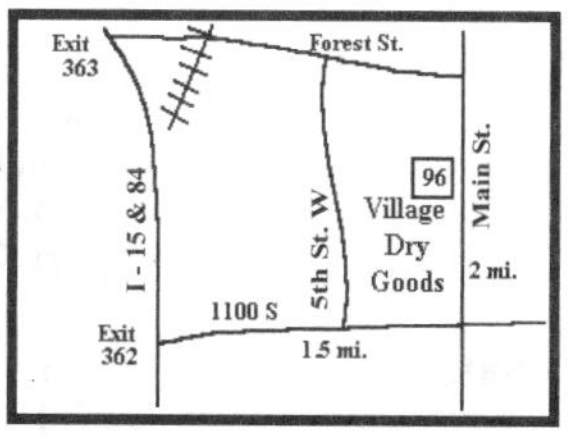

Logan, UT #12

Mon - Fri 10 - 6 Sat 10 - 5

Red Rooster

Quilts & Treasures

New Location in Historic Downtown Logan.
27 N. Main 84321 (435) 787-8857
Owner: Kaye Neilson
Est: 2003 2500 sq.ft.
redroosterquilt@gmail.com
www.redroosterquilt.com
A delightful assortment of quilting fabrics, overdyed wool, books, notions, gifts and FUN!

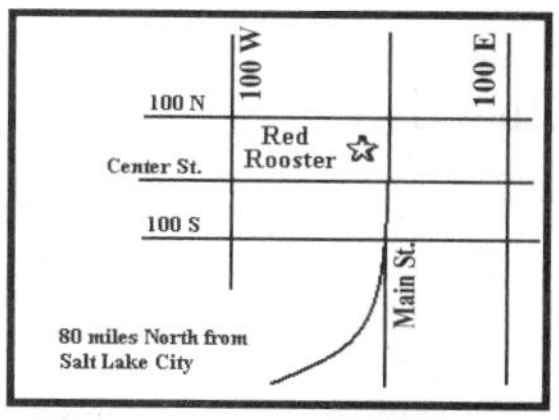

Mom's Crafts and Fabrics

Mon - Sat 10 - 6

313 South 100 West 84624

Biggest and Best Selection of Quilting Fabrics South of Provo, Utah.
100 Antique Sewing Machines on Display.
Est: 1973
4800 sq.ft.

(435) 864-3325
Owner: Peggy Overson
E-Mail:
peggyo@frontiernet.net

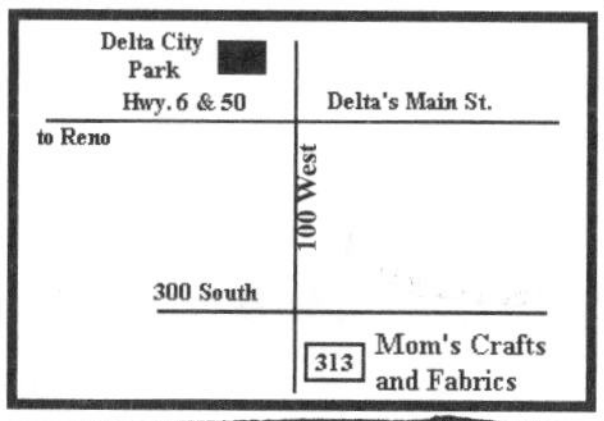

Delta, UT #13

Richfield, UT #14

Mon - Sat 9 - 6

MARCIA'S

25 N. Main St. 84701
(435) 896-8354
Est: 1989

Central Utah's largest fabric shop. We cater to quilters. Custom hand quilting and edging.
Gifts - Fabric - Quilting - Classes

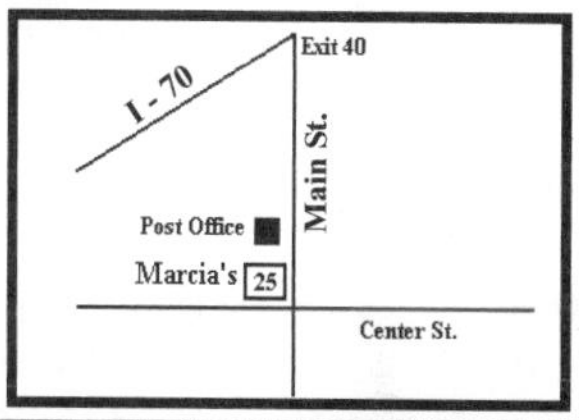

Moab, UT #15

Tues - Fri 10 - 6 Sat 10 - 4

IT'S SEW MOAB Quilting Shop

40 W. Center St. 84532
(435) 259-0739

Moab's only Quilt Shop!
100% Cotton Fabrics.
Patterns - Notions - Classes - Books - Kits
Rental Machines Available.

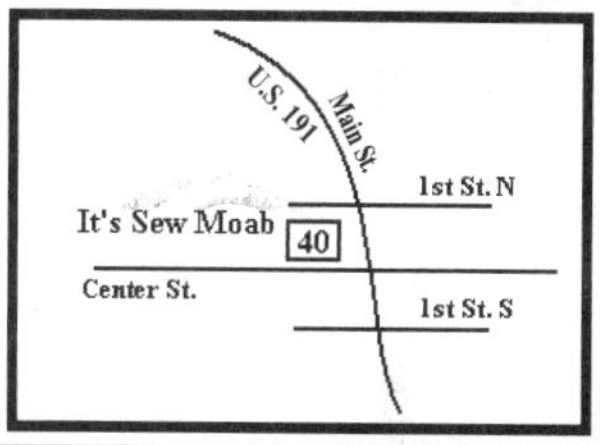

St. George, UT #16

Mon - Fri 10 - 5:30 Sat 10 - 4:30

LAZY DAISY COTTAGE

46 N 100 W 84770
(435) 673-5659 Fax: (435) 673-5513
www.lazydaisycottage.blogspot.com
Owner:
Dana Brooks
Est: 2003
2100 sq.ft.
1800 Bolts

Stop by our cozy historical home which is filled with fabrics, patterns, notions and a large variety of homespun cottage gifts.

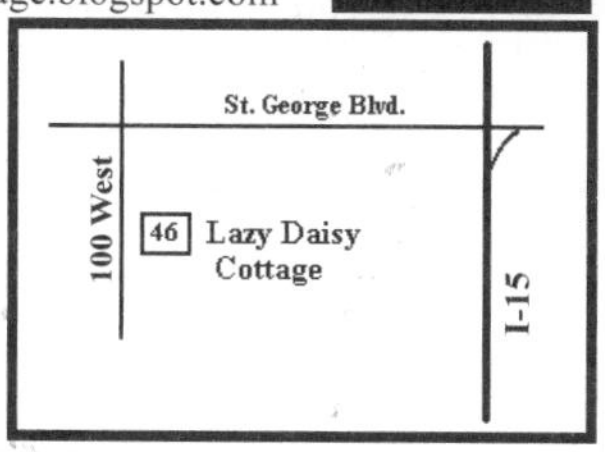

St. George, UT #17

Mon - Fri 10 - 6 Sat 10 - 4

Quilted Works, Inc.

140 N 400 W #A7 84770
(435) 674-2500
Owners: Sharla & Barb Johnson Est: 2005
quiltedworks@yahoo.com
www.quiltedworks.com

Great selection of quality fabric: bright, trendy & traditional. Pfaff sales and service.
Fun & Friendly Atmosphere.

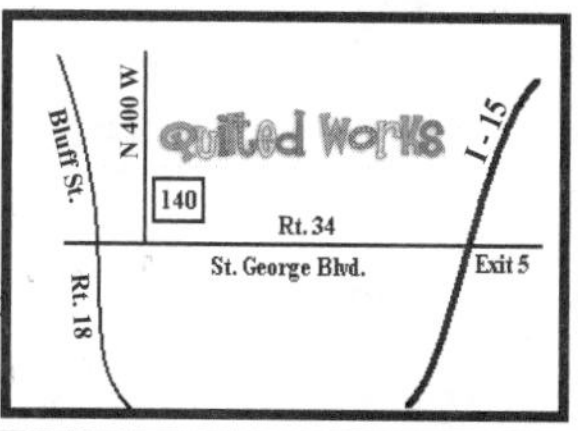

St. George, UT #18

Mon - Sat 10 - 6

SCRAP APPLE QUILTS

144 W. Brigham Rd. #23 84790
(435) 628-8226 or (800) 994-0097

- 5000+ Bolts
- Notions
- Janome Sewing Machines

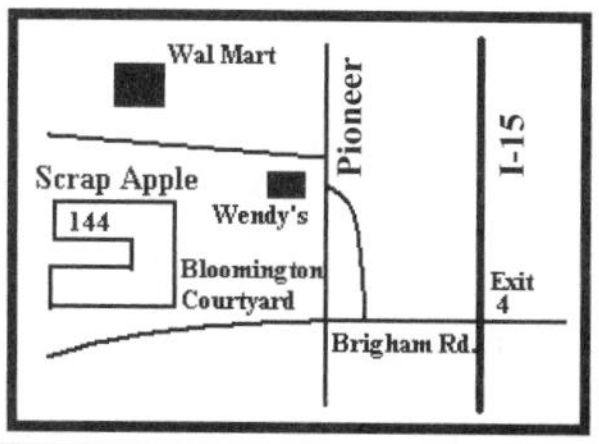

"Southern Utah's Quilting Destination"
www.scrapapplequilts.com
Est: 2005 3000 sq.ft. Free Newsletter

Utah Quilt Shops

American Fork	**The Quilting Cottage, 38 S 100 E**	**801-492-6119**	**See ad #4, page 544**
American Fork	Nuttall's Bernina & Fabrics, 53 W. Main	801-756-2223	
Bountiful	**Quilter's Haven, 583 W. 2600 S, Conionol Sq.**	**801-292-1846**	**See ad #9, page 544**
Bountiful	Brooks Fabrics, 220 N. Main	801-295-2941	
Brigham City	**Village Dry Goods, 96 S. Main**	**435-723-1315**	**See ad #11, page 545**
Cedar City	Granny's Quilts, Inc., 535 S Main #4	435-867-1828	
Cedar City	Sew Swanky, 60 N. Main St.	435-586-6300	
Clearfield	Bernina Sewing Center, 2465 N. Main St.	801-544-5911	
Clearfield	Sew N Save, 1475 S. State	801-825-2177	
Cottonwood Heights	**Elaine's Quilt Block 6970 S 3000 E**	**801-947-9100**	**See ad #1, page 542**
Delta	**Mom's Crafts and Fabrics, 313 S 100 W**	**435-864-3325**	**See ad #13, page 545**
Draper	**Thimbles & Threads, 12215 S 900 E**	**801-576-0390**	**See ad #5, page 544**
Gunnison	Quilt S'More, 98 S. Main St.	435-528-5393	
Gunnison	White Hills Trading Co., 74 S. Main St.	435-528-5100	
Highland	Just Sew, 11073 N Alpine Hwy # 101	865-847-9929	
Hurricane	Main Street Quilt Cottage, 72 N Main	435-635-4748	
Lehi	Broadbent's Quilt Shop, 128 N 100 E	801-768-9201	
Lehi	Quilt-N-Cuzzins, 605 W 900 N	801-768-2102	
Logan	**Red Rooster Quilts & Treasures, 27 N. Main**	**435-787-8857**	**See ad #12, page 545**
Logan	Stylish Fabrics, 138 N. Main St.	435-752-4186	
Midvale	Mormon Handicraft, 1110 E. Fort Union	801-561-8777	
Midway	Seasons of Home, P.O. Box 845	435-654-2844	
Moab	**It's Sew Moab, 40 W. Center St.**	**435-259-0739**	**See ad #15, page 545**
Orem	**The Stitching Corner, 631 E 1700 S**	**801-426-6900**	**See ad #3, page 544**
Orem	American Quilting, 426 W 800 N	801-802-7841	
Panguitch	The Scrappy Appleyard, 190 N. Main	435-676-8677	
Payson	Morganson's Sew Forth, 51 South Main	801-465-9133	
Price	Mrs. Guppy's, 42 E. Main	435-613-1470	
Providence	The Quilt House, 135 S. 100 E	801-752-5429	
Provo	Daines Cotton Shop, 164 West 500 North	801-373-6210	
Provo	Fabric Mill, 90 W. Center St.	801-375-4818	
Richfield	**Marcia's 25 N. Main St.**	**435-896-8354**	**See ad #14, page 545**
Roy	The Quilter's Basket, 4684 S 3600 W	888-703-7031	
Salem	Gracie Lou's, 446 N. State Rd.	801-423-1339	
Salt Lake City	**Pipers Quilts, 1944 S 1100 E**	**801-484-5890**	**See ad #7, page 544**
Salt Lake City	**Whimsy Cottage, 4647 S. 2300 E.**	**801-274-1443**	**See ad #8, page 544**
Salt Lake City	Stitches Quilting, 2798 E Pine View Dr	801-918-8792	
Salt Lake City	Nuttall's Bernina & Fabrics, 4742 S 900 E	801-262-6665	
Sandy	**Quilt Quilt Quilt, Etc., 11 E. Main St.**	**801-255-2666**	**See ad #2, page 543**
Sandy	Daines Cotton Shop, 9441 S 700 E	801-572-1412	
Sandy	Quilted Keepsakes, 1897 Falcon Way	801-571-9671	
Santa Clara	The Clover Patch, 2721 Santa Clara Dr	435-986-9070	
Smithfield	Stitches, 45 S. Main St.	435-563-0230	
South Ogden	**Gardiner's Sew & Quilt, 3789 Wall Ave**	**801-394-4466**	**See ad #10, page 544**
South Jordan	Material Girls Quilts, 1645 W Town Center	801-495-4290	
Springville	Corn Wagon Quilt Company, 303 E. 400 S	801-491-3551	
St. George	**Lazy Daisy Cottage, 46 N 100 W**	**435-673-5659**	**See ad #16, page 545**
St. George	**Quilted Works, Inc., 140 N. 400 W., # A7**	**435-674-2500**	**See ad #17, page 545**
St. George	**Scrap Apple Quilts, 144 W. Brigham Rd. #23**	**435-628-8226**	**See ad #18, page 545**
St. George	Mormon Handicraft, 735 S. Bluff	435-628-4495	
Tooele	Sew Sweet, 289 N. Main	435-833-0370	
Vernal	Quilted Hens, 38 S 600 W	435-789-2411	
Vernal	Dinaland Quiltworks, 2280 S 2000 E	435-789-6426	
West Jordan	**Pine Needles LLC, 1100 W 7800 S #3**	**801-233-0551**	**See ad #6, page 544**
West Jordan	The Quilt Shop, 9135 S. Redwood Rd.	801-966-7915	
West Jordan	Gardner Village Quilt Shop, 1100 W 7800 S	801-566-1846	
West Jordan	Floyd's Sewing Machines, 2263 W 7800 S	801-255-4130	

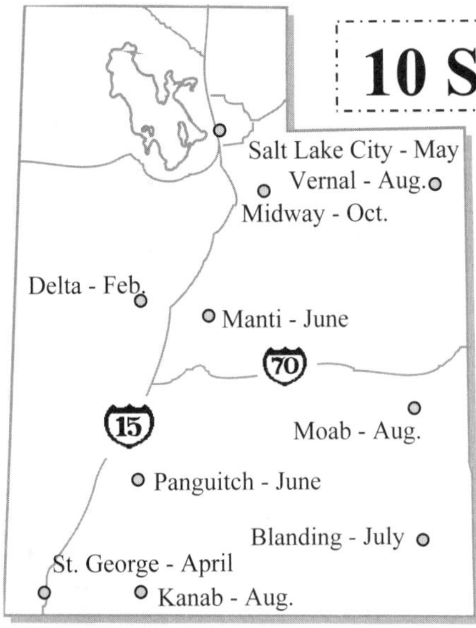

10 Shows

Utah Quilt Shows

About Shows: We are listing only the very basic information about shows that happen on a regular schedule here. Please check out our website for more details on each show. Also this information tends to change quite often so please verify the event with our website or a local source before you venture far. Or if you're in the right area at the right time, give it a shot.

Month	City	Schedule	Show	Location with address
February				
	Delta	Annual, 4th weekend of February	Snow Goose Quilt Show	Millard County Fair Bldg.
April				
	St. George	Odd Years, 3rd weekend of April	Dixie Quilt Guild Show	Dixie Convention Center, 1885 Convention Center
May				
	Salt Lake City	Annual, 2nd weekend in May	Home Machine Quilting Association Show	South Towne Exposition Center, 9575 S State St
June				
	Manti	Annual, 2nd & 3rd weekend in June	Horseshoe Mountain Quilt Guild & The Quilt Keepers	Old City Hall, 2nd North and Main St.
	Panguitch	Annual, 2nd week in June	Panguitch Quilt Walk Festival	Panguitch High School 185 S 400 E
July				
	Blanding	Annual, July 4th	Grayson Country Quilters Show	Blanding Elementary, 100 W 300 S
August				
	Vernal	Annual, 2nd & 3rd week of August	Quilters on the Edge Show	Western Heritage Museum, 328 E 200 S
	Kanab	Annual, 4th weekend in August	Western Legends Quilt Show	LDS Church, 20 W. Center St.
	Moab	Odd Years, August or September	Delicate Stitchers Quilt Guild Show	Grand Center, 182 N 500 W
October				
	Midway	Annual, 1st weekend in October	Utah Quilt Festival	Zermatt Resort

VERMONT

12 Featured Shops

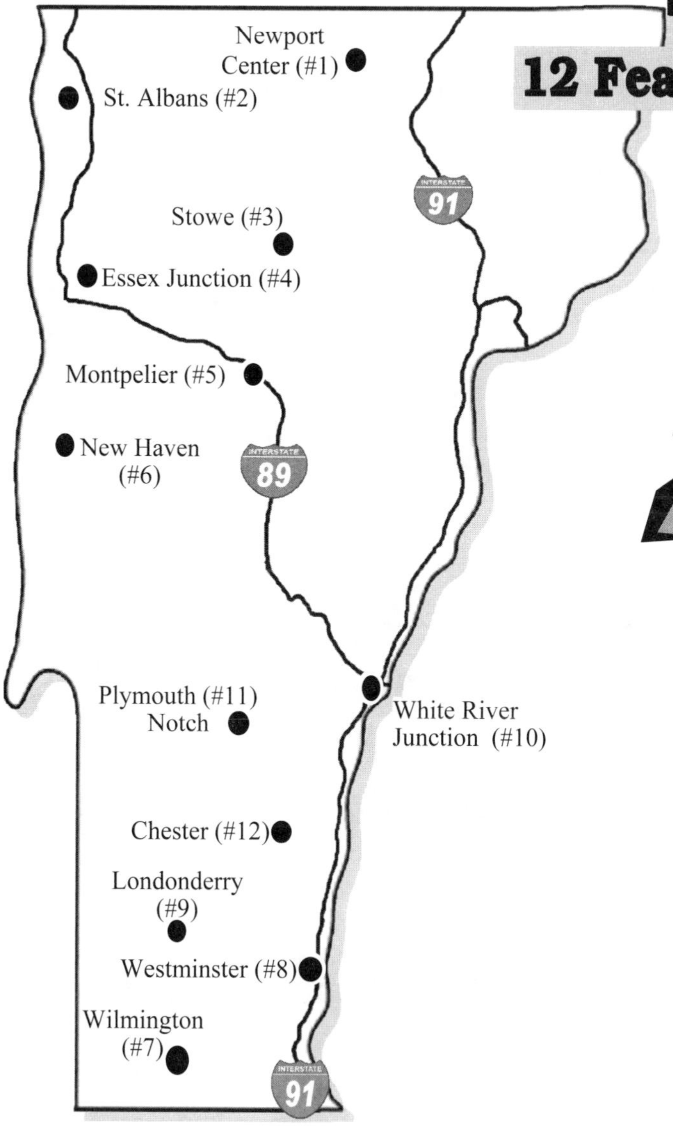

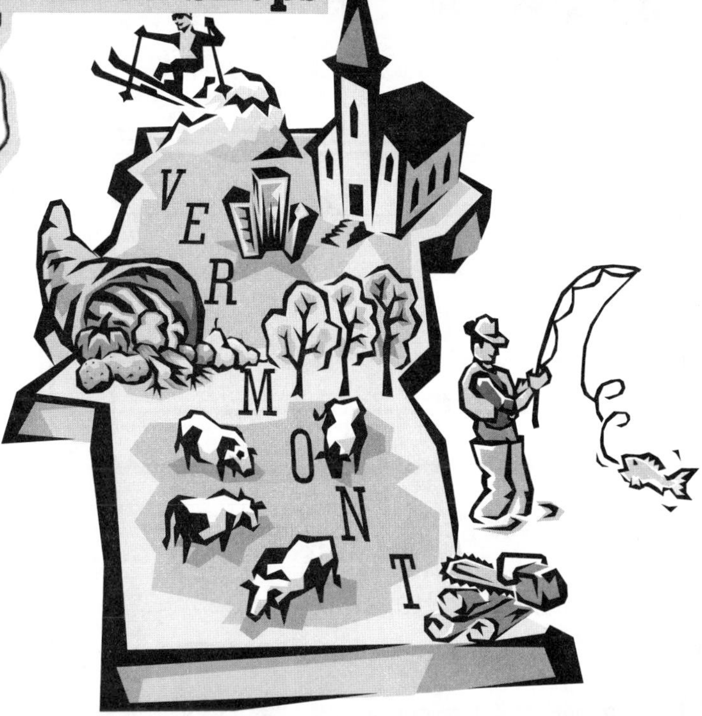

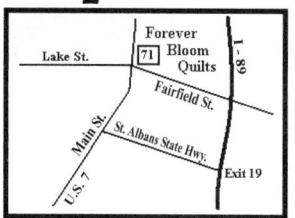

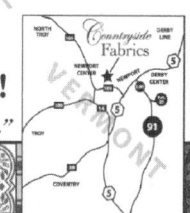

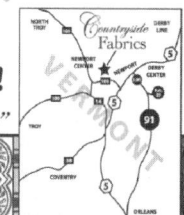

Stowe, VT #3

Mon - Fri 9 - 6
Sat & Sun 10 - 5

STOWE FABRIC & YARN

82 Park St., P.O. Box 422
05672
(802) 253-6740

Owners: Carla & Kristy

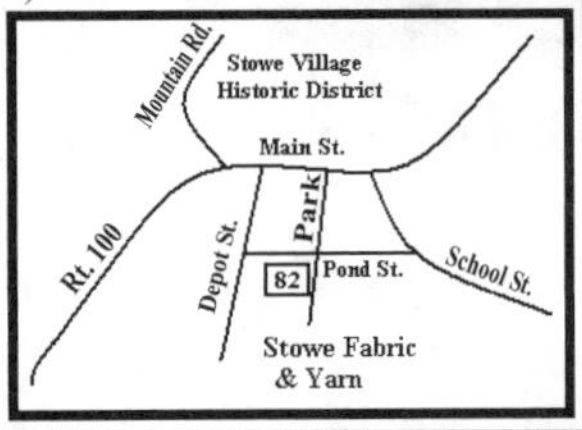

stowefabricandyarn@gmail.com
Stop in and browse through our hand dyed yarns, fine fabrics, quilts, and wonderful home decorating items & gifts.

Essex Junction, VT #4

Mon 10 - 5
Tues - Fri 10 - 6
Sat 10-5
Sun 12-4

Yankee Pride

9 Main St. 05452
(802) 872-9300
Est: 1981 5000 Bolts
info@yankeepridequilts.com
www.yankeepridequilts.com
All the top brands of fabrics, the newest books and notions, classes.
Friendly, knowledgeable service.

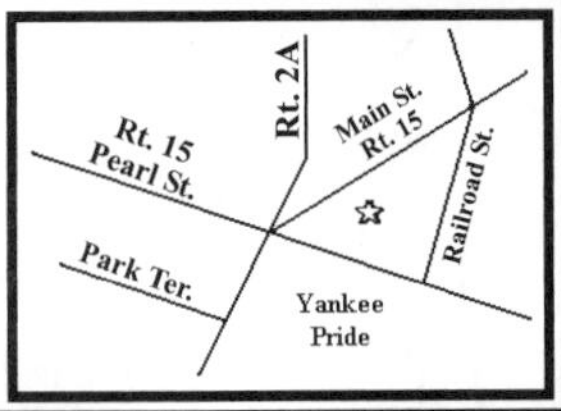

Montpelier, VT #5

Est: 2007

A Quilter's Garden Inc.

342 River St. (Rte. 302) 05602
(802) 223-2275
www.aquiltersgarden.net

- Quality Quilting Fabrics
- Notions
- Recent Publications of Books & Patterns
- Kits
- Classes for ALL Levels
- Programs & Clubs
- Long Arm Quilting
- Gifts

Tues - Fri 10 - 5
Sat 10 - 4

Helpful-Experienced Service in a Fun & Inviting Place

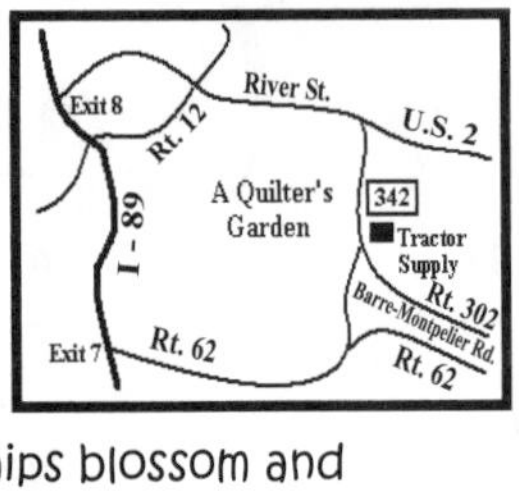

"Where Friendships blossom and inspiration Blooms!"
Owner: Dee Lamberton

New Haven, VT #6

Mon - Fri 9 - 5
Thur til 6
Sat 9 - 4

Knits & Bolts
Fine Yarns & Fabrics
Handmade Gifts

5343 Ethan Allen Hwy. 05472
(802) 453-7477
Owner: Jean Clark
Est: 2003
4000+ bolts

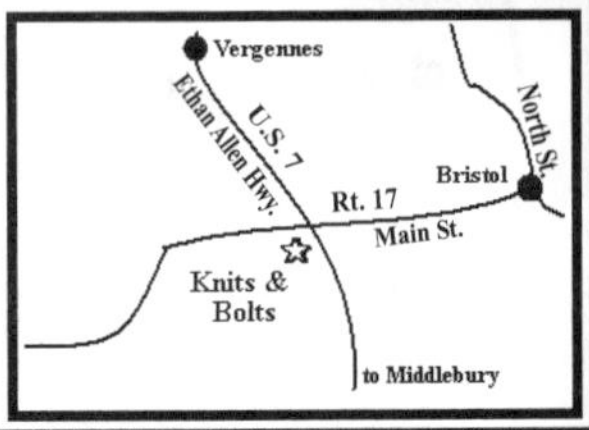

We carry an extensive selection of fabrics, yarns and notions to meet all of your sewing/quilting, knitting and crocheting needs.
jean@knitsandbolts.com
www.knitsandbolts.com

Wilmington, VT #7

Norton House

A Quilter's Paradise !

Over 4000 100% Cotton Fabrics.
The most beautiful fabric at the best prices!

Our Fabric Sale Attic is stuffed with 100% top quality cottons specially priced at 20 to 50% off.

Books - Notions - Patterns
Needlework - Puzzles - Craft Kits - Toys
Shop online: www.nortonhousequilting.com

Open 7 Days a Week, 9 - 5, all year

30 W. Main St., P.O. Box 579
Wilmington, VT 05363
(802) 464-7213
info@nortonhousequilting.com
Owner: Suzanne Wells Wurzberger
Est: 1967 2000 sq.ft.

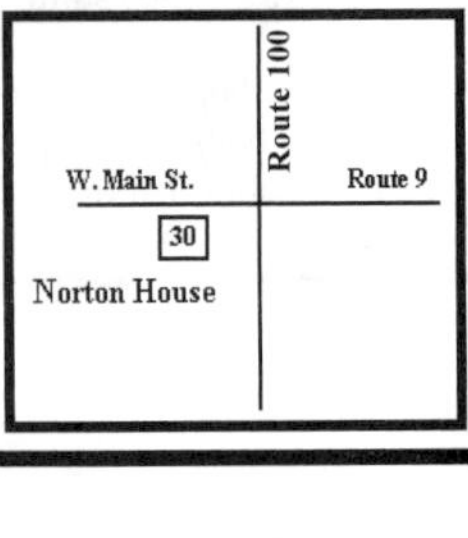

Westminster, VT #8

M, T, Th, F 12 - 4
Sat 10 - 4
or by Appt.

Quilt-a-way

190 Back Westminster Rd.
(802) 722-4743 05159
Toll Free Order Line 866-217-4743
Owner: Carol Coski
3200 sq.ft. 8000+ bolts 2300+ bolts of Batiks.
www.quiltaway.com
"She who dies with the most fabric wins!"
Every day is a sale day & we discount everything we sell.

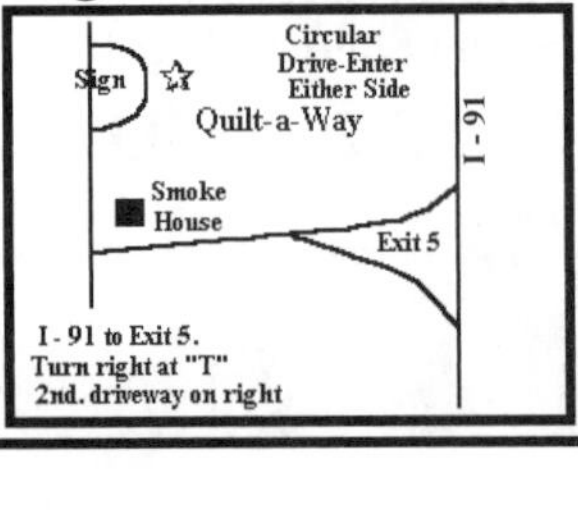

Londonderry, VT #9

Not Your Granny's Quilt Shop!

Waterwheel House Quilt Shop

6795 VT Rt. 100 05148
802-824-5700
Fax: 802-548-4176
Owner: Shelley Sas
Est: 2009
2600 sq.ft. 1000 Bolts
A Creative new sewing center in beautiful Southern Vermont.

Tues - Sat 10 - 5
Sun 12 - 5

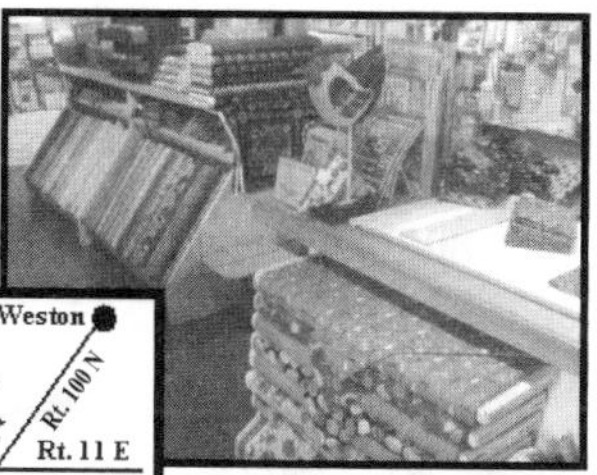

We carry Kaffe Fassett, Amy Butler, Lakehouse, Valerie Wells, Batiks and more.

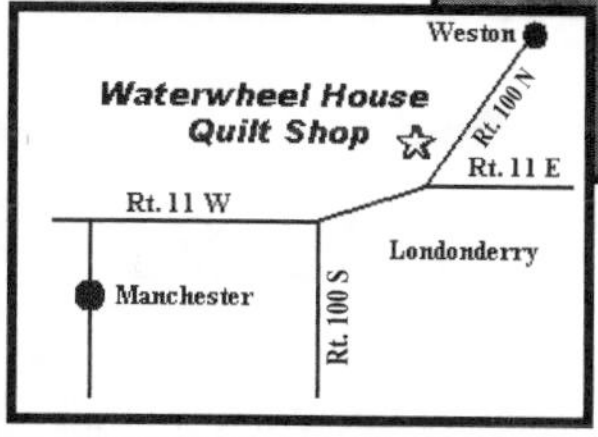

Embroidery, Wool Applique and Art Quilting supplies too.
shellesas@aol.com
www.waterwheelhouse.com

White River Junction, VT #10

Tues - Fri 10 - 5
Sat 10 - 4

Hen House Fabric

246 Holiday Dr. #2 05001
(802) 295-4436

Quilting Supplies, Classes, Gift Certificates
Friendly, knowledgeable service.
Inspiration & advice is always FREE.

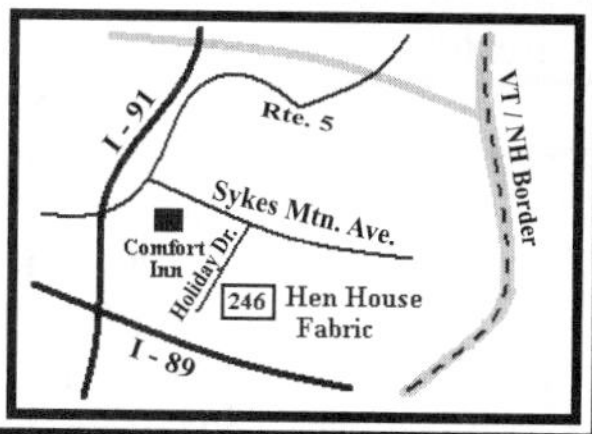

Plymouth Notch, VT #11

Daily Late May - mid Oct
9:30 - 5

President Calvin Coolidge State Historic Site

Plymouth Notch Historic District
(802) 672-3773 Est: 1956
P.O. Box 247 05056
11 Museum Buildings

Several late 19th Century Quilts on Permanent exhibition. Including one pieced by Calvin Coolidge when he was 10 years old. (Tumbling Blocks)

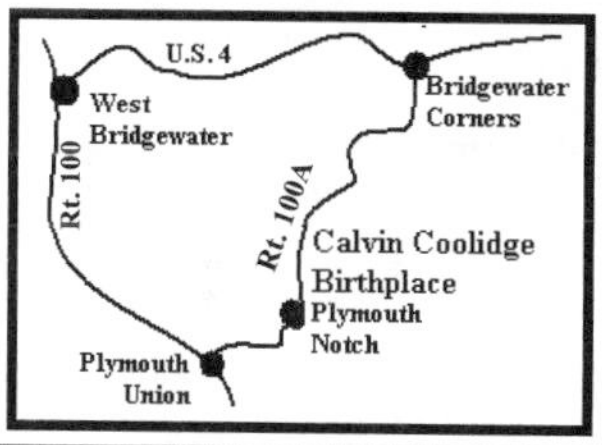

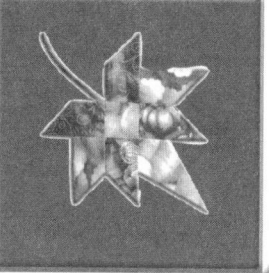

Chester, VT #12

Country Treasures

Fabric • Quilts • Gifts • Books

One of the premier quilt shops in New England!

Stocked with over **8,000 BOLTS** of fabric, including flannels and brushed homespuns

Fat quarters bundles, color coordinated or complete lines

Great selection of books and patterns!

Quilt classes for every skill level

(802)875-4377
12 Common St.,
Chester, VT 05143
vermontquilting.com
sue@vermontquilting.com

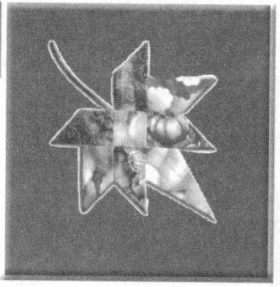

Open: Monday ~ Saturday 10am - 5pm • Sunday 12pm - 4pm • Closed in April

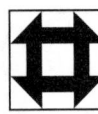

Vermont Quilt Shops

Town	Shop	Phone	Ad
Bethel	The Garden of Stitches, 768 S. Main St.	802-234-9965	
Center Rutland	Country Quilt & Fabric, 123 Ave. A	802-773-3470	
Chester	**Country Treasures, 12 Common St.**	**802-875-4377**	**See ad #12, page 549 & 196**
Danville	Sewin' Love Fabric Shoppe, 15 Hill St. #B	802-684-9790	
Derby	Country Thyme Vermont, 60 Rte. 11	802-766-2852	
Essex Junction	**Yankee Pride, 9 Main St.**	**802-872-9300**	**See ad #4, page 548**
Essex Junction	Backcountry Threads, 169 Brigham Hill Rd.	802-872-7855	
Londonderry	**Waterwheel Quilt Shop, 6795 VT Rt. 100**	**802-824-5700**	**See ad #9, page 549**
Montpelier	**A Quilter's Garden, 342 River St. Rte. 302**	**802-223-2275**	**See ad #5, page 548**
New Haven	**Knits & Bolts, 5343 Ethen Allen Hwy**	**802-453-7477**	**See ad #6, page 548**
Newfane	Newfane Country Store, 598 Rte. 30,	802-365-7916	
Newport Center	**Countryside Fabrics, 1778 VT Rt. 105**	**802-334-8879**	**See ad #1, page 547**
Newport	Quilters Quisine, 383 E. Main St.	802-334-3033	
North Clarendon	Quilt Barn of Vermont, 1943 East St.	802-775-0988	
Northfield	Maplewood Quilts, 1680 Rte 12 S	802-485-4325	
Plymouth	**Plymouth Notch Historic Dist P.O. Box 247**	**802-672-3773**	**See ad #11, page 549**
St. Albans	**Forever Bloom Quilt Shop, 71 N. Main St.**	**802-370-3111**	**See ad #2, page 547**
Stowe	**Stowe Fabric & Yarn, 82 Park St.**	**802-253-6740**	**See ad #3, page 548**
Waitsfield	Cabin Fever Quilts, 4276 Main St. #1	802-496-2287	
Wallingford	Ann's Pin Cushion, 238 S. Main St.	802-4462693	
Westminster Station	**Quilt-a-way Fabrics, 190 Back Westminster**	**802-722-4743**	**See ad #8, page 548**
White River Junction	**Hen House Fabric, 246 Holiday Dr. #2**	**802-295-4436**	**See ad #10, page 549**
Williston	Strawberry & Rhubarb, 20 Walnut Walk	802-878-2290	
Williston	Sew Many Treasures, 8016 Williston Rd.	802-878-3373	
Wilmington	**Norton House, A Quilters Paradise, 30 W. Main St.**	**802-464-7213**	**See ad #7, page 548**
Wilmington	Quilt & Fiber Arts, 15 Higley Hill Rd.	802-464-3762	

Vermont Quilt Shows

About Shows: We are listing only the very basic information about shows that happen on a regular schedule here. Please check out our website for more details on each show. Also this information tends to change quite often so please verify the event with our website or a local source before you venture far. Or if you're in the right area at the right time, give it a shot.

If you are a show organizer, please keep us updated on your event.
shows@quilterstravelcompanion.com www.quilterstravelcompanion.com

On our website you will also find:

- Exact dates (when we have them)
- Contact Information
- Events happening on a one-time basis
- Sponsor Information
- Description of Event

Month	City	Schedule	Show	Location with address
April				
	Rutland	Even Years--Spring	Festival of Quilts	College of St. Joseph, 71 Clement Rd.
	St. Albans	Annual, 1st weekend in April (unless Easter)	Quilting in Franklin County	St. Albans City Hall, 100 N Main St
June				
	Essex Junction	Annual, last weekend of June	Vermont Quilt Festival	Champlain Valley Exposition, 105 Pearl St. (Rt. 15)
August				
	Woodstock	Annual, August & September	Quilt Exhibition	Billings Farm & Museum, Rte 12 N & River Rd.
September				
	Bennington	Annual, 2nd weekend after Labor Day	Bennington Quiltfest	Mount Anthony Union High School, Park St.
October				
	Morrisville	Odd Year, Early weekend in October	Common Threads Quilt Guild	People's Academy Gymnasium, 202 Copley Ave.
	Westminster	Odd Year, 3rd weekend in October	Westminster Quilt Show	Westminster Center School, 301 School St.
November				
	Shelburne	Annual, 2nd weekend of November	Champlain Valley Quilters' Guild Show	Shelburne Farms Coach Barn, Harbor Rd. (Off Rte. 7)

VIRGINIA

43 Featured Shops

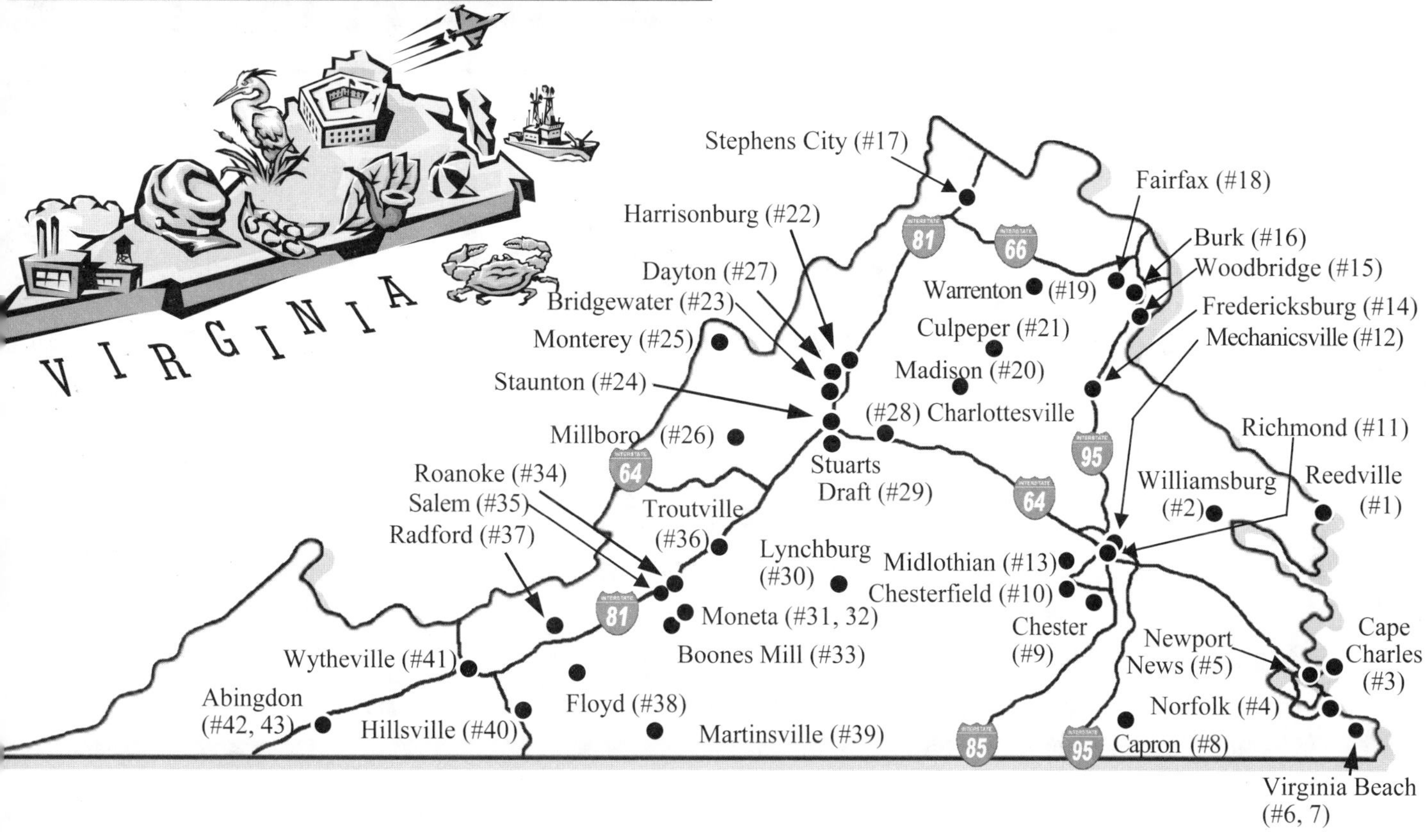

Reedville, VA #1

Tues - Sat 10 - 5

Material Girl Quilt Shop

16658 Northumberland Hwy.
22539
(804) 453-6003
materialgirl@nnwifi.com
www.materialgirlnn.com

Supplies for Quilting, Punchneedle and Rug Hooking.

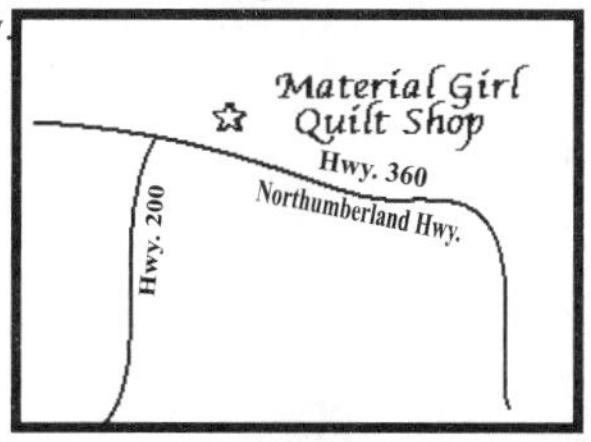

Williamsburg, VA #2

Mon - Sat 10 - 5 Winter Sat 10 - 4

LOVE 2 QUILT & more

In The Village Shops at Kingsmill
1915 Pocahontas Drive 23185
(757) 565-0978 www.love2quilt.com
3300 sq.ft. 3000+ Bolts

Stop by to see our fabulous fabrics including reproductions, Asian & contemporary prints.

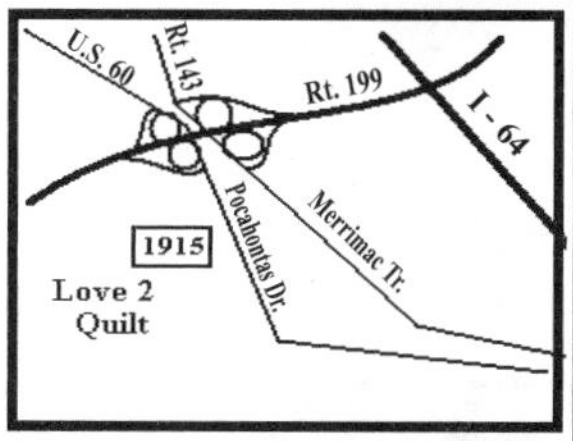

Cape Charles, VA #3

Mon - Sat 10 - 5

Quilts & More Fabric Outlet

27376 Lankford Hwy 23310
(757) 331-3642
Owner: Henrietta Morris
Est: 1990 3900 sq. ft.

Quilting, curtain, upholstery and clothing fabrics, also leather. Sewing supplies & notions. Much more at reasonable prices.

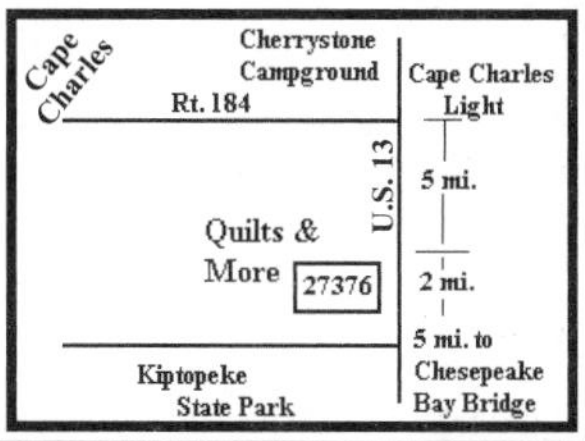

Norfolk, VA #4

Mon - Fri 10 - 7 Sat 10 - 6

FABRIC HUT Where Friends and Fabric Meet
Shop@
www.FabricHut.com

2340 E. Little Creek Rd. 23518
Roosevelt Gardens
Shopping Center
(877) 4Fab-Hut
(757) 588-1300

Largest Selection of Quilting Cottons in the Hampton Roads Area. Shop our wall of over 700 bolts of name brand quilting cottons at $3.88/yd. 10% discount to Sewing Guilds. Celebrating over 40 years.

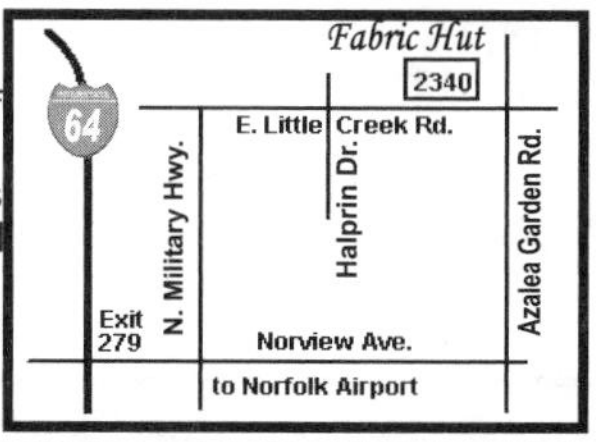

BERNINA • BERNINA • BERNINA • BERNINA • BERNINA • BERNINA • BERNINA

NANCY'S CALICO PATCH

On Warwick Blvd.
21 Hidenwood Shopping Center
Newport News, VA 23606
(757) 596-7397

Newport News, VA #5

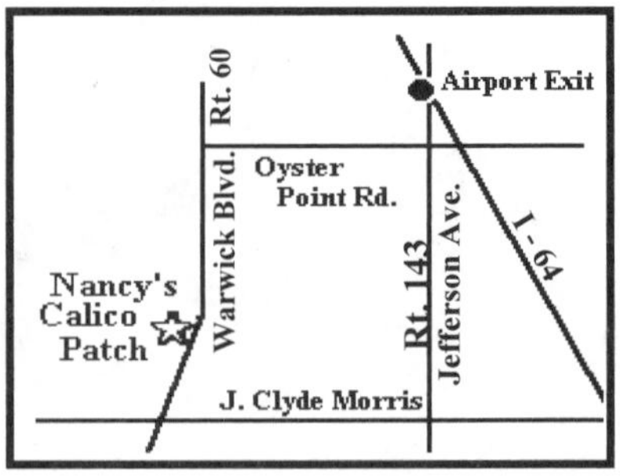

~ Sewing Machines ~ Sergers ~ Software! ~
~ Accessories ~ Embroidery Cards ~
~ Notions ~ Threads ~ Books
~ Fabric ~ & ~ Lots of Inspiration ~
Authorized Bernina Dealer

BERNINA

Mon - Sat 10 - 5

www.ncpquilting.com

Virginia Beach, VA #6

Mon - Sat 10 - 5:30 Thur til 8 Sun 12 - 4

What's Your Stitch'n Stuff

5350 Kempsriver Dr. #104 23464
(757) 523-2711
www.whatsyourstitchnstuff.com
Owners: Holly Erdei-Zuber & Irene Erdei
Over 3000 bolts!
100% Cotton Fabrics, Books, Patterns, Notions, Primitive Rug Hooking, Penny Rugs & Wool Applique.
PLUS ALWAYS FRIENDLY SERVICE!

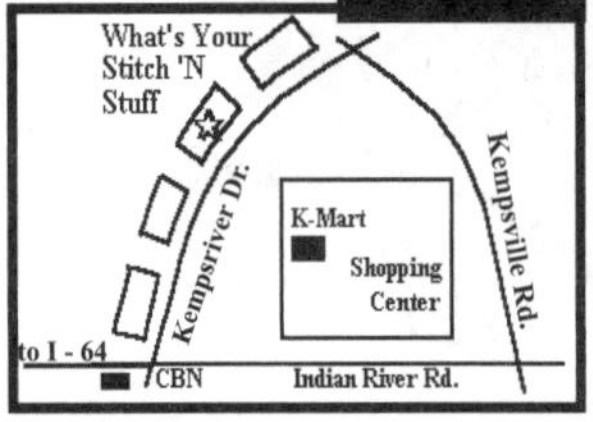

Virginia Beach, VA #7

Tues - Sat 10 - 5:30

Sarah's Thimble Quilt Shoppe

2245 W. Great Neck Rd. #5 23451
(757) 481-1725 Fax: (757) 481-1776
Owner: Sarah Norman Est: 2005
sarah@sarahsthimble.com
www.sarahsthimble.com

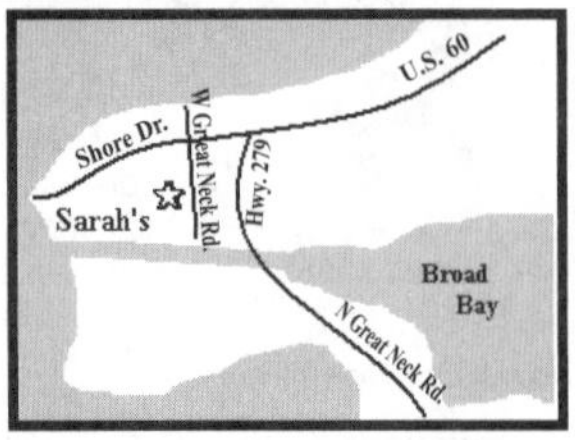

Great fabrics from Kaffe Fassett, Amy Butler, Timeless Treasures, Island Batik and more.
Kits, Classes, Gammill Quilter

Quilters -N- Friends

17293 Pinopolis Rd.
P.O. Box 63 23829
(434) 658-4564
Fax: (434) 658-9240
quilters287@aol.com
Est: 2007 1800 bolts

Capron, VA #8

Fabrics, Patterns, Notions, Books, Classes
Color of the Month 25% off.
Custom longarm quilting with a Statler Stitcher by Gammill

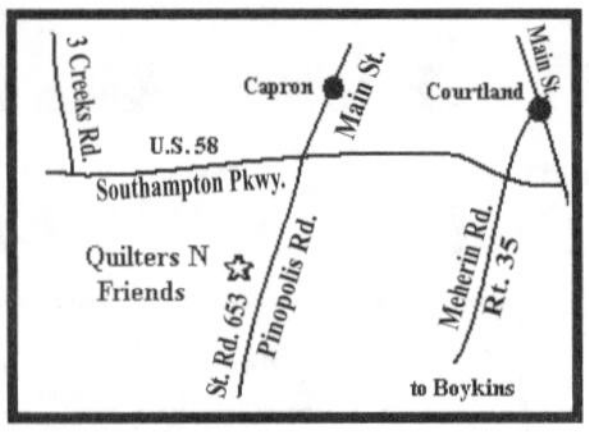

Statler Stitcher

Wed & Thur 11 - 6:30
Fri & Sat 10 - 5

Proprietors: Louann & Dean Gram

#9 The Busy Bea

Est: 1976

Bea & Cathy Chase

11934 Centre St., Chester, Va.

(804) 748-4951

Mon.-Fri., 9:00-6:00
Sat., 9:00-4:00
Closed Sun.

Fax: (804) 748-2126

busybea.chester.va31@verizon.net

Sulky of America · Mettler Threads · Coats & Clark Threads · Elna Sewing Machines · Horn Sewing Cabinets

Cathy is a certified teacher in Eleanor Burns..."QUILT IN A Day" Techniques

3,000+ bolts of 100% Cotton Fabric, Notions, Books and Assorted Supplies. Finished quilts (all sizes), restored 1800's trunks and gifts.

Pre-Beginner to Post-Grad Classes

Just South of Richmond I-95: Take the Chester (61B) Exit, Rt. 10 West. Start counting traffic lights. Turn RIGHT at light #6 (approximately 2 miles). We are the 2nd business on left.

I-295: Take the Chester (15B) exit. Rt. 10 West. Start counting traffic lights. Turn RIGHT at light #10 (approximately 6 miles). We are the 2nd business on left.

From Western Part of State: Follow I-64 East to Route 288, south to Chester Rd. Exit. Turn RIGHT off Exit. Turn RIGHT at 2nd light (Route 10W). Turn RIGHT at next light. We are 2nd business on left.

#10 JoJo's Quilt Shop

PIECING IT ALL TOGETHER

WWW.JOJOSQUILTSHOP.COM

804-778-7566

Best Selection of Quality Fabrics!
Books, Patterns, Notions and Classes
Floriani Threads & Horn Cabinets

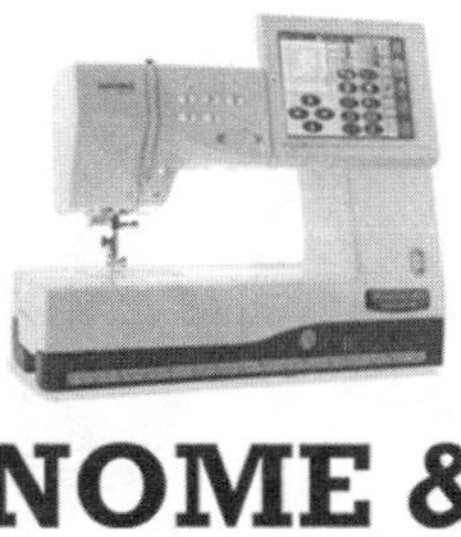

JANOME & TIN LIZZIE

MON-FRI - 10am-5pm SAT - 10am-4pm SUN - 1pm-5pm
7056 COMMONS PLAZA – CHESTERFIELD, VA 23832
Ironbridge (Route 10 East) & Beach Rds-one mile off Route 288

Richmond, VA #11

Mon 10 - 6
Tues - Fri 10 - 8
Sat 10 - 6
Sun 12 - 5

1601 Willow Lawn Dr. #108 23230
The Shops at Willow Lawn
(804) 262-0005

Quilting Adventures

"The friendly shop for everyone who creates with fabric."
info@quiltingadventures.com
www.quiltingadventures.com
Fabric, books, supplies & classes for both traditional & contemporary quilters.

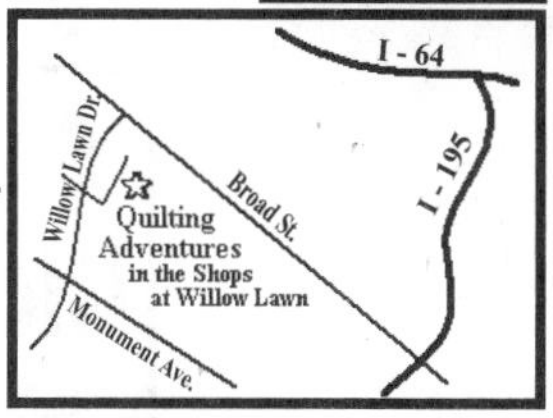

Mechanicsville, VA #12

Tues - Fri 10 - 5
Sat 10 - 4

Millstone Quilts

8074 Flannigan Mill Rd. 23111
(804) 779-3535 Fax: (804) 779-3900
Owners: Chris & Regina Simmons
Est: 2002 1200 sq.ft. 3000+ Bolts
Free Online Newsletter
www.millstonequilts.com

Come see an historical civil war grist mill, with everything you need for quilting and more...

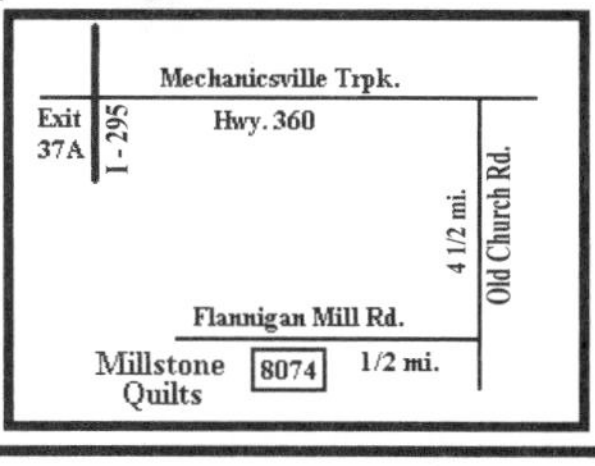

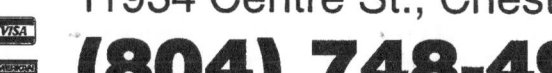

Midlothian, VA #13

Open Seven Days A Week

Quilter's Corner

1257 Sycamore Square Dr. 23113
(804) 794-1990

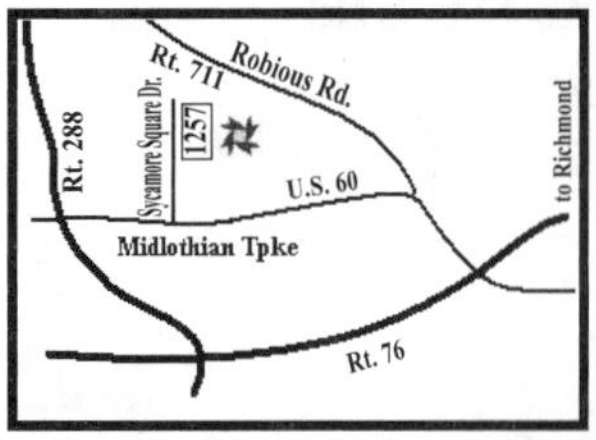

www.QuiltersCornerVA.com
Quality Fabric & Quilting Supplies
Kits • Books • Patterns • Notions • Classes
Richmond's Premier Quilt Shop
is located in Sycamore Square -
a delightful mix of unique shops and
restaurants. Authorized Brother Dealer.

Fredericksburg, VA #14

Mon - Sat 10 - 5:30
Sun 12 - 5

Quilt and Sewing Center

3940 Plank Rd., Suite Y 22407
(540) 548-2377 Fax: (540) 548-2910
3600 sq.ft. 3000+ bolts
www.quiltandsewwonline.com

Authorized Bernina Sales and Service.
Horn Sewing Furniture Dealer
We sell beautiful high quality cotton fabric, thread, patterns and notions. Classes for Bernina machines, quilt construction and machine quilting.

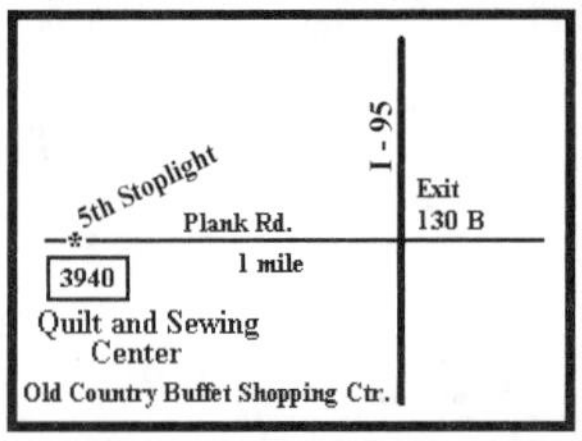

Where Being the Best Begins

Circle Sewing Studios

2212 Tackett's Mill Dr. 22192
(703) 910-7516
Fax: (703) 910-7517
Owner: Parker Chiudioni
circlesewingstudios@yahoo.com
www.circlesewingstudios.com

Woodbridge, VA #15

We embrace new technology and love to incorporate new tools and techniques. We carry many batiks. Authorized JANOME dealer.
Online Newsletter

Tues, Thurs & Fri 10 - 7
Wed 10 - 8 Sat 10 - 6

On the lower level of Tackett's Mill Shp. Ctr.

The Artful Quilter

Top Ten Quilt Sampler® Featured Shop

"The Most Delightful Creative Solutions"

- Personal and Professional Service
- Classes and Workshops
- Handi-Quilter Representative
- Fabric, Patterns, Books, and Notions
- On Site Longarm Quilting
- Online Shopping

Better Homes and Gardens Quilt Sampler Featured Shop

#16

The Artful Quilter
9570-L Burke Road
Burke, VA 22015
703 266-3250
www.artfulquilter.com

Mon-Sat 10-5 Sun 12-5

Stephens City, VA #17

Mon - Fri 10 - 5
Sat 10 - 3
Open to the Public

Cloth Peddler Quilt Shop

5330 Main St. 22655
(540) 868-9020
Est: 2007
www.clothpeddler.com

Off I-81 in the Shenandoah Valley, this pre civil war home offers rooms full of fabrics: Moda, Hoffman, Timeless Treasures, Blank, Northcott, Kona Bay, RJR and more.

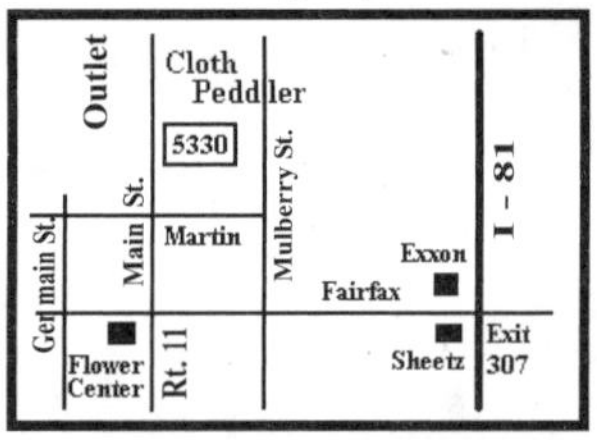

Rachel's QUILT PATCH

Enjoy a unique shop
in Historic Downtown Staunton
at the Train Station

Our shop features
100% cotton fabric collections
from top of the line
designers and manufacturers,
as well as Patterns, Books, & Notions
selected for today's
Quilter and Fabric Crafter.

Hours
Mon. Wed. Fri. & Sat.
10:00 a.m.- 5:00 p.m.
Tues. & Thurs.
10:00 a.m.- 7:00 p.m.

Owner:
Rachel W. N. Brown
Author of :
Adoration Quilts &
Small Camel
Follows the Star

Serving quilters
and crafters for
14 years

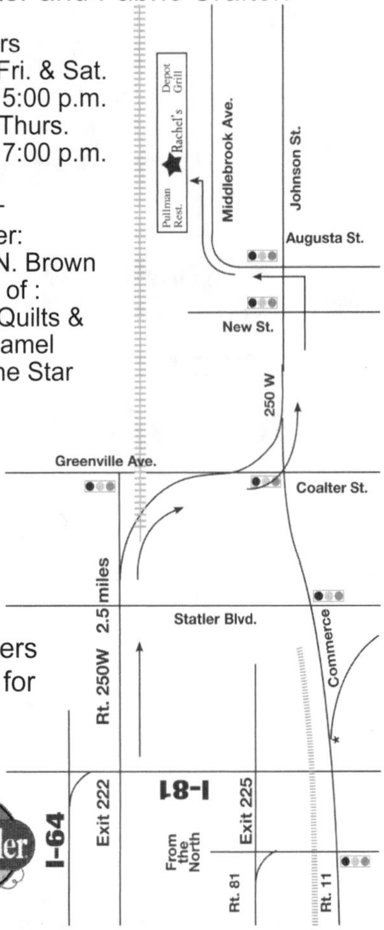

Better Homes and Gardens Quilt Sampler FEATURED SHOP

40 Middlebrook Ave. 24401
(540) 886-7728
www.rachelsquiltpatch.com

Staunton, VA #24

Culpeper, VA #21

Mon - Sat 10 - 6
Sun 12 - 5

145 Art & Design Studio

145 E. Davis St. 22701
(540) 825-5620 • (540) 727-8372
info@145artanddesignstudio.com
www.145artanddesignstudio.com
Sewing Machines & Accessories • Art Supplies • Fabrics • Yarns • Notions
Machine service and repair
Located in historic downtown Culpeper.

BERNINA Authorized Dealer

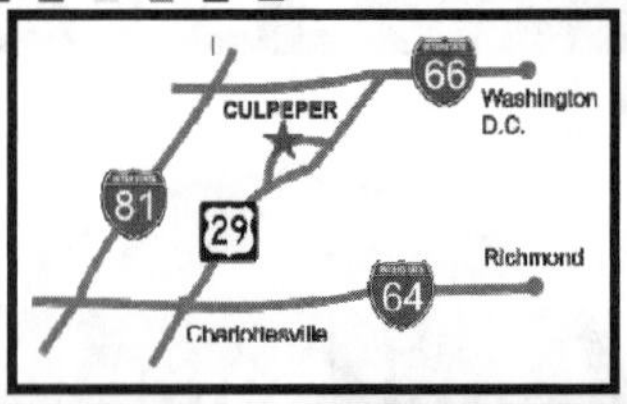

Harrisonburg, VA #22

Mon - Wed 9 - 5
Th & F 9 - 7
Sat 9 - 4

Ragtime Fabrics

60 W. Market St. 22801
(540) 434-5663
www.ragtimefabrics.com
Owner:
Laura "Belle" Stemper
Est: 2003 4800 sq.ft.
belle@ragtimefabrics.com

Fabrics and trims for apparel, home decorations, costuming and handmade creations.
Baby Lock Dealer.
Become a fan on Facebook

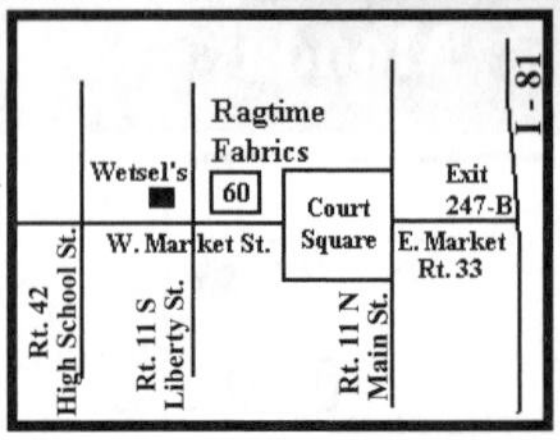

Bridgewater, VA #23

Mon - Sat 9:30 - 6

Spring Creek Fabric

7689 Nazarene Church Rd. 22812
(540) 828-6728 Fax: (540) 828-3320
Owner: Christina Zimmerman Est: 1997

Quilting, Clothing, Flannels, and Polar Fleeces, Fabrics.
Books, greeting cards and classic Toys.
Melissa & Doug Wooden Toys & Puzzles.

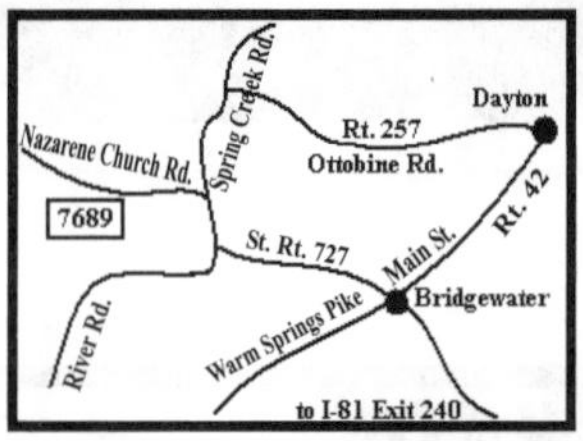

Monterey, VA #25

Mon - Fri 12 - 5
Sat 10 - 4

Wool Becomes Ewe

50 Fleisher Ave.
P.O. Box 24 24465
(540) 468-2007
Owner:
Theresa Wagner
contact@woolbecomesewe.com
www.woolbecomesewe.com
Nestled in the Allegheny Highlands, we offer beautiful yarns, quality fabrics and unique "crafty" gifts.

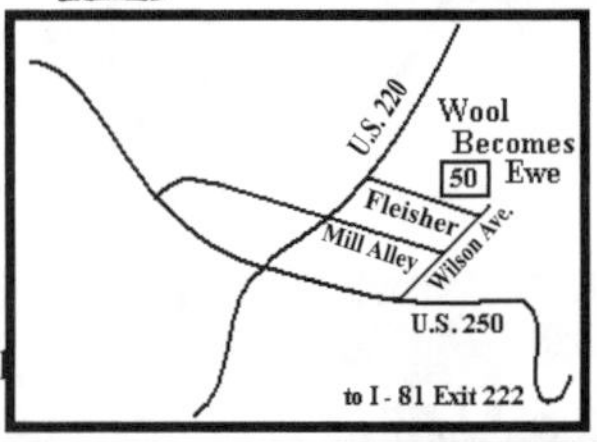

Millboro, VA #26

Please Call for Hours

Tender Heart Quilts

4434 Cowpasture River Hwy.
24460
(540) 862-4718 1200 sq.ft.
cheryl@tenderheartquilts.com
www.tenderheartquilts.com

We carry 1,500+ bolts of quality fabric, quilt & craft classes, notions, handmade gift items and mission work with quilts.

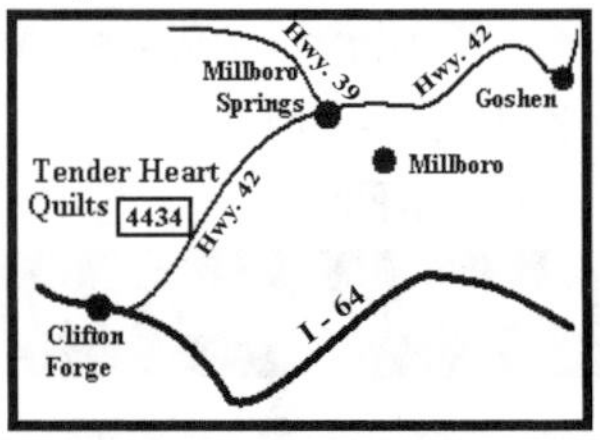

Dayton, VA #27

Patchwork Plus INC.

HOURS: Mon--Wed 9-5
Thur--Sat 9-6
Closed Major Holidays

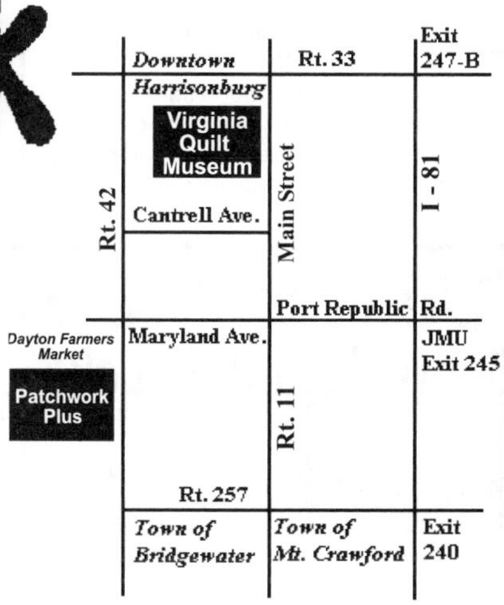

- ***A Full Service Shop*** offering the best of what quilters need
- ***9,000 Sq. Ft.*** Showroom, Classroom, Office & Service Area
- ***Knowledgeable Staff*** with over 600 years combined experience
- ***Major Brands*** of quality fabrics, notions, books, & patterns
- ***A Full Line*** of Bernina® & Janome sewing machines, sergers, embroidery machines, software and accessories

Handi Quilter®

17 Killdeer Lane (off Rt. 42), Dayton, VA 22821
(on the hill above Dayton Farmers Market)
Phone 540-879-2505
Toll Free 1-877-674-4821
patchworkplus@verizon.net
www.patchworkplus-quilting.com

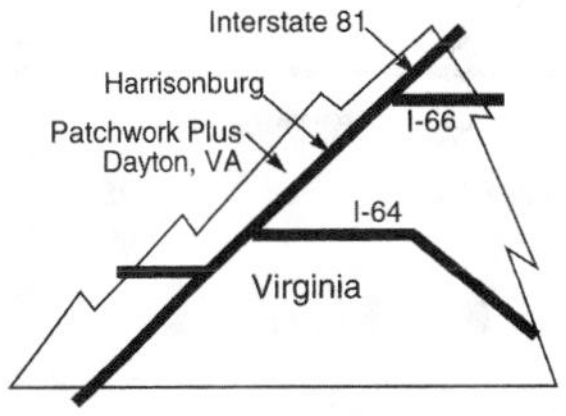

Charlottesville, VA #28

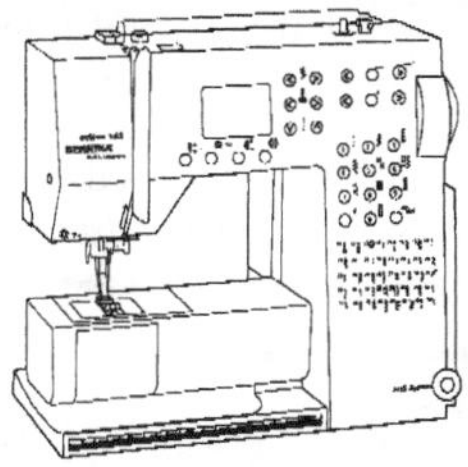

COTTONWOOD

Meadowbrook Shopping Centre
2035 Barracks Road, Charlottesville, VA 22903
(434) 244-9975 fax: (434) 244-5072
E-Mail: shop@cottonwoodquiltshop.com
Web Site: www.cottonwoodquiltshop.com
Est: 1995 4500 sq.ft.

Come visit our shop in **Charlottesville.**
Over 3000 Bolts of Quilting Cottons, Batiks,
Homespun Plaids, Flannels, and Wools
Books, Patterns, Supplies
BERNINA Sewing and Embroidery Machines and Sergers
Embroidery Software and accessories.
Service of all brands of sewing machines

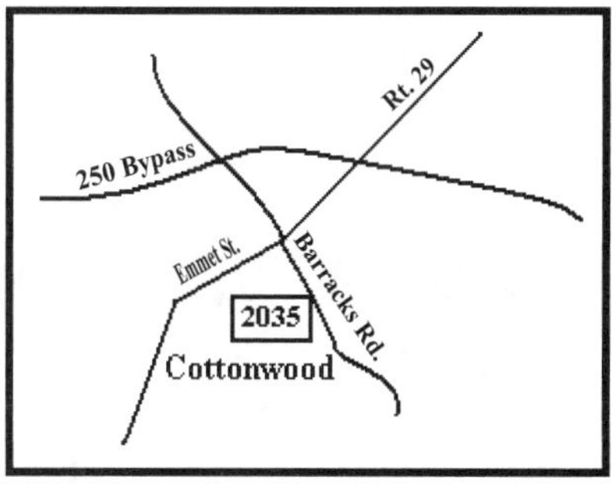

Classes for Quilting, Rug Hooking,
Redwork and Primitive Stitchery

5 minutes from I-64. At Exit 118B take 29N/250 Bypass to Barracks Rd. Turn right onto Barracks Rd., go through 2 stop lights. Meadowbrook Shopping Centre is on right.

Shop Hours:
Mon - Sat 10:00 - 6:00 pm; Wed 10:00 - 8:00 pm
Sun 12:00 - 4:00 pm

Stuarts Draft, VA #29

Mon - Sat 10 - 6

Valley Fabrics

2701 Stuarts Draft Hwy. 24477
540-324-0548
Est: 2001 5000 sq.ft.
valleyfabrics@opexonline.com
A Community Sewing Together
We carry a full line of quilting and apparel fabrics, notions and upholstery.

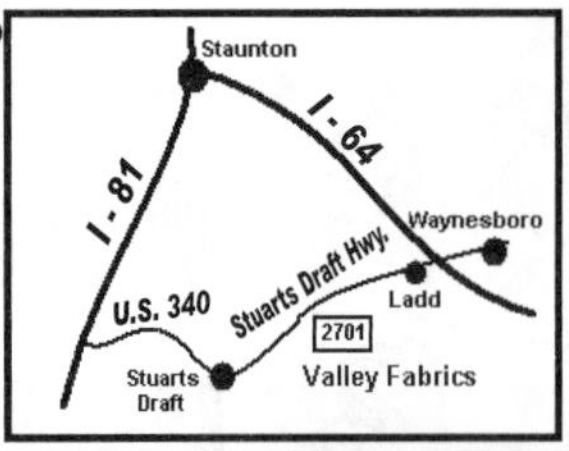

Moneta, VA #31

Mon - Fri 10 - 5
Wed 12 - 6
Sat 10 - 3

Smith Mountain Lake Quilting

130 Scruggs Rd. #214 24121
(540) 719-7845
Fax: (540) 420-0941
Owner: Margaret Brush
Est: 2007 1600 sq.ft
contact@smithmountainlakequilting.com
www.smithmountainlakequilting.com
We specialize in high quality quilting fabrics and supplies. Our goal is to help every customer leave happy, and ready to create something wonderful. Stop by to view our specials. Newsletter.

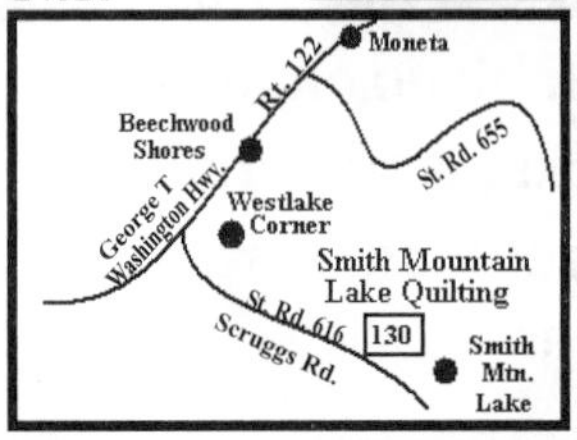

Moneta, VA #32

Mon - Sat 9:30 - 6

The General Store

213 Scruggs Rd. #214 24121
(540) 721-3009 3600 sq.ft.
vicki@generalstoresml.com
www.generalstoresml.com

1000+ bolts of quilting fabric - RJR, Michael Miller, Batiks, Moda, Avlyn and More.
Notions / Books / Patterns / Quilt Classes

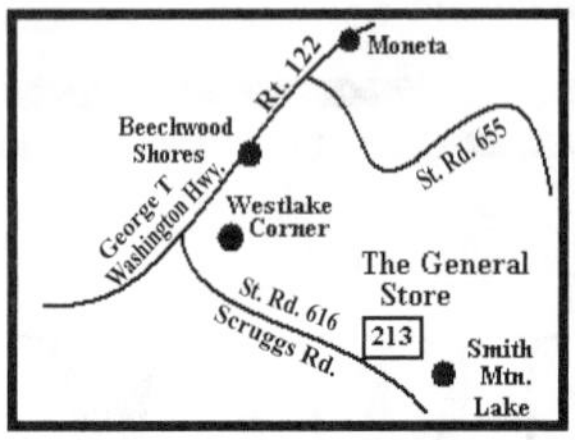

Boones Mill, VA #33

Tues - Sat 9:30 - 5:30

Boone's Country Store

2699 Jubal Early Hwy. 24065
(540) 721-2478
Owners: Randy & Elva Boone
Est: 1975 3588 sq.ft

Old Fashioned Quality -- Up to date Values. Calicoes, broad cloth, sheetings, quilting supplies, books, gifts. Homemade breads, pies, cakes & sweet rolls. 9 miles from Boones Mill.

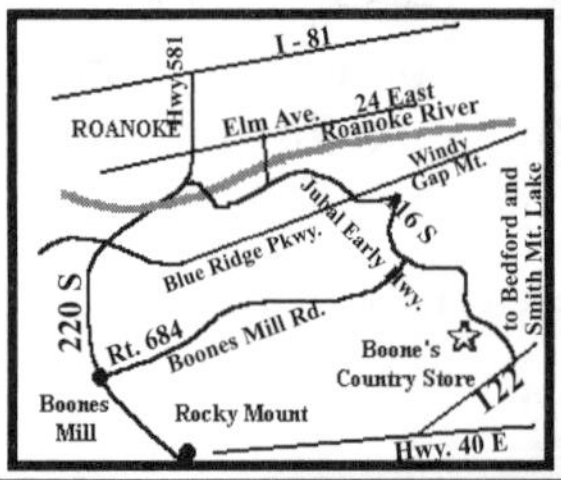

Roanoke, VA #34

Mon - Fri 9:30 - 4
Tues til 6
Sat 10 - 3

Creative Quilting

6342 Peters Creek Rd. 24019
(540) 362-4721
creativequilt@gmail.com

Specializing in quality quilting fabrics, books, patterns, notions, and classes.

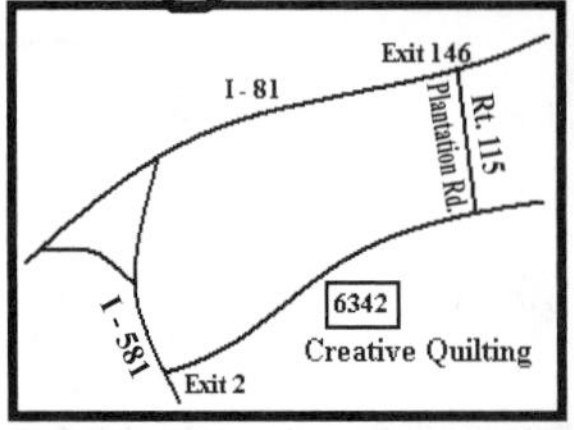

Lynchburg, VA #30

QUILTED EXPRESSIONS & Sewing Possessions

Almost 20 years in business and over 3000 bolts of top quality 100% cotton fabrics. We offer a wide range of fabric including brights, novelties and reproductions. We carry a wide array of notions, patterns and books along with lots of samples on display to inspire you! We offer a variety of classes from kids to advanced. Our friendly and courteous staff is ready to help with all your quilting needs - we are glad you stopped by! **Mail Order** inquiries are invited. We offer complete kits as well as die cut jelly rolls and charm squares. Large groups are welcome - please call ahead so we can prepare a special event for you. Check out our website www.QuiltedExpressions.com for more details on our shop, events and our quarterly class schedule as well as detailed driving directions.

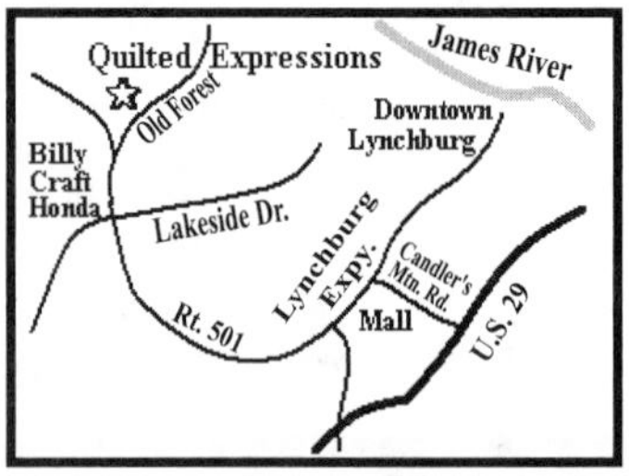

3622 Old Forest Rd.
Lynchburg, VA
24501
(434) 385-6765
Opened: 1992

Mon-Sat 10am-5pm
Thur 10am-7pm

QUILTING ESSENTIALS

405 Apperson Dr., Salem, VA 24153
540-389-3650

2000+ bolts of 100% Cotton Fabrics including a great selection of Flannels & 104" to 108" Quilt Backing Fabrics.

Books, Patterns, Notions, Quilting Supplies, Kits and Classes. Also Anchor Floss and Aurifil Thread.

We carry the Alto Quilt Cut 2 Fabric Cutting System, the Alto Pro and most all other Alto Supplies

We carry Locker Hooking supplies & provide classes.

#35 Mon-Fri 10-5:30
Sat 10-4

Owner: Pat Langheim
quiltingessentials
@comcast.net

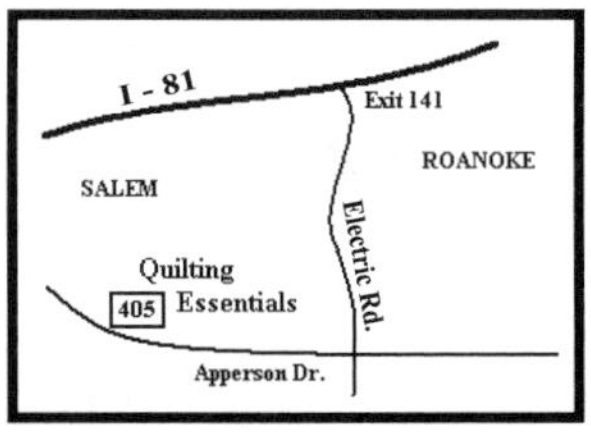

Old Trinity Schoolhouse Quilt Shop

#36

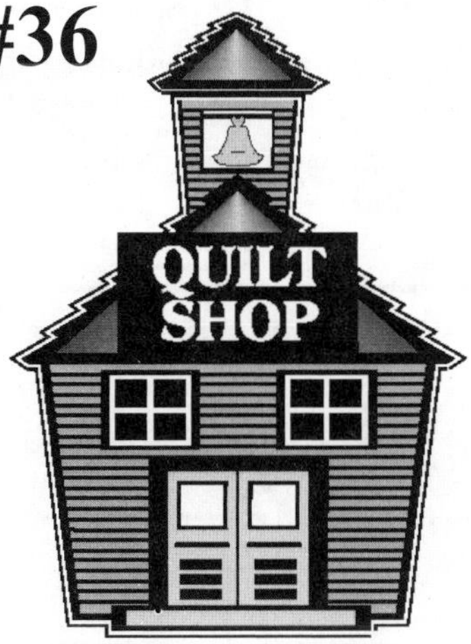

3200 Trinity Road
(corner of US 220 & Trinity Road)
Troutville, Virginia 24175

540 • 992 • 1233

Speciality: *Reproduction Fabrics (1770-1930)*
Books: *Over 400, Many with a Historical Focus*

Broad Selection of more than 4,000 Quilt Fabrics including: Orientals, Batiks, Florals, Windham, Marcus Brothers, Hoffman, Thimbleberries, P&B, Moda, and many others,

Notions, Block of the Months, Kits, and Classes

Visit our shop:
9am - 6pm
Monday thru Saturday

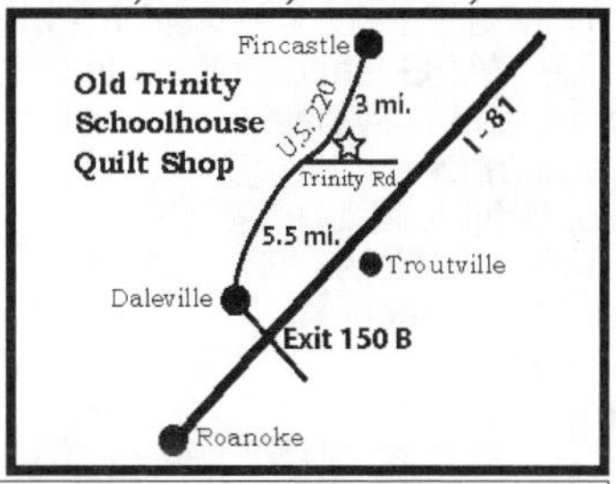

Order Directly from our Web Site,
www.TrinityQuilts.com

Radford, VA #37

Mon - Sat
9 - 5:30
Thur til 8

Sew Biz inc.

92 & 94 Harvey St. 24141
(540) 639-1138
sewoften@aol.com
Est: 1981
3600 sq.ft.
2000+ Bolts
www.sewbiz.com

Historic 1889 building with two floors of beautiful fabrics for Quilting & Apparel. Extensive selection of books, patterns, tools--with accessories for your Bernina & Elna as well.

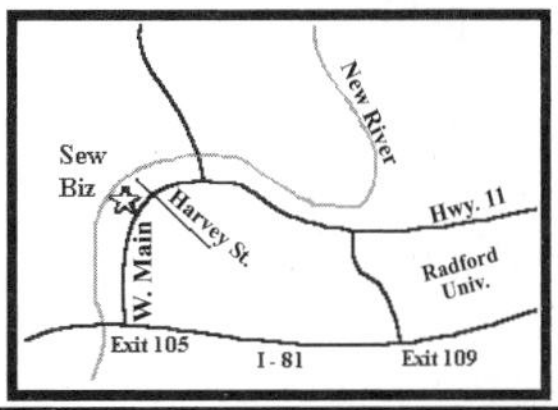

Floyd, VA #38

Mon - Sat
9 - 5:30

Schoolhouse Fabrics

"A Sewing Paradise"

220 N. Locust St. 24091 Est: 1971
(540) 745-4561 Fax: (540) 745-4168
Located in old School House built in 1911.
3 floors with 12 rooms filled with fabrics, patterns & books, notions, quilting frames, etc.

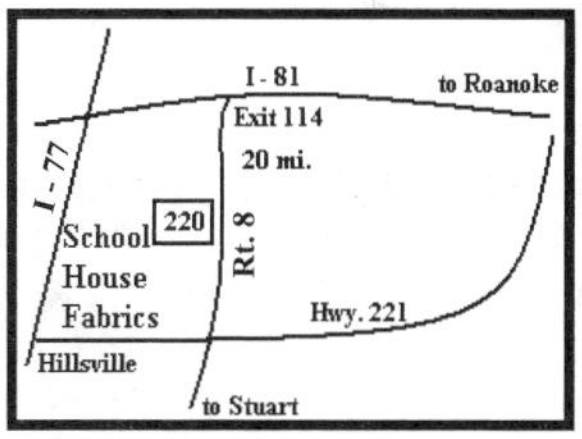

Martinsville, VA #39

Mon - Fri
8:30 - 5
Sat 10 - 2

The Sewing Studio, Inc.

1310 Memorial Blvd. South 24112
(276) 632-5700 Fax: Same
Owner: Brenda S. Feeny
Est: 1992 5000 sq.ft. 3000+ Bolts
bfeeny@embarqmail.com
www.thesewingstudio.com

Large selection of fabric, books & notions.
BabyLock dealer. Sales - Service. Classes.

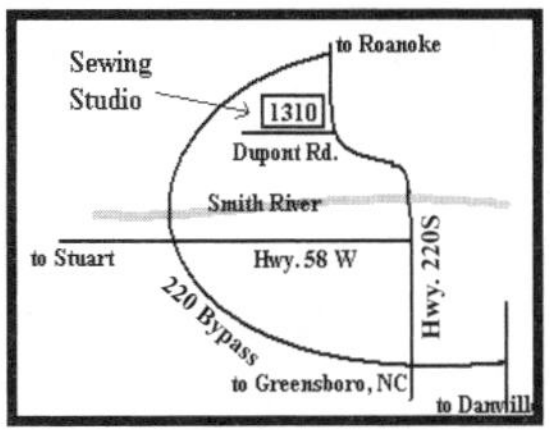

Hillsville, VA #40

Mon - Sat
9 - 5

Mountain Plains Fabrics

4505 Fancy Gap Hwy. 24343
(276) 728-7517
Est: 1960 8000 sq.ft. 2500 Bolts
www.mtnplainsfabrics.com
Quilting Fabric & Supplies * Quilt Frames
* Buttons * Polyfoam * Lace * Drapery
Upholstery Material * Vinyl * Leather

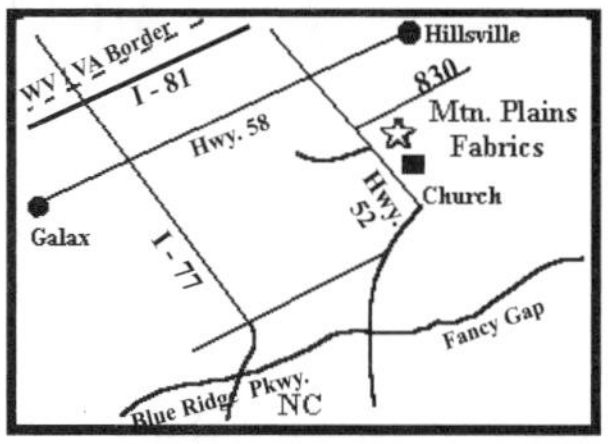

Wytheville, VA #41

Mon - Sat 10 - 5:30

Batiks Etcetera & Sew What Fabrics

460 East Main Street, Wytheville, VA 24382
276-228-6400 or 800-228-4573 Fax: 276-228-9597
Owner: Carol C. Britt www.batiks.com info@batiks.com
Est: 1982 4200 sq.ft. 8000 bolts

The most complete retail source for batik fabrics! Batiks Etcetera & Sew What Fabrics is located in an 1840's home in old town Wytheville, VA. Gourmet cottons, Indonesian & Malaysian batiks, flannel, and lively classes are available with expert, friendly assistance.

New! Batik Nickel Club and Batik Jelly Rolls. Check out our secure web site. Come have a ball!

Abingdon, VA #42

Mon - Fri 10 - 5 Sat 10 - 4 Closed Sun & Wed

Abingdon Quilt Cottage

267 E. Valley Street 24210
(276) 628-1433
www.abingdonquiltcottage.com
info@abingdonquiltcottage.com

Over 1,000 bolts of "Quilt Shop Only" designer fabric, as well as jelly rolls, charm packs, layer cakes and quilter's candy! Be sure to check out our "$4 Fabric Frenzy".

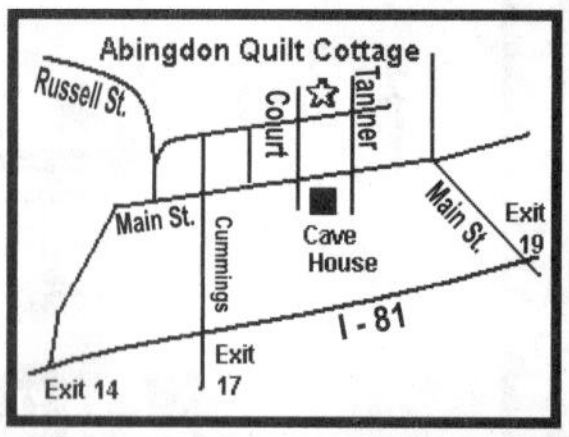

Abingdon, VA #43

Mon - Fri 9:30 - 5 Sat 9:30 - 4

Jeannine's Fabrics & Quilt Shop

414 W. Main St. 24210
(276) 628-9586
Owners: Jeannine & Gene Widener
Est: 1968 3000 sq.ft. 1000+ Bolts

Full Line Quilting Supplies including 100% cotton from RJR, P&B, Hoffman, Springs, VIP, Concord, Fabri-Quilt. Books, Patterns, Rulers, Stencils.

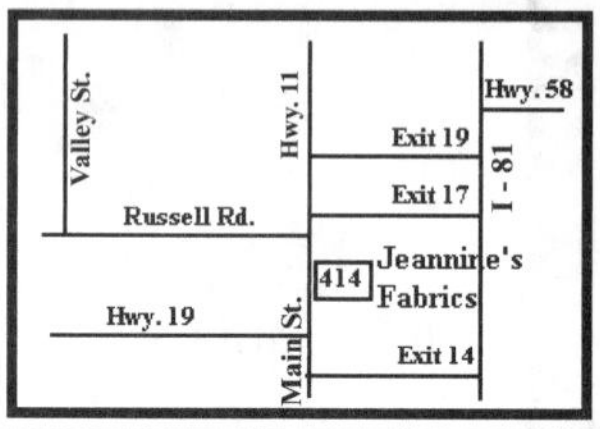

Virginia Quilt Shops

Abingdon	**Abingdon Quilt Cottage, 267 E. Valley St.**	**276-628-1433**	**See ad #42, this page**
Abingdon	**Jeannine's Fabrics, 414 W. Main St.**	**276-628-9586**	**See ad #43, this page**
Amelia	Amelia Fabrics and More, PO Box 276	804-561-5221	
Amelia	B&K Fabrics, 16121 Goodes Bridge Rd.	804-561-5221	
Boones Mill	**Boone's Country Store, 2699 Jubal Early Hwy.**	**540-721-2478**	**See ad #33, page 558**
Bridgewater	**Spring Creek Fabrics, 7689 Nazarene Church**	**540-828-6728**	**See ad #23, page 556**
Bristol	Quilted Blessings, 2000 Euclid Ave.	276-466-8552	
Burke	**The Artful Quilter, 9570 L Burke Rd**	**703-266-3250**	**See ad #16, page 554**
Cape Charles	**Quilts & More Fabric, 27376 Lankford Hwy.**	**757-331-3642**	**See ad #3, page 551**
Capron	**Quilters N Friends, 17293 Pinopolis Rd.**	**434-658-4564**	**See ad #8, page 552**
Carrollton	Bella Fabrics, 13478 Carrollton	757-238-7747	
Centreville	G Street Fabrics, 5077 Westfields Blvd.	703-818-8090	
Charlottesville	**Cottonwood, 2035 Barracks Rd.**	**434-244-9975**	**See ad #28, page 557**
Chesapeake	A Different Touch, 1107 S Military Hwy #B	757-366-8830	
Chester	**The Busy Bea, 11934 Centre St.**	**804-748-4951**	**See ad #9, page 553**
Chesterfield	**JoJo's Quilt Shop, 7056 Commons Plaza**	**804-778-7566**	**See ad #10, page 553**
Council	Betty's Fabric & Crafts, HC4, Box 57	276-794-7979	
Culpeper	**145 Art & Design Studio, 145 E Davis St**	**540-825-5620**	**See ad #21, page 556**
Dayton	**Patchwork Plus, 17 Killdeer Lane**	**540-879-2505**	**See ad #27, page 557**
Fairfax	**The Quilt Patch, 10381 Main St.**	**703-273-6937**	**See ad #18, page 555**
Falls Church	G Street Fabrics, 6250 Seven Corners Cntr.	240-283-8300	
Falls Church	Appalachian Spring, 102 W. Jefferson St.	703-533-0930	
Floyd	**School House Fabrics, 220 N. Locust St.**	**540-745-4561**	**See ad #38, page 559**
Forest	Quilt & Sew Studio, 18013 Forest Rd.	434-385-4080	
Fredericksburg	**Quilt and Sewing Center, 3940 Plank Rd.**	**540-548-2377**	**See ad #14, page 554**
Gainesville	Quilting Cellar, 4198 Stepney Dr.	703-354-2061	
Great Falls	Jinny Beyer Studio, 776-F Walker Rd.	703-759-0250	
Harrisonburg	**Ragtime Fabrics, 60 W. Market St.**	**540-434-5663**	**See ad #22, page 556**
Hillsville	**Mountain Plains Fabrics, 4505 Fancy Gap**	**276-728-7517**	**See ad #40, page 559**
Kenbridge	Keeping You In Stitches, 118 S. Broad St.	434-676-4000	
Lovingston	Stitches & Shavings, 605 Front St.	434-263-6359	
Lynchburg	**Quilted Expressions, 3622 Old Forest Rd.**	**434-385-6765**	**See ad #30, page 558**
Madison	**That Little Quilt Shop, 212 N. Main St.**	**540-948-4147**	**See ad #20, page 555**
Manassas	Old Town Needlecrafts, 9774 Center St.	703-330-1846	
Martinsville	**The Sewing Studio, 1310 Memorial Blvd. S**	**276-632-5700**	**See ad #39, page 559**
Merchanicsville	**Millstone Quilts, 8074 Flannigan Mill Rd.**	**(804) 779-3535**	**See ad #12, page 553**
Midlothian	**Quilter's Corner, 1257 Sycamore Square**	**804-794-1990**	**See ad #13, page 554**
Millboro	**Tender Heart Quilts, 4434 Cowpasture River Hwy.**	**540-862-4718**	**See ad #26, page 556**
Moneta	**The General Store, 213 Scruggs Rd.**	**540-721-3009**	**See ad #32, page 558**
Moneta	**Smith Mountain Lake Quilting, 130 Scruggs Rd. #214**	**540-719-7845**	**See ad #31, page 558**
Monterey	**Wool Becomes Ewe, 50 Fleisher Ave.**	**540-468-2007**	**See ad #25, page 556**
Newport News	**Nancy's Calico Patch, 21 Hidenwood Shopping Ctr**	**757-596-7397**	**See ad #5, page 552**
Norfolk	**Fabric Hut, 2340 E Little Creek Rd**	**757-588-1300**	**See ad #4, page 551**
Occoquan	Epicurean Crafts, 305 Mill St. #A3	703-490-0777	
Occoquan	Attic Treasures, 204 Washington St.	703-490-1536	
Portsmouth	Sew E-Z, 2858 Airline Blvd.	757-488-9449	
Portsmouth	Addicted Quilter, 3232 Academy Ave.	757-484-7752	

Pound — Fabric House, 8424 West Main St. 276-796-4500
Purcellville — Webfabrics, 116 N. Bailey Ln. 703-727-4458
Radford — Sew Biz, Inc. 92 Harvey St.
540-639-1138 **See ad #37, page 559**
Reedville — Material Girl Quilt Shop, 16658 Northumberland
804-453-6003 **See ad #1, page 551**
Richmond — Quilting Adventures, 1601 Willow Lawn Dr
804-262-0005 **See ad #11, page 553**
Richmond — Bernina of Richmond, 7590 W. Broad St. 804-755-4499
Roanoke — Creative Quilting, 6342 Peters Creek Rd.
540-362-4721 **See ad #34, page 558**
Salem — Quilting Essentials, 405 Apperson Dr.
540-389-3650 **See ad #35, page 558**
Staunton — Rachel's Quilt Patch, Ltd., 40 Middlebrook
540-886-7728 **See ad #24, page 556**
Stephens City — Cloth Peddler Quilt Shop, 5330 Main St.
540-868-9020 **See ad #17, page 554**
Stuarts Draft — Valley Fabrics, 2701 Stuarts Draft Hwy.
540-324-0548 **See ad #29, page 558**
Suffolk — Quilt With ME, 2999 Corporate Ln. #B9 757-539-0009
Troutville — Old Trinity Schoolhouse, 3200 Trinity Road
540-992-1233 **See ad #36, page 559**
Vienna — Vienna Quilt Shop, 396 Maple Ave. E 703-281-4091
Virginia Beach — Sarah's Thimble, 2245 W Great Neck Rd. #5
757-481-1725 **See ad #7, page 552**
Virginia Beach — What's Your Stitch 'N Stuff, 5350 Kempsriver
757-523-2711 **See ad #6, page 552**
Warrenton — Kelly Ann's Quilting, 9 S. 5th St.
540-341-8890 **See ad #19, page 555**
West Point — Ps & Qs Primitives and Quilts, 618 Main St 804-843-4555
Williamsburg — Love 2 Quilt, 1915 Pocohontas Dr. #B04-B06
757-565-0978 **See ad #2, page 551**
Woodbridge — Circle Sewing Studios, 2212 Tackett's Mill
703-910-7516 **See ad #15, page 554**
Woodstock — Shenandoah Sew & Vac, 498 N. Main St. 540-459-1888
Wytheville — Batiks Etc. & Sew What Fabrics, 460 E. Main St.
276-228-6400 **See ad #41, page 560**

Virginia Quilt Shows

15 Shows

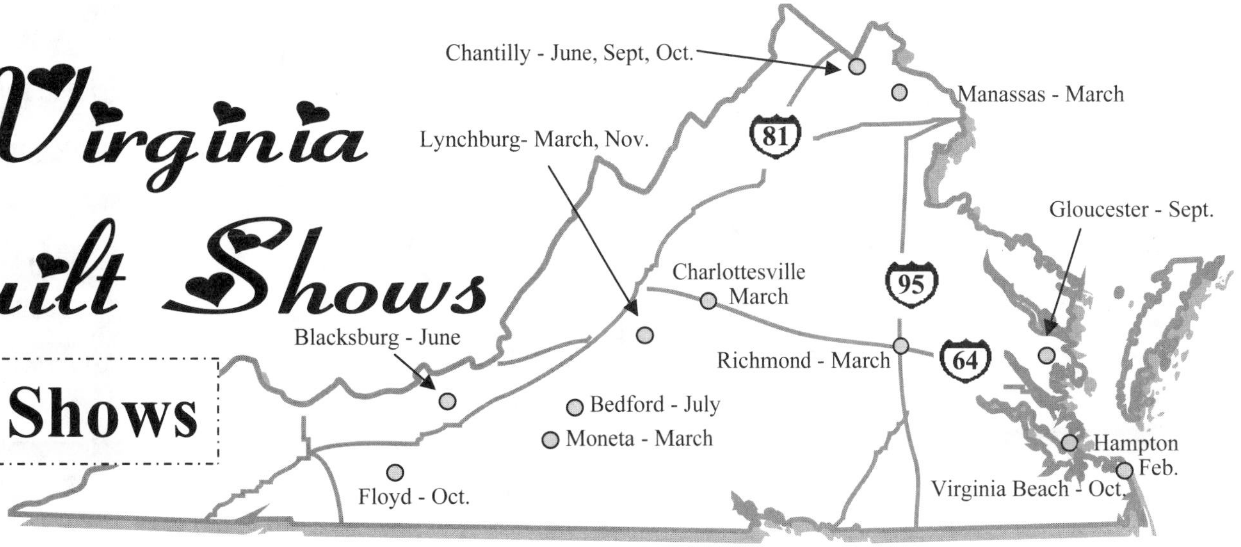

About Shows: We are listing only the very basic information about shows that happen on a regular schedule here. Please check out our website for more details on each show. Also this information tends to change quite often so please verify the event with our website or a local source before you venture far. Or if you're in the right area at the right time, give it a shot.

If you are a show organizer, please keep us updated on your event.
shows@quilterstravelcompanion.com www.quilterstravelcompanion.com

Month	City	Schedule	Show	Location with address
February				
	Hampton	Annual, 4th weekend in February	Mid-Atlantic Quilt Festival	Hampton Roads Convention Center, I-64 & I-664
March				
	Richmond	Annual, 2nd weekend in March	Virginia Spring Show	The Show Place Exhibition Center, 3000 Mechanicsville Trpk.
	Lynchburg	Every 3 years in March (from 2010)	Patches and Pieces Quilt Show	Holy Cross School, 2125 Langhorne Rd.
	Manassas	Annual, 3rd weekend in March	Cabin Branch & Stone House Quilters' Show	Prince William Cty Fairgrounds, 10624 Dumfries Rd.
	Charlottesville	Odd Years, late March or Early April	Jefferson Country Quilt Show	East Rivana Volunteer Fire Station, Rt. 250 E. at Glenmore
	Moneta	Even Years, 4th weekend in March	Lake Quilters Guild Show	Trinity Ecumenical Parrish, Rt. 122
June				
	Chantilly	Annual, 1st weekend in June	Quilters Unlimited Quilt Show	Dulles Expo Center--North Hall, 4320 Chantilly Shopping Ctr
	Blacksburg	Annual, 3rd weekend in June	Blue Ridge Quilt Festival	New Blacksburg Middle School, 3109 Price's Fork Rd.
July				
	Bedford	Annual, mid two weeks of July	Peaks & Pieces Quilt Guild Show	Bedford Central Library, 321 N. Bridge St.
September				
	Chantilly	Annual, 2nd Sun in Sept.	Sully Quilt Show & Sale	Sully Historic Site, 3601 Sully Rd.
	Gloucester	Odd years, 2nd Fri & Sat in September	River Country Quilters Show	Historic Court Circle, 6509 Main St.
	Chantilly	Annual, late September or early October	Original Sewing & Quilt Expo	Dulles Expo Center, 4368 Chantilly Shopping Center
October				
	Floyd	Annual, 1st weekend in October	Old Church Gallery Quilt Guild Show	Floyd Elementary School Gym, 531 Oak Hill Dr.
	Virginia Beach	Even Years, 2nd weekend of October	Quilt Show Memories	Church of the Ascension Community Center, 4853 Princess Anne
November				
	Lynchburg	Annual, first Sat. of November	Rainbow of Hope Quilt Auction	Mountain View United Church Rte. 221, just off Perrowville Rd.

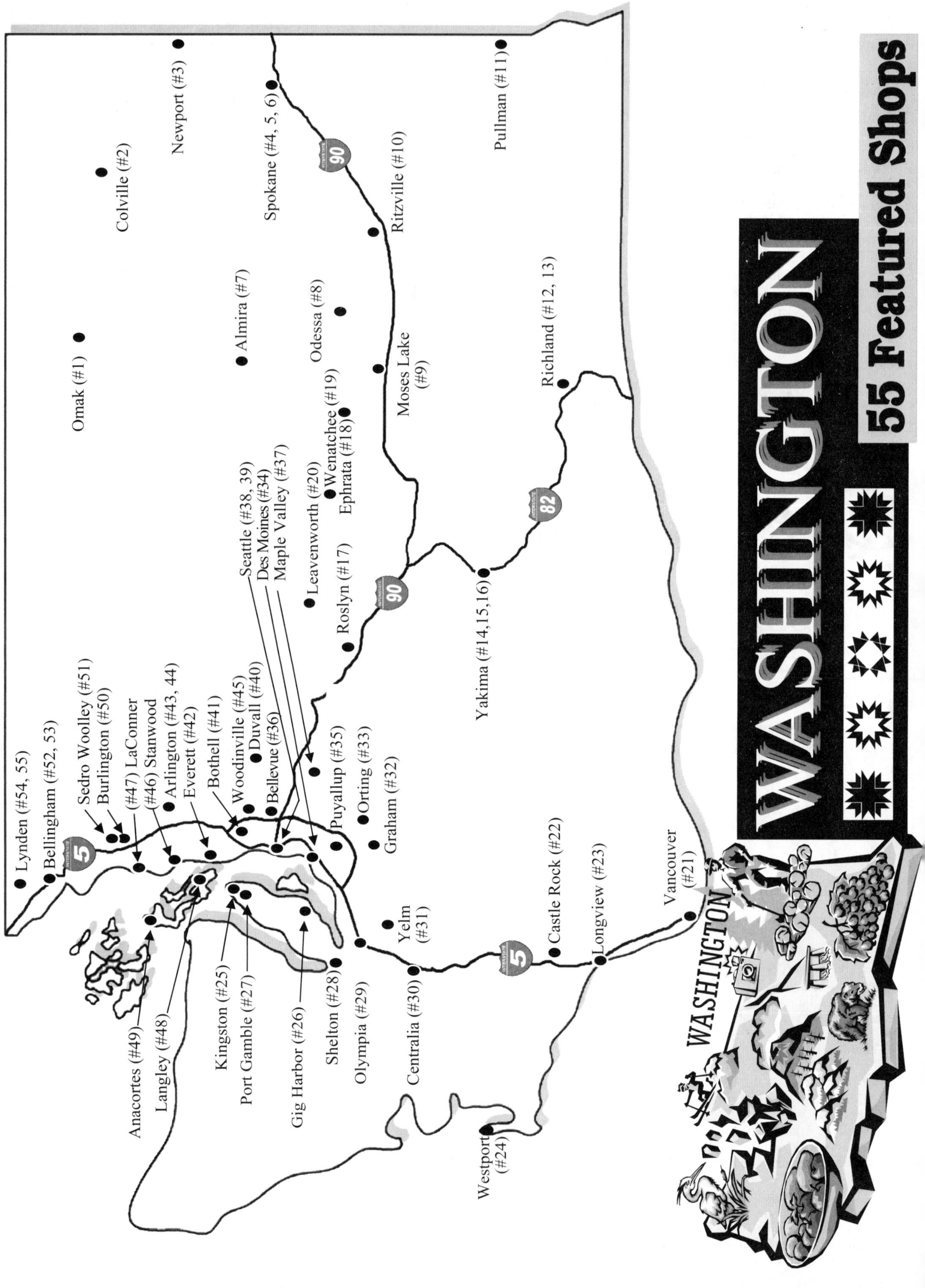
WASHINGTON
55 Featured Shops
Omak (#1)
Colville (#2)
Newport (#3)
Spokane (#4, 5, 6)
Almira (#7)
Odessa (#8)
Moses Lake (#9)
Ritzville (#10)
Pullman (#11)
Richland (#12, 13)
Yakima (#14,15,16)
Roslyn (#17)
Ephrata (#18)
Wenatchee (#19)
Leavenworth (#20)
Vancouver (#21)
Castle Rock (#22)
Longview (#23)
Westport (#24)
Kingston (#25)
Gig Harbor (#26)
Port Gamble (#27)
Shelton (#28)
Olympia (#29)
Centralia (#30)
Yelm (#31)
Graham (#32)
Orting (#33)
Des Moines (#34)
Puyallup (#35)
Bellevue (#36)
Maple Valley (#37)
Seattle (#38, 39)
Duvall (#40)
Bothell (#41)
Everett (#42)
Arlington (#43, 44)
Woodinville (#45)
(#46) Stanwood
(#47) LaConner
Langley (#48)
Anacortes (#49)
Burlington (#50)
Sedro Woolley (#51)
Bellingham (#52, 53)
Lynden (#54, 55)
5
90
82
WASHINGTON

Omak, WA #1

Mon - Fri 9:30 - 6
Sat 9:30 - 5:30

Needlelyn Time

9 N. Main St. 98841
(509) 826-1198
Est: 1986
3000 sq.ft.
3000 Bolts
lyn@needlelyntime.com
www.needlelyntime.com

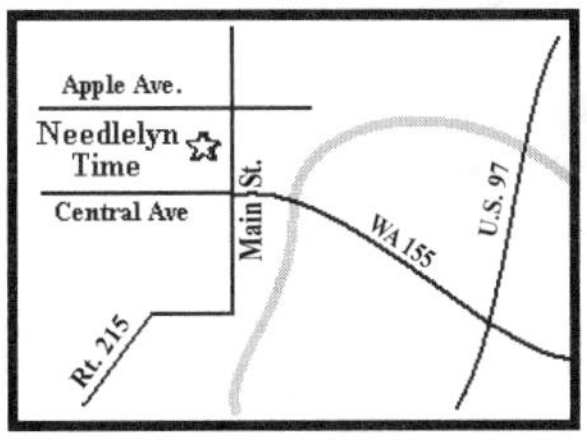

Visit us for all your Quilting and Pfaff Sewing Machine supplies and classes. Proud to serve the Okanogan Valley and beyond.

Colville, WA #2

Mon - Sat 9 - 5:30

E - Z Knit Fabrics

165 N. Main 99114
(509) 684-2644 Fax: (509) 684-6659
Owner: Vickie Black
Est: 1969 3000 sq.ft.
mail@ezknit.com
www.ezknit.com

3 stores in one — Beads — Fabrics — Yarn

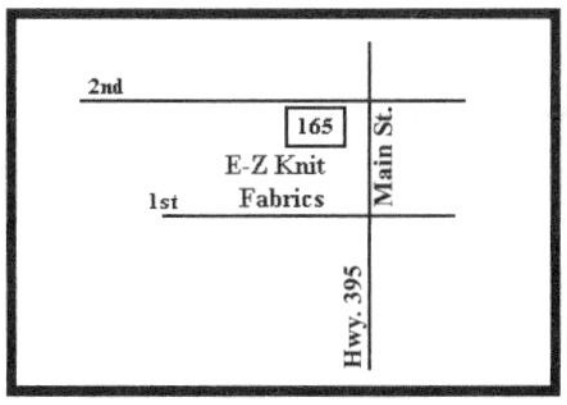

Newport, WA #3

Tues - Fri 10 - 5
Sat 10 - 4

Cottage Quilting

Corner of North Shore Rd. and Wakefield Rd.
Exit off U.S. 2 at Northshore/Diamond Lake Rd.
(509) 447-0208
Est: 2006 2500 sq.ft. 2000+ Bolts
cottagequilting@cottagequiltshop.com
www.cottagequiltshop.com
"The Quilt Shop in the Woods"
We are a full service quilt shop with everything you need for your next project. Wonderful kits too.

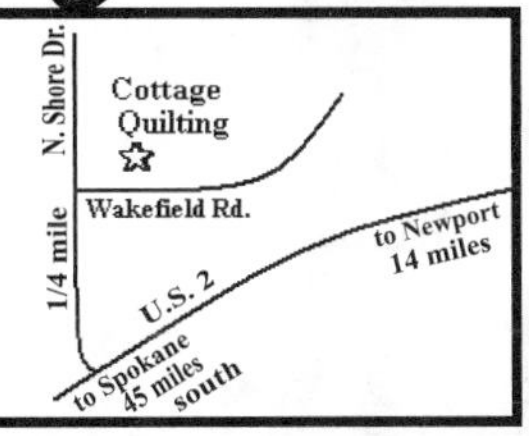

Spokane, WA #4

The Quilting Bee Inc.
BERNINA

Store Hours
M&F 10:00-8:00
Tues, Wed, Thur 10:00-6:00
Sat 10:00-5:00
2nd Sun 12:00-5:00

"Where lasting friendships are pieced together"

- Authorized BERNINA Dealer
- Machine Service & Repair All Makes
- Fabric, Kits, Notions
- Machine Embroidery Supplies
- Quilting Classes-ALL Levels

12117 E. Mission
Spokane, WA
99206
1-888-928-6037

www.quiltingbeespokane.com

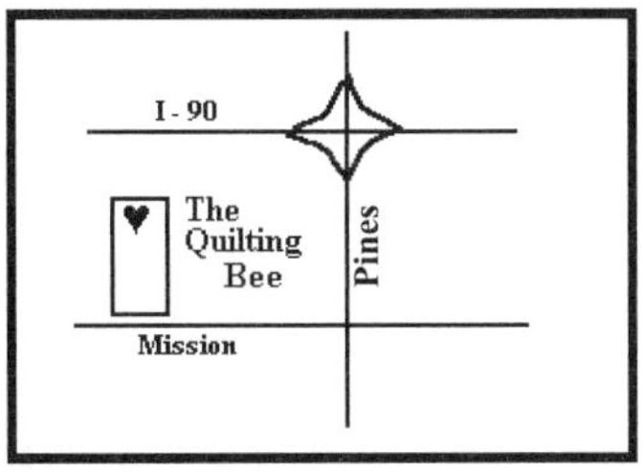

1998 Award Winning Quilt Shop
"American Patchwork and Quilting"
The 10 Best Quilt Shops in the USA

Spokane, WA #5

Mon - Thur 9 - 7
Fri & Sat 9 - 6

Sew E-Z, Too

603 W. Garland 99205
(877) 417-4694 or (509) 325-6644
Owner: Vickie Black Est: 1997
mail@ezknit.com
www.ezknit.com

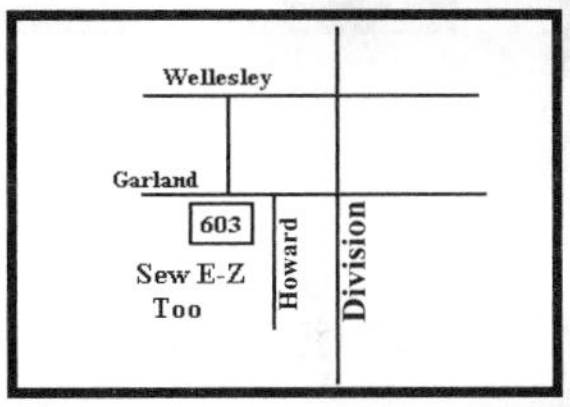

Designer Fabrics and More. Large selection of quality cottons, books, patterns.

Spokane, WA #6

Mon - Thur 10 - 6
Fri & Sat 10 - 5

the Cozy Quilt

9413 N. Newport Hwy. 99218
(509) 464-2425

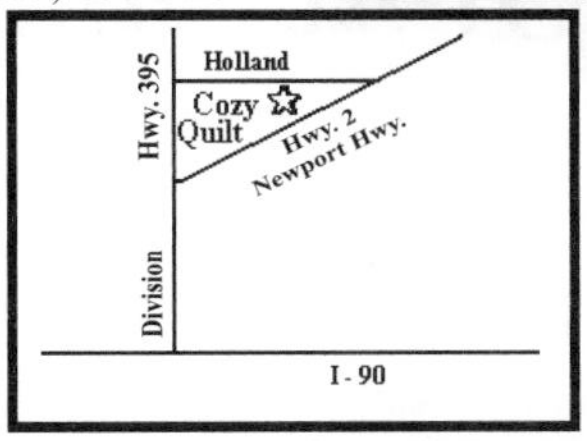

Owner: Carol Jones Est: 2004 4500 sq.ft.
www.thecozyquilt.net

Quality fabrics in a friendly atmosphere. Exclusive Baby Lock Dealer.

Almira, WA #7

Wed, Thur & Fri 10 - 5

Nana's Quilts & More

318 W. Maple Ave. 99103
(509) 639-2648
Owner: Karen Ertz Newsletter
Est: 2002 1200 sq.ft. 1000+ Bolts
heifer@centurytel.net

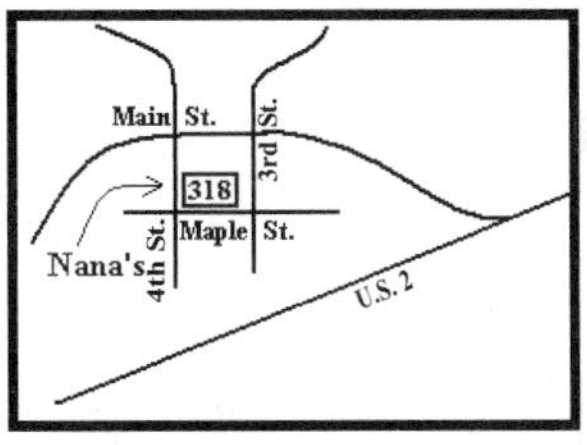

The Quilt Shop with country flair and down home feel. Assortment of fabrics including Western. Notions and longarm quilting.

Odessa, WA #8

Mon - Fri 10 - 5
Sat 10 - 4

The Quilt Crossing

4 W. First Ave., P.O. Box 206 99159
(509) 982-2194
Est: 1993
quiltcrossing@odessaoffice.com

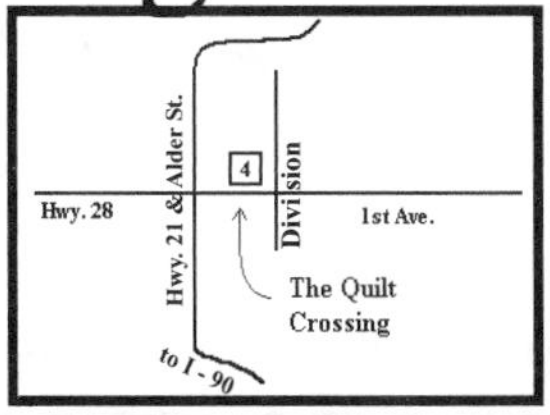

100% Cotton Fabrics, Patterns, Books, Stencils & Notions. Embroidery supplies. Classes, Friday night "Free Sew" quilting, first & third Fridays open till 9.

Moses Lake, WA #9

Tues - Fri 10 - 5:30
Sat 8:30 - 2

COLUMBIA BASIN QUILTWORKS AND BERNINA

122 W. 3rd Ave. 98837
(509) 764-2238
Est: 1998 4500 sq.ft. 2500+ Bolts
www.cbquiltworks.com

HandiQuilter, Bernina, Happy Dealer
"Sewing Workshop" garment kits.

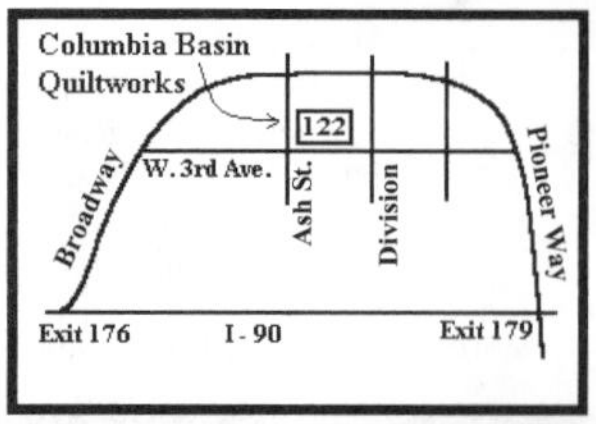

Ritzville, WA #10

Tues - Sat 10 - 6

Wild Flowers
Quilt Shop & Liquor Store

213 W.. Main St. 99169
(509) 659-4450
Ami Danekas * Proprietor
wildflowers@ritzville.com

1 mile off of
I - 90 in
Downtown
Ritzville

Pullman, WA #11

Mon - Sat 10 - 5

134 N. Grand Ave. 99163
(800) 324-5516 or (509) 334-7544
Est: 1993 3000 sq.ft.

Quilted Heart LLC
Encouraging the Fabric Arts

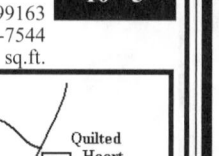

sales@quiltedheart.com
www.quiltedheart.com
Idea Central! Everything for top quality quilting and knitting projects.

- Books, Notions, Patterns
- 2500+ Designer Fabrics
- Gorgeous Yarns • Fun Staff

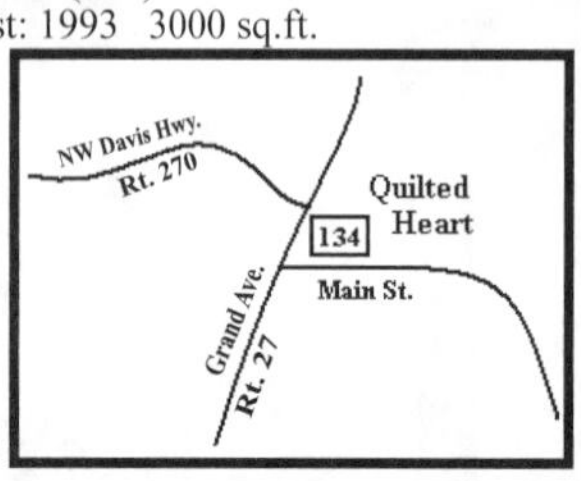

Richland, WA #12

1442 Jadwin Ave. #C 99354
(509) 946-PINS (7467)

Quiltmania!!

Owner: Debi Merhar
Est: 1991 10,000 Bolts
Rent time on our longarm quilting machine or let us do it.

Mon - Thur 10 - 6
Fri & Sat 10 - 5
Sun Noon - 5

Classes, Notions, Fabric.
Over 1000 book titles to choose from.
Quilts for Sale.

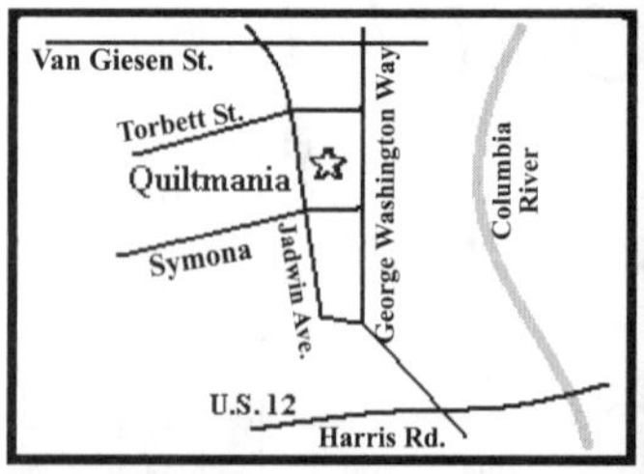

Village Quiltworks

Richland, WA #13

QUEENSGATE VILLAGE
1950 Keene Road, Suite B, Richland, WA 99352
(509) 628-0652
Est: 2001 3000 sq.ft. Over 3000 bolts

www.villagequiltworks.com

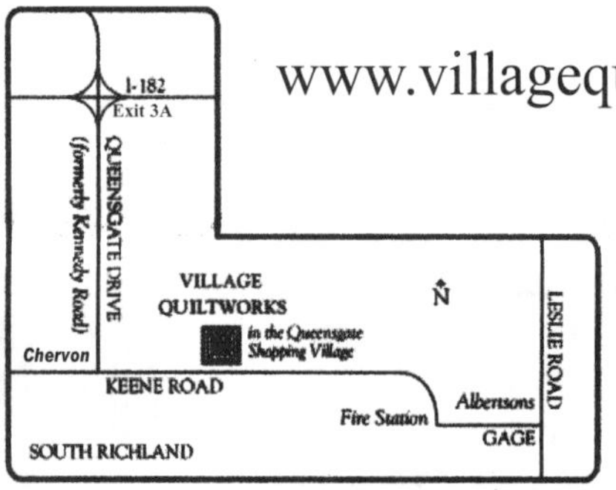

Mon -Fri 10-6
Sat 10-5

Village Quiltworks is a full service quilt shop located in a charming shopping village.

PROMOTING the ART of QUILTING

OFFERING
Authorized Handi Quilter Dealer · Classes
Machine quilting service · Friendly & helpful staff

Yakima, WA #14

By Appt Only

Sunbonnet Sue

1517 Summitview Ave. 98902
(509) 452-4112 Fax: (509) 452-4812
yakimasunbonnetsue@hotmail.com
Owners: Sue Lee & Brenda Oaks
Est: 2004 Free Newsletter
Long Arm Machine Quilting. We specialize in "Photo", custom made quilts and friendly service. Backing and batting available.

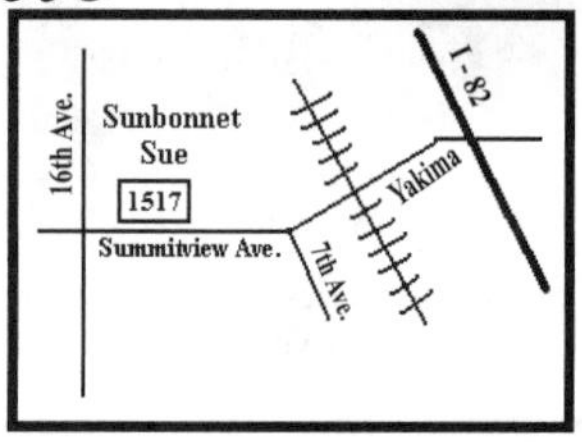

Yakima, WA #15

Tues - Fri 10 - 5
Sat 10 - 4

Stitch n' Quilt

8405 Ahtanum Rd. 98903
(509) 945-2560
Owner: Jolou Catron
Est: 2008 1500 sq.ft. 1500 Bolts
tneedle@qwest.net Online Newscard
Long arm quilting, P&B, Northcott, Kona Bay, Cloth Works, South Seas, Windham, Andover, Troy and Benartex fabrics.

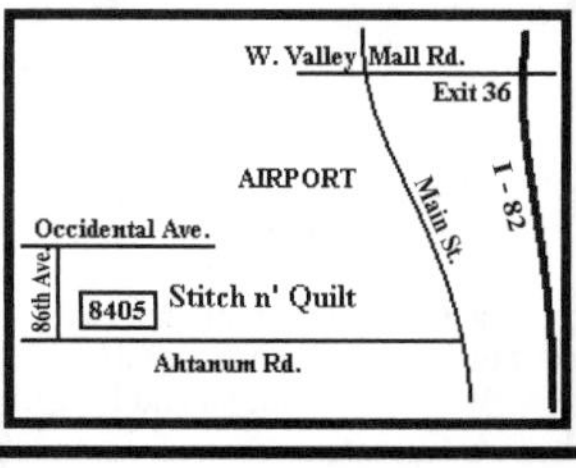

Yakima, WA #16

BERNINA Sewing & Vacuum Center

103 S. 7th Ave. 98902
509-248-0078 Fax: 509-248-0348
support@berninayakima.com
Owners: Brad & Sue McMillan
Est: 1968 3500 sq.ft.

Mon - Fri 9 - 5:30 Sat 9 - 5

Over 2000 Bolts of Quilt Fabric. Large Selection of Books, Patterns, Notions, Classes. Bernina Sales & Service.

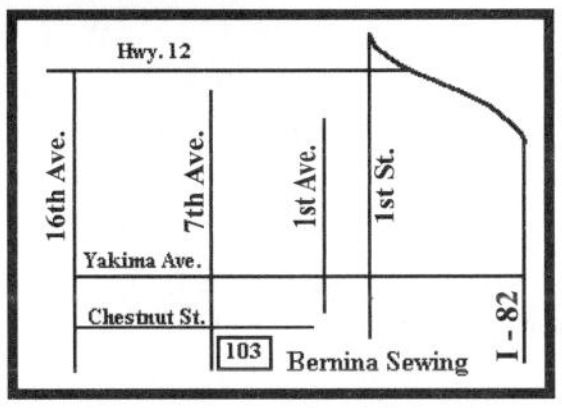

Crazy Quilt Shop

104 E Pennsylvania Ave
Roslyn, WA 98941-237
509-649-3777

Proprietor: Nancy L Bronk
crazyquiltshop@hotmail.com

Explore Historic Roslyn and The Crazy Quilt Shop

Tues - Sat
11 - 5

#17

The Crazy Quilt Shop embodies the Roslyn experience, where the famous televison show Northern Exposure was filmed. Not only do we provide a relaxed and friendly shopping experience, we specialize in retreats. Retreat guests have 24hour access to the Shop workspace and the adjacent Hummingbird Inn.

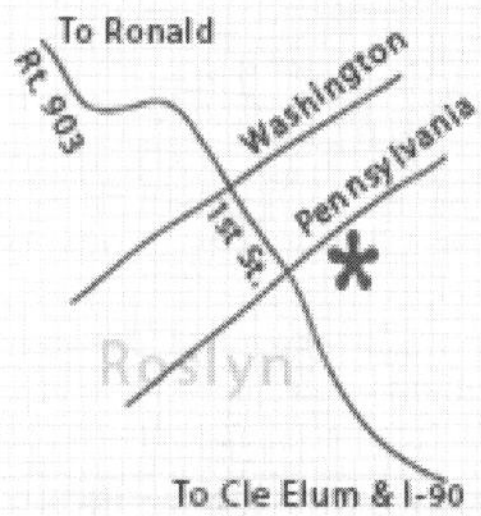

Visit our website:
www.thecrazyquiltshop.com

Attend our Annual "Crazy for Quilts Show"
The weekend before Labor Day weekend.

And Always a Friendly Northwest Welcome

The Fabric Patch

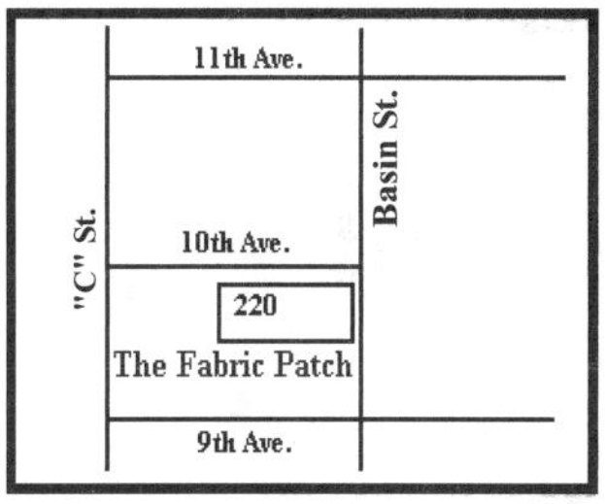

Ephrata, WA #18

220 Tenth Ave. SW, Ephrata, WA 98823
509-754-8280
www.fabricpatch.net
Est: 1999 2500 sq.ft.
Owners: Cindi & Brianna Rang

Visit our new Yarn Shop:
Two Sticks & A String
Right next door!

We are the Washington dealers for the Innova Quilting Machine.
Stop in for a demo, or rent one to finish your quilt!

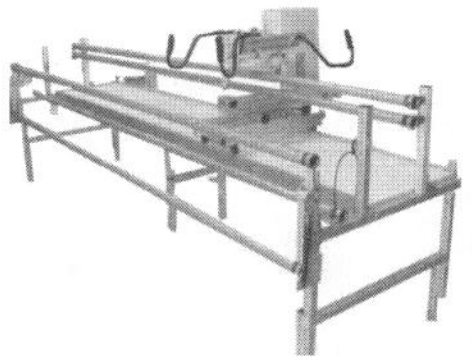

5500+ bolts of 100% cotton in Batiks, flannels, novelties and more. 900+ book titles. Complete line of notions and hundreds of patterns. Extensive classroom schedule.

Mon - Fri 9:00 - 5:30 Sat 9:00 - 5:00

Wenatchee, WA #19

Mon - Thur 9:30 - 6
Fri 9:30-5:30
Sat 10 - 5
Sun 12 - 4

The Attic Window Quilt Shoppe

1630 N. Wenatchee Ave. #8 98801
(509) 888-2006 Est: 2006
Owners: Marilyn Martin & Diane Garlini
2400 sq.ft. 2000 bolts Online Newsletter
atticwindow@nwi.net
www.theatticwindowquiltshoppe.com
A complete quilting supply store for the beginner or expert. We carry many lines of the highest quality fabrics and a full line of notions and books.

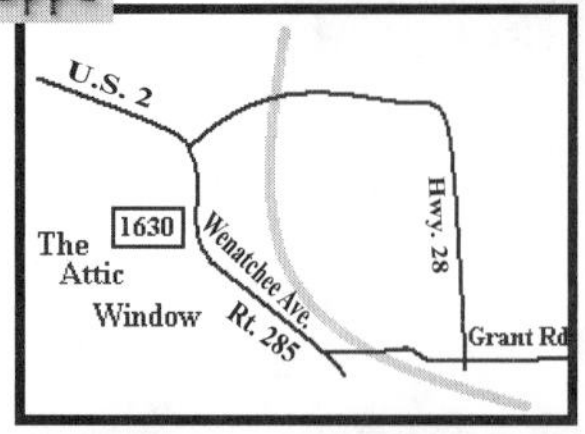

Leavenworth, WA #20

All Year 9 a.m. to 6 p.m.

Dee's Country Accents

917 Commercial St. 98826
(800) 253-8990
info@quiltersheaven.com
www.quiltersheaven.com

Largest selection of Fabrics, Books and Patterns in the Pacific Northwest, plus Mrs. Anderson's Lodging House, a ten room Bed & Breakfast specializing in Christian, quilting retreats.

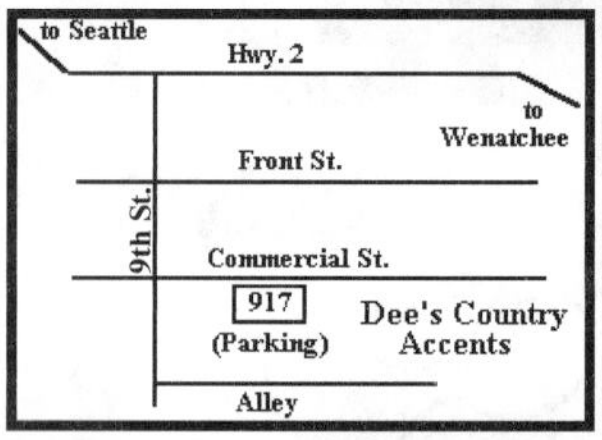

Vancouver, WA #21

Tues - Sat 10 - 5

Art & Sew'l

2727 E. Evergreen Blvd.
98661
(360) 696-9215 or (360) 904-7157

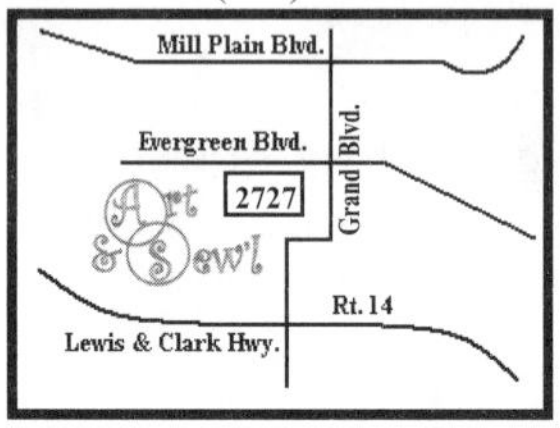

www.artandsewl.com
Quilting Gathers the Fabric of Life, Colors the Imagination and Binds our Dreams.

Castle Rock, WA #22

Mon - Fri 10 - 5:30
Sat & Sun 10 - 4

The Quilt Nest

105 Cowlitz St. W
P.O. Box 1287 98611
(360) 274-4663 Fax: Same
Owner: Tina Keele
quiltnest@hotmail.com

We have 3000 plus Bolts of 1st quality fabric. Friendly hands-on service.

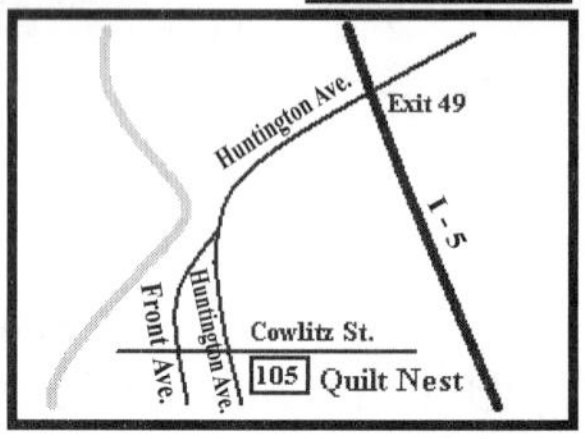

★ Momma Made It ★
*A Quilt Shop
Since 1996

We specialize in the warm, traditional look...
Civil War era reproductions, homespuns, Jo Morton, and hand dyed wool.

2121 8th Avenue, Longview, WA 98632
360.636.5631

WWW.MOMMAMADEIT.COM

Take I-5 Exit #39 - turn West on Allen St. - turn right on 5th Ave. - turn left on Cowlitz Way - cross bridge - turn right on 8th Ave. just past McDonalds.

Store Hours: Mon. 10 to 6, Tues - Fri. 10 to 5, Sat. 10 to 4
Sunday - Closed

Longview, WA #23

Westport, WA #24

Tues - Sat 10 - 5
Summer Sun 10 - 2

The Quilter's Stash

714 N. Montesano St. 98595
(360) 268-7370
Fax: (360) 268-7381
Est: 2001 1250 sq.ft.
Owners: Anne Howard & Dee Sidney
1100 bolts Online newsletter & catalog
info@thequiltersstash.com
www.thequiltersstash.com
Wide variety of 100% cotton quality fabrics, notions, books, patterns, kits and quality gifts.
New classes quarterly.

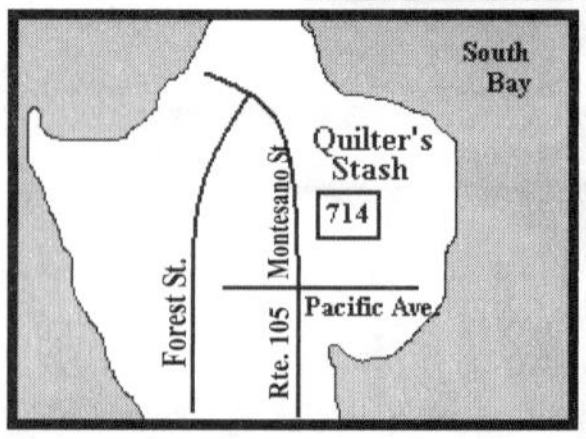

HARBOR QUILT inc

7716 D Pioneer Way Gig Harbor WA 98335
253-858-5414 800-743-9995 www.harborquilt.com
Mon - Sat 10am - 5 pm Sun 12noon - 5pm

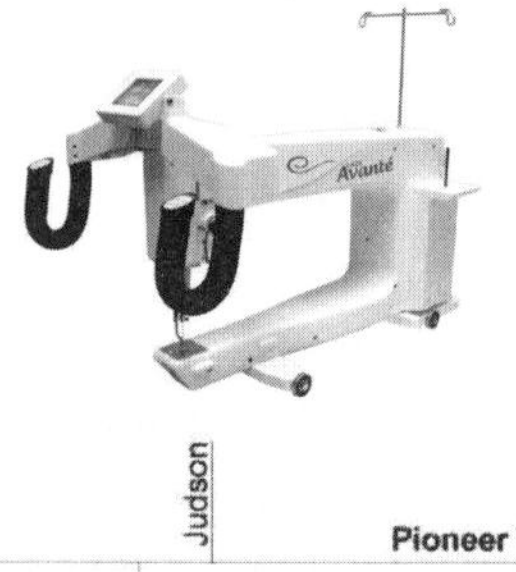

- Fabrics
- Notions
- DMC Floss
- Books
- Patterns
- Classes

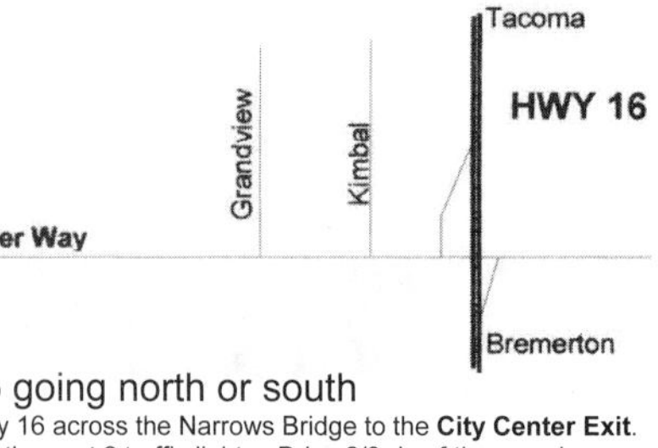

From I-5 going north or south
Take the Bremerton Exit. Follow Hwy 16 across the Narrows Bridge to the **City Center Exit**. Turn **right** at the light. Go through the next 2 traffic lights. Drive 2/3rds of the way down the hill and turn **left** at the building with the teal roof trim.

Bremerton, Port Orchard
Follow Hwy 16 to the **Wollochet/City Center Exit.** Turn **left** at the light. Go through the next 2 traffic lights. Drive 2/3rds of the way down the hill and turn **left** at the building with the teal roof trim.

Gig Harbor, WA #26

Kingston, WA #25

Mon - Sat 10 - 5
Sun 1 - 5

Kingston Quilt Shop

11264 NE State Hwy. 104 98346
(360) 297-2729

We have everything you need for exquisite quilts, and we love what we do! Located just feet from the Kingston Ferry.

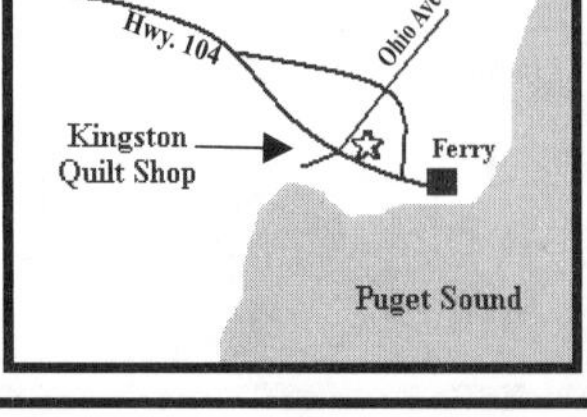

www.kingstonquiltshop.com

Quilted Strait

Quilting and Needlework Supplies

Store Hours:
Mon - Sat: 10 am to 6 pm
Sunday: 11 am to 5 pm

New Location

in Historic Port Gamble
Washington

1½ miles from the Hood Canal Bridge on Highway 104 on the Kitsap Peninsula.

32280 Puget Way
Port Gamble, WA 98364
info@quiltedstrait.com
www.quiltedstrait.com

Our 100 year old building is full of quilts for inspiration as well as more than 3500 bolts of quilting fabrics. Our eclectic inventory includes batiks, Asian inspired fabrics, flannels, contemporary prints, 1800's reproductions, wools, lots of basics, novelties, and a variety of extra wide quilt backings.

We also carry linens, patterns and floss for cross stitch as well as supplies for needle felting and wool appliqué.

Shop at our online store at www.quiltedstrait.com

Port Gamble, founded in 1853, is a 120-acre National Historic Landmark complete with picturesque, turn-of-the-century buildings, breathtaking views, expansive grounds, New England Style houses and unique shops on maple and elm lined streets. www.portgamble.com

360-930-8145

Port Gamble, WA #27

Shelton, WA #28

Mon - Sat
10 - 5:30

Sue's Stitch In Time

927 W. Railroad Ave. 98584
(360) 427-6164
Owner: Annie Gajadhar
Est: 2000
3400 sq.ft.
7000+ bolts

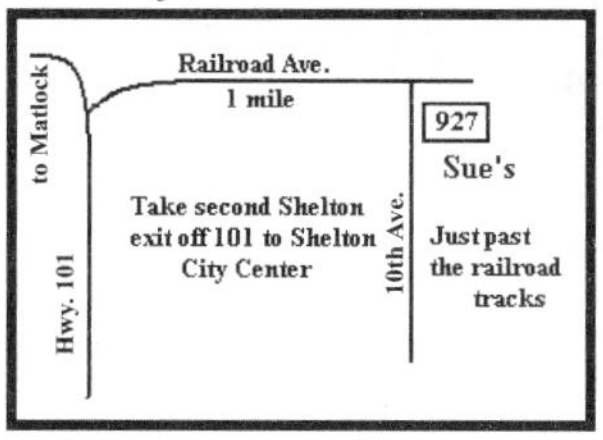

- Extensive Flannels Collection
- Exquisite Patterns
- Exceptional Heirloom Quality Fabrics
- Top Grade Quilting Supplies and Notions
- Superior Classes and Training
- "Best in Class" Customer Service

ONE OF AMERICA'S TOP TEN SHOPS!

DON'T MISS THIS!
1000'S OF BOLTS OF FABRIC, INSPIRATION, FRAMES AND *FUN* IN DOWNTOWN OLYMPIA

DIRECTIONS

I-5 Southbound take Exit 105A,
I-5 Northbound take Exit 105,
both are for Capital & City Center.
Go straight through the first stoplight and through the tunnel. At the second stoplight, take a right onto Capitol Way. Head straight North on Capitol Way to the 5th stoplight. Turn right on 4th Ave, which is a oneway going to your right. Get in the left lane. Turn left on Franklin.
Turn left on State Ave.
Then a quick left into our parking lot.
Enjoy!

BAYSIDE QUILTING
www.baysidequilting.com

Open Daily at 10:00
225 STATE AVE NE
OLYMPIA, WA 98501
LOCAL (360) 357-2000
TOLL FREE (877) 357-8822
FAX (360) 252-6110
info@baysidequilting.com

Olympia, WA #29

Centralia, WA #30

Mon - Sat
10 - 5:30

Quilters Junction

1728 S. Gold St. 98531
(360) 807-1255
Owner: Evelyna Manier Est: 1997
quilters_junction@comcast.net
www.quiltersjunctionusa.com

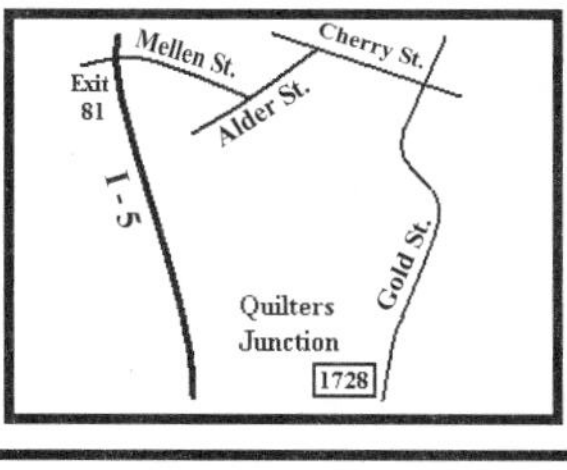

Fabrics, Patterns, Books & Notions.
Located in the Fairway Center.
"We put quality in your quilts."

Gee-Gee's Quilting INC

Crafts & Gifts

100% Cotton Fabrics, 15,000+ bolts,
over 700 bolts of Flannels,
over 600 Quilting Books,
over 200 Patterns, stencils, notions,
craft supplies, and yarns.
Plus Collectible Gifts,
& Finished Quilts.

Mon - Fri 9 - 6
Sat 9 - 5
Sun 11 - 4

601 Yelm Ave. W 98597
(360) 458-5616
sales@geegeesquilting.com
www.geegeesquilting.com
Est: 1978 6000 sq.ft.

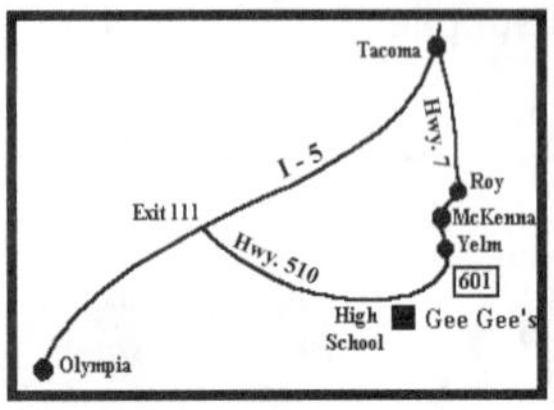

Yelm, WA #31

Creative Quilter

Graham, WA #32

Large selection of Books, Patterns, Notions & Machine Quilting Aids. Full line **BERNINA** Dealer. Moda, RJR, Benartex, Blank, Princess Mira.

Mon - Sat 10 - 5

21110 Meridian Ave. E
Suite C, Graham, WA 98338
(253) 262-3230

Est: 2002 2400 sq.ft. 2500 Bolts
Monthly Broadcasts of the "Virtual **BERNINA** Clubs"
quilters@creativesewing.net
Sign up for our E-Newsletter on our homepage.

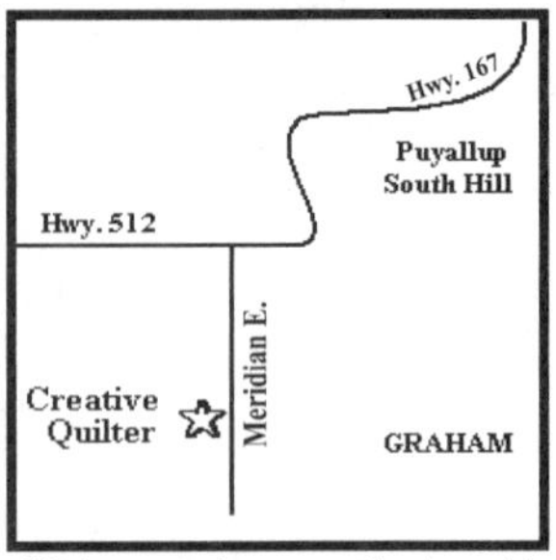

We're next door to a dentist with the "Huge White Tooth" on his sign

www.creativesewing.net

Wild Rose

Quilt Shop & Retreat

Nestled in a picturesque little town with a stunning view of Mt. Rainier, you'll find a gorgeous quilt shop and 10-person Retreat Center.

Built to look like an 1880's saloon, our modern shop has over 3200 bolts and a huge selection of reproduction, florals, "go-withs," contemporaries and flannels. We have a wide and current range of books, patterns and notions. Our fully equipped Retreat Center is like no other...AND we have an elevator so you don't have to carry your machine and other equipment up the stairs. Sew upstairs, shop downstairs....it just doesn't get any better than that!

www.thewildrosequiltshop.com

Orting, WA #33

Mon-Sat 9-5
Sun 11-4

125 Van Scoyoc Ave SW
~ Orting, WA 98360 ~
360-893-0202

Fine Fabrics ♥ Wool ♥ Folk Art ♥ Quilt Kits ♥ Books ♥ Patterns ♥ Fine Fabrics ♥ Wool ♥ Folk Art ♥ Quilt Kits ♥ Books ♥ Patterns ♥ Fine Fabrics ♥ Wool ♥ Books ♥ Patterns ♥ Fine Fabrics ♥ Wool ♥ Folk Art ♥ Quilt Kits

Carriage Country Quilts

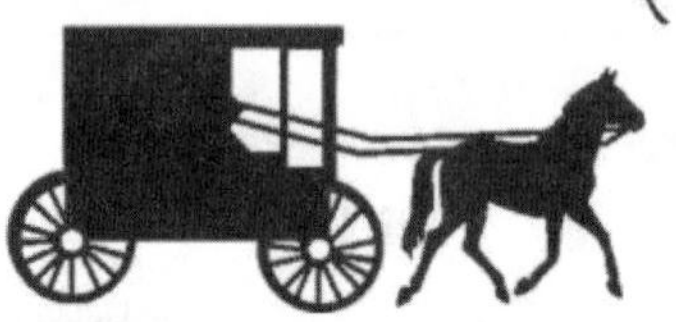

22214 Marine View Drive S. ♥ Des Moines, WA 98198
Phone: 206-878-9414
email: info@carriagecountryquilts.com
www.carriagecountryquilts.com
Hours: Mon-Fri 10-7 ♥ Sat 10-5 ♥ Sun 11-4

A Quilter's Fantasy

Offering you the latest in fabric, books, patterns, notions, classes and kits. You will also find the largest selection of wool, Civil War era reproduction fabrics and Jo Morton fabrics in Washington State.

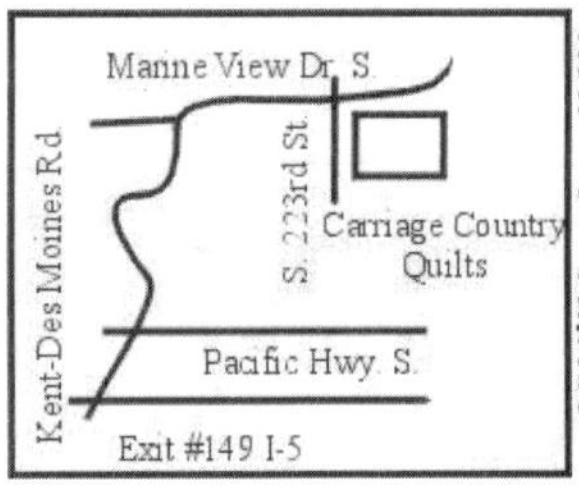

Exit #149 from I-5 North or South

Better Homes and Gardens Quilt Sampler Featured Shop 2007

Nationally recognized as a Top 10 Shop

#34

The Quilt Barn

2102 E. Main #102, Puyallup, WA 98372
(253) 845-1532

Regular Business Hours:
Mon. thru Fri. 10-6 p.m.
Sat 10-5 p.m. Sun. 12-4 p.m.
e-mail: thequiltbarn@comcast.net
Web site: www.quiltbarn.com

Serving Quilters for over 29 years

- **Over 9,000 bolt selection of 100% fine cotton quilting fabrics ~ specializing in brights, batiks, novelty prints and flannels**
- **Complete quilting supplies and notions**
- **Large selection of books and patterns**
- **Friendly and knowledgeable staff**
- **Open 7 day a week**

Puyallup, WA #35

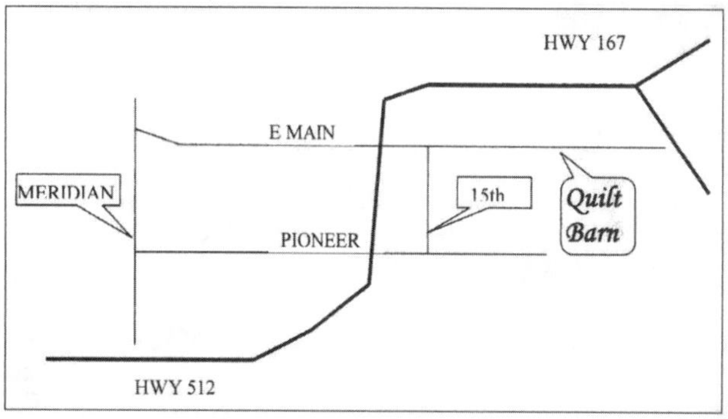

From Hwy 167: Going south, follow signs to Hwy 410. Take 1st exit (Traffic Ave). At stop sign, turn right and go 1 ¼ miles. We are on the left.

From I-5: Take the hwy 512 exit. Take Pioneer exit. At stop sign turn right. Make left at 15th. then right at E. Main. We are on the right.

Bellevue, WA #36

QuiltWorksNorthwest

www.quiltworksnw.com

Where Materials Meet Inspiration

Mon/Wed/Fri/Sat
10 am - 6 pm
Tues/Thurs
10 am - 9 pm
Sun Noon - 5 pm

Fabrics • Notions • Patterns • Books • Beads
Jewelry Supplies • Beading Classes • Sewing Classes

BERNINA
Nothing Sews Like A BERNINA. Nothing.
Full-line, Full Service Dealership with On-Site Technicians, FREE Lifetime Machine and Software Mastery Classes.

Inspiration for the Traditional, Contemporary or Art Quiltmaker: Batiks, Asian Prints, Yarn Dyes, Solids, Reproductions, Moda, Novelties, Contemporary Designers, Weeks Dye Works, Surface Design & Embellishment Supplies.

121 A 107th Ave. NE
Bellevue, WA 98004
877-295-7222
425-453-6005

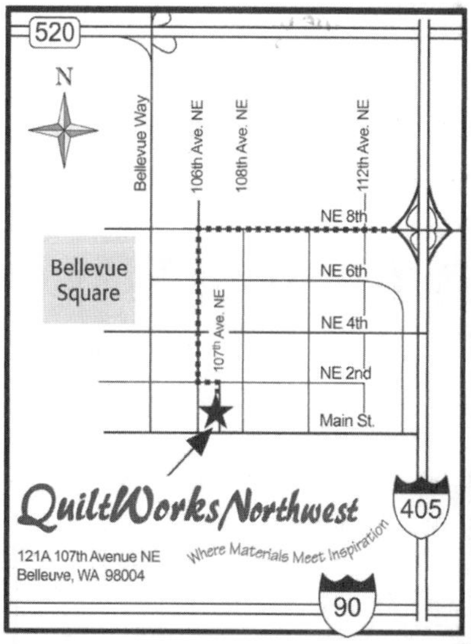

We're proud to be the new home of
BEADS AND BEYOND
Offering beads, buttons, beading and wire classes and much more!

Maple Valley, WA #37

7 Days a Week 10 - 4

21639 Renton-Maple Valley Rd. SE Ste B
(425) 432-8277 98038
www.des-mar.com/quilts/index.html
Fax: (423) 432-8278
Owner:
Joanne Lee
Est: 2007
1050 sq.ft.
1400+ bolts Batiks too!
Free Newsletter
snowkittens_designs@msn.com

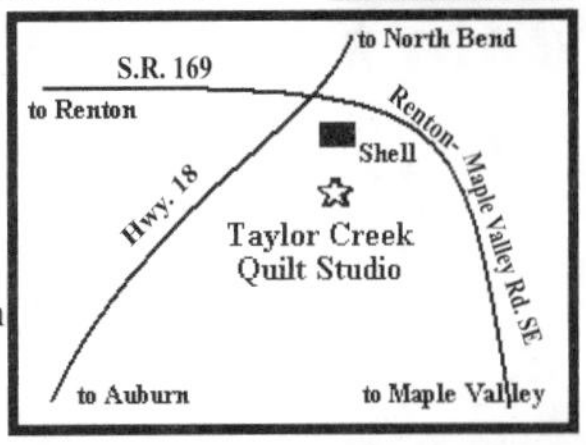

Taylor Creek has a focus on fabrics from the Pacific Rim. SW & PAC NW Indian fabrics & patterns.

Seattle, WA #39

Mon - Sat 10 - 6 Sun 10 - 5

1411 1st Ave. #106 98101
Inside the South Arcade Bldg.
(800) 469-6511 or (206) 622-6382
Owner:
Linda Hitchcock
Est: 1990 1000 sq.ft.
3000 bolts
quilts@serv.net
500 book titles, notions, supplies, gifts. Exclusive quilting patterns. Largest Selection of American Made New and Antique Quilts & Tops in the Pacific Northwest! www.undercoverquilts.com

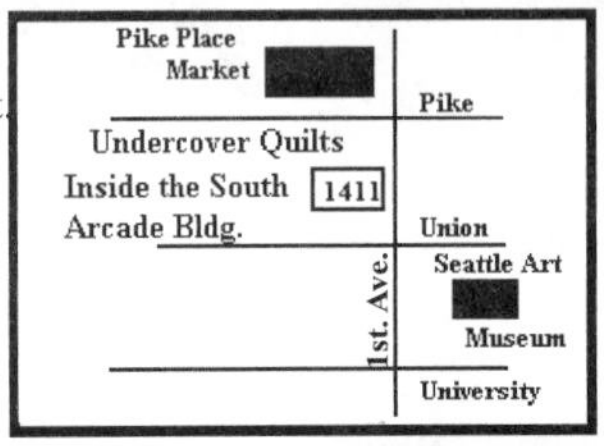

THE QUILTING LOFT

M, W, F: 10am-6pm
T & Th: 10am-8pm
Sat: 10am-5pm
Sun: 12pm-5pm

Fabric Boutique
Quilting Classes
Strip Club
Buck-A-Block
Quilt Kits
Long-arm Services

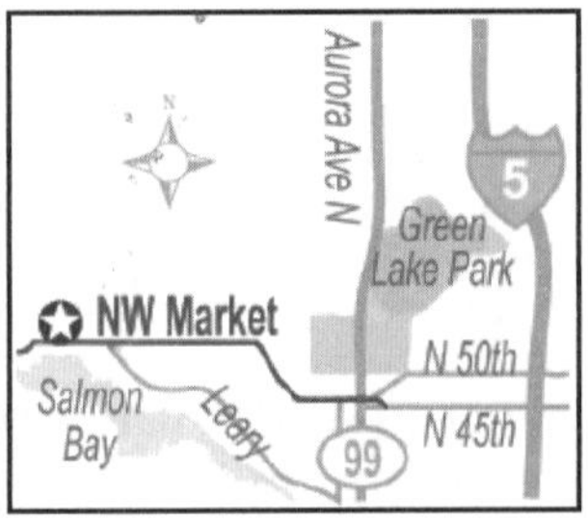

2601 NW Market St
Seattle, WA 98107
206-706-0445
#38

Visit us on the web!
www.thequiltingloft.com

Duvall, WA #40

Tues - Thurs 10 - 6 Fri & Sat 10 - 5

The Quilter's Garden

15705 Main St. NE,
P.O. Box 306 98019
(425) 844-1621
Est: 2002
1300 sq.ft. 2500+ Bolts
Free online Newsletter
www.duvalquiltshop.com
Friendliest shop in the Cascade Foothills!
Unbelievable selection! Fun Classes!
Shop here for what you see in the Magazines!

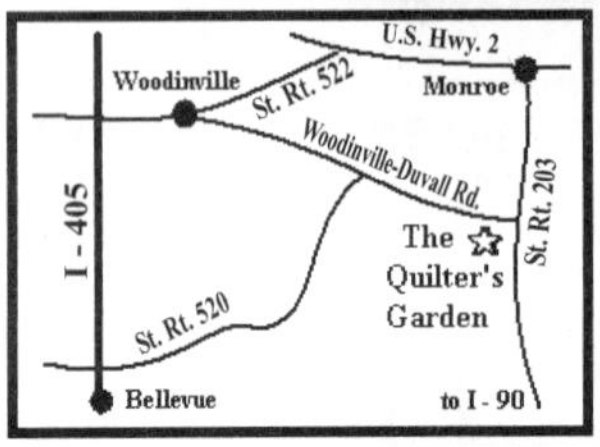

Bothell, WA #41

Mon - Sat 10 - 6 Sun 11 - 5

Keepsake Cottage Fabrics

818 238th St. SE. 98021
(425) 486-3483
Owner: Julie Stewart
Est: 1985 2000 sq.ft.
quilter@keepsakecottagefabrics.com
www.keepsakecottagefabrics.com

Quilting Fabrics, patterns and notions.
In the heart of Bothell's Country Village.

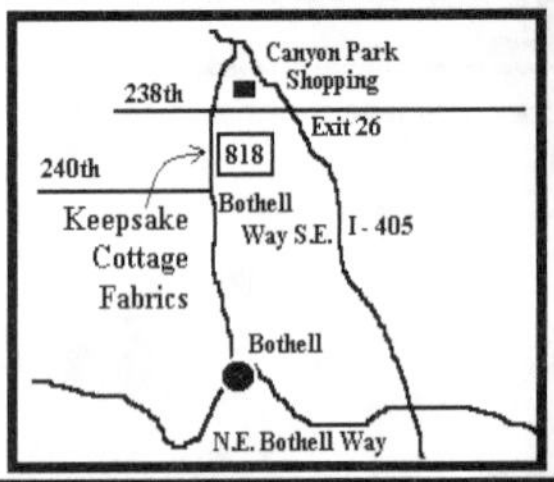

Everett, WA #42

Mon - Sat 10 - 9 Sun 10 - 7

The Needle & I

Authorized **BERNINA**® Dealer
4727 Evergreen Way 98203
(425) 259-3013 Est: 2006
5000 sq.ft. 3000+ bolts Online newsletter
theneedleandi@comcast.net
www.theneedleandi.com

For all your sewing needs!
Quality fabrics, patterns, notions, classes and service for your sewing machines!

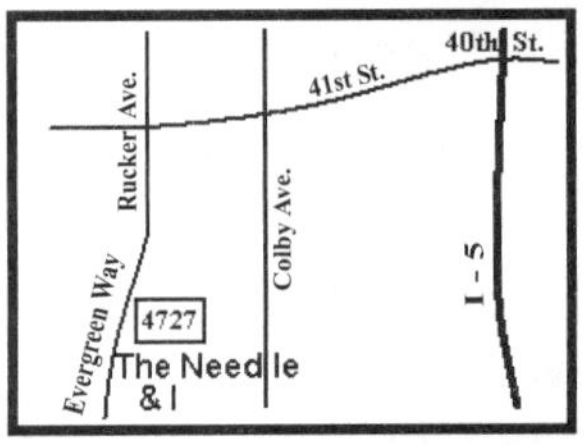

Aunt Mary's Quilt Shop

Mon - Fri 9 - 6
Sat 10 - 5
Sun 10 - 3

Full Espresso Bar open.

Specializing in Contemporary Quilting Fabrics with vibrant colors.
We strive to be a Comfortable, Fun place to visit.

www.auntmarysquiltshop.com

3323 169th Pl. NE, Suite I
Arlington, WA 98223
360-657-1116
Est: 2001 1500 sq.ft.
carrol@antmarysquiltshop.com
Online newsletter

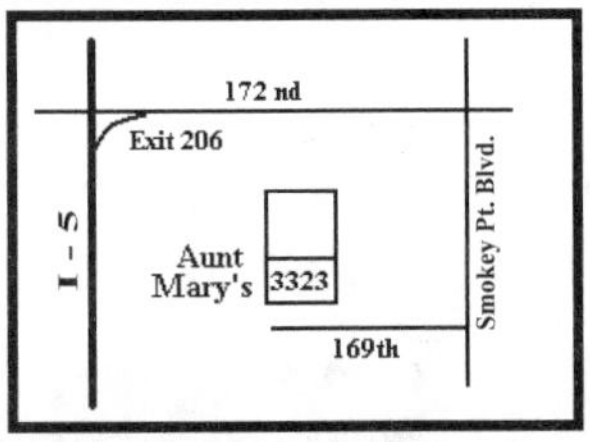

Arlington, WA #43

Arlington, WA #44

Mon - Fri 10 - 5:30 Sat 10 - 4

The Quiltmaker's Shoppe

315 N. Olympic Ave. 98223
(360) 435-3993

TheQuiltmakersShoppe@verizon.net
www.TheQuiltmakersShoppe.com

Stop in and visit one of the friendliest shops around! We specialize in beautiful fabric, notions, books, and classes.

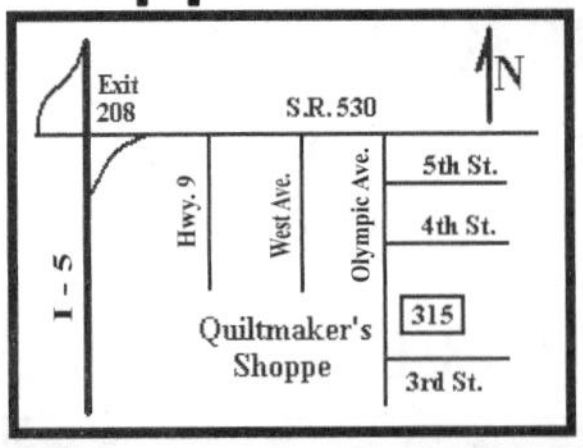

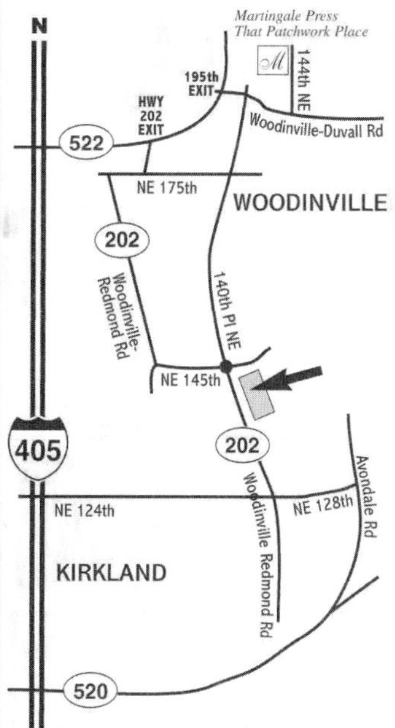

From the north: take WA State Route 522
From the south: take 124th St exit (Kirkland)

Gathering Fabric Quilt Shop

Fabric, Notions, Books, Classes, Events & Retreats for the Quiltmaker, Homemaker and Textile Artisan

14450 Woodinville Redmond Road NE • Woodinville, WA 98072
425-402-9034

www.gatheringfabric.com

Regular Shop Hours: Monday & Tuesday 10-5 • Wednesday-Friday 10-6
Saturday 10-5 • Sunday 12-4

Woodinville, WA #45

Visit our newly expanded "courtyard shop" located in the Sammamish Valley in the heart of Wine Country in historic Woodinville, Washington

Stanwood, WA #46

Cotton Pickins'

Mon - Sat 10 - 5:30 Thursday until 7:00

Choose from a wonderful selection of notions, books, patterns, kits and special gifts. Featuring quality 100% cotton quilting fabrics, homespuns and flannels from Hoffman, Moda, South Seas, Bali, RJR, Thimbleberries, Benartex and More!

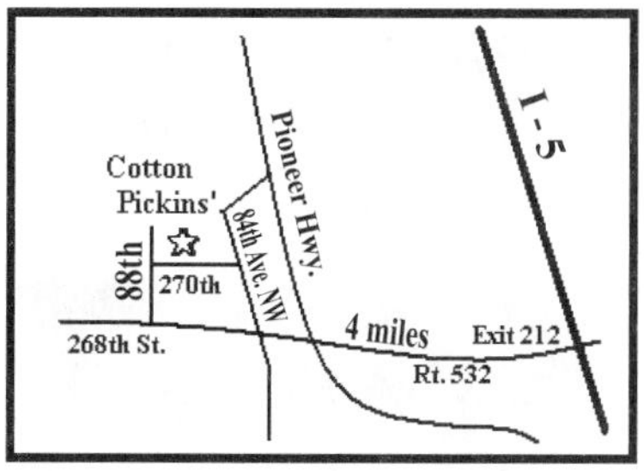

8718 270th St. NW
Stanwood, WA 98292
360-629-4771
CottonPickins@aol.com
Owner: Kathy Blank
Est: 2000 3000 Bolts

American Patchwork & Quilting Top 10 Shop

Authorized BERNINA Dealer

www.CottonPickins.com

LaConner, WA #47

Wed - Sun 11 - 5

LA CONNER QUILT & TEXTILE MUSEUM

703 S. 2nd St.,
P.O. Box 1270 98257
(360) 466-4288
Admission $5, member free
info@laconnerquilts.com
www.laconnerquilts.com

New exhibits of quilts & textiles every 3 months in this 3-story 1891 Victorian Mansion.

Langley, WA #48

Mon-Sat 10 - 5
Sun 11 - 3

QUILTING • BY • THE • SEA

221 2nd St. 98260 (360) 221-8171
www.quiltingbythesea.com

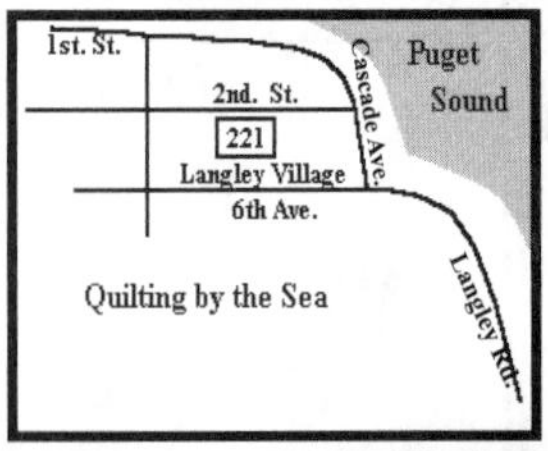

Extraordinary quilt shop in Quaint Village.
✂ Fabrics ✂ Books ✂ Patterns ✂ Notions ✂
Fully equipped OVERNIGHT RETREAT
Bernina Sewing Machines

Burlington, WA #50

Mon - Sat 10 - 9
Sun 10 - 7

Sewers Dream Fabric Outlet

Largest Fabric Outlet in Western Washington

316 Fashion Way 98233
(360) 757-1812 Fax: (360) 757-4650
Owner: Peggy Schafer
Est: 2000 2000 bolts
service@sewandquilt.com
www.sewandquilt.com
5,000 sq. ft. of fabrics and notions priced at outlet prices, quilting cottons, upholstery, batting, beads, sequins and more!

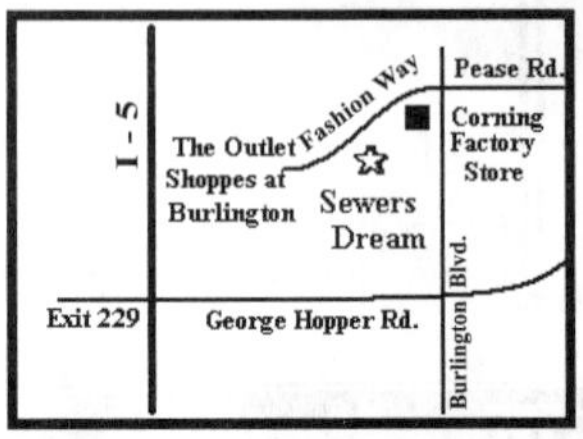

the Quilt Shop

Mon - Sat 9:30 - 5:30
Sun 11 - 4

Everything for the Quilter! Fabrics, patterns, books, notions & classes.

Owners:
Cathy Berk
& Mary Gillman
3000+ Bolts

820 Commercial Ave. 98221
(360) 293-2146
www.anacortesquilts.com

Anacortes, WA #49

Sedro Woolley, WA #51

Mon - Fri 9:30 - 5:30
Sat 9:30 - 5

Cascade Fabrics

824 Metcalf 98284
(360) 855-0323
Owner: Paul Kelley
Est: 1978 3000 sq.ft.

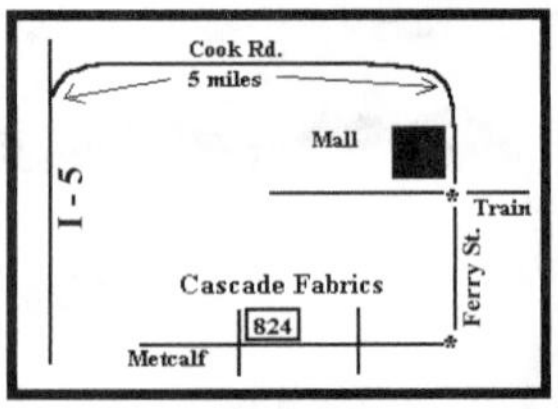

Quilting Supplies, Books and Classes. Experienced Staff. Always 20% off all cotton fabric. Wide Selection of other Fabrics.

FOURTH CORNER QUILTS

- Janome Sewing Machine Sales & Service
- Handi Quilter sales, installation, training, repair and rental
- Textile Surface Design Supplies, Angelina fibers, paint, ink, and threads
- Quilting Classes for All Skill Levels
- Rent, sell & service HandiQuilter Long Arms.

1844 N State Street Bellingham WA 98225

•I-5 N - exit 254. Left on Iowa, left on State
•I-5 S - exit 254. Veer right, left on State

#52

Regular Store Hours:
Monday - Saturday
10:00 am - 6:00 pm

360•714•0070
www.fourthcornerquilts.com

Bellingham, WA #53

Mon - Sat 10 - 6

Fabric-Etc

1633 Birchwood Ave. 98225
(360) 671-5277
info@fabric-etc.com
www.fabric-etc.com
Est: 1997 1800 sq.ft.

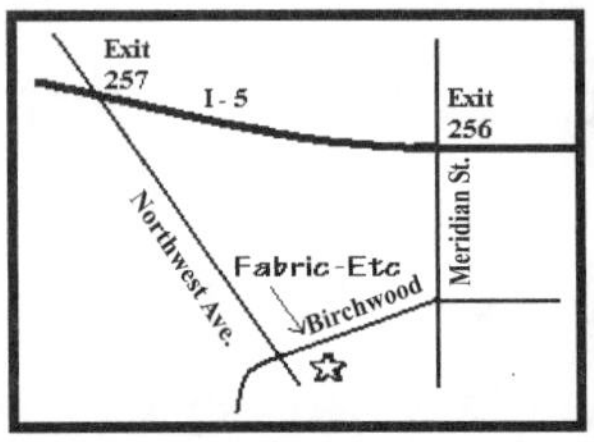

- 2500+ bolts of quality quilting cottons
- Large selection of fashion fabrics
- Books, patterns, notions

Lynden, WA #54

Mon - Sat 10 - 5

Folktales

1885 Kok Rd. 98264
(360) 354-0855
Owner: Linda Kroon
Est: 1995 1000+ Bolts
folktales@netzero.net

"A Little Shop Full of Big Ideas"
Fabric, patterns & supplies.
Unique handcrafted collectibles.

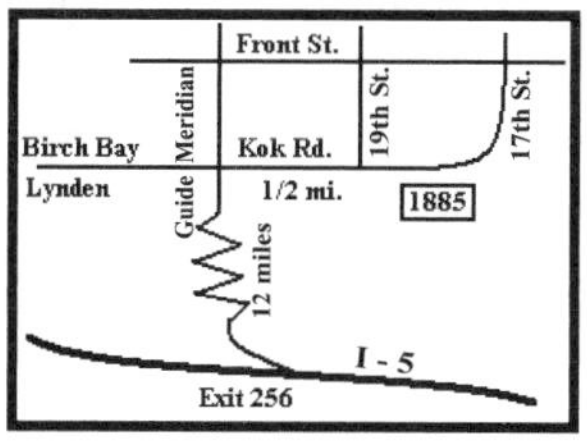

Lynden, WA #55

Mon - Sat 9:30 - 5:30

CALICO COUNTRY™

Fairway Center
1722 Front St. 98264
(360) 354-4832
calico_country@msn.com
3500 bolts of cottons & flannels, quilting supplies, custom lampshades, classes, alterations & custom sewing.
Bernina sewing machine sales and service.
Celebrating 27 years of personalized service.

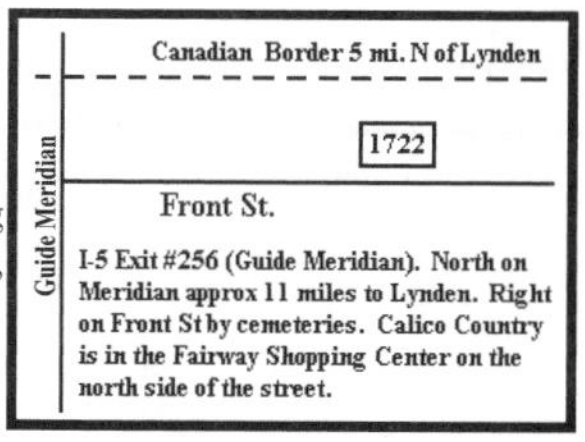

Washington Quilt Shops

Almira — **Nana's Quilts & More, 318 W. Maple Ave.**
509-639-2648 See ad #7, page 563

Anacortes — Fabrics Plus, 608 Commercial Ave 360-293-7641

Anacortes — **The Quilt Shop, 820 Commerical Ave.**
360-293-2146 See ad #49, page 572

Arlington — **Aunt Mary's Quilt Shop, 3323 169th Pl NE #I**
360-657-1116 See ad #43, page 570

Arlington — **The Quiltmaker's Shoppe, 315 N. Olympic**
360-435-3993 See ad #44, page 570

Bainbridge Island — Esther's Fabrics, 181 Winslow Way E # D 206-842-2261

Bainfridge Island — Beach Garden Quilts, 9723 Olympus Beach Rd NE 206-842-5118

Battle Ground — Country Manor Fabrics, 7702 NE 179th 360-573-6084

Battle Ground — Quilted Memories, 23513 NE 229th St. 360-687-9393

Bellevue — Block Butter, Inc., 1004 141st PL NE 425-644-4242

Bellevue — **QuiltWorks Northwest, 121 A 107th Ave NE**
425-453-6005 See ad #36, page 569

Bellevue — Pacific Fabrics & Crafts, 1645-140th NE 425-747-3551

Bellingham — Lynda's Quilting & Needle Art, 5021 Northwest Dr 360-380-0886

Bellingham — Two Thimbles, 1805 Cornwall Ave. 360-715-1629

Bellingham — **Fabric-Etc, 1633 Birchwood Ave.**
360-671-5277 See ad #53, page 572

Bellingham — **Fourth Corner Quilts, 1844 N. State St.**
360-714-0070 See ad #52, page 572

Bothell — **Keepsake Cottage Fabrics, 818 238th St. SE**
425-486-3483 See ad #41, page 570

Bremerton — Pacific Fabrics & Crafts, 4214 Wheaton Wy 360-479-4214

Burlington — **Sewer's Dream Fabric Outlet**
316 Fashion Way
360-757-1812 See ad #50, page 572

Castle Rock — **The Quilt Nest, 105 Cowlitz Ave. W**
360-274-4663 See ad #22, page 566

Centralia — **Quilters Junction, 1728 S. Gold St.**
360-807-1255 See ad #30 page 567

Chehalis — Sister's Fabric Shop, 476 N. Market 360-748-9747

Chewelah — Akers United Drug, N. 406 Park 509-935-8441

Clinton — Casey's Fabric & Crafts, Hwy. 525 & Howard Rd. 360-321-0577

Colville — **E-Z Knit Fabrics, 165 N. Main St.**
509-684-2644 See ad #2, page 563

Deer Park — Quilt Lounge and Knittery, 110 W. Crawford, Ste. A 509-276-3030

Des Moines — **Carriage Country Quilts**
22214 Marine View Dr. S
206-878-9414 See ad #34, page 568

Duvall — **The Quilter's Garden, 15705 Main St. NE**
425-844-1621 See ad #40, page 570

Eastsound — Poppies, 294 "A" St., P.O. Box 1075 360-376-2686

Eatonville — Country Mouse, 755 Eatonville Hwy. E 360-832-8065

Ellensburg — The Sewing Corral, 411 N. Pine St. 509-933-4567

Ephrata — **The Fabric Patch, 220 10th Ave. SW**
509-754-8280 See ad #18, page 565

Evans — Wumpkins Whole Caboodle Quilt Shop, 1072 A Williams Lake Rd 509-684-3838

Everett — **The Needle and I, 4727 Evergreen Way**
425-259-3013 See ad #42, page 570

Gig Harbor — **Harbor Quilts, 7716 D Pioneer Way**
253-858-5414 See ad #26, page 566

Graham — **Creative Quilter, 21110 Meridian Ave E Ste C**
253-262-3230 See ad #32, page 568

Kennewick — Sandy's Fabrics & Machines, 24 N. Benton 509-585-4739

Kennewick — Stitch N Bug, 130 Vista Way 509-736-3698

Kettle Falls — Red Rooster, 130 E. 3rd Ave. 509-738-4418

Kingston — **Kingston Quilt Shop**
11264 NE State Hwy. 104
360-297-2729 See ad #25, page 566

Kirkland — Quality Sewing & Vacuum Centers , 13501 100th Ave NE 425-821-1747

La Conner — **La Conner Quilt & Textile Museum**
703 S. 2nd. St.
360-466-4288 See ad #47, page 572

Lakewood — The Shibori Dragon, 11124 Gravelly Lake Dr. SW 253-582-7455

Langley — **Quilting By The Sea, 221 Second St.**
360-221-8171 See ad #48, page 572

Leavenworth — **Dee's Country Accents, 917 Commercial St.**
509-548-5311 See ad #20, page 566

Longview — Longview Sewing & Vac, 945 Washington Way 360-578-2628

Longview — **Momma Made It, 2121 8th Ave**
360-636-5631 See ad #23, page 566

Lynden — **Calico Country, 1722 Front St.**
360-354-4832 See ad #55, this page

Lynden — **Folktales, 1885 Kok Rd.**
360-354-0855 See ad #54, this page

Lynden — Tangled Threads Quilt Shop, 202 6th St. 360-318-1567

Lynnwood — Quality Sewing & Vacuum Centers, 3105 Alderwood Mall Blvd. Suite A1 425-775-6612

Maple Valley — **Taylor Creek Quilt Studio**
21639 Renton-Maple Valley Rd SE
425-432-8277 See ad #37, page 570

Marysville — The Quiltery, 6710 45th Place NE 425-377-8646

Metaline Falls — Sweet Creek Creations, 219 E 5th Ave 509-446-2429

Morton — Sugar-n-Spice, 680 Airport Way 360-496-6629

Moses Lake — **Columbia Basin Quiltworks, 122 W. 3rd Ave.**
509-764-2238 See ad #9, page 564

Moses Lake — Country Fabrics, 711 N. Stratford #B 509-764-4706

Mossyrock Kathy's Kountry Fabrics, 121 Aijune Rd. 360-983-8171
Mount Vernon Ellen's Arlington Fabric, 2522 A Old Hwy. 99 S 360-424-9293
Moxee Common Thread Quilting, 240 Meadowlark 509-248-3878
Mukilteo Peacock & Periwinkle, 11700 Mukilteo Speedway, Ste 201 425-232-1355

Newport Cottage Quilting, 52 Wakefield Rd.
509-447-0208 See ad #3, page 563

Nine Mile Falls Sew Shabby Quilt Shoppe, 7415 W. Ridgecrest Ave. 509-499-2343
Northgate Quality Sewing & Vacuum Center, 842 NE Northgate Way 206-363-1634
Oak Harbor Quilters Workshop, 715 SE Fidalgo Ave. 360-675-7216
Oakesdale Ditzy's Neats & Dumb-Dumbs 103 E. Steptoe Ave. 509-285-4265
Oakville The Quilting Cottage, 208 E. Pine St. 360-273-5523
Ocean Shores Cranberry Bay, 897 Minard Ave. NW #3 360-289-0984

Odessa The Quilt Crossing, 4 W 1st. Ave.
509-982-2194 See ad #8, page 563

Olympia Bayside Quilting225 State Ave. NE
360-357-2000 See ad #29, page 567

Omak Needlelyn Time, 9 N. Main St.
509-826-1198 See ad #1, page 563

Orting The Wild Rose Quilt Shop & Retreat
125 Van Scoyoc Ave. SW
360-893-0202 See ad #33, page 568 & 410

Palouse Small Towne Quilts, 124 E Main St. 509-878-1253
Pasco Janean's Bernina, 6303 Burden Blvd. #C 509-544-7888
Pomeroy Rather-Be's Quilting Shop, 382 Hwy. 12 E. 509-843-6162

Port Gamble Quilted Strait, 32280 Puget Way
360-930-8145 See ad #27, page 567

Port Orchard Rochelle's Fine Fabric & Quilting 1700 SE Mill Hill Dr. #300 360-895-1515
Poulsbo Heirloom Quilts, 18833-B Front St. 360-697-2222
Prosser Quilters Garden, 1205 Meade Ave. 509-786-2766
Prosser The Sewing Basket & The Quilted Country Inn 1108 Wine Country Rd. 509-786-7367
Prosser The Wheat Wagon, P.O. Box 9 509-786-2377

Pullman The Quilted Heart. LLC, 134 N. Grand Ave.
509-334-7544 See ad #11, page 564

Puyallup The Quilt Barn, 2102 E. Main #102
253-845-1532 See ad #35, page 569

Quilcene Blueberry Ewe, 295549 Hwy. 101 360-765-4957
Reardan The Buggy Barn, 28848 Tramm Rd N. 509-796-2188
Renton Pieces Quilt Shop, 364 Renton Center Way SW #59 425-271-7160

Richland Village Quiltworks, 1950 Keene Rd. Suite B
509-628-0652 See ad #13, page 564

Richland Quiltmania, 1442 Jadwin Ave. #C
509-946-7467 See ad #12, page 564

Ritzville Wild Flowers Quilt Shop, 213 W. Main St.
509-659-4450 See ad #10, page 564

Roslyn The Crazy Quilt Shop, 104 E. Pennsylvania
509-649-3777 See ad #17, page 565 & 404

Seattle Undercover Quilts from the USA
1411 1st. Ave. #106
206-622-6382 See ad #39, page 570

Seattle The Quilting Loft, 2601 NW Market St.
206-706-0445 See ad #38, page 570

Seattle The Brick Sewing Room, 5708 27th . NE 206-369-5585
Seattle Quilt Haus, 3511 NE 196th St. 206-362-0719

Sedro Woolley Cascade Fabrics, 824 Metcalf St.
360-855-0323 See ad #51, page 572

Shelton Sue's Stitch in Time, 927 W. Railroad Ave.
360-427-6164 See ad #28, page 567

Silverdale Material Girls Quilt Shop, 10404 NW Silverdale Way 360-692-0286

Spokane Quilting Bee, Inc., 12117 E. Mission
509-928-6037 See ad #4, page 563

Spokane Sew E-Z, Too, 603 W. Garland
509-325-6644 See ad #5, page 563

Spokane The Cozy Quilt, 9413 N. Newport Hwy.
509-464-2425 See ad #6, page 563

Stanwood Cotton Pickins', 8718 270th St. NW
360-629-4771 See ad #46, page 571

Spokane The Log Cabin, 4922 E. Union 509-747-0315
Spokane This N' That, 9826 N. Andrew St. 509-467-9496
Spokane Valley Quilt cottage, 17 N. Bowdish Rd. 509-891-6624
Stanwood Granny's House, 9300 271st St. NW 360-629-3947
Tacoma Quality Sewing & Vacuum Centers, I-5 & S 38th St. 253-471-3899
Tacoma Trains & Fabrics, Etc., 1315 S. 23rd 253-779-0219
Tacoma Evergreen Quilting, 4106 South M St. 253-476-9800
Tacoma Parkland Parish Quilt Co., 12152 Pacific Ave. S 253-531-4309
Toppenish Hope Chest Crafts, 508 W. 2nd Ave. 509-865-5666

Vancouver Art and Sew'l, 2727 E. Evergreen
360-696-9215 See ad #21, page 566

Vancouver Primitive Thimble Quilt Shoppe, 1503 NE 78th St. Suite 1A 360-574-3949
Vashon Island Quilter, 17626 Vashon Hwy. SW 206-713-6000
Walla Walla Walla Walla Sew & Vac, 102 E. Main St. 509-529-7755
Waterville Yesteryear Quilting, 107 W. Locust 509-745-9306

Wenatchee The Attic Window Quilt Shoppe
1630 N. Wenatchee Ave. #8
509-888-2006 See ad #19, page 566

Westport The Quilter's Stash, 714 N. Montesano St.
3602687370 See ad #24, page 566

Woodinville Gathering Fabric Quilt Shop
14450 Woodinville Redmond Rd NE
425-402-9034 See ad #45, page 571

Yakima Bernina Sewing Center, 103 South 7th Ave.
509-248-0078 See ad #16, page 565

Yakima Stitch n' Quilt, 8405 Ahtanum Rd.
509-945-2560 See ad #15, page 564

Yakima Sunbonnet Sue, 1517 Summitview Ave.
509-452-4112 See ad #14, page 564

Yakima Fiddlesticks, 1601 Summitview 509-452-7718
Yakima Ann's Quilts and Things, 3504 Ahtanum Rd 509-965-2313
Yakima Viking Sewing Center, 2614 A Nobhill 509-966-3430

Yelm Gee Gee's Quilting Inc., 601 Yelm Ave. W
360-458-5616 See ad #31, page 568

Washington Quilt Shows

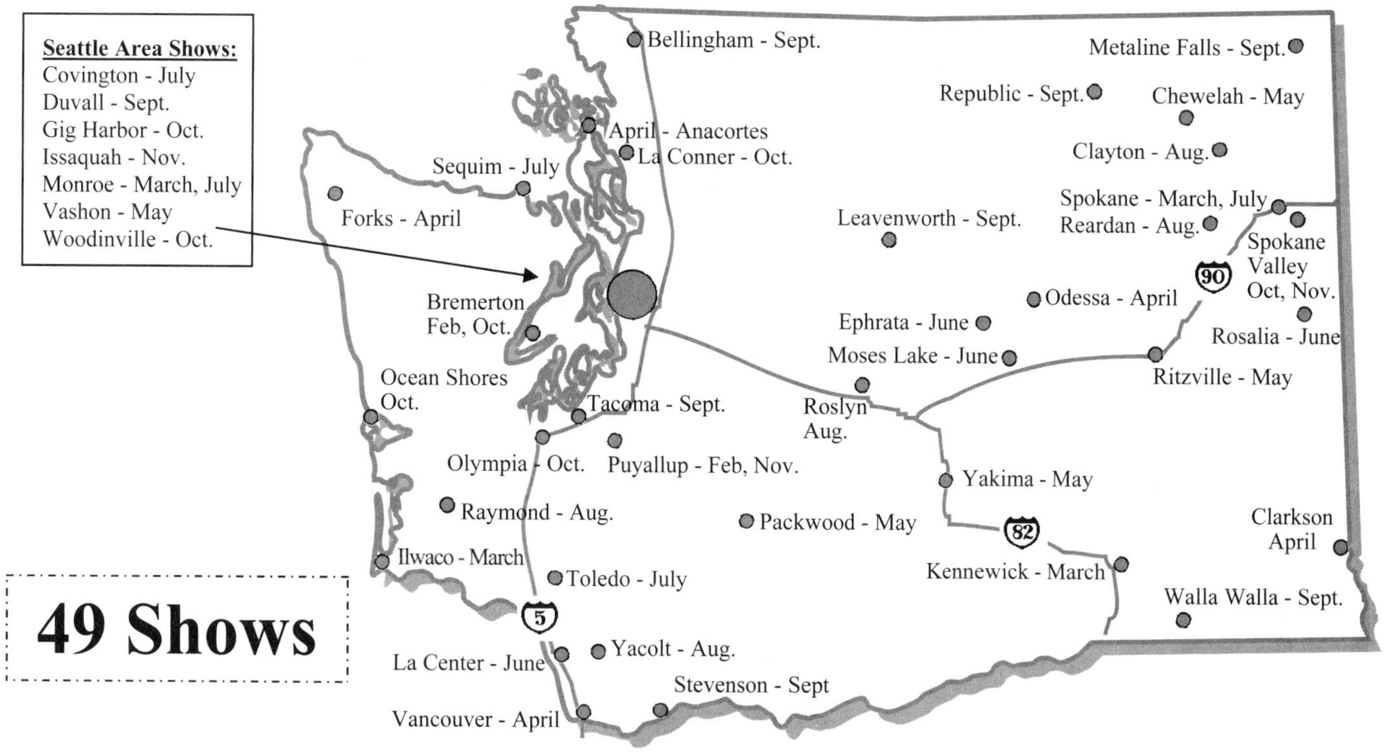

About Shows: We are listing only the very basic information about shows that happen on a regular schedule here. Please check out our website for more details on each show. Also this information tends to change quite often so please verify the event with our website or a local source before you venture far. Or if you're in the right area at the right time, give it a shot.

If you are a show organizer, please keep us updated on your event.
shows@quilterstravelcompanion.com www.quilterstravelcompanion.com

On our website you will also find:

- Exact dates (when we have them)
- Contact Information
- Events happening on a one-time basis
- Sponsor Information
- Description of Event

Month	City	Schedule	Show	Location with address
February				
	Bremerton	Annual, 3rd Fri & Sat in February	Kitsap Quilters Show	Kitsap County Fairgrounds, Presidents' Hall, 1200 NW Fairgrounds (Off Rt. 303)
	Puyallup	Annual, late February / early March	Sewing & Stitchery Expo	Best Western Park Plaza, 9620 S. Hill Park Pl. E
March				
	Kennewick	Annual, 4th weekend in March	Tri-City Quilters' Guild Show	Three River Convention Center, 7016 W. Grandridge Blvd.
	Ilwaco	Annual, 3rd weekend in March	Peninsula Quilt Guild Show	Ilwaco Heritage Museum, 115 SE Lake
	Monroe	Annual, 3rd weekend in March	Quilters Anonymous Show	Evergreen State Fairgrounds, 14405 179th Ave SE, Bldgs 400
	Spokane	Annual,2nd weekend in March	Waterford Quilt Show	Waterford on South Hill, 2929 W Waterford Dr
April				
	Anacortes	Annual, 1st weekend in April	Fidalgo Island Quilters Show	Anacortes Middle School, 2202 M Ave
	Anacortes	Annual, April	Fidalgo Island Quilt Walk	Various Shops
	Vancouver	Annual, 1st Thur. - Sat. April	Clark County Quilters Show	Vancouver Church of Christ, 9019 NE 86th St.
	Forks	Annual, 3rd weekend in April	Rainfest	Forks High School, Auxiliary Gym, 261 S. Spartan Ave.
	Clarkston	Annual, last weekend in April	Seaport Quilters' Guild Show	Clarkston High School, 401 Chestnut
	Odessa	Annual, Last Friday and Saturday in April	Odessa Quilt Club Show	Odessa High School Gym, 107 E 4th St

Washington Show Continued

May			
Packwood	Annual, 1st weekend in May	Packwood Quilt Show	Packwood Elementary Gym, 12990 U.S. Hwy. 12
Ritzville	Annual, 1st Saturday in May	Peace by Piece Quilt Guild Show	Ritzville Grade School Gym, 601 S. Chelan
Vashon	Odd Years, 1st weekend in May	Vashon Island Quilters	Camp Burton's Gresham Hall, 9326 SW Bayview Dr.
Yakima	Odd Years, May	Yakima Valley Quilters' Guild Show	Modern Living Building at State Fair Park, 1301 S. Fair
Chewelah	Annual, Last weekend in May	Chewelah Arts Guild Show	Chewelah Museum, 501 N 3rd St E
June			
Rosalia	Annual, 1st Saturday in June	Rosalia Battle Days Quilt Show	Rosalia Community Center, 614 S Whitman
Ephrata	Annual, 2nd weekend in June	Sun Country Quilt Festival	Ephrata High School Gym, 333 4th Ave NW
Moses Lake	Odd Years in June Basin	Piecemakers Quilt Guild Show	Moses Lake High School, 803 E. Sharon
La Center	Annual, 4th Saturday in June	La Center Annual Quilt Show	Evangelical Church Hall, 111 E 5th St
July			
Toledo	Annual, 2nd Sat. in July	Toledo Cheese Days Quilt Show	Toledo High School, 1200 St. Hwy. 505
Sequim	Annual, 3rd weekend of July	Sunbonnet Sue Quilt Club Show	Sequim Middle School, 301 W. Hendrickson Rd.
Spokane	Annual, 3rd Sat. in July	Kindred Spirits Outdoor Quilt Show	Downtown Spokane, 9th & Arthur
Covington	Annual, last weekend of July	Covington Quilters Guild Show	Cedar Heights Middle School, 19640 SE 272nd St. (Off Kent-Kangley Hwy 516)
Monroe	Annual, late July	Busy Bee Quilters Show	Monroe High School, 17001 Tester Rd.
August			
Clayton	Annual, 1st Sat in August	Clayton Fat Quarters Quilters Show	Clayton Grange, 4478 Railroad Ave.
Raymond	Annual, 1st weekend in August	Willapa Harbor Quilt Guild Show	Raymond Elementary School Gym, 9th & Commercial
Yacolt	Annual, 1st weekend in August	Quilt Festival	Pomeroy Living History Farm, 20902 NE Lucia Falls Rd.
Roslyn	Annual, last weekend in August	Crazy for Quilt Show	Crazy Quilt Shop & other businesses, 104 E. Pennsylvania Ave.
Reardan	Annual, last weekend of August	Outdoor Quilt Show & Folk Art Sale	The Buggy Barn, 28848 Tramm Rd. N
September			
Leavenworth	Annual, 1st Wed. - Sun in September	Leavenworth Quilt Show	Leavenworth Village, 1016 Commercial St.
Metaline Falls	Annual, 1st weekend of September	Forgotten Corners Quilt Guild Show	208 E. 5th Ave.
Republic	Annual, Labor Day weekend in September	Ferry County Quilt Exhibit	Ferry County Fairgrounds, Hwy. 20 (3 mi. NE of town)
Stevenson	Annual, 3rd weekend in September	Columbia River Gorge Quilt Show	Skamania Co. Fairgrounds, 720 SW Rock Creek Dr.
Tacoma	Annual, 3rd Wed - Sat. of September	Innovations	Tacoma Convention Center, 1500 Broadway
Walla Walla	Annual, 3rd weekend of Sept.	Walla Walla Valley Quilt Festival	SE Washington Fairgrounds, 360 Orchard St.
Bellingham	Even Years, 4th weekend in September	Quilted from the Heart of the Northwest	New Horizon Community Church, 4600 Guide Meridian
Duvall	Annual, last Sat. of September	Duvall Outdoor Show	Downtown Main St.
October			
La Conner	Annual, 1st weekend in October	LaConner Quilt Fest	Historic Gaches Mansion (Quilt Museum), 703 S. 2nd St.
Ocean Shores	Annual, 1st weekend of October	SeaPals Quilters of Ocean Shores	Ocean Shores Convention Center, 120 W. Chance A La Mer Ave.
Gig Harbor	Annual, 2nd weekend of October	Gig Harbor Quilt Festival	Chapel Hill Presbyterian Church, 7700 Skansie Avenue
Olympia	Odd Years, 2nd Fri & Sat in October	Washington Stars Quilt Guild	Thurston County Fairgrounds, 3054 Carpenter Rd. SE
Woodinville	Annual, 2nd weekend in October	Woodinville Harvest Festival Quilt Show	Stromson Manor HouseChateau
Bremerton	Annual, last weekend of October	West Sound Quilters	President's Hall, Kitsap County Fairgrounds, 1200 NW Fairgrounds Rd.
Spokane Valley	Annual, 3rd weekend in October	Washington State Quilters Show	Spokane County Fair & Expo, 404 N. Havana St.
November			
Issaquah	Annual, 1st weekend in November	Block Party Quilters Culb Show	Issaquah Community Center, 1st Ave. South & SE Bush
Spokane Valley	Annual, 1st Saturday in November	Spokane Valley Partners	East Valley High School, 15711 E. Wellesley
Puyallup	Annual, 3rd weekend in November	Quilt, Craft & Sewing Festivals	Western WA Fairgrounds, 110 9th Ave. SW

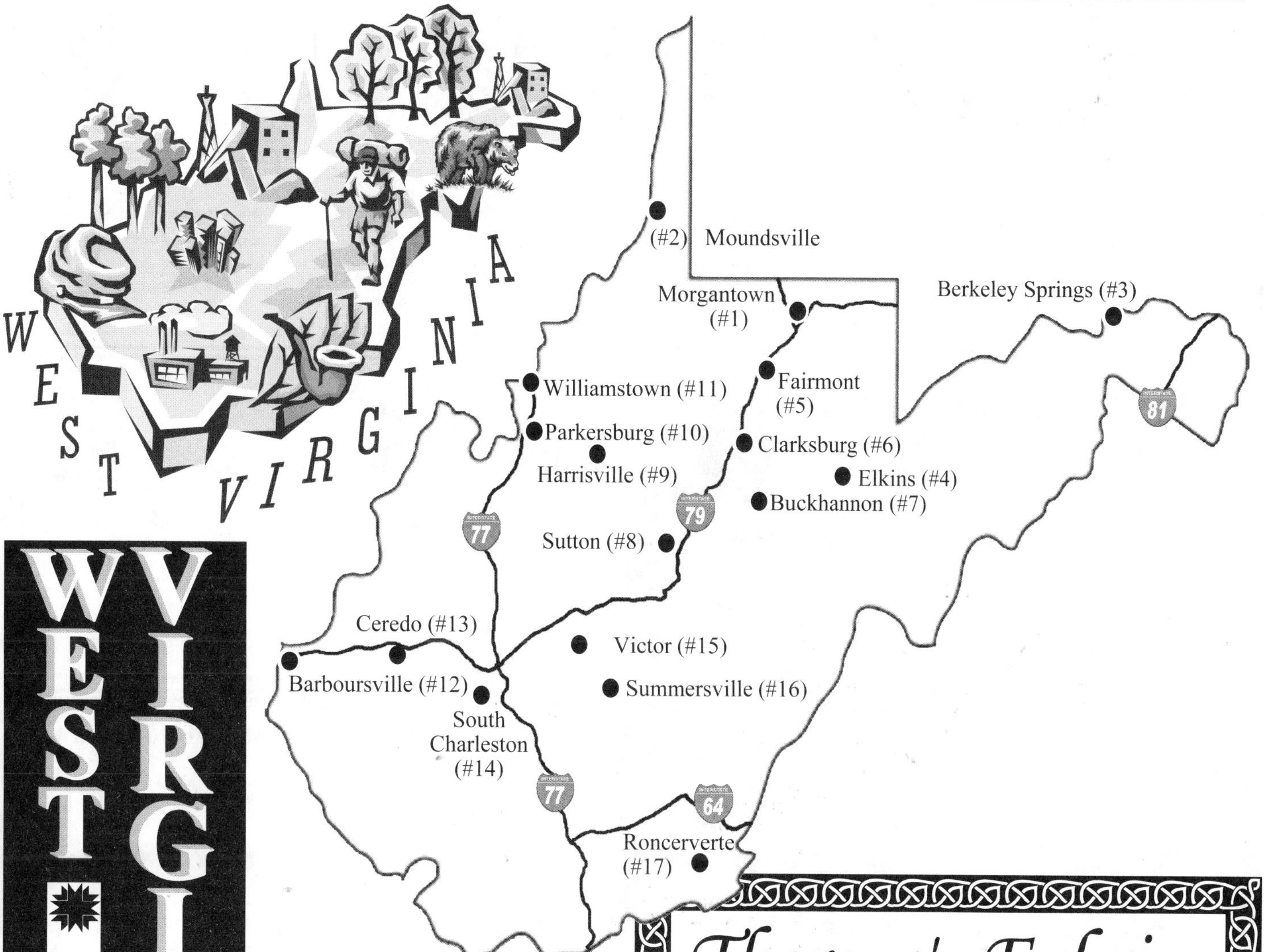

WEST VIRGINIA

17 Featured Shops

Morgantown, WV #1

Mon - Fri 10 - 6
Sat 10 - 5

The Sew Inn, Ltd.

120 High St. 26505
(304) 296-6802
thesewinn@msn.com
Owner: Virginia Showers Est: 1973
2500 sq.ft. over 3000 Bolts

Wonderful collection of quilting cottons, books, notions & classes. Knowledgeable & Friendly service. Authorized Viking Dealer. Participant in "Mountain Quilt Quest"

Easy Access from I - 79 or I - 68. Located downtown across from The Hotel Morgan.

Theresa's Fabrics

Located in historic Moundsville.
We carry over 5000 bolts of fabrics, books, notions, everything for quilting.

264 Jefferson Ave., Moundsville, WV 26041
(304) 845-4330
theresa@theresasfabrics.comcastbiz.net
Owner: Theresa M. Gouldsberry
Est: 1986 5500 sq.ft. 5000+ Bolts

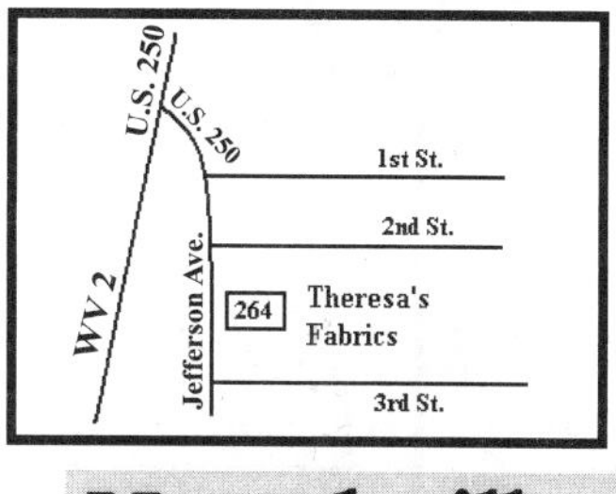

Mon - Fri 10 - 4:30
Sat 10 - 2

Moundsville, WV #2

Berkeley Springs, WV #3

By Appt. Only

ACORNS & OAKS
...QUILTS AND MORE

P.O. Box 1017 25411 (304) 702-3202
acornsandoaks@verizon.net Est: 2005
www.acornsandoaks.com
We've closed our shop and gone on the road to shows and quilt guilds. We come to you bringing kits, notions, fat quarters, yard cuts and classes. We also present trunk shows for groups or guilds.

Elkins, WV #4

Mon - Sat 9 - 5 Fri til 7

Elkins Sewing Center

300 Davis Ave. 26241
(304) 636-9480
Fax: (304) 636-9486
Owners: Sue & Jim Pifer sueesc@aol.com
www.elkinssewingcenter.com

Serving Quilters and Needlecrafters since 1982
Quilting Fabrics, Supplies and Classes
Cross Stitch, Punchneedle and Needlefelting

Husqvarna Viking Sewing Machines

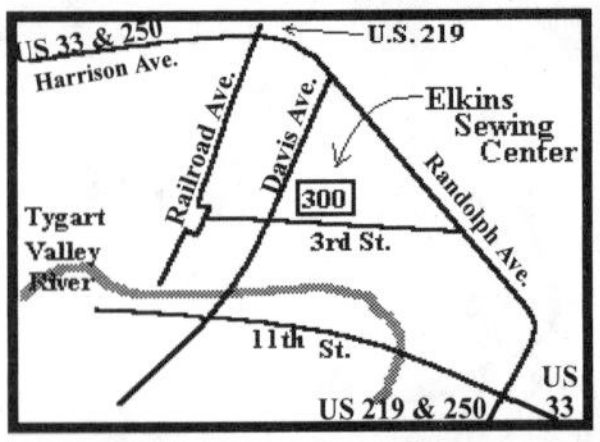

Sew Chic

I - 79 Exit 139

348 Meadowdale Rd. Fairmont, WV 26554
(877) 366-4135 or (304) 366-4135
Owner: Sue Henderson Est: 1996
Participant in Mountain Quilt Quest Shop Hop

- Over 2500 bolts of designer cottons
- Complete line of quilting supplies, books, patterns, and notions
- Huge thread assortment
- Machine Embroidery
- Year round classes
- Mail orders welcome
- Free newsletter online or by request
- Friendly, Knowledgeable Staff

BERNINA

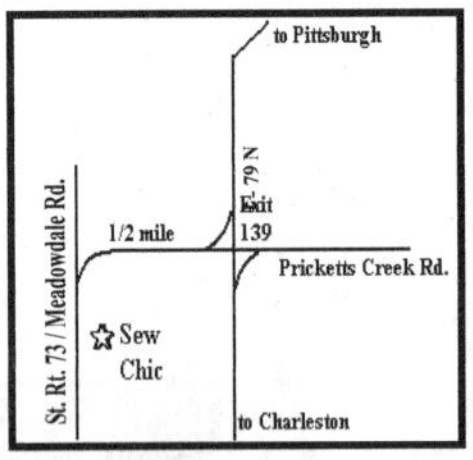

Fairmont, WV #5

Mon - Fri 10 - 6 Sat 10 - 2

www.sewchic.com

Clarksburg, WV #6

Tues 9 - 9 Wed - Fri 9 - 5 Sun 9 - 3

Classic Quilt Shop

1704 W. Pike St. 26301
(304) 326-6969
classicquiltshop.wvdsl.net
www.classicquiltshop.com

Friendly service, Easy-to-Find.
We love Thimbleberries, Kansas Troubles, Civil War Repros, black & whites, and feedsack prints.

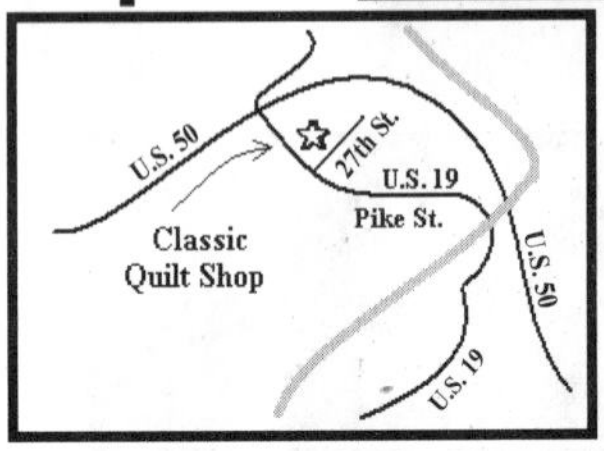

Mon-Fri 10-5, Sat 10-4

The Stitching House
and Sew Much More, LLC

- Longarm Machine Quilting Services Available (Custom and Edge to Edge designs)
- Quality fabrics, notions, books, patterns, batting, backings, kits, classes and Sew Much More!
- Member of Mountain Quilt Quest and Mystery Harvest Shop Hops
- Antique machines on display, Gammill Showroom, free parking behind shop, friendly front porch seating...Come visit us.

www.theStitchingHouse.com

29 S. Kanwha St. 26201
304-472-8188
Owners: Linda & Beth Childers
Est: 2007
Online Newsletter
info@theStitchingHouse.com

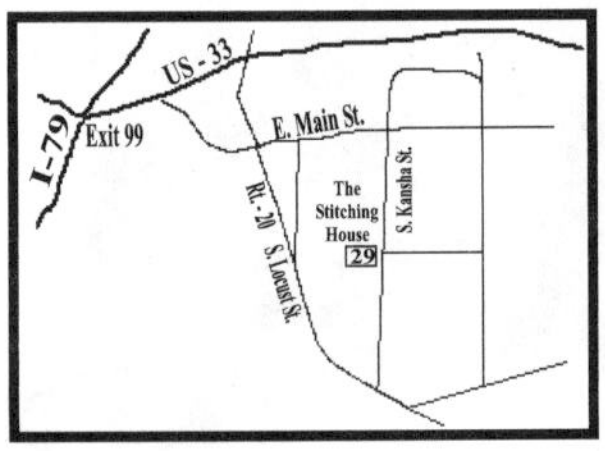

Buckhannon, WV #7

Sutton, WV #8

Tues - Fri 9 - 5 Sat 9 - 12

The Needle Basket

208 Main St. 26601
(304) 765-7505
Owner: Rita Sniffin
Est: 2007 1000 Bolts

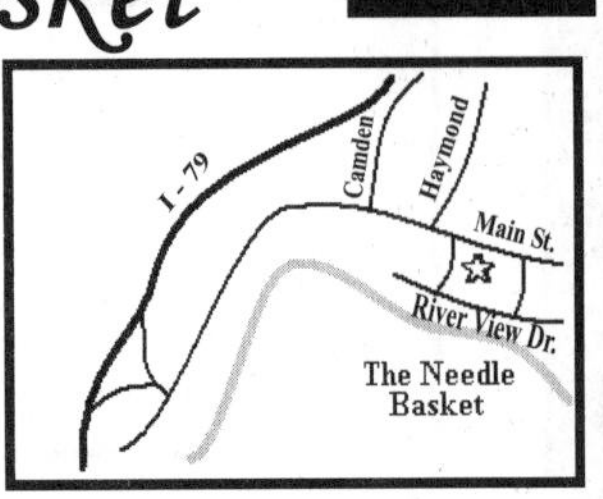

We are a full line quilt and sewing shop with everything you need for your latest project. We have quilting classes and also offer sewing machine repairs.

Harrisville, WV #9

Tues - Sat 10 - 4

Pieces of the Past Quilt Shop

Rt. 1, Box 61C3 26362
(304) 643-2077
Owner: Kathy Lanham
momcpo@aol.com
A small shop with a big personality, settled in a quaint country setting. Quilting and crafting supplies and classes, candles, gifts and more. Located between Ellenboro and Harrisville, 15 min. to North Bend State Park.

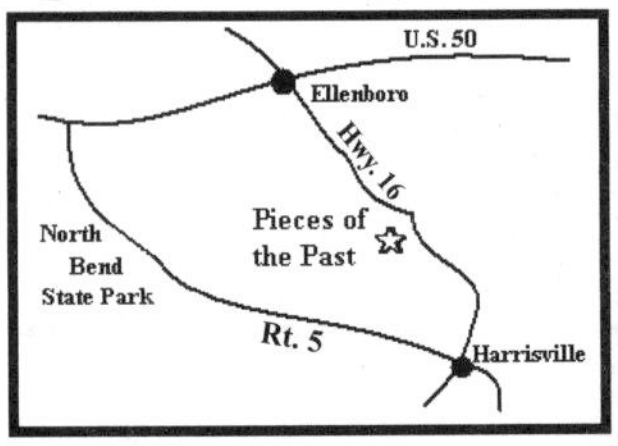

Parkersburg, WV #10

Mon - Sat 10 - 5

Parkersburg Sewing & Quilting

1809 Dupont Rd. #3 26102
look for 1050 Division St.
(304) 428-4933
Est: 2006 2000 sq.ft. 2000 Bolts
Newsletter on website
www.sewwithsheryl.com
Full service quilt shop. We sell Singer & HQ Avanté. Machine quilting available. AccuCut Go and dies.

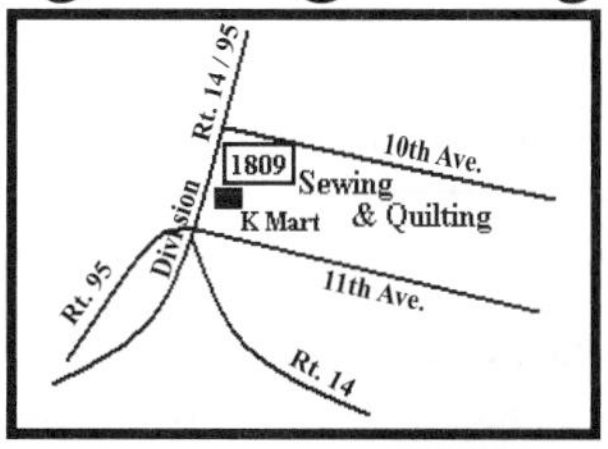

Barboursville, WV #12

Mon - Fri 10 - 5 Sat 10 - 3

WV QUILT

642 Main St. #101 25504
(304) 302-5400
6000 sq.ft. 3000+ bolts
www.wvquilt.com
Fabric by the Pound

Chenille Sew Easy

Located in the quaint, historic downtown Barboursville WV. Come see our quilts and bolts of fabric on display. Buses Welcome. Easy off I-64, exit 18, 1/2 mile

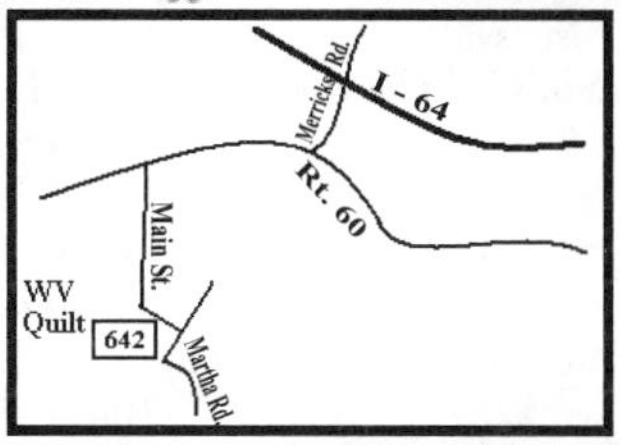

Ceredo, WV #13

Mon & Wed 10 - 5 Tues & Thur 10 - 8 Fri 10 - 6 Sat 10 - 3

Rt. 60 & 4th Sts. P.O. Box 549 25507
(304) 453-5650
sewmanyblessings@zoominternet.net
Est: 2006 1500+ bolts
Free Newsletter

SEW MANY BLESSINGS

Full service quilt shop carrying the latest from Moda, RJR, Benartex, Maywood, P&B, etc. Large selection of patterns and notions.
www.sewmanyblessingswv.com

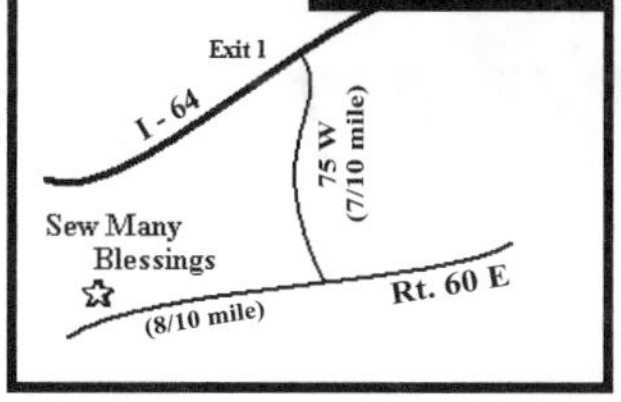

The Woolen Willow

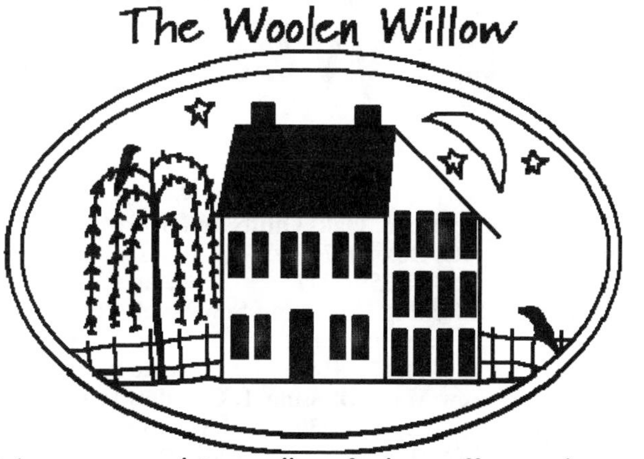

We are a complete needlecraft shop, offering almost 2000 bolts of quilt fabric, beautiful fine yarns and a comprehensive selection of rug hooking kits and supplies. Classes and demonstrations.
Tour groups welcome.

Better Homes and Gardens Quilt Sampler FEATURED SHOP

www.woolenwillow.com
Catalog $5

Mon - Sat 10 - 5

901 Highland Ave.
26187
(304) 375-WOOL (9665)
Owners: Gretchen Streeter & Jenifer Gaston
woolenwillow@aol.com
Est: 2004 3000 sq. ft.

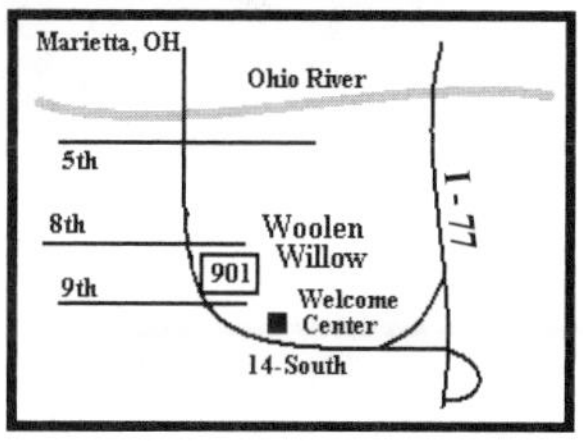

Williamstown, WV #11

South Charleston, WV #14

Mon - Sat 9:30 - 5:30 Mon & Thur til 9

Textile Mills

5303 MacCorkle Ave. SW 25309
(304) 768-6661 Fax: (304) 768-3686
Est: 1955 6000 sq.ft. 20,000 bolts
Owner: Lynda Happe
textilemills@verizon.net
Your complete fabric store.

Quilting, drapery, upholstery fabrics
Fat Quarters. Celebrating 55 years.

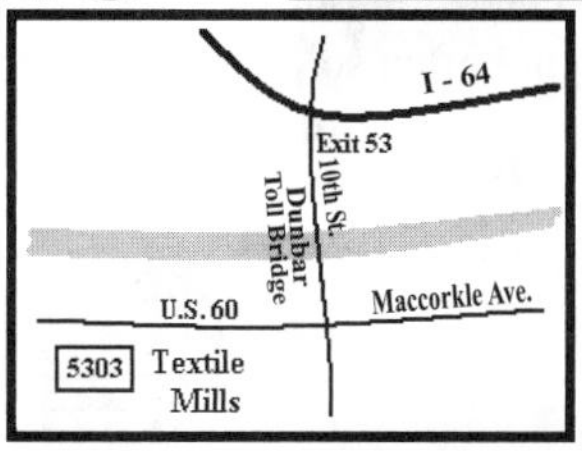

Victor, WV #15

Mon, Wed, Thur, Fri 10 - 5 Tues & Sat 10 - 4

QUILTS & MORE

23746 Midland Trail 25938
(304) 658-3606 Owner: Debra Davis
wvquilter1@aol.com

Quality Fabrics From Top Designers and Manufacturers. Books, Patterns, Notions, Threads. Custom Quilts, New and Collectible Quilts. Custom Pre-Cut Quilts
Antiques and Collectible Consignment Shop
Home of Emma & Estella's Pattern Company

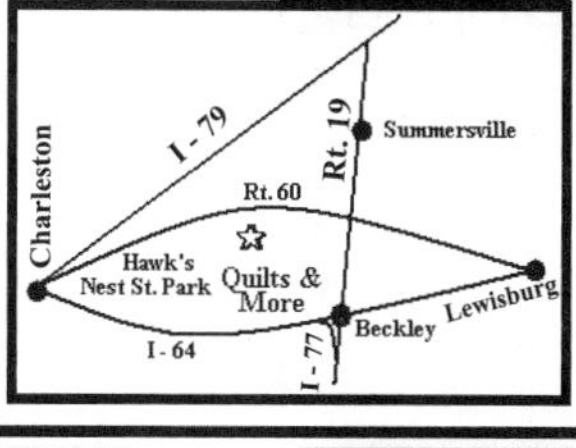

Summersville, WV #16

Tues - Fri 10 - 5 Sat 10 - 3:30

The Quilt Shoppe INC.

508 Main St. #A 26651
(304) 872-0959
Owner: Vickie Fleer
Est: 2002 1600 sq.ft. 3000+ bolts
wvquiltshoppe2@verizon.net
Cozy small shop in the mountains with a great variety of quilters "needful things" just minutes from Rt. 19 in downtown Summersville.

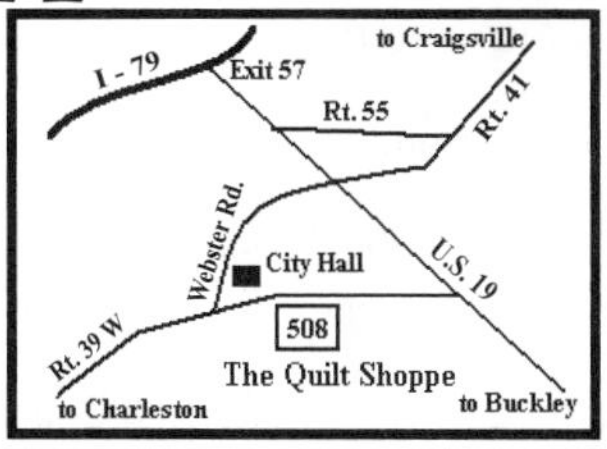

Ronceverte, WV #17

Mon-Thurs 10 - 6 Fri 10 - 5 Sat 9 - 2

Nancy's Fabrics

In Loving Memory

218 W. Edgar Ave. 24970
(3040) 645-0010 Est: 2007
2000 sq.ft. 800+ bolts
www.nancysfabrics.com

We carry high-quality cotton quilting fabrics from Moda, Timeless Treasures, Benartex and other quality fabric manufacturers.

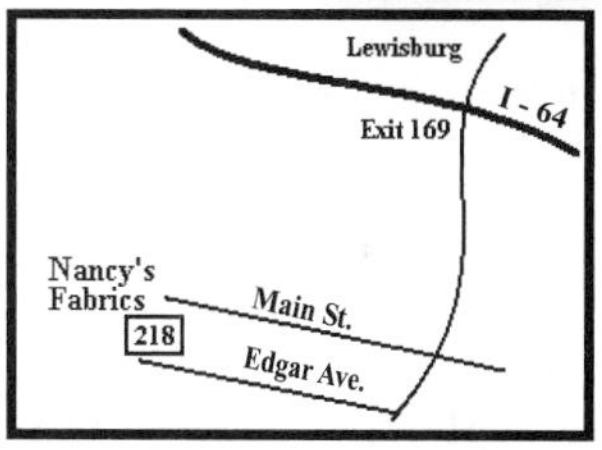

West Virginia Quilt Shops

Barboursville — **WV Quilt, 642 Main St. #101** — **304-302-5400** — **See ad #12, page 579**

Beckley — Speckled Hen, LLC, 501 S. Eisenhower Dr. — 304-253-4367

Berkeley Springs — **Acorns & Oaks Quilts and More, P.O. Box 1017** — **304-258-2277** — **See ad #3, page 578**

Buckhannon — **Stitching House and Sew Much More, 29 S. Kanawha St.** — **304-472-8188** — **See ad #7, page 578**

Ceredo — **Sew Many Blessings1, Ceredo Plz. #7** — **304-453-5650** — **See ad #13, page 579**

Charles Town — Gatehouse Quilting, 4490 Sumit Point Rd. — 304-728-0809

Clarksburg — **Classic Quilt Studio, 1704 W. Pike St.** — **304-326-6969** — **See ad #6, page 578**

Danville — Town Square Fabrics, 28 Town Square — 304-369-6269

Elkins — **Elkins Sewing Center, 300 Davis Ave.** — **304-636-9480** — **See ad #4, page 578**

Fairmont — **Sew Chic LLC, 348 Meadowdale Rd.** — **304-366-4135** — **See ad #5, page 578 & 204**

Harrisville — **Pieces of the Past Quilt Shop, Rt. 1 Box 61, C3** — **304-643-2077** — **See ad #9, page 578**

Hinton — Heart's Content Quilts, 309 Temple St. — 304-923-1622

Hurricane — Quilts by Phyllis, 2943 Putnam Ave. — 304-562-7404

Kingwood — Creative Stitches, 106 E. Main St. — 304-329-8280

Marlinton — Hudson's Variety, 213 Main St. — 304-799-4996

Morgantown — **The Sew Inn, Ltd., 120 High St.** — **304-296-6802** — **See ad #1, page 577**

Moundsville — **Theresa's Fabrics, 264 Jefferson Ave.** — **304-845-4330** — **See ad #2, page 577**

Parkersburg — **Parkersburg Sewing & Quilting, 1809 Dupont Rd. Ste 3** — **304-428-4933** — **See ad #10, page 579**

Point Pleasant — Seams To Be Fabric Shop, 2413 Jackson — 304-674-0328

Rainelle — Marie's Fabric & Crafts, 705 Main St. — 304-438-5500

Reedsville — Eleanor's Quilts & Fabric Shop, Rt. 7 E., Kanes Creek — 304-864-6330

Roncerverte — **Nancy's Fabrics, 218 W Edgar Ave.** — **304-645-0010** — **See ad #17, page 579**

Sistersville — Quintilla's Fabrics, 946 Allen Run Rd. — 304-758-2890

So. Charleston — **Textile Mills Cloth Shop, 5303 MacCorkle Ave., SW** — **304-768-6661** — **See ad #14, page 579**

Summersville — **The Quilt Shoppe, LLC, 508 Main St. #A** — **304-872-0959** — **See ad #16, page 579**

Sutton — **The Needle Basket, 208 Main St.** — **304-765-7505** — **See ad #8, page 578**

Victor — **Quilts & More, 23746 Midland Trail** — **304-658-3606** — **See ad #15, page 579**

Williamstown — **The Woolen Willow, 901 Highland Ave.** — **304-375-9665** — **See ad #11, page 579**

Winfield — Fern's Quilt Shoppe, 6130 St. Rt. 34 — 304-757-3047

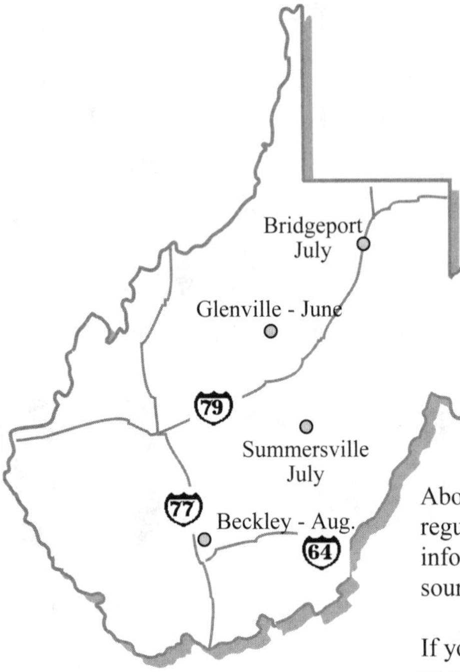

5 Shows

West Virginia Quilt Shows

About Shows: We are listing only the very basic information about shows that happen on a regular schedule here. Please check out our website for more details on each show. Also this information tends to change quite often so please verify the event with our website or a local source before you venture far. Or if you're in the right area at the right time, give it a shot.

If you are a show organizer, please keep us updated on your event.
shows@quilterstravelcompanion.com
www.quilterstravelcompanion.com

Month	City	Schedule	Show	Location with address
May				
	Berkeley Springs	Annual, Weekends only early May to early June	Delectable Mountains Quilt Guild Show	Morgan Arts Council Ice House, Corner of Independence & Mercer St.
June				
	Glenville	Annual, 3rd weekend of June	Patchwork Gathering Quilt Shop	Trinity Methodist Church, 112 E. Main St.
July				
	Summersville	Even Years, 3rd weekend in July	West Virginia State Guild Quilt Show	Summersville Arena & Conference Center, 3 Armory Way
	Bridgeport	Annual, 2nd Fri & Sat in July	Millennium Quilters' Guild Quilt Show	Bridgeport High School, 531 Johnson Ave.
August				
	Beckley	Annual, last weekend of August	Appalachian Treasures	Raleigh County Armory, 200 Armory Dr.

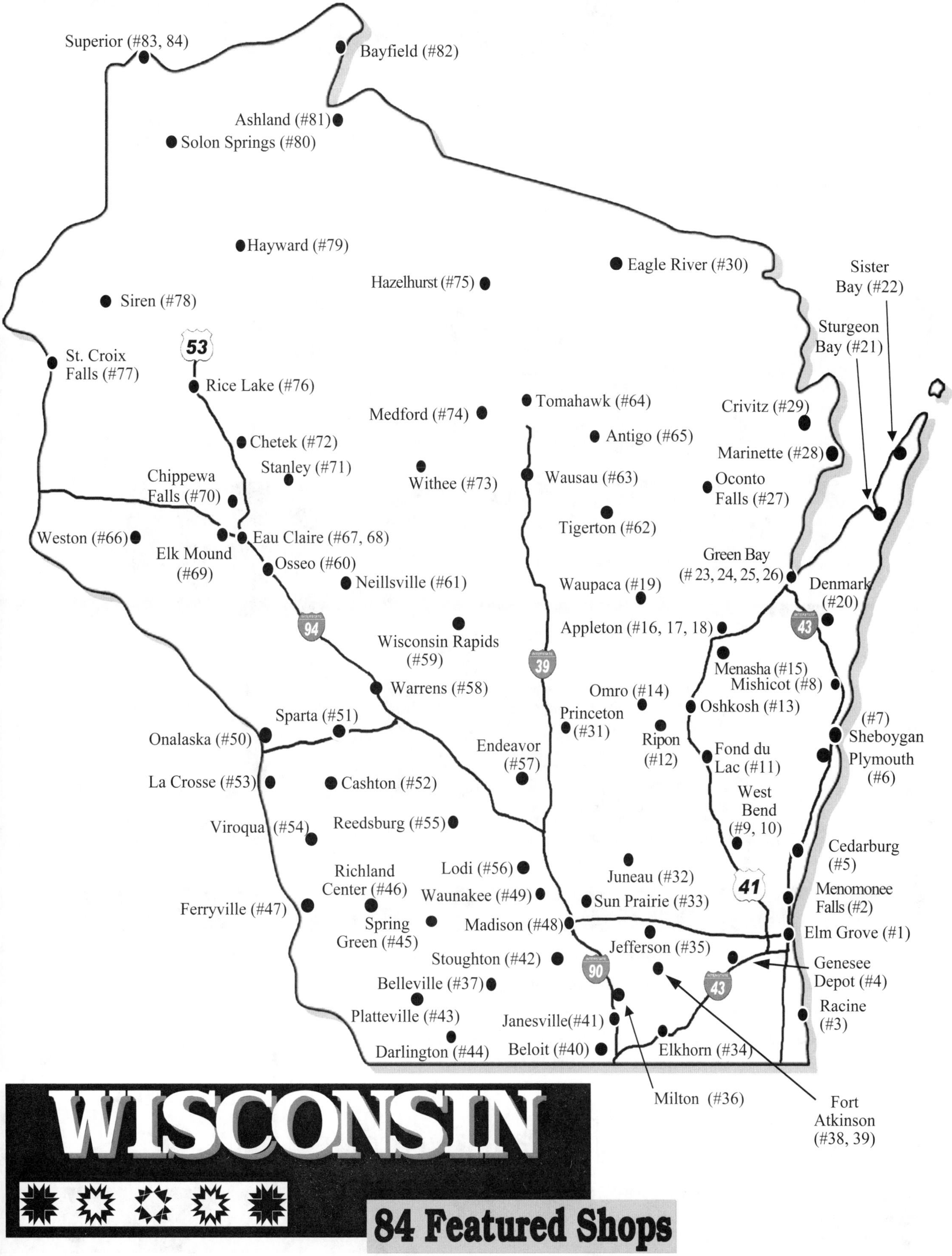
Superior (#83, 84)
Bayfield (#82)
Ashland (#81)
Solon Springs (#80)
Hayward (#79)
Eagle River (#30)
Hazelhurst (#75)
Siren (#78)
Sister Bay (#22)
Sturgeon Bay (#21)
53
St. Croix Falls (#77)
Rice Lake (#76)
Tomahawk (#64)
Medford (#74)
Crivitz (#29)
Chetek (#72)
Antigo (#65)
Marinette (#28)
Stanley (#71)
Chippewa Falls (#70)
Withee (#73)
Wausau (#63)
Oconto Falls (#27)
Weston (#66)
Eau Claire (#67, 68)
Tigerton (#62)
Elk Mound (#69)
Osseo (#60)
Green Bay (# 23, 24, 25, 26)
Neillsville (#61)
Waupaca (#19)
Denmark (#20)
94
Appleton (#16, 17, 18)
43
Wisconsin Rapids (#59)
39
Menasha (#15)
Mishicot (#8)
Warrens (#58)
Omro (#14)
Oshkosh (#13)
Sparta (#51)
Princeton (#31)
(#7) Sheboygan
Onalaska (#50)
Ripon (#12)
Endeavor (#57)
Fond du Lac (#11)
Plymouth (#6)
La Crosse (#53)
Cashton (#52)
West Bend (#9, 10)
Viroqua (#54)
Reedsburg (#55)
Cedarburg (#5)
Richland Center (#46)
Lodi (#56)
Juneau (#32)
41
Menomonee Falls (#2)
Waunakee (#49)
Sun Prairie (#33)
Ferryville (#47)
Spring Green (#45)
Madison (#48)
Elm Grove (#1)
Jefferson (#35)
Stoughton (#42)
Genesee Depot (#4)
90
Belleville (#37)
43
Racine (#3)
Platteville (#43)
Janesville(#41)
Darlington (#44)
Beloit (#40)
Elkhorn (#34)
Milton (#36)
Fort Atkinson (#38, 39)

WISCONSIN

84 Featured Shops

Elm Grove, WI #1
PATCHED WORKS
YOUR QUILT SHOP DESTINATION IN SOUTHEASTERN WISCONSIN
OVER
eight thousand bolts
in stock and on display, every single day!
BOOKS · THREADS · NOTIONS · MACHINE QUILTING SERVICES & MORE!
13330 Watertown Plank Road • Elm Grove, WI 53122
Phone: 262.786.1523 • Fax: 262.786.1562 • Email: julie@patchedworks.com
MON & TUE 10am - 5pm • WED 10am - 8pm • THU & FRI 10am - 5pm
SAT 10 am - 5 pm • SUN 12 pm - 4 pm
JOIN A CLUB
BATIK CLUB
Strip Club
30's CLUB
Moda U
BUSES WELCOME!
NORTH AVE
PATCHED WORKS
MAYFAIR
WATERTOWN PLANK ROAD
I-45
BLUEMOUND ROAD
ELM GROVE RD.
I-94
ESTABLISHED 1978 · WWW.PATCHEDWORKS.COM

The Quilted Basket

N88 W16599 Main St., Menomonee Falls, WI 53051
(262) 251-8791
Owners: Ann & Tom Wanke
www.thequiltedbasket.com

Menomonee Falls, WI #2

The shop offers an extensive selection (over 6,000) of bolts of beautiful quilting fabric along with hand dyed wools, wool felts, and chenille.
In stock are over 800 book and pattern titles.
Check out our garment sewing fabric also.

<u>May-Labor Day Summer Hours</u>
Mon, Wed, Fri 9 - 5
Tues & Thurs 9 - 8
Sat 9 - 3 Sun - Closed
<u>Winter Hours</u>
Mon, Wed, Fri 9 - 5
Tues & Thur 9 - 8
Sat 9 - 4 Sun 11 - 4

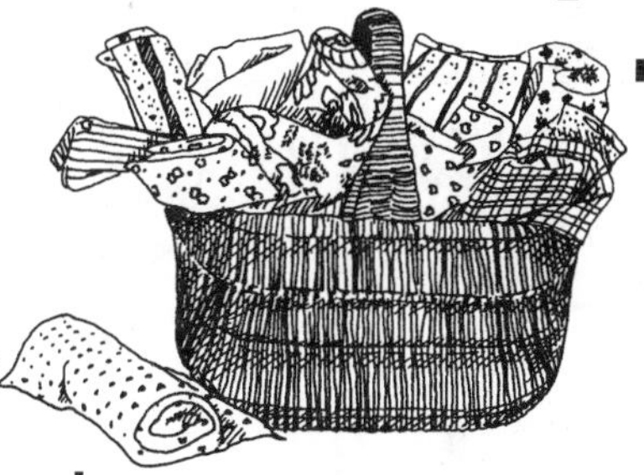

Fabrics featured include reproductions, batiks and the largest selection of Christmas fabrics.
Check out our complete Thimbleberries Department.

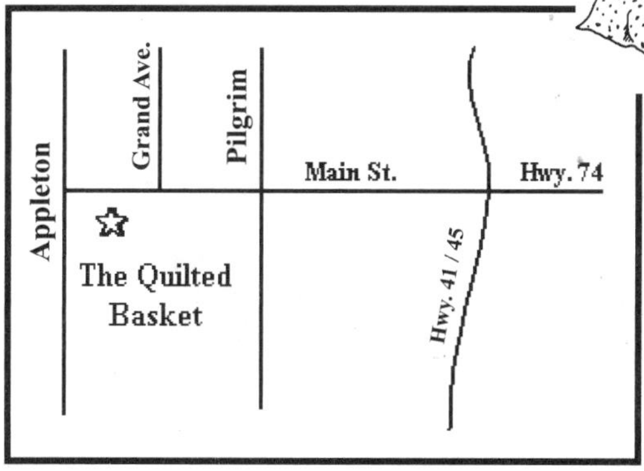

Authorized Husqvarna Viking Sewing Machine Dealer.

Husqvarna VIKING

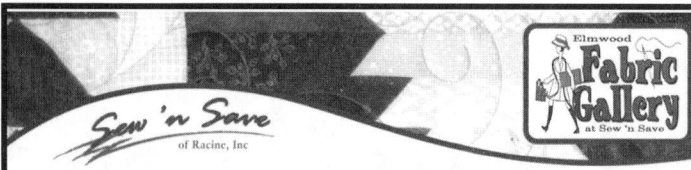

Elmwood Fabric Gallery at Sew 'n Save

Sew 'n Save of Racine, Inc

- Quality Cottons—from Moda, Benartex, Northcott, Andover and many more.
- Specializing in batiks from Hoffman, Island Batik and more
- Check out our Thimbleberries Club and Fabric
- Samples to motivate and inspire
- Quilting supplies, patterns, & books
- Machine Embroidery supplies and patterns
- Classes, Clubs & Workshops
- 6000 sq. ft.
- Over 3000 bolts premium fabrics

STORE HOURS:
MON, WED & FRI
10 - 8
TUES & THURS
10 - 6
LATER ON CLASS NIGHTS
SAT 9:30 - 3
CLOSED SUN

ELMWOOD PLAZA
3701 Durand Ave.
Racine, WI 53405
262-554-8708

www.sewnsaveofracine.com

WIDE ASSORTMENT OF SEWING, EMBROIDERY, QUILTING MACHINES AND SERGERS.

Husqvarna VIKING elna

CUSTOM HAND-MADE CUTTING TABLES & QUILTING/SEWING FURNITURE.

LARGE SELECTION OF QUILTING CLASSES.

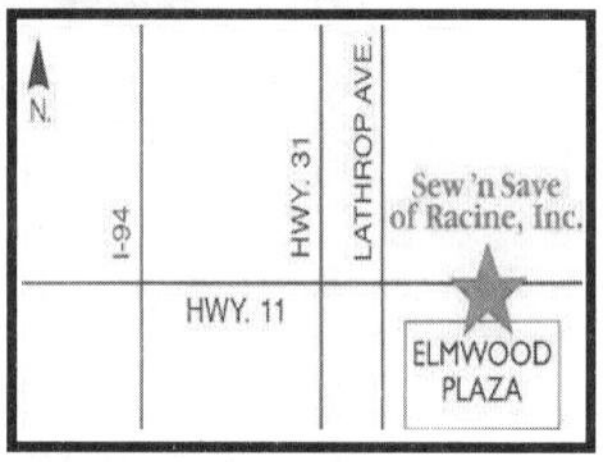

Racine, WI #3

Genesee Depot, WI #4

Mon - Fri 9:30 - 6
Tues til 8
Sat 9:30 - 4

Pamella's Place

S 42 W 31230 St. Rd. 83 53127
(262) 968-3821
Owner: Pamella Gray
Est: 1987 3200 sq.ft. 2500 Bolts
sewing@wi.twcbc.com
www.pamellasplace.com

Bernina sewing machines.
Inspiring Quilting & Fashion fabrics.
Creating Sewing Excitement!

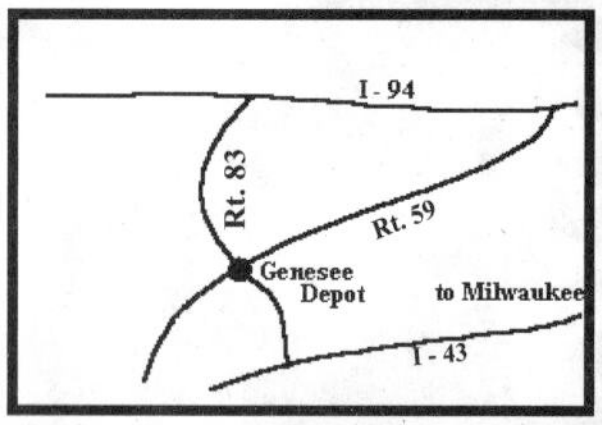

Cedarburg, WI #5

Wed 10 - 8
Thurs 10 - 5
Fri & Sat 10 - 4

Ye Olde Schoolhouse

318 Green Bay Rd. 53012
(262) 377-2770

Quilts, Reproduction and Homespun Fabric, Rughooking, Hand Dyed Wool Redware and Primitive Folkart. See our website for a tour of the shop: www.yeoldeschoolhouse.com

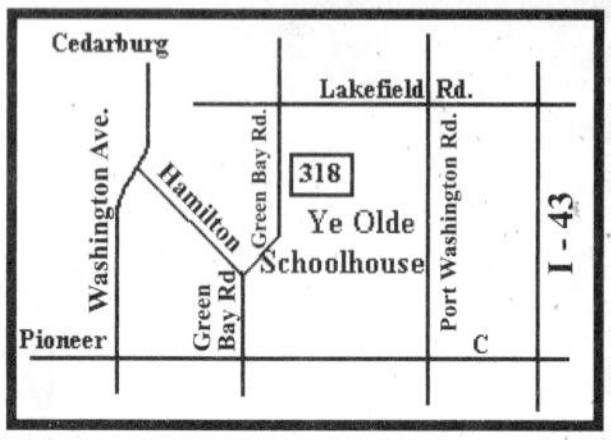

Sewing Basket

426 E Mill St. Plymouth, WI 53073

3 hours from Chicago
What a Deal Purse Cards
www.sewingbasket.biz
1 hour from Milwaukee
1 hour from Green Bay
quilt @sewingbasket.biz
Accuquilt GO! Dealer
2 hours from Madison

HOURS
Mon & Fri
9-5
Tue, Wed, Thur
9-6
Saturday
9-4

PHONE
920-892-4751

QFL QUILTING FOOTBALL LEAGUE

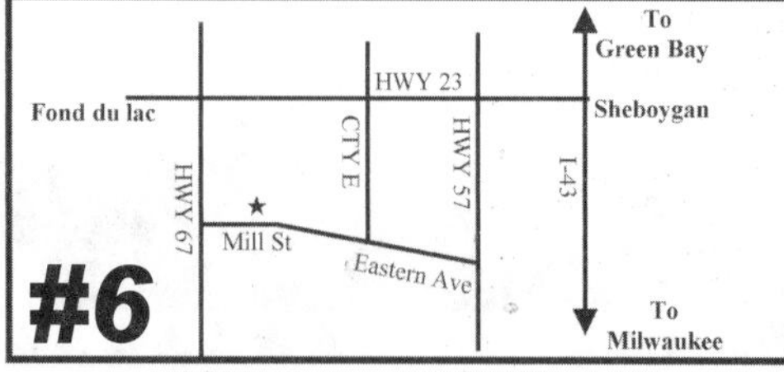

#6

A Big Shop With Small Town Hospitality

Sheboygan, WI #7

Mon - Fri 10 - 6
Thur 10 - 8
Sat 10 - 3

my sister's QUILT SHOPPE

1224 Weeden Creek Rd. #15 53081
(920) 457-4787

in the Sunnyside Mall
Est: 2008 2700 sq.ft. 2300 Bolts
sisters@msqsonline.com Free Newsletter
www.msqsonline.com
Everything to satisfy quilters needs.
Patterns, books, kits, notions and fabric.
Visit our shoppe or shop online.
Long-Arm quilting services and rental.

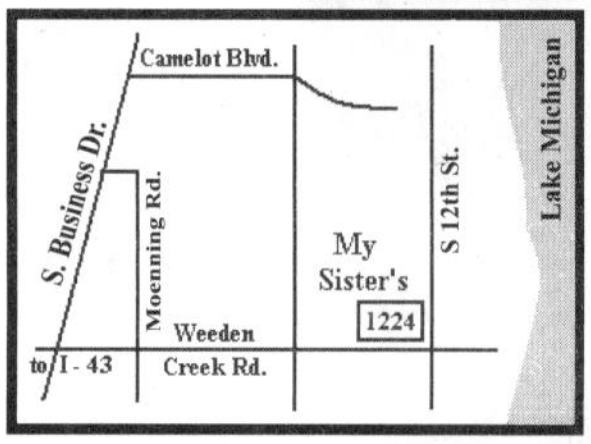

Mishicot, WI #8

Mon 11 - 3
Tues - Fri 10 - 5
Sat 10 - 4

Lisa's PhotoQuilting & More...

316 E. Main St.
P.O. Box 136 54228
(920) 755-4217
1600+ Bolts
Online Newsletter
lisa@lisasphotoquilting.com
We specialize in doing your photo transfers. Our shop offers a kids room, northwoods, flannels, gifts & More.
Retreats in March and November.

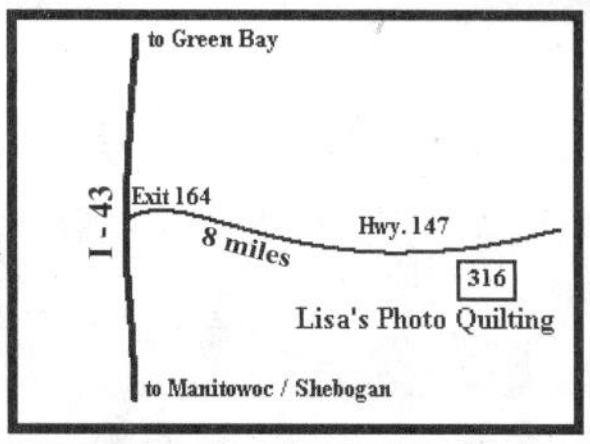

Material matters Quilt Shop & Training Center

We carry a huge selection of longarm and machine quilting supplies.
Longarm quilting machines available for rent.
Longarm Quilting Training and Demonstrations.
Large selection of Books and Classes
We carry a wide variety of Batiks , Basics, Backings and Batting.
Stop in to try a wide variety of machines and frames.

Just North of Milwaukee off Hwy 45 or I43.
www.material-matters.com
1-800-443-5800

Open most days, hours by appointment
Call for hours and location.

West Bend, WI #9

Royce Quilting

BERNINA Sewing Center

West Bend, WI #10

840 S. Main 53095
(262) 338-0597

Mon - Tues 9:30 - 8
Wed, Thur, Fri 9:30 - 5
Sat 9:30 - 4

roycequilting@sbcglobal.net
Owner: Jerry Quasius
Est: 1971 3000 sq.ft.

Specializing in Moda,
30's Prints and
Reproduction Fabrics.
3000+ Bolts.
Books, Soft Patterns,
Quilting Classes.

Authorized Bernina Sales &
Service for the last 37 years.

Willett Sew

23 N. Main St. 54935
920-929-9690

- Fabrics & Notions
- Patterns & Books
- Hand Dyed Wools
- Bernina Sewing Machines

BERNINA

Fond du Lac, WI #11

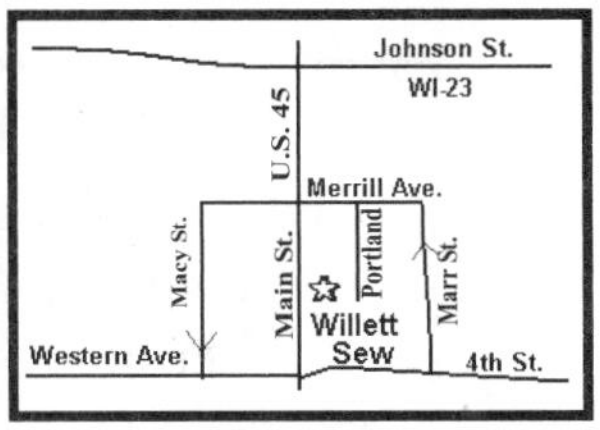

Mon - Fri 10 - 5
Sat 10 - 2

Owner: Robyn Willett
Est: 2006 1500 sq.ft.
Online Newsletter
willettsew@sbcglobal.net

Ripon, WI #12

Mon - Fri 8 - 5
Winter Mon - Fri 8 - 4
Always Sats 9 - 3

Goosebearys Village Quilter

3 Harris St. 54971
(920) 748-1233
Owner: Jan Horn

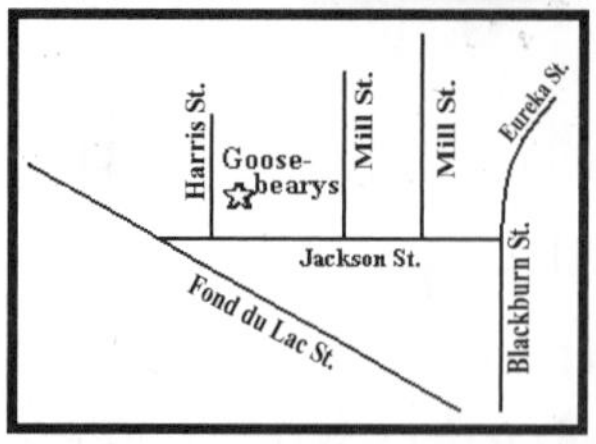

goosebeary@centurytel.net
www.goosebearys.com

* Civil War and Reproduction Fabrics
* Kits & samples or choose your own fabric
* Cozy Atmosphere

Oshkosh, WI #13

Mon - Fri 10 - 6
Sat 9 - 4
Sun 11 - 2

Quilt Essentials

1928 S. Washburn St. 54904
(920) 230-3680
quilt@quiltessentials.biz
www.QuiltEssentials.biz
Located near the intersection of 20th & Washburn St. next to Renee Michelle's Salon.

The Friendliest Quilt Shop in the Fox Valley

Omro, WI #14

Mon - Fri 10 - 4
Sat 10 - 3

YDS

5530 St. Rd. 116 54963
(920) 582-7196
Owner: Mary K. Yaroch
Est: 1976 1500 sq.ft. 2500+ Bolts

"Biggest, little quilt shop in Winnebago County"

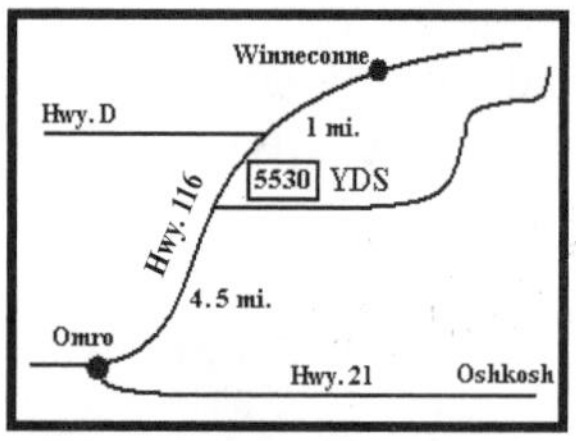

#15

PRIMITIVE GATHERINGS QUILT SHOP

"A 2006 Top Ten Quilt Shop"

Owners: Nick and Lisa Bongean
Established: 2004

850 Racine Street
Menasha, WI 54952
www.primitivegatherings.us
primitivegatheringsquiltshop@yahoo.com
(920)722-7233

A new quilt shop with an old fashion look, featuring the area's largest selection of reproduction fabrics, homespuns, and hand-dyed wool. Also a large selection of wool and fabric kits as well as many blocks of the month!

Shop Hours:

Monday-Wednesday	9:30-5:00
Thursday	9:30-8:00
Friday	9:30-5:00
Saturday	9:30-4:00

Easy to Find....

Piece By Piece

1350 W. College Ave.
Appleton, WI 54914
(920) 749-1957
Piecebypiece@earthlink.net
www.piecebypiecellc.com

An inviting unique shop located ½ mile west of historic downtown and 2 miles east of the Fox River Mall. ***Come in and see our new expanded store and classroom.***

Visit our shop and view the 200 samples that are sure to inspire anyone.
Kits are available for most samples.

We feature a large selection of quality fabrics for the quilter including florals, many kid's prints, 200 batiks, flannels, seasonal prints, Marbles, Crystals, Fairy Frost.

Blocks of the Month, Classes, Books, Patterns.

Hours: Monday and Thursday 10-8
Tuesday, Wednesday, Friday 10 - 5
Saturday 10-4

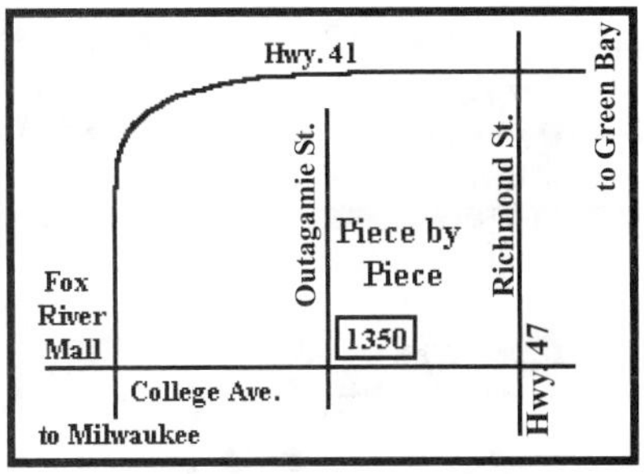

Appleton, WI #16

Appleton, WI #17

Mon - Fri 9:30 - 5:30
Thurs til 7:30
Sat 9:30 - 3

Keep Me In Stitches

3402 N. Richmond St. #B
54911
(920) 734-0852

Owner:
Jacqi Levy
Est: 2010
1550 sq.ft.

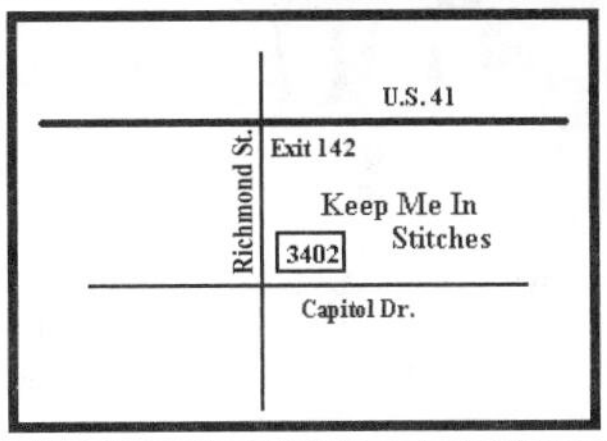

Quilt shop and creative sewing center.
Large selection of Batiks.

Sew 'n Sew

2 Great Shops!

Mon - Fri 9 - 5
Sat 10 - 4

Quilting Fabric • Patterns Books • Notions.
Heirloom supplies • Classes Year Round
Premier Dealer for Husqvarna Viking Sewing Machines

Appleton, WI #18

1881 N. Silverspring Dr. 54915
920-830-9372
Fax: 920-830-9379
Est: 2000 2500 sq.ft. 1500 Bolts

112 S. Main 54981
715-256-1071
Fax: 715-256-1198
Est: 1997 2100 sq.ft. 2000 Bolts

Waupaca, WI #19

Owners: Bonita & Samuel Welsch sewnsew@gglbbs.com

Husqvarna VIKING

Denmark, WI #20

Mon - Fri 10 - 6
Sat 10 - 3

Kindred Spirits Quilt Shop

"Where creative souls gather"
148 E. Main St. 54208
(920) 863-8855
www.KindredSpiritsQuiltShop.net
(Just 10 min. South of Green Bay on I-43!)

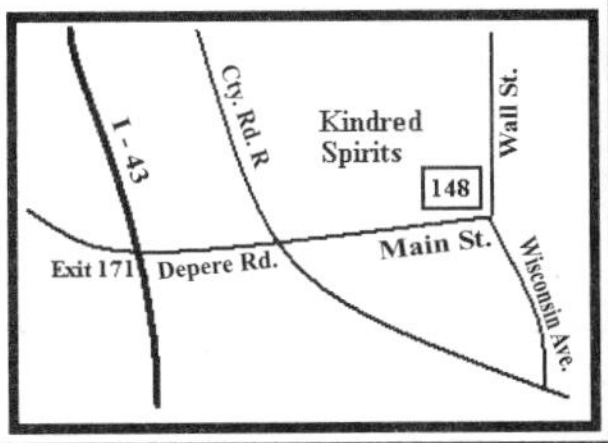

Barn Door Quilt Shop

154 N. Third Ave. 54235
(920) 746-1544
Est: 2004 2200 sq. ft.
3000 Bolts Free Newsletter

Mon - Sat 9 - 5 Sun 10 - 3

Full Service Quilt Shop. Extensive collection of reproduction fabrics, batiks, and other top quality cottons and wool. Classes. Special Orders. Scissor and Rotary Blade sharpening.

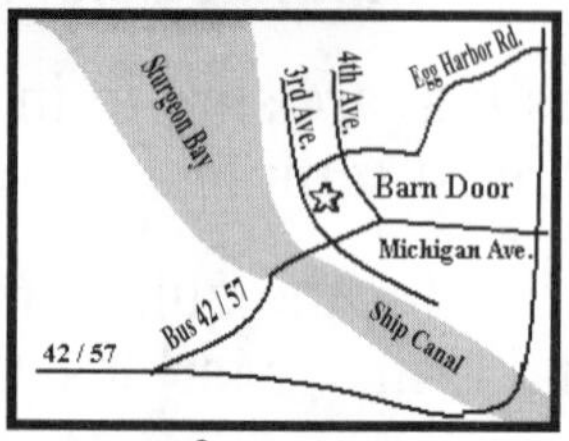

www.barndoorquilts.com

Sturgeon Bay, WI #21

QUILTER'S QUEST

10590 Country Walk Dr., #3, Sister Bay, WI 54234
(920) 854-1824 • Toll Free (866) 854-1824
quiltersquest@charterinternet.net
www.doorcountyquilts.com
IN BEAUTIFUL NORTHERN DOOR COUNTY

Sister Bay, WI #22

Over 3000 bolts
Specialty Notions,
Books, Patterns
Needlework Supplies
Warm, Friendly Service

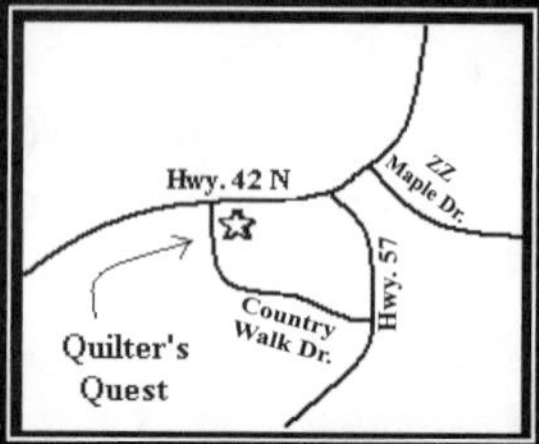

Special Hours on Request, just call
(920) 854-6538
No Obligation to Purchase

Linda Batley, Owner

May - Oct Daily 10 - 5 Nov - April Thurs - Sat 10 - 5

A Truly Unique Shopping Experience!

Green Bay, WI #23

Quilter's Connection

2269 True Ln. 54304
(920) 497-8787
Owner: Pam Zeratsky
6000 sq.ft. 10,000+ Bolts
www.quiltersconnection.net

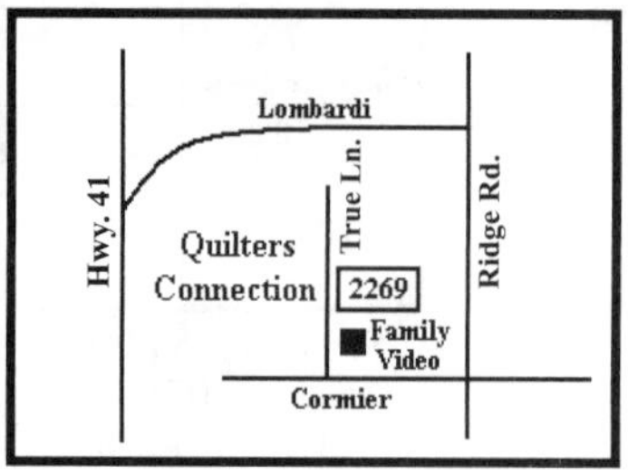

Mon & Fri 10 - 6
Tues, Wed, Thur
10 - 5
Sat 10 - 3

Located west of the Ridge Rd. & Cormier intersection next to Family Video

We are a full service quilt shop featuring:
Fabrics - Notions - Hand dyed wool
Specializing in Civil War
and Kaffe Fassett.
Our friendly staff is waiting to help you.

Green Bay, WI #24

Mon - Fri
9:30 - 5:30
Sat 9:30 - 3

MY FAVORITE QUILT SHOP

1550 Dousman St. 54303
(920) 965-2085 or (866) 437-5906
Fax: (920) 965-7224 Est: 2002
Owner: Jana Anderson-Laes 2000 Bolts
jana@favoritequiltshop.com
www.favoritequiltshop.com

We will easily become your favorite quilt shop. Books, patterns, & kits. Fabric lines: Kaffe Fassett, infant & juvenile, floral, batiks, outdoor and flannels. Wide backing fabrics, Batting by the yard. Friendly.

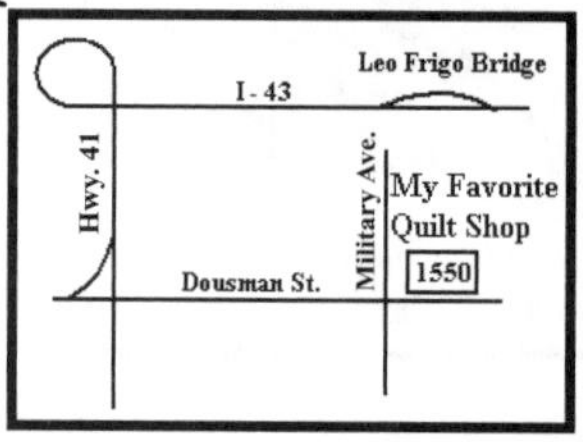

Green Bay, WI #25

Please Call for Appointment

Cordy's Quilting

3093 Westpoint Rd. 54313
(920) 494-3491
Owner: Cordy Wescott
Est: 2005
imcordy@aol.com

Custom quilting.
No panagraphs or computer stitching.

Call for Directions

Silver Thimble

Quilt and Gift Shoppe

Est: 1990

2475 University Ave. University Courtyard 54302
(800) 469-1495 or (920) 468-1495
www.silverthimblequilts.com silverthimble@tds.net
Owners: Nanette Guzzonato & Elaine Corson

- Over 3000 bolts 100% cotton fabric
- Books - Patterns - Notions
- Kona Bay Orientals, Moda, RJR, etc.
- Help with color/fabric selection
- Thimbleberries fabric, books & patterns at reduced prices
- Classes
- Finished quilts & quilt tops for sale
- Hand-dyed Wool
- Large Selection of Batiks (including Hoffman, Moda, Island Batiks)
- Wheelchair Accessible

Mon & Thur
9:30 - 8
Tues & Wed
9:30 - 5
Fri 9:30 - 4
Closed Sat
Sun 11 - 4

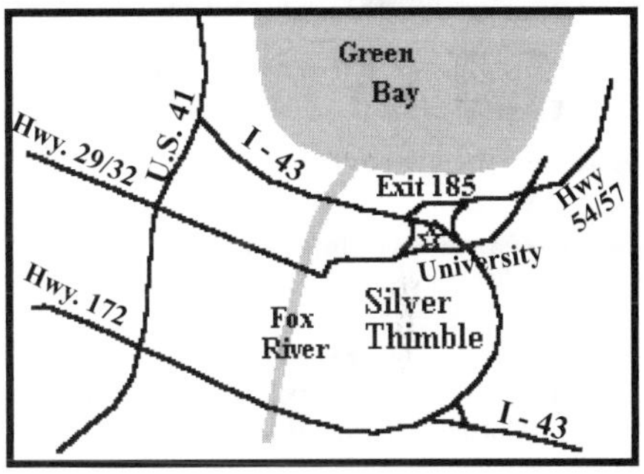

Take I - 43, exit 185, to Green Bay
Turn left at first stoplight.
Go one block & left into parking lot

Green Bay, WI #26

Oconto Falls, WI #27

The Quilter's Escape

Mon - Fri
10 - 6
Thur til 8
Sat 10 - 4

323 E. Highland Dr., P.O. Box 98 54154
(920) 846-8222
Owner: Tammy Walters
Est: 2007 1200 sq.ft. 1200 bolts
quiltersescape@centurytel.net
Get inspired with the latest and greatest fabrics, kits, patterns, books, classes, and block of the month.
Long Arm quilting service available.

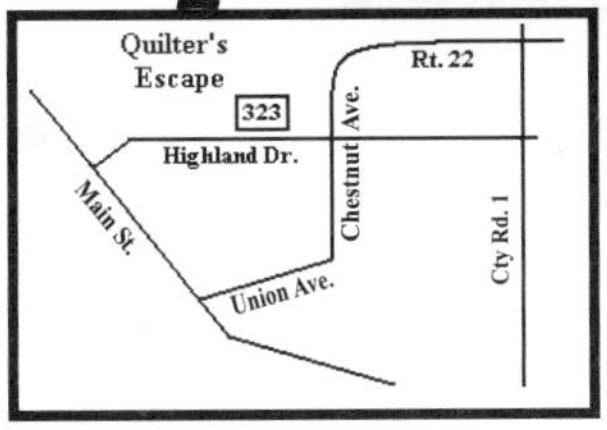

Marinette, WI #28

Pine St. Quilts

Mon - Fri
9 - 5
Sat 9 - 3

801 Marinette Ave. 54143
(715) 735-9806
Owner: Cyndie Halfmann
Est: 2002 1500+ bolts

Friendly small town Quilt Shop.
Janome and Tin Lizzie Dealer
Just 50 miles north of Green Bay.

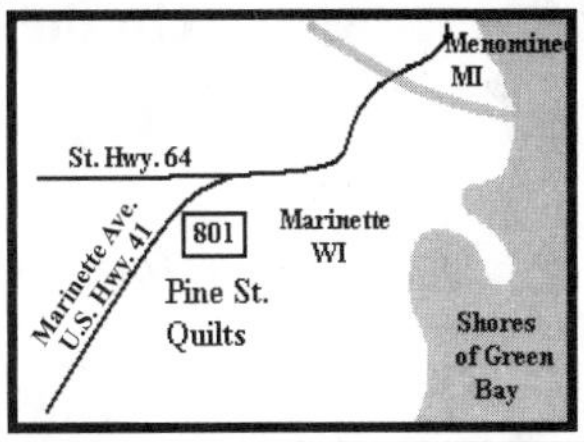

Crivitz, WI #29

Sew Much More

Mon - Fri
9 - 5
Sat 9 - 4
Sun 10 - 4

709 Dyer St. 54114
(715) 854-2621
Owners: Vicki Markert & Jane Belschner

Quilting Fabrics, Notions, Classes, Patterns.
Authorized Elna Dealer QFL Member
Located in Dyer Business Park
www.sewmuchmoreincrivitz.com

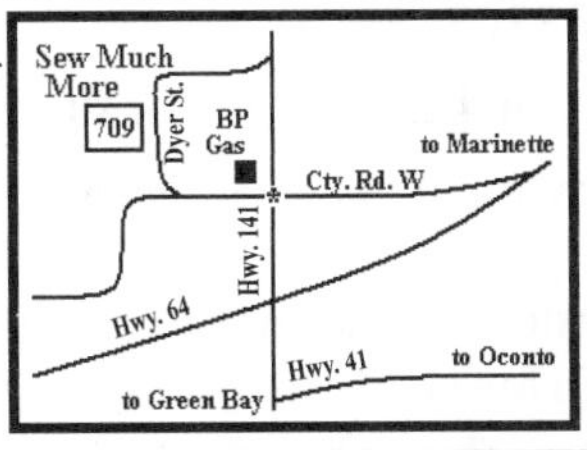

Eagle River, WI #30

Karen's Quilt Corner

Mon - Fri
9 - 5:30
Sat 9 - 5
Sun 11 - 3 from Memorial Day to Labor Day

330 W. Pine St. 54521
(715) 477-2603
Owner: Karen Kuphal

karensqc@verizon.net Est: 2003 2400 sq.ft.
www.kquiltcorner.com 3000+ bolts
Always met with a smile, Classes - Beginner to Advanced, Batiks, flannels, 30's, Thimbleberries, Northwoods and many more.
Large selection of thread & notions.
Bernina & Babylock dealer.

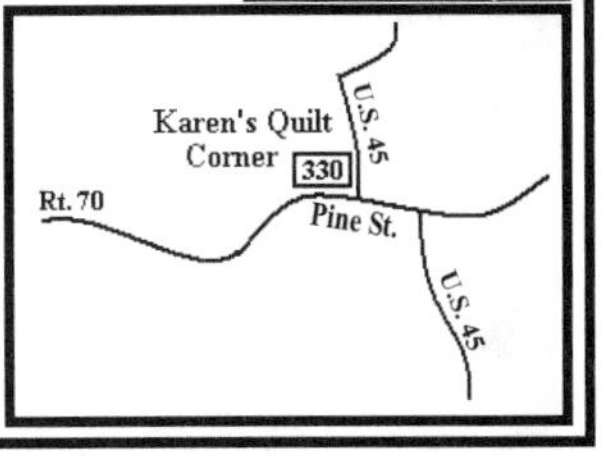

Princeton, WI #31

Tues - Fri 9 - 4
Sat 9 - 3

Quilts & Quilting

607 W. Main St. (920) 295-6506
P.O. Box 362 54968 Est: 1971
Owners: Sandy & Ron Mason
Machine Quilting & Kit Brochure SASE
quilteacher@verizon.net

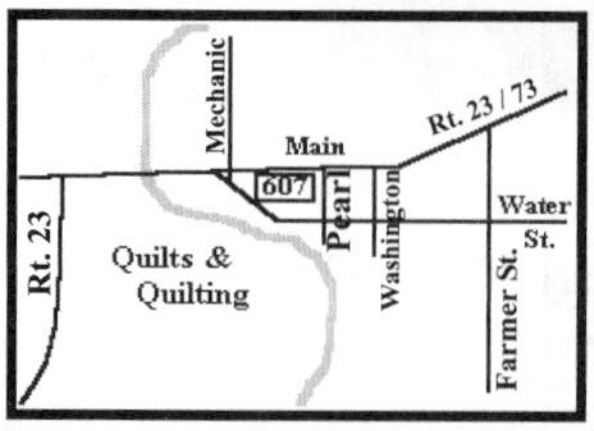

Custom Machine Quilting Since 1971. Fabric, and Notions. Antique calico feed sacks. Die-Cut Quilt Top Kits—pillows to king size.

Juneau, WI #32

Tues - Fri 10 - 6
Sat 10 - 5

J & A Stitches

N3914 Welsh Rd. 53039
(920) 696-3827
jastitches@wildblue.net
www.twosistersandaquilt.com

* 2000+ Bolts of Cotton Fabric
* 100+ Books and Patterns
* Many Kaffe Fassett Prints, Landscapes, 30's, Batiks, Novelty Prints, Brights and much more to choose from.

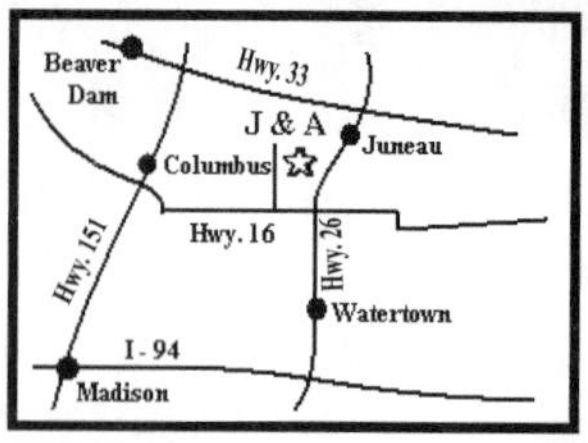

Sun Prairie, WI #33

Mon - Fri 9:30 - 5:30
Sat 10 - 5

J.J. STITCHES

221 E. Main St. 53590
(608) 837-2266
www.jjstitches.com
Est: 1975 5000 Bolts

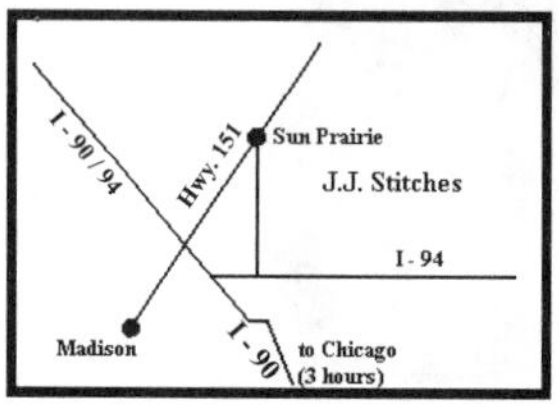

Featured shop in Quilt Sampler 2002. Store features homespuns, tickings, and vintage replica fabrics.

Elkhorn, WI #34

Mon - Fri 10 - 5
Sat 10 - 4

Sawdust & Stitches LLC

13 S. Wisconsin St. 53121
(262) 723-1213 Fax: Same
www.sawdustandstitches.net
Owner: Sharon Lauderdale Est: 1996

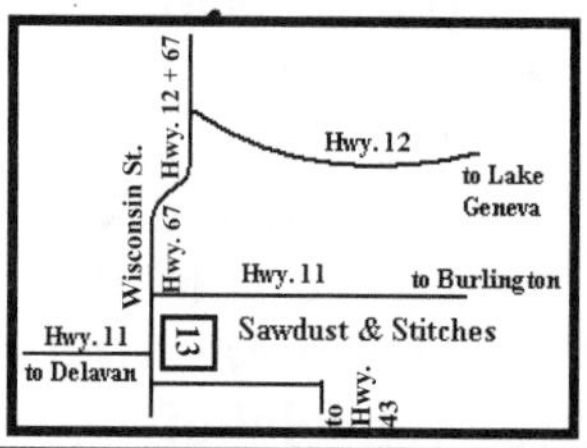

100% cotton prints & solids for Quilting needs. Patterns, Books, & Stitchery. Quilting Classes

"Home of Courageous Fabric"

Tea and Textiles Quilt Shop, LLC

107 S Main Street Jefferson, WI 53549-1631
On the SW corner of Hwy 26 & Hwy 18
920-674-9017

Bring in your Travel Companion for your *Free Fat Quarter*

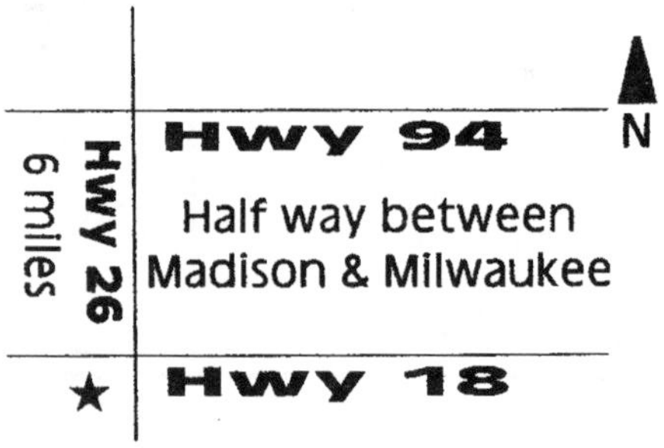

Join us for a Complimentary Cup of Tea

Jefferson, WI #35

Tues-Wed	10:00 AM - 7:00 PM
Thur	3:00 PM - 7:00 PM
Fri-Sat	9:00 AM - 5:00 PM
Sun	10:00 AM - 5:00 PM

100% Cotton Fabrics
90" - 116" wide Quilt Backings

Books - Patterns - Notions - Classes - Software - Gift Certificates

Jefferson Patchworkers Guild Meetings 6:30 pm 4th Tuesday of the Month. All Welcome.

Annual Fat Quarter Frenzy Show and Tell - 3rd Sunday - 1:00 PM

Free Use of Flannel Board for Design Play and Tables for Layering and Pinning Quilts
Linus Quilt Drop-Off Site

Milton, WI #36

8005 N. Hwy. 26 53563
(608) 868-7912
lthreads@hotmail.com
"Samples Are Us"

HOURS
Mon 10 - 2
Tues - Fri 10 - 5
Sat 10 - 4
Sun 12 - 4

Southern Wisconsin's Largest Quilt Shop

Loose Threads
FULL SERVICE QUILT & YARN SHOP
MILTON, WISCONSIN

Our building is rich in history. Built in 1852 as a one room schoolhouse, the building has seen two expansions and now houses over 4000 bolts of 100% cotton. Enjoy our bright room, homespun room, baby room, and of course the largest selection of flannel fabrics for miles around.
Our knowledgeable, friendly staff is always willing to assist with all your quilting and knitting needs. Guaranteed to be an "inspirational experience"!

www.loosethreadsllc.com

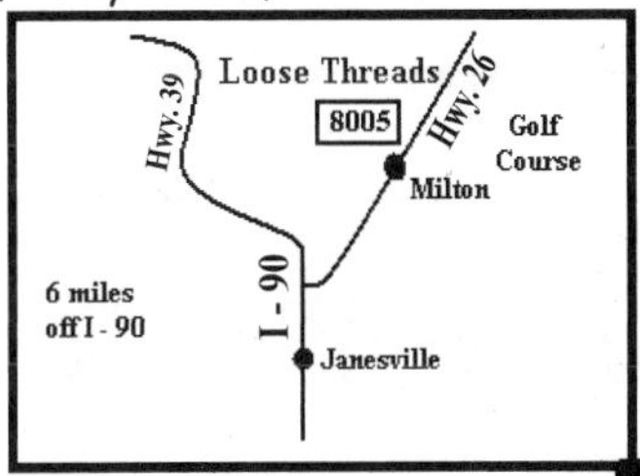

Patches and Petals

A Quilter's General Store

A cozy and inviting shop located in a historical building. We have something for everyone. We have a unique blend of quilting fabrics, kits, antiques and collectibles. Home of Sweet Pea Designs.

13 W. Main St
Belleville, WI 53508
Phone (608) 424-1516
Fax (608_ 424-1730
www.patchesandpetals.com
patches_1@verizon.net

Hours:
Tuesday - Friday: 10 -6
Saturday: 9 - 4 p.m.
Sunday: Noon - 4 p.m.
Closed Mondays

We are located 20 minutes from Madison on Hwy 69-92.

Belleville, WI #37

Fort Atkinson, WI #38

Tues - Thur 11 - 5
Fri 10 - 4
Sat 9 - 4

The Quilt Patch LLC

W 3352 Lower Hebron Rd. 53538
(262) 593-8462
www.thequiltpatchstore.com
Owners: Wayne & Jane Strunk
Est: 2003 1200 sq.ft.

Country quilting at its best. Wonderful selection of fabrics, patterns, books, and gifts to choose from. Worth the trip. Classes and custom long arm quilting.

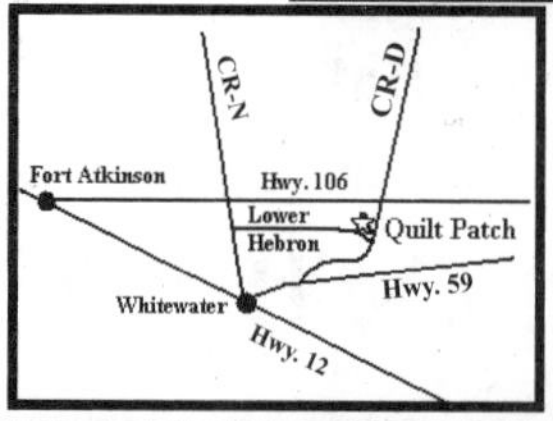

Fort Atkinson, WI #39

Tues 10 - 6
Wed - Fri 10 - 5:30
Sat 10 - 4
Sun 12 - 4

Backyard Quilt Shop & Custom Quilting

N1541 Knaack Ct. 53538
(920) 568-1974 Est: 2004
Owner: Kathy Knaack 1200 sq.ft.
4000 Bolts Online newsletter
backyardquilts@charter.net
www.backyardquiltshopwi.com
Full service shop set in a lovely country subdivision.

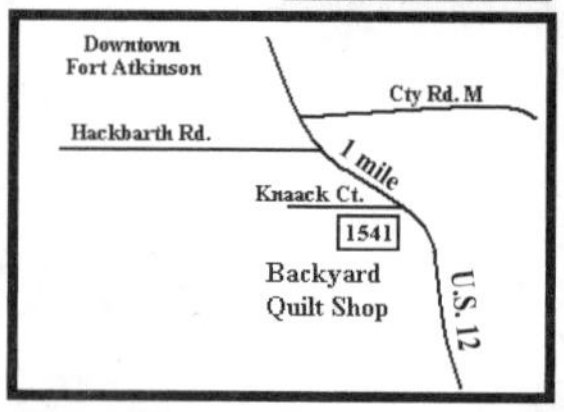

Beloit, WI #40

Mon - Thurs 10 - 5
Fri 10 - 8
Sat 10 - 4

Attic Quilts

314 State St. 53511
(608) 364-4037 Fax: (608) 368-2913
smquilts@aol.com Est: 1997
www.atticquilts.net 3000 sq.ft.
Owner: Sally McFerren 4000 Bolts

Books, Patterns, Notions, Yarn. 100% Cotton Fabrics: Batiks, Flannels, Homespuns, Thimbleberries, 30's & 1800's Reproductions, Moda, Benartex, Hoffman, Kona Bay & more.

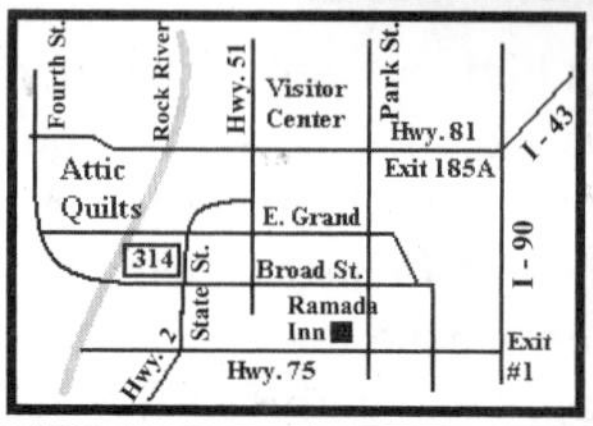

Saving Thyme

233 W. Main St., Stoughton, WI 53589
(608) 877-0075 Fax: (608) 877-0076
gstehley@choiceonemail.com Owner: Gloria Stehley
Est: 2000 1700 sq.ft.

Stoughton, WI #42

Located in a 4 level Victorian style shop on the river in Historic Downtown Stoughton. Houses a unique blend of quilting fabric, notions, and kits and Scandinavian Imports with local art enhancing the unique atmosphere.

Mon - Thur 10 - 7
Fri 10 - 5
Sat 9 - 5
Sun 12 - 4

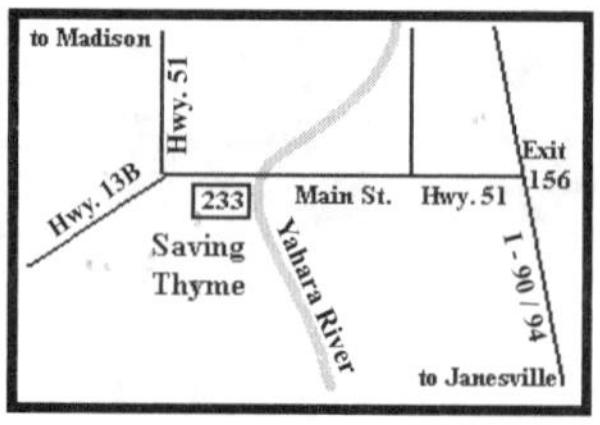

www.savingthyme.net

Janesville, WI #41

Life's A Stitch
QUILT SHOPPE

Better Homes and Gardens Quilt Sampler FEATURED SHOP 2008

5130 E US Highway 14, Janesville, WI 53546
(608) 756-9850 Fax: (608) 756-9860
lifesastitch@sbcglobal.net
Est. 2003 2400 sq. ft. 4000 Bolts

Located 1.5 miles off I-90 on Hwy 14/11 east (exit 175B).

Enjoy our 1863 Victorian Farmhouse while shopping through a wonderful assortment of reproduction fabrics, along with a wide variety of designer lines and hand-dyed wools.
We now have open day retreats available.
Call us for more information.
It's more than quilting, it's an inspiration!

Tues ~ Sat 10 ~ 5
Thur 10 ~ 6
Sun 12 ~ 4

Owner: Patricia Riley

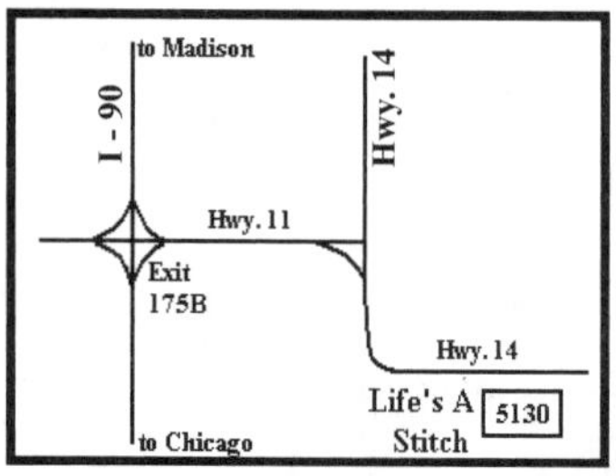

www.lasquiltshoppe.com

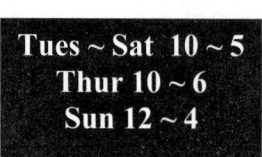

Hidden Quilts LLC

Tues - Fri 10 - 6
Sat 10 - 4

- Over 1750 bolts of 100% cotton fabrics
- Large selection of Hoffman Batiks
- Blank Quilting Fabrics
- RJR Thimbleberries
- Kid's Brights & Flannels
- 1930's Reproductions
- Black & Whites • Orientals
- Hand Dyed wools
- Weeks Dye Works Floss
- Books, Patterns, Notions & Kits
- Many Models on Display
- Finished quilts for sale
- Annual May Fat Quarter Frenzy
- Home of Hidden Quilts Designs
- Longarm Quilter on site
- Arrow Cabinet Dealer

915 B East Mineral St.
Platteville, WI 53818
(608) 348-4977
hiddenquilts@centurytel.net
Est: 2002 1500 sq.ft.
www.hiddenquilts.com

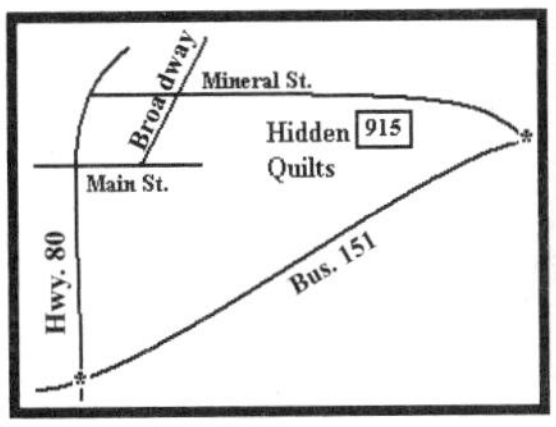

Platteville, WI #43

Darlington, WI #44

Pins & Pieces Quilt Shop

Mon - Fri 9:30 - 5:30
Sat 9ish - 3ish

208 Main St. 53530
(608) 776-2116
Owner: Heidi Brenum Est: 2009
pinspiecesquilt@centurytel.net

Quality quilting fabrics, classes, patterns, books, notions.
Scrapbooking supplies & classes.
Tuxedo rentals.

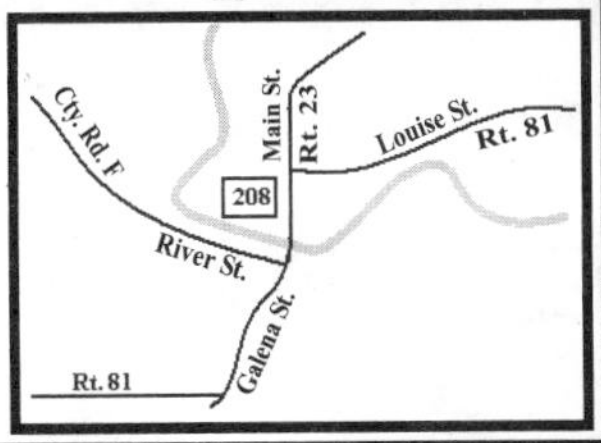

Richland Center, WI #46

Thimble N Thread LLC

Tues - Fri 10 - 5
Sat 10 - 4

2315 Hwy. 14 E, Suite #1 53581
(608) 649-2222
Est: 2004 1500 sq.ft. 1500 Bolts
www.thimblenthread.net
"Love Quilting? You'll Love Our Shop"
Baby Lock Sewing Machines, Authorized Sewing Technician on staff, Quilting classes, Quilting Fabrics & Kits, Gutermann Thread, Quilters Dream Batting, Large Assortment of Books & Patterns, Friendly Service & Support, Gift Certificates.

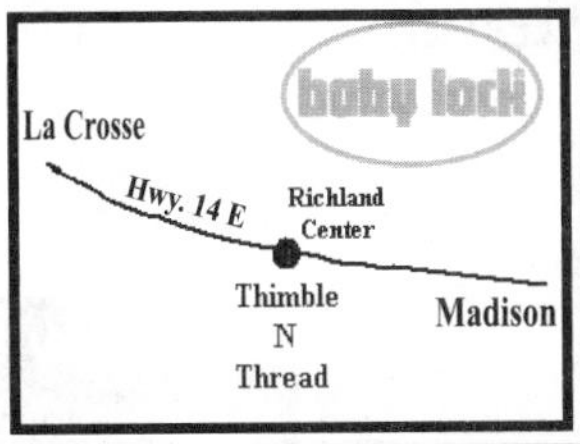

Ferryville, WI #47

Olde Tyme Quilt Shoppe

Mon - Sat 10 - 5

62682 Rush Creek Rd. 54628
(608) 648-2081
Owner: Virginia Johnson 900 sq.ft.
otymequilt@mwt.net Est: 1986
www.Ferryville.com
Virginia's original quilts. Hand painted fabric. Longarm machine quilting. Call for estimate.
Notions - 100% cotton thread.

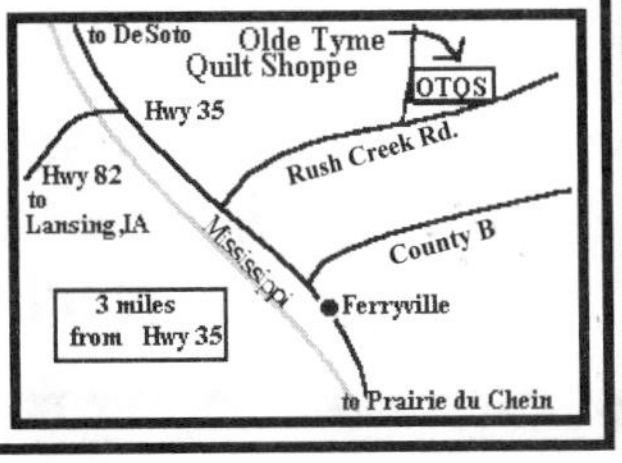

Country Sampler & 2nd Story

A Top 10 Quilt Shop in Quilt Sampler ®2000
Celebrating 27 Years
www.sgcountrysampler.com
Phone 608-588-2510

Sign up on our website for our weekly email newsletter. This will keep you in the loop of what's new in the shop and our coming events.

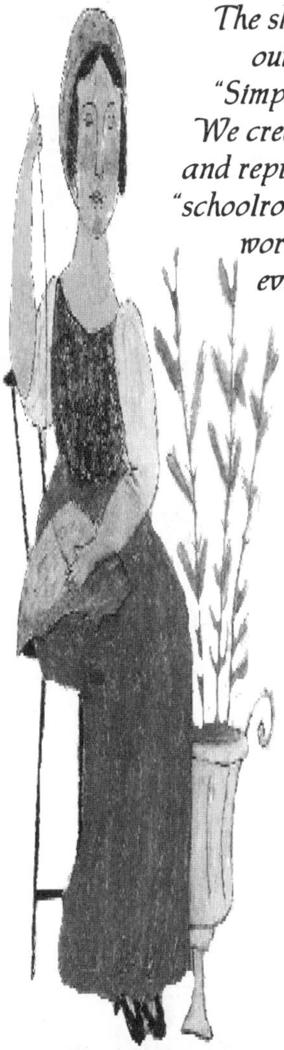

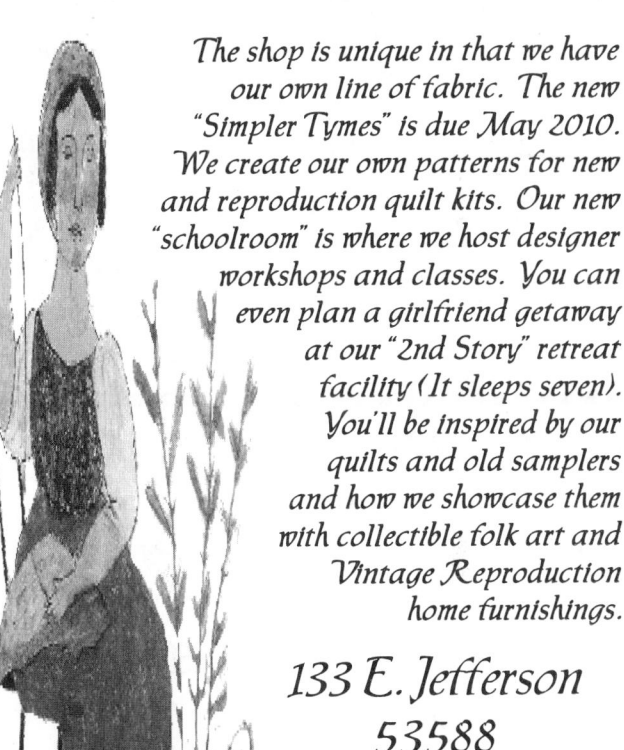

The shop is unique in that we have our own line of fabric. The new "Simpler Tymes" is due May 2010. We create our own patterns for new and reproduction quilt kits. Our new "schoolroom" is where we host designer workshops and classes. You can even plan a girlfriend getaway at our "2nd Story" retreat facility (It sleeps seven). You'll be inspired by our quilts and old samplers and how we showcase them with collectible folk art and Vintage Reproduction home furnishings.

133 E. Jefferson
53588
Fax: 608 • 588 • 3530
Owner: Jeanne Horton
Est: 1983 1800 sq. ft.
2000+ Bolts
stchgirl@yahoo.com

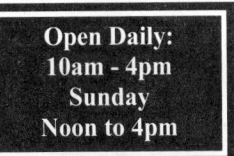

Open Daily:
10am - 4pm
Sunday
Noon to 4pm

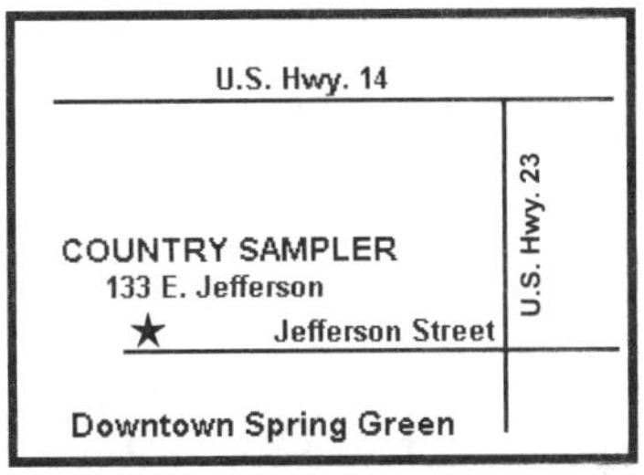

Spring Green, WI #45

Madison, WI #48

"2003 Top Ten Quilt Shop"
"2007 Best Of Quilt Sampler"

Open Daily

Mon-Fri
9:30-6:00
Thur til 8:30
Sat 9:30-5:00
Sun 12:00-4:00

Stitcher's Crossing

6122 Mineral Point Road 53705
608.232.1500 tel

info@stitcherscrossing.com
www.stitcherscrossing.com
Owner: Sharon Luehring
Est: 1980 4600 sq. ft.

- Great selection of fabrics, books and patterns for quilting, knitting and cross stitch
- Inspiring models
- Knowledgeable and friendly staff
- Extensive class schedule

"where traditional meets contemporary"

Mill House Quilts

Waunakee, WI #49

Come shop for all your quilting supplies in our beautifully restored 1875 grain mill.

- Wide selection of fabric, books, bales, patterns, kits and notions
- Classes and clubs
- A "Top Ten" shop
- Knowledgeable, friendly staff

Monday to Saturday 9 to 5
Thursdays 9 to 8
Sundays 12 to 4

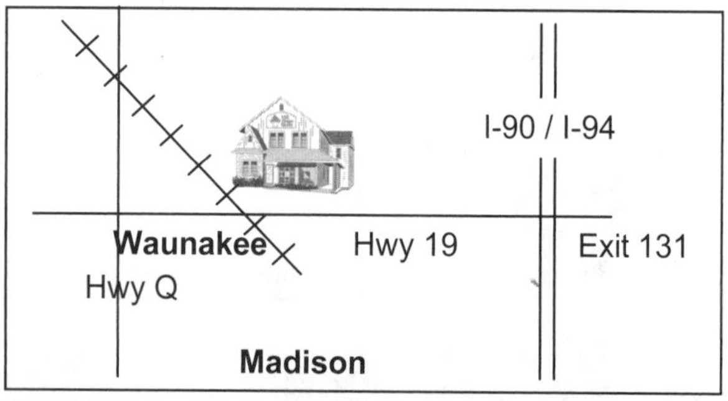

Minutes from I 90/94, Exit 131
100 Baker Street, Waunakee , WI
Downtown at the railroad tracks

608-849-6473
www.millhousequilts.com
info@millhousequilts.com

#50

olive juice Quilts LLC

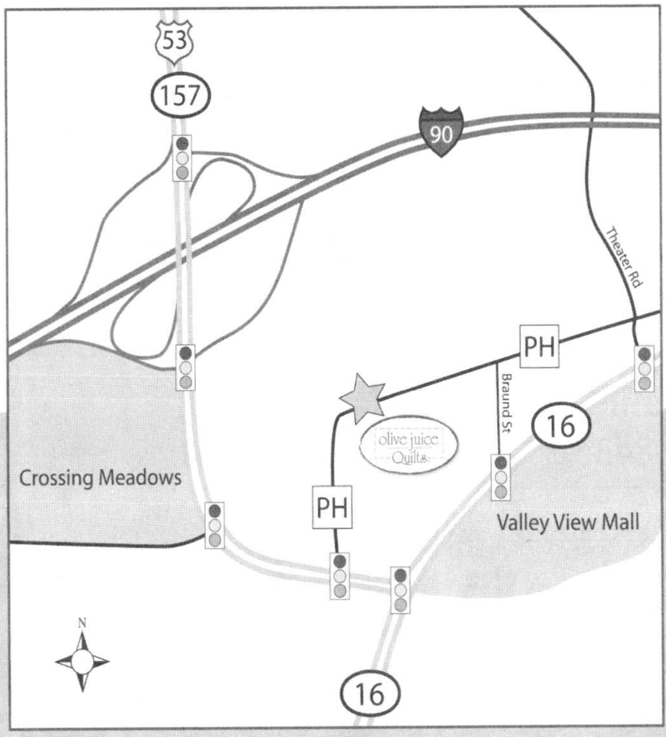

BERNINA

300 Book Titles • Notions
4,000 Bolts of Fabric
Arrow Cabinets • Horn Cabinets
Classes • Clubs • Newsletters

All Model Machine Repair
with 90 day guarantee

1258 County Road PH
Onalaska, WI 54650
(608) 782-3257
www.olivejuicequilts.com

mon - sat 10 - 5 | thurs 10 - 8 | sun 12 - 4

Sparta, WI #51

Mon - Fri 9 - 5
Sat 9 - 4

Quilt CORNER

219 N. Water St. 54656
(608) 269-1083
contactus@quiltcorner.net

A Large 2 Story House that is ALL Quilt Shop!

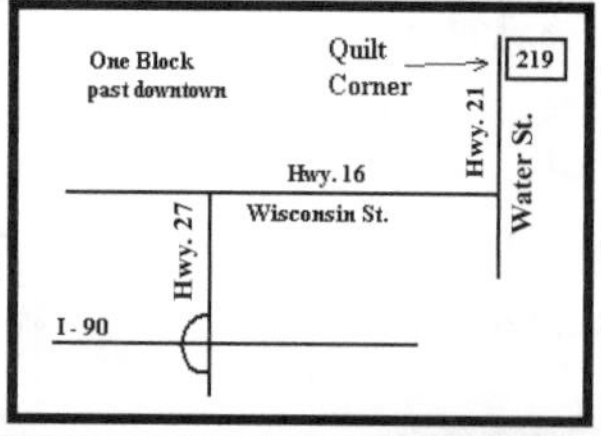

We have over 5000 bolts of fabric, a large sale room and everything to help you make a quilt.
Thimbleberries Quilt Club
Block of Month Clubs - Kansas Troubles Teas

Cashton, WI #52

N 43.44.842
W 90.40.788

Inspirations at Dovetail Farm

Largest Quilt Shop in the Heart of Amish Country
29553 Nevada Rd. 54619
(608) 654-5727
www.Dovetailfarm.com
"An enjoyable shop for the whole family."
Quilting supplies, books, kits, fabrics & beads.
Also Antiques & Amish Gift Items

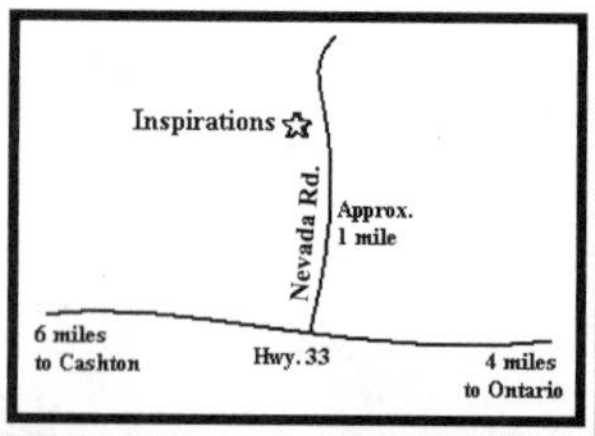

La Crosse, WI #53

Mon - Fri 9 - 6
Sat 10 - 5
Sun 12 - 4

River Road Quilt Shop at Nelson Flag

2501 South Ave. 54601
(608) 788-2990
Est: 2007 Online Newsletter
nelsonflag@centurytel.net
www.nelsonflag.com

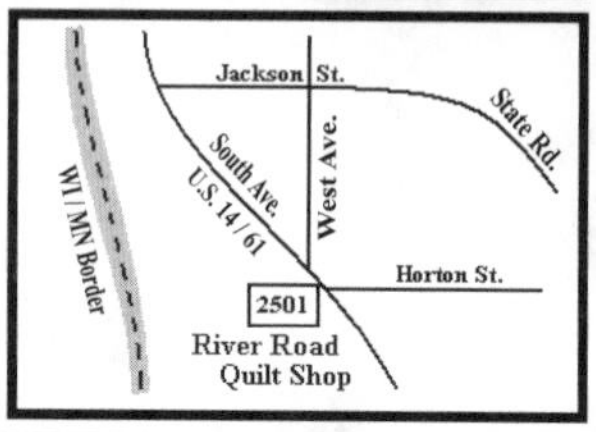

Family owned neighborhood Quilt Shop on the Great River Road. Two shops in one - Gifts & Garden in front, Fabric in back.

Viroqua, WI #54

Mon - Sat 9 - 5

Quilt Basket 'n' Creations

117 F. S. Dr. 54665
(608) 637-7002
or (608) 629-5664
Fax: (608) 637-8049
Owner: Karen L. Swenson Est: 1999

Great selection of 100% cotton fabrics, books, patterns and notions. We have yarn and supplies. Bus Tours Welcome.
Long Arm Quilting Services Available.

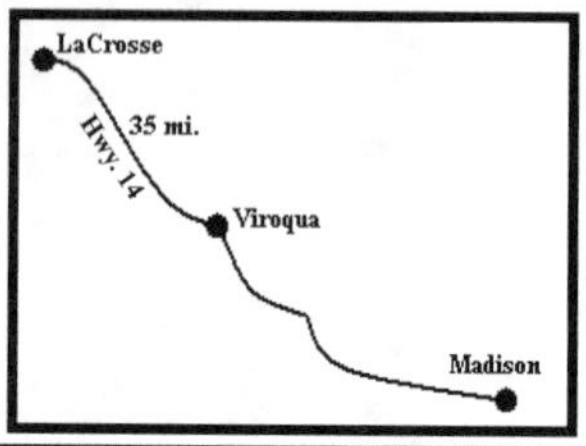

Quintessential Quilts

Located in a "Victorian House"

www.qquilts.com
email: qquilts@rucls.net

We carry a variety of **Patterns, Books & Notions.**
Classes offered for beginners to advanced.
We carry 9 - 10,000 bolts of Fabric.

Bring in this ad for a 10% discount on your purchases.

We are your full sales & service
Husqvarna VIKING
Sewing Machine dealer.

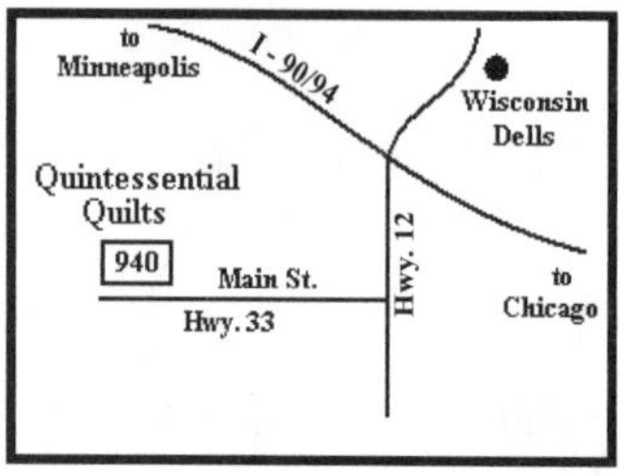

940 E. Main St.
608-524-8435

Mon - Sat 9 - 5 Sun 12 - 4

Reedsburg, WI #55

We have everything a Quilter needs except more time!

Lodi, WI #56

Tues - Fri 10 - 5
Sat 9 - 2

Village Creek LLC

123 S. Main St. 53555
(608) 592-5793
www.villagecreeklodi.com

Cozy little shop in the center of downtown Lodi. 1/2 block south of 4 way stop at Hwy. 60. 20 minutes North of Madison off I - 90 / 94

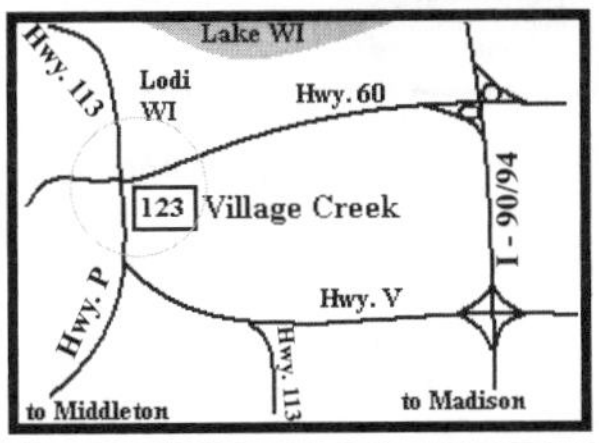

Endeavor, WI #57

Mon, Tues Thur 9:30 - 5
Fri & Sat 9:30 - 4

Homespun Fabrics

N149 County Road T 53930
(608) 742-6400
homespun@maqs.net
www.homespunfabrics.net
Owner: Louise Back
Est: 1995 1000 Bolts

Great Selection of 100% Cotton Fabrics, Books, Notions & Patterns.
Machine Quilting.

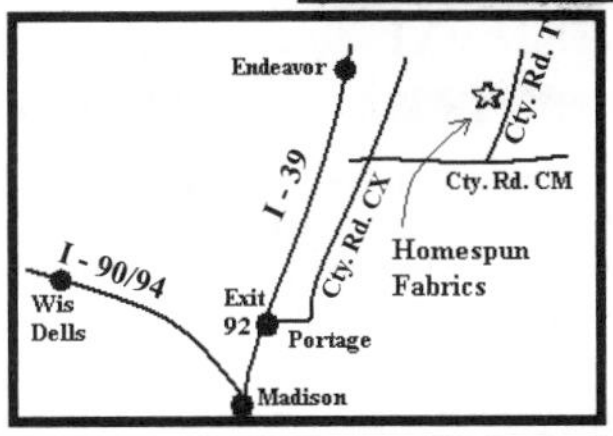

Warrens, WI #58

Tue - Sat 9 - 5
Thur til 8

Quilting Plus LLC

103 Main St. 54666
(608) 378-4585 quiltingplus@gmail.com
Owner: Connie J. Johnson Est: 2006
quiltingplus.wordpress.com
Huge selection of fabrics - patterns - books - notions & kits - Classes & Clubs - Clearance Crib. Carry all colors of DMC floss and many embroidery patterns.
"Your Small Town Quilt Shop with a Friendly Atmosphere."

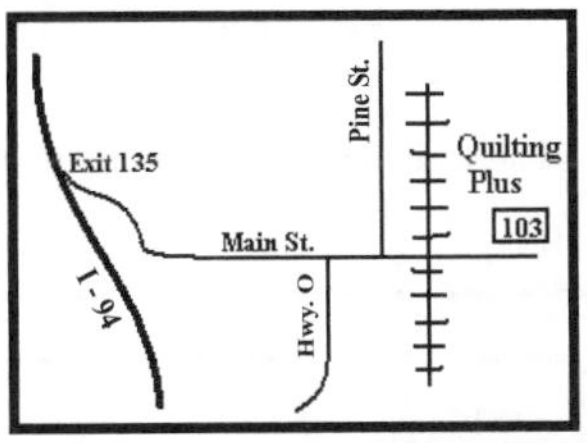

Wisconsin Rapids, WI #59

Mon - Fri 10 - 5
Sat 10 - 4

The COTTON Thimble
FOR YOUR QUILTING NEEDS

540 Daly Ave. 54494
(715) 424-1122
Owner: Carol Prahl Est: 1993
cthimble@wctc.net

Over 8000 Bolts of 100% Cottons and 1400 bolts of Batiks. Books, Patterns, Stencils, & Quilting Notions.

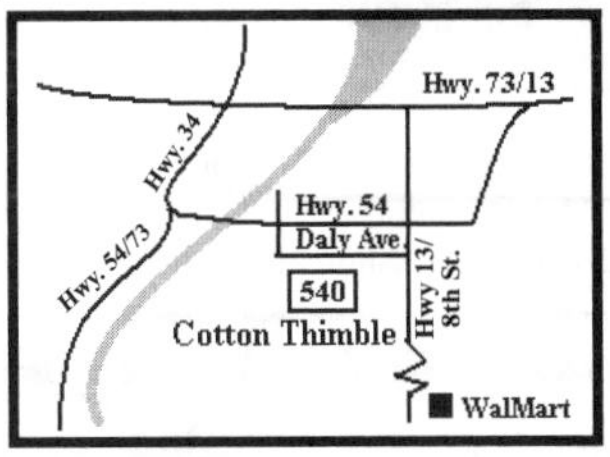

Osseo, WI #60

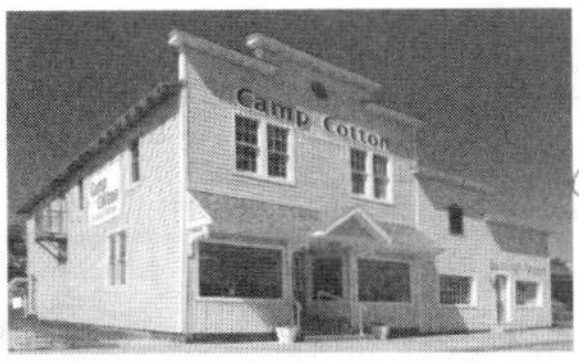

Camp Cotton Quilting Retreat

Camp Cotton is a retreat with comfort in mind.

- **18 beds. Sheets, pillows and quits included**
- **1,200 square foot workroom**
- **Five bathrooms, five showers, towels provided**
- **Full kitchen with refrigerator, stove, microwave, pot, pans, dishes, silverware, coffepots and filters**
- **Secure wireless internet**
- **Available for sewing, quilting and craft groups**

Join us for week long Cotton Theory Camps hosted by Betty Cotton.

Visit www.campcotton.com for more information or call 715-597-2452

"Because nice matters"

We specialize in:

- Cotton Theory Quilting
- Large selection of designer cotton fabric
- Notions, patterns and books
- 100's of samples
- Fabric kits available
- Mailing list, newsletter and mail orders available

Est. 1996

Hours:
Mon-Sat 9:30-5:00

Bus tours and large groups always welcome

Quilt Yard®

13900 7th Street, PO Box 277
Osseo, WI 54758
(715) 597-2452
sales@quiltyard.com
www.quiltyard.com
Owners: Jack & Betty Cotton

PFAFF Authorized Dealer

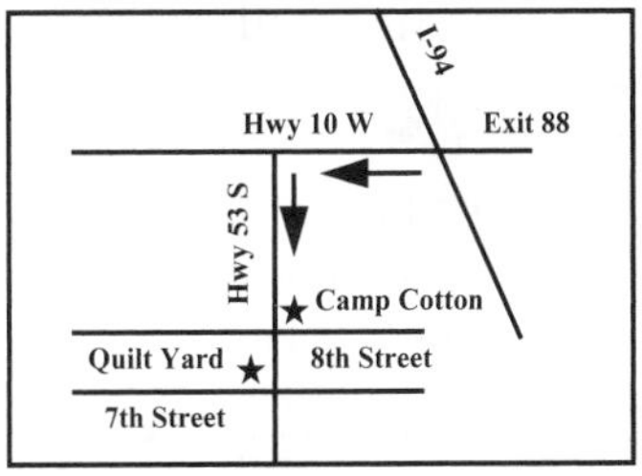

Located 1 mile off I-94 at Exit 88. Hwy 10 West to Hwy 53 South, turn left. Quilt Yard is located 2 blocks on the right.

Neillsville, WI #61

Mon - Fri 9:30 - 5
Wed til 8
Sat 9:30 - 3

HEART 2 HANDS QUILT SHOP

100 E. Division St.
54456
(715) 743-2284

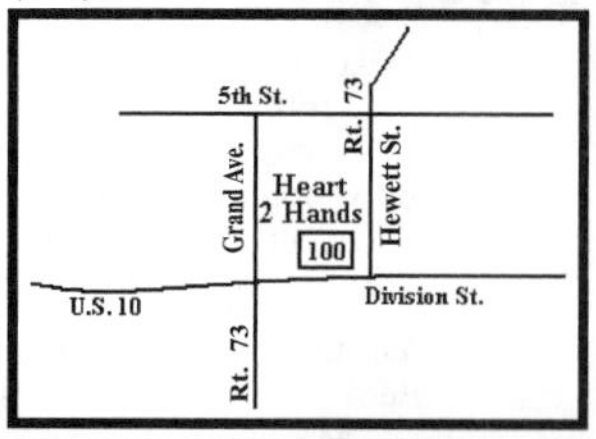

One of the best classrooms in the state.
heart2hands@tds.net www.heart2hands.net
We're a small-town quilt shop with big value, a great selection and many classes to suit your needs.
Great selection of Moda Pre-cuts. Newsletter.

Tigerton, WI #62

Wed - Sat 9 - 6
Sun 12 - 6

PINERY PATCHES LLC

N 4647 Hwy. 45 54486
(715) 535-2277 Est: 2003
pinery_patches@frontiernet.net
www.pinerypatches.com
Fabric, patterns and books for all levels of quilting. Kits for the quilter on the go.
"Coffee pot's always on!"
Show us this ad for a one time 10% discount.

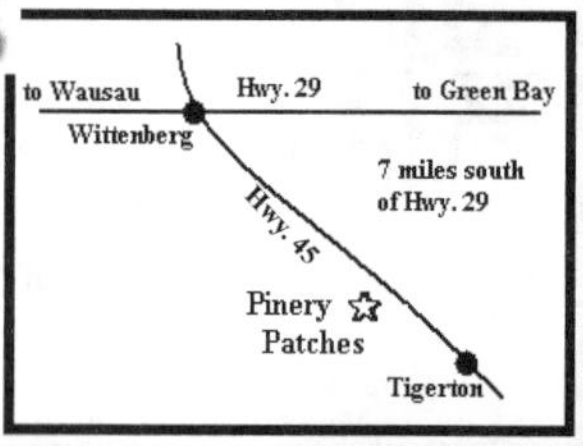

Wausau, WI #63

Mon - Thur 10 - 5
Fri 10 - 7
Sat 10 - 5

The Quilting Workshop

314 S. First Ave. 54401
(715) 848-5546
Est: 2003 1200 sq.ft. 3000 Bolts
swanmum@dwave.net

Wausau's only quilt shop! We carry quilting fabrics, supplies and wool, adjoining The Needle Workshop all in one historic building.

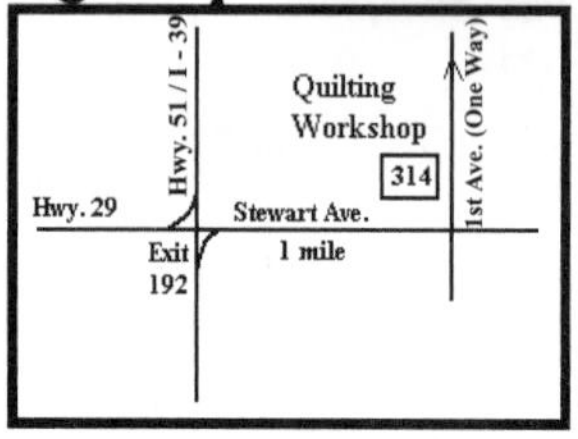

Tomahawk, WI #64

Mon - Fri 8:30 - 4:30
Sat 9 - 1

Sew Pieceful Quilting

118 W. Wisconsin Ave. 54487
(715) 453-7126 Fax: (715) 453-5672
Owner: Marie Daigle
Est: 2009 1745 sq.ft.
sewpiecefulquilting@verizon.net
www.sewpiecefulquiltshop.com
Fabric, Patterns, Notions, Hand-made Gifts, Sewing Classes and more!
"Bringing generations together under one roof!"

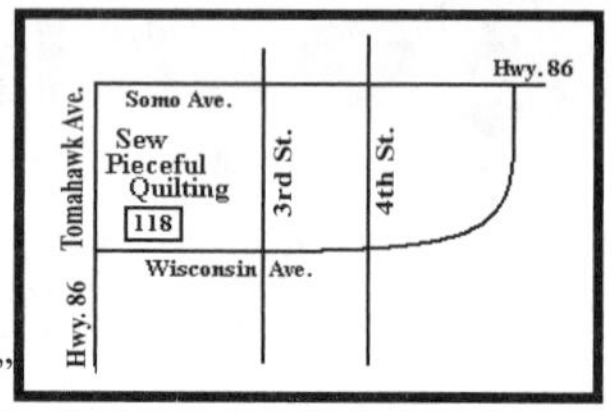

APQS AMERICAN PROFESSIONAL QUILTING SYSTEMS

The Cutting Edge

Fabric & Craft Supply Shoppe, LLC

816 5th Ave., Antigo, WI 54409
(715) 623-3590
3910 Schofield Ave., Suite 7, Weston, WI 54476
(715) 359-2407
www.cuttingedgequilts.com

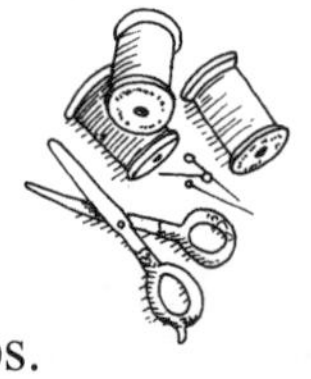

Your one stop quilting resource centers. Dealer of APQS George, Husqvarna Viking, TinLizzie
Full service quilt stores and yarn shops.

Antigo, WI #65

Established 1990
Store Hours:
Mon-Fri 10-5
Sat 9-4

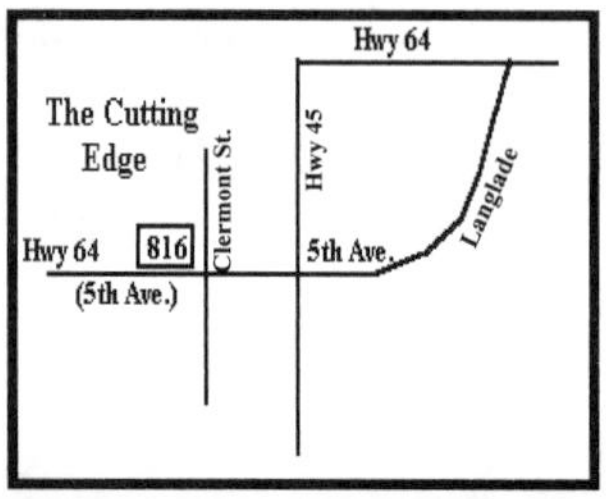

Weston, WI #66

Established 2003
Store Hours:
Mon, Wed, Fri 10-5
Tues & Thur 10-8 Sat 9-4

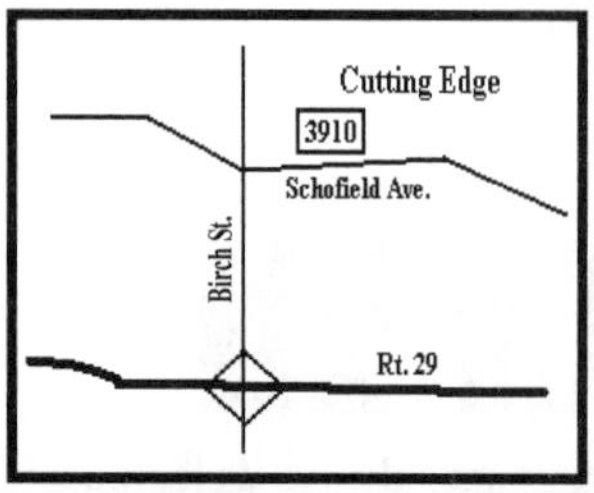

Husqvarna VIKING

Eau Claire, WI #67

Mon - Fri 10 - 5
Thur til 8
Sat 10 - 4

The Calico Shoppe

214 S. Barstow St. 54701
(715) 834-9990
www.calicoshoppe.com
Owner: Lynn Goelzer
Est: 1993 3500+ Bolts
Our shop is located in Eau Claire's Downtown area. Our unique shop offers the latest fabrics, books, patterns, notions & classes; along with a charming gift shop, "The Purple Petunia"
Make a Quilt . . . Make a Memory!

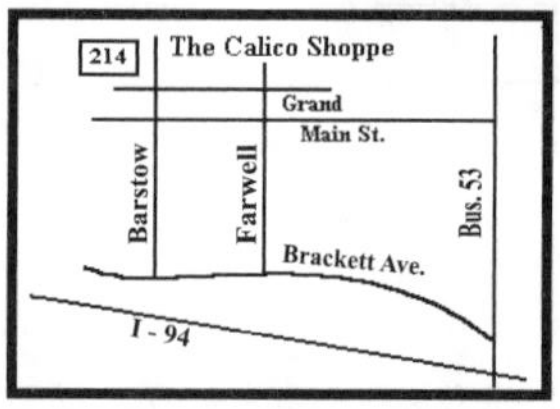

Eau Claire, WI #68

Large Groups

Bridge Creek Cottage

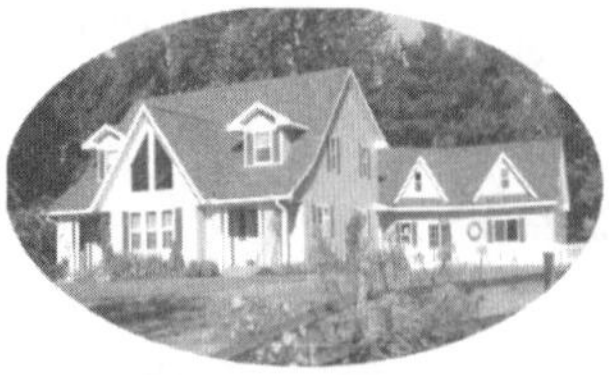

Quilting Retreat 715-529-3344
www.bridgecreekcottage.com
"A gift to women" is how one guest describes this beautiful retreat nestled on the banks of Bridge Creek in the heart of Amish country. Fully equipped with plush accommodations for up to 20 guests, Bridge Creek Cottage is a quilter's paradise!

Elk Mound, WI #69

Small Groups

Meadow Ridge Cottages

Quilting Retreat 715-529-3344
www.meadowridgecottages.com
These brand new cottages are designed to privately host up to 6 guests each, or the soundproof double doors can be opened to accommodate 12 guests.
The spacious, fully equipped cottages are set on beautiful acreage among rolling hills 10 miles west of Eau Claire, WI

Chippewa Falls, WI #70

Tues - Fri 10 - 5:30
Sat 9 - 3

Cotton Club

5503 County Hwy. K 54729
(715) 726-9612
Owner: Mary Machler Online Newsletter
cottonclub9612@charter.net
www.cottonclubquilting.com
Over 1100 square feet of fabrics (including children's), books, patterns, notions, classes, retreats and country gift items such as benches and birdfeeders. Custom quilt racks are made to your specifications.

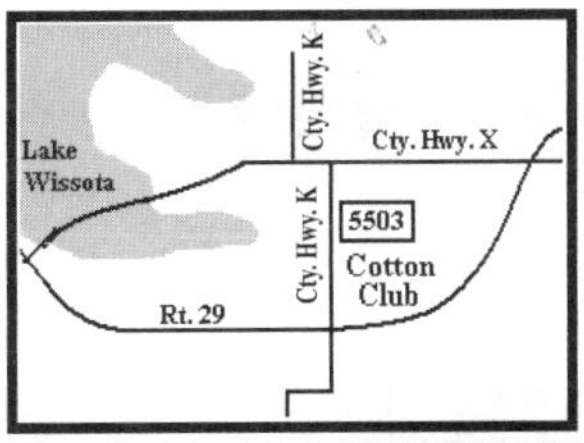

Stanley, WI #71

Mon - Fri 9 - 5
Evenings & Sat by Appt.

Sew N Sew Quilts & Fabrics

36360 Cty. Hwy. MM 54768
(715) 644-5563 Fax: Same
djhaas@centurytel.net
www.seweasytriangles.com
Owner: Donna Haas
Machine Quilting, Machine Embroidery, Also Home of Pieceful Patches.
A Small Country Shop with a Big Atmosphere.
Fabrics, Notions, Books, Classes & Fun!

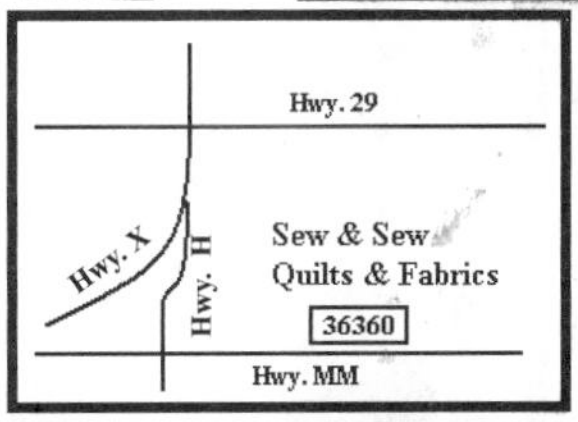

Chetek, WI #72

Mon - Fri 10 - 5
Sat 9 - 1

ELLY'S SHEARED SHEEP

Yarn & Fabric Shop

603 Second St., Center Court Bldg. 54728
(715) 925-9276 Est: 2003
yarnshop@charterinternet.com
www.ellysshearedsheep.com
We have hundreds of the highest quality cotton fabrics for your quilting needs. There is a bountiful variety of wool and wool blend yarns to choose fronm for your knitting pleasures. Sewing notions & embellishments.

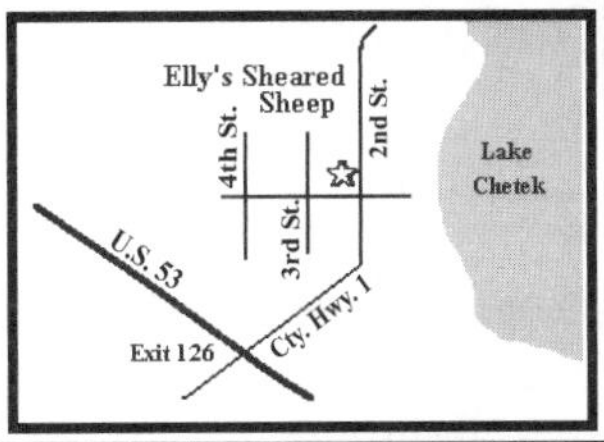

Withee, WI #73

Mon - Fri 8 - 8
Sat 8 - 4

Brubaker Sewing & Furniture

N 14590 Cty. Hwy. O 54498
(715) 229-2851 Fax: (715) 229-2956
Bernina Sewing Machine Sales & Service. Over 2500 Bolts of fabric. Fabric, Quilts & Batting, Baby Supplies, Hosiery, Underwear, Childrens Shoes, Sweaters, Sewing Notions, Disposable Diapers, & Hair Accessories.
Plus High Quality Furniture.

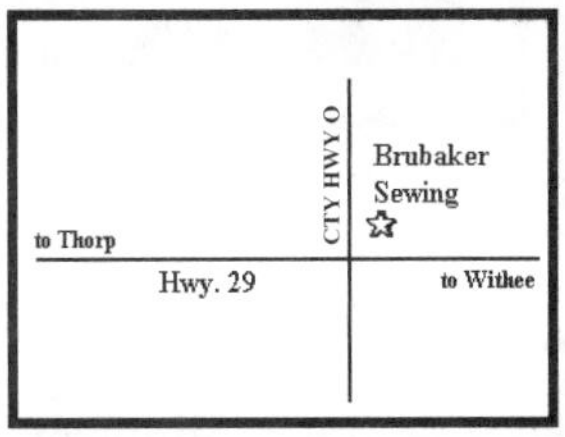

Medford, WI #74

Mon - Fri 9 - 5
Sat 9 - 2

Hoffman's

Fabric, Floral & Crafts

142 S. Main 54451
(715) 748-4770
ehoffmaninc@charterinternet.com
We are a locally owned business for all your creative quilt, craft, floral and gift needs. Since 1935 we have been your helpful and creative outlet with a huge selection of goods.

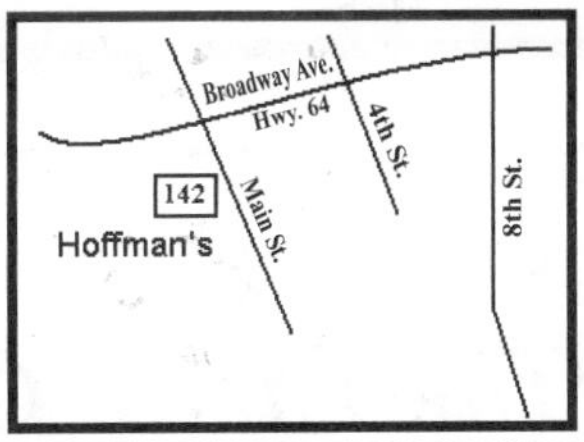

Hazelhurst, WI #75

The Quilt Cottage

Mon - Fri 10 - 4
Sat 10 - 3
Summer Suns 10 - 3

6823 Hwy. 51 S 54531
(715) 358-7074
Fax: Same
thequiltcottage@gmail.com
Owner: Barbara Zawistowski

Better Homes and Gardens American Patchwork & Quilting Top Ten Quilt Shop in 2004. We specialize in Civil War Reproductions and Wool with over 5,000 bolts of fabric.

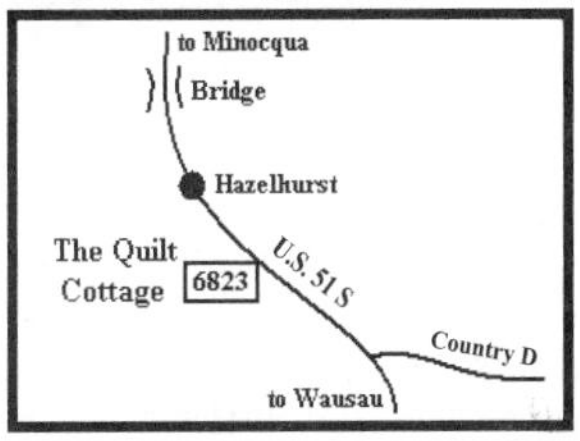

Rice Lake, WI #76

Busy Bobbin

Large selection 100% Cotton fabrics, patterns, books, and quilting notions. Classes offered. Authorized Janome dealer and Horn of America sewing tables.

Mon - Fri 9:30 - 5 Sat 9:30 - 3

234 N. Wilson Ave. 54868
(715) 234-1217
www.busybobbin.com
Fax: (715) 234-6326
Owner: Diann Raymond
diann@busybobbin.com
Est: 1981 1300 sq.ft. 4000 Bolts

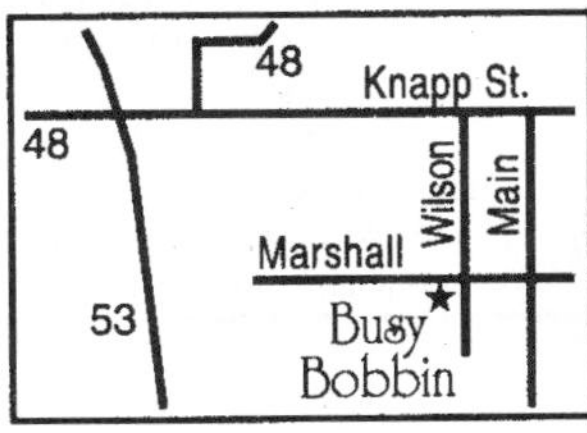

St. Croix Falls, WI #77

Mon - Sat 9:30 - 5:30

Pins 'N' Needles Quilt Shop

126 N. Washington 54024
(715) 483-5728 Est: 2000
Owner: Mary E. Anderson 4000 sq.ft.
Over 3000 bolts of fabric along with books, patterns, and notions. We've added a "Wool N Mittins" yarn shoppe Friendly people waiting to help you. . Come see us!
www.pinsnneedlesquiltshop.com

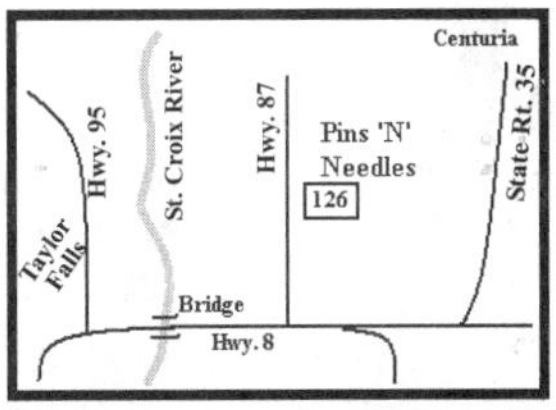

Bear Den Quilt Co.

Siren, WI #78

24665 State Road 35-70, Suite C
Siren, WI 54872
715-349-2250

Owner: Karen Miller
www.BearDenQuiltCo.com

Hours :
Summer (June 1 - Oct 31)
Mon - Fri 9:30 - 5 PM
Saturday 9:30 - 4 PM
Sunday 11:00 - 3 PM
Winter (Nov 1 - May 31)
Mon - Fri 10 - 5 PM
Saturday 10 - 4 PM

While visiting beautiful Northwestern Wisconsin don't miss a stop at the area's premier Quilt Shop. You will find over 4,000 bolts of quality fabric and walls filled with samples in full view. Surely you will be inspired for your next quilt project. Our shop is spacious and well lit and we are known for our friendly atmosphere and personal service. We specialize in batiks and the "Northwoods" look and have an extensive flannel selection too! Don't miss our fat quarter aisle, it's been called "Fat Quarter Heaven". You will find many unique gift items and numerous Fabric PACs for the discerning quilter. We host quilt retreats four times a year and offer classes and clubs year around. We also offer Long-Arm Quilting services.

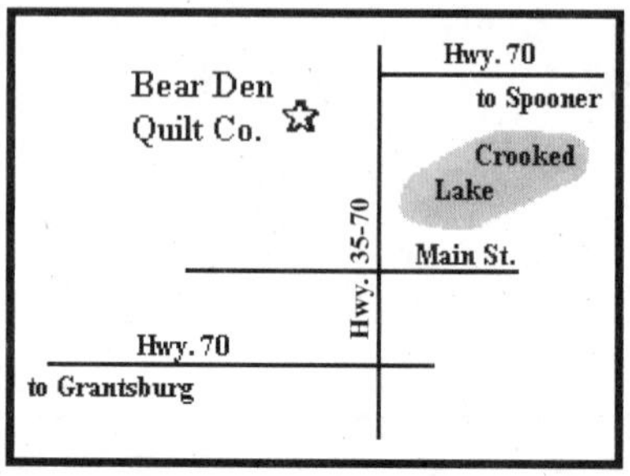

Travel 1.5 miles north of Siren's Main Street on Highway 35-70 and we are on the left-hand side of the highway. Look for the blue Quilt Shop sign.

Hayward, WI #79

River's Edge Antiques & Quilt Loft, Ltd.

Two floors of quality antiques plus over 4000 bolts of 100% cottons & flannels, books, patterns & notions.

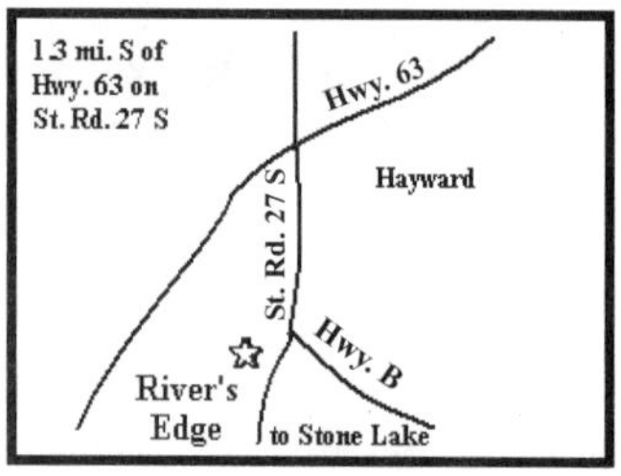

Located 1 1/3 miles South of Hwy. 63 on State Road 27 South

10103 State Road 27, Hayward, WI 54843
www.shopriversedge.com
(715) 634-0706

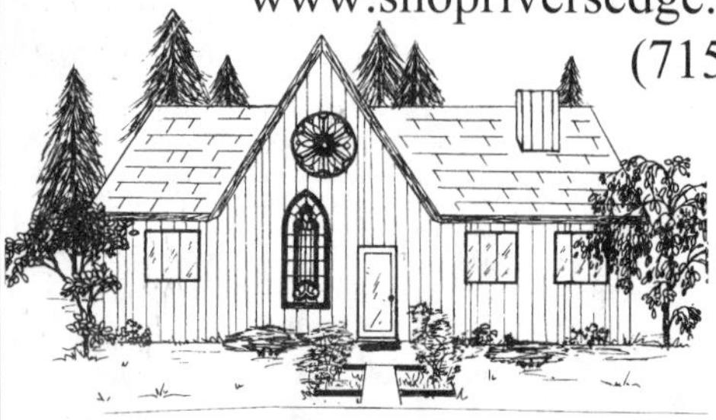

Mon - Sat 10 - 5

Discover "*The Best Kept Secret in the Northwoods.*"

Solon Springs, WI #80

Mon - Sat 10 - 5
Sun 10 - 2

The Little Gift House

9234 E. Main St., P.O. Box 297 54873
(715) 378-4170
Est: 1974 2000 sq.ft.
www.littlegifthouseonline.com
100% cotton fabrics. Large selection of flannels, batiks, plaids, and novelties.
Books & notions. Great gifts.
Good Customer Service is our goal.

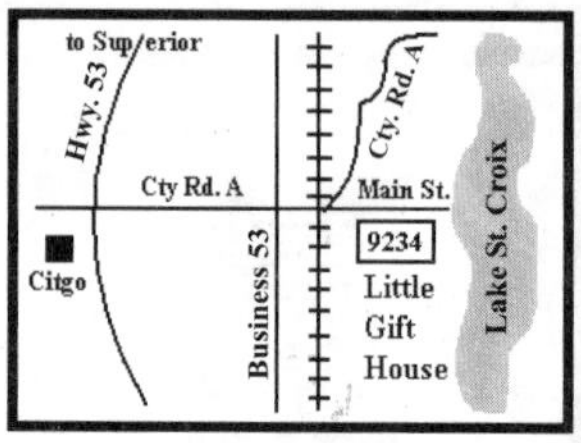

Ashland, WI #81

Mon - Sat 10 - 6

Ashland Area Quilt & Fabric Company

805 Lake Shore Drive West 54806
(715) 682-4646
Owners: Barb and Bruce Hoekstra
Est: 2010 1700 sq.ft.
barb@ashlandquilt.com
www.ashlandquilt.com
2,000 bolts of fabric, notions and Lake Superior Lighthouse patterns.
Long arm quilting services.

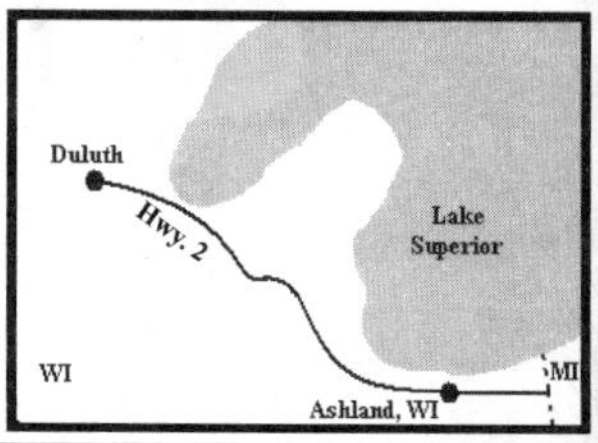

Bayfield, WI #82

Mon - Sat 10 - 5

Orchard's Edge Quilting

87740 County Hwy. J 54814
(715) 779-9822
Est: 2007 1200 sq.ft. 1000+ bolts
mary@orchardsedgequilting.com
www.orchardsedgequilting.com
Fabric, Kits, Notions, Patterns, Quilts
Gather your family, friends, neighbors to join us at our beautiful northwoods classroom.
Machine Quilting Service also Available.

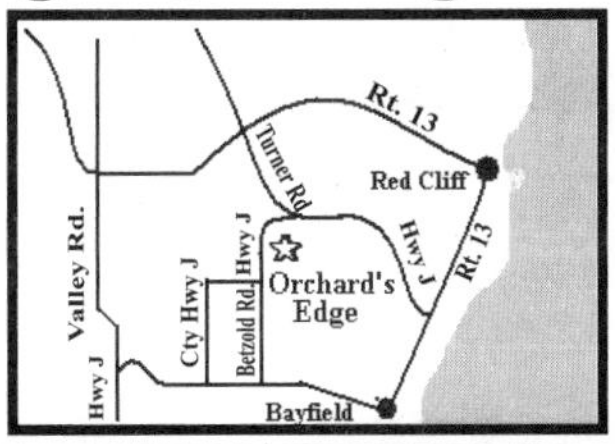

Superior, WI #84

Mon - Fri 9:30 - 5
Thur til 8
Sat 10 - 4

Fabric Works

1320 Tower Ave. 54880
(715) 392-7060
Owner: Barb Engelking
Est: 1991

Over 2000 Bolts of 100% Cotton Fabric.
Yarn, knitting and quilting supplies.

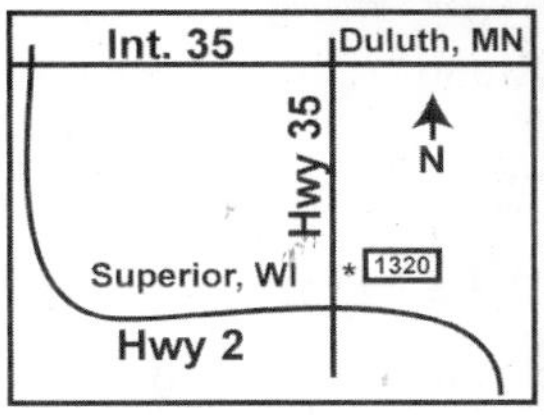

Featuring "Up North" fabrics, flannels,
Moda, Kaufman, Hoffman, Red Rooster, etc.
We're known for great kits for all our samples.
Baby Lock Dealer-Quilters Dream Series.

Mon - Fri 10 - 5 Sat 10 - 2

2104 E. 5th St. 54880
(715) 398-0150
CtrySchlhs@aol.com
Est: 2001
www.country-schoolhouse.com

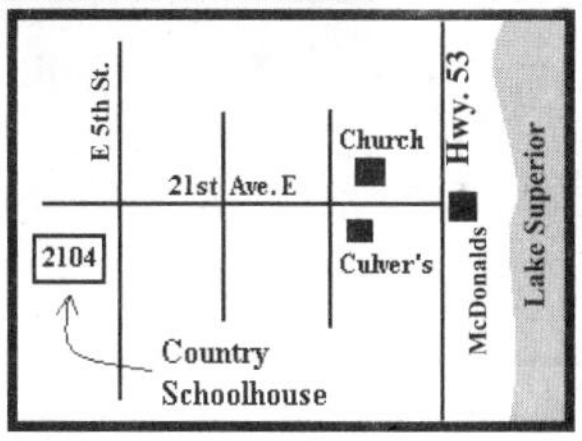

Superior, WI #83

Wisconsin Quilt Shops

Antigo — **The Cutting Edge, 816 5th Ave.**
715-623-3590 — **See ad #65, page 598**

Appleton — **Keep Me In Stitches, 3402 N Richmond St #B**
920-734-0852 — **See ad #17, page 587**

Appleton — **Sew n Sew, 1881 N. Silverspring Dr.**
920-830-9372 — **See ad #18, page 587**

Appleton — **Piece by Piece, 1350 W. College Ave.**
920-749-1957 — **See ad #16, page 587**

Ashland — **Ashland Area Quilt & Fabric Company**
805 Lake Shore Drive West
715-682-4646 — **See ad #81, page 600**

Ashland — Bear Trap Trading Post, 67151 US Hwy. 2 — 715-682-5004

Bayfield — **Orchard's Edge Quilting, 87740 Cnty Hwy J**
715-779-9822 — **See ad #82, this page**

Beaver Dam — Nancy's Notions, 333 Beichl Ave. — 920-887-7321

Belleville — **Patches & Petals, LLC 13 W. Main St.**
608-424-1516 — **See ad #37, page 591**

Beloit — **Attic Quilts, 314 State St.**
608-364-4037 — **See ad #40, page 592**

Cashton — **Inspiration at Dovetail Farm, 29553 Nevada**
608-654-5727 — **See ad #52, page 596**

Cedarburg — **Ye Olde Schoolhouse, 318 Green Bay Rd.**
262-377-2770 — **See ad #5, page 584**

Cedarburg — Cedarburg Woolen Mill, W 62 N 580 Washington Ave.
262-377-5000

Chetek — **Elly's Sheared Sheep, 603 Second St**
715-925-9276 — **See ad #72, page 599**

Chippewa Falls — **Cotton Club, 5503 County Hwy. K**
715-726-9612 — **See ad #70, page 599**

Clear Lake — Sew Country, 464 3rd Ave. — 715-263-2384

Cornell — Uncommon Creations, 23132 Cnty Hwy Z — 715-239-3379

Crivitz — **Sew Much More, LLC 709 Dyer St.**
715-854-2621 — **See ad #29, page 589**

Darlington — **Pins & Pieces Quilt Shop, 208 Main St.**
608-776-2116 — **See ad #44, page 593**

Delavan — The Stitchery, N2482 County Rd. O — 262-728-6318

Denmark — **Kindred Spirits Quilt Shop, 148 E. Main St.**
920-863-8855 — **See ad #20, page 587**

DePere — Life's A Stitch, 124 N. Broadway — 920-338-1381

Dorchester — Cow Country Fabrics & Quilts, 800 E. Center Ave.
715-654-5250

Eagle River — **Karen's Quilt Corner**
330 W Pine St Hwy 70 W
715-477-2603 — **See ad #30, page 589**

Eau Claire — **The Calico Shoppe, 214 S. Barstow St.**
715-834-9990 — **See ad #67, page 598**

Eau Claire — **Bridge Creek Cottage, 415 Southwood Ct.**
320-420-0250 — **See ad #68, page 598**

Elk Mound — **Meadow Ridge Cottages, 415 Southwood Ct**
320-420-0250 — **See ad #69, page 598**

Elkhorn — **Sawdust & Stitches, 13 S. Wisconsin St.**
262-723-1213 — **See ad #34, page 590**

Elkhorn — The Quilting Connection, 21 Adams St. — 262-723-6775

Elm Grove — **Patched Works, Inc., 13330 Watertown Plank**
262-786-1523 — **See ad #1, page 582**

Endeavor — **Homespun Fabrics, N149 County Rd. T**
608-742-6400 — **See ad #57, page 597**

Ferryville — **Olde Tyme Quilt Shoppe, 62682 Rush Creek**
608-648-2081 — **See ad #47, page 593**

Fond du Lac — **Willett Sew, 23 N. Main St.**
920-929-9690 — **See ad #11, page 585**

Fort Atkinson — **The Quilt Patch LLC, W3352 Lower Hebron**
262-593-8462 — **See ad #38, page 592**

Fort Atkinson — **Backyard Quilt Shop & Custom Quilting**
N1541 Knaack Ct.
920-568-1974 — **See ad #39, page 592**

Genesee Depot — **Pamella's Place, S42 W31230 St. Rd. 83**
262-968-3821 **See ad #4, page 584**

Gordon — Kunert Kreations, 9586 E. County Y 715-376-4722

Green Bay — Door County Quiltworks, 1043 S. Quincy St.

Green Bay — **My Favorite Quilt Shop, 1550 Dousman St.**
920-965-2085 **See ad #24, page 588**

Green Bay — **Quilter's Connection, 2269 True Ln.**
920-497-8787 **See ad #23, page 588**

Green Bay — **Silver Thimble Quilt & Gift Shoppe**
2475 University Ave.
920-468-1495 **See ad #26, page 589**

Green Bay — **Cordy's Quilting3093, Westpoint Rd.**
9204943491 **See ad #25, page 588**

Hayward — **River's Edge Antiques & Quilt Loft**
10103 State Rd. 27
715-634-0706 **See ad #79, page 600**

Hazelhurst — **The Quilt Cottage, 6823 Hwy. 51 S**
715-358-7074 **See ad #75, page 599**

Janesville — **Life's A Stitch Quilt Shoppe, 5130 E. Hwy. 14**
608-756-9850 **See ad #41, page 592**

Janesville — A Quilt Lovers Shoppe, 1604 S. Crosby 608-754-6497

Jefferson — **Tea and Textiles Quilt Shop, 107 S. Main St.**
920-674-9017 **See ad #35, page 590**

Juneau — **J & A Stitches, N3914 Welsh Rd.**
920-696-3827 **See ad #32, page 590**

La Crosse — **River Road Quilt Shop, 2501 South Ave.**
608-788-2990 **See ad #53, page 596**

Lodi — **Village Creek, 123 S. Main St.**
608-592-5793 **See ad #56, page 597**

Madison — **Stitcher's Crossing, 6122 Mineral Point Rd.**
608-232-1500 **See ad #48, page 594**

Marinette — **Pine Street Quilts, 801 Marinette Ave. #2**
715-735-9806 **See ad #28, page 589**

Marinette — Quilt Stitchery, 2456 Elm St. 715-735-3099

Markesan — All About Quilting, 47 E. John St. 920-398-2009

Marshfield — Sew Smart, 125 S. Central Ave. 715-384-3465

Medford — **Hoffman's Fabric Floral & Crafts**
142 S. Main
715-748-4770 **See ad #74, page 599**

Menasha — **Primitive Gatherings, 850 Racine St.**
920-722-7233 **See ad #15, page 586**

Menomonee Falls — **The Quilted Basket, N 88 W 16599 Main St.**
262-251-8791 **See ad #2, page 583**

Milton — **Loose Threads Quilt & Yarn, 8005 N Hwy 26**
608-868-7912 **See ad #36, page 591**

Mishicot — **Lisa's Photo Quilting Retreat & Lodging**
316 E. Main St.
920-755-4217 **See ad #8, page 584**

Montello — Teapot Quilt Cottage, 505 Main St. 608-297-7849

Neillsville — **Heart 2 Hands, LLC, 100 E. Division St.**
715-743-2284 **See ad #61, page 598**

Oakfield — Stitches 'N Tyme, LLC, 203 S. Main St. 920-583-2625

Oconomowoc — Ben Franklin Crafts, 1083 Summit Ave. 262-567-0271

Oconto Falls — **The Quilter's Escape, 323 E Highland Dr.**
920-846-8222 **See ad #27, page 589**

Omro — **YDS, 5530 St. Rd. 116**
920-582-7196 **See ad #14, page 586**

Onalaska — **Olive Juice Quilts, 1258 CTH PH**
608-782-3257 **See ad #50, page 595 & 205**

Oshkosh — **QuiltEssentials, 1928 S. Washburn St.**
920-230-3680 **See ad #13, page 586**

Osseo — **The Quilt Yard, LLC, 13900 7th St.**
715-597-2452 **See ad #60, page 597**

Platteville — **Hidden Quilts, 915 B East Mineral St.**
608-348-4977 **See ad #43, page 593**

Plymouth — **The Sewing Basket, 426 E. Mill St.**
920-892-4751 **See ad #6, page 584**

Potosi — Quilt Spot, 446 Hwy 61S 608-763-2646

Prairie du Chien — The Pickett Fence, 100 W. Blackhawk Ave. 608-326-4593

Prairie du Chien — Front Porch Quilts, 216 N Marquette Rd 608-326-4371

Princeton — **Quilts & Quilting, 607 W. Main**
920-295-6506 **See ad #31, page 590**

Racine — **Elmwood Fabric, 3701 Durand Ave.**
262-554-6445 **See ad #3, page 584**

Reedsburg — **Quintessential Quilts LLC, 940 E. Main St.**
608-524-8435 **See ad #55, page 596**

Rhinelander — Sew Smart , 33 W. Davenport St. 715-362-8321

Rice Lake — **Busy Bobbin, 234 N. Wilson Ave.**
715-234-1217 **See ad #76, page 599**

Richland Center — **Thimble N Thread LLC**
2315 Hwy. 145 E Suite #1
608-649-2222 **See ad #46, page 593**

Ripon — **Goosebeary's Village Quilter, 3 Harris St.**
920-748-1233 **See ad #12, page 586**

Sheboygan — **My Sister's Quilt Shoppe**
1224 Weeden Creek Rd.
920-457-4787 **See ad #7, page 584**

Siren — **Bear Den Quilt Company**
24665 State Rd. 35-70, Suite C
715-349-2250 **See ad #78, page 600**

Sister Bay — **Quilters Quest, 10590 Country Walk Dr. #3**
920-854-1824 **See ad #22, page 588**

Solon Springs — **The Little Gift House, 9234 E. Main St.**
715-378-4170 **See ad #80, page 600**

Sparta — **Quilt Corner 219 N. Water St.**
608-269-1083 **See ad #51, page 596**

Spring Green — **Country Sampler, 133 E. Jefferson St.**
608-588-2510 **See ad #45, page 593**

St. Croix Falls — **Pins "N" Needles, 126 N. Washington**
715-483-5728 **See ad #77, page 599**

Stanley — **Sew N Sew Quilts and Fabric**
36360 County Hwy. MM
715-644-5563 **See ad #71, page 599**

Stockholm — Amish Country, 119 Spring St. 715-442-2015

Stone Lake — Jan McKichan, 16719 W. Sissabagama Rd. 715-865-6406

Stoughton — **Saving Thyme, 233 W. Main St.**
608-877-0075 **See ad #42, page 592**

Sturgeon Bay — **Barn Door Quilt Shop, LLC, 154 N. 3rd Ave.**
920-746-1544 **See ad #21, page 588**

Sun Prairie — **J. J. Stitches, 221 E. Main St.**
608-837-2266 **See ad #33, page 590**

Sun Prairie — Prairie Quiltworks LLC, 229 East Main St. 608-837-9201

Superior — **Fabric Works, 1320 Tower Ave.**
715-392-7060 **See ad #84, page 601**

Superior — **Country Schoolhouse Quilt Shop, 2104 E 5th**
715-398-0150 **See ad #83, page 601**

Sussex — Country At Heart, N 70 W 23748 Prides Rd 262-246-8537

Tigerton — **Pinery Patches LLC, N4647 Hwy. 45**
715-535-2277 **See ad #62, page 598**

Tomahawk — **Sew Pieceful Quilting, 119 W. Wisconsin Ave.**
715-453-7126 **See ad #64, page 598**

Two Rivers — Sew Much Wool, 1815 Washington St. 920-553-9669

Viroqua — **Quilt Basket 'N' Creations, 117 FS Drive, #C**
608-637-7002 **See ad #54, page 596**

Warrens — **Quilting Plus, LLC, 103 Main St.**
608-378-4585 **See ad #58, page 597**

Waukesha — Bits N Pieces Quilt Shop, N4 W22496 Bluemound Rd.
262-547-6022

Waunakee	**Mill House Quilts, 100 Baker St.**	**608-849-6473**	**See ad #49, page 594**
Waupaca	**Sew n Sew, 112 S. Main**	**715-256-1071**	**See ad #19, page 587**
Waupaca	Stoney Acres Quilt Shop, 700 Hill Crest Dr	715-258-2296	
Wausau	**The Quilting Workshop, 314 S. First Ave.**	**715-848-5546**	**See ad #63, page 598**
Wausau	Sew Smart, 2907 Rib Mountain Dr.	715-845-9675	
West Allis	Homespun Creations, 7633 W. Beloit Rd.	414-454-0955	
West Bend	**Royce Quilting, 840 S. Main St.**	**262-338-0597**	**See ad #10, page 585**
West Bend	**Material Matters, 2805 E. Progress Dr.**	**800-443-5800**	**See ad #9, page 585 & 408**
West Bend	Quilt Factory, 5046 S. Oak Rd.	262-338-0054	
Weston	**The Cutting Edge 3910 Schofield Ave.**	**715-359-2407**	**See ad #66, page 598**
Whitewater	Woodland Quilts, 147 W. Main St.	262-473-2978	
Wisconsin Rapids	**The Cotton Thimble, 540 Daly Ave.**	**715-424-1122**	**See ad #59, page 597**
Withee	**Brubaker Sewing, N14590 Cty. Hwy. 0**	**715-229-2851**	**See ad #73, page 599**

Wisconsin Quilt Shows

37 Shows

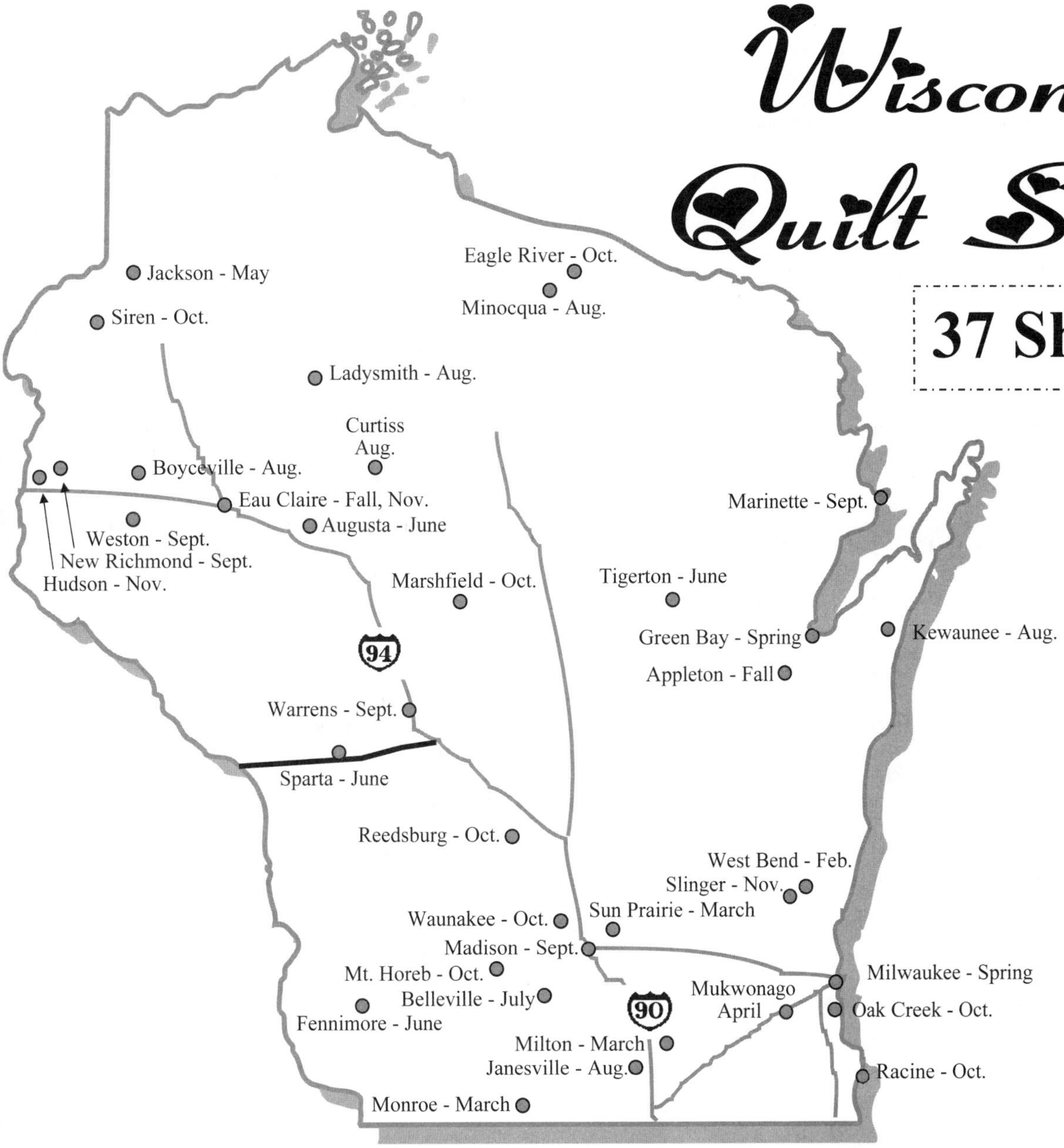

About Shows: We are listing only the very basic information about shows that happen on a regular schedule here. Please check out our website for more details on each show. Also this information tends to change quite often so please verify the event with our website or a local source before you venture far. Or if you're in the right area at the right time, give it a shot.

If you are a show organizer, please keep us updated on your event.
shows@quilterstravelcompanion.com www.quilterstravelcompanion.com

On our website you will also find:

- Exact dates (when we have them)
- Sponsor Information
- Contact Information
- Description of Event
- Events happening on a one-time basis

Month City	Schedule	Show	Location with address
February			
West Bend	Annual, 4th Saturday in February	Winter Quilt Show	Washington County Fair Park, 3000 Hwy. PV
March			
Monroe	Odd Year, March or April	Quilts of Life	Monroe High School, 1600 26th St.
Sun Prairie	Annual, 2nd weekend in March	Prairie Heritage Quilt Show	St. Albert's Parish Center, 2420 St. Albert Dr.
Milwaukee	Even Years, Spring	West Suburban Quilt Guild Show	Mount Mary College, 2900 N. Menomonee River Pkwy.
Milton	Odd Years, Last weekend of March	RVQG Quilt Show	Milton High School, 114 W. High
April			
Mukwonago	Annual, Weekend after Easter	Crazy Quilters Quilt Guild Show	Park View Middle School, Hwy. 83 & NN
Green Bay	Even Years, Spring	Evergreen Quilters Guild	Ashwaubenon High School, 2391 S. Ridge Rd.
May			
Jackson	Annual, 1st weekend in May	It's A Stitch Quilt Show	Kettle Moraine Lutheran High School, 3399 Division Rd.
June			
Fennimore	Annual, 1st weekend of June	Sewing & Quilting Expo	Southwest Wisconsin Technical College, 1800 Bronson Blvd.
Sparta	Annual, 1st weekend in June	Butterfest Quilt Show	Maplewood Elementary School, 900 E. Montgomery
Tigerton	Odd Years, 2nd Sat. in June	Woven Hearts Quilt Show	Tigerton High School, 213 Spaulding St.
Augusta	Annual, last weekend of June	A Celebration of Quilts	Augusta Senior Center, 601 Main St.
July			
Belleville	Odd Years, 3rd weekend in July	Belleville Chamber of Commerce Quilt Show	Belleville High School, 635 W. Church St.
August			
Curtiss	Annual, 1st weekend in August	Curtiss Corners Quilt Show	Curtiss Corners Community Center, W of Abbotsford on Hwy. 29, 1/4 mi. N on Hwy. E
Janesville	Annual, first Saturday in August	Quilts in the Park	Sportsmans Park, 3411 N. US Hwy. 51
Minocqua	Every 3rd year, next 2010, 1st weekend of August	Ladies of the Lakes Quilt Show	Lakeland Union High School, 9573 St. Hwy. 70
Kewaunee	Odd Years, 2nd weekend in August	Fabric of the Kewaunee Lakeshore	Agricultural Heritage & Resources, N 2251 St. Rd. 42
Ladysmith	Second weekend in Aug.	Flambeau Area Piecemakers Quilt Show	Rusk County Library, 418 W. Corbett Ave.
Boyceville	Annual, 3rd weekend of August	Heart and Hand Quilt Guild Show	Boyceville Middle School, 505 Tiffany St.
September			
Madison	Annual, 2nd weekend of September	Quilt Expo	Exhibition Hall--Alliant Energy Center, 1919 Alliant Energy Ctr Way
Marinette	Odd Years, 1st weekend after Labor Day	Northwoods Quilters Quilt Show	Marinette Middle School, 1011 Water St.
Eau Claire	Odd Years, Fall	Clear Water Quilt Guild	Historic Schlegelmilch House, 517 S. Farwell
Weston	Odd Years, Late weekend in September	Pine Tree Quilters Show	Greenheck Fieldhouse, adjacent to DC Everest H.S., 6400 Alderson St.
New Richmond	Annual, last weekend in September	The Willow River Piecemakers Quilt Guild	Wisconsin Indianhead Technical College, Cahsman Conference Center
Warrens	Annual, last weekend of September	Warrens Cranberry Festival Quilt Show	Warrens School Gym, Main St.
Appleton	Odd Years, Fall	Darting Needles Quilt Show	Fox Valley Lutheran High School, 5300 N. Meade St.
October			
Eagle River	Odd Years, first Saturday in October	Cranberry Country Quilters Show	First United Church of Christ, 105 N. First St.
Mt. Horeb	Annual, 1st weekend in October	Fall Heritage Quilt Show	Mt. Horeb Community Center, 107 N. Grove St.
Racine	Odd Years, 1st weekend in October	Lighthouse Quilters' Guild Show	Case High School, 7345 Washington Ave. (Hwy. 20)
Siren	Annual, 2nd weekend in October	Mixed Sampler Quilt Guild Show	Siren High School, 24022 4th Ave.
Oak Creek	Annual, 3rd weekend in October	Wandering Foot Quilters	Oelschlaeger-Dallman American Legion Post, 9327 S. Shepard Ave.
Reedsburg	Even Years, Late October	Threads of Warmth Quilt Show	St. Peter's Lutheran School Gym, 346 N. Locust St.
Marshfield	Annual, last weekend of October	Piecemakers Quilt Guild Show	Marshfield High School, 1401 Becker Rd.
Waunakee	Annual, Late October or early November	St. John's Piecemakers Show	St. John's School Gym, 114 E. 3rd St.
November			
Hudson	Odd Years, 1st weekend of November	Patchwork Harvest Quilt Show	Hudson Middle School, 1300 Carmichael Rd.
Slinger	Annual, 1st Sat in November	Ties that Bind Guild Show	Slinger Middle School, 521 Olympic Dr.
Eau Claire	Annual, 2nd weekend of November	Holidaze Arts Festival	Ramada Convention Center, 205 S. Barstow St.

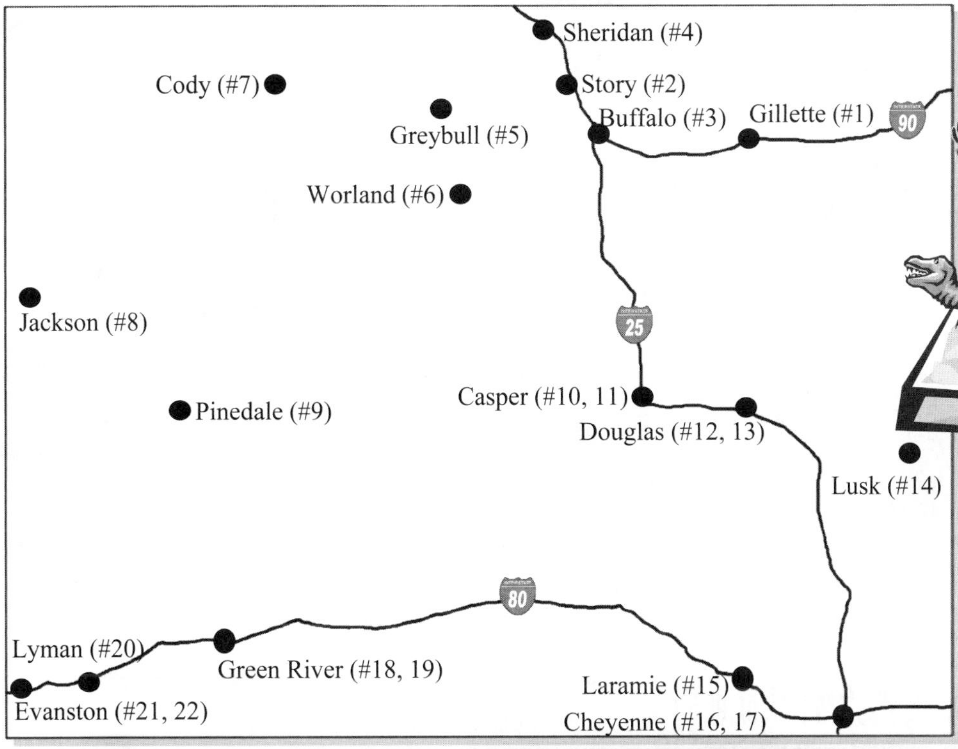

WYOMING

22 Featured Shops

Gillette, WY #1

Northeastern Wyoming's One Stop Quilt Shop!

Quilt Nook, Inc.

211 West 2nd Street
Gillette, WY 82716
(307)682-9196 (888)268-3381

Over 5000 square feet of Quilter's Heaven!

SHOP HOURS:
Tuesday 9:00am to 7:00pm
Wednesday – Friday 9:00am to 5:00pm
Saturday 9:00am to 3:00pm
CLOSED Sunday - Monday

* Koala Cabinets
* Kits, Books, Patterns
* Janome Sewing Machines
* Quilting Notions, Stabilizers, Needles
* Guterman, YLI, Star, Mettler, Quilting Threads
* Over 8,000 Bolts of 100% Cotton Quilting Fabrics

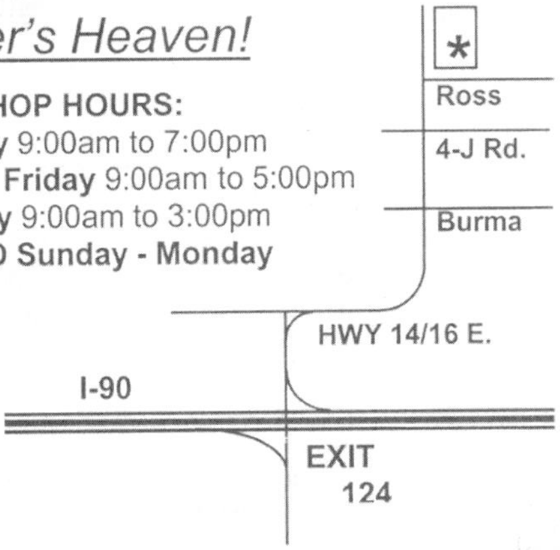

JANOME

Authorized Dealer, Sales and Service Center!

Story, WY #2

Located in the scenic mountain village of Story, between Buffalo and Sheridan.
1500 bolts of quality fabric, unique collectibles & gifts, books & notions. Ongoing quilt display & classes. Owner: Janet Ludwig of Chickadee Charms Pattern Company

"Look for a brown cottage with footbridge, fountains, and picket fence."

Mon-Wed-Fri 1 - 5
Sat 10 - 4
Extended Summer Hours TBA

36 No. Piney Road
P.O. Box 250 82842
877-814-8608
307-683-2900
sales@chickadeecharms.com
www.chickadeecharms.com

From I - 90, take either Exit 44 or 33. Follow the signs for 5 - 8 miles. At the end of Story's Main business street. Featured as a destination quilt shop by Quilt Magazine.

The cheerful Chickadees are ready with a big Western Welcome!

Buffalo, WY #3

Mon - Fri 10 - 5
Sat 10 - 4

E.J. Quilts
Buffalo, Wyoming

80 S. Main St. 82834
1-877-ETQUILTS or (307) 684-9006
Fax: (307) 684-5540
Owner: Terry Foust
Est: 2000
3600 sq.ft.
1000 Bolts

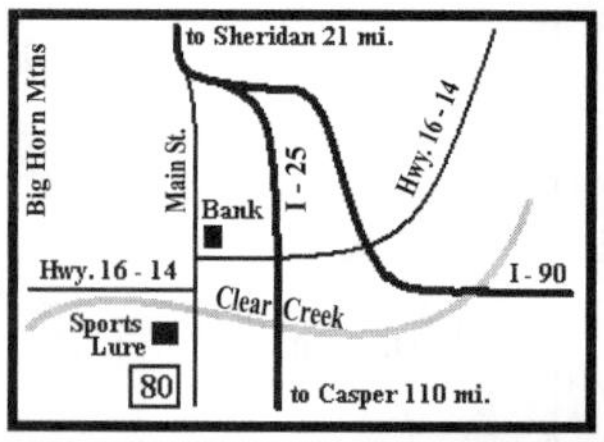

terry@etquilts.com www.etquilts.com
Quality Fabrics, Notions, Kits, Patterns, Books & Quilts. Salt City Candles, Needlecraft, Boyd's Bears and Kona Bay Asian Fabrics. Free Online Newsletter.

Sheridan, WY #4

Mon - Fri 10 - 6
Sat 9 - 4

The Quilters' Fix

1135 N. Main 82801
(307) 674-0558 Fax: (307) 674-6633
Owners: Julie Way & Jackie Jolovich
Est: 2008 quiltersfix@fiberpipe.net
www.quiltersfix.com

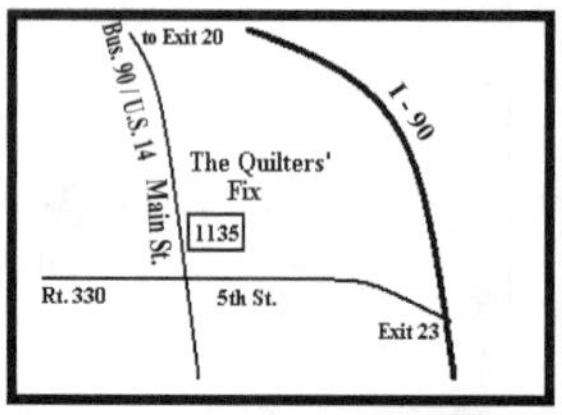

Large Selection of Batiks, Flannel, Novelties & Children Prints. Great Variety of Wildlife and Western Prints. Classes. Handicap Accessible.

529 Greybull Ave. 82426
(877) 586-9150
or (307) 765-2604

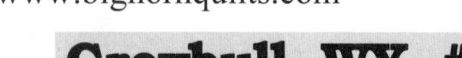

Big Horn Quilts

www.bighornquilts.com

Greybull, WY #5

Mon - Fri 10 - 4, Sat 9 - 3

Julie@bighornquilts.com
Owners: David & Julie Owens
Est: 1998 6000 Bolts
Online Catalog

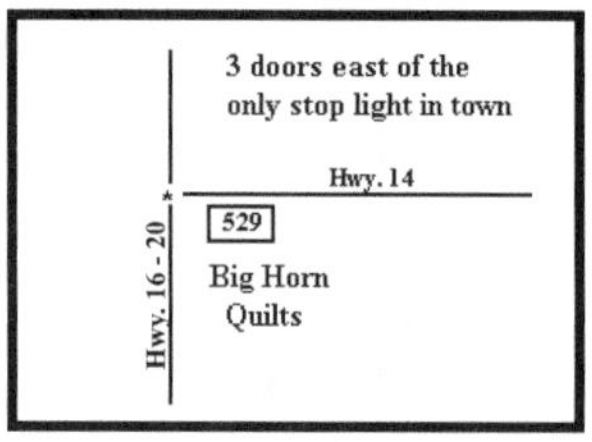

Worland, WY #6

Mon - Fri 9 - 5:30
Sat 10 - 2

Heart-N-Home

1201 Big Horn Ave. 82401
(307) 347-4954
Owners: Marcy & Richard Buckman

Full line Craft Supply Store.
Quilting Cottons & much more.
Quilt books, notions, patterns, etc.

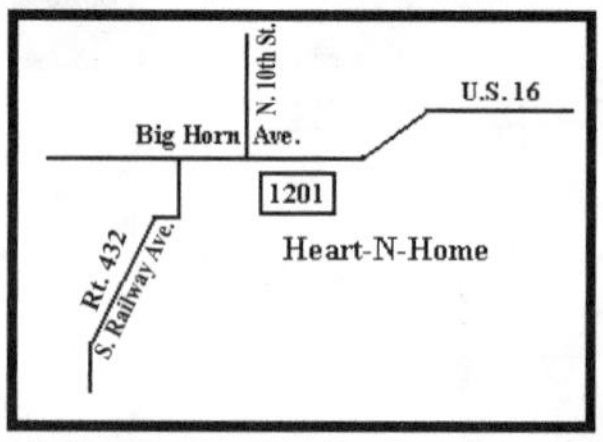

Cody, WY #7

Mon - Sat 10 - 6

Friends & Co.

402 Warren 82414
(307) 527-7217
Fax: (307) 527-7217
friendsandcoquilts@yahoo.com www.friendsandco.net
Owners: Arnold & Vicki Mollett

Est: 2004
4000 sq. ft.
5000+ bolts
Fabrics & Supplies
Quilts and Gifts
Husqvarna Viking Machines, HQ 16 with ProStitcher

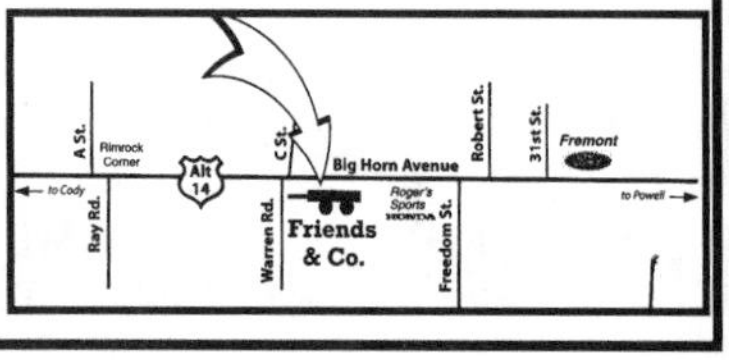

Jackson, WY #8

Stitch 'n Time, Inc.

Jackson Hole's Largest Fabric, Quilting and Craft Center

Mon - Fri 9 - 6
Sat 9 - 5

955 Alpine Ln., P.O. Box 13070
Jackson, WY 83002
(888) 565-5634 or (307) 733-6800
sales@stitchntimeinc.com
www.stitchntimeinc.com
Owner: Kim Kerr

Est: 1971
5000 sq.ft. 4000 Bolts

A unique array of fabrics and notions that expand the imagination to creative expression.

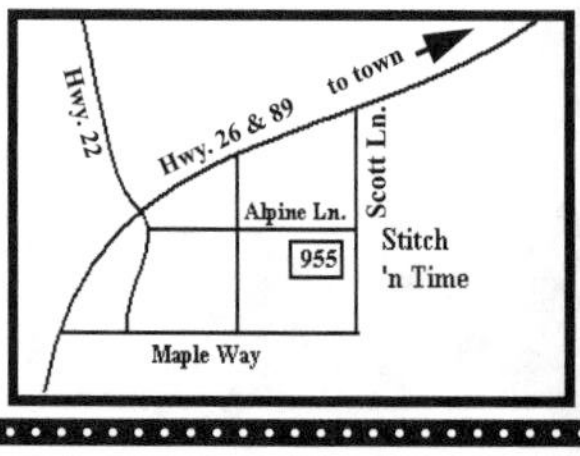

Heritage Quilts & Fabric Shoppe

THE AREA'S FRIENDLIEST QUILT STORE

www.HeritageQuiltsFabricShoppe.com

Over 4500 bolts of cottons & flannel fabric to choose from the deep hues of Kansas Troubles & Holly Taylor to the vibrant colors of Bali hand dyes and batiks. Books, patterns, notions & distinctive gifts. Classes Offered. Authorized Husqvarna-VIKING dealer

Quilt programs by:
McKenna Ryan of Pine Needles

Pinedale, WY #9

Owner: Sue Wells
21 East Pine St.,
P.O. Box 1517 82941
(307) 367-7397 (SEWS)

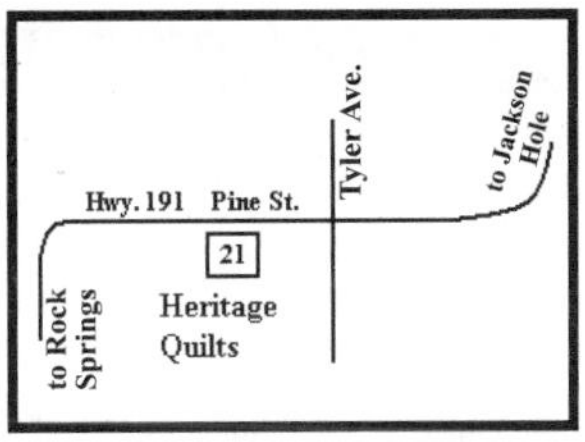

HOURS:
Mon - Fri
9 - 5:30
Sat
10 - 4:30

The building with the Cattle Drive mural, next door to the new Visitors Center

Casper, WY #10

Mon - Sat 10 - 5

Prism Quilt

114 E. 2nd St. 82601
(307) 234-4841
www.prismquilt.com
Owners: Becki & Bill Marsh
Est: 1987 4800 sq.ft.

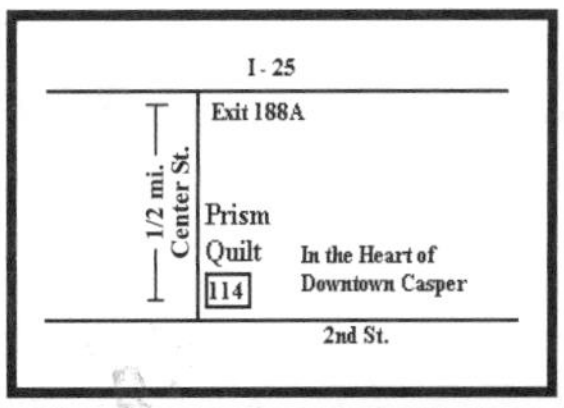

4800+ cotton fabrics, 5000 fat quarters, Pfaff Sewing Machines, Quilts, Books, Patterns, Notions, Quilting Supplies and Service.

Casper, WY #11

Mon - Thur 10 - 6
Fri & Sat 10 - 5

Kalico Kat Quilt Shop

350 W. Collins Dr. 82601
(307) 237-8458
Owner: Sandie Swanson
Est: 2005 2000 sq.ft.
www.kalicokatquilts.com

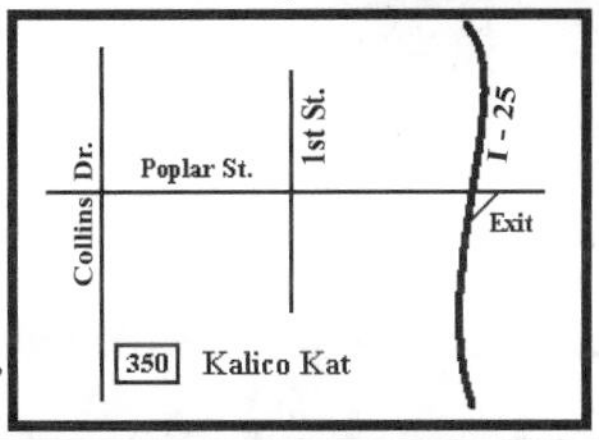

3500+ bolts of quality cotton fabrics; Hoffman Batiks, RJR, Thimbleberries, Moda, Kansas Troubles, Blacks/Whites Wall, Books, Patterns, and Notions. Many Classes.

Douglas, WY #12

Mon - Fri 9 - 5:30
Sat 9 - 4

Above the Cellar

132 N. 2nd St. 82633
(307) 358-2206
Owners: Vicki Weiss & Paulette Dunn
Est: 1983 2000 sq.ft. 300+ bolts

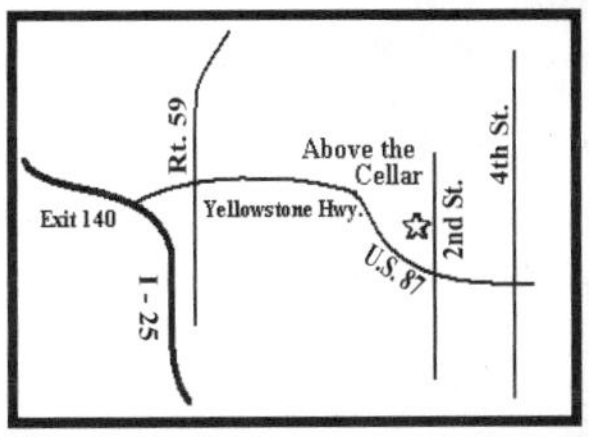

Art & Craft Supplies, Nice selection of fine fabrics. Cake & Candy Supplies. Rubber Stamping & Scrapbooking Supplies. Boyd's Bears & Webkinz. Gourmet Coffee Beans, Jewelry.

Douglas, WY #13

Mon - Fri 9 - 5:30
Sat 9 - 4

The Prairie Stitcher

120 N. 3rd St. 82633
(307) 358-5571

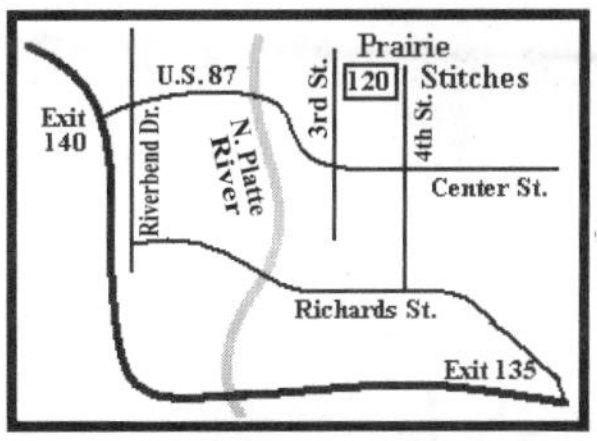

Quilting - Yarns - Stitcheries - Fleece
Gifts - Gooseberry Patch Books
Novels - Mysteries - Specialty Threads

Lusk, WY #14

Tues - Sat 9 - 5

LICKETY Stitch QUILTS
A Creative Sewing Center

206 S. Main St. 82225
(307) 334-9963
Est: 2010

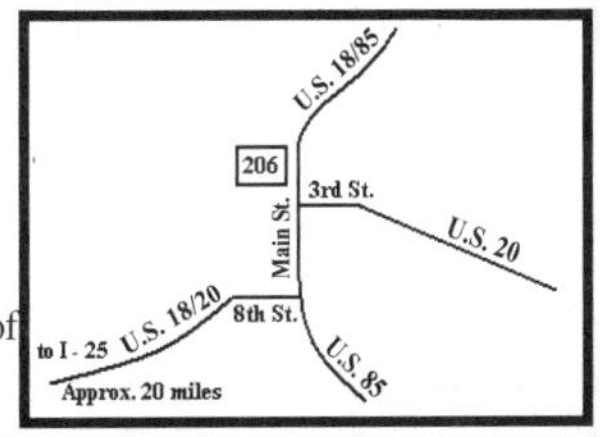

licketystitch@hughes.net
www.licketystitchquilts.com
Quilt shop and creative sewing center. Large variety of fabrics, books, patterns, notions and kits. Finished quilts and machine quilting services.

QuiltEssentials

314 S. 2nd St. 82070
(307) 742-6156
quiltessentials@qwestoffice.net
www.quiltessentials.org
Owners: Cynthia Deveraux & Rose McNerney
Est: 2002 3100 sq.ft. 3000 Bolts

A full line of Fabrics, Books, Notions and Gift Items. Located in Historic Downtown Laramie.

Laramie, WY #15

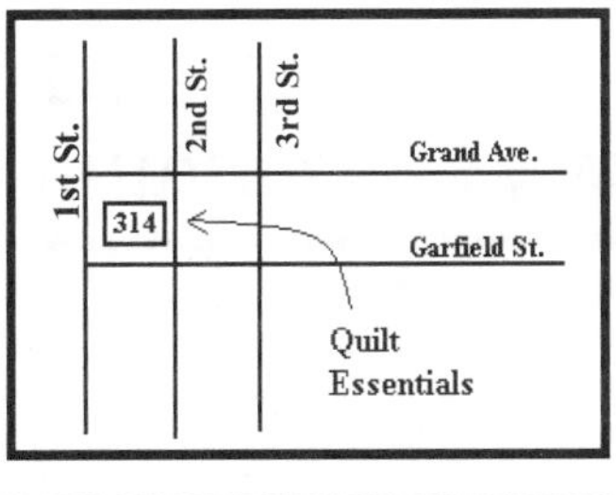

Mon - Sat 10 - 5:30

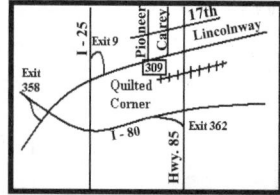

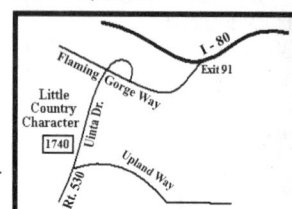

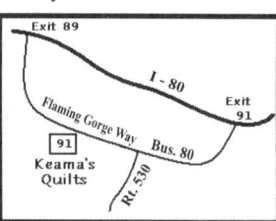

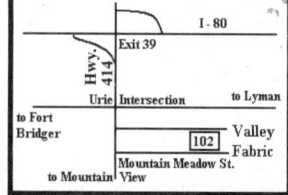

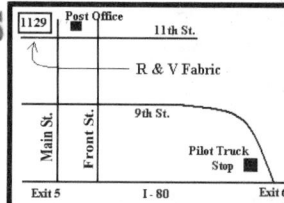

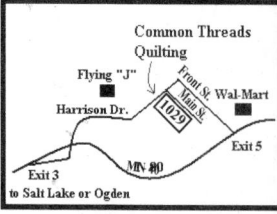

Wyoming Quilt Shops

Afton — The Cottage, 419 S. Washington St. 307-885-2522

Buffalo — **ET Quilts 80 S. Main St.**
307-684-9006 See ad #3, page 606

Casper — **Prism Quilt, 114 E. 2nd St.**
307-234-4841 See ad #10, page 607

Casper — **Kalico Kat Quilt Shop, 350 W. Collins Dr.**
307-237-8458 See ad #11, page 607

Casper — Buzy Bee Quilt and Sew Shop, 1831 E. 12th 307-237-6876

Cheyenne — **The Quilted Corner, 309 W. Lincolnway**
307-638-2002 See ad #17, page 608

Cheyenne — **Around the Block, 453 Vandehei Ave. #120**
307-433-9555 See ad #16, page 608

Clearmont — The Best Kept Secret, 1617 New York Ave. 307-758-4456

Cody — **Friends & Co. Quilt Shop, 402 Warren Rd.**
307-527-7217 See ad #7, page 606

Douglas — **The Prairie Stitcher, 120 N. 3rd St.**
307-358-5571 See ad #13, page 607

Douglas — **Above the Cellar, 132 N. 2nd St.**
307-358-2206 See ad #12, page 607

Evanston — **R&V High Country Fabrics, 528 Cty Rd.**
307-789-7300 See ad #21, page 608

Evanston — **Common Threads Quilting, 1029 Main St.**
307-444-1675 See ad #22, page 608

Gillette — **Quilt Nook, 211 W. 2nd St.**
307-682-9196 See ad #1, page 605 & 416

Green River — **A Little Country Character, 1740 Uinta Dr.**
307-875-7172 See ad #18, page 608 & 202

Green River — **Keama's Quilts, 91 W. Flaming Gorge Way**
888-875-5461 See ad #19, page 608

Greybull — **Big Horn Quilts, 529 Greybull Ave.**
307-765-2604 See ad #5, page 606

Hulett — Witches Stitches, 101 Sager St. 307-467-5343

Jackson — **Stitch 'N Time, 955 Alpine Lane**
307-733-6800 See ad #8, page 606

Kemmerer — Ace Hardware Fabric & Gifts, 709 Pine 307-877-6956

Lander — Wyoming Quilts, 305 Main St. 307-332-4123

Laramie — **QuiltEssentials, 314 S. 2nd St.**
307-742-6156 See ad #15, page 607

Laramie — Snowy River Quilts, 216 E. Custer 307-721-3160

Lovell — Mayes Fabrics, 435 Oregon Ave. 307-548-7715

Lusk — **Lickety Stitch Quilts, 206 S Main St**
307-334-9963 See ad #14, page 607

Lyman — **Valley Fabric Shop, 102 Meadow St.**
307-786-2653 See ad #20, page 608

Pinedale — **Heritage Quilts & Fabric Shoppe, 21 E. Pine**
307-367-7397 See ad #9, page 607

Powell — Cut & Sew, 217 N. Bent 307-754-7247

Rock Springs — Willow Ridge Crafts, 625 Broadway St. 307-362-2556

Rock Springs — The Huckleberry Patch, 513 Elbow Ln. 307-362-2245

Sheridan — **The Quilters Fix, LLC, 1135 N. Main St.**
3076740558 See ad #4, page 606

Shoshoni — Sheep Camp Quilts, 865 Paradise Valley 307-856-1468

Story — **Pinewood Cottage Quilts, 36 N. Piney Rd.**
307-683-2900 See ad #2, page 606

Worland — **Heart - N - Home, 1201 Big Horn Ave.**
307-347-4954 See ad #6, page 606

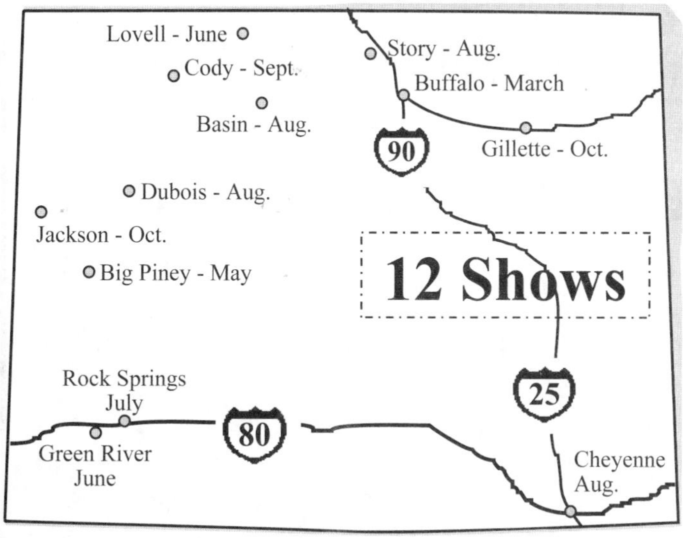

Wyoming Quilt Shows

About Shows: We are listing only the very basic information about shows that happen on a regular schedule here. Please check out our website for more details on each show. Also this information tends to change quite often so please verify the event with our website or a local source before you venture far. Or if you're in the right area at the right time, give it a shot.

If you are a show organizer, please keep us updated on your event.
shows@quilterstravelcompanion.com
www.quilterstravelcompanion.com

Month	City	Schedule	Show	Location with address
March				
	Buffalo	Annual, most of March	Buffalo Quilting Gals Quilt Show	Johnson County Library, 171 N. Adams
May				
	Big Piney	Annual, 3rd Fri & Sat in May	Big Piney and Pinedale Quilt Guilds Show	Big Piney Annex, 950 Piney Dr
June				
	Green River	Annual, weekend after Memorial Day	Quilting on the Green	Expedition Island Pavilion, 475 S 2nd East St.
	Lovell	Annual, last weekend in June	Pindropper's Club Show	National Guard Armory, 360 E 5th St
July				
	Rock Springs	Annual, 3rd weekend in July	Wyoming State Quilt Guild Show	Western Wyoming Comm. College
August				
	Basin	Annual, 1st weekend in August	Big Horn County Fair Quilt Show	Big Horn County Fair Main Bldg, 315 Holdrege Ave.
	Cheyenne	Annual, 1st Thurs - Sat in August	Cheyenne Heritage Quilter's Show	Cheyenne Civic Center, 510 W. 20th St. (Just off I-25, exit 362)
	Dubois	Annual, 2nd weekend in August	Never Sweat Needlers Quilt Show	Headwaters Arts and Conference Center, 20 Stalnaker St.
	Story	Annual, 4th Saturday of August	Mountain Village Outdoor Quilt Show	Pinewood Cottage Quilt & Gift Shop, 36 N. Piney Rd.
September				
	Cody	Annual, 2nd weekend in September	Yellowstone Quilt Fest	Cody Auditorium, 16 Sunburst Dr.
October				
	Gillette	Annual, 1st weekend of October	North East Wyoming Quilt Show	Cam-Plex Energy Hall, 1634 Reata Dr.
	Jackson	Annual, 1st week of October	Quilting in the Tetons	Tetons County Fair Bldg., 350 W. Snow King Ave.

12 Featured Shops

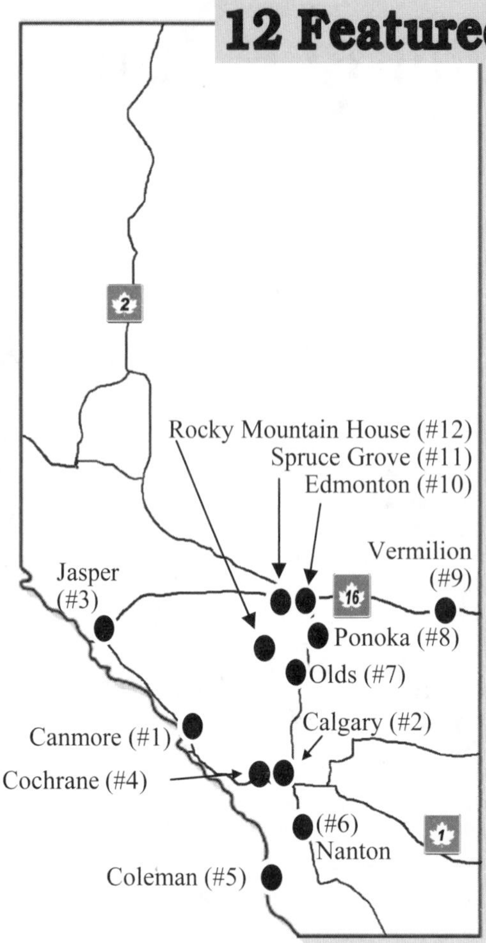

ALBERTA CANADA

#1

The Sugar Pine Company

Award-Winning Quilt Shop · Canmore, Alberta

(403) 678-9603 www.thesugarpine.com

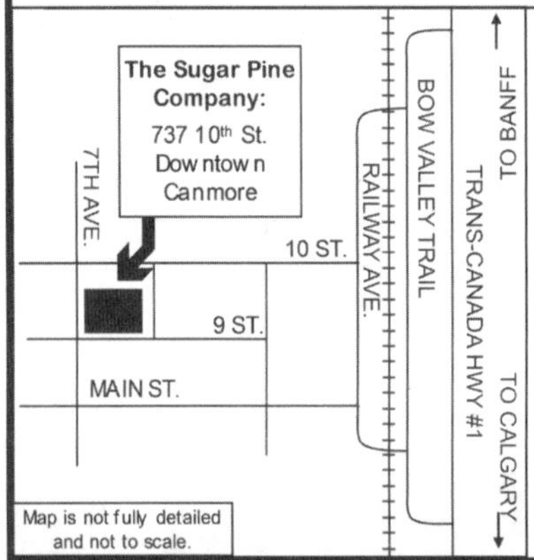

- 8,000 Bolts
- Open Evenings & Weekends
- Lots of Quilt Kits
- Knitting & Gifts
- Featured Shop
  Quilt Sampler Magazine

Mon - Sat: 9 - 9
Sun: 11 - 8

737 Tenth Street, Canmore, Alberta T1W 2A3 Phone: (403) 678-9603
Fax: (403) 678-4703 www.thesugarpine.com

Present this ad & SAVE 10% on Cotton Fabrics*

*Restrictions Apply. Expires December 31, 2012

My Sewing Room

www.mysewingroom.ca

Canada's Largest Quilt Shoppe!

"Still small enough to care."

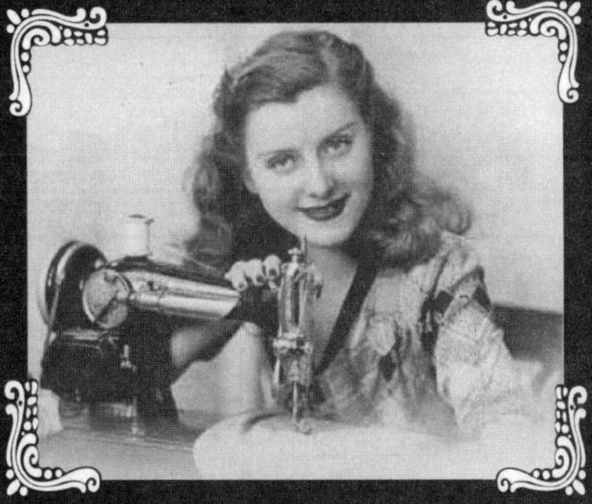

- Enormous selection of quality cotton fabrics! Over 10,000 bolts. "Fabric Rooms" of Asian, Retro, Novelty, Flannel, Seasonal, Batik and much more!
- A friendly shoppe in an easy to find location with terrific hours and great staff.
- Bernina & Brother sewing machine dealer.
- On site Computerized Long-Arm Quilting.
- On Site Sewing Machine Repair.

Take a tour online at :
www.greatcanadianshophop.com

Let us know where you are visiting from. Buses are welcome, please call ahead.
Check out our class schedule on-line.

Est. 2001, Proprietor: Anne Dale
info@mysewingroom.ca

Shop Hours:
9:30 - 9:00 Monday - Friday
9:30 - 5:00 Saturday
11:00 - 5:00 Sunday
Closed Most Holidays

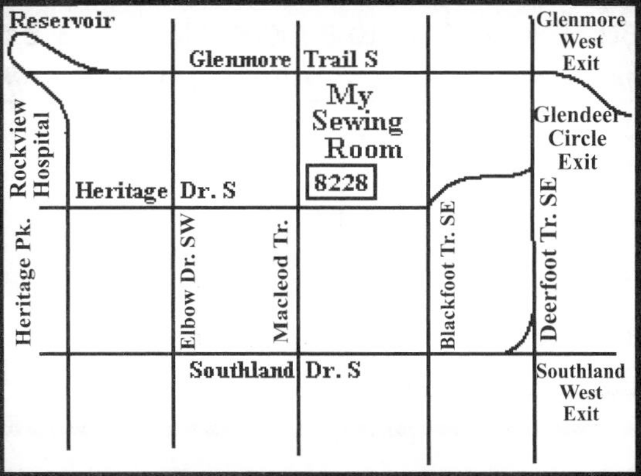

148, 8228 Macleod Trail SE
Calgary, Alberta T2H 2B8
403-252-3711

2

Jasper, AB #3

Summer Daily 10 - 8
Winter Closed Monday

STYCHEN TYME QUILT & YARN SHOP

Est: 2000
1000 sq.ft.
4000 Bolts

402 Patricia St.
P.O. Box 2230 T0E 1E0
(780) 852-7490 or (866) 852-7490
Owner: Romy Quackenbush
www.stychentyme.ca

Large selection of fabric, yarn and cross-stitch available. Specializing in "Lodge" and "Nordic" designs. Featuring Canadian designers. Stitch a Rocky Mountain Memory.

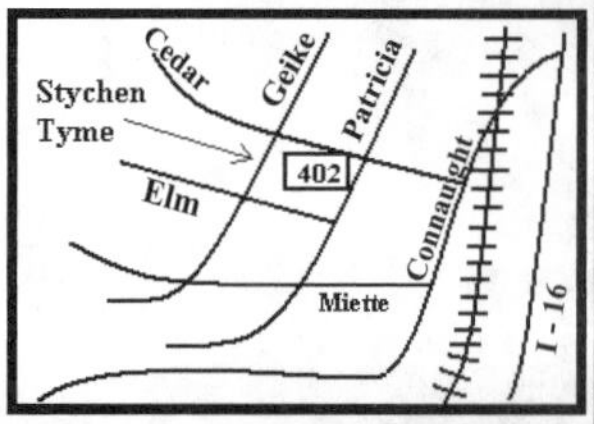

Cochrane, AB #4

Tues - Sat 10:30 - 5:30
Sun 12 - 4

Addie's

420 First St. West
Box 1047 T4C 1B1
(403) 932-1500

Free Newsletter
2addies@telus.net
www.addiescreativefabrics.com
Addie's is a popular destination quilt shop with travelers across Canada & around the world.

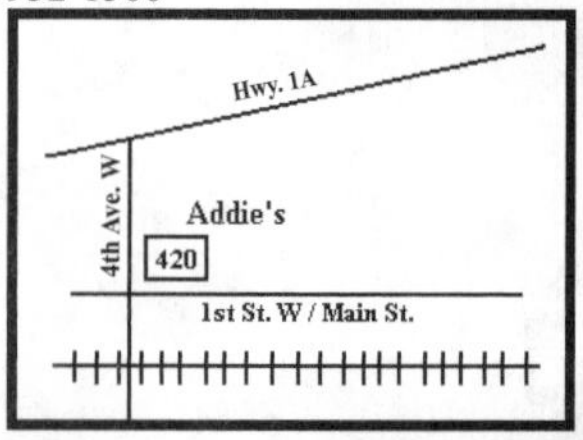

Coleman, AB #5

Tues - Fri 11 - 5:30
Sat 9:30 - 5:30

Cozy Corner

baby lock
accuquilt

7801 - 17 Avenue, P.O. Box 366 T0K 0M0
(403) 562-2699 (COZY)
Owner: Pam York Est: 2005
1950 sq. ft. 2200 bolts cozycor@shaw.ca
www.aquiltersplayground.com

Located on Heritage Rte 3 in downtown Coleman.
Stop in for a free gift. Lots of books, tools, notions. Patterns & Books by Canadian Designers. Our website is Paypal friendly.

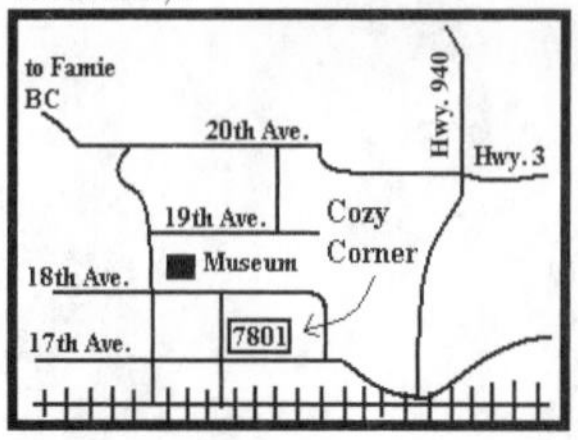

Nanton, AB #6

Tues - Fri 10 - 5
Sat 10 - 4

Cottonwoods

2109 - 20th St., P.O. Box 1021 T0L 1R0
(403) 646-2086 Fax: (403) 646-2398
cotwoods@telusplanet.net
Est: 1998 5000 sq.ft. 1500 Bolts
Toll Free 1-866-646-9970
Quilting fabrics, classes, books, notions & patterns. Quilts for Sale.
Authorized Pfaff Dealer.

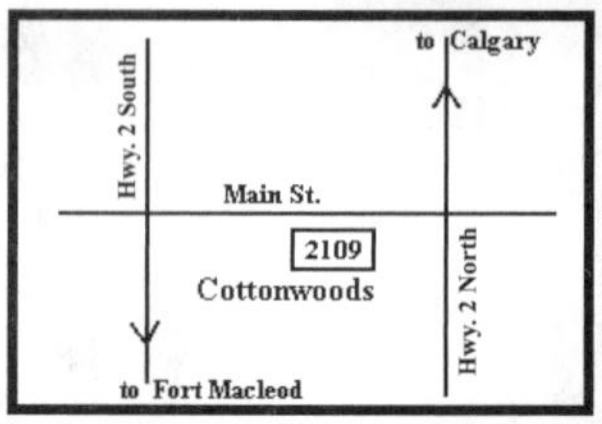

Olds, AB #7

THE QUILTING BEE

Established—2000

5026 51 Street
Olds AB T4H 1P7
403-507-8825

www.thequiltingbee.ca

Owner: Cheryl Naglis

STORE HOURS
Monday to Saturday
10 am—5 pm

For small town charm and friendly faces, we can't be beat! Take a drive to a more relaxing pace of life.

The Quilting Bee is your Hive of Inspiration

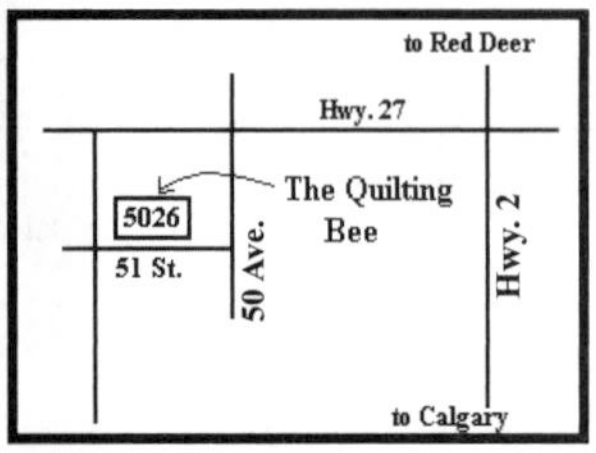

- Cotton & Specialty Fabrics
- Yummy Yarns
- Threads to Inspire
- Classes & Lectures
- Quilting Frames
- Wools & Kits

Ponoka, AB #8

Mon - Fri 9 - 5:30
Sat 9 - 4

Dot's Crafts & Yarn Supplies

5023 - 51Ave. T4J 1S1
(403) 783-4091

Lots of 100% Quilting Fabrics.
A wonderful selection of Yarns.
Notions, books & cross stitch supplies.
Also uniforms.

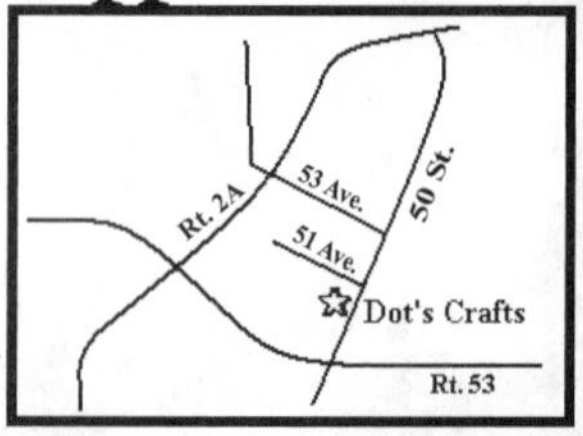

Vermilion, AB #9

Mon - Sat 10 - 6
Thur til 8

EXTRAORDINARY EXTRAS
QUILTING & GIFTWARE

Located in the Lakeland Mall
4420 Railway Ave. T9X 1G1
(780) 853-6626

Owner: Carol Wasylik Est: 1997
eextras@telus.net Newsletter available.
www.extraordinaryextras.com

We offers a variety of fabrics and giftware. Patterns, Books, Notions, Kits and Classes.

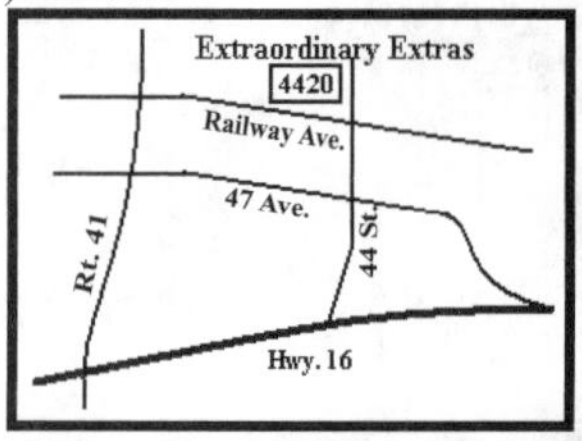

Edmonton, AB #10

Mon - Fri 9 - 8
Sat 9-5 Sun 12-5

Earthly Goods

5848 111th St. T6H 3G1
Lendrum Shopping Center
(780) 433-7179 Fax: (780) 430-1508
Est: 1985
Owner:
Patti Hansen
4000 sq.ft.
3000 Bolts

info@earthlygoodsquilting.com
www.earthlygoodsquilting.com
Featured in Quilt Sampler Magazine.
Everything you need for quilting including Cottons, Notions & Books. Great Classes.

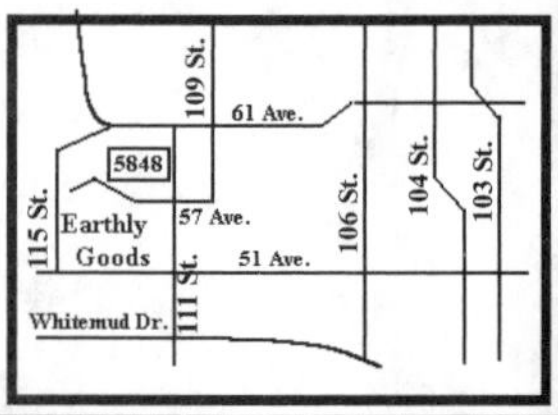

Spruce Grove, AB #11

Mon - Sat 9:30 - 5 Thur til 8

Woodland Quilting Co.
"the little store with lots of fabric"

323 McLeod Ave.,
P.O. Box 5171 T7X 3A3
(780) 962-2599 Est: 2007
Owner: Maureen Lipiec 1000+ Bolts
maureen@woodlandquilting.com
www.woodlandquilting.com

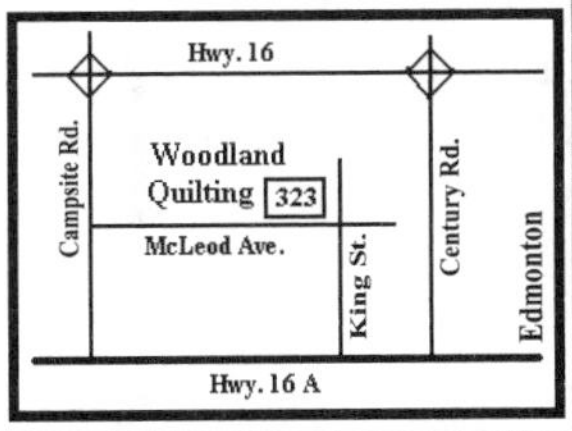

Woodland Quilting offers a large selection of fabrics, including flannels and homespuns. Our friendly staff members look forward to helping you find the perfect fabric for your project!

Rocky Mtn. House, AB #12

Mon - Sat 9:30 - 5:30

Big Horn Plaza, Hwy 11, PO Box 249 T4T 1P1
(403) 845-4314
Est: 2004 cornerquilts@hotmail.com
www.quilterscorner.ca

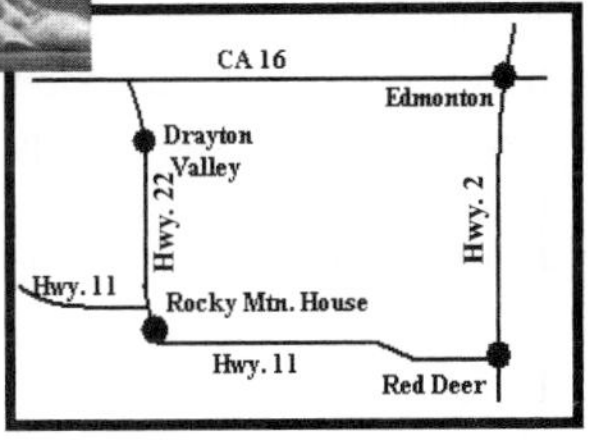

We offer a wide range of quality cottons and flannels, books, patterns and notion. Many of our patterns and kits are our very own designs. Classes, retreats and long arm quilting.

Alberta Quilt Shops

Airdrie	Material Girls Quilt Co., 129 Bowers St. NE	403-948-2171
Athabasca	Whispering Hills Fabrics, 4910A 50 St.	780-675-7075
Beaver Lodge	Around the Block, 1040 1St. Ave., PO Box 1078	780-354-3423
Boyle	Homespun Gallery, 5124 3 St.	780-689-5151
Brooks	Deanna's Quilted Garden, #114 - 2nd St. W.	403-362-6606
Calgary	**My Sewing Room, 148, 8228 Macleod Trail S.E. 403-252-3711**	**See ad #2, page 611**
Calgary	Needleworks Fabrics, 759 Northmount Dr. NW	403-210-2883
Calgary	A Sewing Sensation-CC, 3832 19th St. NW	403-288-8288
Calgary	Along Came Quilting #12, 5920 11th St. SE	403-253-4419
Calgary	Out of Hand, 12-6449 Crowchild Tr. SW	403-217-4871
Calgary	Traditional Pastimes, 7 Parkdale Cres. NW	403-286-9421
Calgary	Freckles Quilt Shop, Ltd., 13A-728 Northmount Drive NW	403-270-2104
Camrose	Quilting From the Heart, 5710 - 48th Ave.	877-679-5492
Camrose	Sewing Center Inc., 4944-50th St.	780-672-2732
Canmore	**The Sugar Pine Co., #1 - 737 Tenth St 403-678-9603**	**See ad #1, page 610**
Cardston	Imagination Unlimited, 257 Main St.	403-653-2633
Carstairs	Custom Woollen Mill, R.R. # 1	403-337-2221
Claresholm	Log Cabin Quilts, Box 1083	403-625-3478
Coaldale	Hopscotch Quilt Shop, 1401 - 20 Ave.	403-345-3910
Cochrane	**Addie's Creative Fabrics, 420 1st St. West 403-932-1500**	**See ad #4, page 612**
Cold Lake	Quilted Gems, 5214 50 Ave.	780-594-5200
Coleman	**Cozy Corner, 7801 - 17th Ave. 403-562-2699**	**See ad #5, page 612**
Crooked Creek	Country Stitches Quilts & Fabrics, R.R. 1 Site 5	780-957-2446
Drayton Valley	Material Matters, 5119 51st St., P.O. Box 6702	403-542-3233
Drumheller	Bits & Pieces Keepsake Quilting, 332 Center St.	403-823-5828
Edmonton	**Earthly Goods Quilting Corner, 5848 111th St. 780-433-7179**	**See ad #10, page 612**
Edmonton	Quilters' Dream, 4359 99 St. NW	780-496-9375
Edmonton	C & M Cottons & More, 8645 63 Ave. NW	780-431-9816
Edmonton	J & J Quilting and Needle Work, 10219 106th St	780-421-9973
Edmonton	Quilter's Dream , 10736 - 124 St. NW	403-452-1133
Grande Prairie	Cotton Candy Crafts & Quilts, 12405 99th St.	780-532-2202
High River	Chinook Fabrics, 149 MacLeod Tr., Box 5482	403-652-3145
Irma	Creative Klutter, 4907 50th St.	780-754-2227
Jasper	**Stychen Tyme Quilt & Yarn Shop, 402 Patricia 780-852-7490**	**See ad #3, page 612**
Killam	Tatters, 5007 - 50th St.	780-385-2292
Lacombe	Wildflower Creations, 5025 50 Ave.	403-782-4141
Lamont	L.A. Sewing Centre, 5028 50 Ave.	780-895-2599
Lethbridge	The Fabric Addict, #1038, 2045 Mayor Magrath Dr S	403-394-1440
Lethbridge	Sewing Lane, 2020A Mayor Magrath Dr. S	403-320-9700
Lethbridge	Village Crafts, #23 - 1240 2nd Ave. A North	403-320-1817
Linden	Jo-Al Styles & Fabrics, 113 Central Ave.	403-546-3882
Lloydminster	Quilter's Cupboard, Ltd., 5732 44th St.	780-875-0001
Lloydminster	B & H Fabrics LTD-CC, 4010 So. Ave., Bay 2	780-871-2830
Mannville	Village Treasures, 5009 50 St.	780-763-2202
Mayerthorpe	Kountry Krafts, 5015 50 St., Box 1109	780-786-2821
Medicine Hat	Quilters Country Cottage, #2 1023 Allowance Se	403-580-8227
Medicine Hat	Sew Many Treasures, 117-3030 13 Ave. SE	403-528-8889
Milk River	Stitch in Time, 207 Main St. NW	403-647-3931
Mundare	The Chicken Coop, 5103 50 St	780-764-3727
Nanton	**Cottonwoods, 2109 20th St. 403-646-2086**	**See ad #6, page 612**
Nanton	Fabrique Boutique, 2119 20 St	403-646-2106
Okotoks	Rumpled Quilt Skins, 64 N. Railway St.	403-938-6269
Olds	**The Quilting Bee, 5026 51st St. 403-507-8825**	**See ad #7, page 612**
Olds	The Stitchery, Box 6, Site 1, R.R. #2 Olds	403-556-6221
Olds	Craig's, 5102 50th Ave.	403-556-3717
Peace River	Seams Easy, 10003-A 102 Ave.	780-624-2750
Ponoka	**Dot's Crafts & Yarn Supplies, 5023 51st Ave. 403-783-4091**	**See ad #8, page 612**
Red Deer	Sew You Like 2 Quilt, Inc, 1018 A 4419 50th	403-348-8880
Red Deer	Cotton Threads Quilt Co., 5020 Gaetz Ave.	403-346-5510
Rocky Mountain House	**Quilters Corner, Hwy 11, Box 249 403-845-4314**	**See ad #12, this page**
Sherwood Park	Lori's Country Cottage, 70 - 130 Broadway Blvd	403-464-9697
Spruce Grove	**Woodland Quilting Co., 323 McLeod Ave. 780-962-2599**	**See ad #11, this page**
St. Albert	Quiltessential Co., 0A Perron St.	780-418-7845
Stettler	Homespun Seasons, 5004 - 50 Ave	403-742-0295
Stony Plain	Sawdust 'n Tangled Threads, 4810 50th Ave.	780-968-9186
Stony Plain	Sewing With Class, #114-3806 49th Ave.	780-963-5992
Strathmore	Cotton & Candy Quilt Shop, 55 Wheatland #2	403-934-3832
Vegreville	The Quilt Rack, 4927 50 St.	7806-327-890
Vegreville	Cotton Pick'n Quilt & Gift Shoppe, 5146 51 Ave	780-632-2342
Vermilion	**Extraordinary Extras, 4420 Railway Ave. 780-853-6626**	**See ad #9, page 612**
White Court	Sew Right, 5106 50th St., Box 2157	780-778-5717

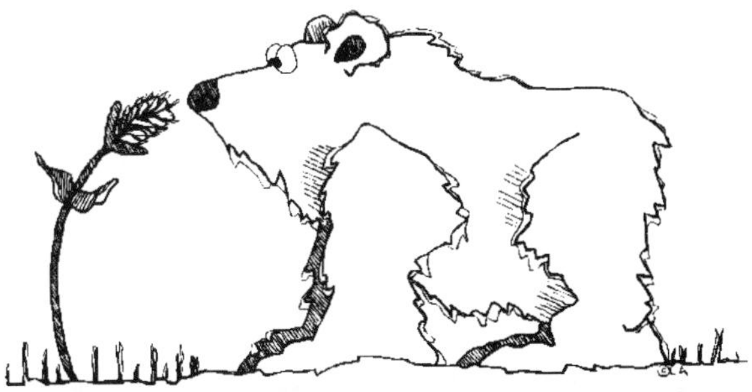

Alberta Quilt Shows

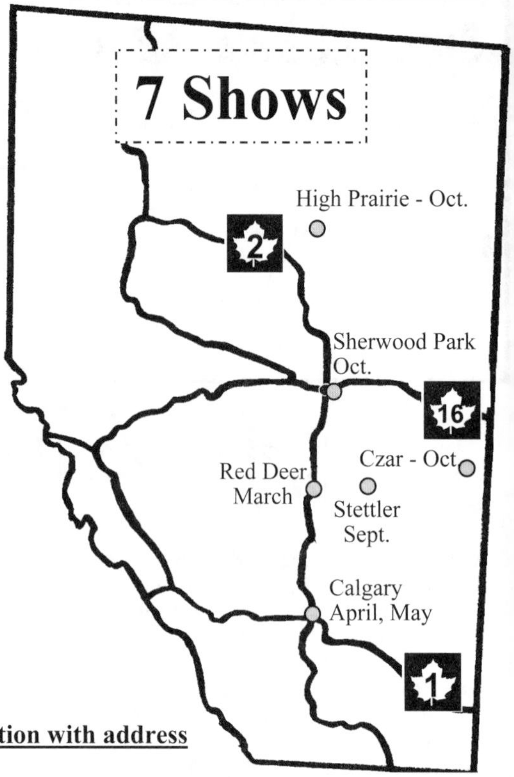

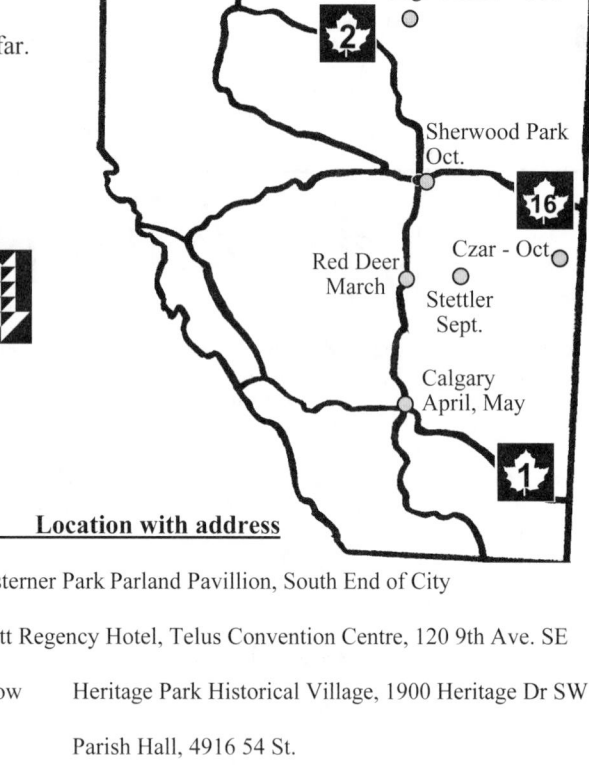

About Shows: We are listing only the very basic information about shows that happen on a regular schedule here. Please check out our website for more details on each show. Also this information tends to change quite often so please verify the event with our website or a local source before you venture far. Or if you're in the right area at the right time, give it a shot.

If you are a show organizer, please keep us updated on your event.
shows@quilterstravelcompanion.com www.quilterstravelcompanion.com

On our website you will also find:

- Exact dates (when we have them)
- Contact Information
- Events happening on a one-time basis
- Sponsor Information
- Description of Event

Month	City	Schedule	Show	Location with address
March				
	Red Deer	Annual, late March or early April	Central Alberta Quilt Show	Westerner Park Parland Pavillion, South End of City
April				
	Calgary	Even Years, Late April	Quilt Canada	Hyatt Regency Hotel, Telus Convention Centre, 120 9th Ave. SE
May				
	Calgary	Annual, Last weekend in May	Heritage Park Historical Village Show	Heritage Park Historical Village, 1900 Heritage Dr SW
September				
	Stettler	Annual, 3rd weekend in September	Heartland Quilters Guild Show	Parish Hall, 4916 54 St.
October				
	High Prairie	Annual, 3rd weekend in October	Happy to be Scrappy	St. Andrews School Gym, 53rd Ave.
	Sherwood Park	Odd Years, 3rd Fri & Sat in October	Sherwood Park Quilt Guild Show	Sherwood Park Pentecostal Assembly, 1 Brower Dr.
	Czar	Annual, last Fri & Sat of October	Quilt Show	Czar Recreation & Cultural Center, Center of Town

Notes

9 Featured Shops

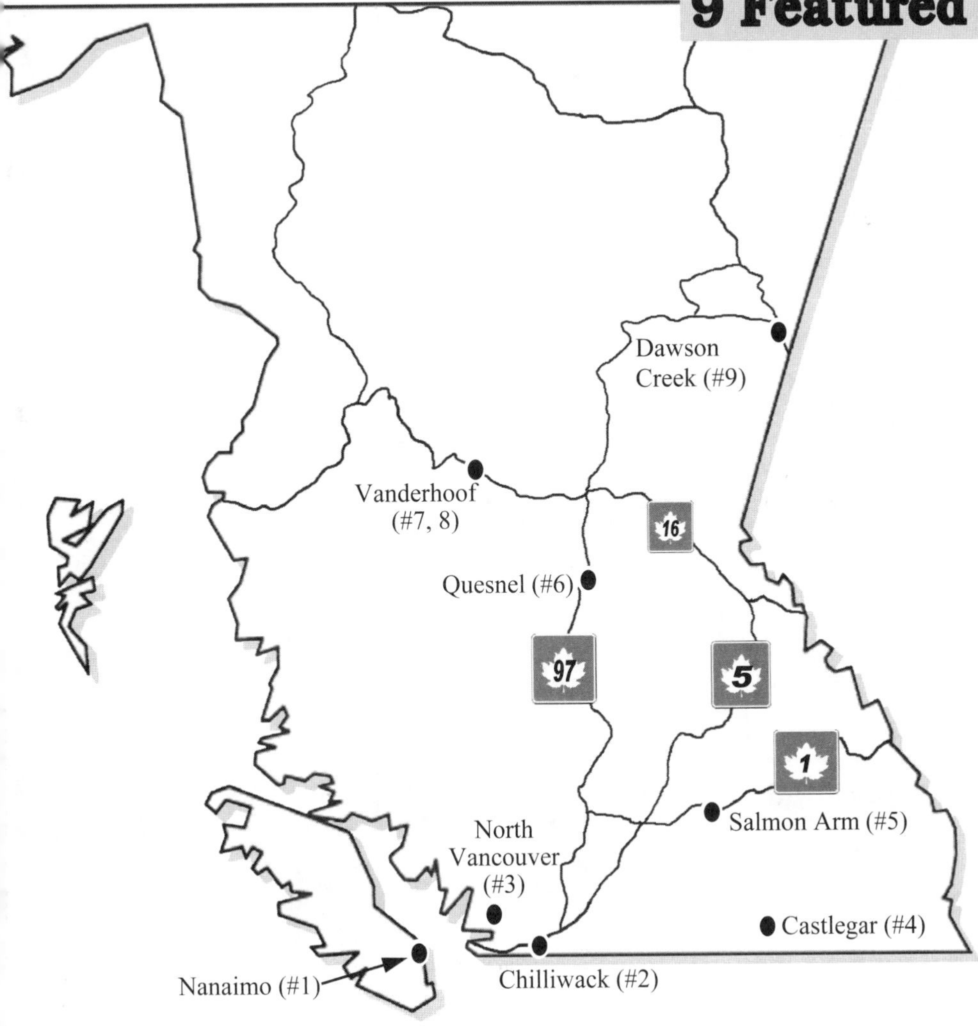

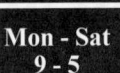

BRITISH COLUMBIA

Snip & Stitch
SEWING CENTRE
NANAIMO

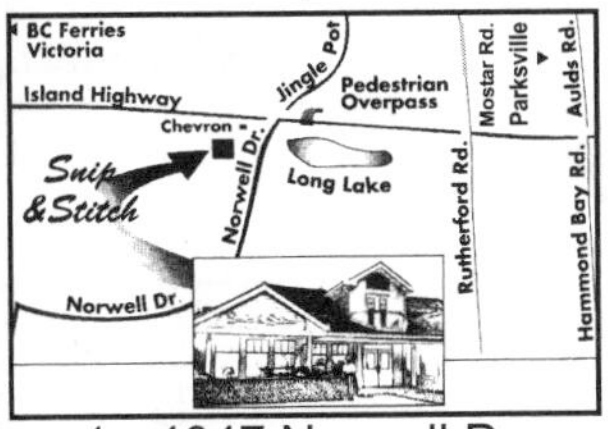

1 - 4047 Norwell Dr.
V9T 1Y6
(800) 789-1730
or (250) 756-2176
info@snipandstitch.com
www.snipandstitch.com

9:30 - 5:30 Mon - Sat
12:00 - 4:00 Sundays
Closed Holidays

Your "One Stop Quilting & Sewing Store" on Vancouver Island

Conveniently situated, one block off the Island Highway in North Nanaimo, we offer a wide selection of classes, books and notions as well as the "BEST" selection of quilting cottons on Vancouver Island.

Come wander throughout the store for a refreshing experience. We look forward to meeting you.
Kathy & Perry Schroter & Staff

Nanaimo, BC #1

Chilliwack, BC #2

Mon - Sat 9 - 5

Hamels Fabrics

5843 Lickman Rd.
V2R 4B5
(604) 846-4350

Quality Cotton Fabrics
Books and Quilting Notions
Kits & Block of the Months

Canada's largest online Quilt Shop

Many Quilts on Display.
Mail Order through our Web-Site: www.hamelsfabrics.com
hamelsfabrics@shawcable.com
toll free: 1-877-774-2635
Owner: Pauline Southgate

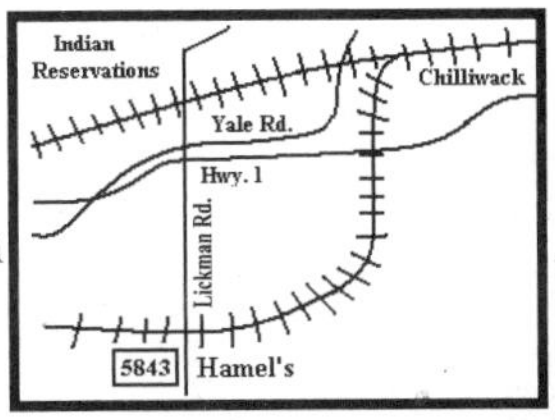

North Vancouver, BC #3

Tues - Sat 10 - 5
Sun 12 - 4

Creative Edge Quilting & Sewing

2055 Old Dollarton Rd. V7H 1A6
(604) 982-0088
Owner: Maureen Van Den Dool Est: 2008
creativedge@telus.net

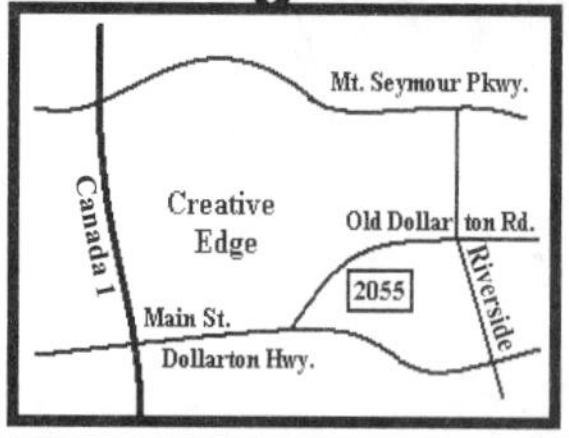

- Specialize in Hoffman Batiks
- Moda - Kaffe Fassett
- Local and Australian Patterns
- South African hand-dyed specialty fabric

Castlegar, BC #4

Mon - Sat 9 - 4:30

Jean's Material Things

650 23rd St. V1N 3X1
(250) 304-2337
Est 2004 Newsletter
jeansmaterialthings@shaw.ca
www.jeansmaterialthings.com
Supplying you with the very finest in top quality quilting material, notions, patterns, threads, yarns and classes. We strive to offer the very best in customer service and satisfaction.

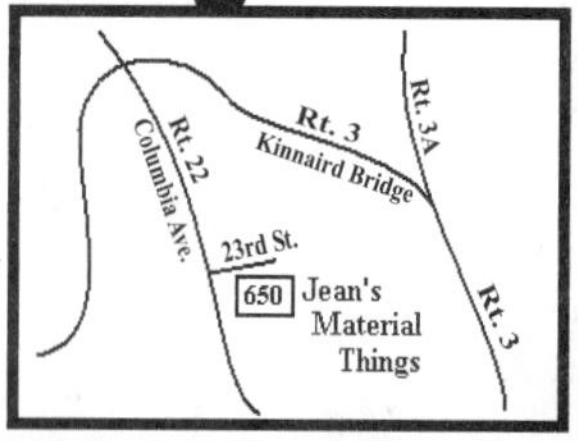

Salmon Arm, BC #5

The Sewing Basket

Quilts & Crafts

168 Macleod, P.O. 327,
V1E 4N5
Located behind the Chevron Station
(250) 832-3937
www.SewingBasket.ca

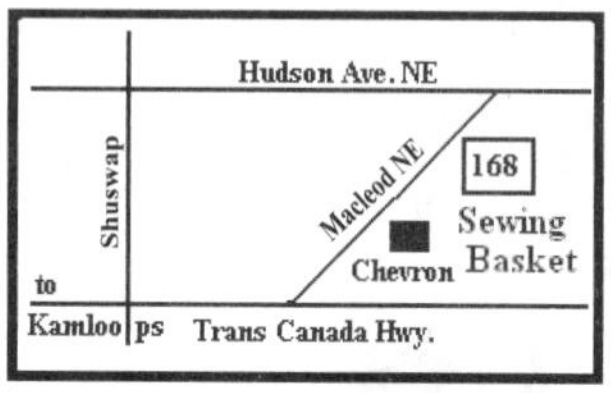

We're a ***"One Stop Shop"*** with:
*A Huge Selection of Quilting Fabrics
*All the latest Notions & Books
*Great Selection of Quilting Kits
*The Most Fabulous Displays--Classes
*Authorized JANOME dealer

Mon - Sat 9:00 - 5:30

A Big City Selection with a Small Town Friendly Atmosphere. It's worth a special trip and the Prices are great too.

Quesnel, BC #6

Mon - Fri 10 - 5
Sat 10 - 3

Expressions By Ewe

222 McNaughton Ave. V2J 2G6
(250) 992-8896
Owner: Marjorie Sales
Est: 1987

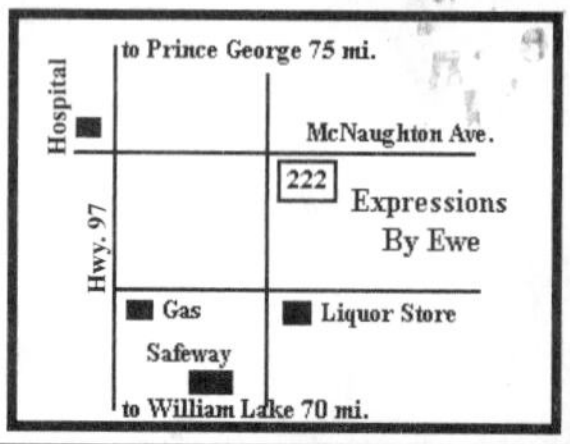

More than 1000 bolts of great fabrics. Large selection of books & supplies for quilting & cross-stitch. Authorized Pfaff dealer.

Vanderhoof, BC #7

Mon - Sat 9 - 5:30

Quilters Corner in Vanderhoof Dept. Store

2465 Burrard Ave., P.O. Box 249 V0J 3A0
(250) 567-2311 Fax: (250) 567-3818
vds@uniserve.com
Owners: Janet & Larry Bangs
Est: 1930 2000 sq.ft. 2000+ Bolts
Large selection of quilting fabrics & notions. Large selection of Bali and Asian Fabrics, also blender fabrics, Moda and Fusions.
Friendly atmosphere.

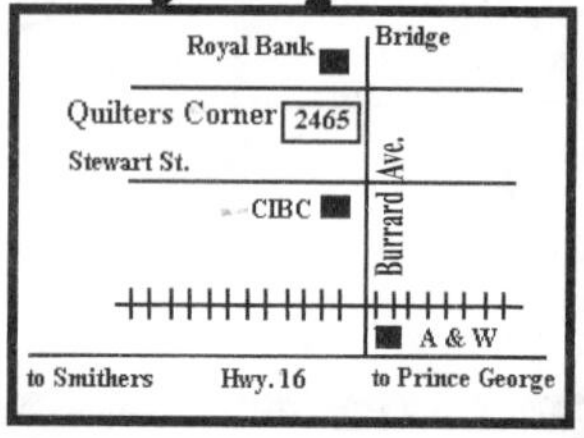

Vanderhoof, BC #8

Mon - Sat 9:30 - 5

Quilters Nook

185 W. Stewart St. V0J 3A0
(250) 567-2828
Owner: Helen Wiebe
Est: 2002 Newsletter
cambiequiltersnook@hotmail.com

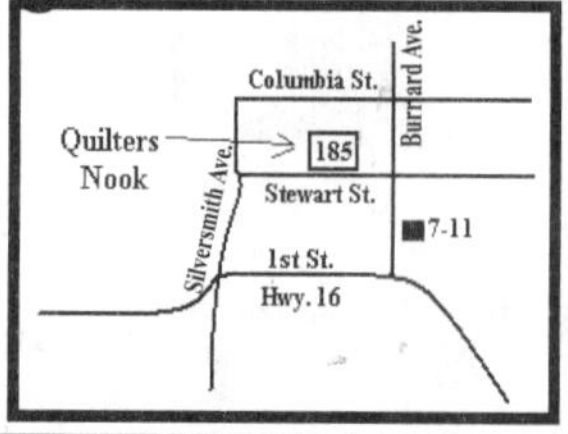

Specializing in fine yarns and quilting fabrics. We carry Amy Butler and Kaffee Fassett prints. A great little quilt shop in the center of BC.

Dawson Creek, BC #9

Mon - Fri 9:30 - 5:30
Sat 10 - 5

The Sew & Sew's QUILT SHOPPE

Husqvarna VIKING

1323 - 102 Ave. V1G 2C8
(250) 782-8777 Fax: (250) 782-8779
thesewandsews@shawcable.com
Owner: Chamie Pekrul Est: 1994
2000 sq.ft. 2000 Bolts Free Newsletter
We specialize in quality Quilting fabrics, notions, books & classes.

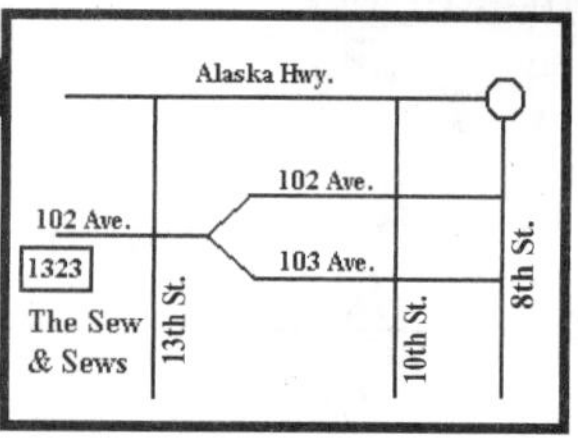

British Columbia Quilt Shops

Abbotsford	Start to Finish Notions, 35366 Doneagle Pl.	604-850-8406
Abbotsford	Quilt Essentials, 100-2622 Montrose Ave.	604-853-5444
Abbotsford	A Great Notion QuiltWorks, #101 - 32526 George Ferguson	604-853-8930
Armstrong	Pleasant Valley Quilting, #2 - 3495 Pleasant Valley Rd.	250-546-0003
Campbell River	Sew 'N' Sew Fabrics, 58 C Adams Rd.	250-923-6065
Castlegar	**Jean's Material Things , 650 23rd St.**	**250-304-2337** **See ad #4, page 616**
Cherryville	Weeping Willow Creek, 63 Begbie Rd.	250-547-0110
Chilliwack	**Hamels Fabrics, 5843 Lickman Rd.**	**604-846-4350** **See ad #2, page 615**
Chilliwack	Countryfolk Fabrics & Gifts, #5 - 45802 Luckakuck Way	604-824-5643
Coquitlam	Fabricana Imports, 348 United Blvd.	604-524-5454
Coquitlam	Quilted Treasures, 40 1140 Austin Ave.	604-936-4778
Cranbrook	Cottage Rose Quilt Shop, 106 Van Home S	250-417-2990
Cranbrook	The Cotton Tree Quilt Shop, 38 Cranbrook St. N	250-426-3358
Dawson Creek	**The Sew & Sews Quilt Shop, 1323 102nd Ave.**	**250-782-8777** **See ad #9, page 616**
Delta	The Quilted Bear, 4867 Delta St.	604-940-7051
Duncan	Creative Quilting, 102-5859 York Rd.	250-746-8033
Fernie	Cotton Tree Quilt Shop, Box 1709	250-423-3358
Fort Langley	A Quilted Stitch, 110-23343 Mavis Ave.	604-455-0115
Fort St. James	Kettle Creek Quilts, 3600 Necoslie Rd.	250-996-7929
Gibsons Carola's	Quilt Shop, #205-938 Gibsons Way	604-886-1245
Grand Forks	Heart N' Sole Quilts, 325 75th Ave.	250-442-0661
Grand Forks	Caba's Quilting Cottage, 7578 8th St.	250-442-2875
Grand Forks	Uptown Sew and Serge, 7354 2nd St.	250-442-0171
Hagensbourg	Crafty Lady Gifts & Hobbies, PO Box 114	250-982-2358
Invermere	Purcell Mountain Quilting Co., #9 - 492 Arrow Rd.	250-341-3115
Invermere	Essentials Department Store, 729 12th St.	250-342-9313
Kamloops	Katja's Quilt Shoppe, #101 - 1967 E. Trans Canada Hwy.	250-851-0324
Kelowna	Dragonfly Quilt Studio, 1863 Bredin Rd.	250-860-8827
Kelowna	Linda's Quilt Shoppe, 114-948 McCurdy	250-491-9770
Kelowna	Cottage Quilting, #6 - 2070 Harvey Ave.	250-860-1120
Kimberley	Sew Creative Chalet, 260 Spokane St.	250-427-3393
Ladysmith	Sweet Pea Quilting, 25 Roberts	250-245-2114
Langford	Cloth Castle, 786 Goldstream Ave Hwy 1A	250-478-2112
Maple Ridge	Quiltopia Quilting & Sewing, 22626 Loughheed Hwy	604-467-8806
N Vancouver	**Creative Edge Quilting & Sewing 2055 Old Dollarton Rd.**	**604-982-0088** **See ad #3, page 616**
Nanaimo	**Snip & Stitch Sewing Centre #1 - 4047 Norwell Dr.**	**250-756-2176** **See ad #1, page 615**
Nanaimo	Serge and Sew, #105 - 6750 N. Island Hwy.	250-390-3602
Nelson	Shannon's Fabrics Ltd., 560 Baker St.	250-352-6104
Oliver	Miss Molly's Quilt Shoppe, 35664 97th St.	250-498-0115
Oliver	Wine Country Quilters Market, 38285 Hwy. 97	250-498-5460
Parksville	Gramma's Quilting Cupboard, 1-1180 Craig	250-248-8449
Pemberton	Bog Fabrics, 1355 Aster St.	604-894-6164
Penticton	Poppin's Quilt Parlour, 350 Main St.	250-493-1815
Port Alberni	Kismet Quilts, 5334 Argyle St.	250-723-6605
Port Alberni	Pincushion, 3218 3rd Ave.	250-723-8831
Prince George	Prince George Sewing Center 1210 5th	250-563-1533
Prince George	Kathy's Quilt Shop, 1260 4th Ave.	250-960-1021
Princeton	Kettle Valley Quilting, 290 Bridge St.	250-295-7795
Pritchard	Di-Versity Quilting Supplies, Nordkinn Rd.	250-577-3494
Quesnel	**Expressions by Ewe, 222 McNaughton Ave.**	**250-992-8896** **See ad #6, page 616**
Quesnel	Quilted Accents, 1706 Lawlor Rd.	250-747-2366
Revelstoke	Just A Notion, 101 1st St. W	250-837-9350
Richmond	Fabricana & Interior Delights, 4591 Garden City Rd.	604-273-5316
Salmon Arm	**The Sewing Basket, 168 Macleod St.**	**250-832-3937** **See ad #5, page 616**
Salt Spring Island	Stitches Quilts & Yarns, 120 Hereford Ave.	250-537-8985
Sechelt	Sew Easy, 15 Trail Bay Centre, 5755 Cowrie St.	604-885-2725
Smithers	Fabrications, 3892 3rd Ave.	250-847-3250
Surrey	Wineberry Fabrics, 6355 - 152nd St. #205	604-597-7934
Surrey	Castle's Sewing Centre, 18543 Fraser Hwy.	604-574-5333
Surrey	A Great Notion QuiltWorks, #108 - 19289 Langley ByPass	604-575-9028
Surrey	The Quilted Garden, 101 15953 Fraser Hwy.	604-597-0933
Taylor	Windy Willow Fabrics, Collins Rd. Mile 30	250-789-9248
Terrace	Fabricland, 117-4717 Lakels Ave.	250-635-2164
Terrace	Cotton Pick n' Quilt Patch, 101-3239 Kalem	250-638-1335
Trail	Allan's Sewing Center, 1268 Pine Ave.	250-368-8485
Trail	Sugar Shack Quilting Co., 907 Spokane St.	250-364-1744
Vancouver	The Cloth Shop, 4415 W 10th Ave.	604-224-1325
Vancouver	Dressew Supply Ltd., 337 W. Hastings St.	604-682-6196
Vanderhoof	**Quilters Corner in the Vanderhoof Dept Store 2465 Burrard Ave.**	**250-567-2311** **See ad #7, page 616**
Vanderhoof	**Quilters Nook, 185 W. Stewart St.**	**250-567-2828** **See ad #8, page 616**
Victoria	Capitol Iron, 1900 Store St	250-385-9703
Victoria	Calico Cupboard, 5134 Cordova Bay	250-658-2722
Victoria	Satin Moon Quilt Shop, 1689 Government	250-383-4023
Victoria	Bib 'N Tucker Quilting, 343 D Bay St.	250-386-6512
West Kelowna	Tyjo's Fabrics, 2959 Lakeview Cove Rd.	250-769-8094
Williams Lake	E & E Sewing Centre, 65 - S 1st Ave.	250-392-4055
Williams Lake	Ibea's Quilting & Craft Galore!, 96 - 3rd N	250-392-7748

British Columbia Quilt Shows

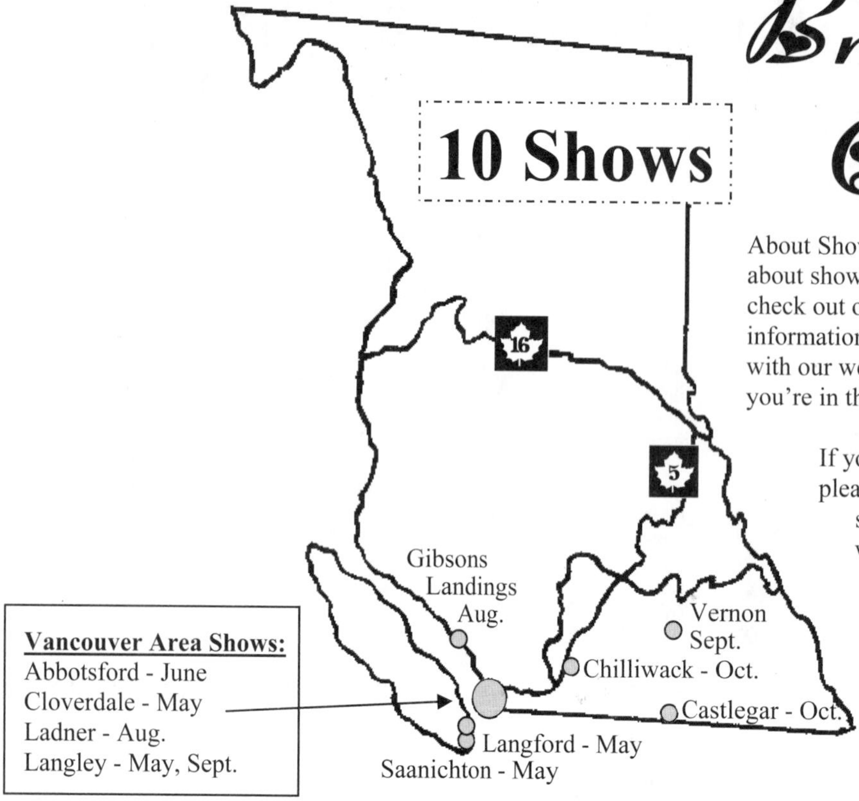

About Shows: We are listing only the very basic information about shows that happen on a regular schedule here. Please check out our website for more details on each show. Also this information tends to change quite often so please verify the event with our website or a local source before you venture far. Or if you're in the right area at the right time, give it a shot.

If you are a show organizer,
please keep us updated on your event.
shows@quilterstravelcompanion.com
www.quilterstravelcompanion.com

On our website you will also find:

- Exact dates (when we have them)
- Sponsor Information
- Contact Information
- Description of Event
- Events happening on a one-time basis

Month	City	Schedule	Show	Location with address
March				
	Langford	Odd Years, 4th Fri - Sun in March	Symphony of Quilts	Eagle Ridge Communtiy Centre, 1089 Langford Pkwy.
May				
	Langley	Even Years, 2nd Fri & Sat in May	Langley Quilters' Guild Show	George Preston Recreation Center, 20699 42nd Ave. (208th St. and 42nd Ave.)
	Saanichton	Even Years, 1st weekend in May	Victoria Quilters' Guild Show	Saanich Fairgrounds, 1528 Stelly's Cross Rd.
	Cloverdale	Odd Years, 3rd weekend in May	Fraser Valley Quilters' Guild	Cloverdale Catholic Parish Hall, 17475 59th Ave
June				
	Abbotsford	Odd Years, June	Abbotsford Quilters' Guild Show	
August				
	Gibsons Landings	Annual, 3rd Wed - Sat in August	Gibsons Landing Fibre Arts Festival	
	Ladner	Annual, 3rd Sun. in August	Ladner Village Quilt Walk & Classic Car Show	Ladner Village
September				
	Vernon	Every 3rd year in Sept., next year 2010	Vernon Silver Star Guild Show	Vernon Recreation Center, 31 St.
	Langley	Annual, 3rd weekend in September	Langley Quilters' Guild Show	Campbell Valley Regional Park, 16 Ave.
October				
	Castlegar	Even Years, 3rd weekend in October	Castlegar Quilters Guild Show	Castlegar Community Complex, 2101 6th Ave.
	Chilliwack	Odd Years, 4th Sat in Oct.	Chilliwack Quilters' Guild Show	Chilliwack Alliance Church Hall, 8700 Young Rd.

MANITOBA

4 Featured Shops

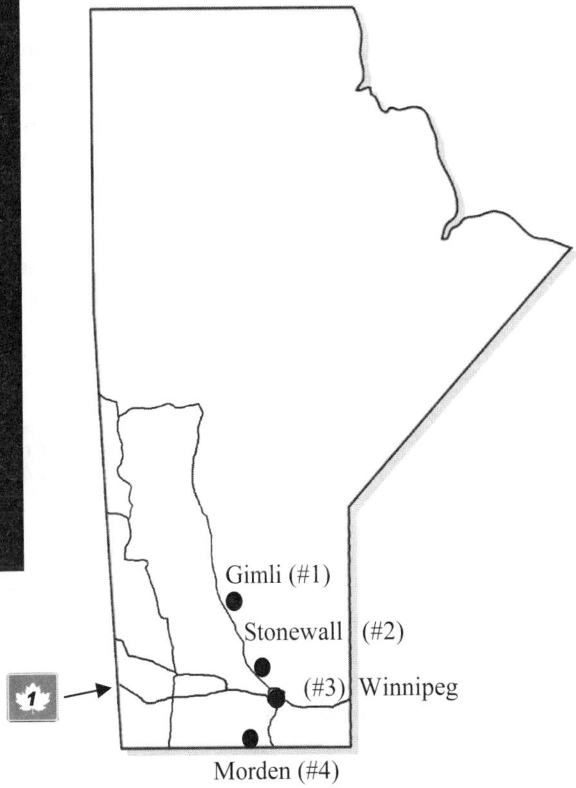

Gimli, MB #1

Mon - Sat 10 - 5:30
Summer: 7 days a week

Jocelyn & Co.

77 1st Ave. Lakeview Resort R0C 1B0
(204) 642-5537
Owner: Jocelyn Barlow Est: 1988

Right around the corner from the beach!
Hundreds of bolts of only the best quilting fabrics, batting and notions.
Browsers welcome!

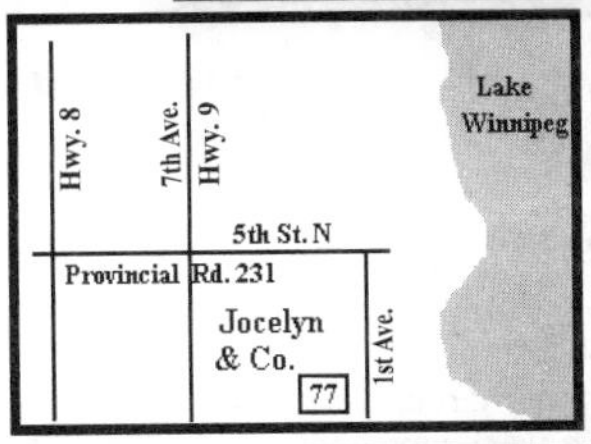

Winnipeg, MB #3

Mon - Sat 9:30 - 5:30

Quilt As Desired

661 Pembina Hwy. R3M 2L5
(204) 942-0035
Fax: (204) 942-0037
Owners: Kelly & Rob Truthwaite
Est: 1969 2500 sq.ft. Online newsletter
quiltasdesired@mts.net
www.quilt-as-desired.com
Winnipeg's Largest Full Service Quilt Shop.
Janome, Husqvarna & Baby Lock Dealer with year round classes, 3000 fabric bolts, notions & more.

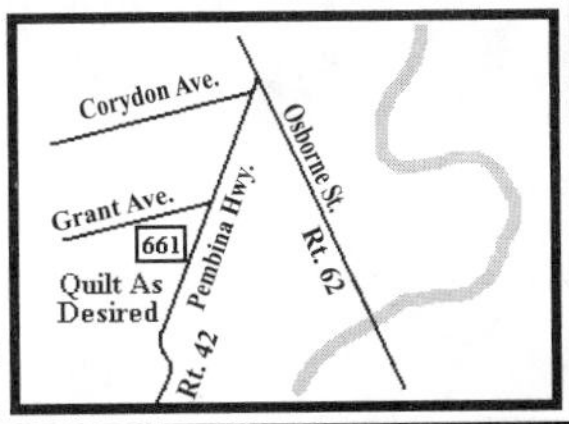

Morden, MB #4

Mon - Sat 10 - 4

the Quilters' Jewel

The big brown barn at11th & Stephen St.
(204) 822-3105
www.thequiltersjewel.com

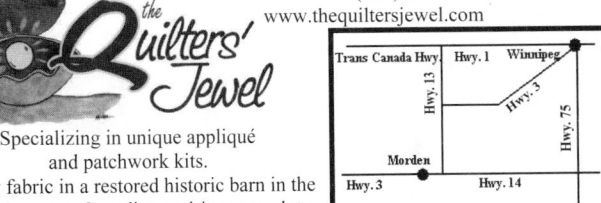

Specializing in unique appliqué and patchwork kits.
Quality fabric in a restored historic barn in the heart of a pretty Canadian prairie town…lots to see and do.

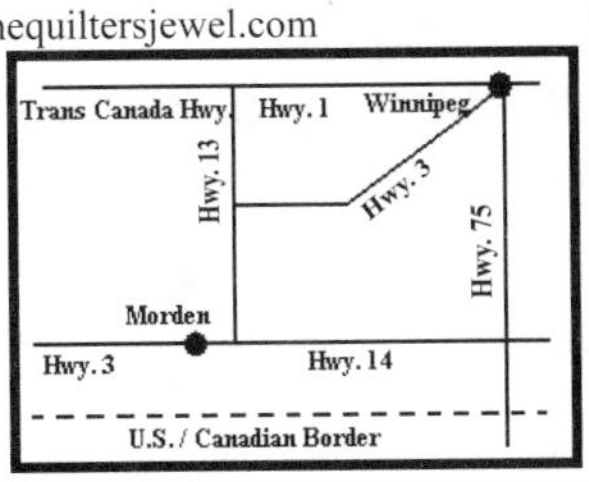

QUILTER'S COTTAGE

Quaint old cottage located on Main Street
We specialize in friendly atmosphere and customer service.
Great selection of top of the line fabrics, patterns, gifts and notions.
Classes for all levels of Quilters.

277 Main St., P.O. Box 1220 R0C 2Z0
(204) 467-2453

Stonewall, MB #2

Owner: Stacy Thiessen
Fax: (204) 467-7551
Est: 2001 1100 sq. ft.
4000 Bolts

Mon - Sat 10 - 5

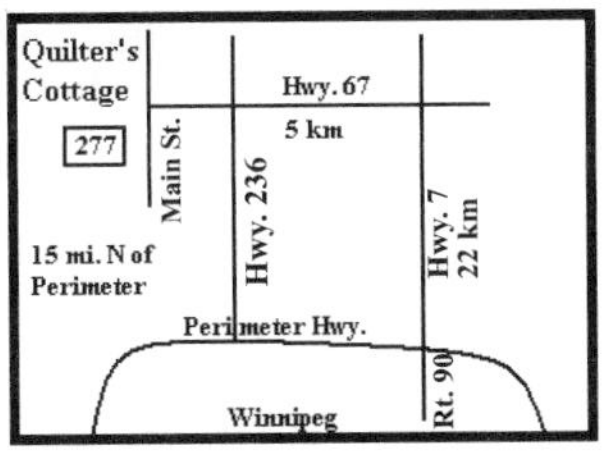

www.quilterscottage.ca

Manitoba Quilt Shops

Carman	Kathy's Fabrics, 2 1st Ave. SW	204-745-3074
Gimli	**Jocelyn & Co., 77 1st Ave. Lakeview Resort**	
	204-642-5537	**See ad #1, page 619**
Grunthal	Oma's Quilt Shop, Box 961	204-434-6747
Killarney	Simply Sewing, 516 Broadway Ave.	204-523-7424
Morden	**The Quilters' Jewel, 565A Stephen St.**	
	2048223105	**See ad #4, page 619**
Reston	Bernice's Fabric Gallery, 111 4th St.	204-877-3955
Steinbach	Tanell's Quilting & Sewing Shop, 354 Main	204-320-9132
Stonewall	**Quilter's Cottage, 277 Main St.**	
	204-467-2453	**See ad #2, page 619**
Winnipeg	**Quilt as Desired, 661 Pembina Hwy.**	
	204-942-0035	**See ad #3, page 619**
Winnipeg	Croft House Quilt Shop, 1846 Portage Ave.	204-888-3370
Winnipeg Beach	Keepers Quilts, 60 Main St.	204-389-4333

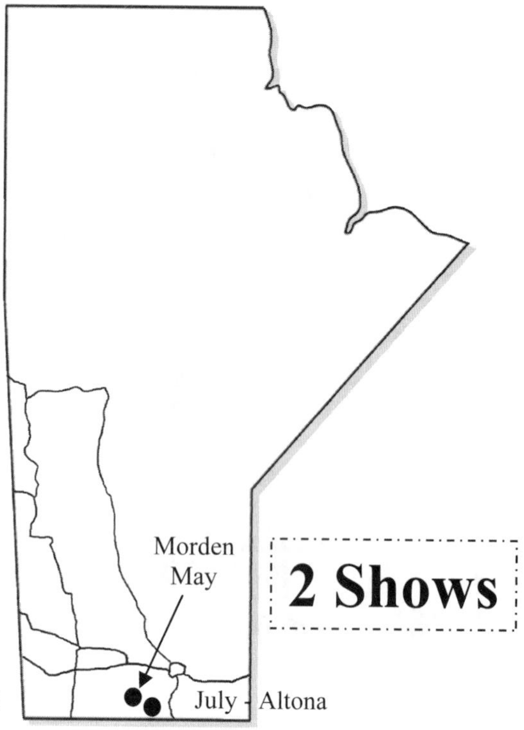

2 Shows

Manitoba Quilt Shows

Month	City	Schedule	Show	Location with address
May				
	Morden	Annual, 1st weekend of May	Barnswallow Quilt Show	Morden Recreation Centre, North end of 2nd St.
July				
	Altona	Annual, 4th weekend in July	Sunflower Festival Quilt Show	South Park Mennonite Brethren Church, 335 6th St. SE

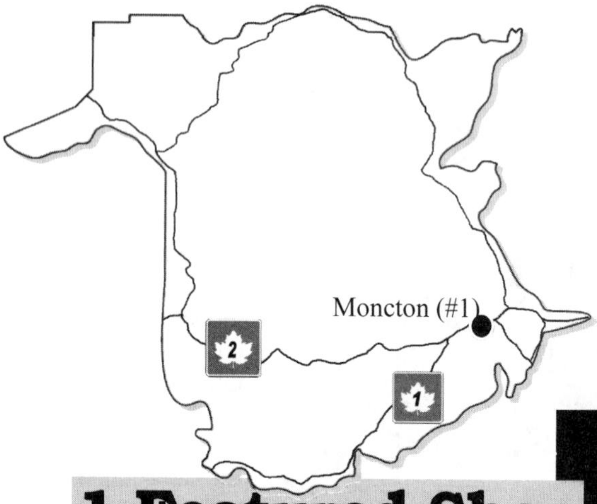

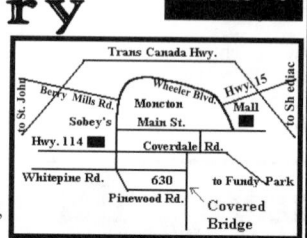

NEW BRUNSWICK

1 Featured Shop

Campbellton	Camille Sewing Center, 36-A Roseberry St.	506-753-3229
Fredericton	Sewing World, 564 Prospect St.	506-459-7324
Fredericton	Country Crafts and Curtains, 334 York St.	506-454-2572
Glenwood	River Gallery Studio, 7310 Route 102	506-468-9004
Riverview	**The Covered Bridge Quiltery**	
	630 Pinewood Rd.	
	506-386-2888	**See ad #1, this page**
Rothesay	Town & Country Quilts, 124 Hampton Rd.	506-847-4099
St. Andrews	Mariner's Compass Quilt Shop, 144 Water	506-529-8351

1 Show

Month	City	Schedule	Show	Location with address
September				
	Quispamsis	Annual, 3rd Thurs - Sat in September	Quilt Show & Sale	Island View Lions Club, 9 Market St.

Newfoundland

2 Featured Shops

Conception Bay South, NL #1

Mon - Sat 10 - 5
Thur also 7 - 9
Sun 2 - 5

Piece Makers Quilt Shop

251 Conception Bay Hwy.
(709) 834-9558 A1W 5J8
Fax: (709) 834-9568
Owner:
Cathy Pittman
Est: 2006
2400 sq.ft.

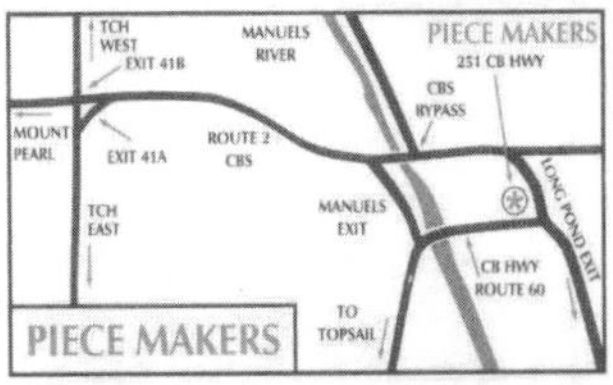

cathypittman@nf.sympatico.ca
www.piecemakers.ca
Excellent selection of fabrics, batting, notions, books, patterns and thread. Also, there are kits and finished items available to buy.
Newfoundland's Bernina and Babylock Dealer.

Springdale, NL #2

Mon - Sat 10 - 5:30
Fri til 9

This That N' Fabrics

141 A Main St. A0J 1T0
(709) 673-3311 Fax: (709) 673-3313
Owners: Tammy & Wavey Est: 2003
tammykanstey@hotmail.com

We carry a large selection of quilting cottons, flannels, yarns and scrapbooking supplies.

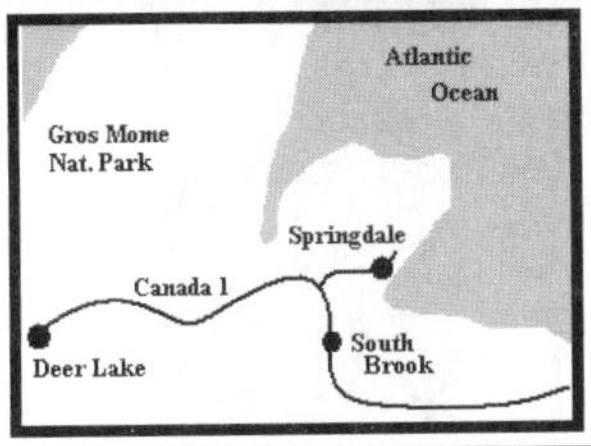

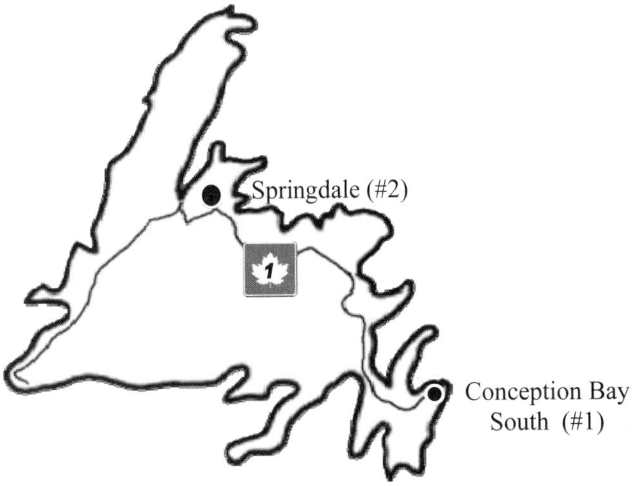

Newfoundland Quilt Shops

Carmanville	C & M Crafts 'N' Stuff, 49 Howells Ave.	709-534-2173
Conception Bay South	**Piece Makers Quilt Shop 251 Conception Bay Hwy.**	**709-834-9558 See ad #1, this page**
Gander	The Needle Nook, 35 B Armstrong Blvd.	709-256-8358
Grand Falls	Fabric Boutique, 114 Main St.	709-489-7384
Labrador City	Crafters Attic, 221 Humber	709-944-2072
Mount Pearl	Fashionable Fabrics, 7 Commonwealth Ave.	709-747-9710
Port Aux Basques	Material World, Grand Bay Mall	709-695-9595
Springdale	**This That N' Fabrics, 141A Main St.**	**709-673-3311 See ad #2, this page**
St. Johns	Sew Much More, 30 Ropewalk Ln.	709-722-6550
St. John's	St. John's Fabrics, Quilt & Yarn, Hamlyn Road Plaza St. #52	709-747-4100
Victoria	Magical Threads, PO 1080 159 Main Rd	709-964-059

Newfoundland Quilt Shows

We don't know of any shows in Newfoundland.
Please submit any shows you may know of, thanks.

Northwest Territory

Northwest Territory Shop

Yellowknife	Quilter's Getaway, 100 Borden Drive Unit 4	867-920-2935

Northwest Territory Quilt Shows

We don't know of any shows in the Northwest Territory
Please submit any show you may know of, thanks.

Nova Scotia

2 Featured Shops

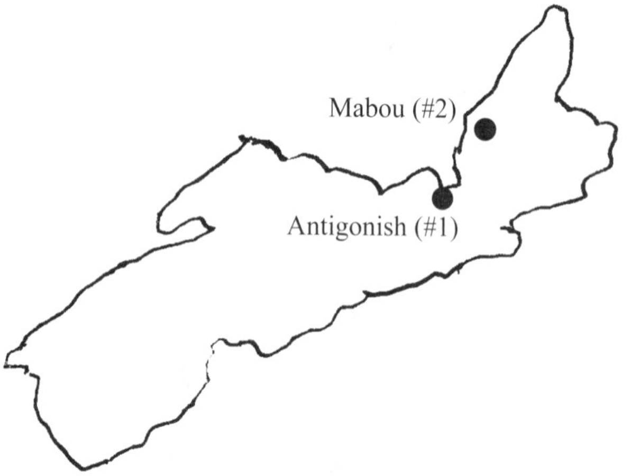

Antigonish County, NS #1

Mon - Sat 10 - 5

Harbour Quilt Company

365 S. Side Harbor Rd. B2G 2L4
info@harbourquiltcompany.com
www.harbourquiltcompany.com Est: 2000
(866) 863-6801
Quilting Supplies, Quilts & Museum in a 100 year old farmhouse. Member of the ECONOMUSEE Network of Artisans.

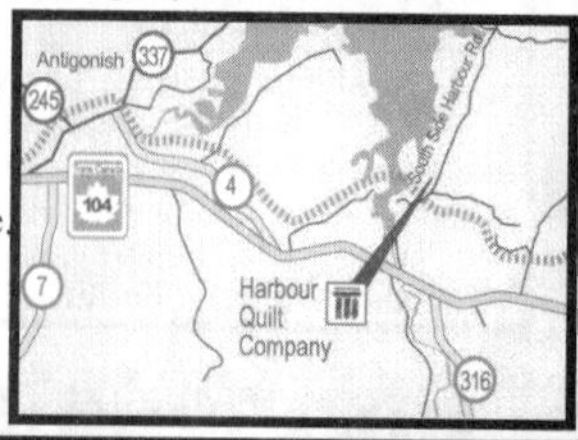

Mabou, NS #2

Mon - Fri 10 - 5
Sat 10 - 3
Sun 11 - 1

11485 Route 19 B0E 1X0
(902) 945-2880
lynda.campbell@ns.sympatico.ca

Owner: Lynda Campbell
Est: 2005
1000 sq.ft.

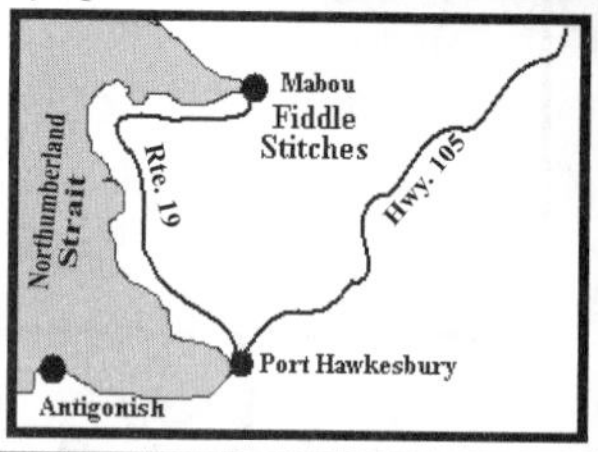

We Sell Quality Fabrics & Notions, Quilts-Crib through King Size & Gifts. Machine Quilting Done on Site.

Antigonish County	**Harbour Quilt Company** **365 S. Side Harbour Rd.** **902-863-6801**	**See ad #1, this page**
Avonport	Avonport Discount Fabrics, 12725 Old Hwy. 1	902-542-3247
Blockhouse	Quilts by the Sea, 18 Cornwall Rd.	902-531-3010
Bridgewater	Atlantic Fabrics, 2304 Hwy. 325, R.R. #7	902-527-2212
Concession	L & S Boudreau Store LtdD., 1474 Patrice Rd.	902-769-2325
Dartmouth	Atlantic Fabrics Staples Plaza, 114 Woodlawn	902-434-7220
Digby County	Panier d'Art, 464 Comeauville, Box 120 B	902-769-3457
Greenwood	Altantic Fabrics, Greenwood Mall	902-765-0600
Mabou	**Fiddle Stitches, 11485 Rt. 19** **902-945-2880**	**See ad #2, this page**
Mahone Bay	Suttles and Seawinds, 466 Main St.	902-624-8375
New Glasgow	Lucy's Fabric and Gifts, 859 Abercrombie Rd.	902-755-3939
New Glasgow	Atlantic Fabrics, 980 E. River Rd.	902-752-1234
New Minas	Knit 'n' Stitch, 8927 Commercial St.	902-681-7410
River John	Timeless Stitches Fabric & Quilt Shop 621 Joudrey Rd., R.R. #3	902-351-2165
Sidney	Quilting on the Mira, 89 Disco St.	902-539-6340
Truro	Mary's Creative Sew & Serge, 333 Main St.	902-895-1369
Upper Tantallon	The Purple Frog Sewing School 5288 St. Margaret's Bay Rd. #5	902-826-1829
Yarmouth	Dayton Fabrics, 261 Hwy. 1	902-742-6363
Yarmouth	K&K Fashion Design, 610 Main St.	902-742-0139
Yarmouth	Le's Fashions, 12 Kirk St	902-742-9495
Yarmouth	The Cotton Mill Fabric & Crafts, 314 Main St.	902-742-8313

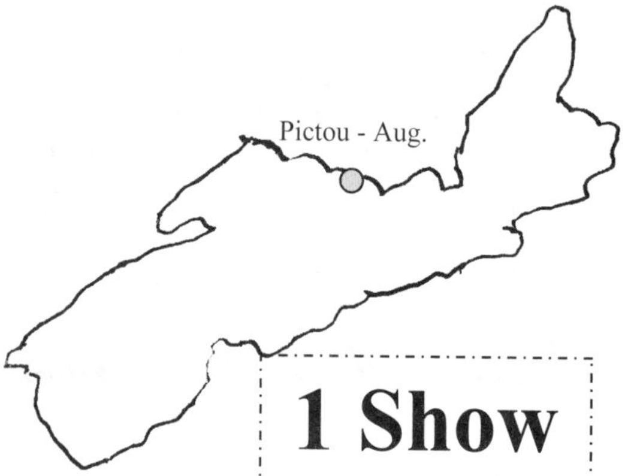

1 Show

Month	City	Schedule	Show	Location with address
August				
	Pictou	Annual, 1st weekend of August	Northumberland Quilt Guild Show	DeCoste Entertainment Center, 99 Water St.

Nunavut Territory Shops & Shows

We don't know of any shops or shows in Nunavut
Please let us know if you know of any.

ONTARIO

36 Featured Shops

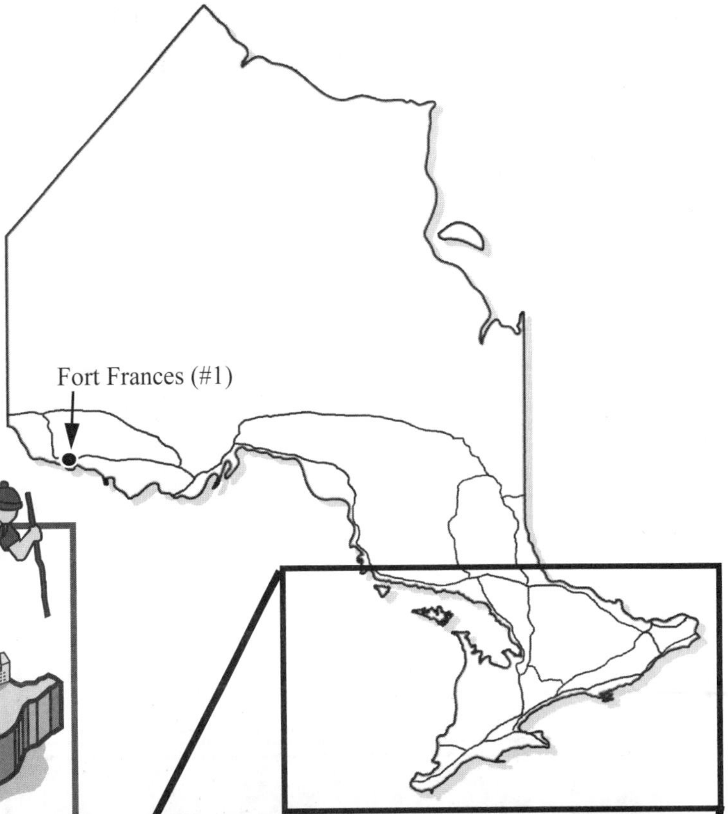

LOWER ONTARIO

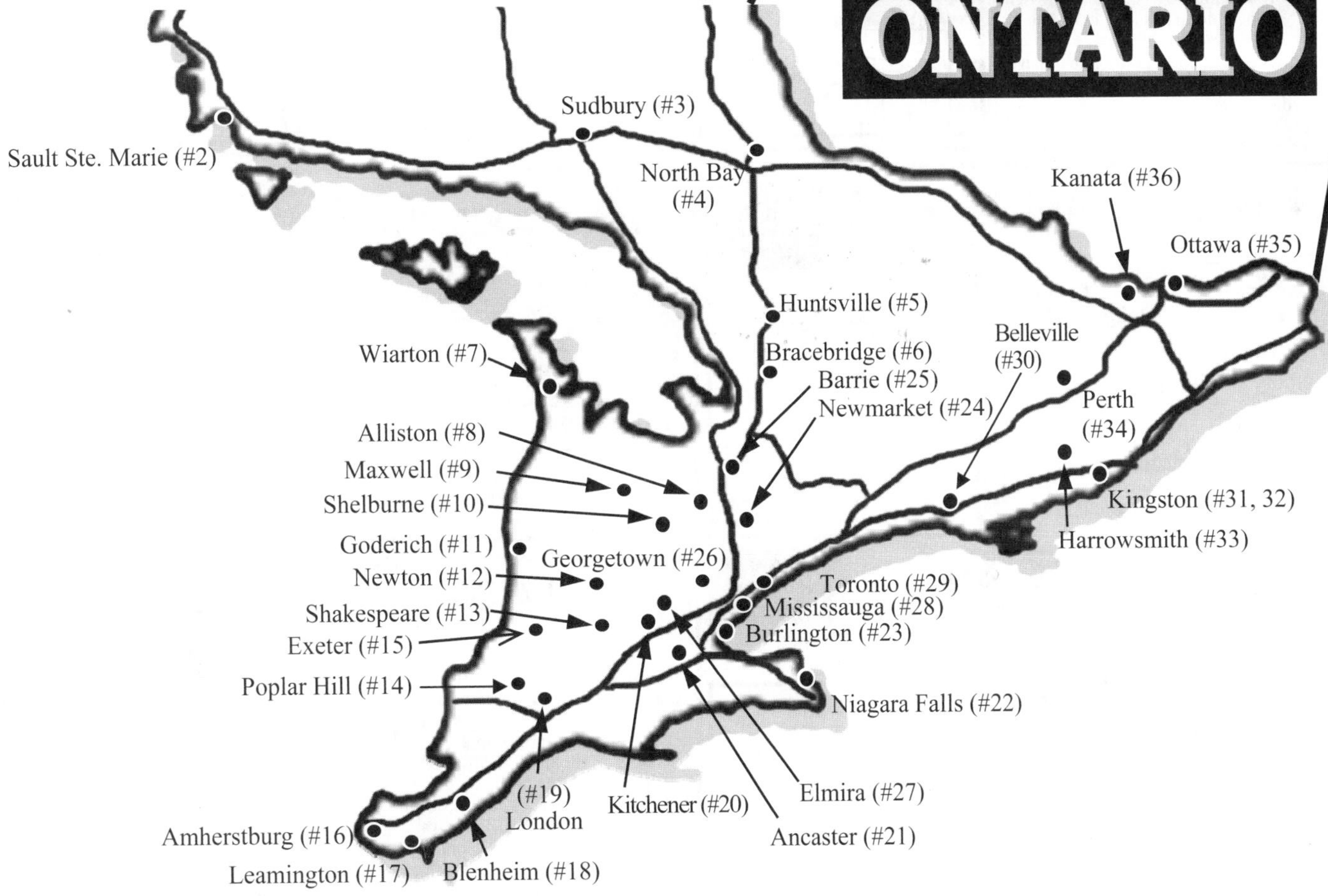

Fort Frances, ON #1

Tues & Thur 12 - 6
Wed & Fri 10 - 4

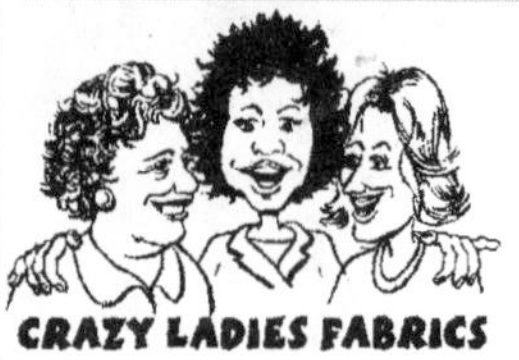

330 Scott Street P9A 1G9
(807) 274-6665
Fax: (807) 274-3168
Owner:
Phyllis Johnson
Est: 1998
1400 sq. ft.
1500 Bolts.
www.crazyladiesfabrics.com

Located on the U.S.-Canada border in NW Ontario. Carrying the most popular cottons and cotton flannels from top companies.

Sault Ste. Marie, ON #2

Mon - Fri 10 - 5:30
Sat 10 - 4

516 Queen St. E P6A 2A1
(866) 570-2062
(705) 254-3339
Fax:
(705) 254-3358
Est: 1997
info@lifesastitch.ca
www.lifesastitch.ca

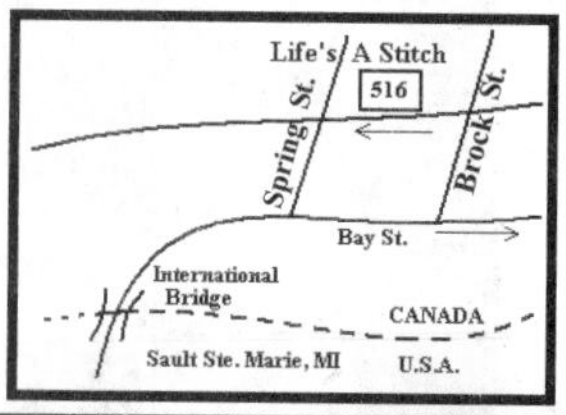

Husqvarna Viking Sewing Machines and Sergers, Quilting Fabrics and Notions, Polarfleece and knits, Books, Patterns, Notions, Accessories and Classes.

Sudbury, ON #3

Mon - Wed 9:30 - 5:30
Thur & Fri 9:30 - 7
Sat 9:30 - 4:30

It's Sew Easy
A Stitch Above The Rest

1313 Lorne St., Unit 4 P3C 5M9
(705) 675-1788 Fax: Same
Owners: Christel Brandle & Tim Robson
Est: 1990 1300 sq.ft. 1000+ Bolts
itsseweasy@persona.ca Online Newsletter
www.its-sew-easy.ca
New Quilter, Experienced Quilter it doesn't matter, come and have a Funtastical time.

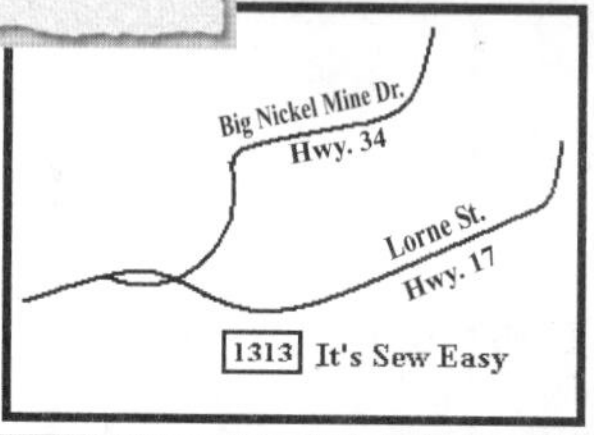

North Bay, ON #4

Mon - Fri 9 - 5
Sat 9 - 4

CREATION UNIQUE
Sewing Emporium

1169 Cassells St. P1B 4B4
(705) 472-5900
Fax: (705) 472-8653

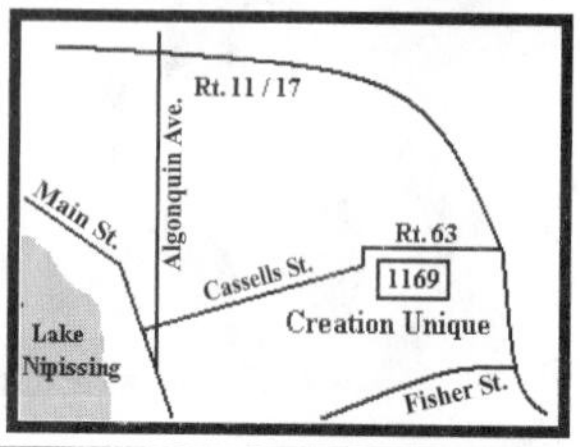

stitches@creationunique.com
www.creationunique.com
We stock all the new products introduced by Husqvarna Viking including the New Emerald 203 & New Sapphire 875Q. Come and have a demonstration. Free classes machine purchase. Fabric, Notions, and Quilting classes.

Huntsville, ON #5

Mon - Fri 9:30 - 5:30
Sat 9:30 - 5

Gone Quilting! INC.
FOR THE QUILTING & SEWING ENTHUSIAST

#1 - 14 Main St. E.
P1H 2C8
(705) 788-9982

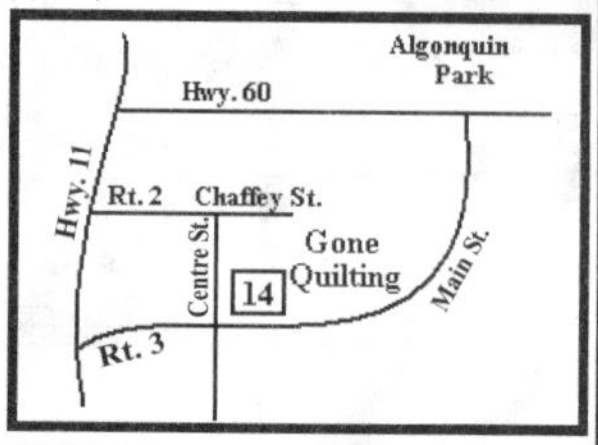

Est: 2005 1800 sq.ft. Owner: Joanne Misener
gonequilting@bellnet.ca
www.gonequilting.ca
Batiks, current collections, homespuns, flannels & more. Books, patterns, notions, custom designs & sewing machines.
Year-round classes at all skill levels.

Bracebridge, ON #6

Mon - Wed 10 - 5
Thurs & Fri 10 - 5:30
Sat 10 - 3

The Muskoka Quilting Co.

161 Manitoba St. P1L 2B7
(705) 645-4446
Owner: Debbie Suffern
quilting@muskoka.com
www.muskokaquilting.com

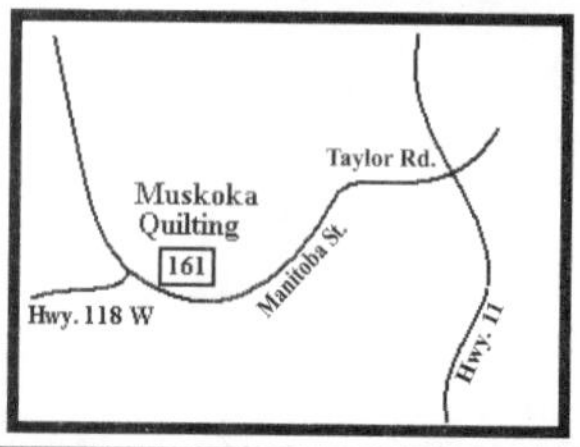

Come see our new look and browse the new fabrics, notions, books and patterns. Charm Packs and Kits Ready to pick up and stitch.
PFAFF sewing machine dealer.
Check out our great class schedule.

Wiarton, ON #7

Mon - Sat 9 - 5

Mothers' Fabric
@ the Spirit Rock Motel

877 Berford St., P.O. Box 873 N0H 2T0
(519) 534-5168
2000 sq.ft. 3000 Bolts
www.mothersfabricquiltshop.com

Located in a beautiful Log Home
Stop in and be amazed!
Ask about our birthday gift to you!

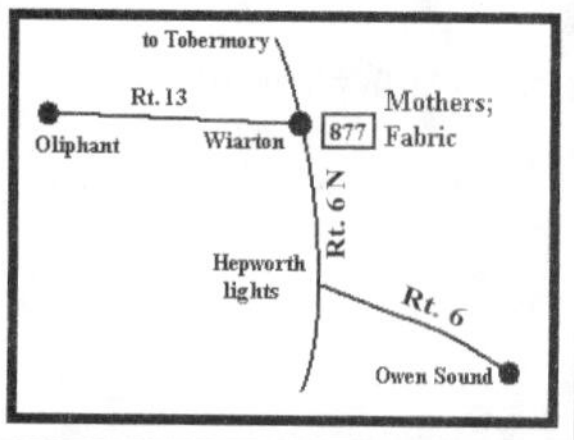

Alliston, ON #8

Mon - Sat 9:30 - 5:30
Sun & most Holidays 11 - 4

Lilac Lane Quilts

180 Parsons Rd. #27
L9R 1E8
(705) 435-2746
(866) 435-1041
Owners: Liz & Carl Schueler
Est: 2002 1300 sq.ft. Free Online Newsletter
liz@lilaclanequilts.com
www.lilaclanequilts.com
Your complete quilt shop. Online shopping, knowledgeable in-store help and 2 longarm Gammills to quilt your project at your service.

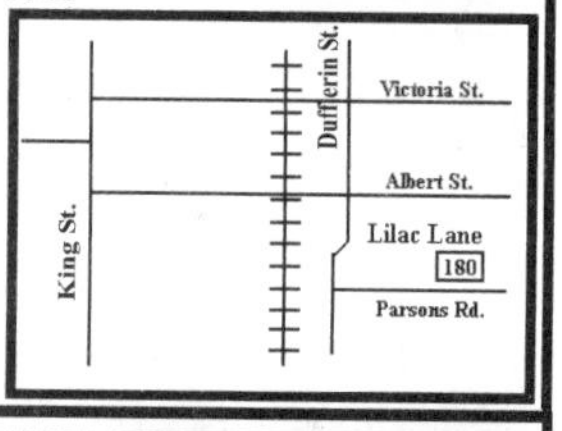

Maxwell, ON #9

Mon - Fri 9 - 5
Sat 9 - 3

Threads That Bind
Today's gifts...tomorrow's heirlooms

408002 Hwy. #4
P.O. Box 76 N0C 1J0
(519) 922-1010 Fax: (519) 922-3198

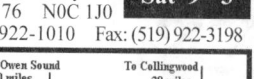

Owner: Lois Plantt Online Newsletter
sales@threadzthatbind.com
www.threadzthatbind.com
Full service quilt shop offering 100% quilting cottons and friendly country service. Patterns, Books, Notions, Classes, plus a great gift shop!

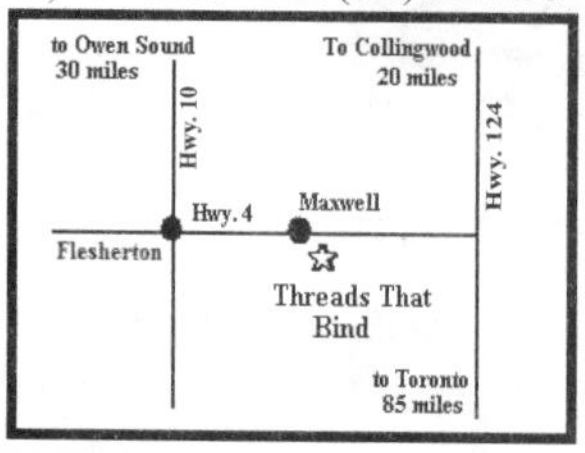

Shelburne, ON #10

Mon 12 - 5
Tues & Wed 10 - 5
Thur & Fri 10 - 8
Sat 10 - 5

Cobwebs & Caviar

Coffee, tea & a Quilting Adventure! Lotsa quiltin' stuff, feast on samples & kits, sewing studio & an Awesome gift shop too! Join us!
127 Main St. E L0N 1S0
(519) 925-2254
Owners: A.J. Cavey & Jacky Hill
Online Newsletter
Est: 2003 2000+ Bolts
cobwebsandcaviar@sympatico.ca
www.cobwebsandcaviar.ca

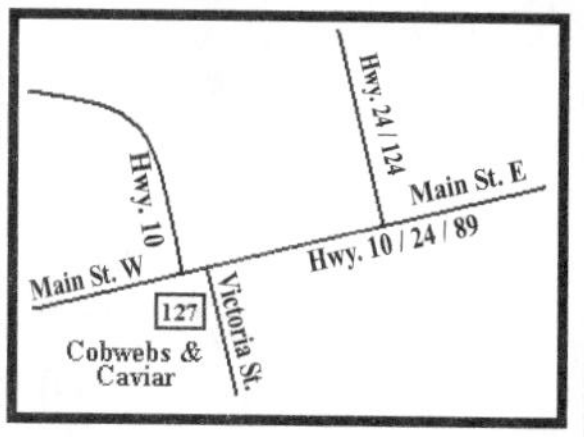

Goderich, ON #11

Mon - Sat
10 - 5:30

Quilters by the Square

32 West St. N7A 2K3
(519) 524-4333
www.quiltersbythesquare.ca

A wide variety of 100% Cotton Fabrics, Quilting Books, Patterns, Notions, DMC Floss, Bear Supplies & Classes available. Visit our friendly knowledgeable staff.

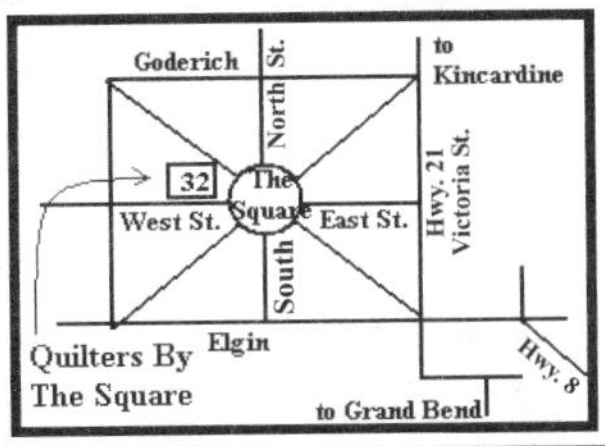

Newton, ON #12

Mon - Fri
8:30 - 5:30
Sat 9 - 5

E & E'S Cloth and Creations

4463 Perth Line 72 N0K 1R0
(519) 595-8569
Owner: Edgar and Emmaline Wagler Est: 1990
emmaline@cyg.net

Excellent prices on over 2000 bolts of quality quilting cottons and flannels. We specialize in customer service and in helping you with all your sewing needs.

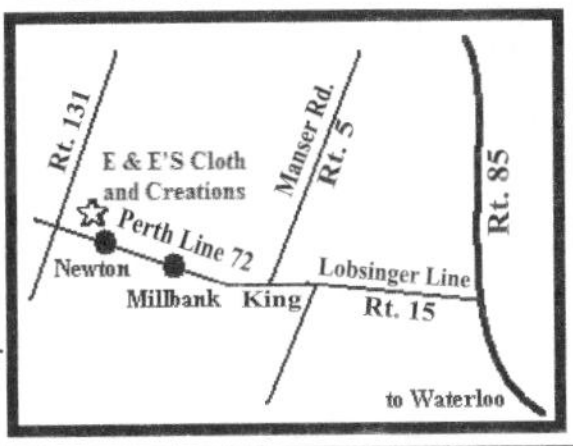

Shakespeare, ON #13

Mon - Sat
10 - 5:30
April - Dec
Sun 12 - 5

THE QUILT PLACE

3991 Perth Rd. #107 N0B 2P0
(519) 625-8435 (888) 457-7077
heather@thequiltplace.ca
Owner:
Heather Stock
1200 sq.ft.
2000+ Bolts
Est: 1986

Your place to find a timeless and elegant quilt for your home or choose the supplies to make a family heirloom.
Friendly, knowledgeable staff!!

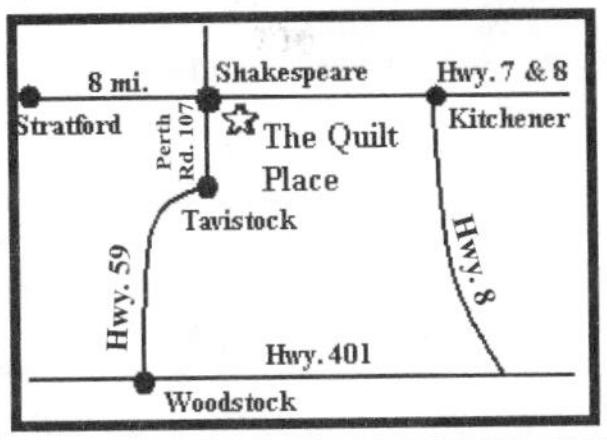

Poplar Hill, ON #14

Mon - Sat
10 - 5

The Marsh Store

10266 Ilderton Rd. in Coldstream N0M 2A0
(519) 666-3330
Owners: Shirley & Tim Bobier
themarshstore@execulink.com
www.themarshstore.com
Experience the charm of an historic general store as a quilt shop. We welcome you into the world of quilting with a wide variety of fabrics, quilting supplies, fibre art media and longarm machine quilting services.

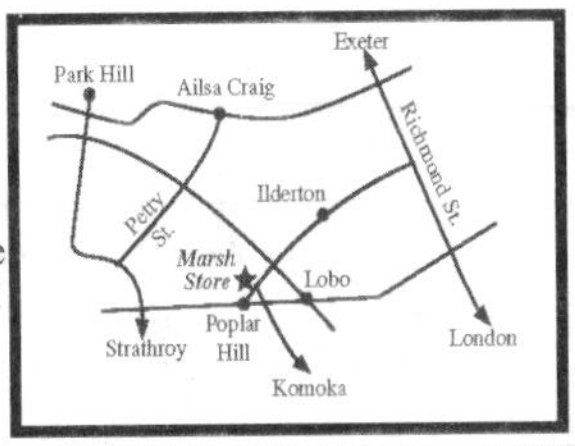

We feature a wide array of 100% cotton fabrics, the latest quilting notions, books, patterns and batting. Authorized dealer for Husqvarna Viking sewing machines and sergers.
Classes for all skill levels offered year round.
In short, your one stop quilt shop. We ship anywhere.

Mon - Fri
9 - 5:30
Sat 9 - 5

www.quilts-calicos.on.ca

Exeter, ON #15

Also be sure to visit "The Cottage"
Quilts and Calicos
Premier Teaching Facility
287 Main Street South, Exeter, ON N0M 1S6
519-235-4856
Open Wednesdays and Thursdays 9:00am - 5:30pm
Over 1500 bolts of 100% cottons just $8.98 per metre.

Unique quilt shop located in a restored century old building.

392 Main St. S, P.O. Box 42,
Exeter, Ontario N0M 1S6
(888) 305-0949 (519) 235-4084
Fax: (519) 235-4967 Est: 1993
Owner: Linda Bartlett 4500 Bolts
quiltscalicos@on.aibn.com

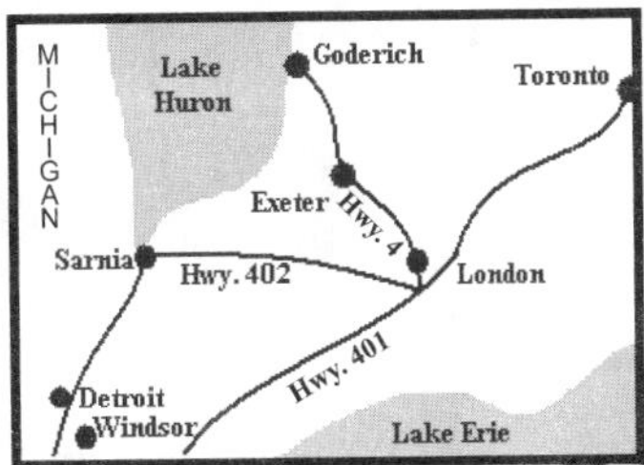

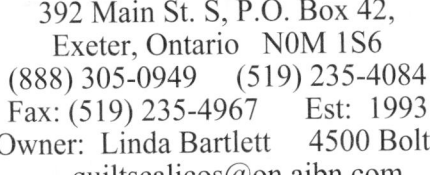

Amherstburg, ON #16

Tues - Fri 10 - 5
Sat 10 - 4

Rose Cottage Quilt Shoppe

276 Dalhousie St. N9V 1W9
(519) 730-1172
Owner: Rosemary Uiberlacher
Est: 2006 Online Newsletter
rosecottagequilts@hotmail.com
www.rosecottagequilt.com
"The Little Quilt Shop with the Big Heart"
We have the 100% cotton fabrics, notions and tools that you'll need, classrooms and courses to expand your skills and the advice you'll value.

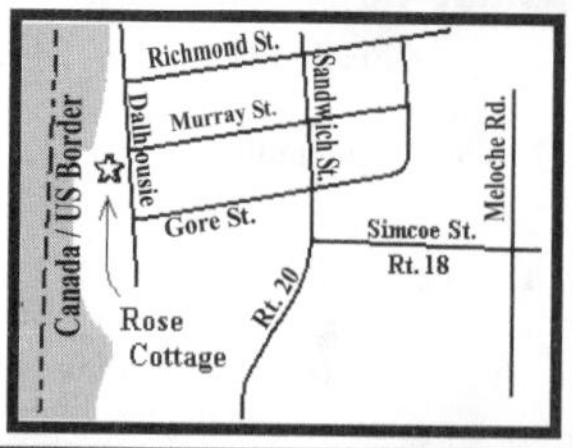

Leamington, ON #17

Mon - Fri 9:30 - 5
Sat 9:30 - 4

A Stitch in Time

30 Mill St. West N8H 1S8
(519) 322-4690
Fax: (519) 322-2614

Owner: Mary Beth Sharpe Est: 1994
astitchintime@cogeco.ca 6600 sq.ft.
www.astitchintime.ca
Janome machines. 6,000 bolts of Quilting Cottons, Dress & Bridal. Cross-stitch, unique yarns & Commercial Embroidery.
We Have It All!

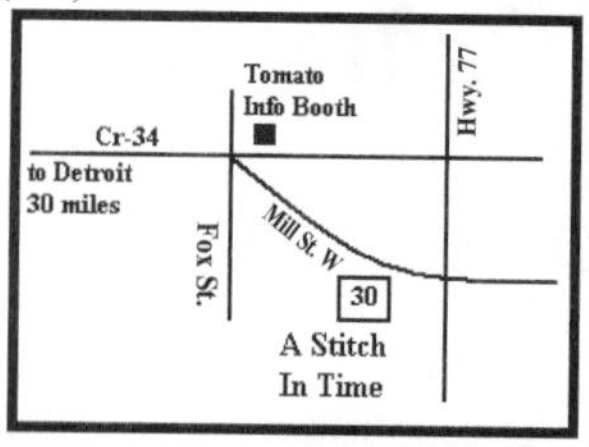

Blenheim, ON #18

Call for Appt.

Pastime Pieces

11175 Brush Line N0P 1A0
(519) 676-5059
Owner: Marlene Wymenga

marlene@pastimes.com
www.pastimepieces.com
Quilting fabrics, books, patterns and kits.

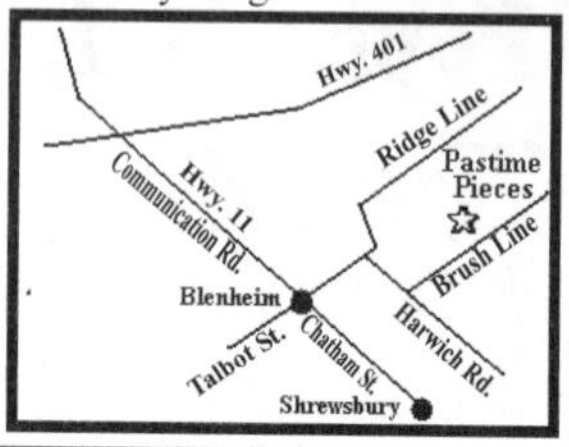

Kitchener, ON #20

Mon - Fri 10 - 5
Sat 9 - 4

Creative Sisters Quilt Studio

321 Lancaster St. W N2H 4V4
(519) 584-2130
http://www.creativesisters.ca
Over 200 bolts of wide backings 108" - 118" including Batiks & Flannels.
Oriental and Batik Fabrics.
Machine Quilting Services.

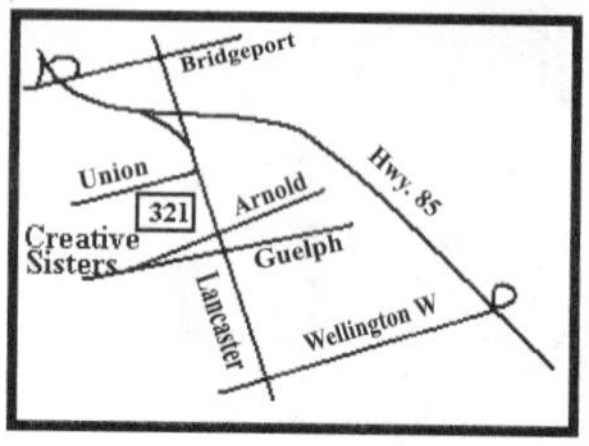

The LARGEST Quilt Shop in Southwestern Ontario

21581 Richmond St. N
London, ON N0M 1C0
Toll Free: (866) 765-2215
(519) 518-6134
suzanne@cotton-by-post.com
www.cotton-by-post.com

Cotton-By-Post Quilt Shoppe

Mon - Fri 9 - 5 Sat 10 - 4

Owner: Suzanne Agnew
Est: 1995 On-line Catalogue
Classes available for all skill levels.
Bernina & Pfaff Dealership

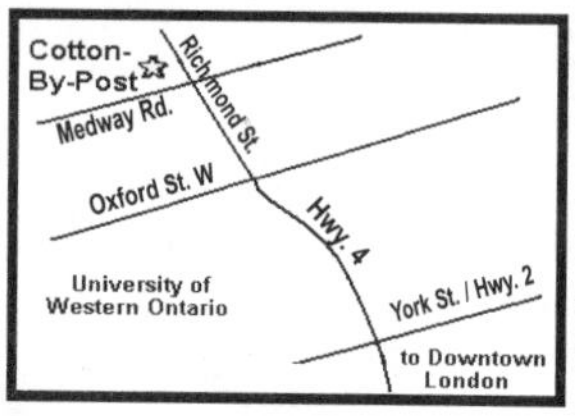

London, ON #19

Ancaster, ON #21

Mon - Sat 10 - 5
Fri til 6

The Quilt Rack

356 Wilson St. E. L9G 2C2
(905) 304-0180
thequiltrack@sympatico.ca
www.thequiltrack.ca

Great selection of fabrics, classes, quilt finishing and long arm machine quilting.
Come to be motivated and inspired!

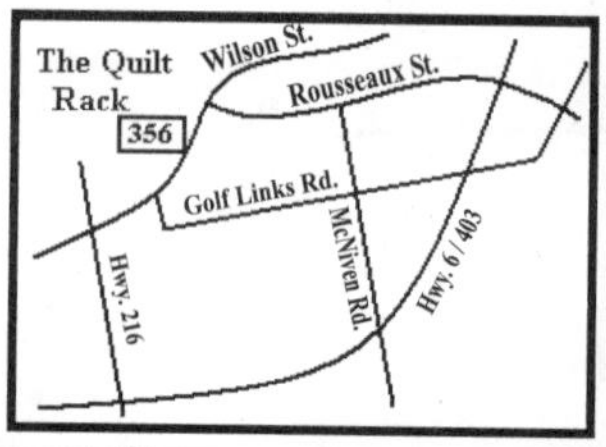

Niagara Falls, ON #22

Mon - Sat 9 - 5:30

The Patchwork Porch

6131 Virginia St. L2E 5Y2
(905) 354-3741 Est: 2002
2400 sq.ft. 2000 Bolts
www.thepatchworkporch.ca
We carry a wide variety of Fabrics. Also batting, sewing essentials (threads, needles, buttons, cutters, cutting boards and almost every gadget you might want) and kits galore.
BOM's, classes, long-arm quilting services.

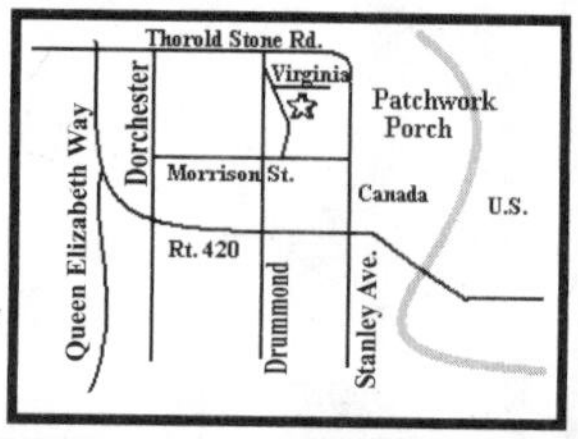

Burlington, ON #23

Mon - Sat 9:30 - 5:30
Sun 12 - 5

Quilters Dream

700 Guelph Line L7R 3M8
(905) 689-3434
info@quiltersdream.ca
Est: 2005
1900 sq.ft.
900 Bolts
www.quiltersdream.ca
Quality cotton quilting fabrics.
Notions/Classes
Authorized Pfaff Dealer
Long Arm Services. Sewing Machine repairs.
Drop in for tea & inspiration! Buses Welcome!

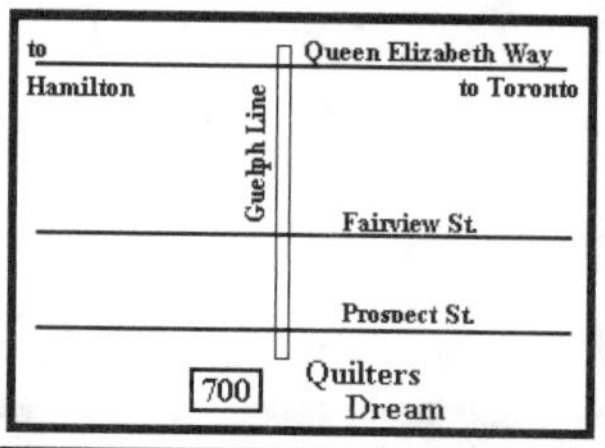

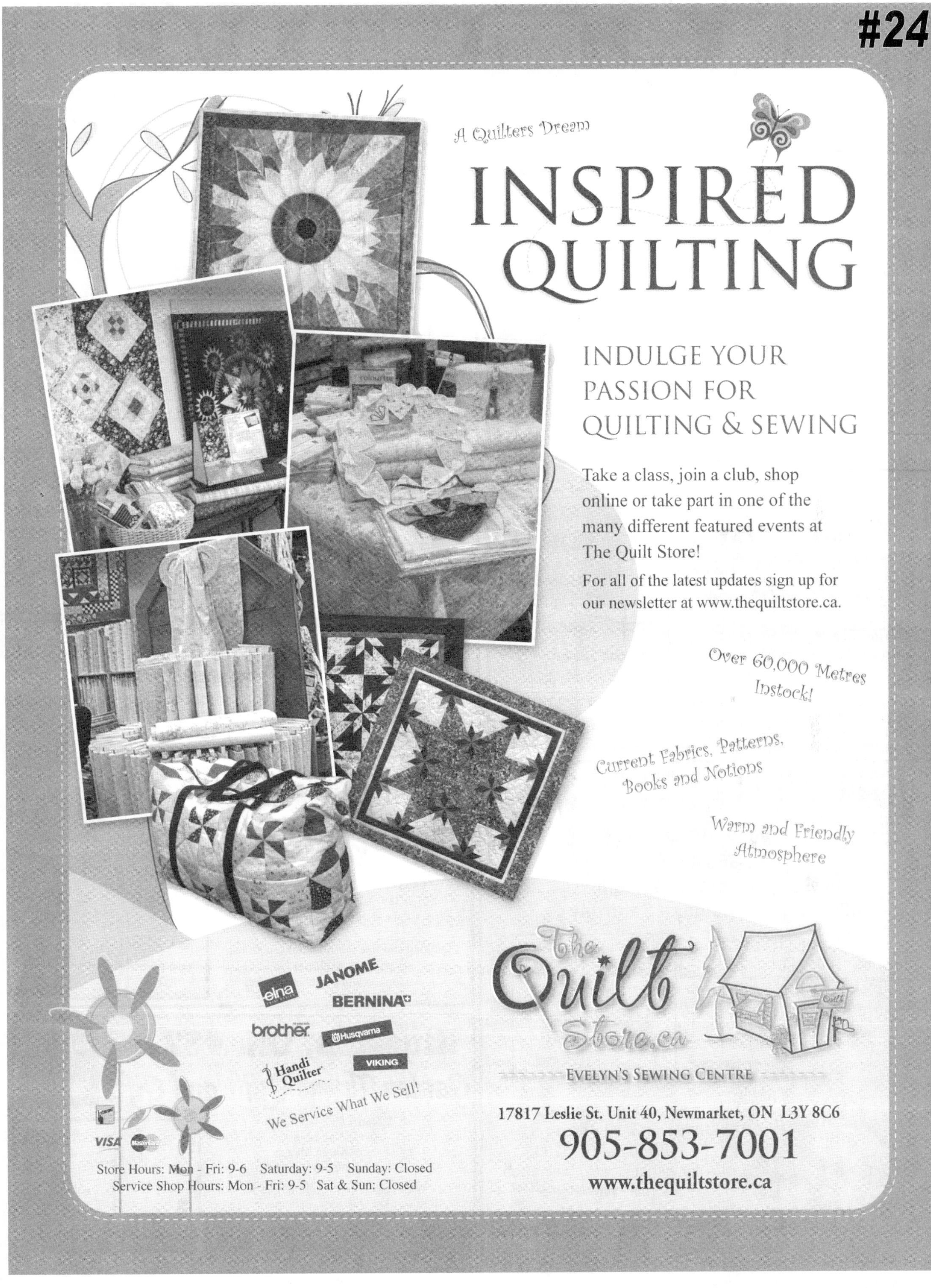
#24
A Quilters Dream
INSPIRED QUILTING
INDULGE YOUR PASSION FOR QUILTING & SEWING
Take a class, join a club, shop online or take part in one of the many different featured events at The Quilt Store!
For all of the latest updates sign up for our newsletter at www.thequiltstore.ca.
Over 60,000 Metres Instock!
Current Fabrics, Patterns, Books and Notions
Warm and Friendly Atmosphere
elna
JANOME
BERNINA
brother
Husqvarna
VIKING
Handi Quilter
We Service What We Sell!
VISA
MasterCard
Store Hours: Mon - Fri: 9-6 Saturday: 9-5 Sunday: Closed
Service Shop Hours: Mon - Fri: 9-5 Sat & Sun: Closed
The Quilt Store.ca
EVELYN'S SEWING CENTRE
17817 Leslie St. Unit 40, Newmarket, ON L3Y 8C6
905-853-7001
www.thequiltstore.ca

Barrie, ON #25

Mon - Sat 9:30 - 5

Knit & Quilt

79 Anne St. S. L4N 2E2
(866) 249-8063 (705) 737-4422
info@knitandquilt.com
www.knitandquilt.com

4,000 square foot shop specializing in top quality quilting fabrics and knitting yarns. Largest shop north of Toronto.

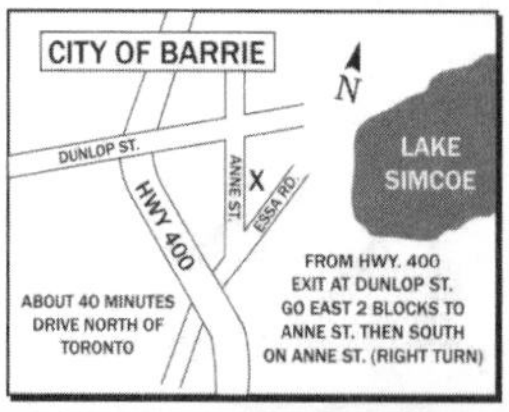

Georgetown, ON #26

Mon - Sat 9:30 - 5:30 Sun 12 - 4

The Hobby Horse Quilt Shoppe

12707 9th Line L7G 4S8
(905) 877-9292 or (800) 565-5366
Owner: Gail Spence Est: 1982
kelly@thehobbyhorse.on.ca
www.thehobbyhorse.on.ca
Featured in quilt Sampler 1996.
We're filled to the brim with bolts of cotton fabrics, quilting supplies, patterns, books, kits and much more. Come Visit Our Store.

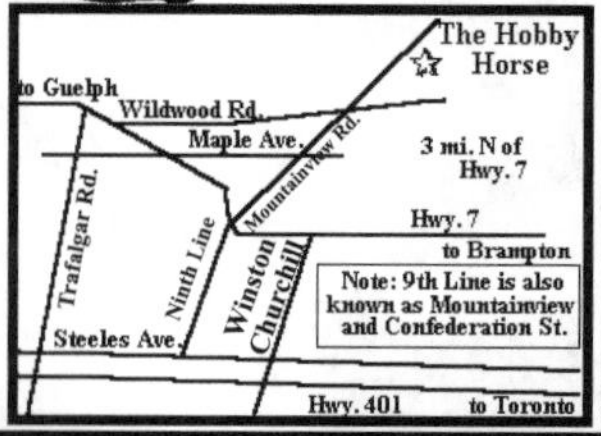

Elmira, ON #27

Tues, Wed Fri 9:30 - 6 Thur 9:30 - 8 Sat 9:30 - 6 Sun 12 - 7

Quilter's Nine Patch

384 Arthur St. S N3B 2P4
(519) 669-9511
quiltersninepatch@gmail.com Est: 2009
www.quiltersninepatch.ca 1600 sq.ft.

1500 bolts of fine quilting fabric:
Civil War, Moda, Amy Butler, Children's Prints, Art Gallery and more. Wool & Rug Hooking.

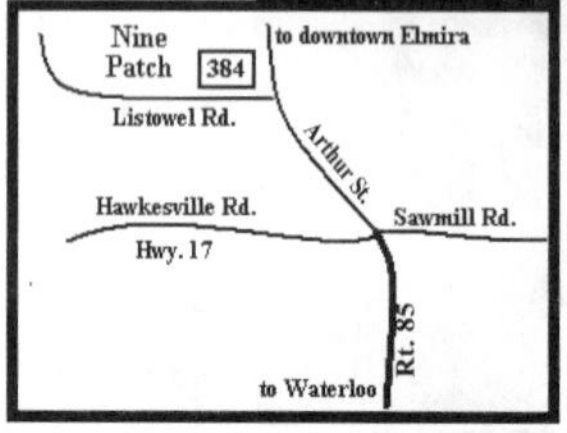

Mississauga, ON #28

Mon - Fri 10 - 5:30 Wed til 7 Sat 10 - 5

Ruti's Needlebed

Lots & Lots of Help - Lots & Lots of Classes

10 Thomas St. L5M 1Y5
(905) 821-9370
Owner: Ruthie Snell
Online Free Newsletter
www.ruti.ca
Very friendly staff - Huge Selection, 5000+ Bolts
All your quilting, sewing, hand knitting, machine knitting and fibercraft needs!
Bring in this ad for your free meter of fabric!

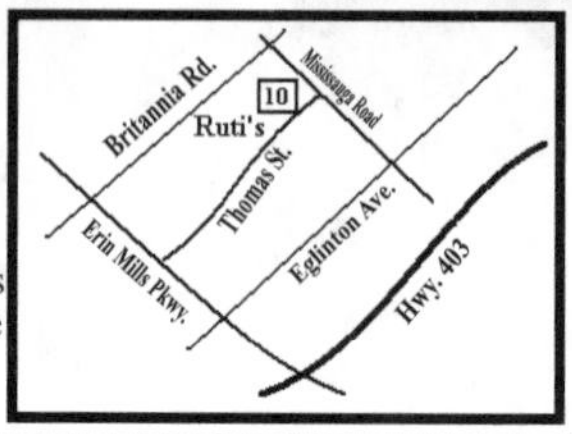

Toronto, ON #29

Mon - Sat 10 - 5:30 Thur til 7 Sun 12 - 4 call for summer hours

the Quilter's Palette

4947 Dundas St. W M9A 1B6
(416) 916-0398 (800) 455-4372
info@quilterspalette.ca
www.quilterspalette.ca

We are Toronto's Fun and Friendly Quilt Store, Conveniently located near major highways, Pearson Airport and Islington Subway Station.

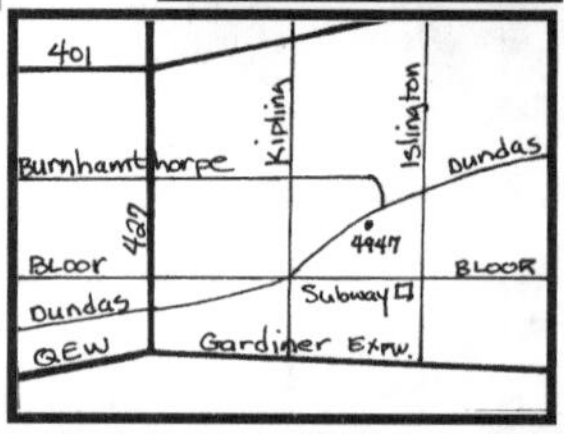

FUN WITH STITCHES

1977 Old Hwy. 2, RR#2 K8N 4Z2
613-966-4715
www.funwithstitches.com
9:30 - 5:00 Monday - Saturday

Quality quilting fabrics & notions. Lots of books and patterns to make that special quilt.
Machine quilting services.
Janome Dealer.

JANOME

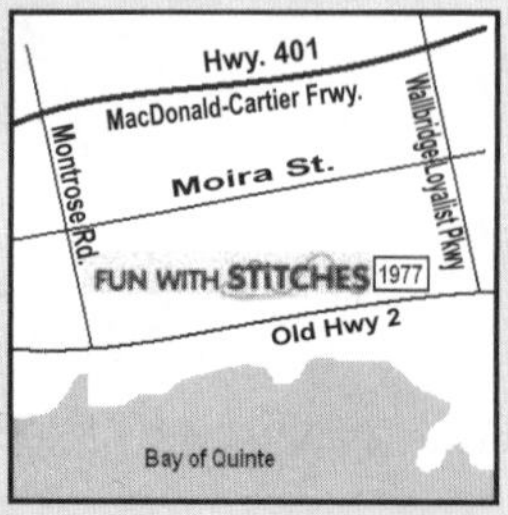

Est: 2004 2000 sq.ft.
3000 Bolts
fax: 613-966-3283
funwithstitches@bellnet.ca
Online Newsletter

Belleville, ON #30

Kingston, ON #31

Mon - Fri 9:30 - 5:30 Sat 9:30 - 5

Quilt & Stitch

645 Gardiners Rd. K7M 8K2
(613) 389-2223 or (800) 207-5417
www.quiltandstitch.ca

Quilting and fine fabrics, books, notions, patterns, & classes.
Kingston's sewing machine center.

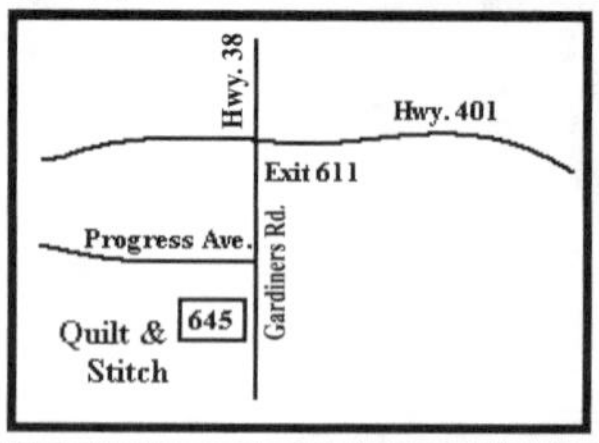

Kingston, ON #32

Tues - Fri 10 - 5 Sat 9 - 4

Garden Thyme Quilt and Gifts

637 Norris Ct. K7P 2R9
(613) 384-8028
Owner: Karen Magee
www.gardenthymequiltfabricandgifts.ca

Wide selection of Quilting Fabric.
1000's of Fat Quarters. Patterns, books, punch needle supplies, primitive décor, Christmas décor, Gourmet food.
Friendly Service.

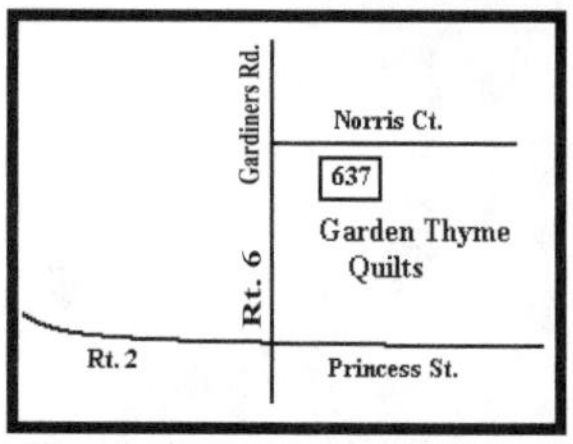

Harrowsmith, ON #33

Tues - Sat 9 - 5

Wilton Creek Fabrics

4909 Hwy. 38 K0H 1V0
(613) 372-1972
wiltoncreekfabrics@yahoo.ca
www.wiltoncreekfabrics.com

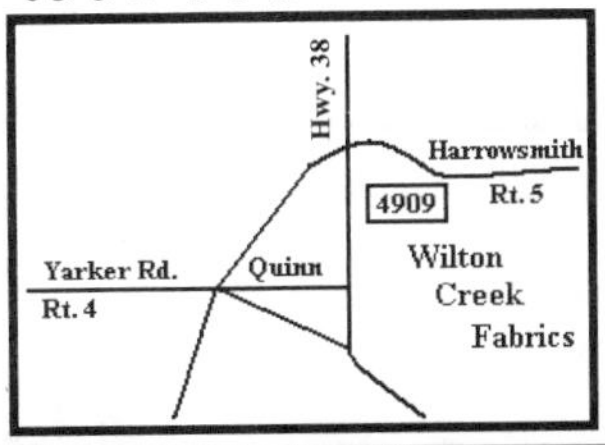

Full service quilt shop. We carry Moda, Hoffman, RJR & much more.
Patterns - Books - Notions - Classes
Official Dealer of Bernina Sewing Machines.

Perth, ON #34

Mon - Fri 9:30 - 5:30 Sat 9 - 5

Perth Fabrics Crafts'n More

14 Gore St. E K7H 1H5
(613) 267-7990 Fax: (613) 267-5587
perthfabrics@rogers.com Est: 1992
www.perthfabrics.com

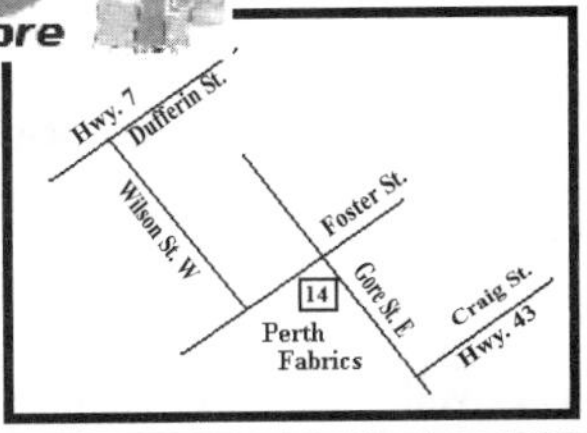

We stock 1,000,001 items.
All types of fabrics.
Have lunch in our beautiful Heritage Town.
Be sure to see our Heritage Quilting Mural.

Ottawa, ON #35

Mon - Fri 10 - 5:30 Fri til 7 (except July & Aug) Sat 10 - 5

dragonfly fabrics for fashion and quilting

2679 Alta Vista Dr. K1V 7T5
(613) 521-9839
www.dragonflyfabrics.ca

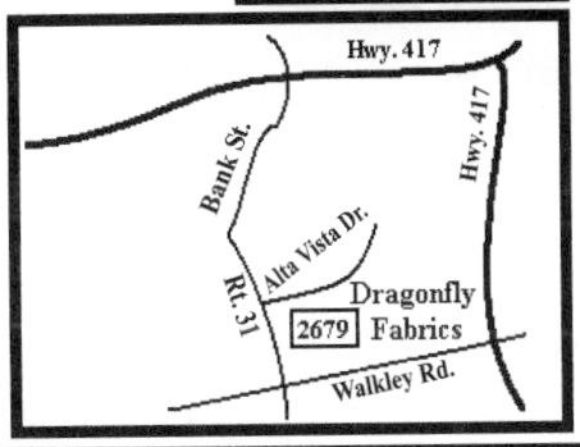

We also carry embellishment products, smocking supplies and fine natural fiber fabrics.

Kanata, ON #36

Mon - Fri 10 - 6 Sat 10 - 5

www.The Running Stitch.ca
613-836-5908
462 Hazeldean Rd, Kanata, ON K2L 1V3
"...Where we Inspire You to Create"
BERNINA

Fax: (613) 836-8865
Owner: Michele Santerre
Est: 1993 2800 sq.ft.

therunningstitch@on.aibn.com
www.therunningstitch.ca

A large selection of fabrics, notions, patterns and books. A cozy atmosphere. Knowledgeable and helpful personnel. Come enjoy yourself!

Ontario Quilt Shops

Alliston — **Lilac Lane Quilts, 180 Parson Rd. #27** — **705-435-2746** — **See ad #8, page 624**
Almonte — Textile Traditions, 87 Mill St. — 613-256-3907
Almonte — The Quilting Quarters, 14 Industrial Dr. — 613-256-4248
Amherstburg — **Rose Cottage Quilt Shoppe, 276 Dalhousie St.** — **519-730-1172** — **See ad #16, page 626**
Ancaster — **The Quilt Rack, 356 Wilson St. E** — **905-304-0180** — **See ad #21, page 626**
Arkona — Quilts 'n Things, 43 Ann St PO Box 251 — 519-518-6228
Arnprior — My Country Quilt Shop, 104 Elgin St. West — 613-623-0500
Barrie — **Knit & Quilt, 79 Anne St.** — **705-737-4422** — **See ad #25, page 628**
Belleville — **Fun With Stitches, 1977 Old Hwy 2. RR#2** — **613-966-4715** — **See ad #30, page 628**
Blenheim — **Pastime Pieces, 11175 Brush Line** — **519-676-5059** — **See ad #18, page 626**
Blenheim — Quilts & Other Cover Ups, 90 McGregor St. — 519-676-2074
Bowmanville — Quilters Boutique, 51 King St. W — 905-623-2404
Bracebridge — **The Muskoka Quilting Co., 161 Manitoba St.** — **705-645-4446** — **See ad #6, page 624**
Brighton — The Robbins Nest, 53 Main — 613-475-0578
Brockville — Taylor Sewing Centre, 7712 Kent Blvd. — 613-342-3153
Brockville — Picket Fence Fabrics, 71 King Street West — 613-498-4874
Burlington — **Quilters Dream Inc., 700 Guelph Line** — **905-689-3434** — **See ad #23, page 626**
Campbellford — Your #1 Sewing Centre, 62 Bridge St — 705-653-5642
Cookstown — Country Concessions, 1 Dufferin St. — 705-458-4546
Dresden Verna's — Sewing Centre, 462 St. George S — 519-683-4244
Dryden — A J's, Hwy. 17 W — 807-223-8700
Dryden — Qustom Quilts & More, 291 Johnston Rd. — 807-937-5116
Dundas — The Cotton Mill Threadworks, 2 Crowly Ct — 905-628-5267
Elmira — **Quilter's Nine Patch, 384 Arthur St. S** — **519-669-9511** — **See ad #27, page 628**
Erin Alice's — Quilt Shoppe, 8 Thompson Cres., #4 — 519-833-0444
Espanola — Cindy Bee's Quilt Shoppe, 70 McCulloch — 705-869-2548
Exeter — **Quilts & Calicos, 392 Main St. S** — **519-235-4084** — **See ad #15, page 625**
Fergus — Undercover Quilts and More!, 181 St. Andrew St. E — 519-546-5411
Fonthill — The Quilting Bee, 155 Hwy. 20 — 905-892-7926
Fort Frances — **Crazy Ladies Fabrics, 330 Scott St.** — **807-274-6665** — **See ad #1, page 624**
Georgetown — **The Hobby Horse, R.R. #5, 12707 9th Line** — **905-877-9292** — **See ad #26, page 628**
Goderich — **Quilters by the Square, 32 West St.** — **519-524-4333** — **See ad #11, page 625**
Guelph — Greenwood Quiltery, 275 Woolwich — 519-822-2790
Guelph — Triangle Sewing Centre, 386 Woolwich St. — 519-822-9910
Harrowsmith — **Wilton Creek Fabrics, 4909 Hwy. 38** — **613-372-1972** — **See ad #33, this page**
Huntsville — **Gone Quilting!, #1 - 14 Main St. E** — **705-788-9982** — **See ad #5, page 624**
Kanata — **The Running Stitch, 474 Hazeldean Rd.** — **613-836-5908** — **See ad #36, this page**
Keewatin — Cottage Country Quilts, Site 1, Box 63, R.R. #1 — 807-547-8458
Kemptville — Kemptville Fabric Shoppe, 31 Clothier St E — 613-258-4437
Kenora — Subtle Creations, 26 Peter St. W — 807-468-6650
Kenora — Quilters Quarters, 25 Main Street South — 807-467-8865
Kincardine — Retail Dry Goods, R.R. #5 — no phone
Kingston — **Quilt & Stitch, 645 Gardiners Rd.** — **613-389-2223** — **See ad #31, page 628**
Kingston — **Garden Thyme Quilt & Gift Emporium, 637 Norris Ct.** — **613-384-8028** — **See ad #32, page 628**
Kingston — Abbey Dawn Quilts, Crafts & Antiques, 1619 Abbey Dawn — 613-542-6247
Kitchener — **Creative Sisters Quilt Studio, 321 Lancaster St. W** — **519-584-2130** — **See ad #20, page 626**
Kitchener — Creative Sewing Centre, 1375 Weber St. E #21 — 519-746-0910

L'Amable	Country Quilts & Fabrics, 739 Upper Turriff Rd., R.R. #1	613-332-2540
Leamington	**A Stitch in Time, 30 Mill St. West**	**519-322-4690** **See ad #17, page 626**
Linwood	Retail Dry Goods, 7546 Rd 116, RR#1	no phone
Lion's Head	Greig's Fabrics, 66 Main St.	519-793-4500
London	**Cotton-By-Post Quilting Studio 21581 Richmond St N**	**519-518-6134** **See ad #19, page 626**
London	Joyce's Sewing Shop, 325 Wortley Rd.	519-433-5344
London	Quilt Works of London, 699 Wilkins St.	519-668-7470
Markdale	Quilters' Line, 57 Main St. W	519-986-2244
Maxwell	**Threads That Bind, 408002 Hwy #4**	**519-922-1010** **See ad #9, page 624**
Meaford	The Fabric Shoppe, 35 Sykes St North	519-538-3955
Midhurst	Simcoe Quilt Shoppe, 6 Wattie Rd.	705-734-1441
Millbrook	Quilts n Critters, 28 King St.	705-932-7848
Mindemoya	Wool 'n' Things, 6135 Hwy 542	705-377-7140
Mississauga	**Ruti's Needlebed, 10 Thomas St.**	**905-821-9370** **See ad #28, page 628**
Mississauga	Dye-Version, 3659 Loyalist Drive	905-569-3299
Mount Albert	Gemini Fibres, 5062 Mt. Albert Rd.	905-473-1033
Mount Forest	Fabric Expressions, 233 Main St. S	519-323-1683
Navan	Aunt Beth's Quilt World, 3217 Navan Rd.,	613-837-6222
Nepean	Sew for It!, 418 Moodie Dr.	613-820-2201
New Hamburg	Heart "N Home Creations, 115 A Peel St.	519-662-4362
New Liskeard	The Quilting Barn, 097460 Jelly Rd	705-647-0081
Newmarket	**Evelyn's Sewing Centre, 17817 Leslie St., # 40**	**905-853-7001** **See ad #24, page 627 & 415**
Newmarket	Cut N Quilt, 232 Lancaster Ave.	905-898-8863
Newton	**E and E'S Cloth and Creations 4463 Perth Line 72**	**519-595-8569** **See ad #12, page 625**
Niagara Falls	**The Patchwork Porch, 6131 Virginia St.**	**905-354-3741** **See ad #22, page 626**
Normandale	Black Bird Country Quilt Works, 2309 Front Rd.	519-426-0736
North Bay	**Creation Unique, 1169 Cassells St.**	**705-472-5900** **See ad #4, page 624**
North Bay	Homestead Stitches 164 Main St W	705-476-9923
North Bay	Three Gables Studio - Quilt Shop, 174 Main Street East	705-475-0900
Orangeville	Cotton Threads Quilt Shop, Inc., 88 First St.	519-938-0842
Orillia	Thimbles & Things, 1282 Brodie Dr.	705-326-9357
Oshawa	Ultimate Sewing Centre, 191 Bloor St. E	905-436-9193
Oshawa	Joyce Hancock's Teaching & Sewing Studio 1396 Winchester Rd. E	905-404-8496
Ottawa	**Dragonfly Fabrics, 2679 Alta Vista Dr**	**613-521-9839** **See ad #35, page 629**
Perth	**Perth Fabrics Crafts 'n More, 14 Gore St. E**	**613-267-7990** **See ad #34, page 629**
Petawawa	Algonquin Sewing Center, 2096 Petawawa	613-732-4789
Peterborough	Your #1 Sewing Centre, 182 George St. N	705-742-3337
Peterborough	Tangled Threads Quilt Shoppe, 261 Charlotte	705-876-8707
Pickering	The Quilt Shoppe Sewing Centre, 1099 Kingston Rd.	905-420-1101
Picton	Picton Fabric World, 261 Main St.	613-476-6397
Poplar Hill	**The Marsh Store, 10266 Ilderton Rd.**	**519-666-3330** **See ad #14, page 625**
Port Hope	Cozy Quilts, 74 Queen St., Unit D	905-885-5777
Red Lake	The Yarn Shop, 150 Harvey St.	807-727-2564
Red Lake	Gail's Stitches, 281 Hwy. 105	807-727-3161
Renfrew	Dolan's Fabric Shop & Yarn, 172 Raglan St. S	613-432-6434
Richmond	Country Quilter, 3444 McBean St.	613-838-5541
Rideau Ferry	Sew Crafty, 1068 Rideau Ferry Rd.	613-264-1547
Sault Ste. Marie	**Life's A Stitch, 516 Queen St. E**	**705-254-3339** **See ad #2, page 624**
Scarborough	Sewing Machine Factory Outlet, 2082 Lawrence Ave. E #1	416-751-7170
Shakespeare	**The Quilt Place, 3991 Perth Rd. #107**	**519-625-8435** **See ad #13 page 625**
Shelburne	**Cobwebs and Caviar, 127 Main St.**	**519-925-2254** **See ad #10, page 624**
Simcoe	Quilter's Haven, 1094 Cockshutt Rd. #5	519-429-2811
Sioux Lookout	Dori's Sewing Studio, 3 Loon Lake Rd	807-737-3674
Smiths Falls	Quilter's Rack, 16 Beckwith St. N	613-284-1551
St. George	Lyn Bell's Designs, 48 Main St. S	519-448-3739
St. Jacobs	Reichard's - The Quilter's Store, 4 Hachborn St Unit 2	519-664-3307
St. Mary's	Simply Sew, 97 Queen St. E.	519-284-0856
Stittsville	Heirloom Quilt Studio, 30 Manchester St.	613-836-6301
Stouffville	Ann's Fabrics & Sewing Centre, 6350 Main	905-640-5635
Stratford	Ye Olde Fabric Shoppe, 327 Erie	519-273-5773
Streetsville	Quiltessential, 228 Quilt St. S	905-542-9194
Sudbury	**It's Sew Easy, 1313 Lorne St. Unit 4**	**705-675-1788** **See ad #3, page 624**
Sudbury	Country Quilter, 1191 Lansing Ave	705-524-6235
Tara	Karen's Country Fabrics, 117538 Grey Road #3, R.R.#4	519-376-4839
Thedford	Country Accents Quilt Shoppe, 8698 Bog Line, R.R. #4	519-296-4738
Thunder Bay	All Sewing & The Quilters Stash, 920B Memorial Ave.	807-345-7174
Tiverton	Creative Quilts & Gifts, 3006 Hwy. 21, R.R. #1	
Toronto	**The Quilters Palette, 4947 Dundas St. W**	**416-916-0398** **See ad #29, page 628**
Toronto	Cock A Doodle Quilts, 115 Miranda Ave.	416-785-4449
Toronto	The Quilting Patch Inc, 88 Dearham Wood	416-281-5561
Toronto	Quilters Fancy, 4 Norbert Crescent	416-232-1199
Trenton	Andjareenas Place, 60 Carrying Place Rd.	613-394-4990
Uxbridge	Quilters Cupboard, 202 Brock St. E	905-862-0666
Uxbridge	Sew Many Fabrics, 4 Banff Rd. #4	905-852-2111
Waterloo	Kallisti Quilts, 66 John St. West	519-569-8718
Waterloo	Len's Mill Store, 130 Moore Ave. S	519-743-4672
Whitby	One Patch At A Time Designs, 25 Foothill	905-666-0243
Wiarton	**Mother's Fabric @ the Spirit Rock Motel 877 Berford St. N**	**519-534-5168** **See ad #7, page 624**
Woodstock	Country Patchworks, #515533 11th Line	519-537-8753

Ontario Quilt Shows

About Shows: We are listing only the very basic information about shows that happen on a regular schedule here. Please check out our website for more details on each show. Also this information tends to change quite often so please verify the event with our website or a local source before you venture far. Or if you're in the right area at the right time, give it a shot.

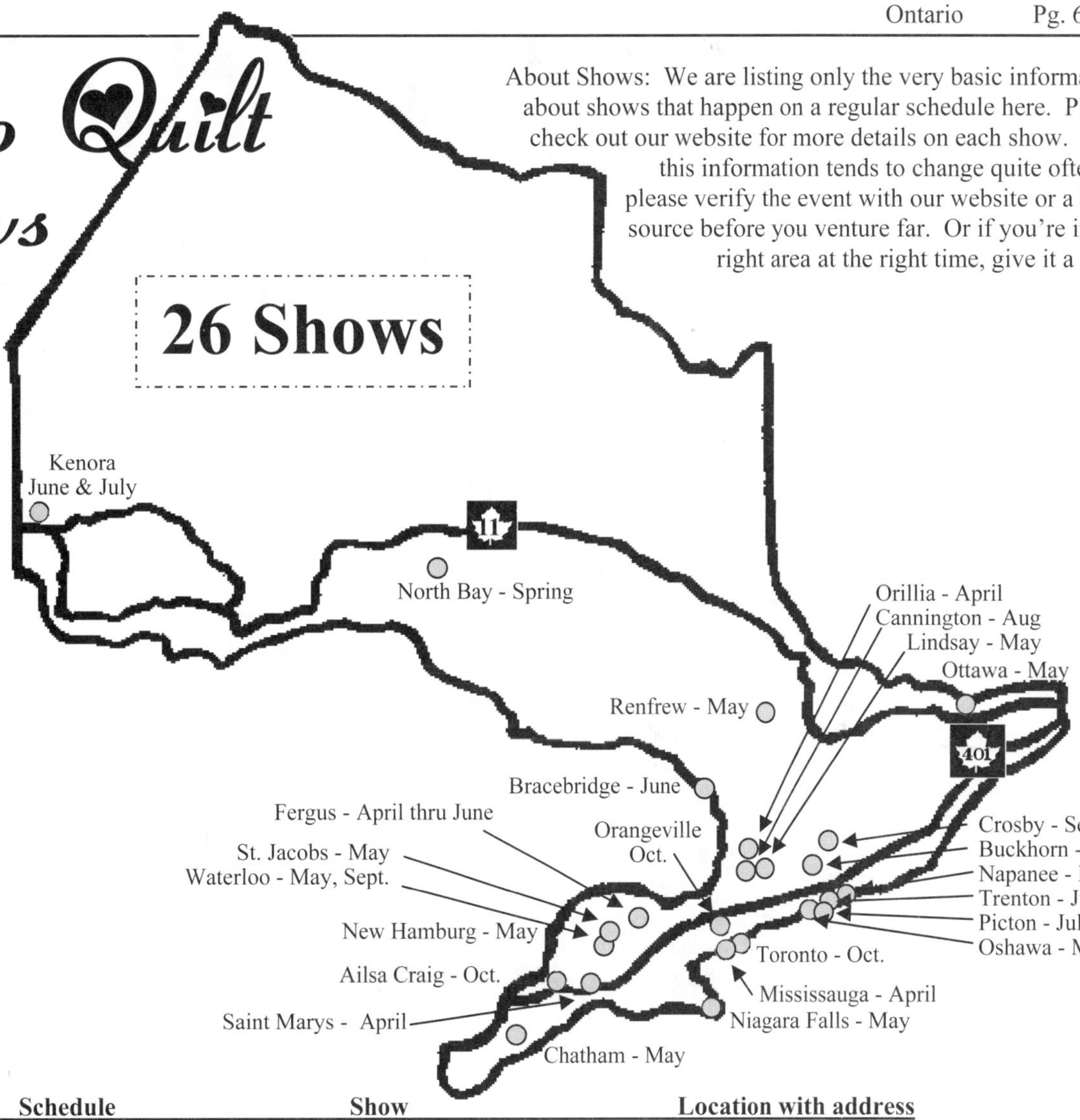

Month	City	Schedule	Show	Location with address
April				
	Orillia	Annual, 3rd weekend in April	Orillia Quilters Guild Show	6 Bed & Breakfasts
	Mississauga	Annual, Last weekend in April	CreativFestival--Spring Show	International Centre, 6900 Airport Rd.
	St. Marys	Even Years, last Thur - Fri of April	Piecemakers Quilt Show	Pyramid Recreation Centre, 317 James St. S
May				
	Chatham	Every 3rd Year, May	2010 Stitches in Bloom	St. Paul's Congregational Church, 450 Park Ave. W
	Fergus	Every 3 Years, April - June	Threadworks	Wellington County Museum, 0536 Wellington Rd. 1, R.R. 1
	Napanee	Odd Years, 1st weekend of May	Quilts - Heritage Quilter's Guild Show	Strathcona Paper Center, 16 McPherson Dr.
	North Bay	Odd Years, Late Spring	Quilts by the Bay	Widdifield Secondary School, 320 Ski Club Rd.
	Niagara Falls	Odd Years, 2nd Fri & Sat in May	Under the Rainbow Quilt Show	Lundy's Lane United Church, 5825 Lowell Ave.
	Oshawa	Annual, Mid May	Tomorrow's Memories	General Sikorski Polish Veteran's Hall, 1551 Stevenson Rd. N
	Ottawa	Odd Years, 2nd weekend in May	Ottawa Valley Quilters Guild	
	Lindsay	Every Other Year, Late May	Lindsay Creative Quilters' Show	Lindsay Curling Club, 18 Peel St.
	New Hamburg	Annual, Last Fri & Sat in May	New Hamburg Minnonite Quilt Auction	New Hamburg Arena, 251 St. Jacob St.
	Renfrew	Even Years, Late May/Early June	Quilters Guild of Renfrew Quilt Show	Mateway Activity Centre, 1 Mateway Park Dr.
	St. Jacobs	Annual, last weekend of May	St. Jacobs Quilt Shows	Various Locations around Town
	Waterloo	Annual, last weekend in May	Quilt & Fibre Art Festival	
June				
	Trenton	Odd Years, 1st weekend in June	The Fabric of Our Lives	Knights of Columbus Hall, 57 Stella Crescent
	Bracebridge	Every third year in June next 2011	Muskoka Quilt Show	Bracebridge Fairgrounds, JD Lang Activity Park, 331 Fraserburg Rd
	Kenora	Annual, June & July	Lake of the Woods Quilters' Guild Show	Lakeside Inn & Conference Center, 470 1st Ave. S .
July				
	Picton	Even Years, 2nd weekend in July	Prince Edward Cty. Quilters' Guild	Prince Edward Comm. Center, 375 Main St. E
August				
	Cannington	Annual, 2nd weekend in August	Cannington & Area Historical Society Show	McLeod Park, Peace St.
September				
	Buckhorn	Even Years, 1st weekend in September	Buckhorn Area Quilters' Guild Show	Buckhorn Community Centre, 1801 Lakehurst Rd.
	Crosby	Annual, 3rd Tues - Sat of September	International Country Festival	Township of Rideau Lakes, Hwy. #15 & Cty. Rd. #42
	Waterloo	Odd Years, last weekend of September	Waterloo County Quilters' Guild Show	Forbes Hall--Rim Park
October				
	Ailsa Craig	Annual, 3rd week of October	East Africian Quilts	Cotton By Post, 135 Main St.
	Orangeville	Every 3rd Year, 3rd weekend in October	The Magic of Cloth	Orangeville Fair Grounds, 247090 5 Sideroad
	Toronto	Annual, 3rd or 4th Fri-Sun in October	Creative Festival	Metro Toronto Convention Centre, 222 Bremner Blvd

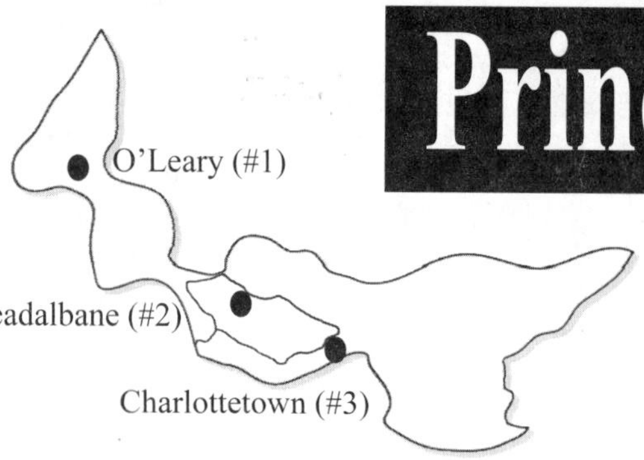

Prince Edward Island

3 Featured Shops

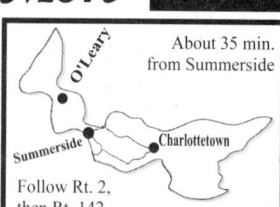

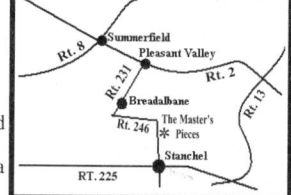

Prince Edward Island Quilt Shops

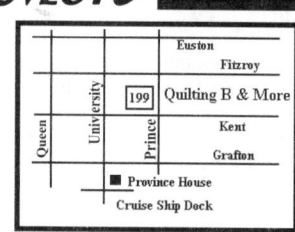

Bedeque	The Village Quilt Shop, Box 4108	902-887-2191
Breadalbane	**The Master's Pieces, 3664 Dixon Rd RR 4**	
	902-621-0569	**See ad #2, this page**
Charlottetown	**Quilting B and More, 199 Prince St.**	
	902-628-1998	**See ad #3, this page**
O'Leary	**Fabric, Crafts 'n More, 538 Main St.**	
	902-859-1888	**See ad #1, this page**
Souris	Jean's Quilting Crafts & Things, 75 Main St., McPhee Mall	902-687-1367
Stratford	Singer Sewing Centre, 9 Aintree Drive	902-569-2762
Summerside	Pins & Needles, 624 Water	902-888-3434
Summerside	Bargain Fabric Outlet, 11 MacMurdo Rd.	902-887-2189
Tignish	Saw & Save Fabrics, Pleasant View	902-882-3616

Prince Edward Island Quilt Shows

We don't know of any shows on Prince Edward Island.
Please submit any shows you may know of, thanks.

Quebec Quilt Shop

Kahnawake Calico Cottage Quilt & Gift Shop, Rt. 132 E (450) 632-7070

Quebec Quilt Shows

Month	City	Schedule	Show	Location with address
September				
	Lennoxville	Annual, weekend after Labor Day		Lennoxville Quilters Show, St. Georges Church Hall, 84 Queen St.
	Saint-Sauveur	Odd Years, Last weekend of September		Laurentian Quilters' Guild Show, Mont Habitant, 12, chemin des Skieurs

Saskatchewan

6 Featured Shops

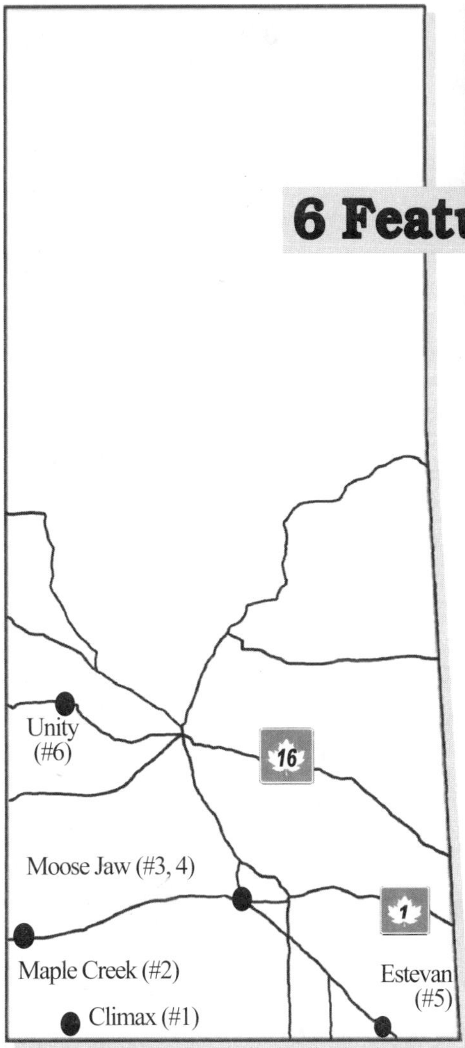

Maple Creek, SK #2

Mon - Sat 9:30 - 5

Cat's Meow Quilts & Gifts

200 Jasper St. S0N 1N0
(306) 662-2180 Fax: Same
Est: 2003 1000 Bolts
catsmeowqg@sasktel.net

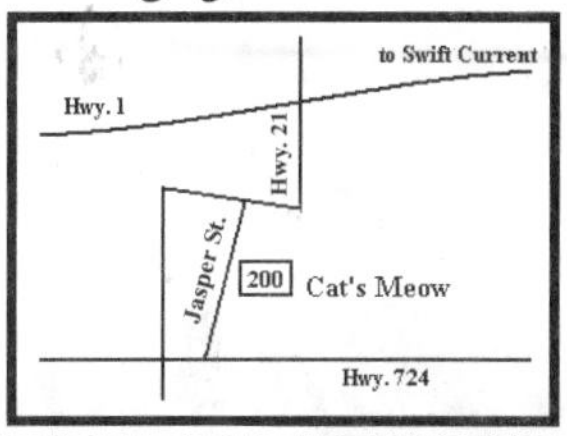

Lots of Fabric, Notions, Books & Patterns
Your One-Stop Shop
Stop in and experience our friendly service.

Moose Jaw, SK #3

Mon - Sat 9:30 - 5:30

Quilters Haven

20 River St. East S6H 0A8
(306) 693-8523 Fax: (306) 693-8524
Owners: Arlyce Thompson & Heather Carruthers
Est: 2005 1200 sq.ft. 1500+ bolts
quiltershaveninc@sasktel.net Online Newsletter
www.quiltershaveninc.ca

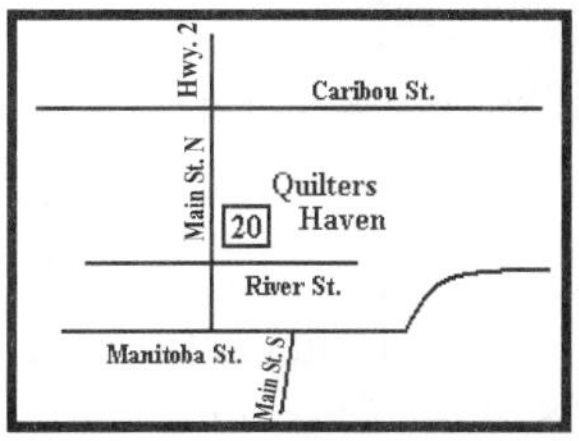

Large selection of quilting cottons, Asian and batik fabrics available in a delicious array of colors, designs and textures.

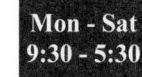

Sweet Material Things

Quilting Supplies & Sew Much More ...

308 1st St. W
Climax, SK S0N 0N0
(306) 293-2976
Fax: (306) 293-2201
sweetmaterialthings
@sasktel.net

Climax, SK #1

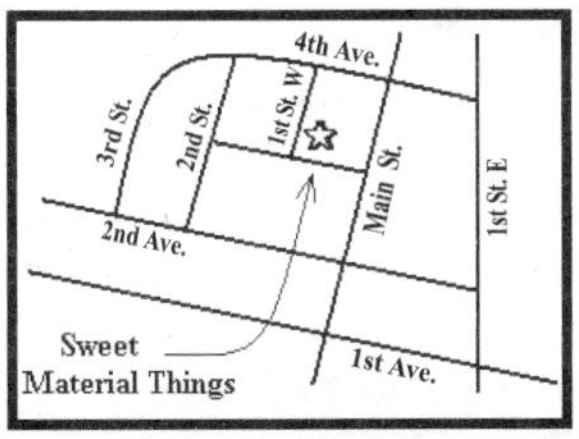

We supply most everything you need for your quilting or sewing projects. This includes hundreds of quality fabrics, new and always needs notions with dozens of patterns for your projects. Also a seasonal change of giftware for birthdays, babies and all life's celebrations.

Tues - Fri 1 - 5:30 **www.sweetmaterialthings.com**

Moose Jaw, SK #4

Mon - Sat 9:30 - 5:30
Sun 1 - 4

The Quilt Patch

35 High St. E
S6H 0B7
(306)692-3360

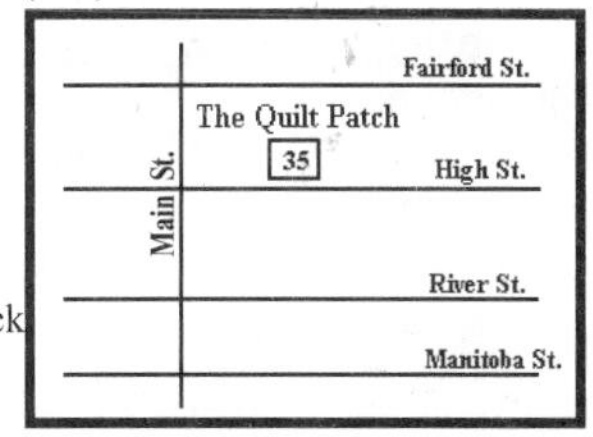

www.thequiltpatch.ca
Free Newsletter
The newest fabrics housed in a beautiful old brick building in the heart of downtown. Fabulous Block-of-the-Month programs & classes.

Estevan, SK #5

Mon - Sat 10 - 5

TIGER LILY QUILTS

1228 4th St. S4A 0W9
(306) 634-2900
Owner: Liz Friswell
Est: 2001 2500 sq.ft
Newsletter

Fabrics, Flannels, Kits, Clubs, Notions, BOM's, Quilts for Sale & Classes. Husqvarna Viking, Babylock, Janome Sewing Machine Dealer
tigerlilyquilts@sasktel.net
www.tigerlilyquilts.com

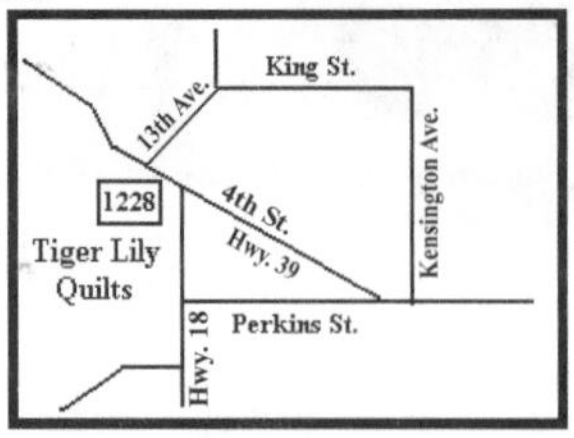

Unity, SK #6

Mon-Sat 10-5:30

IQ+ Ilene's Quilting Plus

120 3rd Ave. E S0K 4L0
(306) 228-2288
Newsletter
ilenesquilting@hotmail.com

Fabrics, patterns, notions, Batiks, fat quarters. Long arm services available.

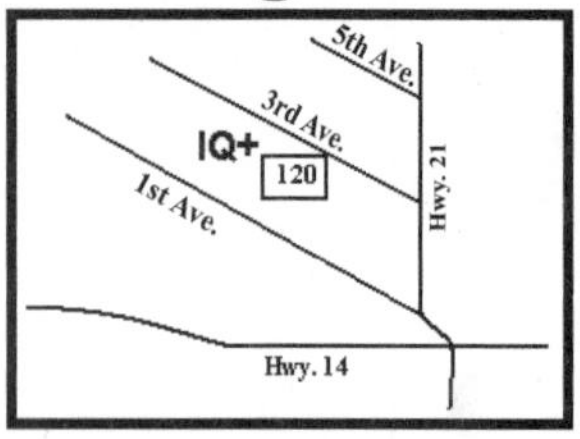

Saskatchewan Quilt Shops

Carlyle	Sew & Sews Quilt & Fabric Shop, 207 Main St.	306-453-2562
Climax	**Sweet Material Things, 308 1st St. W**	
	306-293-2976	**See ad #1, page 633**
Estevan	**Tiger Lily Quilts, 1228 4th St.**	
	306-634-2900	**See ad #5, this page**
Foam Lake	Quiltworks Studio Quilt Shop, 323 Main St.	306-272-4420
Hague	Prairie Chicks Quilting, 205 Main St., Box 752	306-225-4787
Humboldt	Saskatchewan Haus of Stitches, 626 Main St.	306-682-0772
Kindersley	Veronica's Sewing Supplies, 100 Main St.	306-463-4505
Macklin	Corner House Quilts, 4902 Herald St. Box 392	306-753-2902
Maple Creek	**Cat's Meow Quilts & Gifts, 200 Jasper St.**	
	306-662-2180	**See ad #2, page 633**
Melfort	Clothworks & Crafts, 502 Main St.	306-752-9449
Moose Jaw	Heather's Quilting Palette, 361 Main St. N	306-693-1393
Moose Jaw	**Quilters Haven inc., 20 River St. East**	
	306-693-8523	**See ad #3, page 633**
Moose Jaw	**The Quilt Patch, 35 High St. East**	
	306-692-3360	**See ad #4, page 633**
Moosomin	Shirley's Sewing Room, 506 Main St.	306-435-3633
Regina	Peachtree Heirlooms Quilt Shop, 140 Albert St.	306-569-1552
Regina	Bears & Bees Quilt, 522 Victoria Ave. E	306-347-0990
Rosetown	Sew Special, 211 Main St.	306-882-4432
Saskatoon	Unique Textiles Studio, 500-234 1st Ave. S	306-653-4977
Saskatoon	Periwinkle Quilting, 2105 8th St. E #105	306-933-3072
Spirit Wood	Thoughts & Things, 332 First St. E. Box 97	306-883-3800
Unity	**Ilene's Quilting Plus, 120 3rd Ave. E Po Box 1949**	
	306-228-2288	**See ad #6, this page**
Yorkton	Colette's Sewing Machines Plus, 206 Smith E	306-782-3520

Saskatchewan Quilt Shows

About Shows: We are listing only the very basic information about shows that happen on a regular schedule here. Please check out our website for more details on each show. Also this information tends to change quite often so please verify the event with our website or a local source before you venture far. Or if you're in the right area at the right time, give it a shot.

If you are a show organizer, please keep us updated on your event.
shows@quilterstravelcompanion.com www.quilterstravelcompanion.com

On our website you will also find:

- Exact dates (when we have them)
- Contact Information
- Events happening on a one-time basis
- Sponsor Information
- Description of Event

Month	City	Schedule	Show	Location with address
September				
	Carlyle	Annual, 3rd weekend in September	Homespun Craft Show & Sale	Carlyle Sports Arena, 100 Main St.
October				
	Saskatoon	Odd Years, October	Saskatoon Quilters Guild Show	Prairieland Park Trade Centre, Hall D, 503 Ruth St. W

Yukon Quilt Shops

Whitehorse	Golden Thimble Fabrics, 102-4133 4th Ave.	867-667-6760
Whitehorse	Sew Far So Good, 54 Tigereyes Crescent	867-633-6548
Whitehorse	Bear Paw Quilt, 2093 2nd Ave.	867-393-2327

Yukon Quilt Shows

We don't know of any shows in the Yukon..
Please submit any shows you may know of, thanks.

Bahamas Shop

Nassau Silk Cotton Quilts, #3 Winton Hwy. 242-324-1073

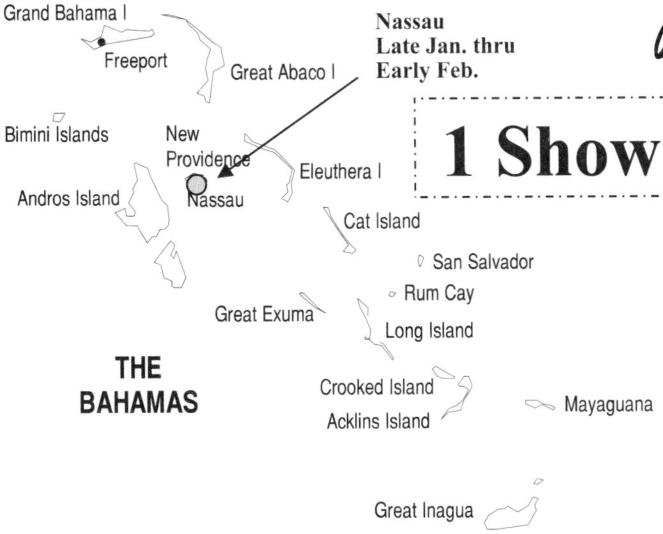

Bahamas Quilt Show

1 Show

About Shows: We are listing only the very basic information about shows that happen on a regular schedule here. Please check out our website for more details on each show. Also this information tends to change quite often so please verify the event with our website or a local source before you venture far. Or if you're in the right area at the right time, give it a shot.

If you are a show organizer,
please keep us updated on your event.
shows@quilterstravelcompanion.com
www.quilterstravelcompanion.com

January

Nassau Annual, last week of Jan - beginning of February Stepping Stone Quilters Show Trinity Methodist Church, Frederick St.

Retreat Facility ads in this edition of the Quilters' Travel Companion

Plan a great event at one of these wonderful locations.

Idaho
- Page 131 Quilt House B&B, Kamiah, ID Ad #4

Illinois
- Page 140 Threads and Beds, Danville, IL Ad #26
- Page 146 Quilter's Garden, Princeton, IL Ad #49

Indiana
- Page 162 Lucky Breezes Crafter's Cottage, Plymouth, IN Ad #5
- Page 165 Cheryl's Quilt Shop, West Lafayette, IN Ad #29
- Page 166 Quilters Harvest Shop, Lafayette, IN Ad #30

Iowa
- Page 180 LouAnn's Quilt Garden, Oelwein, IA Ad #27
- Page 180 Vintage Threads, Dyersville, IA Ad #28
- Page 182 The Cottage Rose, Marion, IA Ad #42
- Page 185 Quilters Paradise, Mt. Pleasant, IA Ad #59

Kansas
- Page 212 All About Quilts, Manhattan, KS Ad #17

Kentucky
- Page 227 Calico Patch Quilt Shop, Morehead, KY Ad #22

Maine
- Page 237 Threads Galore Quilt Shop, Rangeley, ME Ad #2
- Page 237 Kedar Quilts, Waterfrod, ME Ad #3

Michigan
- Page 265 So South Haven, South Haven, MI Ad #32

MARION, IA

KEDARBURN INN WATERFORD, ME

W. LAFAYETTE, IN

DANVILLE, IL

SEWED INN-MOREHEAD, KY

SOUTH HAVEN, MI

PRINCETON, IL

PLYMOUTH, IN

LAFAYETTE, IN

RANGELEY, ME

HUMMINGBIRD INN
ROSLYN, WA

MRS. ANDERSON'S LODGING
LEAVENWORTH, WA

OSSEO, WI

KINGSVILLE, MO

VANDERBUILT, PA

QUILTING RETREAT
Seams like Home
BED & BREAKFAST

G BAR M RANCH
BOZEMAN, MT

WAITE PARK, MN

ARCHBOLD, OH

SUNSET RANCH
JOSHUA, TX

EAU CLAIRE, WI

CEDAR HILL, TX

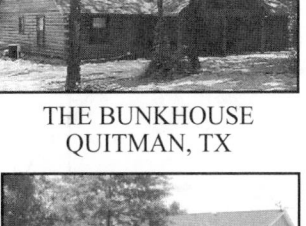

THE BUNKHOUSE
QUITMAN, TX

LANGLEY, WA

THE MAIN HOUSE
KERRVILLE
TX

LAKESIDE LODGE
INLET, NY

MAGGIE VALLEY, NC

WHIPPLE, OH

ORTING, WA

THE QUILTER'S INN
COSBY, TN

BUTTERFLY MEADOWS INN
FRANKLIN, TN

THE QUILT INN
GRANBURY, TX

ELK MOUND, WI

THE BARN QUILT ARTS MOVEMENT

Historic barns and corncribs adorned with quilt blocks. Quilt blocks are proudly displayed on close to 70 barns all over this Iowa county. You'll also find many other interesting attractions along the way. Check out our "Area Lodging and Dining" section on our website.

www.barnquilts.com

The website lists all the addresses for the spruced-up barns, a map and links to google maps.
We also offer a full-color book.

Pick up a brochure describing the Barn quilts of Sac County at Welcome Centers throughout the state. Many local shops also have maps locating the barn quilts around the county.

Sac County also sponsors "Quilt-A-Fair" quilt show in September of Odd Years.
Next Show is Sept. 24 & 25, 2011

One of the flower beds planted in a quilt design.

As you're traveling it would be great fun if you can work in a 'Barn Quilt' tour.

The idea of barn quilts began in Adams County Ohio in 2001. It was conceived as a way to draw traffic off a busy four-lane highway as it wound through this economically depressed area of southern Ohio. Local artists painted traditional quilt blocks on weathered tobacco barns and the project began to attract travelers to the area. Then many other projects sprang up to draw traffic back to rural areas bypassed when a major highway was rerouted.

Please see our listings on the next page for ***some*** of the many quilt barn projects around the country. You may want to include a nice country drive in your travels.

If you're in Northern Indiana or close to Kansas City Missouri, be sure to make time to visit the ***"Quilt Gardens"***
We're sure many more will be 'popping' up.
These are flower gardens planted in quilt block patterns.

Check out:

Quilt Gardens along the Heritage Trail, Indiana
www.amishcountry.org
Amish Acres Quilt Gardens
www.amishacres.com
Many tours are also being offered to visit the Northern Indiana gardens.

Quilt Gardens along the Heritage Trail

The Heartland Harvest Garden
Kingsville, Missouri
www.powellgardens.org

Quilt Gardens Tour

The pictures below are from the Sac County project. There are barn quilts projects in other Iowa counties and in about 25 different states, but you'll see more quilts in Sac County than just about anywhere else.

COLORADO
Barn Quilts of Morgan County, Colorado
www.mcbarnquilts.blogspot.com

GEORGIA
Barn Quilts of Cobb County, Georgia
www.southernquilttrail.com

KENTUCKY
Kentucky Quilt Trails, Various Counties
www.kentuckyquilttrail.org
Barn Quilts of Bracken County
http://home.windstream.net
Breckinridge County Quilt Barns
www.visitbreckinridgecountyky.com
Quilt Trail Project, Campbell County, KY
http://cckyquilts.wordpress.com
Western Kentucky Quilt Trail http://kentuckyquiltline.com
Buffalo Gals Barn Quilt Trail www.georgetownky.com
Grayson County Clothesline of Quilts
www.graysoncountytourism.com
The Barn Quilts of Harrison County
www.harrisoncountybarnquilts.com
Hart County Clothes Line of Quilts
http://ces.ca.uky.edu/hart/node/69
Henry County Barn Quilt Project
www.henrycountyky.com/extension/barnquilts.htm
Hickman County Quilt Trail
http:// hickmancoquilttrail.wordpress.com/
Jessamine Quilt Trail
http://kentuckyquilttrail-jessaminecounty.com
Lewis County Quilt Trail www.visitlewiscountyky.com
Kentucky Quilt Trail of Madison County
http://ce3.ca.uky.edu/madisonquilttrail/trail.html
Marion County Quilt Trail www.visitlebanonky.com
Rowan County Kentucky Foothill Quilt Trail
http://rcquilttrail.tripod.com/
Washington County Barn Quilt Trail
http://ces.ca.uky.edu/washington-files
ILLINOIS
Barn Quilts of Kankakee County, Illinois
www.web.extension.illinois.edu
McHenry County Quilted Barn Program, Illinois
www.mchsonline.org/quilted_barn_prog.htm

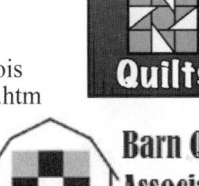

INDIANA
Marshall County Barn Quilt Trail, Indiana
www.marshallcountytourism.org

IOWA
Butler County Barn Quilts, Iowa
www.butlercountyiowa.com/barnquilts.html
Barn Quilts of Clay County, Iowa
www.travelclaycountyiowa.com
Barn Quilts of Buchanan County, Iowa
www.buchanancountyhistory.com
Fayette County Barn Quilts, Iowa
www.wadenaiowa.com/barnquilts.htm
Barn Quilts of Grundy County, Iowa
www.grundycountyia.com
Humbolt County Barn Quilts of Iowa
www.humboltcountybarnquilts.com
Barn Quilts of O'Brien County, Iowa
www.obriencounty.com
Barn Quilts of Washington County Iowa
www.barnquiltsiowa.com

MARYLAND
Barn Quilts of Garrett County, Maryland
www.garrettbarnquilts.org

MICHIGAN
Alcona County Quilt Trail
http://alconaquilttrail.com
Michigan Barn Network
www.barnsofoldmission.com

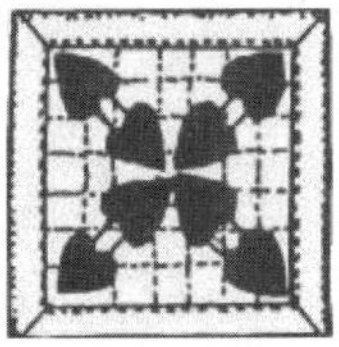
Upper Cumberland Quilt Trail

MINNESOTA
Caledonia Area Barn Quilts www.caledoniamn.gov

NEBRASKA
Cass County Barn Quilts
http://embarn.freehostia.com/index.html

NEW JERSEY
New Jersey Barn Quilts
www.njbarnquilts.com/warencoquilts/html
also /susexcoquilts.html and
middlesexcoquilts.html

NORTH CAROLINA
"Way Back When" Barn Quilts of N Carolina
www.wbwbarnquilts.com
Ashe County Arts Barn Project of NC
www.ashecountyarts.org
Avery Quilt Tour
www.averycountyartscouncil.org
Macon County Quilt Trail
www.maconcountyquilttrail.org
Madison County Barn Quilts
www.madisoncountyarts.com
McDowell Quilt Trail http://mcdowellquilttrail.org
Watauga County Quilt Trail www.watauga-arts.org
Barn Quilt Project of Wilkes County
www.cacwilkes.org
Yadkin Valley Quilt Trail www.shacktownnc.com

OHIO
Adams County Quilt Barn Trail
www.adamscountytravel.org/quiltbarntrail.asp
Athens County Quilt Barn Tour
www.athensohio.com
Ohio Clothesline of Quilts Trail
www.browncountytourism.com
Harrison County Quilt Barn Project
http://bender.frog.net/~harrisoncic/community
Miami County Quilt Barns
http://visitmiamicounty.org
Pike's Patches Quilt Barn Trail
www.piketravel.com
Vinton County Quilt Barns
www.vintoncountytravel.com/quilt_barns.htm

SOUTH CAROLINA
Oconee Heritage Quilt Trail
www.oconeeheritagequilttrail.com

TENNESSEE
Tennessee Quilt Trail--Anderson, Grainger, Union, Claiborne, Hawkins, Cocke, Know, Hamblen, Carter, Green, Johnson, Sullivan, Washington, Hancock, Unicoi, Blunt Counties
www.vacationaqt.com
Houston County Celtic Quilt Trail
www.houstoncochamber.com
Jefferson County Quilt Trail
http://jeffersoncountyvacation.com

TEXAS
Terry County Quilt Trail
www.terrycountyquilt.com

WISCONSIN
Barn Quilts of Green County, Wisconsin
www.greencountybarnquilts.com
Kewaunee County Barn Quilts, Wisconsin
www.agriculturalheritage.org
Barn Quilts of SW Wisconsin
www.uwex.edu
Racine County Quilts on Barns
www.quiltsonbarns.com
Barn Quilts of Walworth County, Wisconsin
http://Walworth.uwex.edu